Interest Formulas

Simple Interest

$I = Prt$

I = simple interest

P = principal

r = rate of interest

t = number of time periods

$A = P + I$

A = simple interest amount

$I = A - P$

I = interest

Compounded Interest

$A = P(1 + r)^t$

A = compounded amount

P = principal

r = interest rate per time period

t = number of time periods

Continuously Compounded Interest

$A = Pe^{rt}$

A = amount compounded continuously

P = principal

r = annual interest rate compounded continuously

t = number of years

$e \approx 2.718$ (irrational number)

Temperature Formulas

Fahrenheit Temperature (F)

$F = \dfrac{9}{5}C + 32$ C = Celsius temperature

Celsius Temperature (C)

$C = \dfrac{5}{9}(F - 32)$ F = Fahrenheit temperature

Other Formulas

Distance Traveled

$d = rt$

d = distance traveled

r = rate (speed)

t = time traveled

Vertical Position (in feet)

$s = -16t^2 + v_0 t + s_0$

s = position in feet above ground level

t = time in seconds

v_0 = initial velocity in feet per second

s_0 = initial position in feet above ground level

Vertical Position (in meters)

$s = -4.9t^2 + v_0 t + s_0$

s = position in meters above ground level

t = time in seconds

v_0 = initial velocity in meters per second

s_0 = initial position in meters above ground level

Quadratic Formula

$x = \dfrac{-b \pm \sqrt{b^2 - 4ac}}{2a}$

a, b, and c are real numbers

$a \neq 0$ and $ax^2 + bx + c = 0$

Distance between Two Points

$d = \sqrt{(x_2 - x_1)^2 + (y_2 - y_1)^2}$

(x_1, y_1) and (x_2, y_2) are coordinates of two points

Pendulum

$T = 2\pi\sqrt{\dfrac{L}{32}}$

T = period in seconds

L = length in feet of suspension

Products of Polynomials

Two Binomial Factors (FOIL Method)

$(a + b)(c + d) = ac + ad + bc + bd$

Squaring a Binomial

$(a + b)^2 = a^2 + 2ab + b^2$

$(a - b)^2 = a^2 - 2ab + b^2$

Sum and Difference of the Same Two Terms

$(a + b)(a - b) = a^2 - b^2$

Other Special Products

$(a + b)(a^2 - ab + b^2) = a^3 + b^3$

$(a - b)(a^2 + ab + b^2) = a^3 - b^3$

Experiencing Introductory & Intermediate Algebra

THROUGH FUNCTIONS AND GRAPHS

JoAnne Thomasson

Pellissippi State Technical Community College

Bob Pesut

Pellissippi State Technical Community College

with contributions by
Tracey Hoy

College of Lake County

PEARSON

Prentice
Hall

Upper Saddle River, New Jersey 07458

Executive Editor: Paul Murphy
Editor in Chief: Christine Hoag
Project Manager: Dawn M. Nuttall
Production Editor: Prepare, Inc.
Senior Managing Editor: Linda Mihatov Behrens
Executive Managing Editor: Kathleen Schiaparelli
Manufacturing Buyer: Maura Zaldivar
Manufacturing Manager: Alexis Heydt-Long
Director of Marketing: Patrice Jones
Senior Marketing Manager: Kate Valentine
Marketing Assistant: Jennifer de Leeuwerk
Media Project Manager: Audra J. Walsh
Editorial Assistant: Abigail Rethore
Art Director: Kenny Beck
Interior Designer: Suzanne Behnke
Cover Designer: Suzanne Behnke
Art Editor: Thomas Benfatti
Creative Director: Juan R. López
Director of Creative Services: Paul Belfanti
Cover Photo: Gavin Hellier / Robert Harding World Imagery / Getty Images, Inc.
Manager, Cover Visual Research & Permissions: Karen Sanatar
Director, Image Resource Center: Melinda Reo
Manager, Rights and Permissions: Zina Arabia
Manager, Visual Research: Beth Brenzel
Image Permission Coordinator: Angelique Sharps
Photo Researcher: Rachel Lucas
Art Studios: Precision Graphics/Laserwords
Composition: Prepare, Inc.

© 2007, 2003, 1999 by Pearson Education, Inc.
Pearson Prentice Hall
Pearson Education, Inc.
Upper Saddle River, New Jersey 07458

Printed in the United States of America
10 9 8 7 6 5 4 3 2 1

ISBN 0-13-221518-7 (Instructor's Edition)
ISBN 0-13-221517-9 (Student Edition)

Pearson Education Ltd., London
Pearson Education Australia Pty. Limited, Sydney
Pearson Education Singapore, Pte. Ltd
Pearson Education North Asia Ltd, Hong Kong
Pearson Education Canada, Ltd, Toronto
Pearson Educación de Mexico, S.A. de C.V.
Pearson Education—Japan, Tokyo
Pearson Education Malaysia, Pte. Ltd

Contents

We dedicate this text to the memory of Karin Wagner,
who first encouraged and supported us in the preparation of this text.
Karin was the acquisitions editor for the first edition of the text.

We also dedicate this text to our families:

Jack	*Gretchen*
Tom	*Lauren*
Isabell	*Katherine*
Tracy	*Tracy*
Shawn	*Jim*
Cameron	*Emma*
Caitlin	*Robert*
Chloe	*—B. P.*
Carter	
—J. T.	

Preface

The third edition of *Experiencing Introductory & Intermediate Algebra Through Functions and Graphs* continues to embrace the goal of promoting a new approach to teaching and learning developmental mathematics. This approach combines a traditional model with the reform movements presented in the National Council of Teachers of Mathematics (NCTM) *Principles and Standards for School Mathematics* and the American Mathematical Association of Two-Year Colleges (AMATYC) *Beyond Crossroads*. The NCTM process standards of problem solving, communication, reasoning and proof, connections, and representation are all incorporated in this text. The AMATYC *Beyond Crossroads* emphasizes the importance of students being actively engaged. Active learning presented in this text consists of discovery-based learning, question posing, and writing. AMATYC also recommends the use of technology to facilitate a kind of learning that is durable, has substance, is engaging to students, and provides mathematical insights through high-level understanding of the mathematics being taught.

The contents of this edition are still organized by families of functions, according to the AMATYC standards. Consequently, the first five chapters of the text focus on linear expressions, equations, and functions. The next four chapters, Chapters 6 through 9, focus on polynomial expressions, equations, and functions. Chapter 10 presents rational expressions, equations, and functions, Chapter 11 examines radical expressions, equations, and functions, and Chapter 12 features exponential and logarithmic expressions, equations, and functions.

In order to present families of functions, certain topics may be taught on an as-needed basis. Tables of values and graphing are introduced in Chapter 1 so that linear equations in one variable may be solved numerically and graphically, as well as algebraically, in Chapter 2. Quadratic functions are first presented in Chapter 6, using the graphing calculator as support, so that real-world quadratic models can be used in the applications presented in Chapters 7, 8, and 9. The properties of square roots are discussed in Chapter 9 with quadratic equations in order to solve quadratic equations by completing the square and the quadratic formula at the same time that we solve quadratic equations algebraically by factoring.

In this text, complex numbers and equations with imaginary solutions have been placed at the end of Chapter 11, following the discussion of radical expressions, equations, and functions. We believe that that is the appropriate place for complex numbers for two major reasons: students will have just learned the algebra of radicals, and the new location provides a perfect opportunity to revisit the quadratic formula, thereby reinforcing their understanding of the concept. However, the section on complex numbers and equations with imaginary solutions has been written as a stand-alone section, and if an instructor so chooses, it could be presented after the discussion of the quadratic formula in Chapter 9.

The first half of the text presents a balanced discussion of algebraic, numerical, and graphical methods for solving linear equations, so that students have a solid understanding of what the concepts represent. In the second half, the discussion of polynomial equations continues to utilize the same algebraic, numerical, and graphical techniques. This approach provides an opportunity for students who enter the sequence at that late point to gain an understanding of those methods. However, as we progress further into the second half of the text, the emphasis increasingly is on algebraic methods. Numerical and graphical methods are used only for checking solutions, rather than obtaining them. This way of teaching the topics will strengthen the students' algebraic skills for their subsequent math courses.

The project at the end of each chapter enriches the study of the material presented in the chapter and provides connections to other areas of mathematics and other disciplines. Students may be asked to research the history of mathematical topics, collect and interpret data for use in their mathematical modeling activities, and build on the applications they have studied.

NEW TO THIS EDITION

In this third edition, we have incorporated recommendations and suggestions from instructors and reviewers of the text. Instructors who currently use the text valued the real-world applications and encouraged us to expand it. At the same time, they recommended that the text be streamlined to reduce its volume. We also added vocabulary review exercises to the chapter summary, encouraging students to use the key terms from the chapter instead of just seeing a list.

We have condensed the discussion of the real-number system and the introduction to variables and equations into a review of prealgebra topics. We have combined Chapters 1 and 2 of the previous edition into this one chapter and added the presentation of inequalities to this discussion. This chapter may be taught as a whole or by sections of choice.

Feedback from reviewers indicated the need for expanding and strengthening the discussion of slope, so we have created a separate section on slope in Chapter 3. In this new section, we offer more examples, exercises, and real-world applications.

Instructors using the text also suggested expanding the chapter on quadratic and polynomial equations. The section on solving by using square roots in the previous edition has been separated into two sections so that more attention can be given to the properties of square roots. We have added a new section in this chapter entitled "More Quadratic Functions and Their Graphs." In this section, we return to the topic of quadratic functions and expand our analysis of quadratic functions and their graphs as a conclusion to the discussion of the family of quadratic functions.

APPROACH

We have carefully written *Experiencing Introductory & Intermediate Algebra Through Functions and Graphs* in a positive manner to help students build confidence in their ability to do algebra. After completing the course, students should be able to do all of the following:

- Model real-world situations.
- Reason mathematically and develop convincing mathematical arguments.
- Use an appropriate method—numeric, graphic, or algebraic—to solve problems.
- Connect algebra to other disciplines.
- Communicate mathematically.
- Use appropriate technology.
- Work collaboratively in groups.

To teach these skills, we introduce a problem-solving procedure in Chapter 2 and use this approach throughout the text. Numeric, graphic, and algebraic approaches to solving problems are described, and students are encouraged to choose that method which is appropriate to solve their problems. Every section of the text addresses real-world situations, so students can see reasons for learning algebra and can connect up what they learn with other disciplines, both inside and outside of mathematics. Students are asked to discover mathematical ideas on their own, to strengthen their mathematical reasoning skills, and to communicate their results. We then explain these results mathematically to reinforce the concepts the students have found.

CONTENT

The text is written for a two-semester course in introductory and intermediate algebra. However, it is also flexible enough for use in a one-semester course. In both courses, topics are covered with a minimal amount of repetition.

In Chapter P, we introduce the set of real numbers, develop the properties of the real-number system, and present the rules for operations on real numbers. We complete these numeric topics with discussions of integer exponents, scientific notation, and radicals. We introduce variables, algebraic expressions, equations, and inequalities. We discuss geometric formulas and other formulas used in the first five chapters of the text. This early introduction to these formulas allows us to integrate geometric and other applications throughout the book.

In Chapter 1, we examine additional topics needed for the study of algebra: ordered pairs, relations, functions, and graphs. This early discussion of functions supports the structure of the remainder of the text, which focuses on the study of various families of functions.

Chapters 2, 3, 4, and 5 cover topics related to linear functions. In Chapter 2, we begin the explicit study of algebra by solving linear equations in one variable and absolute-value equations. Here and throughout the text, we teach how to solve equations numerically, graphically, and algebraically. Chapter 3 focuses on the concept of slope, on linear equations in two variables, and on functions. Chapter 4 presents methods for solving systems of linear equations in two variables, emphasizing solutions by graphing, by the substitution method, and by the addition method. Inequalities and solutions of linear inequalities are discussed in Chapter 5. We recommend the first five chapters as an introductory algebra text.

We designed Chapter 6 as the first chapter in the second semester of study, allowing for a review of graphical methods and the concept of a function. The remainder of the text follows a standard pattern consisting of the introduction of a family of functions, rules for operating with the expressions that define the functions, and methods for solving related equations numerically, graphically, and algebraically. We follow this pattern in discussing polynomial functions in Chapter 6, polynomial expressions in Chapter 7, factoring polynomials in Chapter 8, and polynomial equations and inequalities in Chapter 9.

In Chapter 9, we solve quadratic equations numerically, graphically, and algebraically by factoring, by completing the square, and by using the quadratic formula. This arrangement allows for closure on quadratic equations and enables the student to choose an appropriate method for solving equations by examining the equation given. We also solve quadratic inequalities. We complete our discussion of quadratic functions by analyzing quadratic models.

In Chapter 10, we describe rational functions, operations with rational expressions, and the solution of rational equations. We complete the coverage of radical functions, expressions, and equations in Chapter 11, along with functions, expressions, and equations having rational exponents. The chapter also includes a section on the complex-number system, describing equations in one variable with complex solutions. This section is designed to stand on its own or to be incorporated into earlier chapters if desired. Finally, Chapter 12 focuses on inverse functions, exponential functions, and logarithmic functions. It also presents a discussion of the properties of exponents and logarithms and the methods for solving exponential equations and logarithmic equations in one variable.

PEDAGOGY

Use of Technology

Graphing calculators allow students the freedom to experiment with and explore mathematical ideas. Using graphing calculators helps boost confidence and increase motivation. Skills such as estimating, computing, graphing, and analyzing data can be developed and reinforced with the use of a calculator. When students are relieved of tedious computations, they can focus on processes instead. They can also go beyond the limitations of traditional paper-and-pencil work and deal directly with real-world numbers.

Students should learn not only *how* to use technology, but also *when* to do so. The text assumes that all students have a TI-84 (or 83) Plus graphing calculator available for use at all times. This requirement will minimize the amount of time necessary to demonstrate particular calculator functions. Technology boxes in the text are designed as stand-alone discussions of topics of interest and present the keystrokes required to produce selected calculator screens. Additional calculator activities and instructions are included in the calculator exercises at the end of each section.

Multiple Approaches

Throughout the text, concepts are developed using *numeric, graphic, algebraic,* and *verbal* approaches. The *numeric* presentation emphasizes tables of values, constructed either manually or by using a calculator. *Graphical* techniques follow naturally from the numeric methods. The *algebraic* approach is introduced and supported by the numeric and graphic methods. Students are encouraged to decide which approach is the most appropriate for solving particular problems. They are also challenged to express their solutions both *orally* and in *writing.*

Interactive and Collaborative Learning

We believe students should learn to read, write, and speak mathematically. We have written this text at a level that developmental readers can understand. Several features, including the guided discovery boxes, the objective checkup exercises at the end of each objective, the writing exercises at the end of every section, the reflections in each chapter review, the chapter tests, and the chapter projects, ask students to write mathematically. These activities may be assigned as individual or group work.

Experiencing Mathematics

The graphing calculator enables students to explore and experiment with mathematical ideas as they discover algebraic concepts in the guided discovery boxes. After a student discovers a concept, the text explains why the concept applies. Students develop a sense of ownership of the algebraic principles through this discovery process. As a result, the students acquire a better understanding of the reasoning behind the mathematics.

To help students keep a positive attitude toward mathematics while experiencing algebra, we provide frequent "Take Notes" (previously Helping Hands) to reinforce skills. Students review their skills at the end of each chapter in the section-by-section review and in the mixed review, as well as in the various cumulative reviews. In addition, each chapter test begins with a test-taking tip designed to further bolster students' confidence and improve their ability to perform well on tests.

Connection with Other Experiences

For a meaningful experience in this course, students must make a connection between algebra and the world around them. To help students make this connection, we begin each section of the text with a real-world application and solve this application before the section ends. Each section also presents a list of objectives, one of which is to model real-world situations by using concepts discussed in that section. Calculator exercises, chapter projects, and writing exercises within each set of section exercises often involve connections to disciplines and fields outside of mathematics, as well as to areas of applied mathematics, such as geometry, probability, and statistics.

RESOURCES FOR THE INSTRUCTOR

Instructor's Edition (0-13-221518-7)
Identical to the student text, except that it also features an answer appendix which includes answers to all section, calculator, and end-of-chapter exercises in the text.

Instructor's Solutions Manual (0-13-221484-9)
This resource includes full, worked-out solutions to all section, calculator, and end-of-chapter exercises in the text as well as answers to the Guided Discovery exercises.

Instructor's Resource Manual with Tests (0-13-221485-7)
This resource includes six sample tests for each chapter, as well as sample final exams. Answers to all tests are also provided.

TestGen (0-13-227983-5)
TestGen enables instructors to build, edit, print, and administer tests using a computerized bank of questions developed to cover all the objectives of the text. TestGen is algorithmically based, allowing instructors to create multiple but equivalent versions of the same question or test with the click of a button. Instructors can also modify test bank questions or add new questions. Tests can be printed or administered online. The software is available on a dual-platform Windows/Macintosh CD-ROM.

MyMathLab Instructor Version (0-13-147898-2)
MyMathLab is a series of text-specific, easily customizable online courses for Prentice Hall textbooks in mathematics and statistics. Powered by CourseCompass™ (Pearson Education's online teaching and learning environment) and MathXL® (our online homework, tutorial, and assessment system), MyMathLab gives you the tools you need to deliver all or a portion of your course online, whether your students are in a lab setting or working from home.

MathXL® Instructor Version (0-13-147895-8)
MathXL is a powerful online homework, tutorial, and assessment system that accompanies Prentice Hall textbooks in mathematics or statistics. With MathXL, instructors can create, edit, and assign online homework and tests using algorithmically generated exercises correlated at the objective level to the textbook.

RESOURCES FOR THE STUDENT

Student Solutions Manual (0-13-221486-5)
This resource includes full, worked-out solutions to the odd section and calculator exercises, as well as all end-of-chapter exercises in the text. Also includes answers to all the Guided Discovery exercises.

MathXL® Tutorials on CD (0-13-221492-X)
This interactive tutorial CD-ROM provides algorithmically generated practice exercises that are correlated at the objective level to the exercises in the textbook. Every practice exercise is accompanied by an example and a guided solution designed to involve students in the solution process. Selected exercises may also include a video clip to help students visualize concepts. The software provides helpful feedback for incorrect answers and can generate printed summaries of students' progress.

Prentice Hall Tutor Center: www.prenhall.com/tutorcenter (0-13-064604-0)
Staffed by developmental math faculty, the Tutor Center provides live tutorial support via phone, fax, or email. Tutors are available Sunday through Thursday 5 P.M. EST to midnight, 5 days a week, 7 hours a day. The Tutor Center may be accessed through a registration number that may be bundled with a new text or purchased separately with a used book. Comes automatically within MyMathLab.

InterAct Math Tutorial Web site: www.interactmath.com

Get practice and tutorial help online! This interactive tutorial Web site provides algorithmically generated practice exercises that correlate directly to the exercises in the textbook. Students can retry an exercise as many times as they like with new values each time for unlimited practice and mastery. Every exercise is accompanied by an interactive guided solution that provides helpful feedback for incorrect answers, and students can also view a worked-out sample problem that steps them through an exercise similar to the one they're working on.

MORE TOOLS FOR SUCCESS!

MyMathLab

MyMathLab is a series of text-specific, easily customizable online courses for Prentice Hall textbooks in mathematics and statistics. Powered by CourseCompass™ (Pearson Education's online teaching and learning environment) and MathXL® (our online homework, tutorial, and assessment system), MyMathLab gives you the tools you need to deliver all or a portion of your course online, whether your students are in a lab setting or working from home. MyMathLab provides a rich and flexible set of course materials, featuring free-response exercises that are algorithmically generated for unlimited practice and mastery. Students can also use online tools, such as video lectures, animations, and a multimedia textbook, to independently improve their understanding and performance. Instructors can use MyMathLab's homework and test managers to select and assign online exercises correlated directly to the textbook, and they can also create and assign their own online exercises and import TestGen tests for added flexibility. MyMathLab's online gradebook—designed specifically for mathematics and statistics—automatically tracks students' homework and test results and gives the instructor control over how to calculate final grades. Instructors can also add offline (paper-and-pencil)

grades to the gradebook. MyMathLab is available to qualified adopters. For more information, visit our Web Site at www.mymathlab.com or contact your Prentice Hall sales representative.

MathXL®

MathXL® is a powerful online homework, tutorial, and assessment system that accompanies Prentice Hall textbooks in mathematics or statistics. With MathXL, instructors can create, edit, and assign online homework and tests using algorithmically generated exercises correlated at the objective level to the textbook. They can also create and assign their own online exercises and import TestGen tests for added flexibility. All student work is tracked in MathXL's online gradebook. Students can take chapter tests in MathXL and receive personalized study plans based on their test results. The study plan diagnoses weaknesses and links students directly to tutorial exercises for the objectives they need to study and retest. Students can also access supplemental animations and video clips directly from selected exercises. MathXL is available to qualified adopters. For more information, visit our Web site at www.mathxl.com, or contact your Prentice Hall sales representative.

ACKNOWLEDGMENTS

This text was completed with the help of many individuals who offered encouragement, suggestions, and criticisms. We would like to thank the following individuals who reviewed the text:

Caroline Best	*Pellissippi State Technical Community College*
Donna Carlson	*College of Lake County*
Terry S. Darling	*Lewis and Clark Community College*
Susan Fitzpatrick	*Northeast State Technical Community College*
Shelle Hartzel	*Lake Land College*
Tracey Hoy	*College of Lake County*
Byron Hunter	*College of Lake County*
Dennis Kimsey	*Rogue Community College*

Steve O'Donnell	*Rogue Community College*
Zoe Lynda Pine	*Northeast State Technical Community College*
Claire Suddeth	*Pellissippi State Technical Community College*

To the students who participated in the various research projects, class tests, and tests of new materials, your involvement has been invaluable. To the mathematics faculty at Pellissippi State Technical Community College who supported us in this project, we offer our thanks. Many faculty members throughout the college encouraged our undertaking of this project, and we want to acknowledge their support. We wish to thank the college administration and faculty for their recognition of our efforts.

We want to thank Tracey Hoy for her contributions of new material for this edition. We thank Helen Medley and Byron Hunter for their help with the accuracy of this edition. We also want to thank the editorial, production, and marketing staff at Prentice Hall for their patience, assistance, and contributions to the project. We thank Paul Murphy and Dawn Nuttall, who guided us through the production process to bring the third edition of the text to fruition.

Last, but certainly not least, we thank our spouses, children, family, and friends for the encouragement, support, and sacrifices they have made in order to allow us to complete the project.

JoAnne Thomasson
Bob Pesut
Pellissippi State Technical Community College

Prealgebra Review

In this chapter, we introduce the set of rational numbers and write numerical expressions that use them. We evaluate these expressions by means of the basic operations of addition, subtraction, multiplication, and division. We also evaluate expressions containing exponents and radicals, which often include irrational numbers. Together, these two categories of numbers form the set of real numbers, the basis for most of this text. We then generalize arithmetic by introducing algebra. We define variables, algebraic expressions, equations, and inequalities, and we discuss geometric formulas and other formulas.

The word *algebra* comes from the Arabic word *al-jabr*, which appears in the title of one of the earliest algebra books known. The book was written in about 825 A.D., which is about the same time as the setting for the stories of the Arabian Nights. The book's author was an astronomer and mathematician named Muhammed ibn Musa al-Khwarizmi, and the full title may be translated as "the science of restoring and reduction." We will see in this chapter how the Arabian mathematicians solved equations by moving terms around ("restoring") and combining like terms ("reduction").

Many of the formulas that we discuss in this chapter were written in ancient times and are accompanied by an interesting history. As you proceed through the chapter, you may want to research the history behind the different formulas introduced. We will conclude the chapter with a project that features one of these historical events, the search for a value of π.

P.1 RATIONAL NUMBERS AND THE NUMBER LINE

OBJECTIVES

1 Identify a number as a member of the set of natural numbers, whole numbers, integers, or rational numbers.
2 Graph rational numbers on a number line.
3 Determine the order of rational numbers, and use the symbols $=$, $<$, $>$, $\leq$, and $\geq$ to complete an equation or inequality.
4 Evaluate the absolute value of a rational number.
5 Evaluate the opposite of a rational number.
6 Model real-world situations with rational numbers.

APPLICATION

Human body temperature is about 98°F. According to the *Guinness Book of World Records*, the coldest inhabited place in the Northern Hemisphere is the Siberian village of Oymyakon (called the "Cold Pole"). The unofficial recorded lowest temperature there is the same as the opposite of the human body temperature. Write and evaluate an expression for the lowest temperature of Oymyakon.

We will discuss this application further. See page 10.

Objective P.1.1

Identifying Rational Numbers and Their Subsets

A **set** is a group or collection of objects. The objects, which we call **members** or **elements** of the set, could be anything, such as state capitals of the United States, baseball players who have hit over 500 home runs in one season, or stars in the sky. In mathematics, we often discuss sets of numbers.

A set with no members is called an **empty set** or **null set**. For example, the set of baseball players who have hit over 500 home runs in one season is an empty set.

If it is possible to list all members of a set, it is called a **finite set**, such as the state capitals of the United States. If it is not possible to list all members of a set, it is called an **infinite set**, such as the set of points on a line.

We indicate a set by enclosing its members in a pair of braces: { }. If the set is infinite, we include enough members to show the pattern of the set. Then we add three dots, called an **ellipsis**, to indicate that the pattern continues.

The following are examples of sets of numbers:

$$A = \{\ \}$$ Empty set A (no members)
$$B = \{1, 3, 5, 7, 9\}$$ Finite set B (odd numbers between 0 and 10)
$$C = \{1, 3, 5, \ldots\}$$ Infinite set C (odd numbers greater than or equal to 1)

A set that is contained in another set is called a **subset** of the latter set. In the three previous sets, set B is a subset of set C. In this section, we discuss the set of rational numbers and several of its subsets.

The first set of numbers we consider is the set N of **natural numbers**, also called **counting numbers**.

$$N = \{1, 2, 3, \ldots\}$$

If we extend the set of natural numbers by including 0 as an element, we have the set W of **whole numbers**:

$$W = \{0, 1, 2, 3, \ldots\}$$

To extend the set of whole numbers, we include the opposites of all the natural numbers. The **opposite** of a natural number is a negative number and is written with a negative sign, −, in front of the number.

The opposite of 1 is negative 1, or −1.

The opposite of 2 is negative 2, or −2.

The opposites of all natural numbers form a set of negative numbers, $\{-1, -2, -3, \dots\}$, or, since the order does not matter, $\{\dots, -3, -2, -1\}$. If we combine this set of negative numbers with the set of whole numbers, we have the set Z of **integers**:

$$Z = \{\dots -3, -2, -1, 0, 1, 2, 3, \dots\}$$

To visualize these sets, we use a **number line**. We construct a number line by drawing a line and labeling equally spaced intervals with numbers in consecutive order. We can represent the integers on a number line like this:

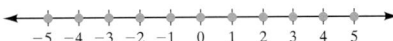

If we examine the number line of integers, we see a space between each pair of consecutive integers. The numbers located between each pair include fractions and decimals. Fractions are simply ratios of integers, while some decimals are equivalent to fractions. We can name many fractions and decimals between 0 and 1, such as $\frac{1}{8}, \frac{1}{4}, \frac{1}{3}, 0.5, \frac{2}{3}, 0.75$, and $\frac{7}{8}$. On the number line, they look like this:

In fact, if we could name and locate all fractions and decimals between 0 and 1, the entire space between 0 and 1 would appear to be filled with numbers.

We can extend the set of integers by including all fractions and their decimal equivalents. This gives us the set Q (quotient of integers) of **rational numbers**.

Rational numbers are numbers that can be written as a fraction (a quotient or ratio of integers), excluding the possibility of a zero denominator.

All integers are rational numbers, because we may write them with a denominator of 1. Thus,

$$6 = \frac{6}{1} \qquad -5 = \frac{-5}{1}$$

All terminating decimals are rational numbers, such as

$$0.25 = \frac{25}{100} = \frac{1}{4} \qquad 0.9 = \frac{9}{10} \qquad 0.125 = \frac{125}{1000} = \frac{1}{8}$$

All repeating decimals are rational numbers. (We use a bar over the numbers that repeat.) For example,

$$0.3333\dots = 0.\overline{3} = \frac{1}{3} \qquad 0.5454\dots = 0.\overline{54} = \frac{6}{11} \qquad 0.8333\dots = 0.8\overline{3} = \frac{5}{6}$$

Other forms of decimals will be discussed later.

All of these examples of rational numbers are written in fractional notation in simplest form. **Fractional notation** (in simplest form) is a form of a rational number written as a ratio of an integer numerator to a nonzero integer denominator, with the numerator and denominator having no common factors other than 1.

$$\frac{3 \text{ numerator}}{4 \text{ denominator}}$$

is in fractional notation in simplest form because 3 and 4 are integers that have no common factors other than 1.

In summary, since the set of rational numbers includes all possible ratios of integers (excluding a denominator of 0), it includes all integers, which includes all whole numbers, which includes all natural or counting numbers, as shown in the following chart:

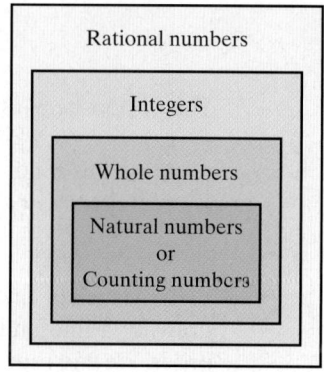

EXAMPLE 1 Identify the possible sets of numbers (natural numbers, whole numbers, integers, or rational numbers) to which the given number belongs.

a. 123   **b.** 0   **c.** −386   **d.** 36.25   **e.** $-\dfrac{2}{3}$ **f.** $2\dfrac{3}{4}$ **g.** $-3\dfrac{1}{4}$

Solution

a. natural number, whole number, integer, rational number

b. whole number, integer, rational number

c. integer, rational number

d. rational number   **e.** rational number

f. rational number   **g.** rational number

You will need to know how to enter rational numbers into your calculator. First, you must be able to distinguish between the negative symbol key (−) and the subtraction sign key that is an operation sign (−). Next, you will need to know how to enter fractions and have the calculator return an answer in the form of a fraction.

EXAMPLE 2 Enter the following rational numbers on your calculator.

a. $-\dfrac{2}{3}$ **b.** $2\dfrac{3}{4}$ **c.** $-3\dfrac{1}{4}$

Solution

The solutions are shown in **Figure P.1**.

T E C H N O L O G Y Rational Numbers and Opposites

Enter $-\dfrac{2}{3}, 2\dfrac{3}{4}, -3\dfrac{1}{4}$.

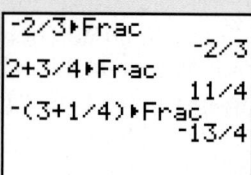

Figure P.1

For **Figure P.1**,

Enter the fraction, $-\frac{2}{3}$, as a quotient, and choose to have your answer displayed as a fraction by selecting ▶ FRAC, option 1, under the MATH menu. The negative symbol is (-).

[(-)] [2] [÷] [3] [MATH] [1] [ENTER]

Enter the mixed number, $2\frac{3}{4}$, as a sum of the whole number, 2, and the fraction, $\frac{3}{4}$. Choose to have the answer displayed as a fraction.

[2] [+] [3] [÷] [4] [MATH] [1] [ENTER]

Enter the negative mixed number as the opposite of a sum of the whole number, 3, and the fraction, $\frac{1}{4}$. Use (-) as an opposite sign. Choose to have the answer displayed as a fraction.

[(-)] [(] [3] [+] [1] [÷] [4] [)] [MATH] [1] [ENTER]

Note that the mixed-number answers are displayed as improper fractions. Directions for changing an improper fraction to a mixed number are given in Section P.2, "Calculator Exercises."

> **TAKE NOTE** In keying a negative mixed number into your calculator, the negative sign must always be outside the parentheses containing the value.

✓ Objective P.1.1 *CHECKUP*

1. Identify the possible sets of numbers (natural numbers, whole numbers, integers, or rational numbers) to which the given number belongs.
   a. 15   b. -3 c. 0   d. -15.4
   e. $\frac{1}{3}$ f. $3\frac{1}{4}$ g. $-2\frac{3}{7}$

2. Enter the following rational numbers into your calculator.
   a. $-\frac{3}{4}$ b. $3\frac{2}{5}$ c. $-1\frac{2}{3}$

3. Define *set*, *empty set*, *finite set*, and *infinite set*.

4. Describe the following sets of numbers: the integers; the whole numbers; the natural numbers; the rational numbers.

Objective P.1.2   Graphing Rational Numbers

We used a number line to visualize sets of numbers. We can also use a number line to understand relationships between numbers. To **graph**, or **plot**, a number on a number line, we place a dot on the line at the location of the number.

EXAMPLE 3   Graph 2, $\frac{3}{4}$, -1.5, $\frac{7}{4}$, and $-2\frac{1}{4}$ on a number line.

Solution

Construct a number line. Label equally spaced intervals with integers in increasing order. Place a dot on the number line at the location where the number appears. Thus,

2 is located 2 units to the right of 0.

$\frac{3}{4}$ is located $\frac{3}{4}$ units to the right of 0.

-1.5 is located 1.5 units to the left of 0, or 0.5 $\left(\frac{1}{2}\right)$ unit to the left of -1.

$\frac{7}{4}$ is located $1\frac{3}{4}$ units to the right of 0, or $\frac{1}{4}$ unit to the left of 2.

$-2\frac{1}{4}$ is located $2\frac{1}{4}$ units to the left of 0, or $\frac{1}{4}$ unit to the left of -2.

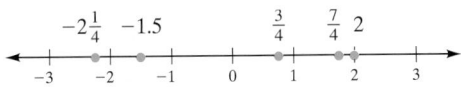

Objective P.1.2 *CHECKUP*

Graph the following numbers on a number line:

$$-2, \frac{3}{5}, 4.75, 3\frac{1}{3}, -5\frac{1}{6}$$

Objective P.1.3   ## Ordering Rational Numbers

Two numbers have the same value, or are **equal** to each other, if they are located in the same position on a number line. For example, 3.5 and $3\frac{1}{2}$ have the same location on the number line.

$$3.5 = 3\frac{1}{2} \quad \text{3.5 is equal to } 3\frac{1}{2}.$$

Numbers that are not of equal value can be compared by using their locations on a number line. The farther a number is located to the right, the larger the number is. The farther a number is located to the left, the smaller the number is. We use **inequality (order) symbols** of "is greater than," $>$, and "is less than," $<$, to write these statements. For example, use $>$ or $<$ to compare

$$7 \underline{} 2$$
$$2 \underline{} 7$$

In comparing 7 and 2 on a number line, we notice that 7 is to the right of 2; therefore, 7 is greater than 2.

$$7 > 2$$

We can also see that 2 is to the left of 7. Therefore, 2 is less than 7.

$$2 < 7$$

TAKE NOTE We can think of the inequality symbol as an arrow pointing to the smaller number.

The two inequalities, $7 > 2$ and $2 < 7$, are **equivalent**, or mean the same thing. To write equivalent inequalities, the numbers are exchanged and the inequality symbol is reversed. (The arrow is still pointing to the smaller number.)

| **EXAMPLE 4** | Use $>$, $<$, or $=$ to compare the following numbers: |

a. $0 \underline{} -\frac{1}{2}$ **b.** $-6 \underline{} -2$ **c.** $-1\frac{1}{4} \underline{} -1.25$

Solution

a. $0 \underline{>} -\frac{1}{2}$ *0 is to the right of $-\frac{1}{2}$. Therefore, $0 > -\frac{1}{2}$.*

b. $-6 \underline{<} -2$ *-6 is to the left of -2. Therefore, $-6 < -2$.*

c. $-1\frac{1}{4} \underline{=} -1.25$ *$-1\frac{1}{4}$ and -1.25 are located in the same position on the number line. Therefore, the numbers are equal.*

If we combine each of the inequality symbols with the equals symbol, we obtain the inequality symbols $\geq$ (is greater than or equal to) and $\leq$ (is less than or equal to).

The following inequalities are true:

$$-1 \le 0 \qquad \text{-1 is less than or equal to 0.}$$

$$-1 \le \frac{-5}{5} \qquad \text{-1 is less than or equal to } \tfrac{-5}{5}.$$

We may also write a **compound inequality** containing more than one inequality symbol:

$$-1 \le 0 < 5 \qquad \text{-1 is less than or equal to 0, and 0 is less than 5.}$$

On a number line, we will observe that 0 is between the values of -1 and 5.

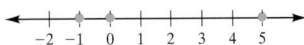

The conventional way to write this form of a compound inequality is to use the "is less than" or the "is less than or is equal to" symbol. This is easy to remember, because we are reading the number line from left to right. Therefore, at times we will need to write an equivalent compound inequality.

EXAMPLE 5

Write equivalent order relations for the following statements:

a. $0.6 < 0.85$ **b.** $-0.5 = -\dfrac{1}{2}$ **c.** $-2 \ge -2.5 \ge -3$

Solution

a. $0.85 > 0.6$ Exchange the numbers and replace $<$ with $>$.

b. $-\dfrac{1}{2} = -0.5$ Exchange the numbers. The $=$ does not change.

c. $-3 \le -2.5 \le -2$ Exchange the numbers and replace $\ge$ with $\le$.

✓ Objective P.1.3 *CHECKUP*

1. Use one of the symbols $>$, $<$, or $=$ to compare the two numbers.
 a. 0 _____ -2
 b. $1\dfrac{1}{2}$ _____ 1.5
 c. -2.3 _____ -3.5

2. Write an equivalent order relation for each statement.
 a. $6 > -2$
 b. $2.75 = \dfrac{11}{4}$
 c. $4 > 0 \ge -3$

Objective P.1.4 **Evaluating Absolute Values**

We are now ready to consider mathematical expressions. An **expression** is a combination of numbers and mathematical operations. (By a mathematical operation, we mean addition, subtraction, multiplication, or division.) The quantity $2 + 3$ is a mathematical expression, as is the quantity 2×3. We **evaluate** expressions by finding their numerical value. The expression $2 + 3$ has a value of 5, and the expression 2×3 has a value of 6.

The distance (number of units) a number is from 0 on the number line is called the **absolute value** of the number. The absolute value of a number is always nonnegative (positive or zero), because distance is always measured in nonnegative units.

To write an absolute-value expression, enclose the number in a set of vertical bars, $|\ \ |$. Do not confuse these bars with parentheses, $(\ )$, brackets, $[\ ]$, or braces, $\{\ \}$.

$$|6| = 6 \qquad \text{The absolute value of 6 is 6.}$$
$$|-6| = 6 \qquad \text{The absolute value of } -6 \text{ is 6.}$$

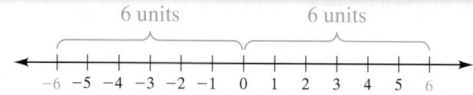

EXAMPLE 6   Evaluate.

a. $|3.5|$ **b.** $\left| -\dfrac{1}{2} \right|$ **c.** $|0|$

Solution

a. $|3.5| = 3.5$ 3.5 is 3.5 units from 0.

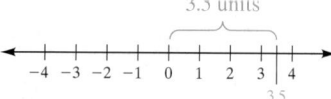

b. $\left| -\dfrac{1}{2} \right| = \dfrac{1}{2}$ $-\frac{1}{2}$ is $\frac{1}{2}$ unit from 0.

c. $|0| = 0$ 0 is 0 units from 0.

The checks for Example 6a and 6b are shown in **Figure P.2**.

TECHNOLOGY   **Absolute Value**

Evaluate $|3.5|$, $\left| -\dfrac{1}{2} \right|$.

```
abs(3.5)
              3.5
abs(-1/2)▶Frac
              1/2
```

Figure P.2

For **Figure P.2**,
To enter an absolute-value expression on your calculator, use the abs function found under the MATH NUM menu option 1. Close the set of parentheses that are opened for you to enclose each of the numbers, 3.5 and $-\frac{1}{2}$, in a set of parentheses.

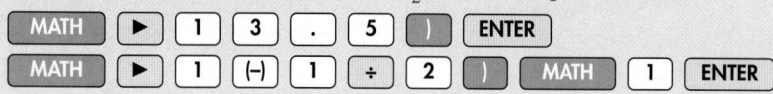

Objective P.1.4   **CHECKUP**

1. Evaluate the absolute-value expressions.

   a. $|-15|$ **b.** $|-3.3|$ **c.** $\left| \dfrac{2}{7} \right|$

2. What does the absolute value of a number represent?

Objective P.1.5   **Evaluating Opposites**

Previously, we defined the opposite of a natural number to be a negative number. More generally, two numbers with different signs, but with the same absolute value, meaning the same distance from 0, are called opposites. The opposite of a positive number is a negative number. The opposite of a negative number is a positive number. To write an opposite expression, enclose the expression in a set of parentheses, ( ), with a negative sign in front of it. In the preceding discussion, 6 and -6 are both 6 units from 0; therefore, 6 and -6 are opposites.

$$-(6) = -6 \quad \text{The opposite of 6 is } -6.$$
$$-(-6) = 6 \quad \text{The opposite of } -6 \text{ is } 6.$$

EXAMPLE 7

Evaluate:

a. $-\left(1\dfrac{1}{2}\right)$ **b.** $-\left|-\dfrac{3}{4}\right|$ **c.** $-(-(75))$

Solution

a. $-\left(1\dfrac{1}{2}\right) = -1\dfrac{1}{2}$ $-1\frac{1}{2}$ is the same distance from 0 as $1\frac{1}{2}$.

b. $-\left|-\dfrac{3}{4}\right| = -\dfrac{3}{4}$ Evaluate the absolute value of $-\frac{3}{4}$ and obtain $\frac{3}{4}$. Then take the opposite of $\frac{3}{4}$ and obtain $-\frac{3}{4}$.

c. $-(-(75)) = 75$ Evaluate the opposite of 75 and obtain -75. Next, the opposite of -75 is 75. In other words, the opposite of the opposite of a number is the number itself.

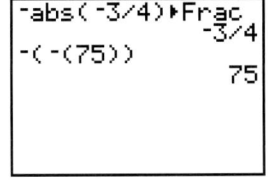

Figure P.3

The checks for Example 7b and 7c are shown in **Figure P.3**. The opposite symbol is .

■

TAKE NOTE In evaluating an expression with more than one set of parentheses, you should always work from the inside out.

✓ Objective P.1.5 *CHECKUP*

1. Evaluate.

a. $-\left(-3\dfrac{1}{3}\right)$ **b.** $-(-(15))$ **c.** $-\left|-\dfrac{4}{7}\right|$ ■

Objective P.1.6   Modeling the Real World

In our daily lives, many things can be expressed as rational numbers. For example, positive and negative numbers are used to define geographic elevations above or below sea level and temperatures above or below zero degrees. Many other situations also lend themselves to being expressed as rational numbers.

EXAMPLE 8

Mount McKinley is 20,320 feet above sea level. Rounded to the nearest 10 feet, the depth of Agulhas Basin in the Indian Ocean is the same distance below sea level. Write an expression, using an opposite symbol, to represent the depth of Agulhas Basin. Evaluate the expression.

Write an expression, using an absolute-value symbol and a rational number, to represent the distance Agulhas Basin is from sea level. Evaluate the expression.

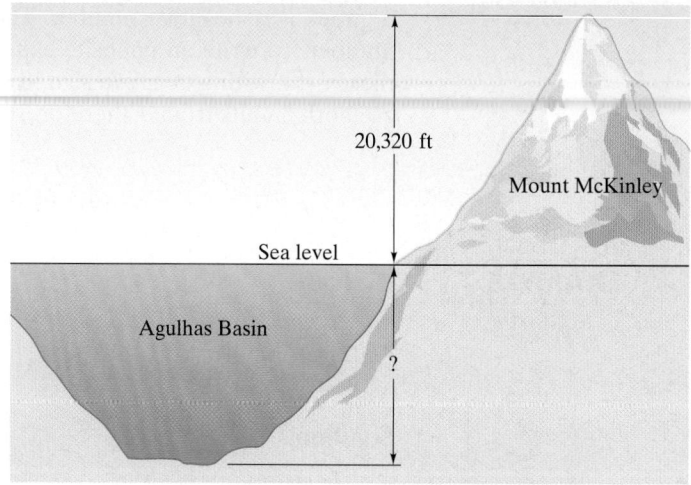

Solution

The depth of Agulhas Basin is the opposite of the height of Mount McKinley. Thus,

$$-(20{,}320) = -20{,}320$$

Agulhas Basin is approximately −20,320 feet. The absolute-value symbol means the distance from 0, or, in this case, sea level. Therefore,

$$|-20{,}320| = 20{,}320$$

Agulhas Basin is approximately 20,320 feet below sea level. ■

APPLICATION

Human body temperature is about 98°F. According to the *Guinness Book of World Records*, the coldest inhabited place in the Northern Hemisphere is the Siberian village of Oymyakon (called the "Cold Pole"). The unofficial recorded lowest temperature there is the same as the opposite of the human body temperature. Write and evaluate an expression for the lowest temperature of Oymyakon.

Discussion

Oymyakon has a temperature that is the opposite of the human body temperature, 98°F. Therefore,

$$-(98) = -98$$

The unofficial lowest temperature in Oymyakon is −98°F.

✓ Objective P.1.6 *CHECKUP*

1. The coldest temperature (Fahrenheit) on record in the United States was 80 degrees below zero (−80°F) at Prospect Creek Camp in the Endicott Mountains of northern Alaska on January 23, 1971. Write an expression, using an absolute-value symbol and a rational number, to represent the number of degrees Fahrenheit that this temperature is away from zero.

2. Between 2000 and 2003, the population of the state of South Dakota increased by 1.3%. During the same period, the population of the state of North Dakota experienced the opposite change. Write an expression, using an opposite symbol, for the percentage change in North Dakota's population. ■

P.1 EXERCISES

 Student Solutions Manual  PH Math/Tutor Center   CD Video Math XL MathXL® MyMathLab MyMathLab   Interactmath.com

Identify the possible sets of numbers (natural, whole, integer, or rational) to which each number belongs.

1. a. -15 **b.** 29 **c.** 1 million   **d.** $\dfrac{3}{7}$ **e.** $-4\dfrac{1}{3}$

2. a. 278 **b.** $-15\dfrac{2}{3}$ **c.** 5 billion   **d.** -14.2 **e.** $5\dfrac{1}{2}$

3. a. 0 **b.** 12.75 **c.** $2\dfrac{4}{9}$ **d.** -8.35 **e.** $\dfrac{4}{5}$

4. a. $\dfrac{9}{3}$ **b.** -199 **c.** $-\dfrac{11}{15}$ **d.** 0.009 **e.** $\dfrac{3}{2}$

5. On the number line, between what two integers would you graph the rational number $\dfrac{17}{3}$?

6. On the number line, between what two integers would you graph the rational number $-\dfrac{3}{2}$?

7. Graph the numbers on a number line.

$$-2, 1.5, \dfrac{1}{2}, -3.5, \dfrac{9}{4}, -1\dfrac{1}{4}, -\dfrac{4}{5}, 4$$

8. Graph the numbers on a number line.

$$\dfrac{7}{2}, -2.25 - 1.5, 0.5, 2, -2\dfrac{1}{4}, -1, -\dfrac{1}{5}$$

Use one of the symbols $>$, $<$, or $=$ to compare the two numbers.

9. -9 ____ -5 **10.** -7 ____ -4 **11.** 0 ____ -6 **12.** 0 ____ 11

13. 5 ____ 3 **14.** 12 ____ 9 **15.** $-\dfrac{1}{2}$ ____ $-\dfrac{2}{5}$ **16.** $-\dfrac{1}{3}$ ____ $-\dfrac{2}{7}$

17. $\dfrac{3}{7}$ ____ $\dfrac{7}{10}$ **18.** $\dfrac{3}{8}$ ____ $\dfrac{2}{7}$ **19.** $2\dfrac{3}{5}$ ____ $-2\dfrac{3}{5}$ **20.** $-4\dfrac{3}{7}$ ____ $4\dfrac{3}{7}$

21. $1\dfrac{4}{5}$ ____ 1.8 **22.** $2\dfrac{2}{5}$ ____ 2.4 **23.** -3.7 ____ -5.8 **24.** -6.2 ____ -4.6

25. 1.7 ____ 3.2 **26.** 4.1 ____ 3.9 **27.** $|-7|$ ____ 7 **28.** 6 ____ $|-6|$

29. $|-3.5|$ ____ -3.5 **30.** -14.3 ____ $|14.3|$ **31.** $\left|\dfrac{1}{2}\right|$ ____ $-\left(-\dfrac{1}{2}\right)$ **32.** $-\left(-\dfrac{3}{4}\right)$ ____ $\left|-\dfrac{3}{4}\right|$

33. $-|2|$ ____ -2 **34.** -5 ____ $-|5|$

Write an equivalent order relation for each statement.

35. $0.7 > 0.295$ **36.** $-2.56 < 0.06$ **37.** $0 \geq -1 > -5$

38. $25 > 24 \geq 20$ **39.** $\dfrac{2}{5} = 0.4$ **40.** $-0.86 = -\dfrac{43}{50}$

In exercises 41–56, evaluate.

41. $|15.34|$ **42.** $|25|$ **43.** $|-15.34|$ **44.** $|-25|$

45. $\left|-\left(-3\dfrac{1}{3}\right)\right|$ **46.** $|-(-25)|$ **47.** $-|23|$ **48.** $-|25|$

49. $-|-23|$ **50.** $-|-25|$ **51.** $-(15)$ **52.** $-\left(\dfrac{1}{2}\right)$

53. $-(-25)$ **54.** $-(-35)$ **55.** $-\left(-\left(-\dfrac{3}{2}\right)\right)$ **56.** $-\left(-\left(-\dfrac{5}{4}\right)\right)$

57. In a Monopoly game, a player gets $45 from the sale of a stock on one play. On another play, a player is assessed $115 for street repairs for a hotel. On a third play, a player collects $200 due to a bank error in her favor. Write rational numbers for each of these situations, using positive numbers for money received and negative numbers for money paid out.

58. On Monday, S & S stock rose 1.25 points; on Tuesday, it dropped 0.75 point; on Wednesday, it dropped 2 points; on Thursday, it rose 1.75 points; and on Friday, it rose 1.50 points. Write rational numbers for each of these situations, using positive numbers for rises in stock prices and negative numbers for drops in stock prices.

59. In 2002, Khalid Khannouchi of USA set the world record for a man running a marathon. If a runner beats this record, the time is recorded as the number of seconds below the record, written as a negative number. In the year 2003, Paul Tergat of Kenya beat Khannouchi's record by 43 seconds. Write an expression, using an opposite symbol, to represent Tergat's time.

60. In 2002, Paula Radcliffe set the world record for a woman running a marathon. In 2003, she beat her record by 113 seconds. Write an expression, using an opposite symbol, to represent Radcliffe's 2003 time.

61. On a true–false test, an instructor awards five points for every correct answer, deducts five points for each incorrect answer, and deducts two points for each unanswered question. Write rational numbers for the situations in which (a) a student answers a question correctly, (b) a student answers a question incorrectly, and (c) a student leaves a question unanswered.

62. In a game of Jeopardy, write rational numbers for the situations in which a player (a) answers a $100 question correctly and (b) answers a $200 question incorrectly.

63. On a number line, graph the points 3.5 and −2.3.
   a. Write an expression for the distance 3.5 is from zero using absolute-value symbols.

b. Write an expression for the distance −2.3 is from zero using absolute-value symbols.
   c. Using the expressions in part **a** and in part **b**, write an expression for the distance between the two points, 3.5 and −2.3, and evaluate.

64. On a number line, graph the points −3.5 and 2.3.
   a. Write an expression for the distance −3.5 is from zero using absolute-value symbols.
   b. Write an expression for the distance 2.3 is from zero using absolute-value symbols.
   c. Using the expressions in part **a** and in part **b**, write an expression for the distance between the two points, −3.5 and 2.3, and evaluate.

P.1 Calculator Exercises

The number line is used in statistical analysis to display data. In statistics, such a graph is called a **dot plot**. In plotting data on a dot plot, if a number occurs more than once, dots are placed one above another, at the same location on the number line to indicate that a value occurs a multiple number of times. As an example, suppose the following sets of numbers were collected for a statistical study on Fahrenheit temperatures:

$$32°, 34°, 35°, 34°, 33°, 37°, 31°, 38°, 42°, 39°, 32°, 33°,$$
$$30°, 31°, 35°, 36°, 33°, 38°, 39°, 35°$$

The dot plot for these data is shown in the following diagram:

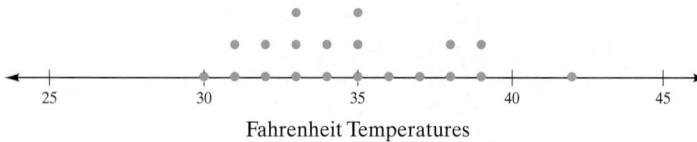

Fahrenheit Temperatures

The plot can be graphed on the calculator using a program. To key the program into your calculator, press [PRGM], scroll over to NEW, and press [ENTER]. The calculator will ask for the name of the program. Since the calculator will be set to ALPHA mode, just type the letters of the name. Each time you press [ENTER], the calculator will move to the next line of the program. Most of the instructions can be found under the [PRGM] key in the edit mode. Just search through the menus until you find the instruction you are looking for, and select it by pressing [ENTER]. The instruction will appear in the program listing. Instructions not found under the [PRGM] menu are identified to the left of the following listing of the program:

PROGRAM: DOTPLOT
ClrList L₂ — Found under the [STAT] key; L₂ is above the [2] key

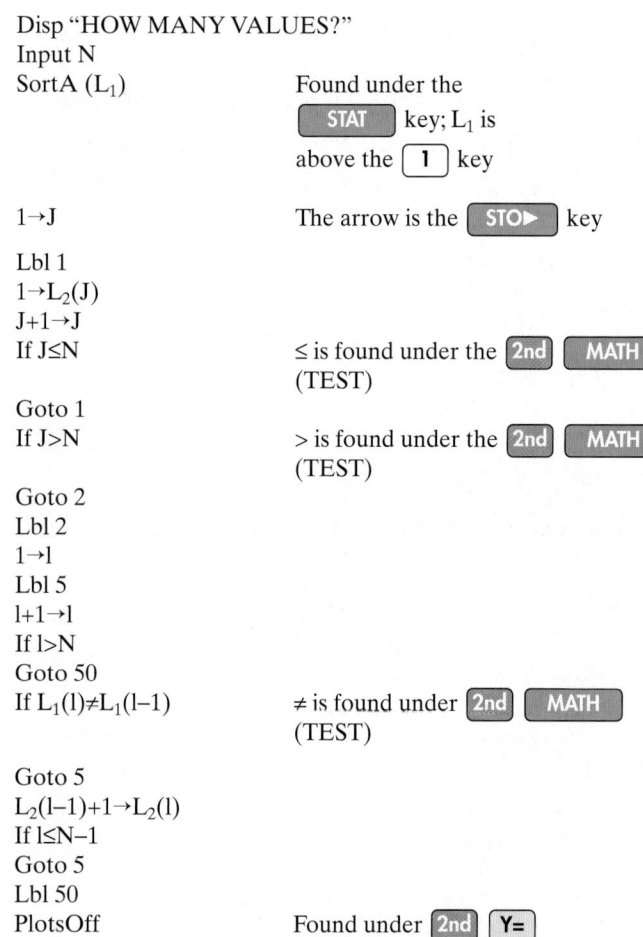

Disp "HOW MANY VALUES?"
Input N
SortA (L₁) — Found under the [STAT] key; L₁ is above the [1] key
1→J — The arrow is the [STO▶] key
Lbl 1
1→L₂(J)
J+1→J
If J≤N — ≤ is found under the [2nd] [MATH] (TEST)
Goto 1
If J>N — > is found under the [2nd] [MATH] (TEST)
Goto 2
Lbl 2
1→I
Lbl 5
I+1→I
If I>N
Goto 50
If L₁(I)≠L₁(I−1) — ≠ is found under [2nd] [MATH] (TEST)
Goto 5
L₂(I−1)+1→L₂(I)
If I≤N−1
Goto 5
Lbl 50
PlotsOff — Found under [2nd] [Y=] (STATPLOT)
Plot1(Scatter, L₁, L₂, □) — Found under [2nd] [Y=] (STATPLOT); Scatter is found in [2nd] [Y=] (STATPLOT), TYPE; The symbol is found there under MARK
L₁(1)−1→Xmin — Xmin is found under [VARS], Window

$L_1(N)+1 \rightarrow Xmax$

$5 \rightarrow Xscl$

$-5 \rightarrow Ymin$

$N/2 \rightarrow Ymax$

$2 \rightarrow Yscl$

DispGraph

All Window settings are found under VARS , Window

The screen displays for this program are as follows:

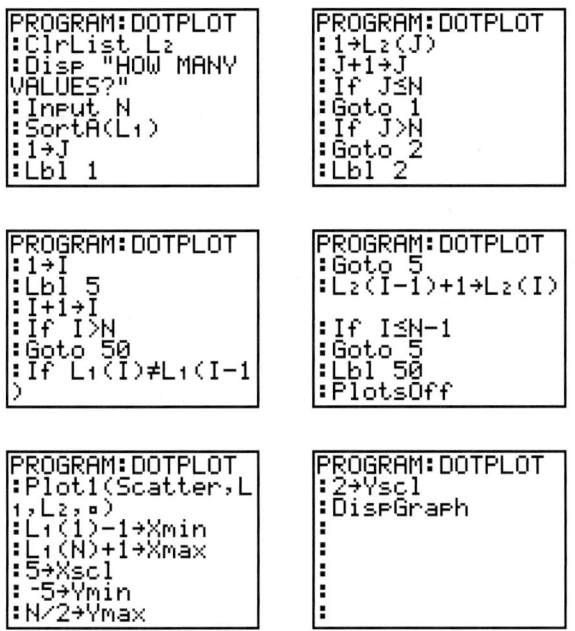

To use the program, first store the data in L_1 of the calculator:

- Press STAT
- Choose Edit
- Move the cursor to list L_1
- Clear the list by placing the cursor on the title, press CLEAR, and move the cursor down.
- Enter the values in L_1, pressing ENTER after each value.

Keep track of how many values were keyed into L_1.

Press Y= , and clear out any equations stored there.

Next press PRGM , choose DOTPLOT, and press ENTER to begin running the program. The program will ask you how many values you entered into L1. Type the number in, and press ENTER . The program will display the dot plot. To identify points press the TRACE key and use the arrows to move from one point to another.

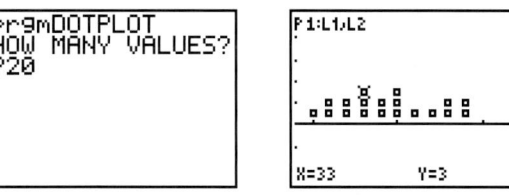

Try drawing dot plots for the following sets of data, and check them with the calculator program:

1. The New England Patriots won the Super Bowl XXXIX by defeating the Philadelphia Eagles. The number of points scored in each of the Patriot's regular-season games is as follows:

   27 23 31 24 30 13 20 40 29 27 24 42 35 28 23 21

2. Tiger Woods won the 2005 Masters Tournament with a score of 276. The following are the scores of the winners of the Masters from 1986 to 2005.

   279 285 281 283 278 277 275 277 279 274 276 270 279
   280 278 272 276 281 279 276

P.1 Writing Exercises

How do you feel about mathematics? Has it always been an easy subject for you, or have you always struggled with it? This is your chance to tell your instructor about your feelings toward the subject. Send an e-mail message or write a short letter to your instructor about your feelings toward math. Be sure to give reasons for your feelings—either good or bad past experiences with a math class, a math instructor, or whatever. Suggest to your instructor what would be helpful to you and what would cause you problems in the class. Describe any personal situations that might affect your study of mathematics, such as work, family responsibilities, or course load. Explain how you plan to handle these situations.

 OPERATIONS WITH RATIONAL NUMBERS

OBJECTIVES

1 Evaluate the sum of rational numbers.
2 Evaluate the difference of rational numbers.
3 Evaluate the product of rational numbers.
4 Evaluate the quotient of rational numbers.
5 Model real-world situations by using arithmetic operations of rational numbers.

APPLICATION

Mount Everest, the highest point in Tibet, is estimated to be 8850 meters above sea level. The lowest point in China, Turpan Pendi, is 154 meters below sea level. Determine the range of the terrain (the difference of the highest and lowest points).

After completing this section, we will discuss this application further. See page 31.

Objective P.2.1

Evaluating Sums of Rational Numbers

When we add two rational numbers, we obtain a **sum**. The numbers that we add are called **addends**. We will find these terms helpful as we discuss the rules for adding rational numbers.

$$8 + 4 = 12 \qquad\qquad 4 + 8 = 12$$

addend + addend = sum   addend + addend = sum

Note that the order in which we add two rational numbers does not change the sum.

$$8 + 4 = 4 + 8$$

COMMUTATIVE LAW FOR ADDITION

Changing the order of two rational-number addends does not change the sum.

To evaluate an expression with grouping symbols, operate on the grouping symbols first.

$$(6 + 2) + 4 = 8 + 4 = 12 \qquad 6 + (2 + 4) = 6 + 6 = 12$$

Note that changing the grouping of three rational-number addends does not change the sum.

$$(6 + 2) + 4 = 6 + (2 + 4)$$

ASSOCIATIVE LAW FOR ADDITION

Changing the grouping of three rational-number addends does not change the sum.

In addition to the commutative and associative properties, two other properties of addition should be noted. The first property we will discuss is the identity property of 0. Adding 0 to any rational number results in the number itself. In other words, when we add 0 to any rational number, the number's "identity" does not change. Therefore, 0 is called the **additive identity**.

$$0 + 4 = 4$$

The second property we use in addition is the additive-inverse property. When we add a rational number and its opposite, the sum is 0. Therefore, the opposite is sometimes called the **additive inverse** of a rational number.

$$6 + (-6) = 0$$

In this text, we use the calculator to do simple problems quickly, so that we can use the results to discover rules of mathematics. The rules of mathematics do not depend on the calculator, and the rules we discover are more basic and fundamental in mathematics than are calculator operations. In fact, the people who designed and built your calculator used those rules to do so.

When we add two nonzero rational numbers, there are two possible combinations: The two numbers may have the same signs (**like signs**) or different signs (**unlike signs**). In order to discover rules for adding these combinations, complete the following sets of exercises with your calculator. (Remember to use the $\boxed{(-)}$ for a negative number.)

Guided Discovery 1   Adding Two Rational Numbers

Evaluate each expression, and compare the results obtained in part **a** with the corresponding results in the part **b**.

1. a. $6 + 2 =$ _____   **b.** $|6| + |2| =$ _____

2. a. $3 + 9 =$ _____   **b.** $|3| + |9| =$ _____

3. a. $-6 + (-2) =$ _____   **b.** $|-6| + |-2| =$ _____

4. a. $-3 + (-9) =$ _____   **b.** $|-3| + |-9| =$ _____

5. a. $6 + (-2) =$ _____   **b.** $|6| - |-2| =$ _____

6. a. $3 + (-9) =$ _____   **b.** $|-9| - |3| =$ _____

7. a. $-6 + 2 =$ _____   **b.** $|-6| - |2| =$ _____

8. a. $-3 + 9 =$ _____   **b.** $|9| - |-3| =$ _____

For exercises 1–4, state a rule for writing the sum of two rational numbers with like signs.

For exercises 5–8, state a rule for writing the sum of two rational numbers with unlike signs.

In part **a** of exercises 1 and 2, we add two positive rational numbers. Each sum results in a positive number. In part **b**, we add the absolute values of the addends. The results are the same.

In part **a** of exercises 3 and 4, we add two negative rational numbers. Each sum results in a negative number. In part **b**, we add the absolute values of the addends. The results are the opposite of those in part **a**.

In part **a** of exercises 5 through 8, we add a positive and a negative rational number. Each sum results in a number whose sign is the same as the sign of the addend with the larger absolute value. In part **b**, we subtract the smaller absolute-value addend from the larger absolute-value addend. The results are the same as the absolute value of the sum in part **a**.

ADDITION OF RATIONAL NUMBERS

To add two rational numbers with like signs (both positive or both negative),

- Add the absolute values of the addends.
- The sign of the sum is the sign of the addends.

To add two rational numbers with unlike signs (one positive and one negative),

- Subtract the smaller absolute-value addend from the larger absolute-value addend.
- The sign of the sum is the sign of the addend with the larger absolute value.

To help you understand the addition rules we have just discovered, let's add rational numbers by using a number line. This will help you visualize how the signs of the addends determine the sign of the sum. We will do three of the exercises in the previous discovery set on a number line.

To perform addition on a number line, we start at the **origin**, 0, we move to the right if an addend is positive, and we move to the left if an addend is negative.

Adding Two Positive Rational Numbers: 6 + 2

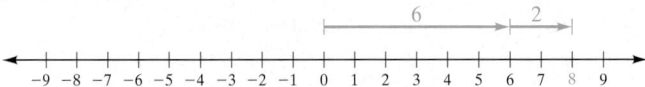

The sum is 8. The result is positive, because both moves were in the positive direction. The absolute value of this sum is the sum of the absolute values of the addends, because both moves were in the same direction from 0.

Adding Two Negative Rational Numbers: −6 + (−2)

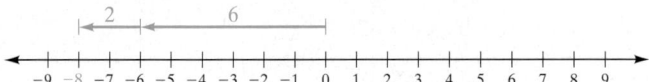

The sum is −8. The result is negative, because both moves were in the negative direction. The absolute value of this sum is the sum of the absolute values of the addends, because both moves were in the same direction from 0.

Adding a Positive and a Negative Rational Number: 6 + (−2)

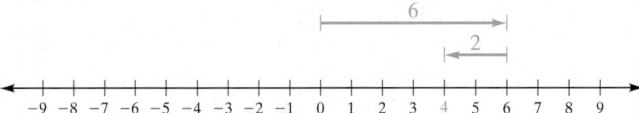

The sum is 4. The result is positive, because although the moves were in opposite directions, the larger move was in the positive direction. The absolute value of this sum is the difference in the absolute values of the addends, because the moves were in different directions and overlapped each other.

We are now ready to use the addition rules we have discovered and illustrated. Let's begin with examples of integers to prepare us for the more complicated exercises that follow.

| EXAMPLE 1 | Add and check using your calculator.

a. $8 + (-2)$ **b.** $-6 + (-5)$ **c.** $-7 + 3$

Solution

Check

a. $8 + (-2) = 6$

Unlike signs: The sum is positive because $|8| > |-2|$ and 8 is positive. The difference of the absolute values of the addends is $|8| - |-2| = 6$. Therefore, the sum is positive 6.

b. $-6 + (-5) = -11$

Like signs: The sum is the same sign as the addends: negative. The sum of the absolute values of the addends is $|-6| + |-5| = 11$. Therefore, the sum is negative 11.

c. $-7 + 3 = -4$

Unlike signs: The sum is negative because $|-7| > |3|$ and -7 is negative. The difference of the absolute values of the addends is $|-7| - |3| = 4$. Therefore, the sum is negative 4.

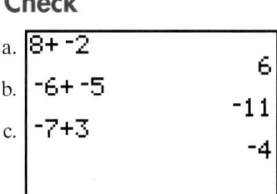

EXAMPLE 2   Add and check.

a. $-4.89 + 6.4$ **b.** $-12.5 + (-2)$ **c.** $\dfrac{1}{2} + \left(-\dfrac{2}{3}\right)$ **d.** $-1\dfrac{2}{3} + 2\dfrac{3}{5}$

Solution

a. $-4.89 + 6.4 = 1.51$

Unlike signs: The sum is positive because $|6.4| > |-4.89|$ and 6.4 is positive. The difference of the absolute values of the addends is $|6.4| - |-4.89| = 1.51$. Therefore, the sum is positive 1.51.

b. $-12.5 + (-2) = -14.5$

Like signs: The sum is the same sign as the addends: negative. The sum of the absolute values of the addends is $|-12.5| + |-2| = 14.5$. Therefore, the sum is negative 14.5.

c. $\dfrac{1}{2} + \left(-\dfrac{2}{3}\right) = \dfrac{3}{6} + \left(-\dfrac{4}{6}\right)$

$= -\dfrac{1}{6}$

Unlike signs: First, convert the fractions to their lowest common denominator: $\frac{1}{2} = \frac{3}{6}$ and $-\frac{2}{3} = -\frac{4}{6}$. The sum is negative because $|-\frac{4}{6}| > |\frac{3}{6}|$ and $-\frac{4}{6}$ is negative. The difference of the absolute values of the addends is $|-\frac{4}{6}| - |\frac{3}{6}| = \frac{1}{6}$. Therefore, the sum is negative $\frac{1}{6}$.

d. $-1\dfrac{2}{3} + 2\dfrac{3}{5} = -1\dfrac{10}{15} + 2\dfrac{9}{15}$

$= -\dfrac{25}{15} + \dfrac{39}{15}$

$= \dfrac{14}{15}$

Unlike signs: Convert the fractions to their lowest common denominator: 15. Convert the mixed numbers to improper fractions. The sum is positive because $|\frac{39}{15}| > |-\frac{25}{15}|$ and $\frac{39}{15}$ is positive. The difference of the absolute values of the addends is $|\frac{39}{15}| - |-\frac{25}{15}| = \frac{14}{15}$. Therefore, the sum is positive $\frac{14}{15}$.

The checks for Examples 2c and 2d are shown in **Figure P.4**.

TECHNOLOGY   Adding Rational Numbers

Add.   **c.** $\dfrac{1}{2} + \left(-\dfrac{2}{3}\right)$ **d.** $-1\dfrac{2}{3} + 2\dfrac{3}{5}$

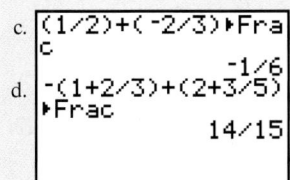

Figure P.4

(continued on page 18)

For **Figure P.4**,

c. Enter the fractions, $\frac{1}{2}$ and $-\frac{2}{3}$, in parentheses for proper grouping and ease in reading. Choose to have the answer displayed as a fraction. This option, ▶ FRAC, is located under the MATH menu option 1.

(1 ÷ 2) + ((−) 2 ÷ 3) MATH 1 ENTER

d. Mixed numbers are written as the sum of the whole number and the fraction. Negative mixed numbers have the negative sign outside the parentheses. Choose to have the answer displayed as a fraction by using option 1 under the MATH menu.

(−) (1 + 2 ÷ 3) + (2 + 3 ÷ 5)
MATH 1 ENTER

EXAMPLE 3   Add and check.

a. $13 + 15 + (-17) + 14 + (-16)$

b. $-\frac{2}{3} + \left(-\frac{1}{6}\right) + \frac{3}{8} + \left(-\frac{5}{12}\right)$

Solution

a. $13 + 15 + (-17) + 14 + (-16)$
$= 28 + (-17) + 14 + (-16)$ Add the numbers
$= 11 + 14 + (-16)$ from left to right.
$= 25 + (-16)$
$= 9$

Check

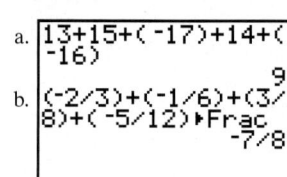

a. 13+15+(-17)+14+(
-16)
                    9
b. (-2/3)+(-1/6)+(3/
8)+(-5/12)▶Frac
                 -7/8

Another way to do Example 3a is to determine the sum of the positive numbers and the sum of the negative numbers:

$13 + 15 + 14 = 42$ Sum the positive numbers.
$-17 + (-16) = -33$ Sum the negative numbers.

Then add these results:

$42 + (-33) = 9$

b. $-\frac{2}{3} + \left(-\frac{1}{6}\right) + \frac{3}{8} + \left(-\frac{5}{12}\right) = -\frac{16}{24} + \left(-\frac{4}{24}\right) + \frac{9}{24} + \left(-\frac{10}{24}\right)$ Change to the LCD of 24.

$= -\frac{20}{24} + \frac{9}{24} + \left(-\frac{10}{24}\right)$ Add from left to right.

$= -\frac{11}{24} + \left(-\frac{10}{24}\right)$

$= -\frac{21}{24} = -\frac{7}{8}$ Reduce to lowest terms.

✓ Objective P.2.1 CHECKUP

Im exercises 1–3, add and check.

1. a. $9 + (-4)$ **b.** $-7 + (-8)$
   c. $-9 + 3$

2. a. $-5.9 + 4.32$ **b.** $-4 + (-2.6)$
   c. $-\frac{5}{7} + \frac{3}{4}$ **d.** $3\frac{1}{4} + \left(-1\frac{2}{3}\right)$

3. a. $-13 + 52 + 2 + (-13) + (-21)$

   b. $\frac{1}{4} + \left(-\frac{3}{5}\right) + \frac{1}{2} + \left(-\frac{3}{10}\right) + \left(-\frac{3}{20}\right)$

4. When you use your calculator to add mixed numbers, it is necessary to enclose the number in parentheses, with any negative signs outside the parentheses. Explain why this is so.

Objective P.2.2   **Evaluating Differences of Rational Numbers**

When two rational numbers are subtracted, we obtain a **difference**. The numbers that we subtract are called the **minuend** and **subtrahend**. We do not use these terms often, but they are useful for describing the process of subtraction.

$$10 \quad - \quad 4 \quad = \quad 6 \qquad\qquad 4 \quad - \quad 10 \quad = \quad -6$$

minuend — subtrahend = difference   minuend — subtrahend = difference

Note that the order in which we subtract does change the difference. Subtraction is *not* commutative.

Once again, we will use the calculator to explore the rules underlying mathematical operations. This time, we investigate the subtraction of rational numbers.

When we subtract two nonzero rational numbers, we have any of three combinations. The two numbers may be both positive, both negative, or a positive number and a negative number. Complete the following sets of exercises with your calculator. (Remember to use $\boxed{(\text{--})}$ for a negative number and $\boxed{-}$ for subtraction.)

💡 **Guided Discovery 2**   Subtracting Two Rational Numbers

Evaluate each expression, and compare the results obtained in part **a** with the corresponding results in part **b**.

1. a. $6 - 2 =$ ____   **b.** $6 + (-2) =$ ____

2. a. $3 - 9 =$ ____   **b.** $3 + (-9) =$ ____

3. a. $-6 - (-2) =$ ____   **b.** $-6 + 2 =$ ____

4. a. $-3 - (-9) =$ ____   **b.** $-3 + 9 =$ ____

5. a. $6 - (-2) =$ ____   **b.** $6 + 2 =$ ____

6. a. $-3 - 9 =$ ____   **b.** $-3 + (-9) =$ ____

For exercises 1 and 2, state a rule for writing the difference of two positive rational numbers.

For exercises 3 and 4, state a rule for writing the difference of two negative rational numbers.

For exercises 5 and 6, state a rule for writing the difference of a positive and a negative rational number.

Note that the same rule was used to describe all of the exercises.

In part **a**, we subtract two rational numbers. In part **b**, we add the minuend and the opposite of the subtrahend. The results are the same.

SUBTRACTION OF RATIONAL NUMBERS

To subtract two rational numbers, add the minuend to the opposite of the subtrahend.

To check the rules of subtraction that we discovered, we need to remember that subtraction is related to addition. Therefore, we can write a subtraction expression as a related addition expression:

$$8 \quad - \quad 3 \quad = \quad 5 \text{ is related to } 5 \quad + \quad 3 \quad = \quad 8.$$

minuend — subtrahend = difference   difference + subtrahend = minuend

We will check examples from the previous discovery sets using this relationship.

$$6 - 2 = \underline{\quad} \text{ is related to } \underline{\quad} + 2 = 6$$

The missing difference is 4.

$$-6 - (-2) = \underline{\quad} \text{ is related to } \underline{\quad} + -2 = -6$$

The missing difference is −4.

$$6 - (-2) = \underline{\quad} \text{ is related to } \underline{\quad} + -2 = 6$$

The missing difference is 8.

We are now ready to use the subtraction rules we have discovered and illustrated. We first perform subtraction on integers in order to prepare ourselves for the more complicated problems that follow.

EXAMPLE 4   Subtract and check using your calculator.

a. $8 - 12$ **b.** $-9 - (-6)$ **c.** $-7 - 3$ **d.** $4 - (-12)$

Solution   **Check**

a. $8 - 12 = 8 + (-12)$ *Change the subtraction to addition*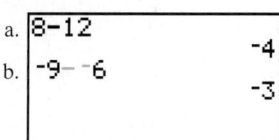

$ = -4$ *and take the opposite of 12.*
Then add.

b. $-9 - (-6) = -9 + 6$ *Change the subtraction to addition*
and take the opposite of -6.

$ = -3$ *Then add.*

c. $-7 - 3 = -7 + (-3)$ *Change the subtraction to addition*
and take the opposite of 3.

$ = -10$ *Then add.*

d. $4 - (-12) = 4 + 12$ *Change the subtraction to addition*
and take the opposite of -12.

$ = 16$ *Then add.*

> **TAKE NOTE** In Example 4b and 4d, the calculator will display different symbols for the minus sign and the opposite symbol.

EXAMPLE 5   Subtract and check.

a. $9.6 - (-3.8)$ **b.** $0 - (-8.9)$ **c.** $-\dfrac{2}{5} - \dfrac{1}{3}$ **d.** $\dfrac{1}{4} - \left(-1\dfrac{1}{2}\right)$

Solution

a. $9.6 - (-3.8) = 9.6 + 3.8$ *Add the opposite of -3.8.*

$ = 13.4$

b. $0 - (-8.9) = 0 + 8.9$ *Add the opposite of -8.9.*

$ = 8.9$

c. $-\dfrac{2}{5} - \dfrac{1}{3} = -\dfrac{2}{5} + \left(-\dfrac{1}{3}\right)$ *Add the opposite of $\frac{1}{3}$.*

$\phantom{-\dfrac{2}{5} - \dfrac{1}{3}} = -\dfrac{6}{15} + \left(-\dfrac{5}{15}\right)$ *Change to the lowest common denominator, LCD, of 5 and 3.*

$\phantom{-\dfrac{2}{5} - \dfrac{1}{3}} = -\dfrac{11}{15}$

d. $\dfrac{1}{4} - \left(-1\dfrac{1}{2}\right) = \dfrac{1}{4} + 1\dfrac{1}{2}$ *Add the opposite of $-1\frac{1}{2}$.*

$\phantom{\dfrac{1}{4} - \left(-1\dfrac{1}{2}\right)} = \dfrac{1}{4} + 1\dfrac{2}{4}$ *Change to the LCD of 4 and 2.*

$\phantom{\dfrac{1}{4} - \left(-1\dfrac{1}{2}\right)} = 1\dfrac{3}{4}$

The checks for Examples 5a and 5d are shown in **Figure P.5**.

TECHNOLOGY   Subtracting Rational Numbers

Subtract.   **a.** $9.6 - (-3.8)$ **d.** $\dfrac{1}{4} - \left(-1\dfrac{1}{2}\right)$

```
a. 9.6--3.8
              13.4
d. (1/4)--(1+1/2)▶F
rac
               7/4
```

Figure P.5

For **Figure P.5**,

a. Negative integers and decimals may be entered without the parentheses. Note the difference in the negative, ⎡(–)⎤, and the minus. ⎡–⎤.

⎡9⎤ ⎡.⎤ ⎡6⎤ ⎡–⎤ ⎡(–)⎤ ⎡3⎤ ⎡.⎤ ⎡8⎤ ⎡ENTER⎤

d. Enter the fraction, $\frac{1}{4}$, in parentheses for proper grouping and ease in reading. Negative mixed numbers have the negative sign outside the parentheses. Choose to have the answer displayed as a fraction. This option, ▶ FRAC, is located under the MATH menu option 1.

⎡(⎤ ⎡1⎤ ⎡÷⎤ ⎡4⎤ ⎡)⎤ ⎡–⎤ ⎡(–)⎤ ⎡(⎤ ⎡1⎤ ⎡+⎤ ⎡1⎤ ⎡÷⎤ ⎡2⎤ ⎡)⎤ ⎡MATH⎤
⎡1⎤ ⎡ENTER⎤

✓ Objective **P.2.2** **CHECKUP**

In exercises 1 and 2, subtract and check.

1. a. $10 - 12$ **b.** $-8 - (-9)$ **2. a.** $-8.75 - 3$ **b.** $0 - 4.5$
   c. $-4 - 8$ **d.** $3 - (-6)$ **c.** $-\dfrac{5}{7} - \dfrac{3}{4}$ **d.** $1\dfrac{1}{3} - \left(-2\dfrac{2}{3}\right)$

Objective **P.2.3**   **Evaluating Products of Rational Numbers**

When two rational numbers are multiplied, we obtain a **product**. The numbers that we multiply are called **factors**. We will use these terms as we discuss multiplying rational numbers.

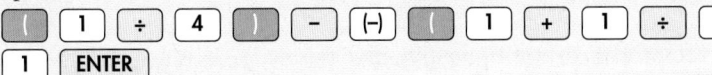

$$6 \times 3 = 18 \qquad 6 \cdot 3 = 18 \qquad (6)(3) = 18$$
factor × factor = product   factor · factor = product   (factor)(factor) = product

The order in which we multiply two rational numbers does not change the product.

$$6 \cdot 2 = 2 \cdot 6$$

COMMUTATIVE LAW FOR MULTIPLICATION

Changing the order of two rational-number factors does not change the product.

Also, changing the grouping when multiplying three rational numbers does not change the product.

$$(6 \cdot 2) \cdot 4 = 6 \cdot (2 \cdot 4)$$

ASSOCIATIVE LAW FOR MULTIPLICATION

Changing the grouping of three rational-number factors does not change the product.

Four additional properties of multiplication should be noted. The first property we discuss is the **identity property of 1**. Multiplying any rational number by 1 results in the number itself. Therefore, 1 is called the **multiplicative identity**.

$$(6)(1) = 6$$

An extension of this property is multiplying a rational number by -1. The product is the opposite of the rational number. Therefore, the **multiplication property of -1** states that the product of -1 and a rational number is the opposite of the rational number itself.

$$6(-1) = -6$$

Another property we use in multiplication is the **multiplicative inverse property**. When we multiply a nonzero rational number by its **reciprocal**, the product is 1. Therefore, the reciprocal is sometimes called the **multiplicative inverse** of a rational number.

$$\frac{2}{3} \cdot \left(\frac{3}{2}\right) = 1$$

Thus, $\frac{2}{3}$ and $\frac{3}{2}$ are reciprocals or multiplicative inverses.

The result of multiplying any rational number by 0 is 0. This property is referred to as the **multiplication property of 0**.

$$0 \cdot 5 = 0$$

As before, we use the calculator to perform mathematical operations so that we can discover the rules that govern these operations. In this case, we want to discover the rules for multiplication of rational numbers.

When we multiply two rational numbers, there are two possible combinations: The two numbers may have like signs; the two numbers may have unlike signs. Complete the following set of exercises with your calculator.

Guided Discovery 3   Multiplying Two Rational Numbers

Evaluate each expression, and compare the results obtained in part **a** with the corresponding results in part **b**.

1. a. $3 \cdot 2 =$ _____   **b.** $|3| \cdot |2| =$ _____

2. a. $-3 \cdot (-2) =$ _____   **b.** $|-3| \cdot |-2| =$ _____

3. a. $3 \cdot (-2) =$ _____   **b.** $|3| \cdot |-2| =$ _____

4. a. $-3 \cdot 2 =$ _____   **b.** $|-3| \cdot |2| =$ _____

For exercises 1 and 2, state a rule for writing the product of two rational numbers with like signs.

For exercises 3 and 4, state a rule for writing the product of two rational numbers with unlike signs.

In part **a** of the first two exercises, we multiply two rational numbers with like sign. Each product results in a positive number. In part **b**, we multiply the absolute values of the factors. The results are the same.

In part **a** of the last two exercises, we multiply two rational numbers with unlike signs. Each product results in a negative number. In part **b**, we multiply the absolute values of the factors. The results are the opposite of those in part **a**.

MULTIPLICATION OF RATIONAL NUMBERS

To multiply two rational numbers with like signs (both positive or both negative),

- Multiply the absolute values of the factors.
- The sign of the product is positive.

To multiply rational numbers with unlike signs (one positive and one negative),

- Multiply the absolute values of the factors.
- The sign of the product is negative.

To understand the rules of multiplication that we have just discovered, we need to remember that multiplication is a shortcut for repeated addition. If we work two examples in the preceding discovery set, the results are

$$3 \cdot 2 = 2 + 2 + 2 = 6 \qquad \text{three two's}$$
$$3 \cdot (-2) = (-2) + (-2) + (-2) = -6 \qquad \text{three negative two's}$$

A problem occurs when we try to multiply two negative numbers.

$$-3 \cdot (-2) = \qquad \text{How do we write negative two a negative three times?}$$

Let's look at the following pattern and see if we can infer that this product is really 6:

$$2(-2) = -4$$
first factor decreases by one $$1(-2) = -2 \qquad \text{product increases by two}$$
$$0(-2) = 0$$
$$-1(-2) = 2$$
$$-2(-2) = 4$$
$$-3(-2) = \underline{\quad} \qquad \text{(Using the preceding pattern, we see that this answer must be 6.)}$$

Therefore, $-3(-2) = 6$.

We are now ready to use the multiplication rules we have discovered and illustrated. Once again, we begin with examples of integers.

EXAMPLE 6

Multiply and check using your calculator.

a. $8(-2)$ **b.** $-6(-5)$ **c.** $-7 \cdot 3$

Solution

a. $8(-2) = -16$ Unlike signs: The product is negative. The product of the absolute values of the factors is $|8| \cdot |-2| = 16$. Therefore, the product is negative 16.

b. $-6(-5) = 30$ Like signs: The product is positive. The product of the absolute values of the factors is $|-6| \cdot |-5| = 30$. Therefore, the product is positive 30.

c. $-7 \cdot 3 = -21$ Unlike signs: The product is negative. The product of the absolute values of the factors is $|-7| \cdot |3| = 21$. Therefore, the product is negative 21.

Check

```
a. 8*-2
              -16
b. -6*-5
               30
c. -7*3
              -21
```

EXAMPLE 7

Multiply and check.

a. $(-4.89)(-6.4)$ **b.** $(-8.9)(0)$ **c.** $\frac{1}{2} \cdot -\frac{1}{3}$ **d.** $-1\frac{2}{3} \cdot 2\frac{3}{5}$

Solution

a. $(-4.89)(-6.4) = 31.296$ Like signs: The product is positive. The product of the absolute values of the factors is $|-4.89| \cdot |-6.4| = 31.296$. Therefore, the product is positive 31.296.

b. $(-8.9)(0) = 0$ *The product of a number and 0 is 0.*

c. $\dfrac{1}{2} \cdot -\dfrac{1}{3} = -\dfrac{1}{6}$ *Unlike signs: The product is negative. The product of the absolute values of the factors is $\left|\frac{1}{2}\right| \cdot \left|-\frac{1}{3}\right| = \frac{1}{6}$. Therefore, the product is negative $\frac{1}{6}$.*

d. $-1\dfrac{2}{3} \cdot 2\dfrac{3}{5} = -\dfrac{5}{3} \cdot \dfrac{13}{5}$ *Unlike signs: The product is negative. Change the mixed numbers to improper fractions and multiply. The product of the absolute values of the factors is $\left|-\frac{5}{3}\right| \cdot \left|\frac{13}{5}\right| = \frac{65}{15}$. Therefore, the product is negative $\frac{65}{15}$.*

$\qquad\qquad = -\dfrac{65}{15}$

$\qquad\qquad = -\dfrac{13}{3}$

$\qquad\qquad = -4\dfrac{1}{3}$ *Reduce the fraction and change to a mixed number.*

The checks for Examples 7a and 7d are shown in **Figure P.6**.

TECHNOLOGY   Multiplying Rational Numbers

Multiply.   **a.** $(-4.89)(-6.4)$ **d.** $-1\dfrac{2}{3} \cdot 2\dfrac{3}{5}$

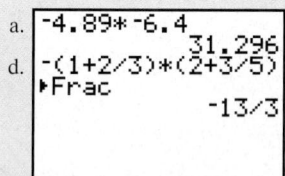

a.
```
-4.89*-6.4
            31.296
```
d.
```
-(1+2/3)*(2+3/5)
▶Frac
            -13/3
```

Figure P.6

For **Figure P.6**,
a. There is no need to place the decimal numbers in parentheses. You may use the multiplication sign instead.

[(-)] [4] [.] [8] [9] [×] [(-)] [6] [.] [4] [ENTER]

d. Place the negative mixed number as a sum in parentheses with the negative outside the grouping. Choose to have your answer displayed as a fraction. This option, ▶ FRAC, is located under the MATH menu option 1.

[(-)] [(] [1] [+] [2] [÷] [3] [)] [×] [(] [2] [+] [3] [÷] [5] [)]
[MATH] [1] [ENTER]

We again use the calculator to perform mathematical operations so that we can discover underlying rules. In this case, we want to discover the rules for multiplication of multiple factors. Complete the following exercises with your calculator.

💡 Guided Discovery 4   Multiplying Three or More Nonzero Rational Numbers

Evaluate each expression, and compare the results obtained in exercise 1 with the results in exercise 2.

1. a. one negative factor $-6 \cdot 3 \cdot 4 \cdot 1 = $ _____

  b. three negative factors $-6 \cdot (-3) \cdot (-4) \cdot 1 = $ _____

2. a. two negative factors $-6 \cdot (-3) \cdot 4 \cdot 1 = $ _____

  b. four negative factors $-6 \cdot (-3) \cdot (-4) \cdot (-1) = $ _____

State a rule for determining the sign of the product of three or more rational numbers.

In exercise 1, an odd number of negative factors results in a negative product. In exercise 2, an even number of negative factors results in a positive product. This discovery is an extension of the rules of multiplication of nonzero factors.

EXAMPLE 8   Multiply and check.

a. $\left(\dfrac{1}{3}\right)\left(-\dfrac{5}{8}\right)\left(-\dfrac{5}{7}\right)$

b. $(-380)(257)(0)(25)$

Solution

a. $\left(\dfrac{1}{3}\right)\left(-\dfrac{5}{8}\right)\left(-\dfrac{5}{7}\right) = \dfrac{25}{168}$ This is an even number of negative factors (two). The product is positive. Multiply the absolute values of the factors from left to right.

b. $(-380)(257)(0)(25) = 0$ A factor of 0 results in a product of 0.

Check

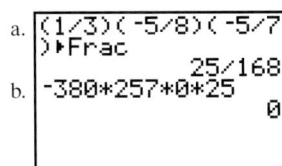

Objective P.2.3 **CHECKUP**

In exercises 1–3, multiply and check.

1. **a.** $-8(-4)$ **b.** $3(-5)$
   c. $-9 \cdot 8$

2. **a.** $(-7.2)(0.02)$ **b.** $0(-3.2)$
   c. $-\dfrac{1}{3} \cdot \left(-\dfrac{3}{4}\right)$ **d.** $2\dfrac{1}{4} \cdot \left(-1\dfrac{1}{3}\right)$

3. **a.** $\left(1\dfrac{5}{7}\right)\left(-3\dfrac{5}{9}\right)\left(-\dfrac{3}{4}\right)\left(-\dfrac{2}{3}\right)$
   b. $(2.5)(-3.5)(0)(5.6)(0)(3.9)$

Objective P.2.4   **Evaluating Quotients of Rational Numbers**

When two rational numbers are divided, we obtain a **quotient**. The numbers we divide are called the **dividend** and the **divisor**. We will use these terms when we discuss the division of rational numbers.

$$15 \ \div \ 3 \ = \ 5 \qquad\qquad 3\overline{)15}\,^{5} \qquad\qquad \dfrac{15}{3} \ = \ 5$$

dividend ÷ divisor = quotient   divisor)dividend quotient $\dfrac{\text{dividend}}{\text{divisor}}$ = quotient

When we divide two rational numbers, there are the same two combinations—like and unlike signs—as in the case of the multiplication rules. Complete the following set of exercises with your calculator.

💡 **Guided Discovery 5**   Dividing Two Rational Numbers

Evaluate each expression, and compare the results obtained in part **a** with the corresponding results in the part **b**.

1. **a.** $8 \div 2 =$ _____   **b.** $|8| \div |2| =$ _____

2. **a.** $-8 \div (-2) =$ _____   **b.** $|-8| \div |-2| =$ _____

3. **a.** $8 \div (-2) =$ _____   **b.** $|8| \div |-2| =$ _____

4. **a.** $-8 \div 2 =$ _____   **b.** $|-8| \div |2| =$ _____

In exercises 1 and 2, state a rule for writing the quotient of two rational numbers with like signs.

In exercises 3 and 4, state a rule for writing the quotient of two rational numbers with unlike signs.

In part **a**, when we divide two rational numbers with like signs, each quotient is a positive number. In part **b**, we divide the absolute values of the dividend and divisor. The results are the same.

In part **a**, when we divide two rational numbers with unlike signs, each quotient is a negative number. In part **b**, we divide the absolute values of the dividend and divisor. The results are the opposite of those in part **a**.

We may divide expressions involving 0. Complete the following set of exercises with your calculator.

 Guided Discovery 6   Division Involving Zero

Evaluate each expression.

1. $8 \div 0 =$ _____

2. $-8 \div 0 =$ _____

3. $0 \div 2 =$ _____

4. $0 \div (-5) =$ _____

5. $0 \div 0 =$ _____

In exercises 1 and 2, state a rule for dividing a rational number by 0.

In exercises 3 and 4, state a rule for dividing 0 by a rational number other than 0.

In exercise 5, state a rule for dividing 0 by 0.

Dividing a nonzero rational number by 0 results in an error on the calculator. That is, the quotient cannot be found when the divisor is 0. We call this quotient **undefined**.

Dividing 0 by any rational number other than 0 results in 0. Dividing 0 by 0 results in an error. The quotient is **indeterminate**.

🖉 **TAKE NOTE** "Undefined" and "indeterminate" do not mean the same thing. This is explained on the next page.

DIVISION OF RATIONAL NUMBERS

To divide two nonzero rational numbers with like signs (both positive or both negative),

- Divide the absolute values of the numbers.
- The sign of the quotient is positive.

To divide two nonzero rational numbers with unlike signs (one positive and one negative),

- Divide the absolute values of the numbers.
- The sign of the quotient is negative.

To divide 0 by a nonzero rational number, the result is 0.
To divide a nonzero rational number by 0 is undefined.
To divide 0 by 0 is indeterminate.

To check the rules of division that we have just discovered, we need to remember that division is related to multiplication. Therefore, we can write any division expression as a related multiplication expression. For example,

$$12 \div 4 = 3 \quad \text{is related to} \quad 3 \cdot 4 = 12$$

dividend ÷ divisor = quotient   quotient   divisor = dividend

If we use this fact, we can find a quotient by completing a multiplication expression. We will work examples from the previous discovery sets to understand this concept.

$$8 \div 2 = \underline{\quad} \text{ is related to } \underline{\quad} \cdot 2 = 8.$$
The missing quotient must be 4.

$$-8 \div (-2) = \underline{\quad} \text{ is related to } \underline{\quad} \cdot (-2) = -8.$$
The missing quotient must be 4.

$$8 \div (-2) = \underline{\quad} \text{ is related to } \underline{\quad} \cdot (-2) = 8.$$
The missing quotient must be -4.

$$-8 \div 2 = \underline{\quad} \text{ is related to } \underline{\quad} \cdot 2 = -8.$$
The missing quotient must be -4.

The divisions involving zero are especially important to understand. Study the following very carefully:

$$8 \div 0 = \underline{\quad} \text{ is related to } \underline{\quad} \cdot 0 = 8.$$
The missing quotient cannot be found, because 0 times any number results in 0, not 8. Therefore, we say the quotient is undefined.

$$0 \div 2 = \underline{\quad} \text{ is related to } \underline{\quad} \cdot 2 = 0.$$
The missing quotient must be 0.

$$0 \div 0 = \underline{\quad} \text{ is related to } \underline{\quad} \cdot 0 = 0.$$
The missing quotient could be any number. Since it is impossible to determine only one number that correctly completes this statement, we say the quotient is indeterminate.

We are now ready to use the division rules we have discovered and illustrated. Let's begin with examples of integers.

EXAMPLE 9

Divide and check using your calculator.

a. $8 \div (-4)$ **b.** $\dfrac{-6}{-2}$ **c.** $\dfrac{2}{-6}$

Solution

a. $8 \div (-4) = -2$ Unlike signs: The quotient is negative. The quotient of the absolute values of the numbers is $|8| \div |-4| = 2$. Therefore, the quotient is negative 2.

Check

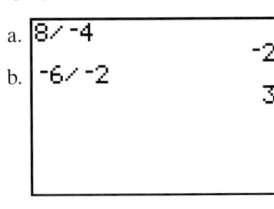

b. $\dfrac{-6}{-2} = 3$ Like signs: The quotient is positive. The quotient of the absolute values of the numbers is $|-6| \div |-2| = 3$. Therefore, the quotient is positive 3.

c. $\dfrac{2}{-6} = -\dfrac{1}{3}$ Unlike signs: The quotient is negative. The quotient of the absolute values of the numbers is $|2| \div |-6| = 0.33$, or $\frac{1}{3}$. Therefore, the quotient is negative 0.33, or negative $\frac{1}{3}$.

Even though it is correct to do so, there is no need to place the numbers in parentheses; enter the numbers with the division sign between them for faster entry. ■

EXAMPLE 10

Divide and check.

a. $1.2 \div (-3)$ **b.** $\dfrac{-12}{-0.8}$ **c.** $\dfrac{0}{-0.34}$ **d.** $-8.9 \div 0$ **e.** $0 \div 0$

Solution

a. $1.2 \div (-3) = -0.4$ Unlike signs: The quotient is negative. The quotient of the absolute values of the numbers is $|1.2| \div |-3| = 0.4$. Therefore, the quotient is negative 0.4.

b. $\dfrac{-12}{-0.8} = 15$ Like signs: The quotient is positive. The quotient of the absolute values of the numbers is $|-12| \div |-0.8| = 15$. Therefore, the quotient is positive 15.

c. $\dfrac{0}{-0.34} = 0$ *The quotient of 0 divided by a rational number other than 0 is 0.*

d. $8.9 \div 0$ is undefined.   *The quotient for a rational number other than 0 divided by 0 is undefined.*

e. $0 \div 0$ is indeterminate.   *The quotient 0 divided by 0 is indeterminate.*

The checks for Examples 10c and 10d are shown in **Figures P.7a** and **P.7b**.

TECHNOLOGY   Dividing Rational Numbers

Divide.   **c.** $\dfrac{0}{-0.34}$ **d.** $8.9 \div 0$

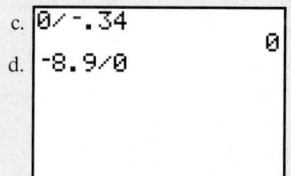

         Figure P.7a   Figure P.7b

For **Figures P.7a** and **P.7b**,
c. There is no need to enter the whole number 0 in the decimal -0.34.

[0] [÷] [(−)] [.] [3] [4] [ENTER]

d. Since it is not possible to divide by 0, an error is displayed on the screen when you enter the expression.

[(−)] [8] [.] [9] [÷] [0] [ENTER]

Press [ENTER] to quit the error screen and return to the default home screen.

✎ **TAKE NOTE** The calculator error message "Divide by 0" is not the answer for a division expression. You must determine if the quotient is "undefined" or "indeterminate."

We must remember that, to divide proper fractions, we change the division symbol to a multiplication symbol and change the divisor to its reciprocal. We then multiply the results.

EXAMPLE 11   Divide and check.

a. $-\dfrac{3}{4} \div \left(-\dfrac{1}{2}\right)$ **b.** $-1\dfrac{2}{3} \div 2\dfrac{3}{5}$ **c.** $\dfrac{2}{3} \div (-3)$

Solution   **Check**

a. $-\dfrac{3}{4} \div \left(-\dfrac{1}{2}\right) = -\dfrac{3}{4} \cdot \left(-\dfrac{2}{1}\right)$ *Change division to multiplication and change the divisor to its reciprocal. Use the rules of multiplication. The quotient is positive $\frac{3}{2}$.*

$= \dfrac{6}{4}$

$= \dfrac{3}{2}$

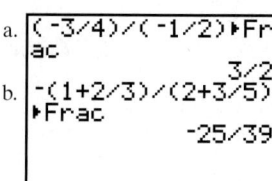

b. $-1\dfrac{2}{3} \div 2\dfrac{3}{5} = \dfrac{-5}{3} \div \dfrac{13}{5}$

$= \dfrac{-5}{3} \cdot \dfrac{5}{13}$

$= -\dfrac{25}{39}$

Change the mixed numbers to equivalent improper fractions. Change the division to multiplication and change the divisor to its reciprocal. Use the rules of multiplication. The quotient is negative $\frac{25}{39}$.

c. $\dfrac{2}{3} \div (-3) = \dfrac{2}{3} \div \left(\dfrac{-3}{1}\right)$

$= \dfrac{2}{3} \cdot \left(\dfrac{-1}{3}\right)$

$= -\dfrac{2}{9}$

Change the whole number to a fraction: $-3 = \frac{-3}{1}$. Change the division to multiplication and change the divisor to its reciprocal, $\frac{-1}{3}$. Use the rules of multiplication. The quotient is negative $\frac{2}{9}$.

c.
```
(2/3)/-3►Frac
              -2/9
```

When using your calculator, enter fractions in sets of parentheses for proper grouping and ease in reading.

✓ Objective P.2.4 *CHECKUP*

In exercises 1–3, divide and check.

1. a. $-12 \div (-4)$ **b.** $\dfrac{63}{-21}$ **c.** $\dfrac{-3}{-5}$

2. a. $36.9 \div (-9)$ **b.** $\dfrac{-18}{-0.5}$ **c.** $0 \div (-13.257)$ **d.** $\dfrac{3.14}{0}$ **e.** $\dfrac{0}{0}$

3. a. $-\dfrac{1}{3} \div \left(-\dfrac{3}{4}\right)$ **b.** $2\dfrac{1}{4} \div \left(-1\dfrac{1}{3}\right)$ **c.** $-\dfrac{1}{5} \div 2$

Objective P.2.5

Modeling the Real World

The rules for arithmetic operations on rational numbers are the same rules that govern situations involving these operations in our daily lives. Operations that involve totals or balances, such as totaling an amount spent in a store or balancing a bank account, can be written as rational expressions. Once we've decided how to represent real data as rational expressions, we add or subtract the expressions.

In our daily lives, many situations can be expressed as products of rational numbers. Whenever there is a repeated process, such as writing a check for the same amount several weeks in a row or paying rent every month for a year, we may represent the amount as a multiplication expression. Also, when we take a "percentage of" or "fractional part of" a value, we write a multiplication expression. In these cases, the rules for multiplication of rational numbers may be applied to obtain a product.

Many situations in our daily lives also involve the division of rational numbers. When we compare two quantities, we use a ratio. A **ratio** is the quotient of the two quantities. When the ratio compares two different kinds of measure, we call the ratio a **rate**. The rate (or speed) at which you travel in an automobile is given in miles per hour or kilometers per hour. The word *per* means division.

When we model real-world situations, it is best to always follow a logical set of steps.

MODELING REAL-WORLD SITUATIONS

To model a real-world situation,

- Read and understand the situation.
- Write an expression with the information given.
- Evaluate the expression.
- Check the value obtained.
- Write an answer to the question, using complete sentences.

EXAMPLE 12

Lorenzo is the owner of a handcrafted-furniture business. He is balancing his accounting records of transactions for the day. He took in three sales: $123.00, $798.00, and $563.00. He paid out to suppliers $699.38 for wood and $76.93 for varnish. He also received a credit from the phone company for $12.75 for an overpayment of his last bill. What is his account balance at the end of the day?

Solution

First, understand the situation. We begin with the sum of the positive numbers that represent amounts taken in from sales. We subtract from these positive numbers the amount paid out to each supplier. A credit is a return of an amount paid out. We subtract (a return) a negative amount (amount paid out).

Second, write an expression:

$$\underset{\text{sales}}{123.00} + \underset{\text{sales}}{798.00} + \underset{\text{sales}}{563.00} - \underset{\text{supplies}}{699.38} - \underset{\text{supplies}}{76.93} - \underset{\text{credit}}{(-12.75)}$$

Third, evaluate the expression. Change all subtractions to additions and the number following each subtraction symbol to its opposite. Note that subtracting a credit is the same as adding a positive amount. The result is

$$123.00 + 798.00 + 563.00 + (-699.38) + (-76.93) + 12.75$$

Next, add all the positive numbers and all the negative numbers, and find the sum of the two sums:

$$123.00 + 798.00 + 563.00 + 12.75 = 1496.75$$
$$-699.38 + (-76.93) = -776.31$$
$$1496.75 + (-776.31) = 720.44$$

Check your results.
Finally, answer the question.
Lorenzo had a balance of $720.44 at the end of the day. ■

Check

```
123.00+798.00+56
3.00-699.38-76.9
3--12.75
            720.44
```

EXAMPLE 13

According to the American Association of Community Colleges, women make up 58% of the community college enrollment. In 2004, 10.4 million students were enrolled in community colleges in the United States. Determine the number of women enrolled in community colleges in 2004.

Solution

To determine the number of women enrolled, determine 58% of 10.4 million. Change 58% to a decimal (58% = 0.58) and multiply.

$$58\% \text{ of } 10.4 = 0.58 \cdot 10.4$$
$$= 6.032$$

The number of women enrolled in community colleges in the United States in 2004 is 6.032 million. ■

EXAMPLE 14   The human heart pumps 4 liters of blood in 90 seconds. Determine the human heart rate in liters per second. How many liters are pumped in 1 minute?

Solution

The heart rate is given in liters per second, so we will divide the number of liters by the number of seconds.

$$\frac{4 \text{ liters}}{90 \text{ seconds}} = \frac{2 \text{ liters}}{45 \text{ seconds}} = \frac{2 \text{ liters}}{45 \text{ seconds}}$$

The human heart rate is $\frac{2}{45}$ liter per second. In one minute, or 60 seconds, the heart will pump 60 times the rate per second.

$$\frac{60 \text{ seconds}}{1 \text{ minute}} \cdot \frac{2 \text{ liters}}{45 \text{ seconds}} = \frac{120 \text{ liters}}{1 \text{ minute}} = \frac{8 \text{ liters}}{1 \text{ minute}} = 2\frac{2}{3}\frac{\text{ liters}}{1 \text{ minute}}$$

The heart will pump $2\frac{2}{3}$ liters of blood per minute. ■

APPLICATION

Mount Everest, the highest point in Tibet, is estimated to be 8850 meters above sea level. The lowest point in China, Turpan Pendi, is 154 meters below sea level. Determine the range of the terrain (the difference of the highest and lowest points).

Discussion

The elevation of Mount Everest is 8850 meters, and that of Turpan Pendi is −154 meters. The range is determined by the difference of the highest point and the lowest points.

$$8850 - (-154) = 8850 + 154 = 9004$$

The range of the terrain in China is 9004 meters.

✓ Objective P.2.5 *CHECKUP*

1. At the start of the month, Beverly's checking account showed a balance of $897.63. During the month, she added to her account by making two deposits: one for $355.00 and another for $572.00. During the same month, she decreased her account by making two withdrawals: one for $120.00 and another for $300.00. She wrote three checks for $185.23, $104.50, and $231.97. However, she stopped payment on the last check, thereby subtracting the deduction from her account. The bank charged $10.00 to stop payment on the check. Write an addition-and-subtraction problem to represent these transactions. What is the current balance in Beverly's account?

2. According to the American Association of Community Colleges, men make up 42% of the community college enrollment. In 2004, 10.4 million students were enrolled in community colleges in the United States. Determine the number of men enrolled in community colleges in 2004.

3. The caseload in a hospital ward is 15 patients for two nurses. Determine the rate of assignment of cases per nurse. How many cases can a ward handle if it employs 12 nurses?

4. The dormant volcano Mauna Kea could be considered the tallest mountain. Its base in the Hawaiian Trough is 19,680 feet below sea level. Its summit is 13,796 feet above sea level. Determine the height of the volcano. ■

P.2 EXERCISES

Student Solutions Manual   PH Math/Tutor Center   CD Video   MathXL®   MyMathLab   Interactmath.com

Add and check.

1. $-7 + 9$ **2.** $-5 + 6$ **3.** $-9 + (-2)$ **4.** $(-2) + (-3)$

5. $5 + (-7)$ **6.** $7 + (-9)$ **7.** $32 + (-579)$ **8.** $703 + (-21)$

9. $2.7 + 3.96$ **10.** $0.06 + 3.1$ **11.** $1.2 + (-2.5)$ **12.** $-5.5 + 2.7$

13. $-2.73 + 4.1$ **14.** $3.9 + (-1.81)$ **15.** $-1.1 + (-2.27)$ **16.** $-3.5 + (-7.9)$

17. $-\dfrac{3}{5} + \left(-\dfrac{1}{2}\right)$ **18.** $-\dfrac{1}{4} + \left(-\dfrac{3}{7}\right)$ **19.** $-\dfrac{7}{9} + \dfrac{1}{6}$ **20.** $-\dfrac{3}{8} + \dfrac{1}{12}$

21. $\dfrac{2}{3} + \left(-\dfrac{2}{9}\right)$ **22.** $\dfrac{5}{6} + \left(-\dfrac{1}{3}\right)$ **23.** $-2\dfrac{3}{4} + 3\dfrac{2}{3}$ **24.** $-1\dfrac{4}{5} + 4\dfrac{2}{3}$

25. $17 + (-23) + 0 + 13$ **26.** $32 + 0 + (-14) + 72$ **27.** $23 + 56 + (-34) + (-12) + (-68) + 31$

28. $132 + 239 + (-141) + (-53) + 75 + (-18)$ **29.** $-\dfrac{1}{2} + \dfrac{1}{3} + \left(-\dfrac{1}{4}\right)$ **30.** $\dfrac{2}{5} + \left(-\dfrac{1}{2}\right) + \left(-\dfrac{3}{4}\right)$

31. $1\dfrac{1}{5} + \left(-2\dfrac{3}{10}\right) + \dfrac{4}{5} + \dfrac{7}{10} + \left(-\dfrac{3}{5}\right)$ **32.** $1\dfrac{1}{3} + 2\dfrac{3}{5} + \left(-5\dfrac{2}{3}\right) + 1\dfrac{2}{5} + \dfrac{4}{15}$

Subtract and check.

33. $-7 - 9$ **34.** $-10 - 2$ **35.** $-9 - (-2)$ **36.** $-12 - (-6)$

37. $5 - (-13)$ **38.** $12 - (-4)$ **39.** $1.2 - (-2.5)$ **40.** $-3.5 - (-7.9)$

41. $-1.1 - (-2.27)$ **42.** $3.9 - (-1.81)$ **43.** $-\dfrac{3}{5} - \left(-\dfrac{1}{2}\right)$ **44.** $-\dfrac{1}{4} - \left(-\dfrac{3}{7}\right)$

45. $-\dfrac{7}{9} - \dfrac{1}{6}$ **46.** $-\dfrac{3}{8} - \dfrac{1}{12}$ **47.** $\dfrac{3}{7} - 3$ **48.** $\dfrac{3}{5} - 2$

49. $-5 - \left(-1\dfrac{4}{5}\right)$ **50.** $-7 - \left(-3\dfrac{2}{3}\right)$ **51.** $3\dfrac{2}{3} - 5$ **52.** $4\dfrac{1}{4} - 6$

Multiply and check.

53. $-3 \cdot (-8)$ **54.** $-4 \cdot (-7)$ **55.** $5 \cdot (-3)$ **56.** $9 \cdot (-4)$

57. $-2 \cdot 10$ **58.** $-8 \cdot 6$ **59.** $45 \cdot (-3)$ **60.** $56 \cdot (-4)$

61. $-32 \cdot (-4)$ **62.** $-55 \cdot (-11)$ **63.** $0 \cdot (-15)$ **64.** $-2 \cdot 0$

65. $(-1.7)(-0.2)$ **66.** $(-34.2)(-2)$ **67.** $(24.3)(0.3)$ **68.** $(0.5)(10)$

69. $(-0.25)(50)$ **70.** $(-5.7)(0.19)$ **71.** $\left(\dfrac{2}{5}\right)\left(\dfrac{25}{48}\right)$ **72.** $\left(\dfrac{11}{17}\right)\left(\dfrac{2}{3}\right)$

73. $\left(1\dfrac{2}{3}\right)\left(-\dfrac{3}{4}\right)$ **74.** $\left(-1\dfrac{1}{5}\right)\left(-\dfrac{5}{6}\right)$ **75.** $\left(-\dfrac{4}{7}\right)\left(\dfrac{3}{16}\right)$ **76.** $\left(-\dfrac{15}{17}\right)\left(\dfrac{5}{9}\right)$

77. $(-2)(-3)(-4)(-10)(20)$ **78.** $(-5)(-4)(6)(-100)(-5)$ **79.** $\left(-\dfrac{1}{5}\right)\left(-\dfrac{2}{3}\right)\left(-\dfrac{4}{5}\right)\left(\dfrac{1}{2}\right)$

80. $\left(-\dfrac{5}{7}\right)\left(\dfrac{14}{25}\right)\left(-\dfrac{2}{5}\right)\left(\dfrac{1}{3}\right)$ **81.** $(5.2)(-0.1)(-2.2)$ **82.** $(-2.9)(-1.1)(0.2)$

83. $(14)(0)(-35)(0)(-312)$ **84.** $(-1.4)(0)(3.76)(0)(-45.2)$

Divide and check.

85. $15 \div (-3)$ **86.** $32 \div (-4)$ **87.** $-32 \div (-4)$ **88.** $-55 \div (-11)$

89. $27 \div 3$ **90.** $16 \div 2$ **91.** $0 \div (-15)$ **92.** $0 \div 12$

93. $26 \div (-0.13)$ **94.** $-54 \div 0.6$ **95.** $-1.7 \div (-0.2)$ **96.** $0.5 \div 10$

97. $-2.7 \div (-2.7)$ **98.** $3.4 \div (-3.4)$ **99.** $\dfrac{5}{-25}$ **100.** $\dfrac{-3}{6}$

101. $\dfrac{0.88}{-1.1}$ **102.** $\dfrac{-0.25}{50}$ **103.** $-\dfrac{1}{3} \div \left(-\dfrac{3}{7}\right)$ **104.** $-\dfrac{2}{5} \div \left(-\dfrac{5}{9}\right)$

105. $-\dfrac{4}{7} \div \dfrac{3}{16}$ **106.** $-\dfrac{15}{17} \div \dfrac{5}{9}$ **107.** $-\dfrac{2}{3} \div \left(-\dfrac{2}{3}\right)$ **108.** $-\dfrac{2}{3} \div \dfrac{3}{2}$

109. $\dfrac{8}{9} \div 4$ **110.** $-\dfrac{7}{8} \div 2$ **111.** $1\dfrac{2}{3} \div \left(-\dfrac{3}{4}\right)$ **112.** $2\dfrac{1}{5} \div \left(-\dfrac{1}{3}\right)$

Write and evaluate an addition or subtraction expression for each situation. Interpret the result.

113. In 2003, projections of the resident populations for states showed that the state of California grew by 1,612,000 people over its 2000 census of 33,872,000. What was the 2003 projected population for California?

114. In 2003, projections of the resident populations for states showed that the state of North Dakota decreased by 8,000 people from its 2000 census of 642,000. What was the 2003 projected population for North Dakota?

115. According to the *Guinness Book of World Records,* one of the greatest temperature ranges in the world occurs in Siberia. Temperatures at Verkhoyansk have ranged from $-90°$F to $98°$F. What is the range of these temperatures? (The range is calculated as the high value minus the low value.)

116. One of the greatest temperature variations recorded in one day occurred at Browning, Montana, from $44°$F to $-56°$F, on January 23–24, 1916. What was the range of temperatures that day?

117. The mean surface temperature of the Moon has been reported to be $130°$C during the lunar day and $-180°$C at night. What is the change in mean surface temperature from lunar day to night?

118. The mean surface temperature of the planet Mercury has been reported to be $350°$C during the day and $-170°$C during the night. What is the change in mean surface temperature during these times?

119. The highest point in the United States is Mount McKinley, Alaska, which has an elevation of 20,320 feet above sea level. The lowest point in the United States is Death Valley, California, which has an elevation of 282 feet below sea level. Find the range between the highest point and the lowest point.

120. The highest point in the state of Louisiana is Driskill Mountain, which has an elevation of 163 meters above sea level. The lowest point in Louisiana is New Orleans, which has an elevation of 2 meters below sea level. Find the range between these highest and lowest points.

121. A cookie recipe requires $\frac{1}{2}$ cup of granulated sugar, $\frac{1}{4}$ cup of brown sugar, 1 cup of sifted all-purpose flour, 1 cup of semi-sweet chocolate pieces, and $\frac{1}{2}$ cup of chopped nuts. How many cups of dry ingredients does the recipe use?

122. A quilting pattern requires $1\frac{1}{4}$ yards of solid blue material, $\frac{3}{4}$ yard of yellow floral material, $\frac{1}{2}$ yard of green floral material, and $2\frac{1}{4}$ yards of navy plaid material. How many yards of material does the pattern use?

123. Karin is a saleswoman with a weekly quota of $5000 in sales. She keeps track of her sales by noting how much she is above her quota (a positive number) or how much she is below her quota (a negative number). Last month, her weekly sales in relation to her quota were $255 below, $375 above, $575 below, and $1525 above. What was Karin's overall standing for the month in terms of her quota? Is she above or below quota? How can you tell?

124. For 6 weeks, Karin's sales in relation to her quota were $385 above, $285 above, $555 below, $405 below, $265 above, and $575 above. She keeps track of her sales by noting sales above quota as a positive number and sales below quota as a negative number. What was her overall performance in sales? Is she above or below quota for the six-week period?

125. Lindsay's parents opened a college savings account with an initial deposit of $1500. For each of the next three months, they deposited $150. However, they withdrew $75 for a savings bond, $500 for a stock investment opportunity, and $200 for a municipal bond. The credit union paid the account $12 in interest for the three-month period. What is the balance of Lindsay's account?

126. At Mallory's birth, her grandparents opened a savings account for her by making an initial deposit of $500. Mallory's parents added deposits of $75, $50, and $100, received as gifts from relatives. Her parents withdrew $125 to make a premium payment on a new insurance policy. The bank added $35 interest at the end of the first year. What is the balance in the account?

127. Rosie makes and sells T-shirts. On one morning, she sold three shirts at $19.95 each, paid $25.00 to purchase dyes, paid the electric bill of $59.27, and refunded the price of one shirt that was the wrong size. What was her balance at the end of that morning?

128. Richard runs a bookstore. In one hour, he sold a book for $39.95, another for $27.95, and a third for $19.99. He paid out $175.00 for the monthly rent and paid $29.95 to the newspaper to run an advertisement for him. A customer returned a book for a refund of $14.95. What was his balance at the end of that hour?

129. An interesting application of the skills of adding and subtracting numbers occurs in the reading of parts diagrams for a machine shop. Many times, the diagrams list only the essential measurements and assume that the user of the diagram can obtain the remaining measurements through addition and subtraction. The drawing in **Figure P.8** is an example of such a diagram. It is a drawing of a part called a *taper*, which a machinist produces. All measurements are in inches. Write and evaluate an addition or subtraction expression to determine the length of *A* in the drawing.

130. For the taper in exercise **129**, write and evaluate an addition or subtraction expression to determine the lengths of *B* and *C* in the drawing.

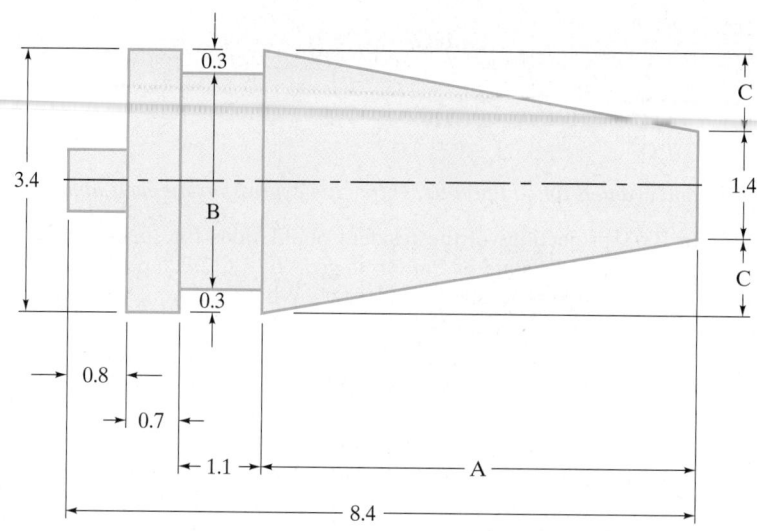

Figure P.8

Write and evaluate a multiplication or division expression for each situation. Interpret the result.

131. The deductions from Sara's paycheck typically amount to 22% of her gross pay. If she grosses $645 every 2 weeks, how much can she expect to have deducted? Deductions are represented by negative numbers. Over a 12-week period, what can she expect her total deduction to be?

132. Ron bets a total of $5 per race on nine races each day at the horse track. Bets are represented as negative numbers, since this is money Ron pays out. If he attends a week's worth of races (six days, since the horses don't race on Mondays), how much money will he bet in the week?

133. Sammy is paid 5 cents for each flyer he distributes. He can distribute 40 flyers per hour. He is permitted to distribute flyers for $1\frac{1}{2}$ hours each weekday. He does so on three weekdays. How much will he earn for the work?

134. Melanie earns 25 cents for her scout troop for each box of cookies she sells. She averages 20 boxes of cookies sold each time she works at the cookie booth in the local mall. She is permitted to work the cookie booth six different times. How much money did she make for her troop?

135. George averages 50 miles per hour on his business trip. He drives approximately $8\frac{1}{2}$ hours each day, and his drive takes him four days to complete. Approximately how many miles did George drive to get to his destination?

136. Michele hikes for $9\frac{1}{2}$ hours per day on the Appalachian Trail. She hikes at an average pace of $1\frac{3}{4}$ miles per hour. How far can she hike in five days?

137. To promote a town fund-raiser, Smallville sets up a clock that ticks off the seconds until the event begins. If the clock starts at 16,000,000 seconds, how many days will it be until the event kicks off?

138. Pioneer Village uses a clock to tick off the seconds until its bicentennial celebration will begin. If the clock starts at 20,000,000 seconds, how many weeks will it be until the event kicks off?

139. Billie wants to buy cabinets to hold her CD collection. She owns 335 CDs. If each cabinet has three drawers and each drawer holds 20 CDs, how many cabinets will she need to buy in order to store her entire collection?

140. Bruce has a collection of 650 LPs (long-playing records). He will buy record cabinets to store his collection. Each cabinet has three shelves, and each shelf holds 125 LPs. How many cabinets will Bruce need to buy for his collection?

141. According to the 2004 *World Almanac*, the population of Vatican City was 770, while its land area measures 0.17 square mile. Determine the density (people per square mile) of the Vatican City in 2004.

142. According to the 2004 *World Almanac*, Greenland has the lowest density in the world. In 2004, Greenland's population was 56,376 and its land area is 839,999 square miles. Determine its density (people per square mile).

143. The giant anteater of South America typically devours about 35,000 ants in a 24-hour period. Determine the anteater's rate of eating. How many ants will the anteater devour in a ten-hour period if the rate of eating is constant?

144. A metal joint 8 feet long requires 45 rivets. Determine the rate, in rivets per foot. How many rivets are required in a joint 5 feet long?

145. Al completes his car trip from Nashville, Tennessee to Washington, DC, a distance of 659 miles. He used 38 gallons of gas. Determine his gas mileage. If he continues his trip to Boston, Massachusetts, a distance of 440 miles, approximate the number of gallons of gas he will need assuming he will have the same gas mileage.

146. Isabell travels by car from Jackson, Mississippi, to Dallas, Texas a distance of 403 miles in 6.5 hours. Determine her car speed. If she continues her trip to Phoenix, Arizona, a distance of 1065 miles, approximate her traveling time assuming she will drive at the same average speed.

147. For the year 2010, the U.S. Census Bureau projected the percentage distribution of the U.S. population by race to be that shown in **Figure P.9**. The Bureau also projects the total U.S. population in the year 2010 to be 308,936,000. Use this total to determine the size of the population projected to be white.

148. Use the information in Exercise **147** determine the size of the population projected to be black in the year 2010.

149. The place where Americans purchase their retail prescription drugs in 2003 is shown in the pie chart in **Figure P.10**. A total of 3,215,000,000 prescription drugs were purchased in 2003. Determine the number of retail prescription drugs purchased in a supermarket.

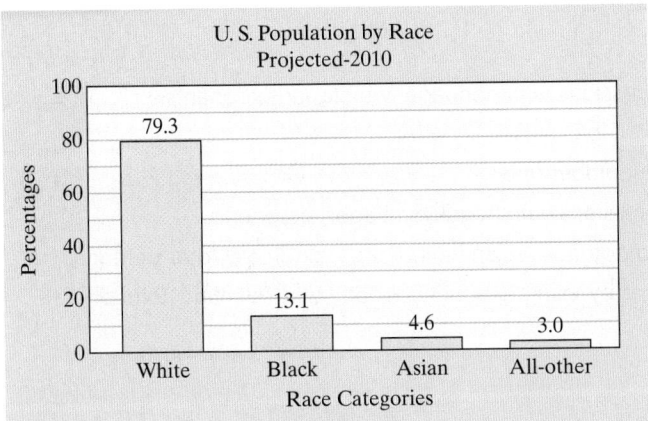

Figure P.9

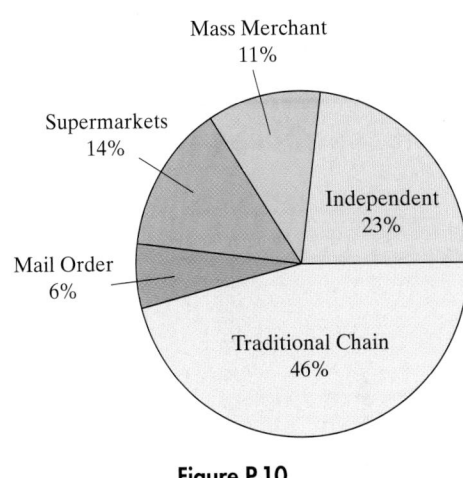

Figure P.10

150. Use the information in Exercise **149** to determine the number of retail prescription drugs purchased in a traditional chain.

 P.2 Calculator Exercises

Converting an Improper Fraction to a Mixed Number

In performing operations with mixed numbers, some calculators may present the result as an improper fraction. If the calculator does not provide an option to convert the improper fraction to a mixed number, the following procedure may be used:

1. Convert the improper fraction to a decimal by dividing on the calculator.
2. Subtract the integer part of the decimal (the part to the left of the decimal point) from the decimal on the calculator.
3. Convert the remaining part of the decimal (the part to the right of the decimal point) to a fraction on the calculator.
4. Add the integer part back to the fraction part to obtain the mixed number.

For example, convert the improper fraction $\frac{43}{15}$ to a mixed number.

1. $\frac{43}{15}$ is 2.86666666....
2. 2.8666666666... − 2 = 0.8666666666...
3. 0.8666666666... **MATH** **1** **ENTER** yields $\frac{13}{15}$.
4. $\frac{13}{15}$ added to 2 yields $2\frac{13}{15}$.

```
43/15
        2.866666667
Ans-2
        .8666666667
Ans▶Frac
            13/15
```

Convert the following improper fractions to mixed numbers, using the preceding approach:

1. $\frac{55}{7}$　　**2.** $-\frac{295}{113}$　　**3.** $\frac{1227}{487}$　　**4.** $-\frac{108}{19}$

P.2 Writing Exercises

Being able to recognize words, phrases, or situations that imply mathematical operations will increase your skills in solving word problems.

1. List as many words or phrases as you can that imply addition.

2. List as many words or phrases as you can that imply subtraction.

3. List as many words or phrases as you can that imply multiplication.

4. List as many words or phrases as you can that imply division.

5. Pick three of the words that imply multiplication, and write a sentence for each that illustrates the use of the word.

6. Pick three of the words that imply division, and write a sentence for each that illustrates the use of the word.

P.3 EXPONENTS, ROOTS, AND SCIENTIFIC NOTATION

OBJECTIVES

1 Evaluate exponential expressions with nonnegative integer exponents.

2 Evaluate square roots and cube roots.

3 Graph real numbers on a number line.

4 Evaluate exponential expressions with negative integer exponents.

5 Write equivalent standard notation, scientific notation, and calculator notation.

6 Model real-world situations by using exponents, roots, and scientific notation.

APPLICATION

Common table salt consists of atoms in the shape of a face-centered cubic structure. The volume of this cube is about 1.68×10^{-28} m^3. Find the length of the edge of the cube.

After completing this section, we will discuss this application further. See page 50.

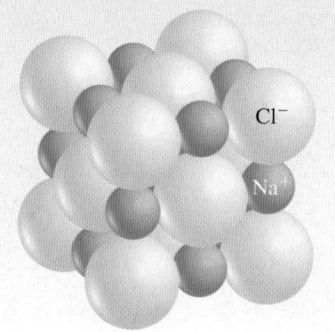

Objective P.3.1 Evaluating Exponential Expressions with a Nonnegative Integer Exponent

When a number is repeated as a factor, the product may be written in exponential form instead of as a multiplicative expression. The repeated factor is the **base** of the expression. The number of times the base is repeated as a factor is written as an **exponent**.

$$2 \cdot 2 \cdot 2 \cdot 2 \cdot 2 \cdot 2 = 2^6$$

2 repeated 6 times   base^{exponent}

The base is 2 and the exponent is 6.

In the preceding example, $2 \cdot 2 \cdot 2 \cdot 2 \cdot 2 \cdot 2$ is called an **expanded form**, and 2^6 is called an **exponential form**, or an **exponential expression**.

For the moment, we will examine expressions with integer exponents greater than 1 and with bases that are positive numbers or 0.

To evaluate any such exponential expression, write it in expanded form and then multiply the factors.

$2^2 = 2 \cdot 2 = 4$ 2 (raised) to the second power is 4, or 2 squared is 4.

$2^3 = 2 \cdot 2 \cdot 2 = 8$ 2 (raised) to the third power is 8, or 2 cubed is 8.

$2^6 = 2 \cdot 2 \cdot 2 \cdot 2 \cdot 2 \cdot 2 = 64$ 2 (raised) to the sixth power is 64. (All powers except 2 and 3 are read in this manner.)

EXAMPLE 1   Write in expanded form and evaluate.

a. $\left(\dfrac{2}{3}\right)^2$ b. 1.5^3 c. 0^4 d. $\left(9\dfrac{1}{3}\right)^5$

Solution

a. $\left(\dfrac{2}{3}\right)^2 = \dfrac{2}{3} \cdot \dfrac{2}{3} = \dfrac{4}{9}$ $\dfrac{2}{3}$ is repeated as a factor two times.

b. $1.5^3 = (1.5)(1.5)(1.5) = 3.375$ 1.5 is repeated as a factor three times.

c. $0^4 = 0 \cdot 0 \cdot 0 \cdot 0 = 0$ 0 is repeated as a factor four times.

d. $\left(9\dfrac{1}{3}\right)^5 = \left(\dfrac{28}{3}\right)\left(\dfrac{28}{3}\right)\left(\dfrac{28}{3}\right)\left(\dfrac{28}{3}\right)\left(\dfrac{28}{3}\right)$ $9\dfrac{1}{3} = \dfrac{28}{3}$ and is repeated as a factor five times.

$= \dfrac{17{,}210{,}368}{243}$

To evaluate an exponential expression on your calculator, it is not necessary to enter the expression in expanded form. The calculator has special keys for exponents. The checks for Example 1a, 1b, and 1d are shown in **Figures P.11a**, **P.11b**, and **P.11c**, respectively.   ■

TECHNOLOGY   Integer Exponents

Evaluate.   a. $\left(\dfrac{2}{3}\right)^2$ b. 1.5^3 d. $\left(9\dfrac{1}{3}\right)^5$

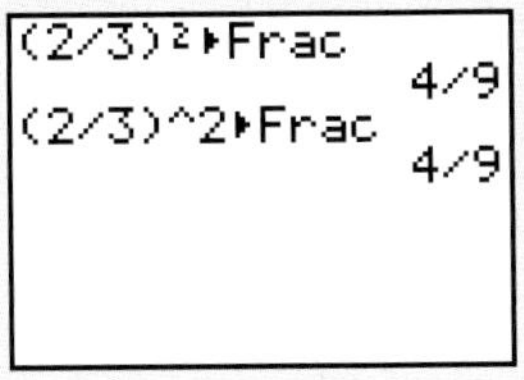

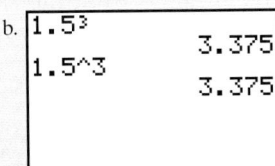

Figure P.11a

Figure P.11b

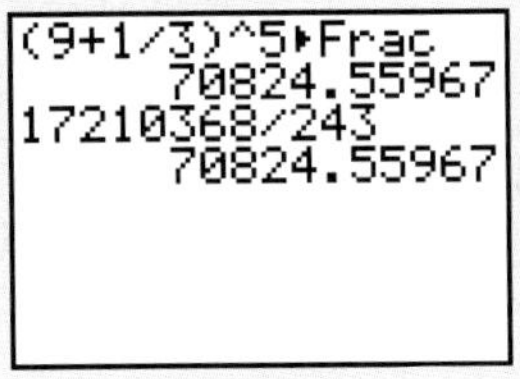

Figure P.11c

To enter an exponent, use the ⌃ key.

For **Figure P.11a**,
a. There is a special key, x^2, that may be used to square a number.
To square a number, enter the base followed by x^2.

(2 ÷ 3) x^2 MATH 1 ENTER or (2 ÷ 3) ⌃ 2 MATH 1 ENTER

For **Figure P.11b**,
b. There is a special function under the MATH menu option 3 that may be used to cube a number.

1 . 5 MATH 3 ENTER or 1 . 5 ⌃ 3 ENTER

For **Figure P.11c**,
d. Enter the mixed number, $9\frac{1}{3}$, as a sum of 9 and $\frac{1}{3}$ enclosed in parentheses.

Use the ⌃ for inserting the exponent.

(9 + 1 ÷ 3) ⌃ 5 MATH 1 ENTER

Since the result is not a fraction, enter the fraction answer that we are checking, $\frac{17210368}{243}$, and compare the decimal values.

1 7 2 1 0 3 6 8 ÷ 2 4 3 ENTER

TAKE NOTE The parentheses in Example 1a are very important, that is, $(2/3)^2$ and $2/3^2$ are not equivalent.

If the repeated factor in an exponential expression is a negative number, write the factor in parentheses as the base. For example,

$$(-2)(-2)(-2)(-2)(-2)(-2) = (-2)^6$$

$$\underbrace{}_{-2 \text{ repeated six times}} \qquad \underbrace{(-2)^6}_{\text{base}^{\text{exponent}}}$$

The parentheses are very important here. If no parentheses are used, the base is not considered to be a negative number. For example,

$$-2^6 = -(2 \cdot 2 \cdot 2 \cdot 2 \cdot 2 \cdot 2) = -64 \qquad \text{— } 2^6 \text{ means the opposite of "2 to the sixth power."}$$

$$(-2)^6 = (-2)(-2)(-2)(-2)(-2)(-2) = 64 \qquad (-2)^6 \text{ means "} -2 \text{ to the sixth power."}$$

Therefore, $(-2)^6 \neq -2^6$ because $(-2)^6 = 64$ and $-2^6 = -64$.

 TAKE NOTE It is very important to understand the difference between -2^6 and $(-2)^6$. Always determine the base of the exponential expression before expanding.

$$-2^6 \qquad \text{2 is the base.}$$

$$(-2)^6 \qquad -2 \text{ is the base.}$$

EVALUATING EXPRESSIONS WITH INTEGER EXPONENTS > I

To evaluate an exponential expression with an integer exponent greater than 1, determine the product of its expanded form.

If the base is positive, the product is positive.

If the base is negative:

- The product is positive if the exponent is even.
- The product is negative if the exponent is odd.

If the base is 0, the product is 0.

EXAMPLE 2   Write in expanded form, evaluate, and check using your calculator.

a. $(-1.8)^5$ **b.** $\left(-\dfrac{3}{4}\right)^4$ **c.** $(-1)^6$ **d.** -1^6

Solution

a. $(-1.8)^5 = (-1.8)(-1.8)(-1.8)(-1.8)(-1.8)$

   The base is -1.8.

   $= -18.89568$

b. $\left(-\dfrac{3}{4}\right)^4 = \left(-\dfrac{3}{4}\right)\left(-\dfrac{3}{4}\right)\left(-\dfrac{3}{4}\right)\left(-\dfrac{3}{4}\right) = \dfrac{81}{256}$

   The base is $-\dfrac{3}{4}$.

c. $(-1)^6 = (-1)(-1)(-1)(-1)(-1)(-1) = 1$

   The base is -1.

d. $-1^6 = -(1 \cdot 1 \cdot 1 \cdot 1 \cdot 1 \cdot 1) = -1$ The base is 1.

Check

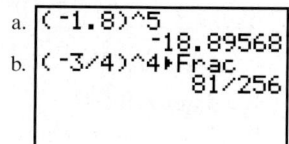

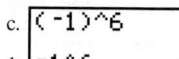
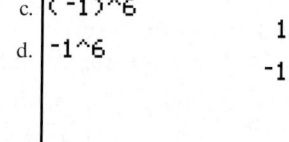

The expanded form of an expression with an exponent of 1 or 0 is not obvious. We need to find a second method for evaluating such expressions.

Complete the following exercises with your calculator.

Guided Discovery 7   Expressions with an Exponent of 1 or 0

Evaluate each expression.

1. 10^1

2. $(-10)^1$

3. 0^1

4. -10^0

5. $(-10)^0$

6. 0^0

     State a rule for evaluating an exponential expression with an exponent of 1.

     State a rule for evaluating an exponential expression with an exponent of 0.

An exponential expression with an exponent of 1 evaluates to the base number.

     An exponential expression with an exponent of 0 and a nonzero base is 1. If the base is 0 and the exponent is 0, the expression is indeterminate.

EVALUATING WITH EXPONENTS OF 1 OR 0

The value of an exponential expression with an exponent of 1 is equal to the base number.

The value of an exponential expression with an exponent of 0 is

- 1 if the base is not 0.
- indeterminate if the base is 0.

To understand these rules, examine the following pattern:

$$10^4 = 10 \cdot 10 \cdot 10 \cdot 10$$
$$10^3 = 10 \cdot 10 \cdot 10 \qquad \text{Divide by 10.}$$
$$\text{Exponent decreases by 1.} \quad 10^2 = 10 \cdot 10$$
$$10^1 = \underline{}$$
$$10^0 = \underline{}$$

Using the preceding pattern, we obtain $10^1 = \underline{10}$ and $10^0 = \underline{1}$. (If we divide by 10, we get 1.) We will explain why 0^0 is indeterminate later in the text.

EXAMPLE 3   Evaluate.

   a. 18^0 **b.** $(-18)^0$ **c.** -18^0 **d.** $(-15)^1$ **e.** -15^1 **f.** 0^0

Solution

   a. $18^0 = 1$ The base is 18.

   b. $(-18)^0 = 1$ The base is −18.

   c. $-18^0 = -1$ The base is 18.

   d. $(-15)^1 = -15$ The base is −15.

   e. $-15^1 = -15$ The base is 15.

   f. 0^0 is indeterminate.   The base is 0.

✓ **Objective P.3.1**   *CHECKUP*

In exercises 1 and 2, write in expanded form and evaluate.

   1. a. 1.3^2 **b.** 0^6 **c.** $\left(\dfrac{2}{5}\right)^5$ **d.** $\left(8\dfrac{3}{5}\right)^5$

   2. a. $(-1.4)^3$ **b.** $\left(-\dfrac{2}{3}\right)^4$ **c.** $(-6)^4$ **d.** -6^4

   3. Evaluate.   **a.** $(-7)^1$ **b.** -7^1 **c.** 7^0 **d.** $(-7)^0$

            e. -7^0 **f.** 0^0

4. In exercise 2, explain the difference between the expressions in c and d, and discuss the impact of this difference on the final answers.

5. When the base of an exponential expression is negative, how can you tell whether the value of the exponential expression will be positive or negative?

Objective P.3.2   Evaluating Roots

Previously, we discussed squaring a number, such as $3^2 = 9$. The result 9 is called a perfect square. A **perfect square** is defined to be the result of squaring a rational number.

If we need to reverse this operation—that is, go from the square of a number back to the number itself—we take the **square root** of the number. For example, $3^2 = 9$ and $(-3)^2 = 9$; both 3 and -3 are square roots of 9. We call 3 the **positive square root** or **principal square root**, $\sqrt{9} = 3$. We refer to -3 as being the **negative square root** of 9 and denote it as the opposite of the positive square root, $-\sqrt{9} = -3$.

Square roots of perfect squares simplify to rational numbers. The square root of a number is one example of a radical expression. In the expression $\sqrt{9}$, the symbol $\sqrt{}$ is called a **radical sign** and 9 is the **radicand**. $\sqrt{9}$ is a **radical expression**.

$$\text{radical sign} \;\rightarrow \sqrt{9} \quad \text{radical expression}$$
$$\uparrow$$
$$\text{radicand}$$

Now, let's find the square root of a negative number, such as -9. To find a value for $\sqrt{-9}$, we must determine what number to square in order to obtain -9. Since squaring a positive number results in a positive number $(3 \cdot 3 = 9)$ and squaring a negative number results in a positive number $(-3 \cdot -3 = 9)$, we know we cannot find a real number whose square is -9 (a negative number). Therefore, $\sqrt{-9}$ cannot be evaluated in the real-number system. We will introduce the *complex-number system*, in which we can evaluate $\sqrt{-9}$, in a later chapter.

EVALUATING SQUARE ROOTS

To evaluate the positive or principal square root of a positive number that is a perfect square,

- Determine the positive number whose square results in the perfect square.

To evaluate the negative square root of a positive number that is a perfect square,

- Determine the negative number whose square results in the perfect square.

The square root of 0 is 0.

The positive and negative square roots of a negative number are not defined among the real numbers.

EXAMPLE 4   Evaluate.

a. $\sqrt{64}$ **b.** $\sqrt{1.44}$ **c.** $\sqrt{\dfrac{4}{9}}$ **d.** $-\sqrt{25}$ **e.** $\sqrt{-25}$ **f.** $\sqrt{0}$

Solution

a. $\sqrt{64} = 8$ *The positive square root of 64 is 8, because $8^2 = 64$.*

b. $\sqrt{1.44} = 1.2$ *The positive square root of 1.44 is 1.2, because $1.2^2 = 1.44$.*

c. $\sqrt{\dfrac{4}{9}} = \dfrac{2}{3}$ *The positive square root of $\frac{4}{9}$ is $\frac{2}{3}$, because $\left(\frac{2}{3}\right)^2 = \frac{4}{9}$.*

d. $-\sqrt{25} = -5$ *The opposite of the positive square root of 25 is -5.*

e. $\sqrt{-25}$ is not a real number.   *There is no real number whose square is -25 (a negative number).*

f. $\sqrt{0} = 0$ *The square root of 0 is 0, because $0^2 = 0$.*

The checks for Example 4c, 4d, and 4e are shown in **Figure P.12a** and **Figure P.12b**.

TECHNOLOGY Square Roots

Evaluate. **c.** $\sqrt{\dfrac{4}{9}}$ **d.** $-\sqrt{25}$ **e.** $\sqrt{-25}$

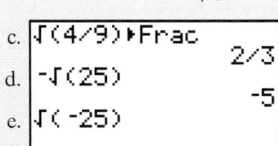

```
c. √(4/9)▶Frac
              2/3
d. -√(25)
               -5
e. √(-25)
```

```
e. ERR:NONREAL ANS
   1:Quit
   2:Goto
```

Figure P.12a   **Figure P.12b**

For **Figure P.12a** and **Figure P.12b**,

To enter a square root, enter [2nd] [x²] (√). Close the parentheses that are opened for you in order to enclose the number in a set of parentheses.

a. [2nd] [x²] (√) [4] [÷] [9] [ )] [MATH] [1] [ENTER]

b. [(-)] [2nd] [x²] (√) [2] [5] [ )] [ENTER]

Since the square root of a negative number is not defined as a real number, if your calculator is in Real mode (the default mode), an error will be displayed when you enter the expression.

e. [2nd] [x²] (√) [(-)] [2] [5] [ )] [ENTER]

Press [ENTER] to quit the error screen and return to the default home screen.

Let's find a value for the square root of a positive rational number that is not a perfect square. Remember, perfect squares are 1, 4, 9, and so on. A number such as 2 is between the perfect squares 1 and 4. Therefore, the value of $\sqrt{2}$ should be between the values of $\sqrt{1}$ and $\sqrt{4}$, or between 1 and 2. Rather than experiment to find $\sqrt{2}$, let's use a calculator.

On a calculator, we find that $\sqrt{2}$ is given by 1.414213562. If we check, we get $(1.414213562)^2 = 1.999999999$. This is a close approximation, but not exactly 2. In fact, we cannot find a rational number whose square is exactly equal to 2. We say $\sqrt{2}$ is approximately equal to ($\approx$) 1.414.

```
√(2)
        1.414213562
1.4142135622
        1.999999999
```

$$\sqrt{2} \approx 1.414 \quad \text{Rounded to the nearest thousandth}$$

The fact that we cannot find a rational number whose square is equal to 2 means that the value of $\sqrt{2}$ is not a rational number. Thus, we cannot write it as a ratio of integers. Therefore, we call $\sqrt{2}$ an irrational number. An **irrational number** is a number that cannot be written as a ratio of integers. **Real numbers** are the set of all rational and irrational numbers.

EXAMPLE 5

Determine between what two integers the values of the following square roots lie, and then approximate the square roots to the nearest thousandth on your calculator.

a. $\sqrt{3}$ **b.** $-\sqrt{5}$ **c.** $\sqrt{99}$

```
a. √(3)
        1.732050808
b. -√(5)
        -2.236067977
c. √(99)
        9.949874371
```

Calculator Solution

a. $\sqrt{3}$ is between $\sqrt{1} = 1$ and $\sqrt{4} = 2$, $\sqrt{3} \approx 1.732$.

b. $-\sqrt{5}$ is between $-\sqrt{4} = -2$ and $-\sqrt{9} = -3$, $-\sqrt{5} \approx -2.236$.

c. $\sqrt{99}$ is between $\sqrt{81} = 9$ and $\sqrt{100} = 10$, $\sqrt{99} \approx 9.950$.

We also can define the roots of expressions with exponents larger than 2. For example, we may want to reverse cubing a number and call the result a **cube root**. In order to use the same notation as with square roots, we will need to add an index to the radical sign. An **index** is the power we are reversing. To write a cube root, in which we are reversing a power of 3, we would write the following:

index
↓

$\sqrt[3]{64}$ What number multiplied as a factor 3 times is 64?

↖
radicand

To evaluate $\sqrt[3]{64}$, we determine that $4^3 = 64$. To evaluate $\sqrt[3]{-64}$, we determine $(-4)^3 = -64$.

$$\sqrt[3]{64} = 4 \qquad \text{The cube root of 64 is 4, because } 4^3 = 64.$$

$$\sqrt[3]{-64} = -4 \qquad \text{The cube root of } -64 \text{ is } -4, \text{ because } (-4)^3 = -64.$$

 TAKE NOTE We can evaluate cube roots of negative numbers in the real-number system.

EVALUATING CUBE ROOTS

To evaluate a cube root of a number that is a perfect cube,

- Determine the number whose cube results in the perfect cube. If the radicand is positive, the number is positive. If the radicand is negative, the number is negative.

To evaluate a cube root of a number that is not a perfect cube,

- Determine a number whose cube is approximately the value of the radicand. A calculator may be needed to find this number.

The value of a radical expression with a radicand of 0 is 0.

EXAMPLE 6   Evaluate, rounding to the nearest thousandth, as appropriate.

a. $\sqrt[3]{-27}$ **b.** $\sqrt[3]{30}$ **c.** $\sqrt[3]{\dfrac{1}{27}}$

Solution

a. $\sqrt[3]{-27} = -3$ The cube root of -27 is -3, because $(-3)^3 = -27$.

b. $\sqrt[3]{30} \approx 3.107232506 \approx 3.107$ The cube root of 30 is between $\sqrt[3]{27} = 3$ and $\sqrt[3]{64} = 4$.

c. $\sqrt[3]{\dfrac{1}{27}} = \dfrac{1}{3}$ The cube root of $\dfrac{1}{27}$ is $\dfrac{1}{3}$, because $\left(\dfrac{1}{3}\right)^3 = \dfrac{1}{27}$.

The checks for Example 6 are shown in **Figure P.13**. ■

TECHNOLOGY   Cube Roots

Evaluate.   **a.** $\sqrt[3]{-27}$ **b.** $\sqrt[3]{30}$ **c.** $\sqrt[3]{\dfrac{1}{27}}$

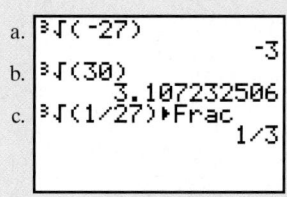

Figure P.13

For **Figure P.13**,
The cube root is located under the MATH menu option 4. Remember to close the set of parentheses that is opened for you.

| MATH | 4 | (–) | 2 | 7 |) | ENTER |

| MATH | 4 | 3 | 0 |) | ENTER |

| MATH | 4 | 1 | ÷ | 2 | 7 |) | MATH | 1 | ENTER |

✓ Objective P.3.2 *CHECKUP*

1. Evaluate.

  a. $\sqrt{49}$ **b.** $\sqrt{0.81}$ **c.** $\sqrt{\dfrac{25}{36}}$

  d. $-\sqrt{16}$ **e.** $\sqrt{-16}$ **f.** $\sqrt{0}$

2. Determine between what two integers the value of each square root lies. Then approximate, using your calculator.

  a. $\sqrt{17}$ **b.** $-\sqrt{15}$ **c.** $\sqrt{70}$

3. Evaluate, rounding to the nearest thousandth, as appropriate.

  a. $\sqrt[3]{-64}$ **b.** $\sqrt[3]{\dfrac{8}{125}}$ **c.** $\sqrt[3]{9}$

4. Explain the difference between the principal root of a number and the negative root of a number.

5. What is meant by an irrational number?

6. What is the index of a radical expression? What is the radicand of a radical expression?

Objective P.3.3 Graphing Real Numbers

In the first section of this text, we discussed the set of rational numbers. A rational number is any number that can be written as a ratio of integers, excluding a zero denominator. We located rational numbers as points on a number line. However, there are points on a number line that we did not identify. These are the irrational numbers. Irrational numbers are numbers that cannot be written as a ratio of integers.

The set of real numbers is the set of all rational and irrational numbers. The set of real numbers makes up a number line. Examples of irrational numbers are as follows:

0.13133133313333 . . .   (Only terminating and repeating decimals can be written as rational numbers.)

π ($\pi \approx 3.141592654$. The value of π is defined to be the ratio of the circumference of a circle to its diameter. (This decimal representation continues without terminating or repeating.)

$\sqrt{2}$ ($\sqrt{2} \approx 1.414213562$. (This decimal representation continues without terminating or repeating.)

$-\sqrt{2}$ ($-\sqrt{2} \approx -1.414213562$. (This decimal representation continues without terminating or repeating.)

$\sqrt[3]{5}$ ($\sqrt[3]{5} \approx 1.709975947$. (This decimal representation continues without terminating or repeating.)

Just as in the first section, we can graph irrational numbers on the real-number line. To graph an irrational number, we need to evaluate the number to determine its approximate value, in order to place it correctly on the line.

EXAMPLE 7   Graph the real numbers $3, \sqrt{3}, -\sqrt{3}, \sqrt{36}, \sqrt[3]{3}$, and π on a number line. Label the points.

Solution

3 is located 3 units to the right of 0.

$\sqrt{3} \approx 1.732050808$, which is approximately 1.7 units to the right of 0.

$-\sqrt{3} \approx -1.732050808$, which is approximately 1.7 units to the left of 0.

$\sqrt{36} = 6$, which is 6 units to the right of 0.

$\sqrt[3]{3} \approx 1.44224957$, which is approximately 1.4 units to the right of 0.

$\pi \approx 3.141592654$, which is approximately 3.1 units to the right of 0.

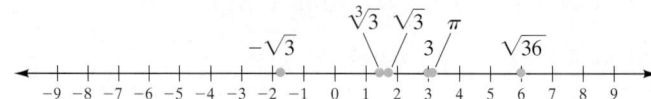

In summary, we have now discussed the entire set of real numbers with its subsets. We have identified natural numbers, whole numbers, and integers as subsets of rational numbers. However, rational numbers are not a subset of irrational numbers. They are mutually exclusive sets: Any number that belongs to one of them does not belong to the other. To visualize this relationship, see the following figure.

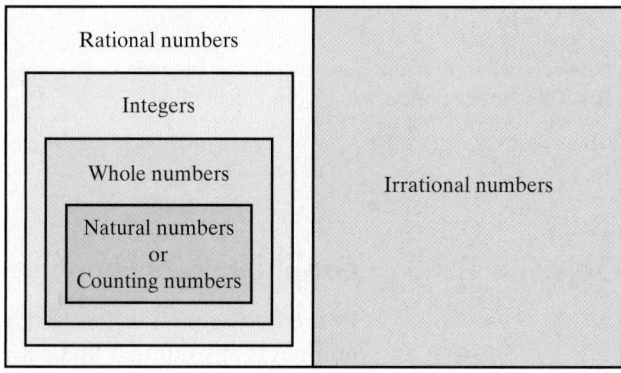

Objective P.3.3 *CHECKUP*

1. Graph the following real numbers on a number line, and label the points:

$$5, \sqrt{5}, -\sqrt{5}, \sqrt[3]{5}, \sqrt{16}$$

2. Explain the difference between irrational numbers and rational numbers.

Objective P.3.4   **Evaluating Exponential Expressions with a Negative Integer Exponent**

If an exponential expression has a negative exponent, it is impossible to determine the number of times to repeat the base when one is writing in expanded form. Therefore, we must discover an alternative method to evaluate these exponential expressions. Complete the following sets of exercises with your calculator.

Guided Discovery 8   Nonzero Integer Bases with Negative Integer Exponents

Evaluate each expression, and compare the results obtained in part **a** with the corresponding results in part **b**.

1. a. $10^{-1} = $ _____   **b.** $\left(\dfrac{1}{10}\right)^{1} = $ _____

2. a. $10^{-2} = $ _____   **b.** $\left(\dfrac{1}{10}\right)^{2} = $ _____

3. a. $10^{-3} = $ _____   **b.** $\left(\dfrac{1}{10}\right)^{3} = $ _____

State a rule for evaluating an exponential expression with a nonzero integer base and a negative integer exponent.

In part **a**, we evaluate an exponential expression with a nonzero integer base and a negative integer exponent. In part **b**, we evaluate an exponential expression consisting of a base that is the reciprocal of the base in part **a** and an exponent that is the opposite of the exponent in part **a**. The results are the same.

EVALUATING EXPRESSIONS WITH NEGATIVE EXPONENTS

To evaluate an exponential expression with a nonzero base and a negative integer exponent,

* Rewrite the expression as the reciprocal of the base with the opposite of the exponent.
* Evaluate the new expression.

An exponential expression with a zero base and a negative integer exponent is undefined.

To understand these rules, examine the following pattern:

$$10^4 = 10 \cdot 10 \cdot 10 \cdot 10$$

Exponent decreases by 1. $$10^3 = 10 \cdot 10 \cdot 10$$ Divide by 10.

$$10^2 = 10 \cdot 10$$

$$10^1 = 10$$

$$10^0 = 1$$

$$10^{-1} = \underline{\quad}$$

$$10^{-2} = \underline{\quad}$$

Using the preceding pattern, $10^{-1} = \frac{1}{10}$ and $10^{-2} = \frac{1}{100}$.

It is impossible to evaluate an exponential expression with a negative exponent and a zero base, because if we take the reciprocal of 0, we obtain $\frac{1}{0}$, which is undefined.

$$0^{-3} = \left(\frac{1}{0}\right)^3, \text{ which is undefined.}$$

EXAMPLE 8   Write an equivalent exponential expression having a positive exponent. Evaluate.

a. $(-10)^{-1}$ **b.** $(-10)^{-2}$

Solution

a. $(-10)^{-1} = \left(-\dfrac{1}{10}\right)^1$ Reciprocal of -10 is $-\frac{1}{10}$.

$= -\dfrac{1}{10}$

b. $(-10)^{-2} = \left(-\dfrac{1}{10}\right)^2$ Reciprocal of -10 is $-\frac{1}{10}$.

$= \dfrac{1}{100}$

Check

a. ```
(-10)^-1►Frac
            -1/10
```
b. ```
(-10)^-2►Frac
            1/100
```

 Objective P.3.4 **CHECKUP**

1. Write an equivalent exponential expression having a positive exponent. Evaluate.

    a. 3^{-1} **b.** $(-3)^{-1}$

2. What is the effect of a negative exponent on an exponential expression?

3. If an exponential expression has a negative exponent, what is the restriction on the value of the base?

Objective P.3.5   **Writing Equivalent Scientific Notation, Standard Notation, and Calculator Notation**

Numbers are usually written in **standard notation**.

5,000,000	five million
−3,458,000,000	negative three billion, four hundred fifty-eight million
0.000034	thirty-four millionths

However, very large and very small numbers are often written in scientific notation. **Scientific notation** is an expression written as the product of a number whose absolute value is between 1 and 10, including 1, and an integer power of 10. We call the number whose absolute value is between 1 and 10, including 1, the **numerical factor**. Since calculators display a limited number of digits, very large and very small numbers are written in an abbreviated scientific notation. We will call this form calculator notation. **Calculator notation** is a display consisting of the numerical factor, followed by "E," followed by the integer exponent of 10.

Standard Notation	**Scientific Notation**	**Calculator Notation**
	numerical factor × 10^integer exponent	numerical factor E integer exponent
$5{,}000{,}000 =$	$5 \times 10^{6} =$	5 E6
$-3{,}458{,}000{,}000 =$	$-3.458 \times 10^{9} =$	−3.458 E9
$0.000034 =$	$3.4 \times 10^{-5} =$	3.4 E−5

 TAKE NOTE Remember that calculator notation is not an appropriate notation for your written answer.

CONVERTING FROM STANDARD TO SCIENTIFIC NOTATION

To convert a number from standard notation to scientific notation, write a product of the numerical factor and an exponential expression.

Determine the numerical factor.

- Move the decimal point in the number so that the resulting number, the numerical factor, has an absolute value between 1 and 10, including 1.

Determine the exponential expression.

- The exponent of the base 10 is positive if the decimal was moved to the left, negative if the decimal was moved to the right, and 0 if the decimal was not moved.
- The absolute value of the exponent is the value of the number of places the decimal was moved.

EXAMPLE 9   Write in scientific notation.

    a. 65,780,000,000,000   **b.** −65,780,000,000,000

    c. 0.00000000002895   **d.** −0.00000000002895

Solution

a. $65,780,000,000,000 = 6.578 \times 10^{13}$ — The decimal was moved 13 places to the left.

b. $-65,780,000,000,000 = -6.578 \times 10^{13}$ — The decimal was moved 13 places to the left.

c. $0.00000000002895 = 2.895 \times 10^{-11}$ — The decimal was moved 11 places to the right.

d. $-0.00000000002895 = -2.895 \times 10^{-11}$ — The decimal was moved 11 places to the right.

Check

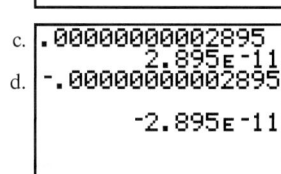

a. 65780000000000
                6.578ᴇ13
b. -65780000000000
               -6.578ᴇ13

c. .00000000002895
              2.895ᴇ-11
d. -.00000000002895
             -2.895ᴇ-11

The calculator will automatically display very large or very small numbers in calculator notation. Other numbers can be displayed by changing the default setting on your calculator. See Section P.3 Calculator Exercises at the end of this section.

 TAKE NOTE In scientific notation, numbers with absolute values greater than or equal to 10 have positive exponents. Numbers with absolute values less than 1 have negative exponents.

CONVERTING FROM SCIENTIFIC TO STANDARD NOTATION

To write a number in standard form if the exponent is positive,

- Move the decimal point in the numerical factor to the right the number of places the absolute value of the exponent denotes.

To write a number in standard form if the exponent is negative,

- Move the decimal point in the numerical factor to the left the number of places the absolute value of the exponent denotes.

If the exponent is 0, a number in standard form is the numerical factor.

EXAMPLE 10

Write in standard notation.

a. 3.86×10^7 **b.** -3.86×10^7 **c.** 7.4×10^{-3} **d.** -7.4×10^{-3}

Solution

a. $3.86 \times 10^7 = 38,600,000$
Move the decimal seven places to the right.

b. $-3.86 \times 10^7 = -38,600,000$
Move the decimal seven places to the right.

c. $7.4 \times 10^{-3} = 0.0074$
Move the decimal three places to the left.

d. $-7.4 \times 10^{-3} = -0.0074$
Move the decimal three places to the left.

CONVERTING FROM CALCULATOR TO SCIENTIFIC NOTATION

To convert a number from calculator notation to scientific notation, write a product of a numerical factor and an exponential expression.

- The numerical factor is the number displayed before the "E."
- The exponential expression consists of a base 10 and an exponent whose value is the number after the "E."

EXAMPLE 11   Write in scientific and standard notation.

a. 3.86 E7   **b.** −3.86 E7   **c.** 7.4 E−3   **d.** −7.4 E−3

Solution

a. 3.86 E7 = 3.86 × 10⁷   = 38,600,000

       3.86 is the numerical factor.   Move the decimal point seven places
       7 is the exponent.   to the right because the exponent is positive.

b. −3.86 E7 = −3.86 × 10⁷   = −38,600,000

       −3.86 is the numerical factor.   Move the decimal point seven places
       7 is the exponent.   to the right because the exponent is positive.

c. 7.4 E−3 = 7.4 × 10⁻³   = 0.0074

       7.4 is the numerical factor.   Move the decimal point three places
       −3 is the exponent.   to the left because the exponent is negative.

d. −7.4 E−3 = −7.4 × 10⁻³   = −0.0074

       −7.4 is the numerical factor.   Move the decimal point three places
       −3 is the exponent.   to the left. because the exponent is negative. ■

The calculator has a special function, EE, to enter a number in calculator notation. The checks for Example 11a and b use this function and are shown in **Figure P.14**.

TECHNOLOGY   Calculator Notation

Write in standard notation.   **a.** 3.86 E7   **b.** −3.86 E7

a. 3.18ᴇ7
             31800000
b. -3.86ᴇ7
             -38600000

Figure P.14

For **Figure P.14**,
"E" is entered using 2nd , (EE)
a. 3 . 8 6 2nd , (EE) 7 ENTER
b. (−) 3 . 8 6 2nd , (EE) 7 ENTER

  Objective P.3.5 **CHECKUP**

Write in scientific notation.

1. a. 78,345,000,000   **b.** −78,345,000,000
    c. 0.00000421   **d.** −0.00000421

Write in standard notation.

2. a. 4.75 × 10⁵   **b.** −4.75 × 10⁵
    c. 3.1 × 10⁻⁶   **d.** −3.1 × 10⁻⁶

Write in scientific and standard notation.

3. a. 5.92 E8   **b.** −5.92 E8
    c. 2.467 E−5   **d.** −2.467 E−5

Objective P.3.6   **Modeling the Real World**

In geometry, we evaluate the area and volume of geometric figures using positive integer exponents. To determine the area of a square, we square the length of its side. This is why raising a number to the second power is referred to as *the number squared*. The length of a side consists of a unit of measure, as well as a number. Therefore, if the number is squared, the unit of measure is also squared. For example, if we have a square of side 2 ft, the area is 4 ft². To determine the volume of a cube, we cube the length of each edge—hence *a number cubed*. As before, we cube the number as well as the unit of measurement. For a cube of edge 2 ft, the volume is 8 ft³.

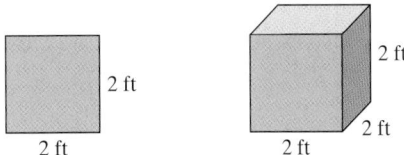

Since we determined the area of a square by squaring the length of its side, we determine the length of the side of a square by taking the square root of its area, including the number and the unit of measure. We also determined the volume of a cube by cubing the length of its edge. Likewise, to determine the length of an edge of a cube, we take the cube root of the volume, including the number and the unit of measure.

EXAMPLE 12

Ernö Rubik, professor at Budapest School of Commercial Art in Hungary, developed a cube with different colored sides divided into three rows and three columns. Each row and column slides up 360 degrees. The object of the game involving Rubik's cube is to rotate the cube until each face is multicolored and then return the cube to its original state. In the United States, Ideal Toys began manufacturing the cube in the late 1970s.

The volume of the original cube is 166.375 cubic centimeters. Determine the length of an edge of Rubik's cube. Determine the length of an edge of one of the small cubes that make up the large cube. Determine the volume of the small cube.

Solution

The length of the edge of the cube is the cube root of its volume.

$$\sqrt[3]{166.375 \text{ cm}^3} = 5.5 \text{ cm}$$

Rubik's cube is 5.5 cm on an edge.

Since there are three rows and three columns on a side, we divide the length of an edge by 3 to determine the length of the edge of the small cube.

$$\frac{5.5}{3} = 1.8\overline{3} \text{ cm}$$

Each small cube is $1.8\overline{3}$ centimeters on an edge.

The volume of the small cube is the length of an edge cubed.

$$(1.8\overline{3} \text{ cm})^3 \approx 6.16 \text{ cm}^3 \quad \text{Do not round your answer until your final calculation.}$$

Each small cube's volume is about 6.16 cubic centimeters.

Scientific notation is used most of the time in dealing with very large and very small numbers. Scientific notation is common in areas such as astronomy, which deals with large distances and huge masses; environmental science, which deals with global populations and resources; biology and chemistry, which deal with very small cells and molecules; and economics, which deals with large amounts of money and financial data.

EXAMPLE 13

Common table salt consists of atoms of the elements sodium (Na) and chlorine (Cl), arranged with alternate atoms at the corners of a cube. The distance between neighboring atoms is 2.76×10^{-10} meter. Determine the length of the edge of the cube. In chemistry, we define an angstrom, Å, as 1×10^{-10} meter. Determine the length of the edge in angstroms.

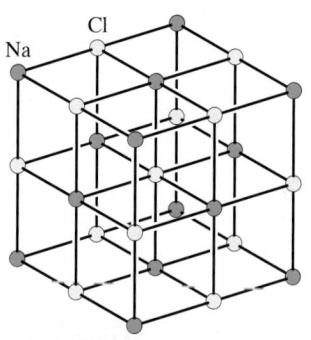

Solution

The length of the cube is about twice the distance between the neighboring atoms.

$$2(2.76 \times 10^{-10}) = 2(2.76 \times 10^{-10}) = (2 \cdot 2.76) \times 10^{-10} \qquad \text{Associative property}$$
$$= 5.52 \times 10^{-10}$$

The length of the edge of the cube is about 5.52×10^{-10} meter. The distance along the edge of the cube is 5.52 Å.

APPLICATION

Common table salt consists of atoms in the shape of a face-centered cubic structure. The volume of this cube is about 1.68×10^{-28} m³. Find the length of the edge of the cube.

Discussion

To determine the length of the edge of a cube, we take the cube root of the volume.

$$\sqrt[3]{1.68 \times 10^{-28} \, m^3} \approx 5.52 \times 10^{-10} \, m$$

The length of the edge is approximately 5.52×10^{-10} m.

Note: This is the same value obtained in Example 13.

✓ Objective P.3.6 **CHECKUP**

1. After the popularity of the Rubik's cube waned, another cube, called Rubik's Revenge, was produced. This cube has an additional row and column on each face. The volume of the cube is approximately 395 cubic centimeters. Determine the length of an edge of Rubik's Revenge. The center square is designed so that the color combinations of its four small squares can be varied. Determine the length of an edge of this center square consisting of four small squares. What is the volume of the center cube?

2. Lithium chloride consists of atoms of the elements lithium (Li) and chlorine (Cl), arranged with alternate atoms at the corners of the cube. The distance between neighboring atoms is 2.02×10^{-10} meters. Determine the length of the edge of the cube. Determine the length of the edge in angstroms. (An angstrom, Å, is 1×10^{-10} meters.)

3. Lithium chloride consists of atoms in the shape of a face-centered cubic structure. The volume of this cube is 6.59×10^{-29} m³. Determine the length of the edge of the cube.

P.3 EXERCISES

 Student Solutions Manual   PH Math/Tutor Center   ⊙ CD Video   Math·XL MathXL®   MyMathLab MyMathLab   Interactmath.com

Write in expanded form and evaluate the following exponential expressions:

1. 3^4
2. 2^6
3. $(-3)^4$
4. $(-2)^6$
5. -3^4

6. -2^6
7. $(-4)^3$
8. $(-3)^5$
9. -4^3
10. -3^5

Evaluate.

11. $(-2.5)^2$
12. $(-0.4)^2$
13. $-\left(-\dfrac{3}{7}\right)^2$
14. $-\left(-\dfrac{2}{3}\right)^4$
15. $\left(1\dfrac{1}{3}\right)^3$

16. $\left(1\dfrac{1}{2}\right)^3$
17. $\left(3\dfrac{2}{11}\right)^4$
18. $\left(7\dfrac{21}{29}\right)^7$
19. 0^8
20. 0^5

21. 1^{32} **22.** 1^{10} **23.** $(-1)^{29}$ **24.** $(-1)^9$ **25.** 1256^1

26. $\left(-\dfrac{4}{17}\right)^1$ **27.** 1256^0 **28.** $(-34.601)^0$ **29.** -4721^0 **30.** -8.23^0

31. $(-325)^0$ **32.** $(-10.8)^0$

Evaluate the following square roots:

33. $\sqrt{36}$ **34.** $\sqrt{81}$ **35.** $\sqrt{256}$ **36.** $\sqrt{324}$ **37.** $-\sqrt{25}$ **38.** $-\sqrt{49}$

39. $\sqrt{0.64}$ **40.** $\sqrt{0.81}$ **41.** $-\sqrt{\dfrac{16}{9}}$ **42.** $-\sqrt{\dfrac{36}{49}}$ **43.** $\sqrt{1}$ **44.** $-\sqrt{1}$

45. $-\sqrt{0}$ **46.** $\sqrt{0}$ **47.** $\sqrt{-16}$ **48.** $\sqrt{-100}$

Determine between what two integers the values of the square roots lie. Then approximate the square roots using your calculator, rounding to three decimal places.

49. $\sqrt{10}$ **50.** $\sqrt{22}$ **51.** $-\sqrt{3}$ **52.** $-\sqrt{14}$

Evaluate the cube roots. Express your answers in fractional notation or round decimals to the nearest thousandth, as appropriate.

53. $\sqrt[3]{64}$ **54.** $\sqrt[3]{8}$ **55.** $\sqrt[3]{1728}$ **56.** $\sqrt[3]{9261}$ **57.** $\sqrt[3]{1234}$

58. $\sqrt[3]{4321}$ **59.** $\sqrt[3]{-125}$ **60.** $\sqrt[3]{-64}$ **61.** $\sqrt[3]{\dfrac{1}{8}}$ **62.** $\sqrt[3]{-\dfrac{729}{1331}}$

63. Graph the following numbers on a number line, and label the points:

$$\sqrt[3]{25},\ -\sqrt{45},\ \sqrt{\dfrac{9}{16}},\ -\sqrt{16},\ -\sqrt{\dfrac{8}{3}},\ \sqrt[3]{8},\ \sqrt{75}$$

64. Graph the following numbers on a number line, and label the points:

$$-\sqrt{9},\ \sqrt{-63},\ -\sqrt{\dfrac{7}{3}},\ \sqrt{17},\ \sqrt{\dfrac{25}{4}},\ \sqrt[3]{64},\ \sqrt[3]{-64}$$

Write an equivalent exponential expression having a positive exponent. Evaluate.

65. 2^{-1} **66.** 5^{-1} **67.** 2^{-2} **68.** 5^{-2}

69. $(-2)^{-1}$ **70.** $(-5)^{-1}$ **71.** $(-2)^{-2}$ **72.** $(-5)^{-2}$

Complete the following table:

	Standard Notation	Scientific Notation	Calculator Notation
73.	23,450,000,000		
74.	18,300,000,000,000,000,000		
75.	−0.000006591		
76.	−0.00000000072193		
77.	3.6943		
78.	9.98031		
79.			−7.1103 E5
80.			−1.005 E11
81.			1.966 E−2
82.			5.555 E−6
83.			−9.95 E0
84.			−8.103 E0
85.		2.7×10^7	
86.		5.47×10^9	
87.		-3.0303×10^{-4}	
88.		-5.11×10^{-9}	
89.		1.26×10^0	
90.		-8.81×10^0	

91. A card table has a surface in the shape of a square with an area of 12 square feet. What are the dimensions of the surface?

92. A square goldfish pond has a surface area of 50 square feet. What are the dimensions of the surface of the pond?

93. The square base of the Great Pyramid, the tomb of Pharaoh Cheops, measures 755 feet on each of its four sides. What is the area of ground covered by the pyramid?

94. The Taj Mahal is one of the most beautiful buildings in the world. It is designed with a high central dome surrounded by small chambers arranged about two intersecting axes so that all four sides of the center structure are the same length. The center structure covers an area of about 377,000 square feet. What is the length of a side of this structure?

95. Instructions for planting a shrub require that a hole be dug in the shape of a cube with a volume of 3 cubic feet. What are the dimensions of the hole?

96. A pit for a luau is shaped like a cube with a volume of 15 cubic feet. What are the dimensions of the pit?

97. For the Great Pyramid, described in exercise **93**, what is the length of the diagonal of the tomb, measured from one corner to the opposite corner. (The length of a diagonal of a square is the square root of the sum of the squares of its two adjacent sides.)

98. For the Taj Mahal, described in exercise **94**, what is the length of the diagonal of the center structure, measured from one corner to the opposite corner? (The length of the diagonal of a square is the square root of the sum of the squares of its two adjacent sides.)

99. St. Peter's Basilica in Vatican City has a dome above the papal altar that spans an area of about 19,400 square feet. The radius of the domed area is the distance from the center of the circle to its outer edge. To find the radius of this circular area, you must divide the area by the mathematical constant π and then take the square root of the quotient. What is the radius of this domed area?

100. One of the largest domes ever constructed is in the Louisiana Superdome. The area of floor covered by the dome measures about 363,000 square feet. Use the calculation method in exercise **99** to determine the radius of the domed area.

101. The degree to which an orbit deviates from a circle is called the *eccentricity* of the orbit. The eccentricity of the Earth's orbit is approximately 0.016722. Write this number in scientific notation.

102. The most massive of all living things are the giant sequoia trees of California's Sequoia National Park, yet a seed from these giants is unusually small. Such a seed weighs about 0.0000078125 pound. Write this number in scientific notation.

103. The longest strait in the world is the Strait of Malacca, between the Malay Peninsula and the island of Sumatra. It's about 500 miles long. This is equivalent to 2,640,000 feet. Write these two numbers in scientific notation.

104. The fastest messages transmitted by the human nervous system travel at a speed of 200 miles per hour, or 1,056,000 feet per hour. Write these two numbers in scientific notation.

105. The planet that passes closest to Earth is Venus, at a distance of 4.2×10^7 kilometers. Write this number in standard notation.

106. The temperature at the Sun's core is estimated to be higher than 2.7×10^7 degrees Fahrenheit. Write this number in standard notation.

107. The lightest atom, hydrogen, weighs 1.7×10^{-24} grams. Write the weight in standard notation.

108. The radius of a Na^+ ion is 9.5×10^{-9} cm. Write this number in standard form.

109. The pyramids at Giza are the most colossal funeral monuments ever built. Each weighs over 6,000,000 tons. Convert this weight to pounds, given that 1 ton equals 2000 pounds. Write the answer in scientific notation.

110. The Great Wall of China is the only human-built structure that can be seen from the space shuttle with the naked eye. Recent discoveries of sections of the wall have increased its estimated length to 4470 miles long. Convert this length to feet, given that 1 mile equals 5280 feet. Write the answer in scientific notation.

111. The Trans-Alaska Pipeline can carry 2.14×10^6 barrels of oil per day. How many barrels of oil will be transported in a four-week period? Write the result in standard notation and interpret it.

112. The largest satellite of any planet in the solar system is Ganymede, which orbits Jupiter. It has a mass of about twice that of the Earth's moon. The moon has a mass of 7.35×10^{25} grams. Approximate the mass of Ganymede. Write the result in standard notation.

113. In 2002, according to the *Statistical Abstract of the United States,* 11,877,000 crimes were reported. The population of the United States in 2002 was estimated to be 288,205,000. Write these numbers in scientific notation. Then determine the rate of the number of crimes to the number of people in the population. Interpret your answer.

114. In 2002, according to the *Statistical Abstract*, 1,426,000 violent crimes were reported. Write this number in scientific notation. Using the population figure in exercise **113**, determine the rate of the number of violent crimes to the number of people in the population. Interpret your answer.

115. In 2003, the Hispanic population of the United States was reported to be 39,899,000. The total U.S. population in 2003 was reported to be 291,049,000. Write the two numbers in scientific notation. What percentage of the U.S. population was Hispanic?

116. In 2002, the number of deaths reported in the United States was 2,448,000. The total U.S. population in 2002 was reported to be 288,205,000. Write these numbers in scientific notation. What percentage of the U.S. population does the number of deaths represent?

117. Silver forms crystals in a face-centered cubic structure measuring 4.07×10^{-10} meter on a side. What is the measure of the perimeter, four times the measure of the length of one side, of one face of the silver crystal?

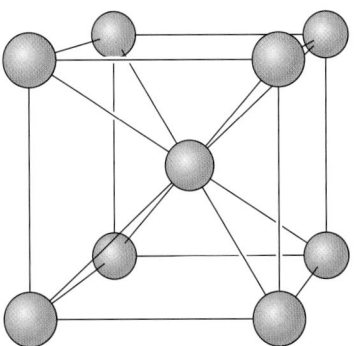

118. Vanadium forms crystals in a body-centered cubic structure (see diagram) measuring 3.03×10^{-10} meter on a side. What is the measure of the perimeter, which is four times the measure of the length of one side, of one face of the vanadium crystal?

119. Vanadium forms crystals in a body-centered cubic structure. The volume of a cell is 2.78×10^{-29} m^3. Find the length of the edge of the cube.

120. Silver forms crystals in a face-centered cubic structure. The volume of a cell is 6.74×10^{-29} m^3. Find the length of the edge of the cube.

P.3 Calculator Exercises

Part 1. Using the calculator to determine other roots

You have seen how to use the square-root key on your calculator to evaluate square roots. You have also seen how to use the MATH key on your calculator to evaluate cube roots. There is another option under the MATH key that can be used to evaluate square roots and cube roots: option 5. Note that this option has the symbol $\sqrt[x]{\ }$ beside it. This means that if you decide to use the option, you must first specify what the index is, then choose the option, and finally specify the radicand.

As an example, suppose you wish to know the square root of 161.29. You can determine the square root using the 2nd option of the square key x^2 or option 5 of the MATH key as shown in the following screen:

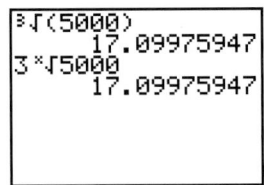

Next, suppose you wish to know the cube root of 5000. You can determine the cube root using option 4 or option 5 of the MATH key as shown in this screen:

Now, you probably would not choose to use option 5 to the MATH key for square roots or cube roots, since it may seem simpler to choose the other method you have learned. However, in later chapters we will be working with expressions in which the index of the radicand is larger than 3. In other words, you may want to know what number is raised to the fourth power, the fifth power, or some other power to yield a certain value. Then option 5 of the MATH key will be handy. As a final example, suppose you want to know what number has to be raised to the sixth power to yield 2,985,984. To determine this, you can use option 5 as follows:

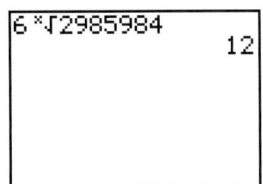

Use option 5 of the MATH key to evaluate the following radicals:

1. $\sqrt[5]{57,392}$ **2.** $-\sqrt[5]{37,652}$ **3.** $\sqrt[4]{\pi}$

4. $\sqrt[6]{\dfrac{64}{729}}$ **5.** $\sqrt[7]{2.5}$ **6.** $\sqrt[5]{-391.35393}$

Part 2. Setting the calculator to scientific mode

Sometimes it is convenient to set your calculator so that all numbers displayed will be in scientific notation. This can be done by pressing the MODE key. The first line of the display will have

"Normal" highlighted. Use the arrow keys to move to "Sci," and press [ENTER]. The calculator is now set to scientific notation (or, rather, calculator notation). Press [2nd] [MODE] (QUIT). Try typing the numbers 3,000,000, −5,000 and −0.00085 into the calculator.

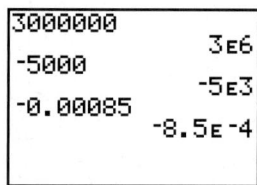

If you multiply 2.58×10^7, by 5.3×10^{-12}, the calculator will display the result in scientific notation.

Try performing the following exercises, using the scientific notation setting on your calculator:

1. $3{,}000{,}000 \div 0.0005$
2. $(1.25 \times 10^5)(4.8 \times 10^{-9})$
3. $(2.35 \times 10^{12}) - (3.87 \times 10^{11})$
4. $2.78 \times 10^{12} + 1.35 \times 10^{13}$

Part 3. Using the calculator applications

The TI-84 Plus has a set of applications. (The TI-83 Plus users must purchase these applications.) These applications are located in the APPS menu. We will use one of these applications to help us visualize and learn about the number systems that we have discussed in this chapter.

First press [APPS] and [3] to choose 3: ALG1PRT1. (If you purchased this APPS, your application number may be different than 3.) To begin the application press [ENTER]. You will see the algebra chapters that are available for your use.

In this section, we discussed the real number system. This topic is found in chapter 1:NUMBER SENSE. Press [1] to choose 1:NUMBER SENSE.

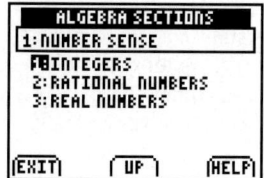

The algebra sections for NUMBER SENSE are listed. Choose the topic you are interested in. Let's view integers. Press [1] to choose 1:INTEGERS

The algebra subsections are listed. Press the number of the subsection that you are interested in. As you proceed in the subsections, you will press [ENTER] or use your arrow keys as prompted. Have fun as you explore the number systems.

P.3 Writing Exercises

Part 1.

Determine the resulting sign of the exponential expressions. Do not evaluate the expressions.

1. $(-55)^8$ 2. $(-85)^{12}$ 3. -55^8 4. -85^{12}
5. $(-55)^5$ 6. $(-85)^7$ 7. -55^5 8. -85^7

Discuss the rules you used to determine the resulting signs for the preceding exercises.

Part 2.

In some radical expressions, the radicand may be negative or positive. In other radical expressions, the radicand must always be positive. Describe the conditions that determine when each of the two situations applies.

P.4 PROPERTIES OF REAL NUMBERS AND ORDER OF OPERATIONS

OBJECTIVES

1 Discover, identify, and illustrate the distributive laws of multiplication over addition and subtraction.

2 Evaluate expressions using the order of operations.

3 Model real-world situations by using expressions and evaluate the expressions by means of the order of operations.

APPLICATION

Federal guidelines on the identification of obesity in adults state that the recommended body weight in pounds of a woman who is 5 feet, 6 inches (or 66 inches), tall is found from the expression

$$2.2[45.5 + 2.3(66 - 60)]$$

Determine this weight.

After completing this section, we will discuss this application further. See page 61.

In previous sections, we have written equivalent expressions for rational numbers. We discussed properties of rational numbers that help us write additional equivalent expressions and understand the ones we have already written. These properties will be useful later on, when we study algebra.

All of the properties of rational numbers that we have discussed are also properties of real numbers. The following is a summary of those properties:

PROPERTIES OF REAL NUMBERS

Identity Property of 0
The sum of a real number and 0 is the number itself.

Identity Property of 1
The product of a real number and 1 is the real number itself.

Multiplication Property of −1
The product of a real number and −1 is the opposite of the number itself.

Multiplication Property of 0
The product of a real number and 0 is 0.

Additive Inverse Property
The sum of a real number and its opposite, or additive inverse, is 0.

Multiplicative Inverse Property
The product of a nonzero real number and its reciprocal, or multiplicative inverse, is 1.

Commutative Law for Addition
Changing the order of two real-number addends does not change the sum.

Commutative Law for Multiplication
Changing the order of two real-number factors does not change the product.

Associative Law for Addition
Changing the grouping of three real-number addends does not change the sum.

Associative Law for Multiplication
Changing the grouping of three real-number factors does not change the product.

We will find that we can discuss properties of a real number even if we don't know its value. In fact, we will sometimes be able to use these properties to figure out the value of an unknown number from information about it.

Objective P.4.1   Identifying the Distributive Law

All of the properties previously described in this section have dealt with only one operation at a time, such as all additions or all multiplications in an expression. The next property involves both multiplication and addition. Complete the following set of exercises with your calculator.

Guided Discovery 9   Combining Multiplication and Addition

Evaluate each expression, and compare the results obtained in part **a** with the corresponding results in part **b**.

In your own words, state a rule for combining multiplication and addition.

1. a. $2(6 + 4) =$ _____   **b.** $2(6) + 2(4) =$ _____

2. a. $-2(-6 + 4) =$ _____   **b.** $-2(-6) + (-2)(4) =$ _____

In part **a** of the exercises, we multiply a sum of real-number addends by a real-number factor. In part **b** of the exercises, we multiply each addend by the real-number factor and then add the products. The results are the same.

DISTRIBUTIVE LAW

Multiplication over Addition
The product of a real-number factor and a sum of real-number addends is the same as the sum of the products of the factor and each addend.

 TAKE NOTE The distributive law applies to other operations as well as multiplication over addition. The other applications are: multiplication over subtraction, division over addition, and division over subtraction.

Combining the multiplication property of -1 and the distributive law results in a very important property. The following example illustrates this property:

$$-(3 + 6) = -1(3 + 6) \qquad \text{Multiplication property of } -1 \text{ (in reverse)}$$
$$= -1(3) + (-1)(6) \qquad \text{Distributive law}$$
$$= -(3) + [-(6)] \qquad \text{Multiplication property of } -1$$

In this example, we see that the opposite of a sum of real numbers is the same as the sum of the opposite of each addend.

$$-(3 + 6) = -(9) = -9 \qquad \text{and} \qquad -(3) + [-(6)] = -3 + (-6) = -9$$

OPPOSITE OF A SUM

The opposite of a sum of real numbers is the same as the sum of the opposites of each addend.

 TAKE NOTE This is also true for taking the opposite of a difference.

$$-(3 - 6) = -(3) - [-(6)] = -3 + 6$$

EXAMPLE 1

Write an equivalent expression for the following expressions, using the distributive law or the opposite-of-a-sum property:

a. $9(3 - 4)$ **b.** $(4 + 2)3$ **c.** $\dfrac{15 + 5}{5}$ **d.** $-(3 + 6)$

Solution

a. $9(3 - 4) = 9(3) - 9(4)$

> Distributive law
> Multiply each addend by the factor 9.

b. $(4 + 2)3 = 4(3) + 2(3)$

> Distributive law
> Multiply each addend by the factor 3.

c. $\dfrac{15 + 5}{5} = \dfrac{15}{5} + \dfrac{5}{5}$

> Distributive law
> Divide each addend by the divisor 5.

d. $-(3 + 6) = -(3) + [-(6)]$ or $-3 - 6$

> Opposite-of-a-sum property
> Take the opposite of each addend.

The reverse of the distributive property is called **factoring**. The following are some examples of factoring:

$$4(3) + 4(2) = 4(3 + 2)$$

> The real-number factor, 4, is called the common factor of the addends.

$$2(3) - 2(4) = 2(3 - 4)$$

> The common factor is 2.

EXAMPLE 2

Factor the expressions by writing an equivalent expression, using the distributive law in reverse. Then evaluate the equivalent expression.

a. $3(5.1) + 3(4.9)$ **b.** $5\left(\dfrac{1}{2}\right) - 3\left(\dfrac{1}{2}\right)$

Solution

a. $3(5.1) + 3(4.9) = 3(5.1 + 4.9)$

> The common factor is 3.

$$= 3(10)$$
$$= 30$$

b. $5\left(\dfrac{1}{2}\right) - 3\left(\dfrac{1}{2}\right) = \dfrac{1}{2}(5 - 3)$

> The common factor is $\frac{1}{2}$.

$$= \dfrac{1}{2}(2)$$
$$= 1$$

✓ Objective P.4.1 *CHECKUP*

1. For each of the following, write an equivalent expression, using the distributive law or the opposite-of-a-sum property.

   a. $5(3 + 7)$ **b.** $(17 - 25)5$

   c. $\dfrac{-46 + 62}{2}$ **d.** $-(-5 + 9)$

2. Factor by writing an equivalent expression, using the distributive law in reverse. Then evaluate the equivalent expression.

   a. $5(1.2) + 5(1.8)$ **b.** $17\left(\dfrac{1}{3}\right) - 23\left(\dfrac{1}{3}\right)$

3. Explain the terms *factoring* and *common factor*.

Objective P.4.2 Evaluating Expressions by Using the Order of Operations

We are now ready to evaluate expressions that involve the four operations of addition, subtraction, multiplication, and division. To do this, we must establish a few rules, so that we all obtain the same results. Complete the following exercises to discover the order of operations for addition, subtraction, multiplication, and division.

Guided Discovery 10 | Order of Operations

Consider the expression $6 \div 2 + 1 \cdot 3 - 5$. Complete the following possible methods of evaluation:

1. Evaluate in order from left to right.

2. First, evaluate all additions and subtractions in order from left to right. Then, evaluate all multiplications and divisions in order from left to right.

3. First, evaluate all multiplications and divisions in order from left to right. Then, evaluate all additions and subtractions in order from left to right.

4. Enter the expression into your calculator.

Write a rule for performing the order of operations by comparing the calculator value with the values obtained in Exercises 1, 2, and 3.

The calculator result is 1. The third set of directions also resulted in 1. Therefore, the calculator is programmed to evaluate the expression in the same order as described in the third set of directions; it performed all multiplications and divisions before additions and subtractions. The calculator evaluated the expression according to the **order of operations**.

With the basic arithmetic operations, we use parentheses, brackets, braces, absolute-value symbols, fraction bars, and radicals as grouping symbols. These grouping symbols change the order of operations of the arithmetic operations (addition, subtraction, multiplication, and division). To evaluate an expression involving grouping symbols, perform the operations within the grouping symbols first. If more than one pair of grouping symbols is present, perform the innermost operation first.

ORDER OF OPERATIONS

To evaluate an expression, perform operations in the following order:

- Perform all operations within grouping symbols. If more than one grouping symbol is present, perform the innermost operation first and work outward.
- Evaluate exponents and roots.
- Evaluate multiplication and division from left to right.
- Evaluate addition and subtraction from left to right.

TAKE NOTE The rule expressing the order of operations does not state that multiplication is completed before division (or addition before subtraction). It does state that multiplication and division are completed in the same pass through the expression, in order from left to right. Likewise, addition and subtraction are completed in the same pass in the order they appear from left to right.

EXAMPLE 3   Evaluate, using the rule for the order of operations.

a. $15 + 7 - 6 \div 3 - 2 \cdot 8$ **b.** $-12(-3) - 6(4) + 8$

Solution

a.
$$
\begin{aligned}
15 + 7 - 6 \div 3 - 2 \cdot 8 &= 15 + 7 - 2 - 2 \cdot 8 &&\text{Divide.}\\
&= 15 + 7 - 2 - 16 &&\text{Multiply.}\\
&= 22 - 2 - 16 &&\text{Add.}\\
&= 20 - 16 &&\text{Subtract.}\\
&= 4
\end{aligned}
$$

b.
$$
\begin{aligned}
-12(-3) - 6(4) + 8 &= 36 - 6(4) + 8 &&\text{Multiply.}\\
&= 36 - 24 + 8 &&\text{Multiply.}\\
&= 12 + 8 &&\text{Subtract.}\\
&= 20 &&\text{Add.}
\end{aligned}
$$

Check

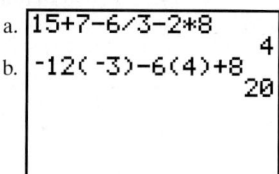

a. 15+7-6/3-2*8
                    4
b. -12(-3)-6(4)+8
                   20

EXAMPLE 4   Evaluate using the order of operations.

a. $-(3^2 - 7) + 8(-2 - 4)$

b. $\dfrac{16 - 2^2 + 3}{3 + 2}$

c. $2\{[2(3 - 4) + 7] - 8\} + 3(-5)$

d. $-\sqrt{25 + 11} + 6$

e. $-|3.5 - 4.26 - 5|$

Solution

a.
$$
\begin{aligned}
-(3^2 - 7) + 8(-2 - 4) &= -(9 - 7) + 8(-2 - 4) &&\text{Evaluate the exponent.}\\
&= -(2) + 8(-2 - 4) &&\text{Subtract within parentheses.}\\
&= -(2) + 8(-6) &&\text{Subtract within parentheses.}\\
&= -2 + 8(-6) &&\text{Take the opposite. (Multiply by } -1.)\\
&= -2 + (-48) &&\text{Multiply.}\\
&= -50 &&\text{Add.}
\end{aligned}
$$

b.
$$
\begin{aligned}
\frac{16 - 2^2 + 3}{3 + 2} &= \frac{16 - 4 + 3}{3 + 2} &&\text{Evaluate the exponent.}\\
&= \frac{12 + 3}{3 + 2} &&\text{Subtract.}\\
&= \frac{15}{5} = 3 &&\text{Add both groups separated by the fraction bar and divide.}
\end{aligned}
$$

c.
$$
\begin{aligned}
2\{[2(3 - 4) + 7] - 8\} + 3(-5) &= 2\{[2(-1) + 7] - 8\} + 3(-5) &&\text{Subtract within parentheses.}\\
&= 2\{[-2 + 7] - 8\} + 3(-5) &&\text{Multiply.}\\
&= 2\{5 - 8\} + 3(-5) &&\text{Add within brackets.}\\
&= 2\{-3\} + 3(-5) &&\text{Subtract.}\\
&= -6 - 15 &&\text{Multiply.}\\
&= -21 &&\text{Subtract.}
\end{aligned}
$$

d.
$$
\begin{aligned}
-\sqrt{25 + 11} + 6 &= -\sqrt{36} + 6 &&\text{Add within the radical sign.}\\
&= -6 + 6 &&\text{Evaluate the radical.}\\
&= 0 &&\text{Add.}
\end{aligned}
$$

e.
$$
\begin{aligned}
-|3.5 - 4.26 - 5| &= -|-5.76| &&\text{Subtract within absolute values.}\\
&= -(5.76) &&\text{Evaluate the absolute value.}\\
&= -5.76 &&\text{Take the opposite.}
\end{aligned}
$$

In entering these examples into your calculator, it may be necessary to add additional parentheses for grouping. Remember to use parentheses for all grouping symbols. This is explained in Section P.4, Calculator Exercises. The checks for Examples 4b, 4c, and 4d are shown in **Figure P.15**. ◼

TECHNOLOGY   Order of Operations

Evaluate.   **b.** $\dfrac{16 - 2^2 + 3}{3 + 2}$ **c.** $2\{[2(3 - 4) + 7] - 8\} + 3(-5)$ **d.** $-\sqrt{25 + 11} + 6$

```
b. (16-2²+3)/(3+2)
                    3
c. 2((2(3-4)+7)-8)+
   3(-5)
                  -21
d. -√(25+11)+6
                    0
```

Figure P.15

(continued on page 60)

For **Figure P.15**,
It is necessary to enter both the numerator and the denominator in a set of parentheses to ensure proper grouping.

`(` `1` `6` `–` `2` `x²` `+` `3` `)` `÷` `(` `3` `+` `2` `)` `ENTER`

Use sets of parentheses instead of brackets and braces.

`2` `(` `(` `2` `(` `3` `–` `4` `)` `+` `7` `)` `–` `8` `)` `+` `3`
`(` `(–)` `5` `)` `ENTER`

Enclose the radicand in a set of parentheses.

`(–)` `2nd` `x²` `(√)` `2` `5` `+` `1` `1` `)` `+` `6` `ENTER`

✓ Objective P.4.2 *CHECKUP*

In exercises 1 and 2, evaluate, using the order of operations.

1. **a.** $11 + 9 - 4 \div 2 - 3 \cdot 4$
  b. $-6(-5) - 2(3) + 7$

2. **a.** $-(4^3 - 15) + 6(-5 - 3)$

  b. $\dfrac{27 - 4^2 + 5}{7 + 1}$

  c. $-2\{4[3 - (5 - 7)] + 6 \div 3\} + 7(-3)$

  d. $-\sqrt{9 + 16} + 1$

  e. $-|3.2 + 5.1 - 7|$

Objective P.4.3   Modeling the Real World

In using real numbers to evaluate real-world data, the same rules for the order of operations apply. Be careful in determining what grouping symbols, if any, are needed to describe the situation correctly, since grouping symbols can change the order of operations. It is often a good idea to check your answer and see whether it seems reasonable to you. For example, if you calculate an average test score and your answer is higher than any of the individual scores, you've made an error somewhere.

EXAMPLE 5   The daily low temperatures (in degrees Celsius) for the week of January 9–15, 2005, for Vancouver, British Columbia, Canada, are given in the following chart:

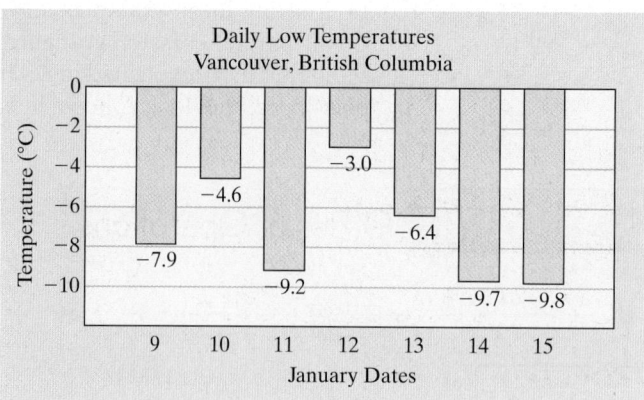

Find the average low temperature for the week.

Solution

In statistics, the average is calculated by adding all of the values and dividing by the count of the values. Therefore, the average low temperature for the week is found by adding the seven low temperatures and dividing the sum by 7, the number of temperatures that were added.

$$\frac{-7.9 + (-4.6) + (-9.2) + (-3) + (-6.4) + (-9.7) + (-9.8)}{7} = \frac{-50.6}{7} = -7\frac{8}{35} \approx -7.2$$

The average low temperature for the week was about 7 degrees Celsius. ▪

APPLICATION

Federal guidelines on the identification of obesity in adults state that the recommended body weight in pounds of a woman who is 5 feet, 6 inches (or 66 inches) tall is found from the expression

$$2.2[45.5 + 2.3(66 - 60)]$$

Determine this weight.

Discussion

$$
\begin{aligned}
2.2[45.5 + 2.3(66 - 60)] &= 2.2[45.5 + 2.3(6)] &&\text{Simplify within parentheses.}\\
&= 2.2[45.5 + 13.8] &&\text{Multiply.}\\
&= 2.2[59.3] &&\text{Add.}\\
&= 130.46 &&\text{Multiply.}
\end{aligned}
$$

The recommended weight for a woman 5 feet, 6 inches is about 130 pounds.

✓ Objective P.4.3 *CHECKUP*

1. The daily high temperatures (in degrees Celsius) for the week of January 9–15, 2005, for Vancouver, British Columbia, Canada, are given in the following chart:

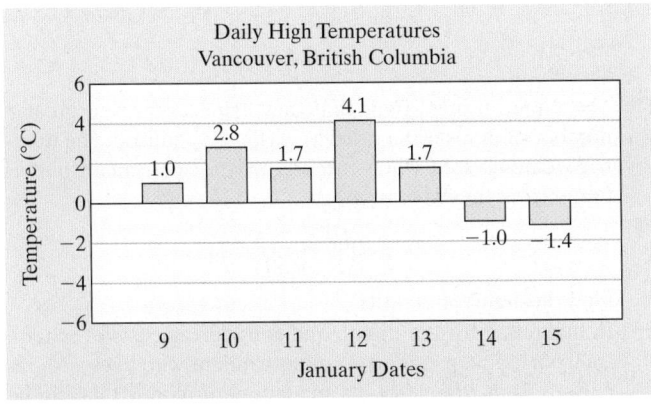

Daily High Temperatures Vancouver, British Columbia

Find the average high temperature for the week.

2. Federal guidelines on the identification of obesity in adult men state that the recommended body weight in pounds of a man who is 6 feet (or 72 inches) tall is found from the expression

$$2.2[50 + 2.3(72 - 60)]$$

Determine this weight. ▪

P.4 EXERCISES

 Student Solutions Manual    PH Math/Tutor Center   CD Video    MathXL®    MyMathLab    Interactmath.com

Write an equivalent expression using the distributive law of real numbers. Check on your calculator.

1. $\left(\dfrac{3}{8}\right)\left(\dfrac{5}{7} - \dfrac{1}{9}\right)$ **2.** $-23(31 + 25)$ **3.** $2.7(-1.5 + 3.2)$ **4.** $\left(1\dfrac{1}{4}\right)\left(5\dfrac{1}{2} - 3\dfrac{1}{8}\right)$

5. $\dfrac{217 - 175}{7}$ **6.** $\dfrac{-78 + 108}{6}$

Write an equivalent expression using the opposite-of-a-sum property of real numbers. Check on your calculator.

7. $-(15 + 19.3)$

8. $-(5.7 + 0.06)$

9. $-\left(-\dfrac{6}{7} - \dfrac{5}{9}\right)$

10. $-(-51 - 19)$

11. $-\left(1\dfrac{1}{7} - 2\dfrac{1}{5}\right)$

12. $-(89 - 17)$

13. $-(19.37 + 15.043)$

14. $-\left(2\dfrac{1}{4} + 3\dfrac{5}{8}\right)$

Factor, using the distributive law of real numbers in reverse. Check on your calculator.

15. $15(17) + 15(23)$

16. $81(22) + 81(8)$

17. $-3(14) - 3(21)$

18. $-13(21) - 13(16)$

19. $6(1.2) - 6(1.3)$

20. $5(4.5) - 5(7)$

Evaluate, using the order of operations. Check on your calculator.

21. $6 \cdot 3 + 27 \div 3 \cdot 3 - 5$

22. $12 - 9 + 14 \div 7 - 3 \cdot 2$

23. $(6^2 - 12) + 5(-3 - 8)$

24. $-(8^2 - 15) + 4(-9 - 11)$

25. $[4(7 - 5) + 2] - 9$

26. $[6(8 - 2) + 1] - 7$

27. $-\sqrt{36 + 64} + 5$

28. $-\sqrt{81 + 144} - 2$

29. $\dfrac{18 - 4^2 + 7}{2 + 1}$

30. $\dfrac{25 - 3^3 + 14}{1 + 5}$

31. $-5(39 - 4^2) - 2(23 - 11)$

32. $-6(100 - 9^2) - (15 - 23)$

33. $4(15 - 8) + 31(14 - 11)$

34. $7(22 - 19) + 16(12 - 14)$

35. $-|5.2 - 31.3 + 3.95|$

36. $-\left|3\dfrac{1}{3} - 7\dfrac{5}{6} + 1\dfrac{1}{2}\right|$

37. $6^2 + 12 \div (-2) - 12 \cdot (-4)$

38. $4^3 + 57 \div (-3) - 7 \cdot (-3)$

39. $\left(\dfrac{2}{3}\right)^2 \div \left(\dfrac{1}{3} + \dfrac{1}{2}\right) \cdot \left(\dfrac{8}{9}\right)$

40. $\left(\dfrac{3}{4}\right)^2 \div \left(\dfrac{1}{2} + \dfrac{1}{6}\right) \cdot \left(\dfrac{2}{5}\right)$

41. $\left(\dfrac{1}{5}\right) \cdot \left(\dfrac{15}{22}\right) \div \left(\dfrac{1}{11} + \dfrac{1}{33}\right) - \left(\dfrac{1}{3}\right)^2$

42. $\left(\dfrac{1}{3}\right) \cdot \left(\dfrac{6}{7}\right) \div \left(\dfrac{1}{7} + \dfrac{1}{2}\right) - \left(\dfrac{1}{3}\right)^2$

43. $100 - (24 + 7^2 - 5) \cdot 3 + 102 \div 2$

44. $214 - (5 + 11^2 - 16) \cdot 4 + 55 \div 11$

45. $2\{3[5 - 2(3 + 4)] + 9 \div 3\} - 9(-8)$

46. $15(7) - 5\{3[8 + 2(5 - 9)] - 14 \div 7\}$

47. $\dfrac{29 + 3 - 2^3}{2^2 + 2^3}$

48. $\dfrac{15 + 3 \cdot 9 - 6}{5 + 2^2}$

49. $15 - \sqrt{2^2 + 3 \cdot 7}$

50. $-\sqrt{9^2 + 19} + 3 \cdot 6$

51. $\dfrac{4 + 3 \cdot 9 - 5^2 - 2 \cdot 3}{6^2 - 5}$

52. $\dfrac{15 - 2^4 + 1^2}{3 \cdot 9 - 5^2}$

53. $\dfrac{8^2 + 3 \cdot 12}{5 - 4 \cdot 6 + 2 \cdot 3^2 + 1^2}$

54. $\dfrac{45 - 7 \cdot 5}{3^3 - 1 + 2 \cdot 19 - 8^2}$

Use the order of operations to answer the following questions.

55. Federal guidelines on the identification of obesity in adult women state that the recommended body weight in pounds of a woman who is 5 feet, 3 inches (or 63 inches) tall is found from the expression

$$2.2[45.5 + 2.3(63 - 60)]$$

Determine this weight in pounds.

56. The same federal guidelines state that the recommended body weight of a man who is 5 feet, 10 inches (70 inches), tall is found from the expression

$$2.2[50 + 2.3(70 - 60)]$$

Determine this man's weight in pounds.

57. A business sells 300 items per week at a price of $15 each. An analysis predicts that sales will increase by 20 for each $0.50 reduction in price. The number of items sold when the price is $13.50 is found from the expression

$$300 + 20\left(\dfrac{15 - 13.50}{0.50}\right)$$

Find this number of units.

58. The same business finds that they can sell an even greater number of items if the price is drastically reduced. The number of items sold when the original price is cut in half is found from the expression

$$300 + 20\left(\dfrac{15 - 7.50}{0.50}\right)$$

Find this number of units.

59. In budgeting for the month and considering costs of school, transportation, and food, a college student who lives with his parents finds that he needs an amount of money that can be found from the expression

$$\dfrac{5000}{9} + 4[3 \cdot 3 \cdot 4 + 7(15)]$$

Determine the amount of money needed. Round your answer to the nearest hundredth of a dollar.

60. If the college student takes the bus and packs his own lunch to save money, his monthly budget needs can be found from the expression

$$\dfrac{5000}{9} + 4[3(5) + 7(10.50)]$$

Determine the amount of money needed. Round your answer to the nearest hundredth of a dollar.

61. An electrical engineer must calculate the current (in amperes) of a three-phase household electrical system as equal to the power delivered (in kilowatts) divided by the voltage (in volts) times $\sqrt{3}$. If the power is 120 kilowatts and the line carries 400 volts, calculate the current. Round your answer to thousandths.

$$\text{Current} = \frac{120}{400\sqrt{3}}$$

62. In exercise 61, refigure the current if the power is 100 kilowatts and the line carries 200 volts. Round your answer to thousandths.

63. A car left a skid mark of 50 feet before crashing. On the basis of research data, police estimated the speed of the car (in miles per hour) as $2\sqrt{5 \cdot 50}$. What is the estimated speed of the car? Round your answer to the nearest mile per hour.

64. According to the same calculation method as in exercise **63**, the estimated speed of a car that left a skid mark of 120 feet is $2\sqrt{5 \cdot 120}$. What is this speed to the nearest mile per hour?

65. If a nozzle has a diameter of 1.5 inches and the static pressure of the water is 40 pounds per square inch, then the flow rate of water through the nozzle is calculated as $(2.97)(1.5^2)\sqrt{40}$ gallons per minute. What is this flow rate to the nearest gallon per minute?

66. According to the calculation method from exercise 65, the flow rate of water through a 2-inch nozzle at 50 pounds per square inch is calculated as $(2.97)(2^2)\sqrt{50}$ gallons per minute. What would this flow rate equal to the nearest gallon per minute?

67. On the New York Stock Exchange, Pfizer, Inc. (PFE) had the following change in stock price for the week of May 23–May 27, 2005.

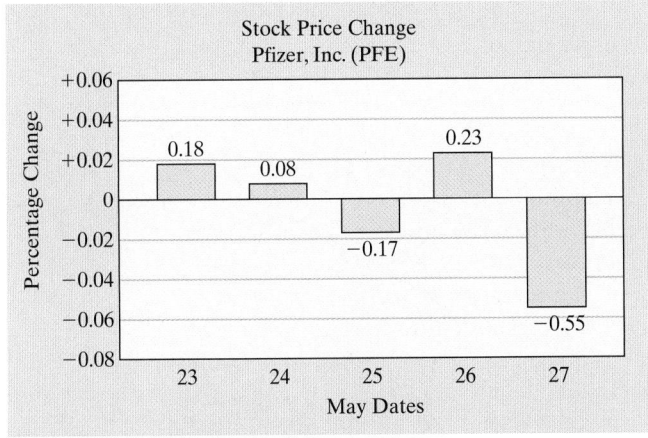

Find the average stock price change for the given week.

68. The daily high temperatures (in degrees Celsius) for the week of January 9–15, 2005, for Watson Lake, Yukon, Canada, are given in the following chart:

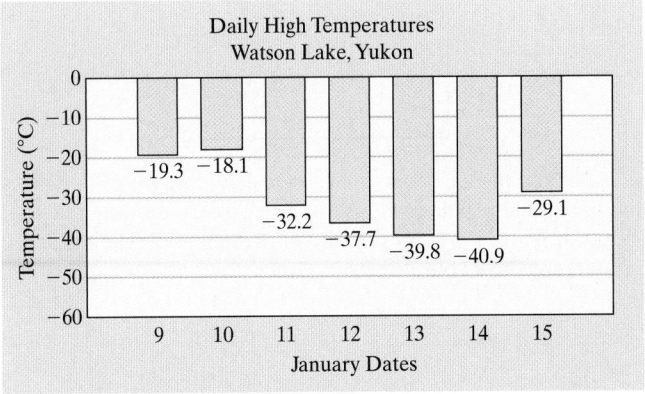

Find the average high temperature for the week.

69. The metal surface area of a can of vegetable shortening (a right circular cylinder) with a height of 6 inches and a radius of 5 inches is approximately $2(3.14)(5)^2 + 2(3.14)(5)(6)$ square inches. Approximate the amount of metal needed to make the can.

70. The cardboard surface area of a large box of oatmeal (a right circular cylinder) with a height of 9.25 inches and a radius of 2.5 inches is approximately $2(3.14)(2.5)^2 + 2(3.14)(2.5)(9)$ square inches. Approximate the amount of cardboard needed to make the box.

71. The surface area of a cone with a height of 5 inches and a radius of 1 inch is approximately $(3.14)(1)\sqrt{(1)^2 + (5)^2} + (3.14)(1)^2$ square inches. Approximate the cone's surface area.

72. The surface area of a cone with a height of 6 inches and a radius of 1.5 inch is approximately $(3.14)(1.5)\sqrt{(1.5)^2 + (6)^2} + (3.14)(1.5)^2$ square inches. Approximate the cone's surface area.

 P.4 Calculator Exercises

In entering information from an exercise involving an order of operations into your calculator, you must be careful not to use the calculator keys for braces and brackets. These keys serve a special function in the calculator and are not meant to be used as grouping symbols. Rather, you should use only the parentheses keys as grouping symbols. If you have one grouping nested within another, the calculator will process your operations properly if you use parentheses for both groupings—the outer one and the nested one.

As an example, suppose you wish to evaluate the expression

$$2\{3(2 + 4) - 5[3(14 - 10) + 7] + 11\} - 4(5 - 6) + 8$$

First, use pencil and paper to prove to yourself that the correct answer is -120.

Then key the expression into the calculator, using parentheses for every grouping symbol. The result is as follows:

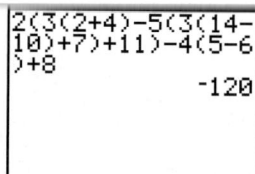

Next, key the expression into the calculator, using the braces and bracket keys. The result is a syntax error, indicating that you are not using the keys for their intended functions. The following two screens show your error:

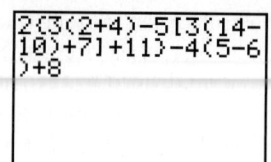

Now that you know you must use only the parentheses keys for grouping symbols, work out the following exercises, first with pencil and paper and then on the calculator:

1. $7 - \{5[2 + 9(4 - 6) - 12] + 8(17 - 12 \div 6)\}$

2. $\dfrac{4 - [2(8 + 3) - 5]}{5 + 2\{3[4 - (8 - 2)] + 11\}}$

P.4 Writing Exercise

Evaluate.

1. $\dfrac{35 + 77}{7}$ **2.** $\dfrac{1}{7}(35 + 77)$ **3.** $\dfrac{1}{7}(35) + \dfrac{1}{7}(77)$ **4.** $\dfrac{35}{7} + \dfrac{77}{7}$

Notice that all the results are the same. The expressions must be equivalent. While this is not a proof, but simply an illustration, the problems demonstrate a relationship between division and multiplication by reciprocals. Explain what this relation-ship is, and describe how the first exercise relates to each of the other three.

Construct a similar illustration in which you divide the differ-ence of two numbers by a real number.

P.5 VARIABLES AND ALGEBRAIC EXPRESSIONS

OBJECTIVES   1 Translate word expressions into algebraic expressions.

2 Evaluate algebraic expressions.

3 Model real-world situations using algebraic expressions.

APPLICATION

The area of a rectangle is found by multiplying its length by its width. The perimeter of a rectangle is twice the sum of its length and width. Write an algebraic expression for the area and perimeter of a rectangle.

According to the *American Football Rules*, the dimensions of a rectangular playing field for football are 120 yards long and $53\frac{1}{3}$ yards wide. Determine the area and perimeter of a football field.

We will discuss this application further. See page 68.

Objective P.5.1   **Translating Word Expressions**

In the previous sections, we worked with **numerical expressions**, which are combina-tions of numbers and mathematical operations, such as

$$14 + 5, \quad -28 - 3, \quad 23 \cdot 5, \quad 45 \div (-5)$$

In algebra, we work with algebraic expressions. Examples of algebraic expressions are

$$14 + x, \quad y - 3, \quad 23a, \quad \frac{s}{t}$$

In an algebraic expression, we use letters as symbols. A symbol representing only one number is called a **constant**. A symbol that can represent more than one number is called a **variable**. In the expression $14 + x$, 14 is a constant and x is a variable. In the expression πd, π is a constant representing one number (approximately 3.14), and d is a variable representing the diameter of a circle. We define an **algebraic expression** as an expression containing variables.

In this section, we will translate word expressions into algebraic expressions. In order to do this, we need to know that certain words translate into operation symbols. **Table P.1** lists examples of these words and their translations.

Table P.1

Addition ($+$)	Subtraction ($-$)	Multiplication ($\cdot$)	Division ($\div$)
add	subtract	multiply	divide
sum	difference	product	quotient
plus	minus	times	divided by
increased by	decreased by	multiplied by	divided into
more than	less than	of	per
total	less	twice	ratio
addends	taken from	double	dividend
	net	triple	divisor
	minuend	factors	
	subtrahend		

To write an algebraic expression,

- Define the variable or variables.
- Translate the words into numbers and symbols.

EXAMPLE 1 Translate each word expression into an algebraic expression.

a. 12 dollars less than the original price

b. 25% of the retail price

c. half of the sum of the length of the larger base and the length of the smaller base

d. the product of the length, width, and height measurements

Solution

a. Let $x =$ the original price

$x - 12$ "Less than" translates into subtraction. Be careful with the order.

b. Let $p =$ the retail price   Define the variable.

$25\% = 0.25$

$0.25 \cdot p$ or $0.25p$ "Of" translates into multiplication.

c. Let $B =$ length of the large base   Define two variables.

$b =$ length of the small base

$\dfrac{1}{2} \cdot (B + b)$ or $\dfrac{1}{2}(B + b)$ "Of" translates into multiplication. "Sum" translates into addition.

d. Let $L =$ length   Define three variables.

$W =$ width

$H =$ height

$L \cdot W \cdot H$,   or LWH "Product" translates into multiplication.

TAKE NOTE You may omit the times sign in multiplication expressions involving variables or parentheses. Capital letters are different variables than their corresponding lowercase letters

 ## Objective P.5.1 *CHECKUP*

1. Translate each word expression into an algebraic expression.
   a. One hundred dollars more than the previous price of the coat
   b. Two times the sum of the length and width
   c. Six less than the product of a number and 8
   d. One-half the product of the base and the height of a triangle

2. Explain the difference between basic arithmetic and algebra.

Objective P.5.2 Evaluating Algebraic Expressions

An algebraic expression can have different values, depending on what value the variable has. To determine the value of the expression, we **substitute** the value of the variable into the expression. For instance, if the variable x has the value 5, then the expression $2x$ has the value 10. If x has the value -3, then the expression $2x$ has the value -6. This process is called **evaluating** the algebraic expression.

> To evaluate an algebraic expression,
>
> - Substitute the given values for the variables.
> - Evaluate the resulting numeric expression, following the order of operations.

 TAKE NOTE When substituting a value for a variable, always enclose the substituted value in parentheses.

EXAMPLE 2 Evaluate $b^2 - 4ac$ for

a. $a = 1$, $b = 3$, and $c = 2$

b. $a = 1$, $b = -5$, and $c = 2$

Solution

a. $b^2 - 4ac = (3)^2 - 4(1)(2)$ *Substitute values.*
   $= 9 - 8$
   $= 1$

b. $b^2 - 4ac = (-5)^2 - 4(1)(2)$ *Substitute values.*
   $= 25 - 8$
   $= 17$

The checks for Example 2 are shown in **Figures P.16a** and **P.16b**.

TECHNOLOGY Evaluating Expressions

Evaluate $b^2 - 4ac$ for

a. $a = 1$, $b = 3$, and $c = 2$

b. $a = 1$, $b = -5$, and $c = 2$

```
(3)²-4(1)(2)
              1
(-5)²-4(1)(2)
             17
```

Figure P.16a

```
1→A:3→B:2→C:B²-4
AC
              1
1→A:-5→B:2→C:B²-
4AC
             17
```

Figure P.16b

For **Figure P.16a**,

a. To evaluate an algebraic expression, we may substitute the value(s) in place of the variable(s) and evaluate the numeric expression. Be sure to enclose the values substituted in parentheses.

For **Figure P.16b**,

b. To evaluate an algebraic expression, we may store the value for the variables and enter the algebraic expression. For ease in editing, we will enter all of these commands as one entry. To do so, we separate each entry with a colon,

[ALPHA] [.] (:).

Store the three values for $a, b,$ and c separated by colons.

[1] [STO▶] [ALPHA] [MATH] (A) [ALPHA] [.] (:) [3] [STO▶] [ALPHA]
[APPS] (B) [ALPHA] [.] (:) [2] [STO▶] [ALPHA] [PRGM] (C) [ALPHA] [.] (:)

Enter the expression.

[ALPHA] [APPS] (B) [x²] [−] [4] [ALPHA] [MATH] (A) [ALPHA]

[PRGM] (C) [ENTER]

In order to enter the second expression without retyping, recall the previous entry and edit it. Press [2nd] [ENTER] (ENTRY) to recall the previous entry. Then edit the previous entry, using the arrow keys in combination with delete, [DEL], and insert by pressing [2nd] [DEL] (INS). [2nd] [ENTER] (ENTRY) Move the cursor to the left, using the arrow keys. Place the cursor on top of the 3 and delete 3, [DEL]. Insert the new value for b, -5, [2nd] [DEL] (INS) [(−)] [5] [ENTER].

 TAKE NOTE The calculator has a special key for x, [X,T,θ,n].

EXAMPLE 3

For $x = 3$, evaluate the following expressions and check on your calculator.

a. $-x$ **b.** $-(-x)$ **c.** x^2 **d.** $-x^2$

Solution

a. $-x$ for $x = 3$

$\quad -x = -(3) = -3$ Substitute 3 for x. The opposite of 3 is −3.

b. $-(-x)$ for $x = 3$

$\quad -(-x) = -(-(3)) = 3$ Substitute 3 for x. The opposite of the opposite of 3 is 3.

c. x^2 for $x = 3$

$\quad x^2 = (3)^2 = 9$ Substitute 3 for x.

d. $-x^2$ for $x = 3$

$\quad -x^2 = -(3)^2 = -(9) = -9$ Substitute 3 for x. The opposite of 9 is −9.

Check

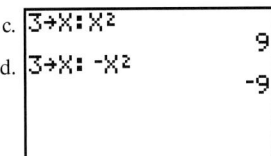

a. 3→X: −X
                    -3
b. 3→X: −(−X)
                    3

c. 3→X: X²
                    9
d. 3→X: −X²
                    -9

| EXAMPLE 4 | Evaluate $-x^2 + x - 3$ for $x = -3$. |

Solution

$$-x^2 + x - 3 = -(-3)^2 + (-3) - 3 \quad \text{Substitute } -3 \text{ for } x.$$
$$= -9 + (-3) - 3$$
$$= -15$$

 Objective P.5.2 CHECKUP

1. Evaluate $\sqrt{a^2 + b^2}$ for
   a. $a = 3$ and $b = 4$ **b.** $a = 2.4$ and $b = 3.2$
2. For $a = -12$, evaluate
   a. $-a$ **b.** $-(-a)$ **c.** a^2 **d.** $-a^2$

3. Evaluate $x^2 - x + 1$ for $x = -2$.
4. Explain what it means to evaluate an algebraic expression.

Objective P.5.3   Modeling the Real World

Algebraic expressions are helpful for evaluating properties of geometric figures, such as areas and perimeters. For example, once you know the expression for the perimeter or area of a rectangle in terms of the lengths of its sides, you can evaluate the perimeter or area of any rectangle, no matter how big or small, given the lengths of its sides. Always remember that whatever operations you perform on the numbers when you evaluate the expression must also be performed on the units of measurement involved. For example,

$$3 \text{ ft} + 2 \text{ ft} = 5 \text{ ft}$$
$$(3 \text{ ft})(2 \text{ ft}) = 6 \text{ ft}^2$$

| EXAMPLE 5 | The daily charge for renting a 24-foot U-Haul truck is $39.95 plus $0.59 per mile driven, with a $5.00 nonrefundable charge. Write an algebraic expression for the cost of renting a truck for x days and driving it y miles. Determine the cost of renting a truck for three days and driving it 543 miles. |

Solution

Let x = the number of days rented   Define the variables.
    y = the number of miles driven
$39.95x + 0.59y + 5.00$ "Plus" translates to addition.
                                 "Per mile" means to multiply.

An expression for the cost of rental is $39.95x + 0.59y + 5.00$ dollars.

$$39.95x + 0.59y + 5.00 = 39.95(3) + 0.59(543) + 5.00 \quad \text{Substitute given values.}$$
$$= 445.22$$

The cost of renting a 24-foot truck for three days and driving it 543 miles is $445.22.

 **APPLICATION**

The area of a rectangle is found by multiplying its length by its width. The perimeter of a rectangle is twice the sum of its length and width. Write an algebraic expression for the area and perimeter of a rectangle.

According to the *American Football Rules*, the dimensions of a rectangular playing field for football are 120 yards long and $53\frac{1}{3}$ yards wide. Determine the area and perimeter of a football field.

Discussion

Let L = length of a rectangle and W = width of a rectangle.

LW is an expression for the area of the rectangle. $2(L + W)$ is an expression for the perimeter of the rectangle.

Area

$$LW = (120 \text{ yd})\left(53\frac{1}{3}\text{yd}\right) \quad \text{Substitute values.}$$

$$= 6400 \text{ yd}^2$$

Perimeter

$$2(L + W) = 2\left(120 \text{ yd} + 53\frac{1}{3}\text{yd}\right) \quad \text{Substitute values.}$$

$$= 2\left(173\frac{1}{3}\text{yd}\right)$$

$$= 346\frac{2}{3}\text{yd}$$

The area of a football field is 6400 square yards, and the perimeter is $346\frac{2}{3}$ yards.

 Objective P.5.3 **CHECKUP**

1. The daily charge for renting a 17-foot U-Haul truck is $29.95 plus $0.59 per mile driven, with a $5.00 nonrefundable charge. Write an algebraic expression for the cost of renting a truck for x days and driving y miles. Determine the cost of renting a truck for two days and driving 318 miles.

2. The length of a diagonal of a rectangle is equal to the square root of the sum of the squares of the length and width of the rectangle. Write an algebraic expression for the length of the diagonal of a rectangle. Determine the length of the diagonal of a playing field for football that is 100 yards long and $53\frac{1}{3}$ yards wide.

P.5 EXERCISES

 Student Solutions Manual  PH Math/Tutor Center   CD Video *Math XL* MathXL® *MyMathLab* MyMathLab   Interactmath.com

Translate each word expression into an algebraic expression.

1. Three-fourths of the total price of a gallon of milk

2. Six percent of the amount invested

3. A total amount divided by 15

4. The quotient of 55 and a count

5. Twenty-five subtracted from the product of 12 and a number

6. Three subtracted from the product of a number and 8

7. Eighty dollars more than triple the cost of a chair

8. Four more than the product of a number and 5

9. One-third of the difference of the length of a rectangle and 5

10. Six more than one-third of the number of adults in a room

11. The product of 2.5 and a number, decreased by the quotient of 19.59 and the number

12. The product of a number and 3, decreased by the quotient of 10 and the number

13. The sum of the lengths of the three sides of a triangle divided by 2

14. The total of three quiz grades divided by 3

15. The square of a number, increased by the product of 3 times the number

16. Five less than twice the length of a side of a square

17. Joe has $10,000 to invest in two separate mutual funds. If he invests x dollars in the first fund, write an algebraic expression for the amount he has left to invest in the second fund.

18. The number of adults and children who attended a school play was 456. If we let a represent the number of adults, write an algebraic expression for the number of children attending the play.

19. A solution of water and salt is 20% saline (salt). If there are x liters of the solution, write an algebraic expression for the number of liters of salt in the solution. Write an algebraic expression for the number of liters of water in the solution.

20. Sue has a collection of nickels and dimes. If she had n nickels and d dimes, write an algebraic expression for the value of the nickels and dimes in her collection.

21. For $x = -3$, evaluate
    a. $-x$ b. $-(-x)$ c. x^2 d. $-x^2$

22. For $x = -1.5$, evaluate
    a. $-x$ b. $-(-x)$ c. x^2 d. $-x^2$

Evaluate $3x + 5$ for

23. $x = -5$ 24. $x = -13$ 25. $x = \frac{2}{3}$ 26. $x = 2\frac{2}{3}$ 27. $x = -2.7$ 28. $x = -1.06$

Evaluate $18 - 3z$ *for*

29. $z = -12.07$ **30.** $z = -0.9$ **31.** $z = 23$ **32.** $z = 33$ **33.** $z = -\dfrac{5}{6}$ **34.** $z = -5\dfrac{4}{9}$

Evaluate $\frac{1}{2}bh$ *for*

35. $b = 56$ and $h = 14$ **36.** $b = 12.8$ and $h = 10.5$ **37.** $b = \dfrac{8}{5}$ and $h = \dfrac{16}{3}$

38. $b = 12$ and $h = 11$ **39.** $b = 6.8$ and $h = 4.2$ **40.** $b = \dfrac{4}{3}$ and $h = \dfrac{5}{2}$

Evaluate $-x^2 + 2x + 9$ *for*

41. $x = -7$ **42.** $x = -8$ **43.** $x = 2.5$ **44.** $x = 1.6$

Evaluate $\sqrt{4x^2 - 20x + 25} + 8$ *for*

45. $x = 3$ **46.** $x = 5$ **47.** $x = -4$ **48.** $x = -1$

Evaluate $|4.5 - 3.1b|$ *for*

49. $b = 2$ **50.** $b = 3$ **51.** $b = -2$ **52.** $b = -3$

Evaluate $\dfrac{-b + \sqrt{b^2 - 4ac}}{2a}$ *for*

53. $a = 1, b = -2, c = -15$ **54.** $a = 1, b = 5, c = -14$ **55.** $a = 2, b = 5, c = -12$ **56.** $a = 3, b = 11, c = -4$

57. At a charity fund-raiser, adult tickets were sold for $6 each and children's tickets were sold for $2 each. Write an algebraic expression for the total amount of money raised from the sale of tickets. How much money was raised if the fund-raiser sold 235 adult tickets and 380 children's tickets?

58. Katie works part time at two different jobs. The first job pays her $9.50 per hour, while the second job pays her $12.25 per hour. Write an algebraic expression for the total amount of money she will earn on both jobs. How much will she earn if she works 15 hours on the first job and 12 hours on the second job?

59. Pablo receives a commission of $200 for each personal computer system he sells and a commission of $50 for each piece of ancillary equipment he sells. He has a fixed monthly expense of $750. Write an algebraic expression for his monthly profit. How much is his profit if he sells 19 personal computer systems and 12 pieces of ancillary equipment in a given month?

60. Shondra is paid a base rate of $1200 per month as a tutor. In addition, she receives $8 per hour spent tutoring and $6 per hour spent administering tests. Write an algebraic expression for her total monthly earnings. How much does she earn if she spent 125 hours tutoring and 30 hours administering tests in a given month?

61. The distance around a circle (circumference) is calculated as the product of π and the diameter of the circle. Write the algebraic expression used to find the circumference of a circle. What is the circumference of a circular wading pool with a diameter of 12 feet? Round your answer to the nearest tenth.

62. The circumference of a circle is calculated as the product of π and twice the radius of the circle. Write the algebraic expression used to find the circumference of a circle. What is the circumference of a circular dining table with a radius of 3 feet? Round your answer to the nearest tenth.

63. The daily charge for renting a 10-foot U-Haul truck is $19.95 plus $0.59 per mile driven. Write an algebraic expression for the cost of renting a truck for one day and driving m miles. Determine the cost of renting a truck for one day and driving 116 miles.

64. The daily charge for renting a 15-kW diesel generator is $145. Write an algebraic expression for the cost of renting the generator for d days. Determine the cost of renting the generator for 3 days.

65. The daily charge for renting a minivan is $64.99 per day plus $0.49 per mile driven. Write an algebraic expression for renting the minivan for d days and driving it m miles. Determine the cost of renting the minivan for eight days and driving it 1250 miles.

66. The daily charge for renting a luxury sedan is $76.99 per day plus $0.49 per mile driven. Write an algebraic expression for renting the luxury sedan for d days and driving it m miles. Determine the cost of renting the luxury sedan for three days and driving it 175 miles.

67. The front of a box fan has the shape of a square. The area of the face is determined as the square of the length of one of its sides. The perimeter of the face is determined as the length of one of its sides multiplied by four. Write algebraic expressions for the area and perimeter of the face of the box fan. Determine the area and perimeter of the face of the fan when its sides measure 21 inches long.

68. The front of a clock has the shape of a triangle. The area of the face of the clock is determined as the product of the length of its base and its height, divided by 2. The perimeter of the face of the clock is determined as the sum of the lengths of its three sides. Write algebraic expressions for the area and perimeter of the face of the clock. Determine the area and perimeter of the face of the clock when its base measures 10 inches, its height measures 13 inches, and the other two sides measure 14 inches each.

69. The sales tax rate is 8.5%. Write an algebraic expression for the tax on a coat whose retail price is a given number of dollars. Write an algebraic expression for the total cost of the coat. What is the total cost of a coat that retails for $149.00?

70. The recommended tip for a restaurant server is 15%. Write an algebraic expression for the tip on a bill for a given number of dollars. Write an expression for the total of the bill and the tip. If a bill totals $87.58 before the tip, what is the total bill, including the tip?

P.5 Calculator Exercises

Evaluate $a^2 + b^2$ for

1. $a = 7$ and $b = 9$
2. $a = 0.8$ and $b = 0.6$
3. $a = \dfrac{9}{5}$ and $b = \dfrac{12}{5}$

4. $a = 6$ and $b = 5$
5. $a = 0.4$ and $b = 0.3$
6. $a = \dfrac{15}{7}$ and $b = \dfrac{8}{7}$

Now use your calculator to evaluate $(a + b)^2$ for the values given in exercises 1–6.

The results are different. Explain the differences between the two expressions, $a^2 + b^2$ and $(a + b)^2$. Can you suggest why they yield different results when they are evaluated for the same values of the variables?

P.5 Writing Exercises

Sometimes we need to translate an algebraic expression into an appropriate word expression. Most of the time, more than one translation will be correct. For example, $3x + 7$ translates into "the product of 3 and a number, increased by 7," "7 more than 3 times a number," or "the sum of triple a number and 7." Write an appropriate word expression for the following four algebraic expressions.

1. $\dfrac{x}{y} + 3$

2. $2\pi r$

3. $a^2 + b^2$

4. $H - L$

5. An algebraic expression for the average of three grades is given by $\dfrac{a + b + c}{3}$, where the letters represent the three grades. Write a word expression for the average of the grades.

6. The gas mileage of a car is determined by $\dfrac{e - b}{g}$, where e is the ending odometer reading, b is the beginning odometer reading, and g is the number of gallons of gas used. Write a word expression for calculating the gas mileage of the car.

P.6 SIMPLIFYING ALGEBRAIC EXPRESSIONS

OBJECTIVES

1 Identify the terms, coefficients, and like terms of an algebraic expression.
2 Simplify algebraic expressions by combining like terms.
3 Simplify algebraic expressions by removing parentheses and combining like terms.
4 Model real-world situations by using algebraic expressions.

APPLICATION

The area of a trapezoid is sometimes written as $\frac{1}{2}h(b + B)$, where h is the height of the trapezoid, B is the length of the base, and b is the length of the top. Write an equivalent form for this expression.

The Great Wall of China has a trapezoidal cross section, with average dimensions of 25 feet for the base, 20 feet for the top, and 30 feet for the height. Use the equivalent form for the area of a trapezoid to determine the area of a cross section of the wall.

After completing this section, we will discuss this application further. See page 77.

Great Wall of China

Understanding the Terminology of Algebraic Expressions

In the previous section, we evaluated algebraic expressions. At times, we do not know the values for the variables in an algebraic expression. However, we would still like to write the expression in its simplest equivalent form. We call this **simplifying** the algebraic expression.

Before we begin simplifying, we need to define the words used with algebraic expressions. A **term** is a number, a variable, or a product of a number and one or more variables. A **variable term** is a term that contains one or more variables. A **constant term** is a term that does not contain a variable. The **numerical coefficient** (often called, simply, **coefficient**) is the numerical factor—both sign and number—of the term.

Algebraic Expression	Number of Terms	Variable Terms	Constant Terms	Coefficients
$6x^2 + 7x + 5$	3	$6x^2, 7x$	5	$6, 7, 5$
$6x^2 + 7x - 5$ or $6x^2 + 7x + (-5)$	3	$6x^2, 7x$	-5	$6, 7, -5$

 TAKE NOTE The constant term is also a coefficient.

Grouping symbols affect the number of terms of an algebraic expression.

$$6x^2 + (7x - 5) \qquad \text{Terms are } 6x^2 \text{ and } (7x - 5).$$

 TAKE NOTE The terms of an expression can be identified as the addends of the expression. Therefore, the terms are separated by plus signs that are not inside grouping symbols.

EXAMPLE 1   Complete the following table:

	Algebraic Expression	Number of Terms	Variable Terms	Constant Terms	Coefficients
a.	$-x^2y - 9xy + x$				
b.	$\dfrac{x}{3} + x - 4$				
c.	$5x(x + 1) - 2(x + 1)$				

Solution

	Algebraic Expression	Number of Terms	Variable Terms	Constant Terms	Coefficients
a.	$-x^2y - 9xy + x$	3	$-x^2y, -9xy, x$	none	$-1, -9, 1$
b.	$\dfrac{x}{3} + x - 4$	3	$\dfrac{x}{3}, x$	-4	$\dfrac{1}{3}, 1, -4$
c.	$5x(x + 1) - 2(x + 1)$	2	$5x(x + 1), -2(x + 1)$	none	$5, -2$

Note:

a. $-x^2y = -1x^2y$ and $x = 1x$

b. $\dfrac{x}{3} = \dfrac{1}{3} \cdot x = \dfrac{1}{3}x$

c. $5x(x + 1) - 2(x + 1) = 5x(x + 1) + (-2)(x + 1)$

The products (terms) are separated by a plus sign.

Two terms are called **like terms** if both are constant terms or both contain the same variables with the same exponents. The expression $6x^2 + 7x - 5$ has no like terms. Notice that the variable terms both have the same variable, x, but the variables have different exponents. However, in the expression $6x^2 + 7x^2 - 5$ there are two like terms, $6x^2$ and $7x^2$, because both variable terms have the same variables with the same exponents.

EXAMPLE 2   Identify the like terms.

a. $x^2 - 4 - y^2 + 6$ **b.** $6x^2 + 7x^2y - 8x^2y + 4x^2y - y^2 - 5xy$

Solution

a. -4 and 6 are like terms. (They are both constants.)

b. $7x^2y$, $-8x^2y$, and $4x^2y$ are like terms. (They are variable terms with the same variables with the same exponents.) ■

 Objective P.6.1 *CHECKUP*

1. Complete the table.

Algebraic Expression	Number of Terms	Variable Terms	Constant Terms	Coefficients
a. $-a^2b + 4ab - b$				
b. $3p(p + 8) - 5(p + 8)$				
c. $\dfrac{2y}{5} + y^2 - 2$				

2. Identify the like terms.
  a. $3y^2 + 7 + 9y - 8$
  b. $3x^2 + 3xy + 6y - 5xy + 7y - 2$

3. How can you identify the terms of an algebraic expression?

4. When are two terms of an algebraic expression like terms?

5. All constant terms in an algebraic expression are coefficients, but not all coefficients are constant terms. Explain. ■

Objective P.6.2   ## Simplifying by Combining Like Terms

To simplify an algebraic expression, we **combine like terms**. In order to do this, we will use the distributive law and factor out the common variables in the like terms.

$$3x + 4x = (3 + 4)x \qquad \text{Factor out the common factor of x.}$$
$$= 7x \qquad \text{Add.}$$

In simplifying a more complicated algebraic expression, first use the associative and commutative properties for addition to rearrange the terms before combining like terms.

$$6x^2 + 8x - 7x^2 + x - 2 = 6x^2 + (-7x^2) + 8x + x - 2 \qquad \text{Rearrange terms.}$$
$$= [6 + (-7)]x^2 + (8 + 1)x - 2 \qquad \text{Factor.}$$
$$= -1x^2 + 9x - 2 \qquad \text{Simplify.}$$
$$= -x^2 + 9x - 2 \qquad \text{It is not necessary to write the } -1 \text{ coefficient.}$$

 TAKE NOTE We must be careful with the signs of the coefficients when we rearrange terms. For example, $x - y = x + (-y) = -y + x$.

To simplify an algebraic expression by combining like terms,

- Rearrange terms if necessary.
- The sum of the coefficients of the like terms is the coefficient of the simplified term.
- The common variable factor for the variable terms does not change in the simplified expression.

 TAKE NOTE It is not necessary to write a coefficient of 1 or -1 with a variable term. For example, $-1x^2$ can be written as $-x^2$. Also, it is not necessary to write a variable term with a coefficient of 0 or a constant term of 0.

EXAMPLE 3 Simplify.

a. $2a^3 + 3a^2 - a^3 - 3a^2 - 3$

b. $2.3xy - 4.4x + 2xy + 6.56x$

c. $\dfrac{x}{2} + \dfrac{3x}{4} - \dfrac{2x^2}{3} - x^2$

Solution

a. $2a^3 + 3a^2 - a^3 - 3a^2 - 3 = 2a^3 - a^3 + 3a^2 - 3a^2 - 3$ Rearrange terms.
$$= 1a^3 \quad\quad + \quad\quad 0a^2 \quad - 3$$ Combine like terms.
$$= \quad a^3 - 3$$ It is not necessary to write the coefficient 1 or the $0a^2$.

b. $2.3xy - 4.4x + 2xy + 6.56x = 2.3xy + 2xy - 4.4x + 6.56x$ Rearrange terms.
$$= 4.3xy + 2.16x$$ Combine like terms.

c. $\dfrac{x}{2} + \dfrac{3x}{4} - \dfrac{2x^2}{3} - x^2 = \dfrac{1}{2}x + \dfrac{3}{4}x - \dfrac{2}{3}x^2 - x^2$

$$= \dfrac{2}{4}x + \dfrac{3}{4}x - \dfrac{2}{3}x^2 - \dfrac{3}{3}x^2$$ Find the least common denominator for like terms.

$$= \dfrac{5}{4}x - \dfrac{5}{3}x^2$$ Combine like terms. ∎

 TAKE NOTE It is customary not to write improper fraction coefficients as mixed numbers.

✓ Objective P.6.2 **CHECKUP**

1. Simplify.

a. $4x^3 + 3x^2 - 5x + 3 - 2x^3 - x^2 + x - 3$

b. $1.7xy + 2.5xz - 3.9yz + 4.3xy - 2.5xz + 1.9yz$

c. $\dfrac{7x}{3} + \dfrac{y}{3} - \dfrac{x}{4} + \dfrac{3y}{4}$

2. What does it mean to collect like terms?

Objective P.6.3 ## Simplifying Algebraic Expressions with Parentheses

In order to simplify algebraic expressions with multiplication, we need to remember the associative law for multiplication.

$$6(3x) = (6 \cdot 3)x$$ Associative law for multiplication
$$= 18x$$

In products involving variables, we multiply numeric coefficients.

In dividing expressions with variable terms by a number, we divide the numeric coefficient of the term by the number.

$$\frac{24x}{8} = \frac{24}{8} \cdot x$$
$$= 3x$$

Algebraic expressions may have parentheses or other grouping symbols. Therefore, in order to simplify these expressions, we must apply the distributive law or opposite-of-a-sum property to remove the grouping symbols.

$$-(4x + 2) = -4x - 2 \qquad \text{Opposite-of-a-sum property}$$
$$3(4x - 1) = 3(4x) - 3(1) \qquad \text{Distributive law}$$
$$= 12x - 3 \qquad \text{Multiply.}$$
$$\frac{6x - 12}{3} = \frac{6x}{3} - \frac{12}{3} \qquad \text{Distributive law}$$
$$= 2x - 4 \qquad \text{Divide.}$$

To simplify algebraic expressions involving mixed operations, use the properties of real numbers and the order of operations.

EXAMPLE 4

Simplify.

a. $4(2a - b) - (6a + 10b)$

b. $[10(x + 2) - 5] + [8 + 4(2x - 6)]$

c. $3\{[2(3x - 4) + 7] - [2(5x + 1) - 6]\}$

d. $\dfrac{5(2x + 4) - 7(x + 2)}{2x - (3x + 3) + x}$

Solution

a. $4(2a - b) - (6a + 10b) = 8a - 4b - 6a - 10b \qquad$ Distributive law
$$= 2a - 14b \qquad \text{Combine like terms.}$$

b. $[10(x + 2) - 5] + [8 + 4(2x - 6)]$
$$= [10x + 20 - 5] + [8 + 8x - 24] \qquad \text{Distributive law}$$
$$= [10x + 15] \quad + [8x - 16] \qquad \text{Combine like terms.}$$
$$= 10x + 15 \quad + 8x - 16 \qquad \text{Remove brackets (addition).}$$
$$= 18x - 1 \qquad \text{Combine like terms.}$$

c. $3\{[2(3x - 4) + 7] - [2(5x + 1) - 6]\}$
$$= 3\{[6x - 8 + 7] - [10x + 2 - 6]\} \qquad \text{Distributive law}$$
$$= 3\{[6x - 1] \quad - [10x - 4]\} \qquad \text{Combine like terms.}$$
$$= 3\{6x - 1 \quad - 10x + 4\} \qquad \text{Opposite-of-a-sum property}$$
$$= 3\{-4x + 3\} \qquad \text{Combine like terms.}$$
$$= -12x + 9 \qquad \text{Distributive law}$$

d. $\dfrac{5(2x + 4) - 7(x + 2)}{2x - (3x + 3) + x} = \dfrac{10x + 20 - 7x - 14}{2x - 3x - 3 + x} \qquad$ Apply the distributive law in the numerator and the opposite-of-a-sum property in the denominator.

$$= \frac{3x + 6}{-3} \qquad \text{Combine like terms.}$$

$$= \frac{3x}{-3} + \frac{6}{-3} \qquad \text{Distributive law}$$

$$= -x - 2 \qquad \text{Divide.}$$

✓ Objective P.6.3 *CHECKUP*

1. Simplify.

   a. $3(6p + 7q) + 4(8p - 5q)$

   b. $-4(5a + 2b + c) - 2(-a + 3b)$

   c. $4\{[2(7p - 3) + 6] - [9(p - 4) - 15]\}$

   d. $\dfrac{9(3x - 7) - 8(6x + 12)}{x - 2(3x + 2) + 1 + 5x}$

2. An algebraic expression may have groupings nested within one another. How should you proceed to remove the grouping symbols?

Objective P.6.4   **Modeling the Real World**

Algebraic expressions can be written for many important business concepts. **Revenue** is the amount of money that is received from sales. A business has **costs**, sometimes made up of **fixed costs**, such as rent, utilities, and setup costs, and **variable costs**, which are the costs that arise for each unit produced. An expression for the **profit** of a business is determined by subtracting the total cost from the revenue. The **break-even point** in a business venture is determined when the revenue is equal to the total cost. At this point, the business does not realize a profit or a loss. The business will realize a profit if the amount of revenue exceeds the amount of the total cost. The business will realize a loss if the total cost exceeds the amount of revenue.

Many algebraic expressions used to describe real-world situations can be simplified by applying the associative or distributive laws. In fact, you will find that calculations are often easier to do if you first simplify the algebraic expression before substituting numbers, instead of substituting numbers first and then trying to simplify.

EXAMPLE 5

A manufacturer of mountain bicycles determines that the cost of the materials is $24.74 per bicycle plus an additional overhead cost of $125.98 per day. Each bicycle sells for $195.99. What is the daily profit for x bicycles? What is the daily profit for 10 bicycles?

Solution

The profit is determined by subtracting the total cost from the revenue. The total revenue is $195.99 (the selling price per bicycle) times x (the number of bicycles), or $195.99x$. The total daily cost is $125.98 (overhead or fixed cost) plus $24.74 (the cost per bicycle) times x (the number of bicycles), or $125.98 + 24.74x$. Therefore, the daily profit (the revenue minus the total cost) is $195.99x - (125.98 + 24.74x)$.

$$195.99x - (125.98 + 24.74x) = 195.99x - 125.98 - 24.74x \quad \text{Distribute.}$$
$$= 171.25x - 125.98 \quad \text{Simplify.}$$

The daily profit for x bicycles is $171.25x - 125.98$ dollars.

The daily profit for 10 bicycles is found by substituting 10 for x in the expression.

$$171.25x - 125.98 = 171.25(10) - 125.98$$
$$= 1586.52$$

The daily profit for 10 bicycles is $1586.52.

APPLICATION

The area of a trapezoid is sometimes written as $\frac{1}{2}h(b + B)$, where h is the height of the trapezoid, B is the length of the base, and b is the length of the top. Write an equivalent form for this expression.

The Great Wall of China has a trapezoidal cross section, with average dimensions of 25 feet for the base, 20 feet for the top, and 30 feet for the height. Use the equivalent form for the area of a trapezoid to determine the area of a cross section of the wall.

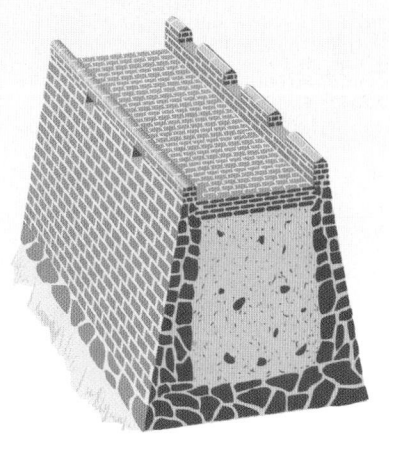

Discussion

$$\frac{1}{2}h(b + B) = \frac{1}{2}hb + \frac{1}{2}hB \qquad \text{Distribute } \frac{1}{2}h.$$

An equivalent form of the area of a trapezoid is $\frac{1}{2}hb + \frac{1}{2}hB$.

To determine the area of the cross section of the Great Wall of China, substitute 25 for B, 20 for b, and 30 for h.

$$\frac{1}{2}hb + \frac{1}{2}hB = \frac{1}{2}(30)(20) + \frac{1}{2}(30)(25)$$
$$= 300 + 375$$
$$= 675$$

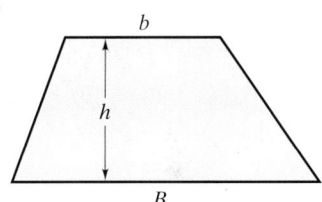

The area of the cross section of the Great Wall of China is about 675 square feet.

✓ Objective P.6.4 **CHECKUP**

1. An artist spends an average of $85 on paints and canvas for each painting she produces. She pays $225 per month to rent a studio for her work. In a given month, she produces and sells x paintings for an average price of $500 each. What is her profit for the month? What is her profit if she produces and sells six paintings?

2. The perimeter of a rectangular figure is sometimes expressed as twice the sum of its length and width. Write an algebraic expression for the perimeter. Write an equivalent expression without using parentheses. Evaluate each expression to find the amount of fringe needed to finish the edges on a rectangular tablecloth if the tablecloth measures 52 inches by 90 inches.

P.6 EXERCISES

 Student Solutions Manual    PH Math/Tutor Center   CD Video   Math XL MathXL®   MyMathLab MyMathLab   Interactmath.com

Without simplifying, (a) determine the number of terms, (b) list the constant terms, (c) list the variable terms, (d) list the coefficient of each term, and (e) identify like terms, for each expression.

1. $2x^2 - 6x + x + 12$ **2.** $3y^5 + y^3 - y + 1 + 4y^3$ **3.** $3.4a - 11.2b - 0.3a$ **4.** $\frac{2}{5}m + \frac{1}{10}n - \frac{3}{10}m + \frac{1}{5}n$

5. $3m(n - 5) + 6(n - 5)$ **6.** $3p(p + q) - q(p + q)$ **7.** $x^2 + 3xy - y^2 + 7$ **8.** $a^2 - b^2 + 6ab - 3$

Simplify.

9. $5x + 9 - 13x + 17 - 12 + 9x$
10. $2a + 3 - 12a + 5 + 7 + 4a$

11. $2x^3 + 7x^2 - 2x + 8 - x^3 - 7x^2 + 3x - 2$
12. $5h^3 + 2h^2 + h - 10 - 4h^2 + 2h^3 - h + 1$

13. $3.05a + 6.29b - 1.18a + 0.49b$
14. $19.92z - 47.08x + 3.076x - 2.572z$

15. $\frac{1}{6}x + \frac{2}{9} - \frac{2}{3}x + \frac{5}{18}$
16. $\frac{3}{4}z - \frac{5}{16} + \frac{7}{8}z + \frac{17}{32}$

17. $6x^3 + 3x^2y - 5xy^2 + 3y^3 - 5x^2y + xy^2 + x^3 + 6y^3$
18. $9d^5 - 7d^3e^2 + 8d^2e^3 - 15e^5 + 6d^2e^3 - 3d^3e^2 + d^5 - e^5$

19. $\frac{2x}{3} + \frac{y}{6} + \frac{5x}{6} - \left(-\frac{y}{3}\right)$
20. $\frac{-7a}{8} + \frac{5b}{8} - \frac{3a}{4} - \left(-\frac{b}{4}\right)$

21. $5x + 4 + (3 - 7x)$ **22.** $9y + 3 + (4y - 7)$ **23.** $(5x - 2) + (2x + 3)$ **24.** $(4 - 2t) + (3t - 3)$

25. $(23 - 12y) - (30 + 3y)$

26. $(43z - 7) - (12 + 23z)$

27. $(x + y + 4z) - (2x - 5y + z)$

28. $(41a + 21b + c) - (a - 12b - 13c)$

29. $-(1.8y - 3.5z) + (4.1y - 2.7z)$

30. $-(2.07t + 5.2r) + (0.15t - 7.6r)$

31. $(a + b) - (a + b) + (a + b) - (a + b)$

32. $(x - y) + (x - y) + (x - y) - (x - y)$

33. $(-x + y) + (x - y)$

34. $-(a - b) - (-a + b)$

35. $(a + 5b) - (-a + 5b)$

36. $-(5m - 10n) + (-5m - 10n)$

37. $-15(2x + 3)$

38. $-12(5z + 1)$

39. $-4(-5z - 14)$

40. $-2(-a - 205)$

41. $2.2(3.5x - 7.3)$

42. $3.6(1.1a - 0.8)$

43. $72\left(-\dfrac{7}{6}m + \dfrac{49}{72}\right)$

44. $55\left(-\dfrac{12}{55}z + 6\right)$

45. $-48\left(-\dfrac{5}{12}b + \dfrac{3}{16}\right)$

46. $-42\left(\dfrac{5}{14}y - \dfrac{20}{21}\right)$

47. $\dfrac{36x + 60}{12}$

48. $\dfrac{-90m - 45n}{15}$

49. $\dfrac{20.4b - 3.4c}{-6.8}$

50. $\dfrac{-2.88m + 9.6n}{-9.6}$

51. $\dfrac{96a + 24b - 115c}{8}$

52. $\dfrac{-75x - 17y + 125z}{5}$

53. $11(-3a + 2b - 4c) - 8(5a - 7b + 2c)$

54. $-31(x - 7y + 9z) + 5(-4x + 7y + 6z)$

55. $-4.6(2x - 5y) + 9.9(5x - 3y)$

56. $16.2(5p - 3q) - 3.8(4p - 8q)$

57. $\dfrac{3}{8}\left(-\dfrac{4}{9}p - \dfrac{2}{9}q\right) + \dfrac{2}{3}\left(\dfrac{7}{8}p - \dfrac{6}{7}q\right)$

58. $-\dfrac{5}{16}\left(\dfrac{2}{5}a + \dfrac{8}{15}b\right) - \dfrac{2}{3}\left(\dfrac{1}{2}a - \dfrac{1}{6}b\right)$

59. $[15 - 2(3x + 6y - 10) + 4x] + [6x + 2(8y - 12)]$

60. $-[23x + 5(2x - 6y) + 9] + [4y - 3(6x + y) - 10]$

61. $2[-5a + 3(2b - 4c) + 15] - [7(2a + 6b - c) + 12]$

62. $-4[5(6x + 4y) + 7z - 22] - [55 - 3(x + y - z)]$

63. $6\{2[x + 2(3y - 4z)] - [x - y + 3(y + 2z)]\}$

64. $2\{3[a + 2(b - 4c) + 3b] - [a + 2(b + c) + 6c]\}$

65. $\dfrac{8(5a + 7c) - 6(2a + 4c)}{4}$

66. $\dfrac{3(x + 2y) + 5(3x - 9y)}{3}$

67. $\dfrac{2.6m + 3(1.2m - 2.6n) - (4.8m + 7.4n) - 1.6n}{3m + 2(-2m + 1) + m}$

68. $\dfrac{2(1.1a + 4.6b) - 3(5.72a - 6.2b)}{(a + 1) - (a - 1)}$

69. The perimeter of a parallelogram may be written as $2(a + b)$, where a is the length of one set of parallel sides and b is the length of the other two parallel sides. Write an equivalent form for this expression. The shape of the state of Tennessee may be approximated by a parallelogram with one set of parallel sides of length 240 miles and the second set of parallel sides of length 360 miles. Approximate the perimeter of the state of Tennessee.

70. The perimeter of a rectangle may be written as $2(L + W)$, where L is the length and W is the width. Write an equivalent form for this expression. The shape of the state of Colorado may be approximated by a rectangle with a length of 380 miles and a width of 270 miles. Approximate the perimeter of the state of Colorado.

71. Paul can mow the front of his yard in x minutes. His brother can mow the back yard in 10 minutes more than twice the time it takes Paul to mow the front yard. Paul's sister mows the two side yards in 5 minutes less than the time it takes Paul to mow.
  a. Write an algebraic expression in terms of x for the total time it takes the three to mow the yard.
  b. Simplify the expression in part **a**.
  c. How long does it take the three to mow the yard if it takes Paul 20 minutes to mow the front yard?

72. The length of one side of a triangle is l inches. The length of the second side is the square of the length of the first side. The third side is twice the difference of the length of the first side less 1 inch.
  a. Write an algebraic expression in terms of l for the perimeter of the triangle (that is, the total distance around the triangle).
  b. Simplify the expression in part **a**.
  c. If the first side of the triangle is 2 inches, what is the perimeter of the triangle?

73. Carl's Carpet Cleaners charges a fee of $20.00 per visit plus $1.55 per square yard of carpeting to clean carpets. The ma-

terials used for the cleaning average $0.65 per square yard of carpeting cleaned, and the cost of each trip averages $6.50. What is the profit for a job where c square yards of carpet are cleaned? What is the profit for a job cleaning 250 square yards of carpet?

74. Pete's Plumbing Company charges $35.00 for each visit to a home. In addition, Pete charges $55.00 an hour for the work he and his helper do on the job. He pays his helper $25.00 an hour. The trip to the house costs him an average of $12.00. What is the profit he makes for a job requiring h hours of work? What is the profit for a job that takes 3.5 hours to complete?

75. Speedy Mail Delivery charges $5.00 plus $1.50 per ounce to deliver a letter overnight. It costs the company about $2.25 for each letter delivered. What is the profit for delivering a letter weighing w ounces? What is the profit for delivering a letter weighing 4 ounces?

76. Tillie's Typing Service charges $10.00 plus $2.00 per page for each manuscript Tillie types. She spends about $3.00 to set up each manuscript and $0.50 per page on supplies. What is her profit for typing a manuscript having p pages? What is the profit for a manuscript having 112 pages?

77. Laurie purchases some compact discs at $9.99 each. The sales clerk adds 8% sales tax to the price of the discs. What is the total cost if Laurie purchases x compact discs? If Laurie pays with a $50.00 bill, what is her change? If Laurie buys three compact discs, what is her cost and what is her change?

78. Mary Lynn paints and sells T-shirts. The shirts cost her $4.50 each. After she paints them, she sells them at craft shows for $15.00 each. She spends $18.50 for the paint kit that she uses for all the T-shirts that she paints and sells. What is her profit for painting and selling x shirts. What is her profit if she sells 22 shirts at the craft show?

P.6 Calculator Exercises

Can the TI-84 Plus calculator simplify $2x + 3x$? To see if it can, type $2x + 3x$ into your calculator and press ENTER . The calculator does not display $5x$. Next, type $5x$ into your calculator. You should see the calculator gives you a numerical value that is the same for both expressions. If you compare the result on your calculator with that of other students, you will most likely find that they also have numerical values displayed, and theirs are different from yours. The reason for this is that when you type an expression into the calculator, it evaluates the expression instead of simplifying it. When it evaluates the expression, it uses whatever

value happened to be stored in the x location from the previous use. The calculator cannot perform algebraic simplifications; it can only perform evaluations. Therefore, you cannot use the calculator to perform algebraic operations. However, you can use the calculator to check your arithmetic when you add coefficients to collect like terms or when you multiply or divide coefficients while applying the distributive law to remove parentheses. Use the calculator this way to check your work on simplifying the expressions that follow.

Simplify. Use your calculator to check your arithmetic.

1. $12.078x + 2.093 - 17.42x - 13.9035$

2. $(2579x - 4302) - (1087x - 306)$

3. $\dfrac{10}{13}x - \dfrac{5}{52}y - \dfrac{17}{20}x - \dfrac{7}{13}y$

4. $\left(2\dfrac{11}{25}\right)x + 5\dfrac{17}{30} - \left(3\dfrac{13}{15}\right)x - 3\dfrac{23}{75}$

5. $(1.0009x + 0.0004) - (0.0909x - 1.0031)$

6. $-(935.3376x + 701.315) - (83.027x - 581.9534)$

7. $3.995x + 12.083 - 2.995x - 9.083$

P.6 Writing Exercises

1. Consider the two terms $3a^4b^3$ and $4a^4b^3$. Are the terms like terms? Explain.

2. Now consider the two terms $3a^4b^3$ and $4a^3b^4$. Are the terms like terms? Explain.

3. What should you look for in order to find like terms?

P.7 EQUATIONS AND INEQUALITIES

OBJECTIVES

1 Identify expressions, equations, and inequalities.
2 Determine whether a number is a solution of an algebraic equation.
3 Represent solutions of inequalities on a number line.
4 Represent solutions of inequalities in interval notation.
5 Model real-world situations by using equations and inequalities.

APPLICATION

According to the American Heart Association, high blood pressure (or hypertension) is a major health problem in the world today. In the United States, 50 million people—about one in every four adults—suffer from the condition. Blood pressure classification is based on the average of two or more readings taken at each of two or more screenings. The systolic and diastolic readings, in mm Hg, for the three stages of high blood pressure are listed in the following table:

Category	Systolic	Diastolic
High blood pressure, Stage 3	180 or more	110 or more
High blood pressure, Stage 2	160–179	100–109
High blood pressure, Stage 1	140–159	90–99

For each of these stages, write an inequality that represents it.
We will discuss this application further. See page 88.

Objective P.7.1   ## Identifying Expressions, Equations, and Inequalities

In the first part of this text, we discussed expressions. We evaluate an expression by finding a numerical value for the expression. If the expression contains variables, we first substitute a value for each of the variables and then find a numeric value for the expression.

In this section, we will form a mathematical statement by combining two expressions with an equals sign. This kind of statement is called an equation. Therefore, an **equation** is a mathematical statement asserting that two expressions have the same (or equal) value.

<table>
<tr><td align="center">We may equate two
numeric expressions:</td><td align="center">Or we may equate two
algebraic expressions:</td></tr>
<tr><td align="center">$2 + 3 = 9 - 4$</td><td align="center">$4x - 3 = 3x + 2$</td></tr>
<tr><td align="center">$14 - (-3) + 8(4) \div 2 = (-5)(-6) + 7$</td><td align="center">$3x + 2y - z = 2x - y + 2z$</td></tr>
</table>

We will also form a mathematical statement by combining two expressions with order symbols. The **order symbols** are "greater than" ($>$), "less than" ($<$), "greater than or equal to" ($\geq$), and "less than or equal to" ($\leq$). This kind of statement is called an inequality. Therefore, an **inequality** is a mathematical statement asserting that two expressions may not have the same (or equal) value.

<table>
<tr><td align="center">Numeric inequality</td><td align="center">Algebraic inequality</td></tr>
<tr><td align="center">$1 < 5$</td><td align="center">$x < 5$</td></tr>
<tr><td align="center">$-6 + 2 \leq -8 - (5 - 2)$</td><td align="center">$2x - 3 \geq 3(x + 1)$</td></tr>
</table>

Two additional symbols used to combine the expressions in an inequality that do not indicate the order of the inequality are "not equal to" ($\neq$) and "approximately equal to" ($\approx$).

$$-7 + (-5) - 4(2) \neq 9(-2) + 4 \qquad \sqrt{2} \approx 1.4$$

It is very important to understand the difference among an expression, an equation, and an inequality.

EXAMPLE 1   Determine whether each of the following is an expression, an equation, or an inequality.

a. $6 + x - y + 3z$ **b.** $6 + x = y + 3z$

c. $6 + x < y + 3z$ **d.** $P = a + b + c$

Solution

a. $6 + x - y + 3z$ is an expression.   (There is no equals sign.)

b. $6 + x = y + 3z$ is an equation.   (There is an equals sign.)

c. $6 + x < y + 3z$ is an inequality.   (There is an ordered symbol.)

d. $P = a + b + c$ is an equation.   (There is an equals sign.)   ■

✓ ## Objective P.7.1 *CHECKUP*

1. Determine whether each of the following is an expression, an equation, or an inequality:

a. $3x + 6 = 17$ **c.** $2L + 2W$

b. $5x - 35$ **d.** $\frac{1}{3}x + 3 > 2$

2. Explain the difference among an algebraic expression, an algebraic equation, and an algebraic inequality.

Determining Solutions of Algebraic Equations

Equations may be true or false. If the expression on the left side of the equation and the expression on the right side of the equation have the same value, then the equation is true. If the two expressions have different values, the equation is false.

An example from the preceding part of this section, $2 + 3 = 9 - 4$, is an equation that is true because when we evaluate the expressions, $5 = 5$.

Here is an other example, taken from the preceding part of this section:

$14 - (-3) + 8(4) \div 2 =$	$(-5)(-6) + 7$
$14 + 3 \quad\quad + 8(4) \div 2$	$30 \quad\quad + 7$
$14 + 3 \quad\quad + 32 \quad \div 2$	37
$14 + 3 \quad\quad + 16$	
33	

The two expressions have different values ($33 \neq 37$). Therefore, the equation is false. (Did you notice this when you first saw this equation? It's not always easy to tell.)

If the expressions in an equation contain a variable, we need to substitute a value for the variable in order to be able to evaluate the expressions. However, not all values of the variable will make the equation true. If there is a value for the variable that makes a true equation, that value is called a **solution** of the equation.

SOLUTION OF AN ALGEBRAIC EQUATION

A solution of an algebraic equation is a value for the variable that will result in a true equation.

To determine whether a number is a solution of an algebraic equation,

- Substitute the possible solution for the variable.
- Evaluate the expression on the left side of the equation and the expression on the right side of the equation.
- Determine whether the expressions are equal.

If the expressions are equal, then the value substituted for the variable is a solution.

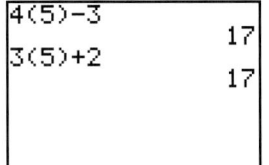

For example, determine whether $x = 5$ is a solution of $4x - 3 = 3x + 2$.

$4x \quad - 3 =$	$3x + 2$	
$4(5) - 3$	$3(5) + 2$	Substitute 5 for x.
$20 \quad - 3$	$15 + 2$	
17	17	

Since $17 = 17$, the equation is true for $x = 5$. Therefore, 5 is a solution of the equation.

On a calculator, as shown in **Figure P.17a**, each expression results in 17. Therefore, 5 is a solution of the equation.

The result is 1 in **Figure P.17b**, which indicates that the equation is true when x is 5; therefore, 5 is a solution of the equation.

TECHNOLOGY   Testing Algebraic Equations

Determine whether $x = 5$ is a solution of the equation $4x - 3 = 3x + 2$.

```
5→X:4X-3
          17
3X+2
          17
```

```
5→X:4X-3=3X+2
              1
```

Figure P.17a   **Figure P.17b**   *(continued on page 82)*

For **Figure P.17a**,
Check the value given by evaluating the expression on the left and the expression on the right.
Store the given value for the variable, $x = 5$.

| 5 | STO▶ | X,T,θ,n |

Separate the entries.

| ALPHA | . | (:) |

Enter the left side and the right side separately.

| 4 | X,T,θ,n | − | 3 | ENTER |

| 3 | X,T,θ,n | + | 2 | ENTER |

Since $17 = 17$, $x = 5$ is a solution.

For **Figure P.17b**,
Check the value by using the TEST function of the calculator.
Store the given value for the variable, $x = 5$.

| 5 | STO▶ | X,T,θ,n |

Separate the two entries.

| ALPHA | . | (:) |

Enter the equation. The equals sign is under TEST menu option 1.

| 4 | X,T,θ,n | − | 3 | 2nd | MATH | (TEST) | 1 | 3 | X,T,θ,n | + | 2 | ENTER |

The calculator returns a 1 to indicate that the equation is true and returns a 0 to indicate that the equation is false. Since the calculator returned a 1, $x = 5$ is a solution of the equation.

TAKE NOTE On some calculators, a solution may wrongly produce a 0 (for "false") if the calculator is working with nonterminating decimals (fractions). In this case, evaluate both expressions separately and visually check for equivalence.

EXAMPLE 2   Determine whether the given value is a solution of the equation.

a. $4(x − 2) + 7x = 6x + 2x + 5x$ for $x = −4$

b. $8 − 3a^2 − (a + 6) = (a + 2) − 2(2a + 4)$ for $a = 1$

Solution

a. $4(x − 2) + 7x = 6x + 2x + 5x$ for $x = −4$

$4(x − 2)$	$+ 7x$	$=$	$6x$	$+$	$2x$	$+$	$5x$
$4[(−4) − 2] + 7(−4)$			$6(−4) + 2(−4) + 5(−4)$				
$4(−6)$	$+ 7(−4)$		$−24 + (−8) + (−20)$				
$−24$	$+ (−28)$		$−52$				
	$−52$						

The solution is $−4$, because $−52 = −52$.

b. $8 − 3a^2 − (a + 6) = (a + 2) − 2(2a + 4)$ for $a = 1$

$8 −$	$3a^2$	$− (a + 6) =$	$(a + 2) −$	$2(2a$	$+ 4)$
$8 − 3(1)^2 − (1 + 6)$			$(1 + 2) − 2[2(1) + 4]$		
$8 −$	3	$− 7$	$3 − 2(2 + 4)$		
		$−2$	$3 − 2(6)$		
			$3 − 12$		
			$−9$		

The solution is not 1, because $−2 ≠ −9$.

Check

a.
```
-4→X:4(X-2)+7X
              -52
6X+2X+5X
              -52
```

b.
```
1→A:8-3A²-(A+6)=
(A+2)-2(2A+4)
               0
```
The calculator display of 0 means false.

✓ Objective P.7.2 **CHECKUP**

Determine whether the given value is a solution of the equation.

1. a. $3x - 5 = 8x - 2$ for $x = -\dfrac{3}{5}$

b. $3c^2 + 5c - 2 = 0$ for $c = 2$

Objective P.7.3

Representing Solutions of Inequalities on a Number Line

Just as numerical equations may be true or false, numerical inequalities may also be true or false. For example,

$1 < 5$	is a true inequality because 1 is less than 5.
$-6 + 2 \le -8 - (5 - 2)$	is a false inequality because -4 is greater than -11, not less than or equal to -11.
$-1 \ge -1$	is a true inequality because -1 is equal to -1.

Linear inequalities that include variables may be true or false, depending on the value of the variable being substituted. A solution of a linear inequality is a number that will make the inequality true. For example,

$x < 5$ is a linear inequality.

There are many possible solutions of this inequality.

4 is a solution because $4 < 5$.
3 is a solution because $3 < 5$.
$4\frac{1}{2}$ is a solution because $4\frac{1}{2} < 5$.
4.75 is a solution because $4.75 < 5$.

In fact, it is impossible to name all the solutions, because there are infinitely many real numbers less than 5. Therefore, we say we have a set of solutions. A **solution set** is a set of all possible solutions. In Section P.3, we discussed a number-line graph for real numbers. Therefore, we can represent this solution set as a graph on a number line.

Since we want to represent all real numbers less than 5, $x < 5$, we say that 5 is the **upper bound** of the solution set. We will graph 5 with an open dot because 5 itself is not a solution and is not included in the solution set. We graph a solid line to the left of 5 to include all real numbers less than 5. We say that the set of real numbers decreases without bound because it has no lower bound.

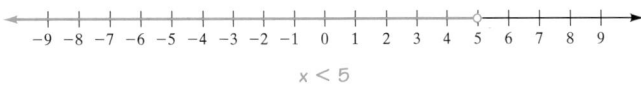

$x < 5$

All real numbers less than 5

Suppose we want to graph the solution set for $x > 5$, all of the real numbers greater than 5. We say that 5 is the **lower bound** of the set of numbers. We graph 5 with an open dot because it is not a member of the solution set, and we graph a solid line to the right of 5 to include all real numbers greater than 5. We say that the set of numbers increases without bound because it has no upper bound.

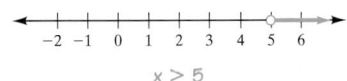

$x > 5$

All real numbers greater than 5

When we graph the solution set for $x \le 5$, all of the real numbers less than or equal to 5, the upper bound of the set of numbers is 5. We graph 5 with a closed dot because it is a member of the solution set, and we graph a solid line to the left of 5 to include all real numbers less than 5.

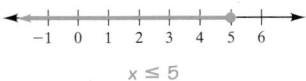

$x \le 5$

All real numbers less than or equal to 5

NUMBER-LINE NOTATION

To graph the solution set of an inequality in the form $x < c$, $x > c$, $x \leq c$, or $x \geq c$ on a number line,

1. Plot the upper or lower bound, c, of the inequality on the number line.
   • Use an open dot if the bound is not included in the solution.
   • Use a closed dot if the bound is a solution.

2. Complete the graph, using a solid line.
   • Cover all points to the left of the upper bound for a "less than" or "less than or equal to" inequality.
   • Cover all points to the right of the lower bound for a "greater than" or "greater than or equal to" inequality.

We can graph an inequality on our calculator. The graph of $x < 5$ is shown in **Figure P.18c**.

TECHNOLOGY   Graphing Inequalities

Graph the solution set of $x < 5$.

Figure P.18a

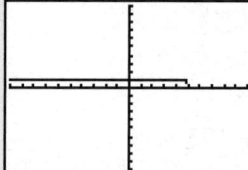

Figure P.18b

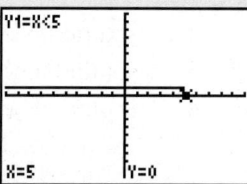

Figure P.18c

For **Figure P.18a**
Enter the inequality $x < 5$ in Y1. The inequality symbols are found under the TEST menu. The "less than" symbol is option 5.

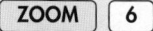

For **Figure P.18b**,
Graph the number line. The calculator will test the inequality for x-values and graph an ordered pair $(x, 1)$ for a true inequality and $(x, 0)$ for a false inequality.

For **Figure P.18c**,
Trace and use the arrow keys to display the coordinates graphed. To check the upper bound of a number line, 5, enter the value while tracing.

[TRACE] [5] [ENTER]

If the upper bound is a solution of the inequality, it will have a y-coordinate of 1. If the upper bound is not a solution of the inequality, it will have a y-coordinate of 0. For $x < 5$, the upper bound is not a solution and is graphed as $(5, 0)$.

EXAMPLE 3   Graph the solution set of $x \geq 5$ on a number line.

Check

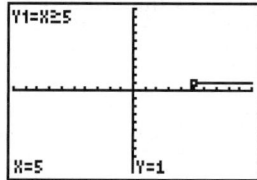

Solution

Since we want to represent all real numbers greater than or equal to 5, we say that 5 is the lower bound of the solution set. We will graph 5 with a closed dot because it is a solution. All real numbers greater than 5 are graphed to the right of 5 on the number line.

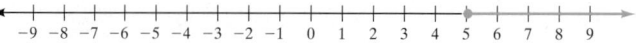

We may combine two inequalities into a **compound inequality**.

$$x > -2 \text{ and } x \le 3$$

The solution set of this compound inequality includes all the real numbers greater than -2 that are also less than or equal to 3. The compound inequality may be written as a **double inequality**.

$$-2 < x \le 3$$

EXAMPLE 4 Graph the solution set of $-2 < x \le 3$ on a number line.

Solution

Since we want to represent all real numbers between -2 and 3, including 3, we will graph the lower bound, -2, with an open dot because it is not a solution and the upper bound, 3, with a closed dot because it is a solution. All real numbers between -2 and 3 are also graphed.

We can check the solution set of a compound inequality on our calculator.

TECHNOLOGY Graphing Compound Inequalities

Graph the solution set of $-2 < x \le 3$ on a number line.

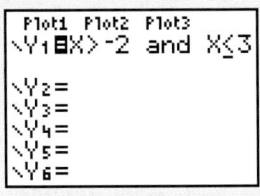

Figure P.19a

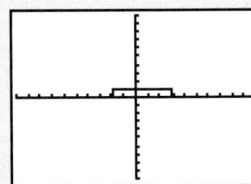

Figure P.19b

For **Figure P.19a**,
Partition the inequality into two inequalities, $x > -2$ and $x \le 3$. Enter the compound inequality using "and," option 1, under "LOGIC" in the TEST menu.

Y= | X,T,θ,n | 2nd | MATH | (TEST) | 3 | (-) | 2 | 2nd | MATH | (TEST) | ▶ | 1

X,T,θ,n | 2nd | MATH | (TEST) | 6 | 3

For **Figure P.19b**,
Graph the number line.

ZOOM | 6

✓ Objective P.7.3 *CHECKUP*

1. Graph the solution set of each inequality on a number line. Check your graph on your calculator.

   a. $x > -2$ **b.** $1 \le x < 5$

2. What is the meaning of the open dot used in graphing a linear inequality on a number line? the closed dot?

Objective P.7.4   ## Representing Solutions of Inequalities in Interval Notation

A solution set of an inequality can also be written in interval notation. **Interval notation** consists of two numbers or symbols representing the lower and upper bounds, if they exist, preceded and followed by parentheses, brackets, or a parenthesis and a bracket, indicating whether the bound is or is not included in the set. If no lower bound exists, we use the symbol $-\infty$ (**negative infinity**) in its place. If no upper bound exists, we use the symbol ∞ (**infinity**) in its place. If the bound is included in the solution, it is preceded by a bracket if it is a lower bound and followed by a bracket if it is an upper bound. (This corresponds to a closed dot on a number line.) If the bound is not included in the set, it is preceded by a parenthesis if it is a lower bound and followed by a parenthesis if it is an upper bound. (This corresponds to an open dot on a number line.) The symbols $-\infty$ and ∞ are not numbers, but indicate that the set continues without bound. Therefore, the symbol $-\infty$ is always preceded by a parenthesis and the symbol ∞ is always followed by a parenthesis.

 TAKE NOTE The interval notation for representing a solution set of all real numbers is $(-\infty, \infty)$.

For example, write the solution set of $x < 5$ in interval notation.

The solution set includes all real numbers less than 5. The upper bound is 5. There is no lower bound, so $-\infty$ will be used in its place. The symbol $-\infty$ must be preceded by a parenthesis. The upper bound, 5, is not included in the solution set, so it is followed by a parenthesis.

$$(-\infty, 5)$$
$$\uparrow \quad \uparrow$$

lower bound, upper bound

INTERVAL NOTATION

To write the solution set of a linear inequality using interval notation,

• Determine the bounds for the solutions if they exist. Write the bounds in increasing order, separated by a comma. If no lower bound exists, use the symbol $-\infty$ in its place. If no upper bound exists, use the symbol ∞ in its place.
• Precede or follow each bound of the inequality with a parenthesis or a bracket. A parenthesis is used to denote that the lower or upper bound is not included in the solution set. A bracket is used to denote that the lower or upper bound is included in the solution set.

Remember, the symbols $-\infty$ and ∞ are not numbers. The symbol $-\infty$ is preceded by a parenthesis and the symbol ∞ is followed by a parenthesis.

EXAMPLE 5   Write the solution set of $x \geq 5$ in interval notation.

Solution

The solution set includes all real numbers greater than or equal to 5. The lower bound is 5. There is no upper bound, so ∞ will be used in its place. The symbol ∞ must be followed by a parenthesis. The lower bound, 5, is included in the solution set, so it is preceded by a bracket.

The solution set is $[5, \infty)$.

EXAMPLE 6   Write the solution set of $-2 < x \le 3$ in interval notation.

Solution

The solution set includes all real numbers between -2 and 3, including 3. The lower bound is -2. The upper bound is 3. The lower bound, -2, is not included in the solution set, so it is preceded by a parenthesis. The upper bound, 3, is included in the solution set, so it is followed by a bracket.

The solution set is $(-2, 3]$. ■

The following table summarizes what we have learned in this section by describing some of the most common inequalities you may encounter:

Description	Inequality	Number Line	Interval Notation
All real numbers less than a	$x < a$		$(-\infty, a)$
All real numbers less than or equal to a	$x \le a$		$(-\infty, a]$
All real numbers greater than a	$x > a$		(a, ∞)
All real numbers greater than or equal to a	$x \ge a$		$[a, \infty)$
All real numbers between a and b	$a < x < b$		(a, b)
All real numbers between a and b, inclusive	$a \le x \le b$		$[a, b]$

✓ Objective P.7.4 *CHECKUP*

1. For each inequality, write the solution set in interval notation.

   a. $x > -2$ **b.** $1 \le x < 5$

2. In the solution of an inequality written using interval notation, what is the meaning of a bound that is preceded or followed by a parenthesis, and what is the meaning of a bound that is preceded or followed by a bracket?

■

Objective P.7.5 Modeling the Real World

One of the most important steps in solving real-world mathematical problems of any kind is correctly translating the given word statements into mathematical equations or inequalities. This is usually the first step in solving problems in physics and chemistry, medicine and biology, economics and business, ecology, and computer science—in fact, any area of human activity that involves mathematical relationships. You need to learn various concepts in these fields so that you know what variables and relationships are available to you. But once you have the right equation or inequality, you can usually figure out what you know and what you need to find in order to solve the problem.

To translate a word statement into an equation or inequality,

- Define the variable or variables.
- Write two algebraic expressions for the word expressions.
- Join the expressions with the appropriate equals or inequality sign.

EXAMPLE 7   Jesse plans to produce and sell get-well baskets. He estimates that each basket will cost $2.25, and it will cost $4.50 per basket to fill them. The cost of advertising is $15.00. If a basket sells for $9.99, write an equation needed to find the break-even point (when the revenue is equal to the total cost).

Solution

Let x = the number of baskets produced and sold
The total revenue is $9.99 per basket, or $9.99x$.
The total cost is $2.25 per basket, plus $4.50 per basket, plus $15.00, or

$$2.25x + 4.50x + 15.00 = 6.75x + 15.00$$

A company is said to break even when the total revenue equals the total cost.

$$9.99x = 6.75x + 15.00$$

EXAMPLE 8   The area of a triangle is the product of one-half its base and its height. Write an equation for this statement.

Solution

Let A = area
b = base
h = height
$A = \dfrac{1}{2}bh$ *"Product" means multiply.*

EXAMPLE 9   Qu is purchasing begonia tubers over the Internet for her garden. The special offer reads, "Buy 12 tubers of one color for $9.65. Free shipping on orders over $30.00." Write a linear inequality to determine the number of different colors Qu can purchase within her budget of $50.00 and receive free shipping.

Solution

Let x = number of colors Qu can order
The cost is $9.65 per color ordered ($9.65x$). The lower bound is $30.00 and the upper bound is $50.00. The lower bound is not included, because she must spend over $30.00. The upper bound is included, as that is the most she can spend.

$$30.00 < 9.65x \le 50.00$$

APPLICATION

According to the American Heart Association, high blood pressure (or hypertension) is a major health problem in the world today. In the United States, 50 million people—about one in every four adults—suffer from the condition. Blood pressure classification is based on the average of two or more readings taken at each of two or more screenings. The systolic and diastolic readings, in mm Hg, for the three stages of high blood pressure are listed in the following table:

Category	Systolic	Diastolic
High blood pressure, Stage 3	180 or more	110 or more
High blood pressure, Stage 2	160–179	100–109
High blood pressure, Stage 1	140–159	90–99

For each of these stages, write an inequality that represents it.

Discussion

Let s = the systolic reading in mm Hg
   d = the diastolic reading in mm Hg

High blood pressure, stage 3	$s \geq 180$	$d \geq 110$
High blood pressure, stage 2	$160 \leq s \leq 179$	$100 \leq d \leq 109$
High blood pressure, stage 1	$140 \leq s \leq 159$	$90 \leq d \leq 99$

✓ Objective P.7.5 *CHECKUP*

1. An enterprising student rents a 26-foot truck from U-Rent-It Truck Rentals. The cost of renting the truck is $141 per day. The student will use the truck to help other students move from a dormitory to off-campus housing. Each student will be charged $49 to help pack his or her belongings onto the truck and to deliver them to their new housing. Write an equation to determine the break-even point for each day's business.

2. In 1826, Georg Simon Ohm studied the effects of resistance in limiting the flow of electricity. He discovered that, for a given resistance, the current is directly proportional to the applied voltage. That is, the resistance, R, of a given conductor can be calculated as the voltage, V, divided by the current, I. Write an equation for this famous relationship.

3. Joseph joined a music club that offered a sale in which he could purchase compact discs for $6.99 each, plus a one-time charge of $5.99 for shipping and handling his order. Write a linear inequality in one variable to determine the number of CDs Joseph can order if he can spend no more than $50.00.

4. The American Heart Association lists the following classifications of blood pressure as being within healthy ranges:

Classification	Systolic	Diastolic
High normal range	130–139	85–89
Normal range	Less than 130	Less than 85
Optimal range	Less than 120	Less than 80

For each of the classifications, write an inequality that represents it.

P.7 EXERCISES

 Student Solutions Manual   PH Math/Tutor Center    CD Video   Math XL MathXL®   MyMathLab MyMathLab   Interactmath.com

Determine whether each item is an expression, equation, or inequality.

1. $3x - 15 = 6$

2. $5x + 9 - 2x$

3. $15x^3 + 7x^2 - 2x + 4$

4. $3x^2 - 6x + 1 = 0$

5. $0.5x^2 - 2.8 \neq 0.7$

6. $1.8x^2 - 7.6x - 0.3$

7. $\dfrac{2}{3}x + \dfrac{6}{7} < 0$

8. $\dfrac{4}{9}x^3 > \dfrac{5}{7}$

9. $\dfrac{4}{9}x^2 - \dfrac{3}{5}x - \dfrac{1}{4}$

10. $\dfrac{1}{2} \neq \dfrac{x}{15}$

11. $y = 3$

12. $\dfrac{x}{3} = \dfrac{5}{7}$

Determine whether the given value is a solution of the equation.

13. $2x + 4 = 10$ for $x = 3$

14. $-3a - 2 = -16$ for $a = 6$

15. $5y - 7 = 9$ for $y = 3$

16. $-12z + 15 = 50$ for $z = -3$

17. $6a + 5 = 3a + 17$ for $a = 3$

18. $5p + 16 = 6p - 12$ for $p = 28$

19. $9z - 23 = 6z - 29$ for $z = -2$

20. $8a + 26 = -5a + 39$ for $a = 1$

21. $3(x - 5) + 9 = 4(6x - 5) - 7$ for $x = 1$

22. $5y + 2(y - 7) = 6 + 3(y - 1)$ for $y = 4$

23. $2[3(x - 4) - 6] + x = 3x$ for $x = 8$

24. $3x - [5(2x + 1) + 3] = x$ for $x = -1$

25. $x^2 + 5 = 33 - 3x$ for $x = 4$

26. $2x^2 - 20 = 3x + 34$ for $x = 7$

Graph the solution set of each inequality on the number line. Check your results on your calculator. Then write the solution set in interval notation.

27. $x \geq 6$

28. $x \leq 9$

29. $z < 12$

30. $c > -7$

31. $b > -\dfrac{13}{5}$

32. $x < 3\dfrac{5}{6}$

33. $x \leq 4\dfrac{2}{3}$

34. $k \geq \dfrac{16}{3}$

35. $p \leq 12.59$

36. $x \geq 5.1$

37. $q > -6.7$

38. $R < 45.65$

39. $5 < x < 13$ **40.** $-2 < x < -1$ **41.** $2 < x < 8$ **42.** $3 \le w \le 6$

43 $-4 < d \le 0$ **44.** $0 \le g < 5$ **45.** $-1 \le m < 6$ **46.** $2 < x \le 7$

47. $2 \le t \le 7$ **48.** $15 \le j \le 30$ **49.** $\dfrac{2}{5} < s \le 3\dfrac{1}{3}$ **50.** $1\dfrac{3}{4} < a < \dfrac{2}{3}$

51. $-2.5 \le q < 3.5$ **52.** $-6.5 < y < -1.5$ **53.** $\dfrac{4}{5} \le x \le 4.5$ **54.** $-2.5 < x < \dfrac{2}{5}$

55. Complete the following table:

Description	Inequality	Number Line	Interval Notation
a. All real numbers less than 4.5			
b.		number line with point at 3	
c.			$(-\infty, -2)$
d.	$z \ge 5.7$		
e.		number line open circle at -7	
f.			$(2, \infty)$
g.	$2 < y < 8$		
h.		number line point at -3, open circle at 2	
i.			$[0, 9]$
j All real numbers between -1 and 1, including 1			

56. Complete the following table.

Description	Inequality	Number Line	Interval Notation
a.			$(-\infty, -9)$
b.		number line point at 4	
c.	$a < \dfrac{1}{2}$		
d.			$[0, \infty)$
e.		number line open circle at -4	
f. All real numbers greater than 2.7			
g.			$(4, 11)$
h.		number line point at 1, open circle at 5	
i.	$-5 \le c \le -1$		
j. All real numbers between -3 and 2, including 2			

Write an equation to represent each situation described. Do not attempt to solve the equation.

57. Jolene purchased a computer for $1300 and a color printer for $350 for her new business endeavor. She estimates the cost of producing the flyers that she plans to sell will be $0.25 per flyer. If she sells flyers for $1.25 each, determine her break-even point.

58. U Rent It purchased an air compressor for $572. The company plans to rent the air compressor for $35 per day. Determine the break-even point.

59. The daily charge for renting a 17-foot Penske truck is $29.95 plus $0.59 per mile driven. If you have budgeted $60.00 for the cost of renting the truck for one day, how many miles is the maximum you would be able to drive?

60. Cox's Furniture Store will carry your loan for 12 months without interest if you pay $250 down and make monthly payments. What would be the amount of the monthly payments if you purchase a dining room set for $2500?

61. The perimeter of a semicircular sector is equal to the diameter added to the product of π and the radius. (This product is one-half the circumference of a circle.)

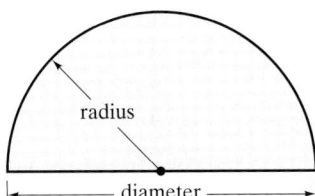

radius

diameter

62. The average rate of speed is equal to the distance traveled divided by the time elapsed.

63. The interest, I, paid on a continuously compounded loan is equal to the difference of the compounded amount, A, less the principal, P.

64. The total amount of a loan, A, is the sum of the principal, P, plus the interest, I.

65. The sum of the number of nickels and the number of dimes is equal to twice the number of nickels.

66. The number of quarters is equal to five more than twice the number of dimes.

67. The sum of 5% of the dollars invested in one account and 7% of the dollars invested in another account is equal to the total interest earned on the investments, $176.

68. The total interest earned on investments, $256, is the sum of 8% of the dollars invested in one account and 10% of the dollars invested in a second account.

69. One angle measures 10 degrees more than triple the measure of another angle.

70. The length of one side of a triangle is 6 inches more than twice the length of a second side.

71. A solenoid is constructed by winding wire on an iron core. An electric current passing through the wire produces a magnetic induction in the core very similar to the magnetic field seen in a bar magnet. The magnetic intensity, H, is equal to the product of the number of turns, N, and the current, I, divided by the length of the solenoid, L. Write an equation to represent this relation.

72. In physics, the number of moles, n, contained in a gas is equal to its mass, m, divided by its molecular mass, M. Write an equation expressing this relation.

For each classification, write a linear inequality that represents it. Seismologists use the Richter scale to classify the magnitude of an earthquake.

73. The following table classifies the magnitudes of less severe earthquakes:

Classification	Richter Magnitudes
Generally not felt, but recorded.	Less than 3.5
Often felt, but rarely causes damage.	3.5–5.4
At most slight damage to well-designed buildings and major damage to poorly constructed buildings over small regions.	under 6.0

74. The following table classifies the magnitudes of earthquakes that are destructive:

Classification	Richter Magnitudes
Destructive in inhabited areas up to about 100 kilometers across.	6.1–6.9
Major earthquake causing damage over larger areas.	7.0–7.9
Great earthquake causing serious damage in areas several hundred kilometers across.	8.0 or greater

Write an inequality to represent each situation described. Do not attempt to solve the inequality.

75. A car rental firm leases a car for $39.95 plus $0.20 per mile. If your cost of rental is not to exceed $150.00, how many miles can you drive the car?

76. The cost of a production run at a factory is the sum of a setup cost of $300 plus a labor and materials cost of $22 per item produced. What is the number of items that can be produced if the production cost is to be less than $1000?

77. Pete is paid a weekly salary of $450 plus 5% commission on his weekly sales. What must his sales be if he wishes his weekly pay to be more than $800?

78. Josephine pays a weekly rental of $125 for a booth at the local mall. She sells handcrafted baskets there for a price of

$15 each. What must be the number of items sold in order for her to realize a profit of at least $250 per week?

79. Sally is planning a shower for her best friend. She has reserved a party room at Le Chien Restaurant, which will charge her $25 for the room and $12.50 per person for lunch. How many people can she invite to the shower if she wishes to spend between $150 and $200 at the restaurant?

80. The local high school is staging *Romeo and Juliet* as a Valentine's Day event. They have spent $350.00 for costumes, props, and so on for the play. They are charging $4.50 per person for admission. How many tickets must they sell in order to realize a profit between $200.00 and $500.00?

P.7 Calculator Exercises

If you have a calculator with split-screen capability, it is often helpful to use the split screen to view an inequality at the same time that you are viewing its graph. As an example, suppose you wish to graph the inequality $x > -3$. The following are the steps used to view this inequality and its graph simultaneously:

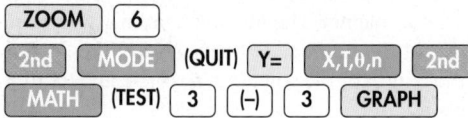

The calculator should exhibit a split screen with the coordinate system above and the home screen below. Now you can enter the instructions to graph the inequality.

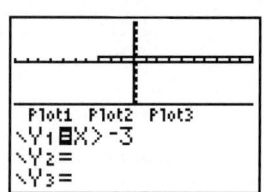

The graph of the inequality is displayed above, and the inequality is displayed below.

Use the split screen to view the graphs of the given inequalities. Trace the graph to view its bounds.

1. $x < -2$ **2.** $x > -2$

3. $x \leq -2$ **4.** $x \geq -2$

Change the window to decimal scale by pressing [ZOOM] [4], and view the following graphs:

5. $-2.5 \leq x \leq 2.5$ **6.** $-2.5 \leq x < 2.5$

7. $-2.5 < x < 2.5$

When you wish to return to a full screen, simply use the [MODE] key, move the cursor down to Full, and press [ENTER]. When you quit the [MODE] function, you will be back to the full screen.

P.7 Writing Exercises

A. Key words that imply order relations.

Consider the following list of phrases that imply an order relation, and assign the correct order relation symbol that applies to each phrase:

1. ____ At least   **2.** ____ At most   **3.** ____ No more than

4. ____ No greater than   **5.** ____ Larger than   **6.** ____ Smaller than

7. ____ Not to exceed   **8.** ____ Below   **9.** ____ Above

10. ____ Greater than   **11.** ____ Greater than or equal to   **12.** ____ Less than

13. ____ Less than or equal to   **14.** ____ No fewer than   **15.** ____ No less than

16. ____ No smaller than   **17.** ____ A maximum of   **18.** ____ A minimum of

19. ____ Up to   **20.** ____ Down to

After completing the list, suggest at least one additional phrase that matches each of the following order relations:

21. $<$ **22.** $>$ **23.** $\leq$ **24.** $\geq$

Use one of the phrases you suggested to write a real-world application that involves an inequality. Write a complete narrative describing the problem. Then write the linear inequality in one variable that represents the application you described.

B. Alternative notation for graphing inequalities.

In this section, you have used open dots and closed dots to graph an inequality on the number line. You also learned to use parentheses and brackets to indicate the inclusion or exclusion of endpoints in the solution set of an inequality. Consider the following graphs of a linear inequality in one variable:

Number Line	Inequality	Interval notation
1. number line from −5 to 5		
2. number line from −5 to 5		
3. number line from −5 to 5		
4. number line from −5 to 5		
5. number line from −5 to 5		

For each graph, write the inequality that corresponds to the graph and write the solution set of the inequality in interval notation. Explain how the graphs differ from those you have seen in this section. Do you think the new notation can be used in place of that shown earlier? Which do you prefer and why?

P.8 FORMULAS

OBJECTIVES

1 Evaluate two-dimensional geometric formulas.
2 Evaluate three-dimensional geometric formulas.
3 Evaluate angle formulas.
4 Evaluate other formulas.
5 Model real-world situations by using formulas.

APPLICATION

Diane plans to remove the carpet in her extra bedroom (br 2 in the house plan) and have it replaced with hardwood flooring. If the hardwood floor that she chose costs $5.98 per square foot installed, determine the cost of replacing the carpet with hardwood flooring, excluding the closet floor.

After completing this section, we will discuss this application further. See page 101.

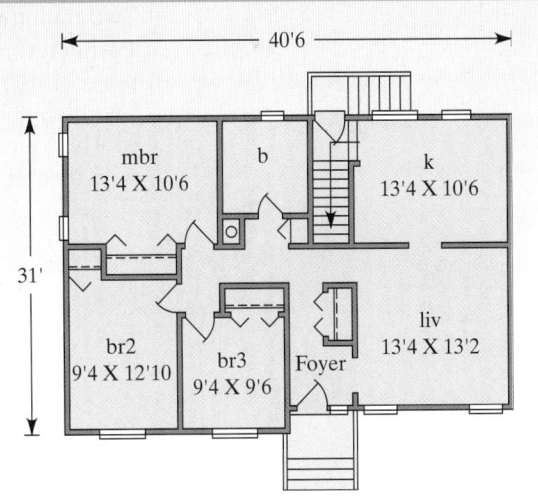

In Example 8 of Section P.7, we wrote a special type of equation called a formula. A **formula** is an equation used to find a numerical value for an unknown variable. We know the values of all the variables in the formula, except one. For example, the formula in Example 8 may be used to find the area, A, of a triangle when the base, b, and height, h, are known.

$$A = \frac{1}{2}bh \quad \text{for } b = \text{base and } h = \text{height}$$

To find a numerical value for the area, A, we substitute values for b and h. We say we *evaluate* the formula.

To evaluate a formula,

- Write the formula.
- Substitute the values for the variables.
- Evaluate the expression containing the substituted values.

For example, evaluate $A = \frac{1}{2}bh$ for $b = 12$ inches and $h = 5$ inches.

$$A = \frac{1}{2}bh \qquad \text{Write the formula.}$$

$$A = \frac{1}{2}(12 \text{ in.})(5 \text{ in.}) \quad \text{Substitute.}$$

$$A = 30 \text{ in}^2 \qquad \text{Evaluate.}$$

The area of the triangle is 30 square inches.

 TAKE NOTE To determine the units of measure, perform the arithmetic operations on the units of measure as well as the numbers.

In this section, we will introduce you to the formulas that you need to work exercises in the first five chapters of this text. Many of these formulas have been discussed in previous sections. However, the formulas have not been presented using variables. In this section, you will evaluate each of these formulas with the information given. In later sections, you will use the formulas to write equations expressing given information.

Objective P.8.1

Evaluating Two-Dimensional Geometric Formulas

Two-dimensional figures have properties of perimeter (circumference) and area. **Perimeter**, P, is the distance around a closed two-dimensional figure. **Circumference**, C, is the distance around a circle. **Area**, A, is the amount of surface covered by a two-dimensional figure.

The following are the two-dimensional figures we will use in this text, together with formulas for their perimeters and areas, as well as other useful formulas:

Triangle

$P = a + b + c$

$A = \dfrac{1}{2}bh$

Rectangle

$P = 2L + 2W$

$A = LW$

Square

$P = 4s$

$A = s^2$

Parallelogram

$A = bh$

$P = 2a + 2b$

Circle

$$d = 2r$$

$$r = \frac{1}{2}d$$

$$C = \pi d \quad \text{or} \quad C = 2\pi r$$

$$A = \pi r^2$$

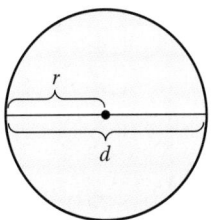

3.141592654

 TAKE NOTE The calculator value for π is more precise than the noncalculator value (3.14) we used earlier. In this text, you need to use the more precise value, unless told otherwise. (See Example 1.) To be as accurate as the calculator, we would need to use a value for π with more decimal places. To determine this value, we can enter ⬛2nd⬛ ⬛^⬛ (π) on the calculator, which will then display a value for π rounded to nine decimal places.

EXAMPLE 1

A soccer field has a center circle that is used for kickoffs. The team taking the kick is allowed as many players inside the circle as it wishes. The length of the radius of the circle depends on the age of the players. For players six years and under, the radius is 5 yards. Find the exact area of the circle, and approximate this area to the nearest tenth of a square yard.

Solution

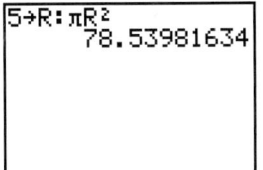

$$A = \pi r^2 \qquad \text{Write the formula.}$$

$$A = \pi(5 \text{ yd})^2 \qquad \text{Substitute.}$$

$$A = 25\pi \text{ yd}^2 \qquad \text{Evaluate.}$$

$$A \approx 78.5 \text{ yd}^2$$

The exact area is 25π square yards. The approximate area is 78.5 square yards. ■

✓ Objective P.8.1 **CHECKUP**

1. For soccer players 9 years and under and 10 years and under, the radius of the center circle of the soccer field is 8 yards. What is the exact area of this circle? What is the area approximated to the nearest tenth of a square yard?

2. What is a formula?

3. What is the difference between the perimeter of a two-dimensional figure and the area of a two-dimensional figure?

Objective P.8.2 **Evaluating Three-Dimensional Geometric Formulas**

Three-dimensional figures have properties of volume and surface area. **Volume**, V, is the amount of space enclosed in a three-dimensional figure. **Surface area**, S, is the total area of all exposed surfaces of a three-dimensional figure.

The following are the three-dimensional figures we will use in this text, together with the formulas for their volume and surface areas:

Rectangular solid

$$V = LWH$$

$$S = 2LW + 2WH + 2LH$$

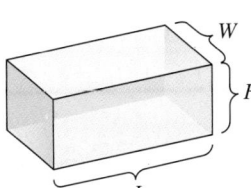

Cube

$$V = s^3$$

$$S = 6s^2$$

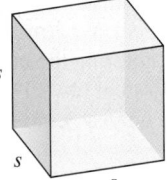

Right circular cylinder

$V = \pi r^2 h$

$S = 2\pi r^2 + 2\pi rh$

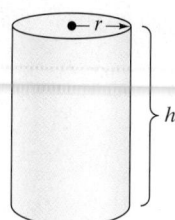

Sphere

$V = \dfrac{4}{3}\pi r^3$

$S = 4\pi r^2$

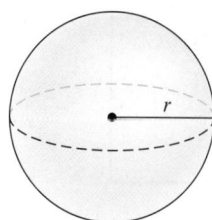

Right circular cone

$V = \dfrac{1}{3}\pi r^2 h$

$S = \pi r\sqrt{r^2 + h^2} + \pi r^2$

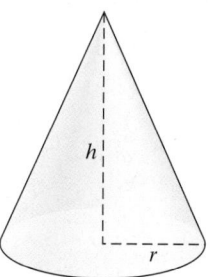

EXAMPLE 2

The 1982 World's Fair centerpiece, the Sunsphere, is a 266-foot-tall steel tower topped by reflective bronze-coated glass windows in the shape of a sphere. The radius of the sphere is 36.5 feet. Determine the exact volume. Approximate the volume to the nearest tenth of a cubic foot.

Solution

$V = \dfrac{4}{3}\pi r^3$ Write the formula.

$V = \dfrac{4}{3}\pi(36.5\text{ ft})^3$ Substitute.

$V = 64836.1\overline{6}\pi \text{ ft}^3$

$V \approx 203{,}688.8 \text{ ft}^3$

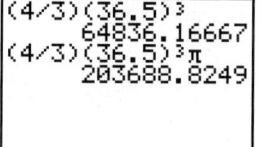

The Sunsphere is exactly $64836.1\overline{6}\pi$ cubic feet or approximately 203,688.8 cubic feet in volume. ∎

✓ Objective P.8.2 *CHECKUP*

1. It was stated that the Sunsphere from the 1982 World's Fair has a radius of 36.5 feet. What is the exact surface area of such a large sphere (ignoring the fact that part of the surface area is resting on the steel tower)? What is the surface area approximated to the nearest tenth of a square foot?

2. What is the difference between the surface area of a three-dimensional figure and its volume?

3. In Example 2, you were asked to find an exact answer and an approximate answer. Explain the differences in the answers.

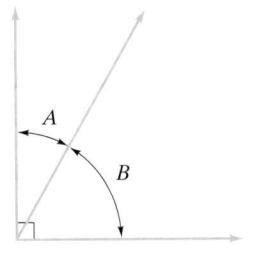

Objective P.8.3

Evaluating Angle Formulas

An **angle** is a geometric figure formed by two lines extending from a common point. An angle can be measured by a unit of measurement called a degree (°). One degree is equal to the rotation of a line through $\frac{1}{360}$ of a complete circle. A **right angle** is an angle whose measure is 90°.

If the sum of the measures of two angles is 90°, we say that the angles are **complementary angles**.

Complementary angles

$$A + B = 90°$$

or

$$A = 90° - B$$

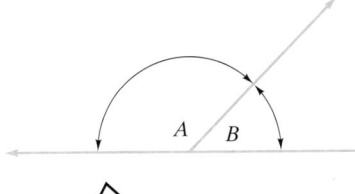

If the sum of the measures of two angles is 180°, we say that the angles are **supplementary angles**.

Supplementary angles

$$A + B = 180°$$

or

$$A = 180° - B$$

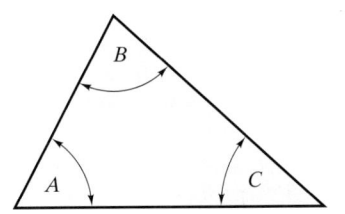

A triangle contains three angles. The sum of the measures of the three angles is 180°.

Sum of the angle measures in a triangle

$$A + B + C = 180°$$

or

$$A = 180° - (B + C)$$

EXAMPLE 3

Find the measure of the third angle in the following triangle:

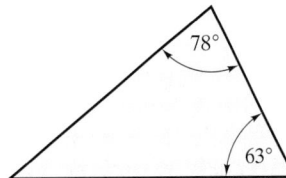

Solution

$$A = 180° - (B + C) \qquad \text{Write the formula.}$$
$$A = 180° - (63° + 78°) \qquad \text{Substitute.}$$
$$A = 180° - 141° \qquad \text{Evaluate.}$$
$$A = 39°$$

The third angle measures 39°.

EXAMPLE 4

Two angles are supplementary. One angle measures 60°. What is the measure of the second angle?

Solution

$$A = 180° - B \qquad \text{Write the formula.}$$
$$A = 180° - 60° \qquad \text{Substitute.}$$
$$A = 120°$$

The second angle measures 120°.

✓ Objective P.8.3 *CHECKUP*

1. One angle of a triangle measures 28 degrees and another angle measures 97 degrees. What is the measure of the third angle of the triangle?

2. Two angles are complementary. One angle measures 59 degrees. What is the measure of the other angle?

3. Explain the difference between complementary and supplementary angles.

Objective P.8.4   Evaluating Other Formulas

Algebraic formulas are used to describe many relationships aside from the properties of geometric figures. In this objective, we briefly present some common and important formulas you are likely to see in a variety of applications.

Two of the most common scales used to measure temperature are the Celsius (C) and Fahrenheit (F) scales. These two scales are defined by assigning 0 degrees Celsius (0°) or 32 degrees Fahrenheit (32°) to the freezing point of water and 100°C or 212°F to the boiling point of water.

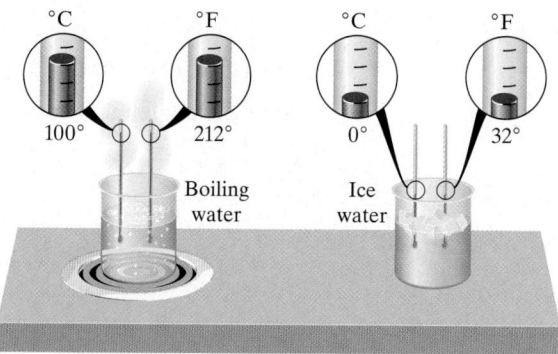

Sometimes it is useful to convert temperatures measured on one scale to the other scale. The following formulas enable us to do this:

<table>
<tr><td>**Celsius to Fahrenheit**</td><td>**Fahrenheit to Celsius**</td></tr>
<tr><td>$F = \dfrac{9}{5}C + 32$</td><td>$C = \dfrac{5}{9}(F - 32)$</td></tr>
</table>

EXAMPLE 5

The average human body temperature is 98.6°F. Convert this temperature to Celsius.

Solution

$$C = \frac{5}{9}(F - 32) \qquad \text{Write the formula.}$$

$$C = \frac{5}{9}(98.6 - 32) \qquad \text{Substitute.}$$

$$C = 37 \qquad \text{Evaluate.}$$

The average human body temperature is 37°C.

Interest, I, is the amount of money a lender charges for borrowing and for investing money. In order to determine the amount of interest, we need to know the **principal**, P, or amount borrowed or invested, the **interest rate**, r, and the period of **time**, t, for which the loan or investment is made.

Interest may be calculated by several different methods. **Simple interest** is interest based on the principal alone. **Compound interest** is based on taking the interest accumulated in one period and adding it to the principal in order to determine the interest applicable in the next period. **Continuously compounded interest** is regular compound interest with very short periods, so that the addition of interest occurs on a continuous basis. In this objective, we will work only with simple interest. Later in the text we will discuss other, more complicated, interest calculations.

Simple interest (I)

$$I = Prt$$ P = principal, r = rate of interest, t = number of periods of time

$$A = P + I$$ A = amount of simple interest and principal, P = principal, I = interest

EXAMPLE 6 According to the American Association of Community Colleges, the 2004 average annual tuition and fees is $1518. Emin applied for a student loan with an annual compounded interest rate of $8\frac{1}{4}\%$. Four years later, the payoff amount would be $2084.41. However, his grandfather offered to lend him the same amount for 9% per year simple interest. Determine the better choice for Emin if he intends to pay off the loan after four years.

Solution

First, determine the amount of simple interest. Change 9% to a decimal, 9% = 0.09.

$$I = Prt$$
$$I = (1518)(0.09)(4)$$
$$I = 546.48$$

Next, determine the total payoff: the amount borrowed plus the amount of simple interest.

$$A = P + I$$
$$A = 1518 + 546.48$$
$$A = 2064.48$$

Emin will pay about $2084.41 for the student loan and $2064.48 to his grandfather. His better choice is to borrow from his grandfather. ■

Another formula we will use often allows us to find the distance traveled, d, if we are given the rate (speed), r, and time traveled, t.

Distance traveled (d)

$$d = rt$$ r = rate (speed), t = time traveled

Two related formulas are $r = \dfrac{d}{t}$ and $t = \dfrac{d}{r}$.

EXAMPLE 7 The X-34, a single-engine rocket plane, can reach altitudes of up to 250,000 feet and travel up to eight times the speed of sound. (Sound travels at 1070 feet per second.) Estimate the length of time it would take for the plane to reach its maximum altitude if it is launched from an L-1011 airliner at an altitude of 40,000 feet and travels at its maximum speed.

Solution

The distance traveled is the difference in the maximum altitude and the altitude at which the plane was launched, or 250,000 − 40,000 − 210,000 feet. The speed is eight times the speed of sound, or 8(1070) = 8560 feet per second.

$$t = \frac{d}{r} \qquad \text{Write the formula.}$$

$$t = \frac{210,000}{8560} \qquad \text{Substitute.}$$

$$t \approx 24.5$$

The X-34 will reach its maximum altitude in about 24.5 seconds from a launch at 40,000 feet. ■

✓ Objective P.8.4 *CHECKUP*

1. Scientists believe that the temperature at the center of the Earth's core could be 7200°F. Convert this temperature to Celsius.

2. Find the amount of simple interest on a loan of $10,000 at a rate of interest of 8.5% per year for two years.

3. A bluefin tuna can swim about 73 feet per second for short periods. At this rate, how far can the tuna swim in two minutes? If one mile is equal to 5280 feet, convert the distance to miles.

Objective P.8.5   **Modeling the Real World**

Many objects in the real world are not perfect geometric shapes. For instance, the Earth is a little wider at the equator than it is through the North and South Poles, so it is not exactly a sphere. Similarly, most rooms in a house tend to be a little out of perfect alignment and so are not exactly rectangular solids. But we can usually approximate real objects by geometrical shapes and use the formulas for volumes, areas, and perimeters introduced earlier in this section. The errors involved in these approximations are often small enough for us to ignore.

EXAMPLE 8

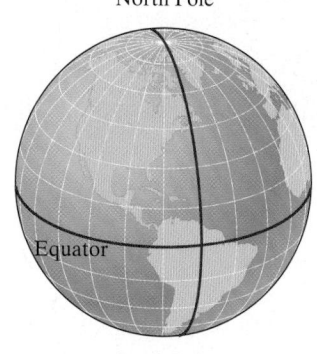

North Pole

Equator

South Pole

a. The equatorial diameter of the Earth is approximately 12,756.34 km. Determine the Earth's equatorial circumference (assuming that our planet is a sphere).

b. The polar diameter of the Earth is approximately 12,713.54 km. Determine the Earth's polar circumference.

c. What is the difference between the equatorial circumference and the polar circumference?

Calculator Solution

a. The equatorial diameter:

$$C = \pi d$$
$$C \approx \pi(12,756.34)$$
$$C \approx 40,075.224$$

The equatorial circumference is approximately 40,075.224 km.

b. The polar diameter:

$$C = \pi d$$
$$C \approx \pi(12,713.54)$$
$$C \approx 39,940.764$$

The polar circumference is approximately 39,940.764 km.

```
a. π(12756.34)
            40075.22403
b. π(12713.54)
            39940.76387
```

c. The difference is 40,075.224 − 39,940.764 = 134.460 km.

Although the difference seems large to us, in comparison to the total circumference of the Earth, it is not. Therefore, approximating the Earth as a sphere is a reasonable approximation for most purposes. A more accurate model would be necessary for calculating the orbit of a satellite. ■

APPLICATION

Diane plans to remove the carpet in her extra bedroom (br 2 in the house plan) and have it replaced with hardwood flooring. If the hardwood floor that she chose costs $5.98 per square foot installed, determine the cost of replacing the carpet with hardwood flooring, excluding the closet floor.

Discussion

The dimensions of the extra bedroom are 9 feet, 4 inches (length), by 12 feet, 10 inches (width). Since we are measuring square feet, we will need to convert these figures to feet. (Remember, 12 inches equal 1 foot!)

$$L = 9 \text{ feet, 4 inches} = 9\frac{4}{12} = 9\frac{1}{3} \text{ feet}$$

$$W = 12 \text{ feet, 10 inches} = 12\frac{10}{12} = 12\frac{5}{6} \text{ feet}$$

$$A = LW \qquad \textit{Area of a rectangle}$$

$$A = \left(9\frac{1}{3}\right)\left(12\frac{5}{6}\right) \qquad \textit{Substitute.}$$

$$A = \frac{1078}{9}$$

$$A = 119\frac{7}{9} \text{ square feet}$$

It costs $5.98 per square foot to install the flooring. The total cost is therefore

$$119\frac{7}{9} \cdot 5.98 \approx 716.27$$

It will cost Diane about $716.27 to install hardwood flooring in her extra bedroom.

br2
9'4 X 12'10

✓ Objective P.8.5 **CHECKUP**

1. The equatorial diameter of the planet Mercury is approximately 4880 km. Determine the equatorial circumference of Mercury, assuming that the planet is a sphere.

2. According to the *Guinness Book of World Records*, the largest corrugated cardboard box was constructed by Kappa Van Dam of the Netherlands in 1999. The box measured 22.9 feet by 8.5 feet by 7.9 feet. Find the volume and surface area of the box. ■

P.8 EXERCISES

Student Solutions Manual   PH Math/Tutor Center   CD Video   MathXL®   MyMathLab   Interactmath.com

In exercises 1–10, find the area and perimeter of each two-dimensional geometric figure.

1. A triangle has a base of 39 inches, a height of 24 inches, and sides of 40 inches and 25 inches.

2. A triangle has a height of 16 millimeters, a base of 75 millimeters, and sides of 20 and 65 millimeters.

3. A rectangle has a length of 6 centimeters and a width of 4 centimeters.

4. A rectangle's length is 8 feet and its width is 5 feet.

5. A square's side measures $2\frac{1}{2}$ feet.

6. A square has sides measuring 5.6 meters each.

7. A parallelogram has a base of 68 meters, a height of 45 meters, and a side of 53 meters.

8. The base of a parallelogram measures 95 inches, its height measures 39 inches, and its side measures 89 inches.

9. A circle has a radius of $5\frac{1}{4}$ inches. Round your answers to the nearest tenth.

10. The radius of a circle measures $2\frac{3}{4}$ feet. Round your answers to the nearest tenth.

11. It is estimated that grizzly bears searching for food range over an area equivalent to a circle with a radius of 16.5 miles. Over how large an area in square miles do they roam? What is the circumference of this circular area?

12. Polar bears are the world's largest land carnivores, and it is estimated that, in their search for food, they roam over an area equivalent to a circle with a radius of 80 miles. Over how large an area in square miles do they roam? What is the perimeter (circumference) of this circular area?

13. When Levittown, New York, was developed as the first mass-housing suburb in the country following World War II, the size of the standard lot was 60 feet by 100 feet. What is the area of this standard lot? What is the perimeter of the lot?

In exercises 19–20, use the following house plan.

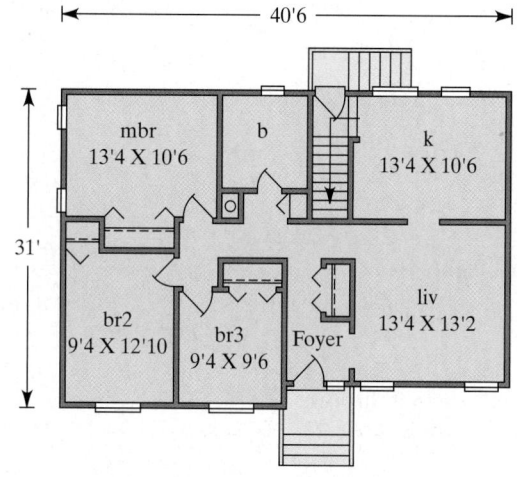

14. Linda has designed a circular area with a fountain in the center for her yard. The circular area has a radius of 5 feet. What is the square footage of this area? How many feet will the border of the area be?

15. Gretchen made a square tablecloth measuring 52 inches on a side. What is the area of coverage? How much fringe material will she need for the perimeter.

16. Marcos built a square raised deck in his yard. The deck was 15 feet on a side. How many square feet of space did the deck contain? Marcos wants to run latticework around the deck, leaving 4 feet along one side for stairs. How many feet of latticework will he need for this?

17. John wants to order outdoor carpeting to cover his patio, which has the shape of a rectangle. The length measures 5 yards and the width measures 4 yards. How many square yards of space will John need to cover? Carpeting is on sale at $6.99 per square yard. How much will it cost for the carpeting?

18. Barbara plans to install laminate flooring in her den. The dimensions of her den are 12 feet by 40 feet. If the flooring costs $2.98 per square foot, what is the cost of the flooring?

19. Diane plans to tile her kitchen (k) as part of her remodeling projects. The ceramic tile costs $1.98 per square foot. (Installation is extra.) Determine the cost of the tile.

20. Diane plans to replace the carpet in the living room (liv) with hardwood flooring. The cost of the hardwood flooring is $2.57 per square foot (not installed). Determine the cost of the hardwood flooring.

In exercises 21–30, find the volume and surface area of each three-dimensional geometric solid.

21. A box has a length of 5 feet, a width of 3 feet, and a height of 1 foot.

22. A chest has a width of 4 feet, a length of 6 feet, and a height of 3 feet.

23. A cube has a side measuring 7.5 inches.

24. Each side of a cube measures 8.2 centimeters.

25. A right circular can has a height of 5 inches and a diameter of 3 inches. Round your answers to the nearest tenth.

26. A can of vegetable shortening has a height of 6 inches and a diameter of 5 inches. Round your answers to the nearest tenth.

27. A sphere has a diameter of 20 centimeters. Round your answers to the nearest whole number.

28. A ball has a radius of 5 inches. Round your answers to the nearest whole number.

29. A right cone has a height of 0.75 foot and a radius of 0.25 foot. Round your answers to the nearest thousandth.

30. A right cone's height measures 8 centimeters, and its radius measures 2 centimeters. Round your answer to the nearest hundredth.

31. Tracy constructed a doll display case out of clear acrylic panes. She built the case in the shape of a cube. If the case is 18 inches on a side, how many cubic inches of space does it contain? How many square inches of acrylic does the surface of the cubic measure?

32. A cube of ice is to be carved into a swan. The cube measures 2.5 feet on a side. How many cubic feet of ice does it contain? What is the total surface area of the cube of ice?

33. Danny bought a spherical tank to store propane gas for his outdoor grill. The tank was listed as having a radius of 10 inches. How many cubic inches of propane gas will the tank hold? How many square inches of surface area does the tank have? Round your answers to the nearest tenth.

34. The crystal base of a table lamp has the shape of a right circular cylinder, with a height of 20 inches and a radius of 4 inches. How many cubic inches of colored pellets will it take

to fill the cylinder? What is the surface area of the base before any holes are made in it? Round your answers to the nearest tenth.

35. A paperweight is shaped as a right cone with a height of 7 inches and a radius measuring 3.5 inches. What is the volume of the paperweight? Round your answer to the nearest hundredth.

36. A cake-decorating kit has a squeeze bag in the shape of a right cone. The bag has a height of 9 inches and a radius of 3 inches. What is the volume of the bag?

37. Jim built a toy box for his grandson. He made the box 4 feet long, 2 feet wide, and 2 feet high. How many cubic feet of toys will the box hold? Jim painted all six sides of the exterior with a high-gloss enamel. How many square feet of surface area did he paint? If one half pint of paint covers 25 square feet, how many half pints of paint did Jim need for one coat?

38. Lindsay designed a toy chest 5 feet by 2.5 feet by 2.5 feet. How many cubic feet of toys will it hold? She painted all six sides. How many square feet of surface area did she paint? If one spray can of paint covers 20 square feet, how many cans of paint does she need to paint one coat?

39. A disco ball at a club in Los Angeles has a diameter of 95.25 inches. What is the radius of the ball? Determine the volume of the ball. Find its surface area. The ball is covered with 6,900 mirrors in the shape of squares measuring 2 inches on a side. How many square inches of the surface is covered with mirrors?

40. In early 2001, space shuttle *Atlantis*'s astronauts installed the $1.4 billion Destiny laboratory on the international space station. Destiny is an aluminum cylinder 28 feet long and 14 feet in diameter. Find the volume of this laboratory. How many square feet of aluminum was needed to construct the cylinder?

41. Two angles are complementary. One angle measures 65 degrees. Find the measure of the other angle.

42. An angle measures 71 degrees. What is its complement?

43. Two angles are supplementary. One angle measures 65 degrees. Find the measure of the other angle.

44. What is the supplement of an angle that measures 124 degrees?

45. Two angles of a triangle measure 33 degrees and 68 degrees. Find the measure of the other angle.

46. One angle of a triangle measures 47 degrees and another angle measures 88 degrees. What is the measure of the third angle?

47. The *pitch* of a roof measures the angle that the roof makes with a horizontal line. The angle that the roof makes with a vertical line is the complement of the pitch. What is the pitch of the roof if its complement measures 50 degrees?

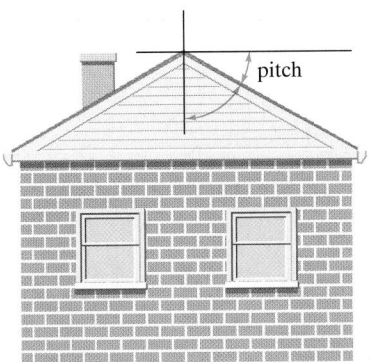

48. A ramp connects a loading dock to a driveway. The ramp forms a 70-degree angle with the vertical edge of the dock. The angle the ramp forms with the horizontal driveway is the complement of this angle. What is the measure of the angle formed with the horizontal driveway?

49. A guy wire forms two angles with the ground. The angles are supplementary. If one of the angles measures 45 degrees, what is the measure of the other angle?

50. An anchoring rope on a tent forms two supplementary angles with the ground. If one of the angles measures 60 degrees, what is the measure of the other angle?

51. Three holes will be bored into a steel plate. They form a triangle, with one angle measuring 30 degrees and another measuring 65 degrees. What is the measure of the third angle?

52. Three stakes in the ground mark off a triangular plot. One angle of the plot measures 55 degrees and another measures 65 degrees. What is the measure of the third angle?

53. Weather station KLOW in Seattle reported a daily low temperature of 25°C. What is the corresponding Fahrenheit temperature?

54. Todd the Weather Guy reported a daily high temperature of 31°C in Atlanta. Convert to the corresponding Fahrenheit temperature.

55. Marti told her friend that the high temperature for the day in Miami was 92°F. Convert this to Celsius measure.

56. The weather channel reported that the low temperature for the day in Boston was 66°F. What was the corresponding Celsius temperature?

57. At sea level, the boiling point of water is 100°C. What is the corresponding Fahrenheit temperature?

58. The melting point of gold is 1063°C. Convert to Fahrenheit temperature.

59. In Denver, the boiling point of water is 95°C. Convert to Fahrenheit temperature.

60. The boiling point of gold is 2966°C. What is the corresponding Fahrenheit temperature?

61. The melting point of mercury is −37.97°F. What is the corresponding Celsius temperature?

62. The boiling point of mercury is 673.84°F. Convert to Celsius temperature.

63. The average high temperature in Rio de Janeiro in January is 84°F. What is the Celsius temperature?

64. The average low temperature in Rio de Janeiro in January is 73°F. Convert to Celsius temperature.

65. JoAnne borrowed $2500 for 1 year at 6.5% simple interest to buy a laptop computer. How much interest did she pay?

66. Jack borrowed $5500 for 1 year at 7% simple interest to buy a used pickup truck. Find the interest on the loan.

67. How much simple interest is earned on $500 at a 7% annual interest rate for 1 month ($\frac{1}{12}$ of a year)?

68. What will be the simple interest and total amount of $100 invested at an 8% annual interest rate for 3 months ($\frac{1}{4}$ of a year)?

69. How much simple interest would be paid on a loan of $1200 at an 8% annual interest rate for 6 months?

70. What is the simple interest on a loan of $2400 at a 12% annual interest rate for 6 months?

71. The drive from home to college took $9\frac{1}{2}$ hours at an average speed of 55 miles per hour. What was the distance covered?

72. The drive to the beach took 8.25 hours at an average speed of 62 miles per hour. How many miles was the trip?

73. In 1911, Ray Harroun won the first Indianapolis 500 with an average speed of 74.602 miles per hour in 6 hours, 42 minutes, and 8 seconds. At this speed, how far did he drive in the first 3 hours of the race?

74. In 2005, Dan Wheldon won the Indianapolis 500 with an average speed of 157.603 miles per hour in 3 hours, 10 minutes, and 21 seconds. At this speed, how far did he drive in the first 2 hours of the race?

P.8 Calculator Exercises

Part 1. Writing a calculator program

It is possible to write a calculator program to perform calculations for the geometric formulas we have studied. As an example, if you enter the following steps into your calculator, you will have created a program to calculate the area, circumference, and diameter of a circle when a number for the radius is entered into the calculator:

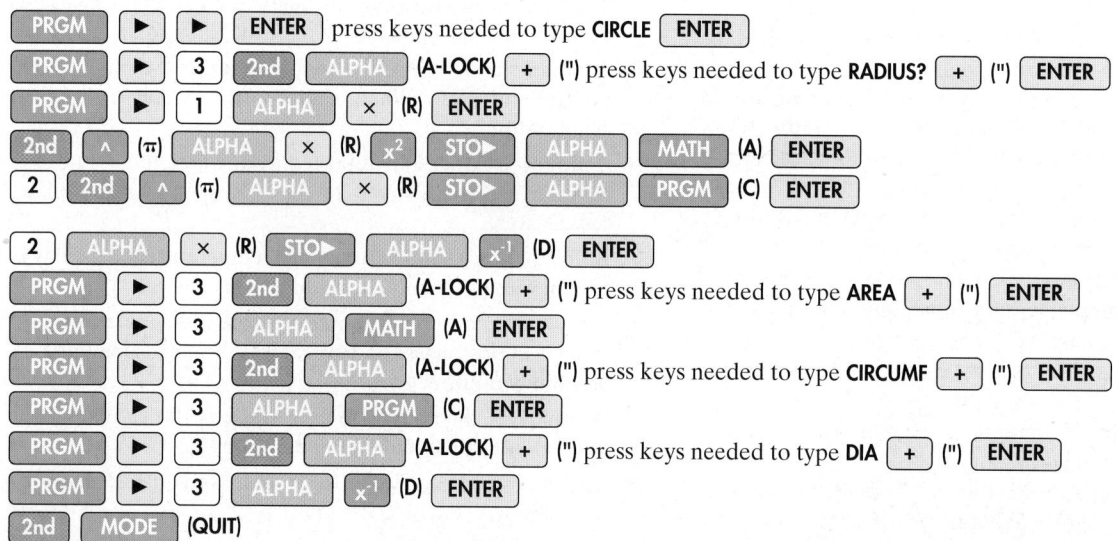

If you have entered the program correctly, you should see the displays shown in **Figures P.20a** and **P.20b**.

```
PROGRAM:CIRCLE
:Disp "RADIUS?"
:Input R
:πR²→A
:2πR→C
:2R→D
:Disp "AREA"
:Disp A
```

Figure P.20a

```
PROGRAM:CIRCLE
:Disp "CIRCUMF"
:Disp C
:Disp "DIA"
:Disp D
:
:
:
```

Figure P.20b

To run the program, perform the following steps:

Enter [PRGM] [1], where "1" is the number of the program in your list.

Press [ENTER], and the calculator will ask for a value for the radius.

Enter a value, and then press [ENTER].

The calculator will display the three measures.

To run the program for another value of the radius, press [ENTER].

Then, repeat the preceding steps.

To quit, enter [2nd] [MODE] (QUIT).

As a check, if you stored a value of 3 for the radius, the calculator should have displayed an area of 28.27433388, a circumference of 18.84955592, and a diameter of 6. You can use this program as a model to develop other programs for the various formulas presented in this section.

Part 2. Using the calculator applications

The TI-84 Plus has a set of applications. (The TI-83 Plus users must purchase these applications.) These applications are located in the APPS menu. We will use one of these applications to help us visualize and learn the area formulas.

First press [APPS] and [4] to choose 4: AreaForm. (If you purchased this APPS, your application number may be different than 4.) To begin the application press [ENTER] [ENTER] to view the menu.

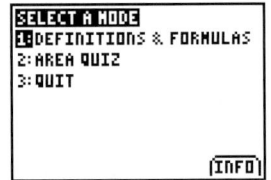

Press [1] to begin with the definitions and formulas. You will now be asked to choose a shape.

Press [6] to choose 6: CIRCLE. You will see a picture and definition of a circle.

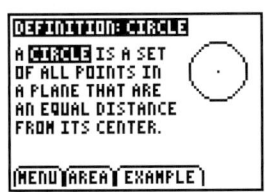

To continue, press [WINDOW] to choose AREA. The formula for the area is displayed.

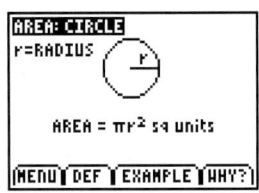

To see the development of the area formula, press [GRAPH] to choose WHY?.

As you read, you will need to continue to press [GRAPH] to choose WHY? when prompted.

Your final display will appears as below.

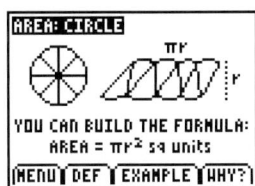

To view an example press [ZOOM].

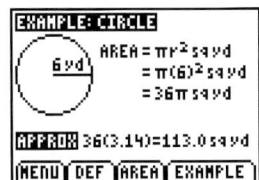

To return to the menu press [Y=]. You may choose a different shape or return to the main menu. To return to the main menu press [Y=]. You may take an area quiz. Press [2] and follow the directions given. Good luck, and return to this APPS if you need additional practice in learning the area formulas for two-dimensional figures.

P.8 Writing Exercises

1. In this section, you learned formulas that are used to measure various properties of two-dimensional and three-dimensional geometric shapes. Write a short definition of what is meant by two-dimensional and three-dimensional shapes. Discuss what can be measured for each, and illustrate your discussion with examples. Explain what distinguishes one from the other.

2. Measure the dimensions of a room. Determine the cost of remodeling the room by replacing the flooring. Write an exercise with your data and show the solution.

■ Chapter P Summary

Vocabulary Review

After completing this chapter, you should be able to define the following terms.

absolute value
area
base
circumference
coefficient
complementary angles
constant

equation
exponent
indeterminate
inequality
members
opposites
order symbols

perimeter
right angle
set
supplementary angles
surface area
undefined
volume

Fill in the blank with one of the words or phrases listed above.

1. A _____ is a collection of objects called _____ of the set.

2. Two numbers that are the same distance from zero are called _____.

3. The distance a number is from zero is called the _____ of the number.

4. The quotient of a number, other than zero, divided by zero is _____, and the quotient of zero divided by zero is _____.

5. In the expression 3^2, the 3 is the _____ and the 2 is the _____.

6. In the expression $-3x^2 - x + 4$, the -3 is a _____.

7. An _____ is a mathematical statement that two expressions are equal.

8. An _____ is a mathematical statement that two expressions are not equal.

9. The symbols $<$, $>$, $\leq$, and $\geq$ are called _____.

10. _____ is the distance around a closed two-dimensional figure.

11. _____ is the amount of surface covered by a two-dimensional figure.

12. _____ is the distance around a circle.

13. _____ is the amount of space enclosed in a three-dimensional figure.

14. A _____ is an angle whose measure is 90°.

15. If the sum of the measures of two angles is 90°, the angles are _____.

16. If the sum of the measures of two angles is 180°, the angles are _____.

Reflections

1. What is a rational number? What types of numbers are included in the set of rational numbers?

2. Explain what is meant by the absolute value of a number.

3. What is meant by the opposite of a number?

4. How do you use absolute values to add two numbers with like signs? with unlike signs? How do you use absolute values to subtract two numbers that may have like or unlike signs?

5. How do you use absolute values to multiply two numbers that have like signs? unlike signs? How do you use absolute values to divide two such numbers?

6. In an exponential expression, what is the effect of a negative integer exponent? What is the effect of a zero exponent? What is the effect of an exponent equal to 1?

7. What is the principal root of a number?

8. When will a radical expression have a positive value? When will it have a negative value? When will it not have a value in the set of real numbers?

9. Why is it important to follow the order of operations in evaluating a mathematical expression?

10. Explain the difference between simplifying an algebraic expression and evaluating an algebraic expression.

11. Define the terms of an algebraic expression. Define like terms in an algebraic expression.

12. Explain the difference between an algebraic expression and an algebraic equation.

13. How can you tell that the given values for the variables in an algebraic equation represent a solution of the equation?

14. What are formulas and why do we use them?

15. What properties of two-dimensional figures are usually represented by formulas?

16. What properties of three-dimensional figures are usually represented by formulas?

Chapter P Section-by-Section Review

P.1

Recall	Examples
Counting numbers, N	$1, 2, 3$
Whole numbers, W	$0, 1, 2, 3$
Integers, Z	$-2, -1, 0, 1, 2$
Rational numbers, Q, are numbers that can be written as a ratio of two integers, excluding the possibility of a zero denominator.	$-\dfrac{2}{3}, 0.75, -5$
To graph or plot a number on a number line, place a dot at the location of the number.	Graph -2 and 1. $-3\ -2\ -1\ \ 0\ \ 1\ \ 2\ \ 3$
Inequality symbols are $<, >, \leq, \geq, \neq,$ and $\approx$.	$-2 < 0 \qquad\qquad -1 \neq 1$ $-5 > -10 \qquad\quad \pi \approx 3.14$ $-3 \leq 0 \leq 5$
Absolute value is the distance a number is from 0.	$\lvert -3 \rvert = 3$ $\lvert 3 \rvert = 3$
Opposites are two numbers that have different signs but the same absolute values.	3 and -3 are opposites. $-(3) = -3$ $-(-3) = 3$

Express your answers in fractional notation or round decimals to the nearest thousandth as appropriate.

1. Identify the possible sets of numbers (natural numbers, whole numbers, integers, rational numbers) to which each of the following numbers belong:

$$-15, 1000, 0, -2000, 13, -\frac{15}{17}, 12.97, 3\frac{5}{8}, \frac{12}{4}$$

2. Graph the following numbers on a number line:

$$-1.1, \frac{3}{4}, -2\frac{1}{2}, 0, 2.5, 1\frac{1}{2}, 4, -3$$

Use one of the symbols $>$, $<$, or $=$ to compare the two numbers.

3. -7 _____ -9

4. $\dfrac{3}{11}$ _____ $\dfrac{1}{3}$

5. -28 _____ 13

6. 331 _____ -331

7. -1.34 _____ -1.04

8. $-\dfrac{3}{4}$ _____ $-\dfrac{5}{8}$

9. $\lvert -10 \rvert$ _____ 10

10. $-\lvert 10 \rvert$ _____ 10

11. $-(-2)$ _____ $\lvert -2 \rvert$

Write an equivalent order relation for each statement.

12. $-23 > -49 \geq -100$

13. $\dfrac{252}{529} < \dfrac{13}{17}$

14. $-34.58 = -\dfrac{1729}{50}$

Evaluate.

15. $-\left\lvert -\dfrac{17}{33} \right\rvert$

16. $\lvert -(-67) \rvert$

17. $-(-32.698)$

18. $-(-(-(257)))$

19. Tiger Woods won the Masters Golf Tournament in 2005 at the Augusta National Golf Course. He scored two over par the first round, six under par the second round, seven under par the third round, and one under par the fourth round. Write a rational-number representation for each of his scores, using positive numbers for scores above par and negative numbers for scores below par.

20. In 1999, NASA lost a $125,000,000 spacecraft, the *Mars Climate Orbiter*. According to NASA, the loss was likely due to the fact that the company which built the spacecraft failed to convert English units of measurement to metric ones. Write a rational-number representation for NASA's loss.

P.2

Recall	Examples
Addition • To add two rational numbers with like signs, add the absolute values of the addends. The sum has the sign of the addends. • To add two rational numbers with unlike signs, subtract the absolute values of the addends. The sum has the sign of the addend with the larger absolute value.	$3 + 4 = 7$ $-3 + (-4) = -7$ $3 + (-4) = -1$ $-3 + 4 = 1$
Laws for Addition • Commutative law for addition: Changing the order of two numbers when adding the numbers does not change the sum. • Associative law for addition: Changing the grouping of three numbers when adding the numbers does not change the sum.	$6 + (-2) = -2 + 6$ $-6 + (2 + 4) = (-6 + 2) + 4$
Subtraction To subtract two rational numbers, add the minuend to the opposite of the subtrahend.	$3 - 4 = 3 + (-4) = -1$ $3 - (-4) = 3 + 4 = 7$ $-3 - 4 = -3 + (-4) = -7$ $-3 - (-4) = -3 + 4 = 1$
Multiplication • To multiply two rational numbers with like signs, multiply the absolute values of the factors. The product is positive. • To multiply two rational numbers with unlike signs, multiply the absolute values of the factors. The product is negative. • The product of any rational number and 0 is 0.	$3 \cdot 4 = 12$ $-3 \cdot (-4) = 12$ $3 \cdot (-4) = -12$ $-3 \cdot 4 = -12$ $3 \cdot 0 = 0$
Laws for Multiplication • Commutative law for multiplication: Changing the order of two numbers when multiplying the numbers does not change the product. • Associative law for multiplication: Changing the grouping of three numbers when multiplying the numbers does not change the product.	$6 \cdot (-2) = -2 \cdot 6$ $-6(2 \cdot 4) = (-6 \cdot 2)4$
Division • To divide two rational numbers with like signs, divide the absolute values of the numbers. The quotient is positive. • To divide two rational numbers with unlike signs, divide the absolute values of the numbers. The quotient is negative. • The quotient of 0 divided by any nonzero rational number is 0. • The quotient of any nonzero rational number divided by 0 is undefined. • The quotient of 0 divided by 0 is indeterminate.	$12 \div 3 = 4$ $-12 \div (-3) = 4$ $12 \div (-4) = -3$ $-12 \div 4 = -3$ $0 \div 4 = 0.$ $4 \div 0$ is undefined. $0 \div 0$ is indeterminate.

Add, and then check, using your calculator.

21. $-27 + 13$ **22.** $-11 + (-34)$ **23.** $-5\frac{2}{9} + 4\frac{5}{9}$ **24.** $\frac{3}{4} + \left(-\frac{5}{6}\right)$ **25.** $-2.3 + 1.47$

26. $12.097 + 1.92$ **27.** $\frac{3}{7} + \frac{5}{9}$ **28.** $-3.57 + (-41.098)$ **29.** $0 + (-123)$ **30.** $15.28 + (-15.28)$

31. 3.7 + (−6.83) + 5.5 + (−9.02) + (−0.8) + 15.2

32. $\frac{4}{5} + \left(-\frac{7}{3}\right) + \frac{8}{9} + \frac{4}{15} + \left(-\frac{2}{3}\right) + 3$

Subtract, and then check, using your calculator.

33. −35 − (−61)

34. $-\frac{3}{8} - \frac{4}{7}$

35. 15.6 − 18

36. 0 − 3.97

37. −2.3 − (−2.3)

38. $3\frac{5}{9} - 5\frac{2}{9}$

39. $-\frac{5}{9} - \frac{2}{3}$

40. 101.02 − (−23.9)

Multiply, and then check, using your calculator.

41. (−13)(−6)

42. (21)(−5)

43. $\left(-7\frac{2}{5}\right)\left(-\frac{5}{7}\right)$

44. (23.05)(−0.04)

45. (−1) · 25

46. $\left(\frac{3}{7}\right)\left(\frac{3}{5}\right)$

47. (−2.04)(−4.12)

48. $-\frac{1}{2} \cdot \frac{8}{9}$

49. (−32)(20)(−1)(5)(−2)(10)

50. (−1.1)(0.2)(−4)(−10)(−0.8)

51. $\left(-\frac{1}{3}\right)\left(\frac{6}{7}\right)\left(-\frac{14}{15}\right)\left(-\frac{25}{8}\right)$

52. (−54)(21)(0)(32)(0)(−25)

Divide, and then check, using your calculator.

53. 220 ÷ (−4)

54. $\frac{5}{9} \div \left(-\frac{2}{3}\right)$

55. −10.557 ÷ 2.3

56. 0 ÷ 25

57. −2 ÷ 0

58. −13.7 ÷ (−1)

59. 0 ÷ 0

60. $-\frac{7}{12} \div \left(-\frac{7}{9}\right)$

Write and evaluate an expression for each situation. Interpret the result.

61. Cleta had a beginning balance of $735.66 in her checking account. She wrote checks for $276.12, $187.05, and $68.57. She made deposits of $75.00, $185.00, and $50.00. The bank deducted a monthly service charge of $4.65 and also charged her $12.00 for her order of blank checks. What was the closing balance on her account?

62. The highest point in California is the top of Mount Whitney, with an elevation of 14,494 feet. The lowest point is in Death Valley, with an elevation of 282 feet below sea level. Determine the range of the elevation from the highest to the lowest point.

63. In 2004, the 1173 U.S. community colleges consisted of public institutions, private institutions, and tribal institutions. The circle graph shows the percentage of community colleges in each of these categories.

64. Clarence records his gasoline usage on a trip from Louisville, Kentucky, to Cleveland, Ohio, to see the Rock and Roll Hall of Fame. He uses 18.7 gallons of gas to drive 345 miles. What was his average gas mileage for the trip? If he continues his trip to St. Louis, a distance of 560 miles, approximate the number of gallons of gas he will need assuming he will have the same gas mileage.

Categories of Community Colleges

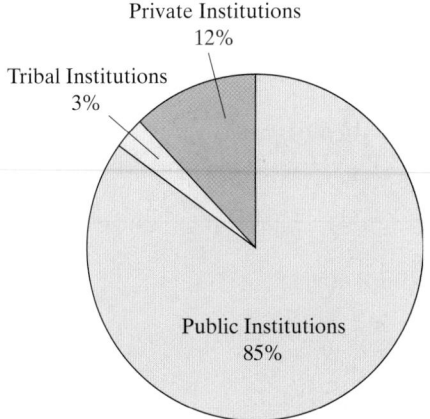

Private Institutions 12%

Tribal Institutions 3%

Public Institutions 85%

Estimate the number of community colleges in each of the categories.

P.3

Recall	Examples
Integer Exponents Greater than 1 • To evaluate, determine the product of the expanded form.	$5^3 = 5 \cdot 5 \cdot 5 = 125$ $(-5)^3 = -5 \cdot -5 \cdot -5 = -125$
Exponent of 1 • The value is the base number.	$5^1 = 5 \qquad (-5)^1 = -5$
Exponent of 0 • If the base is nonzero, the value is 1. • If the base is 0, the expression is indeterminate.	$5^0 = 1 \qquad (-5)^0 = 1$ 0^0 is indeterminate.
Square Roots • The principal square root is positive and must have a radicand that is positive. • The negative square root is negative and must have a radicand that is positive. • A square root is not defined in the real numbers if the radicand is negative.	$\sqrt{25} = 5 \qquad \sqrt{24} \approx 4.899$ $-\sqrt{36} = -6$ $\sqrt{-12}$ is not a real number.
Cube Roots The value of a cube root is • Positive if the radicand is positive. • Negative if the radicand is negative.	$\sqrt[3]{8} = 2$ $\sqrt[3]{-83} \approx -4.362$
Integer Exponents Less than 0 • If the base is nonzero, rewrite the expression as the reciprocal of the base with the opposite of the exponent. Then evaluate the new expression. • If the base is 0, the expression is undefined.	$(5)^{-2} = \left(\dfrac{1}{5}\right)^2 = \left(\dfrac{1}{5}\right)\left(\dfrac{1}{5}\right) = \dfrac{1}{25}$ $\left(-\dfrac{1}{5}\right)^{-2} = (-5)^2 = (-5)(-5) = 25$ $0^{-3} = \left(\dfrac{1}{0}\right)^3$ is undefined.
Converting Standard Notation to Scientific Notation Write a product of the numerical factor and an exponential expression. • Move the decimal point in the number so that the resulting numerical factor has an absolute value between 1 and 10, including 1. • Determine the exponential expression. The exponent of the base 10 is positive if the decimal was moved to the left, negative if the decimal was moved to the right, and 0 if the decimal was not moved. • The absolute value of the exponent is the value of the number of places the decimal was moved.	$3{,}540{,}000 = 3.54 \times 10^6$ $0.00034 = 3.4 \times 10^{-4}$
Converting Scientific Notation to Standard Notation Move the decimal point in the numerical factor the number of places the exponent denotes (its absolute value). • The decimal moves to the right if the exponent is positive. • The decimal moves to the left if the exponent is negative.	$5.2 \times 10^4 = 52{,}000$ $-3.81 \times 10^{-4} = -0.000381$
Converting Calculator Notation to Scientific Notation Write a product of the numerical factor and an exponential expression. • The numerical factor is the number displayed before the "E." • The exponential factor has a base of 10 and an exponent whose value is the number after the "E."	$-5.6\text{E}6 = -5.6 \times 10^6$ $4.38\text{E}{-6} = 4.38 \times 10^{-6}$

Evaluate.

65. $(-3)^5$ **66.** -3^4 **67.** 1.2^2 **68.** 0^{10} **69.** 1^{15} **70.** $(-1)^{18}$

71. $(-1)^{21}$ **72.** $\left(-\dfrac{3}{4}\right)^6$ **73.** $\left(2\dfrac{1}{3}\right)^5$ **74.** $(-15)^0$ **75.** -15^0 **76.** -15^1

77. 0^0 **78.** 0^1 **79.** $\sqrt{0.64}$ **80.** $\sqrt{\dfrac{9}{25}}$ **81.** $-\sqrt{49}$ **82.** $\sqrt{-16}$

83. $-\sqrt{470.89}$ **84.** $\sqrt{15}$ **85.** $\sqrt[3]{0.125}$ **86.** $\sqrt[3]{\dfrac{64}{729}}$ **87.** $\sqrt[3]{-27000}$ **88.** $-\sqrt[3]{10}$

89. Graph the following numbers on a number line, and label the points:

$$9, \sqrt{9}, -\sqrt{16}, \sqrt{18}, -\sqrt{68}, \pi, -\sqrt{7.29}, \sqrt[3]{140}$$

Write an equivalent exponential expression having a positive exponent. Evaluate.

90. 4^{-1} **91.** $\left(\dfrac{1}{4}\right)^{-1}$ **92.** $\left(\dfrac{1}{4}\right)^{-2}$ **93.** $(-4)^{-2}$

Complete the following table:

	Standard Notation	Scientific Notation	Calculator Notation
94.	0.000000189		
95.	−27,085,000,000		
96.		5.89×10^{11}	
97.			−7.093 E−5

98. The diamond in a baseball field is a square-shaped plot that has an area of 729 square meters. What are the dimensions of the diamond?

99. A box for facial tissues is a cube that will be marketed as a bathroom boutique design. The box has a volume of $91\frac{1}{8}$ cubic inches. What are the dimensions of the box?

100. In 2003, the total U.S. export of goods was reported as $742,000,000,000. Write this number in scientific notation.

101. In 2003, the total U.S. import of the goods was reported as 1.2632×10^{12} U.S. dollars. Write this number in standard notation. Using the information in exercise 100, by how many dollars do U.S. imports exceed U.S. exports?

102. Red blood cells of mammals measure about 8×10^{-6} meters in diameter. Write this number in standard notation. The radius of the cell is the diameter divided by 2. What is the radius of the blood cell?

P.4

Recall	Examples
Distributive Laws • The product of a real-number factor and a sum (or difference) of real number addends is the same as the sum (or difference) of the products of the factor and each addend. • The quotient of a real-number divisor and a sum (or difference) of real number addends is the same as the sum (or difference) of the quotients of the divisor and each addend (minuend/subtrahend).	$2(3 + 4) = 2(3) + 2(4)$ $-3(-2 - 5) = -3(-2) - (-3)(5)$ $\dfrac{3 + 5}{2} = \dfrac{3}{2} + \dfrac{5}{2}$ $\dfrac{3 - 5}{2} = \dfrac{3}{2} - \dfrac{5}{2}$
Opposite-of-a-Sum Property The opposite of the sum of real numbers is the same as the sum of the opposites.	$-(3 + 4) = -3 + (-4)$ $-(5 - 7) = -5 - (-7) = -5 + 7$
Factoring Factoring is doing the reverse of the distributive laws.	$7(2) + 7(8) = 7(2 + 8) = 7(10)$
Order of Operations Perform operations from left to right in the following order: grouping symbols, powers and radicals, multiplication and division, addition and subtraction.	$2\{3[2 - (3 - 2^2)]\}$ $\quad = 2\{3[2 - (3 - 4)]\}$ $12 - 6 \div 2 + 3 \cdot (-5)$ $\quad = 2\{3[2 - (-1)]\}$ $\quad = 12 - 3 + 3 \cdot (-5)$ $\quad = 2\{3[3]\}$ $\quad = 12 - 3 + (-15)$ $\quad = 2\{9\}$ $\quad = -6$ $\quad = 18$

Write an equivalent expression using the distributive law or the opposite-of-a-sum property, and then check on your calculator.

103. $-2.6(-1.9 + 3.2)$ **104.** $\dfrac{5}{6}\left(\dfrac{3}{5} \cdot \dfrac{4}{15}\right)$ **105.** $\dfrac{1687 - 1372}{7}$ **106.** $-(2.7 + 3.09)$

Factor. Check for equivalence.

107. $21(18) + 21(42)$ **108.** $5(97) - 5(17)$

Evaluate exercises 109–115, using the order of operations.

109. $16 - 12 \div 4 \cdot 2 + 6$ **110.** $41(-73 + 65) - (52 - 46)$ **111.** $-(27 - 4^2) - 16(-5 - 3)$

112. $[15 + 21(14 - 18)] - 7^2$ **113.** $22 - \sqrt{9^2 - 45} + 5$ **114.** $\dfrac{8 \cdot 9 - 2 \cdot 6^2}{125 - 7^2}$

115. $\dfrac{78 - 3 \cdot 17}{5^2 - 4 \cdot 6 - 1^3}$

116. Federal guidelines on the identification of obesity in adult men state that the lean body weight (in pounds) of a man who is 5 feet, 10 inches tall and weighs 184 pounds is found from the expression

$$2.2[0.5(184) - 4.1(184^2 \div 70^2)]$$

Determine this weight.

117. The average hourly earnings for production workers in natural resources are given in the following table for the years 2000, 2001, 2002, and 2003.

Find the average of the earnings for the four years shown.

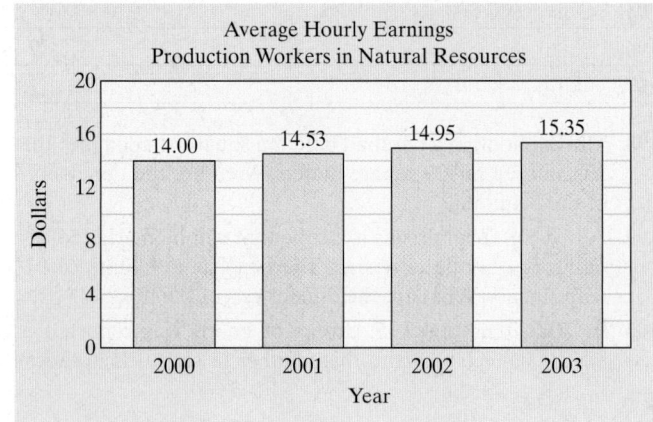

P.5

Recall	Examples
Translate into an algebraic expression. • Define the variables. • Translate the words into numbers and symbols.	One-third of the sum of three test grades Let a = the first test grade b = the second test grade c = the third test grade $\dfrac{1}{3}(a + b + c)$
To evaluate an algebraic expression. • Substitute the values for the variables, enclosing them in parentheses. • Evaluate the resulting numeric expression.	Evaluate $-x^2 + 2x - 3$ for $x = -2$. $-x^2 + 2x - 3 = -(-2)^2 + 2(-2) - 3$ $= -11$

In exercises 118–120, translate each word expression into an algebraic expression.

118. a. Four more than the product of a number and 55

    b. The product of 4 more than a number and 55

119. a. Three-fourths of the sum of a number and 35

    b. The sum of three-fourths of a number and 35

120. a. Twenty less than twice a number

    b. Twenty less twice a number

121. The total cost of a car is the sum of the down payment of $2500 and the product of monthly payments of $275 for n months. Write an algebraic expression for the total cost of the car.

122. Pat's hourly rate of pay for a job is the quotient of his total earnings of $650 divided by the hours he worked, h. Write an algebraic expression for Pat's hourly rate of pay.

123. A telephone salesperson is paid $200 per week plus $5.50 for every customer who purchases the product. What is the person's weekly pay if k customers agree to purchase?

124. A solution of water and antifreeze is 40% antifreeze. If there are x liters of the solution, write an algebraic expression for the number of liters of antifreeze in the solution. Then write an algebraic expression for the number of liters of water in the solution.

125. An auto trip lasted two days and covered 758 miles of travel. If, on the first day of the trip, x miles were traveled, write an algebraic expression for the number of miles covered on the second day of the trip.

126. A dress was placed on sale at a discount of 25%. If the dress originally sold for x dollars, write an algebraic expression for the amount of discount of the dress. Write an expression for the sale price of the dress.

For $x = -\frac{2}{3}$, evaluate the following expressions:

127. $-x$ **128.** $-(-x)$ **129.** x^2 **130.** $-x^2$ **131.** $|-x|$

Evaluate $\sqrt{a^2 + b^2}$ for

132. $a = 9, b = 12$ **133.** $a = 4.5, b = 6$

Evaluate $\dfrac{12y - 84}{6y + 36}$ for

134. $y = 9$ **135.** $y = -6$

Evaluate $|2x^2 - 45x - 75| - 2$ for

136. $x = 0.1$ **137.** $x = 10$

138. The volume of a box is equal to the product of the measures of the length, width, and height of the box.

    a. Write an algebraic expression for the volume of a box.

    b. The Longaberger® Company's home office building is really a basket! It is located in Newark, Ohio. According to information provided by the company's public relations office, the base of the building is 192 feet long and 126 feet wide. Not including the handles, the height of the building is about 103 feet high. While the building is not exactly a rectangular box shape, assume that it is and determine its volume.

P.6

Recall	Examples
Combine like terms. • The sum of the coefficients of like terms is the coefficient of the simplified term. • The common variable factor is the variable factor of the simplified term.	Combine like terms. $2x^2 + 3x - 1 - x^2 - 3x + 4 = 2x^2 - x^2 + 3x - 3x - 1 + 4$ $= x^2 + 3$
Simplify expressions. • Remove parentheses by using the distributive law. • Combine like terms of the resulting expression.	Simplify. $(2a + b - 5) - (a + b + 3) = 2a + b - 5 - a - b - 3$ $= a - 8$ $2[-3(x + 1) + 4(2x - 1)] = 2[-3x - 3 + 8x - 4]$ $= 2[5x - 7]$ $= 10x - 14$

Without simplifying the algebraic expression, complete the following table:

Algebraic Expression	Number Terms	Constant Terms	Variable Terms	Coefficients of Terms	Like Terms
139. $3x - 2y + 4x + 9y$					
140. $2a^2 - a + 3a^2 - 5a^3$					
141. $2.4x + 5.1 + 6.2x$					
142. $4a(a + b) - b(a + b)$					

Simplify.

143. $2.4z + 1.7z - 3.9z$

144. $17x + 51 + 26x - 86 - 19x - 7$

145. $\dfrac{3}{4}x + \dfrac{5}{8}y - \dfrac{2}{3}x + \dfrac{1}{4}y$

146. $15x^2 - 14xy + 12y^2 - 23 + 42xy - 7y^2 + 21 - 6x^2$

147. $(3a + 4b) - (-2a - 6b) + (a - b) - (-a + b)$

148. $-2(3.8a - 4.7b)$

149. $-105\left(\dfrac{6}{7}x - \dfrac{4}{15}y\right)$

150. $2x(3x - 17y)$

151. $\dfrac{27a - 36b + 15c}{9}$

152. $12(7x + 9y) + 15(3x - 7y)$

153. $3[-2(x + 3y) - 5] - [3(2x + y) + 16]$

154. $\dfrac{25(2a - 6b) + 5(4b - 3c) + 75}{4a - 2(2a - 3) - 1}$

155. In gym class, Tom can do x push-ups without stopping. His friend Charles can do 5 less than twice the number Tom can do. Jim can do 7 more than Tom can do. Write an algebraic expression for the total number of push-ups all three students can do. Simplify this expression. What is the total number if Tom can do 45 push-ups?

Write an expression for each situation. Then simplify and evaluate.

156. At the Summer Olympics gift shop, Katie bought some commemorative pins for $5 each. The clerk added 6% sales tax to the cost. Katie paid with a $20 bill. If Katie bought x pins, what was her change? Determine Katie's change if she bought three pins.

157. Margaret buys unfinished frames, which she decorates and sells. She pays $3.25 for each frame. After she decorates them, she sells them at craft fairs for $12.00 each. She spends $52.65 for paint and lace to decorate the frames, which is enough for all the frames she can make and sell. Write an algebraic expression for Margaret's net profit, given that she can sell x frames. What will her profit be if she makes and sells 32 frames?

P.7

Recall	Examples
To determine whether a number is a solution of an algebraic equation	Is 3 a solution of $2x - 5 = 3x - 8$?
• Substitute the possible solution for the variable. • Evaluate both expressions. • If the expressions have equal values, then the number is a solution.	 $\begin{array}{c\|c} 2x - 5 & = \quad 3x - 8 \\ \hline 2(3) - 5 & 3(3) - 8 \\ 6 - 5 & 9 - 8 \\ 1 & 1 \end{array}$ The value 3 is a solution because $1 = 1$.
To represent an inequality on a number line • Plot the upper or lower bound with an open dot if the bound is not included and a closed dot if the bound is included. • Draw a solid line to the left of the upper bound for a "less than" or "less than or equal to" inequality and to the right for a "greater than" or "greater than or equal to" inequality.	Inequality notation Number-line notation $x < 3$ $x > 3$ $x \le 3$ $x \ge 3$ $-1 < x \le 3$

Recall	Examples
To represent an inequality in interval notation • Write the bounds, if they exist, in increasing order, separated by a comma. Use infinity symbols if no bound exists. • Precede or follow each bound with a parenthesis if it is not included in the solution set or a bracket if it is included in the solution set.	Inequality notation $\quad$ Interval notation $x < 3$ $\qquad\qquad$ $(-\infty, 3)$ $x > 3$ $\qquad\qquad$ $(3, \infty)$ $x \leq 3$ $\qquad\qquad$ $(-\infty, 3]$ $x \geq 3$ $\qquad\qquad$ $[3, \infty)$ $-1 < x \leq 3$ $\qquad$ $(-1, 3]$
Translate into algebraic equations. • Define the variables. • Translate the words into numbers and symbols.	The test average of three grades is one-third of the sum of the grades. Let A = the test average $\quad a$ = the first test grade $\quad b$ = the second test grade $\quad c$ = the third test grade $A = \dfrac{1}{3}(a + b + c)$

Determine whether each item is an expression, an equation, or an inequality.

158. $2x + 7y - x$ $\qquad$ **159.** $-2x \leq 7x - 1$ $\qquad$ **160.** $5x = 3y - x$

Determine whether the given value is a solution of the equation.

161. $8a + 2(3a - 7) = 11a - 32$ for $a = -6$ $\qquad$ **162.** $x^3 - 25x = 2x^2 - 3x - 35$ for $x = 5$

163. $2(x - 3.4) = x - 5$ for $x = 1.8$ $\qquad$ **164.** $x - \dfrac{2}{3} = -\dfrac{1}{9}$ for $x = \dfrac{4}{9}$

Graph the solution set of each inequality on a number line. Check your graph on your calculator. Then write the solution set in interval notation.

165. $x < 3$ $\qquad$ **166.** $x > -2$ $\qquad$ **167.** $x \leq -5$

168. $x \geq -3.5$ $\qquad$ **169.** $-2 < a < 4$ $\qquad$ **170.** $-1 < b \leq 0$

In exercises 171–174, define all variables. Do not solve the equation.

171. A writer is advanced $1500 to purchase a personal computer system to be used to author a pamphlet that is to be published by a publishing company. If the writer earns royalties of $1.35 for each pamphlet sold, write an equation to determine the break-even point for the writer.

172. The total interest earned, $1500, is the sum of 6% of the dollars invested in one account and 8% of the dollars invested in another account. Write an equation to represent this situation.

173. Write an equation which says that the dollars invested in one account added to the dollars invested in a second account total $30,000.

174. An equation is used to determine the optimum gauge of wire for a hammer dulcimer. The equation states that the fundamental frequency, f, of the wire is calculated as the square root of the quotient of tension, T, in the wire divided by the mass per unit length of wire, m. The square root is then divided by two times the length of the wire, L. Write the equation in question.

Write an inequality to represent each situation. Do not solve the inequality.

175. One copy machine can make 30 copies per minute, while another machine can make 25 copies per minute. If both machines are used to make copies, how long will it take to make at least 300 copies of a one-page flyer?

176. In designing a roadway, a civil engineer uses the following rules of thumb: The pavement will cost twice the amount of the base material. The sidewalk will cost one-fourth the amount of the pavement. What will the cost of the base material be if the cost of the roadway must be below $200,000?

177. The Fujita Scale (F-Scale) is accepted as the official classification system for tornado damage. The following classifications are used to rate the intensities of less-than-severe tornadoes:

F-Scale Number	Intensity	Wind Speed
F0	Gale tornado	40–72 mph
F1	Moderate tornado	73–112 mph
F2	Significant tornado	113–157 mph

For each of the categories listed, write a linear inequality that represents that category.

P.8

Recall	Examples
To evaluate a formula • Write the formula. • Substitute the value for the variables. • Evaluate the resulting numeric expression.	Evaluate $A = \pi r^2$ for $r = 8$ feet. $A = \pi r^2$ $A = \pi(8 \text{ ft})^2$ $A = 64\pi$ square feet (exact answer) $A \approx 201.06$ square feet (rounded answer)

Find the area and perimeter of each two-dimensional figure.

178. A triangle has a base of 26 m, a height of 16 m, and sides of 22 m and 20 m.

179. A rectangle has a width of 20 inches and a length of 44 inches.

180. A square measures 15 cm on a side.

181. A parallelogram has a base of 10.0 m, a height of 6.5 m, and a side of 7.0 m.

182. A circle has a radius of 12.2 feet.

In exercises 183–187, find the volume and surface area of each three-dimensional figure.

183. A box has a length of 35 inches, a width of 9 inches, and a height of 21 inches.

184. A cubical carton measures 14.6 cm on each side.

185. A right circular cylinder has a height of 54 inches and a radius of 18 inches.

186. A ball has a radius of 32.6 cm.

187. A right circular cone has a height of 7 cm and a radius of 4 cm.

188. Two angles are supplementary. One angle measures 58 degrees. What is the measure of the other angle?

189. Two angles are complementary. One angle measures 58 degrees. What is the measure of the other angle?

190. One angle of a triangle measures 67 degrees. Another angle of the triangle measures 88 degrees. What is the measure of the third angle of the triangle?

191. Dan wants to purchase sod for his backyard. The yard is rectangular, with a width of 60 feet and a length of 85 feet. How much sod should he order? If he fences in the yard, how many linear feet of fencing should he order if he plans a 3-foot gate and attaches the fence to the back of the house, which measures 35 feet across?

192. Amelia marks off a circular plot in the yard for a garden. The plot has a radius of 8 feet. In the center she places a circular tile on which a birdbath will sit. The tile has a diameter of 2 feet. How many square feet of the garden will there be for flowers?

193. Big Ed's Pizza Shop offers 10-inch (diameter) pizzas for $6.75 or 14-inch pizzas for $13.50. Since two of the 10-inch pizzas cost as much as one 14-inch pizza, which is a better deal, two 10-inch pizzas or one 14-inch pizza?

194. A garden shop delivers a truckload of mulch. The bed of the truck measures 8 feet by 5 feet by 2 feet high. How many cubic feet of mulch will the truck hold?

195. What is the surface area of a spherical storage tank with a diameter of 6 feet?

196. Find the simple interest on a loan of $850 at 12.5% per year for one year. What is the total amount of the loan, including the interest?

197. Convert 50°C to Fahrenheit.

198. Convert 80°F to Celsius.

199. LuAnn's automobile trip took $5\frac{3}{4}$ hours of driving time, with an average speed of travel of 62 miles per hour. What was the distance traveled?

■ Chapter P Mixed Review

Complete the following table:

Standard Notation	Scientific Notation	Calculator Notation
1. 355,400,000,000,000,000		
2. −0.000092		
3.	7.94×10^{-12}	
4.		−6.876E4

Factor. Check for equivalence on your calculator.

5. $42(73) - 42(23)$ **6.** $-31(18) - 31(42)$

Use one of the symbols >, <, or = to compare the two numbers.

7. 3.54 _____ 3.65

8. $\dfrac{3}{5}$ _____ $\dfrac{1}{7}$

9. -142 _____ -105

10. $-\dfrac{2}{9}$ _____ $\dfrac{-5}{12}$

11. $\dfrac{3}{8}$ _____ 0.375

12. -3.7 _____ 0.53

13. 0 _____ -197

14. $-|5|$ _____ -5

Evaluate.

15. $-\left|\dfrac{9}{25}\right|$

16. $|-(-102)|$

17. $-(0.085)$

18. $-54 + (-90)$

19. $3.07 + (-2.9)$

20. $-\dfrac{1}{8} + \left(-1\dfrac{1}{4}\right)$

21. $-\dfrac{5}{6} + \dfrac{8}{9}$

22. $-576 - (-394)$

23. $0.52 - 3$

24. $0 - \dfrac{3}{11}$

25. $-4.07 - (-5.1)$

26. $-\dfrac{3}{5} - \dfrac{1}{3}$

27. $4\dfrac{1}{2} - (-2)$

28. $\left(-\dfrac{1}{5}\right)\left(-\dfrac{5}{6}\right)$

29. $\left(-4\dfrac{3}{7}\right)\left(\dfrac{14}{31}\right)$

30. $(-1)(-88)$

31. $(-3.1)(1.1)$

32. $\dfrac{3}{4} \cdot (-6)$

33. $\dfrac{4}{13} \div \left(-\dfrac{12}{13}\right)$

34. $0 \div 0$

35. $-21 \div 0$

36. $-9.02 \div (-1.1)$

37. $-\dfrac{5}{8} \div 10$

38. $5.5 \div 2.2$

39. 13^2

40. $(1.2)^5$

41. $(-5)^3$

42. -5^4

43. $\left(-1\dfrac{2}{5}\right)^3$

44. $(-1)^{24}$

45. $(-1)^{35}$

46. $-\left(\dfrac{1}{3}\right)^5$

47. 22^0

48. $(-22)^0$

49. -22^0

50. 22^1

51. 0^0

52. 10^{-2}

53. $(-10)^{-2}$

54. $\left(\dfrac{1}{10}\right)^{-1}$

55. $\left(-\dfrac{1}{10}\right)^{-1}$

56. $\sqrt{2500}$

57. $\sqrt{-400}$

58. $-\sqrt{\dfrac{5}{400}}$

59. $\sqrt[3]{-64}$

60. $\sqrt{\dfrac{81}{16}}$

61. $-\sqrt[3]{25}$

62. $\sqrt{2.56}$

63. $\sqrt[3]{\dfrac{27}{64}}$

64. $(-55)(12)(-2)(9)(-3)(1)$

65. $\left(-\dfrac{14}{22}\right)\left(\dfrac{8}{21}\right)\left(-\dfrac{11}{4}\right)\left(-\dfrac{3}{5}\right)$

66. $(-11.2)(3.1)(0)(-9.4)(-1)(-7.5)$

67. $2 - \{4[3 + 2(7 - 5)] - 18 \div 3\}$

68. $-(34 - 7^2) - 21(-8 - 4)$

69. $96 - \sqrt{11^2 - 21} - 36$

70. $\dfrac{412 + 204 - 4^2}{5^2 + 35}$

71. $\dfrac{35 - 6 \cdot 22}{6^3 - 4 \cdot 50 - 4^2}$

In exercises 72–74, write an equivalent order relation for each statement.

72. $76 > 75 \geq 74$

73. $-\dfrac{2}{5} < \dfrac{1}{7}$

74. $0.52 = \dfrac{13}{25}$

75. Graph the following numbers on a number line, and label the points:

$$-7,\ \sqrt{7},\ -\sqrt{7},\ \sqrt{25},\ \sqrt[3]{0},\ \sqrt{81},\ -\sqrt[3]{64},\ \sqrt{\dfrac{9}{25}},\ \dfrac{-2}{3},\ 2\dfrac{1}{2},\ -2.7$$

Without simplifying the algebraic expressions, complete the table.

Algebriac Expression	Number of Terms	Constant Terms	Variable Terms	Coefficients of Terms	Like Terms
76. $12x + y - z + 23$					
77. $3(a - 2) + 5(b - 4) + 75$					
78. $12 - 7x + 14x - 18 + x$					
79. $b^2 + 2b - 3b^2 + 6b + b^3$					

Evaluate for $x = -18$.

80. x^2 **81.** $-x^2$ **82.** $(-x)^2$

Evaluate $\sqrt{12y + 20} - 16$ *for*

83. $y = 8$ **84.** $y = -\dfrac{1}{3}$ **85.** $y = -5$

Evaluate $-\dfrac{b}{2a}$ *for*

86. $a = 1, b = -4$ **87.** $a = 2, b = 5$ **88.** $a = \dfrac{1}{2}, b = -3$

Determine whether each of the following is an equation, an expression, or an inequality.

89. $6x + 3 = 2(x - 5)$ **90.** $6x + 3 - 2(x - 5)$ **91.** $6x + 3 > 2(x - 5)$

Determine whether the given value is a solution of the equation.

92. $5x + 17 = 10x + 5$ for $x = 3$ **93.** $2.1x - 1.9 = 0.6x - 4.6$ for $x = -1.8$

94. $3x^2 - 6x - 10 = x^2 + x - 5$ for $x = -5$ **95.** $\dfrac{5}{8}a + \dfrac{2}{3} = \dfrac{1}{4}a - \dfrac{1}{3}$ for $a = \dfrac{3}{8}$

Simplify.

96. $12h + 9h - 4h$ **97.** $6m + 22 - m - 12 + 3m$ **98.** $3x - 35 + 4y - 5x - 6y + 7x + 27 + 17y + 22x$

99. $3x^4 + 5x - 7x^2 + 12x^4 - 17x - 34x + x^3 - 1$ **100.** $(6.2a + 5.3b) + (4.7a - 1.9b)$ **101.** $-(27y - 15)$

102. $5g + 8 - (g + 4)$ **103.** $(-2x + 4y - 7z) - (-x + 6y + 8z)$ **104.** $50\left(\dfrac{11}{25}a + \dfrac{33}{50}b\right)$

105. $\dfrac{104x - 156y + 30z}{13}$ **106.** $\dfrac{-18x + 24y - 36z}{-6}$ **107.** $4(3.9x - 11.1y) + 7(2.9x - 0.7y)$

108. $12[-3(2a - 5b) + 9] + 8[-9(a + 13) - 6(b - 12)]$ **109.** $\dfrac{14.4(2x + 5) - 21.6(5x - 2) + 7.2(x - 1)}{3x - 4(x + 8) + x + 34.4}$

Complete the following table:

	Description	Inequality	Number Line	Interval Notation
110.	All real numbers less than -2			
111.		$x > 5$		
112.				
113.				$[-3, \infty)$
114.		$-3 \leq x < 0$		

For 112, the number line is labeled $-5\ -4\ -3\ -2\ -1\ \ 0\ \ 1\ \ 2\ \ 3\ \ 4\ \ 5$ with a point at -2.

115. The film *Who Framed Roger Rabbit?* has the longest list of credits of any film, with 763 names. It takes $6\frac{1}{2}$ minutes to run the credits. On the average, how many credits run each minute?

116. A National Geographic Society ad stated, "One in seven adult Americans can't find the U.S. on a world map." The Bureau of the Census reported that the resident population 18 years and older in 2003 was 217,766,000. How many of these residents could not find the United States on a world map?

117. On June 9, 2005; stocks fell on prediction of inflation. The following chart presents the changes in value of the indexes at the close of trading for that day.

Index	Dow	NASDAQ	S&P 500	Russell 2000
Change	-6.21	-6.98	-2.59	-3.31

Determine the average of the four indexes.

118. Barium crystallizes in a body-centered cube with a volume of 1.303×10^{-28} cubic meter. Determine the length of each side of the cube.

119. Lakeetha charges a flat fee of $225 plus an hourly fee of $45 for consulting services while writing computer programs for a hospital auditing system. Write an algebraic expression for the amount of money she will make for one of her consulting contracts. How much will she earn for this assignment if she spends 120 hours developing the program?

120. Chum bought a circular above-ground swimming pool for his backyard. The pool has a radius of 10 feet. If he fills the pool to a depth of 4.5 feet, how many cubic feet of water will the pool hold?

121. If the temperature reads 96°F, what is the Celsius reading?

122. What is the distance Randy traveled if he bicycled for 1.25 hours at an average speed of 13 miles per hour?

123. Find the volume and surface area of a circular can that has a height of 1.5 inches and a radius of 1.625 inches.

124. A used book store buys paperbacks at a cost of $0.50 per book. The store then resells the used paperbacks for $2.00 each. The store has a weekly overhead cost for rent and utilities of $175.00. If the store buys and resells x books, write an expression for the profit from the sales. What is the profit if the store buys and sells 250 books in a week?

125. In biology, the speed of an enzymatic reaction is often described by a formula according to which the velocity of the reaction, v, is equal to the product of a and x, divided by the sum of x and k. (a is the maximum reaction velocity, x is the concentration of the substrate, and k is the concentration of the substrate when the velocity is half of the maximum velocity.) Write an equation that represents the speed of the reaction.

126. The diameter of the wire in a standard paper clip is 0.04 inch. If the wire is 4 inches long, use the formula for a right circular cylinder to determine the volume of the wire.

127. What is the measure of the complementary angle of an angle that measures 85 degrees?

128. An angle measures 43 degrees. What is the measure of its supplementary angle?

129. Find the measure of the third angle of a triangle if the other two angles measure 31 degrees and 58 degrees.

130. The surface area of a cone-shaped sand pile with a height of 50 feet and a radius of 20 feet is approximately $(3.14)(20)\sqrt{(20)^2 + (50)^2} + (3.14)(20)^2$ square feet. Approximate the sand pile's surface area.

131. Victoria plans to sell fall flower arrangements. She determines that the cost of advertising would be $50.00, and the cost of materials for an arrangement is $3.50. If she sells the arrangements for $10.50 each, write an equation to determine her break-even point.

132. Based upon data from the U.S. Department of Health and Human Services, body weight classification depends upon a person's height, among other factors. The following table suggests body weight classifications for a person who is 5 feet, 9 inches, tall:

Classification	Weight, lb
Healthy weight	130–165
Moderately overweight	166–190
Severely overweight	Over 190

For each category, write a linear inequality that represents that category.

■ Chapter P Test

A+

Use one of the symbols $>$, $<$, or $=$ to compare the numbers.

1. $\dfrac{4}{9}$ ____ $\dfrac{5}{6}$

2. -18 ____ -23

3. $\dfrac{17}{25}$ ____ 0.68

Write an equivalent order relation for each statement.

4. $\dfrac{5}{16} > \dfrac{1}{4} \geq \dfrac{1}{5}$

5. $-3.2 < -2.3$

6. $\dfrac{3}{50} = 0.06$

In exercises 7–25, evaluate. Express your answers in the same form as the original exercise wherever possible, and round decimals to the nearest thousandth.

7. $|-13.37|$

8. $-|-20|$

9. $59 + (-95)$

10. $-\dfrac{17}{95} + \dfrac{4}{19}$

11. $4.378 - 7.98$

12. $\left(-\dfrac{3}{4}\right)\left(-\dfrac{8}{15}\right)$

13. $\dfrac{-6}{7} - \left(-\dfrac{1}{3}\right)$

14. $(4.7)(-2.3)$

15. $0 \div 0$

16. $-41.3 + (-59.76)$

17. $-819 \div (-9)$

18. $-\dfrac{4}{5} \div \dfrac{3}{10}$

19. $15.9 \div 0$

20. $0 \div (-53)$

21. $2\dfrac{3}{7} \div \dfrac{3}{14}$

22. $-12.03 - 2.4$

23. $(-23)(-4)(0)(-17)(0)(-45)$

24. $\left(-\dfrac{5}{6}\right)\left(-\dfrac{3}{7}\right)\left(\dfrac{1}{2}\right)\left(-\dfrac{2}{15}\right)$

25. $4.3 + (-0.1) + 2 + (-1.1)$

26. Graph the following numbers on a number line, and label the points: $-3.5, 3, \dfrac{1}{2}, 2\dfrac{3}{4}, -1\dfrac{1}{2}, \sqrt[3]{100}, \sqrt{25}$

Write in scientific notation.

27. $5{,}239{,}000{,}000{,}000{,}000$

28. -0.00000203

Evaluate.

29. $(1.5)^2$

30. $\left(\dfrac{4}{3}\right)^4$

31. 1^9

32. -3^4

33. $(-4)^3$

34. $(-4.008)^1$

35. 0^0

36. $(-10)^{-1}$

37. $(-3)^0$

38. $\sqrt{\dfrac{36}{121}}$

39. $-\sqrt{3.6}$

40. $\sqrt{-400}$

41. $\sqrt[3]{17^2 - 6 \cdot 12 - 1} + 126 \div 9$

42. $\dfrac{2(5^2 + 3^2) - 8^2 - 2^2}{3.65}$

Evaluate each algebraic expression for the given value.

43. $\sqrt{4x^2 - 20x + 25} + 8$ for $x = 2$

44. $b^2 - 4ac$ for $b = -1, a = 2, c = 1$

Evaluate for $x = -6$.

45. x^2

46. $-x^2$

47. $(-x)^2$

Without simplifying, consider the algebraic expression.

$$y^3 - 5y^2 + 15y - 3 + 7y^2 - 12 + 4y + 6y^3$$

48. How many terms are in the expression?

49. List the variable terms.

50. List the constant terms.

51. List the coefficients of the terms.

52. List the like terms.

Simplify.

53. $\dfrac{2}{3}x + \dfrac{5}{6}y - \dfrac{8}{9} + \dfrac{1}{6}x + \dfrac{7}{9}y + \dfrac{1}{3}$

54. $-(5p + 2q) - (-9p + q) + (p + q) - (-p - q)$

55. $\dfrac{25x - 45}{-5}$

56. $5[2(x + 3) - 4(2x + 1)]$

Determine whether the given value is a solution of the equation.

57. $-7x - 4 = 6x + 9$ for $x = -2$

58. $8x^2 + 40x + 45 = 2x^2 - 2x - 27$ for $x = -4$

Complete the following table:

Description	Inequality	Number Line	Interval Notation
59.	$x \geq 4$		
60.		$\xleftarrow{\quad} \overset{}{\underset{-5\ -4\ -3\ -2\ -1\ \ 0\ \ 1\ \ 2\ \ 3\ \ 4\ \ 5}{\longmapsto}} \xrightarrow{\quad}$	
61.			$(-1, \infty)$
62. All real numbers between -3 and 5			

63. The average high temperature at North Pole, Alaska, is 75 degrees Fahrenheit in July. The average low temperature in the month of January is 19 degrees below zero Fahrenheit. Determine the range of the average temperatures for North Pole, Alaska.

64. The biggest satellite of any planet in the Solar System is Ganymede, which orbits Jupiter. It has a mass of 1.46×10^{23} tons, approximately twice the mass of the Earth's moon. Approximate the mass of the Earth's moon.

65. The metal surface area of a can of vegetable shortening (a right circular cylinder) with a height of 6 inches and a radius of 5 inches is approximately $2(3.14)(5)^2 + 2(3.14)(5)(6)$ square inches. Approximate the amount of metal needed to make the can.

66. Joseph plans to produce and sell birdhouses. He purchased a miter saw for $350.00. He estimates that the material to make each birdhouse will cost $2.00. If he sells the birdhouses for $10.50 each, write an equation to determine his break-even point.

67. A carton of milk contains 1.89 liters. The milk is labeled as 2% reduced-fat milk. How many liters of the milk are fat? If there are eight servings of milk in the container, how many liters of fat are contained in each serving?

68. Orhan builds a toolbox that is 4 feet long, 2 feet wide, and 1.5 feet high. What is the volume of the box? What is the outside surface area?

69. If Tracy makes a single deposit of $2000 into a savings account that earns simple interest at 5.5% annually, how much will the account contain in 40 years?

70. What does the supplementary angle of a 78-degree angle measure?

71. Find the area and perimeter of a rectangle with a length of 6 meters and a width of 2.5 meters.

72. What is the Fahrenheit temperature if the Celsius temperature is 25°C?

73. The Fujita Scale described in this chapter classifies tornadoes according to the amount of damage they inflict. The following table lists the classifications of tornadoes that are considered severe or even worse:

F-Scale Number	Intensity	Wind Speed
F3	Severe tornado	158–206 mph
F4	Devastating tornado	207–260 mph
F5	Incredible tornado	261–318 mph
F6	Inconceivable tornado	319 or higher

For each of the categories listed, write a linear inequality that represents that category.

74. Explain the difference between the area and the perimeter of a two-dimensional figure.

75. Explain the difference between a constant and a coefficient in a variable expression.

P
Project

The formulas we use in geometry are the results of centuries of study by mathematicians and scientists. The development of a method for determining the value of π has a history as part of the "three famous problems" that the Greeks pondered. Early attempts were empirical – that is, experimental—in nature.

PART I We will conduct an empirical study similar to those used in ancient times to evaluate π. We know that the circumference and diameter of a circle are related by the formula $C = \pi d$, or $\pi = \frac{C}{d}$. In order to use this formula to estimate π, you will need a long piece of string, a meter stick, and three different circular objects.

1. Wrap a string around the top of the circular object and mark the circumference. Lay the string on a meter stick and measure the marked length (the circumference).

2. Place the string across the top of the circular object through its center, marking the distance, and measure the string (the diameter).

3. Determine the ratio of the circumference to the diameter or the quotient of the circumference divided by the diameter, rounded to six decimal places.

Complete the following table with your data:

Object	Circumference	Diameter	Circumference ÷ Diameter

Now determine the average of the three ratios.

The average ratio of the circumference to the diameter is ____.

The answers in the last column should be close to the same value, as well as to the average of these ratios. In fact, if you measured very accurately, the number should be approximately the value of π. Therefore, the real number π is defined as the ratio of the circumference of a circle to its diameter.

PART II You can research the history of the development of methods for estimating the irrational number π in the library and on the Internet. Find a reference that discusses the history of π, and write a one-page paper summarizing your findings. Be sure to list your reference source.

PART III At the beginning of this chapter, there is a photo of the Dome of the Rock. This structure has a circular dome in its center. Search the Internet to find other photos of the interior and exterior of the structure. Print one of the photos, and include it with your report on this structure. Find information on the measurements of the dome. Use them in the formulas for a circle, and apply the formulas to describe the size of the dome. Write a one-page summary of your findings on the Dome of the Rock.

PART IV The real number π has many other applications in mathematics. Do research in the library or on the Internet to determine a different application or formula that involves π. Write a one-page summary describing the application that uses this mathematical constant. Cite your reference source in your paper.

Relations, Functions, and Graphs

In Chapter P, we saw that giving a value to one or more variables in an algebraic expression or equation usually determines the value of other variables. For example, if we know the temperature in degrees Fahrenheit, we are able to determine the temperature in degrees Celsius. An equation or formula relates these two variables; therefore, changing the value of the variable for Fahrenheit temperature changes the value of the variable representing the Celsius temperature.

In this chapter, we will visualize this relationship in a different kind of way. We will use tables to help us organize our data. We will introduce the concept of a graph of an equation and show how it translates into a picture we can see. Finally, we will use the graphs we produce to understand the relationship between two variables in more depth.

Many important relationships between two variables are found in business and science. Tables and graphs help us visualize and analyze these relationships. We will end the chapter with a project in which you will collect the hourly temperature for one day and discuss the relationship between time of day and temperature.

123

1.1   TABLES OF VALUES, ORDERED PAIRS, AND RELATIONS

OBJECTIVES
1. Create tables of values for given data.
2. Write ordered pairs for given data.
3. Identify the domain and range of a relation.
4. Create tables of values for real-world data.

APPLICATION

According to end-of-the-year reports for the year 2003, General Motors (GM) had the largest total revenue in the United States, about $186 billion. The following table gives a 10-year summary of revenue from GM sales:

Year	2003	2002	2001	2000	1999	1998	1997	1996	1995	1994
Sales (in billions of dollars)	186	187	177	185	177	161	166	158	164	151

Write a set of ordered pairs that represent these data. Determine the domain and range of the relation. Interpret.

We will discuss this application further. See page 130.

Objective 1.1.1   Creating Tables of Values

Sometimes we need to evaluate a formula or an equation more than once. It is often convenient to organize our information in a table of values. A **table of values** is a table with at least two columns. One column lists the values substituted for the variable. The second column lists the values obtained for the unknown variable when the formula is evaluated.

For example, suppose a biologist needs to convert Celsius temperatures into Fahrenheit temperatures. Instead of using the conversion formula each time, she decides to make a reference table of all temperatures she is using. A portion of this table will look like the following:

Celsius Temperature (°C)	Fahrenheit Temperature (°F)
20	68
21	69.8
22	71.6
23	73.4

To complete the next three entries in the table, we will extend it to include a middle column (to show our work). The first column is labeled with the independent variable. The **independent variable** is the variable for which we are substituting values. The second column is labeled with the formula or equation we are evaluating. The third column is labeled with the dependent variable. The **dependent variable** is the variable that is determined by the substitutions we make. We refer to the information in the table as **data**.

To construct a table of values, set up a three-column table.

- The first column is labeled with the independent variable.

- The second column is labeled with the formula or equation needed to find the unknown variable.
- The third column is labeled with the dependent variable.

Complete the table.

- Enter a number in the first column.
- Substitute the number from the first column into the formula or equation in the second column, and evaluate the results.
- Enter the results in the third column.

For example, complete the next three entries in the Celsius-to-Fahrenheit temperature table.

°C	$F = \dfrac{9}{5}C + 32$	°F
24	$F = \dfrac{9}{5}(24) + 32$	75.2
25	$F = \dfrac{9}{5}(25) + 32$	77
26	$F = \dfrac{9}{5}(26) + 32$	78.8

You can construct a table of values with the use of your calculator. The calculator is designed to use the variable x for the independent variable and the variable y for the dependent variable. The calculator has two modes, Ask and Auto, for constructing a table of values.

Since we want to complete the next three entries in our table, we will first illustrate the Ask mode.

TECHNOLOGY   Table of Values Using Ask Mode

Set the calculator to generate a table of values, asking for x-values from the user and automatically performing the calculations, for $y = \frac{9}{5}x + 32$, given that $x = 24, 25,$ and 26.

Figure 1.1a

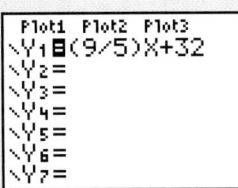

Figure 1.1b

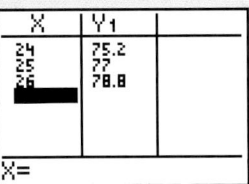

Figure 1.1c

For **Figure 1.1a**,
Set up the table.
[2nd] [WINDOW] (TBLSET)
Set the table to ask mode for the independent variable, x. (Ignore the first two entries.)
[▼] [▼] [▶] [ENTER] [▼] [ENTER]

For **Figure 1.1b**,
Enter the formula in terms of x for the first y.
[Y=] [(] [9] [÷] [5] [)] [X,T,θ,n] [+] [3] [2]

For **Figure 1.1c**,
View the table.
[2nd] [GRAPH] (TABLE)
Enter the values for x (24, 25, and 26).
[2] [4] [ENTER] [2] [5] [ENTER] [2] [6] [ENTER]

If we want additional integer entries, we can use the Auto mode.

TECHNOLOGY   Table of Values Using Auto Mode

Set the calculator to automatically generate a table of values for $y = \frac{9}{5}x + 32$, given that $x = 24, 25,$ and 26.

| Figure 1.2a | Figure 1.2b | Figure 1.2c |

For **Figure 1.2a**,
Set up the table.

[2nd] [WINDOW] (TBLSET)

Set a minimum value for the independent variable, x.

[2] [4] [ENTER] (minimum value 24)

Set the size of increments to be added to the independent variable.

[1] [ENTER] (increments of 1)

Set the calculator to perform the evaluations automatically.

[ENTER] [▼] [ENTER]

For **Figure 1.2b**,
Enter the formula in terms of x for the first y.

[Y=] [(] [9] [÷] [5] [)] [X,T,θ,n] [+] [3] [2]

For **Figure 1.2c**,
View the table.

[2nd] [GRAPH] (TABLE)

You may view additional entries in the table by using the up or down arrow keys.

EXAMPLE 1

a. Construct a table of values for the circumference of a circle, given the set of values $\{5, 10, 15, 20, 25\}$ for the diameter, d.

b. Construct a table of values for $y = 3x$, where x is an integer between -4 and 4.

Solution

a.

d	$C = \pi d$	C
5	$C = \pi(5)$	15.708
10	$C = \pi(10)$	31.416
15	$C = \pi(15)$	47.124
20	$C = \pi(20)$	62.832
25	$C = \pi(25)$	78.540

Check

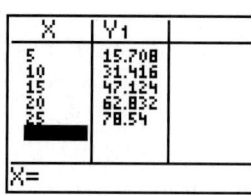

Y1 = πx

The calculator table was generated in Ask mode.

b. The integer values for x are $-3, -2, -1, 0, 1, 2$, and 3.

x	$y = 3x$	y
-3	$y = 3(-3)$	-9
-2	$y = 3(-2)$	-6
-1	$y = 3(-1)$	-3
0	$y = 3(0)$	0
1	$y = 3(1)$	3
2	$y = 3(2)$	6
3	$y = 3(3)$	9

X	Y1	
-3	-9	
-2	-6	
-1	-3	
0	0	
1	3	
2	6	
3	9	
X= -3		

Y1 = 3x

The calculator table was generated in Auto mode.

Objective 1.1.1 CHECKUP

Construct a table of values for each equation and check your results on your calculator.

1. **a.** Convert Fahrenheit temperatures to Celsius temperatures with the formula $C = \frac{5}{9}(F - 32)$, given the set of values $\{86, 77, 68, 59, 50, 41, 32\}$ for F.

   b. Construct a table of values of $a = -6b + 7$, where b is an integer between -4 and 4.

2. What is a table of values, and how can it help you when you work with an equation or a formula?

Objective 1.1.2 Writing Ordered Pairs

Another way to organize the data contained in an equation is to write ordered pairs. An **ordered pair** consists of two numbers in parentheses, separated by a comma. The first number in the ordered pair is the value of the independent variable. The second number in the ordered pair is the value of the dependent variable. The order of the numbers is very important.

For example, the previous temperature conversion table yields the following ordered pairs:

°C	°F	Independent Variable (C,	Dependent Variable F)
20	68	(20,	68)
21	69.8	(21,	69.8)
22	71.6	(22,	71.6)
23	73.4	(23,	73.4)

Ordered pairs are a common and useful way of organizing data for the purpose of graphing an equation, as we will see in Section 1.2.

EXAMPLE 2   Write ordered pairs for the data found in Example 1.

Solution

a. $(5, 15.708), (10, 31.416), (15, 47.124), (20, 62.832), (25, 78.540)$

b. $(-3, -9), (-2, -6), (-1, -3), (0, 0), (1, 3), (2, 6)$, and $(3, 9)$

Objective 1.1.2 CHECKUP

1. Write ordered pairs for the data found in exercises 1a and 1b of Objective 1.1.1 Checkup.

2. In writing an ordered pair for a set of data, why is the order of the numbers important?

Objective 1.1.3   Identifying the Domain and Range of a Relation

A set of ordered pairs is a **relation**. For example,

The set of ordered pairs

$$T = \{(20, 68), (21, 69.8), (22, 71.6), (23, 73.4)\}$$

that the biologist used for temperature conversion is a relation.

The set of all possible values for the independent variable is called the **domain** of the relation. The set of all possible values for the dependent variable is called the **range** of the relation.

$$T = \{(20, 68), (21, 69.8), (22, 71.6), (23, 73.4)\}$$

↓	↓	↓	↓	↓	↓	↓	↓
Domain	20		21		22		23	
Range		68		69.8		71.6		73.4

The domain is $\{20, 21, 22, 23\}$.

The range is $\{68, 69.8, 71.6, 73.4\}$.

The list of ordered pairs in a relation can be finite or infinite. A **finite** list has a definite number of ordered pairs.

$$A = \{(1, 1), (1, 2), (1, 3)\} \quad \text{Finite}$$

The domain is $\{1\}$.

The range is $\{1, 2, 3\}$.

An **infinite** list does not have a definite number of ordered pairs.

$$B = \{\ldots, (-2, -1), (-1, 0), (0, 1), (1, 2), (2, 3), \ldots\} \quad \text{Infinite}$$

The domain is $\{\ldots, -2, -1, 0, 1, 2, \ldots\}$, or the set of all integers.

The range is $\{\ldots, -1, 0, 1, 2, 3, \ldots\}$, or the set of all integers.

A relation can also be written as an equation with two variables. We can use the equation to determine the ordered pairs by substituting a value for the independent variable and determining a value for the dependent variable.

$y = 2x$ for $x = 1, 2, 3$ is a relation of a finite set of ordered pairs,

$$\{(1, 2), (2, 4), (3, 6)\}.$$

The domain is $\{1, 2, 3\}$.

The range is $\{2, 4, 6\}$.

 TAKE NOTE A table of values will help us determine the ordered pairs when an equation is given.

EXAMPLE 3

Determine the domain and range for the following relations, assuming that x is the independent variable and y is the dependent variable:

a. $\{(1, 3), (2, 5), (6, 5)\}$ **b.** $\{(1, 2), (2, 2), (3, 2), \ldots\}$

c. $y = 3x + 2$ for $x = -1, 0, 1$

Solution

a. domain $\{1, 2, 6\}$ *The domain is the set of the x-values.*

range $\{3, 5\}$ *The range is the set of the y-values. There is no need to write more than one 5.*

b. domain $\{1, 2, 3, \ldots\}$,   *The domain is the set of the x-values.*

range $\{2\}$ *The range is the set of the y-values.*

c. A table of values for $y = 3x + 2$ will help us determine the ordered pairs.

x	$y = 3x + 2$	y	
-1	$y = 3(-1) + 2$	-1	$(-1, -1)$
0	$y = 3(0) + 2$	2	$(0, 2)$
1	$y = 3(1) + 2$	5	$(1, 5)$

domain $\{-1, 0, 1\}$
range $\{-1, 2, 5\}$

✓ Objective 1.1.3 *CHECKUP*

1. Determine the domain and range for each relation. Assume that x is the independent variable.

   a. $\{(5, 15), (10, 30), (15, 45)\}$
   b. $\{(0, 4), (1, 6), (2, 8), (3, 10), \dots\}$
   c. $y = x + 15$ for $x = 0.5, 1.5, 2.5$

2. Explain the terms *domain* and *range* of a relation.

3. What is the difference between a finite list of ordered pairs and an infinite list of ordered pairs?

Objective 1.1.4   Modeling the Real World

Real-life situations can often be modeled as relations. Some relations are more convenient to describe by tables of values, other relations can best be described by sets of ordered pairs, and still others are most appropriately described by equations. You need to be familiar with all these forms of relations in order to describe a situation in the most useful manner.

EXAMPLE 4

The daily charge for renting a 24-foot U-Haul truck is $39.95, plus $0.59 per mile driven, with a $5.00 nonrefundable deposit.

   a. Write an equation for the cost of renting a 24-foot U-Haul truck for one day.

   b. Complete a table of values for the cost of renting a 24-foot U-Haul truck for one day for 100 miles, 200 miles, and 300 miles.

   c. List the ordered pairs and interpret.

Solution

a. Let m = the number of miles driven and c = the cost of a one-day rental.

$$c = 39.95 + 0.59m + 5.00$$
$$c = 44.95 + 0.59m$$

b. Add a middle column to the table to show your work.

m	$c = 44.95 + 0.59m$	c
100	$c = 44.95 + 0.59(100)$	103.95
200	$c = 44.95 + 0.59(200)$	162.95
300	$c = 44.95 + 0.59(300)$	221.95

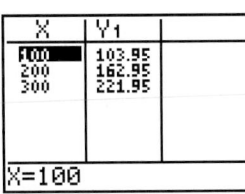

Y1 = 44.95 + 0.59x

c. The ordered pairs are $(100, 103.95)$, $(200, 162.95)$, and $(300, 221.95.)$

The daily charge for renting the truck and driving 100 miles is $103.95, driving 200 miles is $162.95, and driving 300 miles is $221.95.

EXAMPLE 5   Latoya plans to borrow $2500 from her grandmother for her tuition payment. Her grandmother will charge her simple interest of 7% per year. Determine the amount of interest Latoya will need to repay if she repays the loan after one, two, three, or four years.

Solution

Use the simple-interest formula, $I = PRT$, where I = simple interest, P = principal or amount borrowed, R = rate of loan per year, and T = time in years. Substitute the given values for the principal, $2500, and rate, 7% = 0.07, to obtain an equation.

$$I = PRT$$
$$I = 2500(0.07)T$$

Since Latoya needs to know several amounts, a table will help us organize our information. The independent variable is the time in years, and the dependent variable is the amount of interest.

T	$I = 2500(0.07)T$	I
1	$I = 2500(0.07)(1)$	175
2	$I = 2500(0.07)(2)$	350
3	$I = 2500(0.07)(3)$	525
4	$I = 2500(0.07)(4)$	700

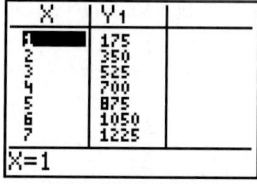

Y1 = 2500(0.07)x

Latoya will need to repay $175 in interest for one year, $350 for two years, $525 for three years, and $700 for four years.

APPLICATION

According to end-of-the-year reports for the year 2003, General Motors (GM) had the largest total revenue in the United States, about $186 billion. The following table gives a 10-year summary of revenue from GM sales:

Year	2003	2002	2001	2000	1999	1998	1997	1996	1995	1994
Sales (in billions of dollars)	186	187	187	185	177	161	166	158	164	151

Write a set of ordered pairs that represent these data. Determine the domain and range of the relation. Interpret.

Discussion

Let x = the year and y = the revenue from sales in billions of dollars. Then we have

{(1994, 151), (1995, 164), (1996, 158), (1997, 166), (1998, 161), (1999, 177), (2000, 185), (2001, 187), (2002, 187), (2003, 186)}

domain: {1994, 1995, 1996, 1997, 1998, 1999, 2000, 2001, 2002, 2003}

range: {151, 158, 161, 164, 166, 177, 185, 186, 187}

GM sales for the 10-year period of 1994 to 2003 ranged from 151 billion dollars to 187 billion dollars.

A second method that will enable us to use smaller numbers is to let x = the number of years after 1994 and y = the revenue from sales in billions of dollars. Then $x = 0$ corresponds to 1994, $x = 1$ corresponds to 1995, $x = 2$ corresponds to 1996, and so on, and we have

(0, 151), (1, 164), (2, 158), (3, 166), (4, 161), (5, 177), (6, 185), (7, 187), (8, 187), (9, 186)

domain: {0, 1, 2, 3, 4, 5, 6, 7, 8, 9}

range: {151, 158, 161, 164, 166, 177, 185, 186, 187}

GM sales for the 10-year period of 1994 to 2003 ranged from 151 billion dollars to 187 billion dollars.

✓ Objective 1.1.4 *CHECKUP*

1. Sven attended a teachers' conference. His school reimbursed him $410 for plane fare, $95 per day for lodging, and $36 per day for meals.
   a. Write an equation for the total reimbursement, r, in terms of the number of days, n, for the trip.
   b. Construct a table showing the possible reimbursements for a trip that lasts from two through five days.
   c. List the ordered pairs found in the table for part **b**.

2. The volume of a videotape cabinet is calculated with the formula $V = LWH$. The cabinet has a width $W = 12$ inches and a length $L = 23$ inches. Determine the volume of the cabinet if the height, H, is 29.5, 38.5, or 47.5 inches.

3. According to end-of-the-year reports for the year 2003, Amazon.com had a total revenue of about $5264 million. The following table gives the 8-year summary of revenue from sales:

Year	2003	2002	2001	2000	1999	1998	1997	1996
Sales (in million dollars)	5264	3933	3122	2762	1640	610	148	16

   a. Let x = the year. Write a set of ordered pairs that represent the data. Determine the domain and range of the relation.
   b. Let x = the number of years after 1996. Write a set of ordered pairs that represent the data. Determine the domain and range of the relation.
   c. Interpret.

4. If x = number of years after 1990, interpret $x = 5$. ■

1.1 EXERCISES

 Student Solutions Manual  PH Math/Tutor Center   CD Video Math XL MathXL® MyMathLab MyMathLab  Interactmath.com

Express your answers in fractional form or round decimals to the nearest thousandth, as appropriate. Construct a table of values, given each set of values for x.

1. $y = 5x + 4$, given $\{-2, -1, 0, 1, 2, 3\}$ for x.

2. $y = -8x - 6$, given $\{-3, -2, -1, 0, 1\}$ for x.

3. $y = \dfrac{3}{5}x - 2$, given $\{-15, -10, -5, 0, 5, 10, 15\}$ for x.

4. $y = \dfrac{7}{9}x + 3$, given $\{-18, -9, 0, 9, 18, 27, 36\}$ for x.

5. $y = 2.3x + 1.6$, given $\{-2, -1, 0, 1, 2\}$ for x.

6. $y = -4.8x - 9.2$, given $\{-3, -1, 0, 1, 3\}$ for x.

7. $y = \dfrac{1}{3}(x + 7)$, given $\{-1, -4, -7, -10, -13\}$ for x.

8. $y = \dfrac{1}{6}(x - 2)$, given $\{-10, -4, 2, 8, 14\}$ for x.

Write a table of values for each equation. Select five values for the independent variable in each table.

9. $y = 6x - 8$

10. $y = -11x + 15$

11. $y = \dfrac{2}{7}x - 2$

12. $y = -\dfrac{3}{8}x + 5$

13. $y = -4.6x + 2.1$

14. $y = 10.6x - 0.8$

15. $y = \dfrac{1}{4}(3x - 2)$

16. $y = \dfrac{3}{8}(x - 5)$

In exercises 17–28, write a table of values for each equation with the given domain.

17. $y = 12x - 13$, where x is an even integer between -5 and 5.

18. $y = -9x + 12$, where x is an odd integer between -4 and 4.

19. $z = \dfrac{1}{3}y + 5$, where y is an integer multiple of 3 between -7 and 7.

20. $p = \dfrac{7}{8}q - 4$, where q is an integer multiple of 8 between -17 and 17.

21. $a = 14.2b + 5.7$, for a domain of integer values between -3 and 3.

22. $m = 1.9n - 3.7$, for a domain of integer values between -4 and 2.

23. $y = 2x^2 + 3x + 1$, with a domain of $\{-3, -2, -1, 0, 1, 2, 3\}$.

24. $y = -3x^2 + 11x - 10$, with a domain of $\{-2, -1, 0, 1, 2, 3, 4\}$.

25. $y = (2x - 3)(3x + 4)$, for integer values of x between -3 and 3.

26. $y = (4x + 1)(-x + 2)$, for integer values of x between 4 and 10.

27. $y = \dfrac{3x + 7}{x - 1}$, for odd integer values of x between -4 and 4.

28. $y = \dfrac{-5x + 2}{-x + 3}$, for odd integer values of x between -2 and 6.

29. Chameeka took a vacation by automobile. She drove at an average speed of 55 miles per hour each day.
   a. Write an equation for the total number of miles she traveled.
   b. Complete a table of values for the total number of miles Chameeka traveled if she drove for 4 hours, 8 hours, 12 hours, 16 hours, and 20 hours.

30. During an auction, the successful bid for place settings of china was $15.50 for each four-piece setting.
   a. Write an equation for the total cost of purchasing a given number of four-piece place settings at the bid price.
   b. Complete a table of values for the total cost of purchasing place settings if the number of four-piece settings purchased was 2, 4, 6, 8, 10, or 12.

31. The daily charge for renting an intermediate class automobile from Avis is $68.99. Lawrence is under 25 years of age and is charged an additional $110.00 fee.

   a. Write an equation for the cost, C, of renting the automobile in terms of d days.

   b. Complete a table of values for the cost of renting the automobile for 5 days, 7 days, and 9 days.

   c. List the ordered pairs and interpret.

32. The daily charge for renting a mini van from Avis is $58.99. Shelley is under 25 years of age and is charged an additional $110.00 fee.

   a. Write an equation for the cost, C, of renting the van in terms of d days.

   b. Complete a table of values for the cost of renting the van for 7 days, 14 days, and 21 days.

   c. List the ordered pairs and interpret.

In exercises 39–44, write tables of values for these formulas with their domains.

33. The volume of a box whose width is 2 feet, whose length is 4 feet, and whose height takes on the values $\{1, 3, 5, 7, 9\}$ feet.

34. The volume of a cube whose edge measures $\{1, 2, 3, 4, 5, 6\}$ feet.

35. The amount of interest earned on an investment of $5000 invested at 4.5% simple interest for a time t, where t starts at 1 year and is repeatedly increased by 1 year until it reaches 12 years.

36. The amount of interest on a loan of $3000 at a rate of simple interest of 7% for a time t, where t starts at 1 year and is incremented by 2 years until it reaches 15 years.

37. Ohm's law in electricity is $I = V \div R$, where I is current (measured in amperes), V is voltage (measured in volts), and R is resistance (measured in ohms). Find the current when the voltage is 9 volts and the resistance assumes values from 1 ohm to 9 ohms in increments of 1 ohm.

38. Ohm's law in electricity may also be stated as $V = I \cdot R$, where V is voltage (measured in volts), I is current (measured in amperes), and R is resistance (measured in ohms). Find the voltage when the current is 5 amps and the resistance varies as a natural number between 1 and 10 ohms, inclusive.

In exercises 39–44, write ordered pairs.

39. $y = 1.2x + 4$ when $x = -2, -1, 0, 1, 2$.

40. $y = 6 - 0.3x$ when $x = -4, -2, 0, 2, 4$.

41. $q = 1 - p$ when $p = \dfrac{1}{6}, \dfrac{1}{5}, \dfrac{1}{4}, \dfrac{1}{3}, \dfrac{1}{2}$.

42. $S = \dfrac{n(n + 1)}{2}$ when $n = 1, 2, 3, 4, 5$.

43. The perimeter of a square when the side measures $2, 4, 6, 8, 10$ inches.

44. The change received when paying with a $10.00 bill for a purchase of $4.00, $6.00, $8.00, $9.50.

45. The average monthly bill (in dollars) for cellular phones, according to the Cellular Telecommunications Industry Association, is presented in the following table:

Year	1994	1995	1996	1997	1998	1999	2000	2001	2002	2003
Average bill	56.21	51.00	47.70	42.78	39.43	41.24	45.27	47.37	48.40	49.91

   a. Write a set of ordered pairs for the data. Let $x =$ the year.

   b. Write a set of ordered pairs for the data. Let $x =$ the number of years after 1994.

46. The net income for all U.S. corporations (in billions of dollars), according to the U.S. Internal Revenue Service, is presented in the following table for the years 1994 through 2001:

Year	1994	1995	1996	1997	1998	1999	2000	2001
Net income	577	714	806	915	838	929	928	604

   a. Write a set of ordered pairs for the data. Let $x =$ the year.

   b. Write a set of ordered pairs for the data. Let $x =$ the number of years after 1994.

47. The Indianapolis 500 is one of the most well-known racing events in the United States. The *Information, Please* almanac notes that the average speed of the winning car varies from year to year due to temperature, humidity, and racing conditions such as number of yellow flag caution laps. The following table summarizes the average speed in miles per hour of the winning car in the Indianapolis 500.

Year	1995	1996	1997	1998	1999	2000	2001	2002	2003	2004
Speed (mph)	153.616	147.956	145.827	145.155	153.176	167.607	141.574	166.499	156.291	138.518

   a. Write a set of ordered pairs to represent these data. Let $x =$ the year.

   b. Write a set of ordered pairs to represent these data. Let $x =$ the number of years after 1995.

48. The U.S. Patent and Trademark Office reported the following summary of number of patents issued (in thousands—for example, 113.6 represents 113,600) for each year between 1994 and 2003.

Year	1994	1995	1996	1997	1998	1999	2000	2001	2002	2003
Patents Issued	113.6	113.8	121.7	124.1	163.1	169.1	176.0	184.0	184.4	187.0

   a. Write a set of ordered pairs to represent these data. Let x = the year.
   b. Write a set of ordered pairs to represent these data. Let x = the number of years after 1994.

In exercises 49–64, determine the domain and range for each relation. Assume that x is the independent variable.

49. $R = \{(3, 15.8), (5, 17.8), (7, 19.8), (9, 21.8)\}$

50. $U = \{(11, 8), (15, 12), (19, 16), (23, 20)\}$

51. $S = \{(4, -3), (4, -1), (4, 1), (4, 3), \ldots\}$

52. $H = \{(3, -1), (2, -1), (1, -1), (0, -1), (-1, -1), \ldots\}$

53. $T = \{\ldots, (2, -2), (2, -1), (2, 0), (2, 1), (2, 2), \ldots\}$

54. $I = \{\ldots, (-2, 0), (-1, 0), (0, 0), (1, 0), (2, 0), \ldots\}$

55. $y = 4x - 5$ for $x = 2, 4, 6$

56. $y = 3x + 5$ for $x = 10, 20, 30$

57. $y = 6 - x$, where x assumes integer values between -1 and 7.

58. $y = -x - 8$, where x assumes integer values between -5 and 5.

59. $y = x^2 + 1$, where x assumes the values $\{0, 0.5, 1, 1.5, 2, 2.5, 3, 3.5, 4\}$

60. $y = x^2 - 2$, where x assumes the values $\{0, 0.5, 1, 1.5, 2, 2.5, 3, 3.5, 4\}$

61. $y = \sqrt{x - 2}$, for $x = 2, 3, 6, 11, 18, 27$

62. $y = \sqrt{x + 2}$, for $x = -2, -1, 2, 7, 14, 23$

63. $y = \dfrac{6}{x - 2}$, for $x = -3, -1, 1, 3, 5, 7$

64. $y = \dfrac{10}{4 - x}$, for $x = -3, -1, 1, 3, 5, 7$

65. A diver jumped off a 50-foot cliff. His position, s feet above water, t seconds after the jump is given by the equation $s = -16t^2 + 50$. Construct a table of values of the diver's position above the water, where t assumes the values $0, 0.5, 1, 1.5$ seconds.

66. A toy rocket is shot upward from the ground with an initial velocity of 225 feet per second. The position of the rocket, s feet above the ground, t seconds after blastoff is given by the equation $s = -16t^2 + 225t$. Construct a table of values of the position of the rocket, where t assumes integer values between 0 and 14, inclusive.

67. Rebecca is traveling on the interstate highway at a constant speed of 65 miles per hour. Write ordered pairs for her distance traveled at the end of each hour for a four-hour trip.

68. David is driving his truck between two turnpike entrances that are 195 miles apart. Write ordered pairs for his speed to the nearest mile per hour if he completes the trip in 2.5, 2.75, 3, 3.25, or 3.5 hours. (The Highway Patrol could use this information to determine whether David exceeded the speed limit on his trip.)

69. An executive lease for an efficiency apartment requires a nonrefundable deposit of $225 and a weekly charge of $175.
   a. Write an equation for the cost of renting the apartment.
   b. Complete a table of values for the cost of renting the apartment for 1, 2, 3, or 4 weeks.

70. A contract for renting a reception hall for a wedding requires a nonrefundable deposit of $300 plus an hourly charge of $75.
   a. Write an equation for the cost of renting the reception hall.
   b. Complete a table of values for the cost of renting the hall for 2, 2.5, 3, 3.5, or 4 hours.

71. The cost of higher education is on the rise. According to the U.S. Department of Education, National Center of Education Statistics, the average cost of undergraduate tuition, room and board, and fees amounted to an estimated $12,111 in school year 2002–2003. The table below illustrates these increasing costs:

School Year	02–03	01–02	00–01	99–00	98–99	97–98	96–97	95–96	91–92	86–87
Cost ($)	12,111	11,380	10,818	10,444	10,076	9588	9206	8800	7077	5206

a. Let x = the number of years after the year 86–87. Write a set of ordered pairs for the data.
b. Determine the domain and range for this relation. Interpret. Does your interpretation support the initial statement in this exercise?

72. The United States has an aging population. According to the U.S. Bureau of the Census, the percent of the population that is 65 and over was just 4.7 in 1920. The following table gives a summary of percent of U.S. population 65 and over.

Year	1920	1930	1940	1950	1960	1970	1980	1990	2000
Percent of U.S. Population 65 and over	4.7	5.4	6.8	8.1	9.2	9.8	11.3	12.5	12.4

a. Let x = the number of years after 1920. Write a set of ordered pairs for the data.
b. Determine the domain and range for this relation. Interpret. Does your interpretation support the initial statement in this exercise?

 ## 1.1 Calculator Exercises

When you set up a table on a calculator, you have the option of setting the independent variable, x, to Auto or to Ask. In this section, you have seen that if you set x to Auto and specify the beginning value and the increment value, the calculator will automatically generate a table. You have also seen that if you set x to Ask, you can input whatever value you want for x, after which the calculator will display the corresponding value for y. These two settings are shown in the following diagrams:

What happens when the dependent variable, y, is set to Ask? The two settings are shown in these diagrams:

In this case, the calculator table will not display a value of y until you select the cell of the table for which you want the value calculated. To do so, you must move the cursor to the column for y, select the cell that corresponds to the value of x displayed, and press ⟨ **ENTER** ⟩. The calculator will display a corresponding value of y for this value of x. If you have both options set to Ask, then you must first enter the values you want to use for x, then move to the column for y, and, finally, select the cell that you want evaluated.

In this chapter, we see no use for this feature, but it is discussed here since many students ask about it out of curiosity. Just remember that we will use the Ask option only for the independent variable, x, but we will always set the dependent variable, y, to the Auto option.

 ## 1.1 Writing Exercises

In this section, you learned several concepts dealing with relations between two variables. Write a brief explanation of each of the following concepts:

1. Describe the various ways in which to define the relation between two variables.

2. Explain dependent and independent variables.

3. Explain the domain and the range of a relation.

1.2 RECTANGULAR COORDINATE SYSTEM AND GRAPHING

OBJECTIVES

1 Construct a coordinate plane.
2 Graph relations.
3 Identify the domain and range of a relation from its graph.
4 Interpret graphs of real-world data.

APPLICATION

The following graph illustrates the revenue from sales, cost of sales, and gross operating profit for General Motors Corporation in the years 1996 through 2003:

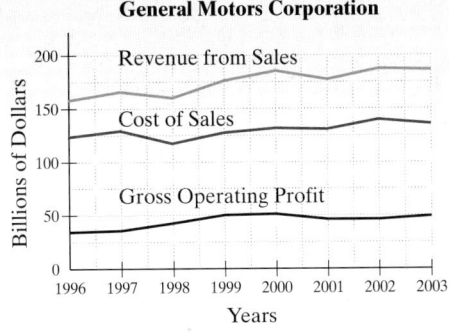

General Motors Corporation

Approximate the domain and range of the revenue, cost, and profit.

After completing this section, we will discuss this application further. See page 147.

Objective 1.2.1 Constructing a Rectangular Coordinate System

We have seen how to organize data in a table of values and in sets of ordered pairs. A third way to organize data is to use a two-dimensional graph. In Chapter P, we graphed numbers on a real-number line. Now we want to graph ordered pairs, consisting of two numbers. We use a **rectangular coordinate system**, or **Cartesian coordinate system**. The word *Cartesian* comes from the name of the great French philosopher and mathematician René Descartes (1596–1650). Sometimes, we simply refer to the system as a **coordinate plane**. A coordinate system combines two real-number lines, perpendicular to each other and intersecting at 0 on each line. Remember, perpendicular lines are lines that intersect at right angles (90°).

The horizontal number line, or horizontal axis, is often called the **x-axis**. The vertical number line, or vertical axis, is often called the **y-axis**. These two lines intersect at a point called the **origin**. We place an arrow at the end of each of the axes to indicate its positive direction.

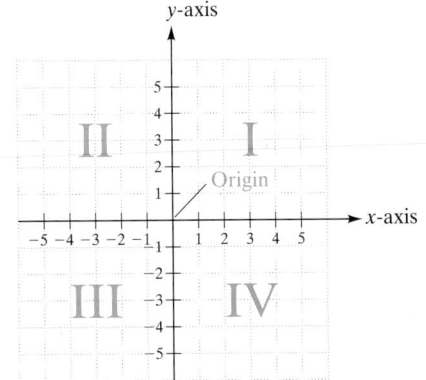

We can draw lines perpendicular to the axes through the locations of all the integers on the two number lines. This network of lines forms a rectangular grid, which may be divided by the *x*-axis and *y*-axis into four regions called **quadrants**. The quadrants are labeled with Roman numerals in a counterclockwise direction, beginning with the upper right-hand region.

We can set up a coordinate plane on the calculator. The calculator has several choices of screens built in for us to use. We will call these screens *default* screens. We can also set the screen to a setting other than a default screen. At times, we will need to change calculator screens in order to view a graph more easily.

The Technology box that follows shows the default calculator coordinate planes. Below each screen in parentheses is the window setting. It is written in the form

(*x* minimum value, *x* maximum value, *x* scale, *y* minimum value,
y maximum value, *y* scale, *x* resolution)

A shorter version may not include the *x* scale, *y* scale, or *x* resolution:

(*x* minimum value, *x* maximum value, *y* minimum value, *y* maximum value)

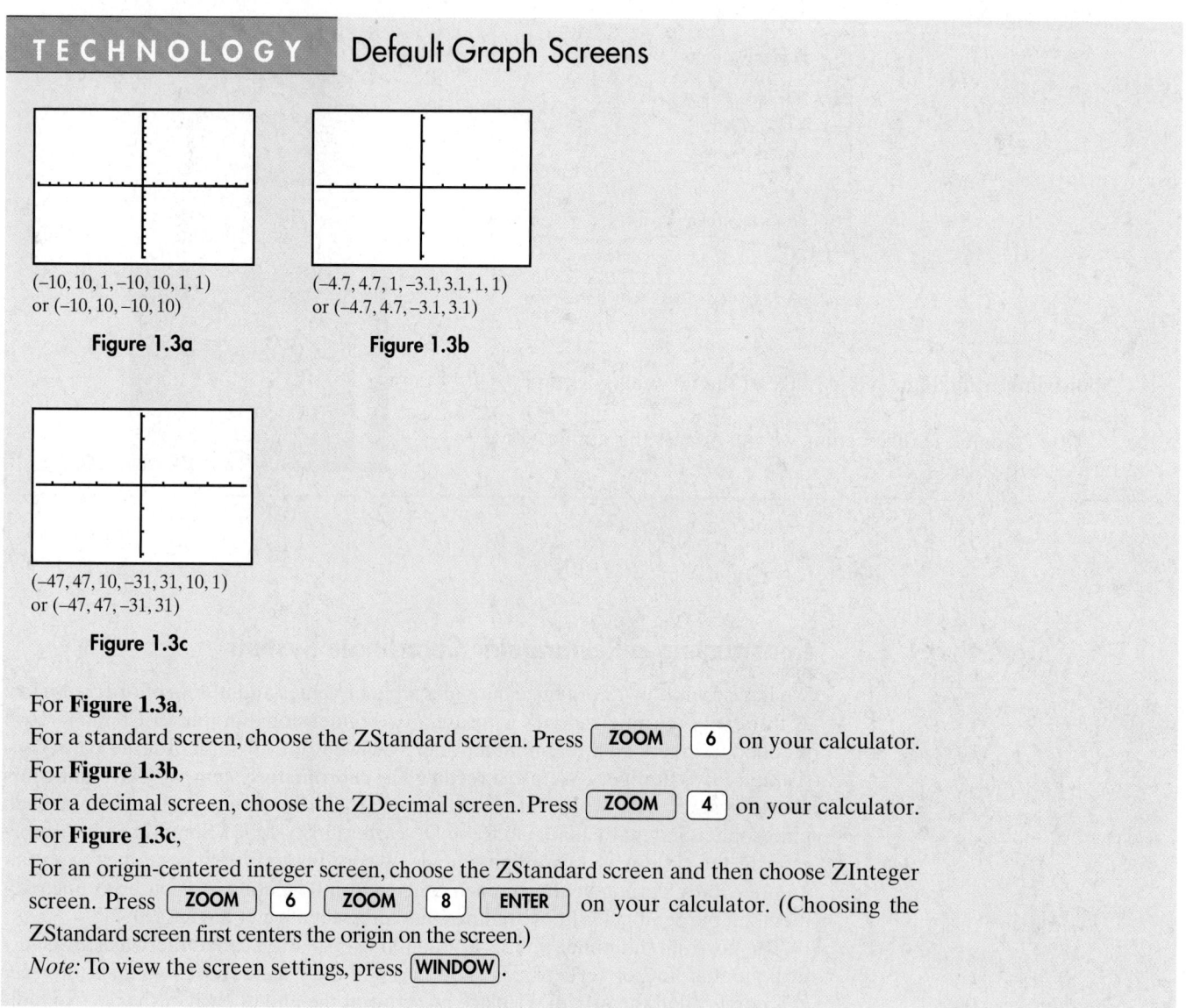

TECHNOLOGY   Default Graph Screens

(–10, 10, 1, –10, 10, 1, 1)
or (–10, 10, –10, 10)

Figure 1.3a

(–4.7, 4.7, 1, –3.1, 3.1, 1, 1)
or (–4.7, 4.7, –3.1, 3.1)

Figure 1.3b

(–47, 47, 10, –31, 31, 10, 1)
or (–47, 47, –31, 31)

Figure 1.3c

For **Figure 1.3a**,
For a standard screen, choose the ZStandard screen. Press [ZOOM] [6] on your calculator.
For **Figure 1.3b**,
For a decimal screen, choose the ZDecimal screen. Press [ZOOM] [4] on your calculator.
For **Figure 1.3c**,
For an origin-centered integer screen, choose the ZStandard screen and then choose ZInteger screen. Press [ZOOM] [6] [ZOOM] [8] [ENTER] on your calculator. (Choosing the ZStandard screen first centers the origin on the screen.)
Note: To view the screen settings, press [WINDOW].

The default screens may not give us a good view of the graph. We can change the default calculator settings to values of our choice. We not only can change the values on the axis, we can change the number of "tic" marks.
For example, set the screen to the following setting, as shown in **Figure 1.4b**:

(−20, 20, 10, −100, 100, 10, 1)

TECHNOLOGY Setting Graph Screens

Set the calculator graph screen to $(-20, 20, 10, -100, 100, 10, 1)$.

```
WINDOW
 Xmin=-20
 Xmax=20
 Xscl=10
 Ymin=-100
 Ymax=100
 Yscl=10
 Xres=1
```

Figure 1.4a   **Figure 1.4b**

For **Figure 1.4a**,
Press $\boxed{\text{WINDOW}}$ and your choice for each setting, followed by $\boxed{\text{ENTER.}}$
$\boxed{(\text{-})}$ $\boxed{2}$ $\boxed{0}$ $\boxed{\text{ENTER}}$ $\boxed{2}$ $\boxed{0}$ $\boxed{\text{ENTER}}$ $\boxed{1}$ $\boxed{0}$ $\boxed{\text{ENTER}}$ $\boxed{(\text{-})}$ $\boxed{1}$ $\boxed{0}$
$\boxed{0}$ $\boxed{\text{ENTER}}$ $\boxed{1}$ $\boxed{0}$ $\boxed{0}$ $\boxed{\text{ENTER}}$ $\boxed{1}$ $\boxed{0}$ $\boxed{\text{ENTER}}$

Note: In this text, the Xres value always equals 1.
For **Figure 1.4b**,
View the graph.
$\boxed{\text{GRAPH}}$

EXAMPLE 1

a. Construct a coordinate plane on graph paper, and label the x-axis from -4 to 4 and the y-axis from -3 to 3, both in increments of 1. This plane is similar to the decimal screen on your calculator. On your calculator, set up a default decimal screen.

b. Construct a coordinate plane on graph paper. Label the x-axis from -140 to 140 in increments of 30. Label the y-axis from -120 to 120 in increments of 40. On your calculator, set up the same window.

Solution

a.

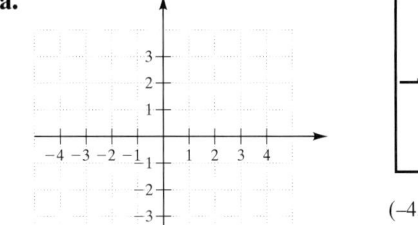 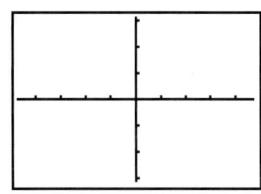

$(-4.7, 4.7, -3.1, 3.1)$

b.

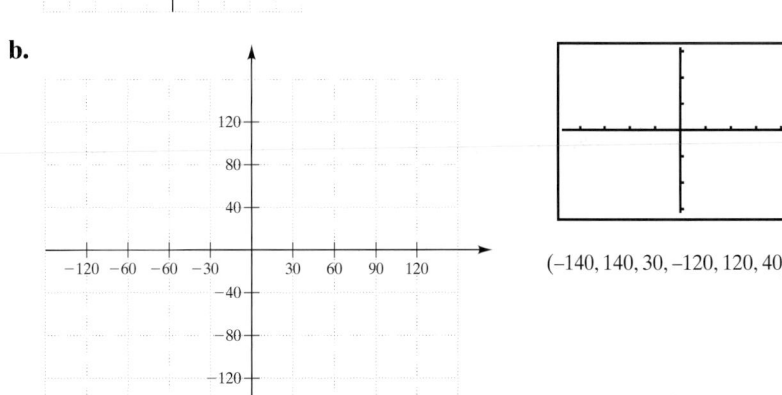

$(-140, 140, 30, -120, 120, 40)$

TAKE NOTE Be very careful to number the lines, not the spaces between the lines.

 ## Objective 1.2.1 *CHECKUP*

1. a. Construct a coordinate system on graph paper, and label the *x*-axis from −10 to 10 and the *y*-axis from −10 to 10, both in increments of 1 unit. To which default graph screen does this scale compare? On your calculator, set up the screen and check the window format to see that you have selected your scales correctly.

b. Construct a coordinate system on graph paper, and label the *x*-axis from −50 to 50 and the *y*-axis from −30 to 30, both in increments of 10 units. To which default graph screen does this scale compare? On your calculator, set up the screen and check the window format to see that you have selected your scales correctly.

2. Define each of the following terms:
a. coordinate plane
b. axes
c. origin
d. quadrants

3. List the default choices on your calculator for graphing within the Cartesian coordinate system and explain what each setting does for graphing.

Objective 1.2.2 — Graphing Relations

Locations in the coordinate plane are written as ordered pairs. The numbers in an ordered pair are called the **coordinates** of the point at that location. Each coordinate corresponds to the distance of the point from the *x*-axis or *y*-axis. The first number in the ordered pair is often called the **x-coordinate**. This corresponds to the distance of the point from the *y*-axis, which we measure along the *x*-axis. Similarly, the second number in the ordered pair is often called the **y-coordinate**, which corresponds to the distance of the point from the *x*-axis, as measured along the *y*-axis.

> To graph an ordered pair (or plot a point), we place a dot at its location on the coordinate plane.
>
> - First, locate the *x*-coordinate on the *x*-axis.
> - Second, locate the *y*-coordinate on the *y*-axis.
> - Place a dot at the intersection of the two lines that are perpendicular to the axes and that go through these locations on the axes.
> - Label the point with its name or coordinates.

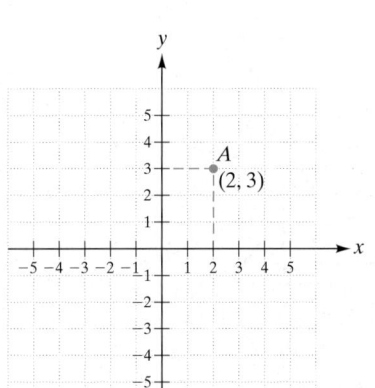

For example, to graph the ordered pair *A*(2, 3), locate the *x*-coordinate, 2, on the *x*-axis and the *y*-coordinate, 3, on the *y*-axis. The intersection of the two lines through these locations is the location of the dot for the ordered pair (2, 3). Label the point by its name, *A*.

EXAMPLE 2 Graph and label each set of ordered pairs on a coordinate plane. Note the difference in the locations of the pairs of points.

a. *A*(1, 3) and *B*(3, 1)

b. *C*(−2, 3) and *D*(3, −2)

c. *E*(2, 0) and *F*(0, 2)

Solution

a.

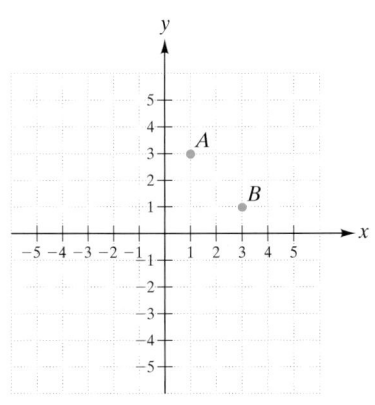

b.

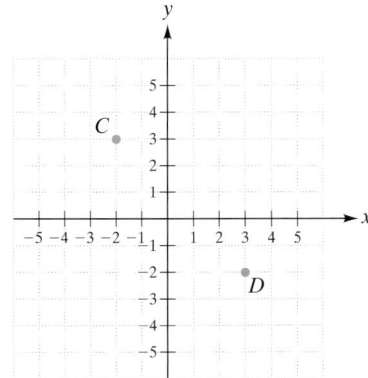

c.

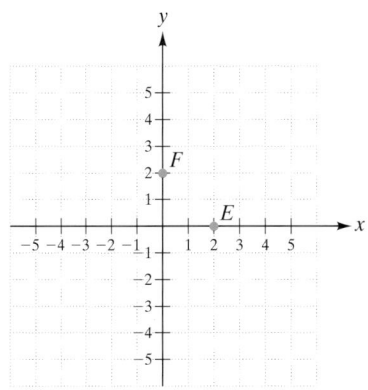

EXAMPLE 3   Using the given graph, state the coordinates of the points shown.

Solution

$$A(0, 5) \quad B(6, 8) \quad C(-3, -4) \quad D(-4, 0)$$
$$E(7, 0) \quad F(-6, 3) \quad G(0, -2) \quad H(5, -2)$$

At times it may be necessary to locate a point in the coordinate plane approximately, without actually plotting it. In such cases, it is useful to know how the coordinates of points vary from one quadrant to another and what coordinates correspond to points located on the axes. Complete the following sets of exercises on your calculator.

Guided Discovery 1   Signs of the Coordinates in Each Quadrant

Set your calculator to the integer screen setting. Use your arrow keys to locate five points in each of the four quadrants. Note that the coordinates of the points are displayed on the screen. Write the ordered pairs.

Write a rule for a condition on the signs of the coordinates in each quadrant.

In quadrant I, both coordinates are positive; in quadrant II, the *x*-coordinate is negative and the *y*-coordinate is positive; in quadrant III, both coordinates are negative; and in quadrant IV, the *x*-coordinate is positive and the *y*-coordinate is negative.

Guided Discovery 2   Location of the Zero Coordinate on the Axes

Set your calculator to the integer screen setting. Use your arrow keys to locate five points on each of the axes. Write the ordered pairs.

Write a rule for a condition on the numbers in an ordered pair for any point on the *x*-axis or the *y*-axis.

On the *x*-axis, the *y*-coordinate is always 0, and on the *y*-axis, the *x*-coordinate is always 0.

SIGNS OF COORDINATES IN THE PLANE

In quadrant I, the x-coordinate is always positive and the y-coordinate is always positive. $(+, +)$

In quadrant II, the x-coordinate is always negative and the y-coordinate is always positive. $(-, +)$

In quadrant III, the x-coordinate is always negative and the y-coordinate is always negative. $(-, -)$

In quadrant IV, the x-coordinate is always positive and the y-coordinate is always negative. $(+, -)$

On the x-axis, the y-coordinate is always 0. $(x, 0)$

On the y-axis, the x-coordinate is always 0. $(0, y)$

EXAMPLE 4

Determine the location of the following points by quadrant or by axis:

a. $(24, 39)$ **b.** $(-24, 39)$ **c.** $(24, -39)$ **d.** $(-24, -39)$

e. $(0, 39)$ **f.** $(-24, 0)$ **g.** $(0, 0)$

Solution

a. quadrant I   Coordinates are $(+, +)$.

b. quadrant II   Coordinates are $(-, +)$.

c. quadrant IV   Coordinates are $(+, -)$.

d. quadrant III   Coordinates are $(-, -)$.

e. y-axis   The x-coordinate is 0.

f. x-axis   The y-coordinate is 0.

g. x-axis and y-axis (origin)   The x-coordinate and the y-coordinate are both 0.

Now we know how to locate a point, represented by an ordered pair, on the coordinate plane. Our next step is to graph a set of ordered pairs—that is, a relation—on the coordinate plane. In fact, since we have shown how to represent a relation by a set of ordered pairs, a table of values, or an equation, we can graph any of these forms in the same fashion.

To graph a relation in list form,

- Plot each ordered pair in the relation.

To graph a relation in table form,

- Write a set of ordered pairs and plot each ordered pair.

EXAMPLE 5

Graph each relation.

a. $A = \{(1, 1), (1, 2), (1, 3)\}$

b.

x	y
-10	-20
-5	-10
0	0
5	10
10	20

Solution

a. Plot each ordered pair.

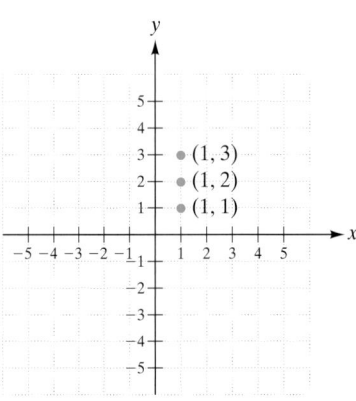

b. Plot the set of ordered pairs from the table.

$\{(-10, -20), (-5, -10), (0, 0), (5, 10), (10, 20)\}$

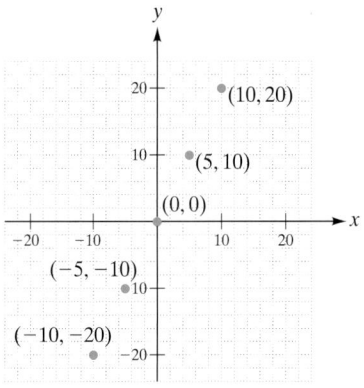

To graph a relation in equation form if the domain is given,

- Set up a table of values for the given domain.
- Plot the set of ordered pairs that the table determines.

To graph a relation in equation form if the domain is not given,

- Choose values for the independent variable that will result in a real-number value for the dependent variable. This will determine a sample of the possible ordered pairs.
- Plot the set of ordered pairs that the equation determines.

EXAMPLE 6

Graph each relation.

a. $y = 2x$ for $x = 1, 2, 3$ **b.** $y = 2x + 3$

Solution

a. In order to graph the relation $y = 2x$ for $x = 1, 2, 3$, we set up a table of values and graph the ordered pairs.

x	$y = 2x$	y
1	$y = 2(1)$	2
2	$y = 2(2)$	4
3	$y = 2(3)$	6

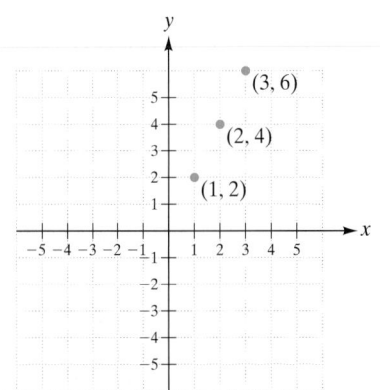

TAKE NOTE In Example 6a, we are given 3 values for x, and we determine a finite set of ordered pairs for the relation. The graph will be the 3 ordered pairs.

b. If a relation is represented by an equation such as $y = 2x + 3$ and the values for x are not given, we find a set of sample ordered pairs. We choose values for x in the domain of the relation. For example, we can choose $x = 1, 1.25, 1\frac{1}{2}$, and 2 and set up a table of values.

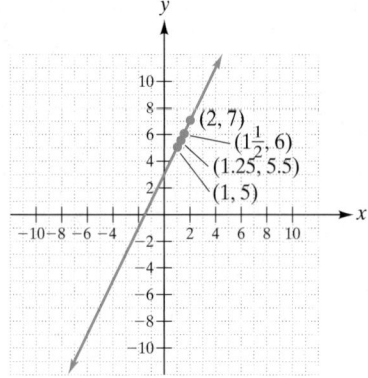

x	$y = 2x + 3$	y
1	$y = 2(1) + 3$	5
1.25	$y = 2(1.25) + 3$	5.5
$1\frac{1}{2}$	$y = 2\left(1\frac{1}{2}\right) + 3$	6
2	$y = 2(2) + 3$	7

When we graph the sample ordered pairs, we see a straight line being formed. In fact, if we could graph all the ordered pairs that satisfy this relation, a solid line would be formed. Therefore, to complete the graph of the relation, draw a line through the sample points. An arrow indicates that the pattern continues. ■

 TAKE NOTE In Example 6b, we are not given values for x. We chose values from the domain and determined a pattern for the graph. The ordered pairs that we determine are in the infinite set of possible ordered pairs. The graph is the set of all possible ordered pair solutions, and we connect the ordered pairs graphed to determine this.

Our calculator is designed to graph relations such as $y = 2x + 3$.

TECHNOLOGY   Graph a Relation

Graph the relation $y = 2x + 3$.

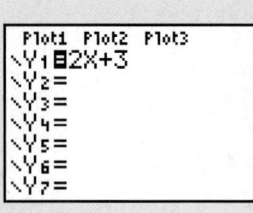

Figure 1.5a

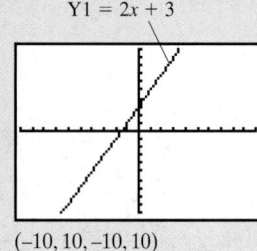

$(-10, 10, -10, 10)$

Figure 1.5b

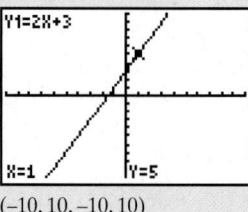

$(-10, 10, -10, 10)$

Figure 1.5c

For **Figure 1.5a,**
Enter the equation into the calculator in the Y = menu.

For **Figure 1.5b,**
Set the calculator to the desired screen setting and graph.
We will use the default standard screen.

[ZOOM] [6]

For **Figure 1.5c**,
To view the points on the graph, we trace the graph and use the left and right arrow keys to move along the graph. To see the coordinates of a point that is not traced, enter the value of the independent variable, and then press ⟨ **ENTER** ⟩. For example, we graphed the point $(1, 5)$ in Example 6b.

⟨ **TRACE** ⟩ ⟨ **1** ⟩ ⟨ **ENTER** ⟩

Not all relations will graph as lines. Some will graph as smooth curves. Viewing a graph on the calculator will help us determine the number of ordered pairs that are needed to draw curves for these relations. There is no magic number, so we will have to judge each relation individually. In this chapter, you will be given a window setting to use in your calculator. However, you should become familiar with the shape of the curve that certain equations graph, because in later chapters you will need to choose a window setting for yourself.

EXAMPLE 7   Graph $y = x^2 + 2x - 8$.

Solution

If we view the curve graphed by the relation on the calculator, we see that a minimum of five points would suggest the curve. We will need to trace the graph or look at the table of values in order to graph this relation.

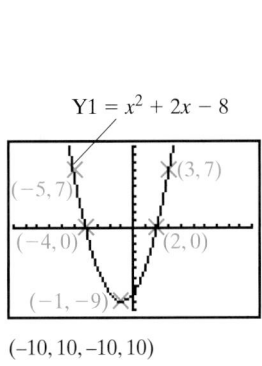

$(-10, 10, -10, 10)$

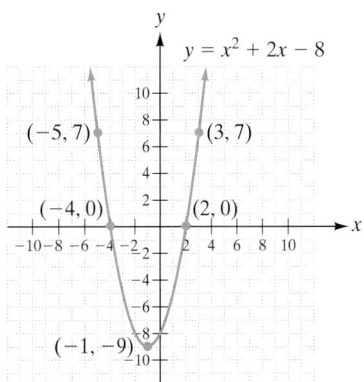

Objective 1.2.2 **CHECKUP**

1. Graph and label each set of ordered pairs on a coordinate plane.
   a. $E(-5, -6)$ and $F(-6, -5)$
   b. $G(3, -3)$ and $H(-3, 3)$
   c. $I(0, -3)$, $J(-3, 0)$

2. State the coordinates of the points graphed in **Figure 1.6**.

3. Determine the location of each point by quadrant or by axis.
   a. $(-16, 95)$ **e.** $(0, 0)$
   b. $(123, 135)$ **f.** $(-3.6, 0)$
   c. $(0.001, -1.009)$ **g.** $\left(0, \dfrac{2}{9}\right)$
   d. $\left(-3\dfrac{1}{3}, -2\dfrac{1}{5}\right)$

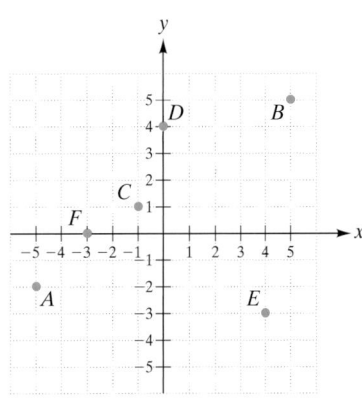

Figure 1.6

In exercises 4–6, graph each relation.

4. a. $R = \{(-2, 1), (0, 1), (3, 1), (7, 1)\}$

   b.

x	y
-3	-9
-2	-6
-1	-3
0	0

5. a. $y = -2x$ for $x = -2, 0, 2$

   b. $y = -3x + 5$

6. $y = 10 - 3x - x^2$

7. In exercise 1, what is the effect of swapping the two values of the coordinate pair? What is the effect of having a negative sign on the x-coordinate? What is the effect of having a negative sign on the y-coordinate?

8. When do we connect the points plotted to determine a graph for a relation?

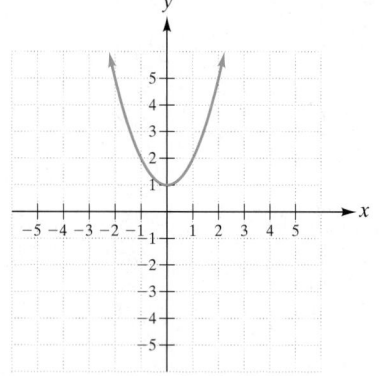

Figure 1.7

Objective 1.2.3   Identifying the Domain and Range

We can determine the domain and range of a relation directly from its graph.

To determine the domain of a relation from its graph, examine the graph to see what values of the independent variable (the x-coordinates) are used to draw the graph.

To determine the range of a relation from its graph, write a set of values of the dependent variable (the y-coordinates) used in the graph.

For example, determine the domain and range of the relation whose graph is shown in **Figure 1.7**.

We see that the graph includes points for every possible value of x, as indicated in the following diagram:

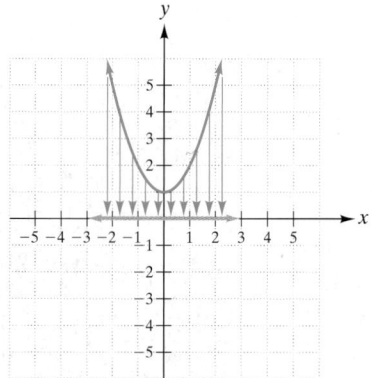

Thus, the domain is the set of all real numbers.

We see that the possible y-values are all greater than or equal to 1 ($y \geq 1$), as indicated in the following diagram:

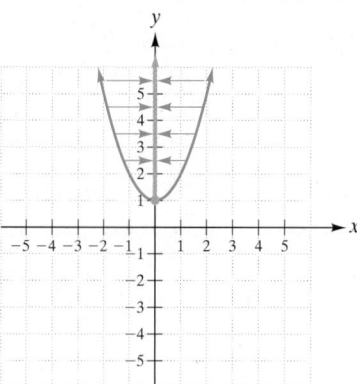

Thus, the range is the set of all real numbers y greater than or equal to 1.

EXAMPLE 8   Determine the domain and range of each relation.

a.
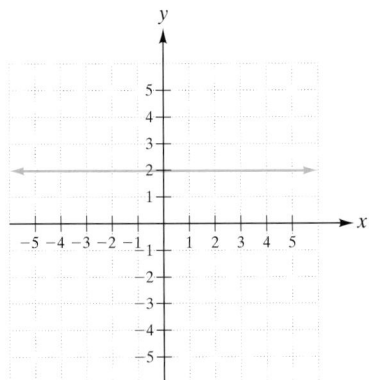

b.
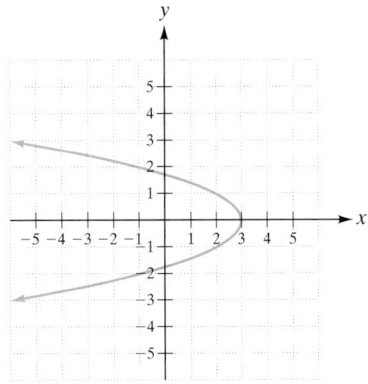

c.
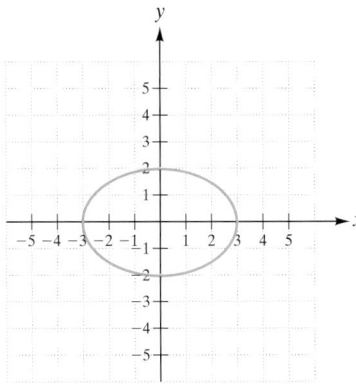

Solution

a.

Domain	Range
The domain is the set of all real numbers	$y = 2$ The range is the set {2}.

b.

Domain	Range
$x \le 3$ The domain is the set of all real numbers less than or equal to 3.	The range is the set of all real numbers.

c.

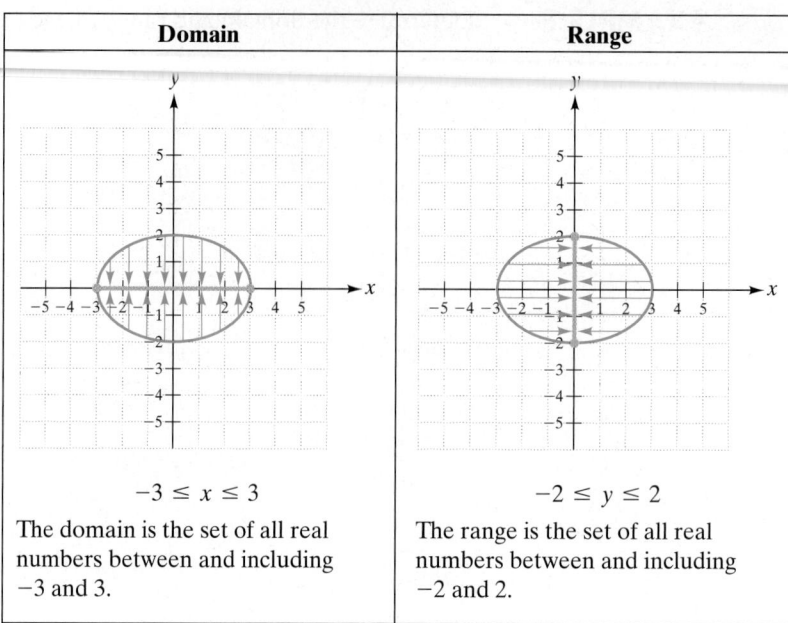

Domain	Range
$-3 \leq x \leq 3$	$-2 \leq y \leq 2$
The domain is the set of all real numbers between and including -3 and 3.	The range is the set of all real numbers between and including -2 and 2.

✓ Objective 1.2.3 *CHECKUP*

Determine the domain and range of each relation.

1.

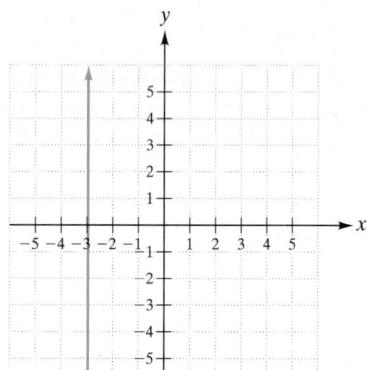

2.

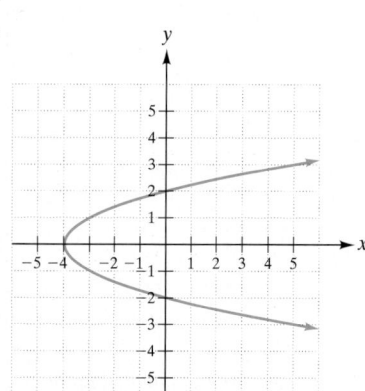

3.

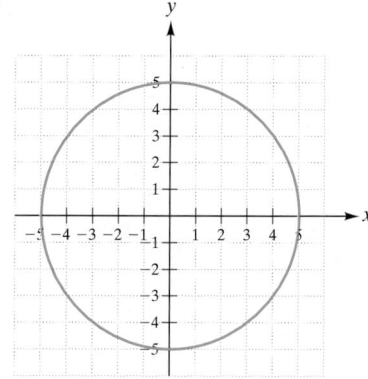

Objective 1.2.4 Modeling the Real World

Many important relations are found in business, science, and social studies—in fact, in almost any area of activity. Graphs are an important tool to help us visualize these relations. However, you should be aware that real situations sometimes impose restrictions on the domain and range of relations. For example, if the independent variable represents time or the number of units sold, then the domain must be limited to nonnegative numbers. If the dependent variable represents cost or height above the ground, then the range must be limited to nonnegative numbers.

EXAMPLE 9

Buddy dropped a pair of pliers from the top of a 30-foot power pole.

a. A relation for the height in feet above ground level of the pliers, s, in terms of time, t, in seconds, is given by $s = -16t^2 + 30$. Graph this relation as $Y1 = -16x^2 + 30$, using $(-2, 2, 1, -30, 30, 10, 1)$ as the graphing window on your calculator.

b. Approximate the domain and range of the relation.

Solution

a.

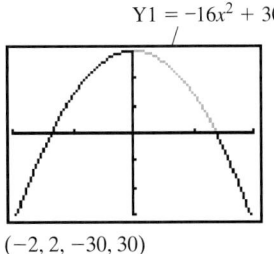

$$Y1 = -16x^2 + 30$$

$(-2, 2, -30, 30)$

b. The independent variable is time, *t*, so it must be nonnegative. The dependent variable, *s*, is height above the ground, so it must also be nonnegative. If we trace the function and view the *t*-values, we see that $0 \le t \le 1.4$ or the domain is the set of all real numbers greater than or equal to 0 and less than or equal to approximately 1.4. If we trace the function and view the *s*-values, we see that $0 \le s \le 30$ or the range is the set of all real numbers greater than or equal to 0 and less than or equal to 30.

APPLICATION

The following graph illustrates the revenue from sales, cost of sales, and gross operating profit for General Motors in the years 1996 through 2003:

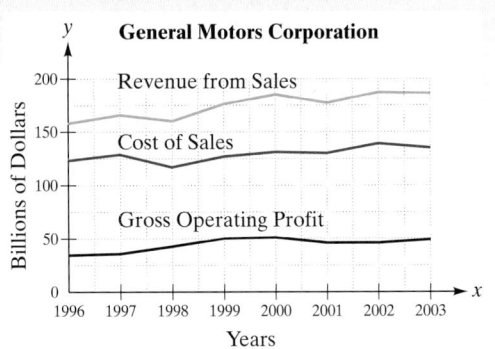

Approximate the domain and range of the revenue, cost, and profit.

Discussion

The domain of the revenue, cost, and profit is {1996, 1997, 1998, 1999, 2000, 2001, 2002, 2003}.

The range of the revenue from sales is the set of all real numbers *y* such that $160 \le y \le 180$. The range of the cost of sales is the set of all real numbers *y* such that $120 \le y \le 140$. The range of the gross operating profit is the set of all real numbers *y* such that $30 \le y \le 50$.

Objective 1.2.4 *CHECKUP*

1. A toy rocket is shot upward from ground level with an initial velocity of 250 feet per second.
   a. A relation for the height in feet above ground level of the rocket, *s*, in terms of time, *t*, in seconds, is given by $s = -16t^2 + 250t$. Graph the relation using $(-20, 20, 5, -1000, 1000, 100, 1)$ as the graphing window on your calculator.
   b. Approximate the domain and range of the relation.
2. The following graph illustrates the revenue from sales, cost of sales, and gross operating profit for Amazon.com in the years 1998 through 2003. Approximate the domain and range of the revenue, cost, and profit.

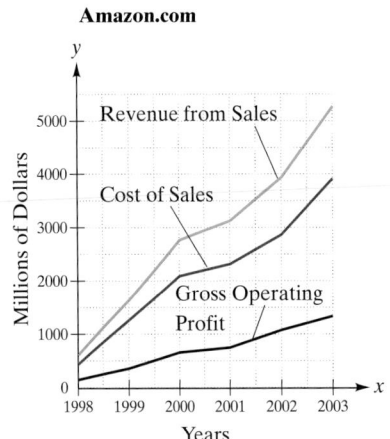

1.2 EXERCISES

Student Solutions Manual   PH Math/Tutor Center   CD Video   MathXL®   MyMathLab   Interactmath.com

Graph and label each ordered pair on a coordinate plane.

1. $A(-7, -5)$ and $B(-5, -7)$ **2.** $C(-2, -4)$ and $D(-4, -2)$ **3.** $E(4, 9)$ and $F(9, 4)$

4. $G(2, 6)$ and $H(6, 2)$ **5.** $I(-5, 5)$ and $J(5, -5)$ **6.** $K(-4, 4)$ and $L(4, -4)$

7. $M(2, -1)$ and $N(-1, 2)$ **8.** $O(3, -4)$ and $P(-4, 3)$ **9.** $Q(3, -1)$ and $R(-3, 1)$

10. $S(2, -7)$ and $T(-2, 7)$ **11.** $U(-8, -2)$ and $V(8, 2)$ **12.** $W(3, 5)$ and $X(-3, -5)$

13. $A(1.2, 2.4)$ **14.** $B(3.4, 1.2)$ **15.** $C(-4.5, -2.6)$

16. $D(-3.6, -2.5)$ **17.** $E(-2.4, 2.1)$ **18.** $F(4.1, -2.4)$

19. $G(1.8, -2.7)$ **20.** $H(-2.7, 1.8)$

Determine the location of each point by quadrant or by axis. Do not graph the point.

21. $(-21, 35)$ **22.** $(-33, -35)$ **23.** $(4, 96)$

24. $(28, -92)$ **25.** $(-3, -19)$ **26.** $(-75, 22)$

27. $(0, -31)$ **28.** $(94, 0)$ **29.** $(90, -100)$

30. $(2, 29)$ **31.** $(24, 0)$ **32.** $(0, -36)$

33. $(-19, 0)$ **34.** $(0, 0)$ **35.** $(0.05, 1.003)$

36. $(-2.09, 8.6)$ **37.** $(0, 3.7)$ **38.** $(-9.3, 0)$

39. $\left(\dfrac{13}{27}, -\dfrac{11}{19}\right)$ **40.** $\left(-\dfrac{57}{105}, -\dfrac{17}{21}\right)$ **41.** $\left(-\dfrac{53}{100}, -\dfrac{39}{100}\right)$

42. $\left(\dfrac{20}{33}, 0\right)$ **43.** $\left(0, \dfrac{28}{51}\right)$ **44.** $\left(3\dfrac{1}{7}, -1\dfrac{4}{5}\right)$

45. State the coordinates of the points graphed in **Figure 1.8**.

46. State the coordinates of the points graphed in **Figure 1.9**.

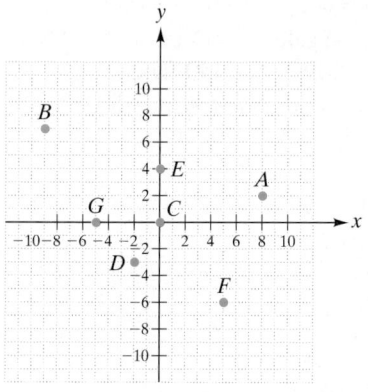

Figure 1.8

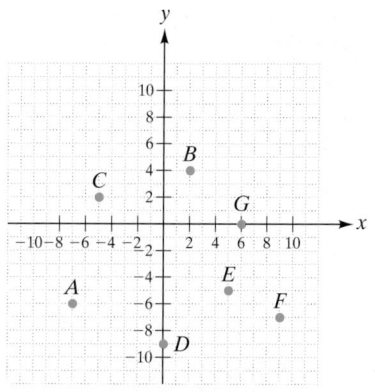

Figure 1.9

In exercises 47–68, graph each relation.

47. $A = \{(-3, -3), (-2, -2), (-1, -1), (0, 0), (1, 1), (2, 2), (3, 3)\}$

48. $B = \{(-2.5, -2), (-1.5, -1), (-0.5, 0), (0.5, 1), (1.5, 2)\}$

49. $C = \{(-4, 4), (-2, 2), (0, 0), (2, -2), (4, -4)\}$

50. $D = \{(0, 2), (1, 3), (2, 4), (3, 5), (4, 6)\}$

51. $E = \{(5, -3), (5, -1), (5, 1), (5, 3)\}$

52. $F = \{(-4, -2), (-2, -2), (0, -2), (2, -2), (4, -2)\}$

53.

x	y
−2	−1
−1	0
0	1
1	2
2	3

54.

x	y
−2	3
−1	2
0	1
1	0
2	−1

55.

x	y
−2	−6
−1	−5
0	−4
1	−3
2	−2
3	−1

56.

x	y
−4	−2
−2	−1
0	0
2	1
4	2

57. $y = 12x - 15$ for $x = -1, 0, 1$

58. $y = 14x$ for $x = -2, -1, 1, 2$

59. $y = \dfrac{1}{2}x + 3$ for $x = -4, -2, 0, 2, 4$

60. $y = -\dfrac{3}{4}x + 5$ for $x = -8, -4, 0, 4, 8$

61. $y = -10x + 9$ **62.** $y = -x - 1$

63. $y = -\dfrac{2}{3}x - 2$ **64.** $y = \dfrac{2}{5}x + \dfrac{1}{5}$

65. $y = 2x^2 - 5$ **66.** $y = -3x^2 - 1$

67. $y = |2x|$ **68.** $y = |-4x|$

Determine the domain and the range of each relation.

69.

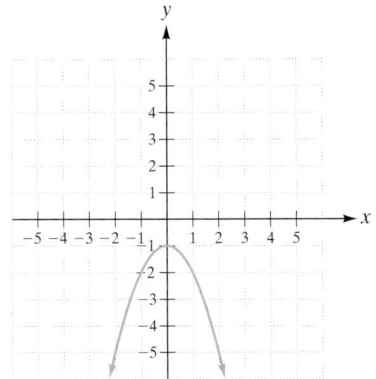

70.

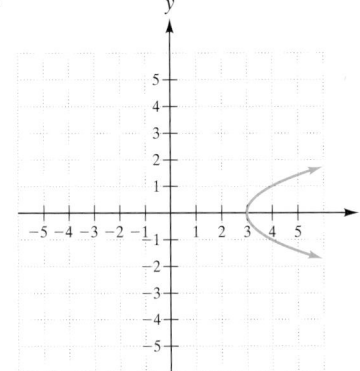

71.

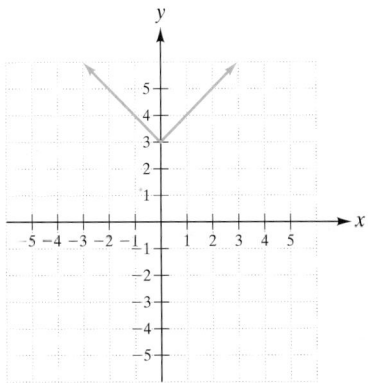

72.

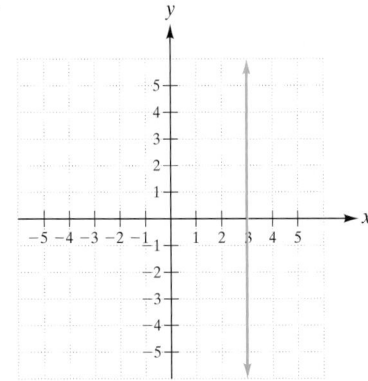

73. Many students do not apply for college financial aid because of a misconception that their parents "make too much money." A U.S. Department of Education, National Center for Educational Statistics report, the *National Postsecondary Student Aid Study*, relates percentages of dependent students receiving aid to the income level of their parents for 2003–2004. ($x = 1$, parent income $< \$20,000$; $x = 2$, parent income $\$20,000$–$\$39,999$; ... $x = 6$, parent income $> \$100,000$) The data are shown in the following figure.

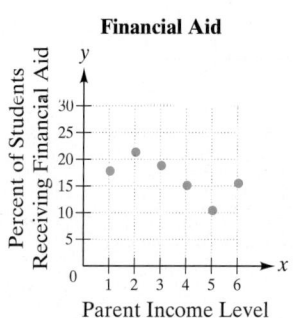

Financial Aid

Determine the domain and range of the relation.

74. A quality-control engineer recorded the numbers of nondefective parts coming off an assembly line that produced 75 parts per day. The data for each day are shown in the following figure:

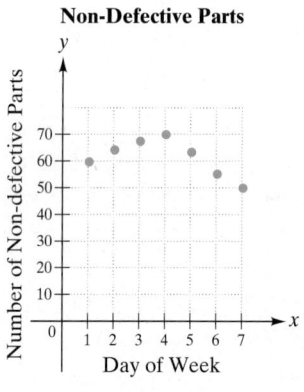

Non-Defective Parts

Determine the domain and range of the relation.

75. The following graph shows violent crime rates of forcible rape and murder in the United States for the years 1993 through 2002, where x is the number of years since 1993. Determine the domain and range of the graphs.

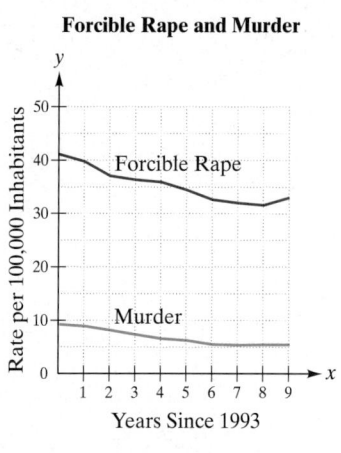

Forcible Rape and Murder

76. The following graph shows violent crime rates of aggravated assault and robbery in the United States for the years 1993 through 2002, where x is the number of years since 1993. Determine the domain and range of the graphs.

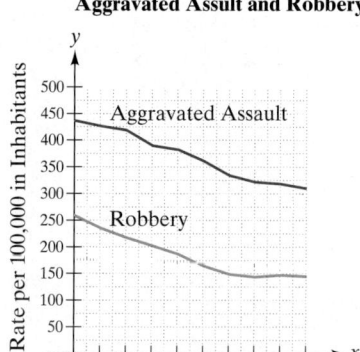

Aggravated Assult and Robbery

77. The following graph shows higher education costs in the United States in thousands of dollars for the school years 1996–2002, where x is the number of years after 1996:

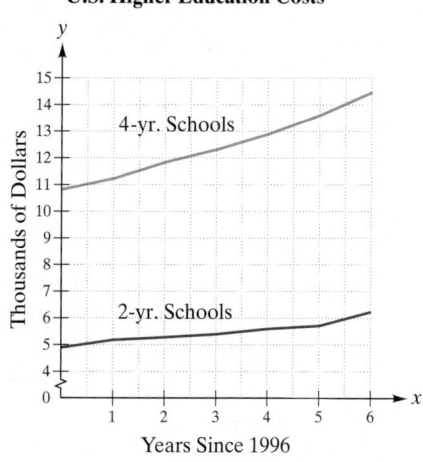

U.S. Higher Education Costs

a. Determine the domain and range for the relation involving 4-year schools.

b. Determine the domain and range for the relation involving 2-year schools.

78. The United States has an aging population. The following graph shows the percent of the U.S. population of varying ages, where x is the number of years since 1950:

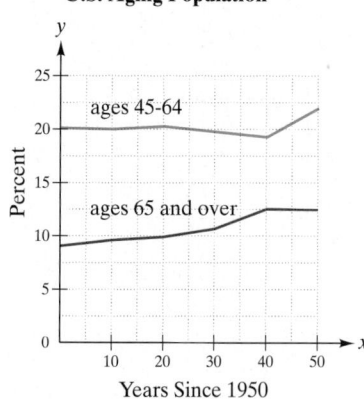

U.S. Aging Population

a. Determine the domain and range if the relation of interest is the age group 45–64.

b. Determine the domain and range if the relation of interest is the age group 65 and over.

79. An egg is dropped from a height of 100 feet.

a. A relation for the height in feet above ground level of the egg, s, in terms of time, t, in seconds, is given by $s = -16t^2 + 100$. Graph the relation, using $(-4.7, 4.7, 1, -124, 124, 40, 1)$ as the graphing window on your calculator.

b. State the domain and range of the relation.

80. A pendulum has a length of x feet.

a. A relation for the period, T, in seconds required for one complete back-and-forth swing of the pendulum is given by $T = 2\pi\sqrt{\dfrac{x}{32}}$. Graph the relation, using $(-4.7, 4.7, 1, -3.1, 3.1, 1, 1)$ as the graphing window on your calculator.

b. State the domain and range of the relation.

1.2 Calculator Exercises

Part 1. Comparing View Screens on the Calculator

To give you an idea of what the various screen settings on a calculator mean, first draw a coordinate plane on a large sheet of graph paper. Place the origin of the coordinate system in the middle of the graph paper, and mark the x-axis in units of 5 from -50 to 50. Also, mark the y-axis in units of 5 from -35 to 35. Make the graph as large as the paper will allow. You will use this graph to draw boxes for the various calculator settings.

Clear the [Y=] screen. Then set your calculator to the decimal setting, ZDecimal, option 4.

Press [WINDOW] to view the setting's limits. Plot the limits on the graph and draw a box. This box represents the portion of a graphed relation you can view with the current setting.

Now set the calculator to the standard setting, ZStandard, option 6. Press [WINDOW] to view this setting's limits. Plot the limits on the same graph and draw another box. This box represents the portion of a graphed relation you can view with the current setting. You should see that you can view much more of a graphed relation with this setting.

Next, set the calculator to the integer setting, ZInteger, option 8. Be sure to press [ENTER] after choosing option 8, in order to move to the new setting. Press [WINDOW] to view this setting's limits. Plot these limits on the same graph and draw a third box. This box represents the portion of a graphed relation you can view with the current setting. Once again, you should see that you can view much more of a graphed relation with this setting.

So if you use a larger setting, you see more of a graph. However, if you use a smaller setting, you may see more detail in a smaller portion of the graph. It's up to you to become familiar enough with these settings in order to make a decision regarding which setting you should use. Be aware that there are other settings you can use. You can set the screen to any setting you choose, and you can also zoom in or zoom out on a setting to see more detail or more of the graph. Try the various settings on the following equations, and decide which is best for viewing them:

1. $y = 2x - 3$

2. $y = 2x^2 - 3x + 1$

3. $y = 2x^3 - 3x^2 + x - 4$

Part 2. Transferring Graphs from the Calculator to Paper

Set your calculator screen to the decimal setting. Then graph the following relations on this setting:

1. $y = 0.6x - 1.2$ **2.** $y = -0.5x + 2.2$

3. $y = |x| - 2$ **4.** $y = |x - 2|$

5. $y = x - 2$

Find the coordinate pairs for each relation using the domain $\{-2, -1, 0, 1, 2\}$. Now plot the points on graph paper, using the coordinate plane. Then sketch the graph connecting these points.

6. Consider the keystrokes needed to enter exercises 3–5 into your calculator. What is the important difference that distinguishes these three exercises? Pay attention to this important difference as you use this calculator method.

1.2 Writing Exercise

In this section, you learned that sometimes a graph is a finite set of points and at other times the graph is an infinite set of points represented by a curve. Explain what must be true about the domain and range of the relation for each type of graph. In your explanation, give an example of a relation that yields each type of graph.

1.3 FUNCTIONS AND FUNCTION NOTATION

OBJECTIVES

1 Determine whether relations written in list form are functions.
2 Determine whether relations represented as graphs are functions.
3 Evaluate functions written in function notation.
4 Use real-world data to determine functions.

APPLICATION

Using data from the 2000–2003 cnd-of the year reports, financial analysts for General Motors determined that the company's profit, in billions of dollars, could be determined by the function $P(x) = 2.25x^2 - 7.65x + 51.85$ for x years after 2000. Estimate the amount of profit for the year 2003.

After completing this section, we will discuss this application further. See page 158.

Objective 1.3.1

Identifying Functions from Ordered Pairs

A function is a special type of relation that we frequently use in mathematics. A **function** is a relation in which every element in the domain corresponds to one and only one element in the range.

A relation

$$M = \{(1, 2), (2, 4), (3, 5), (4, 6)\}$$

written in list form, is a function, because we match every element in the domain, $\{1, 2, 3, 4\}$, to only one element in the range, $\{2, 4, 5, 6\}$.

Domain	**Range**
(Independent variable values)	(Dependent variable values)

1 ⟶ 2
2 ⟶ 4
3 ⟶ 5
4 ⟶ 6

A relation

$$N = \{(1, 2), (1, 3), (2, 4)\}$$

written in list form, is not a function, because we match one element, 1, in the domain $\{1, 2\}$ to more than one element, 2 and 3, in the range $\{2, 3, 4\}$.

Domain	**Range**

1 ⟶ 2
⟶ 3
2 ⟶ 4

EXAMPLE 1

Determine whether each relation is a function.

a. $\{(-5, -10), (-3, -6), (3, 6), (5, 10)\}$
b. $\{(3, 6), (-3, 6), (5, 10), (-5, 10)\}$
c. $\{(3, 6), (3, -6), (5, 10), (5, -10)\}$

Solution

a. Domain   **Range**

$-5 \longrightarrow -10$

$-3 \longrightarrow -6$

$3 \longrightarrow 6$

$5 \longrightarrow 10$

$\{(-5, -10), (-3, -6), (3, 6), (5, 10)\}$ is a function, because every element in the domain corresponds to only one element in the range. The first coordinate is not repeated in the set of ordered pairs.

b. Domain   **Range**

$\begin{array}{l} 3 \\ -3 \end{array} \longrightarrow 6$

$\begin{array}{l} 5 \\ -5 \end{array} \longrightarrow 10$

$\{(3, 6), (-3, 6), (5, 10), (-5, 10)\}$ is a function, because every element in the domain corresponds to only one element in the range. The first coordinate is not repeated in the set of ordered pairs. The repeated elements in the range, 6 and 10, do not matter.

c. Domain   **Range**

$3 \longrightarrow \begin{array}{l} 6 \\ -6 \end{array}$

$5 \longrightarrow \begin{array}{l} 10 \\ -10 \end{array}$

$\{(3, 6), (3, -6), (5, 10), (5, -10)\}$ is not a function, because an element in the domain, 3, corresponds to two elements in the range, 6 and -6. The first coordinate, 3, is repeated in the set of ordered pairs. Likewise, the element 5 in the domain corresponds to two elements in the range. ◼

✓ Objective 1.3.1 *CHECKUP*

1. Determine whether each relation is a function.
   a. $A = \{(-2, 3), (-1, 5), (0, 7), (1, 5), (2, 3)\}$
   b. $B = \{(-3, 5), (-1, 5), (1, 5), (3, 5)\}$
   c. $D = \{(2, -1), (2, 0), (2, 1), (2, 2)\}$

2. What should you look for in a relation to determine whether the relation is a function?

Objective 1.3.2   ## Identifying Functions from Graphs

Relations are sometimes represented as graphs. Therefore, a function may be represented as a graph. We need to determine a method for deciding whether a relation represented as a graph is a function. Complete the following set of exercises.

Guided Discovery 3 Graphs of Functions

The following are graphs of functions:

1.

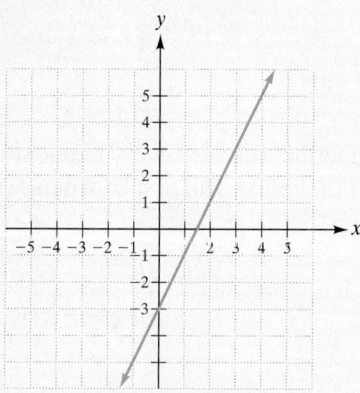

2.

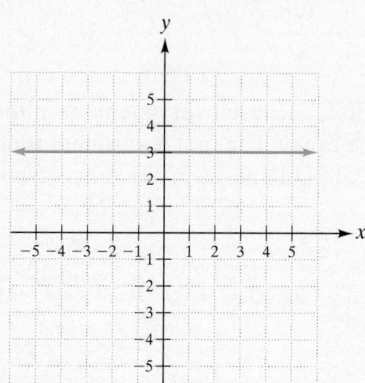

3.

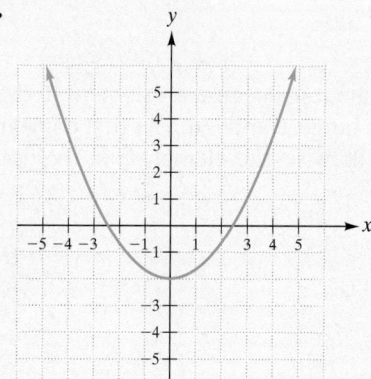

4.

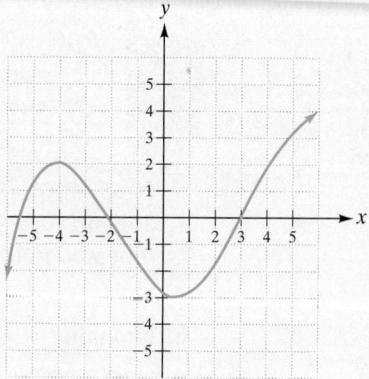

If possible, draw a vertical line through more than one point on the graph.

Write a rule for determining a function from the graph of a relation by drawing a line through points on the graph.

Check your rule on the following two graphs of relations that are not functions:

5.

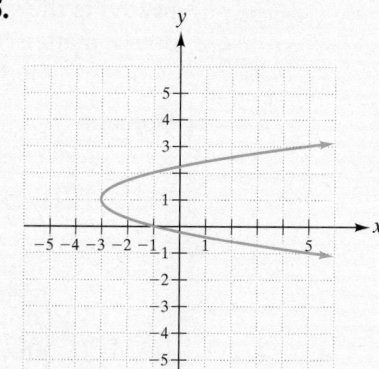

6.

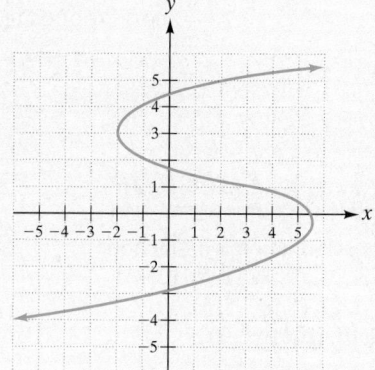

In the set of functions, a vertical line does not cross the graph of a function more than once. In the check, we see that a vertical line crossed the graphs of the relations that were not functions more than once.

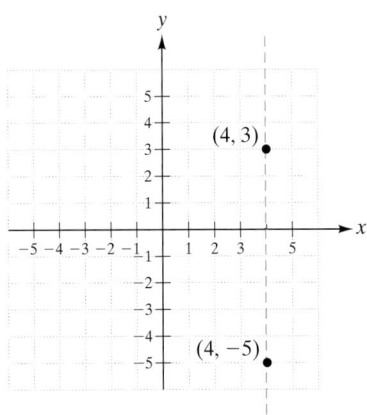

VERTICAL-LINE TEST

If a vertical line can be drawn such that it intersects the graph of a relation more than once, the graph does not represent a function. If every possible vertical line intersects the graph only once, then the graph represents a function.

We know that this rule is a valid test because if we graph two distinct ordered pairs with the same x-coordinate, they will lie on the same vertical line, and a function does not have two ordered pairs with the same x-coordinate. For example, graph the relation $\{(4, 3), (4, -5)\}$, which is not a function.

Examples of applying the vertical-line test are given in the following figures:

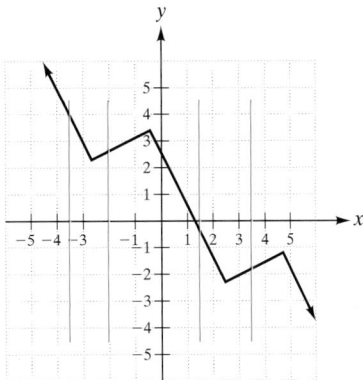

This graph represents a function. All possible vertical lines cross the graph only once.

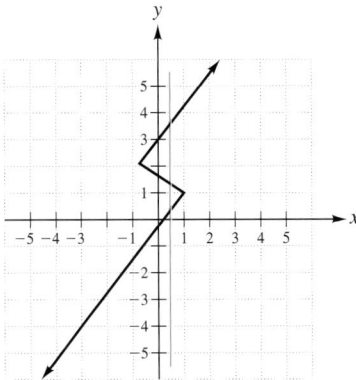

This graph does not represent a function. The vertical line drawn is one of many such lines that cross the graph more than once.

EXAMPLE 2

Determine whether each graph represents a function.

a.

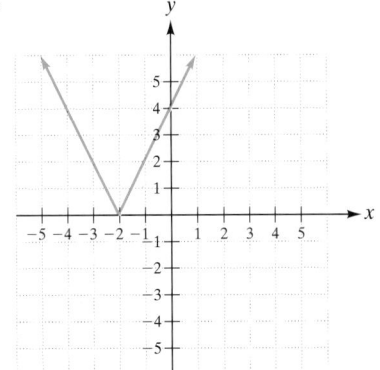

b.

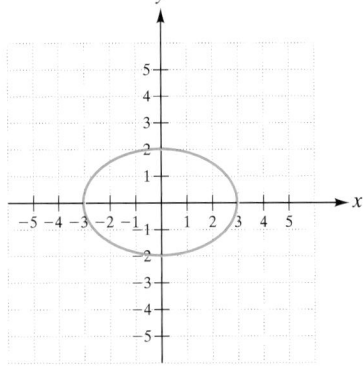

Figure 1.10

Solution

a. The graph represents a function, because all possible vertical lines cross the graph only once.

b. The graph does not represent a function, because a vertical line can be drawn to cross the graph more than once. One such vertical line is shown in **Figure 1.10**. ■

✓ Objective 1.3.2 *CHECKUP*

1. Determine whether each graph represents a function.

a.

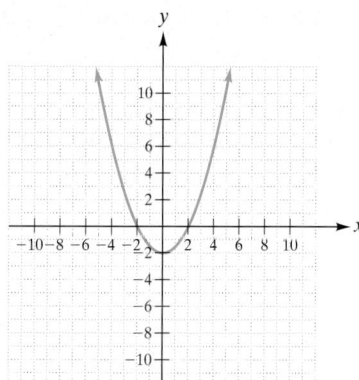

b.

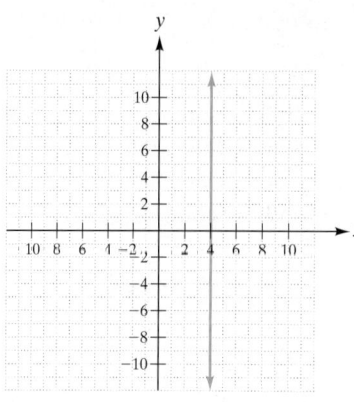

2. Explain how to check the graph of a relation to determine whether it is a function.

Objective 1.3.3   ## Function Notation

A function is a relation, so it may be represented in all of the same ways as a relation. That is, a function may be written as a list of ordered pairs, in equation form, or as a graph. However, there is a notation specific to functions called function notation. **Function notation** is written as an equation with the name of the function, the name of the independent variable in parentheses, and an expression to be evaluated to determine the dependent variable. For example,

$$y = x + 2 \quad \text{Relation} \qquad\qquad u = 3t - 5 \quad \text{Relation}$$
$$f(x) = x + 2 \quad \text{Function notation} \qquad g(t) = 3t - 5 \quad \text{Function notation}$$

The latter is read "f of x equals x plus 2."   The latter is read "g of t equals $3t$ minus 5."

Caution: The notation $f(x)$ does not mean multiplication of f by x.

 TAKE NOTE Function notation is very similar to the equation form of a relation. The difference is that in function notation the y is replaced with the name of the function and the name of the independent variable in parentheses.

We evaluate a function written in function notation just as we evaluate a function written as an equation to determine ordered pairs.

> To evaluate a function for a given number,
> * Substitute the number for the independent variable in the equation.
> * Perform the indicated operations.

For example, evaluate the function $y = x + 2$ for $x = 3$.
    This means

$$\text{Given } f(x) = x + 2, \text{ find } f(3). \quad \text{Function notation}$$
$$f(3) = 3 + 2 \quad \text{Substitute 3 for the variable, } x.$$
$$f(3) = 5 \quad \text{Evaluate.}$$

The ordered pair is written $(x, f(x))$, or $(3, 5)$.

To evaluate a function for an algebraic expression,

- Substitute the expression for the independent variable in the equation.
- Simplify the expression.

For example, given $g(t) = 3t - 5$, find $g(a)$.

$$g(t) = 3t - 5 \qquad \text{Function}$$
$$g(a) = 3(a) - 5 \qquad \text{Substitute the expression, } a, \text{ for the variable, } t.$$
$$g(a) = 3a - 5$$

Given $g(t) = 3t - 5$, find $g(a + 1)$.

$$g(t) = 3t - 5 \qquad \text{Function}$$
$$g(a + 1) = 3(a + 1) - 5 \qquad \text{Substitute the expression, } a + 1, \text{ for the variable, } t.$$
$$g(a + 1) = 3a + 3 - 5 \qquad \text{Distribute and simplify.}$$
$$g(a + 1) = 3a - 2$$

 TAKE NOTE We cannot evaluate $g(a)$ and $g(a + 1)$ on the TI-84 (or 83) calculator, because the calculator will assume a numerical value for any variable in the expression.

EXAMPLE 3

Evaluate each function for the given number or expression.

a. Given $f(x) = x^2 + x + 5$, find $f(2)$ and $f(-2)$.
b. Given $h(x) = -x^2 - x$, find $h(3)$ and $h(-3)$.
c. Given $g(v) = \sqrt{v + 7} + 1$, find $g(8)$ and $g(-8)$.
d. Given $f(x) = 2x - 4$, find $f(a)$ and $f(a + h)$.

Solution

a. Given $f(x) = x^2 + x + 5$, find $f(2)$ and $f(-2)$.

$$f(2) = (2)^2 + 2 + 5 \qquad f(-2) = (-2)^2 + (-2) + 5 \quad \text{Substitute.}$$
$$f(2) = 4 + 2 + 5 \qquad f(-2) = 4 + (-2) + 5 \qquad \text{Evaluate.}$$
$$f(2) = 11 \qquad\qquad f(-2) = 7$$

b. Given $h(x) = -x^2 - x$, find $h(3)$ and $h(-3)$.

$$h(3) = -(3)^2 - (3) \qquad h(-3) = -(-3)^2 - (-3) \quad \text{Substitute.}$$
$$h(3) = -9 - 3 \qquad\quad h(-3) = -9 + 3 \qquad\quad \text{Evaluate.}$$
$$h(3) = -12 \qquad\quad h(-3) = -6$$

c. Given $g(v) = \sqrt{v + 7} + 1$, find $g(8)$ and $g(-8)$.

$$g(8) = \sqrt{8 + 7} + 1 \qquad g(-8) = \sqrt{-8 + 7} + 1 \quad \text{Substitute.}$$
$$g(8) = \sqrt{15} + 1 \qquad\quad g(-8) = \sqrt{-1} + 1 \qquad \text{Evaluate.}$$
$$g(8) \approx 4.873 \qquad\quad g(-8) \text{ is not a real number.}$$

d. Given $f(x) = 2x - 4$, find $f(a)$ and $f(a + h)$.

$$f(a) = 2a - 4 \qquad f(a + h) = 2(a + h) - 4 \qquad \text{Substitute.}$$
$$f(a + h) = 2a + 2h - 4 \qquad \text{Distribute.}$$

The solutions for 3a, 3b, and 3c can be checked using your calculator. However, 3d cannot be evaluated on a calculator. ■

✓ Objective 1.3.3 *CHECKUP*

1. Evaluate each function for the given number or expression.

   a. Given $f(x) = \sqrt{21 - 15x} - 17$, find $f(4)$ and $f(-4)$.

   b. Given $c(x) = -x^2 - x + 3$, find $c(-5)$ and $c(5)$.

   c. Given $h(z) = 3z^3 - 2z^2 + 4z - 8$, find $h(1)$ and $h(-1)$.

   d. Given $g(x) = 4x - 8$, find $g(b)$ and $g(b + 1)$.

2. Explain what the notation $f(x)$ means. ■

Objective 1.3.4 Modeling the Real World

In real-world applications, a function is defined as a process or rule that results in exactly one **output value** for each **input value**. Many business applications involve pairs of values wherein the value of the independent variable (or input value) results in a single value for the dependent variable (or output value). Therefore, these business relations are functions. Given a business function, you can determine the output value by substituting the input value into the function. Some of the most common business relations that we will write as functions are revenue, $R(x)$, cost, $C(x)$, and profit, $P(x)$.

EXAMPLE 4

Dougal plans to decorate sweatshirts. The paint costs \$14.75. The sweatshirts cost \$7.14 each.

a. Write a cost function, $C(x)$, for the cost of x sweatshirts.

b. Determine the cost of two sweatshirts, using the cost function in part **a**.

Solution

a. Let x = the number of sweatshirts decorated
   The cost is 14.75 plus 7.14 times the number of sweatshirts, x.

$$C(x) = 14.75 + 7.14x$$

b. To find the cost of two sweatshirts, find $C(2)$.

$$C(2) = 14.75 + 7.14(2)$$
$$C(2) = 29.03$$

Two sweatshirts cost Dougal \$29.03 to produce. ■

APPLICATION

Using data from the 2000–2003 end-of-the-year reports, financial analysts for General Motors determined that the company's profit, in billions of dollars, could be determined by the function $P(x) = 2.25x^2 - 7.65x + 51.85$ for x years after 2000. Estimate the amount of profit for the year 2003.

Discussion

The year 2003 corresponds to $x = 3$ (three years after 2000).

$$P(x) = 2.25x^2 - 7.65x + 51.85$$
$$P(3) = 2.25(3)^2 - 7.65(3) + 51.85$$
$$P(3) = 49.15$$

In the year 2003, General Motors' profit was approximately \$49,150,000,000.

Note: Check your results on the graph for the Section 1.2 Application.

✓ Objective 1.3.4 *CHECKUP*

1. The charge for renting a chain saw is $10 per day or fraction of a day, with a $5 flat fee for resharpening the saw.
   a. Write a function that represents the charge for renting the saw for d days.
   b. Determine the cost of renting the saw for four days.

2. Using the data from 2000–2003 end-of-year reports, financial analysts for Amazon.com determined that the company's profit, in millions of dollars, could be determined by the function $P(x) = 42x^2 + 109.6x + 641.6$ for x years after 2000. Estimate the amount of profit for the year 2003. ■

1.3 EXERCISES

 Student Solutions Manual    PH Math/Tutor Center   CD Video   Math XL MathXL®   *MyMathLab* MyMathLab    Interactmath.com

Determine whether each relation is a function.

1. $A = \{(-2, 1), (-2, 3), (2, -3), (2, -1)\}$

2. $B = \{(1.2, 2.4), (1.4, 2.8), (1.6, 3.2), (1.8, 3.6)\}$

3. $C = \{(1.1, 1.1), (2.2, 2.2), (3.3, 3.3), (4.4, 4.4), (5.5, 5.5)\}$

4. $D = \{(1, 9), (2, 8), (3, 7), (4, 6), (5, 5)\}$

5. $E = \{(6, -1), (6, -3), (6, -5), (6, -7)\}$

6. $F = \left\{ \left(\frac{1}{2}, 2\right), \left(\frac{1}{2}, 3\right), \left(\frac{1}{2}, 4\right), \left(\frac{1}{2}, 5\right) \right\}$

7. $G = \left\{ \left(-1, \frac{2}{3}\right), \left(-2, \frac{2}{3}\right), \left(-3, \frac{2}{3}\right), \left(-4, \frac{2}{3}\right) \right\}$

8. $H = \{(8, -2), (7, -2), (6, -2), (5, -2), (4, -2)\}$

9.

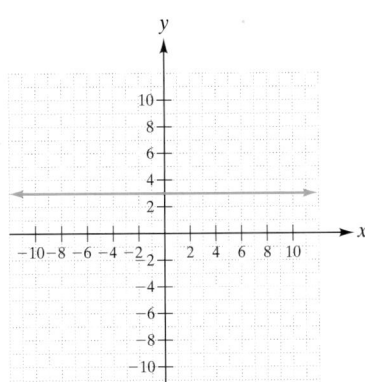

10.

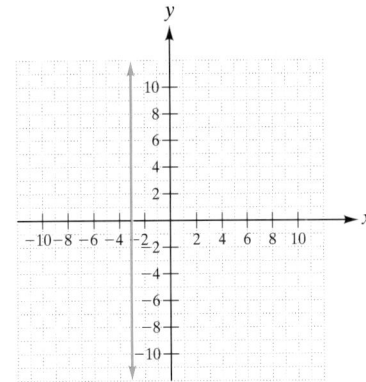

11.

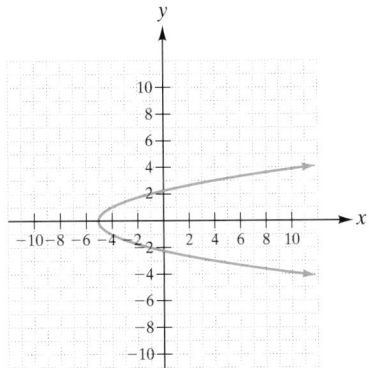

12.

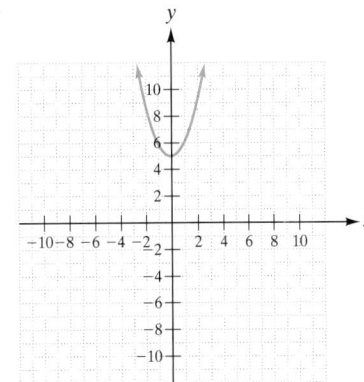

13.

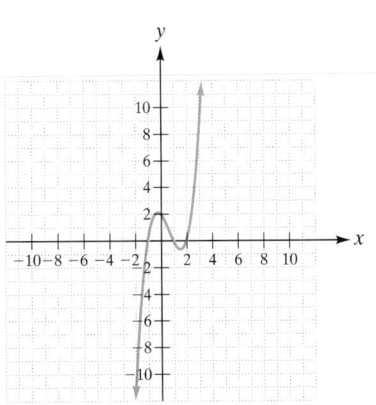

14.

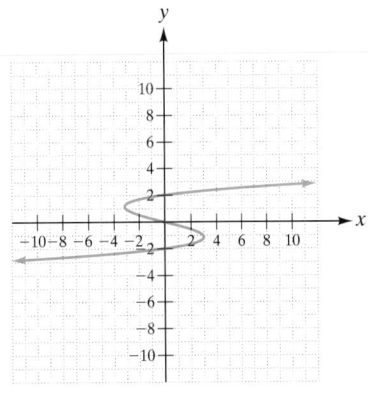

Given $f(x) = 20x + 12$, find

15. $f(5)$ **16.** $f(50)$ **17.** $f(-7)$ **18.** $f(-17)$

19. $f(2.4)$ **20.** $f(-2.4)$ **21.** $f\left(-\dfrac{1}{4}\right)$ **22.** $f\left(\dfrac{1}{10}\right)$

23. $f(a)$ **24.** $f(-a)$ **25.** $f(h+2)$ **26.** $f(h-2)$

27. $f(a-4)$ **28.** $f(4-a)$ **29.** $f(a+h)$ **30.** $f(x+h)$

Given $h(x) = 2x^2 - 4x + 5$, find

31. $h(7)$ **32.** $h(1)$ **33.** $h(-4)$ **34.** $h(-1)$

35. $h(-1.1)$ **36.** $h(0.1)$ **37.** $h\left(-\dfrac{2}{5}\right)$ **38.** $h\left(\dfrac{2}{5}\right)$

39. $h\left(2\dfrac{3}{5}\right)$ **40.** $h\left(-7\dfrac{1}{2}\right)$ **41.** $h(b)$ **42.** $h(-b)$

Given $g(x) = |-3x + 9|$, find

43. $g(5)$ **44.** $g(0)$ **45.** $g(-5)$ **46.** $g(-1)$

47. $g(4.5)$ **48.** $g(0.1)$ **49.** $g(-4.5)$ **50.** $g(-0.01)$

51. $g\left(\dfrac{2}{3}\right)$ **52.** $g\left(-\dfrac{2}{3}\right)$ **53.** $g\left(-4\dfrac{2}{3}\right)$ **54.** $g\left(4\dfrac{2}{3}\right)$

Given $F(x) = \sqrt{x + 15} + 21$, find

55. $F(85)$ **56.** $F(34)$ **57.** $F(-6)$ **58.** $F(-11)$

59. $F(-25)$ **60.** $F(-100)$ **61.** $F(5.25)$ **62.** $F(6.16)$

63. $F\left(-2\dfrac{3}{4}\right)$ **64.** $F\left(2\dfrac{16}{25}\right)$

65. Goodbuy Television's production process for manufacturing television sets has a fixed cost of $1500 for setting up a production run. Materials and labor to produce the sets cost $35 per television. Write a cost function for a production run. What is the cost of a production run that produces 400 televisions?

66. Creaky Car Company is considering setting up a new line in its production plant. The setup cost for each run on the line is estimated to be $25,000. The cost of materials and labor to produce parts is $550 per unit. Write a cost function for a production run. If the company can produce 3000 units on one run of the line, what will be the cost of production?

67. Fixed costs associated with selling CD players amount to $470 for advertising and counter space. The players sell for $125 each. Write a profit function (sales minus costs) for selling the players. What is the profit when 400 players are sold?

68. Truck rental costs to deliver parts to a customer average $185 per delivery. The parts are sold for $1200 per lot. Write a profit function (sales minus costs) for one shipment of a given number of lots. What will be the profit for one delivery of 50 lots of parts to a customer?

69. Trucks-4-U offers to rent a truck for a drop-off fee of $39, plus a daily rental fee of $25. Write a cost function for renting a truck for a given number of days. What will be the charge for renting the truck for three days?

70. Susie Seller is paid $475 per week plus a commission of $165 for each major furniture sale she completes. Write a pay function for her week's pay, given that she completes a certain number of major sales. What will her week's pay be if she makes four major sales this week?

71. Handi Parking charges a fee of $2.50 plus $1.00 for each half hour of parking. Write a cost function for parking for a given number of half-hour increments. What is the charge for parking a car for $3\frac{1}{2}$ hours?

72. Party Palace rents a party room for $140 per evening and charges $18.50 per person for food and refreshments. Write a cost function to rent the room for a party for a given number of guests. What will be the charge for a party of 75 guests?

73. A Musical Mastery bus tour has 25 seats to sell. Each seat on the tour costs $175. However, in order to entice more customers to sign up for the tour, the company advertises that it will reduce the price $3 for each seat filled on the bus. The revenue function, given that x customers sign up for the tour is $R(x) = 175x - 3x^2$. How much revenue will the company collect if 22 customers make reservations for the tour?

74. The landlord of Midrose Place has 40 apartments to rent. In the past, a rent of $375 per month has been low enough that all the apartments will be rented. For each $25 increase in rent, one additional apartment will become vacant. The function for the total monthly rental receipts given the rent increases by x increments of $25 is $R(x) = 15,000 + 625x - 25x^2$. What will be the total monthly rental receipts if the landlord raises the rent $75?

75. Recycled CDs, Incorporated, offers a choice of five used CDs for $25, with each additional CD costing $4. Write a cost function for purchasing five or more CDs. What will be the cost of buying 12 used CDs?

76. Comix Collectors Club offers a sale of 10 comic books for $35, with each additional comic book selling for $1.50. Write a cost function for purchasing 10 or more comic books. What will be the cost of purchasing 18 comic books?

77. According to data from the U.S. Department of Education, higher education costs in four-year schools can be estimated by the function $c(x) = 598x + 10{,}695$, where x is the number of years after 1996. Assuming that costs continue to follow this model, estimate the cost in the year 2007.

78. According to data from the Social Security Administration, the average monthly Social Security benefits for a retired male can be estimated by the function $b(x) = 29.7x + 649.34$, where x is the number of years after 1990. Assuming that the benefits will continue to follow this model, estimate the average monthly social security benefit for a retired male in the year 2006.

79. Using data from the Bureau of Labor Statistics, it is estimated that the price per gallon of gasoline can be represented by the function $p(x) = 0.03x^2 - 0.08x + 1.56$, where x is the number of years after 2000.

a. Use this function to predict the price of gasoline in 2007.
b. Assuming that prices continue to follow this model, in approximately what year will the price of gasoline exceed $4.00? (A table of values will help you determine this answer.)

80. According to the National Health Interview Survey of the Centers for Disease Control (CDC), an increasing number of American adults have mild to severe loss of hearing. One model estimates the percent of people with hearing trouble by using the function $p(x) = 0.01x^2 - 0.03x - 0.5$, where x is the age of an American adult.

a. Use this function to estimate the percent of 25-year-olds who have hearing trouble.
b. At what age does about one quarter of the population have trouble with their hearing? (A table of values will help you determine this answer.)

1.3 Calculator Exercises

The table function of your calculator can be helpful when a function is to be evaluated repeatedly.

As an example, if

$$f(x) = x^3 + x^2 + x + 1$$

this expression can be stored in the calculator, and the "ask" feature can be used to generate evaluations as needed. The keystrokes to do so are as follows:

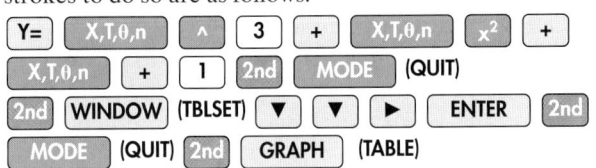

To evaluate the function for a given value, enter the value into the calculator and press [**ENTER**]. Thus, $f(-5) = -104$. Use this setup to find the following values of the function:

1. $f(65)$ **2.** $f(-83)$ **3.** $f(\pi)$
4. $f(\sqrt{2})$ **5.** $f(5634)$ **6.** $f(-\pi)$

Given $F(x) = \sqrt{x^2 + 8x + 16}$, find

7. $F(-8)$ **8.** $F(0)$ **9.** $F(-4)$
10. $F(0.8)$ **11.** $F(-6.3)$ **12.** $F\left(\dfrac{3}{4}\right)$

Given $h(x) = \dfrac{5}{x - 5}$, find

13. $h(10)$ **14.** $h(-5)$ **15.** $h(20)$
16. $h(5.5)$ **17.** $h(5)$ **18.** $h\left(\dfrac{1}{5}\right)$

1.3 Writing Exercise

"Every function is a relation, but not every relation is a function." Discuss this statement, explaining what it means and why it is true. Include examples to illustrate your explanation.

1.4 ANALYZING GRAPHS

OBJECTIVES
1 Identify the intercepts of graphs.
2 Identify the maxima and minima of graphs.
3 Identify the intersection of two graphs.
4 Analyze graphs containing real-world data.

APPLICATION

The total net income of a company is the sum of the company's income from ongoing and discontinued operations, plus all other positive or negative adjustments. The total net income of y billion dollars for the x years after 1991 for General Motors is represented in the following graph:

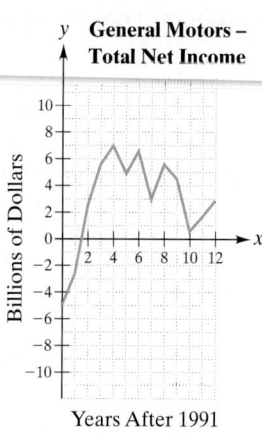

General Motors –
Total Net Income

Years After 1991

a. Approximate the x-intercept and discuss its relevance.

b. The function has a relative _____ of $y = 0.6$ at $x = 10$. Interpret.

c. The function is _____ for $10 < x < 12$. Interpret.

After completing this section, we will discuss this application further. See page 170.

Now we want to analyze a graph of a relation or a function by visually determining its characteristics. We first need to define several terms that will help us describe the graph.

Objective 1.4.1

Identifying Intercepts

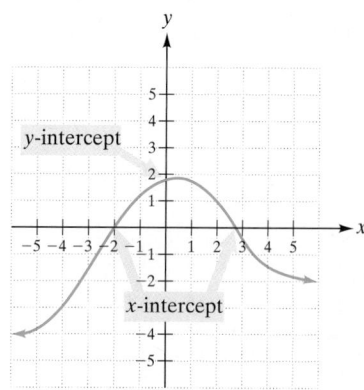

A graph may or may not cross the x-axis. If it does, it may cross the x-axis once or several times. An **x-intercept** is the location where a graph touches or crosses the x-axis. There may be more than one x-intercept for a function. Similarly, a **y-intercept** is the location where a graph touches or crosses the y-axis. There may be more than one y-intercept for a relation but not for a function.

In Section 1.2, we discovered that the y-coordinate is 0 for all points located on the x-axis. Therefore, the x-intercept will always have a y-coordinate of 0. Similarly, the x-coordinate of a point located on the y-axis is 0. Hence, the y-intercept must have an x-coordinate of 0.

✎ **TAKE NOTE** The x-intercept and the y-intercept are always written as ordered pairs.

EXAMPLE 1

Determine the x-intercepts and the y-intercepts for the following graphs:

a.

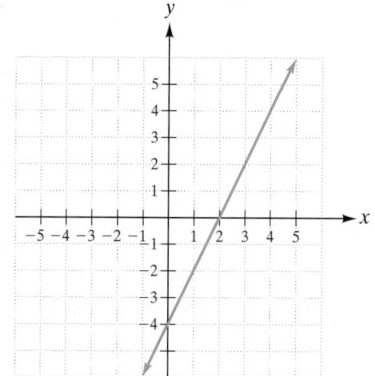

b.

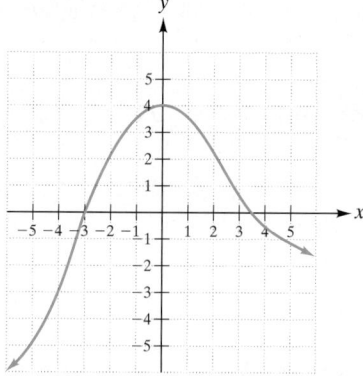

Solution

a. The x-intercept is $(2, 0)$. The y-intercept is $(0, -4)$.

b. The x-intercepts are $(-3, 0)$ and approximately $\left(\frac{7}{2}, 0\right)$. The y-intercept is $(0, 4)$.

The calculator has features that will help you determine the y-intercept of a graph.

EXAMPLE 2
Graph $y = x^2 - 1$ on a decimal screen and with a window setting of $(-5, 10, -5, 10)$. Then determine the y-intercept of the curve.

Calculator Solution

The y-intercept is $(0, -1)$.
See **Figure 1.11a** and **Figure 1.11b**.

TECHNOLOGY *Y-Intercept*

Determine the y-intercept of the graph of $y = x^2 - 1$.

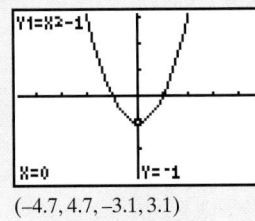
$(-4.7, 4.7, -3.1, 3.1)$

Figure 1.11a

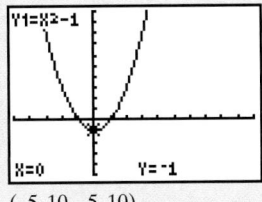
$(-5, 10, -5, 10)$

Figure 1.11b

For **Figure 1.11a**,
Enter the relation $y = x^2 - 1$ in Y1.

| Y= | X,T,θ,n | x² | − | 1 |

Set the window to the default decimal screen, and graph the relation.

| ZOOM | 4 |

Trace the graph to determine the y-intercept. Since the decimal screen is centered in the window, the first point traced is the y-intercept.

| TRACE |

For **Figure 1.11b**,
Enter the relation in Y1.

| Y= | X,T,θ,n | x² | − | 1 |

Set the window to the desired window setting, and graph the relation.

| WINDOW | (−) | 5 | ENTER | 1 | 0 | ENTER | ▼ | (−) | 5 |
| ENTER | 1 | 0 | ENTER | GRAPH |

Trace the graph to determine the y-intercept. Since the graph is not centered in the window, the first point traced is not the y-intercept. Ask for the y-coordinate when $x = 0$.

| TRACE | 0 | ENTER |

The y-intercept is $(0, -1)$.

The calculator also has a feature to help us find the x-intercepts of a graph.

EXAMPLE 3
Graph $y = x^3 + 4.05x^2 + 3.15x$ on a decimal screen, and determine the x-intercepts of the curve.

Calculator Solution

The x-intercepts are $(0, 0)$, $(-3, 0)$, and $(-1.05, 0)$. See **Figure 1.12a**, **Figure 1.12b**, and **Figure 1.12c**.

TECHNOLOGY *X*-Intercepts

Determine the *x*-intercepts of the graph of $y = x^3 + 4.05x^2 + 3.15x$.

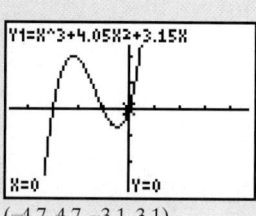

(−4.7, 4.7, −3.1, 3.1)

Figure 1.12a

(−4.7, 4.7, −3.1, 3.1)

Figure 1.12b

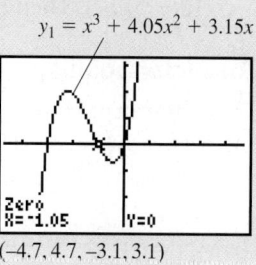

$y_1 = x^3 + 4.05x^2 + 3.15x$

(−4.7, 4.7, −3.1, 3.1)

Figure 1.12c

For **Figure 1.12a** and **Figure 1.12b**,
Enter the relation $y = x^3 + 4.05x^2 + 3.15x$ in Y1.

| Y= | X,T,θ,n | ^ | 3 | + | 4 | . | 0 | 5 | X,T,θ,n | x² | + | 3 | . | 1 | 5 |

| X,T,θ,n |

Set the window to the default decimal screen, and graph the relation.

| ZOOM | 4 |

Trace the graph to determine the *x*-intercepts—that is, the points on the graph where $y = 0$. Press | TRACE |. The first *x*-intercept is also the *y*-intercept, (0, 0). Use the left arrow key to move over to the *x*-intercept, (−3, 0).

For **Figure 1.12c**,

One of the *x*-intercepts cannot be found by tracing the graph. To find the *x*-intercept, choose ZERO, option 2, under the CALC menu. Press | 2nd | | TRACE | (CALC) | 2 |. Move the cursor to the left side of the intercept, called the *left bound*, and press | ENTER |. Move the cursor to the right of the intercept, called the *right bound*. Press | ENTER | | ENTER |. The calculator will display the coordinates of the missing *x*-intercept, (−1.05, 0).

The *x*-intercepts are (0, 0), (−3, 0), and (−1.05, 0).

✓ Objective 1.4.1 *CHECKUP*

1. Determine the *x*-intercepts and the *y*-intercepts of each graph.

a.

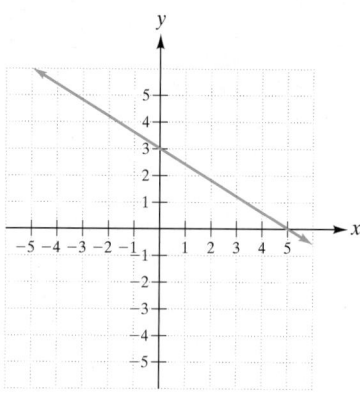

b.

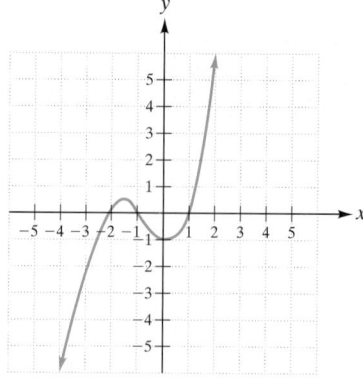

In exercises 2–3, graph each function on your calculator, and determine the x-intercepts and the y-intercepts.

2. $y = x^2 - 4$

3. $y = \dfrac{2}{3}x^3 - \dfrac{5}{6}x^2 - \dfrac{17}{6}x + 3$

4. If the graph of a relation has *x*-intercepts and *y*-intercepts, where do they occur?

5. Which coordinate of an *x*-intercept has a value of 0? Which coordinate of a *y*-intercept has a value of 0?

Objective 1.4.2   **Determining Maxima and Minima**

A function is said to be **increasing** if the values of the function increase as the values of the independent variable increase. A function is said to be **decreasing** if the values of the function decrease as the values of the independent variable increase. A function is **constant** if its values do not change as the values of the independent variable increase.

A function value is called a **relative maximum** (plural, *maxima*) if it is larger than the function values of its neighboring points. A function value is called a **relative minimum** (plural, *minima*) if it is smaller than the function values of its neighboring points.

We can visualize these definitions by tracing the graph of a function. Complete the following set of exercises on your calculator.

 Guided Discovery 4   Increasing and Decreasing Functions, Relative Maximum, and Relative Minimum

Graph $f(x) = x^2 - 4x$ on an integer window.

1. Trace the function from left to right (the *x*-values are increasing), and determine the following function values:

$f(-2) = $ _____ $f(-1) = $ _____ $f(0) = $ _____

$f(1) = $ _____ $f(2) = $ _____ $f(3) = $ _____

$f(4) = $ _____ $f(5) = $ _____ $f(6) = $ _____

2. The function values first _____ and then _____ as the *x*-values increase. (Insert *decrease* or *increase*.)

3. Tracing the graph from left to right, we find that the graph first _____ and then _____. (insert *falls* or *rises*.)

Write a rule to determine, from a graph, whether the function is increasing or decreasing.

4. The function has a relative _____. (Insert *maximum* or *minimum*.)

5. The graph has one _____ point. (Insert *low* or *high*.)

Write a rule to determine, from a graph, whether the function has a relative maximum or minimum.

Tracing the graph from left to right, we see that the graph first falls and then rises. As we trace the graph from left to right, we see that the *x*-values are increasing and the function values are first decreasing and then increasing.

The graph has one low point, $(2, -4)$. At this low point on the graph, the function has a relative minimum value of $f(2) = -4$. This is also where the graph changes from falling to rising and where the function changes from decreasing to increasing.

Similarly, a function would have a relative maximum value at a high point on its graph. The graph would change from rising to falling, and the function would change from increasing to decreasing.

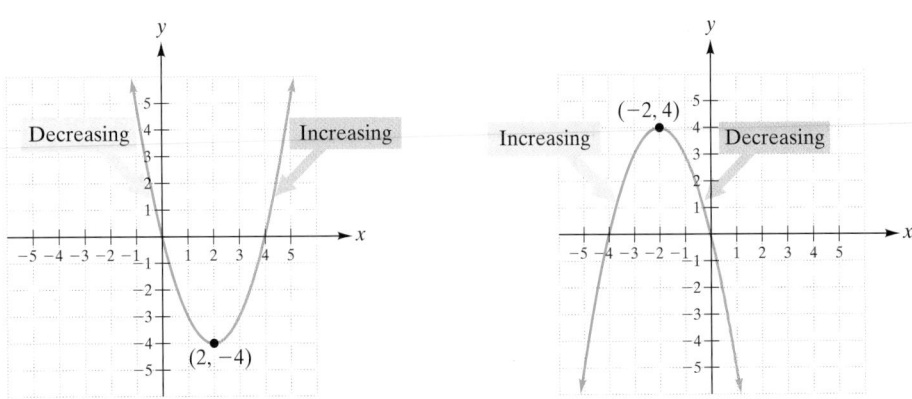

Relative minimum of $y = -4$ at $x = 2$.   Relative maximum of $y = 4$ at $x = -2$.

EXAMPLE 4   Use the following graph to answer the questions that follow:

a. What is the relative maximum value of the function that is graphed?

b. What is the relative minimum value of the function that is graphed?

c. For what x-values is the function increasing?

d. For what x-values is the function decreasing?

Solution

a. The graph does not have a high point.
The function does not have a relative maximum.

b. The graph has a low point at $(1, 2)$.
The function has relative minimum of $y = 2$ at $x = 1$.

c. The graph is rising to the right of $x = 1$.
The function is increasing for $x > 1$.

d. The graph is falling to the left of $x = 1$.
The function is decreasing for $x < 1$.

 TAKE NOTE In analyzing a function, it is easier to first determine any relative maxima and minima and then determine where the function is increasing or decreasing.

We can also determine an approximate relative maximum or relative minimum on our calculator.

EXAMPLE 5   Graph $g(x) = x^3 + 2x^2 - 4x + 4$ on a window $(-4.7, 4.7, -31, 31)$.

a. What are the relative maxima of the function?

b. What are the relative minima of the function?

c. For what x-values is the function increasing?

d. For what x-values is the function decreasing?

Calculator Solution

See **Figure 1.13a** and **Figure 1.13b**.

a. The function has a relative maximum of $y = 12$ at $x = -2$ (a high point).

b. The function has a relative minimum of $y = 2.5$ at $x \approx 0.7$ (a low point).

c. The graph is rising to the left of $x = -2$ and to the right of $x \approx 0.7$.
The function is increasing for $x < -2$ and $x > 0.7$.

d. The graph is falling between $x = -2$ and $x \approx 0.7$.
The function is decreasing for $-2 < x < 0.7$.

 TAKE NOTE Note that the x-values incorporate all real numbers, the domain of the function.

TECHNOLOGY   ## Relative Maximum and Relative Minimum

Determine the relative maximum and relative minimum of the function $g(x) = x^3 + 2x^2 - 4x + 4$.

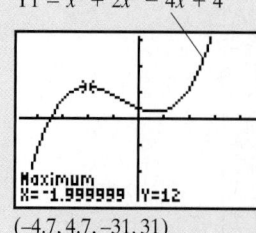

$(-4.7, 4.7, -31, 31)$

Figure 1.13a

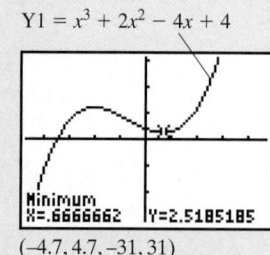

$(-4.7, 4.7, -31, 31)$

Figure 1.13b

For **Figure 1.13a**,
First graph the function as Y1.
A high point on the graph, $(-2, 12)$, can be found by tracing the graph.

The calculator will estimate a maximum function value between two given values called the left bound and the right bound. Choose MAXIMUM under the CALC function, option 4, by pressing `2nd` `TRACE` (CALC) `4`. Move the cursor to the left of the high point and press `ENTER`. Move the cursor to the right of the high point and press `ENTER` `ENTER`.
Note that the approximation is not exact.

For **Figure 1.13b**,
First graph the function as Y1.
A low point on the graph cannot be found by tracing the graph.

The calculator will estimate a minimum function value between two given values called the left bound and the right bound. Choose MINIMUM under the CALC function, option 3, by pressing `2nd` `TRACE` (CALC) `3`. Move the cursor to the left of the low point and press `ENTER`. Move the cursor to the right of the low point and press `ENTER` `ENTER`.

The function has a relative maximum of $y = 12$ at $x = -2$.
The function has a relative minimum of $y \approx 2.5$ at $x \approx 0.7$.

Objective 1.4.2 *CHECKUP*

1. Use the following graph to answer the questions that follow:

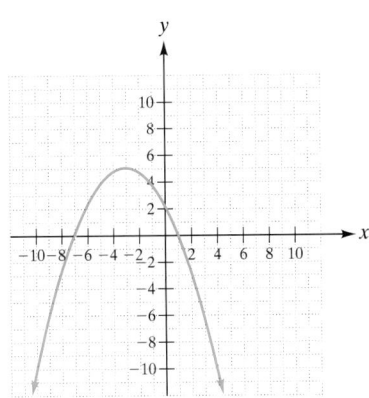

a. What are the relative maxima of the function that is graphed?
b. What are the relative minima of the function that is graphed?
c. For what x-values is the function increasing?
d. For what x-values is the function decreasing?

Use your calculator to determine (a) the relative maxima, (b) the relative minima, (c) for what x-values is the function increasing, and (d) for what x-values is the function decreasing. Use the indicated calculator window.

2. $y = 3x^4 - 14x^3 + 54x - 3$; $(-4.7, 4.7, 1, -62, 62, 20, 1)$.

3. What does it mean to say that a function is increasing or decreasing over a certain part of its domain?

4. Define *relative maximum* and *relative minimum*.

Objective 1.4.3   **Determining Intersections**

The **intersection** of two graphs is the location where the two graphs cross. There may be more than one point of intersection. The intersection is significant because at that point the x-values of the two graphs are equal and the y-values of the two graphs are equal.

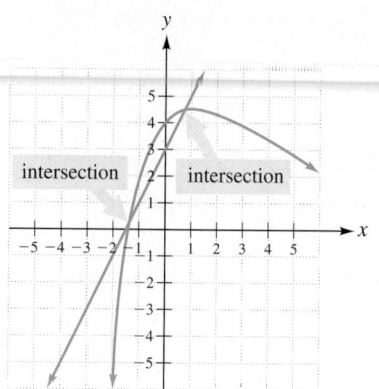

EXAMPLE 6   Determine the point of intersection of the graphs shown in the accompanying figure.

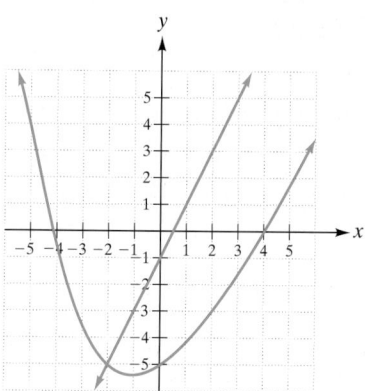

Solution

The point of intersection of the graphs is $(-2, -5)$.   ■

EXAMPLE 7   The calculator has a feature to determine the point of intersection of two graphs.

Graph the functions $y = 2x$ and $y = x + 1$ on a decimal screen. Determine the point of intersection.

Calculator Solution

The point of intersection of the graphs is $(1, 2)$. See **Figure 1.14b**.   ■

TECHNOLOGY   Intersection of Two Graphs

Determine the point of intersection of the graphs of $y = 2x$ and $y = x + 1$.

Figure 1.14a

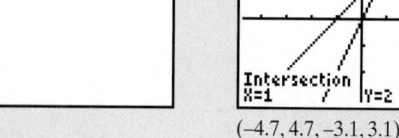

$(-4.7, 4.7, -3.1, 3.1)$

Figure 1.14b

For **Figure 1.14a**,

Enter $y = 2x$ as Y1.   Move to Y2.   Enter $y = x + 1$ as Y2.

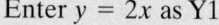

For **Figure 1.14b**,
Graph on a decimal screen.

[ZOOM] [4]

Press [TRACE] and use the left and right arrow keys to find the point of intersection. To move between the graphs, use the up and down arrow keys. The point of intersection is $(1, 2)$. To check the point of intersection, use INTERSECT under the CALC menu, option 5, by pressing [2nd] [TRACE] (CALC) [5]. Move the cursor to the closest location to the intersection on the first graph, and press [ENTER]. Move the cursor to the closest location to the intersection on the second graph, and press [ENTER] [ENTER].
The point of intersection is $(1, 2)$.

✓ Objective 1.4.3 **CHECKUP**

1. In the figure to the right, determine the point or points of intersection of the graphs.

2. Determine the point of intersection of the two graphs for the following functions.

$$y = 2x - 15 \quad \text{and} \quad y = -2x + 5$$

3. What is the term for the location at which two graphs cross? What is important about the coordinates of the point of crossing?

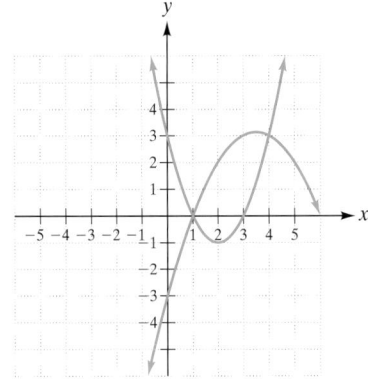

Objective 1.4.4   Modeling the Real World

We have seen that graphs are a very important way of representing functions that model real-world situations. One reason for this is that they make it easier to visualize things such as maximum and minimum values of functions or intersections of functions. However, remember that dealing with real-world situations, the answers you get must make practical sense as well as mathematical sense. For example, suppose your function represents the number of T-shirts you need to sell to make a profit, and you find that your profit is a maximum if you sell 7.89 T-shirts. This means that you need to sell 8 T-shirts, since fractions of a T-shirt are not part of your sales model.

EXAMPLE 8

Dougal plans to decorate sweatshirts and sell them for a profit. She spends $14.75 for paint. The sweatshirts cost $7.14 each. The appliques cost $3.96 per shirt. She plans to sell the shirts for $20.00 each.

a. Write a cost function, $C(x)$, for the cost of the x sweatshirts.
b. Write a revenue function, $R(x)$, for the amount collected from the sale of x sweatshirts.
c. Graph the cost and revenue functions on a calculator. Use the following settings for your window: $(0, 10, 1, 0, 62, 10, 1)$. Determine the intersection of the two graphs. Interpret the meaning of the coordinates of the intersection.

Solution

a. Let x = the number of sweatshirts decorated and sold
The sweatshirts cost $7.14 per sweatshirt, or $7.14x$.
The appliques cost $3.96 per sweatshirt, or $3.96x$.
The paint costs $14.75.

$$C(x) = 7.14x + 3.96x + 14.75 \quad \text{or} \quad C(x) = 11.10x + 14.75$$

Y2 = 20x   Y1 = 11.10x + 14.75

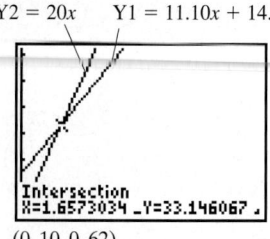

Intersection
X=1.6573034 Y=33.146067

(0, 10, 0, 62)

b. The sweatshirts sell for $20.00 each, or 20.00x.

$$R(x) = 20.00x \quad \text{or} \quad R(x) = 20x$$

c. The intersection of the graphs is (1.657, 33.146). Therefore, Dougal must make and sell approximately 1.657 sweatshirts for approximately $33.15 in order to break even (equal cost and revenue). Actually, Dougal must make and sell 2 sweatshirts, since it is impossible to sell 1.657 sweatshirts.

APPLICATION

The total net income of a company is the sum of the company's income from ongoing and discontinued operations, plus all other positive or negative adjustments. The total net income of y billion dollars for the x years after 1991 for General Motors is represented in the following graph:

a. Approximate the x-intercept and discuss its relevance.

b. The function has a relative _____ of $y = 0$ at $x = 10$. Interpret.

c. The function is _____ for $10 < x < 12$. Interpret.

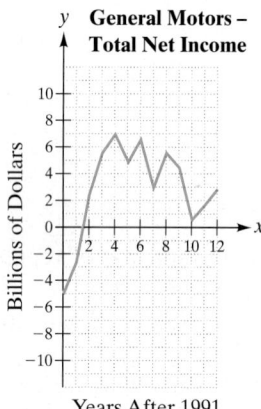

y   **General Motors –**
    Total Net Income

Billions of Dollars

Years After 1991

Discussion

a. According to the graph, the total net income function has an x-intercept between $(1, 0)$ and $(2, 0)$, or about $(1.5, 0)$. General Motors had a negative net income (a loss) when $x = 1$ (the year 1992) and a positive net income (a profit) when $x = 2$ (the year 1993).

b. The function has a relative *minimum* of $y = 0.6$ at $x = 10$. In 2001 ($x = 10$), the net income of General Motors was at a low of 0.6 billion dollars.

c. The function is *increasing* for $10 < x < 12$. In the years 2001 through 2003, the net income of General Motors was increasing.

Objective 1.4.4 *CHECKUP*

1. Aquarius packages the new U.S. Mint's Washington Quarters States Collection quarters in plastic containers and resells them. He pays $0.35 for each container and obtains the quarters at a local bank at their face value of $0.25 each. He spends $35.00 to place an advertisement in the local trading newspaper and sells the packaged quarters for $1.00 each.
a. Write a cost function, $C(x)$, for the cost of packaging and advertising the sale of x quarters.
b. Write a revenue function, $R(x)$, for the amount of money collected from selling x quarters.
c. Graph the cost and revenue functions on a calculator, using (0, 150, 10, 0, 150, 10, 1) as the window. Determine the intersection point and interpret its meaning.

2. The total net income of y million dollars for the x years after 1996 for Amazon.com is represented in the following graph:

Amazon.com–Total Net Income

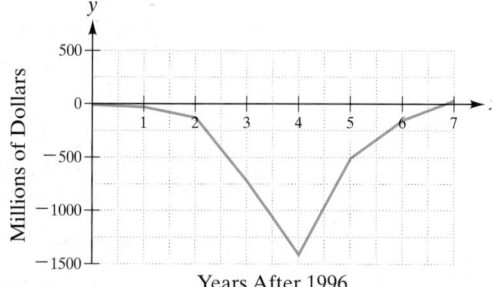

Millions of Dollars

Years After 1996

a. Approximate the x-intercept and discuss its relevance.
b. The function has a relative _____ of $y = -1411$ at $x = 4$. Interpret.
c. The function is _____ for $4 < x < 7$. Interpret.

1.4 EXERCISES

Student Solutions Manual   PH Math/Tutor Center   CD Video   Math XL MathXL®   MyMathLab MyMathLab   Interactmath.com

Use each graph to determine the following:

  a. *x-intercepts*   **b.** *y-intercepts*   **c.** *relative maxima*   **d.** *relative minima*
  e. *x-values for which the function is increasing*   **f.** *x-values for which the function is decreasing*

1.
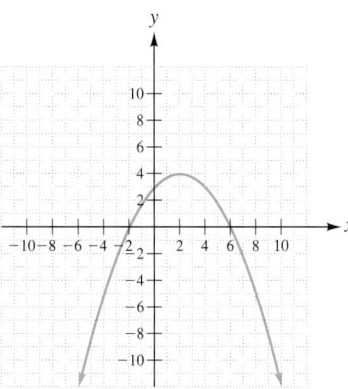

2.
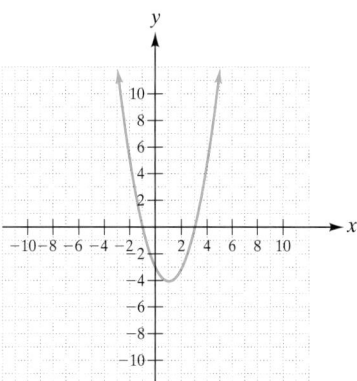

3.
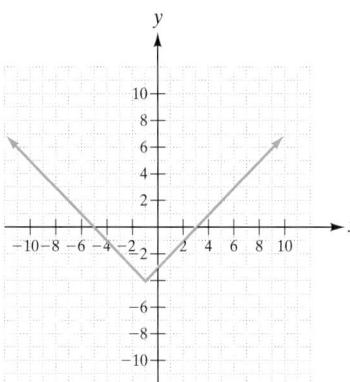

4.
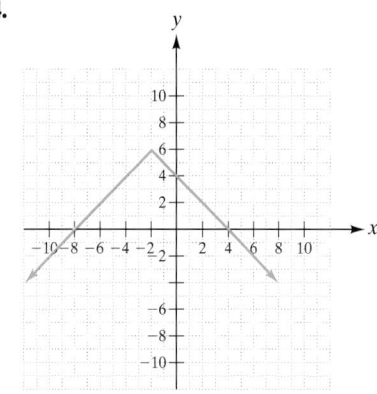

Graph each function and determine the x-intercepts and the y-intercepts.

5. $y = 3x - 6$ **6.** $y = 4x + 8$ **7.** $y = \dfrac{1}{2}x + 1$

8. $y = \dfrac{2}{3}x + 4$ **9.** $y = 1.2x - 6$ **10.** $y = 0.2x + 1$

11. $f(x) = -12x + 24$ **12.** $F(x) = 15x - 45$ **13.** $f(x) = 9x + 15$

14. $G(x) = -8x + 36$ **15.** $y = x^2 - 9$ **16.** $y = x^2 - 16$

17. $y = x^2 + 6x + 9$ **18.** $y = x^2 - 4x + 4$ **19.** $y = 4x^2 + 4x + 1$

20. $y = 4x^2 - 12x + 9$ **21.** $g(x) = x^2 + 10x - 3$ **22.** $f(x) = 0.4x^2 - 0.4x - 6.5$

23. $H(x) = x^2 - 5x - 24$ **24.** $g(x) = 2x^2 + 13x - 70$ **25.** $y = x^3 + x^2 - 2x$

26. $y = x^3 + 4x^2 + 3x$ **27.** $f(x) = x^3 + 2x^2 - x - 2$ **28.** $f(x) = x^3 + x^2 - 4x - 4$

29. $h(x) = |x| - 6$ **30.** $f(x) = |2x| - 6$ **31.** $y = |2x - 3| - 1$

32. $y = 5 - |3x + 1|$ **33.** $y = |x^2 - 2| - 1$ **34.** $y = |x^2 - 3| - 1$

Graph each function. Determine any relative minima and relative maxima. Then determine the x-values for which the function is increasing and the x-values for which the function is decreasing.

35. $y = 2x + 8$ **36.** $y = 4 - x$ **37.** $f(x) = 3 - 2x$

38. $g(x) = x - 2$ **39.** $y = 1 - x^2$ **40.** $y = x^2 + 1$

41. $g(x) = x^2 + 4x + 3$ **42.** $h(x) = 4x - 5 - x^2$ **43.** $y = |x + 3|$

44. $y = |x| + 3$ **45.** $f(x) = -|x + 3|$ **46.** $p(x) = -|x| + 3$

Determine the point or points of intersection of the given pair of graphs.

47.

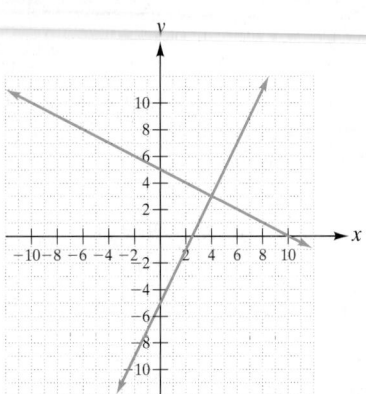

48.

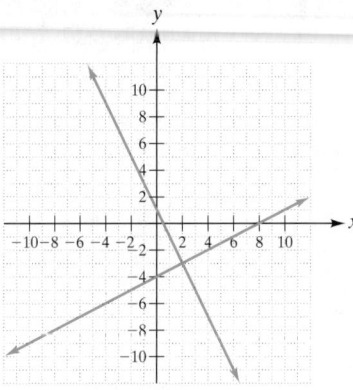

49.

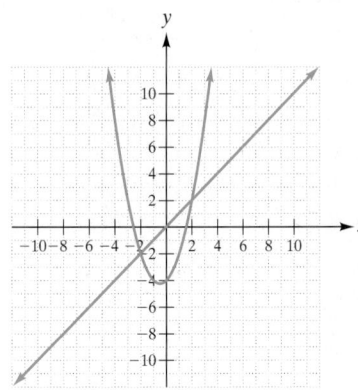

50.

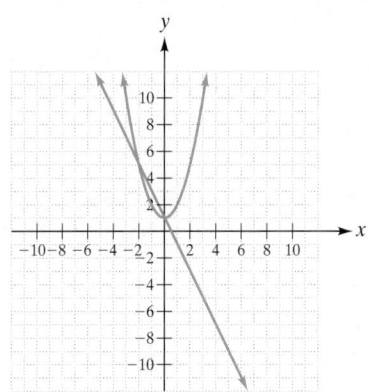

In exercises 51–66, given each pair of functions, find the point or points of intersection of their graphs.

51. $y = 3x - 5$ and $y = -2x + 15$

52. $y = x - 7$ and $y = -x + 9$

53. $f(x) = 2x + 7$ and $g(x) = -x + 1$

54. $f(x) = -x - 3$ and $g(x) = 2x$

55. $y = -5x + 2$ and $y = 3x + 8$

56. $y = -4x$ and $y = -x + 8$

57. $r(x) = 5x - 7$ and $c(x) = 12$

58. $p(x) = 5$ and $q(x) = -3x + 14$

59. $y = 3$ and $y = -x^2 + 4$

60. $y = x^2 - 16$ and $y = 9$

61. $f(x) = 2x^2 - 4x + 5$ and $g(x) = 4x - 1$

62. $m(x) = -2x^2 - 8x - 2$ and $n(x) = 2x + 6$

63. $y = \dfrac{1}{4}x^2 - 2$ and $y = \dfrac{1}{2}x$

64. $y = \dfrac{1}{3}x^2 - 6$ and $y = x$

65. $y = |x| - 5$ and $y = 2$

66. $y = |2x + 8| - 12$ and $y = 4$

67. A promotion to sell laboratory equipment to a school offers each item for a regular price of $400. However, to stimulate sales, the price for each piece will be reduced by $10 times the number of pieces sold, up to a maximum of 25 pieces. A function for the total cost of purchasing x pieces of equipment is given by $c(x) = x(400 - 10x)$, or $c(x) = 400x - 10x^2$.
   a. Graph the function, using a window of (0, 94, 10, −3100, 6200, 1000, 1).
   b. Determine any relative minima or relative maxima.
   c. Determine for which x-values the function is increasing and for which x-values the function is decreasing.

68. Roadrunners Bus Company charges $100 per person for a weekend bus excursion. To promote reservations, the company offers to reduce the price per person by $1 times the number of people who take the trip. The bus can hold up to 65 people. A function for the revenue if x people take the trip is given by $r(x) = x(100 - 1x)$, or $r(x) = 100x - x^2$.

a. Graph the function, using a window of (0, 188, 10, −3100, 6200, 1000, 1).
b. Determine any relative minima or relative maxima.
c. Determine for which x-values the function is increasing and for which x-values the function is decreasing.

69. To operate her craft booth, Jillie has a fixed daily expense of $50. She collects a fee of $5 on each craft sold. (That is, items are priced to sell at $5 above wholesale cost.)
   a. Write a function for Jillie's daily profit after expenses are subtracted from revenue when x items are sold.
   b. Graph the function, using a window of (0, 94, 10, −310, 620, 100, 1).
   c. Determine any relative minima or relative maxima.
   d. Determine for which x-values the function is increasing and for which x-values the function is decreasing.

70. Sierra starts college with a scholarship of $50,000. She withdraws $5,000 per semester for tuition and expenses.

a. Write a function representing the amount of money remaining in the scholarship fund after x semesters of withdrawals.

b. Graph the function, using a window of $(0, 18.8, 2, -31000, 62000, 10000, 1)$.

c. Determine any relative minima or relative maxima.

d. Determine for which x-values the function is increasing and for which x-values the function is decreasing.

71. Charlie's Container Company can build containers at a cost of \$4 per container, with a setup cost of \$50 per run. The company sells the containers for \$10 each.

a. Write a cost function for the cost of making x containers in one run.

b. Write a revenue function for the revenue received for selling x containers.

c. Graph the two functions on the same coordinate plane and determine their point of intersection. Use a window of $(0, 9.4, 1, 0, 124, 20, 1)$.

d. Interpret what this point of intersection tells you.

72. Jim's Carvings, Incorporated, pays a carver \$12 per carving plus a bonus of a \$100 for signing up to supply carvings to the company. The company retails the carvings for \$24 each.

a. Write a cost function for the cost of obtaining x carvings from a carver.

b. Write a revenue function for the money received from selling x carvings.

c. Graph the two functions and locate the point of intersection of the graphs. Use a window of $(0, 18.8, 2, 0, 620, 100, 1)$.

d. What does the point of intersection indicate?

73. Tatyana's employers make a deal with her to encourage her in her college work. They offer her a bonus of \$200 plus \$50 for each credit hour with a passing grade. Alternatively, if she prefers, instead of the \$200, they will pay her \$75 for each credit hour with a passing grade.

a. Write functions to represent how much Tatyana will receive under each offer if she receives x credit hours with passing grades.

b. Graph the two functions on the same coordinate plane and determine their point of intersection. Use a window of $(0, 18.8, 2, 0, 930, 150, 1)$.

c. Explain what the point of intersection means to Tatyana.

74. Dandylawn Mowing Service offers Khalid a job. The service gives him a choice of two payment methods. He can earn a base pay of \$25 per week plus \$10 for each lawn he mows, or he can earn \$15 per lawn mowed with no base pay.

a. Write functions to represent how much Khalid will receive under each payment plan if he mows x lawns a week.

b. Graph the two functions on the same coordinate plane and determine their point of intersection. Use a window of $(0, 9.4, 1, 0, 124, 20, 1)$.

c. What does the point of intersection represent to Khalid?

75. The average high temperature, $a(x)$, and the record high temperature, $r(x)$, recorded at the Grand Canyon (Williams, Arizona) for x months after January is shown in the following graph. (Temperatures are recorded in degrees Fahrenheit.)

High Temperatures at the Grand Canyon

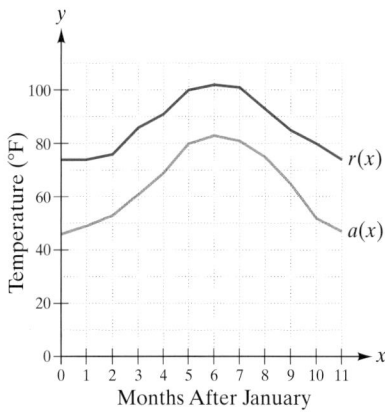

a. For the function, $r(x)$, determine for what x-values the function is constant, increasing, and decreasing.

b. For the function, $a(x)$, determine any relative minima and relative maxima. Then determine for what x-values the function is increasing and the function is decreasing. Interpret the meaning of these values.

76. The average low temperature, $a(x)$, and the record low temperature, $r(x)$, recorded at the Grand Canyon (Williams, Arizona) for x months after January is shown in the following graph. (Temperatures are recorded in degrees Fahrenheit.)

Low Temperatures at the Grand Canyon

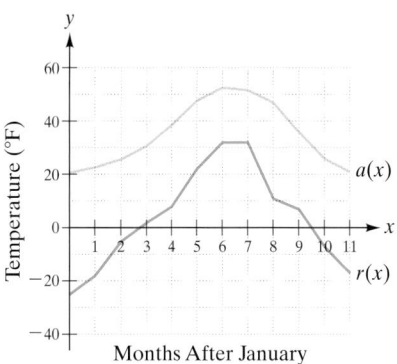

a. For the function, $r(x)$, determine for what x-values the function is constant, increasing, and decreasing.

b. For the function, $a(x)$, determine any relative minima and relative maxima. Then determine for what x-values the function is increasing and the function is decreasing. Interpret the meaning of these values.

77. Astronomers track man-made satellites. One such type of telephone satellite reflects sunlight and creates what are known as Iridium Flares. The following graph measures intensity of the last flare, y, for x days after June 13, 2005.

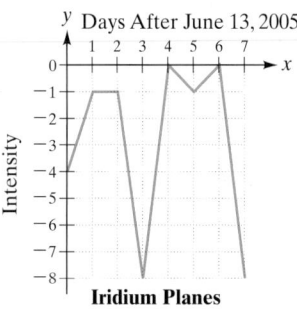

Iridium Planes

Estimate the x-intercepts and the y-intercept and interpret the meaning of each.

78. Some banks offer "overdraft protection" for which the bank charges a monthly fee. When a customer's account falls below $0 the bank will still pay for the checks. A customer's balance y rounded to the nearest dollar, x days after January 20, is shown in the following graph:

Checking Account Balance

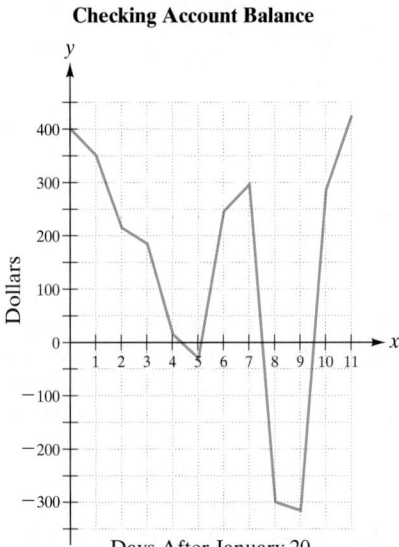

Days After January 20

Estimate the x-intercepts and y-intercept and interpret their meanings.

79. The total net income, y million dollars, for x years after 1995, for Yahoo! Inc., is shown in the following graph:

Total Net Income–Yahoo! Inc.

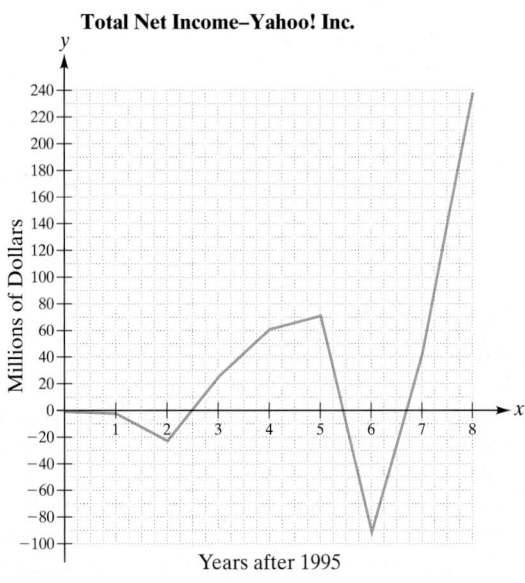

Years after 1995

Estimate the x-intercepts and interpret their meanings.

80. The total net income, y million dollars, for x years after 1993, for Northwest Airlines Corporation is shown in the following graph:

Total Net Income–Northwest Airlines Corporation

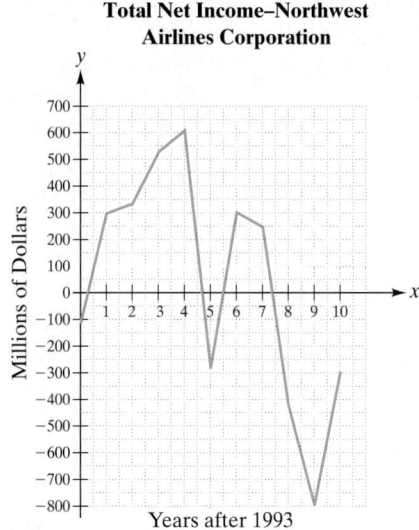

Years after 1993

Estimate the x-intercepts and interpret their meanings.

 **1.4 Calculator Exercises**

Graph the following two functions, using the integer setting for the coordinate screen.

$$y = \frac{2}{3}x^2 - 6 \quad \text{and} \quad y = -2x - 6$$

Can you tell by looking at the screen how many times the line crosses the curve? It is difficult to see, but it does cross twice. Try changing the setting by using the [**ZOOM**] button. First try [**ZOOM**] [**4**]. Is this better? Can you find the points of intersection now? Next, try [**ZOOM**] [**6**]. Is this better? If not, try [**ZOOM**] [**8**] [**ENTER**]. You will learn more about the [**ZOOM**] button later, but you should see that it can help you see the graph better if you learn how to vary the setting. Remember, you can't get lost when you experiment with the [ZOOM] key. You can always get back to the integer setting simply by pressing [ZOOM] [6], waiting until the graph is drawn, and then pressing [ZOOM] [8] [ENTER].

Experiment with the ZOOM setting to find the points of intersection of each pair of functions.

1. $g(x) = \frac{1}{3}x + 3$ and $f(x) = \frac{1}{4}x^2 - 4$

2. $y = |x| - 6$ and $y = -|x| + 4$

3. $y = x^2 - 18$ and $y = -x^2 + 54$

1.4 Writing Exercise

In analyzing graphs of functions, we stated that there may be more than one x-intercept for a function, but that there must not be more than one y-intercept for a function. Explain what we mean when we refer to x-intercepts and y-intercepts, and then explain why a function can have several x-intercepts but only one y-intercept. (*Hint:* Think about the vertical-line test for checking whether a graph is the graph of a function.) Draw an example of a function that has two x-intercepts; one that has three x-intercepts; one with four x-intercepts.

■ Chapter 1 Summary

Vocabulary Review

After completing this chapter, you should be able to define the following key terms.

constant	increasing	relative maximum
coordinate plane	independent variable	relative minimum
coordinates	intersection	x-axis
decreasing	ordered pair	x-coordinate
dependent variable	origin	x-intercept
domain	quadrants	y-axis
function	range	y-coordinate
function notation	relation	y-intercept

Fill in the blank with one of the words or phrases listed above.

1. A _____ is a set of ordered pairs.
2. The variable in a relation for which we substitute values is called the _____.
3. The _____ of a relation is the set of all possible values for the independent variable.
4. The _____ of a relation is the set of all possible values for the dependent variable.
5. The system on which we graph ordered pairs is called a _____.
6. The _____ is the horizontal axis. The _____ is the vertical axis.
7. The _____ is the point of intersection of the horizontal axis and the vertical axis.
8. The four regions formed by the horizontal axis and the vertical axis are called _____.
9. A _____ is a relation in which every element in the domain corresponds to one and only one element in the range.
10. The location where a graph crosses or touches the horizontal axis is called the _____. This point will always have an _____ of 0.
11. The location where a graph crosses or touches the vertical axis is called the _____. This point will always have an _____ of 0.
12. If the graph of a function is rising as we trace it from left to right, the function is said to be _____.
13. If the graph of a function is falling as we trace it from left to right, the function is said to be _____.
14. If the graph of a function is neither rising nor falling as we trace it from left to right, the function is said to be _____.
15. A function would have a _____ at a high point on the graph.
16. A function would have a _____ at a low point on the graph.
17. The _____ of two graphs is the location where the two graphs cross.

Reflections

1. What is the difference between a dependent variable and an independent variable?
2. Explain the importance of order in an ordered pair of values.

3. In mathematics, what is a relation? What is the domain of a relation? What is the range of a relation?

4. Describe the Cartesian coordinate system and discuss its use.

5. What is a function? Are all relations functions? Explain.

6. What is an intercept of a graph?

7. Describe what a relative minimum or a relative maximum of a graph represents.

8. When two relations are graphed on the same coordinate system, what is the significance of any points of intersection?

■ Chapter 1 Section-by-Section Review

Express your answers in fractional form, or round to nearest thousandth, as appropriate.

1.1

Recall	Examples
Table of values	
• First column: values of independent variable • Second column: equation • Third column: values of dependent variable	Construct a table of values for $y = x + 4$ when $x = \{1, 2, 3\}$. | x	$y = x + 4$	y
---	---	---
1	$y = 1 + 4$	5
2	$y = 2 + 4$	6
3	$y = 3 + 4$	7	
Ordered pairs • Two numbers enclosed in parentheses and separated by a comma. • First number is the value of the independent variable. • Second number is the value of the dependent variable.	Ordered pairs for the previous example are $(1, 5)$, $(2, 6)$, and $(3, 7)$.
Domain • Set of all possible values of the independent variable.	The domain of the previous example is $\{1, 2, 3\}$.
Range • Set of all possible values of the dependent variable.	The range of the previous example is $\{5, 6, 7\}$.

Construct a table of values for each equation, given the set of values for the independent variable.

1. $b = -2a + 7$, given $\{-3, -2, -1, 0, 1, 2, 3\}$ for a.

2. $y = \dfrac{2}{3}x + 4$, given $\{9, 6, 3, 0, -3, -6, -9\}$ for x.

3. $y = 0.4x - 1.2$, given $\{-3, -2, -1, 0, 1, 2, 3\}$ for x.

4. $y = 5x^3 - 3x^2 + 2x - 22$, given $\{-18, -7, 0, 6, 21, 22.5\}$ for x.

5. $y = |x^2 - 6x + 5|$, given $\{-2, -1, 0, 1, 2, 3\}$ for x.

6. $y = 3.6x^2 + 1.5x - 14.2$, given $\{-2.7, -1.9, -0.6, 0, 0.8, 1.5, 2.4\}$ for x.

Construct a table of values for each equation. Select five values for the independent variable, x, in each table.

7. $y = -1.6x + 4.5$ 8. $y = \dfrac{3}{2}x - 6$ 9. $y = |2x - 9|$

In exercises 10–12, construct a table of values for each equation with the given domain.

10. $y = (5x + 2)(x - 4)$, for odd integer values of x between -6 and 6.

11. $y = \dfrac{3}{5}x + 8$, where x is an integer multiple of 5 between -20 and 20.

12. $y = 17.1x - 12.9$, where x is an integer value between -4 and 4.

13. In the spring of 2005, the price of unleaded gasoline was posted as $2.099 per gallon.
    a. Write an equation for the total cost of purchasing a given number of gallons of gasoline.
    b. Complete a table of values for the total cost of purchasing 5, 10, 15, and 20 gallons of gasoline.

Construct a table of values for each application with the given domain.

14. The area of a circle for even integer values of the radius between 2 and 12 inches.

15. The measure of an angle with a complementary angle measuring $\{10, 20, 30, 40, 45\}$ degrees.

16. The amount of simple interest on an investment of $2000 at a rate of interest of 6% for t years, where t assumes integer values between 1 and 5.

17. The Celsius temperature when the temperature assumes values of $\{-23, -14, 0, 41, 50, 59, 100\}$ degrees Fahrenheit.

In exercises 18–21, write ordered pairs.

18. $y = 7 - 3x$ when $x = -10, -5, 0, 5, 10$.

20. $d = \dfrac{2}{3}c - 1$ when $c = -6, -3, 0, 3, 6$.

19. $y = \sqrt{x + 8}$ when $x = -8, -7, -4, 1, 8$.

21. The radius of a circle whose diameter measures $2, 4, 6, 8$, and 10 inches.

22. During the 1980s the United States' national debt exceeded one trillion dollars for the first time in history. The table below summarizes the national (or public) debt:

Year	1980	1985	1990	1995	2000	2001	2002	2003
National Debt (in trillions of dollars)	0.9	1.9	3.2	5.0	5.7	5.8	6.2	6.8

Source: U.S. Department of the Treasury

a. Let x = the number of years after 1980. Write a set of ordered pairs for the data.

b. Determine the domain and range for this relation. Interpret.

In exercises 23–28, determine the domain and the range of each relation. Assume that x is the independent variable.

23. $P = \{(1, 2), (3, 6), (5, 10), (7, 14), (9, 18)\}$

24. $C = \{\ldots, (-6, 6), (-4, 4), (-2, 2), (0, 0), (2, -2), (4, -4), (6, -6), \ldots\}$

25. $y = 4(x + 5) - 1$ for $x = -5, -4, -3, -2, -1$

26. $y = x^2 + 2.5$, for $x = 0, 0.5, 1, 1.5, 2$

27. $y = \sqrt{5 + x}$, for $x = -5, -4, -3, -2, -1, 0$

28. $y = \dfrac{12}{1 - x}$, for $x = -4, -2, 0, 2, 4$

29. $T = 2\pi\sqrt{\dfrac{L}{32}}$, where T is the period of a pendulum that has a suspension of L feet. (L is the independent variable.) Construct a table of values of the period, where L assumes the values $1, 8, 16, 24$, and 32 feet.

1.2

Recall	Examples
Graph a relation. • Plot all points given • If no points are given, set up a table of values and plot the ordered pairs determined from the table.	Graph $y = x^2 - 3$. Determine a sample set of ordered pairs. Let $x = -2, -1, 0, 1, 2$.

x	$y = x^2 - 3$	y
-2	$y = (-2)^2 - 3$	1
-1	$y = (-1)^2 - 3$	-2
0	$y = (0)^2 - 3$	-3
1	$y = (1)^2 - 3$	-2
2	$y = (2)^2 - 3$	1

(continued on page 178)

Recall	Examples
Domain • Determine all values that can be graphed for the independent variable.	The domain of the relation in the previous example is the set of all real numbers.
Range • Determine all values that can be graphed for the dependent variable.	Since $y \geq -3$, the range of the relation in the previous example is the set of all real numbers greater than or equal to -3.

Graph and label each ordered pair on a coordinate plane.

30. $A(3, 2)$ **31.** $B(4, -3)$ **32.** $C(-3, 2)$ **33.** $D(-4, -3)$

34. $E(0, 5)$ **35.** $F(-5, 0)$

36. State the coordinates of the points graphed in **Figure 1.15**.

*Using **Figure 1.15**, state the quadrant in which each plotted point lies or the axis on which the point lies.*

37. A **38.** B

39. C **40.** D

41. E **42.** F

43. G

Graph each relation.

44. $S = \{(0, -4), (1, -3), (2, -2), (3, -1), (4, 0), (5, 1)\}$

45.

x	y
-1	-5
0	-3
1	-1
2	1
3	3
4	5

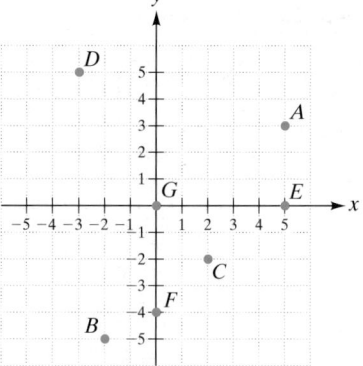

Figure 1.15

46. $y = 3 - 2x$ **47.** $T = \{(-5, 3), (-3, 3), (-1, 3), (1, 3), (3, 3), (5, 3)\}$

In exercises 48 and 49, determine the domain and range of each relation.

48.

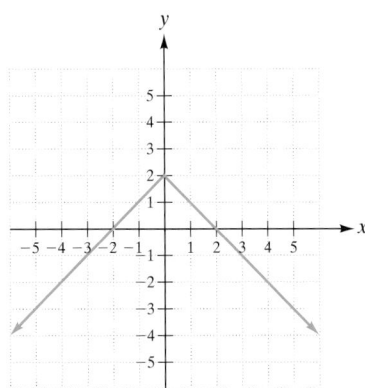

49.

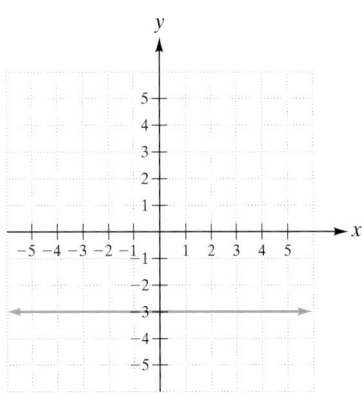

50. Higher educational attainment is usually affiliated with higher earning power. The following chart shows the median annual income by level of education for men for the years 1998–2001, where x is the number of years after 1998.

Education level vs.
Income (Men)

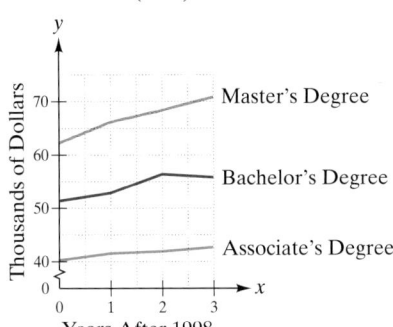

Determine the domain and range if the relation of interest is Bachelor's degree.

51. The weekly charge for a family to send its children to a child-care center is $40 plus $10 per child.
  a. Write a relation for the weekly charge, y, in terms of the number of children, x.
  b. Graph the relation, using $(-4.7, 4.7, 1, -31, 93, 10, 1)$ as the graphing window on your calculator.
  c. State the domain and range of the relation.

52. A square has sides measuring x feet.
  a. Write a relation for the area, y square feet, in terms of the length of a side, x feet.
  b. Graph the relation, using $(-4.7, 4.7, 1, -6.2, 31, 10, 1)$ as the graphing window on your calculator.
  c. State the domain and range of the relation.

1.3

Recall	Examples
Vertical-line test • A graph represents a function if all possible vertical lines intersect or touch the graph only once.	The following graph represents a function. Sample vertical lines are shown.
Function notation • An equation in function notation consists of the name of the function, the name of the independent variable, and an expression to be evaluated to determine the dependent variable. • To evaluate a function for a given value, substitute the value for the independent variable.	Given $f(x) = -x^2 + 2x - 1$, evaluate $f(-3)$ and $f(a)$. $f(-3) = -(-3)^2 + 2(-3) - 1 \qquad f(a) = -(a)^2 + 2(a) - 1$ $f(-3) = -16 \qquad\qquad\qquad\qquad f(a) = -a^2 + 2a - 1$

Determine whether each relation is a function.

53. $S = \{(-2, 3), (-1, 5), (0, 7), (-1, 9), (-2, 11)\}$

54. $T = \{(-2, 3), (-1, 5), (0, 7), (1, 5), (2, 3)\}$

55.

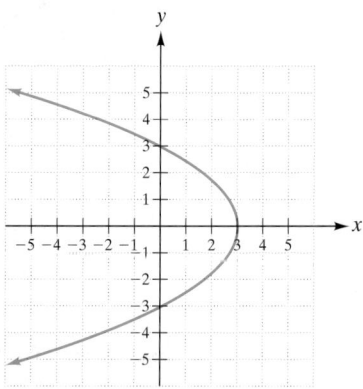

56.

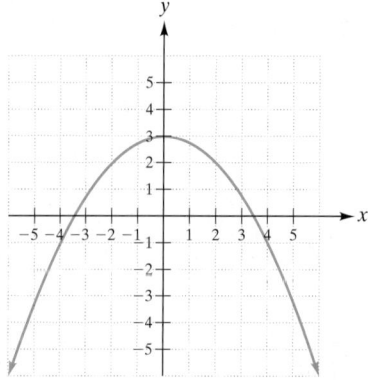

Given $f(x) = -4x + 13$, *find*

57. $f(13)$ **58.** $f(-21)$ **59.** $f(2.5)$ **60.** $f(-3.7)$ **61.** $f(3 + h)$ **62.** $f(-b)$

Given $g(x) = 5x^2 + x - 4$, *find*

63. $g(3)$ **64.** $g(-2)$ **65.** $g(0.5)$ **66.** $g(a)$ **67.** $g(-a)$ **68.** $g\left(-\dfrac{1}{4}\right)$

Given $S(x) = \sqrt{2x + 3} - 5$, *find*

69. $S(3)$ **70.** $S(11)$ **71.** $S(59)$

72. A process requires \$4500 to set up for a production run. The cost of labor and materials to produce a single widget is \$17. Write a cost function for a production run. What is the cost of producing 1200 widgets on one production run?

73. A learning institute will conduct a training session at your company for a fee of \$1500 plus a charge of \$125 per person attending. Write a function for the total charge of a training session. What will be the charge for a training session for 20 employees?

74. Dmitri charges \$1.50 to paint faces at a church carnival. He purchased his supplies for \$15.00. Write a profit function for painting faces. How much profit will Dmitri make for the church if he paints 135 faces?

75. Using data from a financial services organization, analysts can estimate the net annual sales (in billions of dollars) for Wal-Mart Stores by the function $S(x) = -0.5x^2 + 27.3x + 114.5$ for x years after 1998. Assuming that the net annual sales will continue to follow this model, use this function to estimate the net sales for the year 2007.

1.4

Recall	Examples
y-intercept • Location where a graph touches or intersects the *y*-axis.	*y*-intercept $(0, 4)$

Recall	**Examples**
x-intercept • Location where a graph touches or intersects the *x*-axis.	 *x*-intercept $(-2, 0)$ *x*-intercept $(0, 0)$
Relative minimum • A function value that is smaller than its neighboring function values.	 $(1, -3)$ Relative minimum of $y = -3$ at $x = 1$.
Relative maximum • A function value that is larger than its neighboring function values.	 $(-1, 2)$ Relative maximum of $y = 2$ at $x = -1$.
Decreasing function • A function is decreasing if the function values decrease as the values of the independent variable increase.	 $(1, -3)$ The function is decreasing for $x < 1$.

(continued on page 182)

Recall	Examples
Increasing function • A function is increasing if the function values increase as the values of the independent variable increase.	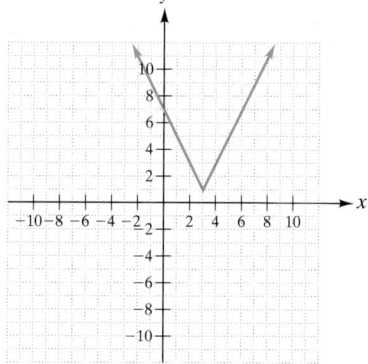 The function is increasing for $x > 1$.
Intersection of two graphs • The point where two graphs cross.	Intersections are $(0, -5)$ and $(3, 4)$.

76. Use the graph at the right to determine the following:
   a. x-intercepts
   b. y-intercepts
   c. relative maxima
   d. relative minima
   e. x-values for which the function is increasing
   f. x-values for which the function is decreasing

Graph each function and determine the x-intercepts and the y-intercepts.

77. $y = 3x + 9$ **78.** $y = \dfrac{3}{4}x - 9$

79. $y = x^2 - 0.36$ **80.** $y = |x| - 4$

Graph each function. Determine any relative minima and relative maxima. Then determine the values of x for which the function is increasing and the values of x for which it is decreasing.

81. $h(x) = 6 - 2x$ **82.** $y = 3 - x^2$ **83.** $y = |x| + 2$ **84.** $f(x) = |x^2 - 1|$

What are the points of intersection of the graphs of each pair of functions?

85. $y = 2x - 2$ and $y = -\dfrac{1}{3}x + 5$ **86.** $y = x^2 - 6$ and $y = x$ **87.** $f(x) = |x + 5|$ and $g(x) = 2$

88. An office contracts to purchase no more than eight desks that ordinarily sell for \$325 each. To encourage multiple sales, the desks are offered at a price of \$$(325 - 15x)$ each, where x is the number of desks purchased. The total cost of purchasing x desks is given by $c(x) = x(325 - 15x)$, or $c(x) = 325x - 15x^2$. Graph this function, using a window of $(0, 9.4, 1, -3100, 3100, 500, 1)$. Determine any relative minima or relative maxima. Then determine for which x-values the function is increasing and for which x-values the function is decreasing.

89. The selling price of a horn switch wiring harness for a car is listed at $10.45. Write a revenue function for x harnesses sold. Graph the function. Determine any relative minima or relative maxima. Then determine for which x-values the function is increasing and for which x-values the function is decreasing.

90. A bank account has a beginning balance of $216.00. There is no activity in the account, except for a monthly service charge of $4.50. Write a function that represents the balance of the account after x months of inactivity. Graph the function. Determine any relative minima or relative maxima. Then determine for which x-values the function is increasing and for which x-values the function is decreasing.

91. Hans can choose to receive a tuition reimbursement stipend of $400 plus $65 per credit hour for each credit hour passed, or he can instead choose to receive $100 per credit hour passed without a stipend.
  a. Write functions that represent how much Hans will receive under each option.
  b. Graph the two functions and determine their point of intersection. Use a window of $(0, 18.8, 1, 0, 3100, 500, 1)$.
  c. What does the point of intersection represent to Hans?

92. The cost of production of certain items includes a setup cost of $500 plus a cost of $12 per item for labor and materials. The finished items sell for $25 each.
  a. Write functions that represent the total cost and total revenue associated with producing and selling x items.
  b. Graph the two functions and determine their point of intersection. Use a window of $(0, 94, 10, 0, 1550, 500, 1)$.
  c. Interpret the point of intersection in business terms.

93. The average minimum temperature, y degrees Fahrenheit, for x months after January in Big Falls, Minnesota, Koochiching County, is shown in the following graph.

Average Minimum Temperature in Big Falls, MN

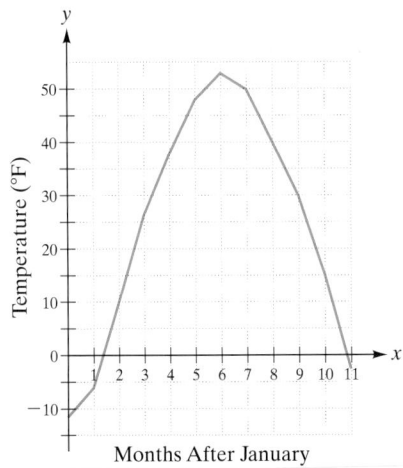

Months After January

  a. Determine for what x-values the function is increasing and decreasing.
  b. Determine any relative minima and relative maxima.
  c. Estimate the y-intercept and interpret its meaning.
  d. Estimate the x-intercepts and interpret their meanings.

94. Students in General Physics conduct an experiment with a ball in which they raise and then drop it over a data collection device which is hooked to their graphing calculators and selected data are displayed. The following graph relates distance above the device in feet, y, to tenths of a second, x.

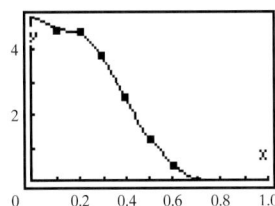

Estimate the x- and y-intercepts and interpret the meaning of each.

■ Chapter 1 Mixed Review

Given $f(x) = -x + 9$, find

1. $f(9)$ **2.** $f(-9)$ **3.** $f(1.8)$ **4.** $f(-2.7)$ **5.** $f(-b)$ **6.** $f(1 + h)$

Given $g(x) = x^2 - 3x - 4$, find

7. $g(4)$ **8.** $g(-1)$ **9.** $g(1.5)$ **10.** $g(v)$ **11.** $g(-v)$ **12.** $g\left(-\dfrac{2}{3}\right)$

Given $S(x) = \sqrt{6x - 8}$, find

13. $S(4)$ **14.** $S(12)$ **15.** $S(44)$

Determine whether each relation is a function.

16. $P = \{(3, 8), (2, 6), (1, 4), (0, 2), (-1, 0)\}$ **17.** $Q = \{(2, -3), (2, -2), (2, -1), (2, 0), (2, 1)\}$

Graph each function and determine the x-intercepts and the y-intercepts. Determine any relative minima and relative maxima. Then determine the values of x for which the function is increasing and the values of x for which it is decreasing.

18. $y = 4.8x - 1.2$ **19.** $y = \dfrac{2}{5}x + 4$ **20.** $y = x^2 - 1.21$ **21.** $y = 2 - |x|$

Determine the points of intersection of the graphs of each pair of functions.

22. $y = 2x + 2$ and $y = -2x - 10$ **23.** $y = x^2$ and $y = 3x$

24. $f(x) = |2x|$ and $g(x) = x + 3$

Determine the domain and the range of each relation. Assume that x is the independent variable.

25. $A = \{(2, 1), (4, 2), (6, 3), (8, 4), (10, 5)\}$

26. $B = \{\ldots, (-6, 3), (-4, 3), (-2, 3), (0, 3), (2, 3), (4, 3), (6, 3), \ldots\}$

27. $y = x^2$ for $x = -5, -4, -3, -2, -1$

28. $y = x^2 - 1.5$ for $x = 0, 0.5, 1, 1.5, 2$

Write ordered pairs.

29. $y = 12 - 8x$ when $x = -6, -3, 0, 3, 6$.   **30.** $y = \sqrt{10 - 3x}$ when $x = 3, 2, 1, 0, -1, -2$.

31. $t = \dfrac{4}{7}s + 5$ when $s = -7, 0, 7, 14, 21$.

Construct a table of values for each relation.

32. $y = (3x - 5)(2x + 1)$, for even integer values of x between -5 and 5.

33. $y = \dfrac{3}{4}x - 5$, where x is an integer multiple of 4 between -13 and 13.

34. $y = 15.8 - 4.7x$, where x is an integer value between -3 and 3.

35. $y = 4x^2 - 17x - 15$, with a domain of $\left\{-2, -\dfrac{3}{4}, 0, \dfrac{3}{4}, 5\right\}$.

36. $y = |1 - 2x - 3x^2|$, given $\{-6, -3, 0, 3, 6, 9\}$ for x.

37. $y = 4.6x^2 + 2.8x + 10.4$, given $\{-3.7, -2.2, -0.7, 0, 0.8, 2.3, 3.8\}$ for x.

Construct a table of values for each relation. Select three values for the independent variable, x, in each table.

38. $y = 4.5x - 1.6$ **39.** $y = \dfrac{1}{4}x + 3$ **40.** $y = |3x - 10|$

41. Write ordered pairs for the circumferences of circles whose radii measure $\frac{1}{4}, \frac{1}{2}, 1, \frac{3}{2}$, and 2 inches.

In exercises 42–45, construct a table of values for each relation.

42. The area of a square for odd integer values of the length of a side between 1 and 7 feet.

43. The measure of the second of two supplementary angles, where one angle measures $\{30, 60, 90, 120, 150\}$ degrees.

44. The simple interest on an investment of $2000 at a rate of interest of 6% for t years, where t assumes integer values between 1 and 5.

45. The Fahrenheit temperature when the temperature assumes values of $\{-10, -5, 0, 5, 10, 15, 20, 25\}$ degrees Celsius.

46. Computer zip disks are on sale for $7.95 each.
   a. Write an equation for the total cost of purchasing a given number of disks.
   b. Complete a table of values for the total cost of purchasing x disks, where x assumes integer values between 0 and 6.

47. The setup costs for a production run for a certain item are $2500. The labor and materials needed to produce a single production item cost $12. Write a function for the total cost of a production run. What will be the total cost of a production run of 1650 items?

48. A rental firm charges $15 to rent a grinder, plus $2 for each hour of rental. Write a function for the total rental cost. What is the cost for renting the grinder for 10 hours?

49. A caterer will arrange an awards luncheon for your employees. He charges $275.00 to rent his party room and $9.50 per person for the luncheon. Write a function for the total charge. What will be the charge for a luncheon for 135 employees?

50. A charity basketball game charges $4 admission. Expenses for the game total $185. Write a function for the profit. What is the profit on 310 admissions?

51. A storage tank holds 250 gallons of fluid when full. The tank dispenses fluid at a rate of 3.5 gallons per minute. Given a tank that was full, write a function for the amount of fluid remaining in the tank after x minutes of dispensing fluid. Graph the function. Determine any relative minima or relative maxima. Determine x-values for which the function is increasing or decreasing.

52. Jillian's grandparents deposited $1000 into a savings account at her birth. From then on, they deposited $50 per month into the account. Write a function for the total amount deposited into the account by her grandparents after x months. Graph the function. Determine any relative minima or relative maxima. Determine x-values for which the function is increasing or decreasing.

53. A contest winner has the option of receiving $25,000 cash initially plus an annual payment of $5000 per year, or no initial cash payment but an annual payment of $6000 per year.
  a. Write functions to represent how much money the winner will receive under each option.
  b. Graph the two functions and determine their point of intersection. Use a window of $(0, 37.6, 4, 0, 248,000, 4000, 1)$.
  c. What does the point of intersection represent to the winner?

54. A retailer purchases appliances at a cost of $22 per appliance plus a total shipping charge of $600 for each lot ordered. She then sells the appliances for $75 apiece.
  a. Write functions that represent her total acquisition cost for a lot of x appliances and her total revenue for selling x appliances.
  b. Graph the two functions and determine their point of intersection. Use a window of $(0, 47, 5, 0, 3100, 500, 1)$.
  c. Interpret the point of intersection in terms of business decisions.

55. Unemployment rates fluctuate due to a variety of economic conditions. The U.S. Bureau of Labor Statistics compiles statistics and creates both monthly and yearly unemployment percentages. The following table gives the unemployment rate as a percent of the labor force since 1980:

Year	1980	1985	1990	1995	2000
Percent unemployed	7.1	7.2	5.6	5.6	4.0

  a. Let $x =$ the number of years after 1980. Write a set of ordered pairs for the data.
  b. Determine the domain and range for this relation. Interpret.

56. This graph summarizes average monthly Social Security benefits for the years 1998–2003, where x is the number of years since 1998.

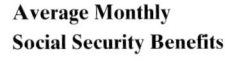

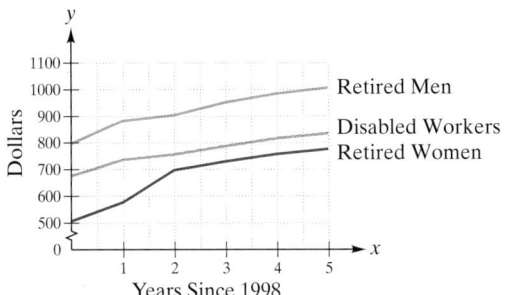

Average Monthly Social Security Benefits

  a. Determine the domain and range if the relation of interest is retired women.
  b. Determine the domain and range if the relation of interest is disabled workers.

57. Social Security reform is of increasing concern to many Americans. Discussion of changing the current formula for retirement benefits is taking place, and various groups have proposed changes to the way in which they are now being computed. The Social Security Administration has published data that relate a worker's average yearly wages in 2005 to the annual benefits promised by the current formula should the person retire in 2045. The function $b(x) = -0.000002x^2 + 0.496x + 4446.646$ can be used to model these data, where b is the annual benefit in 2045 and x is the yearly wages earned in 2005.
  a. What annual benefit is promised in 2045 for a person making $40,000 in 2005?
  b. How much would a person need to earn in 2005 to qualify for a $35,000 benefit in 2045?

58. The quarterly domestic operating profit/loss margin (as a percent), y, reported in quarterly reports for a low-cost carrier, is shown in the following graph, where x is the number of quarters after the fourth quarter of 2003.

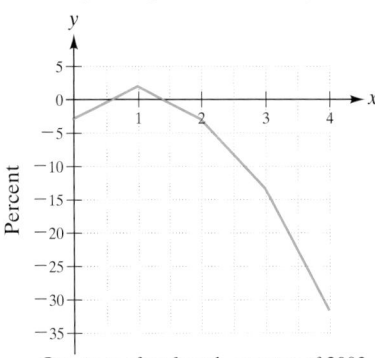

Operating Profit/Loss Margin

Quarters after fourth quarter of 2003

  a. Estimate the x-values for which the function is increasing and decreasing.
  b. Estimate the relative minima and relative maxima.
  c. Estimate the x- and y-intercepts and interpret the meaning of each.

■ Chapter 1 Test

A+   TEST-TAKING TIPS

Before you start a test, you should "dump your brain." By this, we mean that you should use scratch paper to list all the important information that you will need for the test—formulas, terms, tips, and so on. This gives you something to refer to while taking the test. Then you should scan the test questions and pick out those problems that you think will be the easiest to do. Do those problems first. This will accomplish two things. First, it will allow you to expend your energies on the parts that you know best while you are still fresh. Second, it will build your confidence while you are taking the test and will help you relax knowing that you can do the work. Save the difficult problems for last. Even then, don't spend a lot of time on any one problem. If you can't seem to get a handle on it, go on to another problem. Your subconscious will continue to work on the first problem, and when you return to it, you may find that the solution will come easily.

1. Construct a table of values for $y = 2x^2 + 17x - 9$, given $\{-9, 0, 3\}$ as the set of values for x.

2. Consider the relation $y = |2x - 3| - 1$, where x is the independent variable.
   a. Graph the relation.
   b. What are the relative maxima of the relation?
   c. What are the relative minima of the relation?
   d. For what values of x is the relation increasing?
   e. For what values of x is the relation decreasing?
   f. What are the x-intercepts of the relation?
   g. What are the y-intercepts of the relation?

3. Consider the following relation:

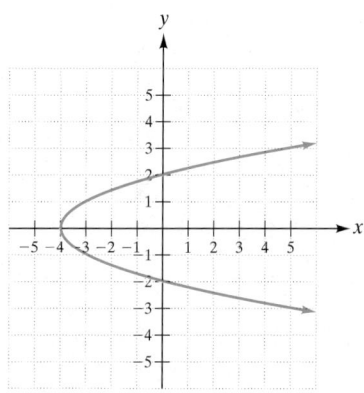

   a. Is this relation a function? Justify your answer.
   b. What is the domain of the relation?
   c. What is the range of the relation?

4. Identify the coordinates of the points in **Figure 1.16**.

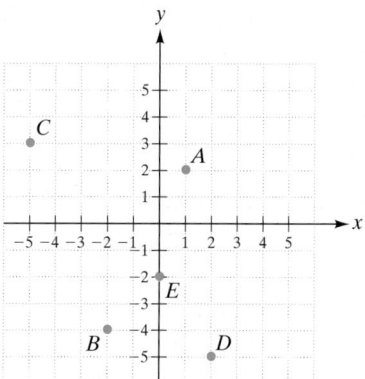

Figure 1.16

5. In **Figure 1.16**, in which quadrant does point D lie?

In exercises 6–8, graph the relations. Label all points used.

6. $y = 2x^2 - 8x$

7. $y = \dfrac{3}{4}x - 2$

8. $y = \sqrt{7 - x} + 1$

In exercises 9–12, for the function $f(x) = \frac{1}{2}x + 6$, find

9. $f(4)$

10. $f(-6)$

11. $f(a)$

12. $f(2 + a)$

13. A production process has a setup cost of $450.00. The cost of labor and materials to produce a single item is $21.50.
   a. Write a function that represents the cost of producing x items in one production run.
   b. The item is sold for $30.50, write a function to represent the revenue of x items.
   c. Graph the cost and revenue function. Determine the point of intersection.
   d. Interpret the point found in part **c**.

14. For the production process described in exercise 13, what is the cost of producing 250 items in one production run?

15. Find the intersection of the graphs of $y = 3x - 10$ and $y = -x - 2$.

16. According to the U.S. Bureau of the Census, young women are waiting longer to get married. Based on census data, a "median age at first marriage" statistic is computed. This information is summarized for women in the following table:

Women Median Age at First Marriage

Year	2002	2001	2000	1999	1998	1997	1996	1995	1994	1993
Age	25.3	25.1	25.1	25.1	25	25	24.8	24.5	24.5	24.5

   a. Let x = the number of years after the year 1993. Write a set of ordered pairs for the data.

   b. Determine the domain and range for this relation. Interpret. Does your interpretation support the initial statement in this exercise?

17. The graph below illustrates the median age at first marriage, where x is the number of years since 1993:

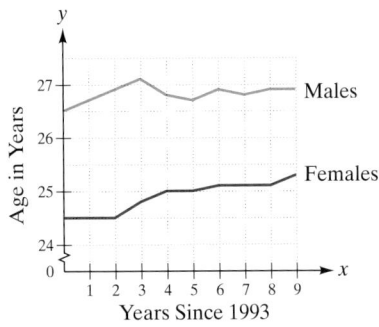

Years Since 1993

Determine the domain and range if the relation of interest is median age at first marriage for males.

18. According to the U.S. Department of Commerce, the median annual income for men with a Master's degree can be represented by the function $i(x) = -356x^2 + 3871x + 62,365$, where x is the number of years after 1998. Assuming that the median income will continue to follow the model, estimate the median income for men with a Master's degree for the year 2008.

19. The total net income of y million dollars for the x years after 1993 for Delta Air Lines is represented in the following graph:

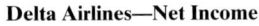

Delta Airlines—Net Income

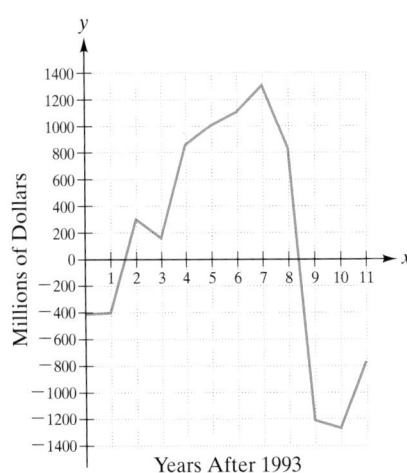

Years After 1993

   a. Approximate the x-intercepts and discuss their meaning.

   b. The function has a relative _____ of $y = 1303$ at $x = 7$. Interpret.

   c. The function has a relative _____ of $y = -1272$ at $x = 10$. Interpret.

   d. The function is _____ for $7 < x < 10$. Interpret.

20. What is meant by the term *ordered pair*, and why is the word *ordered* important?

Project

The temperature outside your home or school usually fluctuates throughout the day and night as well as throughout the seasons of the year. In this project, you will identify temperature data and discuss various aspects of your data.

Identify one of the following sets of temperature data:

1. The hourly temperatures for a 24-hour period (you can use a Calculator-Based Laboratory (CBL) with a temperature probe and your TI calculator to collect these data.

2. The projected hourly temperature for a 24-hour period

3. The average low temperatures for a 12-month period

4. The average high temperatures for a 12-month period

PART I   Use the data identified to complete the exercises that follow. Let x represent the variable for time. Let y be the temperature in degrees Celsius.

1. Write ordered pairs for the set of data collected.

2. Use the data collected to sketch a graph of the daily temperatures. Label all points and the axes.

3. Determine the sets of numbers for the domain and range of this relation. Explain the meaning of these sets of numbers.

4. Does your data represent a function?

5. Does the graph have an x-intercept? If so, explain its meaning. If not, explain why not.

6. Does the graph have a y-intercept? If so, explain its meaning. If not, explain why not.

7. **a.** Determine any relative minima. Where do they occur? Convert each relative minimum to time of day and explain its meaning.
   b. Determine the absolute minimum—the lowest temperature of the day. Is this value also a relative minimum? For what x-value does it occur? Convert the absolute minimum to time of day.
   c. Determine any relative maxima. Where do they occur? Convert each relative maximum to time of day and explain its meaning.
   d. Determine the absolute maximum—the highest temperature of the day. Is this value also a relative maximum? For what x-value does it occur? Convert the absolute maximum to time of day.

8. Between what x-values is the temperature increasing? Between what x-values is it decreasing? Convert the x-values to time of day and explain their meaning.

PART II   Now convert the temperature to Fahrenheit (to two decimal places), and repeat the previous set of exercises with your new data. Let x be the number of hours after data collection began. Let y be the temperature in degrees Fahrenheit. Repeat exercises 1–8 in Part I.

■ Chapters P–1 Cumulative Review

Consider the following real numbers:

$$-\frac{2}{3}, \quad 0, \quad 12, \quad 1\frac{4}{5}, \quad -0.33, \quad \sqrt{7}$$

1. Which numbers are whole numbers?

2. Which numbers are integers?

3. Which numbers are rational numbers?

4. Which numbers are irrational numbers?

Use one of the symbols $>$, $<$, or $=$ to compare the numbers.

5. $\dfrac{3}{8}$ —— $\dfrac{1}{3}$

6. $\dfrac{2}{3}$ —— 0.66

7. -2.8 —— -1.6

8. Graph the following numbers on a number line, and label the points:

$$-3.1 \quad -\frac{1}{2} \quad 2\frac{3}{4} \quad \sqrt{5} \quad -\sqrt{25}$$

Evaluate. Express your answers in fractional notation or round decimals to the nearest thousandth, as appropriate.

9. $-28 + 13$

10. $4.8 - 7.36$

11. $-87 \div (-29)$

12. $-\dfrac{5}{8} - \dfrac{2}{3}$

13. $-2\dfrac{3}{4} \div 1\dfrac{3}{7}$

14. $\left(-\dfrac{2}{3}\right)\left(\dfrac{3}{8}\right)\left(-\dfrac{7}{16}\right)\left(\dfrac{9}{10}\right)$

15. $(12.96)(-4.8)$

16. $(14)(0)(5)(-6)$

17. $(-12)(16) \div 4(-2)$

18. $14 + (-7) + 22 - 16 - (-18)$

19. $-[3.8 - (-2.4)]$

20. $\dfrac{2(3^2 + 7) - 2^5}{3.18}$

21. $-|12 - 20|$

22. $\sqrt{\dfrac{16}{25}}$

23. $-\sqrt{1.2}$

24. $\sqrt{-16}$

25. $\sqrt[3]{1\dfrac{13}{81}}$

26. 14^0

27. 1^{12}

28. 0^0

29. -8^4

30. $(-8)^4$

31. $\left(\dfrac{1}{10}\right)^{-2}$

Write in scientific notation.

32. 0.00000305

33. $-4,235,600$

Write in standard notation.

34. 3.56×10^{-2}

35. 6.78×10^8

36. Evaluate the expression $\sqrt{-x^2 + 5x - 2} + 5$ for $x = 3$.

37. Consider the algebraic expression $a^3 - 2a^2 + a - 2a^3 + 7a - 5$.

    a. How many terms are in the expression?

    b. List the variable terms.

    c. List the constant terms.

    d. Simplify the expression.

Simplify exercises 38–40.

38. $-(3y + 2z) + (4y - 2z) - (-3y - 5z)$

39. $\dfrac{3x}{4} + \dfrac{5y}{8} - \dfrac{1}{16} - \dfrac{3x}{4} + \dfrac{y}{8} - \dfrac{5}{6}$

40. $2[8 + 3(x - 4) - 2(3x + 1)]$

41. Determine whether -2 is a solution of the equation $-x^2 + 3x + 8 = -3x$.

In exercises 42–46, consider the relation $y = 2x^2 + 3$, where x is the independent variable.

42. Graph the relation.

43. What is the domain of the relation? What is the range of the relation?

44. Is this relation a function? Justify your answer.

45. Determine the relative minima if possible.

46. Determine the x-values for which the relation is increasing.

47. For the function $f(x) = \frac{1}{3}x - 5$, find

    a. $f(9)$ **b.** $f(3 + h)$

48. Determine the volume of a rectangular solid with a length of 3.5 feet, a width of 2.25 feet, and a height of 1.75 feet.

49. Kelsie invests $500 for four years with simple interest applied annually at 5.5%. Find the total amount of interest she will receive. What is her total investment amount?

50. The Christmas House produces Christmas decorations. The setup cost for a certain ornament is $35.00. The cost of labor and materials per ornament is $2.80. Write a function to represent the cost of producing x ornaments in one production run. What is the cost of producing 150 ornaments in one production run?

2

Linear Equations in One Variable

In Chapter 1 we saw how to describe relations using tables, equations, and graphs. In this chapter we present methods for solving equations—that is, using the description of a relation to find values of a variable that make the equation true. We work here with linear equations in one variable, which have fewer complications than more general kinds of equations. However, the three different methods we present—numeric, graphic, and algebraic—will apply to other kinds of equations in later chapters, as well as to solving real-world problems.

The real-world situations that we will examine involve linear relationships and may be solved using a linear equation in one variable. These linear relationships are found in many aspects of our lives, including analyzing the weather, renting an automobile, setting up a business, or making an investment. Many geometric relationships can also be linear. We conclude the chapter with a project illustrating a famous geometric relationship, the golden ratio, that has a very interesting history, beginning with the Egyptians, who thought the ratio was sacred. Indeed, some of their hieroglyphics have proportions based on the golden ratio.

2.1 SOLVING EQUATIONS NUMERICALLY AND GRAPHICALLY

OBJECTIVES

1 Identify linear equations in one variable.

2 Solve linear equations numerically.

3 Solve linear equations graphically.

4 Identify linear equations that are contradictions and linear equations that are identities numerically and graphically.

5 Model real-world situations by using linear equations, and solve them numerically or graphically.

APPLICATION

The average high temperature for Washington, DC, in the month of May is 76°F. If the high temperatures for the first six days of the third week of May are 73°, 75°, 77°, 75°, 76°, and 75°, what temperature is needed on the last day of the week to obtain a weekly average that is the same as the monthly average high temperature for May?

We will discuss this application further. See page 202.

Objective 2.1.1   **Identifying Linear Equations in One Variable**

In this text, we will be solving various kinds of equations. In this chapter, we will solve **linear equations in one variable**. These equations can be written in a particular (standard) form.

STANDARD FORM FOR A LINEAR EQUATION IN ONE VARIABLE

A linear equation in one variable (linear equation) is an equation that can be written in the form

$$ax + b = 0, \text{ where } a \text{ and } b \text{ are real numbers and } a \neq 0.$$

For example,

1. $2x + 5 \qquad = 0$ Standard form: $ax + b = 0$

2. $2x - 5 \qquad = 6$ Not standard form

3. $x + 2 + 3(x - 4) = 3x - 8$ Not standard form

The first equation is in the exact form $ax + b = 0$, where $a = 2$ and $b = 5$. The last two equations can be written in this form with algebraic manipulations that we will learn later in the chapter.

 TAKE NOTE The variable x is raised to the first power. This *must* be the case for a linear equation in one variable.

Examples of nonlinear equations that contain variables raised to powers other than 1, variables in denominators of fractions, or roots of variables are listed here. We will solve these equations later in the text.

1. $2x^2 = 4$ x raised to the second power

2. $\dfrac{2}{x} + 1 = 0$ x in the denominator of a fraction

3. $2\sqrt{x} + 5 = x - 3$ x in the radicand of a radical expression

Until we learn algebraic manipulations, we will identify a linear equation in one variable, x, as an equation consisting of two expressions. Each of these expressions can be simplified to the form $ax + b$, where $a \neq 0$ in at least one of the expressions and the coefficient a is not the same in each expression.

 TAKE NOTE   Equations such as $2x + 3 = 2x + 5$ and $2x + 3 = 2x + (5 - 2)$ are not linear. With algebraic manipulations these equations will result in a standard form with $a = 0$.

Using the previous linear examples, we have

Form: $ax + b$ $ax + b$

1. $2x + 5 = 0x + 0$ $a = 2, b = 5; a = 0, b = 0$

2. $2x + (-5) = 0x + 6$ $a = 2, b = -5; a = 0, b = 6$

3. $4x + (-10) = 3x + (-8)$ $a = 4, b = -10; a = 3, b = -8$

These equations are called linear equations because the graphs of the functions defined by the two expressions in the equation turn out to be straight lines. Let's test this statement on the calculator. Complete the following set of exercises with your calculator.

Guided Discovery 1   Graphs of Functions Defined by Expressions in a Linear Equation

On a standard screen, graph the following functions, determined from the given linear equation:

1. $3x - 8 = 6$
   $Y1 = 3x - 8$ $Y2 = 6$

2. $-2x + 5 = -3x - 4$
   $Y1 = -2x + 5$ $Y2 = -3x - 4$

Describe the characteristic of the graph of the function defined by the expression in Y1.

Describe the characteristic of the graph of the function defined by the expression in Y2.

On an integer screen, graph the following functions, determined from the given nonlinear equation:

3. $\dfrac{2}{x} = x$

   $Y1 = \dfrac{2}{x}$ $Y2 = x$

4. $2x^3 = 4$
   $Y1 = 2x^3$ $Y2 = 4$

Describe the characteristic of the graph of the function defined by the expression in Y1.

Describe the characteristic of the graph of the function defined by the expression in Y2.

For linear equations, we see that the graphs of the functions defined by the expressions are straight lines.

EXAMPLE 1   Identify each equation as linear or nonlinear. Check your results graphically on your calculator.

a. $5x + (x - 2) = 3(x - 2)$

b. $\sqrt[4]{x + 2} = 3x - 7$

c. $\dfrac{x}{5} + 3 = 6x$

d. $2x^2 = 4$

Solution

a. Linear, because the equation simplifies to $6x - 2 = 3x - 6$, with both expressions in the form $ax + b$.

b. Nonlinear, because the radical expression has a variable in its radicand.

c. Linear, because the equation simplifies to $\frac{1}{5}x + 3 = 6x$, with both expressions in the form $ax + b$.

d. Nonlinear, because x has an exponent of 2.

Check

Check your results graphically on your calculator. You may graph the expression on the left side of the equation and the expression on the right side of the equation in the same window.

a. $Y1 = 5x + (x - 2)$ $Y2 = 3(x - 2)$

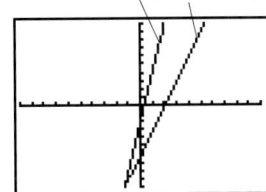

$(-10, 10, -10, 10)$
Linear, because the functions graphed are both lines.

b. $Y2 = 3x - 7$ $Y1 = \sqrt[4]{x + 2}$

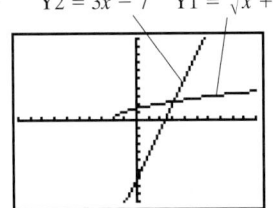

$(-10, 10, -10, 10)$
Nonlinear, because the graph of the function Y1, defined by the radical expression containing a variable in the radicand, is not a line.

c. $Y2 = 6x$ $Y1 = \frac{x}{5} + 3$

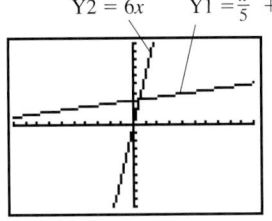

$(-10, 10, -10, 10)$
Linear, because the functions graphed are both lines.

d. $Y1 = 2x^2$ $Y2 = 4$

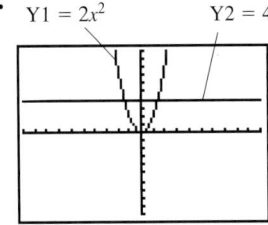

$(-10, 10, -10, 10)$
Nonlinear, because the graph of Y1, defined by the expression containing x^2, is not a line.

Objective 2.1.1   *CHECKUP*

1. Identify each equation as linear or nonlinear.

a. $5x - (x - 7) = x - 5$ **b.** $\frac{1}{7}x - \frac{3}{7} = \frac{5}{14}x + \frac{1}{2}$

c. $2x + 8 = \sqrt{x} + 1$ **d.** $\frac{1}{x^2} + 12 = 5$

2. What is meant by the standard form of a linear equation in one variable?

Objective 2.1.2   Solving Equations Numerically

In Chapter P, we determined whether a number was a solution of an equation by substituting the number for the variable and evaluating the two resulting expressions in the equation. If the expressions were equivalent, then the number substituted was called a solution. The set of all possible solutions is called a solution set. For example, determine whether 0 is a solution of $3x - 9 = -2x + 6$.

$3x - 9 =$	$-2x + 6$	
$3(0) - 9$	$-2(0) + 6$	Substitute 0 for x.
$0 - 9$	$0 + 6$	Simplify.
-9	6	

Therefore, 0 is not a solution, because the resulting values for the expressions, -9 and 6, are not equal.

To find a solution of the equation $3x - 9 = -2x + 6$, we could continue to substitute values for x until we find a number that results in equivalent values for each expression in the equation. To do this, it is convenient to use a table. You can see what we mean by trying the following Guided Discovery exercise.

Guided Discovery 2   Numerical Solutions

To solve the equation $3x - 9 = -2x + 6$, complete the extended table of values shown, compare the values obtained, and determine the difference of the values.

x	$3x - 9$	$=$	$-2x + 6$		
0	-9		6	$-9 < 6$	$-9 - 6 = -15$
1					
2					
3					
4					

Write a rule to determine the solution of an equation from a table of values.

The solution is the number in the first column that, when substituted for the variable, results in two equal expressions. In comparing the values obtained for the expressions, we see that the first expression is first less than, then equal to, and then greater than, the second expression. The difference of the value of the first expression and the value of the second expression changes from negative to zero to positive.

SOLVING A LINEAR EQUATION NUMERICALLY

To solve a linear equation numerically,
Set up an extended table of values.

- The first column is labeled with the independent variable.
- The second column is labeled with the expression on the left side of the equation.
- The third column is labeled with the expression on the right side of the equation.

Complete the table.

- Substitute values for the independent variable.
- Evaluate the second and third columns.
- Continue evaluating until the values of the two expressions (the numbers in the second and third columns) are equal.

The value of the independent variable (the number in the first column) substituted to find the equivalent expressions is the solution.

For example, solve $2x + 3 = x + 5$ numerically for integer solutions.
The following is a sample table to determine an integer solution:

x	$2x + 3$	$=$	$x + 5$		
0	$2(0) + 3$ 3		$0 + 5$ 5	$3 < 5$	$3 - 5 = -2$
1	$2(1) + 3$ 5		$1 + 5$ 6	$5 < 6$	$5 - 6 = -1$
2	$2(2) + 3$ 7		$2 + 5$ 7	$7 = 7$	$7 - 7 = 0$
3	$2(3) + 3$ 9		$3 + 5$ 8	$9 > 8$	$9 - 8 = 1$
4	$2(4) + 3$ 11		$4 + 5$ 9	$11 > 9$	$11 - 9 = 2$

When 2 is substituted for the variable x, the two expressions are equivalent ($7 = 7$). Therefore, 2 is the solution of the linear equation $2x + 3 = x + 5$.

Note that in comparing the values obtained for the two expressions, the first expression is less than the second expression when $x = 0$ and $x = 1$ (values less than the solution), but greater than the second expression when $x = 3$ and $x = 4$ (values greater than the solution).

Note also that the difference of the value obtained for the first expression and the value obtained for the second expression is negative for $x = 0$ and $x = 1$, but is positive for $x = 3$ and $x = 4$.

To solve $2x + 3 = x + 5$ numerically for integer solutions on a calculator, complete the steps in the technology box that follows. As shown in **Figure 2.1c**, the solution is 2, because when $x = 2$, Y1 and Y2 have equal values.

TECHNOLOGY   Solving Equations Numerically

Solve $2x + 3 = x + 5$ numerically for integer solutions.

Figure 2.1a   **Figure 2.1b**   **Figure 2.1c**

Rename the independent variable x if necessary.
For **Figure 2.1a**,
Set up the table.

[2nd] [WINDOW] (TBLSET)

Set up the first column for the independent variable, x, by setting a minimum integer value, 0, and increments of 1 for integers.

[0] [ENTER] (Minimum number in the table is 0.)

[1] [ENTER] (Independent variable values are increasing by 1.)

Set the calculator to perform the operations automatically.

[ENTER] [▼] [ENTER]

For **Figure 2.1b**,
Set up the second column to be the expression on the left side by entering the left expression of the equation, $2x + 3$, in Y1.

[Y=] [2] [X,T,θ,n] [+] [3] [ENTER]

Set up the third column to be the expression on the right side by entering the right expression of the equation, $x + 5$, in Y2.

[X,T,θ,n] [+] [5]

For **Figure 2.1c**,
View the table.

[2nd] [GRAPH] (TABLE)

Move beyond the screen to view additional rows by using the up and down arrows.
The solution is the x-value that results in equal Y1 and Y2 values. The solution of $2x + 3 = x + 5$ is 2 because $7 = 7$.

Linear equations may have a noninteger solution. Try solving this next equation with your calculator.

 Guided Discovery 3   Equations with Noninteger Solutions

$(5x + 4) - 2(3x + 1) = 2(x - 7)$ does not have an integer solution. Complete the table of values, compare the values obtained, and determine their difference.

x	$(5x + 4) - 2(3x + 1)$	$= 2(x - 7)$		
3	-1	-8	$-1 > -8$	$-1 - (-8) = 7$
4				
5				
6				
7				

Write a rule for determining when the solution of an equation is between two integers given in a table of values.

The expression on the left is greater than the expression on the right for x-values of 3, 4, and 5. The expression on the left is less than the expression on the right for x-values of 6 and 7. Therefore, the expression on the left is equal to the expression on the right at some x-value between 5 and 6. The solution is thus noninteger. (We will need a different method to find this solution.)

Note that the differences are positive for the x-values of 3, 4, and 5. The differences are negative for the x-values of 6 and 7.

EXAMPLE 2 Solve numerically if possible.

a. $3a + 5 = 2a$ **b.** $6x - (4x + 3) = 7 - 3x$

c. $4 - 5x - (3x + 2) = 7 - x$

Solution

a. Rewrite the equation in terms of x—that is, $3x + 5 = 2x$.
Let $Y1 = 3x + 5$ and $Y2 = 2x$.
A sample table is shown in **Figure 2.2a**.

X	Y1	Y2		
-7	-16	-14	$-16 < -14$	$-16 - (-14) = -2$
-6	-13	-12	$-13 < -12$	$-13 - (-12) = -1$
-5	-10	-10	$-10 = -10$	$-10 - (-10) = 0$
-4	-7	-8	$-7 > -8$	$-7 - (-8) = 1$
-3	-4	-6	$-4 > -6$	$-4 - (-6) = 2$
-2	-1	-4	$-1 > -4$	$-1 - (-4) = 3$
-1	2	-2	$2 > -2$	$2 - (-2) = 4$

X= -7

Figure 2.2a

The solution is -5 because, when -5 is substituted for the variable a in both expressions, the results are equivalent: $-10 = -10$.

b. A sample table is shown in **Figure 2.2b**.

X	Y1	Y2		
0	-3	7	$-3 < 7$	$-3 - 7 = -10$
1	-1	4	$-1 < 4$	$-1 - 4 = -5$
2	1	1	$1 = 1$	$1 - 1 = 0$
3	3	-2	$3 > -2$	$3 - (-2) = 5$
4	5	-5	$5 > -5$	$5 - (-5) = 10$
5	7	-8	$7 > -8$	$7 - (-8) = 15$
6	9	-11	$9 > -11$	$9 - (-11) = 20$

X=0

$Y1 = 6x - (4x + 3)$ $Y2 = 7 - 3x$

Figure 2.2b

The solution is 2 because, when 2 is substituted for the variable x in both expressions, the results are equivalent: $1 = 1$.

c. A sample table is shown in **Figure 2.2c**.

X	Y1	Y2		
-2	18	9	$18 > 9$	$18 - 9 = 9$
-1	10	8	$10 > 8$	$10 - 8 = 2$
0	2	7	$2 < 7$	$2 - 7 = -5$
1	-6	6	$-6 < 6$	$-6 - 6 = -12$
2	-14	5	$-14 < 5$	$-14 - 5 = -19$
3	-22	4	$-22 < 4$	$-22 - 4 = -26$
4	-30	3	$-30 < 3$	$-30 - 3 = -33$

X= -2

$Y1 = 4 - 5x - (3x + 2)$ $Y2 = 7 - x$

Figure 2.2c

The expression on the left is greater than the expression on the right for $x = -1$ and less than the expression on the right for $x = 0$. The solution is noninteger and between -1 and 0. We will need another method to find the solution of this equation.

Objective 2.1.2 *CHECKUP*

1. Solve numerically if possible. If the solution is a noninteger one, indicate between what two integers it is located.
   a. $3x + 6 = x + 2$
   b. $\frac{1}{2}(3 + 2x) = 2x - \frac{1}{2}$
   c. $4b - (2b + 3) = 10 - 3b$

2. When solving a linear equation numerically, how can you tell between what two integers a noninteger solution will be located?

Objective 2.1.3   ## Solving Equations Graphically

A second method of solving an equation is to graph two functions. The functions to be graphed are written using each expression in the equation as a rule for one of the functions. For example, for the equation $3x - 9 = -2x + 6$, we write the two functions $Y1 = 3x - 9$ and $Y2 = -2x + 6$. Try it yourself in the next Guided Discovery exercise. Complete the exercise on your calculator.

💡 Guided Discovery 4   Graphical Solutions

To solve the equation $3x - 9 = -2x + 6$, graph the functions $Y1 = 3x - 9$ and $Y2 = -2x + 6$. Label the point of intersection of the graphs.

Write a rule for determining the solution of an equation from the graph of the two functions.

Write a rule for determining the numerical value of each expression when the equation is evaluated at its solution.

The solution of the equation is the x-coordinate of the point of intersection. The y-coordinate of the point of intersection is the value of each expression in the equation when x is replaced by the solution.

SOLVING A LINEAR EQUATION GRAPHICALLY

To solve a linear equation graphically,

- Write two functions, using each expression in the equation as a rule.
- Graph both functions on the same coordinate plane by plotting points found in the table of values and connecting the points with a line, to include all values in the domains of the functions.
- Determine the point of intersection of the lines.

The solution of the equation is the x-coordinate of the point of intersection of the two lines.

The y-coordinate of the point of intersection of the two lines is the value obtained for both expressions when the equation is evaluated with the solution.

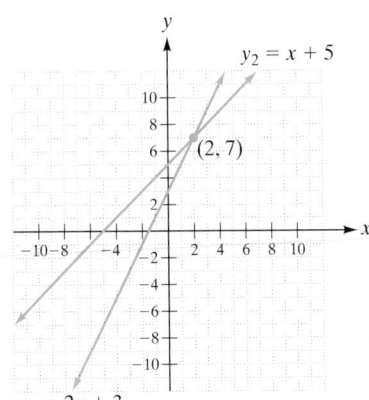

Figure 2.3

For example, solve $2x + 3 = x + 5$ graphically.

Let $y_1 = 2x + 3$ and $y_2 = x + 5$, and graph the equations.

The solution is 2, because the x-coordinate of the intersection is 2, as shown in **Figure 2.3**.

To solve $2x + 3 = x + 5$ graphically on your calculator, complete the steps in the next technology box.

As shown in **Figure 2.4b**, the solution is 2, because the x-coordinate of the intersection is 2.

TECHNOLOGY Solving Equations Graphically

Solve $2x + 3 = x + 5$ graphically.

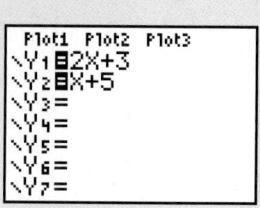

Figure 2.4a

$Y1 = 2x + 3$ $Y2 = x + 5$

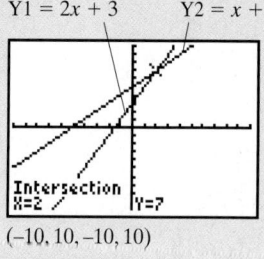

$(-10, 10, -10, 10)$

Figure 2.4b

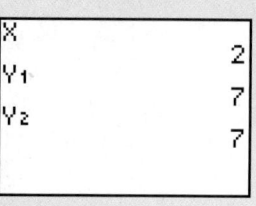

Figure 2.4c

Rename the independent variable x if necessary.

For **Figure 2.4a**,

Enter the expression on the left side of the equation, $2x + 3$, as Y1.

[Y=] [2] [X,T,θ,n] [+] [3] [ENTER]

Enter the expression on the right side of the equation, $x + 5$, as Y2.

[X,T,θ,n] [+] [5]

For **Figure 2.4b**,

Graph the equations. (In this case, we will use the standard window.)

[ZOOM] [6]

Find the intersection of the graphs. First trace the graph.

[TRACE]

Use the arrow keys to find the intersection.

If the intersection cannot be found by tracing, use Intersect, option 5, under the CALC menu.

[2nd] [TRACE] (CALC) [5] [ENTER] [ENTER] [ENTER]

For **Figure 2.4c**,

The solution is the x-value of the intersection point and is stored in x. The y-coordinate of the point of intersection is the value obtained for both the left side (Y1) and the right side (Y2) and is also stored. We can use this feature to check whether Y1 equals Y2.

Quit the graph screen and enter x.

[2nd] [MODE] (QUIT) [X,T,θ,n] [ENTER]

Enter Y1 and Y2.

[VARS] [▶] [1] [1] [ENTER]

[VARS] [▶] [1] [2] [ENTER]

Since $x = 2$ when $7 = 7$ (or Y1 = Y2), the solution of $2x + 3 = x + 5$ is 2.

EXAMPLE 3

Solve graphically.

a. $3a + 5 = 2a$ **b.** $6x - (4x + 3) = 7 - 3x$

c. $(5x + 4) - 2(3x + 1) = 2(x - 7)$

Calculator Graphic Solution

a. To graph the equation with your calculator, change the variable a to x.

$$3x + 5 = 2x$$
$$\text{Let } Y1 = 3x + 5$$
$$Y2 = 2x$$

$Y1 = 3x + 5$ $Y2 = 2x$

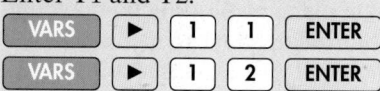

$(-47, 47, -31, 31)$

The solution is -5, because the x-coordinate of the intersection is -5.

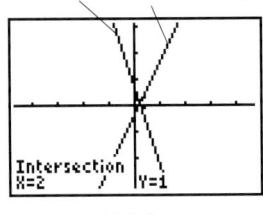

$Y2 = 7 - 3x$ $Y1 = 6x - (4x + 3)$

$(-47, 47, -31, 31)$

b. When using your calculator to graph, you do not have to simplify the expressions on the left side or right side of the equation.

$$\text{Let } Y1 = 6x - (4x + 3)$$
$$Y2 = 7 - 3x$$

The solution is 2, because the *x*-coordinate of the intersection is 2.

c. $(5x + 4) - 2(3x + 1) = 2(x - 7)$

$$\text{Let } Y1 = (5x + 4) - 2(3x + 1)$$
$$Y2 = 2(x - 7)$$

There is no integer solution. Use the Intersect function on your calculator to find the solution.

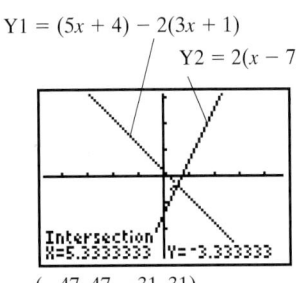

$Y1 = (5x + 4) - 2(3x + 1)$
$Y2 = 2(x - 7)$

$(-47, 47, -31, 31)$

Figure 2.5a

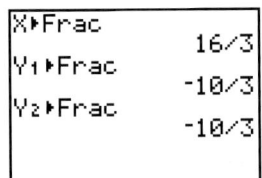

Figure 2.5b

As shown in **Figures 2.5a** and **2.5b**, the solution is $5.\overline{3}$ or $\frac{16}{3}$.

 Objective 2.1.3 CHECKUP

1. Solve graphically.

   a. $3x + 6 = x + 2$

   b. $\frac{1}{2}(3 + 2x) = 2x - \frac{1}{2}$

   c. $4b - (2b + 3) = 10 - 3b$

2. Explain why the *x*-coordinate of the point of intersection of the two functions defined from the original equation represents the solution of the original equation.

Objective 2.1.4 **Identifying Contradictions and Identities**

The equations in Examples 2 and 3 have one solution. This is not always true. Try solving the following equations with your calculator.

Guided Discovery 5 Equations with No Solution

1. Solve $2x + 5 = 2x + 10$ numerically by completing a table of values.

Write a rule explaining how to solve the equation by viewing its table of values.

2. Solve $2x + 5 = 2x + 10$ graphically. Sketch the graph.

Write a rule explaining how to solve the equation by viewing its graph.

Viewing the table of values, we find that the expression on the left is always five less than the expression on the right. The two expressions will never be equal. The equation does not appear to have a solution. Such an equation is called a contradiction. A **contradiction** is an equation with no solution.

The two graphs do not appear to intersect. (The lines are parallel.) Therefore, there is no ordered pair common to both functions, which means that there is no solution of the equation. The equation is a contradiction.

TAKE NOTE The equation $2x + 5 = 2.0000001x + 10$ looks as if it has no solution when we examine a table of values. The table has a constant difference of 5 between the expressions on the left and right. However, other methods will give us a noninteger solution. This fact emphasizes the need to know other methods to check our findings.

For example, if we graphically solve $2x + 5 = 2.000001x + 10$, the lines appear parallel when they are not. However, if we move between the two graphs with the up and down arrows, we can see that the difference of the y-coordinates is not constant for all x-coordinates.

Guided Discovery 6   Equations with Many Solutions

1. Solve $2x + 5 = (x + 3) + (x + 2)$ numerically by completing a table of values.

Write a rule explaining how to solve the equation by viewing its table of values.

2. Solve $2x + 5 = (x + 3) + (x + 2)$ graphically. Sketch the graph.

Write a rule explaining how to solve the equation by viewing its graph.

Viewing the table of values, we find that the two expressions are equal for every value of the independent variable evaluated. (This is also true for any other real-number value chosen for x.) The solution set of the equation is the set of all real numbers. Such an equation is called an identity. An **identity** is an equation for which all permissible replacements of the variable result in a true equation.

Although it seems as if there is only one graph on the screen, actually there are two, but they are the same line. (The lines coincide.) Therefore, all ordered pairs on the graph are common to both functions, and all their x-coordinates are solutions of the equation. The solution set is the set of all real numbers (the domain of the functions graphed). The equation is an identity.

EXAMPLE 4   Solve graphically and numerically.

a. $4(x - 2) = 4x - 8$

b. $3x + 4 = 2x + (x + 10)$

Calculator Solution

a. Let Y1 = $4(x - 2) = 4x - 8$
       Y2 = $4x - 8$

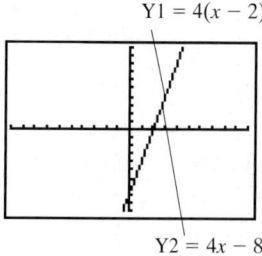

Y1 = $4(x - 2)$

Y2 = $4x - 8$

X	Y₁	Y₂	
0	-8	-8	$-8 = -8$
1	-4	-4	$-4 = -4$
2	0	0	$0 = 0$
3	4	4	$4 = 4$
4	8	8	$8 = 8$
5	12	12	$12 = 12$
6	16	16	$16 = 16$

X=0

The two graphs are the same. The solution set is the set of all real numbers

The expressions are always equal. The solution set is the set of all real numbers.

 TAKE NOTE The solution set of a linear equation is the set of all real numbers when the simplified expression on the left side and the simplified expression on the right side are the same.

b. Let $Y1 = 3x + 4$
$Y2 = 2x + (x + 10)$

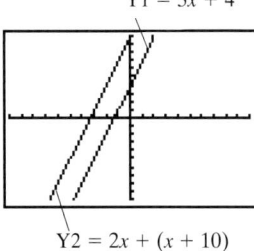

$Y1 = 3x + 4$

X	Y₁	Y₂		
0	4	10	4 < 10	4 − 10 = −6
1	7	13	7 < 13	7 − 13 = −6
2	10	16	10 < 16	10 − 16 = −6
3	13	19	13 < 19	13 − 19 = −6
4	16	22	16 < 22	16 − 22 = −6
5	19	25	19 < 25	19 − 25 = −6
6	22	28	22 < 28	22 − 28 = −6

X=0

$Y2 = 2x + (x + 10)$

The two graphs do not intersect. The table of values confirms this fact. The expressions will never be equal. There is no solution.

The difference of the values of the two expressions is always the same. The expressions will never be equal. There is no solution.

We can summarize the preceding discoveries and exercises.

NUMERICAL SOLUTIONS

To solve an equation numerically for integer solutions, set up an extended table of values. One of four possibilities will occur:

An integer solution exists. The solution is the integer in the first column that corresponds to equal values in the second and third columns.

A noninteger solution exists. The values in the second column change in order from less than to greater than, or from greater than to less than, the values in the third column. The noninteger solution is between the two integers in the first column that correspond to this change.

No solution exists. In the second and third columns, all of the differences of the values are the same.

An infinite number of solutions exist. In the second and third columns, all of the corresponding values are equal.

In conclusion, an equation may be solved numerically by using a table of values. However, if the solution is noninteger, it will be difficult to find by that method. The graphic method will solve noninteger equations.

GRAPHICAL SOLUTIONS

To solve an equation graphically, graph the two functions defined by the expressions on the left and right sides of the equation. One of three possibilities will occur:

One solution exists. The graphs intersect. The solution is the x-coordinate of the point of intersection.

No solution exists. The graphs are parallel.

An infinite number of solutions exist. The graphs coincide.

Objective 2.1.4 *CHECKUP*

1. Solve numerically and graphically if possible.
   a. $(a - 1) + (a - 3) = 2(a - 2)$
   b. $(x + 1) + (3x + 4) = 3(x - 1) + x$
2. In solving a linear equation numerically and graphically, what results indicate that the equation may have no solution? What do we call a linear equation that has no solution?
3. In solving a linear equation numerically and graphically, what results indicate that the equation has many solutions? What do we call a linear equation that has many solutions?

Objective 2.1.5   ## Modeling the Real World

Linear equations in one variable are very common descriptions of real-world situations. In practical terms, you don't always need to solve these equations—for example, you may know that a $50 bill is going to cover the cost of filling your car with gasoline at your local service station, regardless of whether it will take 12 gallons, 13 gallons, or whatever your gas tank will hold. But if you need to know how much money you'll need for gas when you drive across the country, or if you're comparing the costs of two different car rental plans, the equation-solving methods discussed in this section can help you make the right decision.

EXAMPLE 5

Jacques rented a carpet shampooer for $28.50 per day, including all supplies. Jill rented a floor buffer for $18.25 per day, plus $20.50 for the wax. They kept the shampooer and buffer for the same number of days and spent the same amount. Determine how many days the shampooer and buffer were rented and the amount each person spent.

Solution

Let x = the number of days rented

The shampooer rental was $28.50 per day for x days, or $28.50x$. The buffer rental was $18.25 per day for x days plus $20.50, or $18.25x + 20.50$.

$$28.50x = 18.25x + 20.50$$

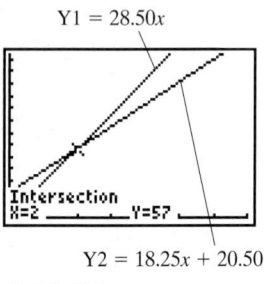

Y1 = 28.50x
Y2 = 18.25x + 20.50

Y1 = 28.50x

Intersection
X=2   Y=57

Y2 = 18.25x + 20.50

(0, 7, 0, 134)

Numeric

Set up a table of values as shown in the figure to the left.

The solution is 2, because $x = 2$ corresponds to the value of 57, where Y1 and Y2 are equal. The shampooer and buffer were rented for two days. Jacques and Jill spent $57.00 each.

Graphic

Graph the two functions Y1 = 28.50x and Y2 = 18.25x + 20.50 as shown in the figure to the left.

The solution is 2, because 2 is the x-coordinate of the point of intersection. The shampooer and buffer were rented for two days. Jacques and Jill spent $57.00 each. ∎

APPLICATION

The average high temperature for Washington, DC, in the month of May is 76°F. If the high temperatures for the first six days of the third week of May are 73°, 75°, 77°, 75°, 76°, and 75°, what temperature is needed on the last day of the week to obtain a weekly average that is the same as the monthly average high temperature for May?

Discussion

Let x = the high temperature for the last day of the week. The average temperature is found by dividing the sum of the temperatures by the number of temperatures, namely, 7.

$$\frac{73 + 75 + 77 + 75 + 76 + 75 + x}{7} = 76$$

Graphic Solution

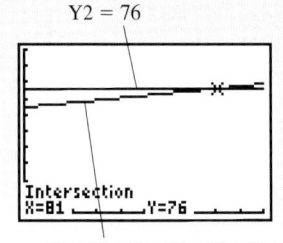

Y2 = 76

Intersection
X=81   Y=76

$Y1 = \dfrac{73 + 75 + 77 + 75 + 76 + 75 + x}{7}$

(0, 100, 0, 100)
The solution is 81.

Numeric Solution

X	Y₁	Y₂
79	75.714	76
80	75.857	76
81	76	76
82	76.143	76
83	76.286	76
84	76.429	76
85	76.571	76

X=79

$Y1 = \dfrac{73 + 75 + 77 + 75 + 76 + 75 + x}{7}$

Y2 = 76
The solution is 81.

The last day of the week, the temperature must reach 81°F to obtain a weekly average high temperature of 76°F.

Note, according to the table and graph, when temperatures are less than 81 degrees, the weekly average will be below the average high. When temperatures are greater than 81 degrees, the weekly average will be above the average high.

✓ Objective 2.1.5 *CHECKUP*

1. Handyman Pete offers to paint your garage for $149. Handywoman Gladys offers to do the same job for $45 plus $13 per hour. How many hours will it take Gladys to complete the job in order to do it for the same cost as Pete?

2. Phillipe scored 83, 88, 91, 90, and 92 on his first five algebra exams. He is trying to earn an average of 90 in the course. What is the score he must get on the next test to achieve an average of 90?

2.1 EXERCISES

 Student Solutions Manual    PH Math/Tutor Center   CD Video    *Math* XL MathXL®   **MyMathLab** MyMathLab   Interactmath.com

Identify each equation as linear or nonlinear.

1. $6x - 55 = x + 72$

2. $5(x - 3) = -(2x - 1)$

3. $4x^2 + 5 = 2x - 6$

4. $70x - 48 = 150x + 102$

5. $\dfrac{7}{9}z - \dfrac{2}{3} = 0$

6. $4.7x^2 - 5.3 = 4.4x + 0.7$

7. $\sqrt[3]{4x + 16} = 27$

8. $x^{1/3} = 64$

9. $3(2x - 5) = x + 3(x - 9)$

10. $235x - 476 = 0$

Use the calculator screens first to write the equation being solved and then to determine the solution or solutions (if any) of the equation.

11.

```
Plot1  Plot2  Plot3
\Y1 ■ 2X-7
\Y2 ■ X+2
\Y3 =
\Y4 =
\Y5 =
\Y6 =
\Y7 =
```

X	Y₁	Y₂
6	5	8
7	7	9
8	9	10
9	11	11
10	13	12
11	15	13
12	17	14

X=12

12.

```
Plot1  Plot2  Plot3
\Y1 ■ (1/2)X-3
\Y2 ■ X-1
\Y3 =
\Y4 =
\Y5 =
\Y6 =
\Y7 =
```

X	Y₁	Y₂
-6	-6	-7
-5	-5.5	-6
-4	-5	-5
-3	-4.5	-4
-2	-4	-3
-1	-3.5	-2
0	-3	-1

X=-6

13.

```
Plot1  Plot2  Plot3
\Y1 ■ .5X+1.25
\Y2 ■ .5(X+2.5)
\Y3 =
\Y4 =
\Y5 =
\Y6 =
\Y7 =
```

X	Y₁	Y₂
0	1.25	1.25
1	1.75	1.75
2	2.25	2.25
3	2.75	2.75
4	3.25	3.25
5	3.75	3.75
6	4.25	4.25

X=0

14.

Plot1 Plot2 Plot3
Y1◻(2/3)X+1
Y2◻X+2-(1/3)(X+3)
Y3=
Y4=
Y5=
Y6=

X	Y1	Y2
-1	.33333	.33333
0	1	1
1	1.6667	1.6667
2	2.3333	2.3333
3	3	3
4	3.6667	3.6667
5	4.3333	4.3333

X=-1

15.

Plot1 Plot2 Plot3
Y1◻X-(4.5-.5X)
Y2◻1.5(X+2)
Y3=
Y4=
Y5=
Y6=
Y7=

X	Y1	Y2
0	-4.5	3
1	-3	4.5
2	-1.5	6
3	0	7.5
4	1.5	9
5	3	10.5
6	4.5	12

X=0

16.

Plot1 Plot2 Plot3
Y1◻X+3(X-5)
Y2◻2(2X-3)
Y3=
Y4=
Y5=
Y6=
Y7=

X	Y1	Y2
0	-15	-6
1	-11	-2
2	-7	2
3	-3	6
4	1	10
5	5	14
6	9	18

X=0

17.

Plot1 Plot2 Plot3
Y1◻(1/3)X+1
Y2◻(3/2)X-1
Y3=
Y4=
Y5=
Y6=
Y7=

X	Y1	Y2
0	1	-1
1	1.3333	.5
2	1.6667	2
3	2	3.5
4	2.3333	5
5	2.6667	6.5
6	3	8

X=0

18.

Plot1 Plot2 Plot3
Y1◻X-1
Y2◻3X+4
Y3=
Y4=
Y5=
Y6=
Y7=

X	Y1	Y2
-6	-7	-14
-5	-6	-11
-4	-5	-8
-3	-4	-5
-2	-3	-2
-1	-2	1
0	-1	4

X=-6

Solve numerically, if possible. Otherwise, solve graphically.

19. $2x - 7 = 35 - x$

20. $4z + 7 = 3z + 12$

21. $3(2x + 11) = 3(5 + x)$

22. $3(x + 10) = -2(x + 5)$

23. $6.8a + 4.3 = 2.6a + 33.7$

24. $\frac{1}{2}(x + 6) = \frac{1}{4}(x + 16) - 1$

25. $7(x + 10) + 15 = 6(x + 15) + (x - 5)$

26. $3(x - 4) = 2(x + 6) - 3(x + 7)$

27. $(a - 4) - (a + 4) = (a + 3) - (a - 2)$

28. $4(x + 1) - 2(x + 3) = 3(x + 1) - (x + 3)$

29. $3.5(z - 1) = 7(0.5z + 0.6) + 2$

30. $2(2.9x - 2.3) = 4.6(x - 1) + 1.2x$

31. $\frac{4}{5}(x - 1) = 6\left(\frac{1}{15}x - \frac{1}{10}\right)$

32. $\frac{1}{2}(x + 1) + \frac{1}{4}(x + 1) = \frac{3}{4}(x + 1)$

Use the calculator screens first to write the equation being solved and then to determine the solution or solutions (if any) of the equation.

33.

Plot1 Plot2 Plot3
Y1◻3X+2
Y2◻4-X
Y3=
Y4=
Y5=
Y6=
Y7=

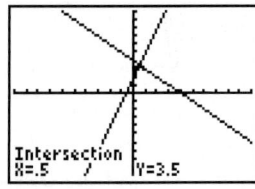

Intersection
X=.5   Y=3.5

34.

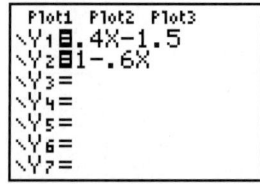

Plot1 Plot2 Plot3
Y1◻.4X-1.5
Y2◻1-.6X
Y3=
Y4=
Y5=
Y6=
Y7=

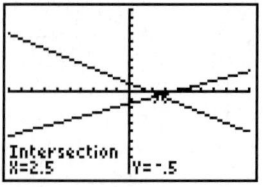

Intersection
X=2.5   Y=-.5

35.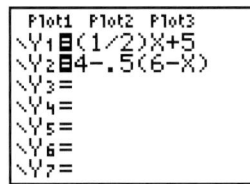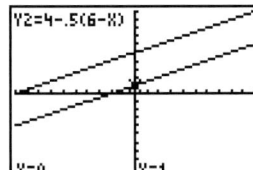

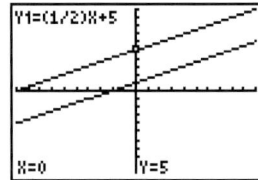

36.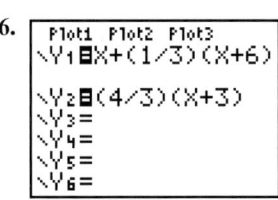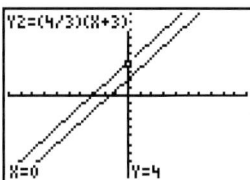

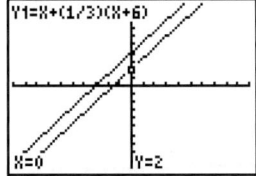

Solve graphically.

37. $x + 6 = 9 + 2x$

38. $(4x - 1) + (x - 6) = 3(2x + 1) - (x + 10)$

39. $(x + 4) + (x + 2) = (x - 1) + (x - 3)$

40. $2x - 8 = x - 6$

41. $2(x + 3) = 3(x - 1) - (x - 9)$

42. $2 - 3x = 4 - x$

43. $1.7x - 22.2 = 13.8 - 0.7x$

44. $5(0.5x + 0.3) = 0.1(25x + 15)$

45. $2.2(x - 1) + 1.7x = 3.5(x + 1) + 0.4x$

46. $7.3x + 23.7 = 2.6x - 13.9$

47. $\frac{4}{5}x + \frac{1}{5} = \frac{1}{5}x + 2$

48. $\frac{17}{24}x + \frac{1}{3} = \frac{1}{4}x + \frac{2}{3}$

49. $\frac{2}{3}(x + 1) - \frac{1}{3} = \frac{1}{3}(x + 1) + \frac{1}{3}x$

50. $\frac{4}{13}x + \frac{17}{4} = \frac{4}{13}x - \frac{7}{2}$

Solve each real-world application numerically or graphically.

Cost/Rental

51. Mathew can rent an Intermediate SUV for $38.99 per day. Since he is under 25 years of age, he must pay an additional fee of $110.00. If he budgeted $500.00 for his trip, how many days can he rent the SUV?

52. Claudette can rent a standard SUV for $43.99 per day. She must also pay an additional $110.00 (because she is 24 years old). If she budgeted $500.00 for her trip, how many days can she rent the SUV?

53. Weston signs a six-month contract with the cellular phone company that charges a monthly fee of $45.00 and $0.20 per minute for minutes beyond 500 because they offer a special deal in which they throw in a camera phone for free. Weston has budgeted $90.00 per month for his cell phone. How many minutes over 500 will this allow him to use?

54. After six months, Weston signed a contract with a cellular phone company that charges a monthly fee of $49.95 and $0.20 per minute beyond 750. He has budgeted $90.00 per month for his cell phone bill. How many minutes over 750 will this allow him to use?

55. Ercille has the choice of paying a flat fee of $25.00 or of paying a fee of $10.00 plus $0.75 per page to have a paper typed. How many pages must the paper be in order to pay the same price for both offers?

56. The Rent-a-Ride car rental company will lease a compact car for $49.95 per day, with unlimited mileage. The Rent-R-Wheels car rental company offers the same car for $29.95 per day plus $0.25 per mile. Determine the number of miles driven that will make the cost of a one-day rental the same for the two offers.

57. Charlene will paper a room for a setup charge of $25, plus $9 per roll of wallpaper and $5 per roll to pay her assistant. Greta does not have an assistant and will do the same work for a setup charge of $25 plus $14 per roll. How many rolls of paper will the job require if Charlene's charge and Greta's charge for the job are the same?

58. Handi-Man Rentals will rent an auger for a flat fee of $20 plus $12 per hour. Tool-Time Rentals will rent the same auger for a flat fee of $25 plus $12 per hour. For what number of hours will the total rental be the same for the two firms?

Breakeven

59. A shoe factory has a daily setup cost of $280. The cost of materials and labor for each pair of shoes produced is $8. The factory sells the shoes at wholesale for $22 a pair. How many pairs of shoes should be produced each day to break even (to have the cost of production equal the revenue from sales)?

60. The cost of producing decorated baskets consists of a setup cost of $150 for materials and a cost of $5 per basket for labor. The baskets sell for $20 each. Determine the number of baskets for which the cost of production equals the revenue received.

Average

61. On a business trip, Ingrid spent $28, $19, $22, and $27 for meals during the first four days of the trip. How much can she spend on the fifth day if she must keep her average daily expense for meals at $25?

62. For the first four weeks of her diet, Caitlin lost 3 pounds, 2 pounds, 3 pounds, and 1 pound. How much must she lose during the fifth week in order to average a loss of 2 pounds per week?

63. The average high temperature for Destin, Florida, in the month of May is 84°F. The high temperatures for the previous six days were 84°, 85°, 85°, 85°, 85°, and 86°. What must the temperature be on the seventh day to achieve a weekly average that is the same as the monthly average high temperature?

64. The average high temperature for Juneau, Alaska, in the month of May is 55°F. The high temperatures for the previous four days were 55°, 55°, 56°, and 58°. What should the temperature be on the fifth day to realize a weekly average that is the same as the monthly average high temperature?

 ## 2.1 Calculator Exercises

Part 1. Using the Zoom Feature to Find Intersection Points

Use your calculator to solve exercises 1 and 2 graphically with the integer screen setting. Even though the lines do not cross on the integer screen, they look as if they will cross if extended. You can still use the intersection method to find the solution. Experiment with other screen settings to find out whether you can see the intersection point. Press ZOOM 3 ENTER to see more of the graph. Afterward, be sure to reset to the integer screen before attempting the second exercise.

1. $10x - 156 = 108 - 2x$

2. $9.2x + 55.8 = 1.4x - 37.8$

In exercises 3 and 4, use the standard screen setting, ZOOM 6 , to graph each equation as two functions. The lines do not appear on the screen, since they are outside the domain and range shown. To see the lines after graphing with the standard screen, repeatedly use the zoom-out feature, ZOOM 3 ENTER , until the lines appear. Now trace toward the point of intersection, and then use the **CALC** function to find the intersection.

3. $7x + 450 = 2x + 1700$

4. $12x + 800 = 8x - 1200$

Before starting another exercise, always reset your screen selection after you have used the ZOOM feature.

Part 2. Using the Test Key to Solve Linear Equations Numerically

When storing the left and right side of the equation in Y1 and Y2, you can also store the condition Y1 = Y2 in Y3. Do this by moving the cursor down to Y3 after entering the functions for Y1 and Y2. Then enter VARS ▶ 1 1 2nd MATH **(TEST)** 1 VARS ▶ 1 2 . Now when you scan the table to find a solution, you can scan the column for Y3, and when you find a row containing a 1, this means that the equation Y1 = Y2 is true, and the value of x for this row is the solution of the equation. Try this additional step on some of the exercises in this section.

Part 3. Using the APPS to Review Topics

In previous sections we have viewed the applications that are in the TI-84 Plus or purchased separately for the TI-83 Plus. In this section, we will view a different algebra chapter that reviews the topics we have discussed in this section, solving numerically and graphically.

First press APPS and 3 to choose 3: ALG1PRT1. (If you purchased this APPS, your application number may be different than 3.) To begin the application press ENTER . You will see the algebra chapters that are available for your use.

If you have used this application, you may need to press ZOOM (UP) to move to this page. In this section, we discussed linear equations. This topic is found in chapter 2:LINEAR EQUATIONS. Press 2 to choose this chapter.

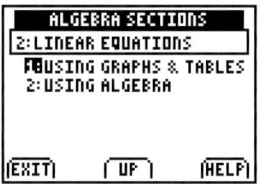

The algebra subsections are listed. Press the number of the subsection that you are interested in. As you proceed in the subsections, you will press ENTER or use your arrow keys as prompted. Have fun as you explore linear equations. After you have completed the next two sections, you may want to return and view the algebra section on using algebra.

In this section, we discussed graphs and tables. Press **1** to choose this algebra subsection, 1: USING GRAPHS AND TABLES.

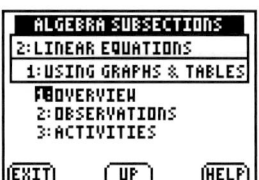

2.1 Writing Exercises

1. When using the numerical method to solve a linear equation in one variable, you construct a table of integer values. When you then search the table for a solution, one of four situations can arise:
   a. There are no solutions of the equation.
   b. There is one integer solution of the equation.
   c. There is one noninteger solution of the equation.
   d. The solution set for the equation is the set of all real numbers in the domain of the relation.

   For each of these outcomes, describe what you would see when you examine the table of values in search of solutions.

   For example, if there are no solutions of the equation, what would you see when you examine the columns for the left and right sides of the equation?

2. When you graphically solve a linear equation in one variable, one of three situations can arise:
   a. There are no solutions of the equation.
   b. There is one solution of the equation.
   c. The solution set for the equation is the set of all real numbers in the domain of the relation.

   For each of these outcomes, describe what you would see when you examine the graph in search of solutions.

2.2 SOLVING EQUATIONS BY USING ADDITION AND MULTIPLICATION

OBJECTIVES

1 Solve linear equations algebraically by using the addition property of equations.

2 Solve linear equations algebraically by using the multiplication property of equations.

3 Model real-world situations by using linear equations, and solve the equations algebraically.

APPLICATION

The U.S. National Center for Education Statistics reports project a 17% increase in public college enrollment from the year 2000 to the year 2012. The projected increase was 1,963,000. What was the enrollment in the year 2000?

After completing this section, we will discuss this application further. See page 214.

Earlier in the text, we defined equivalent expressions to be two expressions with the same value. Similarly, **equivalent equations** are two equations that have exactly the same solutions. In order to write equivalent equations, we will need to know the properties of equations.

Objective 2.2.1

Solving Linear Equations by Using Addition

The addition property of equations is used to write equivalent equations. Let's see if we can discover how it works. Complete the following set of exercises.

 Guided Discovery 7   Addition Property of Equations

Given the equation $7 = 7$, add 2 to both expressions.

$$7 = 7$$
$$\frac{\qquad\qquad\qquad}{}$$
$$7 + 2 \quad | \quad 7 + 2$$
$$9 \qquad | \qquad 9$$

1. Given the equation $7 = 7$, add -2 to both expressions.

2. Given the equation $6 + 1 = 4 + 3$, add 2 to both expressions.

3. Given the equation $6 + 1 = 4 + 3$, add -2 to both expressions.

Write a rule for the addition property of equations.

In each of the preceding exercises, we began with an equation and added the same number to both expressions. The resulting expressions remained equal in value.

This property holds true for subtraction as well, because subtraction is defined to be adding the opposite of a number.

ADDITION PROPERTY OF EQUATIONS

Given expressions a, b, and c,

$$\text{if } a = b, \text{ then } a + c = b + c \text{ and } a - c = b - c.$$

To illustrate why the addition property is true, we can think of an equation as a balanced scale. Each expression weighs the same amount. If an equal weight is added to or subtracted from each side of a balanced scale, the scale will remain balanced. The same is true of a balanced equation. That is, if an expression is added to or subtracted from the equal expressions, the expressions remain equal.

We are now ready to use the addition property of equations to solve algebraically a linear equation consisting of algebraic expressions. Our goal is to find a value for the variable that will make the equation true.

Let's begin with a simple equation: $x - 3 = 5$. We know that the solution of the equation is 8, because if we replace x with 8, the result is $5 = 5$, a true equation. Therefore, we begin with $x - 3 = 5$ and should end with the equation $x = 8$ (the solution). The step in the middle involves the addition property.

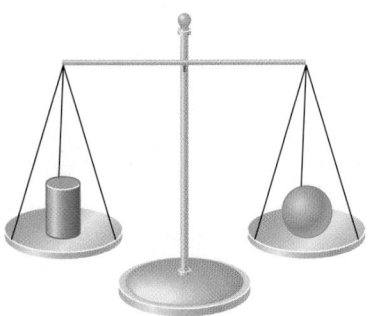

If $a = b$

then $a + c = b + c$

Solve $x - 3 = 5$.

We want to isolate the variable x on one side of the equation to determine the solution. To do this, we want to eliminate the term -3. Therefore, we must add the opposite of the term, 3, to -3 and obtain 0. However, we must add the same value to both sides of the equation in order to produce an equivalent equation.

$$x - 3 = 5$$
$$x - 3 + 3 = 5 + 3 \qquad \text{Add 3 to both sides.}$$
$$x = 8 \qquad\qquad \text{Combine like terms.}$$

The solution is 8.

Similarly, solve $x + 3 = 5$.

We want to isolate the variable x on one side of the equation to determine the solution. To do this, we want to eliminate the term 3. We must add the opposite of the term, -3 (or subtract 3), to 3 and obtain 0. We must add (or subtract) the same value to both sides of the equation.

$$x + 3 = 5$$
$$x + 3 - 3 = 5 - 3 \qquad \text{Subtract 3 from both sides.}$$
$$x = 2 \qquad \text{Combine like terms.}$$

The solution is 2.

SOLVING A LINEAR EQUATION BY USING THE ADDITION PROPERTY OF EQUATIONS

To solve a linear equation by using the addition property, first simplify both expressions in the equation. Then isolate the variable on one side of the equation.

- Add a term if a term is subtracted from the variable, and then combine like terms.

or

- Subtract a term if a term is added to the variable, and then combine like terms.

Check the solution by substituting, solving numerically, or solving graphically.

EXAMPLE 1   Solve each equation algebraically. Check your solution by substituting, solving numerically, and solving graphically.

a. $5 + (x - 7) = 9$ **b.** $14 = (3x - 5) - (2x + 4)$

Solution
a. Algebraic

$$5 + (x - 7) = 9$$
$$5 + x - 7 = 9 \qquad \text{Remove parentheses.}$$
$$x - 2 = 9 \qquad \text{Combine like terms.}$$
$$x - 2 + 2 = 9 + 2 \qquad \text{Add 2 to both sides.}$$
$$x = 11 \qquad \text{Combine like terms.}$$

Substitution Check

$$\frac{5 + (x - 7) = 9}{5 + (11 - 7) \mid 9}$$
$$9 \qquad \mid$$

The solution is 11.

Numeric

X	Y₁	Y₂
7	5	9
8	6	9
9	7	9
10	8	9
11	9	9
12	10	9
13	11	9

X=7

$Y1 = 5 + (x - 7)$
$Y2 = 9$
The solution is 11.

Graphic

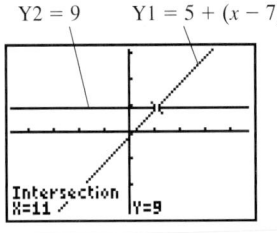

Y2 = 9   Y1 = 5 + (x − 7)

Intersection
X=11   Y=9

$(-47, 47, -31, 31)$
The solution is 11.

b. Algebraic

$$14 = (3x - 5) - (2x + 4)$$
$$14 = 3x - 5 - 2x - 4 \qquad \text{Remove parentheses.}$$
$$14 = x - 9 \qquad \text{Combine like terms.}$$
$$14 + 9 = x - 9 + 9 \qquad \text{Add 9 to both sides.}$$
$$23 = x \quad \text{or} \quad x = 23$$

Substitution Check	Numeric	Graphic

Substitution Check

$14 = (3x - 5) - (2x + 4)$

14	$(3(23) - 5) - (2(23) + 4)$
	14

The solution is 23.

Numeric

X	Y1	Y2
21	14	12
22	14	13
23	14	14
24	14	15
25	14	16
26	14	17
27	14	18
X=21		

$Y1 = 14$
$Y2 = (3x - 5) - (2x + 4)$
The solution is 23.

Graphic

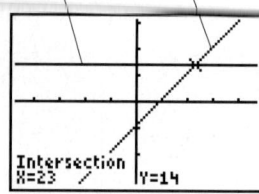

$Y1 = 14$ $Y2 = (3x - 5) - (2x + 4)$

Intersection
X=23   Y=14

$(-47, 47, -31, 31)$
The solution is 23.

 Objective 2.2.1 **CHECKUP**

1. Use the addition property of equations to solve each equation algebraically. Check your solutions.
   a. $8 - (5 - x) = 25$ b. $(5x + 1) - (4x - 3) = 10$

2. What does it mean to solve a linear equation by isolating the variable? How does the addition property of equations enable you to do this?

Objective 2.2.2   **Solving Linear Equations by Using Multiplication**

Another property of equations involves multiplication. It is very similar to the addition property of equations, which is not too surprising, since multiplication is based on repeated additions of numbers. Let's see if we can discover how the multiplication property works. Complete the following set of exercises.

Guided Discovery 8   Multiplication Property of Equations

Given the equation $7 = 7$, multiply both expressions by 2.

$7 = 7$	
$7 \cdot 2$	$7 \cdot 2$
14	14

1. Given the equation $7 = 7$, multiply both expressions by -2.

2. Given the equation $6 + 1 = 4 + 3$, multiply both expressions by 2.

3. Given the equation $6 + 1 = 4 + 3$, multiply both expressions by -2.

Write a rule for the multiplication property of equations.

In each of the preceding exercises, we began with an equation and multiplied both expressions by the same number. The resulting expressions remained equal in value.

This property holds true for division as well, because division is defined to be multiplication by the reciprocal of a number.

MULTIPLICATION PROPERTY OF EQUATIONS

Given expressions $a, b,$ and c,

$$\text{if } a = b, \text{ then } a \cdot c = b \cdot c \text{ and } a \div c = b \div c \text{ (when } c \neq 0).$$

To illustrate why the multiplication property is true, we can think of an equation as a balanced scale. Each expression weighs the same amount. If a weight is multiplied by a value on each side of a balanced scale, the scale remains balanced. The same is true of a balanced equation. That is, if each expression is multiplied by an equal expression, the resulting expressions remain equal.

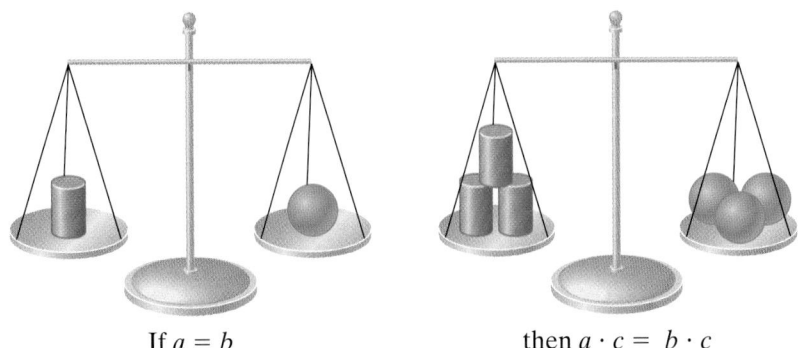

If $a = b$ then $a \cdot c = b \cdot c$

We are now ready to use the multiplication property of equations to solve a linear equation, such as $3x = 15$. We know that the solution of the equation is 5, because if we replace x with 5, the result is $15 = 15$, a true equation. Therefore, we begin with $3x = 15$ and should end with the equation $x = 5$ (the solution). The step in the middle involves the multiplication property.

Solve $3x = 15$.

We want to isolate the variable x on one side of the equation to determine the solution. To do this, we want to eliminate the factor 3. Therefore, we must divide by 3 because division is the inverse operation of multiplication. We obtain a factor 1. However, we must divide both sides of the equation by the same value in order to produce an equivalent equation.

$$3x = 15$$

$$\frac{3x}{3} = \frac{15}{3} \qquad \text{Divide both sides by 3.}$$

$$x = 5 \qquad \text{Simplify.}$$

The solution is 5.

Similarly, solve $\frac{x}{3} = 5$.

$$3\left(\frac{x}{3}\right) = 3(5) \qquad \text{Multiply both sides by 3.}$$

$$x = 15 \qquad \text{Simplify.}$$

The solution is 15.

SOLVING A LINEAR EQUATION BY USING THE MULTIPLICATION PROPERTY OF EQUATIONS

To solve a linear equation by using the multiplication property, first simplify both expressions in the equation. Then isolate the variable on one side of the equation.

- Multiply by an algebraic expression if the variable is divided by an algebraic expression.

or

- Divide by an algebraic expression if the variable is multiplied by an algebraic expression.

Check the solution by substituting, solving numerically, or solving graphically.

EXAMPLE 2   Solve each equation algebraically. Check your solution.

a. $-x = 9$ **b.** $46 = (4x + 3) + 3(2x - 1)$ **c.** $\frac{3}{4}x = 9$

Solution

a. Algebraic

$$-x = 9 \qquad \text{The coefficient of } -x \text{ is } -1.$$

$$\frac{-x}{-1} = \frac{9}{-1} \qquad \text{Divide both sides by } -1.$$

$$x = -9 \qquad \text{Simplify.}$$

The solution is -9.

Substitution Check

$$-x = 9$$

$$\begin{array}{c|c} -(-9) & 9 \\ \hline 9 & \end{array}$$

The solution, -9, checks.

b. Algebraic

$$46 = (4x + 3) + 3(2x - 1)$$

$$46 = 4x + 3 + 6x - 3 \qquad \text{Remove parentheses and distribute.}$$

$$46 = 10x \qquad \text{Combine like terms.}$$

$$\frac{46}{10} = \frac{10x}{10} \qquad \text{Divide both sides by 10.}$$

$$\frac{23}{5} = x \quad \text{or} \quad x = 4.6$$

The solution is 4.6.

Graphic

$$Y1 = 46 \quad Y2 = (4x + 3) + 3(2x - 1)$$

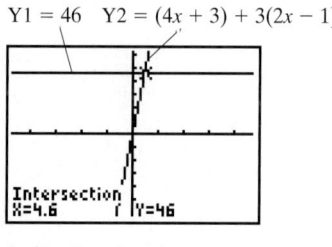

Intersection
X=4.6   Y=46

$(-47, 47, -62, 62)$
The solution is 4.6.

The integer setting $(-47, 47, -31, 31)$ will not result in two graphs, because the range is not large enough for the equation $Y1 = 46$ to be seen. Therefore, we need to double the range of the integer screen. The solution is 4.6.

c. Algebraic

$$\frac{3}{4}x = 9$$

$$\frac{3}{4}x \div \frac{3}{4} = 9 \div \frac{3}{4} \qquad \text{Divide both sides by } \frac{3}{4}.$$

$$x = \frac{9}{1} \cdot \frac{4}{3} \qquad \text{Simplify.}$$

$$x = \frac{36}{3}$$

$$x = 12$$

The solution is 12.

Numeric

X	Y1	Y2
9	6.75	9
10	7.5	9
11	8.25	9
12	9	9
13	9.75	9
14	10.5	9
15	11.25	9

X=9

$$Y1 = \frac{3}{4}x \qquad Y2 = 9$$

The solution is 12.

Note: This example could have been solved in a different way. Dividing by a fraction is equivalent to multiplying by the fraction's reciprocal. For example,

$$\frac{3}{4}x = 9$$

$$\frac{\cancel{3}}{\cancel{4}}x \cdot \frac{\cancel{4}}{\cancel{3}} = \frac{\cancel{9}}{1} \cdot \frac{4}{\cancel{3}} \qquad \text{Multiply both sides by the reciprocal of } \frac{3}{4}, \text{ or } \frac{4}{3}.$$

$$x = 12 \qquad \text{Simplify.}$$

The solution remains 12.

✓ Objective 2.2.2 *CHECKUP*

Use the multiplication property of equations to solve each equation algebraically. Check your solutions.

1. a. $-4a = -\dfrac{8}{15}$ **b.** $8(5x + 12) - 3(32 - 4x) = 260$ **c.** $\dfrac{5}{11}x = -15$

Objective 2.2.3   Modeling the Real World

Solving linear equations by using the addition and multiplication properties of equations is the first big step in using the power of algebra to solve real-world problems. We will see this throughout the rest of this chapter. Remember, as in all real-world problem solving, whatever operation you do on a number must also be done on the number's unit of measurement. You know, for example, that $24 \div 4 = 6$, but remember also that 24 sq ft $\div$ 4 ft = 6 ft.

EXAMPLE 3

Heat bursts are an odd atmospheric event that occurs in thunderstorms. In Glasgow, MT, on September 9, 1994, the temperature at 5:02 A.M. was 67°F. A heat burst from a thunderstorm shot the temperature up to 93°F at 5:17 A.M. Write an equation to determine the number of degrees Fahrenheit the temperature rose. Solve the equation.

Algebraic Solution

Let x = the number of degrees Fahrenheit the temperature rose.

The heat burst temperature is the sum of the temperature before the increase and the number of degrees the temperature rose, or $67 + x = 93$.

$67 + x = 93$	*Write an equation.*
$67 + x - 67 = 93 - 67$	*Subtract 67 from both sides.*
$x = 26$	

Substitution Check

$$67 + x = 93$$
$$\begin{array}{c|c} 67 + 26 & 93 \\ 93 & \end{array}$$

The solution is 26.

The solution is 26.
The temperature rose 26°F due to the heat burst.

EXAMPLE 4

David's small dog needs a pen with an area of 156 square feet for proper exercise. David wants the width of the pen to be 12 feet. If he is constructing a rectangular pen, what is the length he needs?

Algebraic Solution

Let x = length of the pen.
The area formula is $A = LW$.

$156 = x \cdot 12$	*Substitute known values.*
$\dfrac{156}{12} = \dfrac{x \cdot 12}{12}$	*Divide both sides by 12.*
$13 = x$	

The length will be 13 feet.

Substitution Check

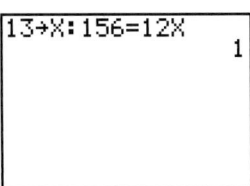

The solution is 13.

EXAMPLE 5 How many liters of a 45% alcohol solution does a nurse need if she wants the solution to contain 1 liter of pure alcohol?

Algebraic Solution

Let L = number of liters of 45% alcohol solution.

Since the amount of alcohol in the solution is 45% of L liters, an expression for this would be $0.45L$. This must equal 1 liter.

$$0.45L = 1$$

$$\frac{0.45L}{0.45} = \frac{1}{0.45}$$ Divide both sides by 0.45.

$$L \approx 2.22$$ Simplify.

Graphic

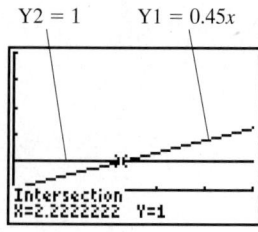

$(0, 5, -1, 5)$
The solution is about 2.22.

The nurse will need approximately 2.22 liters of the 45% solution. ■

APPLICATION

The U.S. National Center for Education Statistics reports project a 17% increase in public college enrollment from the year 2000 to the year 2012. The projected increase was 1,963,000. What was the enrollment in the year 2000?

Discussion

Let x = the enrollment in the year 2000. Seventeen percent of the 2000 enrollment, $0.17x$, is equal to 1,963,000, or $0.17x = 1,963,000$.

Algebraic Solution

$$0.17x = 1,963,000$$

$$\frac{0.17x}{0.17} = \frac{1,963,000}{0.17}$$ Divide both sides by 0.17.

$$x \approx 11,547,058$$ Simplify.

Substitution Check

```
11547058→X:.17X
            1962999.86
```

Since $1,962,999.86 \approx 1,963,000$, the solution is 11,547,058.

The public college enrollment in the year 2000 was about 11,547,058.

✓ Objective 2.2.3 CHECKUP

Write an equation and solve algebraically.

1. The average height of the adult male is approximately 69 inches. Big Bird of TV's "Sesame Street" is 29 inches taller than the average adult male. Determine Big Bird's height.

2. Cheryl plans to put a square flower garden in her backyard. She has 38 linear feet of landscaping bricks to use to border the garden. What will be the length of each side?

3. How many liters of a 20% saline solution is needed to make a solution containing 1 liter of salt?

4. The gravitational pull on the surface of the Moon is about one-sixth as strong as it is on Earth. An astronaut and his space suit would weigh about 60 pounds on the surface of the Moon. Determine the weight of the astronaut and his suit on Earth.

2.2 EXERCISES

Student Solutions Manual   PH Math/Tutor Center   CD Video   MathXL®   MyMathLab   Interactmath.com

Use the addition property of equations to solve algebraically.

1. $x + 33 = 51$

2. $y + 73 = -31$

3. $75 = a - 41$

4. $x - 123 = -47$

5. $-4.91 = y + 3.07$

6. $a - 0.153 = -4.759$

7. $y - \dfrac{1}{6} = -\dfrac{1}{6}$

8. $a - \dfrac{13}{18} = \dfrac{5}{6}$

9. $27 + (x - 13) = 11$

10. $8 = (12 + a) - 54$

11. $(13.9 + x) + 0.88 = -2.07$

12. $(x - 14.75) - 10.5 = -2.65$

13. $5x - (2 + 4x) = -10$

14. $3y - (5 + 2y) = -9$

15. $(5x - 2) - (4x + 7) = 27$

16. $42 = (36x - 21) - (35x + 60)$

17. $\left(\dfrac{1}{3}x + \dfrac{1}{8}\right) + \left(\dfrac{3}{4} + \dfrac{2}{3}x\right) = -\dfrac{3}{16}$

18. $\left(\dfrac{5}{7}z + \dfrac{3}{5}\right) - \left(\dfrac{3}{10} - \dfrac{2}{7}z\right) = \dfrac{13}{15}$

19. $(3x + 76) - (2x - 45) = 31$

20. $(16x + 15) - (15x + 16) = -1$

Use the multiplication property of equations to solve algebraically. Round decimal answers to the nearest thousandth.

21. $-324 = -4y$

22. $7x = -434$

23. $-5.1x = 0.102$

24. $-3.7y = 13.69$

25. $-3\dfrac{1}{3}x = -1\dfrac{1}{3}$

26. $\dfrac{1}{5}a = -3\dfrac{1}{5}$

27. $\dfrac{x}{4} = 1.22$

28. $\dfrac{x}{17.3} = -4$

29. $-x = 57$

30. $-x = -16\dfrac{1}{5}$

31. $57 = 2x + 17x$

32. $4a - 5a = -17$

33. $18.22x - 12.9x = -12.76$

34. $-121 = 2.2x + 9.9x$

35. $\dfrac{5}{14} = \dfrac{9}{14}a + \dfrac{3}{7}a$

36. $\dfrac{1}{5}x - \dfrac{1}{7}x = -\dfrac{2}{49}$

37. $2(3x + 6) + 3(x - 4) = 126$

38. $(a + 17) - (2a + 17) = 41$

39. $4.8(a + 3) + 2.4(a - 6) = -7.2$

40. $2.2(x + 3.7) + 7.4(x - 1.1) = 60.48$

41. $3\left(\dfrac{1}{2}x - \dfrac{3}{4}\right) - 18\left(x - \dfrac{1}{8}\right) = 0$

42. $\dfrac{1}{4}(x + 2) - \dfrac{1}{6}(x + 3) = -\dfrac{1}{12}$

Write an equation and solve algebraically.

43. Chuck's net paycheck was $1784.26 and the deductions amounted to $567.32. What was his gross pay? (*Hint:* Gross pay less deductions equals net pay.)

44. Alberta's net paycheck was $1252.76, and her gross pay was $1640.00. What was the amount of her deductions?

45. A jacket that originally sold for $129.95 was marked down to a sale price of $88.49. What was the amount of the markdown?

46. A shirt was marked down $12.50 to a sale price of $17.99. What was the original price before markdown?

47. Tameka was charged $54.32 for a dress that was priced at $49.95. She had forgotten that sales tax would be added to the selling price. How much money in sales tax did Tameka pay on the purchase?

48. The selling price of a house is $125,000. A down payment of $32,000 is required to purchase the home. How much of a loan will be needed to purchase the home?

49. If Erika's class receives $2.50 for each packet of gourmet coffee it sells, how many packets must the class sell if it wishes to make $1450 to purchase a computer?

50. How many months will it take to pay off a loan of $3150 (with interest already included) if monthly payments are $175?

51. Jane and her two children received $45,240 as their portion of a probated estate. If they received $\frac{3}{5}$ of the estate, how much was the estate worth?

52. Angelo was charged $4.49 for $\frac{3}{4}$ pound of baked ham. What was the selling price per pound of the ham?

53. At the start of an Iditarod dog-sled race from Anchorage to Nome, 12 dogs must be on the towline. If this number represents 75% of the maximum number of dogs a musher can have at the start of the race, what is the maximum number of dogs allowed?

54. The greatest land mountain range in the world is the Himalayas, which contain 88% of the world's peaks that are over 24,000 feet high. If the Himalayas contain 96 of these peaks, how many are there worldwide?

55. How much must you place into savings if you wish to earn $864 in simple interest at 4.5% per year over three years?

56. After two years of making payments, how much did you borrow if you paid $455.00 in simple interest at a rate of 6.5% per year?

57. How many gallons of a 70% antifreeze solution does a mechanic need if he wants the solution to contain 4 gallons of pure antifreeze?

58. How many pints of a 20% insecticide solution does a gardener need if she wants the solution to contain 0.5 pint of pure insecticide?

59. According to the U.S. Bureau of the Census, 7,532,800 males ages 18–24 were living at home in 2002. How many males ages 18–24 were in the United States if 55% of them were living at home in 2002?

60. The U.S. Bureau of the Census reported that 6,252,000 females in the 18–24 age range were living at home in 2002. How many 18–24-year-old females were in the United States if 46% of them were living at home in 2002?

61. What was the average speed for a trip of 855 miles that took 13 hours to complete?

62. What was the average miles per gallon for a trip of 855 miles that took 40.7 gallons of gas?

63. If each of the five partners in a firm earned $12,730 last quarter in profits, what was the firm's quarterly profits?

64. If seven people share a lottery prize, and each receives $6,570,000, what was the jackpot, rounded to the nearest million dollars?

65. The floor in Colonel Mustard's library is in the shape of a parallelogram. The base of the parallelogram from one end of the library to the other is 20 feet. If the covering on the floor is 350 square feet, what is the perpendicular distance (height) across the library?

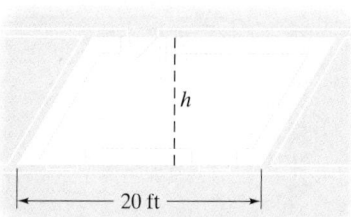

66. In designing a rectangular storage bin, the base is limited to measurements 6 feet long by 4 feet wide. How high must the bin be if it must hold 120 cubic feet?

67. A cylindrical tank is needed to hold 300 cubic feet of water. If the radius of the tank is 4 feet, what must its height be, rounded to the nearest foot?

68. What is the radius (rounded to the nearest inch) of a circle that has a circumference of 100 inches?

69. As of March 2000, the population of the United States was estimated to exceed that of the 1990 census by 32,700,000 people. If the 1990 census reported 248,700,000 people, what is the 2000 estimated population?

70. The highest continuously active volcano in the world is Cotopaxi volcano in Ecuador. The tallest mountain in South America is Aconcagua, which, at a height of 22,831 feet, is 3431 feet taller than the volcano. What is the height of the volcano?

71. In late 1999, Lucent Technologies announced a record-breaking development of a transistor with a minute length of 50 nanometers. (A nanometer is one billionth of a meter.) This is approximately 2000 times thinner than the width of a single human hair. Approximate the width of a single human hair.

72. The highest recorded temperature created by man is 950,000,000°F, claimed to be 30 times hotter than the center of the Sun. It was created in 1994 at the Princeton Plasma Physics Laboratory. Approximate the temperature of the center of the Sun. (You wonder how they can measure these things!)

 2.2 Calculator Exercises

The calculator has a special feature that can be used to solve equations. In order to use this feature, you must enter the following instruction into the calculator:

solve(expression, variable, guess)

In this instruction, "expression" represents the equation's left side after the equation has been rewritten to equal zero on the right side, "variable" instructs the calculator as to which variable is being solved for, and "guess" is a reasonable guess that the calculator uses as a starting point for solving the equation. As an example, suppose you wish to solve $2(3x - 6) + 3(x + 4) = 126$. Begin by rewriting the equation as $2(3x - 6) + 3(x + 4) - 126 = 0$. Then type the following instruction into the calculator:

solve($2(3x - 6) + 3(x + 4) - 126, x, 10$)

The calculator will return a value of 14, the solution of the original equation.

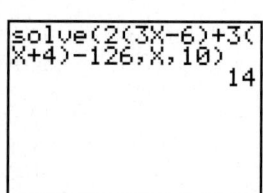

The keystrokes needed to enter the instruction are [2nd] [0] **(CATALOG)** [▼] (repeatedly until you reach the solve instruction), then [ENTER], then the expression followed by [,] [X,T,θ,n] [,] the guess, and, finally, [ )]. Press [ENTER] to execute the instruction.

Following are some applications that you can solve by this method. Write a linear equation to represent each situation, and solve the equation by using the "solve" instruction. Refer to Chapter P for the formulas needed in these exercises.

1. A circular fence is to be placed around a swimming pool. The radius of the enclosed area will be 75 feet. Two gates will be placed at opposite ends of the pool. Each gate measures 5 feet wide. How many linear feet of fencing will be required to surround the area? Round your answer to the nearest tenth of a foot.

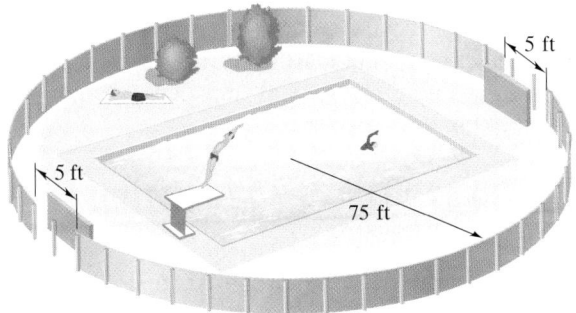

2. A circle has a diameter of 25.8 inches. By how many inches is the circumference larger than the diameter?

3. If a stock account grew by $531\frac{1}{4}$ points for 250 shares of stock, what was the increase per share of stock?

4. How many pieces of tubing, each measuring $5\frac{3}{8}$ inches long, can be cut from a piece measuring $34\frac{1}{2}$ inches long?

5. If a car averages 18.5 miles per gallon for highway driving, approximately how many gallons of fuel will be needed for a trip of 220 miles?

6. In laying brick, a rule of thumb is that 6.5 bricks are needed for each square foot of wall. How many square feet of wall can be constructed from a pallet containing 800 bricks?

7. The label on a package of Choc-o-Block cookies states that one serving of the cookies contains 2.5 grams of fat, representing 4% of the daily recommended amount of fat. Using this information, calculate the daily recommended amount of fat.

8. A bakery states that one serving of its Sweetie-Goo cookies contains 3 grams of fat, representing 5% of the daily recommended amount of fat. Calculate the daily recommended amount from this information. Does your answer agree with that of exercise 7? If not, how do you explain the difference?

9. To measure the velocity of water flow in a stream, a ball is thrown into the stream, and the time it takes to travel 250 feet is measured. Using the formula $d = rt$, find the speed (in feet per second) if the ball took 15 seconds to travel the 250 feet.

2.2 Writing Exercise

You have learned two properties of equations that can be used to help you solve linear equations algebraically: the addition property and the multiplication property. Explain how you would decide when to use each of the properties. In your explanation, state what characteristic you would look for in an equation that would signal the property to use. There are four different characteristics of an equation to consider. In your explanation, give examples of equations with each of the characteristics.

2.3 SOLVING EQUATIONS BY USING A COMBINATION OF PROPERTIES

OBJECTIVES

1 Solve linear equations algebraically by using a combination of properties of equations.

2 Model real-world situations by using linear equations, and solve the equations algebraically.

APPLICATION

Crickets are called the poor man's thermometer, because temperature directly affects their rate of activity. According to weather folklore, the temperature can be related to the number of cricket chirps in a given period. Several variations of this relationship may be found. One relationship uses field crickets to determine the Fahrenheit temperature. To do so, one calculates the average number of chirps in 15 seconds (the number of chirps per minute, divided by 4) and adds 37. If the temperature is 77°F, how many chirps will a field cricket produce in one minute?

After completing this section, we will discuss this application further. See page 224.

Using Combinations of Properties of Equations

The addition property and the multiplication property are the keys to solving all linear equations. Now that we have mastered the basics, we are ready to solve more complicated linear equations. In order to do this, we will need to apply combinations of the properties of equations. When we solve equations with multiple steps, we are reversing the order of operations. Since there are several different ways to solve linear equations, we will set up a few rules so that at least in the beginning we are performing the same steps. When we become more sure of ourselves, we may follow these steps in different orders and obtain the same results.

SOLVING A LINEAR EQUATION BY USING A COMBINATION OF PROPERTIES OF EQUATIONS

To solve a linear equation by using a combination of properties of equations,

- Simplify both expressions in the equation (preferably leaving them without fractions).
- Isolate the variable to one side of the equation (preferably the left side) by using the addition property of equations.
- Isolate the constants to the other side (preferably the right side) of the equation by using the addition property of equations.
- Reduce the coefficient of the variable to 1 by using the multiplication property of equations.

Check the solution by substituting, solving numerically, or solving graphically.

The process of simplifying equations by performing operations on both sides that will isolate the variable on one side is the basis of solving all equations, not just linear ones. Therefore, this process is important to remember.

EXAMPLE 1

Use a combination of the properties of equations to solve the following equations algebraically, and then check your solutions:

a. $2x - 3 = 7$ **b.** $6x + 5 = 2x + 25$ **c.** $5x + 4 = 2(3x - 8)$

Algebraic Solution

a. The order of operations on the left side require us to multiply before we subtract. Therefore, we must undo these operations in reverse order.

$$2x - 3 = 7$$
$$2x - 3 + 3 = 7 + 3 \qquad \text{First, add 3 to both sides.}$$
$$2x = 10 \qquad \text{Second, simplify.}$$
$$\frac{2x}{2} = \frac{10}{2} \qquad \text{Divide both sides by 2.}$$
$$x = 5 \qquad \text{Simplify.}$$

The solution is 5.
The check is left to you.

b.
$$6x + 5 = 2x + 25$$
$$6x + 5 - 2x = 2x + 25 - 2x \qquad \text{Subtract 2x from both sides.}$$
$$4x + 5 = 25 \qquad \text{Simplify.}$$
$$4x + 5 - 5 = 25 - 5 \qquad \text{Subtract 5 from both sides.}$$
$$4x = 20 \qquad \text{Simplify.}$$
$$\frac{4x}{4} = \frac{20}{4} \qquad \text{Divide both sides by 4.}$$
$$x = 5 \qquad \text{Simplify.}$$

The solution is 5.
The check is left to you.

c.

$$5x + 4 = 2(3x - 8)$$

$$5x + 4 = 6x - 16 \qquad \text{Distribute.}$$

$$5x + 4 - 6x = 6x - 16 - 6x \qquad \text{Subtract 6x from both sides.}$$

$$-x + 4 = -16 \qquad \text{Simplify.}$$

$$-x + 4 - 4 = -16 - 4 \qquad \text{Subtract 4 from both sides.}$$

$$-x = -20 \qquad \text{Simplify.}$$

$$\frac{-x}{-1} = \frac{-20}{-1} \qquad \text{Divide both sides by } -1 \text{ (the coefficient of x).}$$

$$x = 20 \qquad \text{Simplify.}$$

The solution is 20.
The check is left to you.

The linear equations in the previous section and in Example 1 of this section all have one solution. However, from the first section in this chapter, we know that that is not always the case: Equations may be contradictions or identities. Let's see what happens when we apply our rules in those cases. Complete the following set of exercises.

 Guided Discovery 9 Equations with No Solution

Solve algebraically the previous example of an equation with no solution: $2x + 5 = 2x + 10$.

Write a rule that explains why the equation has no solution.

When we attempt to isolate the variable term to one side of the equation, that term is eliminated from both sides of the equation. The result is a false equation. Therefore, there is no solution. The equation is a contradiction.

Guided Discovery 10 Equations with Many Solutions

Solve algebraically the previous example of an equation with many solutions: $2x + 5 = (x + 3) + (x + 2)$.

Write a rule that explains why the equation has many solutions.

When we attempt to isolate the variable term to one side, that term is eliminated from the equation. The result is a true equation. Therefore, the solution set is the set of all real numbers. The equation is an identity.

EXAMPLE 2 Solve algebraically.

a. $4(x - 2) = 4x - 8$

b. $3x + 4 = 2x + (x + 10)$

Algebraic Solution

a.

$$4(x - 2) = 4x - 8$$

$$4x - 8 = 4x - 8 \qquad \text{Distribute 4.}$$

$$4x - 8 - 4x = 4x - 8 - 4x \qquad \text{Subtract 4x from both sides.}$$

$$-8 = -8 \qquad \text{Simplify.}$$

Numeric

X	Y1	Y2
-3	-20	-20
-2	-16	-16
-1	-12	-12
0	-8	-8
1	-4	-4
2	0	0
3	4	4

X = -3

Y1 = 4(x − 2)
Y2 = 4x − 8
The solution is the set of all real numbers.

The original equation is an identity. We can confirm this by a numeric or graphic check. Since this is a true equation, the solution is all possible values for x, or the set of all real numbers.

Algebraic Solution	**Graphic**

b. $3x + 4 = 2x + (x + 10)$

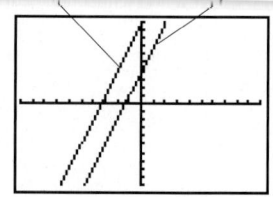

$Y2 = 2x + (x + 10)$ $Y1 = 3x + 4$

$3x + 4 = 2x + x + 10$ Remove parentheses.

$3x + 4 = 3x + 10$ Simplify.

$3x + 4 - 3x = 3x + 10 - 3x$ Subtract 3x from both sides.

$4 = 10$ Simplify.

$(-10, 10, -10, 10)$
There is no solution.

The original equation is a contradiction. We can confirm this by a numeric or graphic check. Since this is a false equation, there is no solution. ■

If an equation has fractional coefficients in the terms, we must be very careful in applying the rules. For example, consider the following algebraic solution:

$$\frac{3}{4}x + \frac{5}{6} = \frac{5}{3}$$

$$\frac{3}{4}x + \frac{5}{6} - \frac{5}{6} = \frac{5}{3} - \frac{5}{6}$$ Subtract $\frac{5}{6}$ from both sides.

$$\frac{3}{4}x = \frac{10}{6} - \frac{5}{6}$$ Simplify and change to LCD.

$$\frac{3}{4}x = \frac{5}{6}$$ Simplify.

$$\overset{1}{\underset{3}{\cancel{4}}}\left(\overset{1}{\underset{1}{\cancel{\frac{3}{4}}}}x\right) = \overset{2}{\underset{3}{\cancel{4}}}\left(\frac{5}{\underset{3}{\cancel{6}}}\right)$$ Multiply both sides by $\frac{4}{3}$.

$$x = \frac{10}{9}$$

The solution is $\frac{10}{9}$.

If an equation has several fractional coefficients in the terms, the multiplication property of equations allows us to solve an equation in an easier way than dealing with the fractions. To clear fractional (decimal) coefficients from terms in an equation, multiply by the least common denominator for all the fractional coefficients. For example,

$$\frac{3}{4}x + \frac{5}{6} = \frac{5}{3}$$

$$12\left(\frac{3}{4}x + \frac{5}{6}\right) = 12\left(\frac{5}{3}\right)$$ Multiply both sides by 12 (LCD of all the fractional coefficients).

$$\overset{3}{\cancel{12}}\left(\frac{3}{4}x\right) + \overset{2}{\cancel{12}}\left(\frac{5}{6}\right) = \overset{4}{\cancel{12}}\left(\frac{5}{3}\right)$$ Distribute 12.

$$9x + 10 = 20$$ Simplify.

$$9x + 10 - 10 = 20 - 10$$ Subtract 10 from both sides.

$$9x = 10$$ Simplify.

$$\frac{9x}{9} = \frac{10}{9}$$ Divide both sides by 9.

$$x = \frac{10}{9}$$

The solution remains $\frac{10}{9}$.

EXAMPLE 3   Solve algebraically. Check your solutions.

a. $-\dfrac{2}{3}x + \dfrac{7}{5} = -\dfrac{5}{6}x$
b. $\dfrac{3}{8}\left(x + \dfrac{1}{4}\right) = \dfrac{5}{6}x + 2$

c. $0.25x - 2.75 = 0.1x + 2$

Algebraic Solution

a.
$$-\dfrac{2}{3}x + \dfrac{7}{5} = -\dfrac{5}{6}x$$

$$30\left(-\dfrac{2}{3}x + \dfrac{7}{5}\right) = 30\left(-\dfrac{5}{6}x\right) \qquad \text{Multiply both sides by 30 (LCD).}$$

$$\overset{10}{30}\left(-\dfrac{2}{\underset{1}{3}}x\right) + \overset{6}{30}\left(\dfrac{7}{\underset{1}{5}}\right) = \overset{5}{30}\left(-\dfrac{5}{\underset{1}{6}}x\right) \qquad \text{Distribute 30.}$$

$$-20x + 42 = -25x \qquad \text{Simplify.}$$
$$-20x + 42 + 20x = -25x + 20x \qquad \text{Add 20x to both sides because the right expression did not have a constant term and this will save steps.}$$

$$42 = -5x \qquad \text{Simplify.}$$
$$\dfrac{42}{-5} = \dfrac{-5x}{-5} \qquad \text{Divide both sides by } -5.$$

$$-\dfrac{42}{5} = x \qquad \text{Simplify.}$$

The solution is $-\frac{42}{5}$.
The check is left to you.

b. $\dfrac{3}{8}\left(x + \dfrac{1}{4}\right) = \dfrac{5}{6}x + 2$

 TAKE NOTE The first fraction in the expression on the left is a factor, not a term. It will be simpler if we distribute before we eliminate the fractions.

$$\dfrac{3}{8}x + \dfrac{3}{32} = \dfrac{5}{6}x + 2 \qquad \text{Distribute.}$$

$$96\left(\dfrac{3}{8}x + \dfrac{3}{32}\right) = 96\left(\dfrac{5}{6}x + 2\right) \qquad \text{Multiply both sides by 96 (LCD).}$$

$$\overset{12}{96}\left(\dfrac{3}{\underset{1}{8}}x\right) + \overset{3}{96}\left(\dfrac{3}{\underset{1}{32}}\right) = \overset{16}{96}\left(\dfrac{5}{\underset{1}{6}}x\right) + 96(2) \qquad \text{Distribute.}$$

$$36x + 9 = 80x + 192 \qquad \text{Simplify.}$$
$$36x + 9 - 80x = 80x + 192 - 80x \qquad \text{Subtract 80x from both sides.}$$
$$-44x + 9 = 192 \qquad \text{Simplify.}$$
$$-44x + 9 - 9 = 192 - 9 \qquad \text{Subtract 9 from both sides.}$$
$$-44x = 183 \qquad \text{Simplify.}$$
$$\dfrac{-44x}{-44} = \dfrac{183}{-44} \qquad \text{Divide both sides by } -44.$$

$$x = -\dfrac{183}{44} \qquad \text{Simplify.}$$

The solution is $-\frac{183}{44}$.
The check is left to you.

c. $0.25x - 2.75 = 0.1x + 2$

▶ TAKE NOTE Decimals are equivalent to fractions. The LCD is determined by the place value of each decimal.

$100(0.25x - 2.75) = 100(0.1x + 2)$	Multiply both sides by 100 (LCD).
$100(0.25x) - 100(2.75) = 100(0.1x) + 100(2)$	Distribute.
$25x - 275 = 10x + 200$	Simplify.
$25x - 275 - 10x = 10x + 200 - 10x$	Subtract 10x from both sides.
$15x - 275 = 200$	Simplify.
$15x - 275 + 275 = 200 + 275$	Add 275 to both sides.
$15x = 475$	Simplify.
$\dfrac{15x}{15} = \dfrac{475}{15}$	Divide both sides by 15.
$x = 31.\overline{6}$	Simplify.

The solution is $31.\overline{6}$.
The check is left to you. ■

ALGEBRAIC SOLUTIONS

To solve an equation algebraically, use the properties of equations to isolate the variable. One of three possibilities will occur:

One solution exists.

No solution exists. Solving results in a contradiction.

An infinite number of solutions exist. Solving results in an identity.

 Objective 2.3.1 CHECKUP

In exercises 1–3, use a combination of the properties of equations to solve algebraically. Check your solutions.

1. a. $2x - 5 = 7$ **b.** $4x + 2 = 3x + 9$
   c. $2x - 5 = 4(x + 2)$

2. a. $6(x - 3) + 23 = 6x + 5$
   b. $x + 5(2x - 7) = 10(x + 4) + (x + 5)$

3. a. $-\dfrac{3}{4}x + \dfrac{3}{8} = -\dfrac{1}{4}$ **b.** $\dfrac{1}{2}\left(x + \dfrac{3}{4}\right) = \dfrac{1}{3}x - \dfrac{1}{8}$
   c. $1.2x - 4 = 0.8x + 1.2$

4. If a linear equation has parentheses in it, what should you do first when attempting to solve it?

5. If a linear equation has coefficients that are fractions or decimals, what can you do to make the equation easier to solve?

■

Objective 2.3.2 Modeling the Real World

Real-world situations tend to be complicated. But many situations can be expressed or approximated by linear equations, and now we know all we need to know in order to solve them. Remember that once you've solved an equation, you will need to look at your solution and see if it makes sense in terms of the original situation. Is it possible to have a negative solution? Is a fractional result realistic? Don't forget to ask yourself these kinds of questions.

EXAMPLE 4	Charles plans to sell flower boxes for $5.00 each. He estimates that the cost of the wood is $3.25 per box. The other materials needed cost $1.75 per box. An advertisement costs $3.50. Determine the break-even point. (That is, determine when the revenue and the cost are equal.)

Solution

Let x = number of flower boxes

The revenue is $5.00 per flower box, or $5.00x$.

The cost is $3.25 per flower box, plus $1.75 per flower box, plus $3.50, or $3.25x + 1.75x + 3.50$.

Algebraic

$$5.00x = 3.25x + 1.75x + 3.50$$
$$5.00x = 5.00x + 3.50 \qquad \text{Simplify.}$$
$$5.00x - 5.00x = 5.00x + 3.50 - 5.00x \qquad \text{Subtract 5.00x from both sides.}$$
$$0 = 3.50$$

Numeric

X	Y₁	Y₂
0	0	3.5
1	5	8.5
2	10	13.5
3	15	18.5
4	20	23.5
5	25	28.5
6	30	33.5

X=0

$Y1 = 5.00x$
$Y2 = 3.25x + 1.75x + 3.50$
Note that the left side is always 3.5 less than the right side.

This is a contradiction. There is no solution. Charles will not break even.

If Charles examines his estimates, he will see that the cost of wood and materials is $5.00 per flower box, his selling price. Therefore, when he adds the cost of the advertisement to the cost of the wood and materials, his cost exceeds his selling price. He must raise the price of his flower boxes in order to break even. ■

EXAMPLE 5

Moria's cell phone plan is $49.99 per month for 500 minutes and an additional $0.40 per minute for all calls over 500. Her sister said that her plan is $0.20 per minute. For how many minutes will the cell phone bills be the same?

Solution

Let x = the number of minutes used

Moria's sister will pay for all x minutes on her plan.
Moria's sister bill will be $0.20x$.
Moria will be charged for the number of minutes over 500 or $(x - 500)$ minutes.
Moria's bill will be $49.99 + \$0.40(x - 500)$.

Algebraic

$$49.99 + 0.40(x - 500) = 0.20x \qquad \text{Equate the bills.}$$
$$49.99 + 0.40x - 200 = 0.20x \qquad \text{Distribute 0.40.}$$
$$-150.01 + 0.40x = 0.20x \qquad \text{Simplify.}$$
$$-150.01 + 0.40x - 0.40x = 0.20x - 0.40x \qquad \text{Subtract 0.40x from both sides.}$$
$$-150.01 = -0.20x \qquad \text{Simplify.}$$
$$\frac{-150.01}{-0.20} = \frac{-0.20x}{-0.20} \qquad \text{Divide both sides by } -0.20.$$
$$x = 750.05 \qquad \text{Simplify.}$$

Numeric

X	Y₁	Y₂
747	148.79	149.4
748	149.19	149.6
749	149.59	149.8
750	149.99	150
751	150.39	150.2
752	150.79	150.4
753	151.19	150.6

X=747

$Y1 = 49.99 + 0.40(x - 500)$
$Y2 = 0.20x$
The solution is about 750.

The sisters' cell phone bills will be approximately the same if both sisters use 750 minutes. ■

EXAMPLE 6   A pharmacist needs a 40% alcohol solution. If she plans to mix 30 cubic centimeters (cc) of a 20% alcohol solution with a 70% alcohol solution, how many cc of the 70% solution does she use? How many cc are in the 40% solution?

Solution

Let x = number of cc of 70% alcohol solution

$x + 30$ = number of cc of 40% alcohol solution

The 40% solution is a mixture of the 20% alcohol solution and the 70% alcohol solution. Therefore, we add the amount of alcohol in the 20% solution, which is 20% of 30, and the amount of alcohol in the 70% solution, which is 70% of x. The result is the amount of alcohol in the 40% solution, 40% of $(x + 30)$.

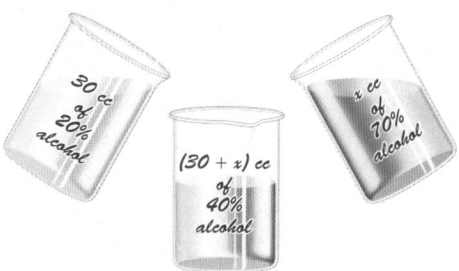

Algebraic

$$0.2(30) + 0.7x = 0.4(x + 30)$$

$6 + 0.7x = 0.4x + 12$ Simplify.

$6 + 0.7x - 0.4x = 0.4x + 12 - 0.4x$ Subtract 0.4x from both sides.

$6 + 0.3x = 12$ Simplify.

$6 + 0.3x - 6 = 12 - 6$ Subtract 6 from both sides.

$0.3x = 6$ Simplify.

$$\frac{0.3x}{0.3} = \frac{6}{0.3}$$ Divide both sides by 0.3.

$x = 20$ Simplify.

Numeric

X	Y₁	Y₂
17	17.9	18.8
18	18.6	19.2
19	19.3	19.6
20	20	20
21	20.7	20.4
22	21.4	20.8
23	22.1	21.2

X=17

$Y1 = 0.2(30) + 0.7x$
$Y2 = 0.4(x + 30)$
The solution is 20.

When 20 cc of the 70% alcohol solution is added to 30 cc of the 20% alcohol solution, the result will be 50 cc of the needed 40% alcohol solution.   ■

APPLICATION

Crickets are called the poor man's thermometer, because temperature directly affects their rate of activity. According to weather folklore, the temperature can be related to the number of cricket chirps in a given period. Several variations of this relationship may be found. One relationship uses field crickets to determine the Fahrenheit temperature. To do so, one calculates the average number of chirps in 15 seconds (the number of chirps per minute, divided by 4) and adds 37. If the temperature is 77°F, how many chirps will a field cricket produce in one minute?

Discussion

Let x = the number of chirps per minute

$\dfrac{x}{4}$ = the average number of chirps in 15 seconds

$\dfrac{x}{4} + 37$ = the sum of 37 and the average number of chirps in 15 seconds

The sum is equal to 77, or $\dfrac{x}{4} + 37 = 77$.

Algebraic		**Numeric**

$$\frac{x}{4} + 37 = 77$$ Write the equation.

$$\frac{x}{4} + 37 - 37 = 77 - 37$$ Subtract 37 from both sides.

$$\frac{x}{4} = 40$$ Simplify.

$$\frac{x}{4} \cdot 4 = 40 \cdot 4$$ Multiply both sides by 4.

$$x = 160$$ Simplify.

X	Y1	Y2
158	76.5	77
159	76.75	77
160	77	77
161	77.25	77
162	77.5	77
163	77.75	77
164	78	77

X=158

Y1 = $\frac{x}{4}$ + 37   Y2 = 77
The solution is 160.

When the temperature is 77°F, the field cricket chirps at a rate of 160 chirps per minute.

✓ Objective 2.3.2 **CHECKUP**

Solve algebraically.

1. Gladys is offered a job to help prepare handcrafted baskets for a bazaar. She will be paid $50.00 per day plus $5.00 per item sold. She must purchase all of her supplies herself. For each day's order, she buys $35.00 worth of dried flowers and $15.00 worth of ribbon. In addition, each basket costs her $3.75, and each basket lining costs her $1.25. Determine Gladys's break-even point.

2. Budget will rent an SUV for $60.99 per day with unlimited miles. Enterprise will rent the same minivan for $47.49 per day plus $0.25 per mile driven over 150 miles. Assuming the number of miles driven will be over 150 miles, determine the number of miles driven that will make the cost of a one-day rental the same for the two rental plans.

3. If x cubic centimeters (cc) of a 40% alcohol solution is mixed with 20 cc of a 70% alcohol solution, a 60% alcohol solution is obtained. How many cc of the 40% alcohol solution were used?

4. To calculate Fahrenheit temperature using the chirps of tree crickets, one calculates the average number of chirps in 7 seconds (the number of chirps in 1 minute, divided by 8.6) and adds 46. How many chirps per minute will you count if the temperature is 81°F?

2.3 EXERCISES

 Student Solutions Manual   PH Math/Tutor Center   CD Video   Math XL MathXL®   MyMathLab MyMathLab   Interactmath.com

Solve algebraically and check. If necessary, round decimal answers to one more decimal place than that shown in the original exercise.

1. $4x + 8 = 0$
2. $5x - 15 = 0$
3. $-x - 41 = 3$
4. $15 - x = 3$
5. $-3x + 7 = 7$
6. $36 = 6x + 9$
7. $15.17 = 5.9x - 4.3$
8. $-4.22x - 0.4 = -21.5$
9. $-9.2x - 4.3 = -70.54$
10. $-6.3p + 1.5 = -4.8$
11. $-\frac{5}{9}b + \frac{11}{12} = \frac{23}{36}$
12. $\frac{5}{12}z + \frac{1}{6} = \frac{4}{9}$
13. $-\frac{2}{3}z - \frac{1}{2} = -\frac{5}{6}$
14. $-\frac{1}{9}y - \frac{5}{18} = -\frac{1}{6}$
15. $5x + 6 = x + 126$
16. $-5x - 18 = 2x - 4$
17. $27x - 49 = -12x - 10$
18. $2x + 17 = 17 - 4x$
19. $156z - 210 = 47z + 662$
20. $728a + 958 = 116a - 878$
21. $4x - (3x + 5) = x - 5$
22. $7x + 4 = 3x + 2(2x + 2)$
23. $6x - (x + 1) = 5x + 7$
24. $6x + (2x + 7) = 2(4x + 9)$
25. $5(0.3x + 8.7) = 2.5x + 41.5$
26. $3.4x + 8.8 = 0.1(17x + 3)$
27. $5.5x = 1.2x + 3.3(x - 2)$
28. $0.2x - 1.5 = 3.2(x - 3)$
29. $\frac{3}{4}x + \frac{1}{2} = \frac{1}{2}x + \frac{1}{4}$
30. $\frac{1}{3}x + \frac{3}{5} = \frac{1}{2}x - \frac{2}{5}$
31. $\frac{3}{5}x + 1 = \frac{2}{5}x + 3$
32. $\frac{3}{8}x + 2 = \frac{1}{8}x + 4$
33. $11x - 12 = 7(3x - 6) - 2(x + 9)$
34. $5(x + 3) - 2x = 2(x + 11) - (2x - 23)$
35. $2(2x - 9) + 3(3x - 4) = 4(x - 3) + 9(x - 2)$
36. $7x - 5(3x + 9) = -2(4x + 35)$

Use the multiplication property of equations to clear the fractions from each equation. Then solve algebraically.

37. $\dfrac{1}{4}x + \dfrac{5}{9} = \dfrac{5}{6}$

38. $\dfrac{3}{7}x + 2 = \dfrac{3}{4}x - 1$

39. $3x + \dfrac{1}{4} = 2x + \dfrac{7}{36}$

40. $\dfrac{9}{11}y - \dfrac{17}{22} = \dfrac{4}{11}y + \dfrac{1}{22}$

41. $\dfrac{2}{5}b - 12 = \dfrac{2}{3}b + 20$

42. $\dfrac{7}{9}x - 15 = \dfrac{4}{9}x - 37$

43. $\dfrac{3}{4}\left(x + \dfrac{4}{5}\right) = -\dfrac{7}{8}x - \dfrac{2}{5}$

44. $\dfrac{3}{4}\left(20p + \dfrac{1}{2}\right) = 13p - \dfrac{3}{8}$

In exercises 45–50, use the multiplication property of equations to clear the decimals from each equation. Then solve algebraically.

45. $0.05x + 10.5 = 0.15x - 0.25$

46. $0.01x + 0.11 = 0.47 - 0.09x$

47. $21.1x + 0.46 = 10.9x + 0.46$

48. $-1.05x - 15.41 = 2.55x - 47.09$

49. $15.2y - 175.43 = -2.4y - 176.31$

50. $81 = 0.5(120 - x) + 0.8x$

Cost/Rental

51. A furniture store will carry your loan without interest for 24 months on any purchase if you pay $200 down. What would the monthly payments be for a living-room set selling for $2252?

52. During a special promotion, Frugal Frieda's furniture company offers to carry your loan without interest for 30 months, with no down payment required. There is an instant rebate of $150 on the purchase to apply to the account. What would the monthly charges be on a purchase of $4350?

53. Budget will rent a compact car for $42.99 per day. Layton must also pay a $5.00 processing fee. If he budgets $600.00 for his trip for car rental, determine the number of days he can rent the car and stay in his budget.

54. Budget will rent a minivan for $74.99 per day. Dorothy has budgeted $700.00 for the minivan rental. She must pay an additional $15.00 processing fee. Determine the number of days she can rent the minivan and stay in her budget.

55. U-haul will rent a 24-foot truck for $39.95 per day plus $0.59 per mile. Budget Rent-A-Truck charges $35.49 per day and $0.65 per mile for the same truck. Determine the number of miles driven that will make the cost of a one-day rental the same for the two rental plans.

56. Penske will rent a 17-foot truck for $29.95 per day plus $0.59 per mile. Budget Rent-A-Truck charges $25.49 per day plus $0.65 per mile. Determine the number of miles driven that will make the cost of a one-day rental the same for the two rental plans.

57. Budget will rent a compact car for $42.99 per day with unlimited miles. Enterprise will rent the same car for $38.93 per day plus $0.30 per mile driven over 150 miles. Assuming the number of miles driven will be over 150, determine the number of miles driven that will make the cost of a one-day rental the same for the two rental plans.

58. Budget will rent a minivan for $74.99 per day with unlimited miles. Enterprise will rent the same minivan for $71.24 per day plus $0.25 per mile driven over 150 miles. Assuming the number of miles driven will be over 150 miles, determine the number of miles driven that will make the cost of a one-day rental the same for the two rental plans.

59. Marshall has a new satellite phone in his car. The charge is $0.30 per minute for all calls. His cell phone company charges $49.99 for 500 minutes and $0.40 per minute for all calls over 500 minutes. For how many minutes will the two plans be the same?

60. Glenna has a choice of two cell phone plans. One charges $69.99 per month for 1000 minutes and an additional $0.40 per minute for all calls over 1000. The second plan charges $0.25 per minute. For how many minutes will the cell phone plans be the same?

61. The sales force at a car dealership has a choice of two pay plans. The first plan pays the salesperson $300 per week plus 4% of the total sales for the week. The second plan pays the salesperson $700 per week plus 4% of the total sales in excess of $5000. Given that sales must exceed $5000, for what value of sales will the two plans be equal?

62. The Flexi-Rental firm will rent a car with a choice of plans. The first plan charges $39.50 plus $0.20 per mile. The second plan charges $49.50 plus $0.20 per mile for every mile over 100 miles. Assuming more than 100 miles will be driven, for what number of miles will the two plans cost the same?

Break Even/Profit

63. Clayton plans to work at home. He purchases a computer and printer for $1300.00. He plans to type papers for local students. The paper costs him $0.05 per page.
   a. If he charges $2.00 per page, determine the number of pages he must type to break even.
   b. Clayton wants to make a profit (revenue minus cost) of $1000 in the first month. Determine the number of pages he must type.

64. Juan does photography shoots. He estimates that he spent $5000 for video equipment. He pays an assistant $8 per hour. He charges $45 per hour.
   a. Determine the number of hours he must work to break even.
   b. Determine the number of hours he must work to realize a profit of $1000.

Mixture

65. A mechanic has a 40% antifreeze mixture and a 70% antifreeze mixture. How many gallons of each should he mix to make 2 gallons of a 60% antifreeze mixture?

66. A chemist has a solution that is 40% acid and another solution that is 65% acid. How many liters of each should he mix to make 2 liters of a solution that is 50% acid?

67. If 4 liters of a 10% vinegar solution is mixed with x liters of a 30% vinegar solution, the result is a 25% vinegar solution. How many liters of the 30% vinegar solution were mixed?

68. Five gallons of a 10% glucose solution is mixed with x gallons of a 40% glucose solution to obtain a 20% glucose solution. How many gallons of the 40% glucose solution were used?

Average

69. Alex wants to make a grade of A in his math class. His grade is the average of his four test grades and his final project. His four test grades are 100, 92, 95, and 87. What must his project grade be to have an average of 93 to make an A?

70. Alexandria wants to make a grade of A in her math class. Her grade is the average of her four test grades and her final project. Her four test grades are 98, 94, 96, and 87. What must her project grade be to have an average of 93 to make an A?

71. The average low temperature for North Pole, Alaska, for the month of December is −15 degrees Fahrenheit. If the low temperatures for the first six days before Christmas Eve were −12, −13, 18, −16, −15, and −11, what should be the low temperature for Christmas Eve to realize a weekly average that is the same as the monthly average low temperature?

72. The average high temperature for North Pole, Alaska, for the month of December is 1 degree Fahrenheit. If the high temperatures for the first six days before Christmas Eve were −1, −2, 3, 5, 2, and −3, what should be the high temperature for Christmas Eve to realize a weekly average that is the same as the monthly average high temperature?

Other

73. Acme Sales pays each member of its sales staff $150 per week plus a commission of 10% of the person's sales. The company deducts 2% of the person's sales from its payment to the sales staff to cover overhead expenses. On the other hand, Mega Sales pays each of its salespeople $200 per week plus a commission of 8% of the person's sales. Mega deducts $50 per week from the payment to its salespeople to cover overhead expenses. For what level of sales will the two companies pay the same weekly amount to their salespeople?

74. During its festival promotion, the Discount Mall will rent a booth to retailers for $285 plus a daily charge of $25. The company also adds to this a daily charge of $20 for janitorial and other support. A license to sell at the Discount Mall costs $15. At the same time, the Christmas Mall next door will rent a booth to retailers for $255 plus a daily charge of $45. There is no charge for support labor, and a license to sell at the Christmas Mall costs $45. Find the number of days for which the two rental options have the same total cost.

75. Justin is working as a server at a restaurant chain near a local mall. He is paid $4.00 per hour and also earns tips. As a part of a team of employees that includes hostesses and bus staff he is also expected to "tip out" 2% of his tips to those who assist him. One busy weekend he works two shifts of five hours each, and after "tipping out" he nets $178. How much had he earned in total tips? Round your answer to the nearest hundredth of a dollar.

76. Working a long shift on a busy Saturday Justin, a waiter, is paid $4.00 per hour plus tips. As in exercise 75, he must "tip out." He earns $168.06 after "tipping out" his support staff from his total tips of $147. How many hours did he work?

 ## 2.3 Calculator Exercises

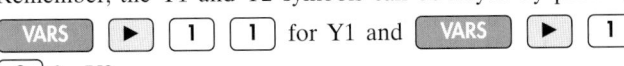

In Section 2.2, we saw how to use the "solve" command as an alternative method for solving a linear equation. The method first required that you rewrite the equation so that its left-hand side was set equal to zero. This can be time consuming and lead to errors. You can obtain the same result if you take the original equation you wish to solve and store the left-hand side in Y1 and the right-hand side in Y2. Then enter the solve command as follows:

Solve (Y1-Y2, x, guess)

Remember, the Y1 and Y2 symbols can be keyed by pressing

[**VARS**] [▶] [1] [1] for Y1 and [**VARS**] [▶] [1]

[2] for Y2.

After finishing one problem, you need only type in the new expressions for Y1 and Y2, and you will be ready to use the same solve command for the next problem.

Write a linear equation which represents each of the applications that follow. Then use the solve command on your calculator to solve the equation.

1. A door-to-door cosmetics salesperson is charged a 3.75% fee on total sales plus $25.00 to participate in the program. If the fee for one month was $49.48, what were the total sales for that month?

2. A nurse must administer 620 grains of a medication to a patient. She has one 200-grain tablet that she must use, and the remainder is in 120-grain tablets. How many of the 120-grain tablets must she administer?

3. A carpenter wants to create a $4\frac{1}{4}$-inch-thick tabletop by layering sheets of different woods on a 2-inch base. The sheets are each $\frac{3}{4}$ inches thick. How many sheets of wood does he need?

2.3 Writing Exercise

At the beginning of this section, we said that you should follow a few rules in solving linear equations, using a combination of properties of equations. The rules first suggested that you use the addition property to isolate the variable to one side of the equation and the constant term to the other side and then use the multiplication property to complete the solution. Explain the advantages of solving in this order, as opposed to using the multiplication principle first. Describe difficulties you might encounter in reversing the order. Since every rule has its exceptions, describe situations in which you might want to apply the multiplication principle first. (*Hint:* In some examples in this section, the multiplication principle was used first.) Finish your discussion by explaining the steps you will follow in applying these properties of equations to solve a linear equation, and illustrate with an example.

2.4 SOLVING EQUATIONS OR FORMULAS FOR A SPECIFIED VARIABLE

OBJECTIVES
1 Solve equations or formulas for a specified variable.
2 Model real-world situations by using linear equations, and then solve the equations.

APPLICATION

Temperature can be recorded in Celsius and Fahrenheit scales. If you know that the conversion formula to calculate Celsius temperatures from Fahrenheit temperatures is $C = \frac{5}{9}(F - 32)$, solve the formula for F to obtain a new formula to calculate Fahrenheit temperatures from Celsius temperatures.

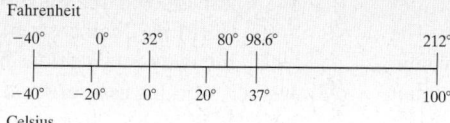

After completing this section, we will discuss this application further. See page 232.

Objective 2.4.1 Solving Equations for a Variable

We defined the term *formula* in an earlier chapter. A formula is a statement equating an unknown variable with an expression that can be evaluated to find a value for the unknown variable. For example, $A = LW$ is a formula used to find a value for the variable A(area) when values for L(length) and W(width) are known for a rectangle.

If $L = 12$ feet and $W = 6$ feet, then

$$A = LW$$
$$A = 12 \text{ feet} \cdot 6 \text{ feet} \qquad \text{Substitute.}$$
$$A = 72 \text{ square feet} \qquad \text{Evaluate.}$$

However, we may know values for A and W, but not for L. If $A = 48$ square feet and $W = 8$ feet, then

$$A = LW$$
$$48 = L \cdot 8 \qquad \text{Substitute.}$$
$$\frac{48}{8} = \frac{L \cdot 8}{8} \qquad \text{Divide both sides by 8.}$$
$$6 = L \qquad \text{Simplify.}$$
$$\text{or} \quad L = 6 \text{ feet}$$

When this type of evaluation must be repeated several times, we need a new formula for L in terms of A and W. That is, we need to solve the formula $A = LW$ for the variable L. We do this by using the same properties of equations that we used in the last two sections.

For example, given $A = LW$, solve for L.

$$A = LW$$

$$\frac{A}{W} = \frac{LW}{W} \qquad \text{Divide both sides by } W.$$

$$\frac{A}{W} = L \quad \text{or} \quad L = \frac{A}{W} \qquad \text{Simplify.}$$

We now have a formula for L in terms of A and W.

 TAKE NOTE The conventional form for writing an equation or formula is to write the variable we are solving for on the left side. Recall that in Chapter 1 we wrote equivalent order relations. For equations or formulas, we simply exchange the expressions on each side.

SOLVING AN EQUATION OR FORMULA FOR A VARIABLE

To solve an equation or formula for a variable by using the properties of equations,

- Clear the equation or formula of fractions.
- Isolate the term(s) involving the desired variable to one side, using the addition property of equations.
- Use the addition property of equations to collect all the other terms to the other side.
- Collect like terms in both expressions. If the terms containing the desired variable are unlike, factor out the desired variable.
- Use the multiplication property of equations to reduce the coefficient of the desired variable to 1.

 TAKE NOTE Since we are using a process we have previously learned, with the only difference being that we are using variables instead of numbers, we can substitute numbers for the variables and solve the equation first. This will help us "see" the steps to use for the variables.

EXAMPLE 1

Solve each formula for the indicated variable.

a. Perimeter of a rectangle, $P = 2L + 2W$, for L.

b. Average of three grades, $A = \dfrac{a + b + c}{3}$, for c.

c. Area of a trapezoid, $A = \dfrac{1}{2}hb + \dfrac{1}{2}hB$, for h.

Solution

a. Perimeter of a rectangle, $P = 2L + 2W$, for L.

$$P = 2L + 2W$$

$$P - 2W = 2L + 2W - 2W \qquad \text{Subtract } 2W \text{ from both sides.}$$

$$P - 2W = 2L \qquad \text{Simplify.}$$

$$\frac{P - 2W}{2} = \frac{2L}{2} \qquad \text{Divide both sides by 2.}$$

$$\frac{P - 2W}{2} = L \quad \text{or} \quad L = \frac{P - 2W}{2} \qquad \text{Simplify.}$$

We could continue to simplify by dividing each term of the expression by 2, yielding $L = \dfrac{P}{2} - W$.

b. Average of three grades, $A = \dfrac{a + b + c}{3}$, for c.

$$A = \frac{a + b + c}{3}$$

$$3A = 3\left(\frac{a + b + c}{3}\right) \qquad \text{Multiply both sides by 3.}$$

$$3A = a + b + c \qquad \text{Simplify.}$$

$$3A - a - b = a + b + c - a - b \qquad \text{Subtract } a \text{ and } b \text{ from both sides.}$$

$$3A - a - b = c \qquad \text{Simplify.}$$

$$\text{or} \quad c = 3A - a - b$$

c. Area of a trapezoid, $A = \dfrac{1}{2}hb + \dfrac{1}{2}hB$, for h.

$$A = \frac{1}{2}hb + \frac{1}{2}hB$$

$$2A = 2\left(\frac{1}{2}hb + \frac{1}{2}hB\right) \qquad \text{Multiply both sides by 2 to clear the fractions.}$$

$$2A = 2\left(\frac{1}{2}hb\right) + 2\left(\frac{1}{2}hB\right) \qquad \text{Distribute.}$$

$$2A = hb + hB \qquad \text{Simplify.}$$

$$2A = h(b + B) \qquad \text{Since we are solving for } h, \text{ which is a factor in two unlike terms, we factor out the common factor } h.$$

$$\frac{2A}{b + B} = \frac{h(b + B)}{b + B} \qquad \text{Divide both sides by } (b + B).$$

$$\frac{2A}{b + B} = h \qquad \text{Simplify.}$$

$$\text{or} \quad h = \frac{2A}{b + B}$$

EXAMPLE 2   Solve for y in terms of x.

a. $3x - y = 6$ **b.** $4x + 2y = 6$ **c.** $y - 3 = \dfrac{1}{2}(x + 1)$

Solution

a.
$$3x - y = 6$$

$$3x - y - 3x = 6 - 3x \qquad \text{Subtract 3x from both sides.}$$

$$-y = 6 - 3x \qquad \text{Simplify.}$$

$$\frac{-y}{-1} = \frac{6 - 3x}{-1} \qquad \text{Divide both sides by } -1.$$

$$y = -6 + 3x \qquad \text{Distribute and simplify.}$$

$$\text{or} \quad y = 3x - 6 \qquad \text{Rearrange the expression on the right with the variable term first.}$$

 TAKE NOTE The conventional form for writing an equation when y is equated to an expression containing a variable term and a constant term is to write the right side of the equation with the variable term followed by the constant term.

b.
$$4x + 2y = 6$$
$$4x + 2y - 4x = 6 - 4x \quad \text{Subtract 4x from both sides.}$$
$$2y = 6 - 4x \quad \text{Simplify.}$$
$$\frac{2y}{2} = \frac{6 - 4x}{2} \quad \text{Divide both sides by 2.}$$
$$y = 3 - 2x \quad \text{Distribute and simplify.}$$
$$\text{or} \quad y = -2x + 3 \quad \text{Rearrange the expression on the right with the variable term first.}$$

c.
$$y - 3 = \frac{1}{2}(x + 1)$$
$$y - 3 = \frac{1}{2}x + \frac{1}{2} \quad \text{Distribute.}$$
$$y - 3 + 3 = \frac{1}{2}x + \frac{1}{2} + 3 \quad \text{Add 3 to both sides.}$$
$$y = \frac{1}{2}x + \frac{7}{2} \quad \text{Simplify.}$$

✓ Objective 2.4.1 *CHECKUP*

1. Solve each formula for the indicated variable.

  a. Perimeter of a rectangle, $P = 2L + 2W$, for W.

  b. Average of four grades, $A = \dfrac{a + b + c + d}{4}$, for a.

  c. Surface area of a rectangular solid,
  $S = 2LW + 2LH + 2WH$, for W.

2. Solve for y in terms of x.

  a. $2x - y = 3$

  b. $44x + 22y = 55$

  c. $y + 5 = \dfrac{7}{3}(x + 6)$

Objective 2.4.2 Modeling the Real World

Many important formulas are used to describe real-world relationships in geometry, science, and business—indeed, just about any subject you can think of. But once you understand how to solve a formula for any variable, you don't need to memorize all the different forms of the same equation. For example, if you know that speed is defined as distance traveled divided by time taken traveling, $r = \frac{d}{t}$, you can solve for d and come up with the distance formula, $d = rt$. Rearranging formulas in this way is a very useful skill to have.

EXAMPLE 3

Linda's class wants to decorate and sell t-shirts. Linda can buy the t-shirts for $4 each and the paint for $12.

  a. Write an equation for the cost, c to decorate n t-shirts.

  b. Use your equation to find a new equation for the number of t-shirts, n, in terms of the cost, c.

  c. Use the equation obtained in part b to determine the number of t-shirts the class can make for $150, $250, and $350.

Solution

  a. Let c = total cost

  n = number of t-shirts decorated

  $c = 4n + 12$

b. Solve $c = 4n + 12$ for n.

$$c = 4n + 12$$

$$c - 12 = 4n + 12 - 12 \quad \text{\small Subtract 12 from both sides.}$$

$$c - 12 = 4n \quad \text{\small Simplify.}$$

$$\frac{c - 12}{4} = \frac{4n}{4} \quad \text{\small Divide both sides by 4.}$$

$$\frac{1}{4}c - 3 = n \quad \text{\small Simplify.}$$

$$n = \frac{1}{4}c - 3 \quad \text{\small Write in conventional form.}$$

c. A table of values will give us the number of t-shirts for different values.

c	$n = \dfrac{1}{4}c - 3$	n
150	$n = \dfrac{1}{4}(150) - 3$	$34\dfrac{1}{2}$
250	$n = \dfrac{1}{4}(250) - 3$	$59\dfrac{1}{2}$
350	$n = \dfrac{1}{4}(350) - 3$	$84\dfrac{1}{2}$

Note: It is not possible to make the 0.5 shirt. To stay within the budget, Linda cannot round up to 35 shirts. Therefore, Linda's class can make 34 shirts for $150, 59 shirts for $250, and 84 shirts for $350. ◼

APPLICATION

Temperature can be recorded in Celsius and Fahrenheit scales. If you know the conversion formula to calculate Celsius temperatures from Fahrenheit temperatures is $C = \frac{5}{9}(F - 32)$, solve the formula for F to obtain a new formula to calculate Fahrenheit temperatures from Celsius temperatures.

Discussion

$$C = \frac{5}{9}(F - 32)$$

$$C = \frac{5}{9}F - \frac{5}{9} \cdot 32 \quad \text{\small Distribute.}$$

$$C = \frac{5}{9}F - \frac{160}{9}$$

$$9C = 9\left(\frac{5}{9}F - \frac{160}{9}\right) \quad \text{\small Multiply both sides by 9.}$$

$$9C = 5F - 160 \quad \text{\small Simplify.}$$

$$9C + 160 = 5F - 160 + 160 \quad \text{\small Add 160 to both sides.}$$

$$9C + 160 = 5F \quad \text{\small Simplify.}$$

$$\frac{9C + 160}{5} = \frac{5F}{5} \quad \text{\small Divide both sides by 5.}$$

$$\frac{9}{5}C + 32 = F \quad \text{\small Distribute.}$$

$$\text{or } F = \frac{9}{5}C + 32$$

Two formulas used to convert between Celsius and Fahrenheit temperatures are $C = \frac{5}{9}(F - 32)$ and $F = \frac{9}{5}C + 32$.

✓ Objective 2.4.2 CHECKUP

1. Happy Harpo's car rental firm offers a weekly special for vacationers: You can rent a car for seven days, paying $49.95 plus a charge of $0.12 per mile.

  a. Write an equation for the cost of renting the car and driving x miles during the week.

  b. Use your equation to find a new equation for the number of miles driven, x, in terms of the cost, c.

  c. Use the equation in part b to find how many miles is the maximum you can drive if your budget is $150; if your budget is $250; if your budget is $500.

2. Solve the Fahrenheit temperature formula, $F = \frac{9}{5}C + 32$, for the Celsius temperature, C.

◼

2.4 EXERCISES

Student Solutions Manual   PH Math/Tutor Center   CD Video   MathXL®   MyMathLab   Interactmath.com

Solve each formula for the indicated variable.

1. The perimeter of a square, $P = 4s$, for s.
2. The area of a parallelogram, $A = bh$, for b.
3. The circumference of a circle, $C = \pi d$, for d.
4. The circumference of a circle, $C = 2\pi r$, for r.
5. The volume of a rectangular solid, $V = LWH$, for L.
6. The volume of a rectangular solid, $V = LWH$, for W.
7. The area of a triangle, $A = \frac{1}{2}bh$, for h.
8. The area of a triangle, $A = \frac{1}{2}bh$, for b.
9. The volume of a cylinder, $V = \pi r^2 h$, for h.
10. The surface area of a cylinder, $S = 2\pi r^2 + 2\pi rh$, for h.
11. Simple interest, $I = Prt$, for P.
12. Simple interest, $I = Prt$, for r.
13. Velocity of an object falling from rest, $v = gt$, where g is the acceleration and t is the time, for g.

14. Velocity of an object falling from rest, $v = gt$, for t.
15. Current in a circuit, $I = \dfrac{V}{R}$, where V is the voltage and R is the resistance, for R.
16. Einstein's law of mass–energy equivalence, $E = mc^2$, where c is a constant (the speed of light), for m, the mass.
17. From statistics, the standardized variable, $z = \dfrac{x - m}{s}$, for m, the mean.
18. The standardized variable, $z = \dfrac{x - m}{s}$, for s, the standard deviation.
19. The surface area of a rectangular solid, $S = 2LW + 2LH + 2WH$, for L.
20. The surface area of a rectangular solid, $S = 2LW + 2LH + 2WH$, for H.

Solve for y in terms of x.

21. $4x + 3y = 0$
22. $5x + 15y = 0$
23. $-5x + 10y = 0$
24. $6x - 18y = 0$
25. $-x - y = 0$
26. $-x + y = 0$
27. $5x + 4y = 20$
28. $-4x - 4y = 12$
29. $-x - y = 7$
30. $13x - y = 13$
31. $7x - 14y = -28$
32. $8x + 7y = -56$
33. $-x + y = -1$
34. $-21x + 7y = -14$
35. $y - 5 = 4(x - 6)$
36. $y - 1 = -4(x - 3)$
37. $y + 6 = -2(x - 7)$
38. $y - 8 = 3(x + 9)$
39. $y + 2 = -1(x + 4)$
40. $y + 12 = -5(x + 10)$
41. $y - 4 = \frac{2}{3}(x + 9)$
42. $y + 6 = -\frac{3}{4}(x - 8)$
43. $y + \frac{5}{9} = -\frac{2}{3}\left(x - \frac{1}{3}\right)$
44. $y - \frac{7}{18} = \frac{4}{9}\left(x - \frac{1}{2}\right)$

45. With a down payment of $200, Jenny purchased a living-room suite, agreeing to make monthly payments of $85, with no interest charges, until the balance is paid up.
   a. Write an equation for Jenny's total payments, P, to pay off the bill in m months.
   b. Find a new equation for the number of months needed to pay off the bill.
   c. How long will it take to pay off a purchase of $2240?
   d. How long will it take to pay off a purchase of $1200?

46. Richard charges a flat fee of $75.00 per job plus $35.00 per hour to do interior painting.
   a. Write an equation for the total cost, c, of a job that takes h hours to complete.
   b. Find a new equation for the number of hours worked on a particular job that costs c dollars.
   c. How many hours did Richard work if the job cost $495.00?
   d. How many hours did he work if the job cost $652.50?

47. Mildred is planning a Halloween party for her kindergarten class. She has already spent $12.50 on decorations for the room.
   a. Write an equation for her total cost of the party, T, if she spends c dollars for favors and treats on each of the 22 students in the class.
   b. Find a new equation for the amount of money she can spend on each child so that she spends T dollars on the party.
   c. How much can she spend on each child if she has $35.00 for the party?

d. How much can she spend on each child if she has $50.00 for the party?

48. The soccer team is planning a fund-raiser to buy equipment and uniforms for its team. The equipment will cost $175.
   a. Write an equation for the total amount needed, T, if the team spends c dollars for each uniform, given that there are 14 members on the team.
   b. Find a new equation for the amount spent on each uniform if the team is limited to spending T dollars total.
   c. How much will each member receive for uniforms if the team raises $675?
   d. How much will each member receive if the team raises $1000?

49. Ted's boss's weekly earnings average $75 more than three times Ted's average weekly earnings. Write an equation for the boss's average weekly earnings, B, in terms of Ted's weekly earnings, T. Find a new equation for Ted's weekly earnings if we know what his boss's earnings are. What are Ted's weekly earnings if his boss averages $725 per week? What are Ted's weekly earnings if his boss averages $1275 per week?

50. In a gender discrimination suit, it was alleged that the average hourly wage of male employees was $0.75 less than 1.5 times the average hourly wage of female employees. Write an equation for the average hourly wage of male employees, M, given that the average hourly wage of female employees is F dollars. Find a new equation for the average hourly wage of female employees if the average hourly wage of male employees is known. What would be the average hourly wage of female employees if male employees average $12.45 per hour? What would be the average hourly wage for females if the male employees average $21.00 per hour?

51. You can rent a tree stump grinder for a flat fee of $85 plus $185 per day. Write an equation to represent the total cost, C, of renting the equipment for d days. Find a new equation for the number of days you can rent the equipment for a fixed cost, C. For how many days can the equipment be rented if you want to limit the total cost to $270? For how many days' rental will the cost be limited to $825?

52. Carol is taking a motor trip around parts of Alaska for her vacation. She has already driven 50 miles from Seward. If she averages 40 miles per hour, write an equation for her total distance traveled, D, after driving h more hours. Find a new equation for the number of driving hours remaining if the total distance of the trip is known. How many driving hours remain if the total distance is about 510 miles to Fairbanks? How many driving hours remain if the total distance is about 130 miles to Anchorage?

53. A storage bin must be built to fit into a corner of a shed. The bin is limited to being 3 feet wide and 5 feet long. Write an equation for the volume of the bin, V, in terms of its height, h. Find a new equation for the height of the bin in terms of its volume. What should the height be if the volume of the bin must be 60 cubic feet? What should the height be if the volume of the bin must be 100 cubic feet?

54. For the storage bin in exercise **53**, write an equation for the total surface area, S, of the bin (including a bottom, top, and four sides) if the width is 3 feet, the length is 5 feet, and the height is h feet. Find a new equation for the height if the total surface area is known. What is the height if the total surface area is 86 square feet? What is the height if the total surface area is 120 square feet?

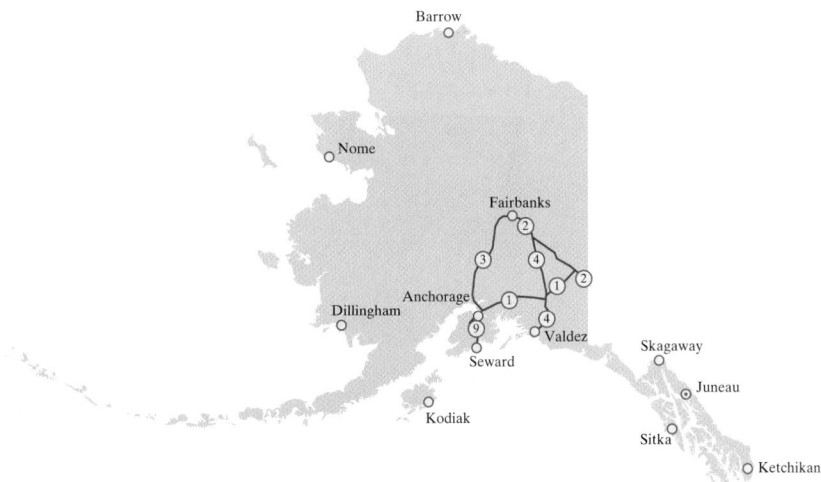

2.4 Calculator Exercises

In Chapter P, various methods for calculating interest on an investment were discussed. One such method, continuously compounded interest, will be discussed in this calculator exercise. An investment of P dollars continuously compounded for t years at an annual interest rate of r percent will accrue to an amount

$$A = Pe^{rt}$$

where e is the irrational number that is approximated by $2.718281828.\ldots$ Find the key for this number on your calculator.

We will use the preceding formula to determine what amount will accrue to an investment of $10,000 at the end of a given number of years when the interest rate is 4.5% per year. Substituting these values into the formula gives us

$$10000 = Pe^{0.045t}$$

as the relation for this particular investment situation. Solve this equation for *P*. Store the new equation in your calculator, using the [Y=] key. To do this, you must replace *P* by *y* and *t* by *x* in your new equation. Then use the table feature of your calculator to complete the following table:

A	r	t	P
$10,000	4.5%	5	
$10,000	4.5%	7	
$10,000	4.5%	10	
$10,000	4.5%	12	

Next, change the amount, *A*, to $25,000 and the interest rate to 7%. Determine the new equation for *P*, store it in your calculator, and complete the following table:

A	r	t	P
$25,000	7%	5	
$25,000	7%	7	
$25,000	7%	10	
$25,000	7%	12	

What do these tables tell you about the relationship between the time over which the investment accrues interest and how much money you must initially invest in order to accumulate a certain amount of money? This type of analysis should impress you with the power of mathematics to help people make important decisions pertaining to managing their finances.

2.4 Writing Exercise

In this section, you learned to take a formula and, by applying the properties of equations, write a new formula by solving for one of the variables. Discuss some of the reasons that you would want to use this technique. Illustrate your reasons with an example in which you start with one of the formulas you have worked with, and use it to solve for another variable. Explain why you are solving for the variable; that is, give reasons as to why you need to solve for another variable. Complete your example by specifying some values for the variables in the formula and calculating the value for the variable for which you solved initially.

2.5 MORE REAL-WORLD MODELS

OBJECTIVES

1 Model real-world situations involving consecutive integers.
2 Model real-world situations involving interest.
3 Model real-world situations involving a percentage of increase or decrease.
4 Model real-world situations involving geometric figures.

APPLICATION

The Vietnam Veterans Memorial was designed by a 21-year-old student, Maya Ying Lin. The memorial consists of two walls, each $246\frac{2}{3}$ feet in length. The walls meet at an angle of 125.2 degrees, with one wall pointing to the Washington Monument and one pointing to the Lincoln Memorial. How many degrees should one of the walls be rotated for the walls to form a straight line? The area enclosed by the walls is in the shape of a triangle with two equal angles. Determine the measure of these angles.

After completing this section, we will discuss this application further. See page 242.

We now know three methods for solving a linear equation: numeric, graphic, and algebraic. We have also solved real-world models with each of these methods. However, numerous other types of models can be solved with such methods.

In this section, we will discuss other types of real-world models involving linear equations. We will also examine some classic algebra exercises that are common in traditional algebra texts. These exercises are not as applicable to the real world as previous exercises in this text, but the ideas needed to solve them will help strengthen your problem-solving skills.

Remember, there is no set way to work all exercises. Also, once a linear equation is written for an exercise, it may be solved with any of the methods we have learned.

MODELING REAL-WORLD SITUATIONS

To model a real-world situation,

- Read and understand the situation. A drawing is often helpful.
- Define a variable for the unknown quantity. Define other quantities in terms of the variable if possible.
- Write an equation with the information given.
- Solve the equation, either numerically, graphically, or algebraically.
- Check the solution with the original problem.
- Write an answer for the question asked, using complete sentences.

The following examples illustrate types of situations that require a linear equation for their solution.

Objective 2.5.1 ## Consecutive-Integer Models

We discussed the set of integers in Chapter P. Remember,

$$Z = \{\ldots, -3, -2, -1, 0, 1, 2, 3, \ldots\}.$$

Now we need to define new terminology that is used in this section. **Consecutive integers** are integers in increasing order with no integers between them. **Consecutive even integers** are even integers in increasing order with no even integers between them. **Consecutive odd integers** are odd integers in increasing order with no odd integers between them. For example,

$$1, 2, 3, 4 \text{ are consecutive integers.}$$

$$-2, 0, 2, 4 \text{ are consecutive even integers.}$$

$$-7, -5, -3, -1 \text{ are consecutive odd integers.}$$

Consecutive integers may be represented with variables. For example, write consecutive integers in terms of the first integer.

Let x = the first integer

The second consecutive integer is 1 more than the first, or $x + 1$.

The third consecutive integer is 1 more than the second, or $(x + 1) + 1$, or $x + 2$.

The fourth consecutive integer is 1 more than the third, or $(x + 2) + 1$, or $x + 3$.

Write consecutive even integers in terms of the first even integer.

Let x = the first even integer

The second consecutive even integer is 2 more than the first, or $x + 2$.

The third consecutive even integer is 2 more than the second, or $(x + 2) + 2$, or $x + 4$.

The fourth consecutive even integer is 2 more than the third, or $(x + 4) + 2$, or $x + 6$.

Write consecutive odd integers in terms of the first odd integer.

Let x = the first odd integer

The second consecutive odd integer is 2 more than the first, or $x + 2$.

The third consecutive odd integer is 2 more than the second, or $(x + 2) + 2$, or $x + 4$.

The fourth consecutive odd integer is 2 more than the third, or $(x + 4) + 2$, or $x + 6$.

 TAKE NOTE Note that the only difference in the consecutive even- and odd-integer representation is the beginning definition for the variable, x, because both even and odd integers are every other integer.

EXAMPLE 1   The sum of three consecutive odd integers is 21. Find the three integers.

Solution

$$\text{Let } x = \text{the first odd integer}$$
$$x + 2 = \text{the second odd integer}$$
$$x + 4 = \text{the third odd integer}$$

The sum of the integers is 21.

$$x + (x + 2) + (x + 4) = 21$$
$$3x + 6 = 21 \qquad \text{Simplify.}$$
$$3x + 6 - 6 = 21 - 6 \qquad \text{Subtract 6 from both sides.}$$
$$3x = 15 \qquad \text{Simplify.}$$
$$\frac{3x}{3} = \frac{15}{3} \qquad \text{Divide both sides by 3.}$$
$$x = 5 \qquad \text{Simplify.}$$

Find the other two integers.

Second odd integer: $x + 2 = 5 + 2 = 7$
Third odd integer: $x + 4 = 5 + 4 = 9$

To check the solution, determine that the sum of the three odd integers, 5, 7, and 9, is 21.

$$5 + 7 + 9 = 21$$

Three odd integers that have a sum of 21 are 5, 7, and 9. ■

EXAMPLE 2   Del is wiring an electrical appliance and has to cut a wire into three pieces. The first piece must be an integer length, and each consecutive piece must be 1 inch longer than the preceding one. He measures the wire to be 27 inches. What are the lengths of the three pieces of wire?

Solution

The wire is to be cut into three consecutive integer lengths.

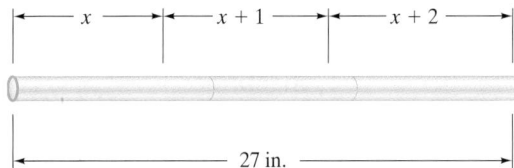

$$\text{Let } x = \text{integer length of the first piece}$$
$$x + 1 = \text{integer length of the second piece}$$
$$x + 2 = \text{integer length of the third piece}$$

The sum of the integers will be 27 inches, which is the total length.

Algebraic

$$x + (x + 1) + (x + 2) = 27$$
$$3x + 3 = 27 \qquad \text{Simplify.}$$
$$3x + 3 - 3 = 27 - 3 \qquad \text{Subtract 3 from both sides.}$$
$$3x = 24 \qquad \text{Simplify.}$$
$$\frac{3x}{3} = \frac{24}{3} \qquad \text{Divide both sides by 3.}$$
$$x = 8 \qquad \text{Simplify.}$$

Numeric

X	Y1	Y2
5	18	27
6	21	27
7	24	27
8	27	27
9	30	27
10	33	27
11	36	27

X=8

Y1 = $x + (x + 1) + (x + 2)$
Y2 = 27
The solution is 8.

Find the other integers (lengths of pieces) by substituting the solution into the other expressions.

Second piece: $x + 1 = 8 + 1 = 9$
Third piece: $x + 2 = 8 + 2 = 10$

To check the solution, we first determine that the values are indeed consecutive integers. Then we total the lengths to see whether the sum is 27 inches: $8 + 9 + 10 = 27$. It is, so the solution is correct.

The three pieces should be cut 8, 9, and 10 inches in length. ■

✓ Objective 2.5.1 **CHECKUP**

1. The sum of three consecutive even integers is 42. Find the integers.

2. Jim is building a scale model for his architecture class. He has a 25-inch piece of balsa wood that he wants to cut into five pieces so that each piece is 1 inch longer than the preceding piece. What are the five lengths he needs to cut?

3. What are the differences in the terms *consecutive integers*, *consecutive even integers*, and *consecutive odd integers*? ■

Objective 2.5.2   Interest Models

We saw in Chapter P that there are several ways to calculate interest on a loan. Compound interest involves exponential functions, but simple interest is a linear relationship. Situations involving calculations of interest or principal at various rates of interest are common and important in business and finance.

EXAMPLE 3

Dennis is building a trailer. He plans to sell it for $2500 when he is finished. He is borrowing the money needed to build the trailer from his father. His father charges 18% simple interest for one year. What is the most Dennis can borrow and know that he will have enough to pay his father at the end of one year?

Solution

Let $x =$ the amount borrowed
   Using the simple-interest formula, we obtain

$$I = PRT$$
$$I = x(0.18)(1) \qquad x = \text{amount borrowed, } R = 0.18, T = 1$$
$$I = 0.18x$$

Dennis will need to repay the amount borrowed, x, plus simple interest, $0.18x$. The maximum amount should be $2500. Therefore, $x + 0.18x = 2500$.

Algebraic

$$x + 0.18x = 2500$$
$$1.18x = 2500 \qquad \text{Combine like terms.}$$
$$\frac{1.18x}{1.18} = \frac{2500}{1.18} \qquad \text{Divide both sides by 1.18.}$$
$$x \approx 2118.64$$

Graphic

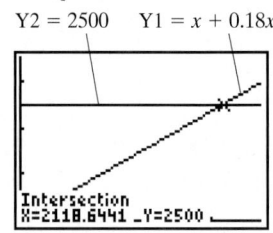

$Y2 = 2500$ $Y1 = x + 0.18x$

Intersection
X=2118.6441 _Y=2500

(0, 2500, 0, 3500)
The solution is about 2118.64.

To check this solution, add the amount borrowed plus interest to see whether we get 2500.

$$2118.64 + 0.18(2118.64) \approx 2500 \text{ (rounded to the nearest cent).}$$

Therefore, the solution is correct.
   Dennis can borrow $2118.64 from his father and repay it at the end of one year. ■

EXAMPLE 4

Nguyen received an inheritance of $10,000 from his great-uncle's estate. He invested part of the money in a simple-interest account paying 9% annually. He invested the remainder of the money in a savings account paying 4.75% simple interest annually. If he earned $815 in interest at the end of one year, how much did he invest in each account?

Solution

Let a = amount invested at 9% interest

$10{,}000 - a$ = amount invested at 4.75% interest

Use the simple-interest formula to determine the amount of interest for each account.

9% account	4.75% account	
$I = PRT$	$I = PRT$	
$I = a(0.09)(1)$	$I = (10{,}000 - a)(0.0475)(1)$	Substitute.
$I = 0.09a$	$I = (10{,}000 - a)(0.0475)$	Simplify.
	$I = 475 - 0.0475a$	Distribute.

The sum of the interest is \$815, or $0.09a + (475 - 0.0475a) = 815$.

Algebraic

$$0.09a + (475 - 0.0475a) = 815$$

$0.0425a + 475 = 815$ Simplify.

$0.0425a + 475 - 475 = 815 - 475$ Subtract 475 from both sides.

$0.0425a = 340$ Simplify.

$$\dfrac{0.0425a}{0.0425} = \dfrac{340}{0.0425}$$ Divide both sides by 0.0425.

$a = 8000$ Simplify.

Graphic

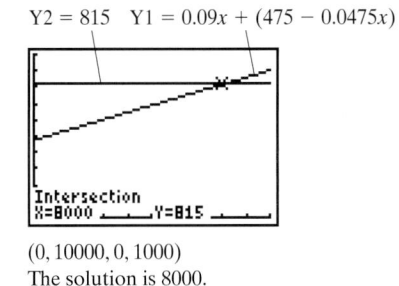

$(0, 10000, 0, 1000)$
The solution is 8000.

The amount deposited in the 9% account is \$8000.
The amount deposited in the 4.75% account is

$$10{,}000 - a = 10{,}000 - 8000 = 2000.$$

To check, determine the amount of interest from each account. Their sum is 815.

$$(0.09)(8000) + (0.0475)(2000) = 720 + 95 = 815$$

Nguyen deposited \$8000 in the 9% account and \$2000 in the 4.75% account.   ■

✓ Objective 2.5.2 *CHECKUP*

1. A bond pays 6.5% simple interest annually. How much should be invested in order to have a total of \$10,000 at the end of one year?

2. Zeke would like to borrow \$5000 at simple interest for one year. He is not able to borrow the total amount from one loan agency, so he must borrow part of it at 7% simple interest and the remainder at 8.5% simple interest. If his total interest payment is to be \$365, how much will he borrow at each interest rate?   ■

Objective 2.5.3   Percentage-of-Increase-or-Decrease Models

One of the most common linear relations in business and consumer finances involves calculating the percentage increase or decrease of some value. The value may be a cost, a sales price, a profit, or some other quantity. In any case, the method of calculating the increased or decreased value (or the calculation of the value before the increase or decrease) is the same.

EXAMPLE 5

Caitlin paid \$39.99 for a battery-and-charger set. The Internet advertisement claimed that this was a savings of \$9.96, or 20%. Determine the original list price. The advertisement also claimed that the original list price was \$49.95. Is the advertisement correct?

List Price: ~~$49.95~~
Our Price: $39.99
You Save: $9.96 (20%)
Availability: Usually ships within 24 hours.

Solution

Let x = the original list price

$0.20x$ = the amount of savings (20% of the original price)

The sale price, $39.99, is the original price minus the savings, or $x - 0.20x = 39.99$.

Algebraic

$$x - 0.20x = 39.99$$
$$0.80x = 39.99 \quad \text{Combine like terms.}$$
$$\frac{0.80x}{0.80} = \frac{39.99}{0.80} \quad \text{Divide both sides by 0.80.}$$
$$x = 49.9875$$

Graphic

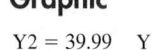

Y2 = 39.99   Y1 = $x - 0.20x$

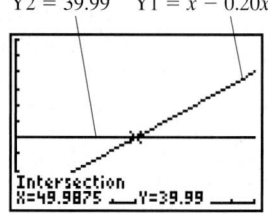

Intersection
X=49.9875 ___ Y=39.99 ___

(0, 100, 0, 100)
The solution is about 49.99.

If Caitlin saved 20%, then the original list price was $49.99, so she saved $49.99 − $39.99, or $10.00. The advertisement stated the original list price incorrectly. There is an error of $0.04. ■

✓ **Objective 2.5.3 CHECKUP**

1. Tillie's Travel Agency adds a 10% surcharge for handling motel reservations for a firm. If the charge for a room is $68.75, what was the charge before the surcharge was added? ▪

Objective 2.5.4   ## Geometric-Formula Models

Geometric formulas are helpful in all kinds of everyday situations. You often need to use these formulas whenever you have to find a measurement of a length, an angle, or an area. The measurement you want to find is your unknown variable, and the geometric formula is the linear equation you want to solve. You will find that a diagram of the situation can help you set up the equation correctly.

EXAMPLE 6   Shawn wants to add baseboards to his study. He measures the dimensions of the study and finds that the perimeter is 47 feet. When Shawn arrives at the home-repair store, he discovers a "manager's special" on carpets. He decides to carpet the floor of his study before adding the baseboards. However, he does not have the room's dimensions. All he can remember is that the rectangular study has a perimeter of 47 feet and the length is $4\frac{1}{2}$ feet more than the width. Determine the area of the floor in the study.

Solution

A figure will help us see the problem.

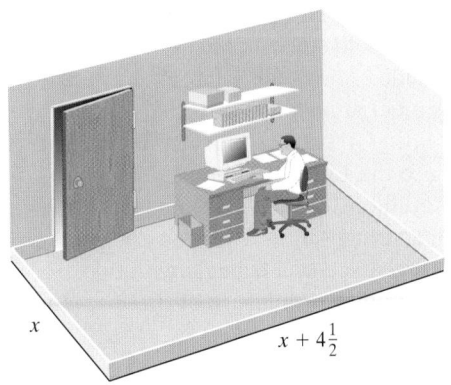

Let x = width of study

$x + 4\frac{1}{2}$ = length of study

To find the area of the floor, Shawn must know the dimensions of the study. He can find them by using the perimeter formula for a rectangle.

Algebraic

$$P = 2L + 2W$$

$$47 = 2\left(x + 4\frac{1}{2}\right) + 2(x) \quad \text{Substitute.}$$

$$47 = 2x + 9 + 2x \quad \text{Distribute.}$$

$$47 = 4x + 9 \quad \text{Simplify.}$$

$$47 - 9 = 4x + 9 - 9 \quad \text{Subtract 9 from both sides.}$$

$$38 = 4x \quad \text{Simplify.}$$

$$\frac{38}{4} = \frac{4x}{4} \quad \text{Divide both sides by 4.}$$

$$9\frac{1}{2} = x \quad \text{Simplify.}$$

Graphic

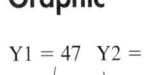

$Y1 = 47 \quad Y2 = 2\left(x + 4\frac{1}{2}\right) + 2x$

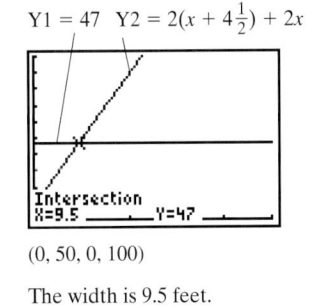

(0, 50, 0, 100)

The width is 9.5 feet.

The width is $9\frac{1}{2}$ feet. To find the length, substitute the solution into the expression: $x + 4\frac{1}{2} = 9\frac{1}{2} + 4\frac{1}{2} = 14$. The length is 14 feet. To check this solution, we check the perimeter formula.

$$P = 2L \quad + \quad 2W$$

47	$2(14) + 2\left(9\dfrac{1}{2}\right)$
	$28 \quad + \quad 19$
	47

The solution checks. The dimensions of the study are $9\frac{1}{2}$ feet by 14 feet.

The area of the rectangular floor is found by substituting the dimensions for the variables into the area formula.

$$A = LW$$

$$A = (14)\left(9\frac{1}{2}\right)$$

$$A = 133 \text{ square feet}$$

The area of the floor is 133 square feet.

APPLICATION

The Vietnam Veterans Memorial was designed by a 21-year-old student, Maya Ying Lin. The memorial is made of two walls, each $246\frac{2}{3}$ feet in length. The walls meet at an angle of 125.2 degrees, with one wall pointing to the Washington Monument and one pointing to the Lincoln Memorial. How many degrees should one of the walls be rotated for the walls to form a straight line? The area enclosed by the walls is in the shape of a triangle with two equal angles. Determine the measure of these angles.

Discussion

If the two walls form a straight line (or 180°), the existing angle of 125.2° is supplementary to the angle through which one of the walls must be rotated.

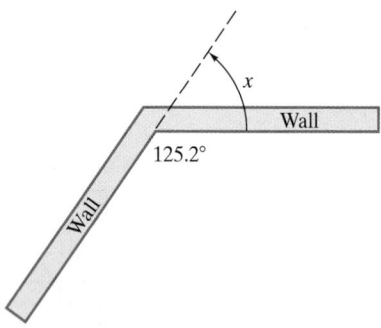

Let x = the measure of the angle
The sum of the angles is 180°.
$$125.2 + x = 180$$

Algebraic Solution

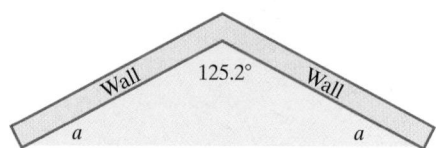

$$125.2 + x = 180$$
$$125.2 + x - 125.2 = 180 - 125.2 \quad \text{Subtract 125.2.}$$
$$x = 54.8$$

In order to form a straight line, one wall must be rotated 54.8°.

The area enclosed by the walls is in the shape of an isosceles triangle (a triangle with two equal sides). The sum of the angles of a triangle is 180°.

Let a = the measure of each equal angle

$$a + a + 125.2 = 180$$
$$a + a + 125.2 = 180$$
$$2a + 125.2 = 180 \qquad \text{Combine like terms.}$$
$$2a + 125.2 - 125.2 = 180 - 125.2 \qquad \text{Subtract 125.2.}$$
$$2a = 54.8$$
$$\frac{2a}{2} = \frac{54.8}{2} \qquad \text{Divide both sides by 2.}$$
$$a = 27.4$$

The two equal angles are each 27.4°.

 Objective 2.5.4 CHECKUP

1. Carlos is building a sandbox for his son, making it triangular to fit into a corner of the patio. He wants two sides to be of equal length and the third side to be 1.5 feet longer than the others. If he has enough material for a perimeter of 12 feet, how long will each side be?

2. Two roads meet at a Y-intersection. The angle between the roads is 56°. A traffic engineer wants to design intersections that are perpendicular. Find the complement of the given angle to determine how much rotation will be needed on one of the roads.

2.5 EXERCISES

Student Solutions Manual   PH Math/Tutor Center   CD Video   Math XL MathXL®   MyMathLab MyMathLab   Interactmath.com

Consecutive Integers

1. The sum of three consecutive integers is 66. Find the three integers.

2. The sum of three consecutive integers is 45. Find the three integers.

3. The sum of three consecutive even integers is 72. Find the three integers.

4. The sum of three consecutive even integers is 102. Find the three integers.

5. The sum of three consecutive odd integers is 99. Find the integers.

6. The sum of three consecutive odd integers is 75. Find the integers.

7. A patient's medication is to be increased in consecutive even-integer dosages in three administrations, for a total of 24 grains of medication. How many grains of medication will be administered each time?

8. A patient's medication is to be decreased in consecutive integer amounts over five administrations, for a total of 70 cc of medication. How many cc will be administered each time?

9. A lottery has four stages of winning. At each stage, the number of winners is increased in consecutive odd numbers. If there are 24 prizes in all, how many will be awarded at each stage?

10. Lottery winnings will be distributed over a five-day period, with the number of winners each day increasing by consecutive even integers. If the lottery will distribute 30 prizes, how many will be awarded each day?

11. An instructor ranks her eight students according to their level of classroom participation and then assigns them consecutive integer numbers as grades. If the total number of points for the eight students is 676, what were the lowest and highest grades given?

12. A movie rating scale has five categories, ranging from "strongly dislike" to "strongly like." Consecutive even integers are assigned left to right so that the sum of the integers is zero. What are the five numbers to be assigned to the scale?

Interest

13. E-Z Loan Agency writes a loan agreement stipulating that the agency will be reimbursed for the amount to be borrowed plus simple interest. What is the amount of money borrowed if $4500 is to be paid back on a one-year simple-interest loan at 12.5% interest? How much interest was paid on the loan?

14. E-Z-R Loan Agency writes a loan agreement stipulating that $1308 is to be repaid for a simple-interest loan for one year at 9%. How much is being borrowed? How much interest is being paid on the loan?

15. A mutual fund will pay 9% simple interest on an investment for one year. If you want to receive a total amount of $5000 at the end of that year, how much must you invest?

16. An investment fund offers 12% simple interest on an investment for one year. How much should be invested to receive a total amount of $12,500 at the end of the year?

17. A wise and successful businessman wants to establish an endowment of $500,000 with a community college. (What a great guy!) He invests money into a simple-interest account for a year. If the account pays 10% simple interest, how much should he invest, rounded to the nearest thousand dollars, in order to be able to establish the endowment?

18. A municipal bond earns 7.8% simple interest annually. How much should be invested in order to have a total amount of $8000 at the end of a year?

19. Megan received $15,000 from a probated estate. She invested part of the money in a simple-interest account paying 8% and the rest in another simple-interest account paying 6.5%. If she earned $1117.50 in interest at the end of the year, how much did she invest in each account?

20. Zach received $15,000 from his great-great-grandfather's estate. He invested part of his money in a corporate bond that paid 9.2% simple interest annually and the rest in a savings account paying 3.5% simple interest annually. If he earned $952.20 interest in one year, how much did he invest in each instrument?

21. Daniel borrowed $18,000 to purchase a car. He borrowed part of the money paying 9.25% per year in simple interest, and the rest he borrowed from his parents paying 5% per year in simple interest. If he paid $1452.50 in interest at the end of the first year, how much did he borrow in each account?

22. Daniel's sister borrowed $10,000 to redecorate her apartment. She borrowed part of the money paying 6.25% per year in simple interest, and the rest she borrowed from her parents paying 5% per year in simple interest. If she paid $587.50 in interest at the end of the first year, how much did she borrow in each account?

23. The Bedrock Savings and Loan Company will pay 7% simple interest on an investment of P dollars for one year. Write an equation for the total amount, A, in a savings account after a year. Find a new equation for the amount to be invested if you know the amount desired after one year. How much should be invested if you wish to have $1350 in an account at the end of the year? How much should be invested if you desire to have $2500 at the end of the year?

24. Friendly Dan's Loan Agency charges 11% simple interest on a loan. Write an equation for the total payback, P, if you take out a loan of L dollars for one year. Find a new equation for the amount of money borrowed if the total amount of the payback is known. How much will you receive as a loan if the payback is $1332? How much will you receive as a loan if the payback is $800?

Percentage of Increase and Decrease

25. Philip is informed that he needs to buy a graphing calculator for his mathematics class. Other students tell him that the college bookstore marks up calculators an automatic 25% over the manufacturer's suggested retail price. If this information is accurate and the bookstore is selling the calculator for $106.25, what is the manufacturer's suggested retail price?

26. Manu needs a laptop computer for his writing class. If the college bookstore marks up computers 25% over the manufacturer's suggested retail price and is selling the computer for $2875, what is the manufacturer's suggested retail price?

27. The sale price of a dress that was reduced by 20% is $68. What was the original selling price of the dress?

28. The sale price of a CD player is $110.49 after a reduction of 15%. What was the original selling price? What was the amount of the reduction?

29. A boutique sells all of its items at a 60% markup over the cost of the items from their suppliers. If an item sells for $19.95, what was the cost to the boutique?

30. An antiques dealer purchases a restored radio and resells it for $350, which represents a 75% markup of the cost. How much did the dealer pay for the radio?

31. A TV set is on sale for $195. The store claims that this is a 25% savings over the regular price. What is the regular price of the TV?

32. A pro shop has its golf clubs on sale, with 20% off the regular price. If a golf club is on sale for $59, what is the regular price of the club?

33. Slippery Sam claims that he can save you 35% of the suggested retail price (SRP) of a car. If he is willing to sell you the car for $12,500, what should the SRP be?

34. What would be the suggested retail price of a car that is on sale for $8995 if this represents a 15%-off sale?

35. Denzel received a cost-of-living increase. His new hourly wage is $13.75 per hour. If the cost-of-living index was 2.2%, what was his hourly wage before the increase?

36. Joan received a 6% merit increase, which raised her annual salary to $32,500. What was her salary before the increase?

37. For large parties, many restaurants automatically add a 15% gratuity to the bill, rather than allowing the customers to add their own gratuity. If the total bill, including gratuity, is $143.24, what was the bill before the gratuity was added?

38. What is the cost before gratuity of a dinner party if the bill plus 15% gratuity is $262.95? How much was the gratuity?

39. An artist notices that the item she sold to a boutique for $9.50 is selling there for $17.10. What is the markup percentage at this boutique?

40. If an antiques dealer sells a vintage radio for $385 and paid $275 for it, what was the markup percentage?

41. A clothing store reduces the original price of a coat by 10% for a sale. Write an equation for the sale price of the coat, y, if the original price is x dollars. Find a new equation for the original price if the sale price is known. What is the original price of a coat that is on sale for $53.96? What is the original price of a coat that is on sale for $98.95?

42. In the country of Erehwon, the sales tax on a purchase is 8.75%. Write an expression for the total cost of a sale, y, if the subtotal before tax is x dollars. Find a new equation for the subtotal if the total cost, including tax, is known. What is the subtotal when the total cost is $27.19? What is the subtotal when the total cost is $143.55?

Geometry

43. The sides of an equilateral triangle are of equal length. What is the length of a side if the perimeter of the triangle is $29\frac{1}{4}$ inches?

44. The second side of a triangle is twice as long as the first side. The third side is 1 centimeter shorter than the second side. If the perimeter is $11\frac{1}{2}$ centimeters, how long is each side?

45. By definition, an isosceles triangle has at least two sides of equal length. What are the lengths of the sides of the triangle if the third side is two-thirds as long as each of the equal sides and the perimeter is 16 feet?

46. If the third side of an isosceles triangle is half as long as each of the equal sides and the perimeter is 38 meters, how long is each side?

47. The perimeter of a rectangle is 400 yards. What are the dimensions of the rectangle if the length is 30 yards more than the width?

48. If the perimeter of a square is 1 inch, what are the dimensions of the square?

49. The width of a rectangle is 55% of the length. What are the dimensions of the rectangle if the perimeter is 294.5 centimeters?

50. The length of a rectangle is 2 inches more than twice its width. If its perimeter is 52 inches, what are the dimensions of the rectangle?

51. Karl wants to build a dog run for his German shepherd. He wants the length of the run to be five times as long as the width. If he has 96 feet of fencing, what should the dimensions of the dog run be? How many square feet of yard will the run cover?

52. See exercise **51**. If Karl builds a square dog run with the fencing, how long would each side be? Will this give him more square feet of yard for the run than in exercise **51**?

53. Regulations state that an access ramp meets the ground at an angle of 175.22°. What is the supplement of this angle? If the triangle below the ramp is in the shape of a right triangle, what are the measures of the three angles of the triangle?

54. A loading ramp meets the ground at an angle of 165°. What is the supplement of this angle? If the triangle below the ramp has the shape of a right triangle, what are the measures of the three angles of the triangle?

55. A second angle of a triangle is twice the measure of the first angle. If the third angle measures six times the measure of the first angle, what are the measures of the three angles?

56. A second angle of a triangle is twice the measure of the first angle. If the third angle measures twenty degrees more than the measure of the first angle, what are the measures of the three angles?

57. A second angle of a triangle is ten degrees more than the measure of the first angle. If the third angle measures fourteen degrees less than twice the measure of the first angle, what is the measure of the three angles?

58. A second angle of a triangle has a measure of ten degrees less than the measure of the first angle. If the third angle measures twenty-eight degrees less than twice the first angle, what is the measure of the three angles?

59. Dylan designed a bay window for her kitchen. The bay window has five equally wide windows. Here is Dylan's sketch:

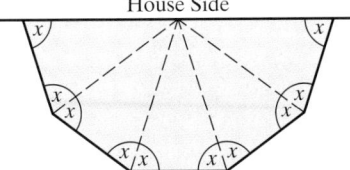

The sketch shows that the bay window has the shape of five triangles of the same shape and size. In order to cut the trim for the windows, she will need to set her saw to bevel the

edges of the trim. To do so, Dylan must know the measure of the angles labeled x on the sketch. Determine the measure of these angles.

60. Dylan altered the design for her kitchen bay window from that shown in exercise **59**. Her new design is shown in the following sketch:

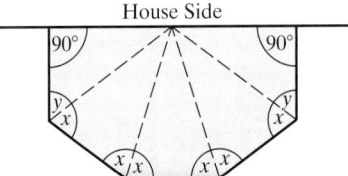

The change she made is that the sides which touch the house now make a $90°$ angle with the house. She still must determine the angles labeled x and y on the sketch. Determine the measures of these angles.

2.5 Calculator Exercises

Many calculators have a list feature that can be used when you wish to evaluate a formula for more than one value. As an example, a mutual fund will pay 9% simple interest for an investment for one year. How much should you invest if you wish to receive the following amounts after a year: $\{\$900, \$1800, \$2700\}$? To solve this problem, let $x =$ the investment P, use the formula $I = Prt$, and substitute the list for the interest I, 9% for the interest rate r, and 1 (year) for the time t.

$$\{900, 1800, 2700\} = (x)(0.09)(1)$$

Solving for x yields

$$x = \frac{\{900, 1800, 2700\}}{0.09}$$

You can use the braces on the calculator to enter this equation, and the calculator will return a set of values in braces, representing the principal invested for each of the interest values.

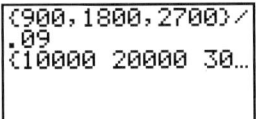 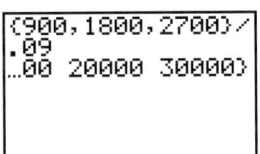

The calculator display is interpreted to mean that $10,000 must be invested to earn $900 interest, $20,000 to earn $1800 interest, and so on. Use the calculator arrows to scroll left and right.

Use this technique in the following exercises:

1. Find the Fahrenheit temperature, given $\{50, 55, 60, 65\}$ as the Celsius temperatures.

2. Find the Celsius temperature, given $\{0, 25, 50, 75, 100\}$ as the Fahrenheit temperatures.

3. Find the complement of an angle whose measure is $\{15, 30, 45, 60\}$ degrees.

4. Find the distance traveled at a rate of 60 miles per hour, given a time of $\{1, 1.5, 2, 2.5\}$ hours driven.

2.5 Writing Exercise

Many business mathematics textbooks use the techniques presented here to solve application problems. Find a textbook that presents an illustration of a business application similar to any of the problems we have studied. It may be a problem dealing with cost-of-living increases, markups or markdowns in selling prices, investments, or something else. Make a photocopy of the page in the text discussing the application. Write a one-paragraph cri-

tique of the illustration. In your critique, state whether you think the author did a good job in presenting the application. Was it clear or was it confusing? If the presentation was not good, suggest what you might have done to present the example differently. Turn in your critique with the photocopy and the library call number of the textbook.

2.6 SOLVING LINEAR ABSOLUTE-VALUE EQUATIONS

OBJECTIVES

1. Identify linear absolute-value equations in one variable.
2. Solve linear absolute-value equations graphically and numerically.
3. Solve linear absolute-value equations algebraically.
4. Model real-world situations by using linear absolute-value equations, and then solve the equations.

APPLICATION

The difference of the tallest mountain on the North American continent, Mount McKinley, and the tallest mountain on the South American continent, Aconcagua, is 765 meters. Mount McKinley is 6194 meters. Determine the height of Aconcagua.

After completing this section, we will discuss this application further. See page 253.

In this section, we will solve a linear equation in one variable that contains an absolute-value expression. Before we begin, we need to review the definition of absolute value. An absolute-value expression is defined to be the distance of the expression from 0 (Chapter P). For example, $|3| = 3$ and $|-3| = 3$. Remember, the result is always nonnegative.

Objective 2.6.1

Identifying Linear Absolute-Value Equations in One Variable

STANDARD FORM FOR A LINEAR ABSOLUTE-VALUE EQUATION IN ONE VARIABLE

A linear absolute-value equation in one variable is an equation written in the form $|ax + b| = c$, where a, b, and c are real numbers and $a \neq 0$.

For example, the following are linear absolute-value equations in one variable:

1. $|2x + 3| = 5$ Standard form: $|ax + b| = c$
2. $|2x + 3| - 6 = 5$ Not standard form
3. $4|2x + 3| = 0$ Not standard form

The first equation is in the exact form $|ax + b| = c$, with $a = 2$, $b = 3$, and $c = 5$. The last two equations can be solved for the absolute-value expression by using the properties of equations. For example,

$$|2x + 3| - 6 = 5, \quad \text{or} \quad |2x + 3| = 11 \quad \text{Add 6 to both sides of the equation.}$$
$$4|2x + 3| = 0, \quad \text{or} \quad |2x + 3| = 0 \quad \text{Divide both sides of the equation by 4.}$$

These equations are called **linear absolute-value equations in one variable** because of the characteristics of the graphs of the functions defined by the two expressions in each equation. To see what we mean, let's graph some absolute-value expressions on the calculator. Complete the following set of exercises on your calculator.

Guided Discovery 11 — Graphs of the Functions Defined by Expressions in a Linear Absolute-Value Equation

On an integer screen, graph the following functions, determined from the given linear absolute-value equation:

1. $|2x + 3| = 5$

    $Y1 = |2x + 3|$ $Y2 = 5$

2. $|2x - 3| = -5$

    $Y1 = |2x - 3|$ $Y2 = -5$

Explain the characteristic of the graphs of the functions defined by the absolute-value expression, Y1.

    Explain the characteristic of the graphs of the functions defined by the constant, Y2.

On an integer screen, graph the following functions, determined from the given linear absolute-value equation:

1. $|2x + 3| - 6 = 5$

    $Y1 = |2x + 3| - 6$ $Y2 = 5$

2. $4|2x + 3| = 0$

    $Y1 = 4|2x + 3|$ $Y2 = 0$

Explain the characteristic of the graphs of the functions defined by the absolute-value expression, Y1.

    Explain the characteristic of the graphs of the functions defined by the constant, Y2.

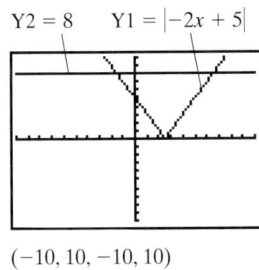

$Y2 = 8$ $Y1 = |-2x + 5|$

$(-10, 10, -10, 10)$

For the linear absolute-value equations in the form $|ax + b| = c$, the graph of the function defined by the absolute-value expression is a V-shaped graph formed by two line segments, and the graph of the constant function is a horizontal line. For the linear absolute-value equations not in $|ax + b| = c$ form, the graph of the function defined by the expression containing the absolute-value expression is formed by lines.

    For example, the equation $|-2x + 5| = 8$ is a linear absolute-value equation. The graph of the function $Y1 = |-2x + 5|$ is a V-shaped graph made up of two line segments. The graph of the function $Y2 = 8$ is a line.

EXAMPLE 1

Identify each equation as a linear absolute-value equation or a nonlinear absolute value equation. Check your results graphically.

a. $-|3x - 5| + 8 = 0$ **b.** $|2x^3 + 3| = 5$

Algebraic Solution

a. $-|3x - 5| + 8 = 0$ Linear absolute value, because it simplifies to $|3x - 5| = 8$.

b. $|2x^3 + 3| = 5$ Nonlinear absolute value, because the x term is raised to the third power.

Graphic Check

a. $Y2 = 0$ $Y1 = -|3x - 5| + 8$

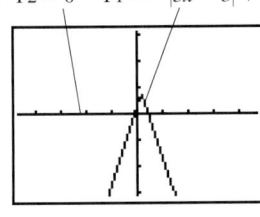

$(-47, 47, -31, 31)$

Note: The graph of $Y2 = 0$ is the x-axis.

The equation is a linear absolute-value equation, because the functions graphed both consist of line segments.

b. $Y2 = 5$ $Y1 = |2x^3 + 3|$

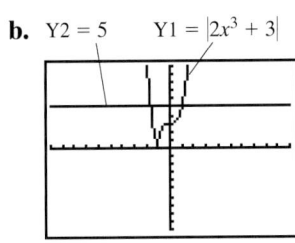

$(-10, 10, -10, 10)$

The equation is a nonlinear absolute-value equation, because the functions graphed are not both made up of line segments. The graph of the function defined by the absolute-value expression is not a line. ■

We will solve linear absolute-value equations by using the three methods we used with linear equations: numerical, graphical, and algebraic.

 Objective 2.6.1 CHECKUP

1. Identify each equation as a linear absolute-value equation or a nonlinear absolute-value equation.
   a. $9 - 2|2x + 1| = 8$ **b.** $|5 - 2x^2| = 10$

2. What does the absolute value of a number represent?
3. What distinguishes a linear absolute-value equation from an absolute-value equation that is nonlinear? ■

Objective 2.6.2 Solving Absolute-Value Equations Graphically and Numerically

Let's solve some linear absolute-value equations graphically and numerically. We will use a calculator to find the solutions of three linear absolute-value equations. Complete the following set of exercises on your calculator.

Guided Discovery 12   Solving a Linear Absolute-Value Equation

Solve each equation graphically and check your solution numerically.

1. a. $|x + 4| = 3$ **b.** $|3 - x| = 2$
2. a. $|x + 4| = -3$ **b.** $|3 - x| = -2$
3. a. $|x + 4| = 0$ **b.** $|3 - x| = 0$

Write a rule for the number of solutions of a linear absolute-value equation when the absolute-value expression equals a positive number, a negative number, and 0.

In the first exercise, in which the absolute-value expression equals a positive number, the equation has two solutions. In the second exercise, in which the absolute-value expression equals a negative number, the equation has no solution. In the third exercise, in which the absolute-value expression equals 0, the equation has one solution.

NUMBER OF SOLUTIONS OF A LINEAR ABSOLUTE-VALUE EQUATION

To determine the number of solutions of a linear absolute-value equation, write the equation in standard form, $|ax + b| = c$.

- If the constant, c, is positive, there are two solutions.
- If the constant, c, is negative, there are no solutions.
- If the constant, c, is 0, there is one solution.

We know this is true because the absolute values of a positive number and its opposite (a negative number) equal the same positive number. Hence, two solutions are possible if c is a positive number. However, an absolute value cannot equal a negative number. Hence, no solution is possible if c is negative. Also, the absolute value of 0 equals 0. Hence, there is only one solution possible if c is 0.

When we solve equations graphically and numerically, we do not rearrange the equation. Therefore, the equation may not be in standard form. We may not be able to determine the number of solutions.

 TAKE NOTE Numerical solutions are sometimes hard to find. It is much easier to solve absolute-value equations graphically and then check the solutions numerically.

EXAMPLE 2   Solve graphically and check numerically.

a. $|2x| + 8 = 8$

b. $\left|\dfrac{x-2}{3}\right| = 5$

c. $3|-2x + 9| + 16 = 9$

Graphic Solution

a. Y2 = 8   Y1 = $|2x| + 8$

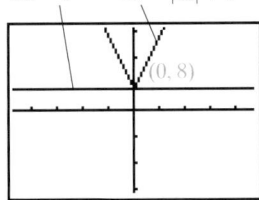

(0, 8)

−47, 47, −31, 31

The solution is 0.

b. Y2 = 5   Y1 = $\left|\dfrac{x-2}{3}\right|$

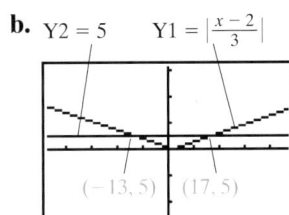

(−13, 5) (17, 5)

(−47, 47, −31, 31)

The solutions are −13 and 17.

c.
Y2 = 9   Y1 = $3|-2x + 9| + 16$

(−47, 47, −31, 31)

There is no solution.

Numeric Check

X	Y1	Y2
-3	14	8
-2	12	8
-1	10	8
0	8	8
1	10	8
2	12	8
3	14	8

X=0

Y1 = $|2x| + 8$
Y2 = 8
The solution is 0.

X	Y1	Y2
-14	5.3333	5
-13	5	5
-12	4.6667	5
-11	4.3333	5
-10	4	5
-9	3.6667	5
-8	3.3333	5

X=-13

X	Y1	Y2
16	4.6667	5
17	5	5
18	5.3333	5
19	5.6667	5
20	6	5
21	6.3333	5
22	6.6667	5

X=17

Y1 = $\left|\dfrac{x-2}{3}\right|$ Y2 = 5

The solutions are −13 and 17.

X	Y1	Y2
2	31	9
3	25	9
4	19	9
5	19	9
6	25	9
7	31	9
8	37	9

X=2

Y1 = $3|-2x + 9| + 16$
Y2 = 9

One must refer to the graph to determine that there is no solution.

Objective 2.6.2 *CHECKUP*

1. Solve graphically. Check numerically.

   a. $|3x| + 1 = 4$　　　**b.** $\left|\dfrac{x + 1}{2}\right| = 3$

   c. $2|-3x + 2| + 13 = 11$

2. How do you determine the solutions of a linear absolute-value equation when you solve the equation graphically?

Objective 2.6.3

Solving Equations Algebraically

We are now ready to solve linear absolute-value equations algebraically. We begin with the rule we found earlier in this section.

> ### SOLVING A LINEAR ABSOLUTE-VALUE EQUATION ALGEBRAICALLY
>
> First, determine the number of solutions of an absolute-value equation by writing it in the form $|ax + b| = c$.
>
> - If the constant, c, is positive, there are two solutions.
> - If the constant, c, is negative, there are no solutions.
> - If the constant, c, is 0, there is one solution.
>
> Second, write and evaluate an equation or equations needed to find the solution(s).
>
> - If there are two solutions, then
>
> $$ax + b = c \quad \text{or} \quad ax + b = -c$$
>
> - If there is one solution, then
>
> $$ax + b = 0 \quad \text{since} \quad c = 0$$

For example, $|x| = 3$ has two solutions, because the absolute-value expression is equal to a positive number. The two solutions are found when the expression within the absolute-value symbols, x, equals -3 or 3. Therefore, $x = -3$ or $x = 3$.

$|x| = -3$ has no solution, because the absolute-value expression equals a negative number.

$|x| = 0$ has one solution, because the absolute-value expression equals 0. The one solution is found when the expression within the absolute-value symbols, x, equals 0. Therefore, $x = 0$.

EXAMPLE 3

Solve algebraically.

   a. $|x + 4| = 3$　　　**b.** $|x + 4| = -3$　　　**c.** $|x + 4| = 0$

Algebraic Solution

a. $|x + 4| = 3$

There are two solutions, because the absolute-value expression equals a positive number.

$x + 4 = 3$	or	$x + 4 = -3$
$x + 4 - 4 = 3 - 4$		$x + 4 - 4 = -3 - 4$
$x = -1$		$x = -7$

The two solutions are -1 and -7.

   The check is left for you.

b. $|x + 4| = -3$

There is no solution, because the absolute-value expression equals a negative number.

c. $|x + 4| = 0$

There is one solution, because the absolute-value expression equals 0.

$$x + 4 = 0$$
$$x + 4 - 4 = 0 - 4$$
$$x = -4$$

The solution is -4.

The check is left for you.

Now let's solve the equations of Example 2 algebraically.

EXAMPLE 4

Solve algebraically. (Remember to isolate the absolute-value expression first.)

a. $|2x| + 8 = 8$ **b.** $\left|\dfrac{x - 2}{3}\right| = 5$ **c.** $3|-2x + 9| + 16 = 9$

Algebraic Solution

a.
$$|2x| + 8 = 8$$
$$|2x| + 8 - 8 = 8 - 8 \quad \text{Subtract 8 from both sides to isolate the absolute-value expression.}$$
$$|2x| = 0 \quad \text{Simplify.}$$
$$2x = 0 \quad \text{Rewrite for one solution.}$$
$$\frac{2x}{2} = \frac{0}{2} \quad \text{Divide both sides by 2.}$$
$$x = 0 \quad \text{Simplify.}$$

The solution is 0.

The check is left for you. (See Example 2a.)

b.
$$\left|\dfrac{x - 2}{3}\right| = 5$$

$$\frac{x - 2}{3} = 5 \qquad \text{or} \qquad \frac{x - 2}{3} = -5 \quad \text{Rewrite for two solutions.}$$

$$3\left(\frac{x - 2}{3}\right) = 3(5) \qquad 3\left(\frac{x - 2}{3}\right) = 3(-5) \quad \text{Multiply both sides by 3.}$$

$$x - 2 = 15 \qquad\qquad x - 2 = -15 \quad \text{Simplify.}$$

$$x - 2 + 2 = 15 + 2 \qquad x - 2 + 2 = -15 + 2 \quad \text{Add 2 to both sides.}$$

$$x = 17 \qquad\qquad x = -13 \quad \text{Simplify.}$$

The solutions are 17 and -13.

The check is left for you. (See Example 2b.)

c.
$$3|-2x + 9| + 16 = 9$$
$$3|-2x + 9| + 16 - 16 = 9 - 16 \quad \text{Add 16 to both sides to isolate the absolute-value expression.}$$
$$3|-2x + 9| = -7 \quad \text{Simplify.}$$
$$\frac{3|-2x + 9|}{3} = \frac{-7}{3} \quad \text{Divide both sides by 3.}$$
$$|-2x + 9| = -\frac{7}{3} \quad \text{Simplify.}$$

There is no solution because the absolute value expression is equal to a negative number.

The check is left for you. (See Example 2c.)

✓ Objective 2.6.3 *CHECKUP*

Solve exercises 1 and 2 algebraically.

1. a. $|x - 9| = 0$ **b.** $|x - 9| = 3$

   c. $|x - 9| = -3$

2. a. $|3x| + 1 = 4$ **b.** $\left|\dfrac{x + 1}{2}\right| = 3$

   c. $2|-3x + 2| + 13 = 11$

3. Describe how you would solve a linear absolute-value equation algebraically.

Objective 2.6.4   Modeling the Real World

Linear absolute-value equations can describe several kinds of real-world situations. In particular, absolute values are used to describe the size, or magnitude, of many quantities that can be positive or negative in direction. Among these quantities are distance, speed, and force. Absolute values can also describe the magnitude of financial transactions, without regard to whether the money is a credit (positive) or a debit (negative). However, remember that when you solve linear absolute-value equations, the answers you get must make sense in terms of the real situation. Sometimes you have to throw away an answer because it doesn't describe the physical situation correctly.

EXAMPLE 5

A plastic disposable hospital bowl is advertised to have an outer diameter of 5.146 inches with a tolerance (allowance for error) of plus or minus 0.015 inch. What is the least and greatest possible length of the diameter?

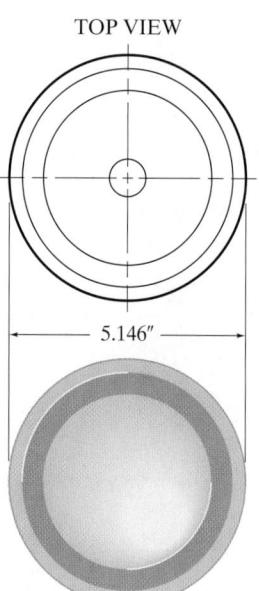

TOP VIEW

5.146"

Algebraic Solution

Let x = the actual length of the diameter

Since we do not know which length is greater—the actual length or the length given on the package—we will take the absolute value of the difference of the lengths and equate it to the absolute value of the tolerance.

$$|x - 5.146| = |\pm 0.015|$$

$$|x - 5.146| = 0.015 \qquad \text{\small Take the absolute value of the right side.}$$

Write equations for the two possible solutions.

$$x - 5.146 = 0.015$$
$$x - 5.146 + 5.146 = 0.015 + 5.146$$
$$x = 5.161$$

or

$$x - 5.146 = -0.015$$
$$x - 5.146 + 5.146 = -0.015 + 5.146$$
$$x = 5.131$$

The greatest diameter measurement is 5.161 inches. The least diameter measurement is 5.131 inches.

Substitution Check

```
5.161→X:abs(X-5.
146)=0.015
                1
5.131→X:abs(X-5.
146)=0.015
                1
```

APPLICATION

The difference of the tallest mountain on the North American continent, Mount McKinley, and the tallest mountain on the South American continent, Aconcagua, is 765 meters. Mount McKinley is 6194 meters. Determine the height of Aconcagua.

Discussion

Let $x =$ the height of Aconcagua in meters

Since we are not told which mountain is taller, we will need to take the absolute value of the difference, $|6194 - x|$, and set it equal to 765.

$$|6194 - x| = 765$$

Algebraic Solution

$$\begin{aligned} 6194 - x &= 765 \\ 6194 - x - 6194 &= 765 - 6194 \\ -x &= -5429 \\ \frac{-x}{-1} &= \frac{-5429}{-1} \\ x &= 5429 \end{aligned} \qquad \text{or} \qquad \begin{aligned} 6194 - x &= -765 \\ 6194 - x - 6194 &= -765 - 6194 \\ -x &= -6959 \\ \frac{x}{-1} &= \frac{-6959}{-1} \\ x &= 6959 \end{aligned}$$

Aconcagua is either 5429 meters high (if it is lower than Mount McKinley) or 6959 meters high (if it is higher than Mount McKinley). More information is needed to determine a final answer.

Since we are taking the absolute value of the difference, we could subtract in either order and obtain the same results. Instead of $|6194 - x| = 765$, we could use $|x - 6194|$. Check for yourself. We can see why we obtain the same solution if we notice that $6194 - x$ is the opposite of $x - 6194$. (The sign of each term is the opposite of that of the corresponding term.) The absolute value of an expression and the absolute value of its opposite are equal.

Objective 2.6.4 CHECKUP

1. An auto manufacturer designs a sports car to comfortably seat a driver who is 6 feet tall (72 inches), give or take 3 inches. Another way of stating this is that the absolute value of the difference between 72 inches and a person's height, h, in inches, equals 3. Write a linear absolute-value equation, and solve it to find the greatest and smallest heights for drivers who will comfortably sit in the car.

2. The range of scores for a test was 28 points. If one of the extreme scores was 66, what are the possible limits for the scores? (Note that 66 could be either the highest score or the lowest score on the test.)

2.6 EXERCISES

Student Solutions Manual | PH Math/Tutor Center | CD Video | MathXL® | MyMathLab | Interactmath.com

Use the calculator screens first to write the equation being solved and then to determine the solution or solutions (if any) of the equation.

1. a.

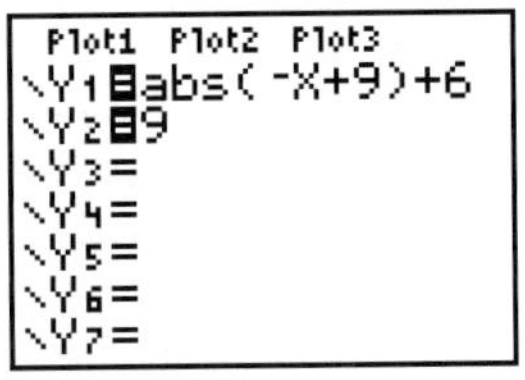
Plot1 Plot2 Plot3
\Y1=abs(-X+9)+6
\Y2=9
\Y3=
\Y4=
\Y5=
\Y6=
\Y7=

b.

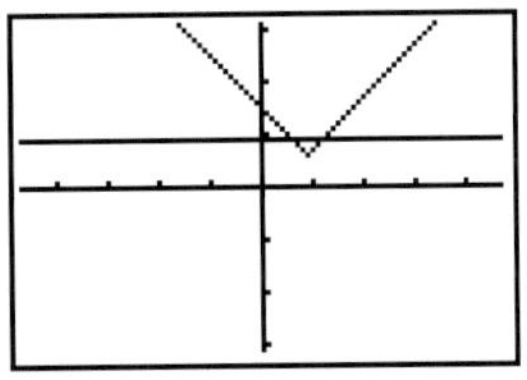

(−47, 47, −31, 31)

c.

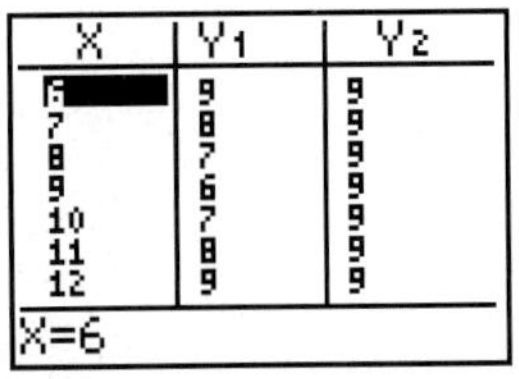
X Y1 Y2
6 9 9
7 8 9
8 7 9
9 6 9
10 7 9
11 8 9
12 9 9
X=6

2. a.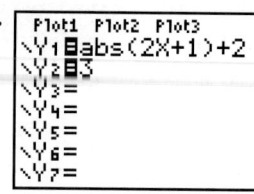

b.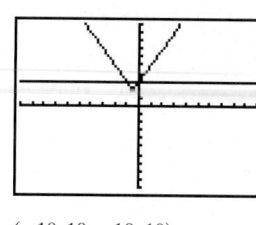

$(-10, 10, -10, 10)$

c.

X	Y1	Y2
-3	7	3
-2	5	3
-1	3	3
0	3	3
1	5	3
2	7	3
3	9	3

X=-3

Solve graphically. Check numerically.

3. $|x + 1| = 3$

4. $|x - 3| = 1$

5. $|6x + 6| = 12$

6. $|3x - 9| = 6$

7. $|-x - 1| = 1$

8. $|-4x - 8| = 4$

9. $|x + 21| - 26$

10. $|x - 19| - 29$

11. $|-x - 19| = 22$

12. $|-x - 1| = 18$

13. $|x - 2.17| = 6.09$

14. $|-x + 22.83| = 0.899$

15. $\left|x + \dfrac{2}{5}\right| = \dfrac{11}{15}$

16. $\left|x + \dfrac{7}{8}\right| = 6\dfrac{9}{16}$

17. $2|x - 15| + 25 = 15$

18. $4|3x - 6| + 19 = 13$

19. $7|x - 32| + 21 = 21$

20. $3|2x + 12| + 14 = 14$

21. $3|x + 5| - 7 = 4$

22. $3|2x - 5| - 16 = 2$

Solve algebraically.

23. $|x| = 138$

24. $|z| = 2400$

25. $|b| = 41.67$

26. $|m| = 0.009$

27. $|a| = -512$

28. $|s| = -22\dfrac{17}{21}$

29. $|c| = 14\dfrac{5}{9}$

30. $|x| = \dfrac{11}{12}$

31. $|x + 578| = 286$

32. $|z + 303| = 471$

33. $|x - 721| = 1942$

34. $|x - 651| = 124$

35. $5|x - 29| - 46 = 74$

36. $4|2x - 18| - 16 = 84$

37. $2|x + 41| + 96 = 48$

38. $3|x + 62| + 76 = 32$

39. $\left|\dfrac{x - 14}{7}\right| = 8$

40. $\left|\dfrac{2x + 3}{5}\right| = 14$

41. $|-3x - 6| - 18 = -6$

42. $|-2x - 16| - 34 = -17$

43. $-4|x + 12| = -16$

44. $-3|-2x + 8| = -15$

Write a linear absolute-value equation for each situation and solve.

45. The maximum depth of Lake Superior differs from that of Lake Michigan by 410 feet. If Lake Michigan has a maximum depth of 923 feet, what are the possible values for the maximum depth of Lake Superior? Given that Lake Superior is deeper, what is its maximum depth?

46. The largest lake in the world is the Caspian Sea, which was incorrectly called a sea by the Romans because of its salty water. One of the most beautiful lakes in the world is Lake Baikal in Russia. The difference in maximum depths of these two lakes is 1952 feet. Given that Lake Baikal has a maximum depth of 5315 feet, what are the possible values for the maximum depth of the Caspian Sea? Given further that Lake Baikal is the deepest lake in the world, what is the maximum depth of the Caspian Sea?

47. Ralph Raffish manufactures sports clothes to fit the average male height, give or take 6 inches. If the average male is 5 feet 9 inches tall, what are the maximum and minimum heights the clothes will fit?

48. Rexus Luxury Cars designs its cars to comfortably seat a driver whose height differs by 4 inches from the average height of buyers of the cars. If the average height of buyers of the cars is established by a customer survey to be 6 feet 1 inch, what are the limits on heights of drivers the car would comfortably seat?

49. The Air and Space Division of the Smithsonian Institution explains that the speed of sound varies with temperature by 81 miles per hour. If the speed of sound at sea level (Mach 1) is 742 miles per hour, what are the possible values for the speed of sound at a high altitude (36,000 feet is considered high)? If the speed of sound decreases as altitude rises, what is its speed at a high altitude?

50. The National Climatic Data Center reports that the highest temperature ever recorded in November in the United States differs from the lowest November temperature ever recorded in the United States by 158 degrees Fahrenheit. If Lincoln, Montana recorded a record temperature of -53 degrees, what are the possible values for temperature for the other record-breaking city, Crafton, California? If Lincoln, Montana's temperature is the colder of the two, what was the maximum November temperature in Crafton?

51. A political survey reports that 42% of the voters support an issue, with a margin of error of 3%. What are the minimum and maximum percentages that may occur?

52. A poll reports that 48% of the voters of a city and county support unification of the city and county charters, with a margin of error of 4.5%. If the poll is accurate, what are the minimum and maximum percentages that could occur in the election?

53. If a bathroom scale has a margin of error of 2 pounds, what is the range for Dee's actual weight if the scale displays a weight of 132 pounds?

54. A scale in a meat market has an allowable margin of error of 0.05 pound. What is the range of weights for a package of hamburger if the scale displays a weight of one pound?

55. The tolerance in cutting a piece of pipe is $\frac{1}{4}$ inch. What are the possible lengths of a piece of pipe that is to be cut to a length of $5\frac{1}{2}$ inches?

56. A metal rod is to be cut to a length of 25.5 inches, with a tolerance of 0.125 inch. What are the possible lengths of the rod?

57. The Wildlife Conservation Society records that the average life expectancy of a squirrel differs from that of a mouse by 6 years. If a mouse's life expectancy is 2.5 years, how long does the average squirrel live?

58. It is estimated by *Ethnologue*, 13th edition, a catalog of the languages spoken in 228 countries, that the number of people speaking English in the world differs from that of people speaking Mandarin Chinese by 561,000,000. If 514,000,000 people speak English, how many speak Mandarin Chinese?

2.6 Calculator Exercises

Some linear absolute-value equations are extremely difficult to solve algebraically, particularly if there is more than one absolute-value expression in the equation. It is then that the graphical method of solving is handy. Following are some such exercises. Solve them graphically. Check your answers numerically.

1. $|x + 2| = |x - 3|$

2. $3|x + 2| - 5 = 3|x + 2| + 5$

3. $|x + 6| - 9 = -|x + 3| + 8$

4. $|x + 2| = -3x + 8$

5. $|x + 3| + |x - 3| = 15$

Could you have solved any of these exercises algebraically? If so, which ones? For those you could not solve algebraically, why couldn't you?

2.6 Writing Exercise

You have seen both ways to solve linear absolute-value equations: graphically and algebraically. Which method did you prefer? Write a brief summary of which method you prefer and why you prefer it. Try to think of situations in which you would be forced to use one method over the other.

■ Chapter 2 Summary

Vocabulary Review

After completing this chapter, you should be able to define the following key terms.

consecutive integer
contradiction
equivalent equations

identity
linear absolute-value equation in one variable

linear equation in one variable

Fill in the blank with one of the words or phrases listed above.

1. A _____ can be written in the form $ax + b = 0$.

2. A _____ can be written in the form $|ax + b| = c$.

3. Equations that have the same solution are called _____.

4. A _____ is an equation with no solution.

5. An _____ is an equation for which all permissible replacements of the variable result in a true equation.

Reflections

1. Explain how the addition property of equations is used to solve a linear equation in one variable.

2. Explain how the multiplication property of equations is used to solve a linear equation in one variable.

3. How can you graphically solve a linear equation in one variable?

4. How can you numerically solve a linear equation in one variable?

5. Explain how you can tell that a linear equation in one variable has no solution.

6. Explain how you can tell that a linear equation in one variable has many solutions.

7. How does a linear absolute-value equation in one variable differ from a linear equation in one variable?

8. What must you do differently when algebraically solving a linear absolute-value equation in one variable, compared with solving a linear equation in one variable?

■ Chapter 2 Section-by-Section Review

2.1

Recall	Examples
Linear equation in one variable • An equation that can be written in the form $ax + b = 0$, where a and b are real numbers and $a \neq 0$.	Linear equations in one variable $\frac{3}{4}x + 5 = 0$; $2x - 5 = -4x - 7$; $x = 9$
Solving numerically • Complete a three-column table of values—one column for the independent variable, one for the left side of the equation, and one for the right side of the equation. • The solution is the value of the independent variable that results in equal values for the left and right sides of the equation.	Solve $2x + 1 = 3x - 5$ numerically.<table><tr><th>x</th><th>$2x + 1$</th><th>$= 3x - 5$</th></tr><tr><td>5</td><td>11</td><td>10</td></tr><tr><td>6</td><td>13</td><td>13</td></tr><tr><td>7</td><td>15</td><td>16</td></tr><tr><td>8</td><td>17</td><td>19</td></tr></table>The solution is 6, because $13 = 13$.
Solving graphically • Graph the two functions defined by the left side of the equation and the right side of the equation. • The solution is the x-coordinate of the point of intersection of the two graphs.	Solve $3x + 2 = 5x - 2$ graphically. The solution is 2, because the intersection is $(2, 8)$.

Identify each equation as linear or nonlinear.

1. $4x^2 - 2x + 1 = 0$ **2.** $5x + 3 = x - 4$ **3.** $5.7x - 8.2(x + 4.6) = 0$

4. $\sqrt{x} + 2 = 3x - 6$ **5.** $\frac{1}{8}x + \frac{3}{4} = \frac{11}{16}$ **6.** $\frac{3}{x} + 5 = 12x$

Use the calculator screens to write the equation being solved and to determine the solution of the equation.

7.
```
Plot1  Plot2  Plot3
\Y1⊟(3/4)(X+7)-5

\Y2⊟(1/3)(X+12)
\Y3=
\Y4=
\Y5=
\Y6=
```

X	Y1	Y2
6	4.75	6
7	5.5	6.3333
8	6.25	6.6667
9	7	7
10	7.75	7.3333
11	8.5	7.6667
12	9.25	8

X=12

Solve numerically for an integer solution if possible.

8. $4x + 7 = 2x - 5$

9. $2.4x - 9.6 = 4.8$

10. $\frac{3}{5}x - \frac{7}{10} = \frac{1}{5}x + \frac{1}{2}$

11. $14x + 12 = 11(x - 5) + 60$

12. $3(x - 2) - 1 = 4(x - 1) - (x + 3)$

13. $2(2x + 1) + x = 3(2x - 1) - (x + 1)$

Use the calculator screens to write the equation being solved and to determine the solution of the equation.

14.

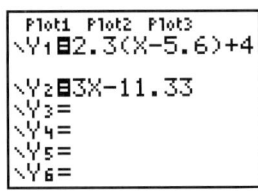

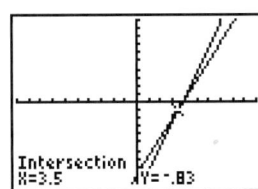

Solve exercises 15–19 graphically.

15. $2x - 2 = -x + 4$

16. $\dfrac{1}{2}x - 2 = -\dfrac{1}{3}x - \dfrac{11}{3}$

17. $(x + 3) + (x + 1) = 3(x + 1) - (x - 1)$

18. $(x + 6) - 3(x + 1) = (2x + 5) - 2(2x + 3)$

19. $1.2x + 0.72 = -2.1x + 8.64$

20. Theresa offers to rake and clean the wooded area of your backyard for a flat fee of $90, or for a fee of $25 plus $6.50 for each hour worked. Determine how many hours of work will make the two offers equivalent.

21. A church receives weekly donations of $2200, $1750, and $1885 for the first three weeks of the month. How much does the church need to receive in the fourth week to meet its average weekly goal of $2000 in donations?

22. The cost of producing an item consists of a setup cost of $250.00 and a cost of $10.00 per item for labor. If the item sells for $20.00, determine the number of items for which the cost of production equals the revenue received.

2.2

Recall	Examples
Solving algebraically by using the addition property of equations • Simplify both expressions in the equation. • To both sides of the equation, add if a term is subtracted from the variable or subtract if a term is added to the variable. • Check the solution.	Solve $3x - 4 - 2x = 3$ algebraically. $3x - 4 - 2x = 3$ $\qquad x - 4 = 3$ $\qquad x - 4 + 4 = 3 + 4$ $\qquad\qquad x = 7$ Check: $\dfrac{3x - 4 - 2x = 3}{3(7) - 4 - 2(7) \;\big|\; 3}$ $\qquad\qquad\qquad 3 \quad$ The solution checks.
Solving algebraically by using the multiplication property of equations • Simplify both expressions in the equation. • To both sides of the equation, multiply if the variable is divided by a number or divide if the variable is multiplied by a number. • Check the solution.	Solve $2x + 3x = 1$ algebraically. $2x + 3x = 1$ $\qquad 5x = 1$ $\qquad \dfrac{5x}{5} = \dfrac{1}{5}$ $\qquad\quad x = \dfrac{1}{5}$ Check: $\dfrac{2x + 3x = 1}{2\left(\dfrac{1}{5}\right) + 3\left(\dfrac{1}{5}\right) \;\Big|\; 1}$ $\qquad\qquad\qquad\quad 1 \quad$ The solution checks.

Solve algebraically.

23. $41 + x = 67$

24. $y - \dfrac{7}{13} = \dfrac{11}{39}$

25. $5 - (2 - x) = 1$

26. $0.59(z - 1) + 0.41(z + 2) = 3.163$

27. $-4x = 272$

28. $45.86z = -1765.61$

29. $\dfrac{a}{7} = 15$

30. $\dfrac{4}{5}x = \dfrac{64}{125}$

31. $15x - 16x = -12$

32. $-y = 2.98$

33. $4(2x - 6) + 6(x + 4) = 49$

Write an equation for each situation and solve algebraically.

34. Total attendance at a benefit luncheon was 247 people. If 189 people purchased tickets, how many tickets were given as complimentary passes?

35. If a graduating class had 154 males, representing 55% of the class, how many students graduated in total?

36. Students at an elementary school are selling coupon books for $15 each as a fund-raiser. If the goal of the school is to raise $80,000 for a computerized classroom, how many books must the students sell?

37. Miyoshi was to receive $\frac{3}{7}$ of the proceeds from the sale of an estate. If she received $18,270, what were the proceeds of the sale?

38. The largest electric current achieved by scientists occurred at the Oak Ridge National Laboratory in 1996. The current of 1000 amperes per square centimeter ordinarily carried by household wires would equal only 0.05 percent of the current achieved by the scientists. Write a linear equation and solve to determine the current achieved by the scientists.

39. How many quarts of a 35% liquid fertilizer solution does a farmer need if he wants the solution to contain 4 quarts of pure liquid fertilizer?

2.3

Recall	Example
Solving algebraically • Simplify both expressions in the equation (preferably without fractions). • Isolate the variable to one side of the equation and the constants to the other side of the equation by using the addition property of equations. • Reduce the coefficient of the variable to 1 by using the multiplication property of equations. • Check the solution.	Solve $\frac{2}{3}x + \frac{1}{2} = x - \frac{1}{4}$ algebraically. $$\frac{2}{3}x + \frac{1}{2} = x - \frac{1}{4}$$ $$12\left(\frac{2}{3}x + \frac{1}{2}\right) = 12\left(x - \frac{1}{4}\right)$$ $$\overset{4}{\cancel{12}}\left(\frac{2}{\cancel{3}}x\right) + \overset{6}{\cancel{12}}\left(\frac{1}{\cancel{2}}\right) = 12(x) - \overset{3}{\cancel{12}}\left(\frac{1}{\cancel{4}}\right)$$ $$8x + 6 = 12x - 3$$ $$8x + 6 - 12x = 12x - 3 - 12x$$ $$-4x + 6 = -3$$ $$-4x + 6 - 6 = -3 - 6$$ $$-4x = -9$$ $$\frac{-4x}{-4} = \frac{-9}{-4}$$ $$x = \frac{9}{4}$$ Check: $$\frac{2}{3}x + \frac{1}{2} = x - \frac{1}{4}$$ $$\frac{1}{\cancel{2}}\left(\frac{\cancel{9}}{\cancel{4}}\right) + \frac{1}{2} \ \bigg| \ \frac{9}{4} - \frac{1}{4}$$ $$2 \ \bigg| \ 2 \qquad \text{The solution checks.}$$

Solve algebraically.

40. $3x + 7 = 4x + 21$

41. $14 - 2x = 5x$

42. $8.7x + 4.33 = -2.4x - 33.41$

43. $\frac{5}{7}a + \frac{11}{14} = \frac{2}{7}a$

44. $2(x + 5) - (x + 6) = 2(x + 2) - x$

45. $3(x - 4) + 2(x + 1) = 5x + 10$

Write an equation for each situation and solve algebraically.

46. Your business trip allows $250.00 for reimbursement of car rental. If you rent a car for a flat fee of $49.95 per week plus $0.22 per mile, what is the maximum number of miles you can drive without exceeding your allowance?

47. One contractor offers to paint your home for a fee of $175 plus $35 per hour. Another contractor offers to do the same job for $100 plus $40 per hour. For what number of hours will the two offers be the same?

48. Glenda wants to make a grade of B in her algebra class. Her grade is the average of her four test grades and her final exam. If her four test grades are 92, 80, 85, and 81, what must her final exam grade be in order to have an average of 85 to make a B?

49. Green's Lawn Service charges $49.99 per application to fertilize lawns in a neighborhood. Bill Green estimated that the fertilizer cost $25.00 per application. His spreader cost $150.30. Determine the number of applications he must do to break even. Determine the number of applications he must do to earn a profit of $500.00.

2.4

Recall	Example
Solving an equation for a variable • Clear the equation of fractions. • Isolate the terms involving the desired variable to one side of the equation and all other terms to the other side of the equation by using the addition property of equations. • If the variable being solved for is in unlike terms, factor out the variable. • Reduce the coefficient of the variable to 1 by using the multiplication property of equations.	Solve $S = 2LW + 2WH + 2LH$ for L. $S = 2LW + 2WH + 2LH$ $S - 2WH = 2LW + 2WH + 2LH - 2WH$ $S - 2WH = 2LW + 2LH$ $S - 2WH = L(2W + 2H)$ $\dfrac{S - 2WH}{2W + 2H} = \dfrac{L(2W + 2H)}{2W + 2H}$ $\dfrac{S - 2WH}{2W + 2H} = L$ or $\qquad L = \dfrac{S - 2WH}{2W + 2H}$

Solve exercises 50–52 for the indicated variable.

50. $A = \dfrac{1}{2}h(b + B)$ for h **51.** $S = 2LW + 2WH + 2LH$ for W **52.** $\dfrac{3}{4}x - \dfrac{5}{8}y = \dfrac{11}{12}$ for y

53. An annuity will pay you $6000 immediately and an annual payment of $8000. Write an equation for the total amount, A, that you will receive from the annuity over n years. Use the equation to solve for n, the number of years the annuity will last for a particular amount. Use the new equation to find how long the annuity will last if the amount is $78,000. How long will the annuity last if the amount is $126,000?

2.5

Recall	Example
	The numbers of people per square mile in Mongolia, Namibia, Australia, and Iceland are consecutive integers.
Modeling real-world situations	The sum of these integers is 22. Determine the density (people per square mile) of these countries.
• Define a variable.	Let $x =$ the density of Mongolia $\qquad x + 1 =$ the density of Namibia $\qquad x + 2 =$ the density of Australia $\qquad x + 3 =$ the density of Iceland
• Write an equation. • Solve the equation.	$x + (x + 1) + (x + 2) + (x + 3) = 22$ $\qquad\qquad\qquad\qquad 4x + 6 = 22$ $\qquad\qquad\qquad 4x + 6 - 6 = 22 - 6$ $\qquad\qquad\qquad\qquad\qquad 4x = 16$ $\qquad\qquad\qquad\qquad \dfrac{4x}{4} = \dfrac{16}{4}$ $\qquad\qquad\qquad\qquad\quad x = 4$
• Check the solution.	The consecutive integers are 4, 5, 6, and 7. Check: The sum of $4 + 5 + 6 + 7 = 22$.
• Write an answer to the question asked.	Mongolia has 4 people per square mile. Namibia has 5 people per square mile. Australia has 6 people per square mile. Iceland has 7 people per square mile.

54. Rob was cutting three lengths of wire from a 3-foot (36 inches) piece. He can't find the instructions that tell how many inches each piece should measure, but he remembers that they were consecutive even integers. What are the lengths he should cut? What would the lengths be if the lengths were consecutive integers instead of consecutive even integers?

55. A privacy fence meets the side of a house at an angle of 138°. What is the measure of the angle behind the fence that is the supplement of this angle? If the owner plants a garden behind the fence and the garden is in the shape of a right triangle, what are the measures of the three angles of the garden?

56. The early Greeks thought that a rectangle whose length is approximately 1.6 times its width was most pleasing to the eye. Many examples of this golden ratio are found in works of art. Julia has 78 inches of framing for a picture that she would like to be in the shape of a golden rectangle. Determine the frame dimensions.

57. An investment fund offers 12% simple interest annually on an investment. How much should be invested to have a total amount of $8100 in the account at the end of the year?

58. Kurre received $15,000 from his grandfather. He invests part of it in a bond paying 8.5% simple interest annually and part of it in a savings account paying 6.5% simple interest per year. If he earns $1225 in interest at the end of the first year, how much did he invest in the accounts?

59. The sale price of a suit was $210. The sale was advertised as a 20%-off sale. Determine the original price of the suit.

60. Casey is in her second semester of college and is dismayed to read in the college's newspaper that the Board has approved a tuition hike of 2.7% for the next school year. If next fall's tuition for a student taking 12 credit hours is $7200, how much is Casey paying this semester for 12 hours?

2.6

Recall	Examples
Linear absolute-value equation in one variable • An equation that can be written in the form $\|ax + b\| = c$, where a, b, and c are real numbers and $a \neq 0$.	Linear absolute-value equation in one variable $\|2x - 5\| = 4; \dfrac{\|x - 2\|}{3} = 1$
Solving graphically a linear absolute-value equation in one variable • Graph the two functions defined by the left side of the equation and the right side of the equation. • The solution(s) are the x-coordinates of the points of intersection of the graphs.	Solve $\|2x - 1\| = 5$. Graphic Solution The solutions are -2 and 3.
Solving algebraically a linear absolute-value equation in one variable • Isolate the absolute value expression and determine the number of solutions to the equation. • Write and evaluate an equation(s) needed to determine the solution(s).	Solve $\|2x - 1\| = 5$. Algebraic Solution $\|2x - 1\| = 5$ $2x - 1 = 5$ or $2x - 1 = -5$ $2x - 1 + 1 = 5 + 1$ $\quad$ $2x - 1 + 1 = -5 + 1$ $2x = 6$ $\qquad\qquad$ $2x = -4$ $\dfrac{2x}{2} = \dfrac{6}{2}$ $\qquad\qquad$ $\dfrac{2x}{2} = \dfrac{-4}{2}$ $x = 3$ $\qquad\qquad\quad$ $x = -2$

Recall	Examples
Checking numerically a linear absolute-value equation in one variable • Set up a table of values. • The solution(s) are the x-values that correspond to equal values for the two expressions.	Check numerically that the solutions of $\|2x - 1\| = 5$ are -2 and 3. Numeric Check x $\quad\|2x - 1\| =\quad$ 5 <table><tr><td>-3</td><td>7</td><td>5</td></tr><tr><td>-2</td><td>5</td><td>5</td></tr><tr><td>-1</td><td>3</td><td>5</td></tr><tr><td>0</td><td>1</td><td>5</td></tr><tr><td>1</td><td>1</td><td>5</td></tr><tr><td>2</td><td>3</td><td>5</td></tr><tr><td>3</td><td>5</td><td>5</td></tr><tr><td>4</td><td>7</td><td>5</td></tr></table> The solutions are -2 and 3 because $5 = 5$.

Use the calculator screens first to write the equation being solved and then to determine the solution or solutions (if any) of the equation.

61.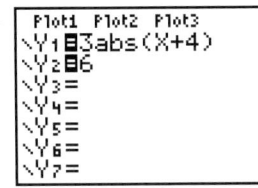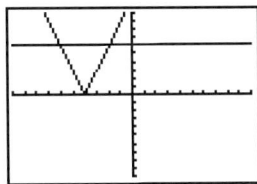

$(-10, 10, -10, 10)$

Solve algebraically and check graphically.

62. $|a - 7| = 0$

63. $|-b + 12| = 4$

64. $|c - 2| = -4$

65. $2|x - 7| - 4 = 8$

66. $5|2x - 7| + 10 = 8$

67. $\left|\dfrac{x + 4}{2}\right| = 6$

Write a linear absolute-value equation that represents each situation and solve.

68. The tolerance on a machining job is 0.04 mm. If the basic dimension of the part is 62.79 mm, what are the permissible limits on the part?

69. A voter survey shows that 49% of the voters are in favor of a consolidation proposal, with a margin of error of 4%. What are the limits on the percentage of voters who favor the proposal?

■ Chapter 2 Mixed Review

Solve graphically.

1. $3(x + 2) - 2(x - 1) = (2x + 5) - (x - 3)$

2. $(2x + 1) - (3x - 7) = (x + 5) - 2(x - 2)$

3. $x + 1 = 2x + 5$

4. $\dfrac{1}{3}x + 3 = 6 - \dfrac{2}{3}x$

5. $1.2x - 6.12 = -2.2x + 4.42$

Solve each equation numerically for an integer solution.

6. $4x - 5 = 7 - 2x$

7. $14(x + 6) - 17 = 12(x + 5)$

8. $1.5x + 5.5 = -2.4x - 6.2$

9. $2(2x - 3) + 3(x + 1) = 6(x - 1) + (x + 3)$

10. $\dfrac{1}{3}x + \dfrac{14}{3} = \dfrac{5}{2} - \dfrac{3}{4}x$

11. $4(x - 2) - (x - 1) = 3x + 1$

Identify each equation as linear or nonlinear.

12. $5 - \dfrac{3}{7}x = \dfrac{2}{3}x + 2$
     13. $2x - 4 = 1 + \dfrac{9}{x}$
     14. $-2x^3 + 3x = x - 5$

15. $15 = 2(x - 7) - (x - 2)$
     16. $3.9(x - 1.2) - 6.7x = 0$
     17. $\sqrt[3]{x + 1} - 5 = 4x$

Solve algebraically.

18. $\dfrac{z}{29} = -12$
     19. $\dfrac{5}{22} = \dfrac{25}{33}y$
     20. $59a = 1888$

21. $-174.243 = 2.41x$
     22. $2.3x - 3.3x = 14$
     23. $-b = 14.59$

24. $3(x - 8) + 8(x + 3) = 77$
     25. $z + 193 = -251$
     26. $\dfrac{13}{17} + a = \dfrac{5}{51}$

27. $0.92(x - 2) + 0.08(x + 1) = 5.73$ **28.** $6.2x + 5.67 = 4.9x + 16.98$
     29. $24.96 - 3.9a = 0$

30. $\dfrac{2}{3}x - \dfrac{3}{4} = -\dfrac{5}{6}$
     31. $\dfrac{4}{9}y + \dfrac{11}{18} = \dfrac{5}{6}y$
     32. $7x - 4 = 3x + 20$

33. $7x = 15 - 3x$
     34. $2(x + 2) + (x + 1) = 5(x + 1) - 2x$
     35. $4(2x - 1) = 3(2x + 1) + 2(x + 1)$

Solve.

36. $|2x + 6| = 0$
     37. $|4 - z| = 4$
     38. $|2x - 1| = -4$
     39. $|5x + 2| = 12$

40. $5|x - 7| - 3 = 12$
     41. $\left|\dfrac{x + 1}{4}\right| - 3 = 2$

Solve each equation for the indicated variable.

42. $y - 6 = \dfrac{2}{3}(x + 9)$ for y
     43. $S = 2LW + 2WH + 2LH$ for H

44. $S = 2\pi r^2 + 2\pi rh$ for h
     45. $I = PRT$ for P

Write a linear absolute-value equation for each situation and solve.

46. The difference in the heights of the Peachtree Tower and the Bank of America Tower, both in Atlanta, is 253 feet. If the Peachtree Tower is 770 feet high, what are the two possible heights for the Bank of America Tower? Given that the Peachtree Tower is not as tall, which height is correct for the Bank of America Tower?

47. The margin of error in a voter poll is 3%. If the survey suggests that 52% of the voters support a new tax levy, what are the limits on the true percentage of voters who will support the levy?

Write a linear equation for each situation and solve.

48. If the sales tax on a purchase was $5.41, which represents 8.25% tax, what was the subtotal of the purchases before taxes? What was the total bill, including sales tax?

49. Chuck was given an advance of $5650 for developing software for a publishing firm. The amount of the advance represented $\frac{2}{5}$ of the total amount he would receive for his work.

How much money does Chuck expect to earn in total for this project?

50. A newspaper delivery service pays its employees $15.00 per day plus $0.25 for each house along the delivery route that purchases a newspaper. To how many houses does an employee need to deliver papers in order to earn $45.00 per day?

51. Instructions for a model-plane kit require a piece of balsa wood to be cut into four pieces, each 1 inch longer than the previous piece. If the wood is 26 inches long, how long will each piece be? What lengths would the strips be if each piece were 2 inches longer than the preceding piece, allowing for 2 inches of scrap?

52. A triangle has one angle measuring 62°. The other two angles are equal in measure. What are the measures of the other two angles? What is the measure of the supplement of each of the two equal angles?

53. If an ink-jet printer was marked down 15% to a sale price of $118.95, what was the price before the markdown?

54. The length of a room is one and one-half times its width. If the perimeter of the room is 84 feet, what are its dimensions?

55. If the price of a television set with 8.75% sales tax was $325.16, what was the price of the set before tax? How much was the sales tax?

56. A company produces and sells greeting cards. The setup costs are $3000, and it costs $2.00 to produce a package of cards. The selling price is $5.50 per package. Determine the number of packages that must be produced and sold to break even. Determine the number of packages that must be produced and sold in order to make a profit of $500.00.

57. Upon retirement Jolene plans to invest $50,000. Part of her money will be in uninsured bonds paying 15% simple interest annually. The rest she will invest in a certificate that pays 8% simple interest annually. If she wants $6000 per year in income from the investment, how much should she have in each account?

58. How many liters of a 30% disinfectant solution must be mixed with 2 liters of a 60% disinfectant solution to make a 50% disinfectant solution?

59. The travel agent offered Bo two plans for his vacation. The first plan has a room for $175 per day. Since he has a small kitchen in the suite, he plans to purchase his food for $250. The second plan is all inclusive (room and food) for $350 per day. For what number of days will the two plans cost the same?

60. The average number of reported tornadoes for the years 2002 through 2004 for the month of May in the United States is 419. The year 2002 reported 204. The year 2003 reported 543. Determine the number of tornadoes in 2004.

61. Chantal signs a contract with a tanning salon as a part of a special promotion. Every month the salon does a bank draft on her account for $15. In addition she pays $3.50 for every 20-minute tanning session. She also gets free tanning products. Write an equation for her total monthly tanning cost, C, if she tans for x 20-minute sessions. Find a new equation for the number of tanning sessions in a month where her total tanning expenditure is C dollars. If she wants to spend $40 a month on tanning, how many tanning sessions can she do?

62. A plumber charges you $40.00 per visit plus $55.50 for each hour worked on a job.
  a. Write an equation for the total amount, A, that you will pay for a job that requires h hours of labor.
  b. Use the equation to solve for h, the hours worked, in terms of the total amount for the job.
  c. Use the new equation to find how many hours a job costing $178.75 lasted.

63. A designer rug is rectangular, with diagonals running from one corner to the opposite corner. If the diagonal makes a 35-degree angle with the length of the rug, how large an angle does it make with the width of the rug?

64. How many gallons of a 60% antifreeze solution does a mechanic need if she wants the solution to contain 2 gallons of pure antifreeze?

■ Chapter 2 Test

A^+ TEST-TAKING TIPS

When you review for an exam, list all the major concepts the exam will cover. Locate exercises that illustrate each of the concepts. Think of how you would recognize them if they were randomly ordered on the exam. Spend more of your study time on those exercises in which you know you are weak. For extra practice, seek out additional exercises in the text that you have not worked out. Try to find someone to study with so that you can help each other with your weaknesses. If you can't complete some exercises, see your instructor or go to a tutoring center well before test time to seek extra help. If you do this, the exam should not be a surprise to you, it won't throw you, and your confidence level will be high.

Identify each equation as linear or nonlinear.

1. $3.14x + 9.07 = 5.72x$ **2.** $5x = 12 + \dfrac{19}{x}$ **3.** $4x + 21 = 5x^2$ **4.** $4(x - 6) = 3(5 - x) + 12$

Solve.

5. $2(2x - 5) - 2(2 - x) = 6(x + 1) + 1$ **6.** $2(x + 5) = -3(x + 1) - 2$

7. $1.41(x + 5.08) + 1.17x + 0.00102 = -3.46x - 5.39334$ **8.** $(x + 1) - 4(x - 1) = 3(2 - x) - 1$

9. $\dfrac{4}{5}x + \dfrac{31}{10} = \dfrac{-4}{3}x + \dfrac{41}{6}$ **10.** $|x + 3| - 1 = -1$

11. $3|2x - 9| + 14 = 5$ **12.** $\left|\dfrac{2x - 2}{3}\right| = 4$

Write a linear equation for each situation and solve.

13. A piece of wire measures 45 inches. For splicing purposes, it will be cut into three pieces, each of which is 1 inch longer than the preceding piece. In what lengths should the three pieces be cut?

14. If a stereo is on sale at 25% off the retail price and its sale price is $179.95, what was the price before it went on sale?

15. Solve $P = 2L + 2W$ for W, where P is the perimeter of a rectangle with length L and width W. Use the formula to find the width of a rectangle whose length is 14.8 inches and whose perimeter measures 44.8 inches.

16. One angle of a triangle measures 42°. The other two angles are equal in measure. What is the measure of the other angles? What is the measure of the supplement of the angles that have equal measure?

17. Fruit drinks are a mixture of fruit juice and water. How many liters of a drink containing 60% apple juice must be mixed with 500 liters of a drink containing 20% cranberry juice to make a drink containing 50% cranberry-apple juice?

18. An Internet music provider charges $9.85 per month to use its service. In addition, it charges a fee of $0.70 to burn a song. If Thom budgets $20.00 per month to use this service, what is the maximum number of songs that he can burn and stay in his budget?

19. Serene Landscaping will clear the wooded area behind Candise's house for a labor charge of $25 per hour and a flat fee of $50 to haul away the brush. Evergreen Yard Service offers to do the same job for a labor charge of $30 per hour and no extra charge for hauling away the brush. For what number of hours will the two plans cost the same?

20. Cathy's Carpet Cleaners charges a fee of $2.95 per square yard of carpeting cleaned. Cathy purchased a heavy-duty carpet cleaner for $549.99. The cleaning materials average $0.65 per square yard of carpet cleaned. Determine the number of square yards Cathy must clean to break even. Determine the number of square yards she must clean to make a profit of $600.00.

21. In a newspaper article, Clint read that the Board had approved a 9.7% increase in tuition for the next school year. The new tuition according to the article will be $3600 for a full-time student. What was the amount of tuition before the increase?

22. Kerk would like to make an A in his biology class. His grade is an average of his midterm, final, and lab grade. If he made 95 on his midterm and 92 for his lab grade, what is the minimum grade that he can make on his final exam to have a 93 average for an A grade?

23. Colleen plans to invest her $1000 in two different accounts. The mutual fund will pay 8% simple interest annually. The savings account will pay 4.5% simple interest annually. If Colleen earned interest of $62.50 in the first year, how much did she invest in each plan?

24. The Pew Internet and American Life Project reports that when nonusers of the Internet are surveyed, 27% report that a major reason for not using the Internet is that it is complicated and difficult to understand. The survey reports a margin of error of plus or minus 3.5%. What are the minimum and maximum percentages of people who feel this way?

25. Describe how to solve a linear equation in one variable graphically. Explain in detail how to locate the solution.

2

Project

Graphing-calculator technology makes it easy to study the golden ratio, one of the most interesting graphical and numerical concepts in algebra. The golden ratio can be found by dividing a line segment into two parts such that the length of the smaller part divided by the length of the larger part is the same as the length of the larger part divided by the length of the line segment.

Let s represent the length of the shorter part, and let the unit length 1 represent the length of the longer part. The following is a sketch of the line segment:

Algebraically, the golden ratio is

$$\frac{\text{shorter length}}{\text{longer length}} = \frac{\text{longer length}}{\text{total length}}$$

$$\frac{s}{1} = \frac{1}{s + 1}$$

This equation will be solved later in the text, but for now just accept it that one of its solutions is $s = \dfrac{\sqrt{5} - 1}{2}$.

Since the ratio of the shorter part to the longer part is s to 1, or $\dfrac{\sqrt{5} - 1}{2}$ to 1, it follows that the shorter part is $\dfrac{\sqrt{5} - 1}{2}$ times the length of the longer part.

PART I   Many philosophers, artists, mathematicians, architects, musicians, and others have been intrigued by the golden ratio and have used it in their undertakings. As an example of how you might use it, suppose you want to construct a rectangle whose length and width are pleasing to the eye. Furthermore, suppose the perimeter of the rectangle is fixed at 50 centimeters. Complete the following steps to determine the length and the width of the rectangle needed:

1. Define the variable x to be the length of the rectangle—the longer side.

2. Write an expression for the width of the rectangle—the shorter side—using s as defined above and x.

3. Draw a rectangle and label its length and width in terms of x.

4. Write an expression for the perimeter of your rectangle (using the expressions for length and width developed in steps 1 and 2), and set the expression equal to the value given in order to obtain an equation.

5. Solve the equation you found in step 4 for the length, x.

6. Approximate the value of the length to one decimal place (by substituting the value for s).

7. Find the width, using the expression from step 2. Substitute the values for s and x, and then round your answer to one decimal place.

8. Check your answer to see that the perimeter is in fact 50 centimeters. If it is not, explain.

Next, construct a rectangle with the dimensions you have determined. Is the rectangle's shape pleasing to the eye? Does the perimeter check?

PART II   Here is another interesting fact: If you mark off a square in your rectangle, with a side measuring the same as the width of the rectangle, the resulting inner rectangle also has dimensions in the golden ratio. You can continue marking off squares in each inner rectangle to obtain another golden rectangle. The resulting picture should be an aesthetically pleasing modern work of art. To do this, hold your rectangle with the width, or shorter side, up. Mark off a square across the top of the rectangle. Turn the rectangle clockwise, and mark off the next square across the top of the remaining rectangle. Continue this procedure and mark off at least five squares. Do you like the pattern? The golden ratio can be tried with other geometric shapes as well.

PART III   Now let's generate a table of dimensions of rectangles whose lengths and widths are in the golden ratio. Set up the table with a column for Length, Width, and Perimeter. Let the length be values from 5 cm to 40 cm in increments of 5 cm.

(*Hint:* You can use your calculator to fill in the table. Begin by storing the expression for the golden ratio, s, under the letter S in the calculator. Then set Y1, the width, equal to SX and Y2 equal to the formula for the perimeter, in terms of S and x. Finally, use the table feature of the calculator to obtain the values needed for the table.)

PART IV   As stated earlier, the golden ratio has a long history of use because of its aesthetic properties. The Egyptians thought that the golden ratio was sacred, and it can be found in the design of their temples, pyramids, and artwork. Even some Egyptian hieroglyphics have proportions based upon the golden ratio. Leonardo da Vinci's drawings often have overlays of rectangles with the golden ratio. The golden ratio also may be seen in many of the rectangles used by Piet Mondrian in his form of art called neoplasticism. The golden ratio can be found in many of the dimensions of the Parthenon, the famous Greek temple. The design of the United Nations building in New York City is said to have windows in the shape of the golden ratio. The music of Beethoven and Mozart are said to have pieces that divide into parts exactly according to the golden ratio. Renaissance writers called it the "divine proportion."

However, there is also controversy about the golden ratio. Is it really as pleasing as is claimed? Does some of the architecture, such as the Greek and Egyptian, conform with the golden ratio as a result of erosion?

As a final task in this project, find a reference on the golden ratio. You may go to the library to search, or use the Internet. Write a short summary of your findings. Be sure to document your reference sources.

Linear Equations and Functions

In Chapter 2 we studied linear equations in one variable, learning to solve them by substituting a suitable value for the variable. In this chapter we examine linear equations in two variables and discuss methods for solving them. Some of the same ideas we learned before will apply here, too. We will also see several new ideas, such as the slope of a line, which is a very important and powerful tool in analyzing equations. With these tools, we will be able to study the relationships between two lines and between two equations. As a result, we will learn how to write linear equations to predict new information. This is an important use of basic mathematics in the real world.

Situations that can be described by linear equations (or functions) often occur in the areas of business and science. One important application of using linear equations to predict new information is illustrated in the chapter project. In the project, you are asked to write linear models from data. Using the linear model of your choosing, you are requested to predict future events for an automobile manufacturing company.

3.1 GRAPHING BY USING THE INTERCEPT METHOD

OBJECTIVES
1. Identify linear equations in two variables.
2. Graph linear equations in two variables by using a set of ordered pairs.
3. Algebraically determine the *y*-intercept and *x*-intercept of a graph.
4. Graph linear equations whose graphs have only one intercept.
5. Graph linear equations in two variables by using the intercept method.
6. Model real-world situations by using linear graphs.

APPLICATION

In 1974, an SR-71 Blackbird jet plane was flown from New York City to London in 1 hour and 55 minutes, the fastest transatlantic flight ever. If we let d represent the plane's distance from London, then an equation representing that distance is $d = 3462 - 1807t$, where t is the flight time in hours. Graph the equation and interpret the intercepts of the graph.

We will discuss this application further. See page 280.

Objective 3.1.1   **Identifying Linear Equations in Two Variables**

In the last chapter, we solved linear equations in one variable. We used this type of equation to solve a problem with one unknown quantity or a problem that can be written in terms of one unknown quantity. However, if we need to solve a problem with two unknown quantities, then we may use a **linear equation in two variables**.

STANDARD FORM FOR A LINEAR EQUATION IN TWO VARIABLES

The standard form for a linear equation in two variables is $ax + by = c$, where a, b, and c are real numbers and a and b are not both equal to 0.

For example, the following are equations in standard form:

$$ax + by = c$$

$2x + 5y = 2$	$a = 2$	$b = 5$	$c = 2$
$x - y = 0$	$a = 1$	$b = -1$	$c = 0$
$2x = 7$	$a = 2$	$b = 0$	$c = 7$
$-3y = 1$	$a = 0$	$b = -3$	$c = 1$

The last two equations, when either $a = 0$ or $b = 0$, are linear equations in one variable, which we discussed in Chapter 2. In the current chapter, they are treated as special cases of linear equations in two variables.

 TAKE NOTE   The variables x and y are each raised to the first power.

The relation $y = -2x + 5$ is a linear equation in two variables because it can be rearranged into standard form by the properties of equations. For example,

$$y = -2x + 5$$
$$y + 2x = -2x + 5 + 2x \quad \text{Add 2x to both sides.}$$
$$y + 2x = 5 \quad \text{Simplify the right side.}$$
$$2x + y = 5 \quad \text{Rearrange the left side.}$$

These equations are called linear equations because their graphs are straight lines. For example, the graph of $y = -2x + 5$ is linear, as shown in the figure at the left.

Y1 = −2x + 5

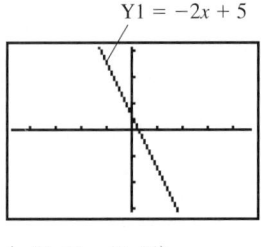

(−47, 47, −31, 31)

All linear equations in two variables are relations. The relation $y = -2x + 5$ is also a function. (The graph passes the vertical line test.) Therefore, it may be written in function notation as $f(x) = -2x + 5$ and is called a **linear function**. (Remember, not all relations are functions.)

EXAMPLE 1   Identify each equation as linear or nonlinear. Express each linear equation in standard form.

a. $2x^2 + 3y = 4$ **b.** $y = -3x$

c. $x = 0$ **d.** $y = 2x + \sqrt{5}$

Solution

a. $2x^2 + 3y = 4$ is a nonlinear equation, because the x term is squared.

b. $y = -3x$ is a linear equation in two variables. Writing the equation in standard form proceeds as follows:

$$y = -3x$$
$$y + 3x = -3x + 3x \qquad \text{Add 3x to both sides.}$$
$$y + 3x = 0 \qquad \text{Simplify.}$$
$$3x + y = 0 \qquad \text{Rearrange the left side.}$$

c. $x = 0$ is a linear equation in two variables. It is written in standard form as $1x + 0y = 0$.

d. $y = 2x + \sqrt{5}$ is a linear equation in two variables. To put the equation in standard form, we write

$$y = 2x + \sqrt{5}$$
$$-2x + y = \sqrt{5}$$

 TAKE NOTE Be careful to examine an equation with a radical expression. If the radical has a radicand containing a variable term, the equation is nonlinear. However, if the radicand contains only a constant term, the equation is linear.

Check your results for parts **a**, **b**, and **d** on your calculator. First solve for y and then graph the equation. Note that you cannot graph part **c** on your calculator using $\boxed{Y=}$. See the Calculator Exercises at the end of this section for a method to graph "X=" equations.

a.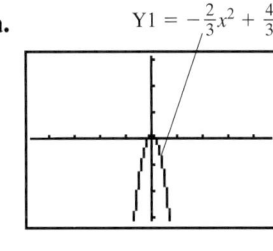

(−47, 47, −31, 31)
nonlinear equation

b.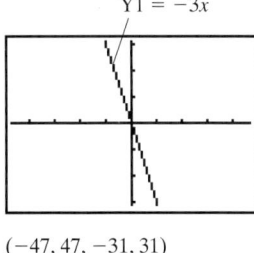

(−47, 47, −31, 31)
linear equation

d.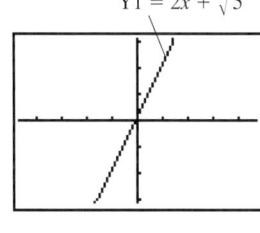

(−47, 47, −31, 31)
linear equation

Objective 3.1.1 *CHECKUP*

1. Identify each equation as linear or nonlinear. Express each linear equation in standard form.

a. $x = 3y^2 + 12$ **b.** $y = -\dfrac{3}{8}$

c. $y = 8x - 3$ **d.** $3\sqrt{x} + 2y = 0$

2. Why is the equation $ax + by = c$ called a linear equation?

Objective 3.1.2

Graphing by Using Ordered Pairs

We determine a solution of a linear equation in one variable by substituting a value for the variable. If the result is a true statement, then the value is a solution. Similarly, we determine a solution of a linear equation in two variables by substituting values for each of the two variables (an ordered pair). If the result is a true statement, then the ordered pair is a solution of the equation. We say the solution satisfies the equation.

SOLUTION OF A LINEAR EQUATION IN TWO VARIABLES

An ordered pair (x, y) is a solution of a linear equation in two variables if the values of the coordinates, when substituted for their corresponding variables, result in a true equation.

Some linear equations in one variable have more than one solution. A linear equation in two variables always has more than one solution. To determine the solutions of a linear equation in two variables, we will use a table of values, as we did with relations in Chapter 1.

To determine solutions of a linear equation in two variables, x and y,

- Solve the equation for y.
- Set up an extended table of values.
- Complete the table with at least three values for x.

EXAMPLE 2

Given $x - y = 3$, determine three ordered-pair solutions.

Solution

Solve for y.

$$x - y = 3$$
$$x - y - x = 3 - x \qquad \text{Subtract x from both sides.}$$
$$-y = 3 - x \qquad \text{Simplify.}$$
$$\frac{-y}{-1} = \frac{3 - x}{-1} \qquad \text{Divide both sides by } -1.$$
$$y = -3 + x \quad \text{or} \quad y = x - 3$$

Complete the table of values. We will use 0, 1, and 2 for x. (Note that we may choose any value for x that is in the domain of the relation.)

x	$y = x - 3$	y	(x, y)
0	$y = 0 - 3$ $y = -3$	-3	$(0, -3)$
1	$y = 1 - 3$ $y = -2$	-2	$(1, -2)$
2	$y = 2 - 3$ $y = -1$	-1	$(2, -1)$

Therefore, $(0, -3)$, $(1, -2)$, and $(2, -1)$ are three possible solutions of the equation.

On your calculator, enter the equation in Y1, set up the table for integers, and view the table. The result is a table of possible ordered-pair solutions. Note that more than three ordered-pair solutions are shown. ∎

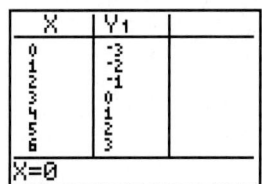

Y1 = $x - 3$

The preceding linear equation in two variables has an infinite number of possible ordered-pair solutions. To illustrate these solutions, we will use a graph.

TAKE NOTE Remember that

1. Every solution of an equation can be represented by a point on its graph.

2. Every point on a graph represents a solution of its equation.

To graph a linear equation in two variables by using ordered pairs,

- Graph at least two ordered-pair solutions found in a table of values.
- Connect the points with a straight line.
- Label the graph with the equation.

A third ordered pair should be used as a checkpoint. Label the coordinates of the points graphed.

EXAMPLE 3

Graph $x - y = 3$.

Solution

Solve for y.

In example 2, we solved $x - y = 3$, $y = x - 3$, and then completed a table of values. We determined three ordered pair solutions of the equation: $(0, -3)$, $(1, -2)$, and $(2, -1)$. Plotting these ordered pairs and connecting the points with a straight line will locate other possible solutions. Label the graph with the original equation.

On your calculator, enter the expression in Y1 and graph it on a standard screen to see the same graph.

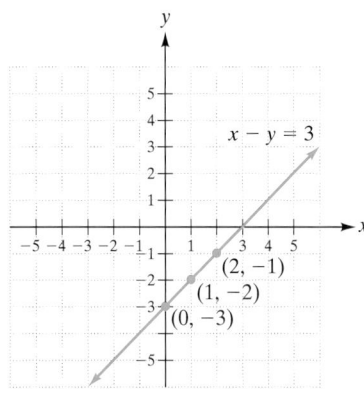

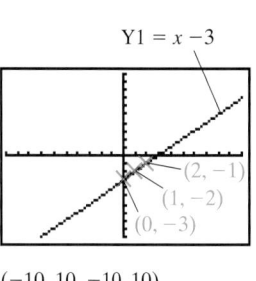

$(-10, 10, -10, 10)$

EXAMPLE 4

Graph $4x - 2y = 6$.

Solution

Solve for y.

$$4x - 2y = 6$$
$$4x - 2y - 4x = 6 - 4x \qquad \text{Subtract 4x from both sides.}$$
$$-2y = -4x + 6 \qquad \text{Simplify.}$$
$$\frac{-2y}{-2} = \frac{-4x + 6}{-2} \qquad \text{Divide both sides by } -2.$$
$$y = 2x - 3 \qquad \text{Simplify.}$$

Set up a table of values. We will use -3, 0, and 2 for x.

x	$y = 2x - 3$	y	(x, y)
-3	$y = 2(-3) - 3$	-9	$(-3, -9)$
0	$y = 2(0) - 3$	-3	$(0, -3)$
2	$y = 2(2) - 3$	1	$(2, 1)$

Graph the ordered pairs and connect them with a straight line. Label the graph with the equation. Check the graph on your calculator.

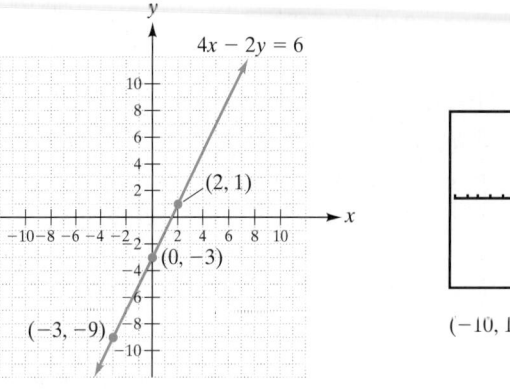

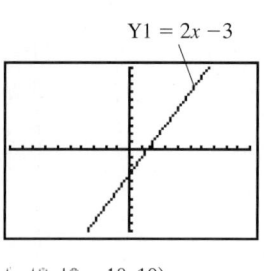

$(-10, 10, -10, 10)$

EXAMPLE 5   Graph $p(x) = \frac{2}{3}x + 1$.

Solution

The given relation, $p(x) = \frac{2}{3}x + 1$, is a function. Set up a table. Choose any number for x. We'll use multiples of 3—that is, $-3, 0,$ and 3—because we are multiplying these numbers by a fraction with a denominator of 3. The result will be an integer.

x	$p(x) = \frac{2}{3}x + 1$	$p(x)$	$(x, p(x))$
-3	$p(x) = \frac{2}{3}(-3) + 1$ $p(x) = -2 + 1$ $p(x) = -1$	-1	$(-3, -1)$
0	$p(x) = \frac{2}{3}(0) + 1$ $p(x) = 1$	1	$(0, 1)$
3	$p(x) = \frac{2}{3}(3) + 1$ $p(x) = 2 + 1$ $p(x) = 3$	3	$(3, 3)$

Therefore, $(-3, -1), (0, 1),$ and $(3, 3)$ are three possible solutions of the linear equation (function).

Graph the ordered pairs and connect them with a straight line. Label the graph with the equation. Check your graph on your calculator.

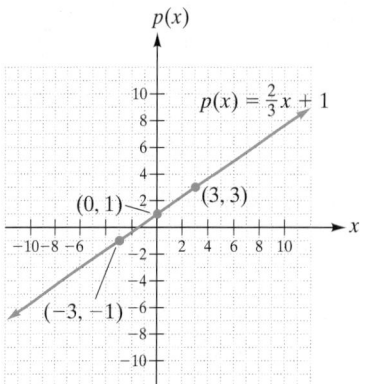

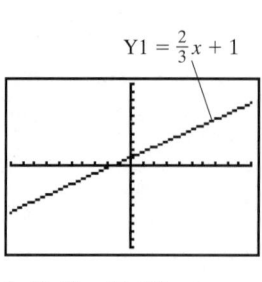

$(-10, 10, -10, 10)$

✓ Objective 3.1.2 *CHECKUP*

Determine three ordered-pair solutions.

1. $x + y = 4$

3. $6x + 2y = 4$ **4.** $g(x) = \dfrac{3}{5}x + 2$

In exercises 2–4, graph.

2. $x + y = 4$

5. How many solutions are there for a linear equation in two variables? ▪

Objective 3.1.3   Algebraically Determining the *y*-Intercept and *x*-Intercept of a Graph

Special solutions of a linear equation in two variables are the *y*-intercept and *x*-intercept of the graph of the equation. Remember that we discussed these points in Chapter 1. The *y*-intercept is the point where a graph touches or crosses the *y*-axis. The *x*-coordinate of this point is 0. Similarly, the *x*-intercept is the point where a graph touches or crosses the *x*-axis. The *y*-coordinate of this point is 0. For example, for the linear equation $x - y = 3$ (Examples 2 and 3), the *x*-intercept is $(3, 0)$ and the *y*-intercept is $(0, -3)$. On your calculator, the intercepts are the same.

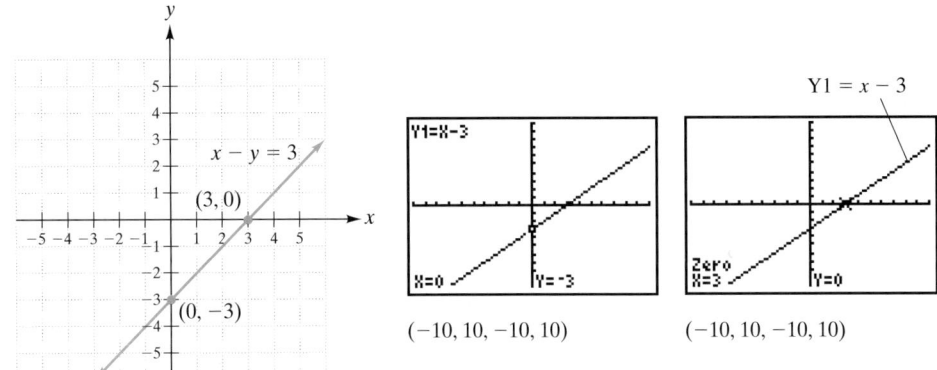

$(-10, 10, -10, 10)$ $(-10, 10, -10, 10)$

 TAKE NOTE It is important to remember that the *y*-coordinate of the *x*-intercept is always 0 (because it is on the *x*-axis). The *x*-coordinate of the *y*-intercept is always 0 (because it is on the *y*-axis). The *x*-intercept and the *y*-intercept are points and are written as ordered pairs.

To determine algebraically the *y*-intercept of a graph from its linear equation,

- Substitute 0 for *x*.
- Solve for *y*.
- Write an ordered pair.

To determine algebraically the *x*-intercept of a graph from its linear equation,

- Substitute 0 for *y*.
- Solve for *x*.
- Write an ordered pair.

For example, given the linear equation $x - y = 3$, find the *y*-intercept and the *x*-intercept algebraically.

To determine the *y*-intercept, we substitute 0 for *x* and solve for *y*.

$$x - y = 3$$
$$0 - y = 3$$
$$-y = 3$$
$$\dfrac{-y}{-1} = \dfrac{3}{-1}$$
$$y = -3$$

Therefore, the *y*-coordinate is -3. The *y*-intercept is $(0, -3)$.

To determine the *x*-intercept, we substitute 0 for *y* and solve for *x*.

$$x - y = 3$$
$$x - 0 = 3$$
$$x = 3$$

Therefore, the *x*-coordinate is 3. The *x*-intercept is $(3, 0)$.

There is another way to determine the graph's *y*-intercept from its linear equation. To see what this method is, complete the following set of exercises on your calculator.

Guided Discovery 1   *y*-Intercepts

Graph each linear equation and label the *y*-intercept.

1. $y = x - 5$ **2.** $y = x + 5$

3. $y = x - 10$ **4.** $y = x + 10$

Write a rule to determine the *y*-coordinate of the *y*-intercept of a graph from its linear equation.

The *y*-coordinate of the *y*-intercept of the graph is the same as the constant term in the equation when the equation is solved for *y*.

To determine algebraically the *y*-intercept of a graph from its linear equation,

- Solve the equation for *y*.
- The constant term is the *y*-coordinate of the *y*-intercept.
- Write an ordered pair. Remember, the *x*-coordinate is 0.

For example, determine the *y*-intercept of the graph of the linear equation $x - y = 3$.

Solve for *y* and obtain $y = x - 3$. The constant term is -3, so the *y*-coordinate of the *y*-intercept is -3. The *y*-intercept is $(0, -3)$.

EXAMPLE 6

Determine algebraically the *x*-intercept and *y*-intercept of the graph of the linear equation $2x + y = 5$.

Solution

To determine the *x*-coordinate of the *x*-intercept, substitute 0 for *y* in the equation and solve for *x*.

$$2x + y = 5$$
$$2x + 0 = 5 \qquad \text{Substitute 0 for } y.$$
$$2x = 5 \qquad \text{Simplify.}$$
$$\frac{2x}{2} = \frac{5}{2} \qquad \text{Divide both sides by 2.}$$
$$x = \frac{5}{2} \qquad \text{Simplify.}$$

The *x*-intercept is $\left(\frac{5}{2}, 0\right)$.

To determine the *y*-coordinate of the *y*-intercept, substitute 0 for *x* in the equation and solve for *y*.

$$2x + y = 5$$
$$2(0) + y = 5$$
$$y = 5$$

The *y*-intercept is $(0, 5)$.

The alternative way to determine the *y*-intercept is to solve the equation for *y*.

$$2x + y = 5$$
$$2x + y - 2x = 5 - 2x$$
$$y = 5 - 2x$$
$$y = -2x + 5$$

The *y*-coordinate of the *y*-intercept is 5. The *y*-intercept is $(0, 5)$.

Objective 3.1.3 *CHECKUP*

1. Determine algebraically the *x*-intercept and *y*-intercept of the graph.

$$6x + y = 12$$

2. Describe how you would determine the *x*-intercept and *y*-intercept of a graph of a linear equation in two variables from the graph. Then describe how you would determine these two points algebraically.

Objective 3.1.4 **Linear Graphs with One Intercept**

Previously, we defined the standard form of a linear equation in two variables, $ax + by = c$, and stated that both *a* and *b* are not equal to 0. Now let us discuss the cases when *a*, *b*, or *c* equals 0. Let's see what some of these graphs look like. First, we will let $c = 0$. Complete the following set of exercises on your calculator.

Guided Discovery 2 Linear Equations in Two Variables, $ax + by = c$, where $c = 0$

Graph the following linear equations in two variables and label the *x*-intercept and *y*-intercept:

1. $x + y = 0$

2. $-2x + 3y = 0$

Write a rule for determining when the graph of an equation has one point that is both the *x*-intercept and *y*-intercept.

Note that the equations are in the standard form $ax + by = c$, with $c = 0$. We see that the graphs of the equations have the same point for the *x*-intercept and the *y*-intercept.

The graph of $ax + by = 0$ has one intercept at the origin, $(0, 0)$.

If only $a = 0$, we have a special case of a linear equation in two variables (a linear equation in one variable). The equation is of the form $0x + by = c$, or $by = c$. An example of such an equation is $2y = 8$. Set up a table of values for this equation.

First, solve the equation for *y*.

$$2y = 8 \quad \text{or} \quad 0x + 2y = 8$$
$$2y = 0x + 8$$
$$y = 0x + 4$$

Since the coefficient of the *x*-term is 0, we will always obtain $y = 4$ for any *x*-value.

x	$y = 0x + 4$	y
0	$y = 0(0) + 4$	4
1	$y = 0(1) + 4$	4
2	$y = 0(2) + 4$	4

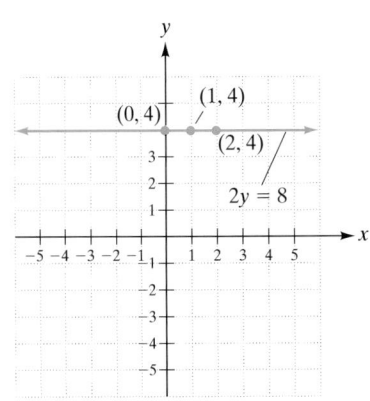

A graph corresponding to the table is shown. There is only one intercept, the *y*-intercept, $(0, 4)$. The line is horizontal.

The graph of $y = k$ is a horizontal line with a *y*-intercept of $(0, k)$.

If only $b = 0$, we have a second special case: an equation of the form $ax + 0y = c$, or $ax = c$.

Set up a table of values for $2x = -12$.

First, we cannot solve the equation for y, since the coefficient of y is 0. Therefore, we solve the equation for x.

$$2x = -12 \quad \text{or} \quad 2x + 0y = -12$$
$$2x = 0y - 12$$
$$x = 0y - 6$$

Now, if we substitute values for x other than -6, the result will be a false statement. Therefore, to obtain ordered pairs, we substitute values for y. Since the coefficient of y is 0, we will always obtain $x = -6$ for any y-value.

x	$x = 0y - 6$	y
-6	$x = 0(0) - 6$	0
-6	$x = 0(1) - 6$	1
-6	$x = 0(2) - 6$	2

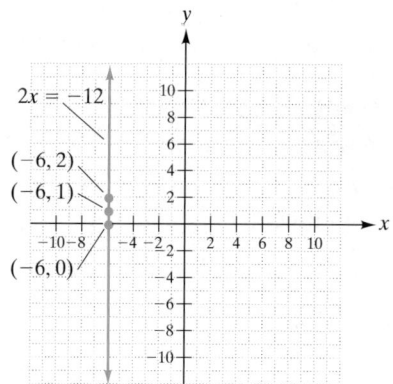

A graph corresponding to the table is shown. There is only one intercept, the x-intercept, $(-6, 0)$. The line is vertical.

This relation is not a function. In fact, a vertical line is the only case in which a linear equation in two variables is not a function. These equations cannot be graphed on a calculator by using the [Y=] menu. (See the Calculator Exercises at the end of this section.)

The graph of $x = h$ is a vertical line with an x-intercept of $(h, 0)$.

EXAMPLE 7   Determine the intercept of the graph of each linear equation in two variables. Then graph the equation.

a. $y - 3 = 0$ **b.** $2x - 6 = 0$ **c.** $x = y$

Solution

a. The equation does not have an x-variable. The coefficient of the x-term is 0. Solve for y.

$$y - 3 = 0$$
$$y = 3$$

The graph is a horizontal line with a y-intercept of $(0, 3)$.

b. The equation does not have a y-variable. The coefficient of the y-term is 0. Solve for x.

$$2x - 6 = 0$$
$$x = 3$$

The graph is a vertical line with x-intercept of $(3, 0)$.

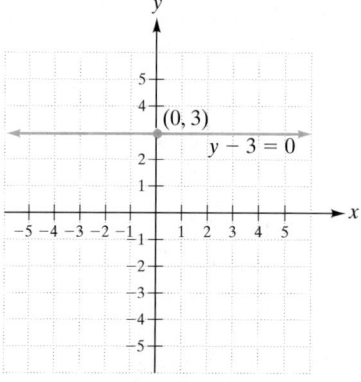

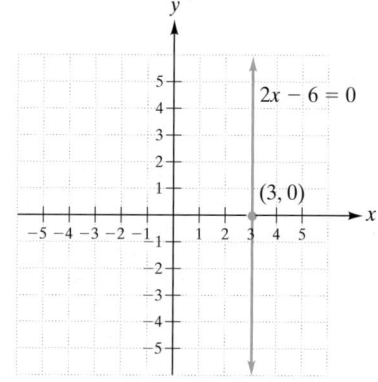

c. In standard form, the equation is $x - y = 0$. Since $c = 0$, the x-intercept and the y-intercept are $(0, 0)$. To complete the graph, determine two additional solutions. We will use 1 and 4 for x.

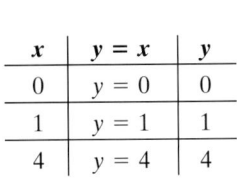

x	$y = x$	y
0	$y = 0$	0
1	$y = 1$	1
4	$y = 4$	4

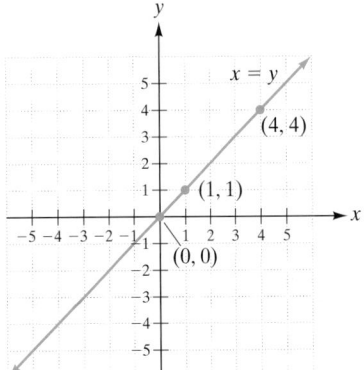

Objective 3.1.4 *CHECKUP*

1. Determine the intercepts of the graph of each linear equation. Then graph the equation as a check.
   a. $2x + 4y = 0$ **b.** $5y = 3$ **c.** $x - 16 = 0$
2. When will the graph of a linear equation have only an x-intercept?

3. When will the graph of a linear equation have only a y-intercept?

4. When will the x-intercept and the y-intercept of the graph of a linear equation be at the same point? What will the coordinates of the point be?

Objective 3.1.5   Graphing Linear Equations in Two Variables by Using the Intercept Method

Now we are ready to graph a linear equation in two variables by using the intercept method. We can use this method only if the graph has two distinct points as the x-intercept and y-intercept. In other words, the equation written in standard form must not have a, b, or c equal to 0.

The intercept method of graphing involves determining the two intercepts and connecting them with a straight line.

To graph a linear equation in two variables by using the intercept method,

- Determine the x-intercept.
- Determine the y-intercept.
- Plot the intercepts and label their coordinates.
- Connect the intercepts with a straight line.
- Label the graph with the equation.
- Check the graph by locating a third point on it, and determine that the coordinates of that point are a solution of the equation.

For example, graph the linear equation $x - y = 3$, using the intercept method.

Graph the two intercepts previously found for the equation, $(3, 0)$ and $(0, -3)$, and connect them with a straight line.

To check the graph, determine a point on it, and check whether that point is a solution of the equation. Let's check the point $(1, -2)$.

$x -$	y	$= 3$	
$1 - (-2)$		3	
$1 + 2$			
	3		

Substitute 1 for x and -2 for y in the equation.

Since $3 = 3$, $(1, -2)$ is a solution. The graph checks.

EXAMPLE 8   Graph the linear equation $3x + 4y = 12$, using the intercept method.

Solution

Determine the y-intercept. Solve for y.

An alternative method is to substitute 0 for x and solve for y.

$$3x + 4y = 12$$

$$3x + 4y - 3x = 12 - 3x$$

$$4y = 12 - 3x$$

$$\frac{4y}{4} = \frac{12 - 3x}{4}$$

$$y = \frac{12}{4} - \frac{3x}{4}$$

$$y = -\frac{3}{4}x + 3$$

$$3(0) + 4y = 12$$

$$4y = 12$$

$$\frac{4y}{4} = \frac{12}{4}$$

$$y = 3$$

The y-coordinate is the constant 3. The x-coordinate is 0. The y-intercept is $(0, 3)$. Determine the x-intercept.
Substitute 0 for y and solve for x.

$$3x + 4(0) = 12$$

$$3x = 12$$

$$\frac{3x}{3} = \frac{12}{3}$$

$$x = 4$$

The x-coordinate is 4. The y-coordinate is 0. The x-intercept is $(4, 0)$.
Graph the two intercepts and connect the points with a straight line.
Check the graph by checking a point on the line. One of the integer ordered pairs located on the graph is $(8, -3)$.

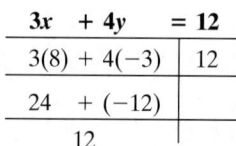

$3x$	$+ 4y$	$= 12$
$3(8)$	$+ 4(-3)$	12
24	$+ (-12)$	
	12	

Substitute 8 for x and -3 for y.

Since $12 = 12$, $(8, -3)$ is a solution. The graph checks.

 TAKE NOTE When the intercepts are not integer pairs, it is difficult to graph them accurately. It is better to use another method.

Objective 3.1.5 *CHECKUP*

1. Graph the equation, using the intercept method. Check your graph by using a third point. Label the intercepts and third point on the graph.

   $2x - 5y = 10$

2. The intercept method of graphing a linear equation works only when none of the coefficients a, b, and c are equal to zero. Explain why this method does not work if a, b, or c equals zero.

3. Given $ax + by = c$, if $a = 0$ and $c = 0$, what is unusual about the graph of the equation?

4. Given $ax + by = c$, if $b = 0$ and $c = 0$, what is unusual about the graph of the equation?

Objective 3.1.6

Modeling the Real World

Graphs of linear equations in two variables are highly useful for representing real-world data, because you need only two ordered pairs of data to determine the straight-line graph of such an equation. Then you can use the graph to determine additional data that satisfy the original equation. So you go easily from knowing two solutions of the equation to knowing as many solutions as you want.

An important point to keep in mind is that real-world data often have practical limitations. A linear equation may be accurate for a period of time, but then the situation may change. This is why the domain and range of a function are so important—they tell you when the relationship is valid and when it is not.

EXAMPLE 9

Mike began his new job as supervisor on a lamp production line. The week before he began, the crew produced 25 lamps. During his first week, 30 lamps were produced. During the second week of Mike's supervision, 35 lamps were produced.

a. Let x = the number of weeks Mike supervised

y = the number of lamps produced during the week

Write three ordered pairs from the information given.

b. Assuming that the same scenario continues, graph a linear representation of lamp production.

c. Using the graph, predict what production will be during week 5.

d. Using the graph, predict what production will be during the 15th week. Is this reasonable to expect? Explain.

Solution

a. Three ordered pairs are $(0, 25)$, $(1, 30)$, and $(2, 35)$.

b.

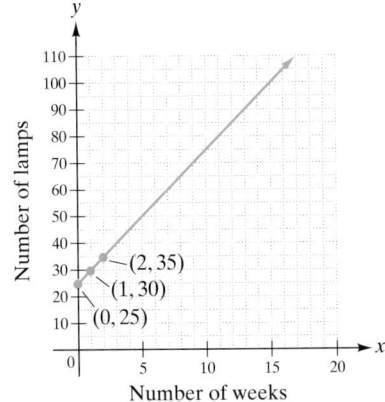

c. Week 5 production is the y-coordinate when $x = 5$. The point $(5, 50)$ is on the graph. Therefore, 50 lamps will be produced during week 5.

d. Week 15 production is the y-coordinate when $x = 15$. The point $(15, 100)$ is on the graph. Therefore, 100 lamps will be produced during the 15th week. This is unlikely, though, unless additional people are hired or new equipment is added. The prediction capabilities are limited in this scenario. ∎

Using the intercept method to graph an equation is often simpler than using other methods, because you can find the intercepts by just substituting 0 for the variables in the equation. When the equation is based on a real-world relationship, you may get an extra bonus because the intercepts may be significant points themselves. For example, if your graph shows a relationship between distance d and time t, then the d-intercept occurs where time (the t-coordinate) is 0—that is, the starting distance. The t-intercept (if there is one) occurs where distance (the d-coordinate) is 0. It is usually worthwhile to find the intercepts of a real-world graph and see what information they can give you.

EXAMPLE 10   Myletta plans to sell her clay flowerpots at a craft fair. A booth costs $50.00 to rent, and she estimates that each pot costs $3.00 to make. If Myletta sells the pots for $10.00, write a linear function for the profit she will obtain. Graph the function by the intercept method. Explain the meaning of the intercepts.

Solution

Let x = the number of flowerpots made and sold

$P(x)$ = the profit from the sale of the flowerpots

The profit is equal to the revenue, $10.00x$, minus the cost, $3.00x + 50.00$.

$$P(x) = 10.00x - (3.00x + 50.00)$$
$$P(x) = 10.00x - 3.00x - 50.00$$
$$P(x) = 7.00x - 50.00$$

The $P(x)$-intercept is $(0, -50.00)$.

To determine the x-intercept, let $P(x) = 0$ and solve for x.

$$P(x) = 7.00x - 50.00$$
$$0 = 7.00x - 50.00 \qquad \text{Substitute 0 for } P(x).$$
$$0 - 7.00x = 7.00x - 7.00x - 50.00 \qquad \text{Subtract 7.00x from both sides.}$$
$$-7.00x = -50.00 \qquad \text{Simplify.}$$
$$\frac{-7.00x}{-7.00} = \frac{-50.00}{-7.00} \qquad \text{Divide both sides by } -7.00.$$
$$x = \frac{50}{7} \qquad \text{Simplify.}$$
$$x \approx 7.14$$

The x-intercept is about $(7.14, 0)$.

Graph the $P(x)$-intercept and the x-intercept. Check the graph by checking a point on the line. One integer ordered pair located on the graph is the point $(8, 6)$.

$P(x) = 7.00x$	$- 50.00$
6	$7.00(8) - 50.00$
	$56.00 - 50.00$
	6.00

The coordinate pair $(8, 6)$ is a solution because $6 = 6.00$. The graph checks.

The $P(x)$-intercept is $(0, -50.00)$. That is, when 0 flowerpots are made and sold, the profit is $-\$50.00$; that is, there is a loss of $50.00. The x-intercept is about $(7.14, 0)$. When 7.14 pots are made and sold, the profit is $0.00. (Myletta will break even.) However, it is not possible to make and sell 7.14 pots, so she must make and sell 8 flowerpots in order to break even (or, in this case, realize a small profit). ■

APPLICATION

In 1974, an SR-71 Blackbird jet plane was flown from New York City to London in 1 hour and 55 minutes, the fastest transatlantic flight ever. If we let d represent the plane's distance from London, then an equation representing that distance is $d = 3462 - 1807t$, where t is the flight time in hours. Graph the equation and interpret the intercepts of the graph.

Discussion

Let t = time   (in hours) in flight

d = plane's distance (in miles) from London

The equation $d = 3462 - 1807t$ is solved for d. The constant term 3462 is the d-coordinate of the d-intercept. The d-intercept is $(0, 3462)$.

We determine the t-intercept by substituting 0 for d and solving for t.

$$0 = 3462 - 1807t$$
$$1807t = 3462$$
$$\frac{1807t}{1807} = \frac{3462}{1807}$$
$$t \approx 1.92$$

The t-intercept is approximately $(1.92, 0)$.

Graph the two intercepts and connect the points with a straight line.

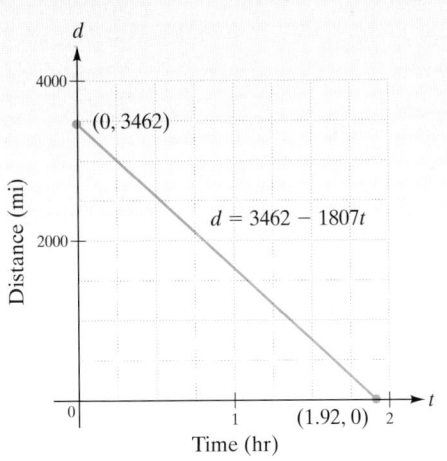

The coordinates of the d-intercept, $(0, 3462)$, mean that at a time of 0 hours (just before the plane begins its flight), the plane is 3462 miles from London. This is the distance from New York City to London.

The coordinates of the t-intercept, approximately $(1.92, 0)$, mean that at a time of approximately 1.92 hours, the plane will be 0 miles from London. In other words, the plane will arrive in London in approximately 1.92 hours.

✓ Objective 3.1.6 *CHECKUP*

1. Dan's Delivery Service charges \$3 to deliver a package weighing 1 pound. The charge for a package weighing 3 pounds is \$7, while the charge for delivering a package weighing 5 pounds is \$11. Let x represent the weight of the package and y represent the delivery charge.
   a. Write three ordered pairs from the information given.
   b. Assuming that a linear relationship exists, graph the relation given by the information.
   c. Using the graph, predict what the cost would be for a package weighing 8 pounds.
   d. What would you say are limitations on the domain of the relation? Do you think Dan would put a limit on the weight of packages he delivers, or would you expect the relationship you graphed to continue for all possible weights of packages? Would the range of the relation have any limits? Explain.

2. Don conducts an abstract algebra preparatory class for students who are returning to graduate school. The setup cost for the class is \$700 to rent space. Don spends \$35 per student for materials for the class. He charges the students \$175 to take the class. Write a linear function for the profit that Don will realize. Graph the function by the intercept method. Explain the meaning of the intercepts.

3. In 1974, an SR-71 Blackbird jet plane was flown from London to Los Angeles in 3 hours and 48 minutes. If we let d represent the plane's distance from Los Angeles, an equation for that distance is $d = 5645 - 1486t$, where t is the flight time in hours. Graph the equation and interpret the intercepts of the graph. From the graph, estimate how long it will take the aircraft to fly 3500 miles (the approximate distance from London to New York City).

3.1 EXERCISES

 Student Solutions Manual    PH Math/Tutor Center    CD Video   Math*XL* MathXL®   **MyMathLab** MyMathLab   Interactmath.com

Identify each equation as linear or nonlinear. Express each linear equation in standard form.

1. $5x + 7y = 35$ 2. $\sqrt{3}x + 2y = 6$ 3. $-4\sqrt{x} + y = 8$ 4. $6x^2 + 2y = 12$

5. $x^2 + y^2 = 1$ 6. $5x - \sqrt{y} = -10$ 7. $2x - 5 = 0$ 8. $7y = 2y + 14$

Determine three ordered-pair solutions of each linear equation, and graph the equation.

9. $x - 6y = 12$ 10. $x + 7y = 21$ 11. $p(x) = \dfrac{4x + 1}{3}$ 12. $q(x) = \dfrac{2x - 3}{5}$

13. $y = 8$ 14. $4y - 16 = 0$ 15. $r(x) = -\dfrac{3}{4}x + 4$ 16. $s(x) = \dfrac{5}{6}x - 3$

17. $y = 2.8x - 1.6$ 18. $y = 4.7 - 1.9x$ 19. $y = \dfrac{3x - 5}{2}$ 20. $y = \dfrac{3x - 2}{5}$

21. $3x + y - 4 = x + 2y - 3$ 22. $7x - 2y + 8 = 5x - 3y + 1$ 23. $5y = -20$ 24. $3y + 7 = 25$

Determine the intercepts of each graph.

25.

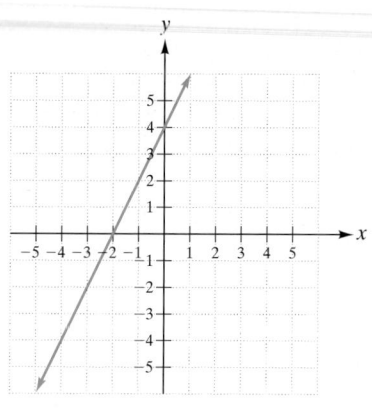

26.

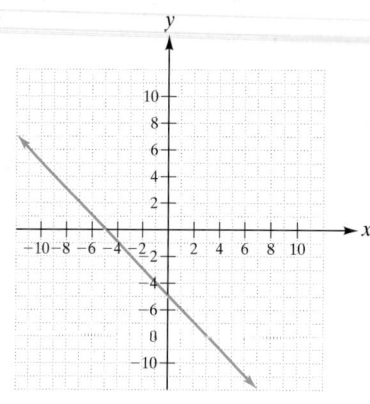

27.

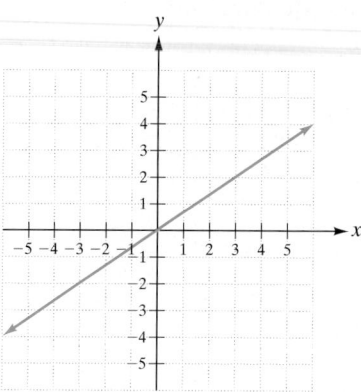

28.

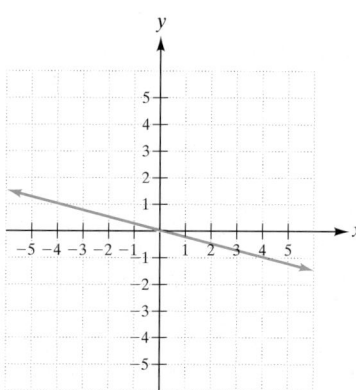

29.

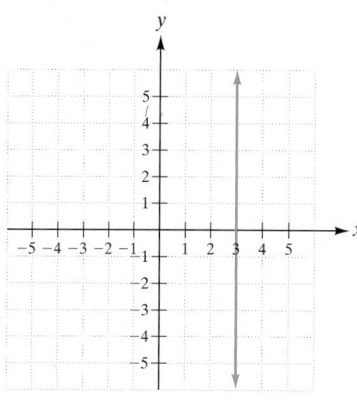

30.

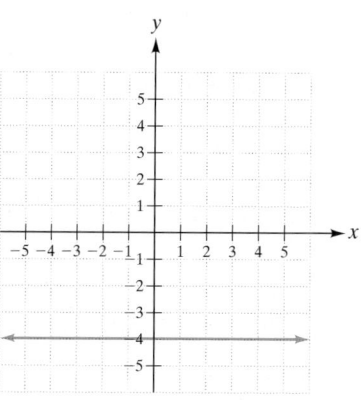

Determine algebraically the intercepts of the graph of each linear equation.

31. $3x + 5y = 12$

32. $7x + 9y = 63$

33. $4x - 7y = 14$

34. $x - y = 31$

35. $-2x - 9y = 27$

36. $-12x - 8y = 36$

37. $6x + 9y - 36 = 0$

38. $5x + 3y + 45 = 0$

39. $3x + 7y = 0$

40. $16x + 3y = 0$

41. $6x - 8 = 2x + 32$

42. $3x - 12 = x - 2$

43. $y = 3y - 22$

44. $6y = y - 25$

Solve each linear equation for y to determine the y-intercept.

45. $12x - y = 24$

46. $x + 9y = 18$

47. $y = 5(x - 3)$

48. $y = 3(x - 7) + 5$

49. $5x - 15y = 0$

50. $14x = 42y$

51. $3y = 12y + 18$

52. $18 - 5y = y$

53. $y + 5 = 5$

54. $3(y + 7) - 4 = 17$

55. $-17.6x + 2.2y = 19.8$

56. $12.6x - 6.3y = 50.4$

57. $x = 12y$

58. $100y = -5x$

In exercises 59–68, graph each equation, using the intercept method. Check your graphs by using a third point. Label the intercepts and a third point on each graph.

59. $3x + 5y = 30$

60. $x + 3y = 33$

61. $4x - 3y = 24$

62. $5x - 7y = 70$

63. $x - y = 9$

64. $-x + y = 9$

65. $-x - y = 9$

66. $x + y = 9$

67. $2x - 7y = -14$

68. $8x - 3y = 24$

69. On an examination, Alex missed none of the questions and received a score of 100. Beth missed 6 questions and scored an 85. Chiyo missed 10 questions and scored 75.
  a. Let x be the number of questions missed, and let y be the score on the test. Write three ordered pairs from the information given.
  b. Assuming a linear relation, graph the information.
  c. Use the graph to predict what score students will receive if they miss 12 questions on the test.
  d. For what domain would it make sense to use this relation?

70. An assembly line is used to pack boxes of candy. When only one person is available, the assembly line cannot operate. When two people are working, they can pack 5 boxes per minute. When four people are working, they can pack 15 boxes per minute.
  a. Let x be the number of persons working the assembly line, and let y be the number of boxes of candy packed per minute. Write three ordered pairs from the information given.
  b. Assuming that the relation continues for other numbers of workers, graph the information.

c. Use the graph to predict how many boxes per minute would be packed by a crew of five people.

d. Are there any limitations on the domain and range of this relation? Is it reasonable to assume that as the number of workers increases, the number of boxes packed per minute could still be estimated by the graph? Explain your answer.

71. Itsu is measuring the borders around equilateral triangles for a science project. He finds that a triangle with a side of 2 inches has a border of 6 inches, one with a side of 3.5 inches has a border of 10.5 inches, and one with a side of 10.5 inches has a border of 31.5 inches.

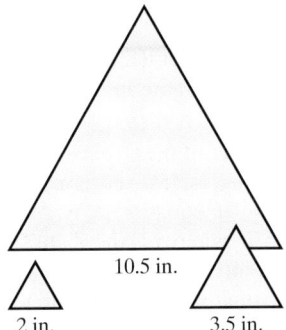

10.5 in.

2 in.   3.5 in.

a. Let x be the length of a side of the equilateral triangle and y be the length of the border around the triangle. Write three ordered pairs from the information given.

b. Graph a linear representation of the information.

c. Predict what the border would be for an equilateral triangle with a side of 4 inches.

d. Is it reasonable to assume that the relation represented by the graph would work for any equilateral triangle? Explain your answer.

72. Carla measured the perimeters of several rectangles, all of which had the same width, but differing lengths. The perimeter of a rectangle with a length of 15 cm was 50 cm. Another rectangle with a length of 25 cm had a perimeter of 70 cm. A third with a length of 10 cm had a perimeter of 40 cm.

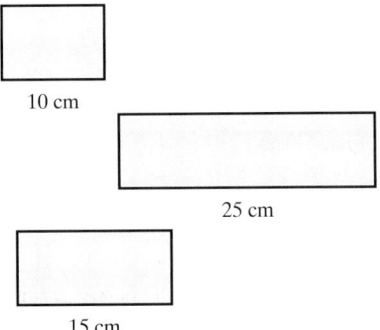

10 cm

25 cm

15 cm

a. Let x be the length of the rectangle and y be the perimeter. Write three ordered pairs from the information given.

b. Graph a linear representation of the information.

c. Using the graph, what would the perimeter be for a rectangle with the same width and with a length of 20 cm?

d. Would this relation hold for all rectangles that had the same width and varying lengths? Explain your answer.

73. According to the U.S. National Center for Health Statistics, major cardiovascular diseases are the leading cause of death. However, the death rate per 100,000 population decreased from 2001 to 2002 from 323.9 to 316.3.

a. Let x = the number of years after 2001, and y = the death rate per 100,000 population. Write two ordered pairs for the data given.

b. If we assume this rate of decrease to continue, graph the linear relation.

c. Predict the death rate for 2008.

d. Describe any limitations for this relation.

74. According to the U.S. National Center for Health Statistics, accidents (unintentional injuries) are one of the leading causes of death. However, the death rate per 100,000 population decreased from 2001 to 2002 from 35.7 to 35.5.

a. Let x = the number of years after 2001, and y = the death rate per 100,000 population. Write two ordered pairs for the data given.

b. If we assume this rate of decrease to continue, graph the linear relation.

c. Predict the death rate for 2008.

d. Describe any limitations for this relation.

75. Krista needs to earn $5000 this summer for school in the fall. A family in a neighboring town hires her as a nanny. They agree to pay her $2000 plus $50 for each day she watches all three of their children. Write a linear function for the amount of money she will make, y, for x days. Graph the function. How many days will she need to watch all three children to earn the money she needs for school?

76. Julie is organizing a birthday party for her son at a local play facility that charges $200 per evening (5–8 P.M.) plus $10 for each child. Write a linear function for the party cost, c, for n children. Graph the function. Using the graph, estimate the cost of a party for 10 children. If Julie has budgeted $350 for the party, how many children can her son invite?

77. Garbage pickup in a suburban town is $75 per quarter. In addition, residents pay an optional recycling fee of $2.50 per week on a week-by-week basis. Write a linear function for the garbage bill for the year (4 quarters), c, in terms of w weeks. Graph the function. For how many weeks can a person get recycling service if he wants to limit his yearly garbage expense to $400?

78. Milk delivery is becoming popular in some metropolitan areas. Weekly delivery guarantees the freshest product. The delivery charge is $2.99 per week, and a standard half gallon of milk costs $3.00. Write a linear function for the monthly (4 weeks) milk bill, c, in terms of the number of half gallons purchased, n. Graph the function. Using your graph, estimate the cost for a family that drinks nine gallons of milk per month. If a family budgets $75 per month for milk, how many half gallons can they afford to buy?

79. The fixed daily cost of operating a water park is $1000, and the cost to provide services is $4.50 per customer. The water park charges $18.75 per person for admission. Write a linear function for the profit that the water park will realize. Graph the function by the intercept method. Explain the meaning of the intercepts.

80. The fixed daily cost of operating a bowling alley is $200, and the cost of operating the lanes is $0.65 per game bowled. The bowling alley charges $2.00 per game bowled. Write a linear function for the profit that the bowling alley will obtain. Graph the function by the intercept method. Explain the meaning of the intercepts.

81. Automobiles lose value quickly. According to *FinanCenter.com*, some vehicles lose as much as 20% of their value in their first year. The value of a particular car, v, in dollars with average depreciation can be given by $v = 15{,}000 - 1750t$, where t is time in years.
    a. Graph the function using ordered pairs.
    b. Find the intercepts of the graph.
    c. Explain the meaning of the intercepts.
    d. From the graph, estimate when the vehicle will have lost half of its value.

82. A more popular and expensive vehicle with desirable features holds its value better and is said to have low depreciation. Its value, v, in dollars can be given by $v = 27{,}000 - 1500t$, where t is time in years.
    a. Graph the function using ordered pairs.
    b. Find the intercepts of the graph.
    c. Explain the meaning of the intercepts.
    d. From the graph, estimate when the vehicle will have lost half of its value.

83. A national fine jewelry chain advertises that the more expensive items that they sell will appreciate (gain) in value. They offer a guarantee in which they will actually buy back or accept as a "trade in" a piece of jewelry at an appreciated value. Thomas buys his fiancée an engagement ring for $3000 with the guarantee that it will appreciate in value by $375 each year. The value of the ring, y, in dollars, can be given by $y = 3000 + 375t$, where t is time in years after purchase.
    a. Graph the function.
    b. Explain the meaning of the y-intercept.
    c. From the graph, estimate when the ring will first be worth more than $5000.

84. In 2005, Beom bought acreage in a resort development in an area becoming increasingly popular for tourists. He paid $20,000 for his parcel. Local real estate agents estimate that the property will increase in value on the average of $2000 per year. The value of the land, v, can be given by $v = 20{,}000 + 2000x$, where x is time in years after 2005.
    a. Graph the function.
    b. Explain the meaning of the intercepts.
    c. From the graph, estimate in which year the property has doubled in value.

85. A Boeing 767 jet aircraft flies from Atlanta to Los Angeles in 4 hours and 34 minutes. If d represents the plane's distance from Los Angeles, an equation representing that distance is $d = 1944 - 425.7t$, where t is the flight time in hours. Graph the equation and interpret the intercepts of the graph. From the graph, approximate how long it will take to fly 1000 miles from Atlanta.

86. A Boeing 747 jet aircraft flies from New York City to London, England, in 8 hours and 55 minutes. If d represents the plane's distance from London, an equation representing that distance is $d = 3471 - 389.3t$, where t is the flight time in hours. Graph the equation and interpret the intercepts of the graph. From the graph, estimate how long it will take to fly 2000 miles from New York City.

 ## 3.1 Calculator Exercises

On the TI-84 Plus, or if you purchase applications for the TI-83 Plus from Texas Instruments, you can obtain an application that enables you to graph vertical lines easily on the calculator. Once you obtain the applications, check the procedure that follows.

To use the applications, press the APPS key on the calculator. Choose the Inequalz application. A logo will appear. Press any key to continue. The calculator will display the menu for the Y= key. To change to the X = format, move the cursor to the top of the display, and highlight $x =$ in the first location. When you press ENTER, the calculator will change the displays to X = displays. The following screens are displayed:

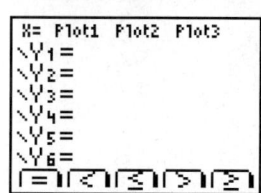 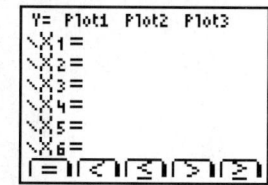

To graph the line for the equation $2x - 3 = x + 5$, first solve the equation for x. You will get $x = 8$. Then store this equation in the first location. Next, proceed to the graph as you normally would by using the ZOOM key or setting the window and using the GRAPH key. ZOOM 6 yields the following graph:

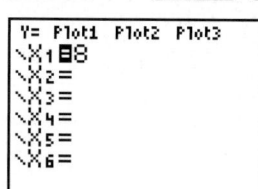 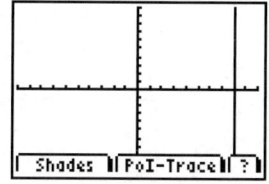

Ignore the choices that are displayed at the bottom of the screen. They cannot be used for our current work. However, they will be useful to us later on, when we want to study the behavior of several lines at the same time.

To return to the previous settings for the calculator, press APPS, choose the Inequalz application again, and then choose option 2 to quit the application. You should get into the habit of doing this when you are through using the application.

Try using this graphing procedure on the following equations:

1. $5(x - 1) = 2x - 4$

2. $\dfrac{3}{4}x + 1 = 7$

3. $4.5x + 1.2 = 2.3x - 5.4$

3.1 Writing Exercises

1. The standard form for a linear equation in two variables is

$$ax + by = c$$

where *a*, *b*, and *c* are real numbers and *a* and *b* are not both equal to 0. Give examples in which *a* or *b* are equal to 0. Then explain why the equation cannot have *a* and *b* both equal to 0.

2. It is important that you fully understand the relationship between the solutions of a linear equation in two variables and the graph of the linear equation. Explain what a graph represents with respect to a linear equation in two variables. Explain what a graph can tell you about a linear equation in two variables. Exactly what is the purpose of graphing a linear equation in two variables?

3.2 SLOPE

OBJECTIVES

1 Determine the slope of a line from its graph.

2 Determine the slope of a line, given two points on the line.

3 Model real-world situations involving slope of a line.

APPLICATION

If you purchase a computer for $2000 to use in your business and determine its useful life to be 5 years, the computer will have no value in 5 years. Let *y* be the value of the computer after *x* years of use. Write two ordered pairs and determine the average rate of change of the computer's value per year.

After completing this section, we will discuss this application further. See page 295.

Objective 3.2.1

Determining the Slope of a Line from Its Graph

In Chapter 1, we discussed functions that were increasing, decreasing, and constant. A function is said to be increasing if the values of the function increase as the values of the independent variable increase. A function is said to be decreasing if the values of the function decrease as the values of the independent variable increase. A function is constant if its values do not change as the values of the independent variable increase.

The graph of a linear function that is increasing appears to rise when viewing the graph from left to right. The graph of a linear function that is decreasing appears to fall when viewing the graph from left to right. The graph of a linear function that is constant is a horizontal line because it does not rise or fall when viewing it from left to right.

A linear equation may also graph as a vertical line. Remember that this type of graph does not represent a function.

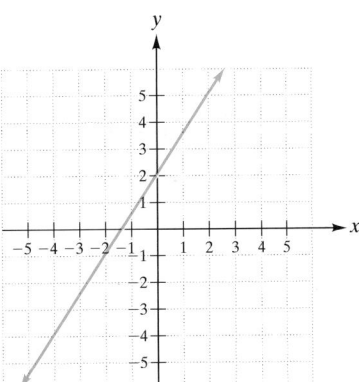

Linear function is increasing.
The graph rises.

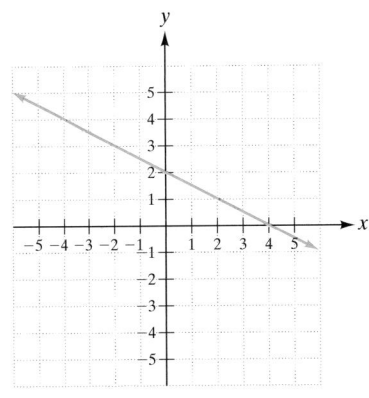

Linear function is decreasing.
The graph falls.

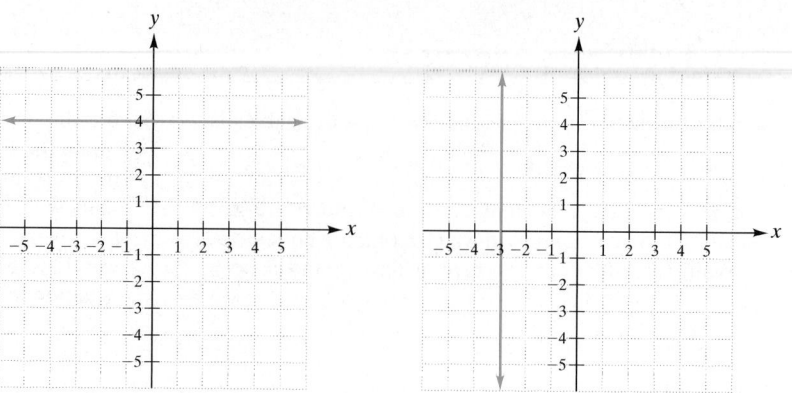

Linear function is constant.
The graph is horizontal.

This graph does not represent a function.
The graph is vertical.

Of two graphs that rise (or fall), one may be more steep or less steep than the other. That is, the function values may increase (or decrease) at different rates.

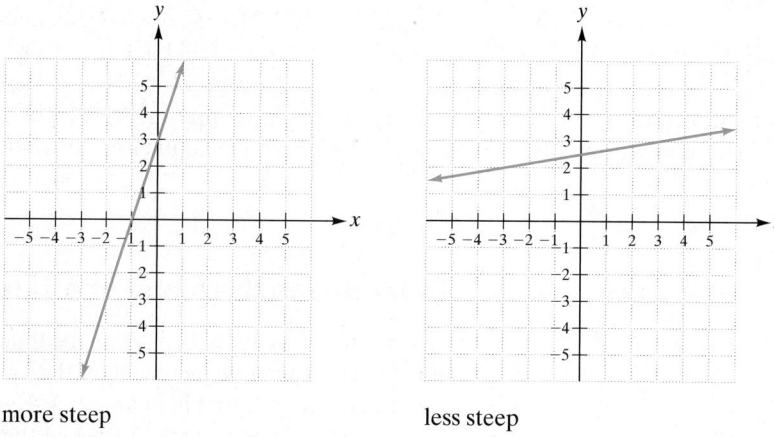

more steep

less steep

We describe the graph of a line by its steepness, which we call the slope of the line. We calculate this slope by determining the change in vertical distance of the line (called the **rise**) that corresponds to a change in horizontal distance of the line (called the **run**). The **slope** of a line is a measure of the steepness of the line and is defined as the ratio of the amount of rise to the amount of run.

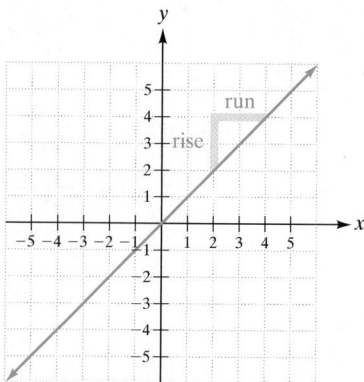

SLOPE OF A LINE

The slope of a line is the ratio of the change in vertical distance to the change in horizontal distance or the amount of rise to the amount of run.

$$\frac{\text{change in vertical distance}}{\text{change in horizontal distance}} \quad \text{or} \quad \frac{\text{amount of rise}}{\text{amount of run}} \quad \text{or} \quad \frac{\text{rise}}{\text{run}}$$

To determine the slope of a line graphically,

- Locate two points on the line whose coordinates are integers.
- Determine the change in vertical distance (rise).
- Determine the change in horizontal distance (run).
- Write a ratio of the amount of rise to the amount of run or $\frac{\text{rise}}{\text{run}}$.

For example, in the following graphs, we determine the slope of the same line. In each case, the slope is $\frac{\text{rise}}{\text{run}} = \frac{2}{5}$.

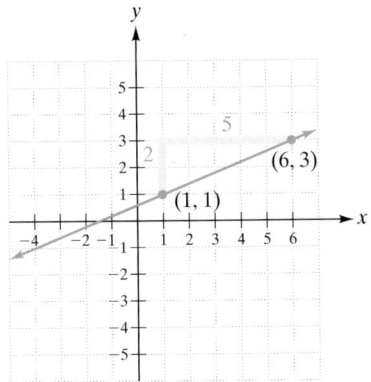

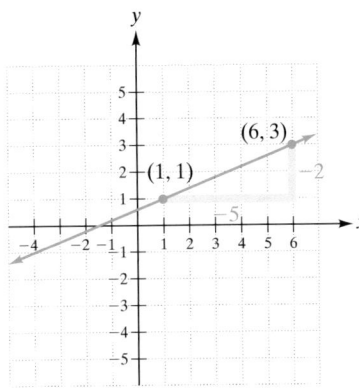

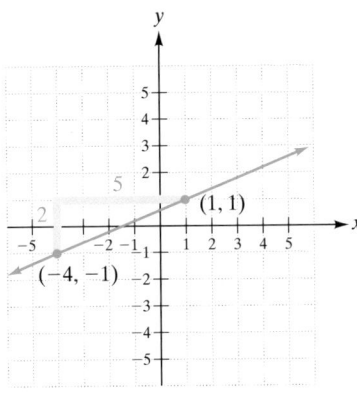

We choose points $(1, 1)$ and $(6, 3)$. Beginning at $(1, 1)$, the vertical change (rise) is 2 units. The horizontal change (run) is 5 units. The slope is $\dfrac{\text{rise}}{\text{run}} = \dfrac{2}{5}$.

We choose points $(1, 1)$ and $(6, 3)$. Beginning at $(6, 3)$, the vertical change (rise) is -2 units. The horizontal change (run) is -5 units. The slope is $\dfrac{\text{rise}}{\text{run}} = \dfrac{-2}{-5} = \dfrac{2}{5}$.

We choose points $(-4, -1)$ and $(1, 1)$. Beginning at $(-4, -1)$, the vertical change (rise) is 2 units. The horizontal change (run) is 5 units. The slope is $\dfrac{\text{rise}}{\text{run}} = \dfrac{2}{5}$.

 TAKE NOTE The slope of the line remains the same for any set of ordered pairs located on the line, including noninteger ones. This is an important characteristic of a straight line.

EXAMPLE 1   Determine the slope of each line.

a.

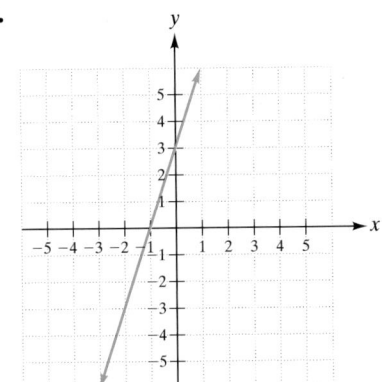

b.

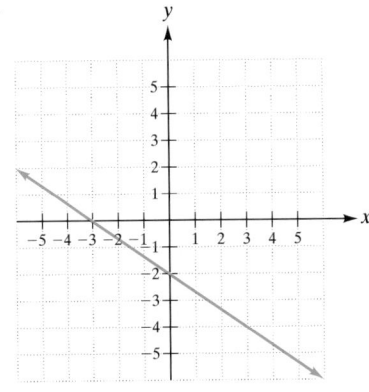

c.

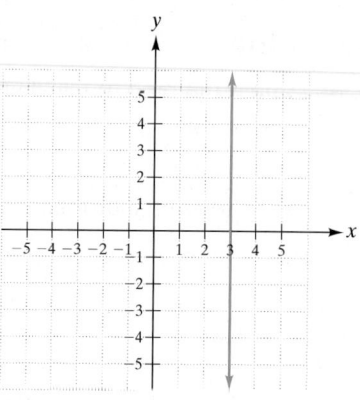

d.

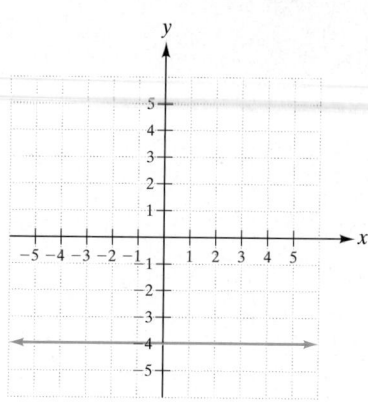

Solution

a.

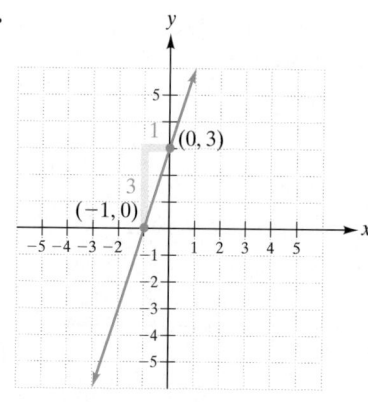

The slope is $\frac{\text{rise}}{\text{run}} = \frac{3}{1} = 3.$

b.

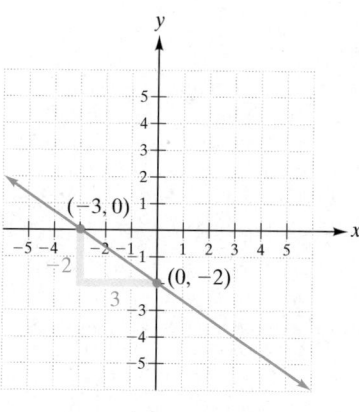

The slope is $\frac{\text{rise}}{\text{run}} = \frac{-2}{3} = -\frac{2}{3}.$

c. The graph is a vertical line. Therefore, the change in the horizontal distance (run) is 0. The slope is $\frac{\text{rise}}{\text{run}} = \frac{\text{any number}}{0}$; that is, the slope is undefined, because division by 0 is undefined.

d. The graph is a horizontal line. Therefore, the change in the vertical distance (rise) is 0. The slope is $\frac{\text{rise}}{\text{run}} = \frac{0}{\text{any number}}$, or 0.

Example 1 shows us that different lines can have slopes that are positive, negative, 0, or undefined. Let's take a closer look at these different slopes. Complete the following set of exercises to discover different types of slopes.

Guided Discovery 3   Types of Slopes

Determine the slopes of the following graphs:

1.

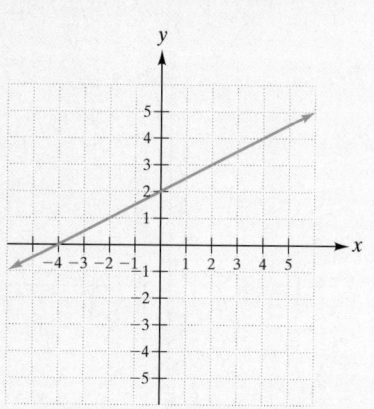

2.

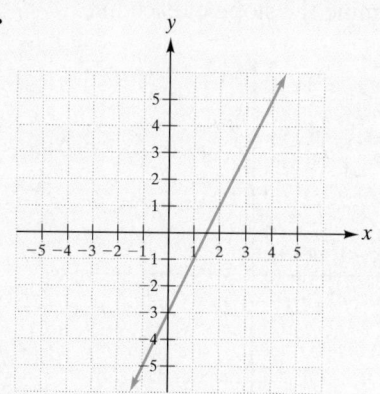

3.

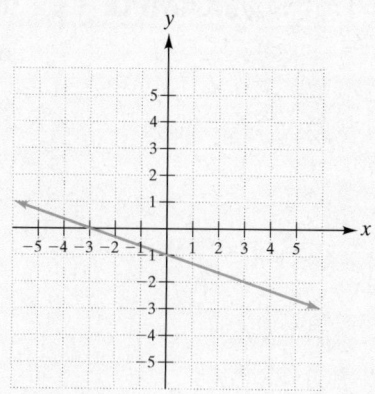

4.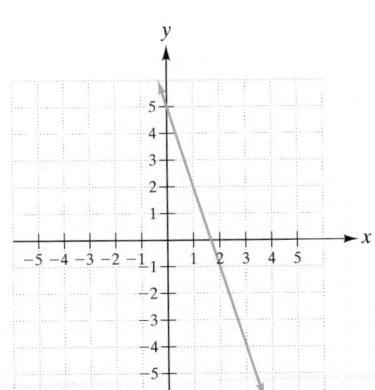

5.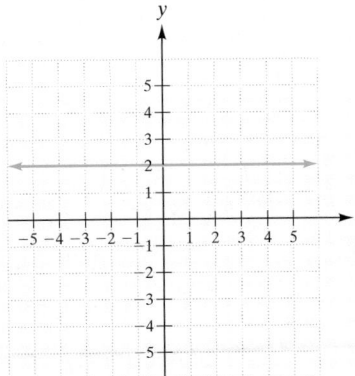

6.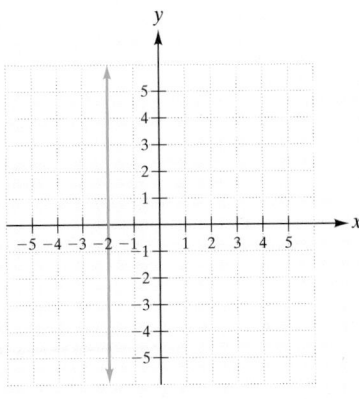

Choose the correct answer.

7. In exercises 1 and 2, the linear function is *increasing/ decreasing/constant*. The slopes have a *positive/ negative* value. Viewing the graphs from left to right, the graphs both *rise/fall*.

8. In exercises 3 and 4, the linear function is *increasing/ decreasing/constant*. The slopes have a *positive/ negative* value. Viewing the graphs from left to right, the graphs both *rise/fall*.

9. In exercise 5, the linear function is *increasing/ decreasing/constant*. The slope is *0/undefined*. The graph is a *vertical/horizontal* line.

10. In exercise 6, the graph does not represent a function. The slope is *0/undefined*. The graph is a *vertical/ horizontal* line.

11. In observing the absolute value of the slope, we see that the larger the absolute value, the *more/less* steep is the graph.

A graph with a positive slope rises from left to right. The function it represents is increasing. A graph with a negative slope falls from left to right. The function it represents is decreasing. A horizontal line has a slope of 0. The function is constant. A vertical line has an undefined slope. It does not represent a function. The larger the absolute value of the slope, the steeper is the graph of the line.

EXAMPLE 2   For each of the graphs that follow, determine whether the graph represents a function. If the graph represents a function, is the function increasing, decreasing, or constant? Determine if the slope of each graph is positive, negative, zero, or undefined. If the slope is positive or negative, find the slope of the line.

a.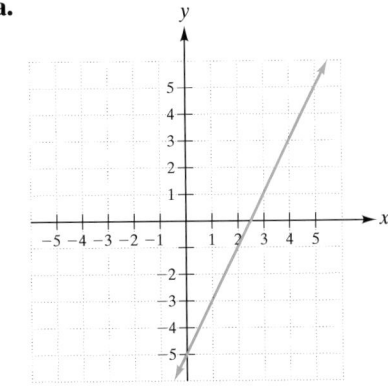

b.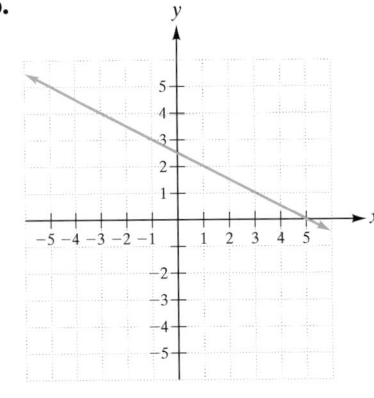

c.

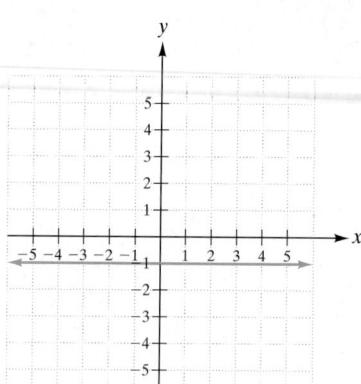

d.

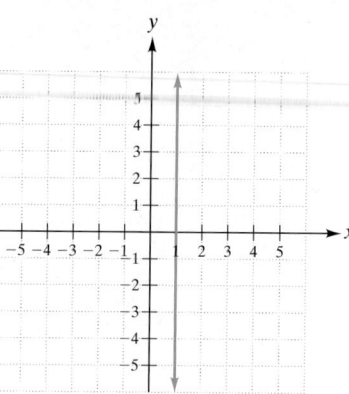

Solution

a. The graph represents a function. (It passes the vertical-line test.) The function is increasing (the graph is rising from left to right and the slope is positive). According to the labeled graph, the slope is $\frac{\text{rise}}{\text{run}} = \frac{2}{1}$, or 2.

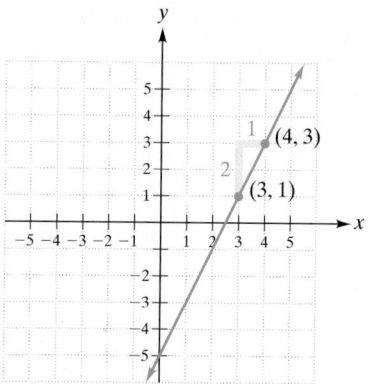

b. The graph represents a function. (It passes the vertical-line test.) The function is decreasing (the graph is falling from left to right and the slope is negative). According to the labeled graph, the slope is $\frac{\text{rise}}{\text{run}} = -\frac{1}{2}$.

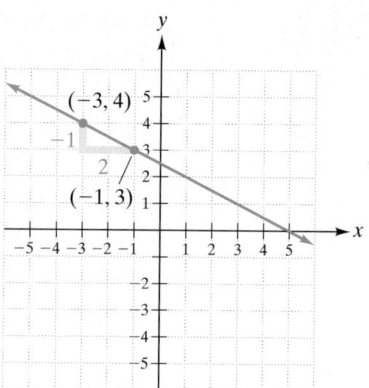

c. The graph represents a function. (It passes the vertical-line test.) The function is constant. The slope of a horizontal line is 0.

d. The graph does not represent a function. (It does not pass the vertical-line test.) The slope of a vertical line is undefined.

✓ Objective 3.2.1 *CHECKUP*

1. Determine the slope of the graph.

a.

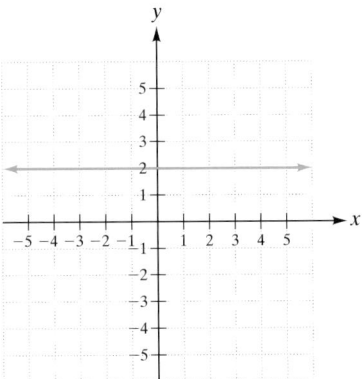

b.

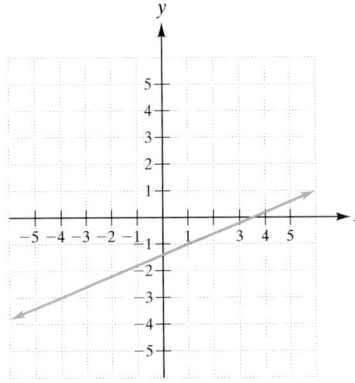

c.

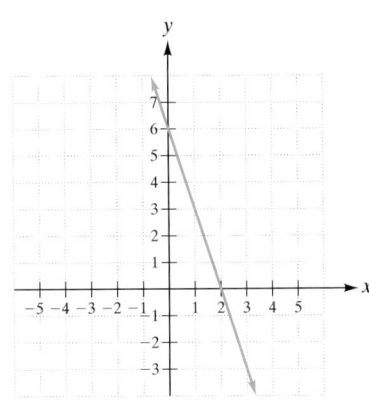

d.

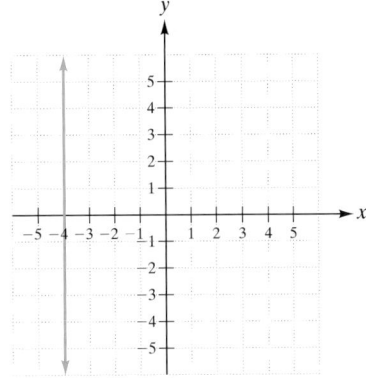

2. For the graphs given in exercise 1, determine whether the graph represents a function. If the graph represents a function, is the function increasing, decreasing, or constant? Determine if the slope of each graph is positive, negative, zero, or undefined.

3. If you know the slope of a linear equation, what can you say about its graph?

Objective 3.2.2   **Determining the Slope of a Line Given Two Points on the Line**

The slope of a line is a very important characteristic of the linear equation represented by that line. In fact, there are times when we might want to determine the slope of a line even when the graph is not drawn for us. For example, suppose we know only two points on the line. We could plot the points, draw the graph, and then determine the slope. But sometimes it's easier to find the slope without drawing the graph. To see how to do this, complete the following set of exercises.

💡 **Guided Discovery 4**   Slope Formula

1. Locate and label the points $(1, 3)$ and $(5, 4)$ on a graph. Draw a line connecting the points.
Draw the legs of a right triangle needed to determine the slope of the line, and label each length.

2. The rise of the graph is _____.

3. The run of the graph is _____.

4. The difference of the y-coordinates of the ordered pairs is $4 - 3 =$ _____.

5. The difference of the x-coordinates of the ordered pairs is $5 - 1 =$ _____.

6. The slope of the graph is _____.

Write a rule to determine the slope of a graph from the coordinates of two ordered pairs.

The rise of the graph and the difference of the y-coordinates of the ordered pairs are the same. The run of the graph and the difference of the x-coordinates of the ordered pairs are the same.

Before we write a formula for the slope of a graph, we need to define some notation. The traditional symbol for the slope is m. To label the coordinates of the two ordered pairs P_1 and P_2, we use subscripts to distinguish the coordinates of the different points. For example, P_1 and P_2 distinguish two different ordered pairs. The numbers 1 and 2 are called **subscripts**. A subscript is written to the right and below a variable. The coordinates of the first point P_1 are written as (x_1, y_1). The coordinates of the second point P_2 are written as (x_2, y_2).

SLOPE OF A LINE THROUGH TWO GIVEN POINTS

Given two ordered pairs, $P_1(x_1, y_1)$ and $P_2(x_2, y_2)$,

$$m = \frac{\text{rise}}{\text{run}} = \frac{\text{difference in } y\text{-coordinates}}{\text{difference in } x\text{-coordinates}} = \frac{y_2 - y_1}{x_2 - x_1}$$

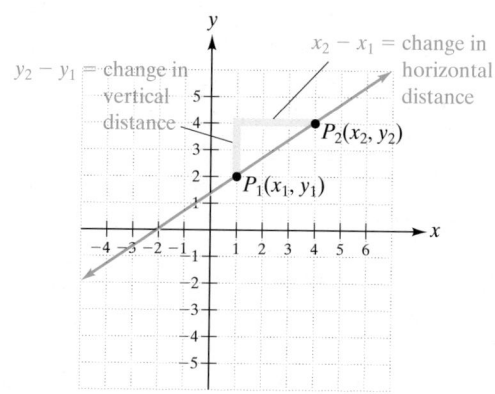

TAKE NOTE Do not mix up the order of coordinates during the subtraction. It is very important to subtract both coordinates of the first point from both coordinates of the second point.

EXAMPLE 3

Determine the slope of a line containing the given points.

a. $(1, 3)$ and $(5, 4)$ **b.** $(9, 2)$ and $(9, -1)$ **c.** $(3, -4)$ and $(2, -4)$

Solution

a. $x_1 = 1, y_1 = 3$

$x_2 = 5, y_2 = 4$

$m = \dfrac{y_2 - y_1}{x_2 - x_1}$

$m = \dfrac{4 - 3}{5 - 1}$

$m = \dfrac{1}{4}$

b. $x_1 = 9, y_1 = 2$

$x_2 = 9, y_2 = -1$

$m = \dfrac{y_2 - y_1}{x_2 - x_1}$

$m = \dfrac{-1 - 2}{9 - 9}$

$m = \dfrac{-3}{0}$

m is undefined.

c. $x_1 = 3, y_1 = -4$

$x_2 = 2, y_2 = -4$

$m = \dfrac{y_2 - y_1}{x_2 - x_1}$

$m = \dfrac{-4 - (-4)}{2 - 3}$

$m = \dfrac{0}{-1}$

$m = 0$

Note that the parentheses in the numerator of part **c** indicate subtraction of a negative number. ■

TAKE NOTE The order of labeling the points does not matter. In Example 3a, the results would be the same if $(x_1, y_1) = (5, 4)$ and $(x_2, y_2) = (1, 3)$. Try this for yourself.

Objective 3.2.2 *CHECKUP*

Determine the slope of the line containing the given points.

1. a. $(-3, -2)$ and $(1, 4)$ **b.** $(4, 2)$ and $(-1, 2)$ **c.** $(2, 1)$ and $(2, -4)$

Objective 3.2.3

Modeling the Real World

The slope has many applications. One real-world application is the **grade** of a road, a measure of how steep the road is. We usually represent a grade as a percent. For example, a 4% grade $\left(4\% = 0.04 = \dfrac{4}{100} \right)$ means that for every vertical distance of 100 feet, the road drops or rises 4 feet. Note that we do not use a positive or a negative percent, because we do not know the orientation of the person viewing the road.

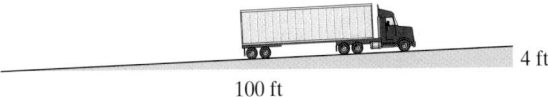

4 ft

100 ft

EXAMPLE 4

The U.S. Army Humvee can drive on road grades rising 30 feet vertically over a horizontal distance of 50 feet. Find the grade of the road.

Solution

The grade of the terrain is the slope, written as a percent.

$$m = \frac{\text{rise}}{\text{run}} = \frac{30}{50} = 0.6 = 60\%$$

The grade of the road for the Humvee is 60%.

When we use a linear equation to represent a real-world situation, the slope can be a very interesting, as well as important, quantity. The slope is the change in the dependent variable produced by a unit change in the independent variable. We call this the **average rate of change** of the dependent variable. From the average rate of change, we can sometimes predict what value a quantity will have in the future or what value it had in the past. A common situation occurs when the independent variable represents time. In this case, the slope tells us how the dependent variable changes over a period of time.

EXAMPLE 5

According to the National Association of Realtors, in 1994 the median price of an existing home was $109,900. In 2004, the median price of an existing home was $185,200. Find the average rate of change per year in the median cost of existing homes from 1994 to 2004.

Solution

Let x = the year
y = the median cost of an existing home

We are given the data points (1994, 109,900) and (2004, 185,200). To determine the average rate of change from 1994 to 2004, we must use $x_1 = 1994$, $y_1 = 109,900$, $x_2 = 2004$, and $y_2 = 185,200$. The order is important in this case.

$$m = \frac{y_2 - y_1}{x_2 - x_1}$$

$$m = \frac{185,200 - 109,900}{2004 - 1994} \quad \frac{\text{cost in dollars}}{\text{years}}$$

$$m = 7530$$

The average rate of change in the mean cost of an existing home from 1994 to 2004 was $7530 per year.

A common average-rate-of-change situation that we encounter daily is the rate at which an object's distance changes with respect to time. That is, the speed at which the object moves. The following example discusses one of these situations. Further investigations are presented in the Calculator Exercises at the end of this section.

EXAMPLE 6 Malcolm walked to school from his home, a distance of 2 miles. After attending his 50-minute class, he ran back home at a rate of twice his walking rate. Let $t =$ the time in minutes of the trip and $d(t) =$ the distance from Malcolm's home in miles. Choose the graph that best illustrates Malcolm's trip.

a.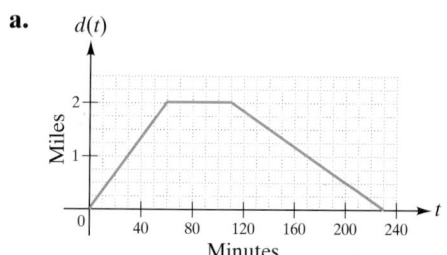

b.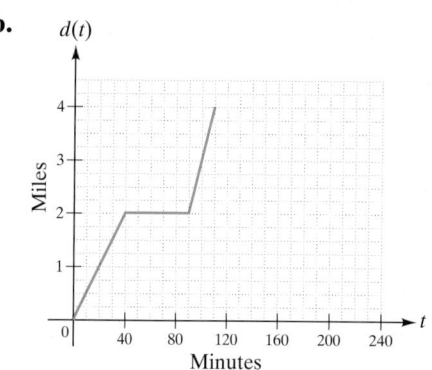

c.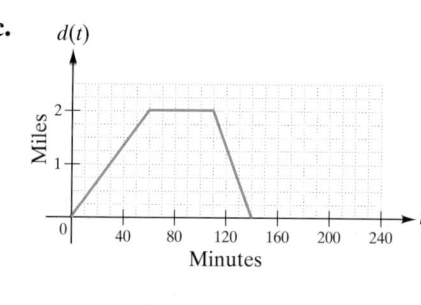

Solution

To interpret the graph, we know that the average rate of change of distance with respect to time, Malcolm's speed, is shown by the slope of the line. The faster the speed, the steeper is the line. The distance function is increasing when Malcolm is moving away from his home (the slope is positive), decreasing when Malcolm is moving toward his home (the slope is negative), and constant when Malcolm is moving neither toward nor away from his home (the slope is zero). Therefore, the graph should have three linear segments. The first segment should have a positive slope. The second segment should have a zero slope for 50 minutes. The third segment should have a negative slope and be twice as steep as the first segment.

a. In the first graph, the first segment has a positive slope. In this segment, Malcolm traveled away from home a distance of 2 miles in 60 minutes at an average speed of 1 mile per 30 minutes. The second segment has a zero slope for 50 minutes; here, Malcolm moved at an average speed of 0 miles per minute. The third segment has a negative slope, indicating that Malcolm traveled toward home for 2 miles in 120 minutes at an average speed of 1 mile per 60 minutes; that is, the slope is half as steep as that of the first segment. In other words, the graph shows that Malcolm's return trip is slower than his trip to school.

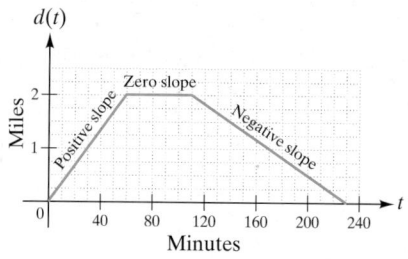

b. In the second graph, the first segment has a positive slope. In this segment, Malcolm traveled away from home 2 miles in 40 minutes at an average speed of 1 mile per 20 minutes. The second segment has a zero slope for 50 minutes; Malcolm moved at an average speed of 0 miles per minute during this segment.

The third segment has a positive slope, indicating that Malcolm traveled away from home 2 miles in 20 minutes at an average speed of 1 mile per 10 minutes. The graph shows that Malcolm's distance from home at the end of his trip is 4 miles. In other words, Malcolm did not return home.

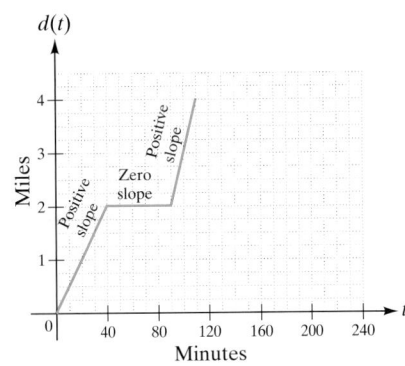

c. In the third graph, the first segment has a positive slope. In this segment, Malcolm traveled away from home 2 miles in 60 minutes at an average speed of 1 mile per 30 minutes. The second segment has a zero slope for 50 minutes here, Malcolm moved at an average speed of 0 miles per minute. The third segment has a negative slope, indicating that Malcolm traveled toward home 2 miles in 30 minutes at an average speed of 1 mile per 15 minutes; that is, the slope is twice as steep here as in the first segment. This graph illustrates Malcolm's trip.

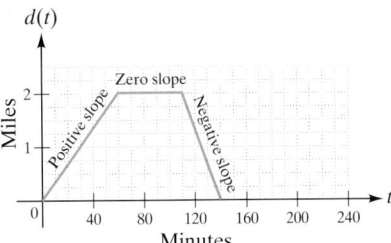

APPLICATION

If you purchase a computer for $2000 to use in your business and determine its useful life to be 5 years, the computer will have no value in 5 years. Let y be the value of the computer after x years of use. Write two ordered pairs and determine the average rate of change of the computer's value per year.

The average rate of change in the computer's value per year is $\dfrac{\text{change in the } y \text{ values}}{\text{change in the } x \text{ values}}$ or the slope of a line through the two ordered pairs.

$$m = \frac{2000 - 0}{0 - 5} \quad \textit{Substitute.}$$

$$m = \frac{2000}{-5}$$

$$m = -400$$

Discussion

When the computer is purchased, it has not been used ($x = 0$) and the value is $2000 ($y = 2000$). After five years of use ($x = 5$), the computer has no value ($y = 0$). Two ordered pairs are $(0, 2000)$ and $(5, 0)$.

The value of the computer is decreasing so the slope is negative. The value of the computer is decreasing at $400 per year.

Objective 3.2.3 CHECKUP

1. A Humvee can drive off the road, rising 30 feet vertically over a horizontal distance of 75 feet. Find the grade of this terrain.

2. In 1994, the average cost of an existing home was $136,800. The average price of an existing home in 2004 was $236,600. Find the average rate of change per year in the average cost of an existing home from 1994 to 2004.

3. Margaret was walking home from the grocery store, which was 1 mile from her home. After walking a quarter of a mile, she stopped to talk with a neighbor who was working in her yard. After talking for 4 minutes, Margaret doubled her walking speed to finish her trip home. Which graph best illustrates Margaret's walk home? Explain your choice.

a.

b.

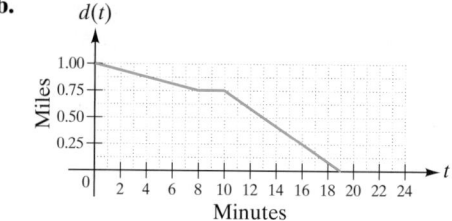

c.

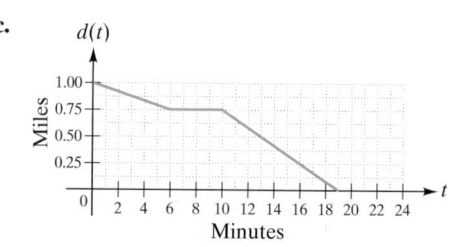

4. A company purchased a machine for $135,000. The company used simple linear depreciation for the machine for tax purposes. If the company estimated the useful life of the machine to be 15 years, determine the average rate of change of the machine's value per year.

3.2 EXERCISES

Student Solutions Manual   PH Math/Tutor Center   CD Video   Math XL   MathXL®   MyMathLab   MyMathLab   Interactmath.com

Determine whether the graph represents a function. If it does, is the function increasing, decreasing, or constant? Determine if the slope of the graph is positive, negative, zero, or undefined. If the slope is positive or negative, find the slope of the graph.

1.

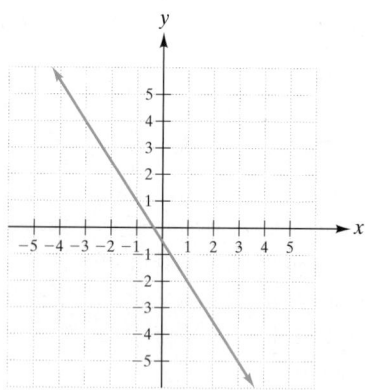

2.

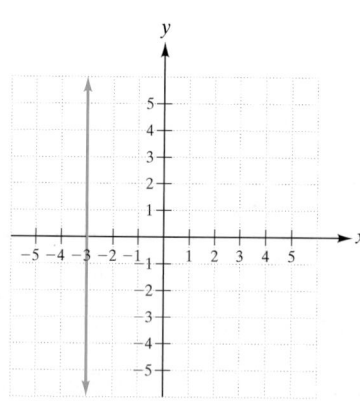

3.

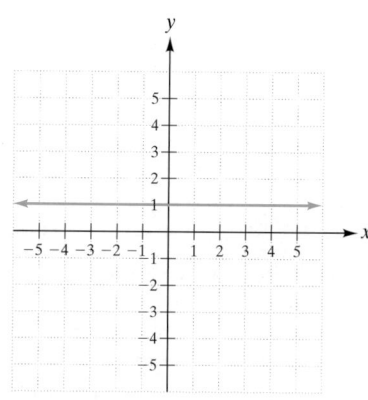

4.

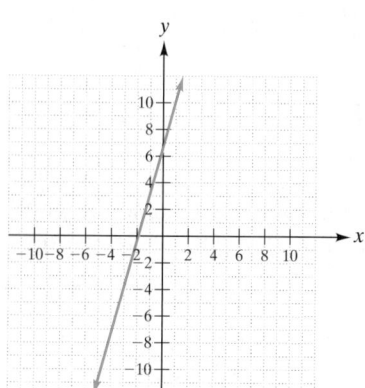

5.

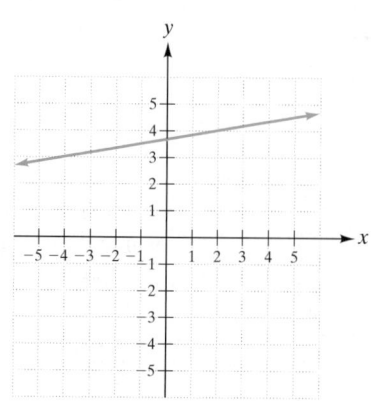

6.

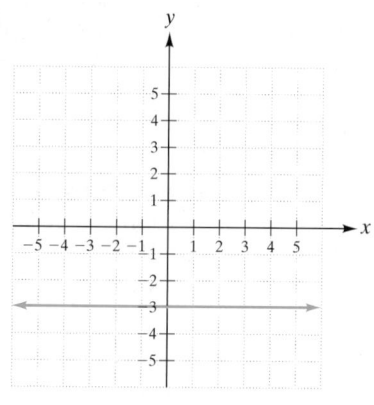

7.

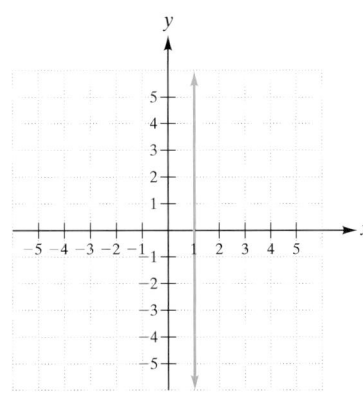

8.

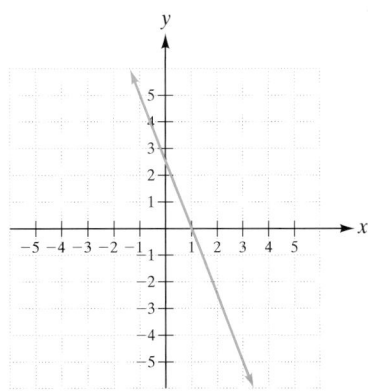

Determine the slope of the line containing the given points.

9. $(-7, -2)$ and $(5, 6)$

10. $(3, -1)$ and $(-2, 8)$

11. $(-12, -9)$ and $(4, -9)$

12. $(-8, 9)$ and $(-8, -5)$

13. $(0, 3)$ and $(0, 8)$

14. $(1, -6)$ and $(8, 9)$

15. $(6, -4)$ and $(7, -6)$

16. $(-5, 0)$ and $(7, 0)$

17. $(0, 4)$ and $(5, 0)$

18. $(-3, 0)$ and $(0, 5)$

19. $(11.5, -9.2)$ and $(6.9, 18.4)$

20. $(-3.8, 1.9)$ and $(5.7, 5.7)$

21. $\left(\dfrac{1}{2}, \dfrac{3}{4}\right)$ and $\left(-\dfrac{1}{2}, -\dfrac{5}{6}\right)$

22. $\left(-\dfrac{3}{7}, \dfrac{1}{4}\right)$ and $\left(\dfrac{5}{14}, -\dfrac{7}{8}\right)$

23. A car dealer advertises that its off-road vehicles can drive on terrain rising 56 feet vertically over a horizontal distance of 160 feet. Find the grade of the advertised terrain.

24. A motor bike drives on a terrain rising 31 feet vertically over a horizontal distance of 124 feet. What is the grade of the terrain?

The pitch of a roof is really the measure of the steepness of the roof. Often the pitch is reported as a fraction whose denominator is 12. A roof that rises 3.6 inches over a horizontal distance of 12 inches is said to have a pitch of 0.30, or 30%.

25. What is the pitch of a roof that rises 3.3 inches over a horizontal distance of 12 inches?

26. Find the pitch of a roof that rises 5 inches over a horizontal distance of 12 inches.

In exercises 27–34, determine whether the graph represents a function. If it does, is the function increasing, decreasing, or constant. Determine the slope of the line.

27.

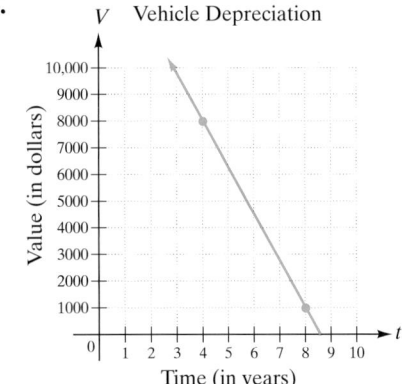

Vehicle Depreciation

28.

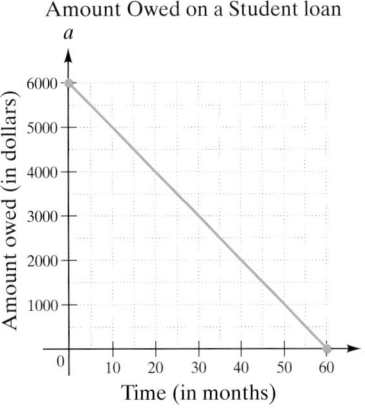

Amount Owed on a Student loan

29.

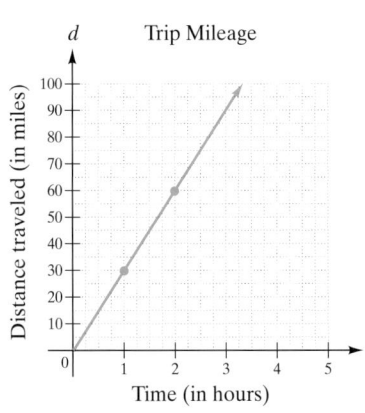

Trip Mileage

30.

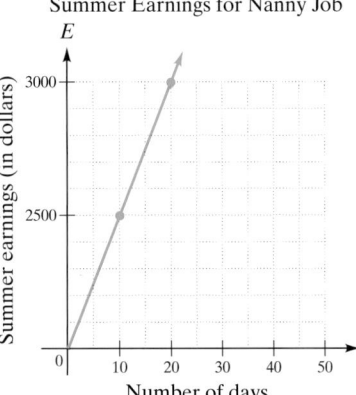

Summer Earnings for Nanny Job

31.

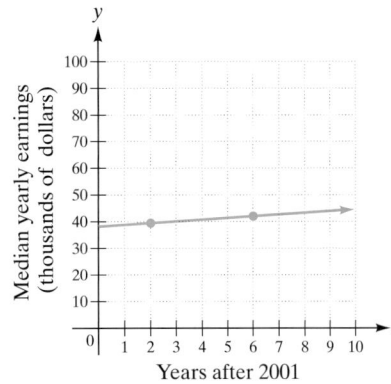

Median Yearly Earnings for Men Working Full-Time

32.

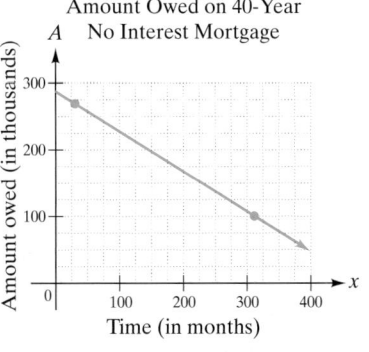

Amount Owed on 40-Year No Interest Mortgage

33.

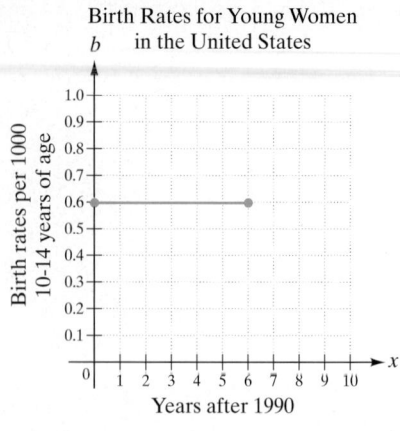

Birth Rates for Young Women
in the United States

34.

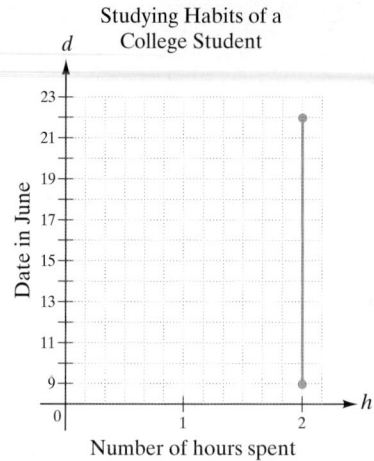

Studying Habits of a
College Student

35. A troop of scouts hiked for three hours to reach a work site that was a distance of 6 miles from their camp. They worked at the site for one hour before starting back to the camp. On the way back, they hiked at the same rate of speed for one hour, then rested for an hour, and then completed the return hike two hours later. Which graph best illustrates their journey? Explain your choice.

a.

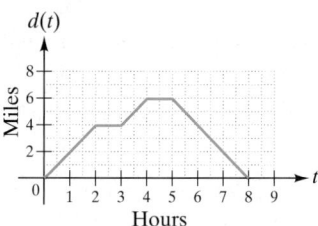

b.

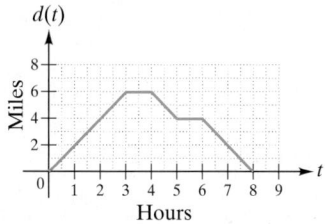

c.

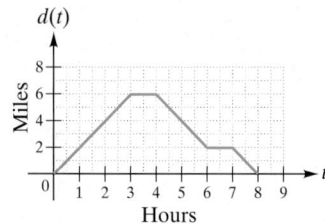

36. Stephanie lived four miles away from the sport center at which she trained. She left the center, jogging toward home. After a half hour, she stopped and spent another half hour cooling down and visiting with her jogging friend. She then walked back to the sport center at a pace that was half as fast as she jogged. Which graph best illustrates her distances from home? Explain your choice.

a.

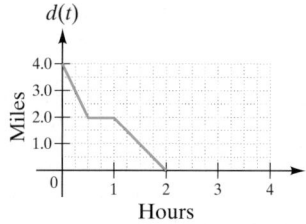

b.

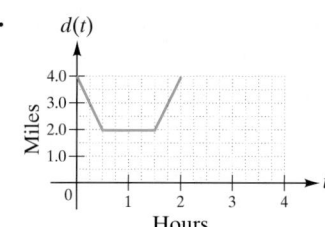

c.

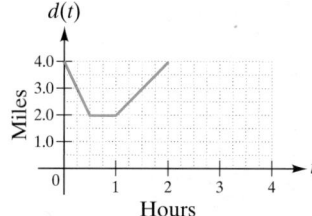

37. Yesterday, the temperature rose steadily from a low of 56°F to a high of 80°F over a 10-hour period. The temperature held constant for 4 hours and then dropped steadily to a low of 60°F over the next 10 hours. Choose the graph that best illustrates this temperature variation.

a.

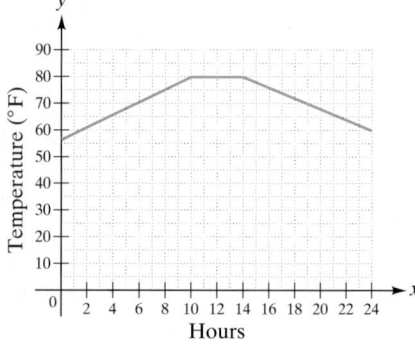

b.

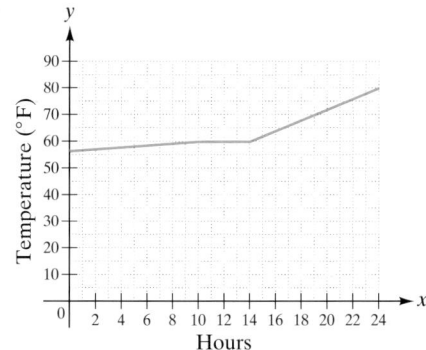

c.

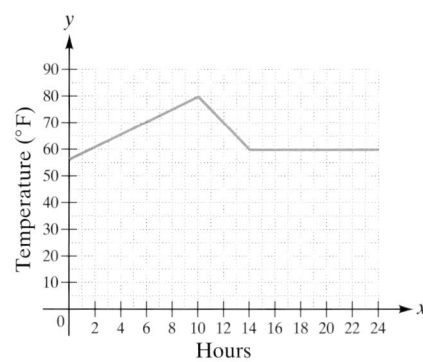

38. In the morning Jose took a frozen chicken from his freezer and set it on the counter to thaw. When his wife got home from work she noticed that it was sitting there and put it in the refrigerator. When Jose got home he put it on the grill. Which graph best illustrates the temperature of the chicken, *y*, with respect to time, *x*?

a.

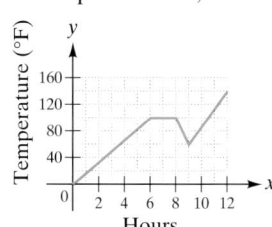

b.

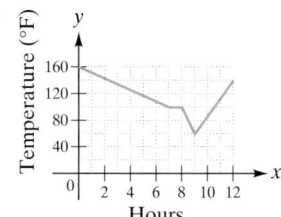

c.

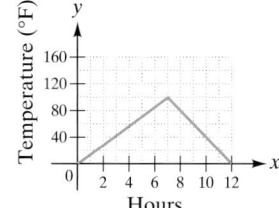

39. The enrollment at a community college grew steadily for the first six years from an initial enrollment of 1500. The enrollment remained constant at 4000 for the next three years.

The enrollment then increased steadily for the next six years at a rate that was half as fast as the beginning rate. Choose the graph that best illustrates this enrollment change.

a.

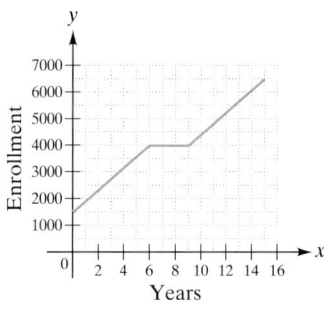

b.

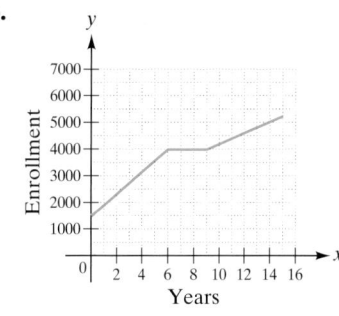

c.

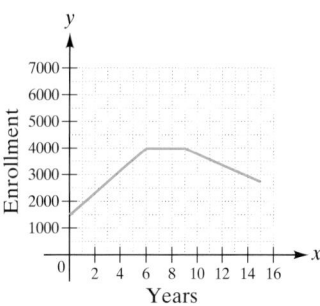

40. When a product is first introduced on the market, sales steadily increase for a period of time, then they may level off, and finally they may decrease as the product loses popularity or is replaced with another product. Suppose a product experiences a steady increase in sales for the first four years that it is marketed, then sales remain level for three more years, and finally sales decrease steadily at a rate that is twice that of the initial increase. Let *x* be the years during which the product is marketed and *y* be the sales, in millions of items, of the product. Choose the graph that best illustrates the sales history of the product.

a.

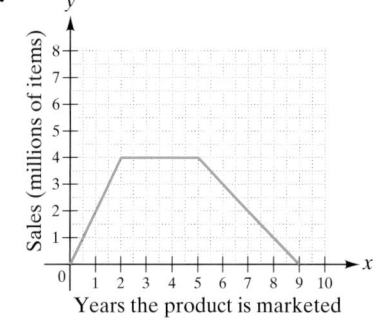

b.

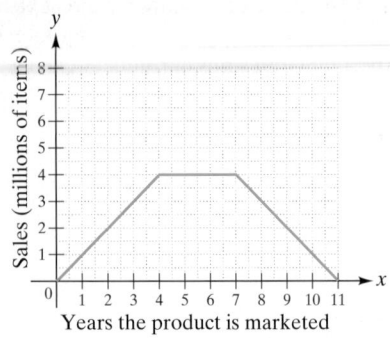

Years the product is marketed

c.

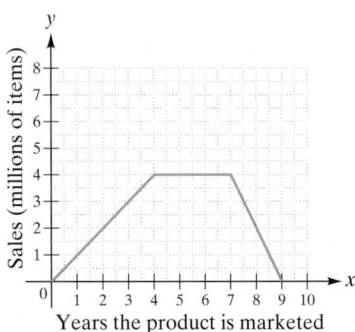

Years the product is marketed

41. A minivan is purchased new for $19,800 by a child-care center that will use straight-line depreciation to depreciate the van over the next five years. Determine the depreciation per year.

42. A lawn service company purchased a pickup truck for $26,800 and used straight-line depreciation to depreciate the truck over the next eight years. Determine the depreciation per year.

43. The U.S. Centers for Medicare and Medicaid Services reported that total private expenditures have steadily increased. The reported 1992 expenditures were 837 billion dollars. The reported 2002 expenditures were 1553 billion dollars. Find the average rate of change in total private expenditures per year.

44. The U.S. Centers for Medicare and Medicaid Services reported that private expenditures on insurance have steadily increased. The reported 1992 expenditures were 274 billion dollars. The reported 2002 expenditures were 550 billion dollars. Find the average rate of change in total private expenditures per year.

45. On a trip the number of hours traveled is related to the distance traveled by the following chart:

Number of hours	1	2	4	5	8	12
Total distance traveled in miles	50	90	150	150	270	400

    a. Find the average rate of change in miles per hour between the first and second hours.
    b. Find the average rate of change in miles per hour between the second and fourth hours.
    c. Find the average rate of change in miles per hour between the first and eighth hours.
    d. Find the average rate of change in miles per hour between the first and twelfth hours.

46. Krista, a nanny, has an arrangement for the summer with a family. They will pay her $2000 plus $50 for each day that she watches all three of their children. The following summarizes her weekly summer earnings:

Week	1	2	3	4	5	6	7	8
Total Earnings	$2100	$2350	$2550	$2560	$2910	$3260	$3510	$4060

    a. What was the average rate of change of her total earnings between weeks 1 and 2?
    b. Between weeks 4 and 6?
    c. Between weeks 1 and 8?

 3.2 Calculator Exercises

The TI-84 Plus with a Ranger program and a Calculator Based Ranger (CBR) may be used to collect data involving the relationship of distance walked with respect to time walked.
In order to run the Ranger program,
    a. Connect the CBR to the TI-84 Plus.
    b. Under programs select RANGER.
    c. Under the MAIN MENU select 2: SETUP/SAMPE.
    d. With the up or down arrow key select a line and press ENTER to change the settings. When the settings are correct, arrow to the top of the page and press ENTER to start. The screen settings should read as shown:

REALTIME: YES

TIME(S): 15

DISPLAY: DIST

BEGIN ON: [ENTER]

SMOOTHING: NONE

UNITS: FEET

    e. Press ENTER to start the program.
    f. Place the CBR on a table. On the floor mark a distance in front of the CBR in feet beginning with 3 feet for a distance of 20 feet.
    g. When you are ready to collect your data, press ENTER again to start the data collection. The CBR will begin to make clicking noises. The calculator will collect data points for 15 seconds.
    h. The calculator will display a graph having time in seconds, T, on the horizontal axis and distance in feet, D, on the vertical axis.
    i. When you are ready to collect additional data, press ENTER and choose 5 for REPEAT SAMPLE.

You will need one person designated as a walker and one person to control the calculator and CBR.

For each of the given situations described below, complete parts **a–e**.

    a. On your paper, set up a table of values to describe the situation. Use integer coordinates $\{0, 1, 2, \ldots, 15\}$ for the independent variable T and determine the dependent variable D.

b. Graph the situation.

c. Perform the situation described using the CBR, the Ranger program, and your TI-84.

d. Compare your graph to the graph on your calculator.

e. Identify the slope of the line as either positive or negative and approximate its value. Determine the y-intercept of the graph. Write an equation for the line.

1. The walker should stand on the 3-foot line. When told to begin, walk away from the CBR at a constant rate of one foot per second for 15 seconds.

2. The walker should stand on the 20-foot line. When told to begin, walk toward from the CBR at a constant rate of one foot per second for 15 seconds.

3. The walker should stand on the 5-foot line. When told to begin, the walker should remain on the 5-foot line for 15 seconds.

3.2 Writing Exercises

The Hudsons have a programmable thermostat. The following graph represents the temperature in their home. Describe a possible scenario.

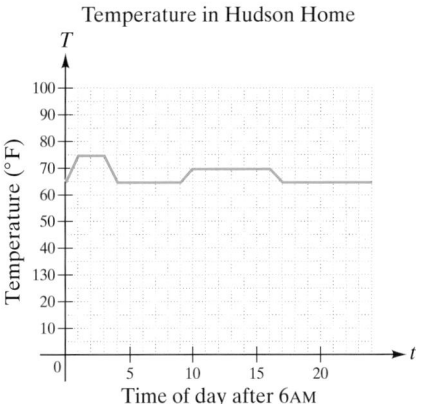

Temperature in Hudson Home

3.3 GRAPHING BY USING THE SLOPE–INTERCEPT METHOD

OBJECTIVES

1 Determine the slope and y-intercept of a line from its linear equation in two variables.

2 Graph linear equations given a point on the line and the slope.

3 Graph linear equations in two variables by using the slope–intercept method.

4 Model real-world situations involving data points and slopes.

APPLICATION

Linear depreciation diminishes the value of an asset by a fixed amount each period until the net value is zero. This is the simplest depreciation calculation to make for tax purposes.

If you purchase a computer for $2000 to use in your business and estimate its useful life to be five years, determine the amount of depreciation per year (the slope of a line).

Given x years of use and the value of the computer in y dollars, determine the y-intercept and graph the equation.

After completing this section, we will discuss this application further. See page 308.

Objective 3.3.1   **Determining the Slope of a Line from Its Linear Equation**

In Section 3.2, we determined the slope of a line given a graph or a set of ordered pairs. We may also need to determine the slope of a line when a graph is not given and only the linear equation is known. Even though we could graph the line from the equation and then determine the slope, it is easier to determine the slope algebraically without drawing the graph. Complete the following discovery to see how to find the slope from the known equation.

Guided Discovery 5 Determining Slope from a Linear Equation

1. Graph the given linear equations in two variables. Label two integer coordinate points.

    a. $y = 2x + 4$

    b. $y = -2x$

    c. $y = \dfrac{1}{2}x - 5$

2. Determine the slope of each of the preceding lines.

3. Determine the coefficient of the x-term in each of the equations in part **1**.

Write a rule to determine the slope of the graph from a linear equation in two variables.

The slope of each graph is the same as the coefficient of the x-term in the linear equation when it is solved for y.

SLOPE OF A LINE, GIVEN A LINEAR EQUATION

Given a linear equation in two variables solved for the dependent variable y, the slope of the line represented by the equation is the coefficient of the independent variable x.

For example, determine the slope of the line for the linear equation $-2x + 3y = 5$. Solve for y.

$$-2x + 3y = 5$$
$$-2x + 3y + 2x = 5 + 2x \qquad \text{Add 2x to both sides.}$$
$$3y = 5 + 2x \qquad \text{Simplify.}$$
$$3y = 2x + 5 \qquad \text{Rearrange the right side.}$$
$$\frac{3y}{3} = \frac{2x + 5}{3} \qquad \text{Divide both sides by 3.}$$
$$y = \frac{2}{3}x + \frac{5}{3} \qquad \text{Simplify.}$$

The slope of the line (m) is the coefficient of the x-term, or $m = \frac{2}{3}$. Recall that the constant term indicates that the y-intercept is $\left(0, \frac{5}{3}\right)$.

TWO SPECIAL CASES OF THE SLOPE OF A LINE GIVEN A LINEAR EQUATION

Given a linear equation in two variables of the form $x = h$, the graph is a vertical line with an undefined slope.

Given a linear equation in two variables of the form $y = k$, the graph is a horizontal line with a zero slope.

 TAKE NOTE A slope of 0 and an undefined slope are not the same.

EXAMPLE 1 Determine by inspection the slope and y-intercept of the line for the given linear equation.

a. $f(x) = -3x + 7$ **b.** $6y = 19$ **c.** $x - 4 = 10$

Solution

a. The coefficient of the x-term is -3. Therefore, $m = -3$. The constant term is 7. The y-intercept is $(0, 7)$.

b. Solve for y.

$$\frac{6y}{6} = \frac{19}{6}$$

$$y = \frac{19}{6} \quad \text{or} \quad y = 0x + \frac{19}{6}$$

The coefficient of the x term is 0. Therefore, $m = 0$. The line has a y-intercept of $\left(0, \frac{19}{6}\right)$.

c. Solve for x because there are no y's.

$$x - 4 = 10$$
$$x - 4 + 4 = 10 + 4$$
$$x = 14$$

The slope m is undefined, because $x = 14$ is a vertical line. The line has an x-intercept of $(14, 0)$. The line does not have a y-intercept. ■

 Objective 3.3.1 CHECKUP

1. Determine by inspection the slope and y-intercept of the line for each linear equation.

a. $t(x) = -\dfrac{7}{11}x + 13$ **b.** $2y - 5 = 3y + 1$

c. $4x - 3 = x + 6$

2. How can you determine the slope of the line for a linear equation by inspecting the equation? How can you determine the y-intercept of the line for a linear equation by inspecting the equation?

Objective 3.3.2   **Graphing Linear Equations Given a Point on the Line and the Slope**

Earlier, we said that the slope of a line is an important characteristic of a linear equation. One reason for its importance is that if you know the slope of a line, you can graph the line even if you know only one point on it, instead of two.

To graph a line when you know both a point on the line and the slope of the line,

- Plot the known point and label its coordinates.
- Count the rise and run from the point you have located. For a positive rise, count upward; for a negative rise, count downward. For a positive run, count to the right; for a negative run, count to the left.
- Place a second point where the next ordered pair is located. Label the coordinates of the point.
- Draw a straight line connecting the two points.

For example, graph a line that contains the point $(2, -1)$ and has a slope of $\frac{3}{5}$.

Plot the point $(2, -1)$. Locate a second point by counting the slope (rise of 3 and run of 5). Draw a straight line connecting the two points.

Since $\frac{3}{5}$ is equal to $\frac{-3}{-5}$, the slope can be counted using different triangles, as shown in the following diagrams:

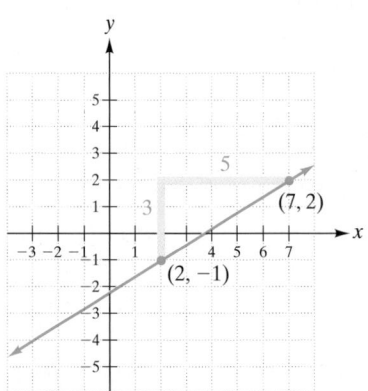
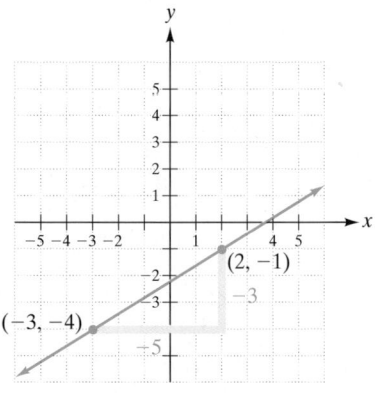

Remember that $\frac{-3}{-5} = \frac{3}{5}$.

EXAMPLE 2   Graph a line that contains the given point and has the given slope. Label two points.

a. $(3, 1); m = -2$ **b.** $(3, 4); m = 0$ **c.** $(-5, -2); m$ is undefined.

Solution

Locate the given point and determine the rise and run.

a.
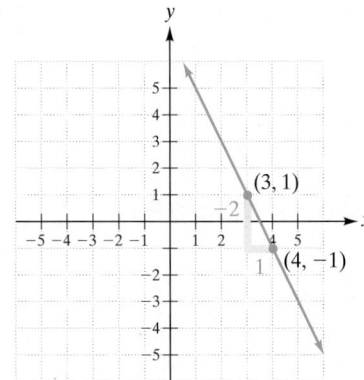

b.
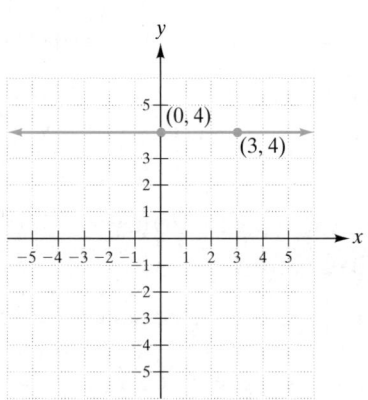

Note: The line is horizontal because $m = 0$.

c.
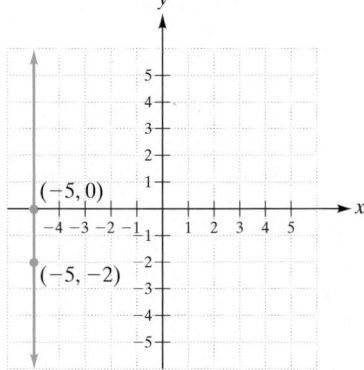

Note: The line is vertical because m is undefined.

✓ Objective 3.3.2 *CHECKUP*

1. Graph a line that contains the given point and has the given slope.
   a. $(-2, 4); m = -1$ **b.** $(6, 0); m$ is undefined.
   c. $(3, 6); m = 0$

2. If it takes two points to draw a line, explain why we can still draw a line if we are given only one point and the slope of the line.

Objective 3.3.3   ## Graphing Linear Equations by Using the Slope–Intercept Method

We have found that if a linear equation in two variables is solved for y, the slope of its graph is the coefficient of the x-term. The constant term is the y-coordinate of the y-intercept. Therefore, we have a linear equation in two variables in what we call the **slope–intercept form**.

SLOPE–INTERCEPT FORM FOR A LINEAR EQUATION IN TWO VARIABLES

The slope–intercept form for a linear equation in two variables is

$$y = mx + b$$

where m is the slope of the graphed line and b is the y-coordinate of the y-intercept of the graph.

We have enough information from the slope–intercept equation to graph a line.

To graph a linear equation in two variables, using the slope–intercept method,

- Solve the equation for y.
- Determine the slope and y-coordinate of the y-intercept from the equation.
- Plot the y-intercept and label its coordinates.
- Locate the next point on the line by counting the slope (rise over run). Label the coordinates of the point.
- Draw a straight line through the two points.

For example, graph the linear equation $3x + y = -1$.

First, solve for y.

$$3x + y = -1$$
$$3x + y - 3x = -1 - 3x \qquad \text{Subtract 3x from both sides.}$$
$$y = -1 - 3x \qquad \text{Simplify.}$$
$$y = -3x - 1 \qquad \text{Rearrange the right side.}$$

Therefore, $m = -3$ and $b = -1$.

The y-intercept is $(0, -1)$ and the slope is -3, or $\frac{-3}{1}$.

Locate the y-intercept and count the slope. Label the coordinates of both points. Draw a straight line through the two points.

EXAMPLE 3

Graph the given linear equation, using the slope–intercept method. Check by graphing on your calculator.

a. $b(x) = -3x + 7$ **b.** $3x - 4y = -4$ **c.** $6y = 19$

Solution

a. $b(x) = -3x + 7$ The slope is -3, or $\frac{-3}{1}$. Starting at the y-intercept $(0, 7)$, move three units down and one unit to the right.

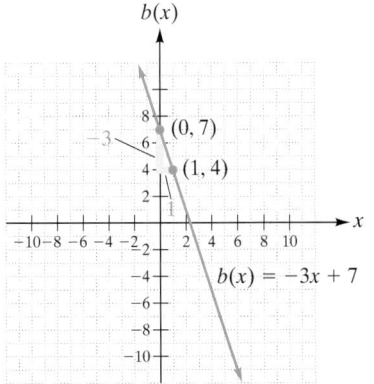

Check

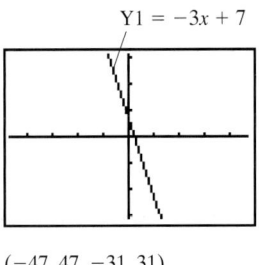

$Y1 = -3x + 7$

$(-47, 47, -31, 31)$

b. Solve for y. $3x - 4y = -4$

$$-4y = -3x - 4$$

$$y = \frac{3}{4}x + 1$$

The slope is $\frac{3}{4}$. Starting at the y-intercept $(0, 1)$, move three units up and four units to the right.

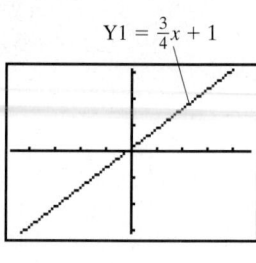

$(-47, 47, -31, 31)$

$3x - 4y = -4$

$(4, 4)$

$(0, 1)$

c. Solve for y. $6y = 19$

$$y = \frac{19}{6}$$

$$y = \frac{19}{6} \quad \text{or} \quad y = 0x + \frac{19}{6}$$

The line is horizontal because the slope is zero. The y-intercept is $\left(0, \frac{19}{6}\right)$.

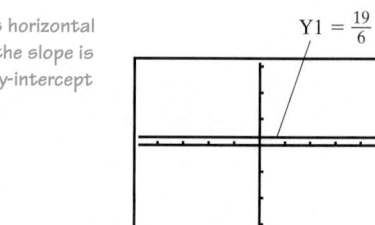

$(-47, 47, -31, 31)$

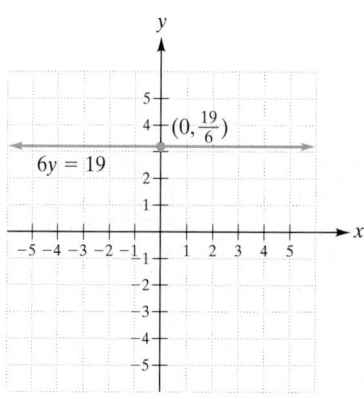

$\left(0, \frac{19}{6}\right)$

$6y = 19$

Objective 3.3.3 CHECKUP

Graph using the slope–intercept method. Check by graphing on your calculator.

1. a. $v(x) = \dfrac{4}{3}x - 2$ **b.** $5x + 2y = 4$ **c.** $6y = 2y + 7$

Objective 3.3.4 Modeling the Real World

Linear equations in two variables are useful in many areas of our lives. If we can write a linear equation, then the graph of the equation allows us to extend our knowledge of the situation to many possible solutions. In the area of business, for example, we can write linear functions for total cost, revenue, and profit. Two other business applications, supply and demand functions, are often used in the study of economics associated with marketing products. The studies associate the price at which you sell a product with the available supply or the quantity demanded of the product. For example, when high-definition televisions were placed on the market, the supply was low, causing the price to be high, and the demand low.

EXAMPLE 4

The manager of the music store has determined that the demand for a popular video, $d(x)$, is related to the price in x dollars by the function, $d(x) = 20 - \frac{1}{2}x$.

a. Graph the function using the slope–intercept method.
b. Use the graph to determine the price of the video if the demand is 17 videos.

Use the graph to determine the demand if the selling price is $10.

Solution

a. Write the demand function in slope–intercept form, $y = mx + b$.

$$d(x) = -\frac{1}{2}x + 20 \qquad m = -\frac{1}{2} \text{ and } b = 20$$

The $d(x)$-intercept is $(0, 20)$. The slope of the line is $-\frac{1}{2}$. Graph the $d(x)$-intercept and count the slope of the line.

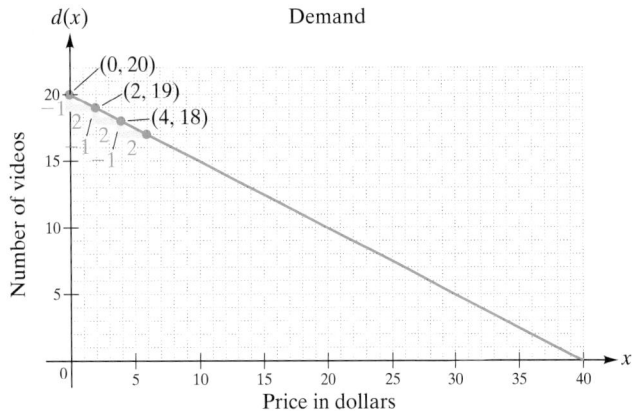

b. According to the following graph, when the demand is 17 videos, the price per video is 6 dollars (red line). When the selling price is $10, the demand for the video is 15 (green line).

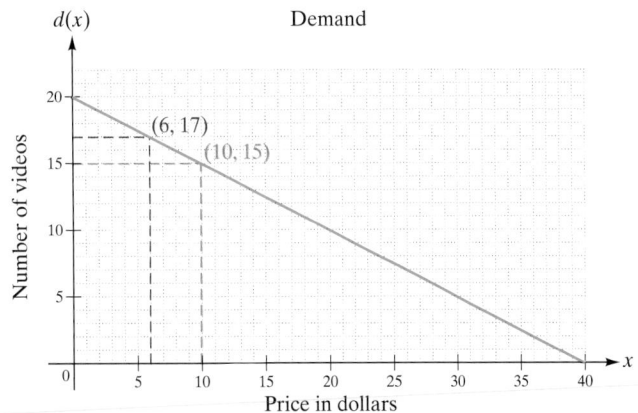

EXAMPLE 5

The supplier of videos has determined that the supply, $s(x)$, for a popular video is related to the price in x dollars by the function, $s(x) = \frac{3}{5}x$.

a. Graph the function using the slope–intercept method.
b. Use the graph to determine the price of the video if the quantity supplied is 12 videos. Use the graph to determine the quantity to be supplied if the selling price is $25.

Solution

a. The supply function is in slope–intercept form, $y = mx + b$.

$$s(x) = \frac{3}{5}x \qquad m = \frac{3}{5} \text{ and } b = 0$$

The $s(x)$-intercept is $(0, 0)$. The slope of the line is $\frac{3}{5}$. Graph the $s(x)$-intercept and count the slope of the line.

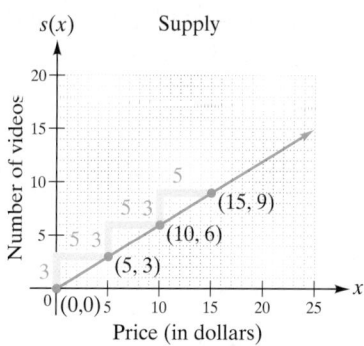

b. According to the following graph, when the supply is 12 videos, the price per video is 20 dollars (red line). When the selling price is $15, the supply for the video is 9 (green line).

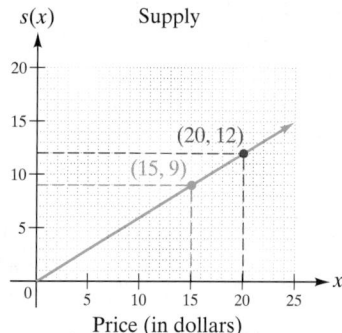

APPLICATION

Linear depreciation diminishes the value of an asset by a fixed amount each period until the net value is zero. This is the simplest depreciation calculation to make for tax purposes.

If you purchase a computer for $2000 to use in your business and estimate its useful life to be five years, determine the amount of depreciation per year (the slope of a line). Given x years of use and the value of the computer in y dollars, determine the y-intercept and graph the equation.

Discussion

The fixed amount of depreciation is $2000 divided by 5 years, or $400 per year. The slope of the line is -400, because the computer is depreciating, or decreasing in value.

To graph this situation, we need to determine the y-intercept. Let $x = 0$ and determine the corresponding y-value. At 0 years after purchase, the value of the computer is $2000. The y-intercept is $(0, 2000)$.

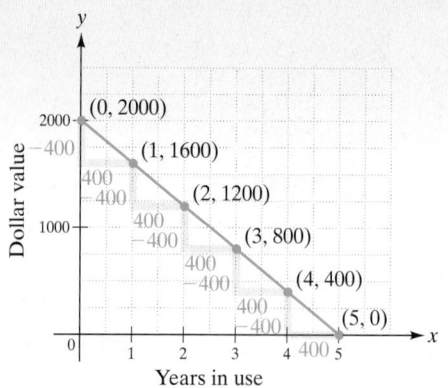

Objective 3.3.4 *CHECKUP*

1. The manager of the music store has determined that the demand, $d(x)$, for a CD player is related to the price in x dollars by the function, $d(x) = 80 - \frac{3}{5}x$.

   a. Graph the function using the slope–intercept method.

   b. Use the graph to determine the price of the player if the demand is 15 CD players. Use the graph to determine the demand if the selling price is $59.

2. The supplier of CD players has determined that the supply, $s(x)$, for the player is related to the price in x dollars by the function, $s(x) = \frac{2}{5}x$.

   a. Graph the function using the slope–intercept method.

   b. Use the graph to determine the price of the player if the quantity supplied is 24 videos. Use the graph to determine the quantity to be supplied if the selling price is $55.

3. If you purchase a car for $20,000 to use in your business and determine its useful life to be 4 years, determine the amount of depreciation per year. Given x years of use and the value of the car in y dollars, determine the y-intercept and graph the equation.

3.3 EXERCISES

 Student Solutions Manual PH Math/Tutor Center CD Video  MathXL®   MyMathLab   Interactmath.com

Determine by inspection the slope and the y-intercept of the line for each equation.

1. $y = 21x + 15$

2. $y = -19x + 28$

3. $y = 5.95x - 2.01$

4. $y = 14.8 - 3.6x$

5. $y = 85,600 - 1255x$

6. $y = 45x + 1250$

7. $16x - 4y = 64$

8. $24x + 3y = 39$

9. $7y + 18 = 2(y + 6) - 4$

10. $12(y + 2) = 5(2y - 4)$

11. $\frac{3}{2}x - \frac{3}{5}y = \frac{21}{10}$

12. $-\frac{5}{3}x + \frac{5}{4}y = \frac{25}{12}$

13. $x = -4\frac{7}{8}$

14. $\frac{5}{9}x = -15$

Graph a line that contains the given point and has the given slope.

15. $(8, 3); m = \frac{4}{7}$

16. $(-7, -6); m = \frac{5}{6}$

17. $(-10, 4); m = -\frac{5}{9}$

18. $(9, -10); m = -\frac{4}{5}$

19. $(5, 7); m = 4$

20. $(-8, 7); m = -6$

21. $(0, 9); m = 0$

22. $(0, 9); m$ is undefined.

23. $(9, 0); m$ is undefined.

24. $(9, 0); m = 0$

Graph exercises 25–36, using the slope–intercept method. Check by graphing on your calculator.

25. $y = \frac{5}{3}x - 4$

26. $y = -\frac{3}{4}x + 6$

27. $16x - 8y = 40$

28. $-21x + 7y = -35$

29. $7x + 2y = -16$

30. $9x - 4y = 24$

31. $14y + 21 = 6y + 5$

32. $31y - 19 = 26y + 6$

33. $5y = 150x + 350$

34. $6y = 300x - 360$

35. $f(x) = 0.3x - 1.2$

36. $m(x) = -0.8x + 2.7$

37. The bookstore manager has studied the daily supply and demand for a computer software package and has determined that the quantity demanded, $d(x)$, is related to the price, x, by the linear demand function, $d(x) = 50 - \frac{1}{2}x$.

   a. Graph the linear function, using the slope–intercept method.

   b. Use the graph to determine the price per software package if the demand is 20. Use the graph to determine the demand if the selling price is $50.

38. The daily demand for a product is given by

$$D(p) = 80 - \frac{4}{5}p$$

where $D(p)$ is the quantity demanded each day by consumers when the price is p dollars per item.

   a. Graph this equation, using the slope–intercept method.

   b. Use the graph to determine what the demand for the product will be when the price is $10 per item; $20 per item; $40 per item; $64 per item.

c. Explain in general what is happening with the demand for the product as the price increases.

d. Are there any practical limits on the price per item, p, for this equation, that would result in an unreasonable price? Explain.

39. The supplier of the computer software package in exercise **37** has studied the daily supply and demand for the software package and has determined a supply function, $s(x)$, $s(x) = \frac{2}{5}x$, where $s(x)$ is the quantity supplied and x is the price.

a. Graph the linear function, using the slope–intercept method.

b. Use the graph to determine the price per software package if the quantity supplied is 20. Use the graph to determine the quantity to be supplied if the selling price is $75.

40. The daily supply of a product is given by

$$S(p) = \frac{5}{8}p$$

where $S(p)$ is the quantity supplied each day when the price is p dollars per item.

a. Graph this equation, using the slope–intercept method.

b. What will the daily supply be if the price is $10 per item; $20 per item; $40 per item; $64 per item?

c. Explain in general what is happening with the supply for the product as the price increases.

d. Are there any practical limits on the price per item for this equation? Explain.

41. Isabell decides to use her home computer to make greeting cards. She purchases a software package for $50.00. She estimates that the cost per card is $0.75. She plans to sell the cards for $5.00 each.

a. Write a function, $c(x)$, for the total cost. Graph the function using the slope–intercept method. Use the graph to determine the cost of producing 8 greeting cards. Use the graph to determine the number of greetings cards produced for a cost of $80.00.

b. Write a function, $r(x)$, for the total revenue. Graph the function using the slope–intercept method. Use the graph to determine the revenue of selling 8 greeting cards. Use the graph to determine the number of greetings cards sold to obtain a revenue of $80.00.

c. Write a function, $p(x)$, for the profit. Graph the function using the slope–intercept method. Use the graph to determine the profit of producing and selling 8 greeting cards. Use the graph to determine the number of greetings cards produced and sold to obtain a profit of $0.00.

42. Thomas decides to use his home computer to design Web pages. He purchases a software package for $150. He estimates that the cost per Web page is $15. He plans to charge $50 per Web page.

a. Write a function, $c(x)$, for the total cost. Graph the function using the slope–intercept method. Use the graph to determine the cost of producing 5 Web pages. Use the graph to determine the number of Web pages produced for a cost of $300.

b. Write a function, $r(x)$, for the total revenue. Graph the function using the slope–intercept method. Use the graph

to determine the revenue of selling 5 Web pages. Use the graph to determine the number of Web pages sold to obtain a revenue of $300.

c. Write a function, $p(x)$, for the profit. Graph the function using the slope–intercept method. Use the graph to determine the profit of producing and selling 5 Web pages. Use the graph to determine the number of Web pages produced and sold to obtain a profit of $0.

43. Charlie's Screen Printers can screen print shirts at a cost of $4 per shirt, with a setup cost of $50 per run. The company sells the shirts for $10 each.

a. Write a function, $c(x)$, for the total cost. Graph the function using the slope–intercept method. Use the graph to determine the cost of producing 5 shirts. Use the graph to determine the number of shirts produced for a cost of $150.

b. Write a function, $r(x)$, for the total revenue. Graph the function using the slope–intercept method. Use the graph to determine the revenue of selling 5 shirts. Use the graph to determine the number of shirts sold to obtain a revenue of $300.

c. Write a function, $p(x)$, for the profit. Graph the function using the slope–intercept method. Use the graph to determine the profit of producing and selling 5 shirts. Use the graph to determine the number of shirts produced and sold to obtain a profit of $0.

44. Jim's Catering Service pays a carver for the meat table $7 per hour. Jim estimates the cost of setup and delivery to be $50. He charges the customer $30 per hour.

a. Write a function, $c(x)$, for the total cost. Graph the function using the slope–intercept method. Use the graph to determine the cost of the carver for 2 hours. Use the graph to determine the number of hours of the service for a cost of $120.

b. Write a function, $r(x)$, for the total revenue. Graph the function using the slope–intercept method. Use the graph to determine the revenue for 2 hours of the service. Use the graph to determine the number of hours of service to obtain a revenue of $120.

c. Write a function, $p(x)$, for the profit. Graph the function using the slope–intercept method. Use the graph to determine the profit from the carving service of 5 hours. Use the graph to determine when the profit is $0.

45. Chloe is planning a trip to visit her cousin, Breanne. She estimates that she can drive an average of 50 miles per hour. Write a linear equation for Chloe's distance from home, d, with respect to the time traveled, t. Graph the equation using the slope–intercept method. Breanne lives 420 miles from Chloe. Use the graph to estimate the time it will take Chloe to drive to Breanne's home.

46. Caitlin is planning a trip to visit her grandmother Marie. She estimates that she can drive an average of 55 miles per hour. Write a linear equation for Caitlin's distance from home, d, with respect to time driven, t. Graph the equation using the slope–intercept method. Marie lives 550 miles from Caitlin. Caitlin plans to stop when she has traveled half of the distance to stretch her legs. Use the graph to estimate the time driven when Caitlin plans to stop.

47. Victoria is visiting colleges. Her first visit is a college 350 miles from her home. If she travels at an average speed of 50 miles per hour toward her home, write a linear equation for the distance from Victoria's home, y, with respect to time driven, t. Graph the equation. Use the graph to estimate the distance to Victoria's home after 1.5 hours of traveling after her first visit.

48. Misty is visiting colleges. Her first visit is a college 350 miles from her home. If she travels to a second college at an average speed of 50 miles per hour away from her home, write a linear equation for the distance from Misty's home, y, with respect to time driven, t. Graph the equation. Use the graph to estimate the distance to Misty's home after 1.5 hours of traveling after her first visit.

3.3 Calculator Exercises

Part 1

Complete the table that follows without graphing. (Remember to first solve the equation for y to obtain the slope–intercept form.) Then check your conclusions by graphing each equation on your calculator.

| Equation | $y = mx + b$ | | Conclusions | |
	Slope m	Constant b	Graph's Inclination ↗ or ↘	Graph's y-Intercept
$y = 3x + 6$				
$y = -2x + 7$				
$y = -x - 3$				
$y = 4x - 1$				
$5x - 3y = 9$				
$4x + 5y = 10$				
$y = \dfrac{7}{8}x - \dfrac{3}{4}$				
$y = -1.7x + 3.2$				

Part 2

Let's explore window settings for graphing linear equations in two variables using real data. The TI-84 Plus will help us set our viewing window.

1. Enter the equation in the $\boxed{\text{Y=}}$ menu.
2. Enter the values for the domain that you wish to graph.
3. The calculator will choose the range values to fit the graph into your viewing window. Press $\boxed{\text{ZOOM}}$ $\boxed{0}$ for ZoomFit.

Use this procedure to graph the exercises involving real data in this section.

3.3 Writing Exercises

You have learned three methods for graphing a linear equation in two variables: using a table of values of coordinate pairs, using the intercept method, and using the slope–intercept method.

State which method you would use for each of the following exercises and why you would use that method.

1. $x + 2y = 4$

2. $y = -x + 3$

3. $3x + 5y = -15$

4. $y = \dfrac{2}{3}x - 1$

5. $7x + y = 18$

6. $y = 2.5x + 4.5$

7. $3y = 2y - 3$

8. $5x - 7 = 3x + 1$

3.4 COINCIDING, PARALLEL, AND PERPENDICULAR LINES

OBJECTIVES
1. Determine whether two linear graphs are coinciding, parallel, intersecting only, or intersecting and perpendicular by inspecting their corresponding equations.
2. Determine from real-world data whether two linear graphs are coinciding, parallel, intersecting only, or intersecting and perpendicular.

APPLICATION

In 1992, Brian J. Whipp and Susan A. Ward of the School of Medicine at UCLA wrote a paper entitled "Will Women Soon Outrun Men?"[1] In a prestigious science journal, the authors graphed the world record track times for both men and women. They noted that the slope of the graph for women was larger than the slope of the graph for men. Using this fact, they predicted that women would eventually overtake men in track competition in the year 1998. In critiquing this article that very year, Randall Woods used current data to write a linear equation for men and one for women, given year x and mean speed y (in meters per minute). The data on running resulted in the equations $y = 0.534x - 430$ for men and $y = 4.58x - 8800$ for women. According to these equations, will the women overtake the men and outrun them? If so, when? What is wrong with these conclusions?

After completing this section, we will discuss this application further. See page 320.

[1]"Will Women Soon Outrun Men?"; *Nature*, January 2, 1992, Vol. 355[25].

Objective 3.4.1

Determining the Relationship of Two Lines

From previous graphing, we know that the graphs of two lines may have one of three relationships. Two **coinciding** lines have all points in common and are said to be **coincident**. Two **parallel** lines have no points in common. Two **intersecting** lines have one common point. In this section, we will see how the concept of the slope enables us to tell which of these three cases we have, just from analyzing the equations of the lines.

Let's first look at the characteristics of coinciding lines. Complete the following set of exercises on your calculator to determine whether the pairs of linear equations graph as coinciding lines.

 Guided Discovery 6 Coinciding Lines

1. Graph the given pairs of linear equations.

   a. $-2x + y = 2$
   $y = 2x + 2$

   b. $2x - 4y = 4$
   $y = \frac{1}{2}x - 1$

   c. $3x + y = -3$
   $y = -3x - 3$

2. Determine the slope and y-coordinate of the y-intercept for each graph.

   a. $-2x + y = 2$
   $y = 2x + 2$

   b. $2x - 4y = 4$
   $y = \frac{1}{2}x - 1$

   c. $3x + y = -3$
   $y = -3x - 3$

Choose the correct answers.

3. The lines graphed are *coinciding/parallel/intersecting/ intersecting and perpendicular*.

4. The slopes, m, in each pair of linear equations are *equal/not equal*.

5. The y-coordinates of the y-intercepts, b, in each pair of linear equations are *equal/not equal*.

Write a rule for determining that the graphs of two linear equations are coinciding.

If two coinciding lines have all points in common, then the slopes between each pair of points are equal and the y-coordinates of the y-intercepts in each pair are equal.

COINCIDING LINES

The graphs of two linear equations are coinciding if the graphs have equal slopes, m, and equal y-coordinates of the y-intercepts, b.

To determine whether two nonvertical lines are coinciding by inspecting their equations,

- Solve both equations for y.
- Determine the slope, m, and y-coordinate of the y-intercept, b, for each equation.

Nonvertical coinciding lines have equal slopes (m) and equal y-coordinates of the y-intercepts (b).

To determine whether two vertical lines are coinciding by inspecting their equations,

- Solve the equations for x. Vertical coinciding lines have the same constant term.

Now let's take a look at the characteristics of parallel lines. Complete the following set of exercises on your calculator to determine whether the two linear equations graph as parallel lines.

Guided Discovery 7   Parallel Lines

1. Graph the given pairs of linear equations.

   a. $-2x + y = 4$
   $\quad\;\; y = 2x - 5$

   b. $x - 2y = 4$
   $\quad\;\; 2x - 4y = -12$

   c. $y = -3x - 5$
   $\quad\;\; 3x + y = 6$

2. Determine the slope and y-coordinate of the y-intercept for each graph.

   a. $-2x + y = 4$
   $\quad\;\; y = 2x - 5$

   b. $x - 2y = 4$
   $\quad\;\; 2x - 4y = -12$

   c. $y = -3x - 5$
   $\quad\;\; 3x + y = 6$

Choose the correct answers.

3. The lines graphed are *coinciding/parallel/intersecting/ intersecting and perpendicular.*

4. The slopes, m, in each pair of linear equations in two variables are *equal/not equal.*

5. The y-coordinates of the y-intercepts, b, in each pair of linear equations in two variables are *equal/not equal.*

Write a rule for determining that the graphs of two linear equations in two variables are parallel.

In each pair of lines graphed, the two lines are parallel. Also, the slopes in each pair are equal. The y-coordinates of the y-intercepts in each pair are not equal.

PARALLEL LINES

The graphs of two linear equations are parallel if the graphs have equal slopes, m, and unequal y-coordinates of the y-intercepts, b.

To determine whether two nonvertical lines are parallel by inspecting their equations,

- Solve the equations for y.
- Determine the slope, m, and y-coordinate of the y-intercept, b, for each equation.

Nonvertical parallel lines have equal slopes (m) and unequal y-coordinates of the y-intercepts (b).

To determine whether two vertical lines are parallel by inspecting their equations,

- Solve the equations for x.

Vertical parallel lines have different constant terms.

 TAKE NOTE Parallel lines never intersect, so they must have a different y-intercept (or x-intercept for vertical lines) and the same slope.

The next Guided Discovery exercise explores the characteristics of intersecting lines. Complete the following set of exercises on your calculator to determine whether the two linear equations graph as intersecting lines.

Guided Discovery 8 Intersecting Lines

1. Graph the given pairs of linear equations.

   a. $-2x + y = 2$
   $y = 3x - 1$

   b. $x - 2y = 4$
   $4x - 4y = -12$

   c. $-3x - y = 6$
   $-3x + y = -6$

2. Determine the slope and y-coordinate of the y-intercept for each graph.

   a. $-2x + y = 2$
   $y = 3x - 1$

   b. $x - 2y = 4$
   $4x - 4y = -12$

   c. $-3x - y = 6$
   $-3x + y = -6$

Choose the correct answers.

3. The lines graphed are *coinciding/parallel/intersecting/ intersecting and perpendicular*.

4. The slopes, m, in each pair of linear equations in two variables are *equal/not equal*.

Write a rule for determining that the graphs of two linear equations in two variables are intersecting.

In each pair of lines graphed, the two lines are intersecting. Also, the slopes in each pair are unequal.

INTERSECTING LINES

The graphs of two linear equations are intersecting if the graphs have unequal slopes, m.

Perpendicular lines are a special case of intersecting lines. Two intersecting lines that form four right angles are called **perpendicular** lines.

 TAKE NOTE A square calculator window is necessary to determine perpendicular lines by inspection. The decimal and integer default windows are two such square windows. See Section 3.4 Calculator Exercises for additional settings.

Complete the following set of exercises on your calculator to investigate this special case of intersecting lines.

 Guided Discovery 9 Perpendicular Lines

1. Graph the given pairs of linear equations.

a. $-2x + 3y = 6$

$y = -\dfrac{3}{2}x - 2$

b. $x - 2y = 4$

$-8x - 4y = -16$

c. $-3x - y = 3$

$-x + 3y = -15$

2. Determine the slope and y-coordinate of the y-intercept for each graph.

a. $-2x + 3y = 6$

$y = -\dfrac{3}{2}x - 2$

b. $x - 2y = 4$

$-8x - 4y = -16$

c. $-3x - y = 3$

$-x + 3y = -15$

Choose the correct answers.

3. The lines graphed are *coinciding/parallel/intersecting/ intersecting and perpendicular.*

4. The slopes, m, in each pair of linear equations in two variables are *equal/not equal.*

5. The two slopes, m, in each pair of linear equations in two variables are reciprocals and have *the same/ opposite* sign.

Write a rule for determining that the graphs of two linear equations in two variables are intersecting and perpendicular.

In each pair of lines graphed, the lines are intersecting and perpendicular. The slopes are opposite reciprocals of each other.

INTERSECTING AND PERPENDICULAR LINES

The graphs of two linear equations are intersecting and perpendicular if the graphs have slopes, m, that are opposite reciprocals of each other.

To determine whether two nonvertical lines are intersecting or are intersecting and perpendicular by inspecting their equations,

- Solve the equations for y.
- Determine the slope, m, and y-coordinate of the y-intercept, b, of each equation.

Intersecting lines have unequal slopes (m). Nonvertical intersecting and perpendicular lines have slopes (m) that are opposite reciprocals of each other.

 TAKE NOTE The product of the slopes of nonvertical perpendicular lines is -1. For example, $m = \dfrac{2}{3}$ and $m = -\dfrac{3}{2}$ are slopes of perpendicular lines, and $\left(\dfrac{2}{3}\right)\left(-\dfrac{3}{2}\right) = -1$. This relationship can be used as a test for perpendicular lines.

A special case of perpendicular lines is when one line is vertical ($x = h$) and the other line is horizontal ($y = k$).

All of the relationships we have just discovered are summarized in the next box.

DETERMINING THE RELATIONSHIP BETWEEN TWO LINES FROM THEIR LINEAR EQUATIONS IN TWO VARIABLES

Two linear equations written in slope–intercept form, $y = mx + b$, have graphs that are

- **Coinciding (or coincident) lines** if the equations have equal slopes (m) and equal y-coordinates of the y-intercepts (b).
- **Parallel lines** if the equations have equal slopes (m) and nonequal y-coordinates of the y-intercepts (b).
- **Intersecting lines** if the equations have nonequal slopes (m).
- **Intersecting and perpendicular lines** if the equations have slopes (m) that are opposite reciprocals of each other.

Two linear equations written in the form $x = h$ have graphs that are

- **Coinciding (or coincident) lines** if the equations have the same constant term.
- **Parallel lines** if the equations have different constant terms.

Two linear equations, one in the form $x = h$, and the other in the form $y = k$, have graphs that are a special case of

- **Intersecting and perpendicular lines**.

EXAMPLE 1 Determine by inspection whether the graphs of the given pairs of linear equations are coinciding, parallel, intersecting only, or intersecting and perpendicular.

a. $y = 2x + 4$
$-y = -2x - 4$

b. $2x - y = 6$
$2x + y = 6$

c. $2x + 3y = 1$
$3x - 2y = 1$

d. $f(x) = 2x - 5$
$g(x) = 2x + 5$

Solution

a. Solve the equations for y.

$y = 2x + 4$ $m = 2$ $b = 4$
$y = 2x + 4$ $m = 2$ $b = 4$

The slopes (m) are equal. The y-coordinates of the y-intercepts (b) are equal. The lines are coinciding.

Check

Y1 = 2x + 4   Y2 = 2x + 4

$(-10, 10, -10, 10)$

b. Solve the equations for y.

$y = 2x - 6$ $m = 2$ $b = -6$
$y = -2x + 6$ $m = -2$ $b = 6$

The lines are intersecting at one point, because the slopes (m) are not equal: $2 \neq -2$. However, even though the slopes have opposite signs, the slopes are not reciprocals of each other; therefore, the lines are not perpendicular.

Y2 = -2x + 6   Y1 = 2x - 6

$(-10, 10, -10, 10)$

c. Solve the equations for y.

$$y = -\frac{2}{3}x + \frac{1}{3} \quad m = -\frac{2}{3} \quad b = \frac{1}{3}$$

$$y = \frac{3}{2}x - \frac{1}{2} \quad m = \frac{3}{2} \quad b = -\frac{1}{2}$$

The lines are intersecting and perpendicular, because the slopes (m) are opposite reciprocals of each other: $-\frac{2}{3}$ and $\frac{3}{2}$. The product of the slopes is -1.

Note, in the calculator graphs to the right, the first setting is a square window and the lines appear perpendicular. In the second graph, the lines do not appear perpendicular.

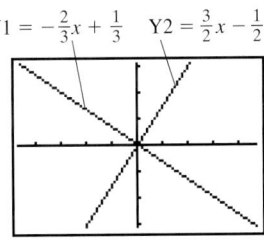

$Y1 = -\frac{2}{3}x + \frac{1}{3}$　　$Y2 = \frac{3}{2}x - \frac{1}{2}$

$(-47, 47, -31, 31)$

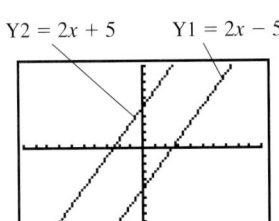

$Y1 = -\frac{2}{3}x + \frac{1}{3}$　　$Y2 = \frac{3}{2}x - \frac{1}{2}$

$(-10, 10, -10, 10)$
Skewed

d. $f(x) = 2x - 5 \quad m = 2 \quad b = -5$

$g(x) = 2x + 5 \quad m = 2 \quad b = 5$

The slopes (m) are equal, but the y-coordinates of the y-intercepts (b) are not equal. The lines are parallel.

$Y2 = 2x + 5$　　$Y1 = 2x - 5$

$(-10, 10, -10, 10)$

EXAMPLE 2　Determine by inspection whether the graphs of the given pairs of linear equations are coinciding, parallel, intersecting only, or intersecting and perpendicular.

a. $x = 5$　　　　　　　　　　　**b.** $y = 5$
$\quad\;\,3x + 4 = 7$　　　　　　　　　　$\quad\;\,x = 5$

Solution

a. Both linear equations, $x = 5$ and $x = 1$ ($3x + 4 = 7$), graph vertical lines. The lines are parallel.

b. The lines are intersecting and perpendicular, because one line is vertical and the other is horizontal.

✓ Objective 3.4.1 *CHECKUP*

In exercises 1 and 2, determine by inspection whether the graphs of the given pairs of linear equations are coinciding, parallel, intersecting only, or intersecting and perpendicular.

1. a. $4x - 5y = 10$
$\quad\;\;\,5x + 4y = 4$

b. $2x - 3y = 9$
$\quad\;\;\,2x - 3y = -9$

c. $5x - y = -1$
$\quad\;\;\,3x + 2y = -4$

d. $y = \frac{2}{3}x - 1$
$\quad\;\;\,2x - 3y = 3$

2. a. $2x = 6$
$\quad\;\;\,y + 3 = 5$

b. $2y = 14$
$\quad\;\;\,y + 3 = 0$

3. Assume that you have two equations, $y = m_1x + b_1$ and $y = m_2x + b_2$. When you graph the two equations, you will obtain two lines. The lines may be intersecting only, intersect- ing and perpendicular, parallel, or coinciding. Complete the following table to identify the relationship between m_1 and m_2 and between b_1 and b_2 for each situation:

Situation	Relationship between Slopes m_1 and m_2	Relationship between y-Intercept Values b_1 and b_2
Graphs coincide.	$m_1 = m_2$	$b_1 = b_2$
Graphs are parallel.		
Graphs intersect only.		
Graphs intersect and are perpendicular.		

4. All perpendicular lines are intersecting, but not all intersecting lines are perpendicular. Explain.

5. Subscripts are used in the description of the coordinate pairs (x_1, y_1) and (x_2, y_2). Explain the meaning of the subscripts.

Objective 3.4.2   Modeling the Real World

How useful is it to know that two graphed lines are coinciding, parallel, or intersecting? If the lines represent equations based on real-world situations, this knowledge can be very useful. For example, economists often graph sales revenue and production costs on the same coordinate system. If the two lines intersect, the point of intersection is called the **break-even point**. The values of the coordinates of this point correspond to how much money you have to make in sales in order to equal the money you spend in production costs. If the two lines don't intersect, you may never be able to earn back in sales the money you spent as costs. This is certainly an important thing to know. In other situations, the point of intersection of two lines may correspond to when one moving object is going to catch up to another. Even without knowing just where the point of intersection is, it's often useful to know from the equations whether there is a point of intersection at all.

EXAMPLE 3

Amy sells wooden Christmas ornaments at a fair booth. The paint costs $0.89 per ornament, the ribbon costs $0.11 per ornament, and the unpainted ornaments cost $0.50 each. The fair charges $25.00 to set up a booth.

a. Write an equation for the total cost, y, required to produce and sell x ornaments.

b. Last year Amy sold the ornaments for $1.50 each. If she plans to sell the ornaments at the same price this year, write an equation for the total revenue, y, for selling x ornaments.

c. Will there be a break-even point (an intersection of the two graphs in parts **a** and **b**)? Explain.

d. Write an equation for the total revenue, y, received for selling x ornaments if Amy decides to sell the ornaments for $2.00. Will there be a break-even point? Explain.

e. Graph the equations on your calculator, using the window (0, 100, 10, 0, 250, 10, 1). Determine the break-even point. Interpret your answer.

Solution

a. The cost per ornament will be $1.50.

$$0.89 + 0.11 + 0.50 = 1.50$$

The total cost will be $1.50 per ornament plus the booth cost of $25.00.

Let y = total cost
x = number of ornaments

$$y = 1.50x + 25.00$$

b. The total revenue will be $1.50 per ornament.

   Let y = total revenue
   x = number of ornaments

$$y = 1.50x$$

c. Using the equations $y = 1.50x + 25.00$ and $y = 1.50x$, we see that the linear equations have equal slopes: $1.50 = 1.50$. They also have unequal y-coordinates of the y-intercepts: $25.00 \neq 0$. Therefore, the lines are parallel and do not intersect, so there is no break-even point.

d. The total revenue will be $2.00 per ornament.

   Let y = total revenue
   x = number of ornaments

$$y = 2.00x$$

Using the equations $y = 1.50x + 25.00$ and $y = 2.00x$, we see that the linear equations have unequal slopes: $1.50 \neq 2.00$. The lines will intersect at one point, and that will be the break-even point.

e. Y1 = 1.50x + 25.00   Y2 = 2.00x

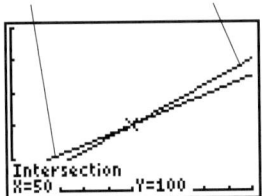

(0, 100, 10, 0, 250, 10, 1)

The intersection is (50, 100). Amy will break even and begin to make a profit if she sells 50 ornaments for a total revenue of $100. ■

Economists graph the demand function and the supply function on the same coordinate system. If the two lines intersect, the point of intersection is called the **equilibrium point**. The coordinate values of the point correspond to the price at which the demand and supply are equal. That is, there is not a surplus or shortage of the item.

EXAMPLE 4

In Section 3.3, we discussed the demand function and the supply function used by the bookstore manager and the supplier of a popular video. The demand function for the quantity demanded, $d(x)$, is related to the price, x dollars, by $d(x) = 20 - \dfrac{1}{2}x$. The supply function for the quantity supplied, $s(x)$, is related to the price, x dollars, by $s(x) = \dfrac{3}{5}x$. Will the graphs of the demand function and the supply function intersect? If so, use your calculator to determine the equilibrium point (point of intersection) and interpret its meaning.

Solution

The demand function in slope–intercept form is $d(x) = -\dfrac{1}{2}x + 20$. The slope of the demand function is $-\dfrac{1}{2}$. The supply function in slope–intercept form is $s(x) = \dfrac{3}{5}x$. The slope of the supply function is $\dfrac{3}{5}$. Since $-\dfrac{1}{2} \neq \dfrac{3}{5}$, the graphs of the lines will intersect.

The equilibrium point (point of intersection) is about (18.18, 10.91). That is, when the price of the popular video is $10.91, there will be an equal demand and supply of about 18 videos. There will be no shortage or surplus of the video at this price. ■

Y1 = $-\dfrac{1}{2}x + 20$ Y2 = $\dfrac{3}{5}x$

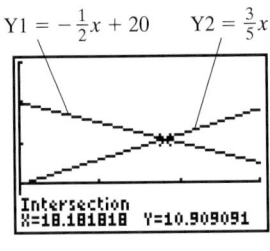

(0, 30, −10, 30)

APPLICATION

In 1992, Brian J. Whipp and Susan A. Ward of the School of Medicine at UCLA wrote a paper entitled "Will Women Soon Outrun Men?" In a prestigious science journal, the authors graphed the world record track times for both men and women. They noted that the slope of the graph for women was larger than the slope of the graph for men. Using this fact, they predicted that women would eventually overtake men in track competition in the year 1998. In critiquing this article that very year, Randall Woods used current data to write a linear equation for men and one for women, given year x and mean speed y (in meters per minute). The data on running resulted in the equations $y = 0.534x - 430$ for men and $y = 4.58x - 8800$ for women. According to these equations, will the women overtake the men and outrun them? If so, when? What is wrong with these conclusions?

Discussion

Given that the two equations have different slopes, we know that the equations will graph intersecting lines. The intersection point of these two graphs will determine the answer to the question, "Will Women Soon Outrun Men?"

   According to the graph, women will outrun men in the year 2068. This conclusion is based on the fact that there are no physical limitations on running and that the rate of increase will continue beyond the time of the most recent data used. Note that both equations would graph lines with a negative y-intercept, meaning that when time was 0 years, the mean speed of the runners was negative. This has no physical meaning.

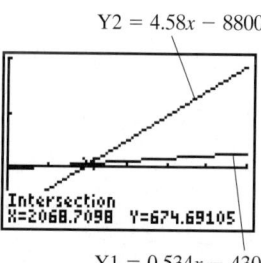

Y2 = 4.58x − 8800

Intersection
X=2068.7098   Y=674.69105

Y1 = 0.534x − 430

(0, 6000, 1000, −10,000, 20,000, 10,000)

✓ Objective 3.4.2 *CHECKUP*

1. Tim has a lawn care business. He spends an average of $8.50 per lawn for fertilizer and an average of $6.50 per lawn for labor to spread the fertilizer. He paid $85 for the spreader.
   a. Write an equation for the total cost, y, of providing Tim's service for x lawns.
   b. Tim charges $20 per lawn for the service. Write an equation for the total revenue, y, from providing the service for x lawns.
   c. Will there be a break-even point? Explain.
   d. Write an equation for the total revenue, y, from providing the service for x lawns if Tim charges $15 per lawn. Will there be a break-even point? Explain.

2. The manager of the music store has determined that the demand for a CD player is related to the price in x dollars by the function, $d(x) = 80 - \dfrac{3}{5}x$. The supplier of CD players

has determined that the supply, $s(x)$, for the player is related to the price in x dollars by the function, $s(x) = \dfrac{2}{5}x$. Will the graphs of the demand function and the supply function intersect? If so, use your calculator to determine the equilibrium point (point of intersection) and interpret its meaning.

3. Using data from *Statistical Abstracts of the United States*, we can represent the number (in millions) of males who listed their marital status as married by the function $m(x) = 0.463x + 55.6$, where x is the number of years since 1990. Likewise, we can represent the number (in millions) of females who listed their marital status as married by the function $f(x) = 0.442x + 56.61$. Will the graphs of these functions intersect? Explain.

3.4 EXERCISES

Student Solutions Manual

PH Math/Tutor Center

CD Video

Math XP
MathXL®

MyMathLab
MyMathLab

Interactmath.com

In exercises 1–26, determine by inspection whether the graphs of the given pairs of linear equations are (a) coinciding, (b) parallel, (c) intersecting only, or (d) both intersecting and perpendicular. Check by graphing.

1. $3x - 2y = 5(y + 7)$
   $7x = 3(1 - y)$

2. $4x + 5 = 0$
   $2(y - 1) = 6 - y$

3. $x = 4(y - 3)$
   $x = 4(y + 5)$

4. $x - 6 = 0$
   $x + 6 = 0$

5. $4x - y = 6$
   $2x - y + 3 = 0$

6. $x + y = 0$
   $x + 4y = 8$

7. $x = 2(y - 7)$
   $y = \dfrac{1}{2}x + 7$

8. $2x - 5 = x + 5$
   $x - 6 = 4$

9. $5x + y = -6$
$3x + y = 0$

10. $y = 3x - 4$
$2x = 3y + 6$

11. $4x + y = 8$
$4x + y + 2 = 0$

12. $y = 4x - 5$
$y + 1 = 4(x - 1)$

13. $y - 5 = 0$
$2x + 6 = x + 9$

14. $5x + y = 3$
$x = 5y$

15. $2y - 3 = 13$
$y + 1 = 4$

16. $x = -6$
$x + 3y = 3$

17. $x + 3 = 0$
$x - 5 = 0$

18. $14x - 2y = -1$
$7x - y = 6$

19. $2x - 9 = 0$
$x - 4 = 5 - x$

20. $y = 1$
$3(y + 3) = 2(y + 4)$

21. $3(y - 3) = 1$
$5y = 10 + 2y$

22. $y + 4 = 0$
$2x - 5y = 15$

23. $x = 2$
$y = 2x - 1$

24. $x + y = 9$
$y = -(x + 3)$

25. $y - 3 = 0$
$2x + 3y = 0$

26. $y + 3 = 0$
$y + 6 = 0$

27. Brook can buy candy bars wholesale for 15 cents each. He wants to resell them in his dormitory to earn some spending money. He hires his roommate Eric to sell the candy for him, paying Eric $2.50 per day, plus 10 cents per candy bar sold. The dorm's resident advisor charges Brook $1.00 a day for permission to sell the candy at the dorm.
  a. Write an equation for the total cost, y, in terms of x candy bars sold by Eric in one day.
  b. Write an equation for the total revenue, y, in terms of x candy bars sold when Eric sells the candy bars for 25 cents each.
  c. Find the break-even point, if there is one, when Brook will start making a profit for each day Eric sells candy for him.
  d. Write an equation for the total revenue, y, in terms of x candy bars sold when Eric sells the candy bars three for a dollar.
  e. Find the break-even point, if there is one, when Brook will start making a profit for each day Eric sells candy for him at this price.
  f. What will be the break-even point if Brook sells his own candy bars for 25 cents each?
  g. What will be the break-even point if Brook sells his own candy bars three for a dollar?
  h. What do you think Brook should do?

28. Joe wants to start a business selling restored antique radios. He can rent a counter in the local antiques mall for $200 per month. Miscellaneous costs average $85 per month. From his past bookkeeping records, he figures that he has purchased antique radios for an average of $70 each. He also figures that the cost of his labor and of parts required to restore the radios average $130 for each radio. (For the calculator graphs, use a window of $(0, 20, 1, 0, 2000, 100, 1)$.)
  a. Write a function for the total cost, y, of setting up shop to restore and sell x radios in a given month.
  b. Write an equation for the total revenue, y, received if Joe sells x radios at $200 each.
  c. Find the break-even point, if there is one, when Joe will start making a profit each month.
  d. Write an equation for the total revenue if Joe sells his radios at $300 each.
  e. Find the break-even point, if there is one, when Joe will start making a profit each month at this price.
  f. What will be the break-even point if Joe sells his radios for $250, reduces his counter rental to $125 per month by moving, and decreases his miscellaneous costs to $50 per month?
  g. What do you think Joe should do?

29. The bookstore manager has studied the daily demand for a computer software package and has determined that the quantity demanded, $d(x)$, is related to the price, x, by the linear demand function, $d(x) = 50 - \frac{1}{2}x$. The supplier of the computer software package has studied the daily supply for the software package and has determined a supply function, $s(x)$, $s(x) = \frac{2}{5}x$, where $s(x)$ is the quantity supplied and x is the price. Will the graphs of the demand function and the supply function intersect? If so, use your calculator to determine the equilibrium point (point of intersection) and interpret its meaning.

30. The daily demand for a product is given by $D(p) = 80 - \frac{4}{5}p$, where $D(p)$ is the quantity demanded each day by consumers when the price is p dollars per item. The daily supply of the product is given by $S(p) = \frac{5}{8}p$, where $S(p)$ is the quantity supplied each day when the price is p dollars per item. Will the graphs of the demand function and the supply function intersect? If so, use your calculator to determine the equilibrium point (point of intersection) and interpret its meaning.

31. Laurie can rent a car for $35.00 per day plus $0.25 per mile from Krazy Kar Rental, or she can rent a car for $60.00 per day with unlimited miles from Rational Car Rental. Write equations that represent her cost for one day of rental from each company if she drives the car x miles. Inspect the equations to determine whether their graphs will intersect. Explain. If the graphs do intersect, graph and find the intersection point, and interpret what it represents.

32. Jim can rent a stump grinder for a day for a flat fee of $65 from Rent All, Inc., or he can rent a grinder for a fee of $15 plus $10 per hour from Best Rental. Write equations that represent his cost for one day of rental from each company if he rents the grinder for x hours. Will the graphs of the equations intersect? Explain. If they do, graph and find the intersection point. Explain what the point represents.

33. Football superstar Archie receives a pass at the 50-yard line. He races in for a touchdown at a speed of 10 feet per second. Write an equation for the distance he will travel in x seconds. Defensive superstar Speedie is behind the 50-yard line. He races to catch Archie at a speed of 15 feet per second and crosses the 50-yard line 4 seconds after Archie. Write an equation for the distance Speedie will travel beyond the 50-yard line. Use both equations to determine whether Speedie will catch Archie before he reaches the end zone, which is 150 feet away.

34. In the Great Automobile Race of 1895, Villainous Victor left the starting line in Paris at 12 noon and averaged 18 miles per hour with his automobile. Trueheart Tom left the starting line 45 minutes later because of startup problems, but he was able to average 21.5 miles per hour with his gasoline-powered carriage. Write equations to determine the distance each man traveled, where x is the number of hours since 12 noon. Use the equations to determine at what distance Tom will overtake Victor, assuming that neither has car trouble in the race.

35. Vehicles bought by consumers for transportation depreciate in value, but some cars, like those bought by collectors, actually increase in value with age. Consider the purchase of a new vehicle in which the value of the vehicle, v, can be estimated by the equation $v = 15,000 - 1050t$, where t is the time in years from the purchase. Likewise, a collectible automobile bought in the same year has value $v = 10,500 + 650t$. Will the graphs of the two equations intersect? If so, find the intersection point and explain what it represents. If not, explain why.

36. A collector of classic cars finds that the value of one of his cars which he bought in 2004 can be estimated by the equation $v = 22,500 + 105t$, where t is the time in years after the year 2004. The same year he purchased a new vehicle in which the value is given by the equation $v = 25,000 - 200t$, where t is the time in years after the year 2004. Will the graphs of these

two equations intersect? If so, find the intersection point and explain what it represents. If not, explain why.

37. According to the United States National Center for Health Statistics, death due to heart disease went down between 2000 and 2001 in this country while death from homicide went up. The death rate per 100,000 people due to heart disease can be modeled by the linear function $c = -9.9t + 257.6$, where t is the number of years after the year 2000. The death rate per 100,000 people due to homicide can be modeled by the linear function $h = 1.2t + 5.9$, where t is the number of years after the year 2000. Will the graphs of the two functions intersect? If so, find the point of intersection and explain what it represents. If not, explain why.

38. The death rate per 100,000 due to accidents can be modeled by the linear function $a = 0.8t + 34.9$, where t is the number of years after the year 2000. Will the graph representing deaths by accident and the graph representing death from heart disease (exercise **37**) intersect? If so, find the point of intersection and explain what it represents. If not, explain why.

39. Based on information from the United States Census Bureau the median earnings of both men and women who work full time, year rounds, increased between 2001 and 2002. If this trend continues, the median earnings in dollars for a male can be given by $e = 38,885 + 544t$, where t is the time in years after the year 2001. The median earnings in dollars for a female can be given by $e = 29,669 + 535t$, where t is the time in years after the year 2001. In what year will women make the same median amount as men? Explain your answer.

40. Americans are spending more money on recreation. According to statistics from the United States Department of Commerce, Bureau of Economic Analysis, the per capita expenditure on books and maps can be estimated by $y = 2x + 23.1$, where y is the amount spent in dollars and x is the number of years after 1995. The per capita expenditure on video and audio products including computer equipment can be estimated by $y = 4.77x + 77$, where y is the amount spent in dollars and x is the number of years after 1995. Assuming that current trends continue, estimate the amount of money spent per capita on each recreational category in 2005. Will the graphs of the two equations intersect? If so, find the point of intersection and explain what it represents.

3.4 Calculator Exercises

Part 1

Let's explore settings of the window for graphing a linear equation in two variables.

1. Clear out any equations in the 〔 **Y=** 〕 menu. Use the 〔 **ZOOM** 〕 key to set the coordinate system to the standard setting. What are the window settings for this choice?

2. Set the coordinate system to the integer setting. What are the window settings for this choice?

3. Reset the integer setting by adding 47 to Xmin and Xmax and 31 to Ymin and Ymax. Then press 〔 **GRAPH** 〕. Use the arrow keys to move the cursor. Do you see that you have been able to reset the coordinate system and still maintain integer pairs for x and y?

4. Repeat steps 1 and 2, and then reset the window by multiplying each setting by 10. Leave Xres set to 1. Press 〔 **GRAPH** 〕. Move the cursor. Are the x- and y-values still integer pairs?

Are you beginning to see how you can adjust the window to be any domain and range that is appropriate for your needs while still maintaining integer pairs? Experiment with other settings.

Remember that you can always go back to 〔 **ZOOM** 〕 〔 **6** 〕 〔 **ZOOM** 〕 〔 **8** 〕 〔 **ENTER** 〕 to get back to your familiar settings.

Use the preceding techniques to experiment with setting the windows for a calculator graph to analyze the following break-even exercises. Determine which pairs of equations will result in intersecting graphs, which will be parallel, which will be perpendicular, and which will be coinciding. For graphs that intersect, find the point of intersection.

5. Cost function: $y = 300x + 450$
Revenue function: $y = 375x$

6. Cost function: $y = 1250 + 725x$
Revenue function: $y = 725x$

7. Cost function: $y = 1800$
Revenue function: $y = 125x$

Part 2

In this section, we stated that to determine perpendicular lines by inspection we must set the calculator to a square window. Let's explore the meaning of this statement.

1. Clear out any equations in the [Y=] menu. Turn on the grid. Press [2nd] [ZOOM] (FORMAT), use the arrow keys to highlight GridOn, and press [ENTER]. Set the calculator graph to the standard window setting $(-10, 10, -10, 10)$. Press [ZOOM] [6]. Note that the grid is not square but a set of rectangles because the calculator screen is a rectangle and we are setting both axes to the same setting, -10 to 10.

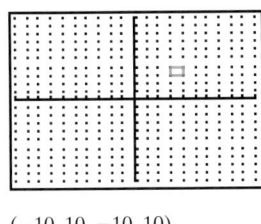

$(-10, 10, -10, 10)$

2. Enter the following set of equations that graph perpendicular lines.

$$y = 2x + 5$$
$$y = -\frac{1}{2}x - 2$$

3. Graph the lines on the standard window. The lines do not appear to be perpendicular.

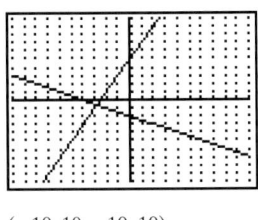

$(-10, 10, -10, 10)$

4. To change this calculator window to a square window, press [ZOOM] [5] (ZSquare). The graphs will now appear to be perpendicular. Also note that the grid is now square. The window setting is now approximately $(-15, 15, -10, 10)$.

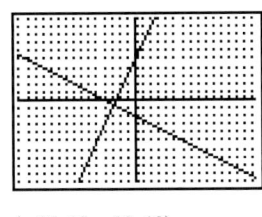

$(-15, 15, -10, 10)$

In this activity we used [ZOOM] [5] (ZSquare) to set a standard window to a square setting. We can use [ZOOM] [5] (ZSquare) to set any window setting to a square window setting. The new square setting will be different according to the original setting.

Use the [ZOOM] [5] (ZSquare) setting to view the following sets of equations that graph perpendicular lines.

1. $y = -4x + 6$
$y = \frac{1}{4}x - 2$

2. $y = -\frac{1}{4}x + 10$
$y = 4x + 5$

3. $y = -x + 25$
$y = x$

3.4 Writing Exercises

Suppose that you intend to graph two linear equations, given by $y = m_1x + b_1$ and $y = m_2x + b_2$.
    Before graphing the equations, you study them to compare the values of their slopes and the y-coordinates of their y-intercepts. Explain what these values can indicate to you. Next, complete the following matching exercise:

_____ **1.** Nonvertical coinciding

_____ **2.** Vertical coinciding

_____ **3.** Nonvertical parallel

_____ **4.** Vertical parallel

_____ **5.** Intersecting

_____ **6.** Nonvertical perpendicular

_____ **7.** Special perpendicular

a. $m_1 = m_2, b_1 \neq b_2$

b. $m_1 \cdot m_2 = -1$ or $m_2 = -\dfrac{1}{m_1}$

c. $m_1 = m_2, b_1 = b_2$

d. $m_1 \neq m_2$

e. $x = c, y = d$

f. $x = c, x = d, c = d$

g. $x = c, x = d, c \neq d$

3.5 WRITING LINEAR EQUATIONS FROM GIVEN DATA

OBJECTIVES

1   Write a linear equation in two variables, given the slope and *y*-intercept of the graph of the equation.

2   Write a linear equation in two variables, given the slope of the graph of the equation and the coordinates of a point through which the graph passes.

3   Write a linear equation in two variables, given the coordinates of two points through which the graph of the equation passes.

4   Write a linear equation in two variables, given the coordinates of a point through which the graph of the equation passes and a description of the line in terms of a second equation.

5   Model real-world situations by using linear equations in two variables.

APPLICATION

In the science fiction movie *Star Games 23: The Comet Strikes Jasper*, astronomers discover the comet Hale–Farewell traveling straight toward the planet Jasper. They measure the speed of the comet as 20,000 km/hr and its position as 3.0×10^7 km from Jasper. Assuming that the comet continues on its course in a straight line at the same speed, write an equation for its distance from Jasper and determine when it will hit the planet.

After completing this section, we will discuss this application further. See page 333.

So far, we have determined graphs for linear equations in two variables. However, suppose we are given information about a graph and need to determine its corresponding equation. Now we will see how to do that.

Objective 3.5.1

Writing a Linear Equation Given a Slope and *y*-Intercept

We already know the slope–intercept form of a linear equation, $y = mx + b$. Therefore, if we are given the slope, m, and the *y*-coordinate of the *y*-intercept, b, of a line, we can use that form to write an equation.

For example, write a linear equation in two variables for a line that has a slope of $\frac{1}{2}$ and a *y*-intercept of $(0, 3)$.

$$m = \tfrac{1}{2} \text{ and } b = 3 \ (y\text{-coordinate of the } y\text{-intercept})$$

Using the slope–intercept form of a linear equation, we have $y = mx + b$,

$$y = \frac{1}{2}x + 3 \qquad \text{Substitute values for } m \text{ and } b.$$

The slope and *y*-intercept may also be determined from a linear graph. Therefore, we can write an equation if we are given such a graph.

To write a linear equation in two variables from a given nonvertical graph,

- Determine the *y*-coordinate of the *y*-intercept (b).
- Determine the slope of the line (m) by counting the rise and the run between two integer coordinate points.
- Write a linear equation in two variables by substituting the values for m and b into the slope–intercept form of the equation $y = mx + b$.

To write a linear equation in two variables from a given vertical graph, write an equation in the form $x = h$, where h is the *x*-coordinate of the *x*-intercept of the graph.

EXAMPLE 1 Write a linear equation in two variables for the given graph

a. 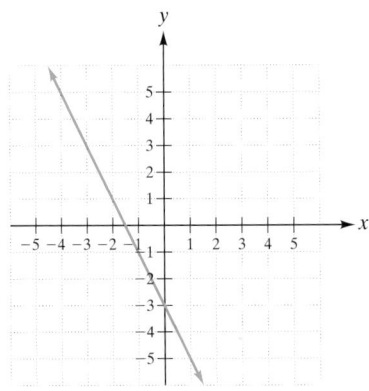 **b.** 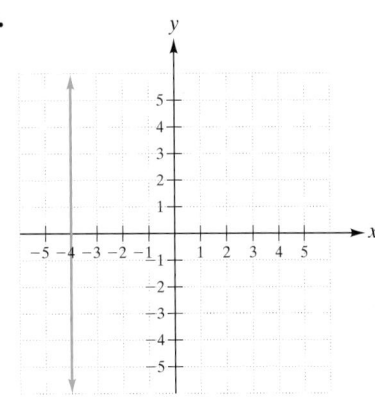 **c.**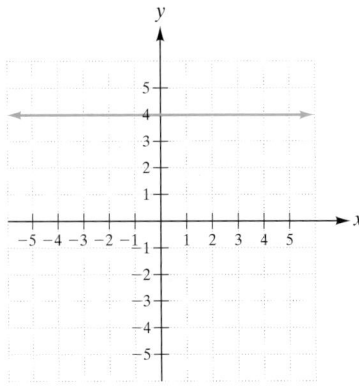

Solution

The graphs are labeled with the information needed to write an equation.

a. 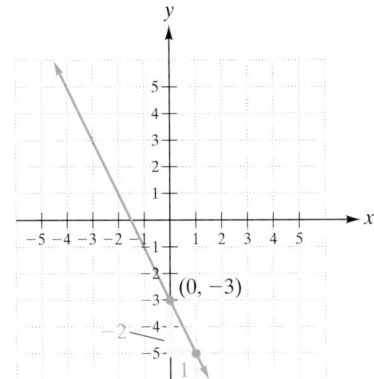 **b.** 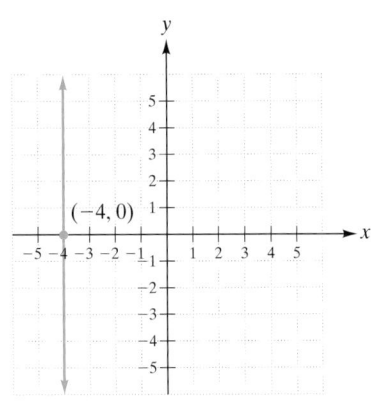 **c.**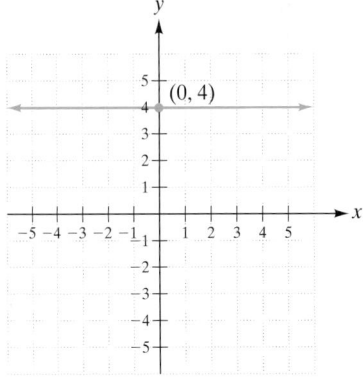

$m = \dfrac{-2}{1} = -2 \quad b = -3$

$y = mx + b$

$y = -2x - 3$

Vertical line with $h = -4$

$x = -4$

$m = 0 \quad b = 4$

$y = mx + b$

$y = 0x + 4$

$y = 4$

EXAMPLE 2 Write a linear equation in two variables from the given information.

    a. $m = 1; b = 0$ **b.** $m = 0; b = 3$ **c.** $m = \dfrac{3}{4}; b = 6$

Solution

a. Substitute $m = 1; b = 0$

$y = mx + b$

$y = 1x + 0$

$y = x$

b. Substitute $m = 0; b = 3$

$y = mx + b$

$y = 0x + 3$

$y = 3$

c. Substitute $m = \dfrac{3}{4}; b = 6$

$y = mx + b$

$y = \dfrac{3}{4}x + 6$

Objective 3.5.1 *CHECKUP*

In exercises 1 and 2, write a linear equation in two variables for the given graph or from the given information.

1. a.

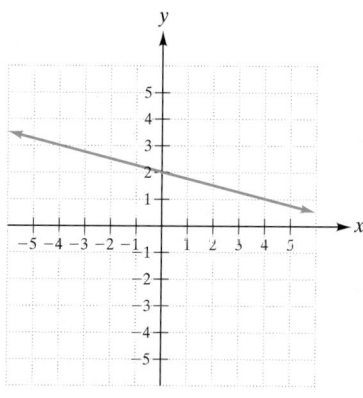

b.

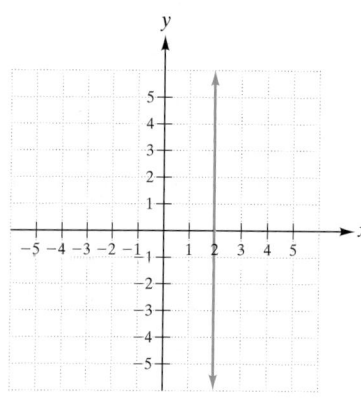

c.

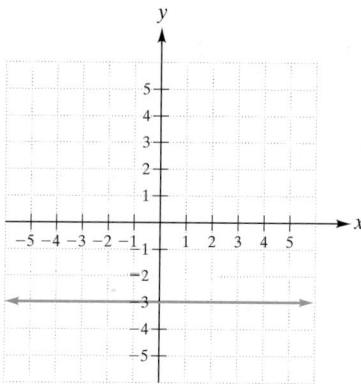

2. a. $m = -2; b = 5$ **b.** $m = 4; b = -1$ **c.** $m = 0; b = 3$

3. Why is $y = mx + b$ called the slope–intercept form of a linear equation?

Objective 3.5.2

Writing a Linear Equation for a Given Point and Slope

Sometimes we know the slope of a line and the coordinates of a point through which the line passes (x_1, y_1), and we want to write a linear equation in two variables for the line. To do so, we need a form for a linear equation in two variables that involves the slope and the coordinates of a point.

To write such a form for a linear equation in two variables, we will use a revised form of the slope formula, $m = \dfrac{y_2 - y_1}{x_2 - x_1}$. Instead of using two points on the line, we will write the variables x and y and use only the coordinates of one point, (x_1, y_1).

$$m = \frac{y_2 - y_1}{x_2 - x_1}$$

$$m = \frac{y - y_1}{x - x_1} \qquad \text{Use x and y instead of } x_2 \text{ and } y_2.$$

$$m(x - x_1) = \frac{y - y_1}{x - x_1}(x - x_1) \qquad \text{Multiply both sides by } (x - x_1).$$

$$m(x - x_1) = y - y_1 \qquad \text{Simplify.}$$

$$y - y_1 = m(x - x_1) \qquad \text{Write an equivalent equation.}$$

This form of a linear equation in two variables is called the **point–slope form**.

POINT–SLOPE FORM FOR A LINEAR EQUATION IN TWO VARIABLES

The point–slope form for a linear equation in two variables is $y - y_1 = m(x - x_1)$, where m is the slope of the line and (x_1, y_1) are the coordinates of a point located on the line.

We can use this point–slope form to write a linear equation in two variables, given the slope of a line and a point through which the line passes.

EXAMPLE 3

Write a linear equation in two variables for a line with a slope of $\frac{1}{2}$ and containing the point $(-3, 2)$.

Solution

Use the point–slope form for a linear equation. Let $m = \frac{1}{2}$, $x_1 = -3$, and $y_1 = 2$.

$$y - y_1 = m(x - x_1)$$

$$y - 2 = \frac{1}{2}[x - (-3)] \quad \text{Substitute values.}$$

$$y - 2 = \frac{1}{2}(x + 3) \quad \text{Simplify.}$$

$$y - 2 = \frac{1}{2}x + \frac{3}{2} \quad \text{Distribute } \frac{1}{2}.$$

$$y = \frac{1}{2}x + \frac{3}{2} + 2 \quad \text{Add 2 to both sides.}$$

$$y = \frac{1}{2}x + \frac{7}{2} \quad \text{Simplify.}$$

First, examine the equation to check the slope. Second, graph the equation on your calculator to determine that the given point is on the line.

$$y = mx + b$$

$$y = \frac{1}{2}x + \frac{7}{2}$$

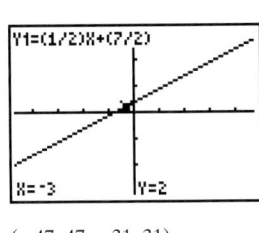

(−47, 47, −31, 31)

By examination of the equation, the slope is $\frac{1}{2}$. On the calculator, we see that the graph of the equation passes through the point $(-3, 2)$. ■

 TAKE NOTE In the writing exercises at the end of this section, another method for finding the equation of a line, given its slope and a point, is presented.

✓ Objective 3.5.2 *CHECKUP*

1. Write a linear equation in two variables for a line with the given slope and containing the given ordered pair. Graph the equation to check your solution.

$$m = \frac{3}{4}; (2, -3)$$

2. Why is $y - y_1 = m(x - x_1)$ called the point–slope form of a linear equation?

■

Objective 3.5.3   **Writing a Linear Equation for Two Given Points**

If we know two ordered pairs (x_1, y_1) and (x_2, y_2) on a line and want to write a linear equation in two variables for the line, we must first determine the slope of the line and then use the point–slope form for a linear equation.

To write a linear equation in two variables, given two data points,

- Determine the slope of the line (m), using the slope formula.
- Write a linear equation in two variables by substituting the values for m and (x_1, y_1) into the point–slope form of the equation, $y - y_1 = m(x - x_1)$.

EXAMPLE 4

Write a linear equation in two variables for a line containing the given ordered pairs. Graph the equation on your calculator to check your solution.

a. $(1, 3)$ and $(2, 7)$ **b.** $(-1, 4)$ and $(2, 4)$ **c.** $(-1, 5)$ and $(-1, -2)$

Solution

a. Let $x_1 = 1$, $y_1 = 3$, $x_2 = 2$, and $y_2 = 7$

$$m = \frac{y_2 - y_1}{x_2 - x_1}$$

$$m = \frac{7 - 3}{2 - 1} \qquad \text{Substitute.}$$

$$m = \frac{4}{1} \qquad \text{Simplify.}$$

$$m = 4 \qquad \text{Simplify.}$$

Now substitute one of the given ordered pairs, (1, 3), and the slope, 4, into the point–slope form.

$$y - y_1 = m(x - x_1)$$

$$y - 3 = 4(x - 1) \qquad \text{Substitute, } (x_1, y_1) = (1, 3) \quad m = 4$$

$$y - 3 = 4x - 4 \qquad \text{Distribute 4.}$$

$$y = 4x - 1 \qquad \text{Add 3 to both sides.}$$

It does not matter which ordered-pair coordinates are used. The results are the same.

$$y - y_1 = m(x - x_1)$$

$$y - 7 = 4(x - 2) \qquad \text{Substitute, } (x_1, y_1) = (2, 7) \quad m = 4$$

$$y - 7 = 4x - 8 \qquad \text{Distribute 4.}$$

$$y = 4x - 1 \qquad \text{Add 7 to both sides.}$$

Graph this equation on your calculator to check that the line contains both points. Enter the equation in Y1, graph the equation, and trace the graph to locate the given points.

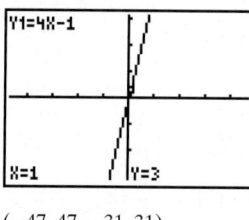

$(-47, 47, -31, 31)$

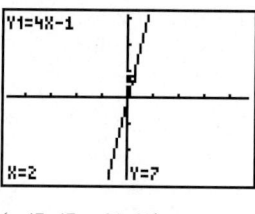

$(-47, 47, -31, 31)$

b. Determine the slope from the two given points.
Let $x_1 = -1$, $y_1 = 4$, $x_2 = 2$, and $y_2 = 4$

$$m = \frac{y_2 - y_1}{x_2 - x_1}$$

$$m = \frac{4 - 4}{2 - (-1)} \qquad \text{Substitute.}$$

$$m = \frac{0}{3} \qquad \text{Simplify.}$$

$$m = 0 \qquad \text{Simplify.}$$

The line is a horizontal line. The constant term is 4, because both ordered pairs have a y-coordinate of 4. The equation is $y = 4$.

If we had not noticed that the line was horizontal, we could have written the equation using the point–slope form. Use $(2, 4)$ as the point.

$$y - y_1 = m(x - x_1)$$
$$y - 4 = 0(x - 2) \qquad \text{Substitute.}$$
$$y - 4 = 0x - 0 \qquad \text{Distribute 0.}$$
$$y - 4 = 0 \qquad \text{Simplify.}$$
$$y = 4 \qquad \text{Add 4 to both sides.}$$

Check

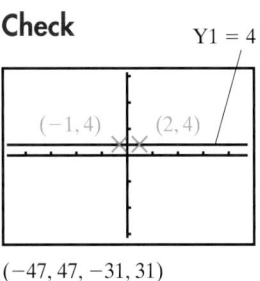

$(-47, 47, -31, 31)$

c. Determine the slope from the two given points. Let $x_1 = -1$, $y_1 = 5$, $x_2 = -1$, and $y_2 = -2$

$$m = \frac{y_2 - y_1}{x_2 - x_1}$$

$$m = \frac{-2 - 5}{-1 - (-1)} \qquad \text{Substitute.}$$

$$m = \frac{-7}{0} \qquad \text{Simplify.}$$

m is undefined.

     The line is a vertical line. The constant term of the equation is -1, because both ordered pairs have an x-coordinate of -1. The equation is $x = -1$. A calculator check is inappropriate. ■

 Objective 3.5.3 CHECKUP

1. Write a linear equation in two variables for a line containing the given ordered pairs. Graph the equation to check that it is correct.

   a. $(2, 3)$ and $(-1, 1)$ **b.** $(2, -3)$ and $(4, -3)$
   c. $(5, 9)$ and $(5, 2)$

2. We know that if you are given two points, you can draw a line between them. How can you find the equation of the line that connects them?

Objective 3.5.4

Writing a Linear Equation for a Graph Described by a Second Equation

In some situations, we need to write a linear equation in two variables when its graph is described in terms of a second equation. The details may vary from case to case, but the procedure always involves finding the slope and a point on the line.

> To write a linear equation in two variables in slope–intercept form when its graph is described in terms of a second equation.
>   Determine the slope of the line.
>
> - If the two lines have the same slope or are parallel, use the slope of the given equation.
> - If the two lines are perpendicular, use the opposite reciprocal of the slope of the given equation.
>
> Write the equation.
>
> - Substitute the values for the slope and the given point into the point–slope form of the equation.
> - Solve for y.
>
> Check the equation.
>
> - Verify that the given conditions have been satisfied.
> - A graph may be needed to check the conditions.

EXAMPLE 5   Write a linear equation in two variables for a line determined by the given information. Graph the equation on your calculator to check that the equation is correct.

a. A line passes through the point $(-1, -3)$ and is parallel to the graph of $2x + 3y = -2$.

b. A line passes through the point $(3, 5)$ and is perpendicular to the graph of $x - 2y = 1$.

Solution

a. Parallel lines have equal slopes. The slope of the given line is found by solving the equation for y to obtain the slope–intercept form, $y = mx + b$.

$$2x + 3y = -2$$
$$2x + 3y - 2x = -2 - 2x \qquad \text{Subtract } 2x \text{ from both sides.}$$
$$3y = -2 - 2x \qquad \text{Simplify.}$$
$$3y = -2x - 2 \qquad \text{Rearrange the right side.}$$
$$\frac{3y}{3} = \frac{-2x - 2}{3} \qquad \text{Divide both sides by 3.}$$
$$y = -\frac{2}{3}x - \frac{2}{3} \qquad \text{Simplify.}$$

The slope of the given line is $-\frac{2}{3}$. A parallel line will have the same slope.
Use the point–slope form with $-\frac{2}{3}$ as the slope and $(-1, -3)$ as the point.

$$y - y_1 = m(x - x_1)$$

$$y - (-3) = -\frac{2}{3}[x - (-1)] \qquad \text{Substitute.}$$

$$y + 3 = -\frac{2}{3}(x + 1) \qquad \text{Simplify.}$$

$$y + 3 = -\frac{2}{3}x - \frac{2}{3} \qquad \text{Distribute } -\frac{2}{3}.$$

$$y + 3 - 3 = -\frac{2}{3}x - \frac{2}{3} - 3 \qquad \text{Subtract 3 from both sides.}$$

$$y = -\frac{2}{3}x - \frac{2}{3} - \frac{9}{3} \qquad \text{Rewrite } -3 = -\frac{9}{-3}.$$

$$y = -\frac{2}{3}x - \frac{11}{3} \qquad \text{Simplify.}$$

Check

$$Y2 = -\frac{2}{3}x - \frac{2}{3}$$

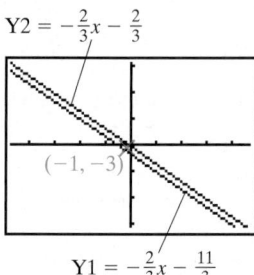

$(-1, -3)$

$$Y1 = -\frac{2}{3}x - \frac{11}{3}$$

b. Perpendicular lines have opposite reciprocal slopes. The slope of the given line is found by solving the equation for y to obtain the slope–intercept form, $y = mx + b$.

$$x - 2y = 1$$
$$x - 2y - x = 1 - x \qquad \text{Subtract } x \text{ from both sides.}$$
$$-2y = 1 - x \qquad \text{Simplify.}$$
$$\frac{-2y}{-2} = \frac{1 - x}{-2} \qquad \text{Divide both sides by } -2.$$
$$y = -\frac{1}{2} + \frac{1}{2}x \qquad \text{Simplify.}$$
$$y = \frac{1}{2}x - \frac{1}{2} \qquad \text{Rearrange the right side.}$$

The slope of the given line is $\frac{1}{2}$. The slope of a line perpendicular to the given line is -2 (the opposite reciprocal of $\frac{1}{2}$).

Use the point–slope form. Use -2 as the slope and $(3, 5)$ as the point.

$$y - y_1 = m(x - x_1)$$
$$y - 5 = -2(x - 3) \qquad \text{Substitute.}$$
$$y - 5 = -2x + 6 \qquad \text{Distribute } -2.$$
$$y - 5 + 5 = -2x + 6 + 5 \qquad \text{Add 5 to both sides.}$$
$$y = -2x + 11 \qquad \text{Simplify}$$

Check

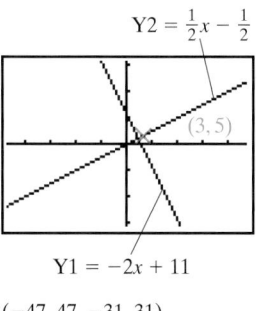

$Y2 = \frac{1}{2}x - \frac{1}{2}$

$(3, 5)$

$Y1 = -2x + 11$

$(-47, 47, -31, 31)$

 Objective 3.5.4 **CHECKUP**

1. Write a linear equation in two variables for a line determined by the given information. Graph the equation on your calculator to check that the equation is correct.
   a. A line passes through the point $(3, 2)$ and is parallel to the graph of $3x + 2y = 3$.
   b. A line passes through the point $(1, -1)$ and is perpendicular to the graph of $2x - 5y = 15$.

2. If you must find the equation of a line that is parallel to the graph of another equation, how can you determine which slope to use for your equation?

3. If you must find the equation of a line that is perpendicular to the graph of another equation, how can you determine which slope to use for your equation?

Objective 3.5.5 Modeling the Real World

Many real-world situations involve complicated relationships described by equations that are difficult to solve. But often, you can use a linear equation in two variables to approximate a solution. All you need to write the linear equation is two points on the line or a point on the line and the slope of the line; then you can use the graph to find an approximate solution to your original problem. This is usually a lot easier to do than solving a more complicated equation, and frequently the approximate solution is reasonably close to the actual solution.

EXAMPLE 6

According to the National Center for Health Statistics, life expectancy at birth for males in the United States has increased at an average rate of 0.23 years per year. In 1970 the life expectancy was 67.1 years.

a. Write a linear equation to determine the life expectancy of males, y, in terms of x years after 1970.

b. Use the equation to determine the life expectancy in 2000. According to the same report, the life expectancy in 2000 was 74.1 years. Compare this figure with your estimate.

c. Use your equation to predict the life expectancy of males in 2010.

Solution

a. The average rate of change is 0.23 years per year, or $m = 0.23$. Since 1970 is 0 years after 1970, the y-intercept is $(0, 67.1)$.

$$y = mx + b$$
$$y = 0.23x + 67.1$$

b. The year 2000 is 30 years after 1970; therefore, $x = 30$.

$$y = 0.23x + 67.1$$
$$y = 0.23(30) + 67.1 \qquad \text{Substitute.}$$
$$y = 74$$

Our estimated life expectancy for males in the United States for the year 2000 is 74 years. This is 0.1 years less than the actual reported figure of 74.1 years.

c. The year 2010 is 40 years after 1970; therefore, $x = 40$.

$$y = 0.23x + 67.1$$
$$y = 0.23(40) + 67.1 \quad \text{Substitute.}$$
$$y = 76.3$$

Our estimated life expectancy for males in the United States for the year 2010 is 76.3 years, assuming that the rate of increase continues to hold. ◼

EXAMPLE 7

Many formulas are found by writing equations to fit given data points. An example of this is the temperature conversion formulas. Two known reference points on the Celsius and Fahrenheit temperature scales are the freezing and boiling points of water. Water freezes at 0 degrees Celsius and 32 degrees Fahrenheit. Water boils at 100 degrees Celsius and 212 degrees Fahrenheit.

a. Write a formula (equation) for the Fahrenheit temperature (F) in terms of the Celsius temperature (C).

b. Using the formula you derived in part a, determine the temperature in degrees Fahrenheit if the temperature is 20 degrees Celsius.

Solution

a. The two data points (C, F) are $(0, 32)$ and $(100, 212)$. First, determine the slope.

$$m = \frac{F_2 - F_1}{C_2 - C_1}$$
$$m = \frac{212 - 32}{100 - 0} \quad \text{Substitute.}$$
$$m = \frac{180}{100} \quad \text{Simplify.}$$
$$m = \frac{9}{5} \quad \text{Simplify.}$$

Use the point–slope form to write an equation. Write the equation in terms of C and F instead of x and y.

$$F - F_1 = m(C - C_1)$$
$$F - 32 = \frac{9}{5}(C - 0) \quad \text{Substitute.}$$
$$F - 32 = \frac{9}{5}C - 0 \quad \text{Distribute } \frac{9}{5}.$$
$$F = \frac{9}{5}C + 32 \quad \text{Simplify.}$$

b. Substitute 20 for C in the equation just determined.

$$F = \frac{9}{5}C + 32$$
$$F = \frac{9}{5}(20) + 32 \quad \text{Substitute.}$$
$$F = 36 + 32 \quad \text{Simplify.}$$
$$F = 68 \quad \text{Simplify.}$$

The temperature is 68 degrees Fahrenheit when the Celsius reading is 20 degrees.

◼

By the age of 18 to 23, human bones are fully formed. After this ossification of the arms and legs, the two major bones in the arm and the two major bones in the leg have grown to a length proportional to the person's height. These relationships are used by forensic scientists and anthropologists to estimate the height of a human given the length of one or more of these four bones.

EXAMPLE 8

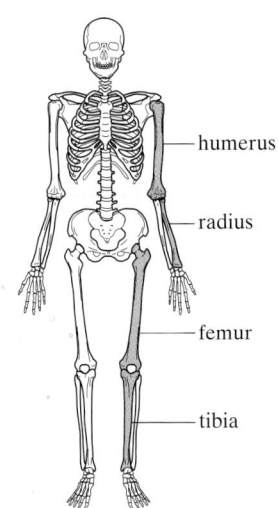

humerus

radius

femur

tibia

Dr. Ward, an archeologist, discovered a male femur that was 17.9 inches in length. She concluded that the male was approximately 65.66 inches or 5 feet 6 inches in height. She also discovered a second male femur that was 21.6 inches in length and estimated his height to be 72.62 inches or 6 feet 1 inch. Let x = the length, in inches, of the male femur, and y = the height of the male in inches. Write a linear equation for the height, in inches, of a male in terms of the length of the femur, in inches. Use the equation to estimate the height of a male given that the femur is 19.6 inches.

Solution

Two ordered pairs given x = the length, in inches, of the male femur, and y = the height of the male in inches are $(17.9, 65.66)$ and $(21.6, 72.62)$. Determine the slope.

$$m = \frac{y_2 - y_1}{x_2 - x_1}$$

$$m = \frac{72.62 - 65.66}{21.6 - 17.9} \qquad \text{Substitute.}$$

$$m \approx 1.88$$

Use the point–slope form to write an equation of the line through the two given points.

$$y - y_1 = m(x - x_1)$$
$$y - 65.66 = 1.88(x - 17.9) \qquad \text{Substitute.}$$
$$y - 65.66 = 1.88x - 33.652 \qquad \text{Distribute 1.88.}$$
$$y - 65.66 + 65.66 = 1.88x - 33.652 + 65.66 \qquad \text{Add 65.66 to both sides.}$$
$$y = 1.88x + 32.008$$

Use the equation and substitute 19.6 for x.

$$y = 1.88x + 32.008$$
$$y = 1.88(19.6) + 32.008 \qquad \text{Substitute.}$$
$$y = 68.856$$

The male was approximately 68.86 inches given the femur was 19.6 inches. ■

APPLICATION

In the science fiction movie *Star Games 23: The Comet Strikes Jasper,* astronomers discover the comet Hale–Farewell traveling straight toward the planet Jasper. They measure the speed of the comet as 20,000 km/hr and its position as 3.0×10^7 km from Jasper. Assuming that the comet continues on its course in a straight line at the same speed, write an equation for its distance from Jasper and determine when it will hit the planet.

Discussion

Let x = the travel time (in hours) of the comet
  y = the distance (in kilometers) the comet is from Jasper

The average rate of change of the distance is decreasing at a rate of 20,000 km/hr (the speed). Therefore, $m = -20,000$ or -2.0×10^4.

At the time of 0 hours, the comet's distance from Jasper is 3.0×10^7 km. This gives us a data point of $(0, 3.0 \times 10^7)$. Therefore, $b = 3.0 \times 10^7$.

$$y = mx + b \qquad \text{Slope–intercept form}$$
$$y = (-2.0 \times 10^4)x + (3.0 \times 10^7) \qquad \text{Substitute values for } m \text{ and } b.$$

The comet will hit Jasper when $y = 0$, because its distance from Jasper, y, will then be 0 km. Therefore, substitute 0 for y and solve for x. (This point is the x-intercept.)

$$y = (-2.0 \times 10^4)x + (3.0 \times 10^7)$$
$$0 = (-2.0 \times 10^4)x + (3.0 \times 10^7)$$
$$0 + (2.0 \times 10^4)x = (-2.0 \times 10^4)x + (3.0 \times 10^7) + (2.0 \times 10^4)x$$
$$(2.0 \times 10^4)x = 3.0 \times 10^7$$
$$\frac{(2.0 \times 10^4)x}{2.0 \times 10^4} = \frac{3.0 \times 10^7}{2.0 \times 10^4}$$
$$x = 1.5 \times 10^3$$
$$x = 1500$$

The comet will hit Jasper in 1500 hours.

The preceding example was science fiction, but astronomers actually did a calculation like that for Comet Shoemaker–Levy, which slammed into Jupiter on July 16, 1994. Of course, the actual calculation was more complicated because the comet wasn't moving at a constant speed or in a straight line, but even so, astronomers were able to pinpoint the time of collision to within minutes for each part of the "string-of-pearls" comet. For example, on July 12, a table of anticipated collision times was published in the *New York Times*. The predicted time for the largest piece, Fragment G, to hit Jupiter was 3:24 A.M. Eastern time. On July 19, the *New York Times* reported that the time of impact for Fragment G on July 16 was 3:28 A.M. Eastern Daylight time, only 4 minutes off the predicted time.

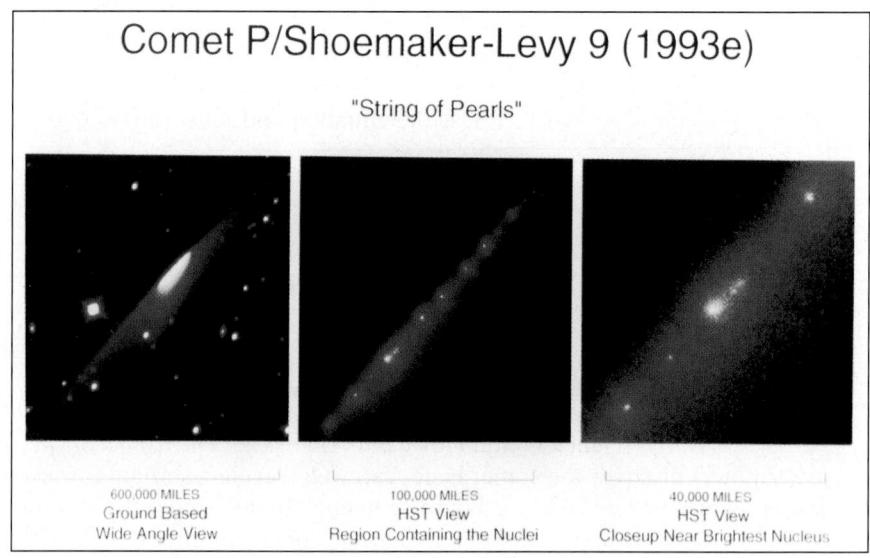

Objective 3.5.5 *CHECKUP*

1. According to the National Center for Health Statistics, life expectancy at birth for females in the United States has increased at an average rate of 0.16 years per year. In 1970 the life expectancy was 74.7 years.
   a. Write a linear equation to determine the life expectancy of females, y, in terms of x years after 1970.
   b. Use the equation to determine the life expectancy in 2000. According to the same report, the life expectancy in 2000 was 79.5 years. Compare this figure with your estimate.
   c. Use your equation to predict the life expectancy of females in 2010.

2. If we reverse the variables in Example 7, the two data points (F, C) will become $(32, 0)$ and $(212, 100)$.
   a. Determine the new slope of the relation between F and C.
   b. Use the point–slope form to write a new equation for C in terms of F.
   c. Using the formula, find the Celsius temperature if the temperature is 75 degrees Fahrenheit.

3. Dr. Ward discovered a female femur that was 17.9 inches in length. She concluded that the female was approximately 63.49 inches or 5 feet 3 inches in height. She also discovered a second female femur that was 21.6 inches in length and

estimated her height to be 70.69 inches or 5 feet 11 inches. Let x = the length, in inches, of the female femur, and y = the height of the female in inches. Write a linear equation for the height, in inches, of a female in terms of the length of the femur, in inches. Use the equation to estimate the height of a female given that the femur is 19.6 inches.

4. The United States Department of Commerce reports that in 1995 the average American family of four spent $1606 on recreation. This number increased at an average rate of $393 per year. Write a linear equation that relates spending, s, to years after 1995, x. If this trend continues, how much will be spent on recreation by a family in the year 2008?

3.5 EXERCISES

 Student Solutions Manual  PH Math/Tutor Center CD Video Math XL MathXL® MyMathLab MyMathLab   Interactmath.com

Write a linear equation for each graph.

1.
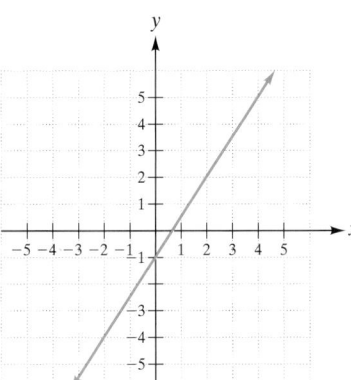

2.
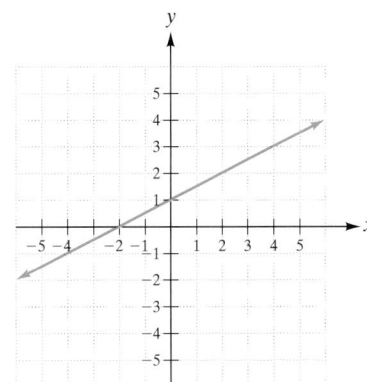

3.
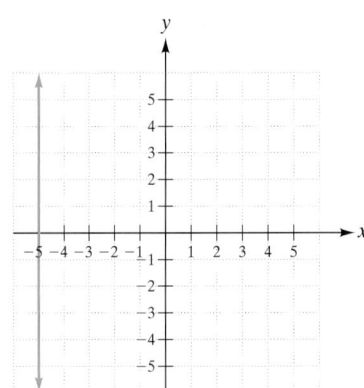

4.
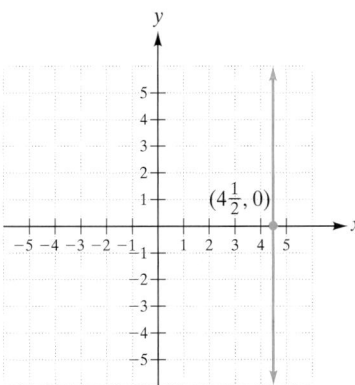

5.
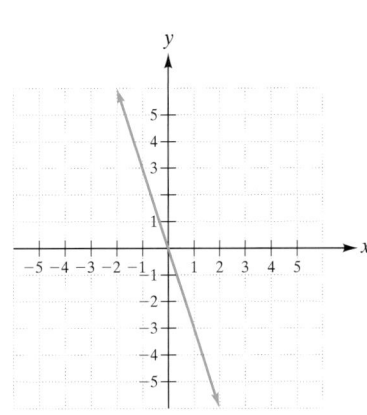

6.
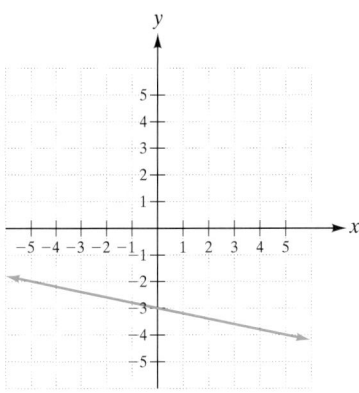

7.
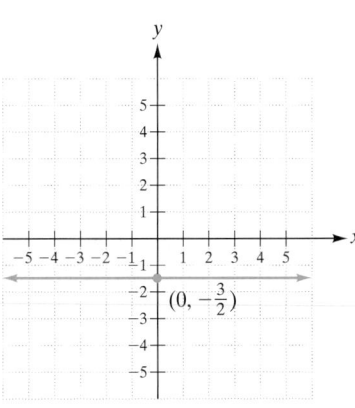

8.
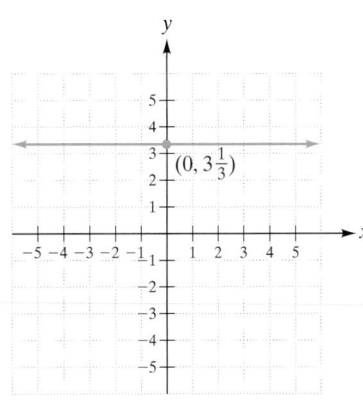

Write a linear equation for the given information.

9. $m = -\dfrac{2}{5}, b = 4$

10. $m = -\dfrac{1}{7}, b = -9$

11. $m = \dfrac{5}{9}, b = 0$

12. $m = \dfrac{1}{7}, b = -1$

13. $m = 4, b = -\dfrac{3}{4}$

14. $m = 11, b = \dfrac{1}{2}$

15. $m = -4.1, b = 0.5$

16. $m = -6.2, b = -2.2$

17. $m = 0, b = -33$

18. $m = -4, b = 0$

Write a linear equation in two variables for a line with the given slope and containing the given ordered pair. Graph the equation to check that it is correct.

19. $m = \dfrac{2}{3}, (3, -3)$ **20.** $m = -2, (4, 0)$ **21.** $m = -3, (0, 4)$ **22.** $m = \dfrac{4}{3}, (-6, -3)$

23. $m = -1.7, (3, -1.5)$ **24.** $m = 1.4, (1.5, -1.2)$

Write a linear equation for a line containing the given ordered pairs. Graph the equation to check that it is correct.

25. $(-1, 1)$ and $(1, -2)$ **26.** $(8, 6)$ and $(1, 6)$ **27.** $(-1, -2)$ and $(-1, 5)$

28. $(1, 6)$ and $(2, 1)$ **29.** $(-1, 1)$ and $(-2, -1)$ **30.** $(-3, 2)$ and $(4, 4)$

31. $(-2, 2)$ and $(4, 2)$ **32.** $(2, 9)$ and $(2, 1)$ **33.** $\left(4\dfrac{1}{2}, 5\dfrac{1}{4}\right)$ and $(1, 4)$

34. $\left(-2, -1\dfrac{1}{3}\right)$ and $\left(2\dfrac{1}{2}, 1\right)$ **35.** $\left(-1\dfrac{1}{3}, 2\right)$ and $(0, 0)$ **36.** $\left(2\dfrac{1}{2}, 5\dfrac{1}{2}\right)$ and $\left(3\dfrac{1}{2}, 1\right)$

37. $(0.5, 0)$ and $(-0.8, 4.2)$ **38.** $(-4, -1)$ and $(-5.1, -4.5)$ **39.** $(2.4, 2.8)$ and $(-2.6, -2.2)$

40. $(1, 6)$ and $(1.5, -3.5)$

In exercises 41–60, write a linear equation for a line determined by the given information. Check by graphing the equations.

41. A line passes through the point $(8, 7)$ and has the same slope as the line whose equation is $3x - 8y = 32$.

42. A line passes through the point $(6, 2)$ and has the same slope as the line whose equation is $5x + 3y = 15$.

43. A line passes through the point $(4, 0)$ and has the same slope as the line whose equation is $x + 2y = 7$.

44. A line passes through the point $(0, -3)$ and has the same slope as the line whose equation is $2x - y = 4$.

45. A line whose y-intercept has a y-coordinate of -5 has the same slope as the line whose equation is $y = 3x + 4$.

46. A line whose y-intercept has a y-coordinate of 2 has the same slope as the line whose equation is $y = -3x + 5$.

47. A line passes through the point $\left(\dfrac{4}{9}, -\dfrac{5}{6}\right)$ and is parallel to the graph of $y = 3x - 10$.

48. A line passes through the point $\left(\dfrac{2}{3}, -\dfrac{1}{6}\right)$ and is parallel to the graph of $y = 2x + 5$.

49. A line parallel to the graph of $y = -1.2x + 3.5$ passes through the point $(4, -2)$.

50. A line parallel to the graph of $y = -0.8x + 2.4$ passes through the point $(9, -3)$.

51. A line parallel to the graph of $2x + 4y = 5$ passes through the origin.

52. A line parallel to the graph of $x - 3y = 6$ passes through the origin.

53. A line passes through the point $(3.6, 5.8)$ and is perpendicular to the line whose equation is $y = 3x + 12$.

54. A line passes through the point $(-3.6, 1.8)$ and is perpendicular to the graph of $y = -6x$.

55. A line passes through the point $(15, -30)$ and is perpendicular to the graph of $y = 5x - 1$.

56. A line passes through the point $(-10, 8)$ and is perpendicular to the graph of $y = 2x + 5$.

57. A line passes through the origin and is perpendicular to the line whose equation is $y = -\dfrac{2}{3}x - 1$.

58. A line passes through the origin and is perpendicular to the line whose equation is $y = \dfrac{5}{4}x + 2$.

59. A line whose x-intercept has an x-coordinate of 3 is perpendicular to the line whose equation is $3x + 2y = 4$.

60. A line whose x-intercept has an x-coordinate of -2 is perpendicular to the line whose equation is $5x - 4y = 4$.

61. Alex purchased a four-wheel-drive truck for $34,000 for his construction business. He plans to use a linear depreciation of its value for tax purposes. He uses a depreciation rate of $6800 per year. Write a linear function for the value of the truck, $v(t)$, in terms of t years in service. Use the function to estimate when the truck will have lost half of its value.

62. Hannah purchased an automobile for $24,000 for her business. She plans to use a linear depreciation of its value for tax purposes. She uses a depreciation rate of $3600 per year. Write a linear function for the value of the automobile, $v(t)$, in terms of t years in service. Use the function to estimate when the automobile will have lost half of its value.

63. The United States Census Bureau reported that in 1995 the median earnings of women working full time was about $26,000 and was growing at about the rate of $675 per year.
 a. Write a linear equation to determine these earnings, y, in terms of x years after 1995.
 b. Use the equation to estimate the earnings in 2002. According to more recent data the earnings in 2002 were about $30,000. Compare this figure with your answer.
 c. Use the equation to predict the median earnings of women in 2010.

64. Data from the League of American Theaters and Producers Inc. shows that gross ticket sales for Broadway shows was 209 million dollars in 1985 and was growing at the rate of about 26.12 million dollars per year.
 a. Write a linear equation to determine the gross ticket sales in million dollars, s, in terms of x years after 1985.
 b. Use the equation to estimate the gross ticket sales in 2001. According to more recent data, the gross ticket sales in 2001 was 666 million dollars. Compare this figure with your answer.
 c. Use the equation to predict the gross sales in 2007.

65. According to the United States Department of Education, the verbal scores on the SAT (Scholarship Aptitude Test) have declined about 1.09 points per year since 1966. If the average verbal score was 543 in 1966, write a linear equation to estimate the score, s, in terms of x years after 1966. Use your equation to estimate the score in 2001 and 2002. More recent data indicates that the score was 507 in 2002. Compare this figure with your answer. Use the equation to predict the score in 2015.

66. According to the United States Department of Education the average female mathematical score on the SAT (Scholastic Aptitude Test) has been rising about 2.5 points per year since 1980. If the average score was 473 in 1980, write a linear equation to estimate the score, s, in terms of x years after 1980. Use your equation to estimate the score in 2002. According to more recent data, the score in 2002 was 503. Compare this figure with your answer. Use the equation to predict the score in 2010. Can this trend continue indefinitely? Why or why not?

67. A consumer article reported that a car weighing 2500 pounds averages 40 miles per gallon of gasoline, while a car weighing 3500 pounds averages 35 miles per gallon. Write a linear equation relating the gas mileage, y, to the weight of the car, x.

68. A consumer article reported that a car weighing 5000 pounds averages 15 miles per gallon of gasoline, while a car weighing 4500 pounds averages 19 miles per gallon. Write a linear equation relating the gas mileage to the weight of the car. How does this equation compare with that of exercise 67? Can you explain any differences?

69. In scientific work, the Kelvin temperature scale measures temperatures from absolute zero, which is the lowest possible temperature. Temperatures on this scale have a linear relationship with the Celsius scale. Given the points (C, K) of $(0, 273)$ and $(-10, 263)$, use the slope–intercept form to write the relationship between the two scales. What Kelvin temperature corresponds to $100°C$?

70. The Rankine temperature scale is used in engineering practice. Temperatures on this scale have a linear relationship with the Fahrenheit scale. Given the points (F, R) of $(32, 492)$ and $(180, 640)$, use the point–slope form to determine the relationship between the two scales. What Rankine temperature corresponds to $75°F$?

71. Dr. Pace, an archeologist, discovered a female humerus that was 29.42 centimeters in length. She concluded that the female was approximately 157.36 centimeters in height. She also discovered a second female humerus that was 32.69 centimeters in length and estimated her height to be 167.64 centimeters. Let x = the length, in centimeters, of the female humerus, and y = the height of the female in centimeters. Write a linear equation for the height, in centimeters, of a female in terms of the length of the humerus, in centimeters. Use the equation to estimate the height of a female given that the humerus is 31.25 centimeters.

72. Dr. Pace also discovered a male humerus that was 33.41 centimeters in length. She concluded that the male was approximately 172.83 centimeters in height. She also discovered a second male humerus that was 31.64 centimeters in length and estimated his height to be 167.54 centimeters. Let x = the length, in centimeters, of the male humerus, and y = the height of the male in centimeters. Write a linear equation for the height, in centimeters, of a male in terms of the length of the humerus, in centimeters. Use the equation to estimate the height of a male given that the humerus is 32.27 centimeters.

73. The United States Bureau of Labor Statistics reports that the average family spent about $150 on reading materials in 1990 and that this amount was growing approximately as shown in the table. Find the linear equation that models this data and verify the data points.

Year	1990	1991	1995	1997	2000
Amount spent (in dollars)	150.00	150.50	152.50	153.50	155.00

74. Between 1995 and 1998 deaths due to chronic lower respiratory diseases increased in a linear fashion. Use the data in the table below to find the linear equation that models this data. Verify the data points.

Year	1995	1996	1997	1998
Death rates per 100,000 population	40.5	41.0	41.5	42.0

75. The number of deaths by liver disease and cirrhosis per 100,000 people in the United States in 1990 was 11.1. In 2000, the number of deaths per 100,000 people decreased to 9.5.
   a. Write a linear equation to determine the number of deaths by liver disease and cirrhosis per 100,000 people, y, for x years after 1990.
   b. Estimate the number of deaths in 1995. According to data, the number of deaths by liver disease and cirrhosis per 100,000 people in 1995 was 10. Compare this number to your estimate and discuss.
   c. Estimate the number of deaths in 2001. According to data, the number of deaths by liver disease and cirrhosis per 100,000 people in 2001 was 9.5. Compare this number to your estimate and discuss.

76. The number of deaths by heart disease per 100,000 people in the United States in 1978 was 409.9. In 1992, the number of deaths per 100,00 people decreased to 306.1.
   a. Write a linear equation to determine the number of deaths by heart disease per 100,000 people, y, for x years after 1978.
   b. Estimate the number of deaths in 1982. According to data, the number of deaths by heart disease per 100,000 people in 1982 was 389. Compare this number to your estimate and discuss.
   c. Estimate the number of deaths in 2001. According to data, the number of deaths by heart disease per 100,000 people in 2001 was 247.8. Compare this number to your estimate and discuss.

77. The United States Bureau of the Census indicates that the number of divorced people has grown from 4.3 million in 1970 to 18.3 million in 1996. Write a linear equation that relates number of divorced people, n, to years after 1970, t. If this trend continues, how many divorced people will there be in 2010? Can this trend continue indefinitely? Why or why not?

78. The number of never-married adults is also increasing: from 21.4 million in 1970 to 44.9 million in 1996. Write a linear equation that relates the number of never-married adults, y, to years after 1970, x. If this trend continues, how many never-married people will there be in 2010? Can this trend continue indefinitely? Why or why not?

3.5 Calculator Exercises

In this section, we wrote an equation for a line given two data points. We then used the equation to estimate additional information. Sometimes the estimate was a "good fit" for this additional information, and sometimes our estimate had limitations. Graphing calculators have statistical procedures that can be used to find the equation of a line through more than two points. The line that best fits the data is called the regression line. We will limit our discussion of the details of these procedures and use the procedures to find the regression line. While this is not the intent of the procedures, they can be used to write such an equation. As an example, suppose you wish to find the equation of the line that passes through the points $(3, 55)$ and $(1, 10)$.

a. Clear any data from the lists L1 and L2, which is where the coordinate pairs will be stored.

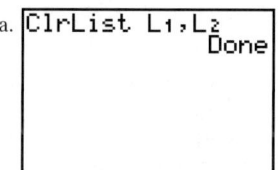

b. Store the coordinate pairs in your calculator, using L1 for the x-coordinate and L2 for the y-coordinate.

STAT 1

Use the arrow keys to move to the L1 column.

3 ENTER 1 ENTER ▶ 5 5 ENTER 1 0 ENTER

c. Graph the points by turning on the Stat Plot feature.

2nd MODE (QUIT) 2nd Y= (STAT PLOT) 1 (Plot 1) ENTER 2nd MODE (QUIT)
ZOOM 9 (ZoomStat)

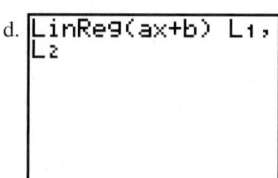

d. Calculate the "linear regression," which will provide the equation.

This instruction directs the calculator to find the x-coordinates in list L1 and the y-coordinates in list L2 and to come up with the equation.

d. `LinReg(ax+b) L₁, L₂`

e. When the ENTER command is keyed, the calculator displays the result. The equation for the line passing through the two points is given by

$$y = 22.5x - 12.5$$

ENTER

e. `LinReg`
`y=ax+b`
`a=22.5`
`b=-12.5`

f. Graph the line. You may enter the equation in Y1 manually or use the calculator feature described below.

Observe that the line passes through both graphed points.

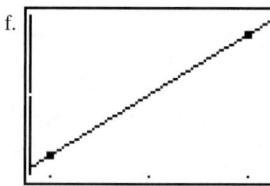

Use this method to find the equations of the lines passing through the given pairs of points. Check the solutions by graphing or substituting the coordinate pairs into the equations.

1. $(5, 47.2)$ and $(11, 66.7)$, where x is the number of years after 1990 and y is the per capita expenditure on toys and sport supplies.

2. $(10, 631.5)$ and $(25, 487)$, where x is the number of years after 1970 and y is cigarette consumption in the United States in billions.

3. $(4, 26,000)$ and $(12, 30,203)$, where x is the number of years after 1990 and y is the median yearly earnings in dollars by a female in the United States.

4. Use this method to find the regression line or line of "best fit" for the following data sets.

Year	1994	1995	1996	1997	1998
Deaths by Heart Disease per 100,000 Population	299.7	296.3	288.3	280.4	272.4

Use your equation to predict the number of deaths due to heart disease in 2001. How does the actual number, 247.8, compare to your number?

5. Use this method to find the regression line or line of "best fit" for the following data sets.

Year	1996	1997	1998	1999	2000
Deaths by Diabetes per 100,000 Population	24	24	24.2	25.2	25.0

Use your equation to predict the number of deaths due to diabetes in 2001. How does the actual number, 25.3, compare to your number? Why do you think that deaths due to diabetes are increasing?

3.5 Writing Exercises

In this section, you learned that if you were given the slope of a line (m) and a point (x_1, y_1) that the line passes through, you can find the equation of the line by substituting the values for m, x_1, and y_1 into the point–slope form,

$$y - y_1 = m(x - x_1)$$

and simplifying the resulting equation. However, if you substitute the values for m, x_1 (for x), and y_1 (for y) into the slope–intercept form,

$$y = mx + b$$

you can solve for b. Then, when you substitute the values for m and b back into the slope–intercept form, you will obtain the same equation as you did using the point–slope form.

Try both methods to find the equation of a line with a slope of $\frac{3}{4}$ and passing through $(4, 1)$. Explain why you think both methods yield the same equation. Then state which method you prefer, and explain why you prefer that method.

■ Chapter 3 Summary

Vocabulary Review

After completing this chapter, you should be able to define the following key terms.

average rate of change	intersecting	rise
break-even point	linear equation in two variables	run
coincident	linear function	slope
coinciding	parallel	slope–intercept form
equilibrium point	perpendicular	standard form
grade	point–slope form	subscripts

Fill in the blank with one of the words or phrases listed above.

1. _____ of a linear equation in two variables is $ax + by = c$.

2. _____ of a linear equation in two variables is $y = mx + b$.

3. _____ of a linear equation in two variables is $y - y_1 = m(x - x_1)$.

4. A _____ is a function that can be written as $f(x) = mx + b$.

5. _____ lines have the same slope and same y-intercept. The lines are said to be _____.

6. _____ lines have the same slope but different y-intercepts.

7. _____ lines and _____ lines have different slopes.

8. Two lines are _____ if the product of their slopes is -1.

9. The _____ of a line is defined as the ratio of the amount of _____ to the amount of _____.

10. The point of intersection of a demand function and a supply function is the _____.

11. The point of intersection of a cost function and a revenue function is the _____.

12. _____ and _____ are two examples of slope of a line.

Reflections

1. How can you determine algebraically the x-intercept and the y-intercept of the graph of a linear equation?
2. If the graph of a linear equation is a horizontal line, what can you say about its intercepts? If the graph of a linear equation is a vertical line, what can you say about its intercepts?
3. Explain how to graph a linear equation in two variables by using the intercept method.
4. What does the slope of a line measure? How can you determine the slope of a line?
5. Describe what the graph of a linear equation in two variables will look like if
   a. the slope of the line is positive.
   b. the slope of the line is negative.
   c. the slope of the line is 0.
   d. the slope of the line is undefined.

6. How would you graph a linear equation in two variables using the slope-intercept method?
7. What can you say about the slopes of two lines if
   a. the lines are parallel?
   b. the lines are intersecting only?
   c. the lines are intersecting and perpendicular?
   d. the lines are coinciding?
8. How can you write an equation for a line if it is described by
   a. its slope and y-intercept?
   b. its slope and a point on the line?
   c. two points on the line?
   d. a point on the line and the equation of another line parallel to the given line?
   e. a point on the line and the equation of another line perpendicular to the given line?

■ Chapter 3 Section-by-Section Review

3.1

Recall	Examples
Linear equation in two variables • The standard form is $ax + by = c$, where a, b, and c are real numbers and a and b are not both 0.	**Linear equations in two variables** $2x + 4y = 5$ $x = 7$ $y = \dfrac{2}{3}$
Graph by using ordered pairs • Determine three ordered-pair solutions of the equation, using a table of values. • Graph and label the three ordered-pair solutions. • Connect the graphed points with a straight line, and add arrows to the ends of the line.	Graph $-2x + 4y = 1$. Solve for y. $y = \dfrac{1}{2}x + \dfrac{1}{4}$ Set up a table. <table><tr><td>x</td><td>$y = \dfrac{1}{2}x + \dfrac{1}{4}$</td><td>$y$</td></tr><tr><td>$-2$</td><td>$y = \dfrac{1}{2}(-2) + \dfrac{1}{4}$</td><td>$-\dfrac{3}{4}$</td></tr><tr><td>$0$</td><td>$y = \dfrac{1}{2}(0) + \dfrac{1}{4}$</td><td>$\dfrac{1}{4}$</td></tr><tr><td>$2$</td><td>$y = \dfrac{1}{2}(2) + \dfrac{1}{4}$</td><td>$\dfrac{5}{4}$</td></tr></table>
y-intercept • To determine the y-coordinate of the y-intercept, b, algebraically, substitute 0 for x and solve for y. • Or solve the equation for y. The constant term is the y-coordinate of the y-intercept, b, where $y = mx + b$. • Write an ordered pair $(0, b)$.	Determine the y-intercept of the graph, $2x + y = 6$. Let $x = 0$. Solve for y. $\quad 2x + y = 6$ $\quad 2x + y = 6$ $\quad 2(0) + y = 6$ $\qquad y = -2x + 6$ $\qquad\quad y = 6$ $\quad$ or $b = 6$ The y-intercept is $(0, 6)$.
x-intercept • To determine the x-intercept algebraically, substitute 0 for y and solve for x. • Write an ordered pair with the second coordinate 0 and the value obtained for x as the first coordinate.	Determine the x-intercept of the graph for $2x + y = 6$. Let $\quad y = 0$. $\quad 2x + y = 6$ $\quad 2x + (0) = 6$ $\qquad\quad 2x = 6$ $\qquad\quad\; x = 3$ The x-intercept is $(3, 0)$.

Recall	Examples	
Graph by using the intercept method • Determine the *x*-intercept and *y*-intercept. • Graph the intercepts. • Draw a line connecting the two points with arrows on both ends. • Check a third ordered-pair solution from the graph.	Graph $2x + y = 6$ by using the intercept method. Use the *x*-intercept and *y*-intercept found in the previous two examples, and graph. Use the point $(1, 4)$ to check for correctness. $$\begin{array}{c c}2x + y = 6 \\ \hline 2(1) + 4 & 6 \\ 6 & \end{array}$$ The solution checks.	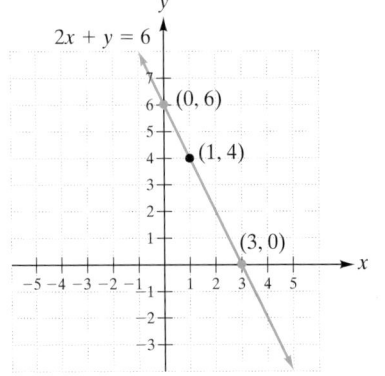

Identify each equation as linear or nonlinear. Express each linear equation in standard form.

1. $y = 0.6x + 2.3$ **2.** $y = 4x^2 - 2$ **3.** $5y - 12 = 7 - y$

Determine three solutions for each equation, and graph the equations.

4. $12x + 6y = 48$ **5.** $y = \dfrac{8}{13}x - 7$ **6.** $y = -9$ **7.** $9x - y = 12$

8. $y = -\dfrac{4}{3}x + 2$ **9.** $5y - 2 = y - 10$ **10.** $2x + 16 = x + 18$

Determine the intercepts of each graph of each linear equation. If possible check your answers with your calculator.

11. $8x + 12y = -24$ **12.** $y = \dfrac{2}{5}x + 4$ **13.** $2y - 4 = y - 7$ **14.** $2(x - 1) + 5 = 9$

Solve each equation for y to determine the y-intercept.

15. $9x - 3y = -12$ **16.** $6x + 2y = x$ **17.** $3y + 2 = 2(y - 4)$

Graph each equation by using the intercept method. Label the points.

18. $7x + 11y = 77$ **19.** $-x - y = 2$ **20.** $7.40x + 14.80y = 29.60$

21. Noriko translates Japanese texts into English as a consultant to a firm that does business in Japan. She is paid $85 to translate 10 pages of text on one job and $160 to translate 20 pages of text on another job.
   a. Let *x* represent the number of pages translated on a particular job, and let *y* represent Noriko's pay for the job. Graph a representation of the information.
   b. Assume that the information is from a linear relation, and connect the points. From the graph, how much will Noriko receive for a job that is 30 pages long?

22. The rental cost for a copy machine is $25 per week. It costs $0.02 to make a copy of a page of a document. The copy center charges its customers $0.04 per copy made. Write a linear function for the weekly profit that the copy center will realize. Graph the function by the intercept method. Explain the meaning of the intercepts.

23. A discount warehouse offers its members a special upgraded membership that costs $100 per year. As part of this membership the customer receives 2% back on all purchases. This promotion can be modeled by the function $M = 100 - 0.02x$, where *M* is the actual membership cost and *x* is the amount of yearly purchases.

a. Graph this function using the intercept method.
b. Interpret the intercepts.
c. If the customer spends $7500, what is his actual membership cost? Interpret this number.

24. A McDonnell Douglas MD80J aircraft can fly from Chicago to Los Angeles in 4 hours and 25 minutes. If we let *y* represent the plane's distance from Chicago, then an equation representing that distance is $y = 1749 - 396x$, where *x* is the flight time in hours. Graph the equation and interpret the intercepts of the graph. From the graph, estimate how long it will take to fly 1000 miles from Chicago.

25. Kari was awarded a scholarship for a year of college. The amount awarded was $5200, to be paid out as $100 weekly. Let *x* represent the number of weeks payment has been made, and let *y* represent the balance of the scholarship account.
   a. Write a linear equation in two variables for the balance of the account after *x* weeks of payments.
   b. Find the intercepts for a graph of the equation. Interpret what the intercepts represent.
   c. Graph the equation by using the intercept method.
   d. From the graph, determine how much money remains in the account after 32 weeks of payments.

3.2

Recall	Examples
Slope of a line • Given a graph, locate two integer coordinate points on the graph, draw a right triangle, count the rise and the run, and write the ratio, $\frac{\text{rise}}{\text{run}}$. • Given two ordered pairs, (x_1, y_1) and (x_2, y_2), use the slope formula, $$m = \frac{y_2 - y_1}{x_2 - x_1}$$ • Given an equation of the line, solve for y. The coefficient of the x-term is the slope.	Determine the slope of the given graph. 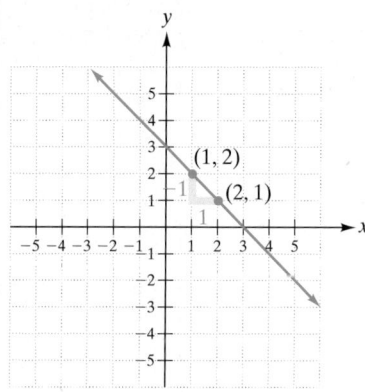 The slope is $\frac{-1}{1} = -1$. Determine the slope of a line passing through the points $(1, 2)$ and $(5, -2)$. $$m = \frac{y_2 - y_1}{x_2 - x_1}$$ $$m = \frac{-2 - 2}{5 - 1}$$ $$m = \frac{-4}{4} = -1$$ Determine the slope of the line, given $y = -x + 3$. The slope is the coefficient of the x-term, or -1.

In exercises 26–31, determine the slope of the graph. Determine whether the graph represents a function. If the graph represents a function, is the function increasing, decreasing, or constant?

26.

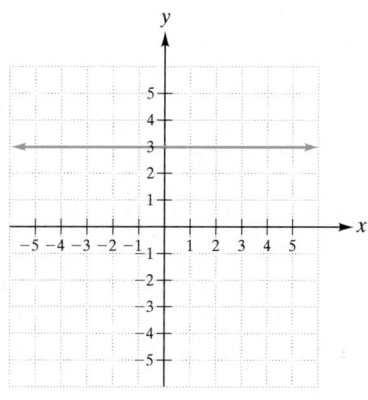

27.

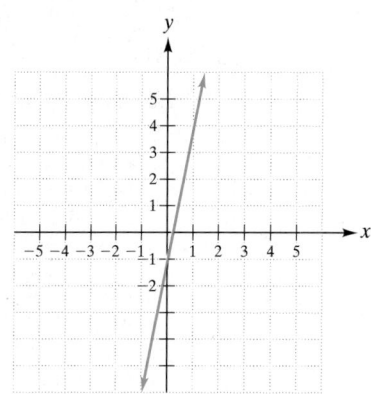

28.

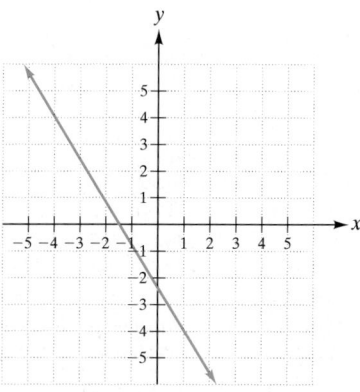

29.

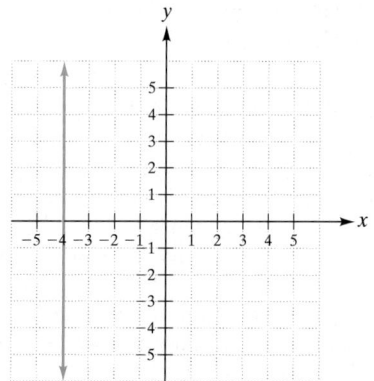

30.

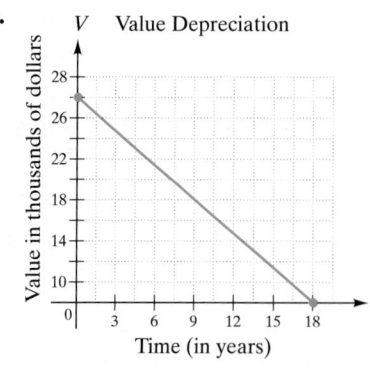

31.

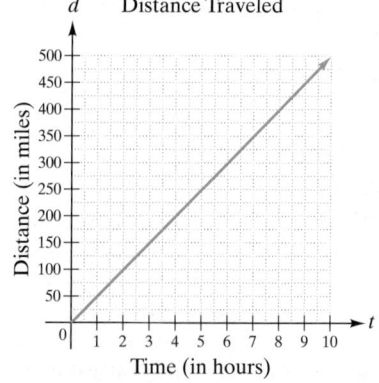

Determine the slope of the line containing the given points.

32. $(-5, -3)$ and $(1, 0)$ **33.** $(-7, 7)$ and $(-4, 2)$ **34.** $(4, -3)$ and $(10, -3)$ **35.** $(4, -3)$ and $(4, 3)$

36. What is the grade of a road that rises 4 feet over a horizontal distance of 160 feet?

37. A professional photographer purchases a digital camera to use in her business. If she uses simple linear depreciation for a camera that cost $485 and estimates its useful life to be 4 years, determine the amount of depreciation per year.

38. Janet left home to walk to the shopping mall that was 2 miles from her home. After walking a mile, she stopped to visit with her sister. She visited for an hour and then continued her walk to the mall. She spent a half hour shopping and then realized that she needed to hurry home, so she quickened her returning pace of walking to twice that of her initial pace. Which graph best illustrates Janet's journey? Explain your choice.

b.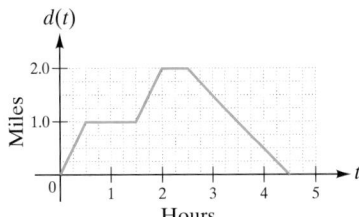

c.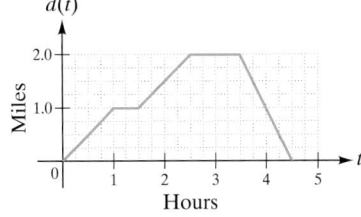

a.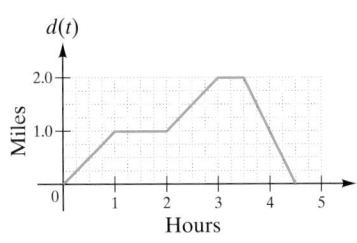

39. James recently went through his Social Security Summary of Contributions that came in the mail. It described his yearly earnings since he got his first summer job in high school.

Year	1994	1995	1996	1997	1998	1999	2000	2001	2002	2003	2004	2005	2006
Earnings	$7800	$8300	$5100	$900	$4000	$4300	$7500	$29,800	$31,000	$45,000	$47,300	$51,000	$46,750

  a. What was the average rate of change of his salary between 1994 and 1995?
  b. Between 1996 and 1997?
  c. Between 2004 and 2005?
  d. Between 2005 and 2006?

3.3

Recall	Examples
Graph by using the slope–intercept method • Graph and label the *y*-intercept. • Count the slope $\left(\frac{\text{rise}}{\text{run}}\right)$. Graph and label the point determined. • For greater accuracy, count the slope from the second point, graph and label a third point. • Connect the points to draw the line.	Graph $y = -2x + 6$ by using the slope–intercept method. The slope intercept form is $y = mx + b$. The slope, m, is -2, or $\frac{-2}{1}$, and the *y*-intercept is $(0, 6)$.

Determine by inspection the slope and the y-intercept of the line for the given equation.

40. $y = 23x - 51$ **41.** $6x + 5y = 12$ **42.** $y - 2 = 4(x + 3)$ **43.** $4(y - 2) = 3(2y - 1) + 4$

Graph a line that contains the given point and has the given slope.

44. $(-2, 3); m = \dfrac{5}{9}$ **45.** $(3, -2); m = -3$ **46.** $(-2, -2); m = 0$ **47.** $(-2, -2); m$ is undefined.

Graph each equation by using the slope–intercept method. Label the points.

48. $y = -\dfrac{5}{3}x + 2$ **49.** $3x + 2y = 12$ **50.** $m(x) = \dfrac{5}{8}x$ **51.** $y = -4$

52. The manager of a music store has determined that the demand function for a DVD player, $d(x)$, is related to the price in x dollars by the function $d(x) = 150 - \dfrac{2}{5}x$. The supplier of the DVD player has determined that the supply, $s(x)$, for the player is related to the price in x dollars by the function $s(x) = \dfrac{1}{2}x$.

   a. Graph the demand function using the slope–intercept method. Use the graph to determine the price of the DVD player if the demand is 100 players. Use the graph to determine the demand if the selling price is $70.

   b. Graph the supply function using the slope–intercept method. Use the graph to determine the price of the DVD player if the supply is 100 players. Use the graph to determine the supply if the selling price is $70.

53. Kristen decides to use her home computer to produce note cards. She purchases a software package for $100. She estimates that the cost per package of note cards is $2. She plans to charge $5 per package.

   a. Write a function, $c(x)$, for the total cost. Graph the function using the slope-intercept method. Use the graph to determine the cost of producing 50 packages. Use the graph to determine the number of packages produced for a cost of $300.

   b. Write a function, $r(x)$, for the total revenue. Graph the function using the slope–intercept method. Use the graph to determine the revenue of selling 50 packages. Use the graph to determine the number of packages sold to obtain a revenue of $300.

   c. Write a function, $p(x)$, for the profit. Graph the function using the slope–intercept method. Use the graph to determine the profit of producing and selling 50 packages. Use the graph to determine the number of packages produced and sold to obtain a profit of $0.

54. David is planning his summer vacation. His first stop is an amusement park 350 miles from his home. If he continues his travels, away from his home, to a beach resort at an average speed of 50 miles per hour, write a linear equation for the distance from David's home, y, with respect to time driven, t. Graph the equation. Use the graph to estimate the distance to David's home after 1.5 hours of traveling from his first stop.

3.4

Recall	Examples
Coinciding lines • Lines that have equal slopes and the same y-intercept.	When solved for y, equations for two coinciding lines are $y = 2x - 3$ and $y = 2x - 3$.
Parallel lines • Lines that have equal slopes but different y-intercepts.	When solved for y, equations for two parallel lines are $y = 2x - 5$ and $y = 2x - 3$.
Intersecting lines • Lines that have different slopes.	When solved for y, equations for two intersecting lines are $y = 2x - 3$ and $y = -2x + 3$.
Intersecting and perpendicular lines • Lines that have opposite reciprocal slopes.	When solved for y, equations for two intersecting and perpendicular lines are $y = 2x - 3$ and $y = -\frac{1}{2}x - 4$.

Determine by inspection whether the graphs of each pair of equations are coinciding, parallel, intersecting only, or both intersecting and perpendicular. Check by graphing.

55. $y = 2x + 6$
    $3y - x = 15$

56. $2y - 2x = y + 3x + 2$
    $5x - y = -2$

57. $4x - 20 = 0$
    $2x + 3 = x + 4$

58. $2x + y = 4$
    $y = -2(x + 2)$

59. $3(y + 2) = 2(y + 4)$
    $2(x - 2) = 0$

60. $5y - 4(y + 3) = -10$
    $y - 1 = -2(x - 1)$

61. $2x - 3y = -9$
    $3x + 2y = 6$

62. $y = x + 7$
    $y = -x + 7$

63. J. R. decides to go into business buying and selling used graphing calculators to students. He spends $25 having posters printed to hang on student bulletin boards and pays $35 to place an ad in the student newspaper. He will buy used calculators at $30 each. Since he is too busy to sell the calculators, he pays Brandon a flat fee of $25 to help him, with the promise of paying him $5 for each calculator he sells.

   a. Let x represent the number of calculators bought and resold, and let y represent the cost of selling calculators. Write a linear equation for the total cost of selling x calculators.

   b. If Brandon sells the calculators at $35 each, write a linear equation for the total revenue of selling x calculators.

   c. Graph the two equations and find the break-even point, if there is one, at which the revenue equals the cost of selling x calculators.

   d. If Brandon sells the calculators at $60 each, write a new linear equation for the total revenue of selling x calculators.

   e. Graph the original cost function and the new revenue function, and determine the new break-even point if there is one.

   f. What would you recommend that J. R. do?

64. The manager of a music store has determined that the demand function for a DVD player, $d(x)$, is related to the price in x dollars by the function $d(x) = 150 - \dfrac{2}{5}x$. The supplier of the DVD player has determined that the supply, $s(x)$, for the player is related to the price in x dollars by the function $s(x) = \dfrac{1}{2}x$. Will the graphs of the demand function and the supply function intersect? If so, use your calculator to determine the equilibrium point and interpret its meaning.

65. Glenda determined that the cost to produce baskets was $3.25 per basket. She plans to advertise in the local newspaper. The advertisement cost $16.00. She plans to sell the baskets for $5.00 each.

   a. Write an equation for the total cost, y, to produce and sell x baskets.

   b. Write an equation for the total revenue, y, for x baskets.

   c. Will there be an intersection point? If so, use your calculator to determine the point of intersection and interpret.

66. The value of a new automobile can be estimated by the equation $v = 24{,}000 - 1200t$, where t is the time in years from the purchase. Likewise, a collector automobile bought the same year has a value $v = 20{,}000 + 600t$. Will the graphs of the two equations intersect? If so, find the point of intersection and explain what it means.

67. From data collected by the U.S. Bureau of the Census, the college population of males in millions can be estimated by the equation $y = 0.9x + 91$, where x is the number of years since 1987 and y is the number of male college students in millions. Likewise, the college population of females in millions can be estimated by the equation $y = 0.9x + 99$, where x is the number of years since 1987 and y is the number of female college students in millions. What can you say about the graphs of these two equations? Justify your answer.

3.5

Recall	Examples
Write an equation of a line	Write an equation of a line with a slope of -3 and a y-intercept of $(0, 4)$.
• Given a slope and the y-intercept, use the slope–intercept form of the equation, $y = mx + b$.	$y = mx + b$ $y = -3x + 4$
• Given a point and the slope of a line, use the point–slope form of the equation, $y - y_1 = m(x - x_1)$.	Write an equation of a line with a slope of -3 and passing through $(-1, 4)$. $y - y_1 = m(x - x_1)$ $y - 4 = -3(x - (-1))$ $y - 4 = -3(x + 1)$ $y - 4 = -3x - 3$ $y - 4 + 4 = -3x - 3 + 4$ $y = -3x + 1$
• Given two points on the line, first determine the slope by using the formula $m = \dfrac{y_2 - y_1}{x_2 - x_1}$, and then use the point–slope form of the equation, $y - y_1 = m(x - x_1)$.	Write an equation of a line passing through $(-1, 4)$ and $(2, 3)$. $m = \dfrac{y_2 - y_1}{x_2 - x_1} \qquad y - y_1 = m(x - x_1)$ $m = \dfrac{3 - 4}{2 - (-1)} \qquad y - 3 = -\dfrac{1}{3}(x - 2)$ $m = -\dfrac{1}{3} \qquad y - 3 = -\dfrac{1}{3}x + \dfrac{2}{3}$ $\qquad\qquad y - 3 + 3 = -\dfrac{1}{3}x + \dfrac{2}{3} + 3$ $\qquad\qquad y = -\dfrac{1}{3}x + \dfrac{11}{3}$

68. Write a linear equation for the graph.

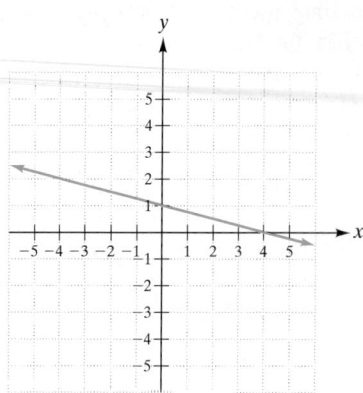

In exercises 69–77, write an equation for a line that satisfies each of the given conditions.

69. The line has a y-intercept of $(0, 3)$ and a slope of -2.

70. The line passes through $(0, -2)$ with a slope of $\frac{3}{5}$.

71. The line is horizontal with a y-intercept of $(0, -3.5)$.

72. The line is vertical with an x-intercept of $(2.6, 0)$.

73. The line has a slope of -5 and passes through $(2, -3)$.

74. The line passes through the points $(9, 5)$ and $(-2, 2)$.

75. The line passes through $(4, 6)$ and has a slope of $\frac{1}{3}$.

76. The line passes through $(1, 1)$ and is parallel to the graph of $y = 4x + 5$.

77. The line passes through $(2, 4)$ and is perpendicular to the graph of $y = 2x - 1$.

78. Dr. Amburn, a forensic scientist, discovered a female femur that was 42.15 centimeters in length. She concluded that the female was approximately 155.4 centimeters in height. She also discovered a second female femur that was 43.45 centimeters in length and estimated her height to be 158.3 centimeters. Let $x =$ the length, in centimeters, of the female femur, and $y =$ the height of the female in centimeters. Write a linear equation for the height, in centimeters, of a female in terms of the length of the femur, in centimeters. Use the equation to estimate the height of a female given that the femur is 43.13 centimeters.

79. According to the U.S. Census Bureau, the median earnings of women since the year 2000 has been increasing at an average of $535 per year. Women's median earnings in 2000 were $29,134.

a. Write a linear equation to determine the median earnings of women, y, in terms of x years after 2000.

b. Use the equation to estimate the median earnings of women in 2002. According to the Census Bureau, women's median earnings in 2002 were $30,203. Compare your figure with your estimate.

c. Use your equation to predict the median earning for women in 2010.

80. Between 1985 and 1995 total expenditures per family for entertainment and reading increased in a linear fashion. Use the data in the table to find the linear equation that models this data. Verify the data points.

Year	1985	1990	1995
Expenditure (to the nearest hundred dollars)	1400	1600	1800

81. The per capita cigarette consumption of people 18 or over in the United States in 1980 was 3851. In 2002, the per capita cigarette consumption had decreased to 2092. Write a linear equation to determine the per capita cigarette consumption, y, in terms of x years after 1980. Estimate the per capita cigarette consumption for 1995. Compare this estimate with the 1995 per capita cigarette consumption of 2515. Predict the per capita consumption of people 18 or over for the year 2018. Is it reasonable to assume that this trend will continue?

■ Chapter 3 Mixed Review

Determine three solutions for each equation, and graph the equations.

1. $y = 8$

2. $8x - 9y = -72$

3. $t(x) = \dfrac{9}{11}x - 8$

Graph a line containing the given point with the given slope.

4. $(2, 6); m = 0$

5. $(2, 6); m$ is undefined.

6. $(1, 4); m = -2$

7. $(0, 3); m = \dfrac{2}{7}$

Graph each equation by using the slope–intercept method. Label the points.

8. $y = \dfrac{-3}{8}x$

9. $y = 7$

10. $5x - 4y = 12$

Graph each equation by using the intercept method. Label the points.

11. $15.50x + 21.70y = 108.50$

12. $12x - 24y = -48$

13. $-x + y = -6$

Determine by inspection whether the graphs of each pair of linear equations are coinciding, parallel, intersecting only, or both intersecting and perpendicular.

14. $2x - 3 = 1$
$4x - 3y = 6$

15. $5x - 4y = 8$
$4x - 5y = -15$

16. $y = 5(x - 1)$
$2(x - 1) = 7x - y + 3$

17. $5(x + 1) = 15$
$3y + 1 = 10$

18. $y = -2x + 3$
$2(x + y) = y + 3$

19. $y = x + 3$
$y = -x - 4$

20. $5y = 20$
$2(y + 3) = -2$

Identify each equation as linear or nonlinear. Express each linear equation in standard form.

21. $y = x$

22. $y = 2x^2 - 8$

23. $8y - 5x = 21$

24. $2x + 3y - 1 = y^2 + x$

Determine by inspection the slope and the y-intercept of the line for each linear equation.

25. $x + 4(x - 2) = 2$

26. $x - 3(y + 2) = 4(x + 1) - y$

27. $12x - 4y = 8$

28. $2y - 6 = 4(y - 2) + 2$

29. $y = 13x - 15$

30. $y = -5.03x + 7.92$

Determine the slope of the line containing the given points.

31. $(5, 5)$ and $(8, 5)$

32. $(-3, -3)$ and $(-3, 3)$

33. $(-4, 4)$ and $(-1, -5)$

34. $\left(-\dfrac{2}{5}, \dfrac{4}{7}\right)$ and $\left(-\dfrac{4}{7}, \dfrac{1}{5}\right)$

For the following graphs, determine the y-intercepts. Determine the slope of the graph. Write an equation of the line. Determine whether the graph represents a function. If the graph represents a function, is the function increasing, decreasing, or constant?

35.

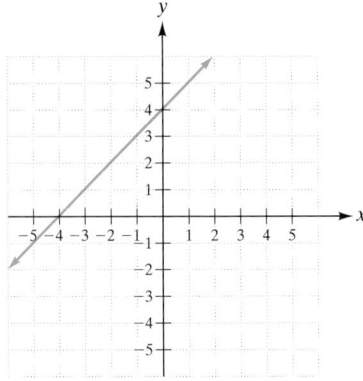

36.

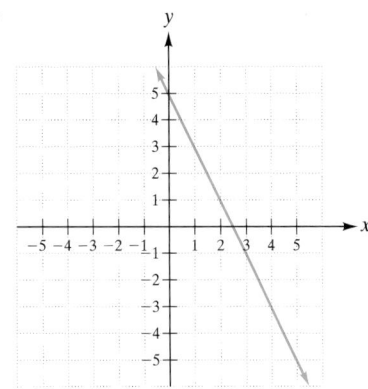

37.

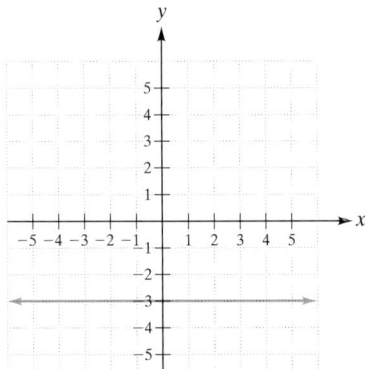

38.

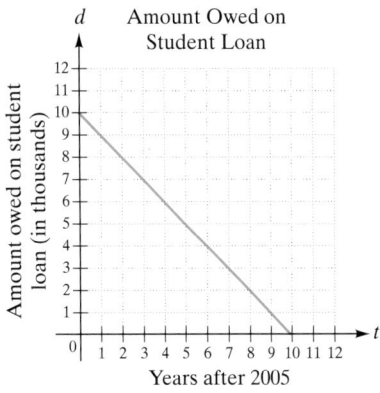

In exercises 39–47, write an equation for a line that satisfies the given conditions.

39. The line contains the points $(4, -2)$ and $(5, 2)$.

40. The line passes through $(-1, -1)$ and has a slope of $-\frac{1}{4}$.

41. The line passes through $(0, 5)$ with a slope of $-\frac{2}{3}$.

42. The line is vertical with an x-intercept of $(4.1, 0)$.

43. The line passes through $(-2, -2)$ and is parallel to the line for $y = -3x + 6$.

44. The line is horizontal with a y-intercept of $(0, 8)$.

45. The line has a slope of 4 and passes through the point $(1.2, 8)$.

46. The line has a y-intercept of $(0, -2)$ and a slope of 3.

47. The line passes through $(0, 2)$ and is perpendicular to the line for $y = -\frac{1}{2}x - 1$.

48. Frank earned money as a freelance umpire for intramural school baseball games. He was paid $24 for a game that lasted 7 innings. For another game that went 9 innings, he was paid $28. Denote his pay as y and the number of innings he worked as x.

a. Graph the two coordinate pairs.

b. Assume that the information is from a linear relation, and connect the points. How much would Frank receive for a game that lasted 8 innings? How much for a game that lasted 10 innings?

49. A sports trainer charges his clients $20 per visit plus $50 per hour to come to their homes and conduct fitness training sessions.

a. Let x represent the number of hours for the training session, and let y represent the total charge for the session. Write an equation to represent the trainer's total charge for a session.

b. Graph the equation.

c. How much would the trainer earn if he trained for 2 hours?

d. How much would he earn for a session that lasted $1\frac{1}{2}$ hours?

50. Shannon set up a business to sell hair bows at a kiosk in the mall during the holiday season. The cost of renting the kiosk is $75.00 per week. She had to purchase supplies that cost $150.00. In addition, the materials used to make each hair bow cost her $0.75 each.

a. Write a linear equation to determine Shannon's total cost, $c(x)$, in terms of the number of hair bows, x, she makes and sells during the week.

b. If she sells the hair bows for $2.00 each, write a linear equation to represent her revenue, $r(x)$, for selling x bows during the week.

c. Graph the two equations, and find the break-even point, if there is one, at which revenue equals cost.

d. Will Shannon make a profit if she sells 150 hair bows during the week? What if she sells 200 bows? What is the minimum number of bows she must sell to avoid a loss?

51. Find the pitch of a roof that rises 2 inches over a horizontal distance of 12 inches.

52. A first edition of a novel was purchased in 1980 for $15.00. The novel was sold to a book dealer in 2000 for $275.00. Find the average rate of change per year in the value of the novel between 1980 and 2000.

53. Jonathan started a new teaching position. His first teaching assignment lasted 6 months, and then he was on summer hiatus for 2 months with no pay. He returned after the hiatus and assumed additional responsibilities that increased his rate of pay. Choose which of the following graphs best represents Jonathan's cumulative pay for the 12-month period:

a.

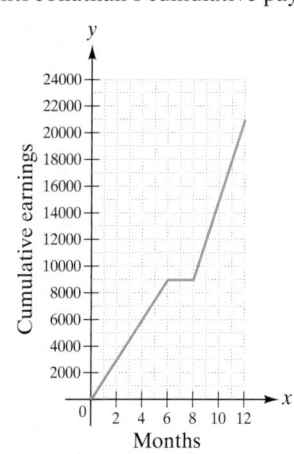

b.

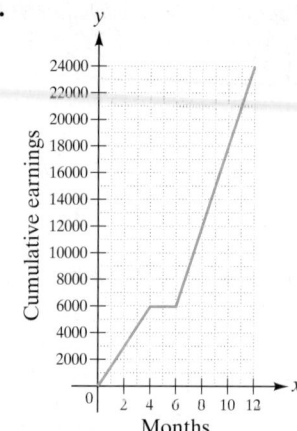

c.

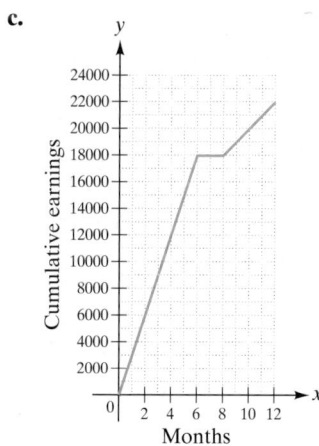

54. Beckie operates a picture-framing operation out of her home. She spends $35.00 per week to advertise in the local paper. She spends an average of $6.50 per picture for framing and matting materials. She charges her customers $40.00 for each picture she frames. Write a linear function for the weekly profit that Beckie can realize. Graph the function by the intercept method. Explain the meaning of the intercepts.

55. The manager of a camera store has determined that the demand function for a digital camera, $d(x)$, is related to the price in x dollars by the function $d(x) = 175 - \frac{3}{5}x$. The supplier of the camera has determined that the supply, $s(x)$, for the camera is related to the price in x dollars by the function $s(x) = 50 + \frac{1}{2}x$.

a. Graph the demand function using the slope–intercept method. Use the graph to determine the price of the camera if the demand is 100 cameras. Use the graph to determine the demand if the selling price is $130.

b. Graph the supply function using the slope–intercept method. Use the graph to determine the price of the camera if the demand is 100 cameras. Use the graph to determine the demand if the selling price is $130.

c. Will the graphs of the demand function and the supply function intersect? If so, use your calculator to determine the equilibrium point and interpret its meaning.

56. Dr. Amburn discovered a male femur that was 45.28 centimeters in length. She concluded that the male was approximately 170.52 centimeters in height. She also discovered a second male femur that was 47.11 centimeters in length and estimated his height to be 174.62 centimeters. Let x = the length, in centimeters, of the male femur, and $y =$ the height of the male in centimeters. Write a linear equation for the height, in centimeters, of a male in terms of the length of the femur, in centimeters. Use the equation to estimate the height of a male given that the femur is 50.27 centimeters.

57. According to the United States Center for Health Statistics, teen birth rates have been declining, although such rates are higher than are those in other developed countries. For white women 15–19 years of age, the birth rate per 100 females is summarized in the following chart. Conclude that the table generates a linear equation by finding the equation and then verifying the data points.

Year	2000	2001	2002
Birth Rate	43	41	39

58. U.S. residents spent $401.60 per capita on recreation in 1995. In 2000, $564.70 per capita was spent on recreation.
 a. Determine the average rate of change in the amount per capita spent on recreation per year.
 b. Write a linear equation for the amount spent per capita on recreation, y, in terms of x year after 1995.
 c. Use the equation to estimate the amount per capita spent on recreation in 2001. According to published reports,

$593.90 per capita was spent on recreation. Compare this figure to your estimate.

59. U.S. residents spent $62.70 per capita on toys and sport supplies in 2000. The average rate of change has increased $3.10 per year.
 a. Write a linear equation for the amount spent per capita on toys and sport supplies, y, in terms of x years after 2000.
 b. Use the equation to estimate the amount per capita spent on toys and sport supplies in 2001. According to published reports, $66.70 per capita was spent on toys and sport supplies. Compare this figure to your estimate.

60. Many banks are now offering 40-year, no-interest loans. Consumers like this idea. Critics charge that people buy houses that they cannot afford and that banks are promoting this so that people default on their loans. A family buys a $288,000 home and arranges a 40-year, no-interest loan. The amount of money they owe the bank is given by the function $P = 288{,}000 - 600t$, where P is the amount owed on their loan and t is the number of months.
 a. Graph the function by the intercept method.
 b. Explain the meaning of the intercepts.
 c. Explain what -600, the coefficient of the variable term, represents.

■ Chapter 3 Test

A⁺ TEST-TAKING TIPS

Rehearse for a test just as you would rehearse for a speech in speech class. By this, we mean "practice, practice, practice." If you have practice tests available, you should study them. Aim for 100% understanding. If you don't understand an exercise, get help immediately. Start practicing at least a week before the test, and do so each day for a reasonable length of time. If you find that you are weak on certain topics, practice with exercises on those topics. Make index card notes summarizing examples that you can review each day. These are like the flash cards you may have used when you were a youngster. Rehearsing moves information from your short-term memory to your long-term memory. It is the only way you can achieve the kind of recall you will need to reach your goal of 100% mastery of the material. Remember, if you don't set this goal, you will have no incentive to reach it!

Identify each equation as linear or nonlinear.

1. $5x - 7y = 2(x + 1) - 3$ **2.** $y = \dfrac{11}{12}x - 5$ **3.** $y^2 - 16 = 0$ **4.** $7x + 2y = 3x^2 + 3$

Graph the equation by using a table of values. Label the points.

5. $2x - 8y = 0$ **6.** $3x + 2y = 7$

Graph by using the intercept method. Label the points.

7. $12x + 15y = 60$ **8.** $2(x - 3) = x + 1$ **9.** $4y - 3 = 2y + 9$

Graph by using the slope–intercept method. Label the points.

10. $g(x) = 3x - 5$ **11.** $3x - 4y = 4$

Determine the slope of the line containing the two points.

12. $(0, -1)$ and $(-1, -1)$ **13.** $(4, -6)$ and $(-5, -1)$ **14.** $(-3, -4)$ and $(1, 0)$ **15.** $(-2, 2)$ and $(-2, 8)$

Determine whether the graphs of each pair of equations are coinciding, parallel, intersecting only, or both intersecting and perpendicular.

16. $y = -8x + 1$

$y = x - 8$

17. $9(y - 2) + 2x = 7x$

$4x = 9(y + 4) - x$

18. $3x - y = 2$

$y - x = 2(x - 1)$

19. $5y - 2 = 3y + 2$

$3x = 2(x + 2)$

Determine the slope and the y-intercept of the graph of each linear equation.

20. $4y = 3x + 12$

21. $7x + 7y = 21$

In exercises 22–25, write an equation of a line that satisfies each of the following conditions:

22. A line passes through $(2, 1)$ and is perpendicular to the graph of $y - \frac{3}{5}x$.

23. A line passes through $(0, 7)$ with a slope of 9.

24. A line passes through $(-1, 2)$ with a slope of 6.

25. A line passes through $(2, 3)$ and $(-4, 1)$.

26. Determine the y-intercept for the following graph. Determine the slope of the graph. Write an equation of the line. Determine whether the graph represents a function. If the graph represents a function, is the function increasing, decreasing, or constant?

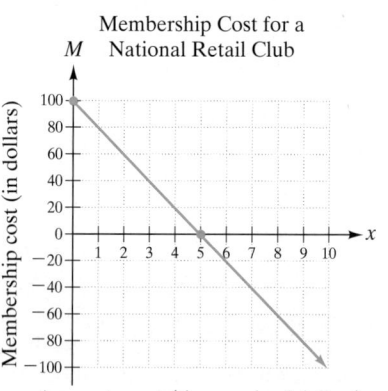

Membership Cost for a National Retail Club

27. According to data from the U.S. Bureau of the Census, the number of farms in the United States has decreased steadily since 1940, but has held relatively constant since 1980. Which of the following charts best illustrates these changes?

a.

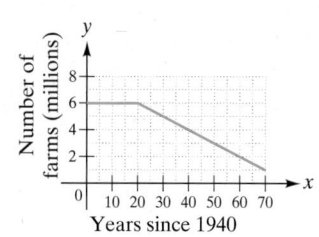

b.

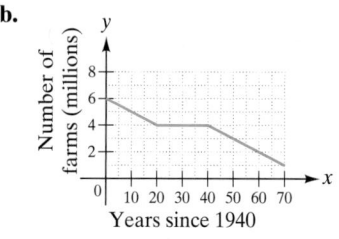

c.

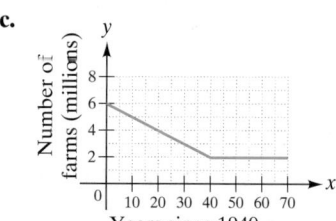

28. A novelty shop purchases a candy-vending machine for $4000. For tax purposes, the shop uses simple linear depreciation and depreciates the machine over a useful life of six years. Determine the amount of depreciation per year.

29. The *World Almanac and Book of Facts* states that in 1940 the typical farm size was 174 acres, in 1980 it was 426 acres, and since then it has remained around 430 acres. Find the average rate of change per year of farm size between 1940 and 1980.

30. Marty is paying off a $1450 loan at the rate of $150 per month.
   a. Write a linear function for his balance, y, in terms of the number of payments, x, he has made.
   b. Graph the function.
   c. Find the intercepts and explain their meanings.
   d. How long will it take to pay off half of his loan?

31. Alex operates a physical training center. He estimates his weekly costs and determines a fixed cost of $500. He pays a trainer $10.00 per hour. He charges a customer $25.00 per hour to train. Write a linear function for the weekly profit Alex can realize. Graph by the intercept method. Explain the meaning of the intercepts.

32. Robert, a forensic scientist, discovered the bodies of two adult males. The length of the tibia of the first male was 42.58 centimeters. The length of the tibia of the second male was 42.75 centimeters. He estimated that the first male was 183.45 centimeters in height. The second male was about 183.85 centimeters in height. Write a linear equation for the height, in centimeters, of a male in terms of the length of the tibia in centimeters. Use the equation to estimate the height of the male given the tibia is 41.96 centimeters.

33. Kris monograms shirts at a cost of $2 per shirt, with a setup cost of $25 per run. She sells the shirts for $5 each.
   a. Write a function, $c(x)$, for the total cost. Graph the function using the slope–intercept method. Use the graph to determine the cost of producing 5 shirts. Use the graph to determine the number of shirts produced for a cost of $65.

b. Write a function, $r(x)$, for the total revenue. Graph the function using the slope–intercept method. Use the graph to determine the revenue of selling 5 shirts. Use the graph to determine the number of shirts sold to obtain a revenue of $65.

c. Write a function, $p(x)$, for the profit. Graph the function using the slope–intercept method. Use the graph to determine the profit of producing and selling 5 shirts. Use the graph to determine the number of shirts produced and sold to obtain a profit of $0.

34. The manager of a camera store has determined that the demand function for a photo printer, $d(x)$, is related to the price in x dollars by the function $d(x) = 175 - \dfrac{3}{5}x$. The supplier of the printer has determined that the supply, $s(x)$, for the printer is related to the price in x dollars by the function $s(x) = 25 + \dfrac{1}{2}x$.

a. Graph the demand function using the slope–intercept method. Use the graph to determine the price of the printer if the demand is 100 printers. Use the graph to determine the demand if the selling price is $85.

b. Graph the supply function using the slope-intercept method. Use the graph to determine the price of the printer if the supply is 100 printers. Use the graph to determine the supply if the selling price is $85.

c. Will the graphs of the demand function and the supply function intersect? If so, use your calculator to determine the intersection point and interpret its meaning.

35. National Motors, Incorporated, advertises that its all-terrain vehicle, the Conqueror, can climb a hill that rises 60 feet vertically over a horizontal distance of 125 feet. Find the grade of the hill.

36. Consumption of cigarettes is dropping in the United States. According to the "Tobacco Outlook Report" by the United States Department of Agriculture, 487 billion cigarettes were consumed in 1995 with this number falling to 425 billion in 2001. Write a linear equation that relates consumption, c, to the number of years after 1995, t. Use your equation to estimate cigarette consumption in 2010.

37. The Bureau of Transportation Statistics reported the domestic operating profit/loss margin percents for several low-cost airline carriers in 2004. One such financially unstable airline's statistics are summarized below:

Month Number	Profit/Loss Margin Percent
3	−8
6	−3.8
9	−0.3
12	−7.3

a. What is the average rate of change of profit/loss margin percent between the third and sixth months?

b. What is the average rate of change of profit/loss margin percent between the ninth and twelfth months?

38. What is the difference between graphing a linear equation by the intercept method and graphing it by the slope–intercept method?

Project

Suppose that you are working for an automobile manufacturing company. The company president (your instructor) wants to know the following:

1. The approximate number of new passenger cars that will be sold in the United States in the year 2015.

2. The average decrease in the number of new passenger cars sold in the United States per year.

You will be assigned a group to complete this report. Each group will present its results to the company president and the board directors (the class) in a 10-minute or less talk.

The U.S. Bureau of the Census releases information about the United States in an annual publication called the *Statistical Abstract of the United States*. This publication is available both on-line and in print form and contains information gathered from a variety of sources, including the American Automobile Manufacturers Association and Ward's Communications. Using information from one of these sources, find the latest data available on new-car sales.

PART I Complete the following exercises to help you justify your answers to the preceding questions:

1. Use data from the latest four years. Let x = the number of years after the earliest of the four years and $N(x)$ = the number of new passenger cars. (For example, if the earliest year is 2000, then let $x = 0$ for 2000.) Complete a table of values for the independent variable x and the dependent variable $N(x)$.

2. Graph the four coordinate pairs found in the table in exercise 1. Do the points appear to lie on a straight line?

3. Using the four data points two at a time, we can determine six different pairs of points. List the six pairs.

4. Write an equation of a line through each pair of points. Name the six equations as $N_1(x)$, $N_2(x)$, $N_3(x)$, $N_4(x)$, $N_5(x)$, and $N_6(x)$.

5. Graph $N_1(x)$. On the same graph, plot and label the four coordinate pairs in exercise 1.

6. Complete the table at the bottom of this page. Note that column three is determined by substituting values of x in column one into the function $N_1(x)$.

7. Repeat exercises 5 and 6 five times, replacing $N_1(x)$ with $N_2(x)$, $N_3(x)$, $N_4(x)$, $N_5(x)$, and $N_6(x)$.

8. Compare the total differences from the six tables. The equation that results in the least total difference may be considered the line of best fit. Statisticians use a similar, but more complicated, process to determine a line of best fit. State the equation that you determined to be the line of best fit.

9. Use the equation from exercise 8 to predict the answers to the president's questions.

PART II The TI-84 Plus has built-in statistical features to find the best-fitting line, called a linear regression line. In 3.5 Calculator Exercises, we used this feature to write an equation for a line given points on the line.

1. Write an equation for $N_7(x)$ by using this statistical feature.

2. Repeat exercise 6 in Part I replacing $N_1(x)$ with $N_7(x)$.

3. Would you consider $N_7(x)$ to be a better fit to the data than the equation found in Part I? If so, why?

4. Use the information that you have gathered to predict the answers to the president's questions.

Number of Years after _____ x	Number of New Automobiles in Thousands $N(x)$	Estimated Number of New Automobiles $N_1(x)$	Difference between Estimate and Given Value $\lvert N(x) - N_1(x) \rvert$
		Total difference	

▪ Chapters P–3 Cumulative Review

1. Use one of the symbols $<$, $>$, or $=$ to compare the numbers.

a. $\dfrac{5}{9}$ _____ $\dfrac{2}{3}$ **b.** $\dfrac{8}{5}$ _____ 1.6 **c.** -5.4 _____ -6.5

2. Graph the following numbers on a number line, and label the points:

$$-\sqrt{9},\ \sqrt{7},\ 3\tfrac{2}{3},\ -\tfrac{3}{4},\ 6.4,\ -5,\ \pi$$

Evaluate. Express your answers in fractional notation, or round decimals to the nearest thousandths, as appropriate.

3. $5.7 - 4.68$

4. $-|17 - 29|$

5. $\sqrt{\dfrac{49}{81}}$

6. $-\sqrt{2.5}$

7. $\sqrt{-4}$

8. $-51 \div (-17)$

9. $-\dfrac{3}{7} - \dfrac{4}{5}$

10. $(-8)(21) \div 3(-7)$

11. $\dfrac{4(5^2 - 9) - 14}{7 + 3}$

12. $15 + (-8) + 13 - 12 - (-7)$

13. $-[14.3 - (-2.68)]$

14. $\left(-\dfrac{3}{5}\right)\left(\dfrac{5}{9}\right)\left(-\dfrac{10}{21}\right)\left(\dfrac{7}{8}\right)$

15. 250

16. -3^4

17. $(-3)^4$

18. $\left(\dfrac{2}{3}\right)^{-2}$

Simplify exercises 19–20.

19. $-(4a - 2b) + (7a - 4b) - (-5a - b)$

20. $2[3(2x + 3y) - (4x + y)] + 7x$

21. Is $x = -3$ a solution of $x^2 + 5x - 3 = 5x + 6$?

22. Consider the algebraic expression
$$x^3 - 2x^2 + 7x - 5x^3 + 2x - 4$$
  a. How many terms are in the expression?
  b. List the variable terms.
  c. List the constant terms.
  d. List the coefficients.
  e. List the like terms.

In exercises 23–27, consider the relation $y = 3x^2 - 1$, where x is the independent variable.

23. Graph the relation.

24. What is the domain of the relation? What is the range of the relation?

25. Is this relation a function? Justify your answer.

26. For which values of x is the relation increasing?

27. What is the maximum or minimum of the relation?

28. For the function $f(x) = 3x + 7$, find
  a. $f(-4)$ **b.** $f(-4 + h)$

Solve.

29. $5x - 3 = x - 7$

30. $2(x - 2) + 1 = 3(x + 6) + 2(x - 7)$

31. $(7x + 4) - (x + 6) = 2(3x - 1)$

32. $4(1.2x + 2) - 0.2(24x + 5) = 6$

33. $|5x - 1| = 6$

Graph using the Cartesian coordinate system. Label enough points to determine the graph.

34. $f(x) = -2x + 6$ **35.** $8x + 2y = -4$ **36.** $3x - 4 = 5$ **37.** $2(y + 4) - 6 = 4$

Determine whether the graphs of the pair of equations are coinciding, parallel, intersecting only, or both intersecting and perpendicular.

38. $4x + 2y = 8$
  $y = -2x + 6$

39. $3x + 2y = -2$
  $-2x + 3y = 3$

Determine the slope of a line that satisfies the following conditions:

40. The line passes through $(-2, 3)$ and $(-3, -1)$.

41. $y = 3x - 6$

42. $x = 4$

In exercises 43 and 44, write an equation for a line that satisfies the following conditions:

43. The line passes through $(1, -2)$ and $(-3, 4)$.

44. The line passes through $(2, 3)$ and is perpendicular to the graph of $4x - y = 1$.

45. Solve for z: $A = \dfrac{x + y + z}{3}$

46. A dress is on sale for $87.49. If the sale price represents a discount of 30% off the original price, write an equation and solve it to find the original price of the dress.

47. Caroline borrowed money for college tuition at a rate of 7.5% simple interest for one year. If she paid $1612.50 to pay off the loan, write an equation and solve it to find the amount of money she borrowed.

48. An independent producer of music CDs pays $300 to set up a production process to manufacture the disks. It costs $2.50 for materials and labor to produce each CD. The CDs are sold for $15 each. Write an equation to find the break-even point. Will the producer make a profit if 20 CDs are made and sold? Will he make a profit if 30 CDs are made and sold?

49. In 2000, the enrollment of students at the local community college was 7500. In 2005, the enrollment had grown to 9500 students. Let x represent the number of years after 2000, and let y represent the enrollment in a given year. Write two co-ordinate pairs for these data.

   a. Find the slope of the line connecting the two coordinate pairs.

   b. Write an equation to estimate the number of students enrolled x years after 2000.

   c. Estimate the number of students enrolled for the year 2010.

   d. What does the equation predict the enrollment will be in the year 2020? Does this number seem reasonable to you? Explain.

50. A car-leasing firm purchases a luxury automobile for $38,500. The firm depreciates the vehicle over a four-year period and then sells the vehicle for $12,500. If the firm uses simple linear depreciation, determine the amount of depreciation per year.

Systems of Linear Equations

We have now seen several methods for solving linear equations in two variables. But many situations in mathematics require more than one equation to describe the relation between two (or three) variables. In this chapter, we examine methods for solving systems of linear equations in two variables and systems of linear equations in three variables. Just like methods for solving single linear equations, these methods provide graphical solutions and algebraic solutions. Under the category of algebraic solutions, we will study two methods: substitution and addition. Then we will apply those methods to solving several types of real-world problems.

In this chapter, we encounter many types of real-world situations that involve systems of equations. Examples of these systems are found in business, economics, science, and social science.

One such application involves travel both in the air and on the water when the rate of travel is determined by more than one force. In the project at the end of the chapter, you will be asked to determine the average rate of travel (speed) of an aircraft in flight between the east and west coasts. This speed not only determines how fast you arrive at your destination, but also determines other factors. One such other factor is the aircraft's point of no return: the point in the flight when the time it takes the plane to return to its point of departure is equal to the time it takes the plane to continue to its destination.

355

4.1 SOLVING SYSTEMS OF TWO EQUATIONS GRAPHICALLY

OBJECTIVES

1 Determine whether a given ordered pair is a solution of a system of linear equations.

2 Solve systems of linear equations graphically and check numerically.

3 Model real-world situations by using systems of linear equations, and solve the equations graphically.

APPLICATION

In earlier chapters, we discussed two different temperature scales: Fahrenheit and Celsius. We know that the freezing point of water is 32 degrees on the Fahrenheit scale and 0 degrees on the Celsius scale. The boiling point of water is 212 degrees Fahrenheit and 100 degrees Celsius. Is there a temperature for which both scales indicate the same temperature? If so, determine this temperature.

We will discuss this application further. See page 363.

Objective 4.1.1

Determining a Solution of a System of Linear Equations

In Chapter 3, we discussed how to solve a linear equation in two variables. But it often happens that the relationships in a situation are described by more than one equation at a time. What do we do then? How do we solve several equations at one time? The first step is to define the situation mathematically.

SYSTEM OF LINEAR EQUATIONS IN TWO VARIABLES

A system of linear equations is a set of two or more linear equations.

For example, a system of linear equations in two variables may be

$$-2x - 3y = 1$$
$$3x - y = -7$$

To determine a solution of a system of linear equations in two variables, we need to find an ordered pair that satisfies *all* of the equations in the system. That is, when the ordered-pair coordinates are substituted into all of the equations, the resulting equations are true.

SOLUTION OF A SYSTEM OF LINEAR EQUATIONS

An ordered pair is a solution of a system of linear equations if it is a solution of every equation in the system.

EXAMPLE 1

Determine whether each ordered pair is a solution of the given system of linear equations.

a. $(-2, 1)$; $-2x - 3y = 1$
$ 3x - y = -7$

b. $(-3, -2)$; $x = -3$
$ y = 2$

Solution

a. Substitute the values for the coordinates.

$$
\begin{array}{c|c}
-2x \quad - 3y \;= 1 & \\
\hline
-2(-2) - 3(1) & 1 \\
4 \quad - 3 & \\
1 &
\end{array}
\qquad
\begin{array}{c|c}
3x \quad - y = -7 & \\
\hline
3(-2) - 1 & -7 \\
-6 \; - 1 & \\
- 7 &
\end{array}
$$

Both equations are true. Therefore, $(-2, 1)$ is a solution of the system.

Check

On your calculator, the solution is determined by storing -2 for x and 1 for y and evaluating the expressions in the equations.

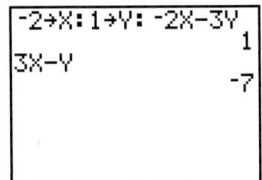

The solution is $(-2, 1)$ because when $x = -2$ and $y = 1$, the equations are true.

b. Substitute the values for the coordinates.

$$
\begin{array}{c|c}
x = -3 & \\
\hline
-3 & -3
\end{array}
\qquad
\begin{array}{c|c}
y = 2 & \\
\hline
-2 & 2
\end{array}
$$

The second equation is false, because $-2 \neq 2$. Therefore, $(-3, -2)$ is not a solution of the system.   ■

 Objective 4.1.1 CHECKUP

1. Determine whether each ordered pair is a solution of the given system of linear equations.

   a. $(3, 1); 2x - 3y = 3$
   $\qquad\;\; x + 2y = 6$

   b. $(5, 0); y = 3x - 15$
   $\qquad\;\; x - 5 = 0$

2. How does the solution of a system of linear equations differ from the solution of a single linear equation?

3. What must be true of a coordinate pair in order for it to be a solution of a system of linear equations?   ■

Objective 4.1.2   **Solving Systems of Linear Equations Graphically**

We know that we can represent the solutions of a linear equation in two variables by graphing. Therefore, if we graph both of the linear equations in a system, we should be able to determine the solution of the system. Let's see how this works. Complete the following set of exercises on your calculator.

 Guided Discovery 1   System of Linear Equations with One Solution

Solve the given system of linear equations by graphing both equations on the same integer screen.

$$y = 2x + 1$$
$$y = 4x - 3$$

1. The point of intersection is _____.

2. Substitute the coordinates of the intersection point into both equations of the system. The solution of the system is _____.

Write a rule for solving a system of linear equations graphically.

The coordinates of the point of intersection of the graphs form an ordered-pair solution of the system.

SOLVING A SYSTEM OF LINEAR EQUATIONS GRAPHICALLY

To solve a system of linear equations graphically, graph the equations on the same coordinate plane. The coordinates of the point of intersection give the ordered-pair solution.

EXAMPLE 2 Solve each system of linear equations graphically and check numerically.

a. $-2x - 3y = 1$ **b.** $x = -3$
        $3x - y = -7$ $y = 2$

Graphic Solution

a. Graph both equations of the system on the same coordinate plane.

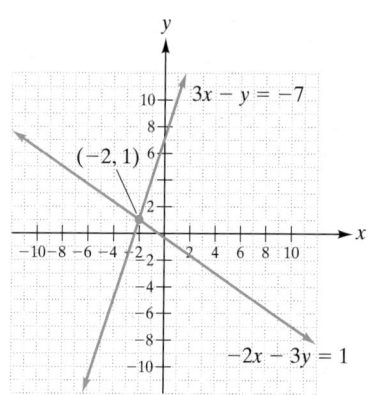

The solution is $(-2, 1)$.

To solve the system on your calculator, solve each equation for y and graph the equations.

$$Y1 = -\frac{2}{3}x - \frac{1}{3} \qquad Y2 = 3x + 7$$

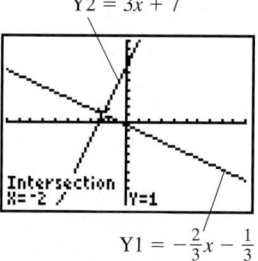

$$Y1 = -\frac{2}{3}x - \frac{1}{3}$$

$(-10, 10, -10, 10)$
The solution is $(-2, 1)$.

Check

Since the solution is an ordered pair of integers, we can check the solution numerically by viewing a table of values.

X	Y₁	Y₂
-4	2.3333	-5
-3	1.6667	-2
-2	1	1
-1	.33333	4
0	-.3333	7
1	-1	10
2	-1.667	13

X=2

$$Y1 = -\frac{2}{3}x - \frac{1}{3}$$
$$Y2 = 3x + 7$$

The solution is $(-2, 1)$.

b. Graph both equations of the system on the same coordinate plane.

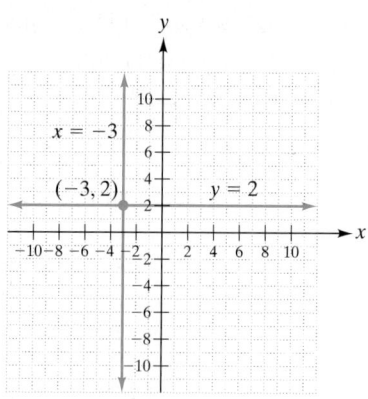

The solution is $(-3, 2)$.

The system contains the equation $x = -3$, which is not a function. Therefore, our calculator won't graph this equation using the $\boxed{Y=}$ menu. However, if you wish to check on the calculator, see the directions in 4.1 Calculator Exercises. ■

Both of the systems in Example 2 had one solution. We call a system with at least one solution a **consistent** system. A system with no solution is called an **inconsistent** system.

In Chapter 3, we determined that two linear graphs can be parallel or coinciding, as well as intersect in one point. We call equations whose graphs coincide **dependent**. We call equations whose graphs do not coincide **independent**.

Both of the systems we solved in Example 2 are consistent, and the equations are independent. Now let's look at inconsistent systems and systems with equations that are dependent. Complete the following sets of exercises on your calculator.

 Guided Discovery 2   Inconsistent System of Linear Equations

Solve the given system of linear equations by graphing both equations on the same integer screen.

$$-2x + y = 1$$
$$-4x + 2y = 10$$

Write a rule for determining, by graphing, that a system of linear equations is inconsistent—in other words, has no solution.

The two graphs are parallel and do not intersect. Since the graphs do not intersect, there is no ordered-pair solution of the system. The system is inconsistent.

We saw in Chapter 3 that two equations graph as parallel lines if their slopes (m) are the same and the y-coordinates of their y-intercepts (b) are different. If the equations in the system are both solved for y (that is, they are put into slope–intercept form), the system has no solution if the equations have the same slope (m) and different y-coordinates of their y-intercepts (b). Therefore, it is not necessary to actually graph the equations to determine that they have no solution.

Guided Discovery 3   System of Dependent Linear Equations

Solve the given system of linear equations by graphing both equations on the same integer screen.

$$-3x - y = -2$$
$$y = -3x + 2$$

Write a rule for determining, by graphing, that a system of linear equations consists of dependent equations—in other words, that it has an infinite number of solutions.

The two graphs are coinciding. Since the graphs coincide at all of their points, all ordered pairs that satisfy one equation also satisfy the second equation in the system. The number of solutions is infinite. In order to represent all these solutions, we need to determine all ordered pairs (x, y) that satisfy one of the linear equations. Since both equations in the system are the same, the solutions are the ordered pairs that satisfy either equation. The equations in this system are dependent.

We also saw in Chapter 3 that two equations graph as coinciding lines if they have the same slope (m) and the same y-coordinates of their y-intercepts (b). If the equations in the system are both solved for y (that is, they are put into slope–intercept form), the system has an infinite number of solutions if the equations have the same slope (m) and the same y-coordinates of their y-intercepts (b). Therefore, it is not necessary to actually graph the equations to determine that they have an infinite number of solutions.

EXAMPLE 3   Determine whether the given systems of linear equations have no solution or infinitely many solutions. If the system has an infinite number of solutions, describe the solution set.

a. $y = -x - 3$ **b.** $y = \dfrac{2}{3}x - \dfrac{1}{3}$ **c.** $x = -7$ **d.** $y = 5$

     $y = -x + 2$ $3y = 2x - 1$ $2x = -2$ $2y - 10 = 0$

Solution

a. The slopes are equal ($-1 = -1$), and the y-coordinates of the y-intercepts are different ($-3 \neq 2$). The graphs will be parallel. There is no solution of the system.

b. Solve the second equation for y: $y = \dfrac{2}{3}x - \dfrac{1}{3}$. The slopes are equal $\left(\dfrac{2}{3} = \dfrac{2}{3}\right)$, and the y-coordinates of the y-intercepts are equal $\left(-\dfrac{1}{3} = -\dfrac{1}{3}\right)$. The graphs will thus be coinciding, and there are an infinite number of solutions of the system. The solution set is the set of all ordered pairs (x, y) that satisfy $y = \dfrac{2}{3}x - \dfrac{1}{3}$.

c. The equations will graph as vertical lines (equal undefined slopes) with different x-coordinates of the x-intercepts ($-7 \neq -1$). The graphs will be parallel. There is no solution of the system.

d. Solve the second equation for y: $y = 5$. The equations will graph as horizontal lines (equal slopes of $0 = 0$) and equal y-coordinates of y-intercepts ($5 = 5$). The graphs will thus be coinciding, and there are an infinite number of solutions of the system. The solution set is the set of all ordered pairs (x, y) that satisfy $y = 5$.

Check

Use your calculator to check your results graphically or numerically. Solve the equations for y, if necessary, and graph both equations of the system on the same window. In part **c**, the system contains two vertical lines. We will not check this answer.

a.   Y2 = −x + 2

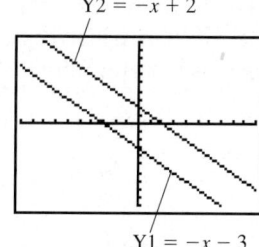

Y1 = −x − 3

$(-10, 10, -10, 10)$

The graphs are parallel.
There is no solution set.

X	Y₁	Y₂
-3	0	5
-2	-1	4
-1	-2	3
0	-3	2
1	-4	1
2	-5	0
3	-6	-1

X = -3

5 − 0 = 5
4 − (−1) = 5
3 − (−2) = 5
2 − (−3) = 5
1 − (−4) = 5
0 − (−5) = 5
−1 − (−6) = 5

Y1 = −x − 3
Y2 = −x + 2
The difference in the value of Y2 and Y1 for each x is always 5. The graphs are parallel. There is no solution.

b.   Y2 = $\frac{2}{3}x - \frac{1}{3}$

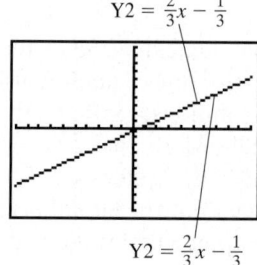

Y2 = $\frac{2}{3}x - \frac{1}{3}$

$(-10, 10, -10, 10)$

The graphs are coinciding. Thus, there are an infinite number of solutions of the system. The solution set is the set of all ordered pairs (x, y) that satisfy $y = \frac{2}{3}x - \frac{1}{3}$.

d.   Y1 = 5

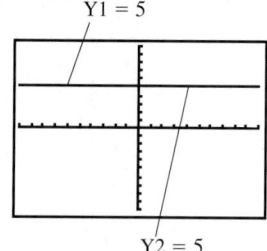

Y2 = 5

$(-10, 10, -10, 10)$

The graphs are coinciding. Thus, there are an infinite number of solutions of the system. The solution set is the set of all ordered pairs (x, y) that satisfy $y = 5$.

GRAPHICAL SOLUTIONS OF A SYSTEM OF LINEAR EQUATIONS

In solving a system of linear equations in two variables graphically, one of three possibilities will occur.

1. The equations have different slopes (m). The graphs intersect.

One solution exists: the ordered-pair intersection.

The system is consistent.

The equations are independent.

2. The equations have the same slope (m) and different y-coordinates of their y-intercepts (b). The graphs are parallel.

No solution exists.

The system is inconsistent.

The equations are independent.

3. The equations have the same slope (m) and the same y-coordinates of their y-intercepts (b). The graphs coincide.

An infinite number of solutions exist. The solution set is the set of all ordered pairs (x, y) that satisfy either equation of the system.

The system is consistent.

The equations are dependent.

✓ Objective 4.1.2 *CHECKUP*

1. Solve each system of equations graphically. Check your solution.

   a. $y = -3x + 4$
      $x + y = 2$

   b. $y = -2x + 3$
      $x = 4$

2. Determine whether each system of equations has no solution or infinitely many solutions. If the system has an infinite number of solutions, describe the solution set.

   a. $y = \dfrac{1}{4}x - 2$
      $4y = x - 6$

   b. $y = 2x + 1$
      $2x - y = -1$

   c. $y = 2x + 3$
      $y - x + 1 = x + 4$

   d. $y = -3$
      $y + 4 = 7$

3. What is meant by a dependent system of linear equations? an independent system? a consistent system? an inconsistent system?

4. You have learned definitions that describe a system of equations as being consistent or inconsistent. You have also learned definitions that describe equations as being dependent or independent. Use your understanding of these definitions to complete the table that follows. When you fill in each cell of the table, draw a diagram of what the graphs of the equations in the system will look like. (One cell of the table is completed for you as an illustration.)

	Consistent System	**Inconsistent System**
Dependent equations	The graphs of the two equations will be *coinciding* lines.	Can a system of equations be inconsistent and at the same time consist of dependent equations? _____
Independent equations	The graphs of the two equations will be _____ lines.	The graphs of the two equations will be _____ lines.

Modeling the Real World

There are two common situations in which graphing two linear equations in two variables at the same time is very helpful. One situation is to compare two different relationships. For example, you might be offered two different car rental plans. Which one should you choose? To find out, you could graph the two equations describing the plans and locate their intersection. Beyond that point, one graph is higher than the other, meaning that the plan it represents will cost more. If you need to rent the car for longer than the time corresponding to the intersection point, you want to choose the plan whose graph is lower *beyond* that time. Likewise, if you need to rent the car for less than the time corresponding to the intersection point, you want to choose the plan whose graph is lower *before* that time.

EXAMPLE 4

Budget will rent a minivan for $74.99 per day with unlimited miles. Enterprise will rent the same minivan for $71.24 per day plus $0.25 per mile driven over 150 miles.

a. Write a system of equations in two variables, relating the daily charges, $c(x)$, in terms of x miles driven.

b. Solve the system graphically on your calculator.

c. Interpret the solution.

Solution

a. Let x = the number of miles driven

$c(x)$ = the daily charges for rental of a minivan

Enterprise does not charge for the first 150 miles. Therefore, we will subtract 150 miles from the total number of miles driven.

$$x - 150 = \text{the number of miles driven over 150}$$

$$c(x) = 74.99 \qquad \text{Budget rental charges}$$

$$c(x) = 71.24 + 0.25(x - 150) \qquad \text{Enterprise rental charges}$$

b. Graph the system.

The intersection point is $(165, 74.99)$.

c. The two rental charges are equal ($74.99) for 165 miles driven. Rental from Enterprise will be less for miles driven less than 165. Rental from Budget will be less for miles driven greater than 165. ∎

Y2 = 71.24 + 0.25(x − 150)   Y1 = 74.99

Intersection
X=165   Y=74.99

(0, 200, 0, 100)

A second situation occurs when the two variables in an equation are related in more than one way. For example, you can receive a bill for plumbing work consisting of two different charges for 7 units of work and 5 units of work. To be able to determine the actual cost per unit of work, you need to know another relationship between the charges.

EXAMPLE 5

Petra recently had a plumber work at her house. She received a bill for $2080. She was billed for 7 units of work on the installation of new pipes and 5 units of work on her existing bathroom tub. The charge for pipe installation is three times as much as it is for working on the tub. Use a system of equations to determine the cost of one unit of plumbing work. How much did the pipe installation and the tub work cost?

Solution

Let x = the cost of one unit of work on the installation of new pipes

y = the cost of one unit of work on bathroom tub

The total charges were $2080 for 7 units of work on the pipes and 5 units of work on the tub.

$$7x + 5y = 2080$$

The charge for the pipe installation is three times the cost of working on the tub.

$$x = 3y$$

To solve graphically the system

$$7x + 5y = 2080$$
$$x = 3y$$

solve the equations for y and graph both equations on the same coordinate system.

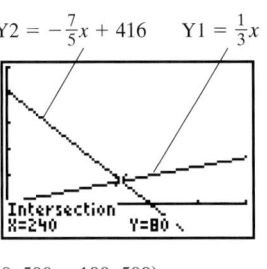

$Y2 = -\frac{7}{5}x + 416$ $Y1 = \frac{1}{3}x$

$(0, 500, -100, 500)$

$7x + 5y = 2080$	$x = 3y$
$7x + 5y - 7x = 2080 - 7x$	$\dfrac{x}{3} = \dfrac{3y}{3}$
$5y = -7x + 2080$	$\dfrac{1}{3}x = y$
$\dfrac{5y}{5} = \dfrac{-7x + 2080}{5}$	
$y = -\dfrac{7}{5}x + 416$	

The solution is (240, 80). The cost of one unit of work on the installation of new pipes is $240, and the cost of one unit of work on bathroom tub is $80. ■

APPLICATION

In earlier chapters, we discussed two different temperature scales: Fahrenheit and Celsius. We know that the freezing point of water is 32 degrees on the Fahrenheit scale and 0 degrees on the Celsius scale. The boiling point of water is 212 degrees Fahrenheit and 100 degrees Celsius. Is there a temperature for which both scales indicate the same temperature? If so, determine this temperature.

Discussion

Let $x =$ the temperature for which both scales are equal
$f(x) =$ the temperature in degrees Fahrenheit
$c(x) =$ the temperature in degrees Celsius

Using the temperature formulas, we obtain the following system of equations:

$$f(x) = \frac{9}{5}x + 32$$

$$c(x) = \frac{5}{9}(x - 32)$$

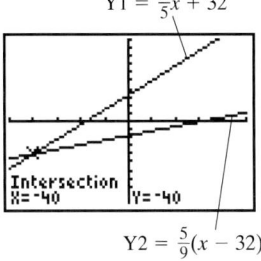

$Y1 = \frac{9}{5}x + 32$

$Y2 = \frac{5}{9}(x - 32)$

$(-50, 50, -100, 100)$

On your calculator, graph each equation in the system. The intersection of the two graphs is $(-40, -40)$. The temperature will be equal on both scales at 40 degrees below zero.

✓ Objective 4.1.3 CHECKUP

1. Tyler is renting a truck for a move and has two choices. One truck rental shop will rent him a truck for one day for $49.95 with unlimited miles. A discount truck rental shop will rent him a truck for one day for $36.23 and charge him $0.15 per mile for all miles over 200 miles. Write two systems of equations and solve each of them to determine the number of miles that make both offers equal. Interpret your results.

2. Amber spends $700 each month on her car payment and car insurance. The amount of the car payment is two and a half times the amount of the insurance. Write a system of equations to represent this situation. Solve the system to find the cost of the monthly insurance payment and the monthly car payment.

3. The percent of both males and females completing four or more years of college has increased since 1990. However, the percent of females is increasing at a much faster rate than the percent of males. The percent of males, $m(x)$, completing four or more years of college x years after 1990 can be estimated by $m(x) = 0.31x + 24.04$. The percent of females,

$f(x)$, completing four or more years of college x years after 1990 can be estimated by $f(x) = 0.52x + 17.95$. Assuming that these rates continue into the future, determine the year in which the percent of males and females completing four or more years of college will be equal.

4.1 EXERCISES

 Student Solutions Manual    PH Math/Tutor Center   CD Video   *Math*XL MathXL®   *MyMathLab* MyMathLab   Interactmath.com

Determine whether each ordered pair is a solution of the given system of linear equations.

1. $(3, 4)$; $y = x + 1$

$2y = x + 5$

2. $(-1, -6)$; $y = 3x - 3$

$y + 6 = 0$

3. $\left(\dfrac{4}{5}, \dfrac{6}{5}\right)$; $y = \dfrac{1}{4}x + 1$

$y = \dfrac{1}{2}x + \dfrac{4}{5}$

4. $\left(7, \dfrac{2}{5}\right)$; $y = \dfrac{1}{7}x - \dfrac{3}{5}$

$7y = x + \dfrac{28}{5}$

5. $(0.3, 2.1)$; $3y = x + 6$

$10y = 25$

6. $(0.8, 0.5)$; $y = 2x - 1$

$10y = 10x - 2$

7. $\left(\dfrac{2}{3}, \dfrac{5}{7}\right)$; $7y + 2 = 7$

$5y + 3 = 0$

8. $\left(\dfrac{1}{8}, \dfrac{1}{8}\right)$; $y = x$

$8y = 1$

9. $(5, -2)$; $2y = -x$

$x = 5$

10. $(-4, -8)$; $y = -2x$

$x = -4$

Solve each system of linear equations graphically and check numerically, if possible. If the system has infinitely many solutions, describe the solution set.

11. $y = 3x - 1$
$y = -2x + 4$

12. $y = 3x - 6$
$y = -5x + 2$

13. $y = \dfrac{1}{2}x + 3$
$y = -\dfrac{3}{2}x + 9$

14. $y = \dfrac{2}{3}x + \dfrac{1}{3}$
$y = -\dfrac{2}{3}x + 1$

15. $2x + y = 5$
$-4x - y = -6$

16. $3x - y = -2$
$-2x + y = -1$

17. $5x - 3y = 15$
$4x + y = 12$

18. $4x - 3y = 12$
$2x + y = 6$

19. $2x + 3y = -6$
$x - 4y = 8$

20. $x - 3y = 6$
$2x + 4y = -8$

21. $a + b = 4$
$a - 2b = 7$

22. $2p + 4q = 8$
$3p + q = -8$

23. $y = \dfrac{1}{2}x + 6$
$x + 3y = 6$

24. $y = \dfrac{1}{2}x + 4$
$x + 3y = 9$

25. $y = 2x + 2$
$y = 2x - 3$

26. $y = -3x + 2$
$y = -3x$

27. $y = -\dfrac{2}{3}x - 2$
$6y = -4x - 12$

28. $x + 4 = 0$
$3x + 2 = -4$

29. $3x + 2y = 12$
$y - 2 = 1$

30. $-x + 2y = 4$
$3x - 2 = 4$

31. $y = 3x - 1$
$6x = -5 - 12y$

32. $y = -2x + 3$
$12x = 8y - 17$

33. $c(x) = 25x + 200$
$c(x) = 15x + 250$

34. $c(x) = 12x + 80$
$c(x) = 15x + 50$

35. $x + 2y = 6$
$x + 2y = 2$

36. $x - y = -1$
$3x - 3y = -3$

37. $5x + 10 = -5$
$2y + 7 = 5$

38. $4y + 8 = -4$
$2x + 6 = -2$

39. Caleb needs to choose between two rental plans. U-Haul will rent a 24-foot truck for $39.95 per day plus $0.59 per mile. Budget Rent-A-Truck charges $25.49 per day and $0.65 per mile for the same truck.

   a. Write a system of equations in two variables, relating the daily cost of rental, $c(x)$, in terms of x miles driven.

   b. Using a window (0, 470, 100, 0, 310, 100, 1), determine a solution of the system on your calculator.

   c. If Caleb plans a daily trip of less than 200 miles, which plan should he choose?

   d. If Caleb plans a daily trip of more than 300 miles, which plan should he use?

40. Penske will rent a 17-foot truck for $29.95 per day plus $0.59 per mile. Budget Rent-A-Truck will rent the same truck for $15.49 per day and $0.65 per mile.

   a. Write a system of equations in two variables, relating the daily cost of rental, $c(x)$, in terms of x miles driven.

   b. Using a window (0, 470, 100, 0, 310, 100, 1), determine a solution of the system on your calculator.

c. If Jonathan plans a daily trip of less than 200 miles, which plan should he choose?

d. If Jonathan plans a daily trip of more than 300 miles, which plan should he use?

41. Marshall has a new satellite phone in his car. The charge is $0.30 per minute for all calls. His monthly cell phone charges are $49.99 for 500 minutes and $0.40 per minute for all calls over 500 minutes.

   a. Write a system of equations in two variables, relating the monthly charges, y, in terms of x minutes used.

   b. Solve the system graphically on your calculator.

   c. Interpret the solution.

42. Budget will rent a compact car for $42.99 per day with unlimited miles. Enterprise will rent the same car for $38.93 per day plus $0.30 per mile driven over 150 miles.

   a. Write a system of equations in two variables, relating the daily charges, y, in terms of x miles driven.

   b. Solve the system graphically on your calculator.

   c. Interpret the solution.

43. An advertising firm needs to decide whether to use presorted or regular first-class mailing in one of its promotions. To use presorted mailing, the company must buy a permit that costs $125 and then pay 23 cents per piece of mail. If the firm uses regular first-class mailing, it will pay 34 cents per piece of mail.

   a. Write a system of linear equations in two variables to represent the cost, y, of mailing x pieces of mail under each option.

   b. Graph the system on your calculator, using a window of (0, 1500, 100, 0, 1000, 100, 1). Determine the solution of the system of equations.

   c. When will it be more cost effective to use the presorted mailing? Explain your answer.

   d. When will it be more cost effective to use the first-class mailing? Explain your answer.

44. A dinner coupon book sells for $50.00. With the book, you save $4.00 on each dinner purchased. The average cost of the dinners is $17.50.

   a. Write a system of linear equations in two variables to represent the total cost, y, of purchasing x dinners with and without the coupon book.

   b. Solve the system of equations.

   c. When will it be beneficial to purchase the coupon book?

   d. When will it be more cost effective not to purchase the coupon book? Explain.

45. Chris is remodeling his basement and needs to rent a nailer and a drywall lift (a piece of equipment that allows him to work alone). He estimates that he needs these tools for an entire work week. The cost of the lift is twelve dollars more per day than the cost of the nailer. Altogether the cost will be $240 for five days. Set up and solve a system to find the cost of renting each tool.

46. Kelly spends a total of $500 per month for rent and car payments. Her rent payment is three times as large as her car payment. Write a system of equations to represent these facts, with x representing the car payment and y representing the rent payment. Solve the system. Explain.

47. Jenny works 40 hours per week at two part-time jobs. One job pays $7.00 per hour and the other pays $8.20 per hour. She wishes to earn exactly $298 to meet her budgeted expenses. Use a system of equations to find how many hours Jenny should work on each job to meet her budget.

48. Hugh earned $316 per week, working part time at two jobs. One job paid $3.00 more per hour than the other job. Hugh worked 18 hours per week at the lower paying job and 22 hours per week at the higher paying job. Use a system of equations to find the hourly wage Hugh earned for each job.

49. Jolie is considering having laser eye surgery so that she will not have to wear glasses. She has investigated a couple of different vision programs with her doctor. One method involves a procedure that costs $5000 and in which there is a $15 charge for each follow-up visit. The other method involves a surgery that costs $3000 with follow-up visits of $250 each. None of this will be covered by her health insurance. Write a system of equations to represent this situation. Solve the system to determine the number of visits that makes both programs equal. Interpret your results.

50. Vehicles bought by consumers for transportation typically depreciate (decline) in value. Joel is considering an automobile purchase and finds one minivan that costs $15,000 with an average depreciation of $1050 per year. Another comparable vehicle is $20,000 and depreciates at a rate of $2500 per year. Use a system of equations to approximate the year in which the two vehicles will be worth the same amount of money.

51. Female participation in high school athletic programs is increasing at a rate that is higher than that for males, according to data published by the National Federation of State High School Associations. The number of males participating, in millions, is estimated by $m(x) = 0.047x + 3.63$, where x is the number of years since 1995. Likewise, the number of females participating, in millions, is estimated by $f(x) = 0.064x + 2.37$. Assuming that these rates continue into the future, determine the year in which the participation by males and females will be equal.

52. The number of foreign visitors from overseas to the United States, in millions, is decreasing and can be estimated by $f(x) = -0.67x + 25.46$, where x is the number of years since 1997. Likewise, the number of U.S. travelers to overseas countries, in millions, can be estimated by $u(x) = 0.49x + 22.56$. These equations were developed with the use of data from the U.S. Department of Commerce. Determine the year in which the number of U.S. travelers to foreign countries will equal the number of foreign travelers to the United States.

53. According to the United States Census Bureau's Social and Economic Supplement, both women and men working full time experienced salary gains between 2001 and 2002, but women had a much higher percentage gain in median yearly earnings. The yearly earnings of women in dollars can be estimated by $w(x) = 27{,}259 + 2944x$, where x is the number of years after 2001. The earnings of men in dollars can be estimated x years after 2001 by $m(x) = 38{,}885 + 544x$. If these trends continue, determine the year in which women and men will have the same median yearly earnings.

54. Between 2000 and 2001 deaths by suicide and deaths due to homicide both went up, but deaths due to homicides went up more drastically. Using data from the United States Center for Health Statistics, the number of deaths by suicide per 100,000 population, $s(t)$, where t is the number of years since 2000, can be estimated by $s(t) = 0.3t + 10.4$. The number of deaths per 100,000 population due to homicide t years after 2000 can be estimated by $h(t) = 1.2t + 5.9$. Assuming these patterns continue, determine the year in which the number of deaths by suicide and the number of deaths due to homicide will be equal.

55. The following table gives male and female employment status for the years 2000 and 2002, a period of increased unemployment.

Year	2000	2002
Number employed in thousands (male)	63,586	63,582
Number employed in thousands (female)	73,305	72,903

    a. Write linear equations that estimate the number of employed males and females, $m(x)$ and $f(x)$, where x is the number of years after 2000.

    b. Create a system of equations and solve the system. Interpret the results.

56. Between 2002 and 2004 the economy rebounded and employment went up. The chart below summarizes employment numbers by sex:

Year	2002	2004
Number employed in thousands (male)	63,582	64,728
Number employed in thousands (female)	72,903	74,524

    a. Write linear equations that estimate the number of employed males and females $m(x)$ and $f(x)$, where x is the number of years after 2002.

    b. Create a system of equations and solve the system. Interpret the results.

4.1 Calculator Exercises

The calculator does not easily graph equations of the form $x = c$, since these are not functions. However, the calculator can still be used to help you solve a system of linear equations when one of the equations in the system is of that form. There are two ways in which to do this. One uses the **TRACE** feature of the calculator, and the other uses the **APPS** feature of the calculator. Each of these is described next.

Part 1. Using the TRACE feature

- Solve the equation that is a function of y. Store this function in Y1.
- Graph the function stored.
- Solve the equation that is not a function, $x = c$, and enter the value of c from this equation into the calculator.
- Trace the function.
- The coordinate pair displayed on the screen represents the solution of the system of equations.

As an example, solve the following system of linear equations:

$$2x + 3y = 8$$
$$4x - 1 = 6$$

Solution:

- The first equation yields $y = \dfrac{-2}{3}x + \dfrac{8}{3}$.
- Store this equation in Y1.
- The second equation yields $x = \dfrac{7}{4}$, or $x = 1.75$.
- Trace the first function and enter the value $\dfrac{7}{4}$ for x.

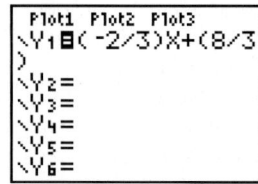 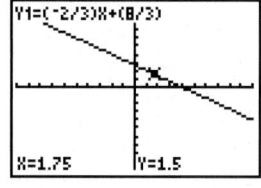

The calculator traces to the solution of the system, which is $(1.75, 1.5)$, or $\left(\dfrac{7}{4}, \dfrac{3}{2}\right)$.

Part 2. Using the APPS feature

If you have a system of equations in which one of the equations graphs to a vertical line, you can use the **APPS** key to graph the system. The **APPS** applications come with the TI-84 Plus but must be purchased for the TI-83 Plus. For example, solve the following system of linear equations:

$$2x + 3y = 8$$
$$4x - 1 = 6$$

- Set up the calculator to graph the equation that is a function.
- To use the applications, press the **APPS** key on the calculator.
- Choose the Inequalz option from the menu. A logo will appear.
- Press any key to continue. The calculator will display the menu for the **Y=** key.
- To change to the X = format, move the cursor to the top of the screen and highlight X = in the first location.
- When you press **ENTER**, the calculator will change the displays to X = displays.
- Enter the value obtained when you solve the second equation for x in the first location.
- Proceed to the graph as you normally would, by using the **ZOOM** key or setting the window and using the **GRAPH** key. **ZOOM** **6** yields the following graph:

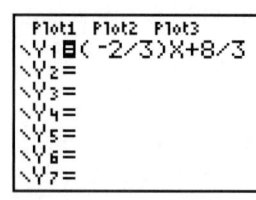 

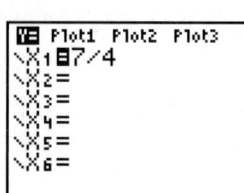 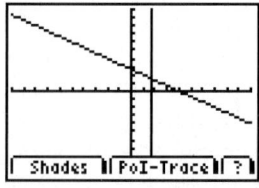

- To find the intersection point of the system, press [ALPHA] [TRACE] or [ALPHA] [ZOOM]. The calculator will display the point of intersection of the two graphs.

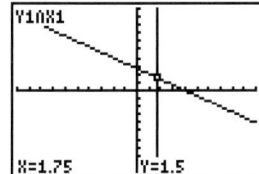

To return to the previous settings for the calculator, press [APPS], choose the Inequalz option again, and then choose option 2 to quit the application. You should get into the habit of doing this whenever you are through with an application.

Try either of these methods on the following systems of equations:

1. $5x + 2y = 5$
   $x + 7 = 10$

2. $5x - y = -19$
   $5x + 20 = 13$

3. $\frac{1}{2}x + \frac{1}{3}y = 7$
   $2x - 7 = x + 1$

4. $x + 5 = 5x - 4$
   $3y + 5 = y - 2$

4.1 Writing Exercises

1. In this section, the following statement was made: "We can represent the solutions of a linear equation in two variables by graphing." Explain what this statement means. In your explanation, discuss the relationship between ordered-pair solutions of a linear equation in two variables and points on the graph of the equation. Explain why the graph is the best way to indicate solutions of such an equation.

2. In the exercises in this section, sometimes it would be best to use the intercept method to graph the system of equations, other times it would be best to use the slope–intercept method, and still other times it might be best to use the table-of-values method or the method of horizontal and vertical lines. First, recall what each of these methods requires. Then look at the equations given in the exercises, and see if you can tell why a particular method would be best for a given form. Write a short paragraph explaining how the form of the equation might lead you to use that method.

4.2 SOLVING SYSTEMS OF TWO EQUATIONS BY THE SUBSTITUTION METHOD

OBJECTIVES
1 Solve systems of linear equations by the substitution method.
2 Model real-world situations by using systems of linear equations, and solve the equations by the substitution method.

APPLICATION

According to the 2005 census, the receipts of the federal government, in trillions of dollars, x years after 2000 may be approximated by $R(x) = -0.067x + 2.022$. Federal government outlays, or expenditures, in trillions of dollars, x years after 2000 may be approximated by $E(x) = 0.135x + 1.757$. Determine the year when the receipts equal the expenditures.

After completing this section, we will discuss this application further. See page 374.

Objective 4.2.1 ## Solving Systems of Linear Equations by the Substitution Method

Sometimes an ordered-pair solution of a system of linear equations may not have integer coordinates. Solving these systems graphically may be difficult. Therefore, algebraic methods are needed. One such method is the **substitution method**.

To understand the substitution method, let's review the process of substitution. We have evaluated equations when we know values of the variables by substituting each value for a variable and simplifying the equation. Let's apply this idea to a system of equations.

Solve the system

$$4x + y = 2$$
$$x = 3$$

Substitute 3 for x in the first equation.

$$4x + y = 2$$
$$4(3) + y = 2 \qquad \text{Substitute 3 for x.}$$
$$12 + y = 2 \qquad \text{Simplify.}$$

Solve for the variable y.

$$12 + y - 12 = 2 - 12 \qquad \text{Subtract 12 from both sides.}$$
$$y = -10 \qquad \text{Simplify.}$$

The solution must have $x = 3$ and $y = -10$ as coordinate values. The ordered-pair solution is $(3, -10)$.

A more complicated example occurs when x equals an expression instead of a number. For example, solve the system

$$4x + y = 2$$
$$x = y + 3$$

Since $x = y + 3$, substitute $(y + 3)$ for x in the first equation.

 TAKE NOTE Be careful to include parentheses around the expression being substituted.

$$4x + y = 2$$
$$4(y + 3) + y = 2 \qquad \text{Substitute y + 3 for x.}$$
$$4y + 12 + y = 2 \qquad \text{Distribute 4.}$$
$$5y + 12 = 2 \qquad \text{Simplify.}$$

Solve for the variable y.

$$5y + 12 - 12 = 2 - 12 \qquad \text{Subtract 12 from both sides.}$$
$$5y = -10 \qquad \text{Simplify.}$$
$$\frac{5y}{5} = \frac{-10}{5} \qquad \text{Divide both sides by 5.}$$
$$y = -2 \qquad \text{Simplify.}$$

To determine the x-coordinate, substitute -2 for y in the second equation of the system, and solve for x.

$$x = y + 3$$
$$x = -2 + 3 \qquad \text{Substitute } -2 \text{ for y.}$$
$$x = 1 \qquad \text{Simplify.}$$

The solution is $(1, -2)$.

SOLVING A SYSTEM OF LINEAR EQUATIONS IN TWO VARIABLES BY THE SUBSTITUTION METHOD

To solve a system of linear equations in two variables by the substitution method,

- Solve one of the equations for a variable. (Preferably, choose a variable with a numerical coefficient of 1.)
- Substitute the expression for the variable found in the first step for the variable in the other equation of the system.

- Solve the resulting equation for the second variable.
- Substitute the value obtained for the second variable into one of the original equations.
- Solve for the remaining variable.

The ordered-pair solution is determined by the values obtained in solving for each individual variable.

 TAKE NOTE Remember to check your solution by substituting it into the original equations or by solving graphically.

EXAMPLE 1   Solve each system of linear equations in two variables by the substitution method. Check the solution.

a. $y = x - 2$
$-x - 2y = 1$

b. $4x + y = 2$
$x - 2y = 3$

Algebraic Solution

a. The first equation is solved for y, $y = x - 2$.
Substitute $(x - 2)$ for y in the second equation.

$$-x - 2y = 1$$
$$-x - 2(x - 2) = 1 \qquad \text{Substitute } x - 2 \text{ for } y.$$
$$-x - 2x + 4 = 1 \qquad \text{Distribute } -2.$$
$$-3x + 4 = 1 \qquad \text{Simplify.}$$

Solve for x.

$$-3x + 4 - 4 = 1 - 4 \qquad \text{Subtract 4 from both sides.}$$
$$-3x = -3 \qquad \text{Simplify.}$$
$$\frac{-3x}{-3} = \frac{-3}{-3} \qquad \text{Divide both sides by } -3.$$
$$x = 1 \qquad \text{Simplify.}$$

Next substitute 1 for x in the first equation and solve for y.

$$y = x - 2$$
$$y = 1 - 2 \qquad \text{Substitute.}$$
$$y = -1 \qquad \text{Simplify.}$$

Since $x = 1$ and $y = -1$, the solution is $(1, -1)$.
Check by substituting the solution back into the original equations.

$y = x - 2$		$-x - 2y = 1$	
-1	$1 - 2$	$-(1) - 2(-1)$	1
	-1	$-1 + 2$	
		1	

The solution checks in both equations.

b. First, we must solve one of the equations for a variable. If we solve the second equation, $x - 2y = 3$, for x, we obtain $x = 2y + 3$. Using the substitution method, we substitute $(2y + 3)$ for x in the first equation, $4x + y = 2$.

$$4x + y = 2$$
$$4(2y + 3) + y = 2 \qquad \text{Substitute } 2y + 3 \text{ for } x.$$
$$8y + 12 + y = 2 \qquad \text{Distribute 4.}$$
$$9y + 12 = 2 \qquad \text{Simplify.}$$

Solve for y.

$$9y + 12 - 12 = 2 - 12 \qquad \text{Subtract 12 from both sides.}$$

$$9y = -10 \qquad \text{Simplify.}$$

$$\frac{9y}{9} = -\frac{10}{9} \qquad \text{Divide both sides by 9.}$$

$$y = -\frac{10}{9} \qquad \text{Simplify.}$$

Next, substitute $-\frac{10}{9}$ for y in the second equation of the system, and solve for x.

$$x - 2y = 3$$

$$x - 2\left(-\frac{10}{9}\right) = 3 \qquad \text{Substitute } -\frac{10}{9} \text{ for } y.$$

$$x + \frac{20}{9} = 3 \qquad \text{Simplify.}$$

$$x + \frac{20}{9} - \frac{20}{9} = 3 - \frac{20}{9} \qquad \text{Subtract } \frac{20}{9} \text{ from both sides.}$$

$$x = \frac{27}{9} - \frac{20}{9} \qquad \text{Simplify and write the right expression with the LCD of the denominators.}$$

$$x = \frac{7}{9} \qquad \text{Simplify.}$$

Check

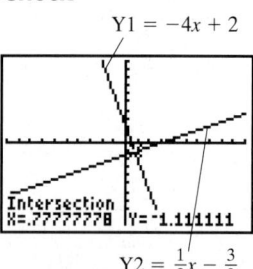

Y1 = $-4x + 2$

Intersection
X=.7777778 Y=-1.111111

Y2 = $\frac{1}{2}x - \frac{3}{2}$

$(-10, 10, -10, 10)$

The solution is $\left(\frac{7}{9}, -\frac{10}{9}\right)$.

To check your solution graphically, solve both equations for y. The intersection point $(0.\overline{7}, -1.\overline{1})$ is the solution $\left(\frac{7}{9}, -\frac{10}{9}\right)$. ■

Each of the systems in Example 1 had one solution. However, we know from the previous section that a system may have no solution or an infinite number of solutions. Let's try substitution on these kinds of systems. Complete the following sets of exercises.

 Guided Discovery 4   Inconsistent System of Linear Equations

Solve the given system of linear equations by the substitution method.

$$-2x + y = 1$$
$$-4x + 2y = 3$$

Write a rule for determining, by the substitution method, that a system of linear equations is inconsistent—in other words, that it has no solution.

A system has no solution if, after applying the substitution method, the resulting equation is a contradiction.

 TAKE NOTE It is important to state that an inconsistent system has no solution.

 Guided Discovery 5   System of Dependent Linear Equations

Solve the given system of linear equations by the substitution method.

$$-3x - y = -2$$
$$y = -3x + 2$$

Write a rule for determining, by the substitution method, that a system of linear equations has dependent equations—in other words, an infinite number of solutions.

A system has an infinite number of solutions if, after applying the substitution method, the resulting equation is an identity.

 TAKE NOTE It is important to describe the solution set for a system of dependent equations as all ordered pairs (x, y) that satisfy the equations.

EXAMPLE 2

Using the substitution method, determine whether each system of equations has no solution or infinitely many solutions. If the system has an infinite number of solutions, describe the solutions. Check by solving graphically.

a. $y = -x - 3$
$\quad y = -x + 2$

b. $y = \dfrac{2}{3}x - \dfrac{1}{3}$
$\quad 3y = 2x - 1$

Algebraic Solution

a. Since the first equation is solved for y, substitute the expression $(-x - 3)$ for y in the second equation.

$$y = -x + 2$$
$$-x - 3 = -x + 2 \quad \text{Substitute } (-x - 3) \text{ for } y.$$

Solve for x.

$$-x - 3 + x = -x + 2 + x \quad \text{Add x to both sides.}$$
$$-3 = 2 \quad \text{Simplify.}$$

The result is a contradiction. There is no solution of the system.
  Checking by solving graphically results in two parallel lines.

Check

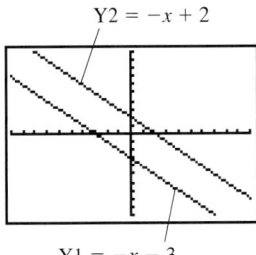

$Y2 = -x + 2$

$Y1 = -x - 3$

$(-10, 10, -10, 10)$

b. Since the first equation is solved for y, substitute the expression $\left(\dfrac{2}{3}x - \dfrac{1}{3}\right)$ for y in the second equation.

$$3y = 2x - 1$$
$$3\left(\frac{2}{3}x - \frac{1}{3}\right) = 2x - 1 \quad \text{Substitute } \left(\tfrac{2}{3}x - \tfrac{1}{3}\right) \text{ for } y.$$
$$2x - 1 = 2x - 1 \quad \text{Distribute 3.}$$

Solve for x.

$$2x - 1 - 2x = 2x - 1 - 2x \quad \text{Subtract 2x from both sides.}$$
$$-1 = -1 \quad \text{Simplify.}$$

The result is an identity. There are an infinite number of solutions. The solutions are all ordered pairs (x, y) that satisfy $y = \dfrac{2}{3}x - \dfrac{1}{3}$.
  Checking by solving graphically results in two coinciding lines.

Check

$Y1 = \frac{2}{3}x - \frac{1}{3}$

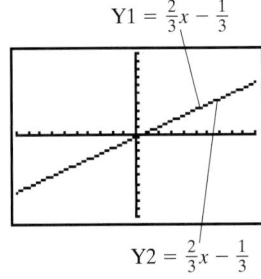

$Y2 = \frac{2}{3}x - \frac{1}{3}$

$(-47, 47, -31, 31)$

The following summary describes the process of algebraically solving a system of linear equations by using the substitution method:

SOLVING A SYSTEM OF LINEAR EQUATIONS BY THE SUBSTITUTION METHOD

In solving a system of linear equations in two variables by the substitution method, one of three possibilities will occur.

(continued on page 372)

1. **A value for both variables will be determined.**

   One solution exists: the ordered-pair coordinates.

   The system is consistent.

   The equations are independent.

2. **Applying the substitution method will result in a contradiction.**

   No solution exists.

   The system is inconsistent.

   The equations are independent.

3. **Applying the substitution method will result in an identity.**

   An infinite number of solutions exist. The solution set is the set of all ordered pairs (x, y) that satisfy either equation of the system.

   The system is consistent.

   The equations are dependent.

Objective 4.2.1 *CHECKUP*

1. Solve each system of linear equations in two variables by the substitution method. Check your solution.

   a. $2x - y = 5$
   $\quad\ 4x = 1$

   b. $-x + 5y = -12$
   $\quad\ \ 2x + y = -2$

2. Determine by the substitution method whether each system of equations has no solution or infinitely many solutions. If the system has an infinite number of solutions, describe the solution set.

   a. $10x - 2y = 6$
   $\quad\ \ y = 5x - 3$

   b. $y = \dfrac{1}{2}x - 7$
   $\quad\ \ 2y = x + 6$

3. In solving a system of equations by the substitution method, one of three outcomes can occur. These are listed in the table that follows. Complete the table to describe the system of equations for each outcome. One row of the table is completed to help you.

Outcome	Number of Solutions	Is the System Consistent or Inconsistent?	Are the Equations Dependent or Independent?
Able to solve the system for a coordinate pair.	One solution exists.	The system is consistent.	The equations are independent.
The system results in an identity.			
The system results in a contradiction.			

Objective 4.2.2 **Modeling the Real World**

The substitution method for solving a system of linear equations works best when one of the equations is relatively easy to solve for one variable. This often happens in geometry problems, where you can frequently solve a geometric formula for a side of a rectangle or the radius of a circle in terms of other variables and numbers.

EXAMPLE 3

If two angles are complementary and one angle is 6 more than twice the other, find the measures of the angles.

Algebraic Solution

Let x = the measure of the first angle

y = the measure of the complementary angle

Since the angles are complementary, the sum of the angle measurements is 90 degrees. We write the following equation:

$$x + y = 90$$

One angle is 6 more than twice the other.

$$x = 2y + 6$$

The system to be solved is

(1) $x + y = 90$

(2) $x = 2y + 6$

We substitute $(2y + 6)$ for x in the first equation and solve for y.

$$
\begin{aligned}
(1)\qquad x + y &= 90 \\
(2y + 6) + y &= 90 \qquad &\text{Substitute } 2y + 6 \text{ for } x. \\
3y + 6 &= 90 \qquad &\text{Simplify.} \\
3y + 6 - 6 &= 90 - 6 \qquad &\text{Subtract 6 from both sides.} \\
3y &= 84 \qquad &\text{Simplify.} \\
\frac{3y}{3} &= \frac{84}{3} \qquad &\text{Divide both sides by 3.} \\
y &= 28 \qquad &\text{Simplify.}
\end{aligned}
$$

Substitute 28 for y in the second equation.

$$
\begin{aligned}
(2)\quad x &= 2y + 6 \\
x &= 2(28) + 6 \qquad &\text{Substitute 28 for } y. \\
x &= 62 \qquad &\text{Simplify.}
\end{aligned}
$$

The check is left to you.

The complementary angles have measures of 28 degrees and 62 degrees.   ■

When we write a system of equations intended to describe real-world situations, we may use function notation. This often is the case for the business applications of total revenue and total cost. To determine algebraically the break-even point, when the total revenue equals the total cost (that is, there is no profit or loss), the substitution method works best.

EXAMPLE 4

The owner of Bateman Camera and Video needs to determine the number of CDs he must produce to break even before he decides to sell this new line of products. He determined that the fixed cost of producing the CDs would be $9000 and that there would be a variable cost of $15 per CD produced. He plans to sell the CDs for $45 each.

a. Write a function for the total cost of producing the CDs.

b. Write a function for the total revenue received from selling the CDs.

c. Write a system of equations and determine the number of CDs that must be produced and sold to break even.

Solution

a. Let x = the number of CDs produced and sold

$C(x)$ = the total cost of producing x CDs

The total cost equals the variable cost plus the fixed cost.

$$C(x) = 15x + 9000$$

b. Let $R(x) =$ the total revenue received from selling x CDs

The total revenue equals the selling price times the number of CDs sold.

$$R(x) - 45x$$

c. Since we want $C(x)$ and $R(x)$ to be equal, we can change the function notation to relation form, using y for both the total cost and the total revenue.

(1) $\qquad y = 15x + 9000$

(2) $\qquad y = 45x$

(1) $\qquad 45x = 15x + 9000$ $\qquad$ Substitute 45x for y in the first equation.

$\qquad 45x - 15x = 15x + 9000 - 15x$ $\qquad$ Subtract 15x from both sides.

$\qquad 30x = 9000$ $\qquad$ Simplify.

$$\frac{30x}{30} = \frac{9000}{30}$$ $\qquad$ Divide both sides by 30.

$\qquad x = 300$ $\qquad$ Simplify.

Substitute 300 for x in the second equation.

(2) $\qquad\qquad y = 45x$

$$y = 45(300)$$

$$y = 13,500$$

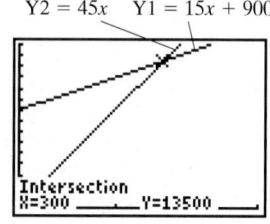

Y2 = 45x   Y1 = 15x + 9000

Intersection
X=300   Y=13500

(0, 500, 0, 15,000)

We can check the solution (300, 13,500) by solving graphically.

The owner will break even if he produces and sells 300 CDs.

APPLICATION

According to the 2005 census, the receipts of the federal government, in trillions of dollars, x years after 2000 may be approximated by $R(x) = -0.067x + 2.022$. Federal government outlays, or expenditures, in trillions of dollars, x years after 2000 may be approximated by $E(x) = 0.135x + 1.757$. Determine the year when the receipts equal the expenditures.

Discussion

To determine when the receipts equal the expenditures, we will write and solve a system of equations.

(1) $R(x) = -0.067x + 2.022$ $\qquad$ or $\qquad y = -0.067x + 2.022$

(2) $E(x) = 0.135x + 1.757$ $\qquad\qquad\qquad\quad y = 0.135x + 1.757$

$$0.135x + 1.757 = -0.067x + 2.022$$ $\qquad$ Substitute (0.135x + 1.757) for y in the first equation.

$$0.135x + 1.757 + 0.067x = -0.067x + 2.022 + 0.067x$$ $\quad$ Add 0.067x to both sides.

$$0.202x + 1.757 = 2.022$$ $\qquad$ Simplify.

$$0.202x + 1.757 - 1.757 = 2.022 - 1.757$$ $\qquad$ Subtract 1.757 from both sides.

$$0.202x = 0.265$$ $\qquad$ Simplify.

$$\frac{0.202x}{0.202} = \frac{0.265}{0.202}$$ $\qquad$ Divide both sides by 0.202.

$$x \approx 1.3$$ $\qquad$ Simplify.

Note that there is no need to determine $R(x)$ and $E(x)$ to answer the question asked.

The receipts will equal the expenditures about 1.3 years after 2000 (or $2000 + 1.3 = 2001.3$). We will need to round up to the next year, 2002.

✓ Objective 4.2.2 *CHECKUP*

1. Two angles are supplementary. The larger angle measures 15 degrees more than twice the smaller angle. Find the measures of the two angles.

2. Deanna set up a bakery in her home to bake German chocolate cakes to sell to local restaurants. She spent $245.00 on supplies such as pans, trays, storage, etc. She estimated that each cake she sold cost her $2.50 to produce. She sold the cakes to restaurants for $20.00 each.
   a. Write a function for the total cost of producing the cakes.
   b. Write a function for the total revenue received from selling the cakes.

   c. Write a system of equations and determine the number of cakes Deanna produced and sold to break even.

3. According to data from the U.S. Social Security Administration, the number of male workers (in millions) with Social Security insured status can be estimated by the function $m(x) = 0.775x + 86.3$, where x is the number of years after 1990. Likewise, the number of female workers (in millions) with Social Security insured status can be estimated by the function $f(x) = 1.121x + 77.3$. Determine the year in which the number of insured female workers will equal the number of insured male workers, assuming that the functions still describe the real world.

4.2 EXERCISES

Student Solutions Manual   PH Math/Tutor Center   CD Video   MathXL®   MyMathLab   Interactmath.com

Solve each system of linear equations by the substitution method. Check the solution. If a system has an infinite number of solutions, describe the solution set.

1. $y = 3x - 1$
$2x + y = 4$

2. $y = 3x - 6$
$5x + y = 2$

3. $y = x - 3$
$2x - y = 19$

4. $y = -x - 3$
$2x + y = 1$

5. $y = \frac{1}{2}x + 3$
$3x + 2y = -2$

6. $y = \frac{3}{4}x + 1$
$2x + 3y = 37$

7. $y = -3x + 4$
$y = x - 4$

8. $y = 2x - 1$
$y = x - 4$

9. $4y = x + 4$
$5y = 2x + 11$

10. $3y = x + 6$
$5y = 10 - x$

11. $y = 3x - 15$
$x - 5 = 0$

12. $y = 2x - 8$
$x + 4 = 0$

13. $2x - 3y = 5$
$2y + 6 = 8$

14. $x - 5y = 20$
$2y + 3 = -7$

15. $y = -4x + 3$
$5(x - 1) = 0$

16. $y = 3x - 3$
$5(y - 5) = 20$

17. $3x + 2y = 12$
$y - 2 = 1$

18. $x - 2y = -4$
$3x - 2 = 4$

19. $2x + 3y = -6$
$x - 4y = 8$

20. $2x + 2y = -6$
$4x - y = 8$

21. $x - 2y = 26$
$5x + 10y = -10$

22. $5x - 3y = -13$
$4x + y = 27$

23. $x + y = 4$
$x - 2y = 7$

24. $x + 2y = -28$
$3x + y = -9$

25. $3x + 5y = 15$
$4x - 2y = 7$

26. $y = x + 1$
$5x - 10y = 3$

27. $y = 2x + 2$
$2x - y = 3$

28. $3x + y = 2$
$y = -3x$

29. $y = 2x + 3$
$y - x + 1 = x + 4$

30. $y = -3x + 2$
$2y + 2x = 2 + y - x$

31. $2x + y = 4$
$x - y = 5$

32. $3x + y = 5$
$x - y = 3$

33. $y = \frac{3}{2}x + 4$
$2x + y = 11$

34. $3x + y = 10$
$y = -\frac{3}{4}x + 1$

35. $x + y = 300$
$5.00x + 3.50y = 1398.00$

36. $x + y = 200$
$2.50x + 3.00y = 553.00$

37. $2x + 2y = 60$
$y = 3x - 2$

38. $2x + 2y = 26$
$x = 4y - 2$

39. $f(x) = 3x - 2$
$f(x) = 6x + 1$

40. $g(x) = -2x + 3$
$g(x) = 2x - 5$

41. $c(x) = 2.50x + 600$
$c(x) = 3.50x + 200$

42. $c(x) = 5.25x + 300$
$c(x) = 4.50x + 600$

43. $5x + 7y = 35$
$2x - 5y = 53$

44. $2x - 5y = 8$
$3x + 4y = 35$

Write a system of equations for each situation, and solve by the substitution method.

Geometry

45. Two angles are complementary. The larger angle measures 10 degrees less than four times the smaller angle. Find the measures of the angles.

46. Two angles are complementary. One angle is 10 degrees more than nine times the other. Find the measure of the angles.

47. Two angles are supplementary. The difference of their measures is 40 degrees. Find the measures of the angles.

48. Two angles are supplementary. The larger of the two is 20 degrees more than three times the smaller. Find the measures of the angles.

49. Two angles of a triangle measure the same. The third angle measures 20 degrees more than the sum of the other two angles. How much does each angle measure?

50. Two angles of a triangle are the same size. The third angle is 15 degrees larger than each of the other two. What is the size of each angle?

51. An isosceles triangle has perimeter 37 feet. Its longest side is 3 feet less than twice the measure of the two equal sides. What is the measure of each side of the triangle?

52. An isosceles triangle has perimeter 40 inches. The third side is 5 inches less than the measure of the two equal sides. What is the measure of the three sides?

53. A rectangle in which the length is 39 centimeters more than the width has a perimeter of 260 centimeters. Find the dimensions of the rectangle.

54. The perimeter of a rectangle is 60 feet. The length is 6 feet less than twice the width. Find the dimensions of the rectangle.

55. The perimeter of a rectangle is 200 feet. The width is 150 feet less than the length. Find the dimensions of the rectangle.

56. The perimeter of a rectangle is 102 feet. The length is 60 feet more than the width. Find the dimensions of the rectangle.

57. The radius of a large circle is 5 inches more than twice the radius of a smaller circle. The larger circle has a circumference of 283 inches. Find the radius of the smaller circle and the radius of the larger circle, to the nearest inch.

58. A large circle has a circumference of 163 cm. Its radius is 10 cm less than three times the radius of a smaller circle. What is the radius of each circle, to the nearest cm?

59. Mr. McDonald had 15 acres of farmland, some of which he planted in corn and the rest in soybeans. The number of acres planted in corn was equivalent to 25 acres of farmland, less the number of acres planted in soybeans. How many acres were planted in each crop?

60. A field has 12 acres of farmland, part of which is planted in wheat and the rest in alfalfa. The number of acres of wheat equals one-half the difference of a 24-acre field, less twice the acreage of the alfalfa. How many acres are planted in each crop?

Business

61. The Homestore sells toaster ovens for $49 each, retail price. The wholesale cost to stock the ovens is $22 each. The fixed cost associated with acquiring the ovens, storing them in inventory, using shelf space, and advertising the ovens for sale is $2500.

a. Write a function for the total cost of stocking the ovens for sale.

b. Write a function for the total revenue received from selling the ovens.

c. Write a system of equations, and determine the number of ovens that must be sold to break even.

62. Handyman Depot sells ceiling fans for a retail price of $89 each. The wholesale cost to stock the fans is $35 each. The cost of ordering the fans from the manufacturer, storing them in inventory, using shelf space, and advertising the fans for sale is $3600.

a. Write a function for the total revenue received from selling the fans.

b. Write a function for the total cost of stocking the fans for sale.

c. Write a system of equations, and determine the number of fans that must be sold to break even.

63. Elaine sells her artwork on consignment at a local store. She pays $200 each month for booth space. She estimates that each piece of art costs $50. The average price of the artwork is $90. How many pieces of artwork will Elaine need to sell to break even?

64. Lowell runs a home improvement company. He does estimates on job cost and then charges customers an hourly rate. For a remodeling job he pays $1500 for materials and then will spend $10 per hour to rent a compressor. He will charge the customer $35 per hour. How many hours will he need to spend on the job to break even?

65. The bookstore manager has studied the daily demand for a computer software package and has determined that the quantity demanded, $d(x)$, is related to the price, x, by the linear demand function, $d(x) = 50 - \frac{1}{2}x$. The supplier of the computer software package has studied the daily supply for the software package and has determined a supply function, $s(x)$, $s(x) = \frac{2}{5}x$, where $s(x)$ is the quantity supplied and x is the price. Solve the system to determine the equilibrium point and interpret its meaning.

66. The daily demand for a product is given by $D(p) = 80 - \frac{4}{5}p$, where $D(p)$ is the quantity demanded each day by consumers when the price is p dollars per item. The daily supply of the product is given by $S(p) = \frac{5}{8}p$, where $S(p)$ is the quantity supplied each day when the price is p dollars per item. Solve the system to determine the equilibrium point and interpret its meaning.

Mixtures

67. Ellie is considering joining a health club during the winter months. One club charges $15 per month and $2 per visit and a second club charges $3.50 per visit with no monthly membership fee. At how many visits will the monthly price of the two clubs be the same?

68. A cell-phone company charges $25 per month plus $0.10 per minute. Another company charges $45 per month with unlimited minutes. How many minutes will a person need to talk to make the two companies' plans cost the same amount monthly?

69. Kevin wants to rent a small tractor to dig a pond in his yard. One company charges $100 for the first three hours and $20 per hour for hours beyond three hours. Another charges $150 for the first five hours and $15 for hours beyond five. Determine the number of hours for which the charges will be equal. Which deal is better if the job takes five hours? Which deal if better if the job takes ten hours?

70. Gary needs some legal work done. One lawyer in town, Mr. Shire, charges a $250 retainer plus $80 per hour for time spent beyond two hours. Another local lawyer, Mr. Hanson, charges a $400 retainer plus an hourly fee of $65 for time in excess of three hours. Determine the number of hours of legal time for which these legal fees will be the same. Assuming Gary's work takes six hours, which lawyer should he use?

Real Data

71. Average monthly Social Security benefits in dollars for disabled workers can be estimated by $D(x) = 21.8x + 566.90$, where x is the number of years after 1990. Similarly, the monthly Social Security benefits average for widows or widowers x years after 1990 can be estimated by $W(x) = 24.28x + 541.10$. These relations are based upon data reported by the Social Security Administration. Determine the year in which the monthly benefit will be equal (assuming that these trends continue). How does your result compare with the following table of actual values?

Year	2000	2001	2002
Monthly earnings (disabled)	787	814.90	834.32
Monthly earnings (widow(er)s)	811.80	840.80	861.09

72. According to data of the International Monetary Fund of the Federal Reserve Board, both the Canadian dollar and Swiss franc have fluctuated in value when compared to the U.S. dollar. The value of the Canadian dollar, d, in U.S. dollars, x years after 1995, can be estimated by $d(x) = -0.012x + 0.73$ while the value of the Swiss franc, s, in U.S. dollars, x years after 1995, can be estimated by $s(x) = -0.018x + 0.84$. Determine the year in which these types of currency will be equal in value when compared to the U.S. dollar. Does the trend shown in the following chart of actual values support your conclusion?

Year	2001	2002	2003
U.S. dollar value of Canadian dollar	0.65	0.64	0.71
U.S. dollar value of Swiss franc	0.59	0.64	0.74

73. According to data from the United States Department of Commerce, the United States' trade balance with Mexico shifted during the 1990s.
  a. Use the following chart and the information from 1993 and 1996 to write a linear equation for U.S. exports to Mexico, $e(x)$, where x is number of years after 1993. Next write an equation for U.S. imports to Mexico, $m(x)$, where x is number of years after 1993.
  b. Solve the system of equations that contains $e(x)$ and $m(x)$. Interpret the results.
  c. What would your equations predict as the trade balance between Mexico and the United States for this year assuming the trends continue?

Year	Exports (in millions of U.S. dollars)	Imports (in millions of U.S. dollars)
1993	41,581	39,917
1994	50,844	49,494
1995	46,292	61,685
1996	56,792	74,297

74. According to Ward's Communications, since 1995 small vehicles have gained as percent of sales in the U.S. automobile market while midsize vehicles have declined as percent of sales.
  a. Use the following chart and the information from 1995 and 2000 to write a linear equation for U.S. car sales as a percent for small vehicles, $s(x)$, where x is the number of years after 1995. Next write an equation for U.S. car sales as a percent for midsize vehicles $m(x)$, x years after 1995.
  b. Solve the system of equations that contains $s(x)$ and $m(x)$. Interpret the results.

Year	1995	2000	2002	2003
Small vehicles (%)	26.5	29.7	30.4	30.9
Large vehicles (%)	49.1	46.1	46.1	45.5

75. The total receipts of the United States for 2000 were estimated to be 1.9563×10^{12} dollars. Some of these receipts were from individual income taxes, and the rest were from other sources, such as corporate income taxes, social security taxes, excise taxes, and miscellaneous taxes. The receipts from other sources were 5.31×10^{10} dollars more than the receipts from individual income taxes. Determine how much was received from individual income taxes and how much was received from other sources.

76. Helium atoms have a much smaller diameter than cesium atoms. The arithmetic average of the two diameters is 2.75×10^{-10} m. The difference in size of the two diameters is 4.5×10^{-10} m. Determine the two diameters.

4.2 Calculator Exercises

The calculator can help you with the arithmetic when you are solving a system of equations by the substitution method, but it cannot do much more. However if you wish to check your solution by solving the system graphically, the calculator can be quite useful. Next is a shortcut that can save you effort when you use the calculator to solve a system graphically.

Whenever you use the calculator to solve a system of linear equations graphically, you must first solve functions for y in order to store them in the calculator. In solving functions for y, it is not necessary to simplify the expressions, since the calculator can handle them in nonsimplified form. This can save you time and keep you from making mistakes in the process. If the function is given to you in standard form, $ax + by = c$, just solve for y without simplifying and store $y = (c - ax) \div b$ in Y1. Do likewise for Y2. As an example, solve the following system of linear equations:

$$\frac{3}{8}x + \frac{7}{16}y = \frac{2303}{5280}$$

$$x + \frac{9}{17}y = \frac{137}{170}$$

We will store the following equations in Y1 and Y2:

$$Y1 = \left(\frac{2303}{5280} - \frac{3}{8}x\right) \div \left(\frac{7}{16}\right)$$

$$Y2 = \left(\frac{137}{170} - x\right) \div \left(\frac{9}{17}\right)$$

Note that you can almost do this step of solving for y in your head as you enter it into the calculator. Note also that we did not simplify these two equations. When we graph the two equations and find the intersection, the calculator displays the values of x and y as follows:

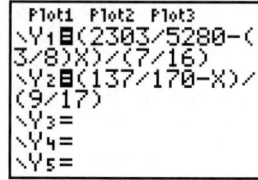
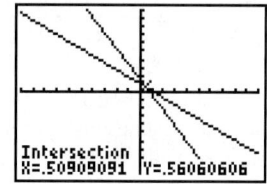

To convert the answers to fractions, simply enter the letters X and Y, followed by the [MATH] [1] command, and the calculator will display the fractions.

Try solving the following systems by using the substitution method. Then use the calculator to check your solution graphically by following the preceding example.

1. $15.80x + y = 2655.10$
   $18.40x + 73.20y = 19361.22$

2. $4.055x - 8.752y = -42.949$
   $x + 0.405y = 2.225$

3. $\frac{7}{13}x + \frac{5}{17}y - \frac{2}{3}$
   $x - \frac{5}{34}y = \frac{19}{42}$

4. $\frac{28}{65}x + \frac{51}{56}y = \frac{43}{35}$
   $\frac{35}{39}x - y = \frac{61}{51}$

4.2 Writing Exercises

You have learned two methods for solving systems of equations: the graphical method and the substitution method. Decide which method is easier to use to solve each system. List the reasons for your decision. Then solve the equations, using the method you chose.

1. $y = 0.0803x + 1.0507$
   $y = -0.8532x + 1.9842$

2. $y = 85x + 300$
   $450x - y = 286,225$

4.3 SOLVING SYSTEMS OF TWO EQUATIONS BY THE ADDITION METHOD

OBJECTIVES

1 Solve systems of linear equations by the addition method.

2 Model real-world situations by using systems of equations, and solve the equations by the addition method.

APPLICATION

According to the U.S. Census Bureau, Hispanics accounted for half of the U.S. population growth from 2003 to 2004. The 2004 total U.S. population is made up of 247.8 million non-Hispanics. The number of Hispanics in 2004 constitutes one-seventh of the total U.S. population. Write and solve a system of linear equations to determine the number of Hispanics in the United States in 2004.

After completing this section, we will discuss this application further. See page 386.

Solving Systems of Linear Equations by the Addition Method

Sometimes neither equation in a system can be solved for one variable in any simple way. Therefore, a second algebraic method is useful. We call this second method for solving a system of linear equations the **addition method**.

In order to understand the addition method, we will review the addition property of equations. This property states that we may add equivalent expressions to both sides of an equation, and the result is an equivalent equation; that is,

If $a = b$ and $c = d$, then $a + c = b + d$ for any expressions a, b, c, and d.

Remember that in Chapter 2 we illustrated why this is true with a balanced scale representing the equation. Now we begin with two equations (balanced scales).

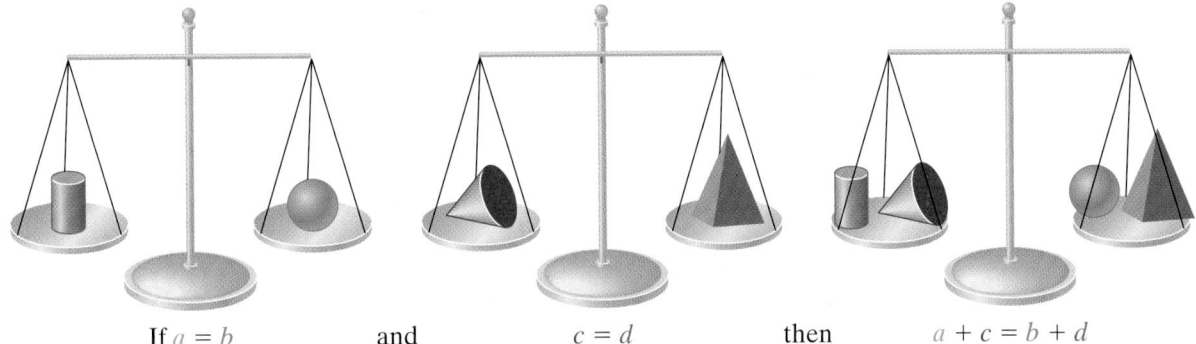

If $a = b$ and $c = d$ then $a + c = b + d$

We will apply the addition property to a system of equations to obtain a new equation with one variable eliminated.

Solve the system

$$2x - y = 8$$
$$y = 4$$

Using the addition property of equations, we obtain

If $2x - y = 8$ and $y = 4$, then $2x - y + y = 8 + 4$.

If $a = b$ and $c = d$, then $a + c = b + d$.

We add to each member of the first equation the corresponding member of the second equation. In other words, we add y to the left side of the first equation, $2x - y$, and 4 to the right side of the first equation, 8.

$$
\begin{array}{rcl}
2x - y & = & 8 \\
y & = & 4 \\
\hline
2x & = & 12 \\
\end{array}
$$ Add corresponding members of the equations.

   Simplify.

$$\frac{2x}{2} = \frac{12}{2}$$ Divide both sides by 2.

$$x = 6$$ Simplify.

Since $y = 4$, the solution of the system is $(6, 4)$.

This process works very nicely if one of the variables is eliminated when we apply the addition property. However, in many cases, we will need to write equivalent equations for the system before we apply the addition property. For example, solve the system

$$2x - y = -1$$
$$4x - y = 3$$

If we add $4x - y$ to the expression on the left side of the first equation, $2x - y$, we obtain $6x - 2y$. No variable is eliminated. However, we should see that if the y-term were positive in one expression and negative in the other expression, the *y*-variable would have been eliminated. In order to get a positive *y*, we need to multiply one of the variable expressions by -1 to change the sign of *y*. To do this, we apply the multiplication property of equations and multiply *both* sides of the equation by the same value, -1.

(1) $2x - y = -1$
(2) $4x - y = 3$
(1) $2x - y = -1$
(2) $-1(4x - y) = -1(3)$ Multiply both sides by -1.

 TAKE NOTE Even though the second equation is the only equation changed in this process, rewrite the entire system each time an equation changes. Doing this helps you keep track of what the system presently looks like.

(1) $2x - y = -1$
(2) $\underline{-4x + y = -3}$
$-2x = -4$ Add corresponding members of the equation.

$\dfrac{-2x}{-2} = \dfrac{-4}{-2}$ Divide both sides by -2.

$x = 2$ Simplify.

Substitute 2 for *x* in the first equation to find the *y*-value of the solution.

(1) $2x - y = -1$
$2(2) - y = -1$ Substitute 2 for x.
$4 - y = -1$ Simplify.
$4 - y - 4 = -1 - 4$ Subtract 4 from both sides.
$-y = -5$ Simplify.
$\dfrac{-y}{-1} = \dfrac{-5}{-1}$ Divide both sides by -1.
$y = 5$ Simplify.

The solution of the system is $(2, 5)$.

In some cases, we will need to rewrite both equations in the system before applying the addition property to eliminate a variable. For example, solve the system

$$2x + 3y = 5$$
$$3x + 2y = -5$$

We see that no variable is eliminated if we apply the addition property of equations. Also, the *x*-variable will not be eliminated if we multiply either expression by an integer. The same is true for the *y*-variable. However, the least common multiple of the coefficients of the variables could be found and then used to determine a number needed to multiply each equation in the system. For example, if we want to eliminate the *x*-variable in the system, we determine the least common multiple, 6, of the *x*-coefficients, 2 and 3. To eliminate the *x*-variable, we want one expression to have 6 and the other expression to have -6 as the coefficient of *x*. One way to accomplish this is by multiplying the members of the first equation by 3 and the members of the second equation by -2.

(1) $2x + 3y = 5$
(2) $3x + 2y = -5$
(1) $3(2x + 3y) = 3(5)$ Multiply both sides by 3.
(2) $-2(3x + 2y) = -2(-5)$ Multiply both sides by -2.
(1) $6x + 9y = 15$
(2) $\underline{-6x - 4y = 10}$
$5y = 25$ Add corresponding members of the equation.
$\dfrac{5y}{5} = \dfrac{25}{5}$ Divide both sides by 5.
$y = 5$ Simplify.

Substitute 5 for y in the first equation to find the x-value of the solution.

(1) $\qquad 2x + 3y = 5$
$\qquad\qquad 2x + 3(5) = 5 \qquad$ Substitute 5 for y.
$\qquad\qquad 2x + 15 = 5 \qquad$ Simplify.
$\quad 2x + 15 - 15 = 5 - 15 \qquad$ Subtract 15 from both sides.
$\qquad\qquad\qquad 2x = -10 \qquad$ Simplify.
$\qquad\qquad\dfrac{2x}{2} = \dfrac{-10}{2} \qquad$ Divide both sides by 2.
$\qquad\qquad\qquad x = -5 \qquad$ Simplify.

The solution of the system is $(-5, 5)$.

SOLVING A SYSTEM OF LINEAR EQUATIONS IN TWO VARIABLES BY THE ADDITION METHOD

To solve a system of linear equations in two variables by the addition method,

- Write both equations in standard form.
- Multiply the members of the equation(s) by a number, if necessary, to obtain coefficients that are opposites but equal in absolute value.
- Add the expressions in the second equation to the corresponding expressions in the first equation, eliminating one of the variables.
- Solve the resulting equation for the remaining variable.
- Substitute the value obtained in one of the original equations, and solve for the other variable.

The ordered-pair solution is determined by the values obtained in solving for each individual variable. Check the solution.

EXAMPLE 1

Solve each system of linear equations in two variables by the addition method. Check the solution by substituting it into the original equations.

a. $2x = -3y + 1$ $\qquad$ **b.** $3x + 2y = 1$ $\qquad$ **c.** $\dfrac{1}{2}x + \dfrac{2}{3}y = 1$

$\quad\ x + 2y = -1$ $\qquad\qquad 2x - 5y = -2$ $\qquad\qquad \dfrac{1}{4}x - \dfrac{1}{5}y = -\dfrac{1}{10}$

Algebraic Solution

a. (1) $2x = -3y + 1$
$\quad$ (2) $x + 2y = -1$

Write the first equation in standard form.

$\quad 2x + 3y = -3y + 1 + 3y \qquad$ Add 3y to both sides of the equation.
$\quad 2x + 3y = 1 \qquad$ Simplify.

The system with equations in standard form is as follows:

(1) $\qquad 2x + 3y = 1$
(2) $\qquad\ x + 2y = -1$
(1) $\qquad 2x + 3y = 1$
(2) $-2(x + 2y) = -2(-1) \qquad$ Multiply both sides by -2.
(1) $\qquad 2x + 3y = 1$
(2) $\qquad \underline{-2x - 4y = 2}$
$\qquad\qquad\qquad -y = 3 \qquad$ Add corresponding members of the equations.
$\qquad\qquad \dfrac{-y}{-1} = \dfrac{3}{-1} \qquad$ Divide both sides by -1.
$\qquad\qquad\qquad y = -3 \qquad$ Simplify.

Substitute -3 for y in the second equation to find the x-value of the solution.

$(2) \qquad x + 2y = -1$

$x + 2(-3) = -1$ Substitute -3 for y.

$x - 6 = -1$ Simplify.

$x - 6 + 6 = -1 + 6$ Add 6 to both sides.

$x = 5$ Simplify.

```
5→X: -3→Y: 2X
                    10
-3Y+1
                    10
X+2Y
                    -1
```

The solution of the system is $(5, -3)$.
The solution checks, because $10 = 10$ and $-1 = -1$.

b. $(1)\ 3x + 2y = 1$

$(2)\ 2x - 5y = -2$

In order to eliminate the x-variable, we determine that the least common multiple of the x-coefficients is 6. Therefore, the members of the first equation must be multiplied by 2 and the members of the second equation by -3 to obtain the x-coefficients 6 and -6.

Note: We could have eliminated the y-variable instead by multiplying the first equation by 5 and the second equation by 2.

$(1) \quad 2(3x + 2y) = 2(1)$ Multiply both sides by 2.

$(2)\ -3(2x - 5y) = -3(-2)$ Multiply both sides by -3.

$(1) \qquad 6x + 4y = 2$

$(2) \quad \underline{\ -6x + 15y = 6\ }$

$19y = 8$ Add corresponding members of the equations.

$\dfrac{19y}{19} = \dfrac{8}{19}$ Divide both sides by 19.

$y = \dfrac{8}{19}$ Simplify.

Substitute $\frac{8}{19}$ for y in the first equation to find the x-value of the solution.

$(1) \qquad 3x + 2y = 1$

$3x + 2\left(\dfrac{8}{19}\right) = 1$ Substitute $\frac{8}{19}$ for y.

$3x + \dfrac{16}{19} = 1$ Simplify.

$3x + \dfrac{16}{19} - \dfrac{16}{19} = 1 - \dfrac{16}{19}$ Subtract $\frac{16}{19}$ from both sides.

$3x = \dfrac{3}{19}$ Simplify.

$3x\left(\dfrac{1}{3}\right) = \left(\dfrac{3}{19}\right)\left(\dfrac{1}{3}\right)$ Multiply both sides by $\frac{1}{3}$.

$x = \dfrac{1}{19}$ Simplify.

The solution of the system is $\left(\frac{1}{19}, \frac{8}{19}\right)$.
The check is left to you.

c. $(1)\ \dfrac{1}{2}x + \dfrac{2}{3}y = 1$

$(2)\ \dfrac{1}{4}x - \dfrac{1}{5}y = -\dfrac{1}{10}$

Eliminate the fractions in the system of equations by multiplying the members of each equation by the least common multiple of the denominators in the equation.

(1) $6\left(\dfrac{1}{2}x + \dfrac{2}{3}y\right) = 6(1)$ Multiply by the LCD of 2 and 3.

(2) $20\left(\dfrac{1}{4}x - \dfrac{1}{5}y\right) = 20\left(-\dfrac{1}{10}\right)$ Multiply by the LCD of 4, 5, and 10.

(1) $3x + 4y = 6$

(2) $\underline{5x - 4y = -2}$

         $8x \qquad = 4$ Add corresponding members of the equations.

         $\dfrac{8x}{8} = \dfrac{4}{8}$ Divide both sides by 8.

         $x = \dfrac{1}{2}$ Simplify.

Substitute $\frac{1}{2}$ for x in the first equation to find the y-value of the solution.

(1) $\dfrac{1}{2}x + \dfrac{2}{3}y = 1$

     $\dfrac{1}{2}\left(\dfrac{1}{2}\right) + \dfrac{2}{3}y = 1$ Substitute $\frac{1}{2}$ for x.

     $\dfrac{1}{4} + \dfrac{2}{3}y = 1$ Simplify.

     $\dfrac{1}{4} + \dfrac{2}{3}y - \dfrac{1}{4} = 1 - \dfrac{1}{4}$ Subtract $\frac{1}{4}$ from both sides.

     $\dfrac{2}{3}y = \dfrac{3}{4}$ Simplify.

     $\dfrac{3}{2}\left(\dfrac{2}{3}y\right) = \dfrac{3}{2}\left(\dfrac{3}{4}\right)$ Multiply both sides by $\frac{3}{2}$.

     $y = \dfrac{9}{8}$ Simplify.

The solution of the system is $\left(\frac{1}{2}, \frac{9}{8}\right)$.
The check is left to you. ■

As we have seen in earlier sections of this chapter, a system may have no solution or an infinite number of solutions. Let's see what happens when we apply the addition method to systems of these types. Complete the following sets of exercises.

🔆 Guided Discovery 6   Inconsistent System of Linear Equations

Solve the given system of linear equations by the addition method.

$$-2x + y = 1$$
$$-4x + 2y = 3$$

Write a rule for determining, by the addition method, that a system of linear equations is inconsistent—in other words, that it has no solution.

A system has no solution if, after applying the addition method, the resulting equation is a contradiction.

Guided Discovery 7 | System of Dependent Linear Equations

Solve the given system of linear equations by the addition method.

$$-3x - y = -2$$
$$y = -3x + 2$$

Write a rule for determining, by the addition method, that a system of linear equations has dependent equations—in other words, an infinite number of solutions.

A system has an infinite number of solutions if, after applying the addition method, the resulting equation is an identity.

EXAMPLE 2 Solve each system of equations by the addition method. If the system has an infinite number of solutions, describe the solutions.

a. $x + y = -3$
$x + y = 2$

b. $y = \dfrac{2}{3}x - \dfrac{1}{3}$
$3y = 2x - 1$

Algebraic Solution

a. (1) $x + y = -3$
(2) $x + y = 2$
(1) $-1(x + y) = -1(-3)$ Multiply both sides of the first equation by −1.
(2) $x + y = 2$
(1) $-x - y = 3$
(2) $\underline{x + y = 2}$
      $0 = 5$ Add corresponding members of the equations.

The result is a contradiction. The system has no solution.

b. (1) $y = \dfrac{2}{3}x - \dfrac{1}{3}$

(2) $3y = 2x - 1$

Write the first equation in standard form.

$$3(y) = 3\left(\frac{2}{3}x - \frac{1}{3}\right)$$ Multiply by the LCD of 3 to clear the fractions.

$$3y = 2x - 1$$ Simplify.

$$3y - 2x = 2x - 1 - 2x$$ Subtract 2x from both sides.

$$-2x + 3y = -1$$ Simplify and rearrange.

Write the second equation in standard form.

$$3y - 2x = 2x - 1 - 2x$$ Subtract 2x from both sides.

$$-2x + 3y = -1$$ Simplify and rearrange.

In standard form, the system is as follows:

(1) $-2x + 3y = -1$
(2) $-2x + 3y = -1$
(1) $-1(-2x + 3y) = -1(-1)$ Multiply both sides of the first equation by −1.
(2) $-2x + 3y = -1$
(1) $2x - 3y = 1$
(2) $\underline{-2x + 3y = -1}$
      $0 = 0$ Add corresponding members of the equations.

The result is an identity. The solutions are all ordered pairs (x, y) that satisfy $y = \frac{2}{3}x - \frac{1}{3}$.

The check is left to you.

The following summary describes the process of algebraically solving a system of linear equations by the addition method:

SOLVING A SYSTEM OF LINEAR EQUATIONS BY THE ADDITION METHOD

In solving a system of linear equations in two variables by the addition method, one of three possibilities will occur.

1. A value for both variables will be determined.

One solution exists: the ordered-pair coordinates.

The system is consistent.

The equations are independent.

2. Applying the addition method will result in a contradiction.

No solution exists.

The system is inconsistent.

The equations are independent.

3. Applying the addition method will result in an identity.

An infinite number of solutions exist. The solution set is the set of all ordered pairs (x, y) that satisfy either equation of the system.

The system is consistent.

The equations are dependent.

Objective 4.3.1 *CHECKUP*

1. Solve each system of equations by the addition method. Check the solution.

  a. $x = 5y + 32$
  $2x + y = -2$

  b. $4x + 7y = -3$
  $7x - 2y = 9$

  c. $\dfrac{1}{2}x + \dfrac{5}{8}y = \dfrac{9}{8}$
  $\dfrac{2}{5}x - \dfrac{1}{2}y = -\dfrac{7}{10}$

2. Solve each system of equations by the addition method. If the system has an infinite number of solutions, describe the solution set.

  a. $x + 2y = 6$
  $3x = 20 - 6y$

  b. $y = 5x + 12$
  $7x + 24 = 2y - 3x$

3. You now know three methods for solving a system of linear equations in two variables: the graphical method, the substitution method, and the addition method. Explain how you would apply each of these methods to obtain the solution of a system of linear equations.

Objective 4.3.2   Modeling the Real World

When two equations are needed to describe the relationship between two variables, we sometimes say that the system consists of **simultaneous equations**, since both equations apply at the same time. The addition method is probably the most common way of solving simultaneous equations, unless we can get one equation into a simple enough form so that the substitution method can be used. In fact, the addition method underlies more complicated techniques that we can use to solve systems of three, four, or more simultaneous equations.

EXAMPLE 3

Melinda's class charged admission of $2.50 for adults and $1.25 for students to its play. Melinda counted 10 chairs remaining empty in the auditorium, which holds 500. If the amount collected was $1013.75, how many adults and students attended?

Algebraic Solution

Let a = number of adults attending

c = number of students attending

(1) $a + c = 490$ — The number attending was 500 − 10 or 490.

(2) $2.50a + 1.25c = 1013.75$ — The cost is the sum of the amount collected for adults, 2.50a, and the amount collected for students, 1.25c.

(1) $-1.25(a + c) = -1.25(490)$ — Multiply both sides by −1.25.

(2) $2.50a + 1.25c = 1013.75$

(1) $-1.25a - 1.25c = -612.50$

(2) $\underline{2.50a + 1.25c = 1013.75}$

$1.25a \quad\quad\quad = 401.25$ — Add corresponding members of the equations.

$\dfrac{1.25a}{1.25} = \dfrac{401.25}{1.25}$ — Divide both sides by 1.25.

$a = 321$ — Simplify.

Substitute 321 for a in the first equation to find the c-value of the solution.

(1) $a + c = 490$

$321 + c = 490$ — Substitute 321 for a.

$321 + c - 321 = 490 - 321$ — Subtract 321 from both sides of the equation.

$c = 169$ — Simplify.

The check is left to you.

There were 321 adults and 169 students attending the play.

APPLICATION

According to the U.S. Census Bureau, Hispanics accounted for half of the U.S. population growth from 2003 to 2004. The 2004 total U.S. population is made up of 247.8 million non-Hispanics. The number of Hispanics in 2004 constitutes one-seventh of the total U.S. population. Write and solve a system of linear equations to determine the number of Hispanics in the United States in 2004.

Discussion

Let h = the Hispanic population in 2004

t = the total U.S. population in 2004

The total U.S. population is the number of non-Hispanics plus the number of Hispanics, or $h + 247.8 = t$.

The number of Hispanics is one-seventh of the total U.S. population, or $\dfrac{1}{7}t = h$.

The system is

(1) $h + 247.8 = t$

(2) $h = \dfrac{1}{7}t$

Rewrite the system in standard form without fractions.

(1) $h - t = -247.8$ — Subtract 247.8 and t from both sides.

(2) $7h - t = 0$ — Multiply both sides by 7 and then subtract t from both sides.

Solve the system.

(1) $h - t = -247.8$

(2) $-1(7h - t) = -1(0)$ — Multiply the second equation by −1.

(1) $h - t = -247.8$

(2) $\underline{-7h + t = 0}$

$-6h \quad\quad = -247.8$ — Add corresponding members of the equation.

$\dfrac{-6h}{-6} = \dfrac{-247.8}{-6}$ — Divide both sides by −6.

$h = 41.3$ — Simplify.

The number of Hispanics in the United States in 2004 was 41.3 million.

Objective 4.3.2 CHECKUP

1. The Pocahontas circle of the Indian Maidens sold 262 cans of nuts as a fund-raiser. Cashews sold for $6.50 per can and peanuts for $4.00 per can. The proceeds from the sale were $1240.50. Members of the circle lost their tally of how many cans of each were sold. Write and solve a system of equations to help them determine how many of each they sold.

2. The United States is increasingly changing as a result of immigration. According to an April 2004 Census Bureau Report, those who speak Spanish at home number about 18.667 times the number of people who speak Chinese at home. The sum of those speaking Spanish or Chinese at home is about 29.6 million people. Write and solve a system of equations to determine the number of people who speak Spanish at home and the number of people who speak Chinese at home.

4.3 EXERCISES

Student Solutions Manual — PH Math/Tutor Center — CD Video — MathXL® — MyMathLab — Interactmath.com

Solve each system of equations by using the addition method. Check your solution.

1. $2x - y = -6$
$5x + y = -8$

2. $5x + y = 8$
$3x - y = 16$

3. $x + 7y = 19$
$-x + 2y = -1$

4. $x + 9y = -12$
$-x + 8y = -5$

5. $5x + y = -24$
$3x - 2y = 9$

6. $4x - 3y = 26$
$2x + y = 18$

7. $x + 3y = 2$
$x + 5y = -2$

8. $x + 8y = 37$
$x + 11y = 52$

9. $2x + 7y = 29$
$4x + 3y = 25$

10. $5x + 11y = -27$
$10x + 13y = -36$

11. $3x - 5y = 66$
$4x + 3y = 1$

12. $2x + 7y = 33$
$3x - 4y = -52$

13. $2x + 9y = 102$
$5x - 11y = -147$

14. $11x + 5y = 133$
$15x + 4y = 187$

15. $40x = 23 + 10y$
$50x + 10y = 94$

16. $15x + 10y = -2$
$5x = 10y + 18$

17. $5x + 40y = 77$
$5x + 15y = 17$

18. $4x + 2y = 15$
$-6x + 2y = -30$

19. $10x - 4y = 28$
$5x + 4y = 35$

20. $2x + y = -7$
$3x - y = -2$

21. $2x + 8y = 29$
$13y = 3x + 39$

22. $5x + 15y = -10$
$19y = 7x + 42$

23. $\frac{1}{4}x + \frac{1}{3}y = \frac{5}{12}$
$\frac{1}{4}x = \frac{1}{3}y - \frac{1}{12}$

24. $\frac{2}{3}x + \frac{3}{5}y = \frac{9}{10}$
$\frac{2}{3}x = \frac{3}{5}y - \frac{1}{10}$

25. $\frac{1}{3}x + \frac{1}{2}y = -\frac{1}{4}$
$\frac{1}{6}x - \frac{5}{6}y = \frac{11}{16}$

26. $\frac{3}{7}x + \frac{4}{5}y = -\frac{1}{6}$
$\frac{3}{7}x - \frac{8}{15}y = \frac{2}{3}$

27. $y = \frac{3}{2}x - 9$
$\frac{1}{6}x - \frac{1}{9}y = 1$

28. $y = \frac{6}{5}x + 2$
$\frac{3}{5}x - \frac{1}{2}y = -1$

29. $\frac{4}{5}x - \frac{3}{5}y = -1$
$\frac{3}{2}x - \frac{9}{8}y = 1$

30. $\frac{1}{12}x - \frac{1}{8}y = -1$
$\frac{1}{3}x - \frac{1}{2}y = 1$

31. $x - 20y = 70$
$3x + 10y = 70$

32. $x + 35y = 300$
$4x + 15y = 200$

33. $3x + y = 40$
$x + y = 20$

34. $x + 4y = 0$
$x + 7y = -30$

35. $x - y = 300$
$2x - y = -100$

36. $x + y = 300$
$x + 3y = 1400$

37. $10x - 10y = 22$
$y = 2x - 11$

38. $5x + 5y = 10$
$y = 9x - 41$

39. $3.2x + 4.2y = 368$
$4.4x - 2.1y = 128$

40. $1.4x + 2.4y = 225$
$3.4x - 1.6y = 123$

41. $0.05x + 0.10y = 0.75$
$x + y = 11$

42. $0.25x + 0.50y = 5.75$
$x + y = 14$

43. $0.3x + 0.45y = 43.5$
$x + y = 110$

44. $0.55x + 0.25y = 49$
$x + y = 100$

45. $12.50x + 6.50y = 1780$
$x + y = 200$

46. $7.95x + 2.25y = 914.70$
$x + y = 214$

Write a system of equations for each application, and solve the equations by using the addition method.

Mixture

47. At Centennial High School's football game, the gate indicated that 683 persons entered. Students were charged $1.50 admission, while nonstudents were charged $5.00 admission. The total receipts at the game were $2645.00. The principal wanted to know how many students attended the game, but unfortunately, the count was not recorded. Can you find the answer for the principal?

48. A church sponsored a bus trip to attend the play *Godspell* at the summer stock theater in a nearby town. Senior citizens were charged $30.00 for the trip, including all expenses, while others were charged $45.00. A total of 56 people took the trip and paid $2190 for the privilege. How many seniors and how many others took the trip?

49. To raise money for a scholarship fund, the faculty and staff at the Community College for Mathematics decided to print a cookbook and a calendar. They sold 50 more cookbooks than calendars and raised $3462.50, selling the cookbooks for $8.50 each and the calendars for $5.00 each. How many of each were sold?

50. For a luncheon, Karlene ordered a tray of ham and cheese from the local deli. The deli advertised the tray as having a weight of 5.5 pounds. The ham sold for $6.00 per pound, and the cheese sold for $4.00 per pound. The total charge for the tray was $29.50. Karlene wanted to know how much ham and how much cheese the deli sold her. Can you help her?

51. Pollstar of Fresno, California shows that the top-grossing concert tour in North America occurred in 1994 with The Rolling Stones. Also in 1994, Pink Floyd had the fourth highest grossing tour of all time. Together the two concerts had total gross of $224.7 million. Pink Floyd's tour grossed $17.7 million less than that of the Rolling Stones. What were the total gross amounts for each band?

52. Athlete Michael Phelps holds the World Swimming Records in both the 200-meter butterfly and the 200-meter medley. His combined times in the two events is about 3.8 minutes. His time in the medley exceeded his time in the butterfly by approximately 2 seconds. What was his time in each event?

53. The number of adults and children at Midtown Nursery's school play totaled 385. Adults were charged $2 admission, and by mistake, the children were also charged $2 each. The receipts for the play amounted to $770. How many adults and how many children attended the play?

54. Mama Mia's Restaurant offers two lists of items on its menu. The items on the first list are all one price, and the items on the second list are all a second price. If a patron selects one item from each list, the price for the meal is $8.95. If a patron selects two items from each list, the price for the meal is $13.95. Find the price of an item from the first list and the price of an item from the second list.

Geometry

55. A triangle has two angles that are equal in size. The third angle measures 30 degrees more than the measure of the equal angles. What is the size of each angle?

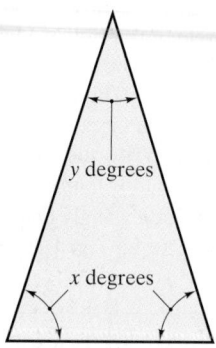

56. The two equal angles of a triangle each measure 30 degrees more than the third angle. Find the measures of the three angles.

57. Two angles are supplementary. One angle is 30 degrees larger than the other. How large is each angle?

58. Two angles are complementary. The second angle is 7 degrees more than three times the first. Find the measure of each angle.

59. Two angles are complementary. Twice the first is equal to 150 degrees minus twice the second. Find the measure of each angle.

60. Two angles are supplementary. One angle measures 180 degrees less the second angle. Find the measure of each angle.

Distance

61. The distance from the Sun to the red planet Mars is approximately 4.864×10^7 miles greater than the distance of the Earth from the Sun. The average of the distances from the Sun for the two planets is 1.1728×10^8 miles. Find the approximate distances of the two planets from the Sun.

62. The planet Mercury is approximately 3.6302×10^9 miles closer to the Sun than the planet Pluto. The average distance from the Sun for the two planets is approximately 1.851×10^9 miles. What are the approximate distances of these planets from the Sun?

Real Data

63. According to data from the U.S. Census Bureau, the median income of males exceeded the median income of females by $12,426 in 2002. The two medians totaled $46,050. Write a system of equations and solve them to determine the median income of males and of females.

64. U.S. Centers for Medicare and Medicaid Services reported in 2002 that the total consumer health expenditure was 762.1 billion dollars. The consumer health expenditure is made up of out-of-pocket expenditures and private insurance costs. The insurance costs were 124.6 billion dollars more than twice the out-of-pocket expenditures. Determine the amount consumers spent in out-of-pocket expenditures.

65. According to the *Forbes* magazine Celebrity 100 list, the celebrity earning the most money in 2004 was George Lucas, and the celebrity with the second highest earnings was Oprah Winfrey. Together, they earned $515 million. Lucas earned $160 million less than twice the amount that Winfrey earned. Write a system of equations and solve them to determine the earnings of each.

66. According to *Forbes* magazine, the athlete with the highest 2004 earnings was Tiger Woods. Shaquille O'Neal ranked second among athletes in 2004 earnings. Their total earnings were \$120.4 million. Tiger earned \$13.2 million less than three times Shaquille's earnings. Write a system and solve to determine the 2004 earnings for Tiger Woods and Shaquille O'Neal.

4.3 Calculator Exercises

A variation of the addition method called the method of alternates can be used to obtain opposite coefficients. Consider the system

(1) $6x - 7y = -21$

(2) $15x - 11y = 6$

Rather than find the least common multiple of 6 and 15, multiply the members of each equation by the coefficient of x in the alternate (other) equation, yielding

(1) $15(6x - 7y) = 15(-21) \rightarrow 90x - 105y = -315$

(2) $6(15x - 11y) = 6(6) \rightarrow 90x - 66y = 36$

Then multiply the members of the second equation by -1 and add.

(1) $90x - 105y = -315$

(2) $\underline{-90x + 66y = -36}$

$-39y = -351$, yielding $y = 9$.

Substituting into one of the original equations yields $x = 7$.

Use this method to solve the exercises that follow. Note that the numbers get large and a calculator may help with the arithmetic.

1. $6x + 35y = -52$
$9x - 14y = 55$

2. $12x - 35y = 81$
$15x - 28y = 54$

3. $21a + 10b = -88$
$14a + 15b = 8$

4. $33x + 7y = -3.1$
$6x + 13y = -33.4$

5. $10x + 21y = 19$
$14x - 9y = 1$

6. $8x - 9y = 8$
$12x + 21y = -11$

4.3 Writing Exercises

You now know three methods for solving a system of equations: graphical, substitution, and addition. Decide which method might be best for each of the exercises that follow. Give reasons for your choices. Then solve the systems.

1. $3x + y = 62$
$5x + 19y = 203$

2. $14x - 3y = -240$
$5x + 3y = -45$

3. $y = 2x - 69$
$y = x - 17$

4.4 MORE REAL-WORLD MODELS

OBJECTIVES
1 Model real-world situations involving a distance traveled.
2 Model real-world situations involving mixtures and collections.

APPLICATION

The U.S. national debt is about \$7.8 trillion. Suppose that the Treasury Department split this debt into two loans. One consists of Treasury bills with an annual interest rate of about 3.6%, and the second loan consists of Treasury constant maturities with an annual interest rate of approximately 4.55%. If about 0.31 trillion dollars is paid in simple interest annually, determine the amount of principal for each loan.

After completing this section, we will discuss this application further. See page 397.

We have now discussed three methods for solving a system of linear equations in two variables: A system can be solved graphically, algebraically by the substitution method, or algebraically by the addition method. We have also discussed real-world situations with each of these methods. In this section, we discuss other applications involving systems of linear equations. Once a system of linear equations is written for a problem, it may be solved with any of the methods we have presented.

Let's review the method we have been using to answer a question about a real-world situation.

MODELING REAL-WORLD SITUATIONS

To model a real-world situation,

- Read and understand the problem.
- Define variables for the unknown quantities, and define other quantities in terms of the defined variables.
- Write equations with the information given.
- Solve the system either graphically or algebraically.
- Check the solution.
- Write an answer for the question asked, in a complete sentence.

Objective 4.4.1

Solving Distance-Traveled Models

In previous chapters, we used the formula for distance traveled. Remember, the distance traveled, d, is equal to the rate of motion, r, times the time traveled, t.

$$d = rt$$

We may be given information about more than one situation involving distance traveled. In such a case, we need to solve a system of equations in two variables.

EXAMPLE 1

Romeo and Juliet live 680 miles apart. They plan to meet each other at a designated location somewhere between their homes. Juliet is planning to drive her sports car at an average speed of 65 mph. However, Romeo is driving his pickup truck and towing a boat, so he plans on driving an average of 45 mph. If they both plan to leave at the same time, how many miles from Juliet's home should they plan to meet?

Algebraic Solution

A picture of the trip may help us to determine the equations.

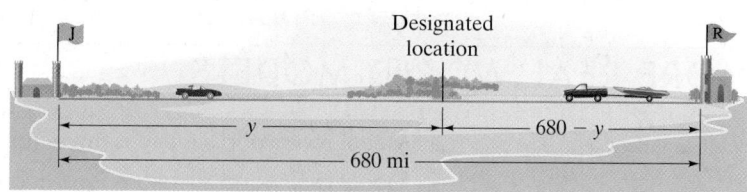

Let y = number of miles from Juliet's home to the meeting place
$680 - y$ = number of miles from Romeo's home to the meeting place
x = time traveled (both drivers travel the same time)

Using the distance-traveled formula, $d = rt$, for each trip, we write the following equations:

$$d = rt$$

(1)   Juliet: $y = 65x$
(2)   Romeo: $680 - y = 45x$

We will use the substitution method to solve this system, since the first equation, $y = 65x$, is already solved for y. Substitute $65x$ for y in the second equation, and solve for x.

(2)
$$680 - y = 45x$$
$$680 - 65x = 45x \qquad \text{Substitute 65x for y.}$$
$$680 - 65x + 65x = 45x + 65x \qquad \text{Add 65x to both sides.}$$
$$680 = 110x \qquad \text{Simplify.}$$
$$\frac{680}{110} = \frac{110x}{110} \qquad \text{Divide both sides by 110.}$$
$$6.182 \approx x \qquad \text{Simplify.}$$

To find the distance from Juliet's home, y, substitute 6.182 for x in the first equation.

(1)
$$y = 65x$$
$$y \approx 65(6.182) \qquad \text{Substitute 6.182 for x.}$$
$$y \approx 401.830 \qquad \text{Simplify.}$$

To check the solution, substitute the solution into both of the original equations.

y	$=$	$65x$
401.830		65(6.182)
		401.830

$680 -$	y	$=$	$45x$
$680 - 401.830$			45(6.182)
278.170			278.190

Remember, we rounded our answer for x. Therefore, the numbers will not check exactly.

The designated location for the meeting place should be about 401.8 miles from Juliet's home.

Graphic Solution

Solve the equations for y and graph them.

(1) $y = 65x$

(2) $y = -45x + 680$

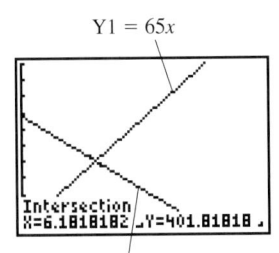

Y1 = 65x

Intersection
X=6.1818182 Y=401.81818

Y2 = −45x + 680

A calculator graph for the solution, $(6.182, 401.818)$, is shown on a window of $(0, 20, 10, 0, 1000, 100, 1)$, using the CALC function to determine the exact intersection. The difference is due to rounding.

The designated location for the meeting place should be about 401.8 miles from Juliet's home. ◼

Sometimes, more than one factor is involved in determining a rate of motion. One such situation involves traveling in the air. High-speed winds that flow between 4 and 6 miles above the earth, mostly from west to east, are called jet streams. Their speeds range between 50 and 250 miles per hour. Over North America there are two (and sometimes three) major jet streams. The force of the wind affects the airspeed by increasing or decreasing the actual speed of an aircraft in relation to the ground. A similar phenomenon occurs in water: Rivers and streams have a current whose speed accelerates or impedes the speed of a boat. In the ocean, streams of water such as the Gulf Stream also exist.

EXAMPLE 2

One evening, Sharon was tracking Delta aircraft between the hubs in Atlanta and Los Angeles, a distance of 1944 miles. The average height above ground of an aircraft was between 5 and 6 miles. The trip from Atlanta to Los Angeles took $5\frac{1}{2}$ hours, and the trip from Los Angeles to Atlanta took $3\frac{1}{2}$ hours. Assuming that the planes were traveling at the same average speed when there was no wind, determine the average speed of the planes in still air and the average speed of the jet stream.

Solution

A picture of the trips between Atlanta and Los Angeles may help us determine the equations we need to describe this example.

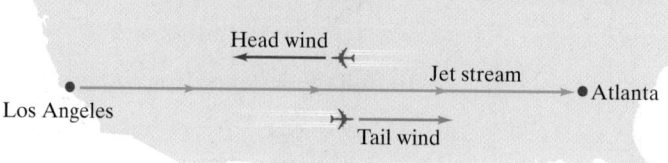

Let x = the speed of the planes in still air
   y = the speed of the wind in the jet stream

The speed a plane travels when it is moving against the wind, with a head wind, is the speed of the plane in still air less the speed of the wind.

$$x - y = \text{the speed of the plane in relation to the ground}$$

The speed a plane travels when it is moving in the same direction as the wind, with a tail wind, is the speed of the plane in still air plus the speed of the wind.

$$x + y = \text{the speed of the plane in relation to the ground}$$

 TAKE NOTE If an object is traveling in the direction of an additional force, add the rates of motion. If an object is traveling in the opposite direction of an additional force, subtract the rates of motion.

A table may help us organize the information.

	Distance	Rate	Time
Leg of trip to Los Angeles	1944	$x - y$	$5\frac{1}{2}$
Leg of trip to Atlanta	1944	$x + y$	$3\frac{1}{2}$

Using the distance-traveled formula, $d = rt$, for each leg of the trip, we write the following equations:

(1)   Leg of the trip to Los Angeles: $1944 = (x - y)\left(5\frac{1}{2}\right)$

(2)   Leg of the trip to Atlanta: $1944 = (x + y)\left(3\frac{1}{2}\right)$

Simplify using the distributive law.

(1) $1944 = \dfrac{11}{2}x - \dfrac{11}{2}y$

(2) $1944 = \dfrac{7}{2}x + \dfrac{7}{2}y$

Clear the fractions in both equations.

(1) $2(1944) = 2\left(\dfrac{11}{2}x - \dfrac{11}{2}y\right)$ or $3888 = 11x - 11y$

(2) $2(1944) = 2\left(\dfrac{7}{2}x + \dfrac{7}{2}y\right)$ or $3888 = 7x + 7y$

To eliminate the variable y, multiply both sides of each equation.

(1)	$7(3888) = 7(11x - 11y)$	Multiply both sides by 7.
(2)	$11(3888) = 11(7x + 7y)$	Multiply both sides by 11.
(1)	$27216 = 77x - 77y$	
(2)	$\underline{42768 = 77x + 77y}$	
	$69984 = 154x$	Add corresponding members of the equations.
	$\dfrac{69984}{154} = \dfrac{154x}{154}$	Divide by 154.
	$x \approx 454.44$	

Substitute 454.44 for x in the second equation, and solve that equation for y.

$$1944 = \frac{7}{2}x + \frac{7}{2}y$$

$$1944 \approx \frac{7}{2}(454.44) + \frac{7}{2}y \qquad \text{Substitute.}$$

$$1944 \approx 1590.54 + \frac{7}{2}y \qquad \text{Simplify.}$$

$$1944 - 1590.54 \approx 1590.54 + \frac{7}{2}y - 1590.54 \qquad \text{Subtract 1590.54 from both sides.}$$

$$353.46 \approx \frac{7}{2}y \qquad \text{Simplify.}$$

$$\frac{2}{7}(353.46) \approx \frac{2}{7}\left(\frac{7}{2}y\right) \qquad \text{Multiply both sides by } \frac{2}{7}.$$

$$y \approx 100.99$$

The check is left for you.

The speed of the plane in still air is about 454.44 miles per hour, and the speed of the wind is about 100.99 miles per hour. ■

✓ Objective 4.4.1 *CHECKUP*

Write and solve a system of equations for each exercise.

1. Patty left her house to attend her cousin's wedding, traveling up the interstate at 55 miles per hour. After she had been gone for half an hour, her father realized she had forgotten to take her bridal-party dress. He immediately left to overtake her. If he drives at the legal speed of 65 miles per hour, how long will it be until he overtakes her on the interstate?

2. A United Airlines flight traveling from Seattle to Washington, DC, flew at an altitude of about 33,000 feet. Traveling with the jet stream, the plane arrived approximately 4 hours after departure. A second United Airlines flight traveling from Washington, DC, to Seattle during the same time frame flew against the jet stream at an altitude of 35,000 feet and arrived approximately 5 hours after departure. Assuming that the two planes fly at the same average speed in still air, determine that average speed and the average speed of the wind due to the jet stream. The two cities are approximately 2350 miles apart. ■

Objective 4.4.2   Solving Mixture and Collection Models

Previously, we solved mixture and collection problems by using a linear equation in one variable. A second method is to use a system of linear equations in two variables. The general method is to set up one equation that expresses the amount of each component in the mixture and a second equation that relates the amounts of each component to one another, according to the statement of the problem. In the previous section (Example 3), we solved this type of problem. In this objective, we will continue to work with examples of this type of problem.

EXAMPLE 3   Su Yung has a collection of 15 antique coins consisting of nickels and dimes. The face value of the coins is $1.10. How many of each denomination does she have?

Algebraic Solution

Let n = number of nickels
d = number of dimes

A table may help us organize the information.

	Nickels	Dimes	Total
Number of coins	n	d	15
Value of collection	$0.05n$	$0.10d$	1.10

Since there is a total of 15 coins, we add the number of nickels, n, and the number of dimes, d.

$$n + d = 15$$

The value of the nickels is 0.05 times the number of nickels, n or $0.05n$. The value of the dimes is 0.10 times the number of dimes, d, or $0.10d$. The value of the collection, 1.10, is equal to the sum of the values of the nickels and dimes.

$$0.05n + 0.10d = 1.10$$

To eliminate the decimals in the equation, multiply both sides of the equation by 100, the LCM of the decimal-place values.

$$100(0.05n + 0.10d) = 100(1.10)$$
$$5n + 10d = 110$$

The system to be solved is

(1) $n + d = 15$
(2) $5n + 10d = 110$

We will use the addition method to solve the system, since both equations are written in standard form. To eliminate the variable n, we will multiply both sides of the first equation by -5.

(1) $-5(n + d) = -5(15)$ Multiply both sides by -5.
(2) $5n + 10d = 110$

(1) $-5n - 5d = -75$
(2) $\underline{5n + 10d = 110}$ Add corresponding members of the equations.
              $5d = 35$

              $\dfrac{5d}{5} = \dfrac{35}{5}$ Divide both sides by 5.

              $d = 7$ Simplify.

Substitute 7 for d in the first equation and solve for n.

(1) $n + d = 15$
            $n + 7 = 15$ Substitute 7 for d.
        $n + 7 - 7 = 15 - 7$ Subtract 7 from both sides.
            $n = 8$ Simplify.

To check the solution, substitute it into both of the original equations.

$$
\begin{array}{c|c}
n + d = 15 \\
\hline
8 + 7 & 15 \\
15 & 15
\end{array}
\qquad
\begin{array}{c|c}
5n + 10d = 110 \\
\hline
5(8) + 10(7) & 110 \\
40 + 70 & \\
& 110
\end{array}
$$

The solution checks.

Su Yung has eight nickels and seven dimes.

EXAMPLE 4 Christine needs 500 milliliters of a 22% saline (salt) solution. She has a 10% saline solution and a 30% saline solution. How many milliliters of the 10% saline solution and the 30% saline solution will she need to mix to obtain her desired solution?

Solution

Let $x =$ the number of milliliters of the 10% saline solution
  $y =$ the number of milliliters of the 30% saline solution

A total of 500 milliliters is needed.

(1) $x + y = 500$

The amount of salt in the 10% solution is 10% of x milliliters, or $0.10x$.
The amount of salt in the 30% solution is 30% of y milliliters, or $0.30y$.
The amount of salt in the 22% solution is 22% of 500 milliliters, or $0.22(500)$.

(2) $0.10x + 0.30y = 0.22(500)$

The system to be solved is

(1) $x + y = 500$ or $x + y - 500$
(2) $0.10x + 0.30y = 0.22(500)$ or $0.1x + 0.3y = 110$

Eliminate the decimal in the second equation by multiplying by 10.

(2) $10(0.1x + 0.3y) = 10(110)$
  $x + 3y = 1100$

The system to be solved by the addition method is

(1) $x + y = 500$
(2) $x + 3y = 1100$
(1) $-1(x + y) = -1(500)$ Multiply both sides by -1.
(2) $x + 3y = 1100$
(1) $-x - y = -500$
(2) $x + 3y = 1100$
           $2y = 600$ Add corresponding members of the equations.
          $\dfrac{2y}{2} = \dfrac{600}{2}$ Divide both sides by 2.
           $y = 300$

Substitute 300 for y in the first equation and solve for x.

(1) $x + y = 500$
         $x + 300 = 500$
    $x + 300 - 300 = 500 - 300$ Subtract 300 from both sides.
          $x = 200$

The check is left for you.
Two hundred milliliters of the 10% saline solution mixed with 300 milliliters of the 30% saline solution will yield 500 milliliters of the 22% saline solution.

EXAMPLE 5   A 40% antifreeze mixture provides freeze-up protection to -10 degrees Fahrenheit. A 70% antifreeze mixture provides freeze-up protection to -62 degrees Fahrenheit. Joe Ben moved to Alaska and needs to lower his freeze-up protection from -10 degrees to -62 degrees. He needs 2 gallons of the 70% antifreeze mixture. How much of the 40% antifreeze mixture must be replaced with pure antifreeze to have a 70% mixture?

Solution

Let x = the number of gallons of pure antifreeze (100% antifreeze)
   y = the number of gallons of the 40% antifreeze

The total amount of liquid is 2 gallons.

(1) $x + y = 2$

The amount of antifreeze in the pure antifreeze mixture is 100% of the amount, or $1.00x$. The amount of antifreeze in the 40% antifreeze mixture is 40% of the amount, or $0.40y$. The total amount of antifreeze in the 70% antifreeze mixture is 70% of the total amount, or $0.70(2)$.

$$1.00x + 0.40y = 0.70(2)$$

(2) $1.00x + 0.40y = 1.40$

The system of equations is

(1) $x + y = 2$
(2) $1.00x + 0.40y = 1.40$

To solve these equations by the substitution method, solve the first equation for y and substitute the resulting expression into the second equation.

(1) $y = -x + 2$
(2) $1.00x + 0.40y = 1.40$

$1.00x + 0.40(-x + 2) = 1.40$ Substitute $-x + 2$ for y.

$1.00x - 0.40x + 0.80 = 1.40$ Distribute.

$0.60x + 0.80 = 1.40$ Simplify.

$0.60x + 0.80 - 0.80 = 1.40 - 0.80$ Subtract 0.80 from both sides.

$0.60x = 0.60$ Simplify.

$x = 1$ Divide both sides by 0.60.

Using the equation $x + y = 2$, substitute 1 for x and solve for y.

(1) $x + y = 2$
     $1 + y = 2$
         $y = 1$

The check is left for you.

Joe Ben will need to add 1 gallon of pure antifreeze to 1 gallon of a 40% antifreeze mixture to obtain 2 gallons of a 70% antifreeze mixture. ∎

EXAMPLE 6   Les finds himself in the situation of owning two homes at once. He has purchased a new home and has not yet sold his existing home. He finds that his best financial strategy is to get both a bridge loan and a mortgage on a monthly basis. He estimates that he needs a loan that is five times as much money for the mortgage (at interest rate 0.675% per month) as for the bridge loan (at interest rate 0.75% per month). With the two loans, Les will be paying $1237.50 monthly in interest. For what amount is the bridge loan? For what amount is the mortgage?

Solution

Let m = the amount of the mortgage
b = the amount of the bridge loan

The amount of the mortgage is 5 times the amount of the bridge loan, or $m = 5b$. The monthly interest is \$1237.50, or $0.00675m + 0.0075b = 1237.50$.

The system is

(1) $\qquad m = 5b$
(2) $\quad 0.00675m + 0.0075b = 1237.50$

Since the first equation is solved for m, we will use the substitution method.

(2) $\quad 0.00675m + 0.0075b = 1237.50$
$\quad 0.00675(5b) + 0.0075b = 1237.50$ Substitute 5b for m.
$\quad 0.03375b + 0.0075b = 1237.50$ Simplify.
$\quad 0.04125b = 1237.50$ Simplify.
$\quad \dfrac{0.04125b}{0.04125} = \dfrac{1237.50}{0.04125}$ Divide both sides by 0.04125.
$\quad b = 30{,}000$ Simplify.

Substitute 30,000 for b and solve for m.

(1) $\quad m = 5b$
$\quad m = 5(30{,}000)$
$\quad m = 150{,}000$

The check is left for you.
The mortgage was for \$150,000 and the bridge loan was for \$30,000.

APPLICATION

The U.S. national debt is about \$7.8 trillion. Suppose that the Treasury Department split this debt into two loans. One consists of Treasury bills with an annual interest rate of about 3.6%, and the second loan consists of Treasury constant maturities with an annual interest rate of approximately 4.55%. If about 0.31 trillion dollars is paid in simple interest annually, determine the amount of principal for each loan.

Discussion

Let x = the amount, in trillions of dollars, borrowed at an annual rate of 3.6% (Treasury bills)
y = the amount, in trillions of dollars, borrowed at an annual rate of 4.55% (Treasury constant maturities)

Simple interest for 1 year is determined by using the formula $I = Prt$.

$I = x \cdot 0.036 \cdot 1 = 0.036x$ = the amount of interest paid for the Treasury bills

$I = y \cdot 0.0455 \cdot 1 = 0.0455y$ = the amount of interest paid for the Treasury constant maturities

The total interest paid is 0.31 trillion dollars.

(1) $0.036x + 0.0455y = 0.31$

The total amount borrowed is 7.8 trillion dollars.

(2) $x + y = 7.8$

The system to solve is

(1) $0.036x + 0.0455y = 0.31$
(2) $\qquad x + y = 7.8$

To eliminate the x, multiply both sides of the second equation by -0.036.

(1) $\quad 0.036x + 0.0455y = 0.31$
(2) $\quad -0.036(x + y) = -0.036(7.8)$
(1) $\quad 0.036x + 0.0455y = 0.31$
(2) $\quad -0.036x + (-0.036y) = -0.2808$ Add corresponding members of the equations.
$\quad 0.0095y = 0.0292$
$\quad \dfrac{0.0095y}{0.0095} = \dfrac{0.0292}{0.0095}$ Divide by 0.0095.
$\quad y \approx 3.07$

Substitute 3.07 for y, and solve for x in the second equation.

(2) $\quad x + y = 7.8$
$\quad x + 3.07 \approx 7.8$
$\quad x \approx 4.73$

Approximately \$4.73 trillion would be in Treasury bills, and about \$3.07 trillion would be in Treasury constant maturities.

Objective 4.4.2 *CHECKUP*

Write and solve a system of equations for each mixture and collection exercise.

1. Rosita had been saving coins to buy Christmas gifts for the family. She had just counted the coins and told her parents there was a total of 498 coins, consisting of 120 nickels and the rest a mix of dimes and quarters. She proudly told them that the coins totaled $63.75. How many dimes and quarters did Rosita have?

2. A chemist needs to mix a 25% glucose solution with a 5% glucose solution to make a new solution that is 10% glucose. If the chemist wants to have 1 liter of the 10% glucose solution, how many liters of the other two should she mix?

3. A chemist needs a 20% glucose solution. She mixes a 50% glucose solution with water (0% glucose). If she needs 1 liter of the 20% glucose solution, how many liters of the other two should she mix?

4. Series EE savings bonds have a fixed rate of 3.50% while I bond rates vary. Recent rates for I bonds were 4.80%. What amounts should you invest at each rate if you wish to earn $1310 in simple interest after one year on a total investment of $30,000?

5. Series EE savings bonds have a fixed rate of 3.50% while I bond rates vary. Recent rates for I bonds were 4.80%. If you wish to be conservative in your investments and invest twice as much at the fixed rate of 3.50% as you invest at the variable rate, how much should you invest in order to earn $11,800?

4.4 EXERCISES

 Student Solutions Manual   PH Math/Tutor Center   CD Video    MathXL®    MyMathLab   Interactmath.com

Write and solve a system of equations for each application.

Distance

1. Nolan lives in Nashville and Monroe lives in Memphis. The distance between their homes is 220 miles. They plan to meet at a location on I-40 between their homes. Nolan drives his truck at an average speed of 60 miles per hour, and Monroe drives his car at an average speed of 65 miles per hour. If they both leave at the same time, how many miles from Nashville will they meet?

2. Henrieta lives in Houston and Dolores lives in Dallas. The distance between their homes is 240 miles. They plan to meet at a location on I-45 between their homes. Henrietta drives her car at an average speed of 65 miles per hour, and Dolores drives her car at an average speed of 55 miles per hour. If they both leave at the same time, how many miles from Houston will they meet?

3. After Kenny's car broke down, he started walking home. Dolly came by and picked him up. The time he walked was twice as long as the time he rode with Dolly. He was walking at an average rate of 3 miles per hour, and Dolly drove at an average rate of 60 miles per hour. If the total distance to his home was 11 miles when he started walking, how much time did Ken spend walking and how much time riding?

4. On an outing, a troop of Boy Scouts canoed at 12 miles per hour for the first leg of their trip. Then they hiked at 3 miles per hour to reach their destination. It took as many hours for the canoe trip as it did for the hike. If the total distance traveled was 30 miles, find the time they spent canoeing and hiking, and find the distance they covered by canoe.

5. Steve is participating in a local 5K Walk/Run event. He estimates that he can run about 2.3 kilometers per hour and walk about 1.2 kilometers per hour. His time for the entire race turns out to be 3.55 hours. About how far did he walk and how far did he run?

6. Wei drives 24 miles to school on both rural and city roads. He can drive 45 miles per hour on rural roads and 35 miles per hour on city streets. It takes him about 40 minutes to commute to school. How much time does he drive on rural routes? How much time does he drive on city streets?

7. Krista, a college student living away from home, arranges to meet her parents partway between her home and school so that they can bring Krista some books she needs. Krista's school is 500 miles from her parents' home. Krista drives 65 miles per hour, and her Dad drives 55 miles per hour. Her parents leave earlier, so it takes them 2 hours longer to drive to the meeting place than it takes Krista. How far did Krista drive? How far did her Dad drive?

8. Kris, a kennel owner, arranges to meet a prospective dog buyer partway between their homes. The distance between the two homes is 600 miles. The buyer drives 50 miles per hour. Kris drives 60 miles per hour and leaves home an hour after the buyer leaves. How far did each drive?

9. An American Airlines flight travels from Miami to San Francisco in approximately 6 hours, flying at an altitude of 39,000 feet. During the same time, another American Airlines flight travels from San Francisco to Miami in approximately 5 hours, flying at an altitude of 30,200 feet. Assuming that the two planes travel at the same average speed, determine their average speed in still air and the average speed of the wind due to the jet stream. The two cities are approximately 2600 miles apart.

10. A United Airlines flight from Chicago to San Diego arrives 4 hours after departure. During the same time frame, an American Airlines flight from San Diego to Chicago arrives 3.5 hours after departure. The planes fly at altitudes above 30,000 feet. Assuming that they travel at the same average speed, determine their average speed in still air and the average speed of the wind due to the jet stream. The flight distance between the two cities is approximately 1750 miles.

11. Two Girl Scouts took a canoe trip up a stream. They paddled for 1.5 hours against the stream's current and reached their destination, which was 6 miles from their starting point.

After resting for a while, they made the return trip in 45 minutes (0.75 hour). How fast were the girls able to paddle in still water, and what was the average speed of the stream's current?

12. Jack cruised 42 miles downriver in 45 minutes (0.75 hour). His return trip took 1 hour. Determine the average speed of his motorboat in still water and the average speed of the river current.

13. While boating in San Francisco Bay near the Golden Gate Bridge, Joel motored with the tidal current for 15 minutes (0.25 hour) and traveled about 13.4 miles. Traveling against the current for 18 minutes (0.3 hour), he returned to his starting point. Determine the average speed of Joel's motorboat in still water and the average speed of the tidal current.

14. Jenny drove her motorboat with the current near Cape Cod Canal for 20 minutes $\left(\frac{1}{3}\text{ hour}\right)$ and traveled 14.4 miles. Returning to her starting point and traveling against the current took her 24 minutes $\left(\frac{2}{5}\text{ hour}\right)$. Determine her motorboat's average speed in still water and the average speed of the current.

Mixtures

15. Gary's Gourmet Coffee Shop mixes French vanilla coffee, which sells for $9.50 per pound, with hazelnut coffee, which sells for $7.00 per pound. The mix, called Croissant blend, sells for $8.50 per pound. If Gary wishes to make 20 pounds of the blend, how many pounds of each should he use?

16. LaToyia's Tea Shop blended orange spice tea, which sold for $3.50 per pound, with lemon honey tea, which sold for $7.50 per pound. The blend, sold as Spicy Citrus, amounted to 10 pounds of tea that sold for $5.00 per pound. How much of each flavor was used to make the blend?

17. Marian budgeted $250 to buy landscaping plants for her home. She needed 30 plants. If azaleas sell for $5 each and rhododendrons sell for $12 each, how many of each can Marian buy on her budget?

18. Sharon went to the local burger palace to buy burgers and hot dogs for a class picnic. She needed to buy 50 sandwiches for the class with the $95.00 she collected. If hot dogs sell for $1.00 each and burgers sell for $2.50 each, how many of each should she order?

19. The first screening of the latest movie sequel, *Cretaceous Park: The Found World*, had a box office take of $1938 at the local theater. Adults paid $7.50 and children paid $4.50 per ticket. There were four times as many children as adults. How many of these were adults and how many were children?

20. The blockbuster movie, *Car Wars, Part 12: The Princess Drives Back*, opened at the local theater. Adults paid $10.00 and children paid $5.50 per ticket for this show. There were twice as many children as adults at the show, and the box office receipts were $5355.00. How many adults and how many children attended the showing?

21. Cher works part time as a waitress in one restaurant and part time as a cook in another restaurant. In one week, she worked 15 hours waitressing and 20 hours as a cook and earned $320. In another week, she worked 18 hours waitressing and 24 hours cooking and earned $384. What is her hourly wage on each job?

22. A sale at Denney's Department Store attracted a throng of customers. One customer bought two shirts and four blouses for a total of $132. Another customer bought three shirts and six blouses from the same counters and paid $180. What were the sale prices of the shirts and blouses?

23. Radio station WALG runs a contest to see whether listeners can guess the makeup of a stack of $5 and $10 bills. The station announces that the stack contains 65 bills and is worth $365. The first listener who calls in with the correct number of each wins the money. Can you quickly determine the correct mix?

24. Tillie, the teller at the bank, has a stack of 35 bills. Some are $20 bills and the rest are $50 bills. If the value of the bills is $1300, how many of each does she have?

25. A grapefruit beverage that is 45% concentrated juice is mixed with an orange beverage that is 75% concentrated juice to produce a blend that is 55% concentrated juice. How many gallons of each must be mixed to produce 200 gallons of the blend?

26. A gardener has a solution that is 70% weed killer. He wants to mix this with another solution that is 40% weed killer, to make 5 pints of a solution that will be 50% weed killer. How many pints of each should he mix?

27. A chemist has a solution that is 60% acid and another solution that is 35% acid. How many liters of each should he mix to make 300 liters of a solution that is 50% acid?

28. A gardener has a solution that is 25% fungicide that she wants to mix with another solution that is 40% fungicide. How many pints of each should she mix to make 8 pints of a solution that is 30% fungicide?

29. An alcoholic drink is made by mixing gin (36% alcohol) with seltzer water, which has no alcohol. How much of each ingredient should be used to make 8 ounces of drink that is 24% alcohol?

30. Infants who are lactose intolerant drink a mixture of soy formula and a pure dairy formula. Forty ounces of a 75% soy formula for one such infant are made by mixing a formula that is 80% soy with a pure dairy formula (0% soy). How much of each type of formula was mixed?

31. Al Falfa, a milk farmer, wants to mix milk that is 4.3% butterfat with skim milk that has no butterfat, in order to make milk that is 2% butterfat. How much of each should he mix to make 200 gallons of the 2% butterfat milk? (Round your answer to the nearest gallon.)

32. How many liters of a 45% ammonia solution should be mixed with sterile water containing no ammonia to make 25 liters of a 35% ammonia solution?

33. The coolant in Mabel's car contains 45% antifreeze. How much should be drained and replaced with pure antifreeze in order for Mabel to have 4 gallons of a 60% antifreeze solution?

34. A car mechanic tests the antifreeze in your car and finds that it is 35% antifreeze. How much antifreeze should be drained and replaced with pure antifreeze in order to bring the car up to 5 gallons of 50% antifreeze? (Round your answer to the nearest tenth of a gallon.)

35. A wine maker has one barrel of wine that is 20% alcohol and another barrel that is 12% alcohol. How many gallons of the 12% alcohol wine must he mix with 5 gallons of the 20% alcohol wine to make a batch of wine with a 15% alcohol content? (*Hint*: Let x = the unknown amount of wine and let y = the total amount of the mixed wine.)

36. A pharmacist has one container of medicine with a strength of 45% medication and another container of medicine with a strength of 75% of the same medication. How many ounces of the 45% strength medication should be mixed with 8 ounces of the 75% strength medication to produce a medication with a strength of 60% medication? (See the hint in the previous exercise.)

37. A vitamin concentrate for pets contains a 1% vitamin C concentration. Five ounces of this concentrate are to be mixed with a 0.5% vitamin C solution. How much of the weaker solution is needed to create a new mixture that has a 0.75% vitamin C concentration?

38. The amount of sand in land of stripped-off soil is 90%. For compacting purposes a developer prefers soil with much less sand content. He mixes 7 cubic yards of topsoil (0% sand) with the 90% sandy soil to get a mixture that is 10% sand. How many yards of low-sand dirt does he have?

Interest

39. In order to reduce her risk, Catherine split her investment in two mutual funds between one that paid 8.5% simple interest annually and another that paid 7% simple interest annually. She had $10,000 to invest, and at the end of the year she received a total of $752.50 in interest. How much did she invest in each fund?

40. Ali received two student loans for school totaling $10,000. He borrowed the maximum allowed at 7% simple interest and the remainder at 8.25% simple interest. After one year, he owed $725 in interest. How much did Ali borrow at each interest rate?

41. Zelda has inherited $16,500, which she would like to invest. She has an opportunity to invest part of the money in a simple-interest savings account paying 5% per year and the rest in a certificate of deposit paying 7.25% per year. If she wishes to earn $1000 in one year for a vacation next year and also wants to keep some money in the savings account in case she needs it sooner, how much should she invest in each account?

42. In exercise **41**, Zelda planned to invest her inheritance. However, she learns that she must pay taxes on the inheritance and will have only $11,000 to invest. She decides to invest the money to earn $600 for a vacation instead. How much should she now invest in each account?

43. A stock club invests $7500 in two stocks. One has an average annual return of 2.5%, and the other, a more risky stock, has a projected return of 7.2%. The stocks performed as expected, and at the end of the year the club had made $243.90 with these purchases. How much did the club invest in each stock?

44. As a part of his will, James left 25% of his real estate holdings and 30% of his stock portfolio to his niece, Amy. The combined value of these assets is 1.5 million dollars. Amy's lawyer estimates that this inheritance is worth $420,000. Find the value of James's real estate holdings and stock portfolio.

45. Zora plans to reduce her risk by investing her inheritance in two separate accounts. One simple interest certificate account pays 7.25% per year. The second simple interest savings account pays 6% per year. If Zora invests twice as much in the certificate account and needs to earn $1230 in interest, how much should she invest in each account?

46. Roby plans to reduce his risk by investing his inheritance in two separate accounts. One simple-interest certificate account pays 7.25% per year. The second simple-interest savings account pays 6% per year. If Roby invests $2000 more in the certificate account than in the savings account and needs to earn $1205 in interest, how much should he invest in each account?

47. Lindsay has two credit cards. Her low-interest card charges 1.6% monthly and her other card charges 2.8% monthly. In July she had three times as much debt on the higher-interest card than on the lower. Her monthly interest payment for that month was $200. What was the balance on each card?

48. Diane went to a storewide sale in which shoes were marked down 20% and all other items in the store were marked down 30%. She spent twice as much on shoes as on other items. Her savings were $55.50. How much did she spend on shoes? How much did she spend on other items?

49. Princess Fiona needed a short-term loan of $100,000. No one loan company would give her the total amount, so she borrowed $45,000 from one company and $55,000 from another company. The total simple interest on the loans was $6450 for one year. The $45,000 loan charged a simple interest rate of 1% more than the loan rate charged on the $55,000 loan. What were the two interest rates for the loans?

50. D. J. deposited $1500 into one savings account and $1200 into another savings account. The two accounts earned $117.90 in simple interest after a year. The $1200 investment paid a simple-interest rate that was 0.3% greater than the interest rate paid on the $1500 investment. What were the two interest rates for the investments?

4.4 Calculator Exercises

In this chapter, we solved a system of linear equations both graphically and algebraically. However, if we know that we are seeking only integer solutions, we may wish to solve the system numerically. To do so, we must first solve each equation in the system for the dependent variable. Next, we store these equations in the calculator, using the $\boxed{Y=}$ key. Then when we view the table, wherever Y1 = Y2, the value of X and of Y1 (or Y2) will represent a coordinate-pair solution of the system.

One application of systems of linear equations in which we may want only integer solutions is the classic "age problem." Consider the following example:

Katie's cousin wants to know Katie's age, so she asks Katie's mom, Brenda. Katie's mom is a math teacher, so she decides to give the cousin the answer by using a math riddle. Brenda tells the cousin, "I am eight times as old as Katie. In 10 years, I will be three times as old as Katie." Use this information to determine how old Katie and Brenda are now.

Solution

Let x = Katie's age now
Let y = Brenda's age now

Brenda is eight times as old as Katie, so

$$y = 8x$$

In 10 years,

$$x + 10 = \text{Katie's age}$$
$$y + 10 = \text{Brenda's age}$$

In 10 years, Brenda will be three times as old as Katie, so $y + 10 = 3(x + 10)$, which simplifies to $y = 3x + 20$

The system of equations is

$$y = 8x$$
$$y = 3x + 20$$

Store these equations in the calculator and view the table.

The table indicates that the solution of the system of equations is (4, 32). Therefore, Katie is now 4 years old and Brenda is 32 years old.

The solution checks, since Brenda is eight times as old as Katie. In 10 years, Katie will be 14 and Brenda will be 42, and then Brenda will be three times as old as Katie.

Use this numerical method to solve the following age problems:

1. Stella is four years younger than three times her son's age. Five years ago, Stella was one year younger than four times her son's age. How old are Stella and her son now?

2. Gulen was daydreaming about her daughter Cecilia. In thinking about their ages, she realized that in 6 years she would be five times as old as Cecilia. In 13 years, she would be three times as old as Cecilia. Can you tell how old Gulen and Cecilia are now?

3. Joe wants to take early retirement in 10 years, when he will be twice as old as his son Paul. Joe is now 25 years older than Paul. How old is Joe now, and how old will he be when he retires?

4. Jenny and Katie bet Susan that she can't solve the riddle about their ages. Jenny is two years younger than Katie. In five years, Katie will be 10% older than Jenny. Help Susan find their ages now.

5. Egan was researching her family history for a school project. In a box of mementos, she found a birthday card from her grandmother to her mom. The card was dated 1965, and the note inside said, "Congratulations, Mary, you are now one-third as old as I am." She found a second card, dated 1977, also from her grandmother to her mother, which read, "Congratulations, Mary, you are now half as old as I am!" When Egan asked her mom how old she was on those two birthdays, her mom (a math teacher) told her to figure it out for herself. How old were her mom and her grandmother in those two years?

6. An antiques dealer found an old dresser and bed with a note attached. The note said that in 1902 the combined age of the bed and dresser was 148 years. It also said that in four more years the dresser would be twice as old as the bed. How old were the two pieces of furniture in 1902?

7. The tiebreaker question in a math contest was an age problem: Fric is three times as old as Frac. In five years, Fric's age will be two years more than twice Frac's age. How old are Fric and Frac now?

4.4 Writing Exercise

Many of the application exercises presented in this section have become classic algebra problems. You will find variations of them in most algebra textbooks. Some students object to these kinds of problems as being contrived and not very practical. For example, students often state that age problems have no practical signifi- cance, and one sometimes sees cartoons that joke about distance-traveled problems. Write a short paragraph describing how you feel about these applications. Do you feel they are worthwhile, and if so, why? Do you think they are contrived? Can you suggest better applications?

4.5 SOLVING SYSTEMS OF LINEAR EQUATIONS IN THREE VARIABLES

OBJECTIVES

1 Determine whether a given ordered triple is a solution of a system of linear equations in three variables.

2 Solve systems of linear equations in three variables algebraically.

3 Model real-world situations by using systems of linear equations, and solve the equations.

APPLICATION

According to Kirchhoff's laws, the currents I_1, I_2, and I_3 shown in **Figure 4.1** are solutions of the system

$$I_1 - I_2 + I_3 = 0$$
$$4I_1 + 2I_2 = 8$$
$$2I_2 + 3I_3 = 7$$

Find the currents, measured in amperes.

After completing this section, we will discuss this application further. See page 410.

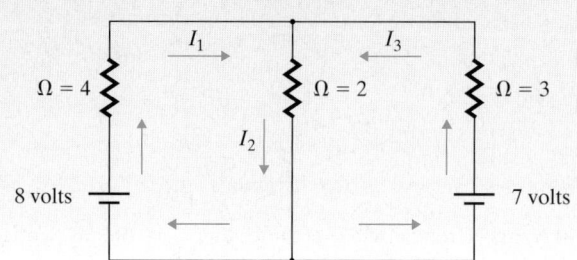

Figure 4.1

Objective 4.5.1

Determining an Ordered-Triple Solution of a System of Linear Equations

In Chapter 3, we examined linear equations in two variables. The standard form of a linear equation in two variables is $ax + by = c$, where a and b are not both equal to zero. In this section, we examine a **linear equation in three variables** and systems of linear equations in three variables.

STANDARD FORM FOR A LINEAR EQUATION IN THREE VARIABLES

The standard form for a linear equation in three variables is $ax + by + cz = d$, where a, b, c, and d are real numbers and a, b, and c are not all equal to 0.

A solution of a linear equation in two variables is an ordered pair (x, y) that satisfies the equation. Similarly, a solution of a linear equation in three variables is an **ordered triple** (x, y, z) that satisfies the equation.

SOLUTION OF A LINEAR EQUATION IN THREE VARIABLES

An ordered triple (x, y, z) is a solution of a linear equation in three variables if the values of its coordinates, when substituted for their corresponding variables, result in a true equation.

 TAKE NOTE If the variables defined are not x, y, and z, the variables are placed in alphabetic order in the ordered triple. For example, an ordered triple could be (k, l, m).

EXAMPLE 1   Determine whether each ordered triple is a solution of the equation $3x - 2y + 8z = -2$.

a. $(2, 0, -1)$ **b.** $(2, 3, 1)$

Solution

a.
$$\begin{array}{c}3x \ - \ 2y \ + \ \ 8z \ = -2 \\ \hline 3(2) \ - \ 2(0) + 8(-1) \ \big| \ -2 \\ 6 \ - \ 0 \ + \ (-8) \\ -2 \end{array}$$

Since $-2 = -2$, $(2, 0, -1)$ is a solution.

b.
$$\begin{array}{c}3x \ - \ 2y \ + \ 8z \ = -2 \\ \hline 3(2) \ - \ 2(3) + 8(1) \ \big| \ -2 \\ 6 \ - \ 6 \ + \ 8 \\ 8 \end{array}$$

Since $8 \ne -2$, $(2, 3, 1)$ is not a solution.

Check

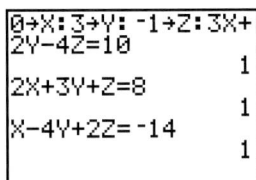

a. ```
2→X:0→Y: -1→Z:3X-
2Y+8Z=-2
                    1
```

b. ```
2→X:3→Y:1→Z:3X-2
Y+8Z=-2
                    0
```

Since 1 indicates true and 0 indicates false, the calculator checks confirm the results obtained. ∎

In the last section, we solved systems of linear equations in two variables. In this section, we solve a **system of linear equations in three variables**. A system of linear equations in three variables is a set of at least two linear equations in three variables.

An ordered triple is a solution of the system if it satisfies every equation in the system.

SOLUTION OF A SYSTEM OF LINEAR EQUATIONS IN THREE VARIABLES

An ordered triple is a solution of a system of linear equations in three variables if it is a solution of every equation in the system.

EXAMPLE 2   Determine whether $(0, 3, -1)$ is a solution of the system

$$3x + 2y - 4z = 10$$
$$2x + 3y + \ z = 8$$
$$x - 4y + 2z = -14$$

Solution

Substitute the values for the variables.

$$\begin{array}{c}3x \ + \ 2y \ - \ \ \ 4z \ = 10 \\ \hline 3(0) + 2(3) - 4(-1) \ \big| \ 10 \\ 10 \end{array} \qquad \begin{array}{c}2x \ + \ 3y \ + \ \ \ z \ = 8 \\ \hline 2(0) + 3(3) + (-1) \ \big| \ 8 \\ 8 \end{array}$$

$$\begin{array}{c}x \ - \ 4y \ + \ \ \ 2z \ = -14 \\ \hline 0 \ - \ 4(3) + 2(-1) \ \big| \ -14 \\ -14 \end{array}$$

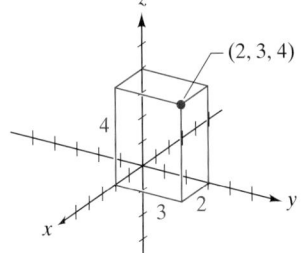

The ordered triple $(0, 3, -1)$ is a solution of the system, because it satisfies all equations in the system. ∎

Check

```
0→X:3→Y: -1→Z:3X+
2Y-4Z=10
                    1
2X+3Y+Z=8
                    1
X-4Y+2Z= -14
                    1
```

Since 1 indicates true, the ordered pair is a solution of the system.

We graph ordered pairs on a two-dimensional rectangular coordinate system, or coordinate plane. We graph ordered triples on a three-dimensional rectangular coordinate system, or **coordinate space**. A coordinate space is formed by three axes that are perpendicular to each other and that pass through the ordered triple $(0, 0, 0)$. For example, plot the ordered triple $(2, 3, 4)$.

The graph of a linear equation in three variables is a plane that extends without end. To help visualize its location, it is conventional to graph a bounded figure. Even though we do not expect you to graph these bounded figures, one of many planes that contain the ordered triple $(2, 3, 4)$ is shown in **Figure 4.2**.

Systems of linear equations in three variables have four possible types of solution sets, illustrated as follows:

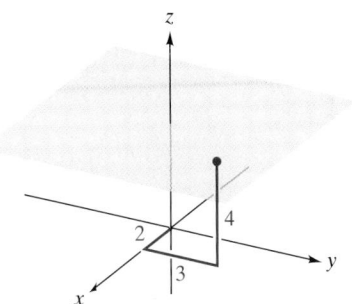

Figure 4.2

1. The three planes have one point in common. The ordered-triple coordinates of the common point represents the solution. The system is consistent.

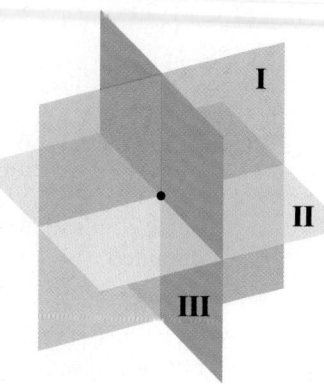

2. The three planes do not have a common intersection. The system has no solution. The system is inconsistent.

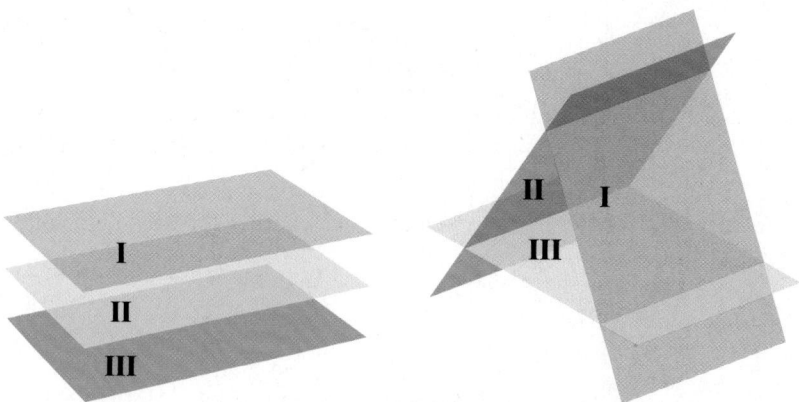

3. The three planes intersect at all points on a line. The system has an infinite number of solutions. The system is consistent.

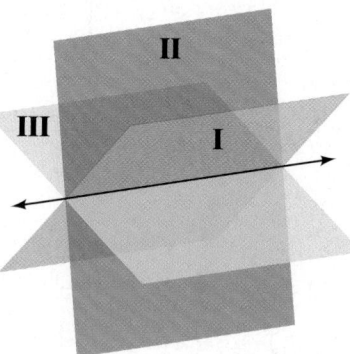

4. The three planes coincide. The system has an infinite number of solutions. The system is consistent, and the equations are dependent.

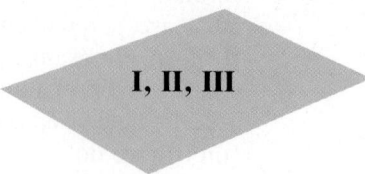

We will not solve these systems graphically. However, this visualization should help you understand the solutions we will obtain algebraically.

✓ Objective 4.5.1 *CHECKUP*

1. Determine whether the ordered triple $(18, 12, -10)$ is a solution of the equation.

$$\frac{2}{3}x - \frac{3}{4}y + \frac{1}{2}z = -2$$

2. Determine whether the ordered triple $(5, -10, 12)$ is a solution of the system.

$$0.5a - 4b + 1.5c = 60.5$$
$$0.3a - 0.2b - 3.4c = -37.3$$
$$1.8a + 2.5b - 4.6c = -71.2$$

3. What is the standard form for a linear equation in three variables?

4. Can a linear equation in three variables have more than one solution? Explain.

Objective 4.5.2 Solving Systems of Linear Equations Algebraically

In this section, we algebraically solve linear equations in three variables, using the addition method to eliminate a variable and obtain a system of linear equations in two variables.

SOLVING A SYSTEM OF LINEAR EQUATIONS IN THREE VARIABLES BY USING THE ADDITION METHOD

To solve a system of linear equations in three variables by using the addition method,

- Write all the equations in standard form.
- Eliminate a variable from a pair of equations. This results in a linear equation in two variables.
- Eliminate the *same* variable from a different pair of equations. This results in a second linear equation in two variables.
- Write a system of linear equations in two variables, using the two equations obtained in the previous steps.
- Solve the system of linear equations in two variables by any method.
- Substitute the known values into one of the original equations containing the third variable, and solve for the third variable.
- Check the solution.

EXAMPLE 3   Solve.

$$2x + 3y + z = 7$$
$$x - 2y + z = -4$$
$$-x + 3y - z = 6$$

Solution

(1) $2x + 3y + z = 7$
(2) $x - 2y + z = -4$
(3) $-x + 3y - z = 6$

We will eliminate the variable z. First use equations (1) and (3), and then use equations (2) and (3).

(1) $\quad 2x + 3y + z = \ 7$	(2) $\quad x - 2y + z = -4$
(3) $\quad \underline{-x + 3y - z = \ 6}$	(3) $\quad \underline{-x + 3y - z = \ 6}$
(4) $\quad x + 6y \quad\ = 13$	(5) $\qquad\quad y \quad\ = 2$

Write a system of equations.

(4) $x + 6y = 13$

(5) $y = 2$

Solve by substituting 2 for y in equation (4).

(4) $x + 6y = 13$

      $x + 6(2) = 13$

      $x + 12 = 13$

(6) $x = 1$

Substitute 2 for y and 1 for x in equation (2).

Check

(2) $x - 2y + z = -4$

     $1 - 2(2) + z = -4$

     $1 - 4 + z = -4$

         $-3 + z = -4$

             $z = -1$

```
1→X: 2→Y: -1→Z: 2X+
3Y+Z=7
                    1
X-2Y+Z= -4
                    1
-X+3Y-Z=6
                    1
```

The ordered-triple solution is $(1, 2, -1)$.
    Check the solution as shown.

EXAMPLE 4   Solve.

$$3x + 2y = 0$$
$$4x - z - 4 = 0$$
$$3y + 2z - 3 = 0$$

Solution

Write each equation in standard form.

(1) $3x + 2y = 0$

(2) $4x - z = 4$

(3) $3y + 2z = 3$

The first equation does not have a term containing the variable z. We eliminate z by using equations (2) and (3). Multiply both sides of equation (2) by 2, and add corresponding members of the equations.

(2) $2(4x - z) = 2(4)$ Yields $8x - 2z = 8$

(3) $3y + 2z = 3$ $\underline{ 3y + 2z = 3}$

                                   (4) $8x + 3y = 11$

Write a system of linear equations in two variables.

(1) $3x + 2y = 0$

(4) $8x + 3y = 11$

We eliminate the variable y. Multiply both sides of equation (1) by -3 and both sides of equation (4) by 2. Then add corresponding members of the equations.

(1) $-3(3x + 2y) = -3(0)$ Yields $-9x - 6y = 0$

(4) $2(8x + 3y) = 2(11)$ Yields $\underline{ 16x + 6y = 22}$

                                        $7x = 22$

$$x = \frac{22}{7}$$

Substitute $\frac{22}{7}$ for x in equation (1), and solve for y.

(1)
$$3x + 2y = 0$$
$$3\left(\frac{22}{7}\right) + 2y = 0$$
$$\frac{66}{7} + 2y = 0$$
$$2y = -\frac{66}{7}$$
$$y = -\frac{33}{7}$$

Substitute $\frac{22}{7}$ for x in equation (2), and solve for z.

Check

(2)
$$4x - z = 4$$
$$4\left(\frac{22}{7}\right) - z = 4$$
$$\frac{88}{7} - z = 4$$
$$-z = -\frac{60}{7}$$
$$z = \frac{60}{7}$$

```
22/7→X: -33/7→Y:6
0/7→Z:3X+2Y=0
                 1
4X-Z-4=0
                 1
3Y+2Z-3=0
                 1
```

The ordered triple $\left(\frac{22}{7}, -\frac{33}{7}, \frac{60}{7}\right)$ is a solution of the system.

Check the solution on your calculator.   ■

Remember that a system may have no solution or many solutions. The results will appear similar to the corresponding results for equations in two variables.

EXAMPLE 5   Solve.

$$x - 2y + 4z - 1 = 0$$
$$-x - 3y + z - 8 = 0$$
$$2x - 4y + 8z = 0$$

Solution
Write each equation in standard form.

(1) $x - 2y + 4z = 1$
(2) $-x - 3y + z = 8$
(3) $2x - 4y + 8z = 0$

We eliminate the variable x. Add corresponding members of equations (1) and (2). Multiply both sides of equation (2) by 2, and add corresponding members of the new equation and equation (3).

(1) $x - 2y + 4z = 1$
(2) $\underline{-x - 3y + z = 8}$
(4) $ -5y + 5z = 9$

(2) $2(-x - 3y + z) = 2(8)$ Yields $-2x - 6y + 2z = 16$
(3) $2x - 4y + 8z = 0$ $\underline{2x - 4y + 8z = 0}$
(5) $ -10y + 10z = 16$

Write a system of linear equations in two variables.

(4) $-5y + 5z = 9$
(5) $-10y + 10z = 16$

Eliminate the variable y. Multiply both sides of equation (4) by -2, and add corresponding members of the new equation and equation (5).

$$
\begin{array}{lll}
(4) & -2(-5y + 5z) = -2(9) & \text{Yields} & 10y - 10z = -18 \\
(5) & -10y + 10z = 16 & & \underline{-10y + 10z = 16} \\
& & & 0 = -2
\end{array}
$$

The result is a contradiction. The system has no solution. ■

EXAMPLE 6 Solve.

$$
\begin{array}{l}
x + 3y - 2z = 4 \\
-2x - 6y + 4z = -8 \\
\dfrac{1}{4}x + \dfrac{3}{4}y - \dfrac{1}{2}z = 1
\end{array}
$$

Solution

$$
\begin{array}{ll}
(1) & x + 3y - 2z = 4 \\
(2) & -2x - 6y + 4z = -8 \\
(3) & \dfrac{1}{4}x + \dfrac{3}{4}y - \dfrac{1}{2}z = 1
\end{array}
$$

Eliminate the variable x. Multiply both sides of equation (1) by 2, and add corresponding members of the resulting equation and equation (2).

$$
\begin{array}{llll}
(1) & 2(x + 3y - 2z) = 2(4) & \text{Yields} & 2x + 6y - 4z = 8 \\
(2) & -2x - 6y + 4z = -8 & & \underline{-2x - 6y + 4z = -8} \\
(4) & & & 0 = 0
\end{array}
$$

The result is an identity. Equations (1) and (2) are equivalent.

Eliminate the fractions in equation (3) by multiplying both sides of the equation by 4 (the LCD).

$$
\begin{array}{lll}
(1) & x + 3y - 2z = 4 & \qquad x + 3y - 2z = 4 \\
(3) & 4\left(\dfrac{1}{4}x + \dfrac{3}{4}y - \dfrac{1}{2}z\right) = 4(1) & \text{Yields} \qquad x + 3y - 2z = 4
\end{array}
$$

Notice that equations (1) and (3) are equivalent. There is no need to eliminate a variable, since all variables would be eliminated and the result would be an identity.

Since equations (1) and (2) are equivalent and equations (1) and (3) are equivalent, all the equations are equivalent. There are an infinite number of solutions. The solution set is all ordered triples that satisfy $x + 3y - 2z = 4$. ■

✓ Objective 4.5.2 *CHECKUP*

Solve exercises 1–4.

1.
$$
\begin{array}{l}
2x - 3y + z = -10 \\
x - y - z = -5.6 \\
3x + y + z = 8.8
\end{array}
$$

2.
$$
\begin{array}{l}
3x + y = -2 \\
x + y + z = 1 \\
x + 2y + 3z = 1
\end{array}
$$

3.
$$
\begin{array}{l}
3x + 4y = z + 6 \\
x + 3z = y + 3 \\
2x - 2y = 10 - 6z
\end{array}
$$

4.
$$
\begin{array}{l}
2x + 4y = 3z + 12 \\
0.4x + 0.8y - 0.6z = 2.4 \\
x + 2y - 6 = 1.5z
\end{array}
$$

5. In solving a system of linear equations in three variables algebraically, how can you tell when there is no solution or when there are an infinite number of solutions? ■

Objective 4.5.3   Modeling the Real World

There are many situations in which three unknowns are related in different ways. Setting up a system of linear equations in three variables is helpful in determining a solution for this type of relationship. For example, you may want to combine three different items and set constraints on them. An ideal algebraic model for this situation would be a system of linear equations in three variables.

EXAMPLE 7

A dietician prepares a dinner for a 27-year-old woman. The meal should have 480 calories, 31 g of fat, and 103 mg of cholesterol. The patient chose roast beef, mashed potatoes, and green beans for her meal. According to the following table, how many servings of each should be prepared?

	Roast Beef (3 oz)	Mashed Potatoes ($\frac{1}{2}$ cup)	Green Beans ($\frac{1}{2}$ cup)
Calories	220	110	20
Fat (in grams)	18	4	0
Cholesterol (in milligrams)	60	13	0

Solution

Let x = the number of 3-oz servings of roast beef

$\quad y$ = the number of $\frac{1}{2}$-cup servings of mashed potatoes

$\quad z$ = the number of $\frac{1}{2}$-cup servings of green beans

The total calories are 480.

$$220x + 110y + 20z = 480$$

The total grams of fat are 31.

$$18x + 4y + 0z = 31$$

The total milligrams of cholesterol are 103.

$$60x + 13y + 0z = 103$$

The system is

(1) $\quad 220x + 110y + 20z = 480$

(2) $\quad\ \ 18x + \ \ 4y + \ \ 0z = 31$

(3) $\quad\ \ 60x + \ \ 13y + \ \ 0z = 103$

Since equations (2) and (3) make a system of two variables, solve the system for x and y.

(2) $\quad 13(18x + 4y) = 13(31)$ $\quad$ Yields $\quad 234x + 52y = 403$

(3) $\quad -4(60x + 13y) = -4(103)$ $\quad$ Yields $\quad \underline{-240x - 52y = -412}$

$$-6x \qquad\quad = -9$$

$$x = 1.5$$

Substitute 1.5 for x and solve for y.

(2) $\qquad 18x + 4y = 31$

$\qquad 18(1.5) + 4y = 31$

$\qquad\quad 27 + 4y = 31$

$\qquad\qquad\quad 4y = 4$

$\qquad\qquad\quad\ y = 1$

Substitute 1.5 for x and 1 for y, and solve for z.

(1) $\qquad 220x + 110y + 20z = 480$

$\qquad 220(1.5) + 110(1) + 20z = 480$

$\qquad\quad 330 + \quad 110 + 20z = 480$

$\qquad\qquad\quad 440 + 20z = 480$

$\qquad\qquad\qquad\quad 20z = 40$

$\qquad\qquad\qquad\qquad z = 2$

The dietician should prepare the following:

1.5 servings roast beef

1 serving mashed potatoes

2 servings green beans

APPLICATION

According to Kirchhoff's laws, the currents I_1, I_2, and I_3 are solutions of the system

$$
\begin{aligned}
I_1 - I_2 + I_3 &= 0 \\
4I_1 + 2I_2 &= 8 \\
2I_2 + 3I_3 &= 7
\end{aligned}
$$

Find the currents, measured in amperes.

Discussion

(1) $1I_1 - 1I_2 + 1I_3 = 0$

(2) $4I_1 + 2I_2 + 0I_3 = 8$

(3) $0I_1 + 2I_2 + 3I_3 = 7$

Equation (2) has only I_1 and I_2. Therefore, eliminate I_3 from a system containing equations (1) and (3).

(1) $-3(1I_1 - 1I_2 + 1I_3) = -3(0)$ Yields $-3I_1 + 3I_2 - 3I_3 = 0$

(3) $0I_1 + 2I_2 + 3I_3 = 7$ $\underline{ 0I_1 + 2I_2 + 3I_3 = 7}$

(4) $-3I_1 + 5I_2 = 7$

Write a new system consisting of equations (2) and (4), and eliminate I_1.

(2) $3(4I_1 + 2I_2) = 3(8)$ Yields $12I_1 + 6I_2 = 24$

(4) $4(-3I_1 + 5I_2) = 4(7)$ Yields $\underline{-12I_1 + 20I_2 = 28}$

$$\frac{26I_2}{26} = \frac{52}{26}$$

$$I_2 = 2$$

Substitute into equation (3).

(3) $2I_2 + 3I_3 = 7$

 $2(2) + 3I_3 = 7$

 $I_3 = 1$

Substitute into equation (2).

(2) $4I_1 + 2I_2 = 8$

 $\underline{4I_1 + 2(2) = 8}$

 $I_1 = 1$

The solution is $(1, 2, 1)$.

Therefore, $I_1 = 1$ ampere, $I_2 = 2$ amperes, and $I_3 = 1$ ampere.

✓ Objective 4.5.3 *CHECKUP*

1. In using Kirchhoff's laws to determine the unknown currents in an electrical circuit, the following system of simultaneous equations resulted:

$$I_1 - I_2 - I_3 = 0$$
$$I_1 + 3I_2 = 8$$
$$I_2 - 2I_3 = -1$$

Solve the system for the three currents, I_1, I_2, and I_3, measured in amperes.

2. At the fast-food counter, Edgar ordered a roast beef sandwich, french fries, and a chocolate shake. The place mat on the tray indicated that this combination had 956 calories, 12.88 grams of saturated fat, and 3.92 grams of unsaturated fat, distributed among the constituents as follows:

	Roast Beef Sandwich	French Fries	Thick Milk Shake
Calories	71 per oz	88 per oz	34 per oz
Saturated fat, grams	0.7 per oz	1.4 per oz	0.49 per oz
Unsaturated fat, grams	0.35 per oz	0.70 per oz	0.035 per oz

How many ounces of each food did Edgar receive?

4.5 EXERCISES

 Student Solutions Manual    PH Math/Tutor Center   CD Video   Math XL MathXL®   MyMathLab MyMathLab   Interactmath.com

Determine whether each ordered triple is a solution of the equation $3x + 4y - 5z = 46$.

1. $(2, -3.5, -10.8)$ **2.** $(-2, 6.5, 5.2)$ **3.** $(0, 8.5, -2.4)$

4. $(10, -2.5, -5.2)$ **5.** $(5, -1.5, 7.4)$ **6.** $(0, 6, -5.2)$

Determine whether each ordered triple is a solution of the equation $\frac{3}{4}a + \frac{1}{3}b = \frac{1}{2}c$.

7. $(8, 12, 10)$ **8.** $(-12, 6, -14)$ **9.** $(-16, 9, -18)$

10. $\left(\frac{5}{6}, -\frac{9}{16}, \frac{7}{8}\right)$ **11.** $\left(\frac{2}{3}, -\frac{3}{4}, -\frac{1}{2}\right)$ **12.** $\left(\frac{8}{9}, -2, 0\right)$

Determine whether each ordered triple is a solution of the given system.

13. $(-3, 5, 8)$
$$5x - 3y + 7z = 26$$
$$4x - 5z = -37$$
$$4y + 9z = 92$$

14. $(5, 0, -4)$
$$4x + 8y - 3z = 32$$
$$2x + 5z = 3y - 10$$
$$x - 4y - 7z = 33$$

15. $(14, 78, 21)$
$$x - \frac{1}{2}y = z - 46$$
$$x + y + z = 113$$
$$2x - 3y + 4z = -122$$

16. $(8, 10, 5)$
$$0.5x - 4.3y + z = -34$$
$$x + 7.1y - 3.2z = 63$$
$$y - 8.4z = 32$$

Solve.

17. $x - y + z = 14$
$x + y + z = 8$
$x + 2y - 5z = -37$

18. $a + b - c = 6$
$2a + b + c = -10$
$a + 4b - 3c = 9$

19. $\frac{1}{3}a + \frac{2}{3}b - \frac{3}{5}c = -\frac{5}{8}$
$2a - \frac{1}{3}b - \frac{4}{5}c = \frac{5}{4}$
$8a + 8b + 8c = 5$

20. $\frac{3}{5}x + \frac{2}{3}y + z = -\frac{1}{15}$
$x - \frac{5}{6}y + 2z = -\frac{3}{2}$
$3x + 5y - 6z = 8$

21. $4x - 5y - 10z = 63$
$2x + 15z = -108$
$x - 5y - 15z = 99$

22. $4x + 5y - z = 1$
$2x - 10y + 7z = 43$
$6x + 8z = 27$

23. $a - b + c = 385$
$2a - 3b + c = 16$
$4a - 5b + 2c = 503$

24. $p + q + r = 321$
$2p + 3q + r = 33$
$p + 2q + 10r = 582$

25. $5x - 3y + 7z = 8$
$x + 4y - 3z = 11$
$6x + y + 4z = 19$

26. $4x + 2y + 3z = 6$
$3x + y + 2z = 8$
$x + y + z = 5$

27. $8a - 3b + 2c = -29$
$5a + b + 7c = 2$
$3a - 4b - 5c = 30$

28. $4a - 3b + 7c = -15$
$5a + 2b + 13c = 14$
$a + 5b + 6c = 29$

Write a system of linear equations in three variables for each situation, and solve the equations to answer the questions asked.

29. At the Holiday Festival of Lights presented at Greenglade Gardens Resort, adults were charged an admission price of $12.00, children were charged $5.00, and resort guests were charged $3.50. The total number of tickets sold was 1257, and the number of children's tickets sold was 87 more than the total of adults and resort guests. If the total receipts for the festival were $9547, how many tickets were sold to each group of people?

30. Deanna found a box of fine china pieces at an antiques store that matched the set she owned. She paid $53.50 for the box. The box had cups selling for $3.50 each, saucers at $1.00 each, and dinner plates at $4.25 each. The number of cups was equal to the total number of saucers and dinner plates. If there were 18 pieces of china in the box, how many pieces of each kind did Deanna buy?

31. Roderick invested $11,200 in three different accounts in order to distribute his investment risk. Each of the accounts was a simple-interest-bearing account, with one account paying 5% interest annually, another paying 5.5%, and the third paying 6%. The amount invested at 5% was $1400 less than the amount invested at 6%. Roderick's total interest on the investments was $623 after one year. How much did he invest in each account?

32. Siegfried paid 1.5% simple interest each month on his credit card balance, 0.75% simple interest per month on his furniture loan balance, and 0.9% simple interest per month on his car loan balance. His furniture loan balance was five times as large as his credit card balance. His total interest payments for the month amounted to $88.28, and the total amount he owed, not including interest, was $9850. What was the balance on each of Siegfried's loans?

33. Ron collected $184 during a charity drive for a shelter for the homeless. The money consisted entirely of $1, $5, and $10 bills. There were three times as many $1 bills as there were $5 bills. If there were 60 bills, how many of each bill did Ron collect?

34. A packet of stamps sold for $12.25. The package contained $0.32 stamps, $0.03 stamps, and $0.35 stamps. The number of $0.32 stamps was the same as the number of $0.03 stamps. The total number of stamps in the packet was 50. How many of each denomination of stamps were in the packet?

35. Henry's Health Foods Market packages healthful cereal in three sizes. A small box (10.8 oz) sells for $2.39, a medium-sized box (13.5 oz) sells for $2.79, and a large box (20.4 oz) sells for $3.59. Henry's receipts indicate that he sold a total of 145 boxes of the cereal, for a total of $446.55. He sold all but 4 oz of his gross stock of 2350 oz of cereal. How many boxes of each size of cereal did he sell?

36. Bakir's Bakery sells Turkish baklava in three sizes. A package of 6 pieces sells for $3.30, a package of 8 pieces sells for $4.00, and a package of 12 pieces sells for $5.40. At the beginning of the day, Bakir made 60 dozen pieces of baklava. When the day was done, he had sold 77 boxes of the treats and had made $336.00 on the sales. Four pieces of baklava were left. How many of each size of package did Bakir sell?

37. A perfume manufacturer is creating a blend of three formulas: fragrance 1 (2% alcohol), fragrance 2 (3% alcohol), and fragrance 3 (7% alcohol). These liquids are mixed together to create 15 oz of a fragrance that is 5.5% alcohol. In order to get an appropriate color, the mixture must contain 3 oz of fragrance 3 for every ounce of fragrance 1 that is used. To the nearest tenth of an ounce, how many ounces of each fragrance should be mixed?

38. In making a rich salad dressing, a chef is careful about the oil content of the finished product. He mixes olive oil (98% oil), vinegar, and mayonnaise (67% oil) to create 10.5 cups of dressing. The oil concentration in the finished dressing is about 50.33%. The sum of the amount of olive oil and the amount of vinegar is twice the amount of mayonnaise. To the nearest tenth of a cup, how many cups of each ingredient should be used?

39. Tenisha invested $7225 to start a portfolio of stocks. She purchased a total of 600 shares. Some shares were gold investments selling for $19.75 each. Others were investments in oil-related industries selling for $9.50 each. The remainder consisted of investments in money market funds selling for $12.00 each. During the first quarter, Tenisha earned a total of $260 in dividends. The gold investment paid $0.50 per share, the oil-related investment $0.10 per share, and the money market funds $0.90 per share. How much did Tenisha invest in each of the three stock funds?

40. Hortense purchased life insurance in units of $1000. Ameritag sold each unit for a premium of $18.00 per year per unit. Bankers Fund sold its units for a premium of $13.20 per year per unit, and Columbia Mutual sold its units for a premium of $15.00 per year per unit. Hortense purchased a mix of 65 units from the three companies at a total annual premium of $942. The companies paid interest each year on the policies. Ameritag paid $1.50 per unit, Bankers Fund paid $0.65 per unit, and Columbia Mutual paid $0.85 per unit. If Hortense received a total of $54.75 in interest payments for one year, how many units of insurance did she purchase from each company?

41. Concetta bakes pastries in her home that she sells to restaurants. She spends $1.25 for each pie, $1.00 for each dozen cookies, and $1.50 for each cake that she bakes. The restaurants pay her $3.50 for each pie, $2.50 for each dozen cookies, and $4.50 for each cake. She bakes three times as many cakes as she does pies. How many of each type of pastry does Concetta bake if she spends $69.50 and receives $200.00 for her efforts?

42. As patient coordinator for a doctor's office, Gretchen schedules patients for visits. Each patient requiring a physical will need 45 minutes, for which the patient will be charged $130. Patients requiring outpatient surgery will need 90 minutes and will be charged $300. Patients requiring diagnostic treatment will need 15 minutes and will be charged $55. Gretchen schedules patients to fill an eight-hour day (480 minutes), for which the total charges are $1595. She schedules one more patient for a physical than she does for surgery. How many of each type of patient does she schedule?

43. In planning Baby Dumpling's meals, the following table is used:

	Cereal (1 oz)	Orange Juice (2 oz)	Milk (2 oz)
Calcium	225 mg	6.8 mg	69.8 mg
Vitamin A	4.5 IU	31.2 IU	116.2 IU
Vitamin C	0.6 mg	35.4 mg	0.6 mg

How many servings of each item should be planned in order for the baby to receive 736 mg of calcium, 505 IU of vitamin A, and 39 mg of vitamin C?

44. Chip will have the items listed in the following table for lunch:

	Hot Dog	Beans (2 oz)	Chips (1 oz)
Protein	6.8 grams	2.7 grams	2 grams
Calcium	11.3 mg	28.4 mg	6.8 mg
Iron	0.8 mg	0.2 mg	0.5 mg

How many servings of each should he have in order to receive 20.3 grams of protein, 64.6 mg of calcium, and 2.8 mg of iron?

45. A triangle's interior angles are designated A, B, and C. The measure of angle C is twice that of angle A. The measure of angle B is half the sum of the measures of angles A and C. Find the measures of each of the three angles.

46. The sum of an angle, its complement, and its supplement is 239 degrees. Find each angle.

4.5 Calculator Exercises

Our calculator can determine the solution of a system of three linear equations in three variables. The calculator uses the mathematical process of matrices to do so. A matrix is a table. Each row of the table contains the coefficients of one of the equations in the system, after the equation is placed into standard form.

The calculator process takes the table and converts it to an equivalent table of coefficients wherein, for each equation, one of the variables has a coefficient of 1 and the other variables in the same equation have coefficients of 0. (This is possible through the properties of equations that you studied before.) The process results in a table that isolates each of the variables in one of the equations, just as you would do if you had one equation with one variable. By reading each row of the resulting table, you are able to read the solution of the system of equations. It is a lovely process to see once you understand it. To determine the solution of a system of equations by using your calculator,

- Rewrite each equation of the system in standard form, $ax + by + cz = d$.
- Create a table in which each row lists only the coefficients a, b, c, and d, in order.
- Store the table as table A in the calculator.

Type each coefficient and press [ENTER] after each.

- After the table is stored, press [2nd] [MODE] (QUIT).
- To create the solution table, choose **rref(** under the **MATRIX** menu

[2nd] [x⁻¹] (MATRIX) [▶] [ALPHA] [APPS] (B).

- Type in the name of table A.

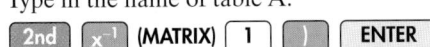

- The calculator will display a table with 1's and 0's in the first three columns and the solution of the system in the fourth column. This really is an equivalent system of equations (having the same solution as the original system), but with new coefficients a, b, c, and d. If you write the new system, you can see its solution.

As an example, solve the system.

$$2x - 3y + z = -9$$
$$x + 2y - 3z = -1$$
$$-2x + y - 4z = -3$$

The table of coefficients is

$$\begin{matrix} 2 & -3 & 1 & -9 \\ 1 & 2 & -3 & -1 \\ -2 & 1 & -4 & -3 \end{matrix}$$

Storing this table in the calculator and obtaining the solution table are shown in the following diagrams:

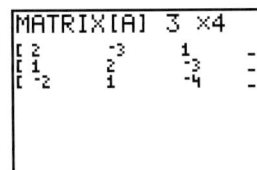 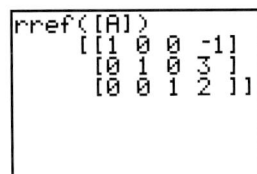

The solution of the system of equations is given by the new equivalent system,

$$1x + 0y + 0z = -1, \quad \text{or} \quad x = -1$$
$$0x + 1y + 0z = 3, \quad \text{or} \quad y = 3$$
$$0x + 0y + 1z = 2, \quad \text{or} \quad z = 2$$

Thus, the solution is $x = -1$, $y = 3$, and $z = 2$. The solution also can be read as the ordered triple $(-1, 3, 2)$, given by the fourth column of the table.

When you write the new equivalent system, if one of the equations is a contradiction, such as $0x + 0y + 0z = 1$, it indicates that the system has no solution.

When you write the new equivalent system, if one of the equations is an identity, such as $0x + 0y + 0z = 0$, it indicates that the system has many solutions.

Use the preceding method to solve the following systems of equations.

1. $x - y - z = 0$
$x + y + z = 4$
$x + y - z = 6$

2. $x + y - z = -4$
$x + 2y + z = -3$
$x - y + z = 6$

3. $2x + 8z = 4$
$4x - y + 8z = 3$
$2x + y = 3$

4. $4x + y - 3z = 2$
$8x - y + 6z = 3$
$y + 9z = 9$

5. $x + 2y + 3z = 6$
$2x - y + z = 2$
$x + 2y - z = 2$

6. $x - 2y + z = 0$
$x - 3y - z = 3$
$2x + y - 4z = 1$

7. $4x + y - z = 30$
$-x + 2y - z = 7$
$9x - 8y + 4z = -3$

8. $3x - y + 3z = 5$
$x + 7y - 2z = 24$
$5x - 6y + 4z = 9$

9. $x - y + z = -2$
$2x + 3y + z = 8$
$3x + 2y + 2z = 10$

10. $3x - 2y + z = -3$
$x - y - 4z = 7$
$4x - 3y - 3z = 4$

4.5 Writing Exercise

In this section, you were shown how to use the addition method to solve a system of linear equations in three variables. Explain how you might generalize what you have learned to solve a system of linear equations in four variables.

■ Chapter 4 Summary

Vocabulary Review

After completing this chapter, you should be able to define the following key terms.

addition method
consistent
coordinate space
dependent

inconsistent
independent
linear equation in three variables
ordered triple

simultaneous equations
substitution method
system of linear equations in three variables

Fill in the blank with one of the words or phrases listed above.

1. A system with at least one solution is called a _____ system.

2. A system with no solution is called an _____ system.

3. Equations whose graphs coincide are called _____.

4. Equations whose graphs do not coincide are called _____.

5. The solution of a linear equation in three variables is an _____ that satisfies the equation.

Reflections

1. Explain the difference between a solution of a linear equation in two variables and a solution of a system of linear equations in two variables.

2. Describe the method of solving a system of linear equations graphically.

3. What do we mean by an inconsistent system of linear equations?

4. What do we mean by a system of dependent linear equations?

5. What can you say about the solutions of a consistent system of independent linear equations?

6. How do you solve a system of linear equations by using the substitution method?

7. How do you solve a system of linear equations by using the addition method?

8. In solving a system of linear equations algebraically, how do you know that there is no solution? How do you know that there are many solutions?

■ Chapter 4 Section-by-Section Review

4.1

Recall	Examples
Solution of a system of linear equations • An ordered pair that satisfies every equation in the system.	Is $(2, 3)$ a solution of the following system? $x + y = 5$ $2x - y = 1$ Substitute the ordered pair in each equation. $\begin{array}{c c} \underline{x + y = 5} & \underline{2x \quad - y = 1} \\ 2 + 3 \mid 5 & 2(2) - 3 \mid 1 \\ 5 \mid & 4 - 3 \\ & 1 \mid \end{array}$ Since $5 = 5$ and $1 = 1$, the ordered pair $(2, 3)$ satisfies both equations and is a solution of the system.
Solve graphically • Graph the equations in the system. • The solution is the coordinates of the ordered-pair intersection of the graphs.	Solve graphically. $y = -x + 5$ $y = 2x - 1$ Graph each equation. The solution is $(2, 3)$.

Determine whether each ordered pair is a solution of the given system of linear equations.

1. $(2, -4); 3x + 2y = -2$
$\quad\quad 4x - 3y = 20$

2. $(0.25, -0.45); 4x - 5y = 3$
$\quad\quad 8x + 5y = 0$

3. $(7, -2); x + 3y = 13$
$\quad\quad x - y = 5$

4. $\left(\dfrac{2}{3}, \dfrac{2}{3}\right); 3x + 6y = -2$
$\quad\quad 6x - 3y = 6$

5. $(1.5, -2.4); 6x + 5y = -3$
$\quad\quad 2x - 10y = 27$

6. $(-3, 5); x + 5 = 2$
$\quad\quad 2y - 3 = 7$

Solve each system of equations graphically. If the system has infinitely many solutions, describe the solution set.

7. $2x + y = 17$
$\quad y = 3x - 18$

8. $3(x + 2) + 1 = -5$
$\quad 2x - y = -10$

9. $x + 6 = 4$
$\quad 2(y + 2) = y + 3$

10. $x - 2y = -3$
$\quad\quad 2x + 4y = 8$

11. $y = 2(x + 2)$
$\quad 2x - y = 5$

12. $y = \dfrac{3}{2}x - 6$
$\quad 3x - 2y = 12$

13. $y = 3x - 6$
$\quad y = -3$

14. $y = \dfrac{1}{2}x - 3$
$\quad x - 4y = -2$

15. $c(x) = 10x + 150$
$\quad c(x) = 8x + 200$

16. $y - 1 = 4$
$\quad 3y - 2 = 13$

17. $2x + 3y = 6$
$\quad x + y = 1$

18. $y = 2x - 15$
$\quad y = -3x + 10$

19. $y = 2x + 1$
$\quad x = 2y + 7$

20. $5y + 6 = 3y + 5$
$\quad 2(x - 3) + 1 = 4$

Write a system of linear equations to represent each situation, and solve the system graphically.

21. Larry hires a mobile computer repair service to work on his two home computers. The pair who came in charge $125 per hour to work on hardware and software and $30 per hour to work on DSL or dial-up lines. The pair was working at Larry's for 5 hours. He was billed $482.50. Determine how many hours were spent on each type of service.

22. An Internet music service charges $9.80 per month for its service and $0.70 per track to burn a song. Another music service charges $1.00 per song to burn a track plus a monthly listening fee of $5.00. Write and solve a system to determine the number of songs that need to be copied in order to make both offers equal. What should a person budget for Internet music service for this number of songs?

23. Bill plans to remodel his house. He can purchase a nailer for $250 or he can rent the same nailer for $25 for the first 2 days and $5 per day after the first 48 hours. For how many days will the rental cost equal the purchase price?

24. According to the U.S. Bureau of Labor Statistics, the median hourly earnings of workers in the sales industry can be estimated by the function $s(x) = 0.064x + 9.69$, where x is the number of years after 2000. The median hourly earnings of workers in production can be estimated by the function $p(x) = -0.067x + 10.379$, where x is the number of years after 2000. Determine the year in which the median hourly earnings will be the same for both industries.

4.2

Recall	Example
Solve by the substitution method.	Solve by the substitution method.
• Solve one of the equations for a variable	$x + y = 5$
• Substitute the expression found in the first step into the other equation, and solve for the second variable.	$2x - y = 1$
• Substitute the value found for the second variable into one of the original equations, and solve for the remaining variable.	Solve the first equation for y.
	$y = -x + 5$
• The ordered-pair solution is determined by the values obtained for each variable.	Substitute into the second equation and solve.
	$2x - y = 1$
	$2x - (-x + 5) = 1$
	$2x + x - 5 = 1$
	$3x - 5 = 1$
	$3x - 5 + 5 = 1 + 5$
	$3x = 6$
	$\dfrac{3x}{3} = \dfrac{6}{3}$
	$x = 2$
	Substitute into the first equation and solve.
	$x + y = 5$
	$2 + y = 5$
	$2 + y - 2 = 5 - 2$
	$y = 3$
	The solution is $(2, 3)$.

Solve each system of linear equations by the substitution method. If a system has an infinite number of solutions, describe the solution set.

25. $8y = 5$
$4x + 8y = 2$

26. $2x + 2y = 180$
$x = y + 10$

27. $4x - y = 5$
$y = 4x + 3$

28. $x - 2y = 71$
$3x - 7y = 275$

29. $3(x + 2) - y = -1$
$y = 3x + 7$

30. $x + 8y = 5$
$12x + y = 10$

31. $y = \dfrac{1}{3}x - 4$
$x - 5y = 0$

32. $y = \dfrac{1}{2}x + 7$
$y = -\dfrac{3}{5}x - 4$

33. $x + y = 150$
$2.00x + 0.50y = 195.00$

34. $c(x) = 2.50x + 200.00$
$c(x) = 5.00x + 100.00$

Write a system of linear equations to represent each situation, and solve the system by the substitution method.

35. Two angles are complementary. The second angle is 12 degrees more than twice the first angle. What is the difference in the measures of the two angles?

36. The perimeter of a rectangle is 116 feet. If the length is 8 feet more than twice the width, determine the dimensions of the rectangle.

37. Kidsports Store wants to feature a promotion on Razor scooters. The store plans to sell the scooters for $89.95 each, much lower than the normal price of $100 to $150 each. Kidsports can acquire scooters for sale at a cost of $29.00 each. There will be a fixed cost of $450.00 for advertising and floor space during the promotion.

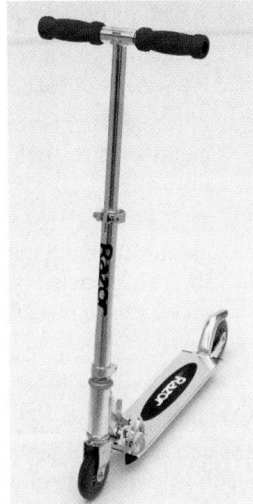

  a. Write a function for the total cost of acquiring scooters, displaying them, and advertising.

  b. Write a function for the total revenue received from selling scooters.

  c. Write a system of equations, and determine the number of scooters that must be acquired and sold to break even.

38. The daily demand for a product is given by $D(p) = 100 - \dfrac{3}{5}p$, where $D(p)$ is the quantity demanded each day by consumers when the price is p dollars per item. The daily supply of the product is given by $S(p) = 20 + \dfrac{2}{5}p$, where $S(p)$ is the quantity supplied each day when the price is p dollars per item. Solve the system to determine the equilibrium point and interpret its meaning.

39. According to data from the U.S. Census Bureau, the population of New Jersey was larger than the population of Georgia in 2001. However, the population of Georgia has increased at a faster rate than the population of New Jersey. Economists have determined that the population of New Jersey can be modeled by the linear function $N(x) = 67x + 8505$, where x is the number of years after 2001 and $N(x)$ is the population in thousands. The population of Georgia can be modeled by the linear function $G(x) = 145x + 8396$, where x is the number of years after 2001 and $G(x)$ is the population in thousands. Determine the year in which the populations of New Jersey and Georgia will be equal. Does the trend shown in the following chart of actual values support your conclusion?

Year	2001	2002	2003
New Jersey	8504	8575	8638
Georgia	8395	8544	8685

4.3

Recall	Example
Solve by the addition method. • Write both equations in standard form. • Determine the least common multiple of the coefficients of the variable to be eliminated. Multiply the members of the equation by a number to obtain coefficients that have the least common multiple and opposite signs. • Add corresponding members of the equations, eliminating one of the variables. • Solve the resulting equation. • Substitute the value obtained into one of the original equations, and solve that equation. • The ordered-pair solution is determined by the values obtained for each variable.	Solve by the addition method. $2x - 3y = 1$ $4x - 5y = 3$ To eliminate the x variable, we need to multiply the first equation by -2 in order to have a coefficient of -4 for x. (1) $\;-2(2x - 3y) = -2(1)$ (2) $\;\;\;\;\;\;4x - 5y = 3$ Add corresponding members. (5) $\;-4x + 6y = -2$ (2) $\;\underline{\;\;4x - 5y = 3\;}$ $\;\;\;\;\;\;\;\;\;\;y = 1$ Substitute into the first equation and solve. (1) $\;\;\;\;\;\;2x - 3y = 1$ $\;\;\;\;\;\;2x - 3(1) = 1$ $\;\;\;\;\;\;2x - 3 = 1$ $\;\;\;2x - 3 + 3 = 1 + 3$ $\;\;\;\;\;\;\;\;\;\;2x = 4$ $\;\;\;\;\;\;\;\;\;\dfrac{2x}{2} = \dfrac{4}{2}$ $\;\;\;\;\;\;\;\;\;\;x = 2$ The solution is $(2, 1)$.

Solve each system of equations by using the addition method. If a system has an infinite number of solutions, describe the solution set.

40. $5x + 3y = -10$
$5x - 3y = 80$

41. $x = 18 - 2y$
$3x + 2y = 30$

42. $\dfrac{1}{2}x + \dfrac{1}{3}y = 3$
$\dfrac{1}{4}x - \dfrac{2}{5}y = -7$

43. $5x + 10y = -55$
$2x - 3y = 6$

44. $2x = 3y + 1$
$15y = 10x + 5$

45. $5x + 7y = 21$
$3x - 2y = 13$

46. $3x + y = 20$
$y = \dfrac{2}{3}x + \dfrac{16}{3}$

47. $7(y - 1) = 5x$
$y = \dfrac{5}{7}x + 1$

48. $3x - 3y = 4$
$9x + 9y = -2$

49. $3x - y = 0$
$2x + 2y = 7$

50. $0.25x + 0.3y = 4$
$0.5x - 0.2y = 4$

51. $0.2x + 0.1y = 5$
$0.02x - 0.01y = 13.5$

Write a system of linear equations to represent each situation, and solve the system by the addition method.

52. According to the *Forbes* magazine Celebrity 100 List, in the year 2004. George Lucas earned 80 million dollars more than Mel Gibson. The combined earnings of the two directors were 475 million dollars. Determine the earnings of each director.

53. A realtor in Chicago is refurbishing a building that is to hold 40 offices. A check of current rates for office rentals indicates that the realtor's competitors are charging about $500 per month for small offices and $1800 per month for large offices. She would like to collect $35,600 per month in rentals

to recover her investment and to make a reasonable profit. How many of each size office should she have?

54. A triangle has two equal angles. The third angle is twice the measure of the equal angles. Determine the measure of the third angle.

55. The mass of the Earth is approximately 5.328×10^{24} kg greater than the mass of the planet Mars. The total mass of the two planets is approximately 6.612×10^{24} kg. Find the mass of each planet.

4.4

Recall	Example
Model a real-world situation. • Read and understand the problem. • Define all variables for the unknown quantities and define other quantities in terms of the defined variables. • Write equations with the information given. • Solve the system. • Check the solution. • In a complete sentence, write an answer to the question asked.	Tony has $20,000 to invest. He wants to diversify his investments by depositing into two accounts, one in mutual bonds at a 7.24% annual interest rate and one in a three-month Treasury bill at a 3.86% annual interest rate. He wants to earn $1279 in interest for one year. Assume that his deposits earn simple interest. How much should Tony deposit in each account? Let x = the amount in mutual bonds at a 7.24% annual rate $\quad y$ = the amount in a three-month Treasury bill at a 3.86% annual rate $\qquad x + y = 20{,}000$ $0.0724x + 0.0386y = 1279$ Solve by any method. The solution is (15,000, 5000). Tony should invest $15,000 in the mutual bonds and $5,000 in the Treasury bill.

Write and solve a system of linear equations for each situation.

56. A plant-food manufacturer wants to blend a fertilizer that is 10% nitrogen with another that is 5% nitrogen to obtain a blend that is 8% nitrogen. If he wants to make 150 pounds of the blend, how many pounds of each component should he use?

57. A food-processing plant is producing frozen vegetables consisting of a mixture of broccoli and cauliflower. The plant will sell the mixture for 69 cents per pound. The plant sells the broccoli separately for 49 cents a pound and the cauliflower for 99 cents per pound. If it wishes to produce 200 pounds of the mixture, how many pounds of each vegetable should be mixed?

58. A trucking company had to send a truck on a delivery 600 miles away. Part of the route was on an interstate highway where the driver drove at 65 mph. The rest was on rural highways where his speed was 45 mph. If the driver made the trip in 10 hours, how many miles did he drive on the interstate?

59. The Buzzards Bay & Vineyard Sound region of Massachusetts has tricky currents that change rapidly and significantly. If a powerboat travels a distance of 20.5 miles with a current for

20 minutes $\left(\frac{1}{3}\text{hour}\right)$ and returns over the same distance in 21 minutes $\left(\frac{7}{20}\text{hour}\right)$, determine the boat's average speed in still water and the average speed of the current. Round your answers to the nearest tenth of a mile per hour.

60. One alloy contains 25% copper and another contains 30% copper. How many pounds of the alloy containing the 25% copper must be combined with 40 pounds of the alloy containing 30% copper to form an alloy that contains 27% copper?

61. Julia invested her salary from her last blockbuster movie in two simple-interest funds. Her salary was $10,000,000. One fund paid 4.5% simple interest, and the other fund paid 6% simple interest. At the end of the year, Julia received a total of $487,500 in interest payments. How much did she invest in each fund?

62. Dorrie makes a sugar solution for her hummingbird feeder by mixing water with a 100% sugar solution that she buys from a birder's catalog. How much water will she need to mix with a cup of the sugar solution to achieve mixture that is 20% sugar? How many cups will she have?

63. Nora traveled 600 miles on a trip. Due to weather conditions, Nora traveled 60 miles per hour and the rest at 30 miles per hour. She estimated that she drove the same amount of time at each speed. How long did it take her to arrive at her destination? How many miles did she travel at each speed?

64. Jordan plans to invest money from his inheritance in two savings bonds. The EE bonds have a fixed rate of 3.25% annual rate, and the I bond has a variable rate that is set for 3.67% annual rate for the next year. If Jordan invests twice as much in the EE bond than the I bond, he will earn $508.50 in simple interest for the year. How much does he plan to invest in each bond?

4.5

Recall	Examples
Solution of a system of linear equations • An ordered triple that satisfies every equation in the system.	Is $(2, 3, -1)$ a solution of the following system? $x + y + z = 4$ $2x - y + z = 0$ $-x + 3y + 2z = 5$ Substitute the ordered triple into each equation. $\begin{array}{c\|c} x + y + z = 4 \\ \hline 2 + 3 + (-1) & 4 \\ 4 & \end{array}$ $\begin{array}{c\|c} 2x - y + z = 0 \\ \hline 2(2) - 3 + (-1) & 0 \\ 4 - 3 - 1 & \\ 0 & \end{array}$ $\begin{array}{c\|c} -x + 3y + 2z = 5 \\ \hline -(2) + 3(3) + 2(-1) & 5 \\ -2 + 9 - 2 & \\ 5 & \end{array}$ Since $4 = 4$, $0 = 0$, and $5 = 5$, the ordered pair $(2, 3, -1)$ satisfies all equations and is a solution of the system.

Solve by the addition method.
• Write all equations in standard form.
• Separate the system into two pairs of equations.
• Eliminate the same variable from each pair of equations.
• Write a system of two variables from the results of the elimination.
• Solve the resulting system of equations.
• Substitute the two values obtained into one of the original equations, and solve that equation for the remaining variable.
• The ordered-triple solution is determined by the values obtained for each variable.
	Solve by the addition method.
	(1) $x + y + z = 4$
	(2) $2x - y + z = 0$
	(3) $-x + 3y + 2z = 5$
	
	Write two pairs of equations.
	(1) $x + y + z = 4$ (2) $2x - y + z = 0$
	(2) $2x - y + z = 0$ (3) $-x + 3y + 2z = 5$
	
	Eliminate the y from each pair.
	(1) $x + y + z = 4$ (2) $3(2x - y + z) = 3(0)$
	(2) $\underline{2x - y + z = 0}$ (3) $-x + 3y + 2z = 5$
	(4) $3x + 2z = 4$
	
	                    (2) $6x - 3y + 3z = 0$
	                    (3) $\underline{-x + 3y + 2z = 5}$
	                    (5) $5x + 5z = 5$
	
	Write a system of two variables and solve by the addition method.
	(4) $-5(3x + 2z) = -5(4)$
	(5) $3(5x + 5z) = 3(5)$
	(4) $-15x - 10z = -20$
	(5) $\underline{15x + 15z = 15}$
	$5z = -5$
	$z = -1$
	(4) $3x + 2z = 4$
	$3x + 2(-1) = 4$
	$3x - 2 = 4$
	$3x = 6$
	$x = 2$

(continued on page 420)

Recall	Examples
	Substitute in an original equation.
	(1) $x + y + z = 4$
	$2 + y + (-1) = 4$
	$y + 1 = 4$
	$y = 3$
	The solution is $(2, 3, -1)$.

Determine whether each ordered triple is a solution of the system.

65. $(3, 4, -2)$

$2x - 3y + 4z = -14$
$5x - 2z = 7$
$3x + 4y = 25$

66. $(0.5, 3.4, -1.2)$

$8x + y + 2z = 5$
$2x - 5y - 5z = -10$
$4x + 2y + 4z = 4$

Solve using the addition method.

67. $4x + y + z = 7$
$x - y + z = 4$
$2x - y + z = 15$

68. $x + y + z = -1$
$x + y - z = 3$
$3y - z = 4$

69. $x + 2y - z = 3$
$3x - y + z = 6$
$2x - 3y + 2z = 3$

70. $x - 3y + 4z = 3$
$4x + y - z = 8$
$3x + 4y - 5z = 5$

Write a system of linear equations in three variables for each situation, and solve the system using the addition method.

71. A charity basketball game charged students $2.50, teachers $5.00, and visitors $7.50 for admission. A total of 140 people attended and $637.50 was raised. The number of students attending was five times the number of teachers. How many of each group attended?

72. Robin had lunch each day at the local deli around the corner from her office. Over a five-day period, she ate sandwiches that had a total fat content of 22 grams, a cholesterol content of 100 mg, and 1446 calories. Her sandwiches were ordered from the following chart:

	Club Sandwich	Veggie Sandwich	Roast Chicken Sandwich
Fat, in grams	5	3	6
Cholesterol in mg	26	0	48
Calories	312	237	348

How many of each sandwich did she eat?

73. A manufacturer of metal wiring is creating a wire that is 42.7% copper. In liquid form a number of ounces of a 35% copper alloy is mixed with a 60% copper alloy and a 30% copper alloy to produce 22 oz of this new metal. The sum of the number of ounces of the 35% and 60% alloys is equal to the number of ounces of the 30% alloy. How many ounces of each type of metal must be used?

74. Kirchhoff's laws yielded the following system of simultaneous equations for an electrical circuit:

$$I_1 - I_2 + I_3 = 0$$
$$2I_1 + 3I_2 = 11$$
$$3I_2 + 4I_3 = 17$$

Solve the system for the three currents, I_1, I_2, and I_3, measured in amperes.

■ Chapter 4 Mixed Review

Solve each system of equations by using the addition method.

1. $y = \frac{4}{7}x + 2$
$x - 3y = 4$

2. $y = \frac{4}{5}x - 6$
$5y + 2 = 4(x - 7)$

3. $1.25x + 3.5y = -25$
$4.5x + 2.8y = 8$

4. $0.55x - 0.68y = 48$
$-0.51x + 0.68y = 0$

5. $8x + 2y = -6$
$6x - 2y = -78$

6. $2x + 8y = -12$
$y = 2x + 3$

7. $3x + y = 4$
$12x + 4y = 9$

8. $3x - 5y = 11$
$4x + 2y = 13$

9. $\frac{1}{3}x - \frac{2}{5}y = 10$
$\frac{1}{2}x + \frac{4}{5}y = -13$

10. $4x + 8y = 68$
$5x - 3y = -6$

11. $2x + y = 0$
$x + 4y = 3$

12. $5x + 3y = 9$
$x - y = 6$

Solve each system of linear equations graphically.

13. $2y + 2 = y$
$\quad y = -x + 1$

14. $2x + 3 = x$
$\quad 2x = 5$

15. $y = 2x + 10$
$\quad 3x + y = -10$

16. $2(x - 1) - 4 = 0$
$\quad 2x + y = 3$

17. $x + y = 9 - x$
$\quad 2x + y = 5$

18. $y = -4x - 3$
$\quad 4x + 2y = y - 3$

19. $3x + 4 = 2x$
$\quad x + 7 = 3$

20. $3y + 7 = 2y + 5$
$\quad y + 9 = 7$

21. $3(x - 3) - 1 = 8$
$\quad 3y - 10 = 15 - 2y$

22. $y = 3x + 7$
$\quad x - y = -1$

23. $x - 5y = 15$
$\quad x + 5y = -5$

24. $y = -4x - 6$
$\quad y = 3x + 8$

25. $y = x$
$\quad x = 2 - y$

26. $x + 9 = 3$
$\quad 3y = 2y - 1$

Solve each system of linear equations by the substitution method.

27. $y = \dfrac{5}{11}x - 43$
$\quad x + 2y = -2$

28. $y = \dfrac{3}{4}x + 14$
$\quad y = -\dfrac{2}{3}x - 3$

29. $2x + 3y = 53$
$\quad 2x - 4y = -248$

30. $y = 4x - 7$
$\quad 2y + 12 = 4x + y + 5$

31. $y = -5x$
$\quad x - y = 1$

32. $5x - 10y = 21$
$\quad 5x = -3$

33. $x + 7y = 3$
$\quad 4x + y = 9$

34. $5x + 6y = 669$
$\quad x - 2y = 1705$

35. $x - y = 5$
$\quad 6x + 2y = 9$

36. $x = 324y$
$\quad 3x - 810y = 90$

37. $y = -2x + 7$
$\quad 2x + y = 0$

38. $2x - y = 60$
$\quad 5x - 3y = 60$

Determine whether each ordered pair is a solution of the given system of linear equations.

39. $\left(\dfrac{5}{6}, -\dfrac{1}{6}\right); 4x + 2y = 3$
$\quad\quad\quad\quad x - y = -1$

40. $(-1.6, 3.8); 3x + y = -1$
$\quad\quad\quad\quad 5x + 5y = 11$

41. $(-4, 2); 5x + 7y = -6$
$\quad\quad\quad\quad 2x - 7y = -22$

42. $\left(\dfrac{13}{9}, -\dfrac{4}{9}\right); x + y = 1$
$\quad\quad\quad\quad 8x - y = 12$

43. $(3, -2); 2x - 1 = 5$
$\quad\quad\quad\quad 3y + 5 = 2$

44. $(-5, -3); x + 10 = 5$
$\quad\quad\quad\quad 3y + 11 = 2$

45. $(-0.44, 1.22); x + 2y = 2$
$\quad\quad\quad\quad\quad 2x + 4y = 5$

46. $(-2, -3); 2x + 5y = -19$
$\quad\quad\quad\quad 3x - 7y = 10$

Write and solve a system of linear equations for each situation.

47. An alloy containing 15% brass is to be combined with an alloy containing 35% brass to form an alloy containing 27% brass. How much of each alloy should be combined to make 200 pounds of the 27% brass alloy? How much more of the 35% alloy will be used than of the 15% alloy?

48. Two-cycle gasoline engines run on a fuel mixture that has a gasoline concentration of 98%. If pure gasoline is used, parts are not lubricated and the engine will seize. Oil must be added to achieve the appropriate concentration. Martin has 5 gallons of pure gasoline. How much oil should he add to it to achieve a 98% gasoline concentration? How many gallons of fuel will he have?

49. Two angles are supplementary. The second angle must measure 10 degrees more than the first angle. What does the smaller angle measure?

50. A survey of 700 people was conducted. Forty percent of the men surveyed supported the issue in question, while 70 percent of the women favored it. A total of 400 people favored the issue. How many more women than men were surveyed?

51. Two angles are complementary. One angle measures 12 degrees more than three times the other angle. Find the measures of the angles.

52. A chemist wants to mix a solution containing 15% sulfuric acid with 18 cc of a solution containing 25% sulfuric acid to make a mixture that is 21% sulfuric acid. How much of the 15% concentration should she use? How many cc's of the mixture will she have?

53. Carter and Michelle are considering two bands for entertainment at their wedding reception. One band, DJam, charges $1000 for setup and $200 per hour. The other, WillRock, asks for $4000 up front and returns $300 per hour for every hour they perform up to a maximum of eight hours. They find that asking for the money in advance prevents customers from canceling. Use a system of equations to determine the number of hours that makes the cost for both bands equal.

54. A coffee shop blends gourmet coffee, which sells for $8.50 per pound, with gourmet Dutch chocolate, which sells for $12.50 per pound. The shop makes a mocha blend that sells for $9.50 per pound. How much coffee should be mixed with how much chocolate to make 50 pounds of the blend?

55. Nikki has been offered two part-time jobs while she attends college. One job pays $10.75 per hour and requires her to work on a production line. The other pays $6.50 per hour as a night clerk and allows her to spend her time studying. She can work a total of 20 hours per week without affecting her studies. She wants to earn exactly $181.00 per week to pay for room and board. How many hours should she work on each job to meet her requirements?

56. A United Airlines flight departs Boston's Logan International Airport and arrives in Los Angeles 5 hours and 45 minutes later. During the same time frame, a United Airlines flight departs Los Angeles International Airport and arrives in Boston 5 hours later. Assuming that the planes travel at the same average speed in still air, determine that average speed, as well as the average speed of the wind caused by the jet stream. The distance between the two cities is 2600 miles.

57. U Rent It will lease a moving van for $39.95 plus $0.15 per mile. Budget Haul It will lease the same type of van for $19.95 plus $0.22 per mile. How many miles must you drive in order for the U Rent It deal to be the less costly choice?

58. A shopkeeper has fixed costs of $75.00 per day and material costs of $2.50 per item produced and sold. The items sell for $6.50 each. How many items must the shopkeeper produce and sell each day in order to break even?

59. Two friends plan to meet at a location between their homes to exchange books. The distance between their homes is 545 miles. If one drives 55 miles per hour and the other averages 60 miles per hour, how long will it take them to meet if they leave at the same time?

60. Sharon inherits $25,000 from her uncle. She decides to invest the money in two different accounts. One account pays 5.6% annually and she can withdraw money from it at any time. The other is a money market fund in which she will leave money without withdrawal for five years. The money market account pays 7.85% annually. Sharon's yearly simple interest income from these accounts is $1580. How much is invested at each rate?

61. Petra plans to invest money from her inheritance in two savings bonds. The EE bonds have a fixed rate of 3.25% annual rate, and the I bond has a variable rate that is set for a 3.67% annual rate for the next year. If she invests twice as much in the I bond than the EE bond, she will earn $529.50 simple interest for the year. How much does she plan to invest in each bond?

62. The daily demand for a product is given by $D(p) = 75 - \dfrac{3}{5}p$, where $D(p)$ is the quantity demanded each day by consumers when the price is p dollars per item. The daily supply of the product is given by $S(p) = 10 + \dfrac{2}{5}p$, where $S(p)$ is the quantity supplied each day when the price is p dollars per item. Solve the system to determine the equilibrium point and interpret its meaning.

63. Nathan has the option of two plans for a small boat rental. One plan charges $150 plus $2 per day. His second choice is $100 for 2 days and $5 per day over the two-day limit. Determine the number of days that Nathan can rent the boat for the plans to be equal.

In exercises 64 and 65, solve the system of equations.

64. $x + y + z = 23$
$2x - y + z = -11$
$x + 3y - z = 5$

65. $x + 2y + z = -1$
$x - 2y - 2z = 5$
$x + 6y + z = 2$

66. Using Kirchhoff's laws on an electrical circuit yields the following system of simultaneous equations:

$$I_1 - I_2 - I_3 = 0$$
$$3I_1 + 4I_2 = 18.5$$
$$4I_2 - 6I_3 = -1$$

Solve the system for the three currents, I_1, I_2, and I_3, measured in amperes.

67. Matthew ate fast-food lunches all last week. He selected sandwiches from the following table:

	Turkey Breast	Ham	Hamburger
Fat	4 grams	5 grams	39 grams
Cholesterol	19 mg	28 mg	90 mg
Calories	289 calories	302 calories	640 calories

His total fat intake from the sandwiches was 92 grams, his total cholesterol intake was 255 mg, and his total calories were 2173. How many of each sandwich did he eat?

68. To maintain his backyard pool Matt needs to keep the chemicals in balance. He uses algicide, shock, and a sanitizer. Each week he adds 7.25 pints of chemical ingredients to his pool. The amount of shock is 1 pint more than four times the amount of algicide, and the amount of shock is also 1 pint less than twice the amount of sanitizer. How many pints of each chemical should he use weekly?

■ Chapter 4 Test

A^+

TEST-TAKING TIPS

Having the right attitude can make the difference between successfully completing a test and failing to do so. Students who say "I've always hated mathematics" or "I've never been good at math" often defeat themselves before they start. Start thinking about ways in which you can overcome "math inability." Pay attention to detail. Don't rush through arithmetic calculations. Check your addition and subtraction. When allowed, repeat the calculation on your calculator. Develop a persistent "don't quit" attitude. Tell yourself that you won't stop working on the test until the time is up. If you are stuck on a problem, start writing on paper what you know. Sometimes the act of writing will unleash thoughts in your mind that will help you solve a problem. Take pleasure in the math exercises you *can* do. This alone may improve your attitude, build up your confidence, and cause you to think more clearly on the test.

1. Determine whether the ordered pair is a solution of the given system of equations.

$$(22.8, -64.3); y = -3.5x + 15.5$$
$$15x + 10y = -301$$

Solve each system of equations graphically.

2. $2y - 8 = 0$
$y = 4$

3. $y = \dfrac{1}{2}x + 3$

$y = \dfrac{1}{2}x - 5$

4. $y = 5x - 9$
$4x + 8y = 16$

Solve each system of equations by the substitution method.

5. $x + 2y = 6$
$5x - 11y = -54$

6. $3x + 6y = 12$
$x + 2y = -5$

7. $x + 6y = -2$
$x - 2y = 1$

Solve each system of equations by the addition method.

8. $3x + 7y = 11$
$6x + 14y = 2$

9. $2x + 9y = 16$
$5y = 8 - x$

10. $5x + 3y = 11$
$2x + 5y = 7$

Write and solve a system of equations for the information given.

11. A factory has a setup cost of $5500 and a cost per item of $65 each to produce. The items sell for $125 each.
   a. Write a function for the total cost of producing the items.
   b. Write a function for the total revenue received for selling the items.
   c. Write a system of equations, and determine the number of items that must be produced and sold to break even.

12. It took Kenny 3 hours to pedal a tandem bicycle built for two to where Dolly was waiting. Dolly's pedaling increased their speed by 4 mph, and the return trip took them only 2 hours. How fast could Kenny pedal alone, and how far did he have to go to find Dolly?

13. A high-speed computer takes 58 nanoseconds to perform six addition and eight multiplication operations. It takes 55 nanoseconds to perform ten additions and five multiplications. How many nanoseconds does the computer take to perform one addition? How many nanoseconds for one multiplication?

14. A candy shop owner is mixing chocolate-covered raisins selling at $1.25 per pound with chocolate-covered peanuts, which sell for $2.00 per pound. He makes a mix to sell at $1.50 per pound. How many pounds of each should he mix in order to make 30 pounds of the mix?

15. Jody has the option of two health club plans. One plan charges $50.00 per month plus a $0.50 towel charge per visit. The club offers another pay-as-you-come plan. The monthly charge is $10.00 for the first two visits and $3.00 per visit after the two visits. Determine the number of visits in which the two plans are equal.

16. A chemist needs 100 cc of a 30% nitric acid solution. She has a 50% solution and a 10% solution in stock. How many cc of each must she mix in order to make the required solution?

17. Two angles are supplementary. One angle is 15 degrees more than twice the other angle. Determine the measure of each angle.

18. Caitlin's investment broker recommended that she invest money in two mutual funds. Mutual Fund A has been earning 9.5% dividends per year, and Mutual Fund B has been earning 7% dividends per year. In order to split her risks over the two funds, Caitlin's broker advises her against putting all her money into one of them. Cailtin wants to invest twice as much in the mutual fund A account than in the mutual fund B account. She would like to realize a total dividend of $780 at the end of the year. How much should she invest in each fund to achieve her goal?

19. Tommy drives his motorboat 36 miles upriver for 36 minutes $\left(\dfrac{3}{5}\text{hour}\right)$ and returns to his starting point in 30 minutes. Determine the average speed of his boat in still water and the average speed of the river current.

20. Mary plans to invest her $15,000 inheritance in two savings bonds. The EE bonds have a fixed rate of 3.25% annual rate and the I bond has a variable rate that is set for 3.67% annual rate for the next year. If she wants to earn $500 simple interest for a trip, how much does she plan to invest in each bond?

21. The owner of Kennel Land agreed to meet a customer at a location between their homes, a distance of 700 miles. He agreed to drive the same length of time that the customer did. If he averages 60 miles per hour and the customer averages 65 miles per hour, at what distance from the kennel should they plan to meet?

In exercises 22 and 23, solve the system of equations.

22. $5x - y + 4z = -1$
$3y + 4z = 0$
$10x - 7y = 0$

23. $3x - 2y + z = -4$
$x - y - z = 3$
$2x - y + 2z = -7$

4 hours to make each table. In a 40-hour work week, Mike spends a total of $29 on materials, and the number of feeders he makes is one more than the number of tables. How many of each item does Mike make each week?

24. Mike makes bird feeders, birdhouses, and snack tables to sell at craft shows. He spends $2.00 on materials for each feeder, $1.50 for each house, and $3.00 for each table. It takes him 3 hours to make each feeder, 2 hours to make each house, and

25. In solving a system of linear equations, one of three outcomes can occur. List the three outcomes, and explain how you would identify them if you were solving the system of equations by means of the graphical method.

4

Project

In this chapter, we discussed the effect of the wind resistance of the jet stream on the velocity of an airplane. In this project, we will track two airplanes in flight traveling between the east coast and the west coast of the United States. A possible choice is to and from Atlanta, Georgia, and Los Angeles, California.

PART I   In order to track a flight in progress,

1. Go to the *www.flightview.com* Web site.

2. Choose "Travel Tools."

3. Choose "Option 2: Track Flights by Cities and Times."

4. Choose an airport on the east coast for the departure, an airport on the west coast for the arrival, and a departure time. When selecting a departure time, remember that there is a three-hour difference between the east coast and west coast time zones. You may have to select several times before you obtain a flight in progress.

5. Record the information from the Web site in the first row of the table in step 7.

6. Choose the same airport on the west coast for the departure, the same airport on the east coast for the arrival, and a departure time. When selecting a departure time, remember that there is a three-hour difference between the east coast and west coast time zones. You may have to select several times before you obtain a flight in progress.

7. Record the information from the Web site in the second row of the following table:

8. Determine the distance (as the crow flies) in miles between the two cities.

9. Use the following guidelines to determine the flight time:
   - The time taken to travel from the east coast to the west coast is three hours more than the difference of Eastern time and Pacific time.
   - The time taken to travel from the west coast to the east coast is three hours less than the difference of Eastern time and Pacific time.
   - Write the time as a mixed number. Fractions of an hour can be determined by dividing the number of minutes by 60.

10. Use the distance-traveled formula, $d = rt$, to write a system of equations. Solve the system to determine the average speed of the airplane in flight and the average speed of the wind, assuming that the jet stream is flowing from west to east. Round the speeds to the nearest whole number.

11. Average speeds and ground (instantaneous) speeds are not always the same. Compare the average speed of the airplane and the instantaneous speed of the airplane recorded in step 7. Note that our average speed is in miles per hour. To convert knots to miles per hour, multiply the number of knots by 1.15 because 1 knot = 1.15 miles per hour. If these numbers are different, explain why.

PART II   The point of no return for an aircraft is the point in its flight when the time needed to complete the flight is equal to the time needed to return to the plane's point of origin.

1. For the flight from the east coast to the west coast, write a system of equations needed to determine the time for the point of no return and the distance from the plane's origin. (*Hint:* Let x be the distance from the plane's origin in miles and y be the time in hours of the point of no return.) Sketch a diagram to illustrate this situation.

2. Determine the time of the point of no return for the trip from the west coast to the east coast and the distance the point is from the plane's origin.

3. Compare the locations of the point of no return for each flight.

Airline and Flight	Airport	Actual Time	Status	Altitude	Ground Speed in Knots	Equipment
	Departing					
	Arriving					
	Departing					
	Arriving					

Linear Inequalities

In the last few chapters, we studied several ways to solve equations. But sometimes it is useful to work with relations in which one quantity is not necessarily equal to some other quantity. Instead, it can be helpful to know that an algebraic expression is simply less than or greater than some other one. In Chapter P, we briefly discussed such inequalities.

In this chapter, we will examine linear inequalities and methods of solving them. We will discuss linear inequalities in one variable and in two variables and systems of linear inequalities in two variables. We will see that the same methods used for solving equations—numeric, graphic, and algebraic—work for solving inequalities as well.

Linear inequalities are important in many areas of practical mathematics. In this chapter we will encounter linear inequalities in the areas of science and medicine. We will also use them to determine the range of scores needed to obtain a final grade average.

Keeping within a budget is a familiar and important application of inequalities, both in large businesses and in our personal lives. We will look at several ways of describing costs and budgets in this chapter and show how to solve some kinds of budgetary problems. In the final project for this chapter, you will be asked to set up a small business venture and determine the number of items you must produce and sell to achieve at least a given profit.

425

5.1 LINEAR INEQUALITIES IN ONE VARIABLE

OBJECTIVES
1. Identify linear inequalities in one variable.
2. Solve linear inequalities in one variable numerically.
3. Solve linear inequalities in one variable graphically.
4. Solve linear inequalities in one variable algebraically.
5. Model real-world situations by using linear inequalities in one variable, and solve the inequalities.

APPLICATION

The body mass index (BMI) is a measure of weight that takes height into account. The BMI of a person 62 inches tall and weighing x pounds is given by the expression $0.2x - 2$. A doctor may prescribe a certain drug if a person has a BMI of 30 or greater. Determine the weights for which a doctor may prescribe this drug for a person 62 inches in height.

After completing this section, we will discuss this application further. See page 439.

Objective 5.1.1 | **Linear Inequalities in One Variable**

In this chapter, we will be solving inequalities of various forms. In this section, we will solve linear inequalities in one variable. A **linear inequality in one variable** (sometimes shortened simply to **linear inequality**) is written by replacing the equals symbol in a linear equation in one variable with an order symbol. The **order symbols** are "greater than" ($>$), "less than" ($<$), "greater than or equal to" ($\geq$), and "less than or equal to" ($\leq$).

STANDARD FORM FOR A LINEAR INEQUALITY IN ONE VARIABLE

A linear inequality in one variable is an inequality in standard form that can be written in one of the following ways:

$$ax + b < 0$$
$$ax + b > 0$$
$$ax + b \geq 0$$
$$ax + b \leq 0$$

where a and b are real numbers and $a \neq 0$.

For example, we might have the following inequalities:

1. $2x + 5 < 0$ Standard form: $ax + b < 0$

2. $2x - 5 < 6$ Not standard form

3. $x + 2 + 3(x - 4) < 3x - 8$ Not standard form

The first inequality is in standard form $ax + b < 0$. The other inequalities can be written in this form with algebraic manipulations that we will learn later in the section.

Note that in a linear inequality, the variable is raised to the first power. An example of a nonlinear inequality, which we will solve later in the text, is $2x^2 - 4 < 0$.

Until we learn algebraic manipulations for inequalities, we will identify a linear inequality in one variable, x, as an inequality consisting of two expressions. Each of these expressions can be simplified to the form $ax + b$, where $a \neq 0$ in at least one of the expressions and the coefficient a is not the same in each expression. Using the previous linear examples, we obtain these inequalities:

$$ax + b \qquad ax + b$$

1. $\qquad 2x + 5 < 0x + 0$

2. $\quad 2x + (-5) < 0x + 6$

3. $4x + (-10) < 3x + (-8)$

EXAMPLE 1

Identify each inequality as linear or nonlinear.

a. $5x + (x - 2) > 3(x - 2)$ 　　　　　　**b.** $x + 5 < x^3 - 2x$

c. $\sqrt[4]{x + 2} \geq 3x - 7$

Solution

a. Linear, because the inequality simplifies to $6x + (-2) > 3x + (-6)$.

b. Nonlinear, because the variable x has an exponent of 3.

c. Nonlinear, because the radical expression contains a variable. ▪

✓ Objective 5.1.1 *CHECKUP*

1. Identify each inequality as linear or nonlinear.

　a. $6x - (3x + 2) < 4(x - 1)$

　b. $\sqrt[3]{x} + 3 \leq 5x + 1$

　c. $\dfrac{1}{x} + 3x \geq 2x - 1$

2. What is the difference between a linear equation in one variable and a linear inequality in one variable?

3. How can you decide whether an inequality in one variable is a linear inequality?

Objective 5.1.2

Solving Linear Inequalities Numerically

In previous chapters, we determined whether a number was a solution of an equation by substituting the number for the variable and evaluating the two resulting expressions. If the expressions were equivalent, then the number substituted was called the solution.

We determine a solution of a linear inequality by using the same method of substituting and evaluating. However, we need to determine whether the resulting inequality is true. For example, determine whether 0 is a solution of $2x + 3 \geq x + 5$.

$$\begin{array}{c|c} \multicolumn{2}{c}{2x + 3 \geq x + 5} \\ \hline 2(0) + 3 & 0 + 5 \\ 3 & 5 \end{array}$$

The number 0 is not a solution, because the resulting inequality, $3 \geq 5$, is not true.

To find a solution of the inequality, $2x + 3 \geq x + 5$, we continue to substitute values for x until we find a number that results in a true inequality. To do this, it is convenient to use a table, as we did when solving equations numerically.

SOLVING A LINEAR INEQUALITY IN ONE VARIABLE NUMERICALLY

To solve a linear inequality numerically,
　Set up an extended table of values.

- The first column is labeled with the name of the independent variable.
- The second column is labeled with the expression on the left side of the inequality.
- The third column is labeled with the expression on the right side of the inequality.

(continued on page 428)

Complete the table.

- Substitute values for the independent variable.
- Evaluate the second and third columns.
- Continue evaluating until the values for the two expressions (the numbers in the second and third columns) result in a true inequality.

The values for the independent variable (the numbers in the first column) used to determine a true inequality are solutions of the inequality.

 TAKE NOTE Not all solutions may be found numerically. We are limited to those numbers substituted for the independent variable.

EXAMPLE 2   Solve numerically $2x + 3 \geq x + 5$ for integer solutions.

Solution

The following is a sample table for determining the integer solutions:

x	$2x + 3$	$x + 5$	
0	$2(0) + 3$ 3	$0 + 5$ 5	$3 \not\geq 5$
1	$2(1) + 3$ 5	$1 + 5$ 6	$5 \not\geq 6$
2	$2(2) + 3$ 7	$2 + 5$ 7	$7 \geq 7$
3	$2(3) + 3$ 9	$3 + 3$ 6	$9 \geq 6$

According to the table, when 2 is substituted for the variable x, the resulting inequality is true ($7 \geq 7$). Therefore, 2 is a solution of the linear inequality $2x + 3 \geq x + 5$. When 3 is substituted for x, the resulting inequality also is true ($9 \geq 6$). Therefore, 3 is a solution of the linear inequality $2x + 3 \geq x + 5$. If the table is extended further, more integer solutions will be found. In fact, all integers completing the obvious pattern will result in true inequalities. Therefore, all integers greater than or equal to 2 will be solutions of the inequality.

The table results in only integer solutions, not all solutions. We could have included noninteger solutions, but it would still be impossible to include all solutions.

To solve $2x + 3 \geq x + 5$ numerically on your calculator, set up the table as shown in **Figure 5.1a**, **Figure 5.1b**, and **Figure 5.1c**. The integer solutions are all integers greater than or equal to 2.

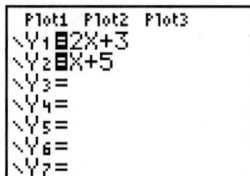

Figure 5.1a

Figure 5.1b

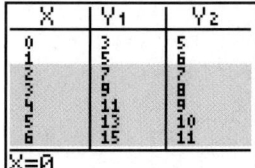

Figure 5.1c

 TAKE NOTE Although not resulting in all solutions, the numerical method may be used as a visualization to check other methods.

✓ Objective 5.1.2 **CHECKUP**

1. Solve numerically for integer solutions. $2x - 5 < 4x - 3$

2. What are the limitations of solving a linear inequality numerically?

Objective 5.1.3   Solving Linear Inequalities Graphically

A second and more inclusive method of solving a linear inequality is to graph two functions. The functions to be graphed are written by using the expression on the left side of the inequality as a rule for the first function and the expression on the right side as a rule for the second function. For example, for the inequality $2x + 3 \leq x + 5$, we write the two functions $y_1 = 2x + 3$ and $y_2 = x + 5$. We then determine the solutions of the inequality $y_1 \leq y_2$. Let's explore this method on the graphing calculator. Complete the following set of exercises on your calculator.

💡 Guided Discovery 1   Graphical Solutions of a "Less Than" Linear Inequality in One Variable

To determine the solutions of the inequality $2x + 3 \leq x + 5$, graph the functions Y1 = $2x + 3$ and Y2 = $x + 5$. Sketch the graphs. Label the point of intersection of the graphs.

1. The intersection of the two graphs is _____.

2. The solution that corresponds to the equality is _____.

For exercise 3, choose the correct answer.

3. To solve a "less than" inequality, Y1 < Y2, locate the portion of the Y1 graph *above/below* the Y2 graph. When tracing the graph of Y1, you will find that this is to the *left/right* of the intersection. The *x*-coordinates of the points in this direction are *less than/greater than* the *x*-coordinate of the point of intersection.

4. Combining the solutions found for the equality and the "less than," we determine that the solution set is _____.

The solution set of the inequality $2x + 3 \leq x + 5$ consists of the *x*-coordinate of the point of intersection and the *x*-coordinates of the points to the left of the intersection. Written as an inequality, the solutions are all *x* that satisfy $x \leq 2$.

Correspondingly, we can solve the inequality $2x + 3 \geq x + 5$ graphically. Complete the following set of exercises on your calculator.

💡 Guided Discovery 2   Graphical Solutions of a "Greater Than" Linear Inequality in One Variable

To determine the solutions of the inequality $2x + 3 \geq x + 5$, graph the functions Y1 = $2x + 3$ and Y2 = $x + 5$. Sketch the graph. Label the point of intersection of the graphs.

1. The intersection of the two graphs is _____.

2. The solution that corresponds to the equality is _____.

For exercise 3, choose the correct answer.

3. To solve a "greater than" inequality, Y1 > Y2, locate the portion of the Y1 graph *above/below* the Y2 graph. When tracing the graph of Y1, you will find that this is to the *left/right* of the intersection. The *x*-coordinates of the points in this direction are *less than/greater than* the *x*-coordinate of the point of intersection.

4. Combining the solutions found for the equality and the "greater than," we determine that the solution set is _____.

The solution set of the inequality $2x + 3 \geq x + 5$ consists of the *x*-coordinate of the point of intersection and the *x*-coordinates of the points to the right of the intersection. Written as an inequality, the solution set is all *x* that satisfy $x \geq 2$.

SOLVING A LINEAR INEQUALITY IN ONE VARIABLE GRAPHICALLY

To solve a linear inequality graphically,

- Write two functions, y_1 and y_2, using the expressions on the left and right sides of the inequality, respectively.
- Graph both functions on the same coordinate plane.
- Determine the intersection, if it exists, of the y_1 and y_2 graphs.
- Locate the portion of the y_1 graph below the y_2 graph if the inequality is "less than." Locate the portion of the y_1 graph above the y_2 graph if the inequality is "greater than."
- Determine the x-coordinates for this portion of the graph.
  - If the portion is to the left of the intersection, then x is less than the x-coordinate of the intersection.
  - If the portion is to the right of the intersection, then x is greater than the x-coordinate of the intersection.

The solution set includes either x-values less than or x-values greater than the x-coordinate of the point of intersection. The solution set also includes the x-coordinate of the point of intersection if the inequality includes equality.

EXAMPLE 3

Solve graphically $2x + 3 > x + 5$. Check numerically.

Solution

Graph $y_1 = 2x + 3$ and $y_2 = x + 5$.

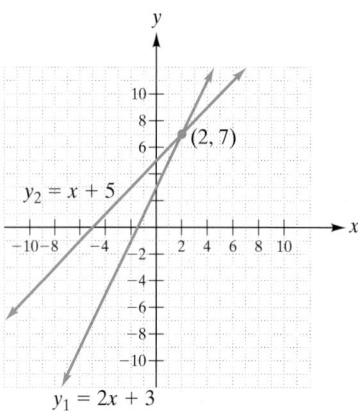   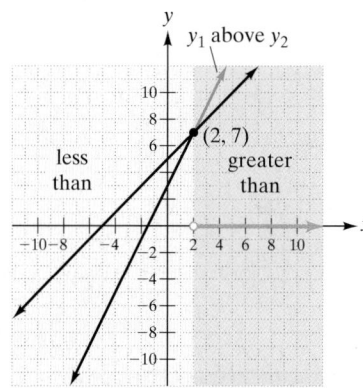

The intersection of the lines is $(2, 7)$. We do not include the x-coordinate of the intersection in the solution, because the inequality does not include equality.

The inequality is "greater than," so the graph of y_1 is above the graph of y_2, to the right of the point of intersection. This is interpreted as an inequality: x is greater than the x-coordinate of the intersection, 2.

The solution set is all x that satisfy $x > 2$.

The graphic and numeric check is shown in **Figure 5.2b** and **Figure 5.2c**. The solution set is all x that satisfy $x > 2$.

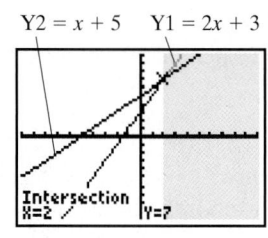

$(-10, 10, -10, 10)$

Figure 5.2a

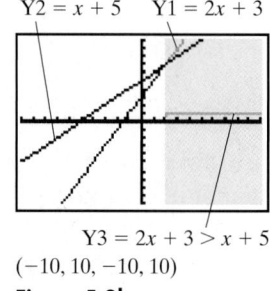

$(-10, 10, -10, 10)$

Figure 5.2b

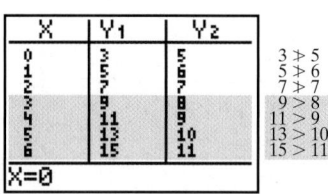

$Y1 = 2x + 3$ $Y2 = x + 5$

Figure 5.2c

EXAMPLE 4   Solve graphically. Check numerically.

a. $6x - (4x + 8) \le 7 - 3x$

b. $(5x + 4) - 2(3x + 1) \ge 2(x - 7)$

Calculator/Graphic Solution   **Check**

a.

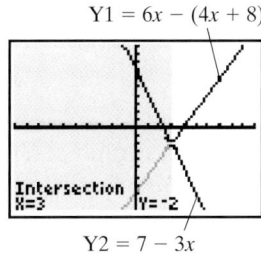

$Y1 = 6x - (4x + 8)$
Intersection X=3 Y=-2
$Y2 = 7 - 3x$
$(-10, 10, -10, 10)$

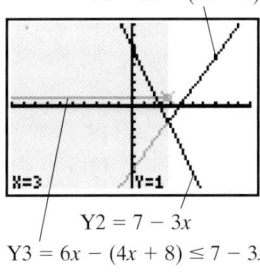

$Y1 = 6x - (4x + 8)$
X=3 Y=1
$Y2 = 7 - 3x$
$Y3 = 6x - (4x + 8) \le 7 - 3x$
$(-10, 10, -10, 10)$

X	Y1	Y2
0	-8	7
1	-6	4
2	-4	1
3	-2	-2
4	0	-5
5	2	-8
6	4	-11

X=0

$-8 \le 7$
$-6 \le 4$
$-4 \le 1$
$-2 \le -2$
$0 \ne -5$
$2 \ne -8$
$4 \ne -11$

$Y1 = 6x - (4x + 8)$
$Y2 = 7 - 3x$

The intersection of the graphs is $(3, -2)$. The inequality is "less than," so we locate the portion of the graph of Y1 that is below the graph of Y2. These points are to the left of the point of intersection and make up the area where x is less than 3. The solution includes the x-coordinate of the point of intersection, because the inequality includes equality. The solution set is all x that satisfy $x \le 3$.

b. $(5x + 4) - 2(3x + 1) \ge 2(x - 7)$ does not have an integer-value intersection. The Trace function will not locate the intersection, so we use Intersect under the CALC function.

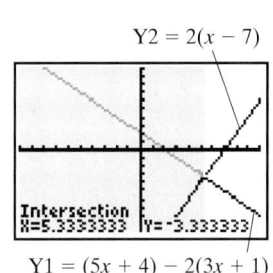

$Y2 = 2(x - 7)$
Intersection X=5.3333333 Y=-3.333333
$Y1 = (5x + 4) - 2(3x + 1)$
$(-10, 10, -10, 10)$

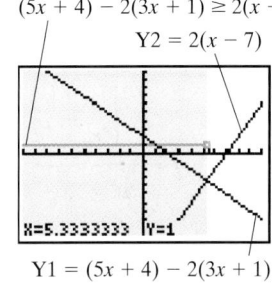

$(5x + 4) - 2(3x + 1) \ge 2(x - 7)$
$Y2 = 2(x - 7)$
X=5.3333333 Y=1
$Y1 = (5x + 4) - 2(3x + 1)$
$(-10, 10, -10, 10)$

X	Y1	Y2
2	0	-10
3	-1	-8
4	-2	-6
5	-3	-4
6	-4	-2
7	-5	0
8	-6	2

X=2

$0 \ge -10$
$-1 \ge -8$
$-2 \ge -6$
$-3 \ge -4$
$-4 \ne -2$
$-5 \ne 0$
$-6 \ne 2$

$Y1 = (5x + 4) - 2(3x + 1)$
$Y2 = 2(x - 7)$

The intersection of the two graphs is $(5.\overline{3}, -3.\overline{3})$ or $\left(\frac{16}{3}, \frac{-10}{3}\right)$. The Y1 graph is above the Y2 graph to the left of the point of intersection. The solution includes the x-coordinate of the intersection point. Note in the numeric check that the solution set is all integer values for x less than or equal to 5. This check does not show the entire solution set. The solution set is all x that satisfy $x \le \frac{16}{3}$. ∎

Remember from Chapter 2 that linear equations may have no solution or may have all-real-number solutions. The same is true for linear inequalities. Graphically solving linear inequalities can result in either of these possibilities.

EXAMPLE 5   Solve graphically.

a. $4(x - 2) < 4x + 10$

b. $3x + 4 \ge 2x + (x + 10)$

c. $2a + 12 \le 2(a + 3) + 6$

Calculator/Graphic Solution

a. Y2 = 4x + 10

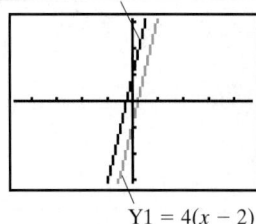

Y1 = 4(x − 2)

(−47, 47, −31, 31)

The graphs are parallel, and the graph of Y1 is always below the graph of Y2. Since the inequality is "less than," the entire Y1 graph will determine solutions of the inequality. The solution set is all real numbers.

b. Y2 = 2x + (x + 10)

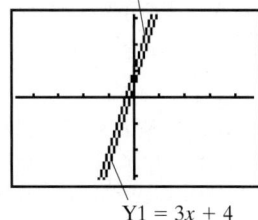

Y1 = 3x + 4

(−47, 47, −31, 31)

The graphs are parallel, and the graph of Y1 is always below the graph of Y2. Since the inequality is "greater than" and the Y1 graph will not have any points above the Y2 graph, the inequality has no solution.

c. Change the variables to x.

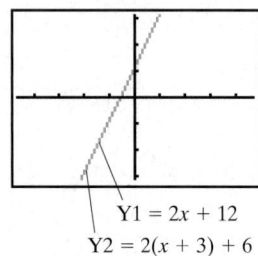

Y1 = 2x + 12
Y2 = 2(x + 3) + 6

(−47, 47, −31, 31)

The graphs are the same line. Since the inequality includes an equals sign, all ordered pairs on the line will determine solutions of the inequality. The solution set is the set of all real numbers.

 TAKE NOTE If the inequality in example **5c** did not include an equals sign, no ordered pair would satisfy the inequality, so it would have no solution. ■

GRAPHICAL SOLUTIONS OF LINEAR INEQUALITIES IN ONE VARIABLE

In solving a linear inequality graphically where Y1 equals the expression on the left side of the inequality and Y2 equals the expression on the right side of the inequality, one of three possibilities will occur.

1. A solution set exists.

2. No solution exists.

This occurs for the following conditions:

Y1 < Y2, and the graph of Y1 is the same as Y2 or always above Y2.
Y1 > Y2, and the graph of Y1 is the same as Y2 or always below Y2.
Y1 ≤ Y2, and the graph of Y1 is always above Y2.
Y1 ≥ Y2, and the graph of Y1 is always below Y2.

3. A solution set of all real numbers exists.
This occurs for the following conditions:

Y1 < Y2, and the graph of Y1 is always below Y2.
Y1 > Y2, and the graph of Y1 is always above Y2.
Y1 ≤ Y2, and the graph of Y1 is the same as Y2 or always below Y2.
Y1 ≥ Y2, and the graph of Y1 is the same as Y2 or always above Y2.

✓ Objective 5.1.3 *CHECKUP*

In exercises 1 and 2, solve graphically. Check numerically.

1. $2x - 5 > 4x - 3$
2. a. $5z + 2 \le 3z$
    b. $3(2x - 1) - (2x + 4) < 2(x - 2) + 2$
3. Solve graphically
    a. $3(x + 2) - 4(2x + 1) > 3(2 - x) + 2(1 - x)$
    b. $3x - (2x + 5) \ge (x + 2) - 7$
    c. $\frac{1}{2}x + 2 > x - \left(\frac{1}{2}x + 1\right)$

4. Explain how you would solve a linear inequality graphically.

5. How would you know from the graphic solution that the solution set is a part of the number line?

6. How would you know from the graphic solution that the solution set is the entire number line or that there is no solution?

Objective 5.1.4   Solving Linear Inequalities Algebraically

To solve a linear equation algebraically, we used the addition and multiplication properties of equations. To solve a linear inequality algebraically, we will need to know similar properties of inequalities. First, let's see if an addition property of inequalities exists. Complete the following set of exercises.

Guided Discovery 3   Addition Property of Inequalities

1. Given the inequality 10 < 12, add 2 to both expressions and check whether the new expression is also true.

$$\begin{array}{c|c} \multicolumn{2}{c}{10 < 12} \\ \hline 10 + 2 & 12 + 2 \\ 12 & 14 \end{array}$$ *True*

2. Given the inequality 10 < 12, add −2 to both expressions and check whether the new expression is also true.

3. Given the inequality 10 < 12, subtract 2 from both expressions and check whether the new expression is also true.

4. Given the inequality 10 < 12, subtract −2 from both expressions and check whether the new expression is also true.

Write a rule for the addition property of inequalities.

In each of the preceding exercises, we began with a true inequality and added (or subtracted) the same number to (or from) both expressions. The result remained a true inequality. We see that if a number is added to (or subtracted from) both expressions in an inequality, the result is a true inequality.

ADDITION PROPERTY OF INEQUALITIES

Given expressions $a, b,$ and $c,$

$$\text{if } a < b, \text{ then } a + c < b + c$$

This property holds true for subtraction as well, because subtraction is defined as adding the opposite of a number. This property also holds for all order symbols.

TAKE NOTE If the same number is added or subtracted from both sides of an inequality, the result is an equivalent inequality.

Now let's consider a property of inequalities involving multiplication. Complete the following set of exercises.

Guided Discovery 4   Multiplication Property of Inequalities

1. Given the inequality $10 < 12$, multiply both expressions by 2 and check whether the new expression is also true.

$$\frac{10 < 12}{10 \cdot 2 \mid 12 \cdot 2}$$
$$20 \mid 24 \qquad \text{True}$$

2. Given the inequality $10 < 12$, multiply both expressions by -2 and check whether the new expression is also true.

3. Given the inequality $10 < 12$, divide both expressions by 2 and check whether the new expression is also true.

4. Given the inequality $10 < 12$, divide both expressions by -2 and check whether the new expression is also true.

Write a rule for the multiplication property of inequalities.

In each of the preceding exercises, we began with a true inequality and multiplied (or divided) both expressions by the same number. When a positive number was used, the result was a true inequality. When a negative number was used, the result was a false inequality. To make the false inequality true, the inequality symbol must be reversed from "less than" to "greater than" or vice versa.

MULTIPLICATION PROPERTY OF INEQUALITIES

Given expressions a, b, and c with $c > 0$,

if $a < b$, then $ac < bc$

Given expressions a, b, and c, with $c < 0$,

if $a < b$, then $ac > bc$

This property holds true for division as well, because division is defined as multiplying by the reciprocal of a number. This property also holds for all order symbols.

 TAKE NOTE If both sides of an inequality are multiplied or divided by a positive number, the result is an equivalent inequality. If both sides of an inequality are multiplied or divided by a negative number, the direction of the inequality symbol must be reversed to form an equivalent inequality.

We are now ready to solve linear inequalities algebraically. To do this, we will need to apply a combination of the properties of inequalities. Since there are several different ways to solve linear inequalities, we will set up a few rules so that, at least in the beginning, we are following the same steps. When we become more sure of ourselves, we may follow these steps in different orders and obtain the same results in the end.

SOLVING A LINEAR INEQUALITY IN ONE VARIABLE ALGEBRAICALLY

To solve a linear inequality by using a combination of properties of inequalities,

- Simplify both expressions in the inequality (preferably, leaving no fractions).

- Isolate the variable in one expression of the inequality (preferably, the expression on the left side) by using the addition property of inequalities.
- Use the addition property of inequalities to isolate the constants in the other expression (preferably, the expression on the right side).
- Use the multiplication property of inequalities to reduce the coefficient of the variable to 1.

Remember to reverse the inequality symbol if a negative number is being used to multiply (or divide) both sides of the inequality.

In Chapter P, we discussed different representations of an inequality.
The following table summarizes what we learned in that chapter by describing some of the most common inequalities you may encounter:

Description	Inequality	Number Line	Interval Notation
All real numbers less than a	$x < a$	open circle at a	$(-\infty, a)$
All real numbers less than or equal to a	$x \leq a$	closed circle at a	$(-\infty, a]$
All real numbers greater than a	$x > a$	open circle at a	(a, ∞)
All real numbers greater than or equal to a	$x \geq a$	closed circle at a	$[a, \infty)$
All real numbers between a and b	$a < x < b$	open circles at a and b	(a, b)
All real numbers between a and b, inclusive	$a \leq x \leq b$	closed circles at a and b	$[a, b]$

EXAMPLE 6   Solve. Represent the solution set as an inequality, in interval notation, and on a number line.

a. $2x + 3 > 7$ **b.** $5x + 4 \geq 6x - 16$

c. $\dfrac{3}{8}\left(x + \dfrac{1}{4}\right) > \dfrac{5}{6}x + 2$

Algebraic Solution

a.
$$2x + 3 > 7$$
$$2x + 3 - 3 > 7 - 3 \qquad \text{Subtract 3 from both sides.}$$
$$2x > 4 \qquad \text{Simplify.}$$
$$\frac{2x}{2} > \frac{4}{2} \qquad \text{Divide both sides by 2.}$$
$$x > 2$$

The solution set is the set of all x that satisfy $x > 2$, which is $(2, \infty)$. $\quad$ We used a parenthesis because 2 is not a solution.
A number-line representation is shown.

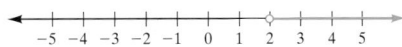

Note that 2 is not included in the solution set and is graphed with an open dot.

b.
$$5x + 4 \geq 6x - 16$$
$$5x + 4 - 6x \geq 6x - 16 - 6x \qquad \text{Subtract 6 x from both sides.}$$
$$-x + 4 \geq -16 \qquad \text{Simplify.}$$
$$-x + 4 - 4 \geq -16 - 4 \qquad \text{Subtract 4 from both sides.}$$
$$-x \geq -20 \qquad \text{Simplify.}$$
$$\frac{-x}{-1} \leq \frac{-20}{-1} \qquad \begin{array}{l}\text{Divide both sides by } -1 \text{ (the coefficient of x).} \\ \text{Remember to reverse the inequality symbol.}\end{array}$$
$$x \leq 20 \qquad \text{Simplify.}$$

The solution set is the set of all x that satisfy $x \le 20$, which is $(-\infty, 20]$. A number-line representation is shown.

We used a bracket because 20 is a solution.

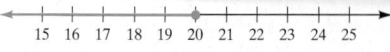

Note that 20 is included in the solution set and is graphed with a closed dot.

c.

$$\frac{3}{8}\left(x + \frac{1}{4}\right) > \frac{5}{6}x + 2$$

$$\frac{3}{8}x + \frac{3}{32} > \frac{5}{6}x + 2 \qquad \text{Distribute.}$$

$$96\left(\frac{3}{8}x + \frac{3}{32}\right) > 96\left(\frac{5}{6}x + 2\right) \qquad \text{Multiply both sides by 96, the LCD of 8, 32, and 6.}$$

$$96\left(\frac{3}{8}x\right) + 96\left(\frac{3}{32}\right) > 96\left(\frac{5}{6}x\right) + 96(2) \qquad \text{Distribute.}$$

$$36x + 9 > 80x + 192 \qquad \text{Simplify.}$$

$$36x + 9 - 80x > 80x + 192 - 80x \qquad \text{Subtract 80x from both sides.}$$

$$-44x + 9 > 192 \qquad \text{Simplify.}$$

$$-44x + 9 - 9 > 192 - 9 \qquad \text{Subtract 9 from both sides.}$$

$$-44x > 183 \qquad \text{Simplify.}$$

$$\frac{-44x}{-44} < \frac{183}{-44} \qquad \begin{array}{l}\text{Divide both sides by } -44.\\ \text{Remember to reverse the inequality symbol.}\end{array}$$

$$x < -\frac{183}{44} \qquad \text{Simplify.}$$

The solution set is the set of all x that satisfy $x < -\frac{183}{44}$, which is $\left(-\infty, -\frac{183}{44}\right)$.

We use a parenthesis because $-\frac{183}{44}$ is not a solution.

A number-line representation is shown.

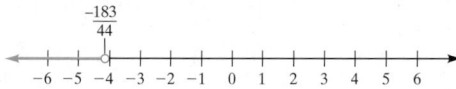

Note that $-\frac{183}{44}$ is not included in the solution set and is graphed with an open dot.

EXAMPLE 7 Solve $-2 < 3x - 5 \le 7$ algebraically.

Algebraic Solution

In order to solve this compound inequality, we will isolate the variable to the middle expression.

$$-2 < 3x - 5 \le 7$$

$$-2 + 5 < 3x - 5 + 5 \le 7 + 5 \qquad \text{Add 5 to all expressions.}$$

$$3 < 3x \le 12 \qquad \text{Simplify.}$$

$$\frac{3}{3} < \frac{3x}{3} \le \frac{12}{3} \qquad \text{Divide all expressions by 3.}$$

$$1 < x \le 4 \qquad \text{Simplify.}$$

The solution set includes all x between 1 and 4, including 4, which is $(1, 4]$. The number-line graph is shown.

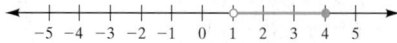

As we mentioned earlier, linear equations may have no solution or all-real-number solutions. In Chapter 2, we algebraically determined that a linear equation may have no solution or a solution set of all real numbers.

When we attempted to isolate the variable to one expression, the variable was deleted. The resulting equation was a contradiction. Therefore, the equation had no solution. Similarly, if the resulting inequality is not true, it has no solution.

When we attempted to isolate the variable to one expression, the variable was deleted. The resulting equation was an identity. Therefore, the solution set was the set of all real numbers. A linear inequality has a solution set of all real numbers if the variable is deleted and the resulting inequality is always true.

EXAMPLE 8

Solve algebraically.

a. $4(x + 2) < 4x - 10$ **b.** $3x + 4 \leq 2x + (x + 4)$

Algebraic Solution

a.
$$4(x + 2) < 4x - 10$$
$$4x + 8 < 4x - 10 \qquad \text{Distribute 4.}$$
$$4x + 8 - 4x < 4x - 10 - 4x \qquad \text{Subtract 4x from both sides.}$$
$$8 < -10 \qquad \text{Simplify.}$$

Since this is a false inequality, it has no solution.

b.
$$3x + 4 \leq 2x + (x + 4)$$
$$3x + 4 \leq 2x + x + 4 \qquad \text{Remove parentheses.}$$
$$3x + 4 \leq 3x + 4 \qquad \text{Simplify.}$$
$$3x + 4 - 3x \leq 3x + 4 - 3x \qquad \text{Subtract 3x from both sides.}$$
$$4 \leq 4 \qquad \text{Simplify.}$$

Since this is a true inequality, the solution set is all real numbers.

ALGEBRAIC SOLUTIONS OF LINEAR INEQUALITIES IN ONE VARIABLE

In solving a linear inequality algebraically, one of three possibilities will occur.

1. **A solution set exists.**

2. **No solution exists.** The solution process results in a false inequality.

3. **A solution set exists, and it is the set of all real numbers.** The solution process results in a true inequality.

✓ Objective 5.1.4 *CHECKUP*

In exercises 1 and 2, solve. Represent the solution set as an inequality, in interval notation, and on a number line, if possible.

1. a. $5x - 8 > 2$ **b.** $3z + 7 \leq 7z - 5$

   c. $\dfrac{2}{3}\left(x - \dfrac{1}{5}\right) < \dfrac{1}{4}x + 3$

2. $-4 \leq \dfrac{1}{2}x + 3 < 2$

3. Solve algebraically

   a. $3(x + 2) - 4(2x + 1) > 3(2 - x) + 2(1 - x)$

   b. $3x - (2x + 5) \geq \dfrac{1}{2}(2x + 4) - 7$

4. In solving a linear inequality algebraically, which property should be used first to isolate the variable to one side of the inequality?

5. How would you know a linear inequality has no solution when you attempt to solve it algebraically?

6. How would you know that the solution set of a linear inequality is the set of all real numbers when you solve it algebraically?

Objective 5.1.5   Modeling the Real World

In real-world situations, the terms *less than or equal to* and *greater than or equal to* may be expressed in a variety of ways. For example, two expressions that are used frequently are *at least* (for *greater than or equal to*) and *at most* (for *less than or equal to*). Situations involving these terms or phrases like them can be analyzed as inequalities and then solved graphically or algebraically as we have described. The same rules apply about including a solution point if the relation includes equality and about reversing the direction of an inequality if you need to multiply or divide by a negative number.

EXAMPLE 9

Eata wants to make a *B* in her algebra class. The grading scale states that the range for a *B* is 85–93. Her first four test grades were 93, 100, 88, and 87. Determine the range of grades she must score on her last test in order to make a *B*.

Solution

Let x = fifth test grade

The average of the test grades must be between 85 and 93, inclusive, in order for Eata to make a B.

Algebraic

$$85 \leq \frac{93 + 100 + 88 + 87 + x}{5} \leq 93$$

$$85 \leq \frac{368 + x}{5} \leq 93 \quad \text{Simplify.}$$

$$5(85) \leq 5\left(\frac{368 + x}{5}\right) \geq 5(93) \quad \text{Multiply by 5.}$$

$$425 \leq 368 + x \leq 465 \quad \text{Simplify.}$$

$$425 - 368 \leq 368 + x - 368 \leq 465 - 368 \quad \text{Subtract 368.}$$

$$57 \leq x \leq 97 \quad \text{Simplify.}$$

Eata must score between 57 and 97, inclusive, on her fifth test in order to make a B.

Graphic

$$Y2 = \frac{93 + 100 + 88 + 87 + x}{5}$$

$$Y3 = 93$$

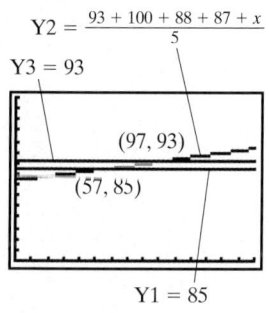

$(97, 93)$

$(57, 85)$

$Y1 = 85$

$(0, 150, 0, 150)$

The intersections are $(57, 85)$ and $(97, 93)$. The portion of the graph of Y2 between Y1 and Y3 is between the intersections. The solution includes the x-coordinates of the intersections. The solution set is the set of all x that satisfy $57 \leq x \leq 97$. ∎

EXAMPLE 10 Jean's Handicrafts sells Christmas wreaths for $25.00 each. Jean estimates that the cost of materials needed to make each wreath is $15.50. The cost of the advertisement is $10.00. If Jean must make a profit of at least $100.00, how many wreaths must she sell?

Solution

Let x = the number of wreaths made and sold

$R(x)$ = the total revenue

$C(x)$ = the total cost

$P(x)$ = the total profit

$$R(x) = 25.00x$$
$$C(x) = 15.50x + 10.00$$

The total profit is the difference of the total revenue and the total cost.

$$P(x) = R(x) - C(x)$$
$$P(x) = 25.00x - (15.50x + 10.00)$$
$$P(x) = 25.00x - 15.50x - 10.00$$
$$P(x) = 9.50x - 10.00$$

Jean must have a profit of at least $100.00, or $P(x) \geq 100.00$.

$$9.50x - 10.00 \geq 100.00$$

Algebraic

$$9.50x - 10.00 \geq 100.00$$

$$9.50x - 10.00 + 10.00 \geq 100.00 + 10.00 \qquad \text{Add 10.00.}$$

$$9.50x \geq 110.00 \qquad \text{Simplify.}$$

$$\frac{9.50x}{9.50} \geq \frac{110.00}{9.50} \qquad \text{Divide by 9.50.}$$

$$x \geq 11.579 \qquad \text{(Rounded to the nearest thousandth.)}$$

Jean must make and sell at least 12 wreaths to make a profit of $100.00.

Numeric

X	Y1	Y2	
8	66	100	66 ≱ 100
9	75.5	100	75.5 ≱ 100
10	85	100	85 ≱ 100
11	94.5	100	94.5 ≱ 100
12	104	100	104 ≥ 100
13	113.5	100	113.5 ≥ 100
14	123	100	123 ≥ 100

X=8

Y1 = 9.50x − 10.00
Y2 = 100

The solution checks.

APPLICATION

The body mass index (BMI) is a measure of weight that takes height into account. The BMI of a person 62 inches tall and weighing x pounds is given by the expression $0.2x - 2$. A doctor may prescribe a certain drug if a person has a BMI of 30 or greater. Determine the weights for which a doctor may prescribe this drug for a person 62 inches in height.

Discussion

Let x = the weight in pounds of a person 62 inches tall

Write an inequality such that the BMI is greater than or equal to 30.

$$0.2x - 2 \geq 30$$

$$0.2x - 2 + 2 \geq 30 + 2 \qquad \text{Add 2 to both sides.}$$

$$0.2x \geq 32 \qquad \text{Simplify.}$$

$$\frac{0.2x}{0.2} \geq \frac{32}{0.2} \qquad \text{Divide both sides by 0.2.}$$

$$x \geq 160$$

A doctor may prescribe a certain drug if a person is 62 inches tall and weighs 160 pounds or more.

✓ Objective 5.1.5 **CHECKUP**

1. A disk exchange store sells used CDs for $6.99 each. The store buys used CDs for $2.99 each. The average daily cost for having the store open for business is $125.00. Assuming that the store buys and sells the same number of CDs in a day, how many CDs must the store buy and sell in order to make a profit of at least $75.00 per day?

2. After the birth of her baby, Jana counted calories to manage her weight. She wanted to average 1300–1350 calories per day. If her intake for the first six days of the week was 1400, 1100, 1200, 1050, 1450, and 1500 calories, what number of calories can she have on the seventh day to achieve her goal?

3. If a person is 6 feet tall, the body mass index (BMI) is approximated by the expression $0.14x - 1$, where x is the person's weight in pounds. If the person has risk factors for heart disease, medication may be prescribed if his or her BMI is at least 27. Determine the weights for which medication may be prescribed.

5.1 EXERCISES

 Student Solutions Manual    PH Math/Tutor Center   CD Video    MathXL®    MyMathLab   Interactmath.com

Solve numerically for integer solutions.

1. $6(x - 12) < 3x$

2. $3x + 6 > 0$

3. $3(x + 5) + 3 > 3x + 18$

4. $a + 3(a + 2) < 6(a + 1) - 2a$

5. $3x + 3 > x + 2$

6. $3x + 5 < 2x - 1$

7. $2(4x + 2) + 2x - 7 < 2(5x + 4)$

8. $x + 5 > 2(x - 1) - (x - 1)$

Solve graphically. Check numerically.

9. $\frac{2}{3}x - \frac{2}{3} \geq -\frac{3}{4}x - \frac{7}{2}$

10. $\frac{1}{4}x - \frac{5}{2} \leq -\frac{1}{2}x - 1$

11. $2(x + 3) - (x - 1) > 8 - (x + 9)$

12. $3(x - 2) - (x - 5) > 7 - (x + 2)$

13. $0.4x - 3.2 \leq -0.6x - 0.2$

14. $0.2(2x + 1) \geq -0.2(x - 7)$

15. $2(x + 1) > 3(x - 1) - x$

16. $5 - (2x + 5) > 2(2x - 1) - 2(3x + 1)$

17. $x - (3x + 1) > -x - (x + 1)$

18. $3(x - 1) - 5x > 2(1 - x)$

Solve algebraically. Represent the solution as an inequality, in interval notation, and on a number line.

19. $4x + 12 > 0$

20. $36 \geq 4x + 8$

21. $-x + 2 > 8$

22. $-3x + 12 \geq 12$

23. $-7x - 12 < -26$

24. $-3x + 11 < -10$

25. $15.17 < 5.9x - 4.3$

26. $3.05y + 0.09 > 31.2$

27. $-4.22c - 0.4 \leq -21.5$

28. $6.1 \geq -0.55a + 6.1$

29. $2.07z + 4.12 \geq 16.54$

30. $-6.3p + 1.5 \geq -4.8$

31. $-\dfrac{5}{9}b + \dfrac{11}{12} < \dfrac{23}{36}$

32. $-\dfrac{4}{7}z + \dfrac{3}{14} > \dfrac{5}{14}$

33. $15x - 2 \geq 7x + 6$

34. $7x + 5 \leq 3x + 9$

35. $-1.05x - 15.41 < 2.55x - 47.09$

36. $21.1x + 0.46 > 10.9x + 0.46$

37. $3x + \dfrac{1}{4} \leq 2x + \dfrac{3}{4}$

38. $5p + \dfrac{3}{8} \geq 3p - \dfrac{3}{8}$

39. $\dfrac{2}{5}b - 12 < \dfrac{2}{3}b + 20$

40. $\dfrac{7}{9}x - 15 > \dfrac{4}{9}x - 37$

41. $4x - (3x + 5) < x - 5$

42. $7x + 4 > 3x + 2(2x + 2)$

43. $4x - (3x + 5) \leq x - 5$

44. $7x + 4 \geq 3x + 2(2x + 2)$

45. $-9 \leq 2x - 3 \leq 11$

46. $-4 \leq 3x + 2 \leq 17$

47. $5 < 4 - 3x \leq 11$

48. $-2 \leq 5x + 3 < 4$

49. $-4 \leq 3(x + 1) - 5 \leq 7$

50. $2 < 6 - 2(x + 5) < 7$

Write a linear inequality to represent each application and solve.

51. Terrance needs braces. His orthodontist estimates that the cost of each visit to put in and maintain the braces will be $215. Terrance's insurance will not cover braces, but he does have a medical reimbursement account in which he has put the maximum amount for the year, $4000. If he has already spent $350 on other medical bills, how many appointments with the orthodontist can he afford while not exceeding the amount in his account?

52. Jeannie recently had a plumber in to work on her bathroom pipes. When she called to set up the appointment, she was told that she would be charged $150 for the call plus $70 per hour for the work. If she wants to spend no more than $400, how many hours of plumbing work can she afford?

53. Richard buys a minivan for $15,000 which has average depreciation of $1050 per year. For how many years will his vehicle be worth more than $5500?

54. Tran was fortunate to qualify for a student loan that did not charge interest. While he was a full-time student he was able to defer payments. Upon graduation he owes $6000, which he plans to pay off at the rate of $200 per month. For how many months will his balance be more than $1500?

55. Luigi is retired, but has a part-time job. He will lose some of his retirement benefits if he earns more than $7500 per year. He makes $9.75 per hour at his job. If he has already earned $5200 this year, how many hours can he work without losing benefits?

56. Bobby rents a stump grinder for $22.00 plus $3.50 per hour. How many hours can he use the grinder and spend no more than $55.00?

57. Angie has invited 120 people to her wedding reception and plans to serve both vegetarian and meat entrée plates. It will cost her $30 per person to serve a vegetarian plate and $35 per person to serve a meat entrée plate. If she plans to spend no more than $4000 for the dinner, how many meat entrée plates can she order?

58. Angie has the replies back from her invitations, and she will now have 75 people attending the reception. The caterer changes his charge because there will be less than 100 guests. It will cost Angie $35 per person for the vegetarian plate and $40 per person for the meat entrée plate. If she plans to spend no more than $2750 for the dinner, how many meat entrée plates can she order?

59. Helen's phone plan is $29.99 per month for unlimited local calls plus $0.05 per minute for long-distance calls. In the mail, she received an offer from her local phone company. The advertised plan was $39.99 per month for unlimited local calls and 500 minutes of long-distance calls. Long-distance calls are $0.10 per minute after the included 500 minutes. Assuming Helen uses more than 500 minutes of long distance each month, determine the number of minutes of long distance Helen can use so that the new offer will be less than her current plan.

60. A recreation vehicle company has two rental plans. The first plan is $49.99 per day and $0.59 per mile driven. The second plan is $35.99 per day plus $0.75 per mile driven over 150 miles. For how many miles will the first plan be less than the second plan? (Assume more than 150 miles are driven.)

61. Lee is trying to earn an A in his algebra class. To do so, he must have an average of no less than 93 points. He scored 93, 97, 92, 89, and 95 on his first five tests. What range of scores on his last test will earn an A?

62. Beckie types student papers for a fee. If her earnings were $38, $62, $56, and $42 for the first four weeks of the term, how much must she earn for the fifth week in order to average more than $50 per week?

63. A rectangular garden is to have a fence placed around it. The perimeter is not to exceed 300 feet of fencing. If the length is to be 10 feet more than twice the width, find the possible widths of the garden.

64. A rectangular swimming pool is to have a perimeter that does not exceed 240 feet. If the length is to be 15 feet more than twice the width, what widths would satisfy that condition?

65. A scalene triangle has a perimeter of less than 25 inches. The second side is twice the length of the first side. The third side is 5 inches more than twice the length of the first side. What lengths of the first side would satisfy these conditions?

66. An isosceles triangle has two sides of equal length and a perimeter of less than 107 feet. The third side is 7 feet less than twice the length of the two shorter sides. What lengths for the shorter sides would satisfy these conditions?

67. A photo-processing kiosk charges $0.25 for each print that it produces. The cost of producing the print is $0.08 per print. The overhead cost is $45.00 per day to rent and staff the kiosk. How many prints must be produced each day to realize a profit of at least $50.00 per day?

68. A coffee shop averages a charge of $3.55 per customer for an order. On the average, it costs the shop $1.25 to fill the order. The daily overhead cost of operating the shop is $165.00. How many orders must be sold each day to make a profit of at least $150.00 per day?

69. A person who is 5 feet 8 inches tall has a body mass index (BMI) that is approximated by the expression $0.146x + 1$, where x is the person's weight in pounds. If the person has no risk factors for heart disease except being overweight, a doctor will not usually prescribe medication if the BMI is below 30. Determine the weights for which the doctor may not prescribe medication.

70. A person who is 6 feet 2 inches tall has a BMI that is approximated by the expression $0.125x + 0.7$, where x is the person's weight in pounds. With other risk factors for heart disease, a doctor may choose not to prescribe medication, so long as the person's BMI remains below 27. Determine the weights for which the doctor may choose not to prescribe medication.

71. Given that an expression for the degrees Fahrenheit is $\frac{9}{5}C + 32$, where C is degrees Celsius, determine the degrees of Celsius between freezing of water, 32°F, and the boiling point of water, 212°F.

72. Given that an expression for the degrees Celsius is $\frac{5}{9}(F - 32)$, where F is degrees Fahrenheit, determine the degrees of Fahrenheit between freezing of water, 0°C, and the boiling point of water, 100°C.

73. Daily high temperatures in Nashville, Tennessee, in the month of July were 82, 83, 88, and 92 degrees Fahrenheit. What would the temperature need to register on the fifth day if the average high temperature for the five days was between 82 and 88 degrees Fahrenheit?

74. The closing price of stock for Cisco Systems, Inc., for the first three Fridays in July were $16.79, $18.74, and $17.99. What must the closing price be for the next Friday if the average closing price on Friday was between $18.00 and $20.00?

75. A vehicle that cost $17,500 new loses its value at a rate of about $3150 per year. For what years after purchase will its value be between $2000 and $10,000?

76. A cell-phone company charges $28.99 per month plus $0.09 per minute. About how many minutes can a person use under this plan and keep his monthly bill between $60.00 and $75.00?

77. The U.S. Census Bureau estimates Las Vegas, Nevada, as one of the fastest-growing cities in the country. Its population, p, can be estimated by $p(t) = 20,730t + 508,604$, where t is time in years after 2002. If this type of growth continues, in what years will the population of Las Vegas exceed 1 million people?

78. Although people are flocking to cities in Nevada, and Arizona, many cities in the Midwest are shrinking in population. According to the U.S. Census Bureau, St. Louis, Missouri, is losing a large percentage of its residents. Its population, p, can be estimated by $p(t) = -4861t + 338,353$, where t is time in years after 2002. If this population decline continues, in what years will the number of St. Louis residents be below 250,000?

79. According to the United States Census Bureau's Social and Economic supplement, women working full time experienced salary gains between 2001 and 2002. The yearly earnings of women in dollars can be estimated by $w(x) = 27,259 + 2944x$, where x is the number of years after 2001. Estimate the years in which women's annual earnings will exceed $50,000.

80. According to the United States Census Bureau's Social and Economic Supplement, men working full time also experienced salary gains between 2001 and 2002, an improvement over the previous year, in which men's earnings held steady. The yearly earnings of men in dollars can be estimated by $m(x) = 38,885 + 544x$, where x is the number of years after 2001. For how many years will men's annual earnings be less than $50,000?

 ## 5.1 Calculator Exercises

In this section, you were shown how to graphically solve an inequality using the calculator. Another way to use your calculator to graphically solve an inequality is to store the expression on the right in Y1 and the expression on the left in Y2 and then graph Y3 = Y1 − Y2 to determine the solution set. If you seek values of x that make Y1 < Y2 (or equivalently, Y1 − Y2 < 0), find the interval where Y3 is below the x-axis (Y3 < 0). If you seek values of x that make Y1 > Y2, find the interval where Y3 is above the x-axis.

For example, use your calculator to solve $2x + 3 > x + 5$ graphically.

- Set the screen to the desired window.

- Enter the expression on the left side of the inequality in Y1.

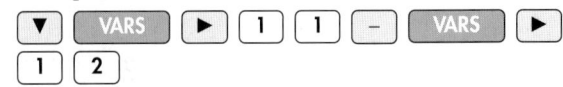

- Enter the expression on the right side of the inequality in Y2.

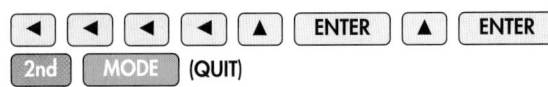

- Set Y3 equal to Y 1 − Y 2.

- Turn off Y1 and Y2.

• Graph Y3.

Since we want Y1 > Y2, find where Y3 is above the x-axis. This occurs where $x > 2$, which can be determined by using the | TRACE | key or by using the | 2nd | | TRACE | (CALC) | 2 | keys to find the "zero" of the graph (that is, the point at which the graph crosses the x-axis).

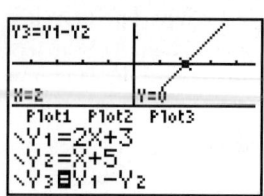

Try this approach on some of the exercises in this section. You must still decide whether to include the bound in your solution set.

5.1 Writing Exercises

Solve the following two inequalities. Discuss the differences in the forms of the inequalities, and explain how these differences affect the solutions of the inequalities. What have you learned from this exercise?

1. $4x - (2x + 5) > 2x - 5$
2. $4x - (2x + 5) \geq 2x - 5$

5.2 LINEAR INEQUALITIES IN TWO VARIABLES

OBJECTIVES

1 Identify linear inequalities in two variables.
2 Graph linear inequalities in two variables.
3 Graph the two special cases of linear inequalities in two variables.
4 Model real-world situations by using linear inequalities in two variables.

APPLICATION

The United States Postal Service (USPS) Priority Mail Service delivery rate chart is as follows:

USPS Priority Mail Rates

Weight in Pounds	Local Zones 1, 2, and 3	Zone 4	Zone 5	Zone 6	Zone 7	Zone 8
1	3.85	3.85	3.85	3.85	3.85	3.85
2	3.95	4.55	4.90	5.05	5.40	5.75
3	4.75	6.05	6.85	7.15	7.85	8.55
4	5.30	7.05	8.05	8.50	9.45	10.35
5	5.85	8.00	9.30	9.85	11.00	12.15

Determine the number of 3-pound packages and the number of 5-pound packages that you can ship to Zone 4 and stay within a shipping budget of $150.00. Give an example of a possible combination of 3-pound packages and 5-pound packages that can be shipped and stay within the budget.

After completing this section, we will discuss this application further. See page 451.

Objective 5.2.1 **Identifying Linear Inequalities in Two Variables**

In this section, we will be solving linear inequalities in two variables. Before we begin, we need to identify a linear inequality in two variables. A **linear inequality in two variables** is written by replacing the equals sign in a linear equation in two variables with an order symbol.

STANDARD FORM FOR A LINEAR INEQUALITY IN TWO VARIABLES

A linear inequality in two variables is an inequality that can be written in the form

$$ax + by < c$$

where $a, b,$ and c are real numbers and a and b are not both equal to 0.

For example,

Standard form: $ax + by < c$

1. $2x + 5y < 0$ $a = 2$ $b = 5$ $c = 0$

2. $3x - y < 12$ $a = 3$ $b = -1$ $c = 12$

3. $2x < 8$ $a = 2$ $b = 0$ $c = 8$

4. $3y < -9$ $a = 0$ $b = 3$ $c = -9$

Each of these inequalities is in standard form. Note that each of the variables, x and y, is raised to the first power. This *must* be the case for a linear inequality in two variables.

However, the inequality $y < 5x + 7$ is also a linear inequality in two variables, because we can use the properties of inequalities to rearrange it into standard form. For example,

$$y < 5x + 7$$
$$y - 5x < 5x + 7 - 5x \quad \text{Subtract 5x from both sides.}$$
$$y - 5x < 7 \quad \text{Simplify.}$$
$$-5x + y < 7 \quad \text{Rearrange the left side.}$$

 TAKE NOTE This property holds true for all order symbols.

EXAMPLE 1

Identify each inequality as linear or nonlinear. Express each linear inequality in standard form.

a. $2x^2 + 3y > 4$ **b.** $y \geq -3x$ **c.** $x \leq 0$

Solution

a. Nonlinear, because the x-term is squared.

b. Linear
   In standard form,

$$y \geq -3x$$
$$y + 3x \geq -3x + 3x$$
$$y + 3x \geq 0$$
$$3x + y \geq 0$$

c. Linear
   In standard form, $x \leq 0$.

✓ Objective 5.2.1 *CHECKUP*

1. Identify each inequality as linear or nonlinear. Express each linear inequality in standard form.

a. $y > 7x - 10$

b. $y < -\dfrac{3}{x} + 7$

c. $x < y$

Graphing Linear Inequalities in Two Variables

To solve a linear inequality in two variables, we will perform the same procedure we used in previous sections to solve linear equations in two variables. That is, to determine if an ordered pair is a solution we will substitute the values for the two variables into the inequality and determine whether the inequality is true. A solution of a linear inequality in two variables is an ordered pair that produces a true statement (that is, that satisfies the inequality). For example, in solving $y \leq x + 5$, we can obtain many possible solutions.

$(4, 9)$	is a solution because, when $x = 4$ and $y = 9$, the inequality results in $9 \leq 9$.
$(5, 7)$	is a solution because, when $x = 5$ and $y = 7$, the inequality results in $7 \leq 10$.
$(0.5, 3)$	is a solution because, when $x = 0.5$ and $y = 3$, the inequality results in $3 \leq 5.5$.

To solve the linear inequality numerically, we begin the same way we did with all other numeric solutions: by completing a table of values. For example, in solving $y \leq x + 5$, we write the following table:

x	$y \leq x + 5$	y	
-3	$y \leq -3 + 5$ $y \leq 2$	$y \leq 2$	This means that when $x = -3$, we have values of y less than or equal to 2.
-2	$y \leq -2 + 5$ $y \leq 3$	$y \leq 3$	This means that when $x = -2$, we have values of y less than or equal to 3.
-1	$y \leq -1 + 5$ $y \leq 4$	$y \leq 4$	This means that when $x = -1$, we have values of y less than or equal to 4.
0	$y \leq 0 + 5$ $y \leq 5$	$y \leq 5$	This means that when $x = 0$, we have values of y less than or equal to 5.
1	$y \leq 1 + 5$ $y \leq 6$	$y \leq 6$	This means that when $x = 1$, we have values of y less than or equal to 6.
2	$y \leq 2 + 5$ $y \leq 7$	$y \leq 7$	This means that when $x = 2$, we have values of y less than or equal to 7.

We can see that the number of solutions is infinite. A table of values is not the most convenient method for expressing all the solutions. Therefore, we will not solve any examples with the numeric method.

We used a rectangular coordinate system and graphical methods to illustrate the solutions of linear equations in two variables because the number of solutions was infinite and the solutions could not be listed numerically. We will do the same for linear inequalities in two variables.

To graph an inequality means to create an illustration that represents the solutions of the inequality. Therefore,

1. Every solution of an inequality can be represented by a point on its graph.

2. Every point on a graph represents a solution of its inequality.

The graph of an equation partitions the coordinate plane into three regions: (1) the coordinate pairs that lie on the line that represents the equation; (2) the coordinate pairs above the line; and (3) the coordinate pairs below the line. (For example, see the graph of the equation $y = x + 5$ at the left.)

If we graph the solutions of $y \leq x + 5$ from the table of values found in the previous section, we obtain a series of vertical-line solutions of the inequality. Each line starts at a boundary point on the line representing $y = x + 5$ and extends below the line representing $y = x + 5$.

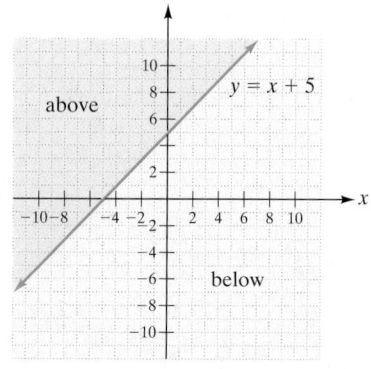

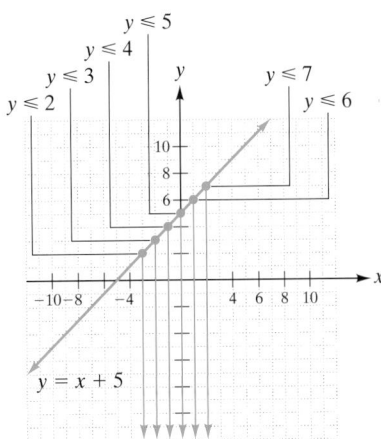

To illustrate the solutions of $y \leq x + 5$, we graph the line for $y = x + 5$ and shade all points below the line.

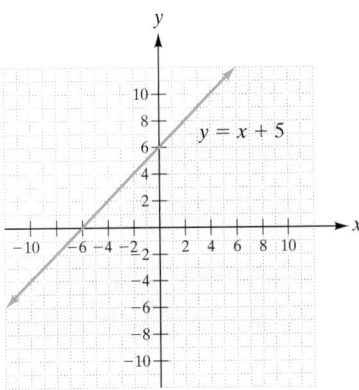

While this method illustrates why we shade a region on one side of the boundary line, it is not the easiest way to graph an inequality. To discover a more straightforward method of graphing a "less than or equal to" inequality, complete the following set of exercises.

Guided Discovery 5 Graphing a "Less Than or Equal To" Linear Inequality in Two Variables

Graph the line determined by the equation $y = 2x + 4$.

1. Use Trace to determine the coordinates of points on the line.
  a. List two of these ordered pairs.
  b. Are the ordered pairs solutions of the inequality $y \leq 2x + 4$?

2. Clear the trace, and use the free-moving cursor (arrow keys) to determine ordered pairs above the line.
  a. List two of these ordered pairs.

  b. Are the ordered pairs solutions of the inequality $y \leq 2x + 4$?

3. Now use the free-moving cursor (arrow keys) to determine ordered pairs below the line.
  a. List two of these ordered pairs.
  b. Are the ordered pairs solutions of the inequality $y \leq 2x + 4$?

Write the rule for graphing a "less than or equal to" linear inequality.

First, we see that the inequality is solved for y. The ordered pairs on the graphed line are solutions of the equation and the "equal to" part of the inequality. We use a solid line to indicate that the ordered pairs on the line are included in the solution. (This is comparable to using a solid dot on a number line for a linear inequality in one variable.) Second, we see that the ordered-pair solutions of the "less than" portion of the inequality are found in the region below the graphed line. We shade this region to indicate that they are included in the solution.

To discover a method for graphing an inequality that does not include equality, complete the following set of exercises.

Guided Discovery 6   Graphing a "Greater Than" Linear Inequality in Two Variables

Graph the line determined by the equation $y = 2x + 4$.

1. Use Trace to determine the coordinates of points on the line.

   a. List two of these ordered pairs.

   b. Are the ordered pairs solutions of the inequality $y > 2x + 4$?

2. Clear the trace, and use the free-moving cursor (arrow keys) to determine ordered pairs above the line.

   a. List two of these ordered pairs.

   b. Are the ordered pairs solutions of the inequality $y > 2x + 4$?

3. Now use the free-moving cursor (arrow keys) to determine ordered pairs below the line.

   a. List two of these ordered pairs.

   b. Are the ordered pairs solutions of the inequality $y > 2x + 4$?

Write the rule for graphing a "greater than" linear inequality.

First, we see that the inequality is solved for y. The ordered pairs on the graphed line are solutions of the equation, but not solutions of the inequality. We use a dashed line to indicate that these ordered pairs are not included in the solution. (This is comparable to using an open dot on a number line for a linear inequality in one variable.) We also see that the ordered-pair solutions of the "greater than" portion of the inequality are found in the region above the graphed line. We shade this region to indicate that these ordered pairs are included in the solution.

GRAPHING A LINEAR INEQUALITY IN TWO VARIABLES WITH A Y-TERM

To graph a linear inequality in two variables,

- Solve the inequality for y (for example, $y < ax + b$).
- Graph the boundary line determined by the related equation $y = ax + b$.
- Use a solid line when the inequality includes equality.
- Use a dashed line when the inequality does not include equality.
- Shade the correct portion of the coordinate plane determined by the inequality solved for y.
- Shade below the line for a "less than" inequality.
- Shade above the line for a "greater than" inequality.
- Check for the correct shading by choosing a test point in the shaded region to determine whether it is a solution of the inequality.

To graph a linear inequality in two variables on a calculator, we need to do the same as we do by hand.

 TAKE NOTE The calculator does not graph dashed lines; it always includes the boundary in the graph. It will be up to you not to include the boundary in your graph when that is appropriate. In 5.2 Calculator Exercises, a procedure whereby dashed lines can be displayed is presented.

EXAMPLE 2   Graph.

   a. $x - y < -5$

   b. $6x + 2y \le -10$

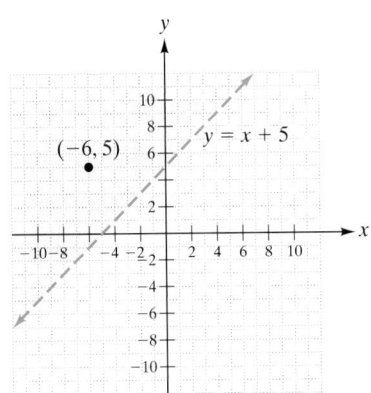

Solution

a. First, solve the inequality for y.

$$x - y < -5$$
$$x - y - x < -5 - x$$
$$-y < -x - 5$$
$$\frac{-y}{-1} > \frac{-x - 5}{-1} \quad \text{\small Reverse the inequality when dividing by a negative number.}$$
$$y > x + 5$$

Graph the boundary line determined by $y = x + 5$. This boundary is a dashed line because there is no equality in the inequality. Since the inequality is "greater than," the boundary line is a lower boundary, so we shade above the boundary line. (Remember, after solving for y, we have a "greater than" inequality.)

Check a point in the shaded portion of the graph. A sample ordered pair is $(-6, 5)$. Substituting this solution into the original inequality results in

$$\begin{array}{c|c} x \quad - y < -5 \\ \hline (-6) - 5 & -5 \\ -11 \end{array}$$

The sample ordered pair is a solution.
The calculator graph is shown in **Figure 5.3b**.

T E C H N O L O G Y Graphing a Linear Inequality in Two Variables

Graph $x - y < -5$.

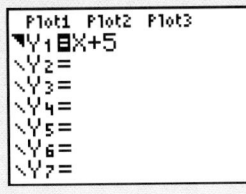

$$Y1 = x + 5$$
$$(-47, 47, -31, 31)$$

Figure 5.3a   **Figure 5.3b**

First solve for y: $y > x + 5$
For **Figure 5.3a**,
Enter the boundary equation $y = x + 5$ in Y1.

Since the inequality is "greater than," shade above the boundary line. Use the left arrow key to move left of Y1.

Choose the "shade above" option. The calculator will display a blinking triangle above a diagonal.

[ENTER] [ENTER]

For **Figure 5.3b**,
Graph.

[GRAPH]

The calculator display shows the shaded graph; it does not show a dashed or solid boundary line.

TAKE NOTE After entering the boundary equation, to shade above press [ENTER] twice; to shade below press [ENTER] three times.

b. Solve the inequality for y.

$$6x + 2y \le -10$$
$$6x + 2y - 6x \le -10 - 6x$$
$$2y \le -6x - 10$$
$$\frac{2y}{2} \le \frac{-6x - 10}{2}$$
$$y \le -3x - 5$$

The boundary line is the graph of the equation $y = -3x - 5$. This boundary is a solid line because the inequality includes equality. The boundary line is an upper boundary for a "less than" inequality, so shade below the boundary.

Check a point in the shaded region. In **Figure 5.4**, we choose the ordered pair $(-4, 2)$ as a solution to check.

$$
\begin{array}{c|c}
6x + 2y \le -10 \\
\hline
6(-4) + 2(2) & -10 \\
-24 + 4 \\
-20
\end{array}
$$

The sample ordered pair is a solution.

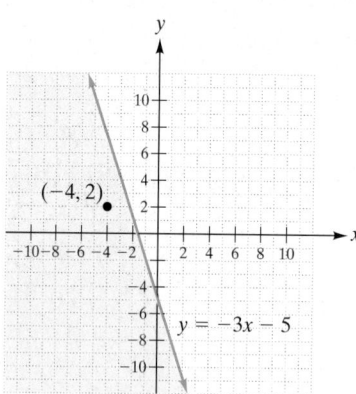

Figure 5.4

Check

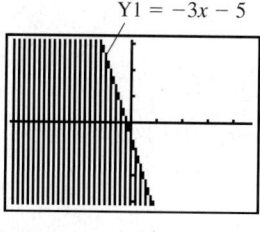

$(-47, 47, -31, 31)$

✓ Objective 5.2.2 CHECKUP

1. Graph. Check each solution on your calculator.
   a. $3x - 2y > 6$ **b.** $y \le -3x + 7$
2. In graphing a linear inequality in two variables, when do you use a dashed boundary line and when do you use a solid one?

3. After graphing a linear inequality in two variables, how should you check that you shaded the proper region of the graph?

Objective 5.2.3   **Graphing Special Cases of Linear Inequalities in Two Variables**

The special cases of linear equations in two variables were the cases when $y = k$ or $x = h$ (Section 3.2). Let's graph inequalities related to each of these cases; that is, we wish to graph the linear inequality $ax + by < c$ when either $a = 0$ or $b = 0$, but not both.

EXAMPLE 3

Graph $y < 5$.

Solution

Graph the boundary line, $y = 5$, with a dashed line. This is a horizontal line. Shade the "less than" portion of the coordinate plane, which is below the upper boundary.

Check a point in the shaded region. (This is left for you.)

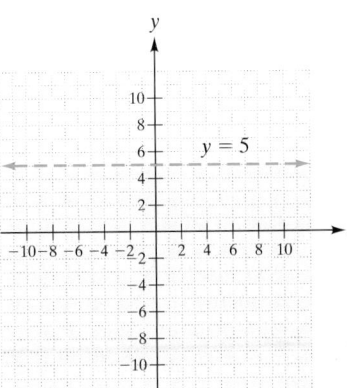

Check

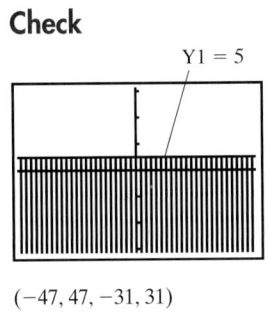

$(-47, 47, -31, 31)$

Inequalities with only a *y*-variable are graphed in the same manner as all other previous inequalities. However, the graph of an inequality not containing a *y*-variable must be determined in a different manner.

The ordered pairs on the graphed line $x = h$ are solutions of the equality portion of the inequality. The line $x = h$ divides the coordinate plane into two parts. Ordered-pair solutions of "less than" inequalities, $x < h$, are located in the region to the left of the graphed line (the right boundary). Ordered-pair solutions of "greater than" inequalities, $x > h$, are located to the right of the graphed line (the left boundary).

GRAPHING A LINEAR INEQUALITY IN TWO VARIABLES WITH NO Y-TERM

To graph a linear inequality in two variables with no *y*-term,

- Solve the inequality for *x*.
- Graph a vertical boundary line for the equation $x = h$.
  - Use a solid line if the inequality includes equality.
  - Use a dashed line if the inequality does not include equality.
- Shade the correct portion of the coordinate plane determined by the solved inequality.
  - Shade to the left of the boundary for a "less than" inequality.
  - Shade to the right of the boundary for a "greater than" inequality.
- Check for the correct shading by choosing a test point in the shaded region to determine whether that point is a solution of the inequality.

Since an inequality with no *y*-variable (such as $ax < 0$ or $ax > 0$) does not have a related function, we cannot use our previous calculator method to graph the inequality. (See 5.2 Calculator Exercises at the end of this section for a calculator method of solving the inequality.)

EXAMPLE 4

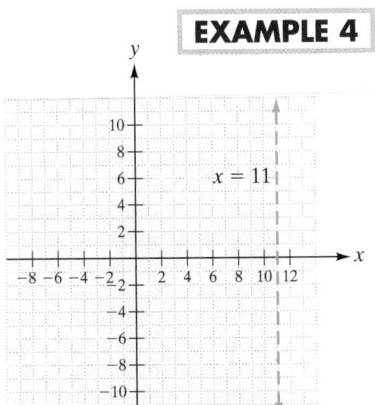

Graph $x - 3 < 8$.

Solution

Solve for *x*.

$$x - 3 < 8$$
$$x - 3 + 3 < 8 + 3$$
$$x < 11$$

Graph the boundary line $x = 11$ as a dashed line because $x < 11$ does not include equality. The boundary is a vertical line. Shade to the left of the boundary because the inequality is "less than."

Since $x = 11$ is not a function, we will choose not to use the calculator to graph the inequality.

Objective 5.2.3 **CHECKUP**

1. Graph.
   a. $y + 3 > 8$ b. $5 - 2x \le 9$
2. What must be true for a linear inequality in two variables if its graph has a vertical boundary line?

3. What must be true for a linear inequality in two variables if its graph has a horizontal boundary line?

Objective 5.2.4   **Modeling the Real World**

Many situations in the real world involve ranges of values rather than single numbers. For example, in business, you want sales income to be greater than cost, regardless of the actual numbers. You want to spend no more than your budget, whatever the budget is, and you want to produce as many items as you can, whatever that number is. Graphing inequalities can give you a picture of these ranges of values, so you can see whether you're close to your budget or you still have room to spend. As with most real-world situations, remember to check the domain of your variables, so that you don't graph negative values of items or time, for example.

EXAMPLE 5

Shanda is a temporary worker for Make or Break Manufacturing Co. She works at most an eight-hour shift with a 30-minute break. (On slow days, she may work shorter hours.) Shanda has been trained to work on two different assembly lines and may be assigned one or both during her shift. One assembly-line job requires 20 minutes per item. The other job requires 10 minutes per item.

a. Write a linear inequality in two variables needed to determine the numbers of items Shanda can complete during one shift.

b. Graph the inequality. Only positive coordinates found in the first quadrant would make sense in this situation. Why?

c. Determine from the graph two possible combinations of 20-minute and 10-minute items Shanda can produce during one shift.

Solution

a. Let x = number of items assembled requiring 20 minutes per item
   y = number of items assembled requiring 10 minutes per item
   The time required to assemble the 20-minute items is $20x$.
   The time required to assemble the 10-minute items is $10y$.
   The total time required to assemble both items is the sum $20x + 10y$. This sum is at most ($\le$) 480 minutes (8 hours × 60 minutes per hour) minus the 30-minute break, or a total of 450 minutes.

$$20x + 10y \le 450$$

b. First, solve the inequality for y.

$$20x + 10y - 20x \le 450 - 20x$$
$$10y \le -20x + 450$$
$$\frac{10y}{10} \le \frac{-20x + 450}{10}$$
$$y \le -2x + 45$$

Only positive values of x and y make sense, because Shanda cannot assemble a negative number of items.

Graph the boundary line, $y = -2x + 45$. This boundary is included as a solid line in the solution and is an upper boundary. Therefore, the region below the line is shaded.

On your calculator, use a window of (0, 47, 10, 0, 62, 10, 1) to view the first quadrant.

Y1 = −2x + 45

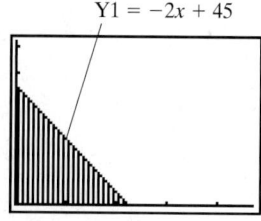

(0, 47, 0, 62)

c.

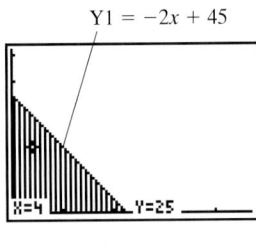

$(0, 47, 0, 62)$

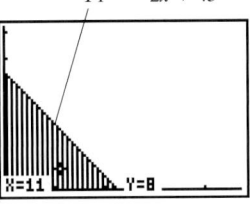

$(0, 47, 0, 62)$

Shanda can produce any combination of 20-minute and 10-minute items determined by the ordered pairs found in the shaded region. For example, $(4, 25)$ and $(11, 8)$ are two ordered pairs in that region.

The ordered pair $(4, 25)$ means that Shanda can produce four 20-minute items and twenty-five 10-minute items during one shift.

The ordered pair $(11, 8)$ means that Shanda can produce eleven 20-minute items and eight 10-minute items during one shift. ■

APPLICATION

The United States Postal Service (USPS) Priority Mail Service delivery rate chart is as follows:

USPS Priority Mail Rates

Weight in Pounds	Local Zones 1, 2, and 3	Zone 4	Zone 5	Zone 6	Zone 7	Zone 8
1	3.85	3.85	3.85	3.85	3.85	3.85
2	3.95	4.55	4.90	5.05	5.40	5.75
3	4.75	6.05	6.85	7.15	7.85	8.55
4	5.30	7.05	8.05	8.50	9.45	10.35
5	5.85	8.00	9.30	9.85	11.00	12.15

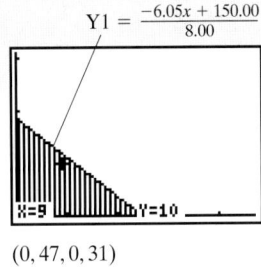

$(0, 47, 0, 31)$

Determine the number of 3-pound packages and the number of 5-pound packages that you can ship to Zone 4 and stay within a shipping budget of $150.00. Give an example of a possible combination of 3-pound packages and 5-pound packages that can be shipped and stay within the budget.

Discussion

Let x = the number of 3-pound packages

y = the number of 5 pound packages

According to the table, the cost of shipping a 3-pound package to Zone 4 is $6.05. The cost of shipping a 5-pound package to Zone 4 is $8.00. The total budget is $150.00; that is, the total shipping costs should be less than or equal to 150.00.

$6.05x$ = the cost of shipping the 3-pound packages

$8.00y$ = the cost of shipping the 5-pound packages

$$6.05x + 8.00y \leq 150.00$$
$$6.05x + 8.00y - 6.05x \leq 150.00 - 6.05x$$
$$8.00y \leq -6.05x + 150.00$$
$$\frac{8.00y}{8.00} \leq \frac{-6.05x + 150.00}{8.00}$$
$$y \leq \frac{-6.05x + 150.00}{8.00}$$

Graph the inequality. (Shown above.) The ordered pairs in the shaded region represent combinations of 3-pound and 5-pound packages that can be shipped and still allow the shipper to stay within the budget. For example, $(9, 10)$ is in the shaded region. Therefore, nine 3-pound packages and ten 5-pound packages can be shipped and still allow the shipper to stay within the budget of $150.00.

Objective 5.2.4 *CHECKUP*

1. Lana is approved for a student loan of no more than $1500 per semester. She figures that she can afford to pay back the loan at the rate of $60 per week. Her parents will contribute $125 occasionally to help her pay back the loan.
   a. Describe Lana's payment plan, using a linear inequality in two variables, where x represents the number of weekly payments Lana makes and y represents the number of occasional payments her parents make on the loan.
   b. Graph the inequality in the first quadrant.
   c. Would a loan such that Lana makes nine weekly payments and her parents make six occasional payments be within the approved loan limit?

   d. Would a loan such that Lana makes 18 weekly payments and her parents make five occasional payments be within the approved loan limit?

2. Use the USPS Priority Mail chart in this section to determine the number of 1-pound packages and 2-pound packages sent to Zone 6 that would overrun a budget of $100.00. Will you overrun the budget by sending thirteen 1-pound packages and nine 2-pound packages to Zone 6? Will you overrun the budget if you send twenty-three 1-pound packages and nine 2-pound packages to Zone 6?

5.2 EXERCISES

Student Solutions Manual | PH Math/Tutor Center | CD Video | MathXL® | MyMathLab | Interactmath.com

Identify each inequality as linear or nonlinear. Express each linear inequality in standard form.

1. $2x + 1.7y > x - 4.6$

2. $y < \sqrt{x-4} + 9$

3. $y < x^2 + 2x - 3$

4. $-5x + 10y \geq 15$

5. $y > \sqrt{x} + 9$

6. $y > x^3 - 27$

7. $\frac{x}{2} - \frac{y}{6} > \frac{1}{12}$

8. $y \geq -\frac{3}{4}x^2 + \frac{5}{8}$

9. $4x + 16 \leq y$

10. $3.5y < 4.2x - 2.8$

11. $y \leq -\frac{2}{5}x + \frac{7}{15}$

12. $\frac{x}{6} + \frac{y}{3} < 2$

Graph each inequality.

13. $2x + y < 3$

14. $5x - y < 6$

15. $5x - 3y \geq 6$

16. $8x + 7y \geq 14$

17. $y < -\frac{3}{4}x + 4$

18. $y < \frac{5}{6}x - 3$

19. $y \geq 2.8x - 1.6$

20. $y \geq 4.7 - 1.9x$

21. $2y > 3x - 5$

22. $5y > 3x - 2$

23. $3x + y - 4 \leq x + 2y - 3$

24. $7x - 2y + 8 \leq 5x - 3y + 1$

25. $5y > -20$

26. $3y + 7 > 25$

27. $3x + 6 \leq 9$

28. $2x - 4 \leq 6$

29. $3x + 5y \geq 12$

30. $7x + 9y \geq 63$

31. $-x - y < 7$

32. $x - y > 3$

33. $-3x - 9y > 27$

34. $-12x - 9y > 36$

35. $\frac{x}{8} + \frac{y}{3} \leq 1$

36. $\frac{x}{9} - \frac{y}{6} \leq 1$

37. $-\frac{4}{7}x + \frac{2}{3}y \geq \frac{10}{21}$

38. $\frac{3}{4}x - \frac{5}{6}y \geq \frac{13}{24}$

39. $1.8x - 3.2y > 0$

40. $58.2x + 19.4y > 0$

41. $4.6y < 3.5y + 5.94$

42. $8.1y + 16.2 < 72.9y$

43. $x - y > 9$

44. $-x + y > 9$

45. $-x - y > 9$

46. $x + y > 9$

47. $y \leq x$

48. $y \geq -x$

In exercises 49–62, write and graph a linear inequality in two variables that represents the situation presented and answer the questions posed.

49. A Christmas shop sells village pieces for $25 each and angel ornaments for $12 each. Rita was given a limit of $225 to spend to buy decorations for the reception area of her office. What combinations can she buy and stay within the limit imposed? Would she be within the budget if she bought four village pieces and seven angel ornaments? What if she bought seven village pieces and nine angel ornaments?

50. The sale of coupon booklets netted the sixth-grade class $240. The money is to be used to buy books and videos for the class library. If the books sell for $12 each and the videos sell for $18 each, what combinations would be within the amount available? Would the class be able to buy 7 books and six videos? Would they be able to buy 12 books and eight videos?

51. The Math Department at KU serves at most 5100 students per semester. Some of their classrooms hold 25 students and others hold 20. What combinations of numbers of sections can be held in each type of room to meet the enrollment needs? If they have teachers for 100 sections in the smaller rooms and 90 sections in the bigger rooms, can they meet their enrollment needs? If they switch and have teachers for 90 sections in the smaller rooms and 100 sections in the bigger rooms, can they meet their enrollment needs?

52. Gordy wants an interior painting job done in which he will pay the contractor "time and material." The painter charges $30 per hour and $20 per gallon for paint and brushes. The estimate, guaranteed to be the maximum bill, for Gordy's total bill is $600. What combinations of time and material were possible given this bill? Is it possible that Gordy's job requires 8 hours and 20 gallons? Is it possible that Gordy's job requires 6 hours and 15 gallons?

53. Pablo will be paid $15 per day for demonstrating crafts, plus $12 for each item he sells at a crafts fair. What combinations will allow the artist to earn at least $400? If he works three days and sells 20 items, will he earn at least $400? If he works five days and sells 30 items, will he earn the minimum?

54. Jason is renting a chain saw for $15 per day. He will charge $10 for each tree he cuts down in his neighbors' yards. What combinations of days and trees will allow him to earn at least $75 for the venture? If he cuts 16 trees in three days, will he make his goal of at least $75? What if he cuts 10 trees in four days?

55. At a school fund-raiser, adults were charged $4.50 each and children were charged $2.00 to attend a chili supper. If the school wished to raise at least $250.00, what combinations of ticket sales would assure that goal? Would 40 adult and 25 children's tickets be enough in sales to make the goal? Would 42 adult and 45 children ticket sales be enough?

56. An elevator has a load limit of 2000 pounds. If the average adult weighs 160 pounds and the average child weighs 65 pounds, what combinations would be safe to ride the elevator? Would a group with 5 teachers and 15 children be safe on the elevator? How about a group with 10 teachers and 12 children?

57. Justin is working as a server at a restaurant chain near a local mall. He is paid $4 per hour and also earns tips of about 18% of his gross sales. He needs to earn at least $180 on the weekend to pay his insurance. What were the possible combinations of hours and gross sales? If he worked eight hours and his gross sales were $1000, can he pay his insurance?

58. A cellular phone company charges a daily fee of $1.50 to use its service. If no calls are made on a given day, there is no fee. To address the issue of unused monthly minutes, the company charges a yearly minute fee of $0.20 per minute for any minutes used beyond 5000. Kelly's father signs her up with this plan and gives her a strict budget of $1000. What combinations of daily use and minutes are possible? If Kelly wants to use her phone every day for a year, can she use 7000 minutes?

59. Barbara bought 220 feet of wallpaper border on sale. What are the limits on the dimensions of a rectangular room if she wants to run the border around the top of the walls? Would she have enough for a 70-by-60-foot room? Would she have enough for a 40-by-60-foot room?

60. In exercise **59**, the rooms Barbara will decorate have 10-foot ceilings. She also bought enough rolls of wallpaper to cover 2400 square feet of wall space. What are the limits on a rectangular room if Barbara wants to paper all four walls, with no allowances for windows or doors? Does she have enough for a 70-by-60-foot room? Does she have enough for a 40-by-50-foot room?

61. An isosceles triangle (two sides are of equal length) has a perimeter at most 107 feet. What combinations of lengths of sides might be possible in this situation? Could one side be 80 feet and another 37 feet? Could the two equal sides be 40 feet each?

62. A scalene triangle has sides in which the longest side is four times the shortest side. The triangle's perimeter is less than 500 cm. What combinations of lengths of sides might be possible in this situation? Could the shortest side be 50 cm? Could the longest side be 400 cm?

For exercises 63 and 64, use the chart for USPS Priority Mail Rates found in the Application.

63. Determine the number of 3-pound packages and the number of 5-pound packages that you can ship to Zone 5 and stay within a shipping budget of $160.00. Give an example of a possible combination of 3-pound packages and 5-pound packages that can be shipped and stay within the budget.

64. Determine the number of 2-pound packages and the number of 5-pound packages that you can ship to Zone 6 and stay within a shipping budget of $125.00. Give an example of a possible combination of 2-pound packages and 5-pound packages that can be shipped and stay within the budget.

 ## 5.2 Calculator Exercises

If you have a TI-84 Plus or obtain the applications package for the TI-83 Plus calculator, you can use features under the APPS key to help you graph linear inequalities in two variables. As an example, graph $x - y < -5$.

- First solve the inequality for y: $y > x + 5$
- Enter the inequality into Y1, using the Inequalz application under the APPS menu:

Press APPS and arrow down to find the Inequalz application.

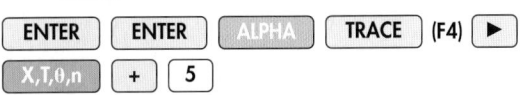

Choose a ZOOM setting:

ZOOM 6

The calculator will display the following screens as you progress through these steps:

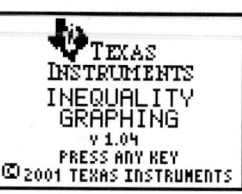 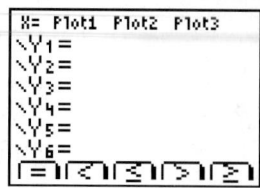  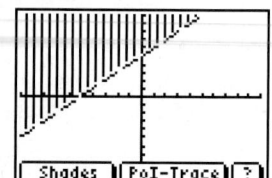

Note that when you use the Inequalz application, the calculator will correctly draw a dashed boundary line for an inequality that does not include equality.

The Inequalz application will also help you graph inequalities in two variables where the boundary line is a vertical line. As an example, graph $3x - 4 > 5 - (x + 1)$.

• First solve the inequality for x: $x > 2$.
• Clear out any equations in Y= .
• Enter the inequality into X =, using the Inequalz application:

  Press APPS

  Arrow down to Inequalz.

  ENTER   ENTER   ▲   ENTER   ALPHA

  TRACE (F4)   ►   2

• Select the ZOOM setting:

  ZOOM   6

The following screens are displayed:

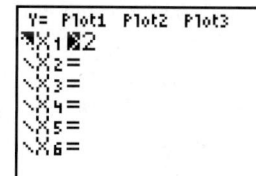 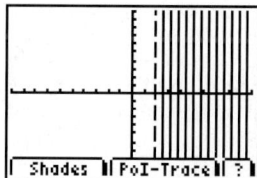

Again, note that the calculator can easily distinguish dashed lines from solid lines when you use the APPS feature.

5.2 Writing Exercises

In this section, you learned two methods for graphing a linear inequality in two variables: with a pencil and paper and with your calculator. It would be helpful to summarize what you have learned. Complete the following table, and keep it as a reference to help you remember details in graphing linear inequalities in two variables:

Inequality	Boundary	Line	Shading
$y < ax + b$	$y = ax + b$		
$y \leq ax + b$			below
$y > ax + b$		dashed	
$y \geq ax + b$			
$y < c$	$y = c$		
$y \leq c$		solid	

Inequality	Boundary	Line	Shading
$y > c$			above
$y \geq c$			
$x < c$		dashed	
$x \leq c$			left
$x > c$	$x = c$		
$x \geq c$			

Summarize what you have learned by answering the following questions:

1. When should the boundary line be dashed, and when should it be solid?
2. When should you shade above the boundary line, and when should you shade below the boundary line?
3. What does the shaded region represent?

5.3 SYSTEMS OF LINEAR INEQUALITIES IN TWO VARIABLES

OBJECTIVES   1 Graph systems of linear inequalities in two variables.
2 Graph systems of linear inequalities in two variables by using a calculator.
3 Model real-world situations by using systems of linear inequalities.

APPLICATION

The United States Postal Service (USPS) Priority Mail Service delivery rate chart is as follows:

USPS Priority Mail Rates

Weight in Pounds	Local Zones 1, 2, and 3	Zone 4	Zone 5	Zone 6	Zone 7	Zone 8
1	3.85	3.85	3.85	3.85	3.85	3.85
2	3.95	4.55	4.90	5.05	5.40	5.75
3	4.75	6.05	6.85	7.15	7.85	8.55
4	5.30	7.05	8.05	8.50	9.45	10.35
5	5.85	8.00	9.30	9.85	11.00	12.15

Your company packages its product in 2-pound packages and 4-pound packages. At most 20 packages can be produced daily. You ship your packages USPS Priority Mail. Determine the number of 2-pound packages and the number of 4-pound packages that you can ship to Zones 1, 2, and 3 and stay within a daily shipping budget of $95.00. Give an example of a possible combination of packages that can be shipped and stay within the budget.

After completing this section, we will discuss this application further. See page 462.

Objective 5.3.1   Graphing Systems of Linear Inequalities in Two Variables

We have solved instances of one linear equation in two variables. But sometimes we may need to know the solution of more than one inequality at a time. A **system of linear inequalities in two variables** consists of two or more linear inequalities in two variables. For example, $x + y < 30$ and $2x - 5y > 40$ is a system of linear inequalities. We usually write this system without the word *and*.

$$x + y < 30$$
$$2x - 5y > 40$$

A solution of a system of inequalities is an ordered pair that makes both inequalities true. We have learned to illustrate graphically the solution set of one linear inequality in two variables by using shaded regions. To solve a system of inequalities, we will need to graph each inequality individually and then determine the ordered pairs that make both inequalities true at the same time. These ordered pairs lie in the overlap of the shaded regions.

GRAPHING A SYSTEM OF LINEAR INEQUALITIES IN TWO VARIABLES

To graph the solution of a system of linear inequalities in two variables,

- Graph each inequality individually on the same rectangular coordinate plane.
- Determine all intersections of the boundary lines.
- Determine the region of the coordinate plane that contains solutions of all inequalities (the overlapping shaded regions).
- Check a point in the overlap region to determine whether that point is a solution.

EXAMPLE 1   Graph the following system of linear inequalities in two variables:

$$2x - y < 7$$
$$-x + y \geq 2$$

a.

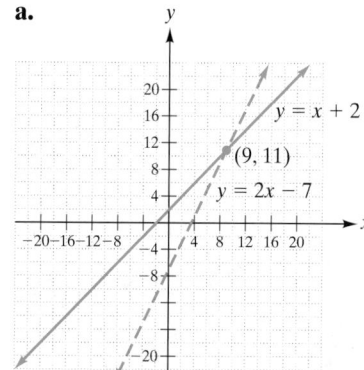

b.

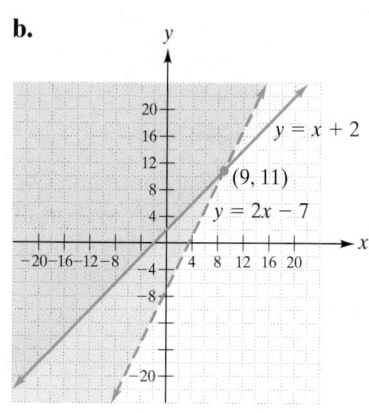

c.

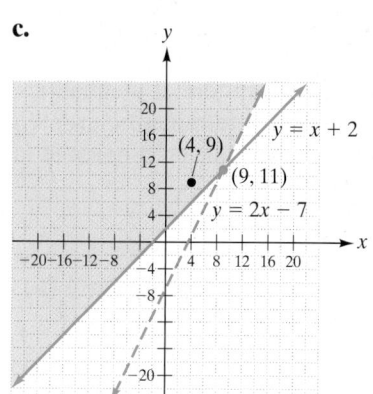

Solution

a. First, solve each inequality for y.

$$2x - y < 7 \quad \text{and} \quad -x + y \geq 2$$
$$y > 2x - 7 \qquad\qquad y \geq x + 2$$

Graph the boundary lines for each inequality. The first inequality has a dashed boundary line (no equality), and the second inequality has a solid boundary line to include the points on the line in the solution set (includes equality).

Determine the intersection of the boundary lines algebraically by solving the related system of equations.

(1) $2x - y = 7$
(2) $-x + y = 2$

By elimination, we obtain

$$x = 9$$

By substitution, we obtain

(1) $-x + y = 2$
$$-(9) + y = 2$$
$$-9 + y = 2$$
$$-9 + y + 9 = 2 + 9$$
$$y = 11$$

The intersection of the boundaries is $(9, 11)$.

b. Shade above both boundaries, because, when solved for y, each inequality was a "greater than" inequality.

The overlap of the shaded regions and the included boundary line shown contains the ordered-pair solutions of the system.

c. Check a point in the overlapping shaded portion. One such point is $(4, 9)$. Check to see whether it is a solution of both inequalities of the system.

$2x - y < 7$	and	$-x + y \geq 2$
$2(4) - 9 \mid 7$		$-(4) + 9 \mid 2$
$8 - 9$		$-4 + 9$
-1		5

The point $(4, 9)$ is a solution.

If the system of linear inequalities has inequalities in which one of the variables has a coefficient of 0, the procedure outlined in Example 1 still applies.

EXAMPLE 2   Graph the following system of linear inequalities in two variables:

$$y < 5$$
$$x + 4 \geq 12$$

Solution

a. Solve the first inequality for y: $y < 5$
The second inequality does not contain a y and should be solved for x.

$$x + 4 \geq 12$$
$$x + 4 - 4 \geq 12 - 4$$
$$x \geq 8$$

a.

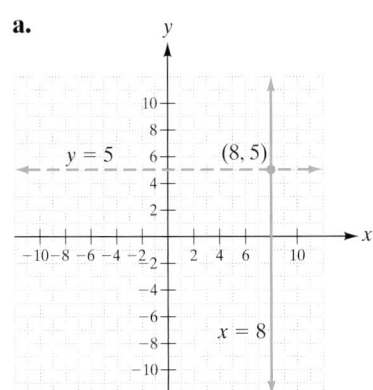

Graph the boundary lines of each inequality. The first line is dashed and the second is solid.

Determine the intersection of the boundary lines algebraically by solving the related system of equations.

$$y = 5$$
$$x = 8$$

The intersection is the ordered pair $(8, 5)$.

b. Shade below the line $y = 5$ for "less than," and shade to the right of the line $x = 8$ for "greater than."

The overlap of both shaded regions and the included boundary line shown contains the ordered-pair solutions of the system.

b.

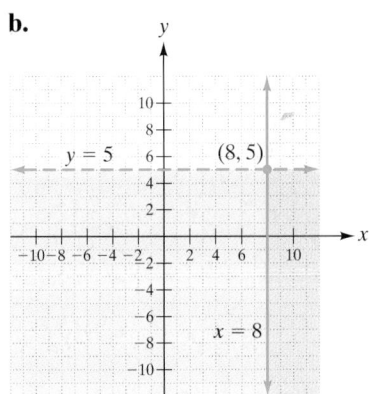

c. Check a point in the shaded portion. One such point is $(10, 3)$. Check to see whether it is a solution of both inequalities of the system.

$$\frac{y < 5}{3 \mid 5} \qquad \text{and} \qquad \frac{x + 4 \geq 12}{\begin{array}{c} 10 + 4 \mid 12 \\ 14 \mid \end{array}}$$

The point $(10, 3)$ is a solution.   ■

c.

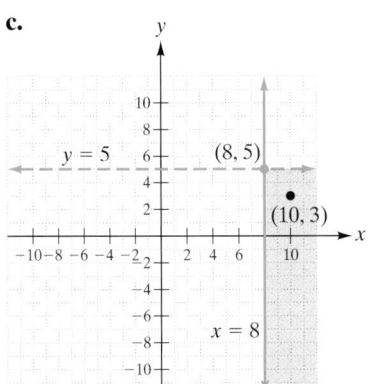

Systems of linear inequalities may have more than two inequalities. A solution of such a system is still an ordered pair that makes all the inequalities true. We graphically illustrate the solutions of the system in the same manner as with two inequalities. That is, we graph all the inequalities on the same coordinate system and determine the overlapping shading of the graphs.

This overlapping shading may be hard to determine. It may be easier to graph the boundary lines, then choose a point in each of the regions of the coordinate plane, and check to see whether that point satisfies all the inequalities in the system.

EXAMPLE 3   Graph the following system of linear inequalities in two variables:

$$x + y \leq 10$$
$$y \leq 4$$
$$y \geq 0$$
$$x \geq 0$$

Solution

a. Solve the first inequality for y.

$$y \leq -x + 10$$

a.

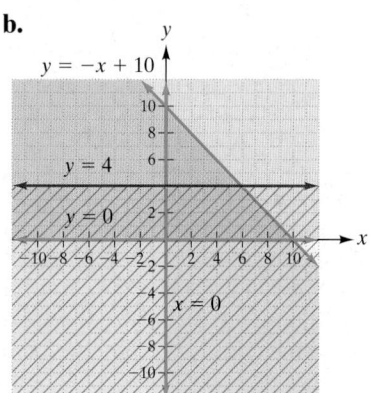

Graph the boundary lines of the inequalities. All the boundaries are solid lines because all the inequalities include equality.

Determine the intersections.

b. Shade the regions for each inequality and determine the overlapping shaded region.

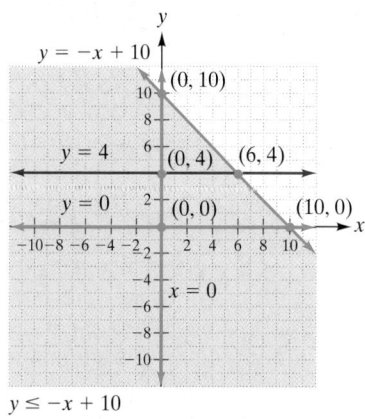

$y \le -x + 10$

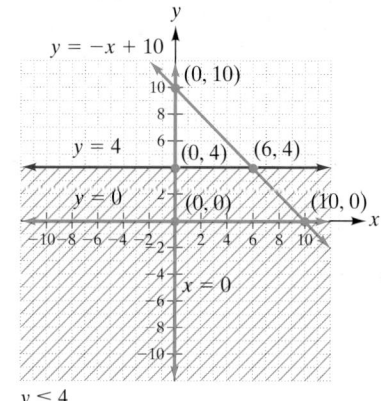

$y \le 4$

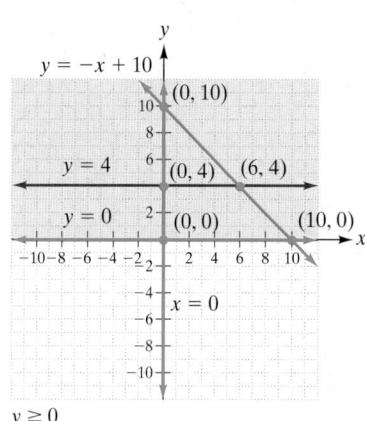

$y \ge 0$

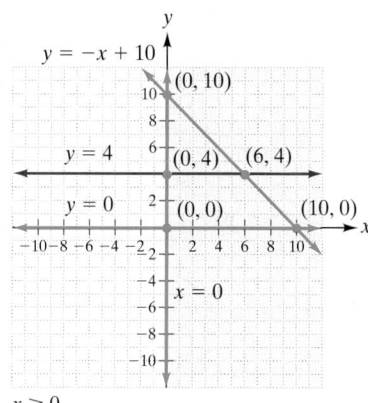

$x \ge 0$

The overlap of all shaded regions and the included boundary lines shown contains the ordered-pair solutions of the system. Because it is so difficult to see the overlapping shading when more than two areas are shaded, it is often advisable to graph only the overlap region, as shown in **Figure 5.5**.

b.

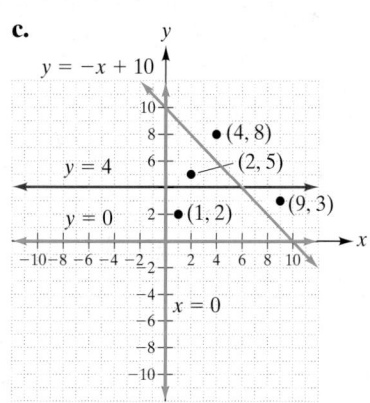

c.

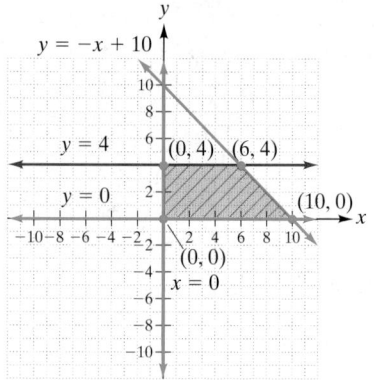

Figure 5.5

c. Alternatively, instead of shading, pick a point in each of the regions defined by the boundaries in the first quadrant. Next, test to determine which of the points you have chosen makes the entire system of inequalities true. Then shade the region which contains that point.

A point in each region is labeled on the graph. Substitute the coordinates of each point into all the inequalities. The ordered pair (1, 2) satisfies all the inequalities. Therefore, shade that region of the first quadrant in which (1, 2) is located. The result is the same as **Figure 5.5**.

Objective 5.3.1 *CHECKUP*

In exercises 1–3, graph each system of linear inequalities.

1. $3x - 5y \leq 5$
$2y + 3 > 7$

2. $y \geq -4x + 3$
$x \geq 1$

3. $x + y < 5$
$y > x + 1$
$x \geq 0$
$y \geq 0$

4. What is the difference between finding the solutions of a linear inequality in two variables and finding the solutions of a system of linear inequalities in two variables?

Objective 5.3.2   Graphing Systems of Linear Inequalities by Using a Calculator

To graph a system of linear inequalities in two variables using a calculator, we perform the same steps as we do by hand.

GRAPHING A SYSTEM OF LINEAR INEQUALITIES IN TWO VARIABLES WITH YOUR CALCULATOR

To graph a system of linear inequalities in two variables with your calculator when both inequalities contain a *y*-term,

- Solve the inequalities for *y*.
- Enter the algebraic expressions in Y1 and Y2.
- Determine the intersection of the boundaries by tracing or using Intersect under the CALC function.
- Shade the coordinate plane determined by the first inequality solved for *y*.
  - For a "less than" inequality, shade below the boundary line.
  - For a "greater than" inequality, shade above the boundary line.
- The second inequality should be entered in the same way as the first.

 TAKE NOTE The calculator does not graph dashed lines; it includes the boundary in the graph. It will be up to you not to include the boundary in your graph. (See 5.3 Calculator Exercises for further guidance.)

EXAMPLE 4

Use your calculator to graph the following system of linear inequalities in two variables:

$$2x - y < 7$$
$$-x + y \geq 2$$

Solution

Solve the inequalities for *y*.

$$y > 2x - 7$$
$$y \geq x + 2$$

Enter the boundaries, graph them, and determine their intersection. Let Y1 = $2x - 7$ and Y2 = $x + 2$, as shown in **Figure 5.6a**.

    Shade above the Y1 graph for a "greater than" inequality. Shade above the Y2 graph for a "greater than or equal to" inequality. The solution set consists of the ordered pairs in the portion of the graph that is shaded twice, as shown in **Figure 5.6b**.

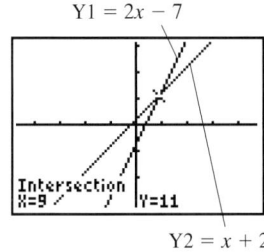

Y1 = 2x − 7

Intersection
X=9   Y=11

Y2 = x + 2
(−47, 47, −31, 31)

Figure 5.6a

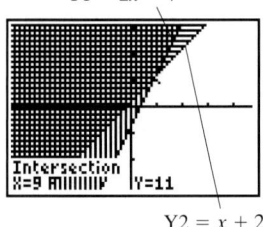

Y1 = 2x − 7

Intersection
X=9 ⊓⊔⊓⊔⊓   Y=11

Y2 = x + 2
(−47, 47, −31, 31)

Figure 5.6b

Solving a system of linear inequalities in two variables when one or more of the inequalities contain a *y*-term with coefficient 0 is more complicated on the calculator. Since the boundary for this type of inequality is not a function, we will not present the calculator procedure here. (See 5.3 Calculator Exercises at the end of this section for instructions.)

When a system of linear inequalities has more than two inequalities, shade the correct portion of the coordinate plane for each inequality that has a boundary line which is a function.

EXAMPLE 5

Use your calculator to graph the following system of linear inequalities in two variables:

$$x + y \leq 10$$
$$y \leq 4$$
$$y \geq 0$$
$$x \geq 0$$

Calculator Solution

We will need to use a close view for this system.

$$(-14.1, 14.1, 1, -12.4, 12.4, 1, 1)$$

Enter the boundaries for the first three inequalities, each of which contains a y-variable.

$$Y1 = -x + 10$$
$$Y2 = 4$$
$$Y3 = 0$$

Because the fourth inequality's boundary, $x = 0$, is not a function, do not graph it. But remember to include it in your description of the solution set of the system of inequalities. (That is, include the y-axis and all points to its right.)

Determine the intersections by tracing. Shade below Y1 and Y2 for a "less than or equal to" inequality. Shade above Y3 for a "greater than or equal to" inequality.

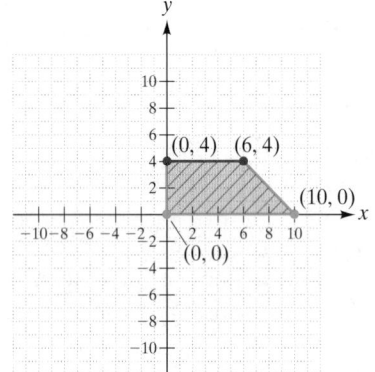

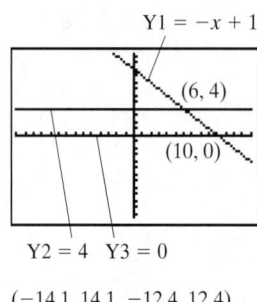

$(-14.1, 14.1, -12.4, 12.4)$

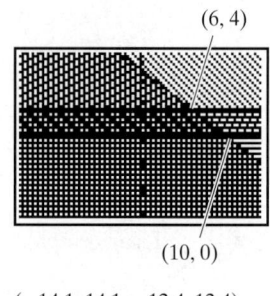

$(-14.1, 14.1, -12.4, 12.4)$

Note: The shaded figure is very difficult to see.

The solution set consists of the ordered pairs that are in the portion of the graph that is shaded three times and that are also on the y-axis or to the right of the y-axis (because $x \geq 0$). ∎

✓ Objective 5.3.2 *CHECKUP*

Graph each system of linear inequalities, using your calculator.

1. $y > -3x + 4$
$\quad x + y > 2$

2. $y \leq \dfrac{2}{3}x + 1$

$\quad y \leq -\dfrac{3}{4}x + 5$

$\quad x \geq 0$

$\quad y \geq 0$

Objective 5.3.3 ## Modeling the Real World

We have seen that systems of inequalities often have many solutions, even an infinite number of solutions. In many real-world situations, we need to restrict the number of solutions to those that make sense, such as restricting solutions to positive values of time. We can do this by adding another inequality to the system, called a **constraint** on the variables. For example, we can add the inequality $t > 0$ to a system involving the variable t for time, so the solutions will include only positive values for t. Or we may want to search a database for unmarried males whose age is over 21 but under 30 and add a constraint that their annual income exceed $100,000. Mathematically, we treat the constraint inequality as just another inequality in the system.

EXAMPLE 6

Donzietta and Kathy make dolls to sell. Donzietta cuts out the patterns and sews and stuffs each doll. This requires 2 hours of work for a rag doll and 6 hours of work for a sculptured doll. Kathy finishes the features and hair of each doll. This requires 3 hours for a rag doll and 2 hours for a sculptured doll. Donzietta plans to work at most 40 hours a week and Kathy at most 32 hours a week.

a. Determine the constraints on producing the dolls for a week.

b. Graph the system of linear inequalities, and determine two possible combinations that satisfy the system.

Solution

a. Let x = number of rag dolls produced per week

y = number of sculptured dolls produced per week

An inequality for Donzietta's contribution is

$$2x + 6y \leq 40$$

An inequality for Kathy's contribution is

$$3x + 2y \leq 32$$

The constraints not stated in the exercise would be that the number of dolls of each kind may not be a negative number.

$$x \geq 0$$
$$y \geq 0$$

Solve each inequality for y.

$$y \leq -\frac{1}{3}x + \frac{20}{3} \qquad \text{\small{Donzietta's contribution}}$$

$$y \leq -\frac{3}{2}x + 16 \qquad \text{\small{Kathy's contribution}}$$

$$y \geq 0$$

The last constraint is solved for x.

$$x \geq 0$$

Graph the boundaries with solid lines for equality, and determine the intersections. Shade each portion of the graph.

For $y \leq -\frac{1}{3}x + \frac{20}{3}$, shade below the boundary line.

For $y \leq -\frac{3}{2}x + 16$, shade below the boundary line.

For $y \geq 0$, shade above the boundary line.

For $x \geq 0$, shade to the right of the boundary line.

b. The solution set consists of all the ordered pairs contained on the boundary lines and in the overlap of the shaded regions. Two possible ordered-pair solutions are $(6, 3)$ and $(8, 4)$.

$(6, 3)$ means that six rag dolls and three sculptured dolls can be produced.

$(8, 4)$ means that eight rag dolls and four sculptured dolls can be produced. ∎

a.

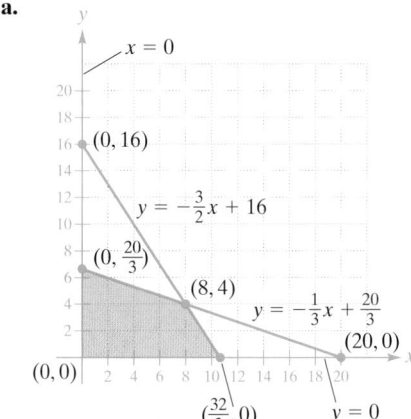

b.

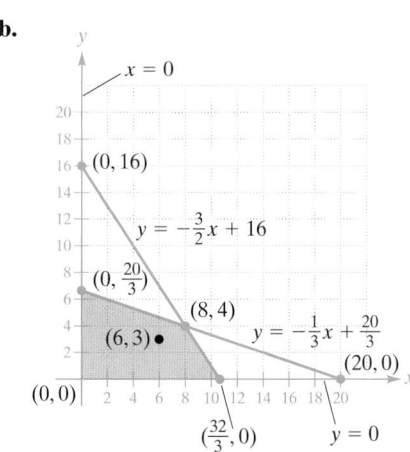

APPLICATION

The United States Postal Service (USPS) Priority Mail Service delivery rate chart is as follows:

USPS Priority Mail Rates

Weight in Pounds	Local Zones 1, 2, and 3	Zone 4	Zone 5	Zone 6	Zone 7	Zone 8
1	3.85	3.85	3.85	3.85	3.85	3.85
2	3.95	4.55	4.90	5.05	5.40	5.75
3	4.75	6.05	6.85	7.15	7.85	8.55
4	5.30	7.05	8.05	8.50	9.45	10.35
5	5.85	8.00	9.30	9.85	11.00	12.15

Your company packages its product in 2-pound packages and 4-pound packages. At most 20 packages can be produced daily. You ship your packages USPS Priority Mail. Determine the number of 2-pound packages and the number of 4-pound packages that you can ship to Zones 1, 2, and 3 and stay within a daily shipping budget of $95.00. Give an example of a possible combination of packages that can be shipped and stay within the budget.

Discussion

Let x = the number of 2-pound packages

y = the number of 4-pound packages

You cannot produce a negative number of packages. Therefore,

$$x \geq 0$$
$$y \geq 0$$

If at most 20 packages can be produced daily,

$$x + y \leq 20 \text{ or } y \leq -x + 20$$

According to the table, the cost of shipping a 2-pound package to Zones 1, 2, and 3 is $3.95. The cost of shipping a 4-pound package to Zones 1, 2, and 3 is $5.30. The total budget for shipping is $95.00. Thus, the total shipping cost should be less than or equal to 95.00.

$$3.95x + 5.30y \leq 95.00$$
$$3.95x + 5.30y - 3.95x \leq 95.00 - 3.95x \quad \text{Subtract 3.95x from both sides.}$$
$$5.30y \leq -3.95x + 95.00 \quad \text{Simplify.}$$
$$\frac{5.30y}{5.30} \leq \frac{-3.95x + 95.00}{5.30} \quad \text{Divide both sides by 5.30.}$$
$$y \leq \frac{-3.95x + 95.00}{5.30} \quad \text{Simplify.}$$

The system of inequalities is

$$x \geq 0$$
$$y \geq 0$$
$$y \leq -x + 20$$
$$y \leq \frac{-3.95x + 95.00}{5.30}$$

$Y1 = -x + 20 \quad Y2 = \frac{-3.95x + 95.00}{5.30}$

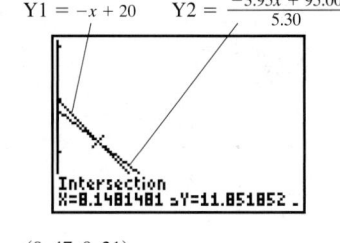

$(0, 47, 0, 31)$

$Y1 = -x + 20 \quad Y2 = \frac{-3.95x + 95.00}{5.30}$

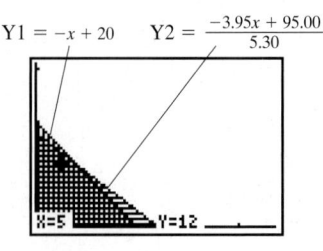

$(0, 47, 0, 31)$

Graph the system of inequalities, and label the point of intersection. The ordered pairs in the shaded region represent combinations of 2- and 4-pound packages that can be produced and shipped while still allowing the shipper to stay within the shipping budget. For example, $(5, 12)$ is found in the shaded region. Therefore, five 2-pound packages and twelve 4-pound packages can be produced and shipped without exceeding the budget.

✓ Objective 5.3.3 *CHECKUP*

1. Donzietta and Kathy decide to streamline their doll-making operation. They purchase kits that shorten the time required to produce the dolls they make. Donzietta can use precut patterns so that she now spends 1.5 hours of work on each rag doll and 4 hours of work on each sculptured doll. Kathy uses doll heads that have been prefinished already, so now she can finish a rag doll in 1.5 hours and a sculptured doll in 1 hour. Donzietta changes her plans to work no more than 30 hours per week, and Kathy changes hers to work no more than 24 hours per week. Determine the new constraints on the production of dolls for a week. Graph the system of linear inequalities, and determine two combinations that satisfy the system.

2. Use the USPS priority chart in this section to determine the number of 2-pound packages and 4-pound packages that can be sent to Zone 6 without exceeding the budget of $125.00 and with the added stipulation that at most 20 packages can be produced each day. If you ship nine 2-pound packages and seven 4-pound packages to Zone 6, will you meet these restrictions? If you ship ten 2-pound packages and eleven 4-pound packages to Zone 6, will you meet the restrictions?

5.3 EXERCISES

Student Solutions Manual   PH Math/Tutor Center   CD Video   MathXL®   MyMathLab   Interactmath.com

Graph each system of linear inequalities. Label the points of intersection.

1. $5x - 3y > 15$
$4x + y > 12$

2. $2x + 3y > -6$
$x - 4y < 8$

3. $2x + 4y \geq 8$
$3x + y \leq -8$

4. $x + y \leq 4$
$x - 2y \leq 7$

5. $y > 3x - 1$
$y > -2x + 4$

6. $y > 3x - 6$
$y > -5x + 2$

7. $y < \dfrac{3}{4}x + 1$
$y < -\dfrac{2}{3}x + 1$

8. $y < \dfrac{1}{2}x + 3$
$y < -\dfrac{3}{2}x - 1$

9. $3x + 2y < 12$
$y - 2 < 1$

10. $-x + 2y > 4$
$3x - 2 < 4$

11. $3y - 2 > 2y + 2$
$x - 1 < 0$

12. $5x + 10 < -5$
$2y + 7 > 5$

13. $y \leq 3x - 5$
$x > 4 - 2y$

14. $y \geq -2x + 3$
$3x \leq 2y + 8$

15. $y \leq \dfrac{1}{2}x + 3$
$x + 2y < 6$

16. $y > x + 1$
$x + y < 1$

17. $y \leq 10 - x$
$2y > x + 6$
$y > 0$
$x < 3$

18. $y > \dfrac{1}{2}x$
$y \leq -2x + 8$
$y \geq 0$
$y \leq 4$
$x \geq 0$

Graph each system of linear inequalities, using your calculator. Determine the points of intersection.

19. $x - 2y > 7$
$5x + 10y < -3$

20. $2x - 3y < 5$
$2y + 6 > 8$

21. $3x - 5y \geq 5$
$10y + 15 > 2$

22. $3x + 5y \geq 15$
$4x - 2y > 7$

23. $y \geq x - 3$
$10x - 5y \geq 14$

24. $y \geq -3x + 4$
$5x - 5y \geq 2$

25. $2x + 9y < 102$
$5x - 11y < -147$

26. $11x + 5y < 133$
$15x + 4y > 187$

27. $3.2x + 4.2y > 368$
$4.4x - 2.1y > 128$

28. $1.4x + 2.4y > 255$
$3.4x - 1.6y > 123$

29. $0.05x + 0.10y < 0.75$
$x + y > 11$

30. $0.25x + 0.50y < 5.75$
$x + y > 14$

For each situation, develop a system of linear inequalities which represents that situation. Graph the system. Determine one possible solution from the solution set.

Geometry

31. A contractor is staking out an area for a rectangular patio. The perimeter of the patio must be no more than 100 feet. The length must be at least 10 feet more than the width. What are the possible dimensions for the patio?

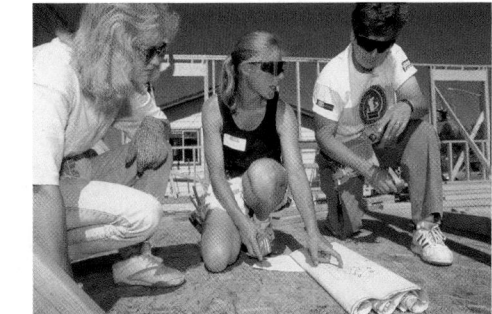

32. After seeing the design for the patio in exercise 31, the customer decides that while the perimeter still should be no more than 100 feet, the length should be at least twice the width. What are the new possible dimensions for the patio?

33. The sum of two angles is no more than 180 degrees. One angle exceeds nine more than ten times the other. Give a possible measure for these angles.

34. The sum of two angles is at least 90 degrees. The larger of the two is at most three times the smaller decreased by seven. Give a possible measure for these angles.

Interest

35. One investment pays 6% simple interest for a year, while another pays 8% simple interest for a year. If you have no more than $3000 to invest, how much can you invest at each rate in order to earn at least $200 in interest for the year?

36. If you have up to $5000 to invest, part at 6% and part at 8% simple interest for a year, how much can you invest at each rate to earn at least $350 in interest?

37. Bob needs two loans to consolidate his debts. He estimates that he needs at least five times more loan money for one loan charging 0.525% per month than for the other, which charges 0.675% per month. A debt consolidation company offers him a deal on both loans which will require a total monthly interest of no more than $90. Give a combination of loan amounts that will meet these conditions.

38. Lindsay has two credit cards. Her low-interest card charges 2.6% monthly and her other card charges 3.8% monthly. In July she had at least three times as much debt on the higher interest card than on the lower. Her monthly interest payment for that month was more than $180. Give a combination of a possible balance on each card.

39. As a part of her financial management strategy, Lauren has 25% of her real estate holdings and 30% of her stock portfolio in a trust for her sons. The combined value of these assets is less than $500,000. For tax purposes, she estimates that the value of the combined trust is more than $25,000. What is a possible value of her real estate holdings and stock portfolio?

40. A real estate investor invests at most $750,000 in two properties. One has an average annual gain in value of 3.5% and the other, a more lucrative investment, has a projected gain of 9.5%. The property values behave as expected, and at the end of the year the investor estimates that he has made at least $2500 with these purchases. What is a possible amount invested at each rate?

Mixtures

41. Hans has two part-time jobs. Because of school, his work is limited to no more than 20 hours per week. He earns $6.50 per hour on the first job and $8.25 on the second job. For what combination of work hours will he earn at least $150.00 per week? Will he earn at least $150.00 if he works 7 hours on the first job and 10 hours on the second job? How about if he works 5 hours on the first job and 15 hours on the second job?

42. Happy Harry's charges $20 per hour to rent its party room and $5 per guest for snacks and beverages. The minimum number of hours of rental is 1.5. For what combination of the number of guests and the number of hours of rental will the cost be no more than $150? Will 15 guests and a 2-hour rental meet the requirements? How about 25 guests and 2.5 hours of rental?

43. Rosie sells two different entrées at her restaurant. Lasagna costs $1.75 per serving to prepare. Veal parmigiana costs $2.25 per serving to prepare. Past experience indicates that she must prepare at least 50 servings of the lasagna and 25 servings of the veal parmigiana each day. If she wants her cost of preparing the entrées to be no more than $200 per day, what combinations of the number of each entrée will do? If she prepares 60 servings of lasagna and 35 servings of veal parmigiana, will the cost be in the permissible range? What if she prepares 60 servings of lasagna and 50 servings of veal parmigiana?

44. Math Academy is considering contracting out its copying operations. It can pay $0.05 per page to copy the manuscript at the local copy center if it contracts for more than 25,000 pages. Or it can purchase a copy machine for a minimum of $1399, after which the cost would be $0.01 per page copied. For what combination of machine cost and number of copies will it be cheaper to buy the machine and do the copying in-house? Will it be cheaper to do copying in-house if 30,000 copies are needed and the cost of a machine is $1500? What if the academy needs 40,000 copies and the machine costs $1400?

For exercises 45 and 46, use the chart for USPS Priority Mail Rates found in the Application.

45. Your company packages its product in 3-pound packages and 5-pound packages. At most 20 packages can be produced daily. You ship your packages USPS Priority Mail. Determine the number of 3-pound packages and the number of 5-pound packages that you can ship to Zone 5 and stay within a daily shipping budget of $160.00. Give an example of a possible combination of packages that can be shipped and stay within the budget.

46. Your company packages its product in 2-pound packages and 5-pound packages. At most 20 packages can be produced daily. You ship your packages USPS Priority Mail. Determine the number of 2-pound packages and the number of 5-pound packages that you can ship to Zone 6 and stay within a daily shipping budget of $125.00. Give an example of a possible combination of packages that can be shipped and stay within the budget.

 ## 5.3 Calculator Exercises

The APPS feature of the TI-84 Plus and TI-83 Plus calculators enhances the graphs of systems of linear inequalities. Using that feature, you are better able to graph boundary lines that are dashed instead of solid, and you are able to graph boundary lines that are vertical lines. An example follows.

Graph $2x - y < 7$
$$3x + 6 < 15$$

• Solve the first inequality for y: $y > 2x - 7$

• Solve the second inequality for x: $x < 3$

- Store the first inequality in Y1:

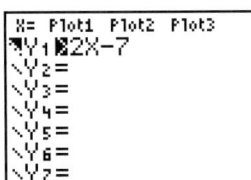

  (Arrow down to the option for "Inequalz".)

  ENTER ENTER ALPHA TRACE (F4) ► 2
  X,T,θ,n – 7

- Store the second inequality in X =:

  ▲ ▲ ENTER ALPHA WINDOW (F2) ► 3

- Select your ZOOM setting:

  ZOOM 6

The calculator displays two dashed boundary lines and an overlapping shaded region indicating coordinate pairs that make the system of inequalities true.

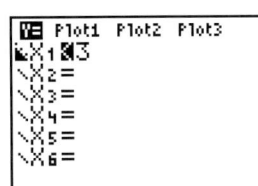

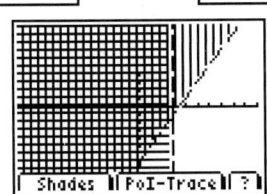

If you wish to see the overlap region more clearly, you may choose a shading option under the Shades menu.

ALPHA Y= (F1) 1

This option selects Ineq Intersection and gives you the following screen:

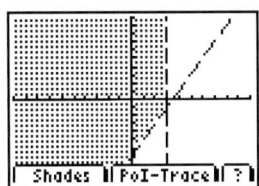

If you wish to determine the intersection point of the boundary lines, enter

ALPHA ZOOM (F3)

and the following screen will show the intersection point, labeled:

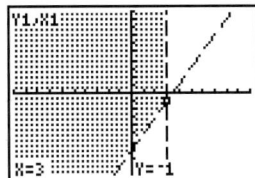

Following are some interesting special cases of systems of linear inequalities that you can graph using the preceding procedure. Describe the solution set of each system.

1. $2x - 3y > -6$
 $-2x + 3y > -6$

2. $x + 2y < 6$
 $x + 2y > 2$

3. $y > -3x + 2$
 $y \le -3x$

4. $y > 2x + 2$
 $y \le 2x - 3$

5. $x + 4 > 0$
 $3x + 2 < -4$

6. $y - 1 < 0$
 $y + 3 > 0$

7. $y < 4 - 2x$
 $2x + y \le -1$

8. $y < x - 7$
 $x > y + 9$

9. $3y \le x + 6$
 $3y - x \ge 6$

10. $y < 2x + 3$
 $y - x + 4 > x + 7$

11. $y < 7$
 $2y - 3 \le y + 4$

12. $y \ge 3x + 4$
 $3x + 5 \le y + 1$

5.3 Writing Exercises

When graphing a system of linear inequalities on your calculator, the choice of an appropriate window is key to being able to see the graph. The window should be large enough to show the intercepts. If any of the inequalities limit the solution space to the first quadrant, the minimum values for x and y should be chosen accordingly. As an example, graph the following system on your calculator using the window indicated.

1. $5.8x + y > 1055.10$
 $18.4x + 73.2y < 19,361.22$
 $x \ge 0$
 $y \ge 0$
 Window: $(0, 1200, 100, 0, 1200, 100, 1)$

Explain the choice of window suggested for exercise 1. Would you graph the third and fourth inequalities? If not, give reasons. After you understand why these choices were made, describe what you would choose as a suitable window for exercise 2, and which inequalities you would graph. Then graph the system and describe the solution set.

2. $487x + 182y < 51,567$
 $182x + 487y < 103,280$
 $x \ge 0$
 $y \ge 0$

■ Chapter 5 Summary

Vocabulary Review

After completing this chapter, you should be able to define the following key terms.

constraint   linear inequality in one variable   system of linear inequalities in two
interval notation   linear inequality in two variables   variables

Fill in the blank with one of the words or phrases listed on the previous page.

1. An example of a _____ is $x + 5 < 4$.
2. An example of a _____ is $2x + 5y \leq x + 4$.
3. An example of a _____ is $3x - 5 > 4$ and $2x - 5y \leq 4$.
4. An example of _____ is $(-\infty, 5)$.

Reflections

1. What is the difference between a linear equation in one variable and a linear inequality in one variable?
2. The solution of a linear inequality can be expressed in interval notation or graphed on the number line. Describe each of these representations.
3. What is the addition property of inequalities? Are there any special considerations you should apply when using this property?
4. What is the multiplication property of inequalities? Are there any special considerations you should apply when using this property?
5. In solving a linear inequality in one variable algebraically, how can you tell that it has no solution? How can you tell that the solution set consists of all real numbers?
6. How does the solution of a linear inequality in two variables differ from the solution of a linear inequality in one variable?
7. How can you show graphically the solution set of a system of linear inequalities in two variables?

■ Chapter 5 Section-by-Section Review

5.1

Recall	Examples
Linear inequality in one variable • The standard forms are $\quad ax + b < 0$ $\quad ax + b > 0$ $\quad ax + b \leq 0$ $\quad ax + b \geq 0$ where a and b are real numbers and $a \neq 0$.	The following are linear inequalities in one variable: $2x + 4 < 0$ $x > -2$ $x \leq 3$ $5x + x - 6 \geq -3x$
Number-line notation • Plot the upper or lower bound with an open dot if the bound is not included and a closed dot if the bound is included. • Draw a solid line to the left of the upper bound for a "less than" or "less than or equal to" inequality and to the right of the lower bound for a "greater than" or "greater than or equal to" inequality.	**Inequality notation** **Number-line notation** $x < 3$ $x > 3$ $x \leq 3$ $x \geq 3$ $-1 < x \leq 3$
Interval notation • Write the bounds, if they exist, in increasing order, separated by a comma. Use infinity symbols if no bound exists. • Precede or follow each bound with a parenthesis if it is not included in the solution set or a bracket if it is included in the solution set.	**Inequality notation** **Interval notation** $x < 3$ $(-\infty, 3)$ $x > 3$ $(3, \infty)$ $x \leq 3$ $(-\infty, 3]$ $x \geq 3$ $[3, \infty)$ $-1 < x \leq 3$ $(-1, 3]$

Recall	Examples
Solving linear inequalities in one variable numerically • Complete a three-column table of values, one column for the independent variable, one for the left side of the inequality, and one for the right side of the inequality. • The solutions are the values of the independent variable that determine a true inequality.	Solve $2x + 1 \leq 3x - 5$ numerically. <table><tr><td>x</td><td>$2x + 1$</td><td>$\leq$</td><td>$3x - 5$</td><td></td></tr><tr><td>5</td><td>11</td><td></td><td>10</td><td>$11 \not\leq 10$</td></tr><tr><td>6</td><td>13</td><td></td><td>13</td><td>$13 \leq 13$</td></tr><tr><td>7</td><td>15</td><td></td><td>16</td><td>$15 \leq 16$</td></tr><tr><td>8</td><td>17</td><td></td><td>19</td><td>$17 \leq 19$</td></tr></table> The solutions are all integers greater than or equal to 6.
Solving linear inequalities in one variable graphically • Graph the two functions, y_1 and y_2, respectively, defined by the left side of the inequality and the right side of the inequality. • Determine the intersection of the graphs. • Locate the portion of the y_1 graph below the y_2 graph for a "less than" inequality or the portion of the y_1 graph above the y_2 graph for a "greater than" inequality. • If the portion located on the graph is to the left of the intersection point, then x is less than the x-coordinate of the intersection point. If the portion located on the graph is to the right of the intersection point, then x is greater than the x-coordinate of the intersection point. • The solution set includes the x-coordinate of the point of intersection if the inequality includes equality.	Solve $2x + 1 \geq 3x - 5$ graphically. 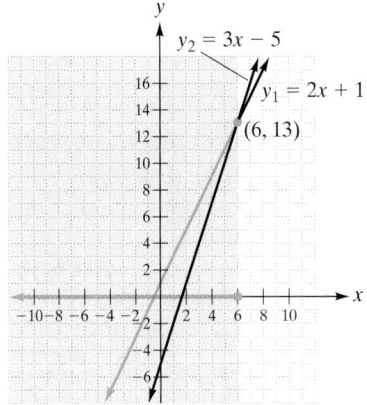 The solution set is the set of all x that satisfy $x \leq 6$.
Solving linear inequalities in one variable algebraically • Simplify both expressions in the inequality (preferably, leaving no fractions). • Isolate the variable on one side of the inequality (preferably, the left side) and the constants on the other side of the inequality by using the addition property of inequalities. • Reduce the coefficient of the variable to 1 by using the multiplication property of inequalities.	Solve $\dfrac{2}{3}x + \dfrac{1}{2} < x - \dfrac{1}{4}$ algebraically. $\dfrac{2}{3}x + \dfrac{1}{2} < x - \dfrac{1}{4}$ $12\left(\dfrac{2}{3}x + \dfrac{1}{2}\right) < 12\left(x - \dfrac{1}{4}\right)$ Multiply both sides by the LCD, 12. $12\left(\dfrac{2}{3}x\right) + 12\left(\dfrac{1}{2}\right) < 12(x) - 12\left(\dfrac{1}{4}\right)$ Distribute 12. $8x + 6 < 12x - 3$ Simplify. $8x + 6 - 12x < 12x - 3 - 12x$ Subtract 12x from both sides. $-4x + 6 < -3$ Simplify. $-4x + 6 - 6 < -3 - 6$ Subtract 6 from both sides. $-4x < -9$ Simplify. $\dfrac{-4x}{-4} > \dfrac{-9}{-4}$ Divide both sides by -4. $x > \dfrac{9}{4}$ Simplify.

Identify each inequality as linear or nonlinear.

1. $3x^2 - 2x + 1 < 0$

2. $5x - 4 > x + 7$

3. $\dfrac{2}{3}x + \dfrac{4}{5} \leq \dfrac{7}{15}$

4. $\sqrt{x} - 3 \geq 6$

5. $x - 3 \geq 6$

6. $\dfrac{1}{x} - 3x \geq 6$

7. $1.5z - 12.6 < 14.7z$

8. $3(a + 2) < 15a - (2a + 1)$

Solve each inequality numerically for integer solutions.

9. $4x + 7 < 2x - 5$ **10.** $2.4x - 9.6 > 4.8$ **11.** $\dfrac{3}{5}x - \dfrac{7}{10} \leq \dfrac{1}{5}x + \dfrac{1}{2}$ **12.** $\dfrac{1}{2}x - 2 \geq -\dfrac{1}{3}x - \dfrac{11}{3}$

Solve each inequality graphically. Represent the solution as an inequality, in interval notation, and on a number line.

13. $2x - 2 > -x + 4$

14. $1.2x + 0.72 \leq -2.1x + 8.64$

15. $(x + 6) - 3(x + 1) < (2x + 5) - 2(2x + 3)$

16. $(x + 3) + (x + 1) \geq 3(x + 1) - (x - 1)$

Solve each inequality algebraically. Represent the solution in interval notation.

17. $412 + x > 671$

18. $y - \dfrac{7}{13} < \dfrac{11}{39}$

19. $3x + 7 < 4x + 21$

20. $14 + 2x < 2x$

21. $8.7x + 4.33 \leq -2.1x - 33.41$

22. $6.8z - 9.52 \geq 0$

23. $2(x + 5) - (x + 6) < 2(x + 2)$

24. $3(x - 4) + 2(x + 1) > 5x + 10$

25. $-3 < 4 - 2x \leq 0$

26. $8 \leq 3(x - 7) + 5 < 20$

For each situation, write and solve an inequality that represents it.

27. Your company has placed a limit on car rentals of no more than $150.00 per trip. If the rental agency charges a flat fee of $49.95 plus $0.18 per mile driven, what range of miles will keep you within budget?

28. Ali must average sales of more than $1500 per month in order to receive his six-month commission. For the first five months, his sales were $2100, $1300, $1650, $1250, and $1725. What should his sales be in the sixth month in order for him to receive his commission?

29. A rectangular flower bed must have a perimeter of no more than 40 feet. If the length must be 4 feet more than the width, what widths would be within the limits?

30. A testing center charges students $35.00 to take a standardized test. The center pays a license fee of $20.00 per student to administer the test. The average daily cost to establish and staff the center is $225.00. How many students must be tested each day to realize a profit of at least $500.00 per day?

31. In order to earn a $B+$ grade for a college mathematics course, a student must have an average of 88 to 92 points. Paul's test scores are 89, 96, 89, 80, and 100. What scores on his last test will earn him a $B+$ in the course?

32. A man who is 5 feet, 6 inches, tall has a body mass index (BMI) given by the expression $0.15x + 2$, where x is his weight in pounds. If the man has other heart risks besides being overweight, a doctor will prescribe medication if his BMI is at least 27. Determine the weights for which a doctor will prescribe medication.

33. Joshua has a choice between two phone plans. One plan charges $39.99 per month with unlimited local minutes and $0.05 per minute for long-distance calls. The second plan charges $49.99 per month for unlimited local minutes and 500 minutes of long-distance calls. Additional long-distance calls are $0.10 per minute. Assuming Joshua uses more than 500 minutes of long distance each month, determine the number of minutes of long distance Joshua can use so that the second plan costs less than the first plan.

34. Between 2000 and 2001, deaths by suicide went up. Using data from the United States Center for Health Statistics, the number of deaths by suicide per 100,000 population, $s(t)$, where t is the number of years since 2000, can be estimated by $s(t) = 0.3t + 10.4$. Assuming this pattern continues, determine the years in which the number of deaths by suicide will exceed 15 per 100,000.

5.2

Recall	Examples
Linear inequality in two variables	Linear inequalities in two variables
• The standard forms are $ax + by < c$ $ax + by > c$ $ax + by \leq c$ $ax + by \geq c$ where a, b, and c are real numbers and a and b are not both 0.	$2x + 4y < 5$ $x \leq 7$ $y \geq \dfrac{2}{3}$
Solution of a linear inequality in two variables • An ordered pair is a solution of a linear inequality in two variables if the value of its coordinates satisfy the inequality.	Is $(1, -4)$ a solution of the inequality $x + 2y > -7$? $\begin{array}{c\|c} x + 2y & > -7 \\ \hline 1 + 2(-4) & -7 \\ -7 & \end{array}$ Because $-7 \not> -7$, $(1, -4)$ is not a solution of the inequality.

Recall	Examples
Graph a linear inequality in two variables • If the inequality contains the variable y, solve for y. If not, solve for x. • Graph the boundary line determined by the related equation $y = mx + b$ or $x = c$. • Use a solid line if the boundary is included and a dashed line if the boundary is not included. • Shade below the boundary if the inequality solved for y is a "less than" inequality. Shade above the boundary if the inequality solved for y is a "greater than" inequality. Shade to the left if the inequality solved for x is a "less than" inequality. Shade to the right if the inequality solved for x is a "greater than" inequality.	Graph $-2x + 4y < 1$. Solve for y: $y < \dfrac{1}{2}x + \dfrac{1}{4}$ 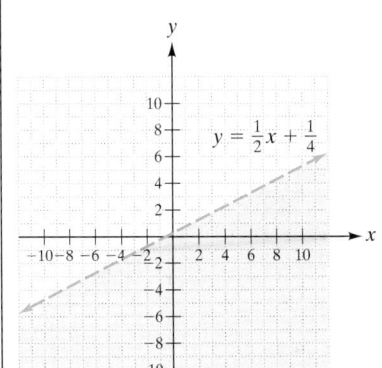 Graph $-2x \geq 6$. Solve for x: $x \leq -3$ 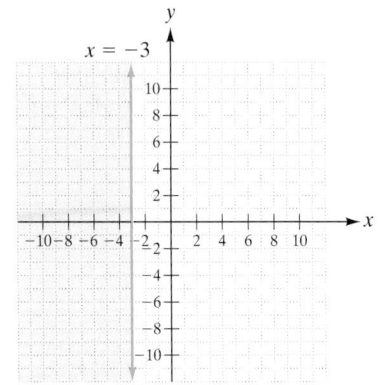

Identify each inequality as linear or nonlinear. Express each linear inequality in two variables in standard form.

35. $x + 2y < 12$

36. $y < \dfrac{2}{3}x + \dfrac{5}{9}$

37. $x^2 + y^2 \geq 1$

38. $0.3x + 2.9 > 1.4y$

39. $y \geq \sqrt{x} - 1.44$

40. $y < x^2 + 9$

Graph each inequality.

41. $12x + 6y < 48$

42. $y > \dfrac{3}{5}x - 6$

43. $4y \leq x + 12$

44. $y + 9 \geq 12$

45. $5y - 2 < y - 10$

46. $2x + 16 > x + 18$

47. $8x - 12y > 24$

48. $4.4x + 1.1y \geq 12.1$

49. $7.4x - 14.8y \leq 29.6$

50. $\dfrac{x}{12} + \dfrac{y}{8} > -\dfrac{5}{4}$

51. $-x - y < 2$

52. $y > -9x + 6$

For each situation, write and graph a linear inequality in two variables that represents the situation. From the graph, determine two possible solutions.

53. Oksana has at most \$85 to spend on plants for her flower garden. She can buy rhododendrons at \$4 a pot and azaleas at \$6 a pot. What combinations of plants can she buy and not go over her budget?

54. Rosa gained 5 points for every homework exercise she solved correctly and lost 3 points for every exercise she solved incorrectly or skipped. What combinations would allow her to score at least 80 points on her homework assignment?

55. A rectangular piece of property has perimeter of at most 1080 feet. Find some possible dimensions of the rectangle. Could the rectangle be twice as long as it is wide? If so, what are its possible dimensions?

56. Chantal signs a contract with a tanning salon as a part of a special promotion. She pays \$3.50 for every 20-minute tanning session plus \$1.50 per application of special moisturizing lotion. If she wants to spend no more than \$40.00 per month, what combinations of tanning time and lotion applications are possible? If she spends 200 minutes tanning, can she afford to get the moisturizing lotion every time? If she wants to get the moisturizing lotion after every tanning session, what is a possible number of minutes she can tan?

5.3

Recall	Examples
Graph a system of linear inequalities • Graph each inequality in the system on the same coordinate plane. • Label all intersections of the boundary lines. • Shade the region of the coordinate plane that contains solutions of all the inequalities. • Check a point in the overlapping region to determine whether that point is a solution.	Graph. $y < 2x + 5$ $y \geq -3x - 2$ You can verify that the point $(2, 1)$ in the shaded region checks. $y < 2x + 5$ $\begin{array}{c\|c} 1 & 9 \end{array}$ $y \geq -3x - 2$ $\begin{array}{c\|c} 1 & -8 \end{array}$

Graph each system of linear inequalities. Label the points of intersection.

57. $2x + y > 10$
$\quad y < 3x - 5$

58. $3(x + 2) + 1 > -5$
$\quad 2x - y < -8$

59. $x + 6 < 4$
$\quad 2(y + 2) > y + 3$

60. $x - 2y \geq 12$
$\quad 2x + 3y < -6$

61. $y < 3x - 6$
$\quad y < -3$

62. $2x + 3y \leq 6$
$\quad x + y \leq 1$

63. $y < 2x - 15$
$\quad y > -3x + 10$

64. $y > 2x + 1$
$\quad x > 2y + 7$

65. $2y + 6 \leq 3y + 5$
$\quad 2(x - 3) + 1 > 5$

66. $y < 6 - x$
$\quad y < 2x + 1$
$\quad x \geq 0$
$\quad y \geq 0$

67. $y < 25 - \dfrac{1}{4}x$

$\quad y < \dfrac{2}{3}x + 5$

$\quad x \geq 0$

$\quad y \geq 0$

For each situation, write a system of linear inequalities in two variables that represents that situation. Graph the inequalities. Determine one possible solution from the graph.

68. Oksana has at most $85 to purchase potted rhododendrons at $4 each and azaleas at $6 each. She needs at least four more rhododendron plants than azaleas. What possible combinations will meet both criteria?

69. If you have $4000 to invest, part at 5% and part at 6% simple interest for a year, how much can you invest at each rate to earn at least $225 interest?

70. A rectangle in which the length is more than the width increased by 15 feet has perimeter less than 175 feet. Find a possible dimension for the rectangle.

■ Chapter 5 Mixed Review

Identify each inequality as linear or nonlinear.

1. $\sqrt{x} - 2 \leq -4$

2. $\dfrac{1}{4}x + \dfrac{3}{4} > \dfrac{1}{2}$

3. $\dfrac{1}{x} - 2 < -5$

Identify each inequality as linear or nonlinear.

4. $y > x + 5$

5. $x^2 - 2y \geq 6$

6. $y - 2 < -5(x + 4)$

Solve numerically for integer solutions.

7. $5x + 3 < 2x - 9$

8. $5.6x - 15.3 > 1.3x + 19.1$

9. $\dfrac{1}{6}x + \dfrac{23}{3} \leq \dfrac{13}{6} - \dfrac{5}{3}x$

10. $\dfrac{3}{7}x + \dfrac{9}{5} \geq \dfrac{4}{5}x - \dfrac{17}{5}$

Solve each inequality graphically. Represent the solution as an inequality, in interval notation, and on the number line.

11. $5x - 13 > 3(1 - x)$

12. $2.1x + 31.71 \leq 8.19 - 3.5x$

13. $3(x - 1) + (x - 1) < 2(x - 1) + 2x - 1$

14. $4(x + 2) - 3(x - 5) \leq 5x + 8 - 4(x + 3)$

Solve each inequality algebraically. Represent the solution in interval notation.

15. $173 - x < 359$

16. $z - \dfrac{4}{17} > \dfrac{15}{34}$

17. $5x + 4 > 3x + 18$

18. $8x < 8x - 16$

19. $3.5x + 19.88 \geq -1.9x + 4.76$

20. $2.6y + 9.62 \leq 0$

21. $3(x + 3) < 4(x + 1) - 2(x - 2)$

22. $3(x - 3) + 2(x + 2) < 5x + 7$

23. $15 < 4(2x - 1) + 5 \leq 25$

Graph each system of linear inequalities. Label points of intersection.

24. $2y + 2 > y$
$\quad y < -x + 1$

25. $2x + 3 > x$
$\quad 2x < 6$

26. $y \geq 2x - 8$
$\quad 3x + y < 8$

27. $2(x - 1) - 4 > 0$
$\quad 2x + y \leq 3$

28. $x + y < 9 - x$
$\quad 2x + y > 5$

29. $3(x - 3) - 1 > 8$
$\quad 3y - 10 < 15 - 2y$

30. $y < 3x + 7$
$\quad x - y > -1$

31. $x - 5y \leq 15$
$\quad x + 5y \leq -5$

32. $y < -4x + 6$
$\quad y > 3x - 8$

33. $y > x$
$\quad x > 2 - y$

34. $x + 9 \leq 3$
$\quad 3y > 2y - 1$

35. $y < -2x + 7$
$\quad y < 2x$
$\quad x \geq 0$
$\quad y \geq 0$

36. $y > \dfrac{3}{4}x - 4$
$\quad y > -\dfrac{2}{3}x + 3$
$\quad x \geq 0$
$\quad y \geq 0$

Graph each linear inequality in two variables.

37. $9x - 5y < 45$

38. $y > \dfrac{4}{3}x - 5$

39. $3y \leq 2x + 9$

40. $y + 13 \geq 8$

41. $-2y - 6 < y - 11$

42. $x - 13 > 3x + 19$

43. $x - 7y > 21$

44. $2.7x + 5.4y \geq 16.2$

45. $4.8x - 1.8y \leq 14.4$

46. $\dfrac{x}{12} + \dfrac{y}{9} > -\dfrac{1}{3}$

47. $x - y < 7$

48. $y > -5x + 7$

For each situation, write and solve a linear inequality in one variable that represents that situation. State one possible solution from the solution set.

49. Ed's Internet music service charges $9.99 per month for its service and $0.75 per track to burn a song. Ed wants to spend less than $15.00 per month for this expense. How many songs can he burn?

50. The setup cost for producing gourmet packs of coffee is $255.00. The materials cost $2.50 per pack. The packs will be sold for $12.50 each. How many packs must be sold in order to make a profit of at least $1200.00?

51. Catherine wants to keep her average telephone bill below $42. Her first five months had bills of $45, $36, $52, $48, and $31. What are the limits on her bill for the sixth month?

52. The width of a rectangular street sign has been set at 18 inches. What must the length be if the area of the sign must be more than 600 square inches?

53. Tony has designed a computer software package that he markets through the Internet. He sells the package for $19.95, including shipping and handling. He estimates that he spends $1.45 for each package that he ships. His only over-

head charge is a monthly charge of $17.00 for his Web site. How many packages must Tony sell in order to realize a profit of at least $600 per month?

54. Tony tracked his profits for the first five months that he sold his software package. His profits were $344, $434, $254, $705, and $723. What should his profit be for the sixth month if he wishes his average profit to be between $500 and $600?

55. According to the National Center for Education Statistics of the United States Department of Education, the percentage of U.S. eighth-grade students attending public schools who scored at or above basic level (denoting "partial mastery of prerequisite knowledge and skills fundamental for proficient work") in mathematics is growing. The percentage of such students, $p(x)$, can be estimated by $p(x) = \dfrac{1}{3}x + 66$, where x is the number of years after 2003. Assuming this trend continues, in what years will the percent of students at or above basic level exceed 75%?

Write and graph a linear inequality in two variables that represents the situation. Determine one possible solution from the graph.

56. A soccer team needs to earn at least 25 points during the season to make the playoffs. If it earns three points for each win, one point for each tie, and no points for a loss, what combinations of wins and ties will land the team in the playoffs?

57. Deepti has her daughter and infant son in her school's Child Care Center. The Center charges $4.14 per hour for her

daughter and $5.50 per hour for her son because he requires more care. Deepti's financial aid covers $90 for child care expenses per week. What combinations of care for her son and daughter can she afford? Can she afford 12 hours per week for each child? If her husband can watch her son for 5 of the 12 hours per week, can she afford it?

For each situation, write a system of linear inequalities in two variables that represents the situation. Graph the inequalities. Determine one possible solution from the graph.

58. Sharon inherits less than $20,000 from her uncle. She decides to invest the money in two different accounts. One account pays 6.5%. The other is a money market fund in which she will leave money without withdrawal and which pays 8.25% annually. Sharon would like to earn yearly interest income of at least $1400. What is a combination of investments that will provide the desired return?

59. An isosceles triangle has two sides of equal length. The third side is at least twice the length of one of the shorter sides. The perimeter is at most 125 meters. What is a possible length of the sides of the triangle and the corresponding perimeter?

60. Farmer McGregor plants oats and wheat on his farm. For conservation purposes, he plants at least twice as many acres of wheat as oats. He can handle up to a total of 540 acres of planting. What combinations of plantings can he realistically consider?

61. A realtor has three efficiency apartments and five regular apartments to rent. The regular apartments will rent for at least $75 more than the efficiency apartments. If the realtor would like to gross at least $6000 per month, what combination of rental rates will meet her wishes?

■ Chapter 5 Test

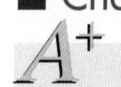

TEST-TAKING TIPS

In attempting to solve a problem on a test, it is helpful to follow some routine procedures. Practice these procedures for homework so that you will be comfortable using them during a test.

- Write down key information about the problem.
- Identify what you need to solve.
- List any formulas or rules you may need for the solution.

- Numerically estimate the answer, using rounded numbers.
- Imagine the same problem with simpler numbers.
- If time permits, solve the problem two different ways (for example, algebraically and graphically) as a check.
- Always check your work.

Identify each inequality as linear or nonlinear. Write the linear inequalities in standard form.

1. $2x - 3y > x + 8$ **2.** $4x^2 + 2x < x - 9$ **3.** $5(x - 3) \geq 4 - (x + 1)$ **4.** $\frac{1}{2}x - 4 \geq y + \frac{3}{8}$

Solve each inequality and represent the solution by using the number line and interval notation, if possible.

5. $7(x + 2) - 3(x + 1) > 4(x + 8)$ **6.** $5x + 9 < 2x - 3$ **7.** $\frac{4}{5}(x - 10) < \frac{1}{5}(4x + 5) + 1$

8. $5a - 7 \geq 8a + 1$ **9.** $-2 < 3(x - 4) - 2 \leq 1$

Graph each linear inequality in two variables.

10. $y < -2x + 5$ **11.** $x + 3 > 2x - 1$

Graph each system of linear inequalities in two variables. Label the points of intersection.

12. $x - y > 4$
$\quad\ x + 2y > 4$

13. $y \geq 4x - 5$
$\quad\ y > -3x + 4$

14. $3y - 1 > 2$
$\quad\ x - 3 \leq -5$

In exercises 15–18, write and solve a linear inequality in one variable to represent the application. Determine one possible solution from the solution set.

15. Bryshon was fortunate to qualify for a student loan that did not charge interest. While he was a full-time student he was able to defer payments. Upon graduation he owes $10,000, which he plans to pay off at the rate of $200 per month. For how many months will his balance be more than $5000?

16. The availability of computers for students in public schools is on the rise. According to data from Quality Education Data, Inc., the number of students per computer can be modeled by $n(x) = -0.167x + 5.4$, where x is the number of years after 1999. If this trend continues, when will the number of students per computer be below three students per computer?

17. On the Fujita Scale, an F3 tornado is considered a severe tornado and has a wind speed between 158 mph and 206 mph inclusive. If the last three recorded tornadoes had wind speeds of 168 mph, 172 mph, and 225 mph, what wind speeds for the next tornado will result in an average wind speed for the four tornadoes that is within the range of a severe tornado?

18. Alexandra opened a shop to sell gift baskets. She sells the baskets for an average price of $49.00 each. The materials, food, and gadgets that she uses to create the baskets cost her an average of $23.50 per basket. She rents the storefront, and her overhead costs average $250.00 per week. How many baskets must she sell in order to make a profit of at least $300.00 per week?

In exercises 19–22, write and graph a linear inequality in two variables to represent the application. Determine one possible solution from the solution set.

19. Jenny uses a mail-order coffee company to buy coffee for the employee lounge at work. The company sells standard blends of coffee for $7.99 per pound and special blends for $12.99 per pound. Her yearly budget is $600.00. How many pounds of coffee might she purchase?

20. A Cub Scout earns 5 points for every good deed and 2 points for every activity sheet completed. If a scout must earn at least 20 points in order to receive a medal, what combinations of good deeds and activity sheets will suffice?

21. A rectangular piece of property has perimeter of at most 504 feet. Find some possible dimensions of the rectangle. Could the rectangle be twice as long as it is wide? If so, what are its possible dimensions?

22. Larry hires a mobile computer repair service to work on his two home computers. The people who came in charged $85 per hour to work on hardware and software and $25 per hour to work on DSL or dial-up lines. The estimated bill was $480. What are the possible combinations of number of hours spent working on each type of task? If the job took four hours on hardware/software, could the technicians have spent six hours on the lines?

In exercises 23 and 24, write and graph a system of linear inequalities that represents the application. Determine one possible solution from the solution set.

23. The perimeter of a rectangular deck must be no more than 100 feet. The length must be at least 10 feet less than twice the width. What are the possible dimensions of the patio? If the width is 20 feet, give a possible length.

24. If you have at most $6000 to invest, part at 4% simple interest and part at 8% simple interest, what investment strategies will assure you of earning at least $400 in interest for a year?

25. What do we mean by the solution of a system of linear inequalities in two variables?

Project

PART I You have decided that you need additional income to balance your budget. In order to receive extra income, you plan to produce and sell a product to consumers for a profit.

Write a report on your business venture. Include the following information:

1. The name of your business
2. The product you wish to produce and sell
3. The fixed and variable costs associated with producing and selling your product (include a list of these costs)
4. A cost function
5. The selling price of your product
6. A revenue function
7. The number of items you must produce and sell to break even on your venture
8. The amount of extra income you need and how many items you need to produce to achieve at least that amount

PART II In this chapter, you have encountered several applications that used real data. For example, one application involved body mass index, and another involved shipping rates for the United States Postal Service deliveries. These data may change over time. To obtain more current data, you may need to research through the library or through Internet sites.

Choose an application in this chapter and either verify that the data has not changed or obtain more current data. Reconstruct the application if more current data exists. Write a short report on your findings, listing the sources for your data, and the results of your update of the application, if the data did indeed change.

■ Chapters P–5 Cumulative Review

Evaluate.

1. $-(-9)$

2. $-|-9|$

3. $\sqrt[3]{-\dfrac{27}{64}}$

4. $\sqrt{10}$

5. $\left(-\dfrac{9}{14}\right)\left(\dfrac{7}{3}\right)$

6. $-\dfrac{3}{8} \div \left(-1\dfrac{2}{3}\right)$

7. $12(-3) \div (-6)(2) \div (-2)$

8. $40 + 16 \div 8 - \sqrt{3^2 + 7 \cdot 5} + 5$

9. $\dfrac{2(5^2 - 10) + 4^2 - 1}{8^2 - 2(32)}$

Simplify.

10. $6x - 2(4x - 1)$

11. $4[2(x - 3) + 1] - [5(2x - 4) - 6]$

Consider the relation $y = 2x^2 - 3$.

12. Graph the relation.

13. What is the domain of the relation? The range?

14. Is the relation a function? Justify your answer.

15. Determine the relative minima and the relative maxima.

16. Determine the x-values for which the relation is increasing and decreasing.

17. Determine the x-intercept and the y-intercept.

Solve.

18. $7x - 3 = 5$

19. $(x + 3) - 2(3x + 4) = 5$

20. $1.2(x + 3) - 4(0.3x + 0.15) = 3$

21. $|2x + 6| = 10$

22. $5|x| + 8 = 8$

Solve. Represent the solution as an inequality, using interval notation, and as a graph on a number line.

23. $-12x + 4 \geq -2x + 8$

24. $4(x + 3) - 3(x - 2) \leq x - 5$

25. $30 < 2x + 10 \leq 70$

Graph. Label enough points to determine the graph.

26. $f(x) = -3x + 4$

27. $6x + 3y = 9$

28. $2x + 3 = 11$

29. $3y - 2 = 5$

30. $y < 4x - 3$

Determine if the graphs of the pair of equations are coinciding lines, parallel lines, only intersecting lines, or both intersecting and perpendicular.

31. $2x + 3y = 21$
   $3x - 2y = 2$

Solve the systems of equations.

32. $y = 3x + 4$
   $y = 2x - 5$

33. $4x + 2y = 8$
   $y = -2x + 4$

Graph the system of inequalities. Determine one possible solution from the graph.

34. $y \geq -x$
   $y < 2x + 4$

Determine the slope of a line that satisfies the following conditions.

35. Passes through $(-2, 3)$ and $(-1, -2)$

36. Passes through $(6, -5)$ and $(6, 3)$

37. $y = 2x + 3$

38. $y = 1.4$

Write an equation for a line that satisfies the following conditions.

39. Passes through $(-2, 3)$ and $(-1, -2)$

40. Passes through $(5, 4)$ and is parallel to the graph of $2x + 3y = 1$.

Write in scientific notation.

41. 5,340,000

Write exercises 42 and 43 in standard notation.

42. 1.2×10^{-4}

43. $-4.783\text{E}{-5}$

44. Solve for L: $P = 2L + 2W$

45. Given $f(x) = x^2 + 2x - 1$, find $f(-3)$.

46. An investment plan offers 11% simple interest on an investment. How much should Lance invest in order to have $2775 in his account at the end of one year?

47. Two angles are complementary. The larger angle measures 25 degrees more than twice the smaller angle. Find the measures of the two angles.

48. Michael's Coffee Shop sells a special blend called Mike's Favorite. For the blend, Michael mixes Hazelnut Coffee, which sells for $7.50 per pound, with Cinnamon Coffee, which sells for $6.75 per pound. How much of each flavor must he use to create 10 pounds of Mike's Favorite blend if he sells it for $7.00?

49. April scored 82, 88, 80, and 95 on the first four tests in her Algebra class. There is one more test in the class. In order to earn a B, she must have a test average of at least 85. Determine the score she must earn on the last test in order to earn a B for the semester.

50. Reliable Rentals is running a special. The cost of renting a chain saw is $35 per day plus $1.50 per hour. Write a cost function to represent the cost of renting the chain saw for one day for x hours. What is the cost of renting the chain saw for 12 hours?

Polynomial Functions

In this chapter, we return to the idea of functions, which we first discussed in Chapter 1. We examine a particular family of functions, referred to as polynomials, starting in this chapter and continuing for the next few chapters. Polynomials are worth special study because of their importance in so many areas of our daily lives, from calculating costs for repairing or selling homes to determining sales and profits for business items.

The motion of an object dropped from a height or thrown into the air is determined by the Earth's gravity. The motion is described by a polynomial function called a quadratic function, which we will discuss in this chapter. We will present several different functions that model the motion of a falling object in typical situations. The fact that the motion of an object due to gravity could be described by a polynomial equation was one of the great scientific and mathematical discoveries of the 17th century and led directly to our present understanding of planetary motion and space travel. We will investigate the motion of a falling object in the project at the end of the chapter.

6.1 INTRODUCTION TO POLYNOMIALS

OBJECTIVES

1 Identify polynomials.
2 Identify the terms of polynomials and classify polynomials by the number of terms they possess.
3 Identify the degree of terms of polynomials and classify polynomials by degree.
4 Write polynomials in one variable in descending and ascending order.
5 Evaluate polynomials.
6 Model real-world situations by using polynomial expressions.

APPLICATION

A contractor charges $9 a square foot to install ceramic tile. The contractor estimates the setup cost to be $75 and materials to be $5 per square foot.

a. Write a polynomial that represents the revenue for installing ceramic tile for a square patio in terms of the length of a side of the square.

b. Write a polynomial that represents the contractor's total cost.

c. Write a polynomial that represents the contractor's profit.

d. What will be the contractor's revenue, cost, and profit if the patio measures 12 feet on a side?

We will discuss this application further. See page 482.

Objective 6.1.1   Identifying Polynomials

In Chapter P, we introduced algebraic expressions. An **algebraic expression** is an expression that contains variables.

The **terms** of an algebraic expression are its addends. There are two types of terms: constant and variable. A **constant term** represents only one number. A **variable term** represents different numbers.

A **numerical coefficient** (or simply, **coefficient**) is the numerical factor of a term.

Two terms are said to be **like terms** if both are constants or if both are variable terms that contain the same variables with the same exponents. We **combine like terms** in order to simplify an algebraic expression. This means that we add the coefficients of the like terms, keeping the variable part intact. For example, $6x^2 - 5x + 3x + 7$ is an algebraic expression. Since we can rewrite $6x^2 - 5x + 3x + 7$ as $6x^2 + (-5x) + 3x + 7$, the addends are $6x^2$, $-5x$, $3x$, and 7, we call these addends terms.

$6x^2$, $-5x$, and $3x$ are variable terms. 6, -5, 3, and 7 are coefficients of the terms.

7 is a constant term. $-5x$ and $3x$ are like terms.

By combining like terms, $6x^2 - 5x + 3x + 7 = 6x^2 - 2x + 7$.

In this chapter, we consider algebraic expressions called monomials. A **monomial** is either a constant term or a variable term consisting of one or more variable factors, each having a nonnegative integer exponent. The following are examples of monomials:

2	is a constant term.
$-3x$	is a variable term with a coefficient of -3 and the variable, x, having an exponent of 1.
$4x^2$	is a variable term with a coefficient of 4 and the variable, x, having an exponent of 2.
$-5x^2y^3z$	is a variable term with a coefficient of -5 and three variables x, y, and z, having exponents of 2, 3, and 1, respectively.

Algebraic expressions are not monomials if they have a variable raised to a power other than a nonnegative integer. Thus, expressions with a variable in the denominator of a fraction and expressions with a variable in the radicand of a radical expression are not monomials. We will explain why this is so later in the text. For example, $x^{2/3}$, x^{-5}, $\dfrac{3}{x^2}$ and $-25\sqrt{4x}$ are not monomials.

A **polynomial** is a monomial or a sum of monomials. Following are some examples:

x^3y	is a monomial.
$x + 2$	is the sum of two monomials: x and 2.
$-7x^2 - 4x$	is the sum of two monomials: $-7x^2$ and $-4x$.
$\dfrac{1}{3}a + 9b^2 - a^3b$	is the sum of three monomials: $\dfrac{1}{3}a$, $9b^2$, and $-a^3b$.

EXAMPLE 1   Determine whether each expression is a polynomial.

a. $\dfrac{2}{3}x^2 + \sqrt{5}xy^3$ **b.** $\dfrac{1}{x^2} - 4\sqrt{xy}$

Solution

a. $\frac{2}{3}x^2 + \sqrt{5}xy^3$ is a polynomial, because the two terms, $\frac{2}{3}x^2$ and $\sqrt{5}xy^3$, are monomials, each consisting of a coefficient and variables with nonnegative integer exponents.

b. $\dfrac{1}{x^2} - 4\sqrt{xy}$ is not a polynomial, because the first term, $\dfrac{1}{x^2}$, and the second term,

$-4\sqrt{xy}$, are not monomials. The first term has a variable in the denominator of a fraction, and the second term has a variable in a radicand. ∎

✓ Objective 6.1.1 *CHECKUP*

1. Determine whether each expression is a polynomial.

   a. $\dfrac{2}{3}x - 3x^2$ **b.** $\dfrac{2}{x} - 5$

2. Explain the difference between the terms of an algebraic expression and the factors of a term.

3. All monomials are polynomials, but not all polynomials are monomials. Explain what this statement means.

4. A polynomial can be simplified by combining its like terms. What are like terms?

Objective 6.1.2   **Classifying Polynomials by Number of Terms**

We can classify a polynomial by the number of its terms. A polynomial with one term is called a monomial. A polynomial with two terms is a **binomial**, and a polynomial with three terms is a **trinomial**. We usually refer to a polynomial with more than three terms simply as a polynomial. Before we classify a polynomial, we must simplify it by combining like terms.

EXAMPLE 2   Combine like terms and classify each polynomial as a monomial, a binomial, a trinomial, or a polynomial.

   a. $6a^2 + 5b^2 + 4ab - a^2 - 2ab + c^2$ **b.** $-x^2 + 2xy - 3x + x^2 - y^3$

Solution

First, simplify each polynomial by combining like terms.

   a. $6a^2 + 5b^2 + 4ab - a^2 - 2ab + c^2 = 5a^2 + 5b^2 + 2ab + c^2$

      There are four terms: $5a^2$, $5b^2$, $2ab$, and c^2.

      The expression is a polynomial.

b. $-x^2 + 2xy - 3x + x^2 - y^3 = 2xy - 3x - y^3$ *Note: $-x^2 + x^2 = 0x^2$, or 0*
There are three terms: $2xy$, $-3x$, and $-y^3$.
The expression is a trinomial.

Objective 6.1.2 CHECKUP

1. Combine like terms and classify each polynomial as a monomial, a binomial, a trinomial, or a polynomial.
  a. $3x - 5 + 7x + 12$ **b.** $6b^3 + 4b^2c - 3bc^2 - c^3$

2. How can you tell whether a polynomial is a monomial, a binomial, or a trinomial?

Objective 6.1.3 | ## Classifying Polynomials by Degree

The **degree of a term** is the sum of the exponents of its variable factors. The **degree of a polynomial** is the largest degree of its variable terms. Remember to simplify the polynomial before determining its degree.

EXAMPLE 3

Determine the degree of each term of each polynomial, and then determine the degree of the polynomial.
  a. $6x^2 + 5x^2y^3 - 7x^2$ **b.** $-5x + 6 + 7x - 2x$ **c.** $9x^2y^3z^4$

Solution

First, simplify each polynomial by combining like terms.

a. $6x^2 + 5x^2y^3 - 7x^2 = -x^2 + 5x^2y^3$
  The terms are $-x^2$, with a degree of 2, and $5x^2y^3$, with a degree of $2 + 3$, or 5.
  The degree of the polynomial is 5, the largest degree of any of its terms.

b. $-5x + 6 + 7x - 2x = 6$
  The constant term, 6, can be written as $6x^0$ (because any nonzero number raised to a power of 0 equals 1) and has a degree of 0.
  The degree of the polynomial is 0.

c. $9x^2y^3z^4$ already is simplified; it is a monomial.
  The polynomial's one term has a degree of $2 + 3 + 4$, or 9.
  The degree of the polynomial is 9.

Objective 6.1.3 CHECKUP

1. Determine the degree of each term of the polynomial, and then determine the degree of the polynomial.
  a. $6x^2 - 3xy^3 + 5y^3$ **b.** $5x + 3x^3 - 2x^2 - 3x^3 + 1$
  c. $-5x^5y^2z^3 + 2x^2y^3z^4$

2. What is the difference between the degree of a term of a polynomial and the degree of a polynomial?

Objective 6.1.4 | ## Writing Polynomials in Descending and Ascending Order

The conventional way to write a polynomial in one variable is to write the terms in order of descending degrees. That is, a polynomial in one variable is written in **descending order** with decreasing values of its variable exponents. Remember that a constant term has a degree of 0 and is always written as the last term. The polynomial $4x^3 - 2x^7 + x^2 - 8$, written in descending order, is $-2x^7 + 4x^3 + x^2 - 8$.

Sometimes it may be desirable to write a polynomial in one variable in ascending order. A polynomial in one variable is written in **ascending order** with increasing values of its variable exponents. The polynomial $4x^3 - 2x^7 + x^2 - 8$, written in ascending order, is $-8 + x^2 + 4x^3 - 2x^7$.

 TAKE NOTE Take special care when arranging polynomials with terms having negative coefficients. The negative sign must remain with these terms.

EXAMPLE 4   Complete the following table by writing each polynomial in descending and ascending order:

Polynomial	Descending Order	Ascending Order
$6x^2 + 8x - 7x^4$		
$5 - x^4 + x$		

Solution

Polynomial	Descending Order	Ascending Order
$6x^2 + 8x - 7x^4$	$-7x^4 + 6x^2 + 8x$	$8x + 6x^2 - 7x^4$
$5 - x^4 + x$	$-x^4 + x + 5$	$5 + x - x^4$

✓ Objective 6.1.4 *CHECKUP*

Complete the following table by writing each polynomial in descending and ascending order:

	Polynomial	Descending Order	Ascending Order
1.	$3 + 2x^3 - 5x - x^2$		
2.	$12 + y^4 + y$		

Objective 6.1.5   Evaluating Polynomials

Like an algebraic expression, a polynomial represents different values, depending on the value(s) of its variable(s).

The process to determine the value of a polynomial is called **evaluating** the polynomial.

> To evaluate a polynomial,
>
> * Substitute a value for each variable.
> * Determine the value of the resulting numeric expression.
>
> To evaluate a polynomial on your calculator,
>
> * Enter the expression with its substituted values.
>
> or
>
> * Store the values of each of the variables and enter the polynomial.

EXAMPLE 5   Evaluate $x^2 + 2xy - 7y^2$

a. for $x = 2$ and $y = -1$. **b.** for $x = \dfrac{3}{4}$ and $y = \dfrac{1}{2}$.

Solution

a. $x^2 + 2xy - 7y^2 = (2)^2 + 2(2)(-1) - 7(-1)^2$ Substitute 2 for x and -1 for y.
$$= 4 - 4 - 7$$
$$= -7$$

b. $x^2 + 2xy - 7y^2 = \left(\dfrac{3}{4}\right)^2 + 2\left(\dfrac{3}{4}\right)\left(\dfrac{1}{2}\right) - 7\left(\dfrac{1}{2}\right)^2$ Substitute $\frac{3}{4}$ for x and $\frac{1}{2}$ for y.
$$= \dfrac{9}{16} + \dfrac{3}{4} - \dfrac{7}{4}$$
$$= \dfrac{9}{16} + \dfrac{12}{16} - \dfrac{28}{16}$$
$$= -\dfrac{7}{16}$$

The two methods of checking with your calculator are shown in **Figure 6.1a** and **Figure 6.1b**.

In **Figure 6.1a**, we substitute the value for the variables and evaluate the polynomial. In **Figure 6.1b**, we store the values of the variables and enter the polynomial. The calculator is programmed to evaluate the polynomial.

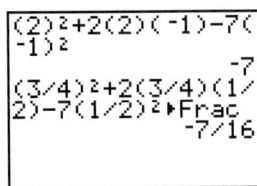

Figure 6.1a   **Figure 6.1b**

> ✎ **TAKE NOTE** When evaluating the same expression more than once, you may recall your last entry by keying [2nd] [ENTER] (ENTRY). Then edit your entry, using the arrow keys. To delete press [DEL] and to insert press [2nd] [DEL] (INS).

✓ Objective 6.1.5 **CHECKUP**

1. Evaluate $2a^2 - 5ab - 9b^2$ for the given values.

   a. $a = -8$ and $b = 2$ **b.** $a = \dfrac{3}{4}$ and $b = -\dfrac{1}{2}$

Objective 6.1.6 ## Modeling the Real World

Many real-life situations can be described by polynomials, including numerous geometric problems, business situations, and scientific relationships. Many other relationships can be approximated by polynomials, which sometimes makes them easier to use.

EXAMPLE 6

A rectangular swimming pool is to be enclosed by a fence. The fenced area is a square.

a. Write a polynomial for the fenced area that is not covered by the pool.

b. Write a polynomial for the cost of the concrete around the pool if the cost per square foot is $5.

c. If the pool is 25 feet by 15 feet, and the fence measures 30 feet on a side, determine the fenced area that is not covered by the pool. What is the cost to concrete this area?

Solution

Let x = length of the pool (in feet)
    y = width of the pool (in feet)
    z = length of the side of the fence (in feet)

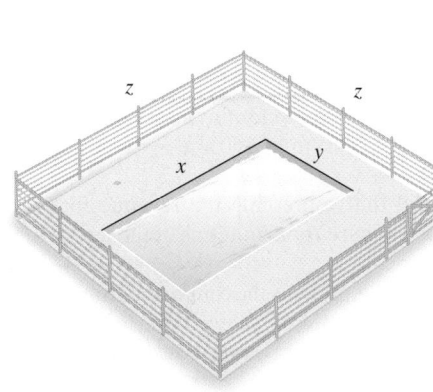

a. Fenced area: The area of a square is determined by the product of the two sides, $z \cdot z$, or z^2.

   Pool area: The area of a rectangle is determined by the product of the length times the width, xy.

   The fenced area not covered by the pool is the fenced area minus the pool area, or $(z^2 - xy)$ square feet.

b. The cost is $5 per square foot, $z^2 - xy$.

$$5(z^2 - xy) = 5z^2 - 5xy$$

The cost to concrete the area around the pool is $(5z^2 - 5xy)$ dollars.

c. Substitute values for the variables. $x = 25$ feet, $y = 15$ feet, and $z = 30$ feet

Fenced area not covered by the pool	Cost
$z^2 - xy = (30)^2 - (25)(15)$	$5z^2 - 5xy = 5(30)^2 - 5(25)(15)$
$= 900 - 375$	$= 4500 - 1875$
$= 525$	$= 2625$

The fenced area not covered by the pool is 525 square feet.
The cost of the concrete is $2625.

APPLICATION

A contractor charges $9 a square foot to install ceramic tile. The contractor estimates the setup cost to be $75 and materials to be $5 per square foot.

a. Write a polynomial that represents the revenue for installing ceramic tile for a square patio in terms of the length of a side of the square.

b. Write a polynomial that represents the contractor's total cost.

c. Write a polynomial that represents the contractor's profit.

d. What will be the contractor's revenue, cost, and profit if the patio measures 12 feet on a side?

Discussion

Let x = the length of the side of the square

a. The area of the square, number of square feet, is x^2. The contractor charges $9 per square foot. Therefore the revenue is $9x^2$.

b. The total cost is $5 per square foot, $5x^2$, plus the setup cost of $75 or $5x^2 + 75$.

c. The contractor's profit is the revenue minus the total cost.

$$9x^2 - (5x^2 + 75) = 9x^2 - 5x^2 - 75$$
$$= 4x^2 - 75$$

d. Substitute 12 for x in each expression.

Revenue	Cost	Profit
$9x^2 = 9(12)^2$	$5x^2 + 75 = 5(12)^2 + 75$	$4x^2 - 75 = 4(12)^2 - 75$
$= 1296$	$= 795$	$= 501$

The contractor's revenue is $1296, the total cost is $795, and the profit is $501.

✓ Objective 6.1.6 CHECKUP

1. A cabin with a square-shaped base is built upon a rectangular lot.

   a. Write a polynomial for the area of the lot that is not covered by the cabin (the yard).

   b. Write a polynomial for the cost to have grass seeded on the yard if the cost per square foot is $0.05.

   c. If the base of the cabin measures 35 feet on a side, and the lot measures 150 feet by 200 feet, determine the area of the lot that is not covered by the cabin. What is the cost of having the yard seeded?

2. A contractor charges $8 per square foot to install terra cotta tile. He estimates his setup cost to be $60 and materials to be $6 per square foot.

   a. Write a polynomial that represents the revenue for installing the tile for a square room in terms of the length of the side of the square.

   b. Write a polynomial that represents the contractor's total cost.

   c. Write a polynomial that represents the contractor's profit.

   d. What will be the contractor's revenue, cost, and profit if the room measures 9 feet on a side?

6.1 EXERCISES

Student Solutions Manual   PH Math/Tutor Center   CD Video   MathXL   MyMathLab   Interactmath.com

Determine whether each expression is a polynomial.

1. $2a + 5$

2. $y^{1/3} + y - 1$

3. $x^2 - 3x + 2$

4. $2z^{-2} - 3z^{-1} + 4$

5. $x^{1/2} - 6x - 7$

6. $a^2 + 4a - 17$

7. $5x^2 + 12xy + 2y^2$

8. $\sqrt{b^2 - 4ac}$

9. $\sqrt{5}x - \sqrt{3}y$

10. $2.44x^2 - 1.05x - 15.7$

11. $5\sqrt{x} - 3\sqrt{y}$

12. $\frac{3}{4}x^2 + \frac{5}{8}x - \frac{9}{16}$

13. $\frac{3}{5}x^3 - \frac{2}{3}x^2 + 4x - \frac{7}{10}$

14. $\frac{1}{a} + a + 1$

15. $\frac{4}{x^2} + \frac{1}{x} - \frac{5}{7}$

16. $0.8x - 2.3$

17. $a^{-2} + 17a^{-1} + 13$

18. $\sqrt{6}r + 5$

19. $0.07b^2 - 2.6b + 13.908$

20. $4p^2 - 6pq + q^2$

Classify each expression as a monomial, a binomial, a trinomial, or a polynomial.

21. $3a + 4b - 5c$

22. $3x^3 - 2x^2y + 5xy^2 + 6y^3$

23. $2z^2$

24. $2 - 4b + 7$

25. $x - y$

26. $\frac{1}{7}x + \frac{2}{7}y + \frac{3}{7}z$

27. $4p^4 - 2p^3 + 11p - 57$

28. $b - 2b + 3b - 4b + 5b$

29. $6x^2 - 12 + 8x - 5x^2 + x - 17$

30. $-14x^3$

31. $3b - 4 + 7b$

32. $p + q$

33. $x + 2x + 3x + 4x + 5x$ **34.** $2a^2 - 6 + a + a^2 - 16a + 6$ **35.** $\frac{1}{2}x + \frac{2}{3}y - \frac{3}{4}z$ **36.** $b^2 - 4ac$

Determine the degree of each term of each polynomial and then the degree of the polynomial.

37. $2 - 15c$

38. $-3,298,175$

39. 123

40. $8x^4 + 5x^3y^3 - y^4$

41. $5 + 5x - 4x - x$

42. $b^2 - 4ac$

43. $7x^5 + 2x^2y^2 - 12$

44. $5a + 7$

45. $\pi r^2 + 2\pi rh$

46. $5a^5bc^3 + 6abc^4 + 3ab^2c^2$

47. $4x^2yz^{12} - 8xy^2z^9 + 3x^3y^3z$

48. $6y^2 + 3y - y + y^2 - 2y$

Write each polynomial in descending order.

49. $5 - 2a + 3a^2 + a^3$

50. $4a^9 - 17 + 3a^3 - 2a^6$

51. $\frac{3}{5}x + \frac{4}{5}x^3 - \frac{7}{15}x - \frac{8}{15}x^4$

52. $p^2 - p^5 + p^3 - p^4 - p - 1$

53. $0.1x^3 - 1.72 + 4.6x^2 + 3.06x^4$

54. $7x + 5x^3 + 9x^5 + 15x^7 + 23x^9 + 33$

In exercises 55–60, write each polynomial in ascending order.

55. $7b^2 - 6b^3 + 11 - 2b$

56. $x^2 - 8x^6 + 6x^5 - 4x^3 + x^4$

57. $\frac{2}{7}x + \frac{1}{7}x^5 - \frac{3}{14}x - \frac{5}{14}x^3$

58. $q^2 - q^5 + q^3 - q^4 - q - 1$

59. $0.5x^7 - 2.77 + 3.2x^3 + 9.76x^5$

60. $x^5 - 4x^4 - 2x^3 + 4x^2 - 2x + 4$

61. Evaluate $3x^2 - 4x + 1$ for the given values.
   a. $x = 4$ **b.** $x = -2$ **c.** $x = 0$

62. Evaluate $3x^3 + 2x^2 + x + 1$ for the given values.
   a. $x = 2$ **b.** $x = -1$ **c.** $x = 0$

63. Evaluate $-x^2 + 4xy + y^2$ for the given values.
   a. $x = 2, y = 3$ **b.** $x = -2, y = -3$ **c.** $x = 0, y = 0$

64. Evaluate $-a^3 + a^2b + ab^2 + b^3$ for the given values.
   a. $a = 2, b = 1$ **b.** $a = -1, b = -2$ **c.** $a = 0, b = 3$

65. Evaluate $1.3m^3 - 2.5m^2 + 3.7m - 4.9$ for the given values.
   a. $m = 1$ **b.** $m = 2.5$ **c.** $m = -1.5$

66. Evaluate $0.6z^2 + 3.7z - 5.8$ for the given values.
   a. $z = 2$ **b.** $z = 4.3$ **c.** $z = -2.5$

67. Evaluate $\frac{2}{3}x^2 - x - 3$ for the given values.

   a. $x = -\frac{3}{2}$ **b.** $x = \frac{1}{4}$ **c.** $x = 3$

68. Evaluate $\frac{3}{4}x^2 - \frac{3}{2}x - \frac{4}{3}$ for the given values.

   a. $x = \frac{2}{3}$ **b.** $x = -\frac{2}{3}$ **c.** $x = 8$

Geometry

Geometric formulas were introduced in Chapter P and are summarized on the inside book cover. Exercises 69–86 refer to these formulas.

69. Write a polynomial for the perimeter of a rectangle given that the length is the square of the width, x. What is the perimeter if the width is 5 feet?

70. Write a polynomial for the perimeter of a rectangle given that the width is twice the square of the length, x. What is the perimeter if the length is 3 meters?

71. Write a polynomial for the perimeter of a triangle whose second side is the square of the length of the first side, x, and whose third side is 1 inch long. What is the perimeter if the length of the first side is 1.2 inches?

72. Write a polynomial for the perimeter of a triangle whose second side is twice the square of the length of the first side, x, and whose third side is 2 centimeters long. What is the perimeter if the length of the first side is 1 centimeter?

73. Write a polynomial for the surface area of a rectangular solid whose width and length are equal and whose height is 3 meters. What is the surface area of the solid if the width measures 1.5 meters?

74. Write a polynomial for the surface area of a rectangular solid whose width is 5 inches, whose length is 10 inches, and whose height is h inches. What is the surface area if the height is $3\frac{1}{2}$ inches?

75. Write a polynomial for the total area of the three geometric shapes shown in **Figure 6.2**. Shape A is a square and shapes B and C are rectangles.

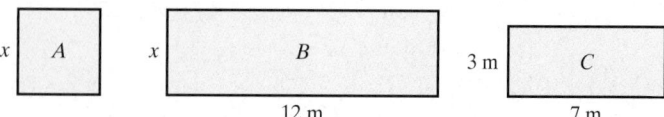

Figure 6.2

76. Write a polynomial for the total area of the three geometric shapes shown in **Figure 6.3**. Shape A is a right triangle and shapes B and C are squares.

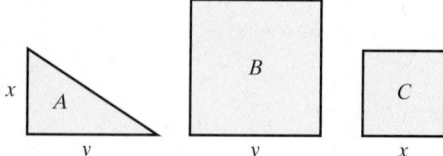

Figure 6.3

77. A rectangular patio measuring 15 feet by 20 feet is placed in a rectangular yard. Write a polynomial for the area of the yard not covered by the patio. What is the area of the yard not covered by the patio if the yard measures 75 feet by 120 feet?

78. A rectangular strawberry patch measuring 8 feet by 16 feet is placed in the back corner of a rectangular yard. Write a polynomial for the area of the yard not covered by the strawberry patch. What is the area of the yard not covered by the strawberry patch if the yard measures 100 feet by 150 feet?

79. A circular swimming pool is placed in a rectangular yard. Write a polynomial for the area of the yard not covered by the pool. What is the area of the yard not covered by the pool if the yard measures 25 meters by 35 meters and the pool has a radius of 4.5 meters?

80. A circular hot tub is placed in a rectangular yard. Write a polynomial for the area of the yard not covered by the hot tub. What is the area of the yard not covered by the hot tub if the yard measures 80 feet by 125 feet and the hot tub has a radius of 5 feet?

81. A flooring company installs prefinished hardwood floors and charges $7 per square foot for installation. Its overhead for a given job is $100, and materials cost the company $4 per square foot.

a. Write a polynomial that represents the revenue for laying the floor in a square room in terms of the length of the side of the square.

b. Write a polynomial that represents the company's total cost.

c. Write a polynomial that represents the company's profit.

d. What will be the contractor's revenue, cost, and profit if the room measures 15 feet on a side?

82. Frank, a carpenter, constructs a wooden deck for his neighbor. He estimates that his overhead on the job is $70 and the material cost is $15 per square foot. Because the neighbor is a friend he charges him less than he would on a regular job and charges him only $20 per square foot.

a. Write a polynomial that represents his revenue for the square deck in terms of the length of the side of the square.

b. Write a polynomial for Frank's cost.

c. Write a polynomial for his profit.

d. Find his revenue, cost, and profit if the deck is 12 feet on a side.

83. The flooring company mentioned in exercise **81** also installs unfinished hardwood floors and charges $10.25. The unfinished flooring is more expensive to install because it must also be sanded, stained, and varnished. The company's overhead for a given job is $225.00, and materials cost the company $3.50 per square foot.

a. Write a polynomial that represents the revenue for laying the floor in a square room in terms of the length of the side of the square.

b. Write a polynomial that represents the company's total cost.

c. Write a polynomial that represents the company's profit.

d. What will be the contractor's revenue, cost, and profit if the room measures 15 feet on a side?

84. Paul, a union tilesetter, creates a square marble hearth for a customer's look-through fireplace. His overhead on the job is $40.00 and the materials cost $10.25 per square foot. He charges the customer $16.50 per square foot for installation.

a. Write a polynomial that represents his revenue for this job in terms of the length of the side of the square.

b. Write a polynomial for his cost.

c. Write a polynomial for his profit.

d. Find his revenue, cost, and profit if the hearth is 5 feet on a side.

85. Ted wants to put in a circular concrete base for a decorative fountain. A contractor estimates that it will cost him $3.15 per square foot to do the job. His overhead is $30.00. He decides to charge Ted $3.60 per square foot.

a. Write a polynomial that represents the contractor's revenue for this job in terms of the radius of the circular base.

b. Write a polynomial for his cost.

c. Write a polynomial for his profit.

d. Find the contractor's revenue, cost, and profit if the job involves a circular concrete base of radius 10 feet.

86. Glenda needs a circular concrete pad poured on which to install a hot tub. A handyman estimates that it will cost him $2.15 per square foot to do the job. His overhead is $15.00. He charges Glenda $3.50 per square foot to do the job.
   a. Write a polynomial that represents the handyman's revenue for this job in terms of the radius of the circular pad.
   b. Write a polynomial for his cost.
   c. Write a polynomial for his profit.
   d. Find his revenue, cost, and profit if the job involves a circular pad of diameter 9 feet.

87. The tire industry advises consumers that they can optimize the mileage of their tires by using recommended tire pressures. A polynomial that relates the expected mileage of the tires (in thousands of miles) to the inflated tire pressure x (in pounds per square inch) is $-1.143x^2 + 75.214x - 1200$. Use this polynomial to estimate the mileage of the tire if the pressure is maintained at 32 pounds per square inch.

88. Use the polynomial in exercise **87** to estimate the mileage of a tire whose pressure is maintained at 34 pounds per square inch.

89. Weather records of the National Climactic Data Center, U.S. Department of Commerce, indicate that extreme low temperatures in the Northwest are related to elevation. A polynomial that relates elevation (in feet) to record low temperature, x degrees Fahrenheit, is $16.671x^2 + 1742.837x + 50,200$. Use this polynomial to estimate the elevation in Colorado at which a temperature of -61 degrees Fahrenheit was recorded.

90. Use the polynomial in exercise **89** to estimate the elevation in Oregon at which a record low temperature of -54 degrees Fahrenheit is recorded.

91. The Council of Tall Buildings and Urban Habitat maintains a list of the tallest buildings in the world. According to the facts in this list, a polynomial that relates height (in feet) of a tall building can be related to its number of stories, n, is $0.306n^2 - 34.081n + 1994$. Use this polynomial to estimate the height of the world's tallest building, Taipei 101 in Taiwan, which has 101 stories.

92. Use the polynomial in exercise **91** to estimate the height of the AT&T Corporate Center in Chicago, which has 60 stories.

 ## 6.1 Calculator Exercises

If you are evaluating a polynomial for several values, it is sometimes helpful to use the LIST feature of your calculator. As an example, suppose you wish to evaluate the polynomial $0.2x^3 - 1.2x + 6.4$ when x equals the values in the list $\{0, 1, 2, 3, 4, 5\}$. We would store these values in a list and then enter the polynomial by using the list symbol in place of the variable. The keystrokes to do this using the list L1 for x are as follows:

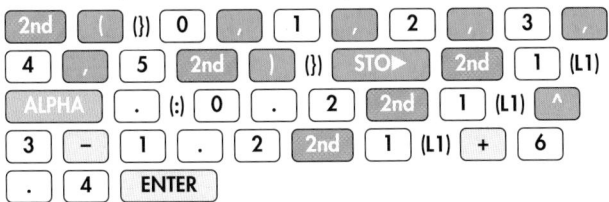

Read the results by using the arrow keys to move the cursor from left to right. The calculator returns the list $\{6.4, 5.4, 5.6, 8.2, 14.4, 25.4\}$, which represents the result of evaluating the polynomial for the list of x-values. You could also have used the TABLE feature of the calculator to do this. However, the LIST feature is more flexible when you have several variables, as the next example illustrates.

Evaluate $a^2 + 2ab - 3b^2$ when a and b equal the pairs of values in the list $\{(2, 6), (3, 7), (4, 8)\}$, where a is the first value of the pair and b is the second value of the pair. Store the a values in

L1 and the b values in L2, maintaining the order of the pairs, and replace a and b by their list notations when you enter the expression. The keystrokes for doing this are as follows:

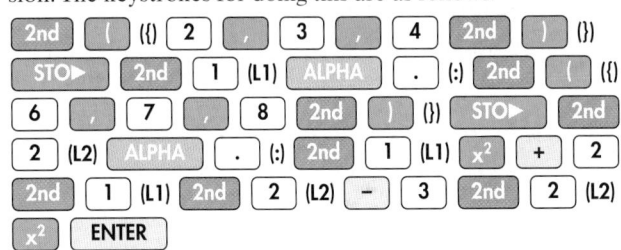

The calculator returns the list $\{-80, -96, -112\}$ as the results of the evaluation.

Use this method to evaluate the following polynomials for the given values:

1. $3x^3 - 8x^2 + 9x - 12$ for $x = \{-3, -1, 1, 3\}$

2. $4a^3 + 2a^2b + 2ab^2 + b^3$ for $\{(-5, 2), (-3, 0), (-1, -2)\}$

3. $\dfrac{1}{2}x^2 + \dfrac{3}{5}xy - \dfrac{1}{4}y^3$ for the (x, y) pairs
$$\left(\frac{1}{2}, \frac{2}{5}\right), \left(\frac{1}{4}, \frac{3}{5}\right), \left(-\frac{1}{2}, 5\right), \left(0, \frac{2}{5}\right)$$

 ## 6.1 Writing Exercises

As you begin the study of polynomials, you will be expanding your knowledge of mathematical models. This would be a good time for you to reflect on your feelings about the study of mathematics. Prepare a short essay describing your experiences to date in studying mathematics. If studying mathematics has been a struggle, try to list reasons why that is so. Do you have personal situations that compete with your studies for your attention? Does your work situation make it difficult to find study time? Have you had a bad past experience in the study of mathematics? Do you have a study group that you can use to help you? Have

you developed a negative attitude toward mathematics? If so, can you understand where this attitude originated?

After you have described your current attitudes and situation, reflect on what you can do to make your further study of mathematics a success. What can you do to develop a more positive attitude? What can you do to ensure adequate study time? What can you do to obtain the help you may need with your studies? Try to list a strategy to which you can refer periodically through your studies to keep you on a positive track.

6.2 POLYNOMIAL FUNCTIONS AND THEIR GRAPHS

1 Create tables of values for polynomial relations.
2 Graph polynomial relations by using sets of ordered pairs.
3 Determine ranges for polynomial relations.
4 Evaluate polynomial functions.
5 Model real-world situations by using polynomial functions.

APPLICATION

During the 1980s the United States' national debt exceeded one trillion dollars for the first time in history. Using data from the United States Department of the Treasury, a third-degree polynomial function for national debt, $n(t)$, in trillions of dollars is generated: $n(t) = 0.014t^3 + 0.058t^2 + 0.069t + 5.688$, where t is the number of years after the year 2000.

a. Use the function to estimate the national debt for the years shown in the following table:

Year	2000	2001	2002	2003
National debt				

b. In 2003 the national debt was 6.8 trillion dollars. How well does the function estimate this number?

c. Estimate the national debt for the current year. Given your knowledge of current events, does this seem reasonable? Why or why not?

After completing this section, we will discuss this application further. See page 497.

Objective 6.2.1   **Creating Tables of Values**

In previous chapters of this text, we developed the concept of a relation. A **relation** is a set of ordered pairs. A relation can be written in equation form. The equation then relates a value for an independent variable to a value for a dependent variable. For example, $y = 3x + 2$ relates a value for the independent variable x to a value for the dependent variable y.

A **polynomial relation** equates a polynomial expression in one independent variable to a dependent variable.

POLYNOMIAL RELATION

A polynomial relation is a relation that can be written in the form

$$y = a_n x^n + a_{n-1}x^{n-1} + a_{n-2}x^{n-2} + \cdots + a_1 x^1 + a_0$$

where n is the degree of the polynomial; $a_0, a_1, a_2, \ldots, a_n$ are real numbers; and $a_n \neq 0$.

By this definition, all linear equations, $y = ax + b$, are polynomial relations.

A set of all possible values for the independent variable is called the **domain** of the relation. In Section 1.2, we determined the domain of a relation from its graph by examining the graph to see what values of the independent variable are used to draw the graph. For example,

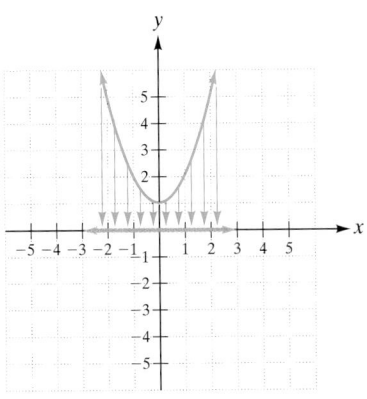

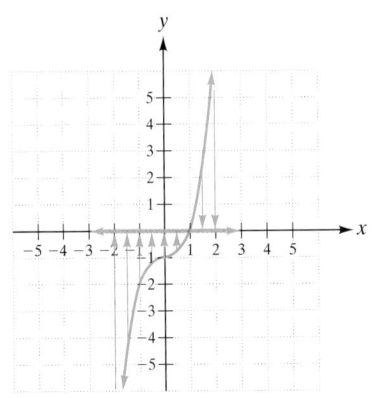

The domain is the set of all real numbers, or $(-\infty, \infty)$.

The domain is the set all real numbers, or $(-\infty, \infty)$.

 TAKE NOTE The domain of a polynomial relation is the set of all real numbers.

An example of a polynomial relation is $y = x^2 + 2x + 7$. The polynomial $x^2 + 2x + 7$, with the independent variable x, equals the dependent variable y. The domain of the relation $y = x^2 + 2x + 7$ is the set of all real numbers.

We can determine an ordered-pair solution of this relation by substituting a value for the independent variable from its domain and obtaining a value for the dependent variable. The corresponding values represent an ordered-pair solution. For example,

$$\text{if } x = 2, \text{ then } y = x^2 + 2x + 7$$
$$y = (2)^2 + 2(2) + 7$$
$$y = 4 + 4 + 7$$
$$y = 15$$

An ordered-pair solution of the relation is $(2, 15)$.

An infinite number of solutions may be found by this method. Previously, we organized the procedure in a table of values. (See Sections 1.1 and 3.1.) A **table of values** is a table with a column for the independent variable and a column for the dependent variable. We may want to add a third column between these to show our work.

To complete a table of values,

- Enter a number from the domain in the first column.
- Substitute this value for the independent variable in the second column.
- Evaluate the expression, and enter the result in the third column.

To construct a table of values on your calculator,

- Rename the independent variable x and the dependent variable y, and enter the equation in Y1.
- Set the calculator to generate the table by entering a minimum value and the amount of the increment to be added to the minimum number. Then set the calculator to perform the evaluations automatically.

An alternative method is to set up the calculator to ask for the x-values.

- Ignore the minimum value and increments. Then set the calculator to ask for the x-values and to perform the evaluations automatically.
- Enter values for x.

EXAMPLE 1   Create a table of values of possible solutions of the given polynomial relation.

a. $y = x^2 + 2x + 7$ 　　　　　　　　　　　 **b.** $y = -2x^3 + 8x - 5$

Solution

a. The domain of $y = x^2 + 2x + 7$ is the set of all real numbers. To determine a table of values, we will select values from the domain. We will use $x = -3, -2, -1, 0,$ and 1.

x	$y = x^2 + 2x + 7$	y
-3	$y = (-3)^2 + 2(-3) + 7$	10
-2	$y = (-2)^2 + 2(-2) + 7$	7
-1	$y = (-1)^2 + 2(-1) + 7$	6
0	$y = (0)^2 + 2(0) + 7$	7
1	$y = (1)^2 + 2(1) + 7$	10

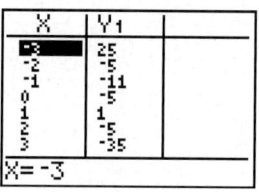

X	Y1
-3	10
-2	7
-1	6
0	7
1	10

X=

Y1 = $x^2 + 2x + 7$
Figure 6.4a

A calculator version of the table is shown in **Figure 6.4a**. This table was generated in ASK mode.

The ordered pairs found in the table, $(-3, 10), (-2, 7), (-1, 6), (0, 7),$ and $(1, 10)$, are solutions of the relation $y = x^2 + 2x + 7$.

b. The domain of $y = -2x^3 + 8x - 5$ is the set of all real numbers. To determine a table of values, we will use $x = -3, -2, -1, 0, 1, 2,$ and 3.

x	$y = -2x^3 + 8x - 5$	y
-3	$y = -2(-3)^3 + 8(-3) - 5$	25
-2	$y = -2(-2)^3 + 8(-2) - 5$	-5
-1	$y = -2(-1)^3 + 8(-1) - 5$	-11
0	$y = -2(0)^3 + 8(0) - 5$	-5
1	$y = -2(1)^3 + 8(1) - 5$	1
2	$y = -2(2)^3 + 8(2) - 5$	-5
3	$y = -2(3)^3 + 8(3) - 5$	-35

X	Y1
-3	25
-2	-5
-1	-11
0	-5
1	1
2	-5
3	-35

X=-3

Y1 = $-2x^3 + 8x - 5$
Figure 6.4b

A calculator version of the table is shown in **Figure 6.4b**. This table was generated in AUTO mode with TblStart = -3. The ordered pairs found in the table, $(-3, 25), (-2, -5), (-1, -11), (0, -5), (1, 1), (2, -5),$ and $(3, -35)$, are solutions of the relation $y = -2x^3 + 8x - 5$. ∎

Objective 6.2.1 CHECKUP

1. Create a table of values with six possible solutions of the given polynomial relation.
   a. $y = -x^2 + 4x - 2$
   b. $y = x^3 + 2x^2 - 5x - 6$

2. Consider the polynomial relation in exercise 1.b.
   a. Which is the independent variable?
   b. Which is the dependent variable?
   c. What is the domain of the relation?

Objective 6.2.2   Graphing Polynomial Relations

Polynomial relations have an infinite number of possible ordered-pair solutions. In order to illustrate these solutions, we use a **graph**.

To graph a polynomial relation means to create an illustration that represents the solutions of the relation. Note that

1. Every solution of a polynomial relation can be represented by a point on its graph, and

2. Every point on a graph represents a solution of its associated polynomial relation.

Since every solution of a polynomial relation can be represented by a point on its graph, we graph a relation using ordered pairs found in a table of values. When we graphed a polynomial of degree 1 in Chapter 3, we observed that the graphs were lines. As we graph polynomials of degree 2, we will observe that the graphs are not lines but have a common shape. We will also notice that polynomials of degree 3 graph in a different shape from polynomials of degrees 1 and 2. We discuss the shape of a graph of a polynomial relation in the calculator exercises at the end of this section. This concept will help us determine the number of points needed to obtain an accurate graph for the polynomial relation. At this point in our discussion, we will use the calculator to help us determine points to be graphed to make an accurate graph.

To graph a polynomial relation using ordered pairs,

- Graph ordered-pair solutions found in a table of values.
- Identify a pattern and complete the pattern.
- Label the coordinates of the points graphed.

To graph a polynomial relation on your calculator,

- Select a viewing screen, such as the standard window, integer window, or decimal window.
- Enter the equation in Y1.
- Graph the equation.

EXAMPLE 2   Graph the given polynomial relations.

a. $y = 2x^2 + 4x + 3$ b. $y = x^3 + x^2 + 6$

Solution

a. In **Figure 6.5a**, we observe that the domain of $y = 2x^2 + 4x + 3$ is the set of all real numbers. If we view the curve graphed by the relation, we see that a minimum of five points would suggest the curve. To determine a table of values, we will use $x = -3, -2, -1, 0,$ and 1 to obtain these points. Graph the ordered pairs and connect them with a smooth curve to include all the possible ordered-pair solutions.

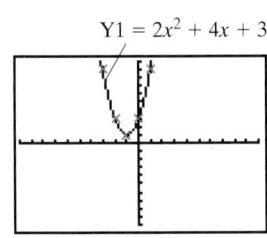

Y1 = $2x^2 + 4x + 3$

$(-10, 10, -10, 10)$

Figure 6.5a

x	$y = 2x^2 + 4x + 3$	y	
-3	$y = 2(-3)^2 + 4(-3) + 3$	9	$(-3, 9)$
-2	$y = 2(-2)^2 + 4(-2) + 3$	3	$(-2, 3)$
-1	$y = 2(-1)^2 + 4(-1) + 3$	1	$(-1, 1)$
0	$y = 2(0)^2 + 4(0) + 3$	3	$(0, 3)$
1	$y = 2(1)^2 + 4(1) + 3$	9	$(1, 9)$

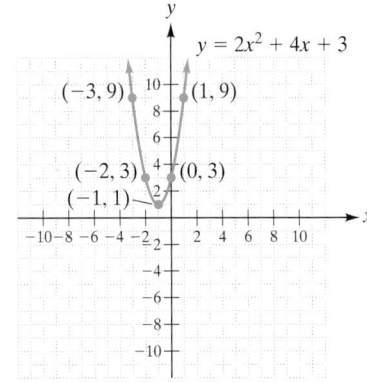

b. In **Figure 6.5b**, we observe that the domain of $y = x^3 + x^2 + 6$ is the set of all real numbers. If we view the curve graphed by the relation, we see that a minimum of six points would suggest the curve. To determine a table of values, we will use $x = -3, -2, -1, 0, 1,$ and 2 to obtain these points. On a coordinate plane, graph the ordered pairs and connect them with a smooth curve to include all the possible ordered-pair solutions.

Y1 = $x^3 + x^2 + 6$

$(-10, 10, -20, 20)$

Figure 6.5b

x	$y = x^3 + x^2 + 6$	y	
-3	$y = (-3)^3 + (-3)^2 + 6$	-12	$(-3, -12)$
-2	$y = (-2)^3 + (-2)^2 + 6$	2	$(-2, 2)$
-1	$y = (-1)^3 + (-1)^2 + 6$	6	$(-1, 6)$
0	$y = (0)^3 + (0)^2 + 6$	6	$(0, 6)$
1	$y = (1)^3 + (1)^2 + 6$	8	$(1, 8)$
2	$y = (2)^3 + (2)^2 + 6$	18	$(2, 18)$

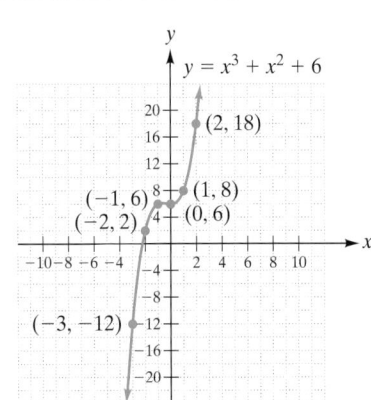

Since every point on a graph represents a solution of its associated polynomial relation, we can obtain solutions of the polynomial relation given a graph of the relation.

EXAMPLE 3   Determine three solutions for the polynomial relation graphed by completing the given table of values.

a.

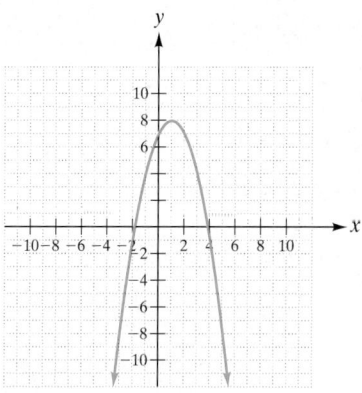

x	y
−3	
3	
	8

b.

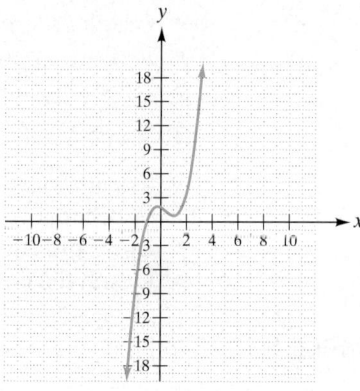

x	y
−2	
2	
	17

Solution

a.

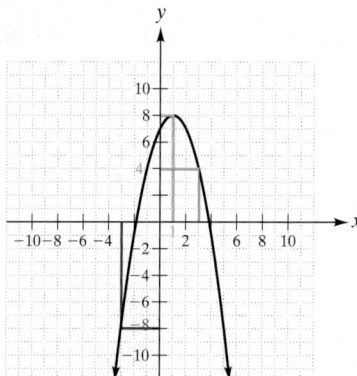

x	y	
−3	−8	When the x-value is −3, the y-value is −8.
3	4	When the x-value is 3, the y-value is 4.
1	8	When the y-value is 8, the x-value is 1.

b.

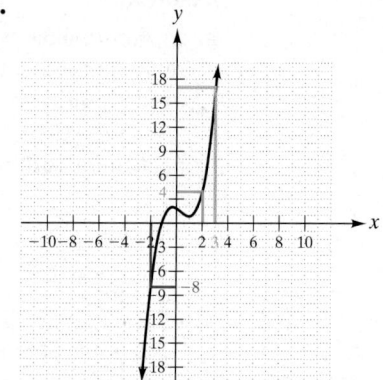

x	y	
−2	−8	When the x-value is −2, the y-value is −8.
2	4	When the x-value is 2, the y-value is 4.
3	17	When the y-value is 17, the x-value is 3.

✓ Objective 6.2.2 CHECKUP

1. Graph the given polynomial relations.

   a. $y = x^3 - 5x + 4$ **b.** $y = x^2 - 4x + 2$

2. Determine three solutions for the polynomial graphed by completing the given table of values.

a.

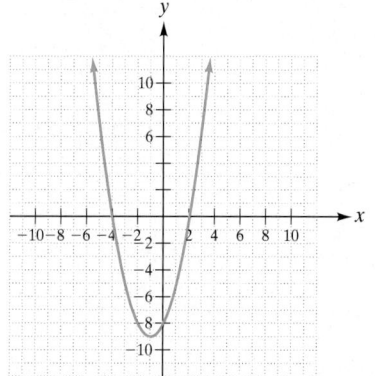

x	y
0	
3	
	−9

b.

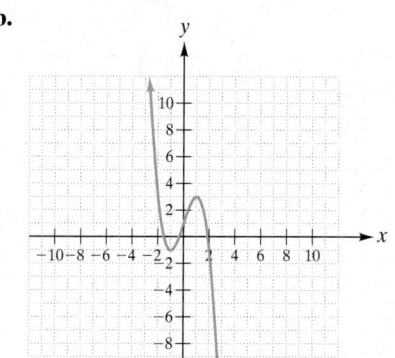

x	y
−1	
0	
	3

3. What are some advantages of representing a polynomial relation with a graph rather than a table?

4. When the domain of a polynomial relation is the set of all real numbers, is it possible to show all solutions of the relation graphically? Explain.

Objective 6.2.3

Determining Ranges for Polynomial Relations

The set of all possible values for the dependent variable of a polynomial relation is called the **range** of the relation. To determine the range, we need to consider the relation for all values in its domain. If the domain is infinite, a more effective method of determining the range is to view the graph of the relation. (See Section 1.4.)

To determine the range of a polynomial relation from its graph, write a set of the values of the dependent variable (y-coordinates) used in the graph. That is, the range lies between and including the **absolute minimum** of the relation (the smallest value of y) and the **absolute maximum** of the relation (the largest value of y), if they exist.

To determine the range of a polynomial relation from its graph,

- Determine the absolute minimum and the absolute maximum of the relation.
- If the relation has no absolute minimum or absolute maximum, the range is the set of all real numbers.
- If the relation has both an absolute minimum and absolute maximum, the range is the set of all real numbers between and including these values.
- If the relation has no absolute maximum, the range is the set of all real numbers greater than or equal to the absolute minimum.
- If the relation has no absolute minimum, the range is the set of all real numbers less than or equal to the absolute maximum.

EXAMPLE 4   Determine the range of each relation.

a.

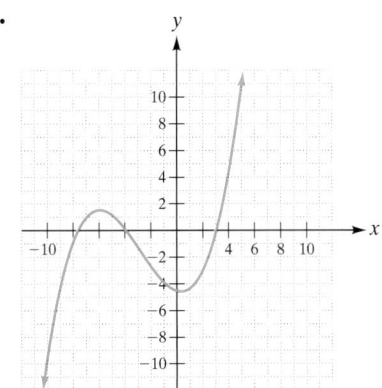

b.

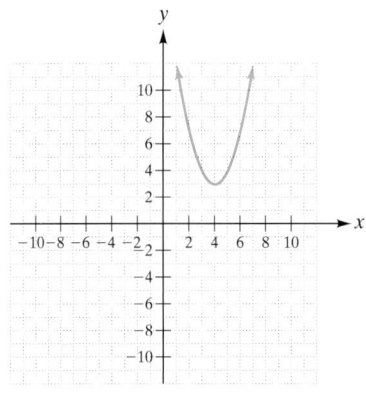

c.

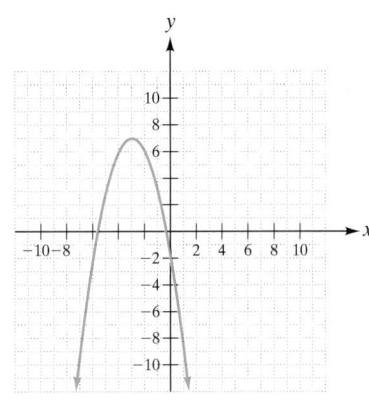

Solution

a.

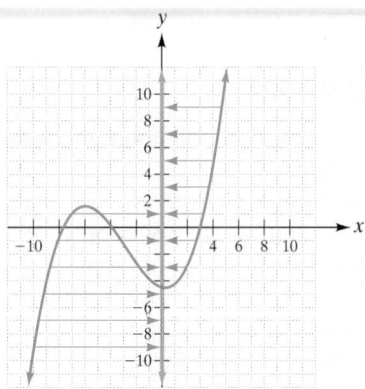

The range is the set of all real numbers, or $(-\infty, \infty)$.

b.

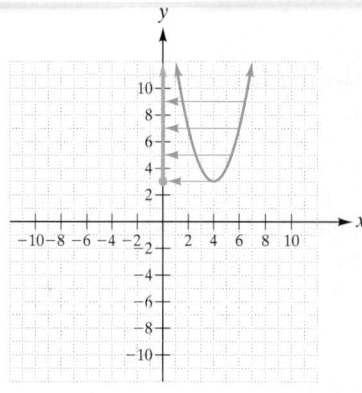

The range is the set of all real numbers greater than or equal to 3, or $y \geq 3$, or $[3, \infty)$.

c.

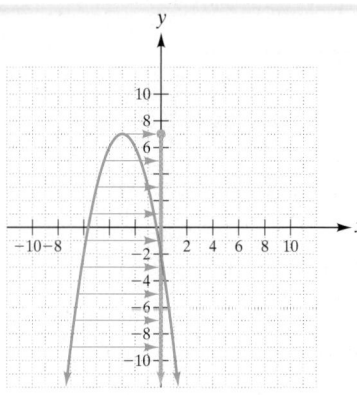

The range is the set of all real numbers less than or equal to 7, or $y \leq 7$, or $(-\infty, 7]$.

To determine the range of a polynomial relation from a calculator graph,

- Trace the graph to determine the y-coordinates of the points. Note the absolute minimum or the absolute maximum.
- Use the CALC function to determine the absolute minimum if it cannot be determined by tracing.
- Use the CALC function to determine the absolute maximum if it cannot be determined by tracing.

 TAKE NOTE The calculator is an excellent tool to help us determine the range of a relation. However, when we calculate the absolute maximum or minimum, the calculator may not display the exact value. We may need to round the answer.

EXAMPLE 5   Determine the range of each relation graphically.

a. $y = x^2 + 2x - 4$ **b.** $y = -2x^3 + 5x - 1$ **c.** $y = -x^4 + x - 5$

Calculator Solution

Graph each relation.

a.   Y1 $= x^2 + 2x - 4$

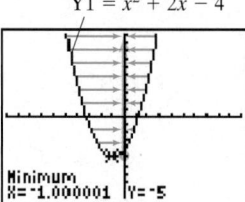

$(-10, 10, -10, 10)$

The y-coordinates have an absolute minimum value of -5. There is no absolute maximum. The range is the set of all real numbers greater than or equal to -5, or $y \geq -5$.

b. Y1 $= -2x^3 + 5x - 1$

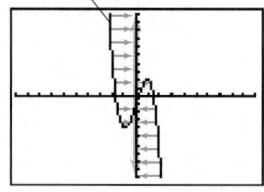

$(-10, 10, -10, 10)$

The y-coordinates have no absolute maximum or absolute minimum value. The range is the set of all real numbers.

c. Y1 $= -x^4 + x - 5$

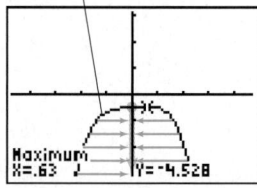

$(-4.7, 4.7, -31, 31)$

The y-coordinates have an absolute maximum value at approximately -4.528. There is no absolute minimum value. The range is the set of all real numbers less than or equal to -4.528.

Objective 6.2.3 *CHECKUP*

In exercises 1 and 2, determine the range of each relation.

1. a.

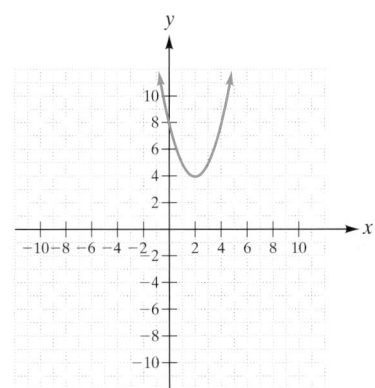

b.

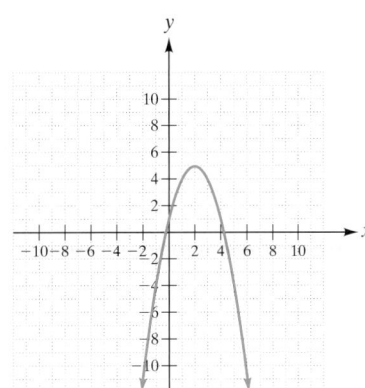

c.

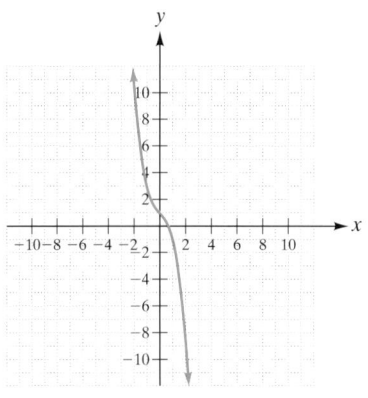

2. a. $y = x^3 + 2x^2 - 5x - 6$ **b.** $y = 8 + 2x - x^2$
c. $y = 0.2x^4 + 0.1x^3 - 0.5x^2 - 0.8x - 1.2$

3. What is the difference between the range of a polynomial relation and the domain of a polynomial relation?

4. If a polynomial relation has an absolute minimum value, what will be true about the range of the relation?

5. If a polynomial relation has an absolute maximum value, what will be true about the range of the relation?

Objective 6.2.4   Evaluating Polynomial Functions

Recall from Chapter 1 that a function is a special type of relation. A **function** relates every element in its domain to only one element in its range. To determine graphically whether a relation is a function, we use the vertical-line test.

VERTICAL-LINE TEST

If a vertical line can be drawn such that it intersects the graph of a relation more than once, the graph does not represent a function. If every possible vertical line intersects the graph only once, then the graph represents a function.

Remember that the vertical-line test works because a function can have only one *y*-value for every *x*-value. Any graph that crosses a vertical line more than once is a relation but is not a function.

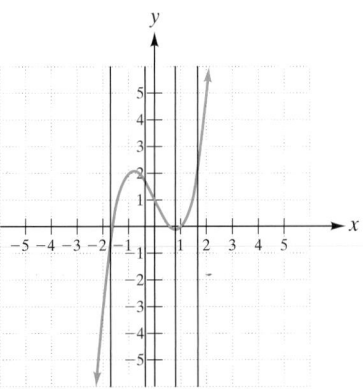

function
All vertical lines intersect graph once.

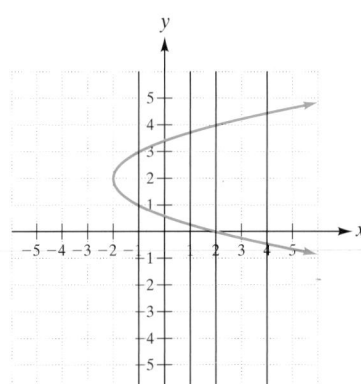

not a function
Vertical lines intersect graph more than once.

Are all polynomial relations also functions? To find out, complete the following set of exercises.

Guided Discovery 1 Graphs of Polynomial Functions

Graph each polynomial relation. Draw a vertical line through more than one point on the graph if possible.

1. $y = x$ **2.** $y = x^2$ **3.** $y = x^3$ **4.** $y = x^4$

Are the polynomial relations graphed in exercises 1–4 functions?

It is not possible to draw a vertical line through more than one point on the graphs of these polynomial relations. Therefore, these polynomial relations are *all* functions. In fact, *all* polynomial relations are functions.

To write a function, we use **function notation**. We replace the dependent variable with the name of the function and put the name of the independent variable in parentheses.

POLYNOMIAL FUNCTION

A polynomial function f is a function that can be written in the form

$$f(x) = a_n x^n + a_{n-1} x^{n-1} + a_{n-2} x^{n-2} + \cdots + a_1 x^1 + a_0$$

where n is the degree of the polynomial; $a_0, a_1, a_2, \ldots, a_n$ are real numbers; and $a_n \neq 0$.

 TAKE NOTE Remember from Chapter 1 that $f(x)$ does *not* mean f times x.

For example, the relation $y = x^2 + 2x + 7$ may be written as the function $f(x) = x^2 + 2x + 7$. We read this as "f of x equals x squared plus 2 times x plus 7."

We may need to evaluate a function for a given value. We use function notation to write the function by replacing the independent variable with the given value. For example, "Evaluate $f(x) = x^2 + 2x + 7$ for $x = 2$" is written "Evaluate $f(2)$, given $f(x) = x^2 + 2x + 7$."

To evaluate a function for a value,

- Substitute the value for the independent variable.
- Evaluate the resulting numeric expression.

EXAMPLE 6

a. Evaluate $f(2)$, given $f(x) = x^2 + 2x + 7$.

b. Evaluate $g(-4)$ given $g(x) = x^3 - x^2 + 5x - 6$.

Solution

a. $f(x) = x^2 + 2x + 7$ *Given function*

$f(2) = (2)^2 + 2(2) + 7$ *Substitute 2 for x.*

$f(2) = 4 + 4 + 7$ *Simplify.*

$f(2) = 15$

b. $g(x) = x^3 - x^2 + 5x - 6$ *Given function*

$g(-4) = (-4)^3 - (-4)^2 + 5(-4) - 6$ *Substitute −4 for x.*

$g(-4) = -64 - 16 - 20 - 6$ *Simplify.*

$g(-4) = -106$

EXAMPLE 7   Given the function $g(x) = x^3 + 50x^2 + 100$, evaluate $g(4000)$ on your calculator.

Solution

$g(4000) \approx 6.48 \times 10^{10}$, or approximately 64,800,000,000.

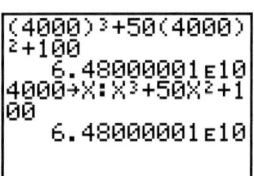

Objective 6.2.4 **CHECKUP**

1. **a.** Evaluate $g(-2)$, given $g(x) = -x^2 + 3x - 5$.
   b. Evaluate $h(-1)$, given $h(x) = 2x^3 - x^2 - 27x + 36$.
2. Given the function $f(x) = x^3 + 20x^2 + 300$, evaluate $f(5000)$ on your calculator.

3. In evaluating a polynomial function, is it important to know the rules for order of operations? Explain.

Objective 6.2.5   **Modeling the Real World**

Often, certain values of a polynomial function have special importance for real-world situations. For example, the absolute maximum value of a polynomial revenue function is the largest amount of revenue. The absolute maximum value of a polynomial profit function is the largest amount of profit. The absolute maximum value of the polynomial function describing the path of a ball thrown into the air tells how high the ball goes before falling back to earth. Graphs of such polynomial functions are often useful for seeing where or when these special values occur and approximately what the values of the variables are at that point or at that time.

When we discuss real-world situations, we may need to add restrictions on the domain of a polynomial function. That is, many times the domain of a polynomial will not include negative numbers. The number of items produced or sold cannot be negative. Time is another independent variable that at times may not be negative. Be sure to remember this when you are working with these situations.

EXAMPLE 8   Josh estimated his weekly sales and determined a profit function, $p(x)$, where x is the number of bicycles sold per week. The following graph represents the function $p(x)$.

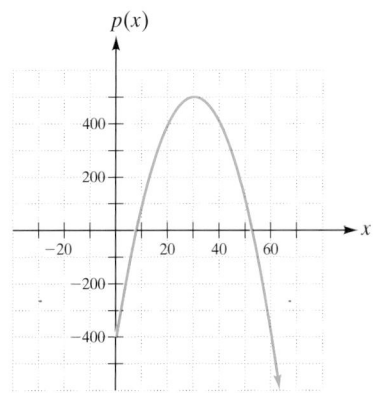

a. Determine the domain of the function.
b. Determine the absolute maximum of the function and interpret.
c. Determine the range of the function. Interpret.

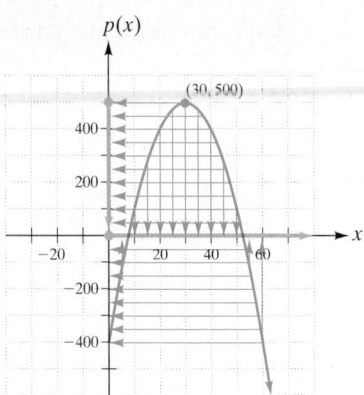

$p(x)$

(30, 500)

Solution

a. The domain is the set of all possible values for x or the set of all real numbers greater than or equal to 0, or $x \geq 0$, or $[0, \infty)$, because the number of bicycles sold, x, cannot be negative.

b. According to the graph, the absolute maximum is located at the point $(30, 500)$. The maximum profit is $500 when 30 bikes are sold per week.

c. According to the graph, the range is the set of all possible values for $p(x)$ or the set of all real numbers less than or equal to 500, or $p(x) \leq 500$, or $(-\infty, 500]$. The profit ranges from negative values (or a loss) to a value of $500 (the maximum profit).

EXAMPLE 9

George makes wooden duck decoys and sells them for $10.00. However, to reduce his inventory before winter, George plans to give a discount of $0.50 for each decoy purchased. If x is the number of decoys a person purchases, then the discount is $0.50 for each decoy purchased, or $0.50x$. The purchase price is $10.00 minus the discount, or $10.00 - 0.50x$. The amount of revenue, $R(x)$, is the purchase price, $10.00 - 0.50x$, times the number of decoys purchased, x:

$$R(x) = (10.00 - 0.50x)x, \text{ which becomes } R(x) = 10.00x - 0.50x^2$$

a. Determine the domain of the revenue function.

b. Determine the amount of revenue if George sells 5 decoys, 10 decoys, or 20 decoys.

c. What is the range of the revenue function?

d. What does this range tell us about George's discount plan?

Solution

a. The number of decoys purchased cannot be negative. The domain is the set of all real numbers greater than or equal to 0, or $[0, \infty)$.

b.
$$R(5) = 10.00(5) - 0.50(5)^2$$
$$R(5) = 37.50$$

If George sells 5 decoys, his revenue is $37.50.

$$R(10) = 10.00(10) - 0.50(10)^2$$
$$R(10) = 50.00$$

If George sells 10 decoys, his revenue is $50.00.

$$R(20) = 10.00(20) - 0.50(20)^2$$
$$R(20) = 0.00$$

If George sells 20 decoys, his revenue is $0.00.

c.

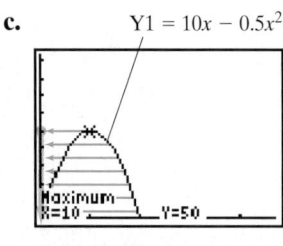

$Y1 = 10x - 0.5x^2$

Maximum
X=10   Y=50

$(0, 44, 0, 93)$

The range is the set of all real numbers less than or equal to 50.00 or $R(x) \leq 50.00$.

d. The range found shows us that if George gives the $0.50 discount, his largest revenue would be $50.00. (According to part (b), this occurs when he sells 10 decoys.) If George does not limit the discount, he would have a revenue of 0 (with 20 decoys sold) or a negative revenue (with more than 20 decoys sold), which is not a good thing to have. If George wants a more accurate picture of how his discount plan affects his possible profits, he should take into account the cost of manufacturing the decoys and the cost of selling them. ■

APPLICATION

During the 1980s the United States' national debt exceeded one trillion dollars for the first time in history. Using data from the United States Department of the Treasury, a third-degree polynomial function for national debt, $n(t)$, in trillions of dollars is generated: $n(t) = 0.014t^3 + 0.058t^2 + 0.069t + 5.688$, where t is the number of years after the year 2000.

a. Use the function to estimate the national debt for the years shown in the following table:

Year	2000	2001	2002	2003
National debt				

b. In 2003 the national debt was 6.8 trillion dollars. How well does the function estimate this number?

c. Estimate the national debt for the current year. Given your knowledge of current events, does this seem reasonable? Why or why not?

Solution

a. The variable t is defined to be the number of years after the year 2000. Therefore, $t = 0$ for 2000, $t = 1$ for 2001, $t = 2$ for 2002, and $t = 3$ for 2003.

t	$n(t) = 0.014t^3 + 0.058t^2 + 0.069t + 5.688$	$N(t)$
0	$n(0) = 0.014(0)^3 + 0.058(0)^2 + 0.069(0) + 5.688$	5.688
1	$n(1) = 0.014(1)^3 + 0.058(1)^2 + 0.069(1) + 5.688$	5.829
2	$n(2) = 0.014(2)^3 + 0.058(2)^2 + 0.069(2) + 5.688$	6.170
3	$n(3) = 0.014(3)^3 + 0.058(3)^2 + 0.069(3) + 5.688$	6.795

b. According to the table, in the year 2003 ($t = 3$) the national debt, $n(3)$, was 6.795. The function was a good predictor of the estimate.

c. Research to determine the national debt for the current year and discuss. Answers will vary.

Objective 6.2.5 **CHECKUP**

1. Josh estimated his weekly sales and determined a profit function, $p(x)$, where x is the number of bicycle tires sold per week.

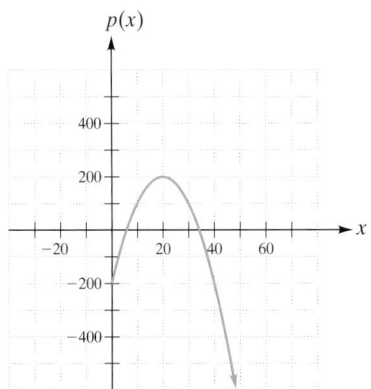

a. Determine the domain of the function.
b. Determine the absolute maximum of the function and interpret.
c. Determine the range of the function and interpret.

2. Consenting Consultants, Inc. (CCI), offers training to a major manufacturer, charging $150 - 4x$ dollars per person, where x is the number of people attending training. (Note that what this amounts to is a discount, depending upon the number of people who attend.) The revenue CCI collects is given by the function

$$R(x) = 150x - 4x^2$$

a. Determine the amount of revenue CCI will realize if 5 people attend the training, if 10 attend, if 15 attend, if 20 attend, if 25 attend, if 30 attend, if 35 attend, and if 40 attend.
b. What is the range of the revenue function?
c. Interpret the range in terms of the discount offered.

3. The United States has an aging population. Using statistics from the U.S. Bureau of the Census, the percent of the population that is between 45 and 64 year of age can be estimated by the third-degree polynomial function $p(x) = -0.0003x^3 + 0.0313x^2 - 0.3820x + 19.6$, where x is number of years after 1980.

a. Use this function to estimate the percent of the population 65 and over for the years in the following table:

Year	1980	1985	1990	2000
Percent of population 65 and over				

b. Data indicate that in the year 2000 the percent of the population between 45 and 64 years of age was 22%. How well did the function predict this number?

c. The Census Bureau published estimated statistics for 2003 which projected the 45–64 population at 23.6%. How well does the polynomial predict this number? ■

6.2 EXERCISES

 Student Solutions Manual  PH Math/Tutor Center CD Video MathXL MathXL® MyMathLab MyMathLab Interactmath.com

Create a table of values of five possible integer solutions of each polynomial relation.

1. $y = x^3 + 2x^2 - 5x - 6$ **2.** $y = x^3 - 2x^2 - 5x + 6$ **3.** $y = x^2 + 4x + 1$ **4.** $y = x^2 - 4x + 1$

In exercises 5–8,

     a. Determine three possible solutions for the polynomial relation graphed by completing the given table of values.
     b. Determine the range of each relation.

5.

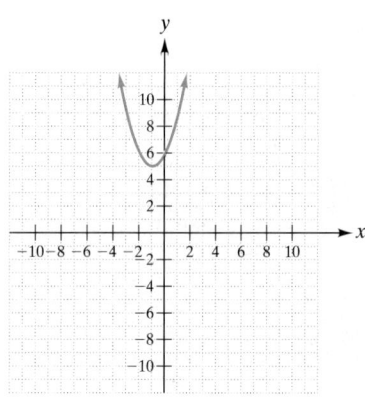

x	y
−2	
1	
	5

6.

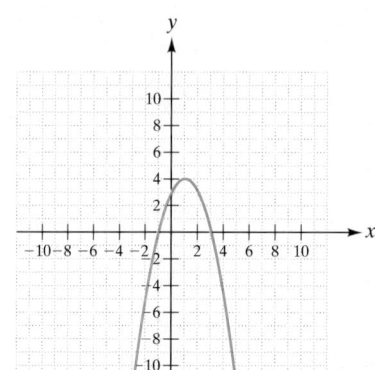

x	y
−2	
3	
	4

7.

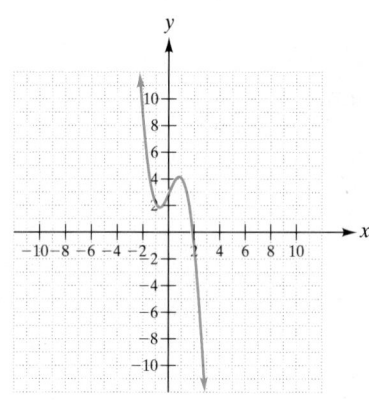

x	y
−1	
1	
	7

8.

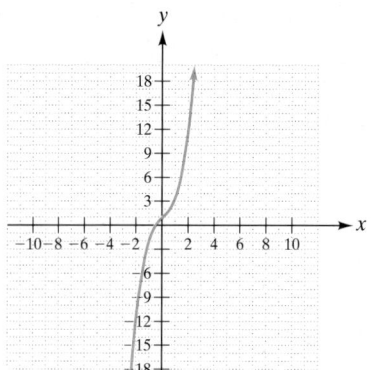

x	y
1	
−1	
	−11

Graph the given polynomial relations. From the graph, determine the range of each relation.

9. $y = 2x - 5$ **10.** $y = -3x + 2$ **11.** $y = -x^2 + 6x - 4$ **12.** $y = -2x^2 - 8x + 1$

13. $y = 2x^2 - 8x + 3$ **14.** $y = x^2 - 4x - 3$ **15.** $y = \frac{1}{2}x^2 + 6$ **16.** $y = \frac{2}{3}x^2 - 4$

17. $y = -\frac{1}{2}x^2 - 4x$ **18.** $y = -\frac{3}{4}x^2 + 6x$ **19.** $y = x^3 - 8$ **20.** $y = x^3 - 1$

21. $y = -\frac{1}{8}x^3 + 1$ **22.** $y = -\frac{1}{27}x^3 + 1$ **23.** $y = x^3 - 4x$ **24.** $y = x^3 - 9x$

25. $y = x^3 + 3x^2 - 10x - 24$ **26.** $y = x^3 - 7x + 6$ **27.** $y = \frac{1}{16}x^4 - x^2$ **28.** $y = \frac{1}{8}x^4 - x^2$

Evaluate the function $f(x) = x^2 + 16x + 64$ at the given values.

29. $f(2)$ **30.** $f(1)$ **31.** $f(-2)$ **32.** $f(-1)$

Evaluate the function $g(x) = 4x^2 - 4x + 1$ at the given values.

33. $g(3)$ **34.** $g(5)$ **35.** $g\left(\frac{3}{2}\right)$ **36.** $g\left(\frac{5}{2}\right)$

Evaluate the function $h(x) = 9x^2 + 12x + 4$ at the given values.

37. $h(-2)$ **38.** $h(-3)$ **39.** $h(-1.5)$ **40.** $h(-1.2)$

Evaluate the function $f(x) = -2x^3 + x^2 - 5x + 8$ *at the given values.*

41. $f(-2)$ **42.** $f(-1)$ **43.** $f(2)$ **44.** $f(3)$

Evaluate the function $g(x) = 2.7x^3 - 1.5x^2 + 3.5x - 6.7$ *at the given values.*

45. $g(2)$ **46.** $g(4)$ **47.** $g(-4)$ **48.** $g(-2)$

49. $g(10)$ **50.** $g(20)$ **51.** $g(1)$ **52.** $g(0)$

Evaluate the function $h(x) = \frac{1}{2}x^3 - \frac{3}{4}x^2 + \frac{3}{8}x - \frac{5}{8}$ *at the given values. Express your results in fraction notation.*

53. $h(2)$ **54.** $h(4)$ **55.** $h(-4)$ **56.** $h(-2)$

In exercises 57 and 58, graphs represent profit functions, where x is the number of items sold.

    a. Determine the domain of the function.

    b. Determine the absolute maximum of the function and interpret.

    c. Determine the range of the function. Interpret.

57.

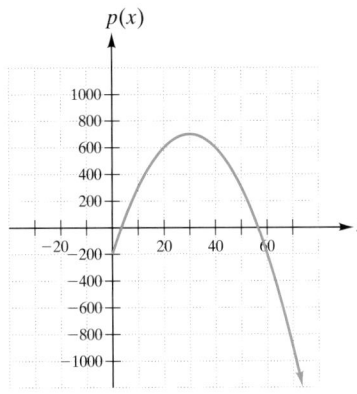

58.

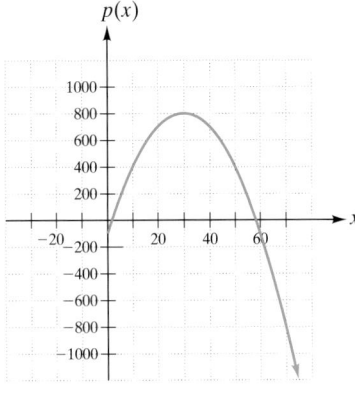

In exercises 59–62, determine the range for the following polynomial relations.

59.

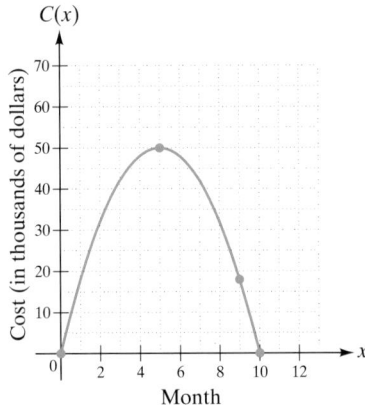

60. Revenues by Quarter

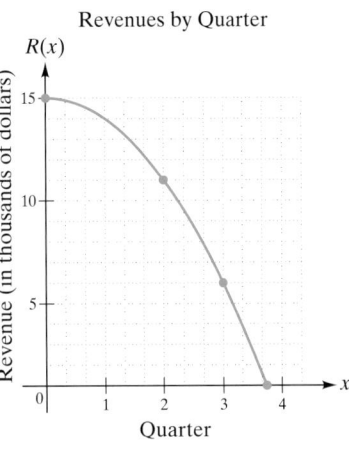

61. World Airline Fatalities

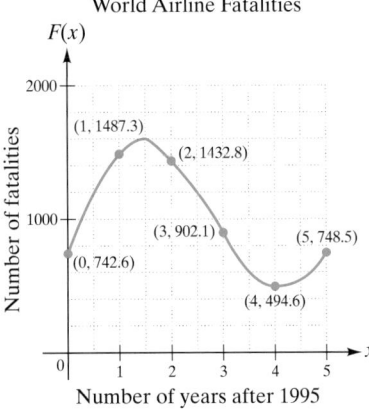

62. U.S. Cigarette Consumption

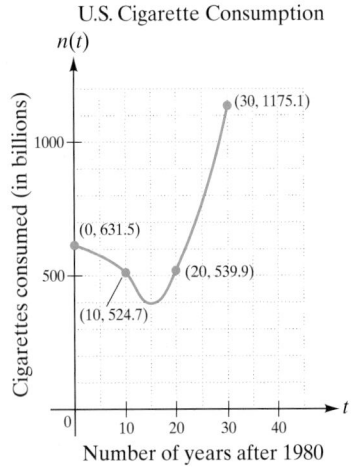

Business

63. In order to encourage multiple purchases, Dave's Wholesale Jewelers sells watches at a price that is a function of the number of watches ordered. For x watches ordered, the price will be $150 - 5x$ dollars per watch. Thus, one watch costs $145, two watches cost $140 each, and so forth. The revenue function for an order of x watches is

$$R(x) = 150x - 5x^2$$

  a. Determine the revenue if 5 watches are ordered, if 10 watches are ordered, if 15 watches are ordered, if 20 watches are ordered, if 25 watches are ordered, and if 30 watches are ordered.
  b. Find the range of the revenue function.
  c. Interpret the range in terms of the discount offered.

64. Honest Al rents space at his merchandise mart and offers sliding-scale rates for multimonth rentals. His rate is $300 - 5x$ dollars per month for x months of rental. Thus, the rate for one month's rental is $295, the rate for two months' rental is $290 per month, the rate for three months' rental is $285 per month, and so forth. The total cost for renting the space for x months is

$$C(x) = 300x - 5x^2$$

  a. Determine the cost of renting space for 10 months, for 20 months, for 30 months, for 40 months, for 50 months, and for 60 months.
  b. Determine the range of the cost function.
  c. Interpret the cost function in terms of the discount offered.

Geometry

65. The perimeter of a rectangle is 200 feet. Its area can be given by using the function $A(x) = 100x - x^2$, where $A(x)$ is the area and x is the measure of the width of the rectangle. What is the domain of this function? Use the function to fill in the following table:

x (width of rectangle)	A(x) (area of rectangle)
10	
20	
30	
40	
50	
60	
70	

What does the table suggest as the maximum possible area?

66. The perimeter of a rectangle is 600 cm. Its area can be given by $A(x) = 300x - x^2$, where $A(x)$ is the area and x is the measure of the length of the rectangle. What is the domain of this function? Use the function to fill in the following table:

x (length of rectangle)	A(x) (area of rectangle)
50	
75	
100	
125	
150	
175	
200	

What does the table suggest as the maximum possible area?

67. The area of a triangle in which the height is 2 feet more than the base can be given by the polynomial $A(x) = 0.5x^2 + x$, where x is the measure of the base and $A(x)$ is the area. What is the domain of this function? What is the range of this function? What is the area if the base is 10 feet? What is the area if the height is 20 feet? What are the measures of the base and the height of the triangle if the area is 150 square feet?

68. The area of an equilateral triangle can be approximated by the polynomial $A(s) = 0.433s^2$, where s is the length of the side of the triangle and $A(s)$ is the area. What is the domain of this function? What is the range of this function? What is the area if the length of a side is 15.8 cm? What is the side of the triangle if the area is 1.4 square centimeters?

Real Data

69. Unemployment rates fluctuate due to a variety of economic conditions. The U.S. Department of Labor compiles statistics and creates both monthly and yearly unemployment percentages. The polynomial function $p(x) = -0.009x^2 + 0.087x + 7.692$ can be used to estimate the percent unemployment, $p(x)$, where x is years after 1980.

  a. Use the function to estimate unemployment rates in the following table:

Year	Percent Unemployed
1980	
1985	
1990	
1995	
1996	
1997	
1998	

  b. Compare your table to the table that shows the actual percentages. Comment on similarities and differences.

Year	Percent Unemployed
1980	7.6
1985	8.3
1990	7.1
1995	7.4
1996	7.2
1997	6.7
1998	6.2

  c. What does the function predict will be the unemployment rate this year? According to your knowledge of current events, does this seem reasonable? Why or why not?

70. According to the United States Health and Human Services Administration for Children and Families, the number of recipients in the Temporary Assistance for Needy Families Program has gone down even though the population of the United States has increased. The actual chart is shown below:

Year	Number of Recipients (in millions)
1994	14.2
1995	13.7
1996	12.6
1997	10.9
1998	8.8
1999	7.2

A polynomial function, $n(t) = -0.17t^2 + 0.74t + 14.2$, is created to estimate the number of recipients, $n(t)$, in millions, where t is the number of years after 1990.

a. Use the function to estimate the number of recipients by year in the table below:

Year	Number of Recipients (in millions)
1994	
1995	
1996	
1997	
1998	
1999	

b. Comment on any similarities or differences between the table of actual data and the table generated by the function.

c. Data suggest that the number of recipients in 2000 was 5.8 million. How well did the function predict this number?

71. Social Security reform is of increasing concern to many Americans. Discussion of changing the current formula for retirement benefits is taking place, and various groups have proposed changes to the way in which they are now being computed. The Social Security Administration has published data that relate a worker's average yearly wages in 2005 to the annual benefits promised by the current formula should the person retire in 2045. The function

$$b(x) = -0.000002x^2 + 0.496x + 4446.646$$

can be used to model these data, where b is the annual benefit in 2045 and x is the yearly wages earned in 2005.

a. Use this function to estimate the promised benefit in 2045 for people with 2005 yearly wages as given in the following table:

Yearly salary in 2005	30,000	50,000	70,000	90,000	110,000
Benefit in 2045					

b. The data suggest that someone making $58,560 in 2005 will earn a benefit of $26,302 in 2045. How well did the function predict this amount?

c. The data also suggest that a person making $36,600 in 2005 will earn a benefit of $19,837 in 2045. How well did the function predict this amount?

72. The United States has an aging population. Using statistics from the U.S. Bureau of the Census, the percent of the population that is 65 and over can be estimated by the polynomial function $p(x) = -0.0015x^2 + 0.165x + 9.8$, where x is the number of years after 1970.

a. Use this function to estimate the percent of the population 65 and over for the years in the following table:

Year	1970	1980	1990
Percent of population 65 and over			

b. Data indicate that in the year 2000 the percent of population 65 and over is 12.4%. How well did the function predict this number?

c. The Census Bureau published estimated statistics for 2003 which projected the 65 and over population at 12.4%. How well does the function predict this number?

73. According to statistics published by the U.S. Department of Education, National Center of Education Statistics, the average cost at two-year institutions of undergraduate tuition, room and board, and fees, $c(x)$, in dollars, can be estimated by the third-degree polynomial function $c(x) = 45.17x^3 - 168x^2 + 239.83x + 5291$, where x is number of years after 1998.

a. Use this function to estimate college costs for the years given in the following table:

Year	1998	1999	2000	2001
Cost				

b. More recent data suggest that the cost in 2001 was $5718. How well did the function predict this amount?

c. More recent data also suggest that the cost in 2002 was $6238. How well does the function predict this amount?

d. According to this model, in what year will costs exceed $10,000? Does this seem reasonable? Why or why not?

74. The average cost of education at four-year institutions is also increasing. The cost of undergraduate tuition, room and board, and fees, $c(x)$, in dollars, can be estimated by the third-degree polynomial function $c(x) = 6.83x^3 + 32.5x^2 + 424.67x + 11,888$, where x is number of years after 1998.

a. Use this function to estimate college costs for the years given in the following table:

Year	1998	1999	2000	2001
Cost				

b. More recent data suggest that the cost in 2001 was $13,639. How well did the function predict this amount?

c. More recent data also suggest that the cost in 2002 was $14,504. How well does the function predict this amount?

d. According to this model, in what year will costs exceed $20,000? Does this seem reasonable? Why or why not?

6.2 Calculator Exercises

Part 1. Influence of Degree of Polynomial

Graph the following polynomial functions with a calculator. To view the graph easily, use the decimal viewing window. Then draw a sketch of each graph, labeling the intercepts.

1. $y = x$ **2.** $y = x^2 + x$

3. $y = x^3 - x$ **4.** $y = x^4 + 2x^3 - x^2 - 2x$

5. $y = x^5 - 5x^3 + 4x$

Determine the degree of each polynomial.

Compare the graphs. How many times does each graph change direction, either moving up from left to right or moving down from left to right? Compare this number with the degree of the polynomial graphed. Complete the following table:

Polynomial	Degree of Polynomial	Number of Changes in Direction
$y = x$		
$y = x^2 + x$		
$y = x^3 - x$		
$y = x^4 + 2x^3 - x^2 - 2x$		
$y = x^5 - 5x^3 + 4x$		

Discuss the apparent relationship between the degree of the polynomial and the number of times the graph changes direction.

Next, notice which graphs have tails that extend in opposite directions and which graphs have tails that extend in the same direction. Discuss and compare this feature with the degree of the polynomials. Do you see a relationship?

Notice also that when the tails extend in opposite directions, there is at least one value of x that will make the polynomial evaluate to 0. Discuss why this is so.

The degree of the polynomial in a polynomial function can be a useful feature to study to understand what the function's graph will look like.

Part 2. Function Notation on the Calculator

The function notation that you used in this section is also used by the calculator to evaluate functions. You have seen that you can evaluate a function by keying it in with the variable replaced by its value. You have also seen that you can evaluate a function by storing the value of its variable and then keying in the function. A third method, using function notation, is explained next.

To evaluate a function on your calculator by using function notation, first store the function under the Y = menu as Y1. Then type the function notation on the home screen, using Y1 with the value enclosed in parentheses. When you press [**ENTER**], the calculator will display the function value, evaluated at the value specified for the variable.

As an example, evaluate the function $f(x) = x^3 - 2x^2 + 5x - 4$ when $x = 7, -5$, and 2.4.

Key the following instructions into the calculator:

- Store the function in Y = as Y1.

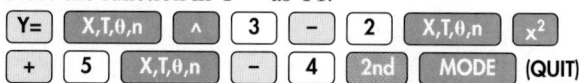

- Key the function notation for the values of x.

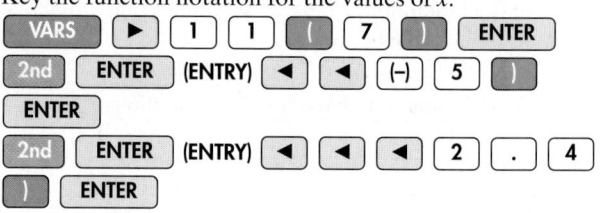

The calculator displays for these instructions are as follows:

```
Plot1 Plot2 Plot3
\Y1▨X^3-2X²+5X-4
\Y2=
\Y3=
\Y4=
\Y5=
\Y6=
```

```
Y1(7)
              276
Y1(-5)
             -204
Y1(2.4)
           10.304
```

Practice this method on the following exercises:

Evaluate the function $f(x) = 2.5x^3 - 1.6x^2 + 4.2x - 9.3$ for the given values.

1. $f(-2.4)$ **2.** $f(155.8)$ **3.** $f(0.944)$

Evaluate the function $h(x) = \frac{2}{3}x^3 + \frac{1}{2}x^2 - 2x + \frac{1}{3}$ for the given values. Use the fraction option of the calculator to display the answer in fractional notation.

4. $h(6)$ **5.** $h\left(\frac{3}{4}\right)$ **6.** (-9)

6.2 Writing Exercise

In this section, several examples or exercises mention statistics as an area of mathematics that often uses polynomials in order to explain the relationship between pairs of observations in actual data collected from an application. In the library, browse some statistics texts to find another example where this is done. (*Note:* In the statistics texts, you will find this done under a method called regression analysis.) Don't try to understand the description of how the relation is developed; just take note of the example presented.

Write a short paragraph describing the independent variable and the dependent variable being studied in the example. Also present the relation developed. Experiment with the relation to see if you can substitute values for the independent variable to estimate what the value will be for the dependent variable. Explain what this example means to you. Footnote the text in which you found the example and provide the library call number for the text.

6.3 QUADRATIC FUNCTIONS AND THEIR GRAPHS

OBJECTIVES   1 Identify quadratic functions.
2 Understand the effects of the coefficients of a quadratic function on its graph.
3 Graph quadratic functions.
4 Model real-world situations using graphs of quadratic functions.

APPLICATION

Pyrotechnicians must take into account many different relationships in designing a fireworks show. However, if we simplify the projection of a firework shell and consider only the force of gravity on the shell, we can write a polynomial function for the position of the shell. The position function for a 6-inch-diameter shell that is shot directly above the launcher at an initial velocity of 203.5 feet per second and an initial height of 5 feet is $s(t) = -16t^2 + 203.5t + 5$, where $s(t)$ is the height above ground level (in feet) and t is the time in seconds after the shell was shot from the launcher.

  a. Find the vertex.

  b. Determine the absolute maximum value of the function.

  c. Determine the range of the function and interpret its meaning.

  d. If the firework explodes 5 seconds after being shot, then the time is $0 \le t \le 5$. Determine the absolute maximum height of the shell.

After completing this section, we will discuss this application further. See page 513.

Objective 6.3.1   ## Identifying Quadratic Functions

In this section, we discuss a special case of a polynomial function, called a quadratic function. A **quadratic function** is a polynomial function with a degree of 2.

STANDARD FORM FOR A QUADRATIC FUNCTION

A quadratic function can be written in the standard form

$$y = ax^2 + bx + c, \text{ where } a \neq 0$$

or

$$f(x) = ax^2 + bx + c, \text{ where } a \neq 0.$$

For example,

Standard form: $y = ax^2 + bx + c$

1. $y = 2x^2 + 3x - 4$	$a = 2, b = 3,$ and $c = -4$
2. $y = x^2 - 2x$	$a = 1, b = -2,$ and $c = 0$
3. $y = -3x^2 + 5$	$a = -3, b = 0,$ and $c = 5$
4. $y = x^2$	$a = 1, b = 0,$ and $c = 0$

The coefficients are identified next to each function. Remember, $a \neq 0$; if $a = 0$, we no longer have a quadratic function. We would then have a linear function of the form $y = bx + c$.

EXAMPLE 1   Identify each function as quadratic or nonquadratic.

  a. $y = x^3 + x^2 - 6x$ **b.** $h(x) = 2x - x^2$ **c.** $y = \dfrac{6}{2x} + 2x - 7$

Solution

a. $y = x^3 + x^2 - 6x$ is not a quadratic function, because $x^3 + x^2 - 6x$ is a third-degree polynomial. (The first term is x cubed.)

b. $h(x) = 2x - x^2$ is a quadratic function, because it can be rearranged into standard form, $h(x) = -x^2 + 2x + 0$.

c. $y = \dfrac{6}{2x} + 2x - 7$ is not a quadratic function, because $\dfrac{6}{2x} + 2x - 7$ is not a polynomial. (A variable is in the denominator of a fraction.)   ■

✓ Objective 6.3.1 *CHECKUP*

1. Identify each function as quadratic or nonquadratic.
   a. $f(x) = 3 - 9x - 7x^2$ **b.** $y = x^3 + x^2 - x$
   c. $y = -\dfrac{3}{x^2} - 4$

2. What must be true about the coefficient of the squared variable term of a quadratic function? Why is this so?

Objective 6.3.2   Understanding the Effects of the Coefficients

Just as the coefficients m and b of a linear function, $y = mx + b$, affect its graph, the values of the coefficients a, b, and c in the standard form of a quadratic function, $y = ax^2 + bx + c$, affect its graph.

All quadratic functions have a U-shaped graph called a **parabola**.

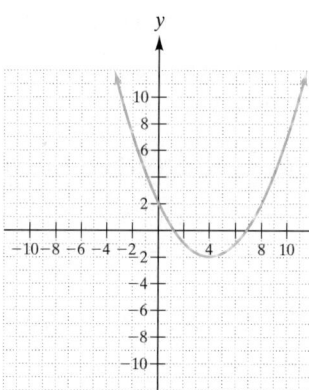   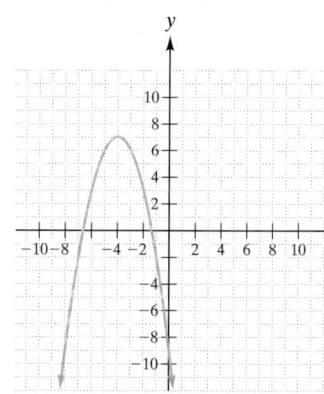

The term ax^2 in the function is called the **quadratic term**. To determine what effect the coefficient a has on the parabola, complete the following set of exercises.

💡 Guided Discovery 2   Effect of the Coefficient a on a Quadratic Graph

Sketch the graphs of the given quadratic functions of the form $y = ax^2$, where $b = c = 0$, on the same coordinate plane. Use the decimal window.

1. $y = 0.2x^2$ **2.** $y = x^2$ **3.** $y = 2x^2$

4. $y = -0.2x^2$ **5.** $y = -x^2$ **6.** $y = -2x^2$

Complete the following sentences by choosing the correct words:

7. In exercises 1–3, a is a *positive/negative* number. All of the graphs open *upward/downward*.

8. In exercises 4–6, a is a *positive/negative* number. All of the graphs open *upward/downward*.

9. In exercises 3 and 6, the absolute value of a is greater than 1. The shape of the parabola is *wider/narrower* than the graphs in exercises 2 and 5, in which $a = 1$ or -1.

10. In exercises 1 and 4, the absolute value of a is less than 1. The shape of the parabola is *wider/narrower* than the graphs in exercises 2 and 5, in which $a = 1$ or -1.

The coefficient a of the quadratic term affects the form of the parabola graphed. If the coefficient is positive, the graph opens upward. We say the graph is **concave upward**. If the coefficient is negative, the graph opens downward, or is **concave downward**.

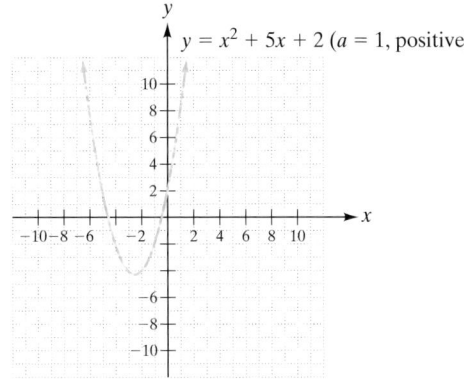

Concave upward

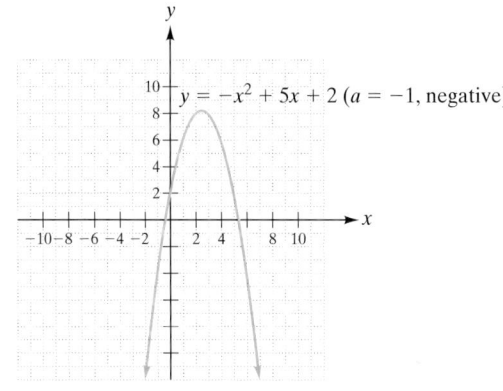

Concave downward

If the absolute value of the coefficient a is greater than 1, the graph is narrower than the graph of a parabola with a coefficient of 1. If the absolute value of the coefficient is less than 1, the graph is wider than the graph of a parabola with a coefficient of 1.

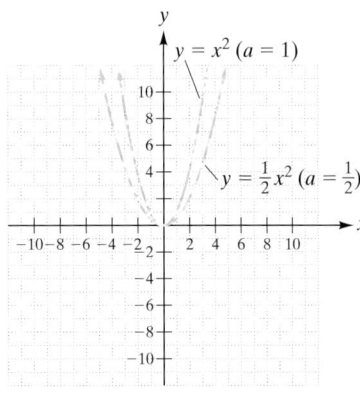

$a = \frac{1}{2}$
Wider since $\left|\frac{1}{2}\right| < 1$

$a = 2$
Narrower since $|2| > 1$

Remember from Chapter 1 that a function value is called a **relative maximum** if it is larger than the function values of its neighboring points. The largest relative maximum is called the *absolute maximum*. If a parabola is concave downward, its quadratic function will have an absolute maximum equal to the function value of the highest point of the parabola.

A function value is called a **relative minimum** if it is smaller than the function values of its neighboring points. The smallest relative minimum is called the *absolute minimum*. If a parabola is concave upward, its quadratic function will have an absolute minimum equal to the function value of the lowest point of the parabola.

The highest point on a concave-down parabola (absolute maximum) and the lowest point on a concave-up parabola (absolute minimum) are each called the **vertex** of the parabola.

A function is said to be **increasing** if the values of the function increase as the values of the independent variable increase. The function is said to be **decreasing** if the values of the function decrease as the values of the independent variable increase.

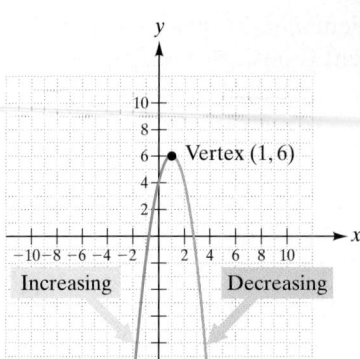

Concave downward
Absolute maximum of 6 at $x = 1$
Function is increasing when $x < 1$
Function is decreasing when $x > 1$

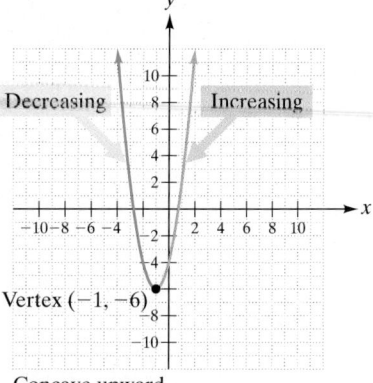

Concave upward
Absolute minimum of -6 at $x = -1$
Function is decreasing when $x < -1$
Function is increasing when $x > -1$

EXAMPLE 2   Use the graph to answer the questions that follow.

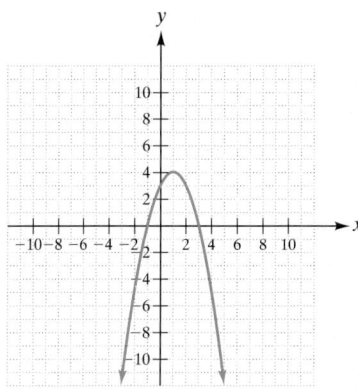

a. Determine the concavity of the graph.

b. Determine the vertex.

c. Determine the absolute maximum or absolute minimum of the function and for what x-value this occurs.

d. Determine the x-values for which the function is increasing.

e. Determine the x-values for which the function is decreasing.

Solution

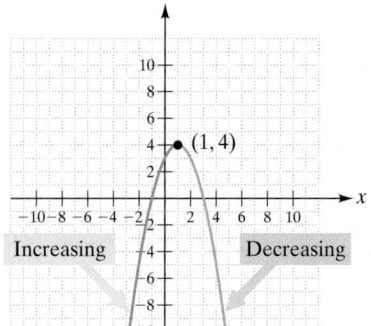

a. The graph is open downward. We say it is concave downward.

b. The vertex is $(1, 4)$.

c. The absolute maximum is 4 at $x = 1$.

d. The function is increasing for $x < 1$ or $(-\infty, 1)$.

e. The function is decreasing for $x > 1$ or $(1, \infty)$.   ■

The coefficients a and b determine the x-coordinate of the vertex. A formula for this is

$$x = \frac{-b}{2a}$$

We use this x-coordinate to find the y-coordinate of the vertex, which is either the absolute maximum or the absolute minimum of the quadratic function.

To determine the vertex of a quadratic function $y = ax^2 + bx + c$,

- Use the formula for the x-coordinate of the vertex of a quadratic function, which is $x = \frac{-b}{2a}$.
- Find the y-coordinate of the vertex by substituting the value of the x-coordinate into the original function and solving for y.

To determine the vertex of a quadratic function on your calculator,

- Enter the function in Y1.
- Graph the function.
- Trace the graph to determine its highest or lowest point.
- Use the CALC function to determine the minimum or maximum if it cannot be found by tracing.

 TAKE NOTE The calculator may display the vertex only approximately, so it may not be exact.

EXAMPLE 3

Given the quadratic function $y = 2x^2 + 4x + 3$, determine the coordinates of the vertex of its graph.

Solution

The coefficients are $a = 2$, $b = 4$, and $c = 3$.

$$x = \frac{-b}{2a}$$

$$x = \frac{-(4)}{2(2)} \qquad a = 2, b = 4$$

$$x = -1$$

To determine the y-coordinate of the vertex, substitute the value of the x-coordinate into the function and solve for y.

$$y = 2x^2 + 4x + 3$$
$$y = 2(-1)^2 + 4(-1) + 3$$
$$y = 2 - 4 + 3$$
$$y = 1$$

The vertex is $(-1, 1)$.

To determine the vertex on your calculator, see **Figures 6.6a** and **6.6b**. Note that in **Figure 6.6a** the vertex is located by tracing. However, in **Figure 6.6b**, the calculated ordered pair is only an approximate location.

Check

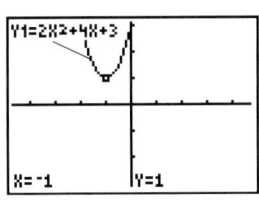

$(-4.7, 4.7, -3.1, 3.1)$

Figure 6.6a

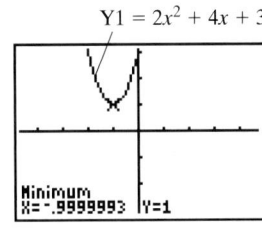

$(-4.7, 4.7, -3.1, 3.1)$

Figure 6.6b

Another feature of a quadratic function's graph is its symmetry. To visualize the meaning of symmetry, complete the following set of exercises on your calculator.

Guided Discovery 3   Symmetric Graph

1. Consider the graph of $y = x^2$. The vertex of the graph is $(0, 0)$. Complete the table of values for the three integer x-values on either side of $x = 0$, the x-coordinate of the vertex.

x	y
-3	
-2	
-1	
0	0 ← vertex
1	
2	
3	

2. Graph the function, using the table of values. Label all points graphed. Compare the y-values for the x-values equidistant from $x = 0$.

3. If $x = 1$ or $x = -1$, then $y = $ _____.

4. If $x = 2$ or $x = -2$, then $y = $ _____.

5. If $x = 3$ or $x = -3$, then $y = $ _____.

The graph of $y = x^2$ is a parabola that is symmetric with respect to the y-axis, or to the line graphed by the equation $x = 0$. The y-values that correspond to the x-values equidistant from $x = 0$ are equal. Therefore, if the graph is folded together along the line $x = 0$, the two sides will coincide. We call the vertical line through the vertex the **axis of symmetry** of the parabola.

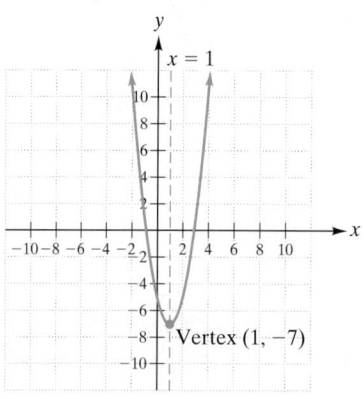

Axis of symmetry: $x = 1$

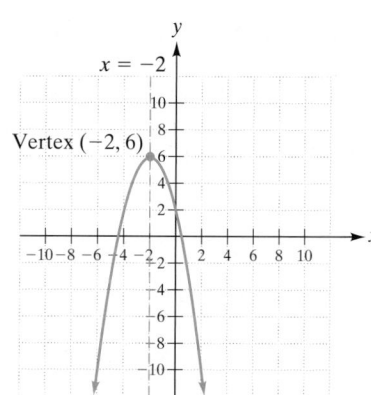

Axis of symmetry: $x = -2$

The constant term c of the quadratic function also affects the graph. To determine the effect of c, complete the following set of exercises on your calculator.

 Guided Discovery 4   Effect of the Coefficient c on a Quadratic Graph

Sketch the graph of the given quadratic functions of the form $y = ax^2 + c$, where $b = 0$, on the same coordinate plane. Use the decimal window and label the y-intercept of each graph.

$$y = 2x^2 \qquad y = 2x^2 + 1 \qquad y = 2x^2 - 3$$

1. Write a rule for determining the y-coordinate of the y-intercept of a parabola from its equation.

2. Check your rule for $y = 2x^2 + 3x - 1$.

The y-coordinate of the y-intercept is the constant term. (This is the same as when we were graphing linear equations.) Therefore, the y-coordinate of the y-intercept of the graph of $y = 2x^2 + 3x - 1$ is -1. The y-intercept is $(0, -1)$. We can determine the y-intercept algebraically in the same manner as we did for a linear equation: Substitute 0 for x and solve for y.

For example, given $y = 2x^2 + 3x - 1$, substitute 0 for x.

$$y = 2x^2 + 3x - 1$$
$$y = 2(0)^2 + 3(0) - 1$$
$$y = -1$$

The y-coordinate of the y-intercept is -1, the constant term of the function.

SUMMARY OF THE EFFECTS OF THE COEFFICIENTS OF A QUADRATIC FUNCTION ON ITS GRAPH

The coefficients of a quadratic function written in standard form, $y = ax^2 + bx + c$, affect the graph of the function.

Coefficient a:

If $a > 0$ (positive), then the graph is concave upward.

If $a < 0$ (negative), then the graph is concave downward.

Absolute value of a:

If $|a| > 1$, then the graph is narrower than when $a = 1$.

If $|a| < 1$, then the graph is wider than when $a = 1$.

Coefficient c:

The coefficient c is the y-coordinate of the y-intercept of the graph.

The y-intercept is at $x = 0$, $y = c$ or at $(0, c)$.

Coefficients a and b:

The x-coordinate of the vertex is $\frac{-b}{2a}$.

The axis of symmetry is the line graphed by $x = \frac{-b}{2a}$.

EXAMPLE 4   Given $y = -2x^2 + 6x - 1$, list the properties of its graph.

Solution

The coefficients of $y = -2x^2 + 6x - 1$ are $a = -2$, $b = 6$, and $c = -1$.

The graph is concave downward, because $a = -2$ (negative).

The graph is narrow compared to the graph of $y = x^2$, because $a = -2$ and $|-2| = 2 > 1$.

The y-intercept is $(0, -1)$. (Note that $c = -1$.)

The x-coordinate of the vertex is

$$x = \frac{-b}{2a} = \frac{-6}{2(-2)} = \frac{-6}{-4} = \frac{3}{2}$$

The y-coordinate of the vertex is

$$y = -2x^2 + 6x - 1$$
$$y = -2\left(\frac{3}{2}\right)^2 + 6\left(\frac{3}{2}\right) - 1$$
$$y = \frac{7}{2}$$

The vertex is $\left(\frac{3}{2}, \frac{7}{2}\right)$.

The axis of symmetry is $x = \frac{3}{2}$.

✓ Objective 6.3.2 *CHECKUP*

1. Use the graph to answer parts **a–e**.

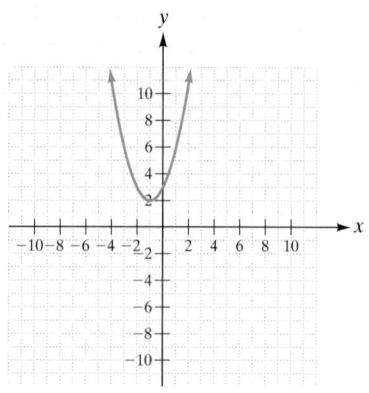

a. Determine the concavity of the graph.
b. Determine the vertex.
c. Determine the absolute maximum or absolute minimum of the function and for what x-value this occurs.
d. Determine the x-values for which the function is increasing.
e. Determine the x-values for which the function is decreasing.

2. Given the quadratic function $y = x^2 + 2x - 1$, determine algebraically the coordinates of the vertex of its graph. Check on your calculator.

3. Given $y = \dfrac{1}{4}x^2 - x + 2$, list the properties of its graph.

4. In graphing the quadratic function $y = ax^2 + bx + c$,
How does the value of the coefficient a affect the graph?
How does the value of the coefficient b affect the graph?
How does the value of the coefficient c affect the graph?

Objective 6.3.3   Graphing Quadratic Functions

When we graphed linear functions, we needed two points to determine the linear pattern. Quadratic functions do not have a linear pattern, so we will need more than two points to determine a pattern.

To graph a quadratic function,

- Determine the coordinates of the vertex by finding the x-coordinate from the formula $x = \frac{-b}{2a}$, substituting the x-coordinate into the original quadratic function, and solving for y to determine the y-coordinate.
- Construct a table of values by choosing at least two x-values greater than the x-coordinate of the vertex and two corresponding x-values less than the x-coordinate of the vertex.
- Graph the function by plotting the vertex and the set of ordered pairs from the table of values and connecting the points with a smooth curve.

🖊 **TAKE NOTE** It helps to graph the axis of symmetry as a dashed vertical line.

EXAMPLE 5

Graph the quadratic function $y = -x^2 + 2x + 1$. Label the vertex. Draw and label the axis of symmetry.

Solution

Given $y = -x^2 + 2x + 1$, we know that $a = -1, b = 2,$ and $c = 1$.
Determine the coordinates of the vertex. Use the formula

$$x = \frac{-b}{2a} = \frac{-2}{2(-1)} = 1$$

Determine the y-coordinate of the vertex.
Substitute 1 for x in the function.

$$y = -x^2 + 2x + 1$$
$$y = -(1)^2 + 2(1) + 1$$
$$y = 2$$

The vertex is $(1, 2)$. The axis of symmetry is the line $x = 1$.

Set up a table of values, using x-values less than and greater than the x-coordinate of the vertex, 1.

x	$y = -x^2 + 2x + 1$	y
-1	$y = -(-1)^2 + 2(-1) + 1$	-2
0	$y = -(0)^2 + 2(0) + 1$	1
1	$y = -(1)^2 + 2(1) + 1$	2
2	$y = -(2)^2 + 2(2) + 1$	1
3	$y = -(3)^2 + 2(3) + 1$	-2

← vertex (1, 2)

Graph the vertex and the points found in the table of values. Connect the points with a smooth curve and graph the axis of symmetry.

Check

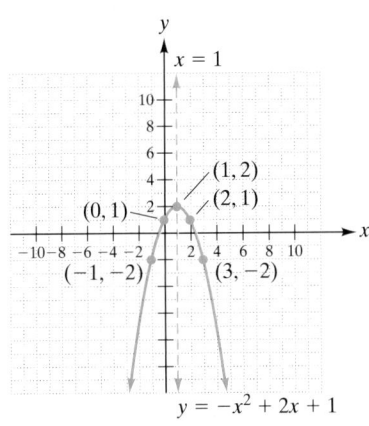

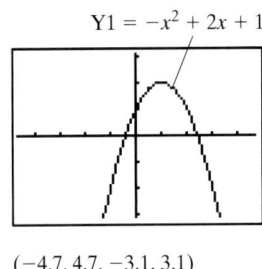

$(-4.7, 4.7, -3.1, 3.1)$

The decimal screen provides a picture.
Trace the graph to check the points found in the table of values.

EXAMPLE 6

Graph the quadratic function $f(x) = x^2 + 3x + 1$. Label the vertex. Draw and label the axis of symmetry.

Solution

The coefficients are $a = 1$, $b = 3$, and $c = 1$.
　First, determine the coordinates of the vertex.
　The x-coordinate is found by the formula

$$x = \frac{-b}{2a} = \frac{-3}{2(1)} = -\frac{3}{2}$$

Determine the y-coordinate of the vertex. Substitute $-\dfrac{3}{2}$ for x in the function.

$$f(x) = x^2 + 3x + 1$$
$$f\left(-\frac{3}{2}\right) = \left(-\frac{3}{2}\right)^2 + 3\left(-\frac{3}{2}\right) + 1$$
$$f\left(-\frac{3}{2}\right) = -\frac{5}{4}$$

The vertex is $\left(-\frac{3}{2}, -\frac{5}{4}\right)$.
　The axis of symmetry is the line $x = -\frac{3}{2}$.
　Complete a table of values by choosing two x-values less than $-\frac{3}{2}$, such as -2 and -3, and two x-values greater than $-\frac{3}{2}$, such as -1 and 0.

x	$f(x) = x^2 + 3x + 1$	$f(x)$
-3	$f(-3) = (-3)^2 + 3(-3) + 1$	1
-2	$f(-2) = (-2)^2 + 3(-2) + 1$	-1
$-\frac{3}{2}$	$f\left(-\frac{3}{2}\right) = \left(-\frac{3}{2}\right)^2 + 3\left(-\frac{3}{2}\right) + 1$	$-\frac{5}{4}$
-1	$f(-1) = (-1)^2 + 3(-1) + 1$	-1
0	$f(0) = (0)^2 + 3(0) + 1$	1

$\leftarrow$ vertex$\left(-\frac{3}{2}, -\frac{5}{4}\right)$

Plot the vertex and the ordered pairs found in the table of values. Connect the points with a smooth curve and graph the axis of symmetry.

On your calculator, enter the function in Y1 and graph it using the decimal screen.

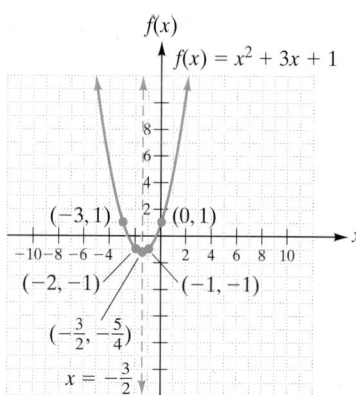

Check

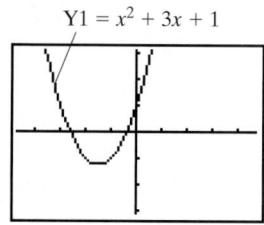

$Y1 = x^2 + 3x + 1$

$(-4.7, 4.7, -3.1, 3.1)$

Objective 6.3.3 **CHECKUP**

Graph the quadratic functions in exercises 1 and 2. Label the vertex. Draw and label the axis of symmetry.

1. $A(x) = 2x^2 - x - 6$

2. $y = -x^2 + 12x - 26$

3. In graphing a quadratic function, why should you first find the vertex?

4. After graphing a quadratic function, how can you use the coefficients of the quadratic polynomial to check that your graph is correct?

Objective 6.3.4   **Modeling the Real World**

Quadratic functions model many real-world applications, as we've seen earlier in this chapter. We can use the methods in this section to find the maximum or minimum values of a quadratic function, which is often useful and important information. For example, we can use a quadratic function to determine the profit of a business. The absolute maximum of the function corresponds to the maximum amount of profit.

EXAMPLE 7

A company manufactures and sells x computer printers per month. The monthly profit function is given by $P(x) = 100x - 0.025x^2$, where x is between 0 and 4000 printers. Determine the maximum profit the company can realize and how many printers should be manufactured and sold to achieve this profit.

Solution

$$P(x) = 100x - 0.025x^2$$
or
$$P(x) = -0.025x^2 + 100x$$

Determine the x-value of the vertex by substituting $a = -0.025$, $b = 100$, and $c = 0$.

Check

Let $Y1 = 100x - 0.025x^2$
Graph and determine the absolute maximum value of the function.

$$x = -\frac{b}{2a}$$

$$x = \frac{-(100)}{2(-0.025)}$$

$$x = 2000$$

The function $P(x) = 100x - 0.025x^2$ evaluated for $x = 2000$ is

$$P(2000) = 100(2000) - 0.025(2000)^2$$
$$P(2000) = 100,000$$

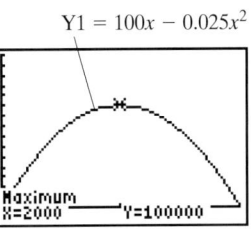

Y1 = 100x − 0.025x²

(0, 4000, −10,000, 150,000)

The vertex is (2000, 100,000). The absolute maximum of the function is 100,000 at $x = 2000$.

The maximum monthly profit for the company is \$100,000, when 2000 computer printers are manufactured and sold. ■

APPLICATION

Pyrotechnicians must take into account many different relationships in designing a fireworks show. However, if we simplify the projection of a firework shell and consider only the force of gravity on the shell, we can write a polynomial function for the position of the shell. The position function for a 6-inch-diameter shell that is shot directly above the launcher at an initial velocity of 203.5 feet per second and an initial height of 5 feet is $s(t) = -16t^2 + 203.5t + 5$, where $s(t)$ is the height above ground level (in feet) and t is the time in seconds after the shell was shot from the launcher.

a. Find the vertex.

b. Determine the absolute maximum value of the function.

c. Determine the range of the function and interpret its meaning.

d. If the firework shell explodes 5 seconds after being shot, then the time t is $0 \le t \le 5$. Determine the absolute maximum height of the shell.

Discussion

Let $Y1 = -16x^2 + 203.5x + 5$, graph the function on your calculator, and find the absolute maximum of the function.

a. The vertex is (6.36, 652).

b. Assuming the shell explodes after 6.36 seconds, the shell reaches a height of about 652 feet at about 6.36 seconds.

c. Assuming that the shell explodes above the initial height, 5 feet, the function values cannot be less than 5. Therefore, the range of the function is all real numbers between and equal to 5 and approximately 652, or $5 \le y \le 652$.

   The position of the firework shell above the ground will range from 5 to 652 feet, assuming that the shell explodes after 6.36 seconds.

d. In parts **b** and **c**, we assumed the shell explodes after 6.36 seconds. If the shell explodes 5 seconds after being shot ($0 \le t \le 5$) and the shell is shot upward, then the absolute maximum height of the shell will occur at $t = 5$ seconds. The maximum height of the shell is 622.5 feet 5 seconds after being shot upward.

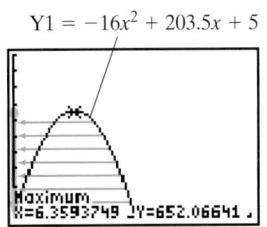

Y1 = −16x² + 203.5x + 5

(0, 25, 0, 1000)

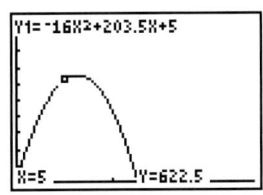

Y1=-16X²+203.5X+5

(0, 25, 0, 1000)

Objective 6.3.4 *CHECKUP*

1. Green Lawns Manufacturing Company determines that the daily cost of producing a tiller is given by $c(x) = 100 + 40x - 0.01x^2$, where the number of tillers, x, is between 0 and 2500. Determine the maximum cost of producing this tiller and how many tillers produced will achieve this cost.

2. A signal flare is shot upward from a cliff 100 meters high. If the initial velocity of the flare was 91.2 meters per second, a position function for the flare is $s(t) = -4.9t^2 + 91.2t + 100$, where $s(t)$ is measured in meters and time, t, is measured in seconds.

   a. Find the vertex.
   b. Determine the absolute maximum value of the function.
   c. Determine the range of the function and interpret its meaning.
   d. If the flare explodes 6 seconds after being shot, then time t is $0 \le t \le 6$. Determine the absolute maximum height of the flare.

6.3 EXERCISES

 Student Solutions Manual  PH Math/Tutor Center   CD Video Math XL MathXL® MyMathLab MyMathLab   Interactmath.com

Identify each function as quadratic or nonquadratic.

1. $y = 1 - x - x^2 - x^3$
2. $g(x) = 1.3x^2 - 4.7$
3. $y = x + 2x^2 - 9$
4. $g(x) = 0.5x^2 + 2.6x - 8.4$

5. $y = 8x^2$
6. $y = -2x^2 - 5x - 7$
7. $r(x) = \dfrac{1}{x^2} - 3$
8. $a = \pi r^2$

9. $s = 4\pi r^2$
10. $y = 3x^3 + 2x - 5$
11. $y = \dfrac{7}{x^2} + 3x - 12$
12. $y = 2x^2 - 2x + 5$

In exercises 13 and 14, given the quadratic function, list the following properties of its graph.

   a. Determine the concavity.
   b. Compare the width of the graph to the graph of $y = x^2$.
   c. Determine the y-intercept.
   d. Determine the vertex.
   e. Determine any absolute maximum or absolute minimum.
   f. Determine for what x-values the function is increasing and decreasing.

13. $y = -5x^2 + 10x + 1$
14. $y = 6x^2 - 6x - 5$

Complete the table. Check your work on your calculator.

	Function	Coefficients			Properties of Graph				
		a	b	c	Wide/Narrow	Concave Upward/Downward	Vertex	Axis of Symmetry	y-Intercept
15.	$y = 0.6x^2 + 6x - 2$								
16.	$y = -x^2 + 6x - 2$								
17.	$y = 2x^2 + 3x + 5$								
18.	$y = -3x^2 + 6x - 5$								
19.	$y = -\dfrac{1}{4}x^2 + x - 3$								
20.	$y = \dfrac{1}{3}x^2 + 2x - 1$								
21.	$f(x) = x^2 + 8x + 1$								
22.	$y = -0.4x^2 + 2.4x - 1.1$								

Graph each quadratic function in exercises 27–42. Label the vertex. Draw and label the axis of symmetry.

23. $y = x^2 + 2x + 5$
24. $y = x^2 + 4x - 5$
25. $y = -x^2 + 4x - 2$
26. $y = -x^2 + 2x + 3$

27. $y = 2x^2 + 5x - 7$
28. $y = 2x^2 + 6x - 5$
29. $y = \dfrac{1}{6}x^2 + 3x + 12$
30. $y = \dfrac{3}{4}x^2 - 6x + 7$

31. $h(x) = 14 + 5x - x^2$
32. $f(x) = 11 - 4x + x^2$
33. $y = -2x^2 + 8x - 3$
34. $y = -3x^2 + 6x + 1$

35. $g(x) = 0.8x^2 - 1.2x$ **36.** $h(x) = 1.2x^2 + 3.6x$ **37.** $y = 0.4x^2$ **38.** $y = -0.7x^2$

39. $y = 3x^2 - 3$ **40.** $y = -6x^2 + 3$ **41.** $f(x) = -0.5x^2 + 3x$ **42.** $g(x) = -0.2x^2 + 4x$

In exercises 43 and 44, list the following properties of the graph of the quadratic function.

   a. Determine the concavity.

   b. Determine the y-intercept.

   c. Determine the vertex.

   d. Determine any absolute maximum or absolute minimum.

   e. Determine for what x-values the function is increasing and decreasing.

43.

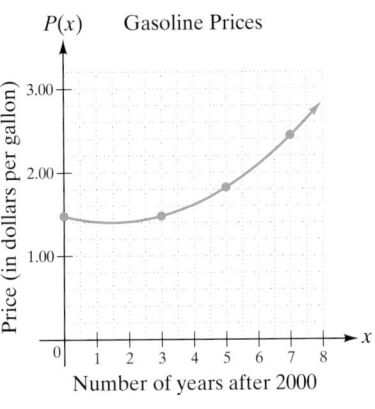

P(x)   Gasoline Prices
Price (in dollars per gallon)
Number of years after 2000

44.

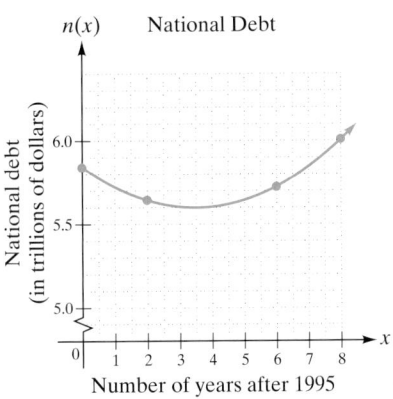

n(x)   National Debt
National debt (in trillions of dollars)
Number of years after 1995

Geometry

45. Gramps is building Granny a cottage. He wants the foundation to be 280 feet around, but isn't sure what width and length to build. If the width of the foundation is x feet, the area of the foundation is given by $A(x) = 140x - x^2$. Graph the function. Find the vertex. Explain what the coordinates of the vertex indicate.

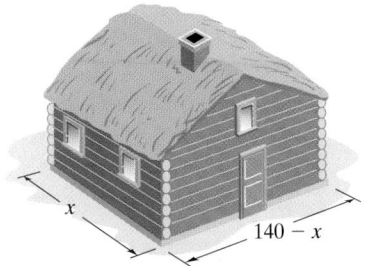

x $140 - x$

46. Farmer Jones plans to build a small animal pen next to his barn. The pen will be rectangular, with one side formed by the barn. The other three sides will be constructed from 120 feet of fencing. The area of the pen is given by the quadratic

function $A(x) = 120x - 2x^2$. Graph the function. Find the vertex. Explain the meaning of the coordinates of the vertex.

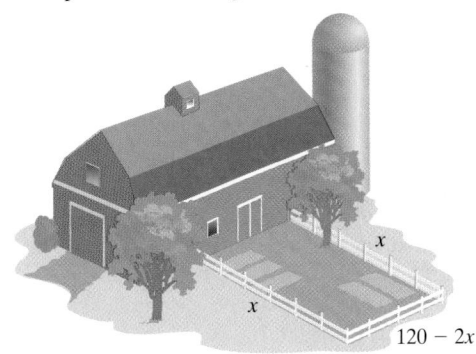

x $120 - 2x$

47. The base of a triangle measures 20 inches minus twice the measure of its height. The area of the triangle is given by $A(x) = 10x - x^2$, where x is the height of the triangle in inches. Graph the function. Find the vertex. Explain the meaning of the coordinates of the vertex.

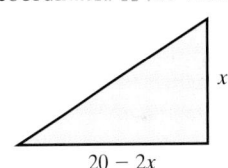

x $20 - 2x$

48. The length of a rectangular billboard is 10 feet more than its width. If the width is denoted by x, the area of the billboard will be given by $A(x) = x^2 + 10x$. Graph the function. Find the vertex. Does the vertex have any physical meaning?

$x + 10$

x SEE ROCKET CITY

Business

49. The price of collectible dolls is varied to encourage customers to buy more than one. If x dolls are purchased, the total revenue for the dolls will be $R(x) = 46x - x^2$. Graph the function. For what value of x will this function be maximized? What is the maximum revenue? Under these conditions, should the seller limit the number of dolls sold?

50. The price of an excursion is discounted to encourage travelers to book multiple reservations. If x travelers book as a group, the total revenue received from the group is given by the function $R(x) = 250x - 25x^2$ dollars. Graph the function. For what value of x will the function be maximized? What is the maximum revenue? Should a limit be placed on the number of travelers in a group that can receive the discount?

51. After subtracting the cost of producing and shipping items to a store from the revenue received from the store, a producer of compact discs realizes a profit $P(x) = 6x - 0.05x^2 - 5$ dollars for an order of x compact discs. Determine the maximum profit the producer can realize and how many discs must be sold to the store to achieve this profit.

52. The producer of major equipment realizes a profit given by $P(x) = 16{,}000x - 200x^2 - 1000$ dollars for selling and delivering x pieces of equipment to the customer. The equation represents the profit after the costs of producing and delivering the equipment are subtracted from the revenues received. Determine the maximum profit the producer can realize and how many pieces of equipment must be sold to achieve this profit.

53. Sod is a lawn option offered by most landscapers. If a particular job involves a triangular lot in which the height is the same as the base, then the landscaper's profit, $P(x)$, where x is the length of the base, can be computed using the function $P(x) = 0.375x^2 - 65.00$. In order to receive this price, a lot must have base and height that are greater than or equal to 15 yards and less than or equal to 40 yards. Find the maximum value of the function. Interpret its meaning.

54. A flooring company installs prefinished hardwood floors. If the floor is to be put down in a square room of side x, then the company's profit, $P(x)$, can be computed using the function $P(x) = 3.00x^2 - 100.00$. The size of a room must be greater than or equal to 8 feet on a side and less than or equal to 50 feet on a side to qualify for this pricing structure. Find the maximum value of the function. Interpret its meaning.

Vertical Position

55. Eve threw an apple upward with a speed of 12 feet per second from a height of 24 feet. The position function for the apple is given by $s(t) = -16t^2 + 12t + 24$. Graph the function. Find the maximum height the apple will reach.

56. A football is kicked with a vertical velocity of 60 feet per second from ground level. The position function for the football is given by $s(t) = -16t^2 + 60t$. Graph the function. Determine the coordinates of the vertex of the graph. Interpret these values.

57. For the Labor Day picnic, an expert pyrotechnician shoots a fireworks rocket from ground level with an initial velocity of 270 feet per second. The position function for the rocket, in feet above ground level, is $s(t) = -16t^2 + 270t$, where t is the time in seconds after the rocket is launched and $0 \le t \le 8$. State the domain and interpret it. Find the absolute maximum value of the function and interpret it. Find the range of the function and interpret it.

58. At the Fourth of July celebration, a professional pyrotechnics expert shoots a rocket straight up from the top of a 20-foot tower. The rocket's initial velocity is 300 feet per second. The position function for the rocket, in feet above ground level, is $s(t) = -16t^2 + 300t + 20$, where t is the time in seconds after the rocket is launched and $0 \le t \le 9$. State the domain and interpret it. Find the absolute maximum value of the function and interpret. Find the range of the function and interpret it.

Real Data

59. Based on data from the Bureau of the Census, Foreign Trade Division, the yearly number of passenger cars imported to the United States from Mexico can be estimated by the function $n(t) = -74{,}147t^2 + 502{,}360t + 22{,}099$, where t is the number of years after 1998. Graph this function. Find and interpret its vertex.

60. The annual number of passenger cars imported to the United States from Germany can be estimated by the function $n(t) = -46{,}649t^2 + 406{,}864t - 306{,}623$, where t is the number of years after 1998. Graph this function. Find and interpret its vertex.

6.3 Calculator Exercises

Sometimes it is desirable to view two screens on your calculator at the same time. For example, suppose you wish to study the impact of various coefficients in quadratic functions by graphing several on the same coordinate plane. At the same time, you want to view the functions along with the graphs. To do so, first split the screen as follows:

Press **MODE** . Use the arrow to move the cursor down to the row Full Horiz G-T.

Use the arrow to move over to Horiz.

Press **ENTER**   **2nd**   **MODE** (QUIT).

The top half of the screen will display graphs, and the bottom half of the screen will be the home screen, where you can key instructions in the same manner as with a full screen.

Graph the following combinations of quadratic functions, using the split screen and a decimal window setting (ZOOM 4):

1. $y_1 = x^2 - 2x$ $y_2 = x^2$ $y_3 = x^2 + 2x$

This will show how the graphs of the functions are affected by the coefficients a and b.

2. $y_1 = x^2 - 1$ $y_2 = x^2$ $y_3 = x^2 + 1$

This will show how the graphs of the functions are affected by the coefficient c.

The bottom half of the screen continues to be available for use, as if you did not have a split screen. This is a handy feature when you graph several functions together. Unfortunately, sometimes the graphs are so compressed that they become difficult to read. You can experiment with changing the window settings to adjust for this compression. When you are through with the split screen, you can return to a full screen:

Press **MODE** . Use the arrow to move the cursor down to the row Full Horiz G-T.

Press **ENTER**   **2nd**   **MODE** (QUIT)

Use the split screen to examine the following sets of quadratic functions:

3. $y_1 = 0.3x^2$ $y_2 = x^2$ $y_3 = 3x^2$
4. $y_1 = -3x^2$ $y_2 = 3x^2$

5. $y_1 = 3x^2$ $y_2 = 3x^2 + 1$ $y_3 = 3x^2 - 2$
6. $y_1 = x^2 + 1$ $y_2 = x^2 + 2x + 1$ $y_3 = x^2 - 2x + 1$

From your examination, describe how the coefficients of the quadratic functions affect the graphs.

6.3 Writing Exercises

Another way to write a quadratic function is to write it in the form

$$y = a(x - h)^2 + k$$

This form has some interesting features, which will become apparent as you graph a function. Graph the given functions. In each case, label the vertex.

1. $y = 2(x - 2)^2 + 3$ **2.** $y = (x - 1)^2 + 3$
3. $y = 0.2(x - 2)^2 - 5$ **4.** $y = -2(x - 1)^2 - 5$

What do you notice about the graphs in exercises 1–4? Compare the coordinates of the vertex of each graph with the values of h and k in the function. Can you tell what the vertex will be for each of the graphs of the functions that follow, without graphing first? Verify your coordinates for the vertices by graphing.

5. $y = (x + 1)^2 + 4$ **6.** $y = (x - 3)^2 + 2$
7. $y = (x - 1)^2$ **8.** $y = x^2 - 3$

State where the vertex will be when the quadratic function is written as $y = a(x - h)^2 + k$. Later, you will learn how to take a quadratic function and transform it into this form by completing the square. This form is called the vertex form of a quadratic function. Write a short summary of what you have learned.

6.4 WRITING QUADRATIC FUNCTIONS

OBJECTIVES

1 Write quadratic functions, given the y-intercept and the two x-intercepts.

2 Write quadratic functions, given three data points.

3 Model real-world situations by using quadratic functions determined from data, and use the functions to make predictions.

APPLICATION

The Ohmishima bridge joining the Japanese islands of Ohmishima and Hakatajima is the longest single-span two-hinged solid rib arch bridge in Japan. The lower width of the arch is 297 meters, and the maximum height of the arch is 49 meters. Determine a quadratic function that will model the arch of the bridge.

After completing this section, we will discuss this application further. See page 523.

Objective 6.4.1   Writing Quadratic Functions, Given Three Intercepts

We have graphed quadratic functions from their equations. However, we may be given information in the form of a graph or data points and need to determine the equation of the function graphed.

We need at least two points to determine a linear function. For a quadratic function, we need at least three points.

The standard form of a quadratic function is the equation $y = ax^2 + bx + c$. If we know a point on the graph, we know that substituting the coordinates of that point into the equation will result in a true statement. Therefore, if we know three points on the graph, we will know three true equations. We can use these equations to determine the values of a, b, and c.

WRITING QUADRATIC FUNCTIONS BY USING THE Y-INTERCEPT AND THE TWO X-INTERCEPTS

To write a quadratic function, given the y-intercept and the two x-intercepts,

- Write three equations by substituting the data points into the standard form of the quadratic function.

(continued on page 518)

- Simplify the three equations.
- Substitute the value determined for c into the other two equations.
- Solve the resulting system of two equations and two unknowns.
- Substitute the values found for a, b, and c into the standard form of the quadratic function.

EXAMPLE 1   Write a quadratic function for the accompanying graph.

Solution

The three intercepts on the graph are $(-1, 0)$, $(5, 0)$, and $(0, -5)$. They result in three equations:

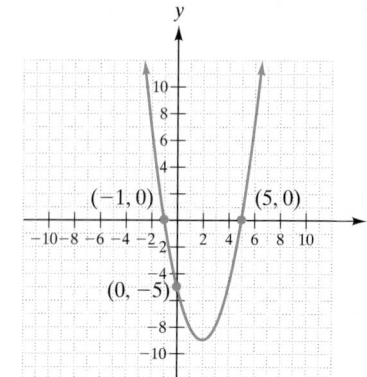

$$y = ax^2 + bx + c \qquad \text{Standard form}$$

(1) $0 = a(-1)^2 + b(-1) + c \qquad$ Substitute $(-1, 0)$.

(2) $0 = a(5)^2 + b(5) + c \qquad$ Substitute $(5, 0)$.

(3) $-5 = a(0)^2 + b(0) + c \qquad$ Substitute $(0, -5)$.

Simplify each equation.

(1) $0 = a - b + c$

(2) $0 = 25a + 5b + c$

(3) $-5 = c$

Substitute -5 for c in the simplified equations (1) and (2).

(1) $0 = a - b + (-5)$

(2) $0 = 25a + 5b + (-5)$

Write the equations in standard form.

(1) $a - b = 5$

(2) $25a + 5b = 5$

Solve the remaining system of linear equations, using the methods presented in Chapter 4. We will use the addition method in the example.

(1) $5a - 5b = 25 \qquad$ Multiply both expressions by 5.

(2) $\underline{25a + 5b = 5}$

$ \quad 30a = 30$

$ \qquad\quad a = 1$

(1) $a - b = 5 \qquad$ Substitute 1 for a in equation (1).

$ \quad 1 - b = 5$

$ \qquad -b = 4$

$ \qquad\quad b = -4$

Therefore, $a = 1$, $b = -4$, and $c = -5$. Substitute these values into the standard form of the quadratic function.

$$y = ax^2 + bx + c$$
$$y = (1)x^2 + (-4)x + (-5)$$
$$y = x^2 - 4x - 5$$

Graph the function, and check to make sure that the graph goes through the three given points.

Check

Y1 $= x^2 - 4x - 5$

$(-1, 0)$

$(0, -5) \quad (5, 0)$

$(-47, 47, -31, 31)$

Objective 6.4.1 *CHECKUP*

1. Write a quadratic function that has the intercepts $(0, -1)$, $(-4, 0)$ and $\left(\frac{1}{3}, 0\right)$. Graph the function and check the points.
2. In this section, you learned how to find the equation of a quadratic function when you know its y-intercept and its two x-intercepts.

a. Will a quadratic function always have a y-intercept? Explain.
b. Will a quadratic function always have two x-intercepts? Explain.

Objective 6.4.2

Writing Quadratic Functions, Given Three Points

If we do not know its y-intercept, it is more difficult to write a quadratic function, given three data points.

WRITING QUADRATIC FUNCTIONS BY USING THREE DATA POINTS

To write a quadratic function, given three data points,
Write three equations by substituting the data points into the standard form of the quadratic function, and then simplify the three equations.
Solve the resulting system of three equations.

- Determine two systems containing two equations each. Use the first and second equation for one system and the second and third equation for the second system.
- Eliminate the same variable in each system. This yields a new system of two linear equations in two variables.

Solve the new system for the two remaining variables. Substitute the values for these two variables into one of the three original equations to solve for the remaining variable.

- Substitute the values found for a, b, and c into the standard form of the quadratic function.

 TAKE NOTE In Chapter 4, we solved a system of three equations.

EXAMPLE 2

Write a function $h(x)$ for a graph that passes through $(-3, -21)$, $(1, -5)$, and $(2, 6)$.

Solution

Substituting the coordinate pairs will result in three equations:

$$h(x) = ax^2 + bx + c \qquad \text{Standard form}$$
$$(1) \quad -21 = a(-3)^2 + b(-3) + c \qquad \text{Substitute } (-3, -21).$$
$$(2) \quad -5 = a(1)^2 + b(1) + c \qquad \text{Substitute } (1, -5).$$
$$(3) \quad 6 = a(2)^2 + b(2) + c \qquad \text{Substitute } (2, 6).$$

Simplify each equation.

$$(1) \quad -21 = 9a - 3b + c$$
$$(2) \quad -5 = a + b + c$$
$$(3) \quad 6 = 4a + 2b + c$$

Since we do not have a value for any variable, we will need to make two systems with two equations each and eliminate the same variable in each system. We will pair equations (1) and (2) to make one system and equations 2 and 3 to make the other system. We will eliminate the variable c.

First system:

$$(1) \quad -21 = 9a - 3b + c$$
$$(2) \quad -5 = a + b + c$$

(1) $21 = -9a + 3b - c$ Multiply both expressions by −1.

(2) $\underline{-5 =\quad a + \ b + c}$

(4) $16 = -8a + 4b$

Second system:

(2) $-5 = a + b + c$

(3) $6 = 4a + 2b + c$

(2) $5 = -a - \ b - c$ Multiply both expressions by −1.

(3) $\underline{6 = 4a + 2b + c}$

(5) $11 = 3a + \ b$

Write a new system containing the two equations in a and b. Solve the system.

New system:

(4) $16 = -8a + 4b$

(5) $11 = 3a + b$

(4) $16 = -8a + 4b$

(5) $\underline{-44 = -12a - 4b}$ Multiply both expressions by − 4.

$-28 = -20a$

$\dfrac{7}{5} = a$

Substitute $\frac{7}{5}$ for a in an equation from the new system. Let's use equation (5) and solve for b.

(5) $11 = 3a + b$

$11 = 3\left(\dfrac{7}{5}\right) + b$

$\dfrac{34}{5} = b$

Substitute a and b in an original simplified equation. Let's use equation (2).

$$-5 = a + b + c$$

$$-5 = \dfrac{7}{5} + \dfrac{34}{5} + c$$

$$-\dfrac{66}{5} = c$$

Therefore, $a = \frac{7}{5}$, $b = \frac{34}{5}$, and $c = -\frac{66}{5}$. Substitute these values into the standard form of the function.

$$h(x) = ax^2 + bx + c$$

$$h(x) = \left(\dfrac{7}{5}\right)x^2 + \left(\dfrac{34}{5}\right)x + \left(-\dfrac{66}{5}\right)$$

$$h(x) = \dfrac{7}{5}x^2 + \dfrac{34}{5}x - \dfrac{66}{5}$$

Graph the function, and check to make sure that the graph passes through the three given points.

Check

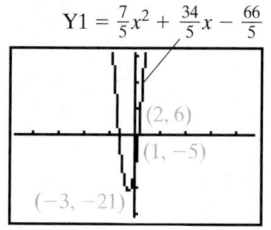

$Y1 = \frac{7}{5}x^2 + \frac{34}{5}x - \frac{66}{5}$

$(2, 6)$

$(1, -5)$

$(-3, -21)$

$(-47, 47, -31, 31)$

✓ Objective 6.4.2 CHECKUP

1. Write a quadratic function for a graph that passes through the points $(1, -4)$, $(2, 0)$, and $(-2, -4)$. Graph the function and check the given points.

2. When you obtain three equations by substituting three coordinate pairs into the standard form of the quadratic function, must you use the addition method to solve the system of equations that results? Are there other methods that can be used to solve the system? Explain.

Objective 6.4.3

Modeling the Real World

We've just seen how to write a quadratic function, given three data points. So what? What's the big deal? The point to realize is that in the real world, you aren't usually given a function all ready for you to graph and analyze. More often than not, you're given some data—observations, computer printouts, whatever—and you need to determine the function that fits these data. This process of determining a function whose graph contains given points is called **curve fitting**. But why bother? Ah, that is part of the power of mathematics: Once you have the function that fits the data, you can use it to predict other pairs of data. As long as the conditions for your model don't change, you can determine new data based on the function you derived from the given data. It's like getting something for nothing—nothing except some work with algebra.

EXAMPLE 3

Your laboratory partner projects a stone upward from a cliff at a height of 250 feet above the ground. After 1 second, the stone is 324 feet above the base of the cliff, and after 2 seconds the stone is 366 feet above the base of the cliff.

a. Write a quadratic function for the height of the stone.

b. Graph the function.

c. Use the graph to predict the length of time required for the stone to hit the ground at the base of the cliff.

d. Use the graph to predict the maximum height of the stone.

2 seconds 366 ft

1 second   324 ft

0 second   250 ft

250 ft

Solution

a. Let t = time in seconds

We need to determine the position function, $s(t)$. We have three data points: $(0, 250)$, $(1, 324)$, and $(2, 366)$.

$$s(t) = at^2 + bt + c \qquad \text{Standard form}$$

(1) $\quad 250 = a(0)^2 + b(0) + c \qquad$ Substitute (0,250).

(2) $\quad 324 = a(1)^2 + b(1) + c \qquad$ Substitute (1,324).

(3) $\quad 366 = a(2)^2 + b(2) + c \qquad$ Substitute (2,366).

Simplify each equation.

(1) $\quad 250 = c$

(2) $\quad 324 = a + b + c$

(3) $\quad 366 = 4a + 2b + c$

Since we know $c = 250$, we substitute 250 for c in the simplified equations (2) and (3).

(2) $\quad 324 = a + b + 250$

(3) $\quad 366 = 4a + 2b + 250$

Write the equations in standard form and simplify.

(2) $\quad a + b = 74$

(3) $\quad 2a + b = 58 \qquad$ Divide both expressions by 2.

Solve the remaining system of linear equations. We will use the addition method in the example.

(2) $\quad -a - b = -74 \qquad$ Multiply both expressions by −1.

(3) $\quad \underline{2a + b = \quad 58}$

$\qquad a \qquad\quad = -16$

$\qquad\qquad a = -16$

(2) $\quad a + b = 74 \qquad$ Substitute −16 for a in equation (2).

$\quad -16 + b = 74$

$\qquad\quad b = 90$

Therefore, $a = -16$, $b = 90$, and $c = 250$. Substitute these values into the standard form of the quadratic function.

$$s(t) = at^2 + bt + c$$
$$s(t) = -16t^2 + 90t + 250$$

b.

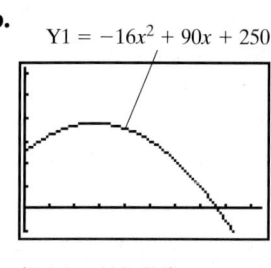

$(0, 9.4, -100, 620)$

c.

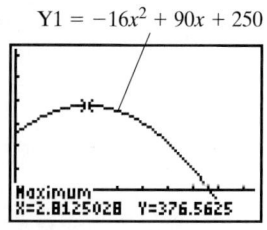

$(0, 9.4, -100, 620)$

Trace the graph or calculate a zero to determine when the stone's position is 0 feet above the ground, or $s(t) = 0$.

The stone will hit the ground in approximately 7.7 seconds.

d.

Y1 = $-16x^2 + 90x + 250$

Maximum
X=2.8125028 Y=376.5625

$(0, 9.4, -100, 620)$

Trace the graph or calculate a maximum to determine the absolute maximum of the function, or the function value of the vertex.

The stone will reach a maximum height of approximately 377 feet. ■

In the study of statistics, a technique is used to "fit" coordinate pairs to a function. The technique, called **regression analysis**, is intended to statistically analyze data, but also can be used to find the quadratic function that passes through three points in the coordinate plane. Many calculators include this feature. We will utilize it to write a function using real data.

A check of the previous example will result in the same equation, $y = -16x^2 + 90x + 250$, as shown in **Figure 6.7c**.

T E C H N O L O G Y   Quadratic Regression

Write a quadratic function that contains the three data points $(0, 250)$, $(1, 324)$, and $(2, 366)$.

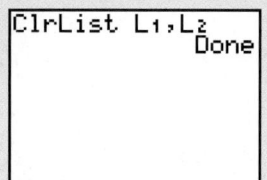

Figure 6.7a

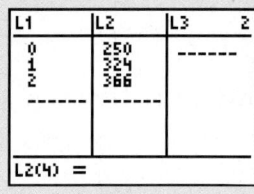

Figure 6.7b

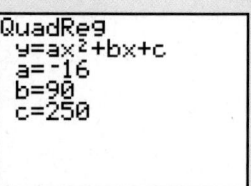

Figure 6.7c

For **Figure 6.7a**,
Clear the lists where the three data points will be stored.

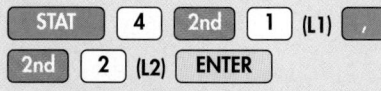

For **Figure 6.7b**,
Enter the coordinate pairs by choosing option 1, EDIT, under the STAT menu.

Enter the values 0, 1, and 2 for x in L1, and then move to L2 and enter the values 250, 324, and 366 for y.

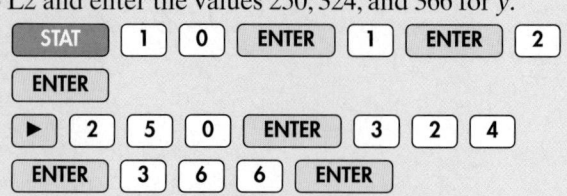

For **Figure 6.7c**,
Exit the EDIT menu.

Calculate the quadratic function by choosing option 5, QuadReg, under the STAT CALC menu.

| STAT | ▶ | 5 | 2nd | 1 | (L1) | , | 2nd |

| 2 | (L2) | ENTER |

Write the function, substituting the given values for a, b, and c into the standard form of the quadratic function. The result is $y = -16x^2 + 90x + 250$.

APPLICATION

The Ohmishima bridge joining the Japanese islands of Ohmishima and Hakatajima is the longest single-span two-hinged solid rib arch bridge in Japan. The lower width of the arch is 297 meters, and the maximum height of the arch is 49 meters. Determine a quadratic function that will model the arch of the bridge.

Discussion

Superimpose a sketch of the bridge on a coordinate plane, placing the origin in the center of the lower width. This will yield 148.5 units ($\frac{1}{2}$ of 297 feet) on each side of the y-axis. Label the three intercepts.

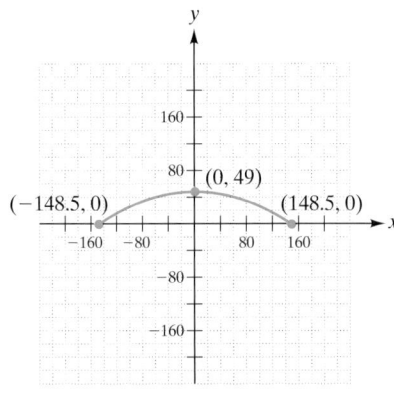

Using the three intercepts, $(0, 49)$, $(-148.5, 0)$, and $(148.5, 0)$, as data points, we observe that the graph is parabolic in shape and a quadratic function will model the data. Since the numbers are not easily manipulated by hand, determine a quadratic regression function on your calculator.

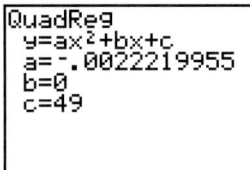

Write the quadratic function by replacing a, b, and c in the standard form of the quadratic equation.

$$y = -0.002222x^2 + 0x + 49$$
$$y = -0.002222x^2 + 49$$

Check the function by graphing it on your calculator.

Note that the value for a was rounded in our function. Therefore, the x-intercepts are not exact. For accuracy's sake, an engineer would not round values as we did.

✓ Objective 6.4.3 **CHECKUP**

1. A message in an attaché case is thrown downward from a plane that is 1500 feet above the water. After 1 second, the case is 1454 feet above the water, and after 2 seconds, it is 1376 feet above the water. Write a quadratic position function for the distance the case is above the water after t seconds. How long will it take the case to reach the water?

2. The Golden Gate Bridge is a suspension bridge that measures a distance of 4200 feet between its towers, which have a height of 500 feet above the roadway. Assuming that the shape of the main span cables is a parabola, write a quadratic function that will model that shape. (*Hint:* A suspension bridge is different from an arch bridge: The parabola opens upward instead of downward. Superimpose a sketch of the bridge on a coordinate plane, placing the origin at the center of the upper width of the parabola. This will yield x-intercepts at 2100 units on each side of the y-axis. The y-intercept will be 500 units below the x-axis. Label the three intercepts and then find the function.)

6.4 EXERCISES

Student Solutions Manual   PH Math/Tutor Center   CD Video   Math XL MathXL®   MyMathLab MyMathLab   Interactmath.com

Write the quadratic function for the graph that passes through the given x-intercepts and y-intercept. Graph the function and check the given points.

1. $(2, 0), (-4, 0), (0, -8)$
2. $(3, 0), (-1, 0), (0, 3)$
3. $(-4, 0), \left(\frac{1}{2}, 0\right), (0, -4)$
4. $(-1, 0), \left(\frac{2}{3}, 0\right), (0, -2)$

5. $(0, 3), (3, 0), (-3, 0)$
6. $(0, 1), (4, 0), (-4, 0)$
7. $(0, -4), (2, 0), (-4, 0)$
8. $(0, -2), (3, 0), (-2, 0)$

9. $\left(0, \frac{2}{3}\right), (-2, 0), (2, 0)$
10. $\left(0, \frac{1}{4}\right), (1, 0), (-2, 0)$
11. $(0, -2), \left(\frac{1}{2}, 0\right), \left(\frac{9}{2}, 0\right)$
12. $(0, 1), \left(\frac{1}{3}, 0\right), \left(\frac{-2}{3}, 0\right)$

Write a quadratic function for a graph that passes through the points specified. Graph the function and check the given points.

13. $(2, -15), (-2, -7), (-4, 9)$
14. $(2, -8), (4, 10), (-5, -8)$
15. $(1, -10), (-2, 5), (2, -7)$

16. $(-1, 10), (1, -12), (3, -10)$
17. $(3, 2), (-3, 14), (6, 5)$
18. $(2, 1), (-2, -3), (-4, 4)$

19. $(-1, -2), (1, 6), (4, 3)$
20. $(2, -3), (-2, 5), (1, 2)$
21. $(-1, -3), (-2, -5), (1, -11)$

22. $(2, -3), (-2, -15), (6, -7)$
23. $(-2, 4), \left(-3, \frac{5}{2}\right), \left(-1, \frac{13}{2}\right)$
24. $\left(5, \frac{13}{3}\right), (6, 4), (3, 7)$

Solve exercises 25–30 by using the position function $s(t) = at^2 + bt + c$. Round your answers to the nearest tenth of a second.

25. A tennis ball is thrown upward from a height of 150 feet. After 1 second, the ball is 146 feet above the ground; after 2 seconds, it is 110 feet above the ground. Write the position function for the ball. How long will it take for the ball to reach the ground?

26. A custard pie is thrown upward from a height of 220 feet. After 1 second, the pie is 222 feet above the ground. After 3 seconds, it is 130 feet above the ground. Write a position function for the pie. How many seconds will it take to reach the ground?

27. A movie stunt dummy is dropped from a height of 400 feet. After 2 seconds, the dummy is 336 feet above the ground. After 4 seconds, it is 144 feet above the ground. Write the position function for the dummy. How many seconds will it take to fall to the ground?

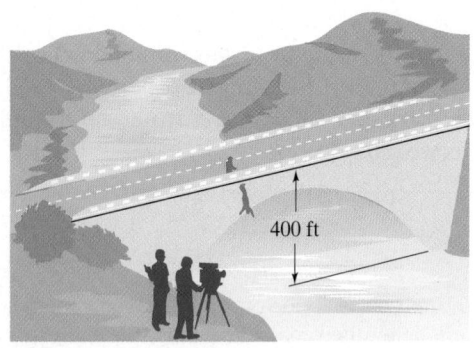

400 ft

28. A child drops a Beanie Baby from a height of 600 feet. After 2 seconds, the toy is 536 feet above the ground. After 3 seconds, it is 456 feet above the ground. Write the position function for the toy. How many seconds will it take to fall to the ground?

29. An empty fuel cylinder is dropped from a lunar module 2000 feet above the surface of the Moon. After 10 seconds, the cylinder is 1730 feet above the lunar surface. After 20 seconds, it is 920 feet above the lunar surface. Determine the position function for the distance of the cylinder above the surface at any time. After how many seconds will the cylinder touch the surface?

30. A probe is ejected upward from a lunar module 3000 feet above the surface of the Moon. After 10 seconds, the probe is 2980 feet above the lunar surface. After 20 seconds, it is 2420 feet above the lunar surface. Determine the position function for the distance of the probe above the surface at any time. How many seconds will it take for the probe to reach the lunar surface?

31. The Brooklyn Bridge opened to vehicular traffic on May 24, 1883, and remains a spectacular sight to this day. The center span of the suspension bridge between its towers is 1595.5 feet long, and the towers rise 130 feet above the roadway. Approximate the curve of the center span, using a quadratic function.

32. The Mackinac Bridge opened to traffic on November 1, 1957. The bridge is one of the world's longest suspension bridges between cable anchorages. The length of the roadway between the main towers is 3800 feet. The towers rise 350 feet above the roadway. Use a quadratic function to approximate the curve of the center span.

33. The New River Gorge Bridge in West Virginia is an arch bridge with a single span of 1700 feet. The rise of the arch is 360 feet. Approximate the curve of the arch with a quadratic function.

34. The Francis Scott Key Bridge arches over Baltimore Harbor, reaching the height of a 36-story building. The main arch span of the bridge is 1200 feet long and has a height of 185 feet. Write a quadratic function to approximate the curve of the arch.

35. In 1990, in the United States the per capita expenditure on radio and television repair was 3.7. In 1995, the per capita expenditure had increased to 4.1. In 2000, the per capita expenditure was 4.1. If *x* is the number of years after 1990 and *y* is the per capita expenditure on radio and television repair, write a quadratic function to fit these data. What would the function predict the per capita expenditure on radio and television repair to be for the year 2005?

36. In 1990, in the United States the per capita expenditure on spectator sports was 4.5. In 1995, the per capita expenditure had risen to 6.1. In 2000, the per capita expenditure had risen further to 9.5. If *x* is the number of years after 1990 and *y* is the per capita expenditure on spectator sports, write a quadratic function to fit these data. What would the function predict the per capita expenditure on spectator sports to be for the year 2005?

37. In 1999, the percentage of U.S. households with TVs that have cable television was 68%. In 2000, the percentage of households with TVs with cable television had declined to 67.8%. In 2001, the percentage had risen to 69.2%. If *x* is the number of years after 1990 and *y* is the percentage of households with TVs that have cable television, write a quadratic function to fit these data. Determine the absolute minimum of the function and compare to the data. When would the function predict the percentage of households with TVs that have cable television reach 100%? Is this possible?

38. In 1991, the number of cable TV systems in the United States was 10,704. In 1994, the number had risen to 11,214. In 2002, the number had declined to 9947. If *x* is the number of years after 1990 and *y* is the number of cable TV systems in the United States, write a quadratic function to fit these data. Determine the absolute maximum of the function and compare to the data. When would the function predict the number of cable TV systems in the United States to fall to 9000?

For exercises 39 and 40, determine a quadratic function to fit the given data and answer the questions.

39.

Year	U.S. Army Personnel on Active Duty
2000	471,633
2001	478,918
2002	485,536

Use your function to predict the number of active Army personnel in 2003. How does this number compare with the actual number, 499,301? What does your function give as the number of active Army personnel in 2004? How does this compare to the actual number 500,203?

40.

Year	Deaths by Heart Disease per 100,000 Population
1995	296.3
1996	288.3
1997	280.4

Use your function to predict the number of deaths due to heart disease in 1998. How does this compare to the actual number of 272.4? What does your function give you as the number of deaths due to heart attack in 2001? How does the actual number, 247.8, compare to your number? Why do you think deaths by heart disease seem to be decreasing?

6.4 Calculator Exercises

Part 1

In this section, we wrote a quadratic equation given three data points. We then used the equation to estimate additional information. Sometimes the estimate was a "good fit" for this additional information, and sometimes our estimate had limitations. Graphing calculators have statistical procedures that can be used to find the equation of a quadratic through more than three points. The curve that best fits the data is called the regression curve. In Section 3.5, we discussed the details of these procedures and used the procedures to find the regression line given more than the two points.

We first graph the data points and observe the pattern graphed. If the data appear to be linear, we would want a regression line. However, if the data appear to have the shape of a parabola, we would want a regression curve and use quadratic regression.

Use this method to find the quadratic function that best fits the data for the following sets. Check your quadratic function by substituting values given and compare your function values with the actual data.

1.

Year	Number of Robberies in the United States
1996	535,594
1997	498,534
1998	447,186
1999	409,371

Use your equation to predict the number of robberies in each of the years 2000, 2001, and 2002. How do your answers compare to the actual numbers: 408,016, 423,557, and 420,637?

2.

Year	Male Professional Golfer's Association Leading Money Winners—Earnings ($)
1998	2,591,031
1999	6,616,585
2000	9,188,321
2001	5,687,777

Use your equation to predict the highest earnings in 2002. How does your estimate compare to the actual earnings of $6,912,625? Use your equation to predict the highest earnings in 2003. How does your estimate compare to the actual earnings of $7,573,907? What might account for fluctuations in the total earnings of the leading money winners?

3.

Year	Female Professional Golfer's Association Leading Money Winners—Earnings ($)
1998	1,092,748
1999	1,591,959
2000	1,876,853
2001	2,105,868

Use your equation to predict the highest earnings in 2002. How does your estimate compare to the actual earnings of $2,863,904? Use your equation to predict the highest earnings in 2003. How does your estimate compare to the actual earnings of $2,029,506? Why do you think women's earnings are more consistent than men's in terms of leading money winners of the Professional Golfer's Association?

4.

Year	1980	1985	1990	1995	2000
U.S. energy production (in quadrillion Btus)	67.24	67.65	70.73	71.16	71.22

Use your equation to estimate U.S. energy production in 2002 and 2003. How does your estimate compare to the actual production of 70.93 quadrillion Btus and 70.47 quadrillion Btus? If your equation did not predict production well for 2002 and 2003, why do you think that was the case?

Part 2

Many models used in mathematics are functions. Some are linear functions, while others are nonlinear. Data gathered from a real-world situation can be used to write mathematical functions to represent the situation. Consider the following data, which come from a production and sales situation:

Number of Items Produced and Sold	5	30	35	40
Cost of production	$155		$335	$365
Revenue from sales	$450	$1200	$1050	
Profit				

1. Make ordered pairs of the data, using the number of items produced and sold as the independent variable and the cost of production as the dependent variable. Plot the data. Does the graph look linear? If so, write a linear function of the form $C(x) = mx + b$ for the relation.

2. Make another set of ordered pairs of data, using the same independent variable, but using revenue from sales as the dependent variable. Plot these data. Does the graph look like a quadratic function? If so, write a quadratic function of the form $R(x) = ax^2 + bx + c$ for the relation.

3. Use the functions you wrote in exercises 1 and 2 to fill in the missing data in the preceding table for cost of production and revenue. Then complete the last line of the table by calculating profit as revenue minus cost of production.

4. Make a third set of ordered pairs of data, using the same independent variable, but using profit as the dependent variable. Graph these pairs of data. Does the relation appear to be a quadratic function? If so, use three of the pairs to write a quadratic function that represents the relation. Check the relation to see whether the fourth pair of data satisfies the function.

5. Find the values of x that make the profit function 0 or less. Discuss what these values represent.

6. Find the coordinates of the vertex of the profit function. Discuss what these values represent.

This is an example of using mathematical models to represent data. Other techniques may be studied to find the "best fit" of a function for a set of data. Once a function has been obtained, it can be used to explain relationships and to answer questions about a relationship. It is a very powerful technique for understanding data. Summarize what the example means to you as a meaningful use of mathematics.

6.4 Writing Exercise

In this section, it was stated that you need two coordinate pairs to determine a linear relationship between two variables and you need three coordinate pairs to determine a quadratic relationship between two variables. Discuss why this is so. Then consider what would happen if you had more than two coordinate pairs and wished to establish a linear relationship. Also, discuss what would happen if you had more than three coordinate pairs and wished to establish a quadratic relationship. What problems could you encounter in each case? How would you deal with these problems?

■ Chapter 6 Summary

Vocabulary Review

After completing this chapter, you should be able to define the following key terms.

absolute maximum
absolute minimum
ascending order
axis of symmetry
binomial
coefficient
combine like terms
concave downward
concave upward
constant term
curve fitting

degree of a polynomial
degree of a term
descending order
evaluating
function
like terms
monomial
numerical coefficient
parabola
polynomial
quadratic function

quadratic term
range
regression analysis
relation
relative maximum
relative minimum
term
trinomial
variable term
vertex

Fill in the blank with one of the words or phrases listed on the previous page.

1. A _____ is a number or the product of a number and variables raised to powers.
2. The _____ is the sum of the exponents of the variables in the term.
3. The _____ is the greatest degree of any term in the polynomial.
4. The _____ of a term is its numerical factor.
5. A polynomial with exactly one term is a _____.
6. A polynomial with exactly two terms is a _____.
7. A polynomial with exactly three terms is a _____.
8. The _____ is the greatest value of a function.
9. The _____ is the least value of a function.
10. The highest point or the lowest point of a parabolic graph is the _____.

Reflections

1. In this chapter, you studied polynomial expressions and polynomial functions (or equations). Explain the difference between the two.
2. What is the difference between the degree of a polynomial expression and the degree of a term of a polynomial expression?
3. What is the difference between simplifying a polynomial expression and evaluating a polynomial expression?
4. Explain how the graph of a quadratic function differs from the graph of a linear function.
5. Given a graph, describe the difference between a parabola that is concave upward and one that is concave downward. Given an equation, explain when the graph of the parabola is concave upward and when it is concave downward.
6. The graph of a polynomial function may have relative maxima and an absolute maximum. Alternatively, the graph may have relative minima and an absolute minimum. Explain the difference between the two situations.
7. In the graph of a quadratic function, what is the relationship between the vertex of the parabola and the axis of symmetry?
8. In order to determine the equation of a line from information about points that lie on the line, you must have two coordinate pairs. In order to determine the equation of a parabola from information about points that lie on the parabola, you must have three coordinate pairs. Can you explain why you need an additional coordinate pair for a parabola?

■ Chapter 6 Section-by-Section Review

6.1

Recall	Examples
Classification of polynomials (Always simplify the polynomial first.) • By number of terms 　One term: monomial 　Two terms: binomial 　Three terms: trinomial 　Four or more terms: polynomial • By degree 　Determine the degree of each term by adding the exponents of the variable terms. The degree of the polynomial is the largest degree of the terms.	Classify the polynomial. $2x^3y + 8x^2 - x^3y + 4$ by number of terms and by degree. First simplify. $x^3y + 8x^2 + 4$ There are three terms: $x^3y, 8x^2, 4$ The degree of each term is as follows: $x^3y: 3 + 1 = 4$ $8x^2: 2$ 4 or $4x^0: 0$ The polynomial is a fourth-degree trinomial.
Order of terms in a polynomial with one variable • Descending: The terms are written in order from largest to smallest degree. • Ascending: The terms are written in order from smallest to largest degree.	Write in descending and ascending order: $-3x^4 - 2x^3 + 8x^2 - 5x - x^5 + 4$ descending order: $-x^5 - 3x^4 - 2x^3 + 8x^2 - 5x + 4$ ascending order: $4 - 5x + 8x^2 - 2x^3 - 3x^4 - x^5$

(continued on page 528)

Recall	Examples
Evaluating a polynomial	Evaluate $-x^2 + 2xy - 4$ for $x = 2$ and $y = -3$.
• Substitute values for the variables, and simplify the resulting numeric expression.	$-x^2 + 2xy - 4 = -(2)^2 + 2(2)(-3) - 4$ $= -4 - 12 - 4$ $= -20$

Determine whether each expression is a polynomial. For those which are polynomials, classify them as monomials, binomials, trinomials, or polynomials.

1. x

2. $5x - 3$

3. $\sqrt{x} + 2$

4. $3x^3 - 4x^2 + x - 1$

5. $\dfrac{3}{a} - 2a + 1$

6. $3a^4 - 2a^2 + 5$

Determine the degree of each term of each polynomial and then the degree of the polynomial.

7. $5x + 3x^3 - 2$

8. $2x^2y + 3xy - 5$

9. $x + 9$

10. $0.5a - 3.1a^2 + 9.6a + 3.1a^2$

11. $12x^2 + 30x + 3$

Write each polynomial in descending order.

12. $5y^2 + 11y^4 + 12 - 6y + 9y^3$

13. $5 - p$

14. $\dfrac{1}{4}z^4 + \dfrac{1}{2}z^2 + z + \dfrac{1}{3}z^3 + 1$

15. $0.6b - 2.3b^5 + 1.8 - 9.1b^3$

Evaluate $2x^3 + 11x^2 - 21x - 90$ for the given values.

16. $x = 3$

17. $x = 0$

18. $x = 1$

19. $x = -6$

20. $x = -\dfrac{5}{2}$

In exercises 21–25, evaluate $a^3 + 2a^2b - 3ab^2 - b^3$ for the given values.

21. $a = 0, b = 1$

22. $a = -1, b = 0$

23. $a = 0, b = 0$

24. $a = 1, b = 1$

25. $a = -1, b = 1$

26. Write a polynomial for the perimeter of a rectangle whose length is numerically equal to the square of its width. What is the perimeter if the rectangle has a width of 7 yards?

27. Write a polynomial for the perimeter of a triangle whose second side is 1 inch more than the square of the first side x, and whose third side is 4 inches. What is the perimeter if the triangle's first side measures 2 inches?

28. Write a polynomial for the total area of the figures shown.

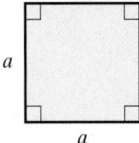 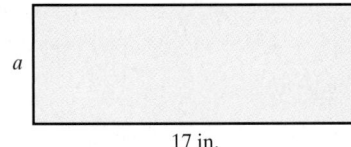 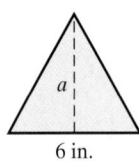

29. A triangular flower garden with a height of x feet and a base of y feet is placed in the center of a square lawn that measures z feet on a side. Write a polynomial for the area of the lawn not covered by the garden. What is this area if the triangle has a height of 6 feet and a base of 10 feet and the lawn measures 80 feet on a side?

30. Industrial engineers conduct time studies to determine how long it will take a production worker to assemble parts on a production line. One such study attempted to estimate the time (in minutes) it takes a worker with x months of experience to perform a particular task on an automobile assembly line. The polynomial used to estimate the time was

$0.01x^2 - 0.67x + 20.09$. Estimate the time it would take a production worker to complete the task if the number of months of experience she has is

a. 3 months

b. 6 months

c. 12 months

31. A handyman makes a square patio out of concrete paving blocks. He charges his customer $9.00 per square foot for installation. His overhead on the job is $50.00, and his material cost is $4.75 per square foot.

a. Write a polynomial that represents his revenue for the patio installation in terms of the length of the side of the square.

b. Write a polynomial for his cost.

c. Write a polynomial for his profit.

d. Find his revenue, cost, and profit if the patio is 7 feet on a side.

32. A flooring outlet sells and installs carpet. They estimate that for a given job their setup cost is $80.00. For a medium quality carpet that costs them $8.95 per square yard the customer is charged $11.95 per square yard for carpet and installation. A customer has a square room.

a. Write a polynomial that represents the flooring outlet's revenue for this job in terms of the length of the side of the square.

b. Write a polynomial for the outlet's cost.

c. Write a polynomial for the outlet's profit.

d. Find the outlet's revenue, cost, and profit if the job involves carpeting a room that measures 9.5 yards on a side.

33. According to data from the International Commission on Large Dams, a dam's height and volume are often related. The volume, in thousands of cubic meters, can be estimated with the polynomial $5.25h^2 - 2835h + 435{,}800$, where h is the height in meters above the lowest formation. Use this polynomial to estimate the volume of the Oroville Dam in California, which has height 235 meters.

6.2

Recall	Examples
Graph a polynomial function • Set up a table of values. • Graph the ordered pairs determined by the table of values. • Connect the graphed ordered pairs with a smooth curve.	Graph $f(x) = x^2 + x - 3$ Set up a table. | x	$f(x) = x^2 + x - 3$	$f(x)$
---	---	---
-4	$f(-4) = (-4)^2 + (-4) - 4$	9
-3	$f(-3) = (-3)^2 + (-3) - 3$	3
-2	$f(-2) = (-2)^2 + (-2) - 3$	-1
-1	$f(-1) = (-1)^2 + (-1) - 3$	-3
0	$f(0) = 0^2 + 0 - 3$	-3
1	$f(1) = 1^2 + 1 - 3$	-1
2	$f(2) = 2^2 + 2 - 3$	3
3	$f(3) = 3^2 + 3 - 3$	9	
Range of a polynomial function • Determine the absolute minimum and absolute maximum of the function from its graph if they exist. • The range is the set of y-values that lie between the absolute minimum and maximum, inclusive. • If the relation has no absolute maximum, the range is the set of all real numbers greater than or equal to the absolute minimum. • If the relation has no absolute minimum, the range is the set of all real numbers less than or equal to the absolute maximum.	Determine the range of $f(x) = x^2 + x - 3$. $Y1 = x^2 + x - 3$ Minimum X=-.4999995 Y=-3.25 The range is $y \geq -3.25$.
Evaluating a polynomial function • Substitute the x-value. • Simplify the resulting numeric expression.	Given $f(x) = x^2 + x - 3$, determine $f(-4)$. $f(x) = x^2 + x - 3$ $f(-4) = (-4)^2 + (-4) - 3$ $\quad\quad = 9$

34. Create a table of values for the polynomial relation $y = x^3 - x^2 - 6x$, where x is an integer between -4 and 4.

35. Use the given polynomial relation.

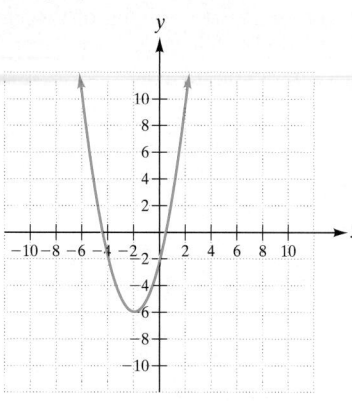

a. Determine three possible solutions for the relation graphed by completing the table of values.

x	y
1	
−1	
	−6

b. Determine the range of the relation.

Graph the given polynomial relations. From the graph, determine the range of each relation.

36. $y = -3x + 5$ **37.** $y = 2x^2 - 2x - 12$ **38.** $y = x^3 + 2x^2 - 5x - 6$

In exercises 39 and 40, evaluate the function $f(x) = 3x^3 - x^2 + 2x - 4$ at the given values.

39. $f(-2)$ **40.** $f(0)$

41. The following graph represents a profit function where x is the number of items sold.

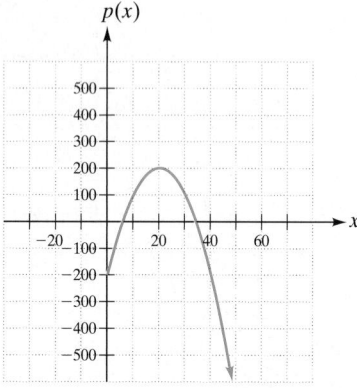

a. Determine the domain of the function.
b. Determine the absolute maximum of the function and interpret.
c. Determine the range of the function. Interpret.

42. Tony's Tees will discount the price of a t-shirt, depending on the number purchased. If a person purchases x shirts, the price per shirt will be $(12 - 0.50x)$ dollars. Tony pays $4 per shirt.

a. If x shirts are sold, the revenue function for the sale is $R(x) = 12x - 0.50x^2$. Determine the revenue if 5 shirts are sold, if 10 shirts are sold, if 15 shirts are sold, if 20 shirts are sold, and if 25 shirts are sold. What does this tell you about limits that should be placed on the price per shirt?

b. If x shirts are sold, the total cost of these shirts to Tony is $C(x) = 4x$. What is the cost of 5 shirts, 10 shirts, 15 shirts, and 20 shirts to Tony?

c. Use the results from parts **a** and **b** to determine how much profit will be made from the sale of 5 shirts, 10 shirts, 15 shirts, and 20 shirts.

d. What would you tell Tony to do in terms of limiting the price per shirt?

43. A statistical study related the cost of milk production, y, to the number of hundreds of gallons produced, x. The relation developed was

$$y = 15{,}800 + 2.2x - 0.001x^2$$

where x is measured in hundreds of gallons and y is measured in dollars. Use the relation to estimate the cost for the following number of gallons produced:

Hundreds of gallons (x)	900	1000	1100	1200	1300	1400
Cost (y)						

What does this relation tell you about the cost of production? If you were the owner of a dairy farm, can you suggest a strategy to contain your cost of production, based upon what this table shows?

44. Cigarette consumption in the United States has fluctuated over the years. Using data from the U.S. Department of Agriculture, a third-degree polynomial function can be generated for number of cigarettes consumed (in billions), $n(x) = 0.083x^3 - 1.88x^2 - 0.18x + 631.5$, where x is the number of years after 1980.

a. Use this function to estimate cigarette consumption for the years shown in the following table:

Year	1980	1985	1990	1995
Cigarette consumption				

b. Data indicate that in year 2000, 430 billion cigarettes were consumed. How well does the function predict this number?

c. In 2001, 425 billion cigarettes were consumed. How well does the function predict this number?

d. The Department of Agriculture estimates that in 2002 consumption of cigarettes actually dropped to 420 billion. Does the function predict this trend? Why or why not?

45. Using data from the Bureau of Labor Statistics, it is estimated that $p(x)$, the price per gallon of gasoline, can be represented by the function

$$p(x) = 0.03x^2 - 0.08x + 1.56$$

where x is the number of years after 2000.

a. Use this function to estimate the price of gasoline in the following years:

Year	2006	2007	2008	2009	2010
Price per gallon					

b. The data included information that in 2005 the price of gasoline was on average $1.92 per gallon. How well did the function predict this price?

c. What is the current price of gas in your area, and how well does the function predict this price?

d. Can this model predict well in the long term? Why or why not?

6.3

Recall	Examples
Standard form for a quadratic function $y = ax^2 + bx + c$ or $f(x) = ax^2 + bx + c$, where $a \neq 0$.	Examples of quadratic functions $y = 2x^2 - 3x + 4$ $g(x) = -\dfrac{1}{2}x^2 + 6x - 2$
Concavity of the graph • Concave upward if $a > 0$. • Concave downward if $a < 0$.	• The graph of $y = 2x^2 - 3x + 4$ is concave upward because the value of a, 2, is positive. • The graph of $g(x) = -\dfrac{1}{2}x^2 + 6x - 2$ is concave downward because the value of a, $-\dfrac{1}{2}$, is negative.
Width of the graph in comparison to the width when $a = 1$. • Narrow graph when $|a| > 1$. • Wide graph when $|a| < 1$.	• The graph of $y = 2x^2 - 3x + 4$ is narrower than the graph with $a = 1$ because the absolute value of a, 2, is greater than 1. • The graph of $g(x) = -\dfrac{1}{2}x^2 + 6x - 2$ is wider than the graph with $a = 1$ because the absolute value of a, $\dfrac{1}{2}$, is less than 1.
Vertex of the graph • The x-coordinate is $\dfrac{-b}{2a}$. • The y-coordinate is the function evaluated at $x = \dfrac{-b}{2a}$.	The vertex of the graph of $y = 2x^2 - 3x + 4$ is $\left(\dfrac{3}{4}, \dfrac{23}{8}\right)$ because $x = \dfrac{-b}{2a} = \dfrac{-(-3)}{2(2)} = \dfrac{3}{4}$ and $y = 2x^2 - 3x + 4$ $\quad = 2\left(\dfrac{3}{4}\right)^2 - 3\left(\dfrac{3}{4}\right) + 4$ $\quad = \dfrac{23}{8}$
Axis of symmetry • The graph of the equation $x = \dfrac{-b}{2a}$.	The axis of symmetry of the graph of $y = 2x^2 - 3x + 4$ is $x = \dfrac{3}{4}$.
y-intercept • The y-intercept is the ordered pair $(0, c)$.	The y-intercept of the graph of $y = 2x^2 - 3x + 4$ is $(0, 4)$ because $c = 4$.

Identify each equation as quadratic or nonquadratic.

46. $y = x^2 + x + 1$ **47.** $y = x^3 - x - 1$ **48.** $y = \dfrac{5}{x^2} + x + 1$ **49.** $y = x^2 + 4x + 4$

Complete the table. Check by using the calculator.

Function	Coefficients			Properties of Graph				
	a	b	c	Wide/Narrow	Concave Upward/Downward	Vertex	Axis of Symmetry	y-Intercept
50. $y = -\dfrac{1}{4}x^2 + \dfrac{1}{2}x + 1$								
51. $f(x) = -2x^2 + 4x$								
52. $g(x) = \dfrac{1}{3}x^2 + x$								
53. $y = 3x^2 - 3x + 1$								

In exercises 54–56, graph each quadratic function. Label the vertex. Draw and label the axis of symmetry.

54. $f(x) = x^2 + 2x - 8$

55. $y = -\dfrac{1}{2}x^2 + x - 2$

56. $h(x) = 2x^2 - 8$

57. Use the graph to discuss the following.

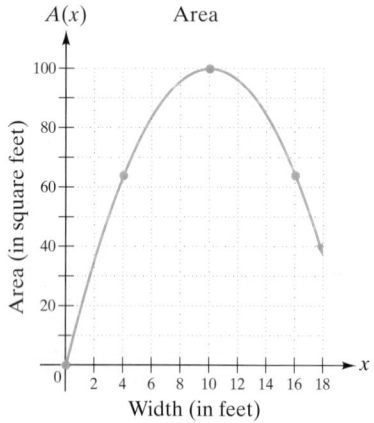

A(x)   Area

Area (in square feet)

Width (in feet)

a. Determine the concavity.
b. Determine the y-intercept.
c. Determine the vertex.
d. Determine any absolute maximum or absolute minimum.
e. Determine for what x-values the function is increasing and decreasing.

58. A bridal photographer sets the price of 8-by-10-inch wedding photos by the number of photos ordered. If the bride orders x photos, the total revenue will be $R(x) = 30x - 0.50x^2$ dollars for the sale. Graph the function and find its vertex. Explain what this vertex represents.

59. At its deepest, the Grand Canyon is 6000 vertical feet from rim to river. If a person stands at the edge of the rim and flings a rock upward with a velocity of 40 feet per second, the distance above the river is given by the function $s(t) = -16t^2 + 40t + 6000$, where $s(t)$ is the height above ground level (in feet) and t is the time in seconds after the rock is flung. Graph the function. Find the maximum height the rock will reach. Determine the range of this function and interpret its meaning.

60. As part of an experiment, a physicist shoots a projectile vertically upward out of a gun from a height of 250 feet. The object has an initial velocity of 200 feet per second. The position function of the projectile, in feet above the ground, after t seconds is $s(t) = -16t^2 + 200t + 250$ with $0 \leq t \leq 5$. Find the maximum value of the function and interpret it.

61. A bricklayer makes a patio out of granite blocks. He charges his customer $11.00 per square foot for installation. His overhead on the job is $35.00, and his material cost is $8.50 per square foot. If the patio is a square with side x, then his profit, $P(x)$, can be computed using the function $P(x) = 2.50x^2 - 35.00$. In order to receive this profit, the patio's dimensions must be greater than or equal to 10 feet on a side and less than or equal to 20 feet on a side. Find the maximum value of the function. Interpret its meaning.

62. The area of a rectangle, $A(w)$, with perimeter 325 meters, can be given by the function $A(w) = -w^2 + 162.5w$, where w is the measure of the width of the rectangle. Graph the function. Find the maximum value of the function and the corresponding width.

63. Data from the Bureau of the Census, U.S. Department of Commerce, indicate that the percentage of foreign-born population in the United States has fluctuated since 1900. The percentage of foreign born for the first part of the century can be estimated by the function $p(x) = -0.013x^2 + 0.24x + 13.6$, where x is the number of years after 1900. Graph this function. Find and interpret its vertex.

6.4

Recall	Example
Writing a quadratic function, given three data points • Write and simplify three equations, substituting the data points into the standard form of the quadratic equation. • Solve the resulting system of three equations.	Write a quadratic function for a graph that will pass through $(1, 9)$, $(2, 16)$, and $(3, 25)$. This will result in three equations: $y = ax^2 + bx + c$ (1) $\quad 9 = a(1)^2 + b(1) + c$ (2) $\quad 16 = a(2)^2 + b(2) + c$ (3) $\quad 25 = a(3)^2 + b(3) + c$ Simplify each equation. (1) $\quad 9 = a + b + c$ (2) $\quad 16 = 4a + 2b + c$ (3) $\quad 25 = 9a + 3b + c$ First system: (1) $\quad 9 = a + b + c$ (2) $\quad 16 = 4a + 2b + c$ (1) $\quad -9 = -a - b - c$ (2) $\quad \underline{16 = 4a + 2b + c}$ (4) $\quad 7 = 3a + \ b$ Second system: (2) $\quad 16 = 4a + 2b + c$ (3) $\quad 25 = 9a + 3b + c$ (2) $\quad -16 = -4a - 2b - c$ (3) $\quad \underline{25 = \ 9a + 3b + c}$ (5) $\quad 9 = \ 5a + \ b$ New system: (4) $\quad 7 = 3a + b$ (5) $\quad 9 = 5a + b$ (4) $\quad -7 = -3a - b$ (5) $\quad \underline{9 = \ 5a + b}$ $\quad\quad 2 = \ 2a$ $\quad\quad 1 = \ \ a$ Substitute 1 for a in an equation from the new system. (4) $\quad 7 = 3a + b$ $\quad\quad 7 = 3(1) + b$ $\quad\quad 4 = b$ Substitute a and b in an original simplified equation. $9 = a + b + c$ $9 = 1 + 4 + c$ $4 = c$ Therefore, $a = 1$, $b = 4$, and $c = 4$. Substitute these values into the standard form of the function. $y = ax^2 + bx + c$ $y = (1)x^2 + (4)x + (4)$ $y = x^2 + 4x + 4$

In exercises 64–66, write the quadratic function for the graph that passes through the given three points. Check by graphing.

64. $(8, 0), (-3, 0), (0, -24)$ **65.** $(0, 5), (5, 0), \left(-\dfrac{1}{2}, 0\right)$ **66.** $(2, -4), (4, -6), (7, 6)$

67. Use the position function, $s(t) = at^2 + bt + c$, to solve the following application: A hammer is thrown upward from a height of 160 feet. After 1 second, it is 176 feet above the ground. After two seconds, it is 160 feet above the ground. Write the position function for the falling hammer. To the nearest tenth of a second, how long will it take the hammer to reach the ground?

68. The Bixby Creek Bridge is one of the largest single-arch concrete bridges in the world. The main span of the bridge is 320 feet long and 280 feet high. Write a quadratic function to approximate the curve of the arch.

69. In 1960, there were 3783 active U.S. Army officers who were female. In 1970, there were 5235 active U.S. Army officers who were female. In 1975, the number of active female U.S. Army officers was 4572. If x is the number of years after 1960 and y is the total number of active female U.S. Army officers, write a quadratic function for these data. Determine the absolute maximum of the function and compare to the data. According to the function, predict when there will be no active female U.S. Army officers.

■ Chapter 6 Mixed Review

Evaluate $2x^3 - 3x^2 - 29x - 30$ *for the given values.*

1. $x = 5$ **2.** $x = 0$ **3.** $x = 1$ **4.** $x = -2$ **5.** $x = -\dfrac{3}{2}$

Evaluate $2a^3 + 4a^2b - 2ab^2 + b^3$ *for the given values.*

6. $a = -1, b = 0$ **7.** $a = 1, b = 1$ **8.** $a = -1, b = 1$ **9.** $a = -1, b = -1$

10. Classify each expression as a monomial, a binomial, a trinomial, or a polynomial. Determine the degree of each term and the degree of the polynomial. Write the polynomial in descending order.
    a. $5 + 3x^2$ **b.** $15a^2 - 5a^3 + 4 + a$ **c.** $5x^4 + x - 2 + x^5 - 3x^2$

11. Classify each expression as a monomial, a binomial, a trinomial, or a polynomial. Determine the degree of each term and the degree of the polynomial.
    a. $7b + 3b^2 - 4 + 6b$ **b.** $3x^2y - 4xy + 3xy^2 + 5 - 4x^2y^2$ **c.** $4xyz - 2 + 3xyz - 5 - xyz + 7$

In exercises 12–16, evaluate the function $f(x) = 2x^3 - 3x^2 - 23x + 12$ *at the given values.*

12. $f(-3)$ **13.** $f(0)$ **14.** $f(4)$ **15.** $f\left(\dfrac{1}{2}\right)$ **16.** $f(2.2)$

17. Construct a table of values for the polynomial relation $y = 2x^3 + 2x^2 - 12x$, where x is an integer between -4 and 4.

In exercises 18–20, graph the given polynomial relation. From the graph, determine the range of each relation.

18. $y = 4x - 2$ **19.** $y = x^2 + 4x - 2$ **20.** $y = x^3 - 3x^2 - 13x + 15$

21. Use the given polynomial relation.
    a. Determine three possible solutions for the relation graphed by completing the table of values.

x	y
0	
5	
	7

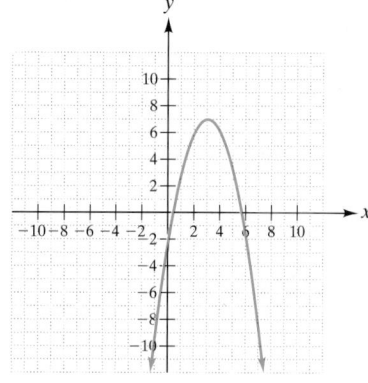

    b. Determine the range of the relation.

Graph each quadratic function, labeling the vertex and drawing the axis of symmetry.

22. $f(x) = 2x^2 + 7x - 4$ **23.** $y = \dfrac{1}{4}x^2 - x + 3$ **24.** $h(x) = -x^2 + 9$

Complete the table. Check by using your calculator.

Function	Coefficients			Properties of Graph				
	a	b	c	Wide/Narrow	Concave Upward/Downward	Vertex	Axis of Symmetry	y-Intercept
25. $y = \dfrac{1}{3}x^2 + \dfrac{2}{3}x + 1$								
26. $f(x) = -3x^2 + 6x$								
27. $y = -\dfrac{1}{4}x^2 + x + 3$								
28. $g(x) = 2x^2 + 4x - 6$								

In exercises 29–30, write the quadratic function for the graph that passes through the given three points. Check by graphing.

29. $(-2, 12), (-4, 8), (-7, 17)$

30. $(9, 0), (-4, 0), (0, -36)$

31. List the following properties of the graph of the quadratic function.

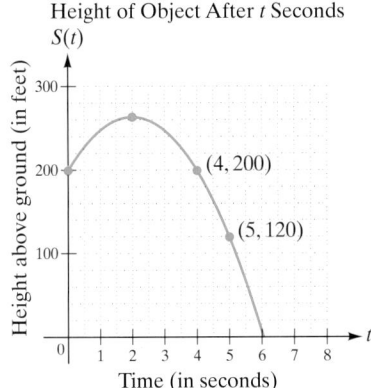

Height of Object After t Seconds

a. Determine the concavity.
b. Determine the y-intercept.
c. Determine the vertex.
d. Determine any absolute maximum or absolute minimum.
e. Determine for what x-values the function is increasing and decreasing.

32. Write a polynomial for the perimeter of a rectangle whose length has a numerical value that is 5 units more than the cube of the numerical value for its width. What is the perimeter if the width of the rectangle is 3 feet?

33. Write a polynomial for the total area of the figures shown.

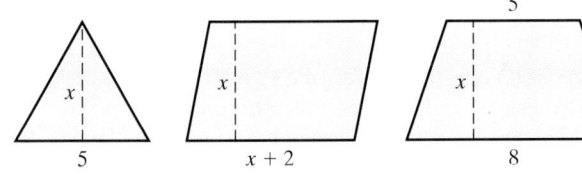

34. A circular pool with a radius of z feet is placed in a rectangular yard with a length of x feet and a width of y feet. Write a polynomial for the area of the yard not covered by the pool. What does this area measure if the pool has a radius of 8 feet and the yard measures 50 feet by 80 feet?

35. A reward system for grades has been designed to be progressive. Pop will pay his child for a report card with no failing grades according to the number of A's earned. If the child earns x grades of A, Pop will pay the child $P(x) = 10x + 2x^2$ dollars.

a. Set up a table of possible values to show how much the child can earn for his report card, given that he is enrolled in seven classes.

b. Interpret the table. What can you say about the payments in relation to the number of A's?

36. A director of a business school graduate program wanted to relate a student's grade point average (GPA) in the school's master-of-business-administration (MBA) program with the student's score on the standardized test given to business school applicants (GMAT). The director developed the mathematical model

$$y = 1.5 + 0.0082z - 0.0000081z^2$$

where y is the student's GPA in the MBA program, and z is the student's score on the GMAT.

a. Using this model, what would you predict a student's GPA to be if her GMAT score was 750?

b. Complete the following table to relate his GPA in the MBA program to his GMAT score:

GMAT score (z)	500	550	600	650	700	750
GPA in MBA (y)						

c. This table should surprise you. What does it say about the relationship between the entrance exam score (GMAT) and the student's performance in graduate school?

37. A supply package is dropped from a lunar module hovering 1500 meters above the surface of the Moon. The position function for the package is $s(t) = -0.8t^2 + 1500$, where t is the number of seconds since the drop. Graph the function. How many seconds will it take for the object to reach the ground?

38. A baseball player throws a ball into the air giving it an initial upward velocity of 20 feet per second. The position function of the ball, in feet above the ground, after t seconds is $s(t) = -16t^2 + 20t + 4$ with $0.1 \le t \le 0.4$. Find the maximum value of the function and interpret it.

39. The deepest gorge on Earth is the Yarlung Tsangpo River Canyon in Tibet, which is more than 3 miles deep at its lowest point. If a rock were to be tossed downward with an initial velocity of 60 feet per second and were to fall directly into the river, its distance above the river would be given by the function $s(t) = -16t^2 - 60t + 19{,}500$, where $s(t)$ is the height above ground level (in feet) and t is the time in seconds after the rock was tossed. Determine the range of this function and interpret its meaning.

40. As a fund-raiser, a school is selling coupon books that give discounts to the purchaser at various stores and restaurants in the community. The school offers reduced prices for multiple purchases in order to increase sales. If a customer purchases x coupon books, the revenue to the school is given by $R(x) = 15x - x^2$ dollars. Determine the maximum revenue the school can receive from one person's multiple purchase and how many books must be sold to receive this maximum revenue.

41. A handyman makes a square patio out of concrete paving blocks. He charges his customer $8.00 per square foot for installation. His overhead on the job is $50.00 and his material cost is $4.75 per square foot. If the patio has side, x, then his profit, $P(x)$, can be computed using the function $P(x) = 3.25x^2 - 50.00$. The patio must be between or equal to 5 and 10 feet on a side to qualify for this price. Find the maximum value of the function. Interpret its meaning.

42. A bricklayer makes a square patio out of granite blocks on a side job. He charges his customer $11.00 per square foot for installation. His overhead on the job is $35.00, and his material cost is $8.50 per square foot.
  a. Write a polynomial that represents his revenue for the patio installation in terms of the length of the side of the square.
  b. Write a polynomial for his cost.
  c. Write a polynomial for his profit.
  d. Find his revenue, cost, and profit if the patio is 7 feet on a side.

43. A flooring outlet sells a high-quality carpet with an expensive pad. For this option the setup cost is $80.00, and the material cost is $10.15 per square yard. The outlet charges the customer $14.25 per square yard for installation. A customer has a square room.
  a. Write a polynomial that represents the flooring outlet's revenue for this job in terms of the length of the side of the square.
  b. Write a polynomial for the outlet's cost.
  c. Write a polynomial for the outlet's profit.
  d. Find the outlet's revenue, cost, and profit if the job involves carpeting for a square room that is 9.5 yards on a side.

44. According to data from the International Commission on Large Dams, a dam's height and volume are often related. The volume, in thousands of cubic meters, can be estimated with the polynomial $5.25h^2 - 2835h + 435,800$, where h is the height in meters above the lowest formation. The Rogun Dam in Tajikistan was recently constructed and is the world's highest dam at 335 meters. Use this polynomial to estimate the volume of the Rogun Dam.

45. Worldwide airline fatalities fluctuate. Using data from the National Safety Council, a third-degree polynomial function can be generated for number of airline fatalities, $f(x)$, where x is the number of years after 1995: $f(x) = 89.7x^3 - 745.7x^2 + 1493.5x + 711$.
  a. Use this function to estimate worldwide airline fatalities by completing the following table:

Year	1995	1996	1998	1999	2000
Airline fatalities					

  b. Data indicate that in year 1996 there were 1146 fatalities. How well does the function predict this number?
  c. In 1999 there were 499 fatalities. How well does the function predict this number?
  d. In 2000 there were 757 fatalities. How well does the function predict this number?
  e. In 2001 this model lost any predictive capabilities it might have had. Why?

46. According to the National Health Interview Survey of the Center for Disease Control and Prevention (CDC), an increasing number of American adults have mild to severe loss of hearing. One model estimates the percent of people with hearing trouble, p, by using the following function, where x is age in years.

$$p(x) = 0.01x^2 - 0.03x - 0.5$$

  a. Use this function to estimate the percent of people with hearing trouble at various ages:

Age in years	35	40	45	60	65	70
Percent with hearing trouble						

  b. The data indicate that more than 50% of adults 75 and older have hearing trouble. How well did the function predict this percentage?
  c. What does the function indicate about the hearing of people in their twenties?
  d. Can this model go on indefinitely? If not, why not?

47. The area of a rectangle, $A(l)$, with perimeter 9 feet can be given by the function $A(l) = -l^2 + 4.5l$, where l is the measure of the length of the rectangle. Graph the function. Find the maximum value of the function and the corresponding length.

48. The percentage of foreign-born population for the second half of the 20th century can be estimated by the function $p(x) = 0.011x^2 - 1.5x + 55.8$, where x is the number of years after 1900. Graph this function. Find and interpret its vertex.

49. In 1960, there were 98,029 active U.S. Army officers who were male. In 1970, there were 138,469 active U.S. Army officers who were male. In 1975, the number of active male U.S. Army officers was 781,316. If x is the number of years after 1960 and y is the total number of active male U.S. Army officers, write a quadratic function for these data. Determine the absolute maximum of the function and compare to the data. According to the function, predict when there will be no active male U.S. Army officers.

50. The Hell Gate Bridge over the East River in New York City provided a much-needed railroad connection when it was completed in 1916. The bridge has an arch that spans 977.5 feet and rises 170 feet from the tracks. Write a quadratic function to approximate the curve of the arch.

■ Chapter 6 Test

Classify each expression as a monomial, a binomial, a trinomial, or a polynomial.

1. $123x^2y^3z$

2. $3a^3 + 5a^2b + 7ab^2 + 9b^3$

3. $2 - c$

Determine the degree of each polynomial.

4. $13 - 3x^3 + 6x - 0.5x^5 + 1.7x^2 - x^4$

5. $5x^2y^3 + 3xy^2 - y + 17$

Write the polynomial in descending order.

6. $15 + 3x^4 - 7x + x^5 + 9x^2 + 21x$

Write the polynomial in ascending order.

7. $a - \dfrac{2}{3}a^3 - \dfrac{5}{6}a^2 - \dfrac{4}{9}$

Evaluate $a^2 + 3ab^3 - 7b^2 - b - 6$ for the given values.

8. $a = 0, b = 3$

9. $a = 2, b = -3$

Given $g(x) = 3x^2 + 7x - 6$, find

10. $g(-3)$

11. $g(0)$

12. $g(1)$

13. Consider the relation $y = \frac{1}{2}x^2 - 2x - 6$.
  a. Find the vertex.
  b. Graph the relation.
  c. Determine the range of the relation graphically.
  d. Is the relation a function? Justify your answer.

14. List the following properties of the graph of the profit function $p(x)$, shown at the right.
  a. Determine the concavity.
  b. Determine the y-intercept.
  c. Determine the vertex.
  d. Determine any absolute maximum or absolute minimum.
  e. Determine for what x-values the function is increasing and decreasing.

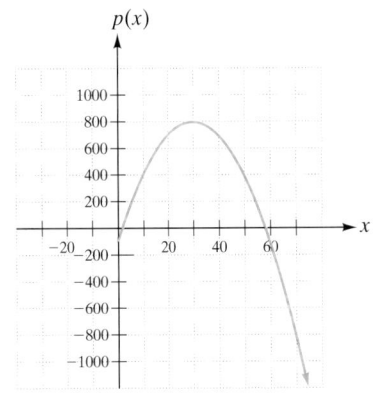

Complete the following table:

	Function	Coefficients			Properties of Graph				
		a	b	c	Wide/Narrow	Concave Upward/Downward	Vertex	Axis of Symmetry	y-Intercept
15.	$y = \dfrac{1}{2}x^2 + 2x + 3$								
16.	$y = 3x^2 - 3x + \dfrac{1}{4}$								

In exercises 17 and 18, write the quadratic function for the graph that passes through the given points.

17. $(0, 8), (2, 0), (4, 0)$

18. $(-1, 6), (1, 4), (2, 9)$

19. Construction on the Tower of London began in 1078 by William of Normandy. It was completed 20 years later, rising nearly 100 feet high. The tower held many famous prisoners, including Sir Thomas More and Anne Boleyn. If they had attempted to drop a note from the top of the tower, its distance above the ground could be approximated by the function $s(t) = -16t^2 + 100$, where $s(t)$ was the height above ground level (in feet) and t was the time in seconds. Determine the range of this function and interpret its meaning.

20. A supplier of ergonomically designed computer keyboards offers a multiple-purchase discount to a firm that plans to purchase them for its employees. If the firm buys x keyboards, the supplier will realize a profit of $P(x) = 75x - 2x^2$ dollars, after subtracting cost from revenue. State the vertex of the graph of this function. Explain what the coordinates of the vertex indicate. What is the maximum profit the supplier can realize, and how many keyboards should be sold to achieve this profit?

21. The Bayonne Bridge is one of the longest steel arch bridges in the world and links Bayonne, New Jersey, with Staten Island, New York. The length of the arch span is 1675 feet, and the height of the arch is 325 feet at the center. Write a quadratic function to approximate the curve of the arch.

22. Jose owns an asphalt sealing business. He makes most of his money working on parking lots. For one job at a mall, the parking lot was square in shape. He determines his overhead is $235.00 and materials cost him $0.07 per square foot. He charges the business owner $0.09 per square foot to do the job.
   a. Write a polynomial that represents his revenue for this in terms of the length of a side of the square.
   b. Write a polynomial for his cost.
   c. Write a polynomial for his profit.
   d. Find his revenue, cost, and profit if the parking lot is a square that measures 300 feet on a side.

23. The Great Lakes are the world's largest body of fresh water (in terms of surface area). According to data from the National Oceanic Service of the U.S. Department of Commerce, the volume of water in cubic miles in one of the Great Lakes can be estimated by the polynomial $0.26x^2 - 130.493x + 16,700$, where x is the length of the lake in miles. Use this polynomial to estimate the volume of Lake Superior, which is 350 miles long.

24. The cost of higher education is on the rise. According to statistics published by the U.S. Department of Education, National Center of Education Statistics, the average cost of undergraduate tuition, room and board, and fees, $c(x)$, in dollars, can be estimated by the polynomial function $c(x) = 3x^2 + 365x + 10,076$, where x is number of years after 1998.

Use this function to estimate college costs for the years given in the following table:

Year	1998	1999	2000	2001
Cost				

   a. More recent data suggest that the cost in 2001 was $11,380. How well did the function predict this amount?
   b. More recent data also suggest that the cost in 2002 was $12,111. How well does the function predict this amount?
   c. Both students at four-year schools and two-year schools have indicated that this function was not accurate when compared to their own personal experiences. How can this be?

25. The annual number of passenger cars imported to the United States from Sweden can be estimated by the function $n(t) = 18,397t^2 - 133,509t + 327,393$, where t is the number of years after 1998. Graph this function. Find and interpret its vertex.

26. Garlic is one of the top-selling medicinal herbs in the United States. The amount sold, in millions of dollars, can be estimated by the function $a(x) = 3.5x^2 - 14.5x + 188$, where x is the number of years after 2000. Graph this function. Find and interpret its vertex.

27. At a Civil War reenactment, a cannonball is shot from a cannon with an initial upward velocity of 35 meters per second. Its position function, in meters above the ground, after t seconds is $s(t) = -9.8t^2 + 35t + 1.8$ with $0 \le t \le 1.5$. Find the maximum value of the function and interpret it.

28. Define what is meant by the term *quadratic function*. Describe the special features of such a function. Explain how you would sketch the graph of a quadratic function.

6

Project

PART I In this chapter, we have given several examples of objects being dropped or propelled upward or downward. In this project, we will use the TI-84 Plus (or TI-83) and a Texas Instrument Calculator-Based Ranger (CBR) to collect our own data involving dropping and tossing a pillow.

You will need the CBR, the Ranger program, and an object (a small pillow is easy to use).

1. Run the Ranger program.

   a. Connect the CBR to the TI-84 (or TI-83) Plus.
   b. Under programs, select RANGER.
   c. Under MAIN MENU, select 1:SETUP/SAMPLE.
   d. With the up or down arrow, select a line, and press ENTER to change the settings. The screen settings should read as follows:

REAL TIME:	YES
TIME(S):	15
DISPLAY:	DIST
BEGIN ON:	[ENTER]
SMOOTHING:	NONE
UNITS:	FEET

   When the settings are correct, use the arrow to move the cursor to the top of the page, and press ENTER to start.

   e. Press ENTER to start the program.
   f. Place the CBR on the floor.
   g. Press ENTER again to start data collection. The CBR will begin to make clicking noises. The calculator will collect data points every 0.2 second.

   h. From a height of about six feet directly above the CBR, drop a pillow on top of it.
   i. When the data have been collected, press ENTER to view the PLOT MENU. Choose 2:SELECT DOMAIN. You will be prompted to choose the left and right bounds of your data set. You will need to eliminate any points before the pillow dropped and after it hit the floor. You may need to do this more than once. You may need to repeat the sample if your data do not appear to be correct. Press 5 to exit. The calculator now has the time in seconds stored in L1 and the distance above the CBR stored in L2.
   j. Calculate the quadratic regression equation for your data. Use the data points to write a quadratic function $s(t)$ representing the height above the motion detector in feet, with t representing the time after the release of the pillow.

2. Repeat the steps in exercise 1, but this time, from a height of about 5 feet, toss the pillow *upward* so that it will fall on top of the motion detector.

   We have discussed the formula $s(t) = -16t^2 + v_0t + s_0$, where $s(t)$ is the vertical distance in feet, t is time in seconds, v_0 is the initial velocity, and s_0 is the initial height. How do your two quadratic equations compare with this theoretical formula? Can you explain why your equation is not in this exact form?

PART II In this chapter, you encountered several exercises that used real data. For example, in Section 6.4, you were asked to write a quadratic function and predict future data.

Search the Internet or library for a similar set of data. List the source of your data. Use the data to write an exercise. Give enough information to write three data points, ask for a quadratic function to model the data, and ask for a prediction of future data.

Exponents and Polynomials

We've seen how to write and evaluate polynomials and how to graph them; our next step is to learn how to work with them. We will look at how to add, subtract, multiply, and divide polynomials. However, before we work with polynomial operations, we will need to look at the rules of exponents.

Scientific notation is an application of exponential expressions and the rules of exponents. Many measurements are either so large or so small that we use scientific notation to write them easily and the rules of exponents to multiply and divide them easily. For example, the distance between the Earth and a star is so large that we resort to scientific notation to write it.

We will also continue to look at geometric applications of polynomials. We will see that many such applications may be described by polynomials. It is important to be able to simplify these polynomials by adding, subtracting, multiplying, and dividing. This will make it easier to work with the polynomials when we are ready to solve polynomial equations.

Raising a polynomial to a power (expanding the polynomial) is sometimes a long and time-consuming process. In the project at the end of the chapter, we will discuss a method that will help us accomplish this expansion more quickly. The method was first published by Blaise Pascal in 1665. Pascal's triangle gives rise to many interesting patterns. One such pattern is called a fractal.

7.1 OPERATIONS INVOLVING NONNEGATIVE EXPONENTS

OBJECTIVES

1 Rewrite exponential expressions by using their definitions.
2 Simplify exponential expressions by using the product rule.
3 Simplify exponential expressions by using the quotient rule.
4 Simplify exponential expressions by using the power-to-a-power rule, product-to-a-power rule, and quotient-to-a-power rule.
5 Simplify exponential expressions by using more than one rule for exponents.
6 Check simplified exponential expressions by using a calculator.
7 Model real-world situations by using exponential expressions.

APPLICATION

The American Bison once roamed the plains states of the United States. They migrated 213 to 395 miles south in the fall of the year and returned north in the spring.

a. Determine the home range (area over which the bison range) of a herd of bison in the summer if the average movement (in a straight line) is estimated as *x* miles.

b. In the winter the average movement is 1.8 times the summer distance. Determine the home range of a herd of bison in the winter.

c. Determine the ratio of the winter home range to the summer home range.

d. If the average movement in the summer is 2.5 miles, determine the summer home range and the winter home range of a herd of bison.

We will discuss this application further. See page 549.

Objective 7.1.1 | Defining Exponential Expressions

We discussed numeric exponential expressions in previous chapters. An exponential expression is an expression that has a base and an exponent. We evaluate an exponential expression by writing it in expanded form and using repeated multiplication. By convention, we do not write an exponent of 1, although we might do so in an intermediate step in solving a problem. In Chapter P, we defined an exponential expression with a nonzero base and a zero exponent as equal to 1.

$$4^3 = 4 \cdot 4 \cdot 4 = 64$$
$$4^1 = 4$$
$$4^0 = 1$$

Remember, 0^0 is indeterminate. We will explain why this is true later in the chapter. We define variable exponential expressions in the same manner as numeric exponential expressions.

INTEGER EXPONENTS

For any base a and nonnegative integer exponent n,

$$a^n = a \cdot a \cdot a \cdot \cdots \cdot a \quad n\text{ factors}$$
$$a^1 = a$$
$$a^0 = 1, \text{ where } a \neq 0$$

The base a may be a constant, a variable, or an expression.

For example,

$$x^4 = x \cdot x \cdot x \cdot x$$
$$x^1 = x$$
$$x^0 = 1 \text{ for all } x \neq 0$$

EXAMPLE 1   Write the given expressions in expanded form.

a. $-2x^4$ **b.** $(-2x)^4$ **c.** a^3b^2 **d.** mn^0 **e.** $(x + 2)^2$

Solution

a. $-2x^4 = -2 \cdot x \cdot x \cdot x \cdot x$
b. $(-2x)^4 = (-2x)(-2x)(-2x)(-2x)$
c. $a^3b^2 = a \cdot a \cdot a \cdot b \cdot b$
d. $mn^0 = m \cdot 1 = m$ Remember, $n^0 = 1$.
e. $(x + 2)^2 = (x + 2)(x + 2)$

 TAKE NOTE It is very important to determine the base of an exponential expression. In Example 1a, the base is x. In Example 1b, the base is $-2x$.

 Objective 7.1.1 **CHECKUP**

1. Write the expressions in expanded form.
  a. $-5y^3$ **b.** $(-5y)^3$ **c.** 3^2x^3 **d.** p^0q^4 **e.** $(a - b)^4$

2. Explain the difference between the definition of *expanded form* and *exponential expression*.

Objective 7.1.2   **The Product Rule**

In order to perform multiplication involving exponential expressions, we need to discover a few rules. Use your calculator to complete the following set of exercises to determine a rule for multiplication of exponential expressions with the same base.

 Guided Discovery 1   Multiplication of Exponential Expressions with the Same Base

Evaluate each expression, and compare the results obtained in part **a** with the corresponding results in part **b**.

1. a. $4^3 \cdot 4^2 = $ _____   **b.** $4^5 = $ _____

2. a. $(-2)^4 \cdot (-2)^2 = $ _____   **b.** $(-2)^6 = $ _____

3. a. $\left(\dfrac{3}{4}\right)^2 \cdot \left(\dfrac{3}{4}\right) = $ _____   **b.** $\left(\dfrac{3}{4}\right)^3 = $ _____

Write a rule for multiplication of two exponential expressions with the same base.

4. Use the rule to simplify $x^4 \cdot x^3 = $ _____.

In part **a**, the base of each factor is the same. In part **b**, the base is the same as the bases of the factors in part **a**, and the exponent is the sum of the factors' exponents. The results are the same. Therefore, to multiply exponential expressions with like bases, add the exponents.

Using this rule, we see that the product of $x^4 \cdot x^3$ is x^{4+3}, or x^7. We can illustrate the rule by rewriting each expression as a product of its factors and simplifying.

$$x^4 \cdot x^3 = (x \cdot x \cdot x \cdot x) \cdot (x \cdot x \cdot x)$$
$$= x \cdot x \cdot x \cdot x \cdot x \cdot x \cdot x$$
$$= x^7$$

PRODUCT RULE FOR EXPONENTS

For any base a and integer exponents m and n,

$$a^m \cdot a^n = a^{m+n}$$

The base a may be a constant, a variable, or an expression.

EXAMPLE 2   Simplify.

a. $y^3 \cdot y$ **b.** $(a + b)^4(a + b)$ **c.** $-2x^3 \cdot x^2 \cdot x$

Solution

a. $y^3 \cdot y = y^{3+1} = y^4$
b. $(a + b)^4(a + b) = (a + b)^{4+1} = (a + b)^5$
c. $-2x^3 \cdot x^2 \cdot x = -2x^{3+2+1} = -2x^6$

Objective 7.1.2 *CHECKUP*

1. Simplify.

a. $z \cdot z^6$ **b.** $(x + y)(x + y)^7$ **c.** $\dfrac{1}{2}a^2 \cdot a \cdot a^5$

2. What is the difference between $x^2 \cdot x^3$ and $x^2 + x^3$? Which of these expressions can be simplified by using the product rule?

Objective 7.1.3   The Quotient Rule

Before we begin to discuss division of polynomials, we must discover rules of exponents involving division. Use your calculator to complete the following set of exercises to determine a rule for division of exponential expressions with the same base.

Guided Discovery 2   Division of Exponential Expressions with the Same Base

Evaluate each expression, and compare the results obtained in part **a** with the corresponding results in part **b**.

1. a. $\dfrac{4^5}{4^2} = $ _____   **b.** $4^3 = $ _____

2. a. $\dfrac{(-2)^4}{(-2)^2} = $ _____   **b.** $(-2)^2 = $ _____

3. a. $\dfrac{\left(\dfrac{3}{4}\right)^3}{\left(\dfrac{3}{4}\right)} = $ _____   **b.** $\left(\dfrac{3}{4}\right)^2 = $ _____

4. a. $\dfrac{0^5}{0^5} = $ _____   **b.** $0^0 = $ _____

Write a rule for division of two exponential expressions with the same base.

5. Use the rule to simplify $\dfrac{x^7}{x^3} = $ _____.

In part **a**, the bases of the divisor and dividend are the same. In part **b**, the base is the same as the bases of the divisor and dividend, and the exponent is the difference of the exponents in the quotient. The results are the same. Therefore, to divide exponential expressions with like bases, subtract the exponent in the denominator from the exponent in the numerator.

Using this rule, we find that the quotient of $\dfrac{x^7}{x^3}$ is x^{7-3}, or x^4. We can illustrate the rule by rewriting each expression as a product of its factors and simplifying.

$$\frac{x^7}{x^3} = \frac{x \cdot x \cdot x \cdot x \cdot x \cdot x \cdot x}{x \cdot x \cdot x}$$

$$= x \cdot x \cdot x \cdot x$$

$$= x^4$$

Note: In the discovery box, we evaluated $\dfrac{0^5}{0^5} = \dfrac{0}{0}$, which we determined to be indeterminate in Chapter P. Now, using the rule we just discovered, we see that $\dfrac{0^5}{0^5} = 0^{5-5} = 0^0$. It follows that 0^0 is indeterminate.

QUOTIENT RULE FOR EXPONENTS

For any nonzero base a and integer exponents m and n,

$$\frac{a^m}{a^n} = a^{m-n}$$

The base a may be a constant, a variable, or an expression.

EXAMPLE 3

Simplify.

a. $\dfrac{y^3}{y}$ **b.** $\dfrac{(a+b)^4}{(a+b)}$ **c.** $\dfrac{-6b^2}{18b}$

Solution

a. $\dfrac{y^3}{y} = y^{3-1} = y^2$

b. $\dfrac{(a+b)^4}{(a+b)} = (a+b)^{4-1} = (a+b)^3$

c. $\dfrac{-6b^2}{18b} = \left(\dfrac{-6}{18}\right)\left(\dfrac{b^2}{b}\right) = \dfrac{-1}{3}b^{2-1} = -\dfrac{1}{3}b$ or $-\dfrac{b}{3}$

✓ Objective 7.1.3 CHECKUP

1. Simplify.

a. $\dfrac{a^{12}}{a^8}$ **b.** $\dfrac{(x+5)^6}{(x+5)^4}$ **c.** $\dfrac{22z^4}{121z}$

2. What is the difference between $\dfrac{x^5}{x^2}$ and $x^5 - x^2$? Which can be simplified by using the quotient rule for exponents?

Objective 7.1.4 Power Rules

Sometimes, we may need to simplify an exponential expression raised to a power. Use your calculator to complete the following set of exercises to determine a rule for simplifying an exponential expression raised to a power.

💡 Guided Discovery 3 Exponential Expressions Raised to a Power

Evaluate each expression, and compare the results obtained in part **a** with the corresponding results in part **b**.

1. a. $(4^3)^2 = $ _____ **b.** $4^6 = $ _____

2. a. $[(-2)^2]^4 = $ _____ **b.** $(-2)^8 = $ _____

3. a. $\left[\left(\dfrac{3}{4}\right)^2\right]^3 = $ _____ **b.** $\left(\dfrac{3}{4}\right)^6 = $ _____

Write a rule for raising an exponential expression to a power.

4. Use the rule to simplify $(x^4)^3 = $ _____.

In part **b**, the base is the same as the base in part **a**, and the exponent is the product of the exponents in part **a**. The results are the same. Therefore, to raise an exponential expression to a power, multiply the exponents.

With this rule, $(x^4)^3$ is $x^{4 \cdot 3}$, or x^{12}. We can illustrate the rule by rewriting the expression as a product of its factors and simplifying.

$$(x^4)^3 = (x \cdot x \cdot x \cdot x)^3$$
$$= (x \cdot x \cdot x \cdot x) \cdot (x \cdot x \cdot x \cdot x) \cdot (x \cdot x \cdot x \cdot x)$$
$$= x \cdot x \cdot x \cdot x \cdot x \cdot x \cdot x \cdot x \cdot x \cdot x \cdot x \cdot x$$
$$= x^{12}$$

POWER-TO-A-POWER RULE FOR EXPONENTS

For any base a and integer exponents m and n,

$$(a^m)^n = a^{mn}$$

The base a may be a constant, a variable, or an expression.

We also need rules to simplify a product or a quotient raised to a power. Use your calculator to complete the following set of exercises to determine a rule for simplifying a product raised to a power.

 Guided Discovery 4   Products Raised to a Power

Evaluate each expression, and compare the results obtained in part **a** with the corresponding results in part **b**.

1. a. $(4 \cdot 2)^3 =$ _____   **b.** $4^3 \cdot 2^3 =$ _____

2. a. $(-2 \cdot 3)^2 =$ _____   **b.** $(-2)^2 \cdot 3^2 =$ _____

3. a. $\left(\dfrac{3}{4} \cdot \dfrac{2}{5}\right)^3 =$ _____   **b.** $\left(\dfrac{3}{4}\right)^3 \cdot \left(\dfrac{2}{5}\right)^3 =$ _____

Write a rule for a product raised to a power.

4. Use the rule to simplify $(xy)^4 =$ _____.

In part **a**, we determine a product and then raise the product to a power. In part **b**, we raise each factor to a power and then multiply the result. The results are the same. Therefore, raising a product to a power is equivalent to multiplying the factors raised to a power.

Applying this rule, we obtain $(xy)^4 = x^4 y^4$. We can illustrate the rule by rewriting the exponential expression as its factors, rearranging the factors by means of the commutative and associative properties, and simplifying.

$$(xy)^4 = (xy)(xy)(xy)(xy)$$
$$= x \cdot y \cdot x \cdot y \cdot x \cdot y \cdot x \cdot y$$
$$= x \cdot x \cdot x \cdot x \cdot y \cdot y \cdot y \cdot y$$
$$= x^4 y^4$$

PRODUCT-TO-A-POWER RULE

For any factors a and b and integer exponent m,

$$(ab)^m = a^m b^m$$

The factors a and b may be constants, variables, or expressions.

The result for a quotient raised to a power is determined in a similar way. For example,

$$\left(\frac{x}{y}\right)^4 = \left(\frac{x}{y}\right)\left(\frac{x}{y}\right)\left(\frac{x}{y}\right)\left(\frac{x}{y}\right) = \frac{x^4}{y^4}$$

QUOTIENT-TO-A-POWER RULE

For any dividend a, nonzero divisor b, and integer exponent m,

$$\left(\frac{a}{b}\right)^m = \frac{a^m}{b^m}$$

The dividend a and divisor b may be constants, variables, or expressions.

EXAMPLE 4   Simplify.

a. $(-2x)^4$ **b.** $(-2x^3)^4$ **c.** $\left(\dfrac{5y}{z}\right)^3$

Solution

a. $(-2x)^4 = (-2)^4 x^4 = 16x^4$ *Product-to-a-power rule*

b. $(-2x^3)^4 = (-2)^4 (x^3)^4$ *Product-to-a-power rule*

$\qquad\qquad = 16x^{3 \cdot 4}$ *Power-to-a-power rule*

$\qquad\qquad = 16x^{12}$

c. $\left(\dfrac{5y}{z}\right)^3 = \dfrac{(5y)^3}{z^3}$ *Quotient-to-a-power rule*

$\qquad\qquad = \dfrac{5^3 y^3}{z^3}$ *Product-to-a-power rule*

$\qquad\qquad = \dfrac{125 y^3}{z^3}$

✓ Objective 7.1.4 *CHECKUP*

1. Simplify.

a. $(-3a)^5$ **b.** $(-4x^8)^3$ **c.** $\left(\dfrac{-2p}{q}\right)^4$

2. What is the difference between $2x^3$ and $(2x)^3$? Which of the two expressions can be simplified with the product-to-a-power rule?

Objective 7.1.5 Combining Rules

Now that we have learned the rules for exponents, we will apply more than one rule to simplify an exponential expression. The order in which we apply the rules may vary to obtain the same simplification.

EXAMPLE 5   Simplify.

a. $-2x^2 y \cdot 3x^3 y^3$ **b.** $\dfrac{12x^4 y}{3x^2 y}$ **c.** $\dfrac{(a^3 b)^2}{a^2 b}$ **d.** $\left(\dfrac{2m^3}{3mn^2}\right)^2$

Solution

a. $-2x^2 y \cdot 3x^3 y^3 = (-2 \cdot 3)(x^2 \cdot x^3)(y \cdot y^3)$

$\qquad\qquad\quad = -6x^{2+3} y^{1+3}$ *Product rule*

$\qquad\qquad\quad = -6x^5 y^4$

b. $\dfrac{12x^4 y}{3x^2 y} = \left(\dfrac{12}{3}\right)\left(\dfrac{x^4}{x^2}\right)\left(\dfrac{y}{y}\right)$

$\qquad\qquad = 4x^{4-2} y^{1-1}$ *Quotient rule*

$\qquad\qquad = 4x^2 y^0$ *Definition: $y^0 = 1$*

$\qquad\qquad = 4x^2$

c. $\dfrac{(a^3 b)^2}{a^2 b} = \dfrac{(a^3)^2 b^2}{a^2 b}$ Product-to-a-power rule

$= \dfrac{a^{3\cdot 2} b^2}{a^2 b}$ Power-to-a-power rule

$= \dfrac{a^6 b^2}{a^2 b}$

$= a^{6-2} b^{2-1}$ Quotient rule

$= a^4 b$

d. $\left(\dfrac{2m^3}{3mn^2}\right)^2 = \dfrac{(2m^3)^2}{(3mn^2)^2}$ Quotient-to-a-power rule

$= \dfrac{2^2 (m^3)^2}{3^2 m^2 (n^2)^2}$ Product-to-a-power rule

$= \dfrac{4 m^{3\cdot 2}}{9 m^2 n^{2\cdot 2}}$ Power-to-a-power rule

$= \dfrac{4 m^6}{9 m^2 n^4}$ $\dfrac{m^6}{m^2} = m^{6-2} = m^4$

$= \dfrac{4 m^4}{9 n^4}$

A second method is to simplify the original quotient before applying the quotient-to-a-power rule. Remember, $\dfrac{m^3}{m} = m^{3-1} = m^2$.

$$\left(\frac{2m^3}{3mn^2}\right)^2 = \left(\frac{2m^2}{3n^2}\right)^2 = \frac{(2m^2)^2}{(3n^2)^2} = \frac{2^2(m^2)^2}{3^2(n^2)^2} = \frac{4m^4}{9n^4}$$

Objective 7.1.5 **CHECKUP**

1. Simplify

a. $\dfrac{1}{2}a^2 b^3\left(-\dfrac{4}{5}a^2 b\right)$ **b.** $\dfrac{21 p^4 q^2}{7 p^4 q}$ **c.** $\dfrac{(-x^2 y)^3}{2xy}$ **d.** $\left(\dfrac{3a^4}{4a^2 b}\right)^3$

2. What is the difference between $(a^m)^n$ and $a^m(a^n)$?

Objective 7.1.6   Checking Simplified Expressions

The calculator can be used to check for equivalence of simplified expressions if the expressions involve a single variable.

TECHNOLOGY   Calculator Check for Equivalence of Simplified Expressions

Is $\left(\dfrac{3}{5}x^3\right)^2 = \dfrac{9}{25}x^6$?

Numeric Check   **Graphic Check**

$Y1 = \left(\dfrac{3}{5}x^3\right)^2$ $Y2 = \dfrac{9}{25}x^6$

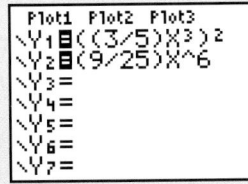

```
Plot1 Plot2 Plot3
\Y1⊟((3/5)X³)²
\Y2⊟(9/25)X^6
\Y3=
\Y4=
\Y5=
\Y6=
\Y7=
```

X	Y1	Y2
0	0	0
1	.36	.36
2	23.04	23.04
3	262.44	262.44
4	1474.6	1474.6
5	5625	5625
6	16796	16796

X=0

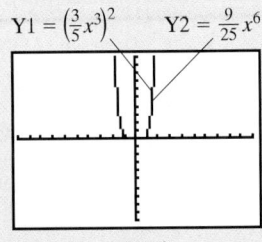

$(-10, 10, -10, 10)$

Figure 7.1a   **Figure 7.1b**   **Figure 7.1c**   *(continued on page 548)*

For **Figure 7.1a**,

Enter the original expression, $\left(\frac{3}{5}x^3\right)^2$, in Y1.

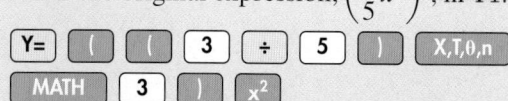

Enter the simplified expression, $\frac{9}{25}x^6$, in Y2.

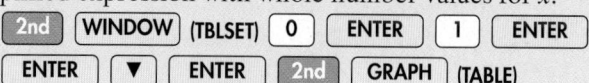

For **Figure 7.1b**,

To check the equivalence numerically, view the table of values of Y1, the original expression, and Y2, the simplified expression with whole number values for x.

Check the values for Y1, the original expression, and Y2, the simplified expression. If the simplification was correct, corresponding values should be equal. (Note that we could have looked at a table of values for other x-values.)

For **Figure 7.1c**,

To check the equivalence graphically, view the graphs of Y1, the original expression, and Y2, the simplified expression.

[ZOOM] [6]

The graphs should coincide. Check by using the TRACE feature of the calculator or by setting the graph of Y2 to be drawn with a bubble.

[Y=] [▼] [◄] [◄] [ENTER] [ENTER] [ENTER]
[ENTER] [GRAPH]

EXAMPLE 6 Simplify. Check numerically and graphically.

$$[(-3x)^2]^3$$

Solution

$$\begin{aligned}
[(-3x)^2]^3 &= [(-3)^2 x^2]^3 &&\text{Product-to-a-power rule} \\
&= [9x^2]^3 &&\text{Simplify.} \\
&= 9^3(x^2)^3 &&\text{Power-to-a-power rule} \\
&= 729x^6 &&\text{Power-to-a-power rule}
\end{aligned}$$

Numeric Check

X	Y₁	Y₂
0	0	0
1	729	729
2	46656	46656
3	531441	531441
4	2.99E6	2.99E6
5	1.14E7	1.14E7
6	3.4E7	3.4E7

X=0

Y1 = $[(-3x)^2]^3$
Y2 = $729x^6$
The values for Y1 = Y2.
The simplification is correct.

Graphic Check

Y1 = $[(-3x)^2]^3$ Y2 = $729x^6$

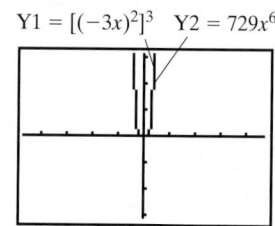

$(-4.7, 4.7, -3.1, 3.1)$

The graphs of Y1 and Y2 are the same. The simplification is correct. ■

✓ Objective 7.1.6 **CHECKUP**

1. Simplify. Check numerically and graphically. $\left(\dfrac{6x^2}{2x^3}\right)^3$

2. When checking a simplification numerically and graphically, are you able to see all the values the variable can assume? Explain.

Objective 7.1.7 **Modeling the Real World**

Exponential expressions occur frequently in all kinds of real-world situations. As always, you must remember to include the units of real quantities in your calculations; that is, raising the quantity 3 feet to the third power gives you, not 27 feet, but 27 *cubic* feet (ft^3).

$$(3 \text{ ft})^3 = 3^3 \text{ ft}^3 = 27 \text{ ft}^3$$

EXAMPLE 7   Determine the area of a square mailroom with sides of length s feet. A publishing company is expanding into new offices, and the new mailroom will still be a square, but with sides of length $2s$ feet. Determine the area of the new mailroom, and compare it with the area of the original mailroom.

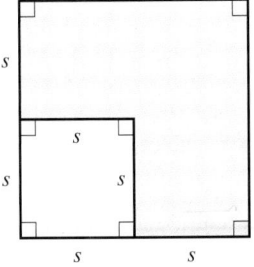

Solution

Let s = length of the side of the original mailroom

The area is found by squaring the length of the side of a square. The original mailroom is $(s \text{ ft})^2 = s^2 \text{ ft}^2$ or s^2 square feet.

Let $2s$ = length of the side of the new mailroom

The area is found by squaring the length of the side of a square. The new mailroom is $(2s \text{ ft})^2 = 2^2 s^2 \text{ ft}^2$ or $4s^2$ square feet.

Since the new mailroom is $4s^2 \text{ ft}^2$ and the original mailroom is $s^2 \text{ ft}^2$, the area of the new room is $\dfrac{4s^2 \text{ ft}^2}{s^2 \text{ft}^2} = 4$ times the area of the original room. ■

In Chapter P, we discussed scientific notation. Scientific notation is used to write very large numbers, which we encounter often in the field of science. Recall the following equivalences:

Standard Notation	Scientific Notation	Calculator Notation
2,340,000	2.34×10^6	2.34E6

At times, it is necessary to perform operations on these large numbers. The rules of exponents allow us to do so.

EXAMPLE 8   The Milky Way galaxy contains roughly 100 billion stars, one of which is the Sun. The galaxy is arranged in a huge disklike structure with a diameter of about 1×10^5 light-years. A light-year, the distance light travels in a year at the speed of 1.86×10^5 miles per second, is about 5.9×10^{12} miles per year. Approximate the length of the diameter of the Milky Way in miles.

Check

```
(1*10^5)(5.9*10^
12)
          5.9E17
(1E5)(5.9E12)
          5.9E17
```

Solution

To determine the length in miles, we will multiply the length in light-years by the number of miles in a light-year.

$$(1 \times 10^5 \text{ years})(5.9 \times 10^{12} \text{ miles per year}) = (1 \times 5.9) \times (10^5 \times 10^{12})\left(\text{years} \cdot \frac{\text{miles}}{\text{years}}\right)$$

$$= 5.9 \times (10^{5+12}) \times \text{miles}$$

$$= 5.9 \times 10^{17} \text{ miles}$$

We can check this result on the calculator by entering the problem two different ways. The diameter of the Milky Way is approximately 5.9×10^{17} miles. ■

APPLICATION

The American Bison once roamed the plains states of the United States. They migrated 213 to 395 miles south in the fall of the year and returned north in the spring.

a. Determine the home range (area over which the bison range) of a herd of bison in the summer if the average movement (in a straight line) is estimated as x miles.

b. In the winter the average movement is 1.8 times the summer distance. Determine the home range of a herd of bison in the winter.

c. Determine the ratio of the winter home range to the summer home range.

d. If the average movement in the summer is 2.5 miles, determine the summer home range and the winter home range of a herd of bison.

(continued on page 550)

Discussion

a. Let x = the number of miles of the average movement of the herd in the summer.

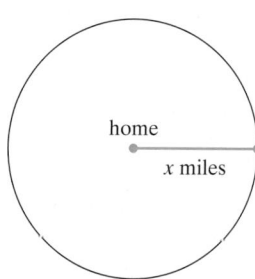

The home range is a circle with a radius of x miles. The area of a circle is $A = \pi r^2$.

$$A = \pi r^2$$
$$A = \pi(x \text{ mi})^2$$
$$A = \pi(x^2 \text{ mi}^2)$$
$$A = \pi x^2 \text{ mi}^2$$

The home range in the summer is πx^2 square miles.

b. Let $1.8x$ = the number of miles of the average movement of the herd in the winter. The area of movement is a circle with a radius of $1.8x$ miles yielding an area of $\pi(1.8x \text{ mi})^2 = \pi(1.8^2 x^2 \text{ mi}^2)$ or $3.24\pi x^2$ square miles.

c. The ratio of the amount of movement in the winter to the amount of movement in the summer is

$$\frac{3.24\pi x^2}{\pi x^2} = \frac{3.24}{1} \text{ or } 3.24 \text{ to } 1$$

In other words, the bison winter home range is 3.24 times its summer home range.

d. If the summer average movement is 2.5 miles, then the summer home range is

$$\pi x^2 = \pi(2.5)^2 = 6.25\pi \text{ square miles}$$

or approximately 19.6 square miles. The winter average movement is

$$3.24\pi x^2 = 3.24\pi(2.5)^2 = 20.25\pi \text{ square miles}$$

or approximately 63.6 square miles.

Objective 7.1.7 CHECKUP

1. A box has the shape of a cube, with each side measuring x inches. Determine the volume of the box. If another box is to be made with each side measuring half the length of the original box, determine the volume of the new box. Compare the volume of the original box with that of the new box. What are the two volumes if the first box has a side measuring 1.5 meters on a side?

2. In a study of the white-tailed deer population in the state of Nebraska, 23 tagged deer were recovered.
   a. Determine the area over which the white-tailed deer ranged if an average movement of x miles was recorded.
   b. In one extreme case, a deer was recovered at about three times the average distance. Determine the area over which this white-tailed deer ranged.

   c. Determine the ratio of the area covered by the deer in part **b** to the area covered by the deer in part **a**.
   d. If the average movement of a deer was 38 miles, determine the area ranged over by the deer for this average and the area ranged over by the deer in the extreme case.

3. It takes moonlight about $1\frac{1}{4}$ seconds to reach the Earth. If light travels at the rate of 1.86×10^5 miles per second, use the distance formula to estimate the distance to the moon in miles. Write your answer in scientific notation. Given that there are 5.28×10^3 feet in each mile, estimate the distance in feet, using scientific notation.

7.1 EXERCISES

 Student Solutions Manual   PH Math/Tutor Center   CD Video    MathXL®    MyMathLab   Interactmath.com

Write in expanded form.

1. $-3x^4$

2. $-4c^3$

3. $(-3x)^4$

4. $(-4c)^3$

5. $a^3 b^0 c^5$

6. $x^2 y z^0$

7. $\left(\frac{3}{4}\right)^3 \cdot x^2$

8. $\left(\frac{2}{3}\right)^2 \cdot x^3$

9. $5(x + y)^2$

10. $-4(p - q)^2$

Simplify.

11. $x^5 \cdot x^8$

12. $a^9 \cdot a^{14}$

13. $y \cdot y^{13}$

14. $b^{23} \cdot b$

15. $\frac{1}{2}x^2 \cdot x \cdot x^5$

16. $\frac{1}{3}y^2 \cdot y^3 \cdot y$

17. $(x + y)^4 (x + y)^2$

18. $(x - y)^5 (x - y)^3$

19. $(x + 3)^2(x + 3)$ **20.** $(x + 9)^{12}(x + 9)$ **21.** $\dfrac{p^{11}}{p^6}$ **22.** $\dfrac{a^5}{a^3}$

23. $\dfrac{54q^7}{18q}$ **24.** $\dfrac{39t^8}{13t}$ **25.** $\dfrac{(2x - 3)^8}{(2x - 3)^3}$ **26.** $\dfrac{(4x + 7)^9}{(4x + 7)^2}$

27. $\dfrac{-3(p + q)^2}{9(p + q)}$ **28.** $\dfrac{-5(xy + 2)^4}{10(xy + 2)}$ **29.** $(a^5)^6$ **30.** $(m^7)^4$

31. $(-3x)^4$ **32.** $(-5y)^3$ **33.** $2(3a)^2$ **34.** $3(2x)^2$

35. $(abc)^{21}$ **36.** $(xyz)^9$ **37.** $(5m^3)^3$ **38.** $(3k^4)^4$

39. $[(x + y)^3]^2$ **40.** $[(a + 2b)^4]^3$ **41.** $(x^2)^0$ **42.** $(x^0)^3$

43. $\left(\dfrac{b}{d}\right)^4$ **44.** $\left(\dfrac{m}{n}\right)^5$ **45.** $\left(\dfrac{3b}{c}\right)^4$ **46.** $\left(\dfrac{5y}{z}\right)^4$

47. $\left(\dfrac{-d}{2c}\right)^6$ **48.** $\left(\dfrac{-m}{3n}\right)^4$ **49.** $-7a^3b \cdot 5a^2b^4$ **50.** $-8c^4d^2 \cdot 3cd^5$

51. $\dfrac{15x^3y^2}{3xy^2}$ **52.** $\dfrac{18ab^2}{3ab}$ **53.** $\dfrac{-27ab^2c^3}{15bc}$ **54.** $\dfrac{-27p^3q^2s}{6ps}$

55. $\dfrac{-4x(4 - x)^4}{2(4 - x)}$ **56.** $\dfrac{5t^2(15 - 4t)^7}{15t(15 - 4t)^3}$ **57.** $\dfrac{(p^5q^7)^3}{p^6q}$ **58.** $\dfrac{(k^4m^6)^2}{k^3m}$

59. $\left(\dfrac{4x^3}{y^2}\right)^2$ **60.** $\left(\dfrac{5a^2}{7b}\right)^2$ **61.** $\left(\dfrac{-3p^4q^2}{p^2q}\right)^3$ **62.** $\left(\dfrac{-5c^2d^3}{cd^2}\right)^2$

63. $[(2a)^2]^5$ **64.** $[(-3t)^2]^2$ **65.** $\left[\left(\dfrac{x}{2y}\right)^2\right]^3$ **66.** $\left[\left(\dfrac{3z}{w}\right)^2\right]^3$

The following calculator screens are samples of checking simplifications numerically and graphically. Choose the correct series of screens that you would use to simplify the given expression and check the simplification numerically and graphically.

67. Simplify $(2x^2)^3$.

a.

b.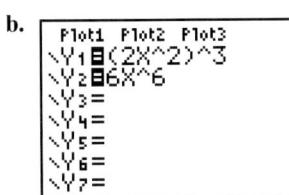

68. Simplify $\left(\dfrac{3x^2}{2x}\right)^3$.

a.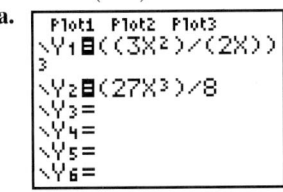

b.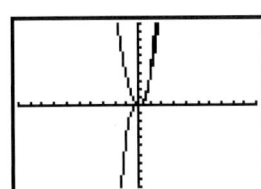

In exercises 69–78, check the simplifications numerically and graphically to determine whether they are correct.

69. $x^3 \cdot x^4 = x^7$ **70.** $x^2 \cdot x^5 = x^7$ **71.** $(3x^4)^2 = 9x^8$

72. $(5x^3)^2 = 25x^6$ **73.** $(3x^4)^2 = 9x^6$ **74.** $(5x^3)^2 = 25x^5$

75. $\left(\dfrac{8x^3}{2x^6}\right)^2 = \dfrac{16}{x^6}$ **76.** $\left(\dfrac{9x^2}{3x^5}\right)^2 = \dfrac{9}{x^6}$ **77.** $\left(\dfrac{8x^3}{2x^6}\right)^2 = \dfrac{16}{x^5}$ **78.** $\left(\dfrac{9x^2}{3x^5}\right)^2 = \dfrac{9}{x^9}$

Geometry

79. A child's square play area is enlarged by increasing each side by a factor of five. (That is, each side is multiplied by 5.) Write exponential expressions for the areas of the original play area and the enlarged play area. Compare the areas of the two squares. What are the two areas if the original area had a side of 6 feet?

80. A department store's square display area is enlarged by increasing each side by a factor of 2.5. Write exponential expressions for the areas of the original and the enlarged display areas. Compare the two areas. What are the two areas if the original area had a side of 12 feet?

81. A storage bin in the shape of a cube is enlarged by increasing each side by a factor of four. Write exponential expressions for the volume of the original bin and the enlarged bin. Compare the volumes of the two bins. What are the two volumes if the original bin had a side of 1.5 feet?

82. A block of ice with the shape of a cube begins to melt. Its size is decreased so that each side is 0.8 of its original length. Write exponential expressions for the volumes of the original cube of ice and the smaller cube of ice. Compare the volumes of the two cubes. What are the two volumes if the larger cube measured 22 inches on a side?

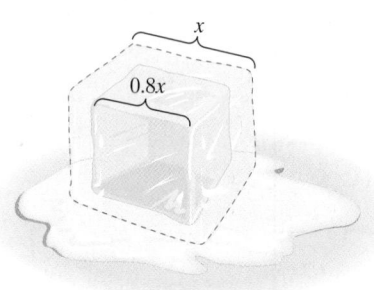

83. A hot-air balloon has the shape of a sphere with a radius of x feet. A second hot-air balloon also has the shape of a sphere, but with a radius that is twice the length of the first balloon. Write exponential expressions for the volumes of the two balloons. Compare the volumes of the balloons. What are the two volumes if the smaller balloon has a radius of 4 feet?

84. A company sells various sizes of exercise balls used in physical fitness conditioning. The company recommends a ball with a radius of x centimeters for a person who is less than 5 feet, 6 inches tall and one with a radius that is 1.5 times as large for a person that is over 6 feet, 5 inches tall. Write exponential expressions for the amount of leather it would take to make the exercise balls (the surface area of each ball). Compare the two surface areas. If the smaller exercise ball has a radius of 27 centimeters, what are the two surface areas?

85. An adult male mountain lion stakes out a home range by leaving markers along the edge. Generally, the cats respect the other's territorial rights.

   a. Determine the home range of an adult male mountain lion in an ideal habitat, such as the west side of the Sierra Nevada, if the average movement (in a straight line) is estimated as x miles.

   b. The average movement in the adult male mountain lion's average home range is 3 times the average movement in an ideal habitat. Determine the average home range of an adult male mountain lion.

   c. Determine the ratio of the average home range to the ideal habitat home range.

   d. If the average movement in an ideal habitat is 1.8 miles, determine the adult male mountain lion's home range in an ideal habitat and the average home range of an adult male mountain lion.

86. An adult female mountain lion has a smaller home range than the adult male mountain lion.

   a. Determine the home range of an adult female mountain lion in an ideal habitat, such as the west side of the Sierra Nevada, if the average movement (in a straight line) is estimated as x miles.

   b. The average movement in the adult female mountain lion's average home range is 1.8 times the average movement in an ideal habitat. Determine the average home range of an adult female mountain lion.

   c. Determine the ratio of the average home range to the ideal habitat home range.

   d. If the average movement in an ideal habitat is 1.1 miles, determine the adult female mountain lion's home range in an ideal habitat and the average home range of an adult female mountain lion.

Physics

87. An object with no initial velocity that starts from rest falls a distance of $9.8t^2$ meters in t seconds. How far will it fall in twice that time? How far will it fall in one-third of that time?

88. An object with no initial velocity that starts from rest falls a distance of $16x^2$ feet in x seconds. How far will it fall in triple that time? How far will it fall in one-half of that time?

89. In a resistor of resistance R with voltage V across it, the power is $\dfrac{V^2}{R}$. What will be the power if the voltage is tripled? What will be the power if the voltage is cut in half?

90. In physics the formula for transitional kinetic energy is $\dfrac{1}{2}mv^2$, where m is the mass of an object and v is its velocity. What is the kinetic energy if the velocity is quadrupled? What is the kinetic energy if the velocity is cut in half?

Scientific Notation

91. The Sun is approximately 2.8×10^4 light-years away from the center of the Milky Way galaxy. Given that a light-year is about 5.9×10^{12} miles, approximate the distance in miles from the Sun to the center of the Milky Way galaxy.

92. If all the stars in the galaxy were placed the same distance from Earth, Deneb would be the brightest star in the sky. Deneb is about 3.23×10^3 light-years away from Earth. Approximate this distance in miles.

93. A popular drug that lowers cholesterol was prescribed 1.8842×10^4 times in 2002. The average person takes 1.46×10^4 milligrams per year. How many total milligrams were prescribed in 2002?

94. According to the *Nutrition Business Journal*, there were 7.36×10^4 chiropractors in the United States in 2003. The average revenue for a chiropractor was 2.25×10^5 dollars in 2003. What were total revenues for chiropractors in this year?

95. To measure the way in which the gravitational fields of planets interact, it is sometimes necessary to square the distance between the planets. If the average distance between the Earth and Neptune is 2.75×10^9 miles, find the square of this distance.

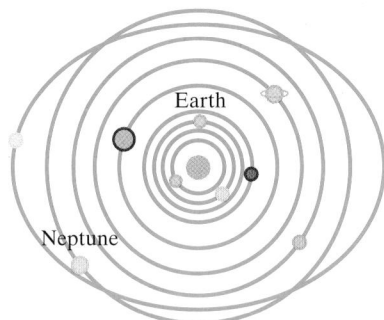

96. If the maximum distance between Pluto and the Sun is 4.6×10^9 miles, find the square of this distance.

97. The radius of the Sun is 6.96×10^5 km. If the Sun is spherical in shape, determine the volume of the Sun.

98. Jupiter is more than twice as massive as all the other planets combined (the mass of Jupiter is 318 times that of Earth). The radius of Jupiter is approximately 1.43×10^5 km. If Jupiter is spherical in shape, determine the volume of Jupiter.

99. A country music radio station broadcasts at a frequency of 107.7 MHz, or 107.7×10^6 cycles per second. Determine the wavelength of these radio waves in meters, by dividing the speed of light, 2.998×10^8 meters per second, by the number of cycles per second.

100. A classic rock radio station broadcasts at a frequency of 103.5 MHz. Using the preceding exercise as a guide, determine the wavelength of these radio waves in meters.

101. In 2002, a popular antidepressant had about 8.32×10^7 total milligrams prescribed. If the average person takes 9.125×10^3 milligrams per year, how many times was the drug prescribed in 2002?

102. According to the *Nutrition Business Journal*, there were 2.35×10^4 acupuncturists in the United States in 2003. The total revenue for people in this field was 2.52×10^9 dollars in 2003. What was the average revenue for an acupuncturist in this year?

 ## 7.1 Calculator Exercises

In this section, you learned how to check to see whether you had properly simplified an expression by using the TABLE or GRAPH features of your calculator. You were instructed to store the original expression in Y1 and the simplified expression in Y2 and then to view the table of values to see whether Y1 was equal to Y2 for each value of the variable, or to view the graphs to see whether they coincided. However, there is another way to use the TABLE or GRAPH features to check expressions.

Instead of storing the two expressions in Y1 and Y2, store both of them in Y1, using an equals sign, since they are presumed to be equivalent. Then, when you view the table, you should see a column of values all equal to 1, indicating that the two expressions are indeed equal to each other. If you see any values of 0 in the table for Y1, this indicates that the two expressions are not equal. Likewise, if you trace along the graph, you should see a horizontal line at Y1 = 1 for a correct simplification and a horizontal line at Y1 = 0 for an incorrect simplification. The calculator screens shown next are for the same example used in the text.

Is $\left(\frac{3}{5}x^3\right)^2 = \frac{9}{25}x^6$?

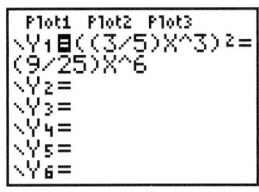 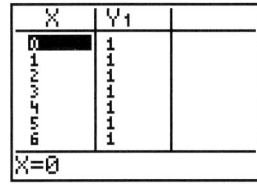

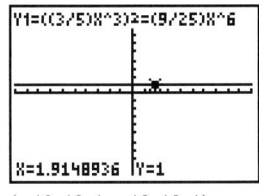

$(-10, 10, 1, -10, 10, 1)$

Use this method to check the following expressions for equivalence:

1. $x^4 \cdot x^5 = x^{20}$?   **2.** $x^4 \cdot x^5 = x^9$?   **3.** $(x^4)^5 = x^{20}$?
4. $(x^4)^5 = x^9$?   **5.** $(3x^4)^2 = 9x^8$?   **6.** $(3x^4)^2 = 9x^6$?

 ## 7.1 Writing Exercises

The rules of exponents sometimes yield results that may run contrary to your intuition. To help you deal with this, explain briefly why the following statements are true, and illustrate each with an example.

1. A negative number raised to an even power results in a positive number.

2. A negative number raised to an odd power results in a negative number.

3. When two exponential expressions have the same base, but different exponents, you may properly write their product as the base raised to the power of the sum of the exponents.

4. When two exponential expressions have different bases, but the same exponent, you may *not* properly write their product as the product of the bases raised to the power of the sum of the exponents.

7.2 OPERATIONS INVOLVING NEGATIVE EXPONENTS

OBJECTIVES

1 Write exponential expressions with negative exponents as equivalent expressions with positive exponents.

2 Simplify exponential expressions with negative exponents by using the rules of exponents.

3 Model real-world situations by using scientific notation.

APPLICATION

Experimental measurements reveal that the diameters of atoms range from 1.4×10^{-10} meters to 5.7×10^{-10} meters. Determine the volume of the smallest atom (assume that the atom is spherical in shape).

After completing this section, we will discuss this application further. See page 559.

Objective 7.2.1   Writing with Positive Exponents

In the last section, we limited our discussion of exponents to nonnegative integers. However, in Chapter P we defined exponential expressions with a numeric base raised to a negative exponent. To evaluate an exponential expression with a nonzero base raised to a negative exponent, rewrite the expression as an exponential expression with the reciprocal of the base and the opposite value of the exponent (a positive number). That is,

$$10^{-1} = \left(\frac{1}{10}\right)^1 = \frac{1}{10^1} = \frac{1}{10} \qquad \left(\frac{1}{10}\right)^{-2} = \left(\frac{10}{1}\right)^2 = 10^2 = 100$$

Remember that 0 raised to a negative exponent is undefined.

$$0^{-2} = \left(\frac{1}{0}\right)^2 = \frac{1^2}{0^2} = \frac{1}{0} \qquad \text{Division by zero is undefined.}$$

While we recognize that expressions with negative exponents are not polynomials, our work with polynomials can result in such expressions. Therefore, in this section, we will complete our discussion of exponential expressions involving integer exponents by discussing negative integer exponents with variable bases. Using the rules of exponents in the last section, we might obtain an expression involving negative exponents. For example, if we use the quotient rule, to simplify $\dfrac{x^3}{x^5}$, we obtain

$$\frac{x^3}{x^5} = x^{3-5} = x^{-2}$$

However, if we simplify $\dfrac{x^3}{x^5}$ by writing it first in expanded form, we obtain

$$\frac{x^3}{x^5} = \frac{x \cdot x \cdot x}{x \cdot x \cdot x \cdot x \cdot x} = \frac{1}{x \cdot x} = \frac{1}{x^2}$$

Therefore, $x^{-2} = \dfrac{1}{x^2}$. The same result is obtained by using the procedure that we used with numeric bases.

For all $x \neq 0$,

$$x^{-4} = \left(\frac{x}{1}\right)^{-4} = \left(\frac{1}{x}\right)^4 = \frac{1}{x^4}$$

$$\frac{1}{x^{-4}} = \frac{1}{\left(\frac{1}{x}\right)^4} = \frac{1}{\frac{1}{x^4}} = 1 \div \frac{1}{x^4} = 1 \cdot \frac{x^4}{1} = x^4$$

 TAKE NOTE As long as only factors are involved, a base with a negative exponent in the numerator is placed in the denominator and given a positive exponent equal to the absolute value of the original exponent. Also, a base with a negative exponent in the denominator is placed in the numerator and given a positive exponent equal to the absolute value of the original exponent.

$$\frac{a^{-n}}{b^{-m}} = \frac{b^m}{a^n}$$

In this text, we will assume that variables represent nonzero values, so that the given expressions are defined.

INTEGER EXPONENTS

For any base a and nonnegative integer exponent n,

$$a^{-n} = \frac{1}{a^n}, \text{ where } a \neq 0$$

$$\frac{1}{a^{-n}} = a^n, \text{ where } a \neq 0$$

The base a may be a constant, a variable, or an expression.

EXAMPLE 1   Write equivalent expressions with positive exponents.

a. $\dfrac{x^{-2}}{y^{-3}}$ **b.** $\dfrac{x^3 y^{-1}}{3^{-2} z^2}$ **c.** $a^3 b^{-2}$

Solution

a. $\dfrac{x^{-2}}{y^{-3}} = \dfrac{y^3}{x^2}$ Rewrite the factor x^{-2} from the numerator into the denominator as the factor x^2.
Rewrite the factor y^{-3} from the denominator into the numerator as the factor y^3.

b. $\dfrac{x^3 y^{-1}}{3^{-2} z^2} = \dfrac{3^2 x^3}{yz^2}$ Rewrite the factor y^{-1} from the numerator into the denominator as the factor y.
Rewrite the factor 3^{-2} from the denominator into the numerator as the factor 3^2.

$\qquad\qquad = \dfrac{9x^3}{yz^2}$ Evaluate 3^2.

c. $a^3 b^{-2} = \dfrac{a^3}{b^2}$ Move the factor b^{-2} into the denominator as the factor b^2.

 Objective 7.2.1 CHECKUP

1. Write each expression with positive exponents.

a. $\dfrac{x^{-4}}{y^{-2}}$ **b.** $\dfrac{5^{-2} a^4}{2^{-3} b^{-3}}$ **c.** $p^{-5} q^5$

2. If an exponential expression has factors with negative exponents, is it always possible to rewrite the expression with nonnegative exponents? Explain.

Objective 7.2.2   ## Simplifying Expressions

Assuming that the variables represent nonzero values so that the given expressions are defined, all of the rules of exponents that we introduced in the previous section are valid for expressions having negative exponents. A summary of these rules follows.

SUMMARY OF RULES FOR EXPONENTS

For any real numbers a and b and integers m and n,

$a^1 = a$	Exponent of one
$a^0 = 1, a \neq 0$	Exponent of zero
$a^m \cdot a^n = a^{m+n}$	Product rule for exponents
$\dfrac{a^m}{a^n} = a^{m-n}, a \neq 0$	Quotient rule for exponents
$(a^m)^n = a^{mn}$	Power-to-a-power rule for exponents
$(ab)^m = a^m b^m$	Product-to-a-power rule for exponents
$\left(\dfrac{a}{b}\right)^m = \dfrac{a^m}{b^m}, b \neq 0$	Quotient-to-a-power rule for exponents

EXAMPLE 2 Simplify and write with positive exponents. Check numerically or graphically.

a. $(2x^4)(-3x^{-2})$ **b.** $\dfrac{4x^{-2}}{8x^{-3}}$

Solution

a. $(2x^4)(-3x^{-2}) = [2 \cdot (-3)](x^4 x^{-2})$

$\qquad = -6x^{4+(-2)}$ *Product rule*

$\qquad = -6x^2$

Numeric Check

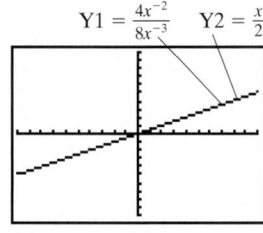

$Y1 = (2x^4)(-3x^{-2})$
$Y2 = -6x^2$
The values of Y1 = Y2.

b. $\dfrac{4x^{-2}}{8x^{-3}} = \left(\dfrac{4}{8}\right)\left(\dfrac{x^{-2}}{x^{-3}}\right)$

$\qquad = \dfrac{1}{2}x^{-2-(-3)}$ *Quotient rule*

$\qquad = \dfrac{1}{2}x^1$

$\qquad = \dfrac{1}{2}x,$ or $\dfrac{x}{2}$

Graphic Check

$Y1 = \dfrac{4x^{-2}}{8x^{-3}}$ $Y2 = \dfrac{x}{2}$

$(-10, 10, -10, 10)$

The graphs of Y1 and Y2 are the same. ■

TAKE NOTE We assume that the variables represent nonzero values so that the expressions are defined. Therefore, Y1 ≠ Y2 when $x = 0$ because Y1 is not defined when $x = 0$.

EXAMPLE 3 Simplify and write with positive exponents.

a. $(3x^{-3}y^4)^{-2}$ **b.** $(3x^2yz)(-4xy^{-2}z^{-1})$

c. $\dfrac{3^{-2}x^{-3}y}{3^{-1}xy^{-4}}$ **d.** $\left(\dfrac{-2a^3b^2}{ab^{-2}}\right)^3$

Solution

a. $(3x^{-3}y^4)^{-2} = 3^{-2}(x^{-3})^{-2}(y^4)^{-2}$ *Product-to-a-power rule*

$\qquad = \dfrac{1}{3^2}x^6y^{-8}$ *Power-to-a-power rule*

$\qquad = \dfrac{1}{9} \cdot x^6 \cdot \dfrac{1}{y^8}$ *Write with positive exponents.*

$\qquad = \dfrac{x^6}{9y^8}$

b. $(3x^2yz)(-4xy^{-2}z^{-1}) = [3 \cdot (-4)](x^2x)(yy^{-2})(zz^{-1})$

$\qquad = -12x^{2+1}y^{1+(-2)}z^{1+(-1)}$ *Product rule*

$\qquad = -12x^3y^{-1}z^0$

$\qquad = \dfrac{-12x^3}{y}$ *Write with positive exponents. Remember, $z^0 = 1$.*

c. $\dfrac{3^{-2}x^{-3}y}{3^{-1}xy^{-4}} = \left(\dfrac{3^{-2}}{3^{-1}}\right)\left(\dfrac{x^{-3}}{x}\right)\left(\dfrac{y}{y^{-4}}\right)$

$\qquad\qquad = 3^{-2-(-1)}x^{-3-1}y^{1-(-4)}$ Quotient rule

$\qquad\qquad = 3^{-1}x^{-4}y^{5}$

$\qquad\qquad = \dfrac{1}{3}\cdot\dfrac{1}{x^{4}}\cdot y^{5}$ Write with positive exponents.

$\qquad\qquad = \dfrac{y^{5}}{3x^{4}}$

d. $\left(\dfrac{-2a^{3}b^{2}}{ab^{-2}}\right)^{3} = \dfrac{(-2)^{3}(a^{3})^{3}(b^{2})^{3}}{a^{3}(b^{-2})^{3}}$ Product-to-a-power rule

           Quotient-to-a-power rule

$\qquad\qquad = \dfrac{-8a^{9}b^{6}}{a^{3}b^{-6}}$ Power-to-a-power rule

$\qquad\qquad = -8\cdot\dfrac{a^{9}}{a^{3}}\cdot\dfrac{b^{6}}{b^{-6}}$

$\qquad\qquad = -8a^{6}b^{12}$ Quotient rule ■

The quotient-to-a power rule may be generalized to the case where the exponent is negative. If the exponent is negative and we apply the rule, we obtain

$$\left(\dfrac{x}{y}\right)^{-4} = \dfrac{x^{-4}}{y^{-4}} = \dfrac{y^{4}}{x^{4}}$$

Since $\dfrac{y^{4}}{x^{4}}$ also equals $\left(\dfrac{y}{x}\right)^{4}$, it follows that $\left(\dfrac{x}{y}\right)^{-4} = \left(\dfrac{y}{x}\right)^{4}$.

The result is the reciprocal of the quotient, raised to the positive power. We will write a special rule for this case.

QUOTIENT-TO-A-NEGATIVE-POWER RULE

For any nonzero dividend and divisor a and b and integer exponent $m > 0$,

$$\left(\dfrac{a}{b}\right)^{-m} = \left(\dfrac{b}{a}\right)^{m} = \dfrac{b^{m}}{a^{m}}$$

The elements a and b may be constants, variables, or expressions.

For example,

$$\left(\dfrac{3}{4}\right)^{-2} = \left(\dfrac{4}{3}\right)^{2} = \dfrac{4^{2}}{3^{2}} = \dfrac{16}{9} \qquad\qquad \left(\dfrac{m}{n}\right)^{-3} = \left(\dfrac{n}{m}\right)^{3} = \dfrac{n^{3}}{m^{3}}$$

EXAMPLE 4   Simplify and write with positive exponents.

    a. $\left(\dfrac{m^{3}}{n^{2}}\right)^{-4}$ **b.** $\left(\dfrac{4xy^{-2}}{16x^{-3}y}\right)^{-2}$

Solution

a. $\left(\dfrac{m^3}{n^2}\right)^{-4} = \left(\dfrac{n^2}{m^3}\right)^{4}$ Quotient-to-a-negative-power rule

$= \dfrac{(n^2)^4}{(m^3)^4}$ Quotient-to-a-power rule

$= \dfrac{n^8}{m^{12}}$ Power-to-a-power rule

b. Before using the rules of exponents, simplify the quotient by writing it with positive exponents.

$\left(\dfrac{4xy^{-2}}{16x^{-3}y}\right)^{-2} = \left(\dfrac{x \cdot x^3}{4y \cdot y^2}\right)^{-2}$ Simplify. $\dfrac{4}{16} = \dfrac{1}{4}$

$= \left(\dfrac{x^4}{4y^3}\right)^{-2}$ Product rule

$= \left(\dfrac{4y^3}{x^4}\right)^{2}$ Quotient-to-a-negative-power rule

$= \dfrac{4^2(y^3)^2}{(x^4)^2}$ Quotient-to-a-power rule
Product-to-a-power rule

$= \dfrac{16y^6}{x^8}$ Power-to-a-power rule

◼

🖊 **TAKE NOTE** As in the case of simplifying positive exponents, the order the rules of exponents are applied may vary. The results will be the same.

 Objective 7.2.2 CHECKUP

In exercises 1–3, simplify and write with only positive exponents.

1. a. $\left(-\dfrac{2}{3}z^6\right)\left(-\dfrac{3}{4}z^{-8}\right)$ **b.** $\dfrac{15b^{-5}}{3b^{-4}}$

2. a. $(2a^{-1}b^3)^{-1}$ **b.** $\left(\dfrac{2}{3}a^3bc^{-2}\right)\left(\dfrac{3}{4}ab^{-4}c^2\right)$

c. $\dfrac{5^{-3}p^2q^{-4}}{5^{-6}pq^{-2}}$ **d.** $\left(\dfrac{-x^2y^3}{5xy^{-1}}\right)^3$

3. a. $\left(\dfrac{h^{-4}}{k^{-2}}\right)^{-3}$ **b.** $\left(\dfrac{8c^{-2}d}{12cd^{-3}}\right)^{-3}$

4. All monomials are exponential expressions, but not all exponential expressions are monomials. Explain.   ◼

Objective 7.2.3 Modeling the Real World

In Chapter P, we discussed scientific notation. In the last section, we discussed scientific notation involving positive exponents and very large numbers. In this section, we will discuss very small numbers written in scientific notation which involves negative exponents. Recall the following equivalences from Chapter P:

Standard Notation	Scientific Notation	Calculator Notation
0.000058	5.8×10^{-5}	5.8E-5

At times it is necessary to perform operations on these small numbers. The rules of exponents allow us to do so.

EXAMPLE 5   Experimental measurements reveal that the diameters of atoms range from 1.4×10^{-10} to 5.7×10^{-10} meters.

a. The size of atoms is usually described by their radius. Determine the range of the radii of atoms.

b. How many times longer is the radius of the largest atom than the smallest atom?

Solution

a. The diameter is twice the radius. To determine the radius we will divide the length of the diameter by 2.

Check

```
(1.4*10^-10)/2
            7E-11
(5.7*10^-10)/2
          2.85E-10
```

(**Note:** Convert the answers to scientific notation.)

$$\frac{1.4 \times 10^{-10}}{2} = \frac{1.4}{2} \times 10^{-10} = 0.7 \times 10^{-10}$$

$$= 7.0 \times 10^{-11}$$

Move the decimal one place to the right and add -1 to the exponent of -10.

$$\frac{5.7 \times 10^{-10}}{2} = \frac{5.7}{2} \times 10^{-10} = 2.85 \times 10^{-10}$$

```
(2.85*10^-10)/(7
.0*10^-11)
        4.071428571
```

b. To determine how many times longer the radius of the largest atom is than the smallest atom, divide the length of the largest radius by the length of the smallest radius.

$$\frac{2.85 \times 10^{-10}}{7.0 \times 10^{-11}} = \frac{2.85}{7.0} \times \frac{10^{-10}}{10^{-11}}$$

$$\approx 0.407 \times 10^{-10-(-11)} \quad \textit{Quotient rule for exponents}$$

$$\approx 0.407 \times 10^{1}$$

$$\approx 4.07$$

The radius of the largest atom is 4.07 times the length of the smallest radius. ■

APPLICATION

Experimental measurements reveal that the diameters of atoms range from 1.4×10^{-10} meters to 5.7×10^{-10} meters. Determine the volume of the smallest atom. (Assume that the atom is spherical in shape.)

Discussion

In Example 5, we determined the radius of the smallest atom to be 7.0×10^{-11} meters. The volume of a sphere is $V = \frac{4}{3}\pi r^3$.

$$V = \frac{4}{3}\pi r^3$$

$$V = \frac{4}{3}\pi(7.0 \times 10^{-11})^3 \qquad \textit{Substitute.}$$

$$V = \frac{4}{3}\pi[(7.0)^3 \times (10^{-11})^3] \qquad \textit{Product-to-a-power rule for exponents}$$

$$V = \frac{4}{3}\pi(7.0^3 \times 10^{-11\cdot3}) \qquad \textit{Power-to-a-power rule for exponents}$$

$$V = \frac{4}{3}\pi(343 \times 10^{-33}) \qquad \textit{Simplify.}$$

$$V = \frac{1372}{3}\pi \times 10^{-33} \qquad \textit{Simplify.}$$

$$V \approx 1436.76 \times 10^{-33} \text{ or } 1.437 \times 10^{-30}$$

Check

```
7.0*10^-11→R:(4/
3)πR³
       1.43675504E-30
```

The volume of the smallest atom is approximately 1.437×10^{-30} cubic meters.

✓ Objective 7.2.3 CHECKUP

1. The mass of a proton is 1.673×10^{-27} kg. The mass of an electron is 9.109×10^{-31} kg. How many times heavier is the mass of a proton than an electron?

2. Experimental measurements reveal that the diameters of atoms range from 1.4×10^{-10} meters to 5.7×10^{-10} meters. Determine the volume of the largest atom. ▪

7.2 EXERCISES

 Student Solutions Manual    PH Math/Tutor Center   CD Video   Math XL MathXL®   MyMathLab MyMathLab   Interactmath.com

In exercises 1–54, simplify. Write with positive exponents.

1. p^{-3}

2. q^{-2}

3. $\dfrac{1}{q^{-5}}$

4. $\dfrac{1}{p^{-3}}$

5. $\dfrac{p^{-3}}{q^{-5}}$

6. $\dfrac{q^{-2}}{p^{-3}}$

7. $\dfrac{d^4}{c^{-3}}$

8. $\dfrac{c^2}{d^{-5}}$

9. $\dfrac{5^{-2}h^3}{2^{-4}k^{-4}}$

10. $\dfrac{3^{-2}x^2}{4^{-3}y^{-3}}$

11. $p^{-3}q^5$

12. p^3q^{-2}

13. $(5a^3)(-4a^{-1})$

14. $(-6h^4)(-5h^{-2})$

15. $\dfrac{4m^{-2}}{16m^{-3}}$

16. $\dfrac{2y^{-3}}{12y^{-4}}$

17. $\dfrac{4^{-3}n^{-2}}{3^{-4}n^{-3}}$

18. $\dfrac{2^{-5}x^{-3}}{5^{-2}x^{-4}}$

19. $(c^{-4})^{-2}$

20. $(p^{-3})^{-2}$

21. $(5a^{-2}b^2)^{-3}$

22. $(5m^{-4}n^2)^{-2}$

23. $(-6p^3q)(7p^{-3}q^{-4})$

24. $(13x^3y)(3x^{-2}y^2)$

25. $(1.4x^2)(4.3x^3y^{-2})$

26. $(5.7yz)(2.7y^2z^{-1})$

27. $\left(\dfrac{3}{7}x^2y^{-1}\right)\left(\dfrac{14}{15}x^{-1}y^4\right)$

28. $\left(\dfrac{5}{9}a^3b^{-4}\right)\left(\dfrac{12}{25}a^{-2}b^2\right)$

29. $(3x^5yz)(-7xy^{-4}z^{-1})$

30. $(-2m^3pq^2)(4m^{-1}p^{-1}q)$

31. $\dfrac{m^{-2}}{m^5}$

32. $\dfrac{k^{-1}}{k}$

33. $\dfrac{-7c^{-5}}{21c^{-7}}$

34. $\dfrac{14d^{-2}}{20d^{-4}}$

35. $\dfrac{8x^2y}{2x^{-1}y^{-3}}$

36. $\dfrac{12cd^3}{4c^{-1}d^{-2}}$

37. $\dfrac{5^{-3}h^{-1}k}{5^{-2}hk^{-6}}$

38. $\dfrac{9^{-4}u^{-2}v^2}{9^{-3}u^3v^{-1}}$

39. $\dfrac{(3x^2)^4}{5x^{-3}}$

40. $\dfrac{(2a^3)^2}{3a^{-4}}$

41. $\left(\dfrac{a^{-3}b}{2ab^{-3}}\right)^3$

42. $\left(\dfrac{-cd^{-3}}{4c^{-2}d}\right)^3$

43. $\left(\dfrac{-4p^3q^2}{2pq^{-3}}\right)^5$

44. $\left(\dfrac{-8km^3}{4k^{-4}m^2}\right)^5$

45. $\left(\dfrac{a}{b}\right)^{-3}$

46. $\left(\dfrac{s}{t}\right)^{-1}$

47. $\left(\dfrac{4x}{y}\right)^{-3}$

48. $\left(\dfrac{3a}{b}\right)^{-5}$

49. $\left(\dfrac{-3p^2}{q^{-2}}\right)^{-4}$

50. $\left(\dfrac{-5c^3}{d^{-1}}\right)^{-2}$

51. $\left(\dfrac{y^{-1}}{z^{-2}}\right)^{-3}$

52. $\left(\dfrac{d^{-3}}{e^{-4}}\right)^{-2}$

53. $\left(\dfrac{5a^{-2}b}{25ab^{-3}}\right)^{-3}$

54. $\left(\dfrac{15s^2t^{-3}}{3s^{-1}t^4}\right)^{-4}$

The following calculator screens are samples of checking simplification numerically and graphically. Choose the correct series of screens that you would use to simplify the given expression and check the simplification numerically and graphically.

55. Simplify $\dfrac{3x^{-2}}{12x^{-5}}$.

a.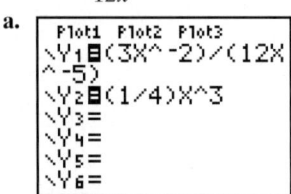

b.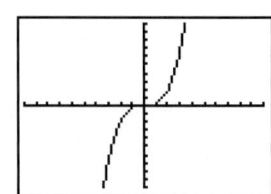

56. Simplify $(3x^{-2})(-5x^{-3})$.

a.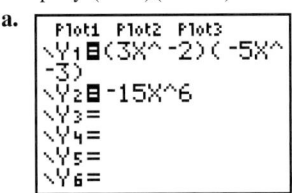

b.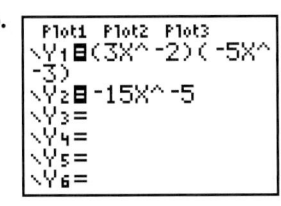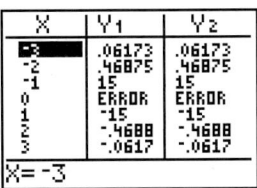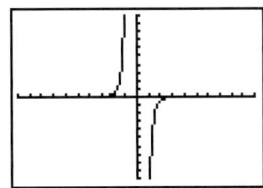

In exercises 57 and 58, simplify. Complete the following screens to check numerically and graphically.

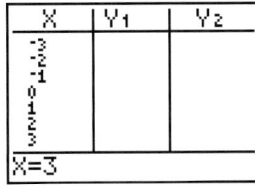 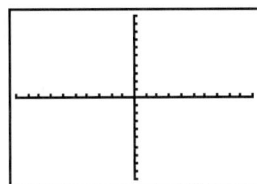

57. $\dfrac{5^{-2}a^{-4}}{3^{-3}a^{3}}$

58. $\left(\dfrac{-2^{-3}b}{3^{2}b^{3}}\right)^{-1}$

59. To convert millimeters to inches, multiply the number of millimeters by 3.937×10^{-2} inches per millimeter. Convert 6.8×10^{-4} millimeters to inches.

60. To convert quarts to liters, multiply the number of quarts by 9.46×10^{-1} liters per quart. Convert 2.3×10^{-5} quarts to liters.

61. One nanometer is 3.97×10^{-8} inches. How many inches in 0.001 nanometers? (Convert 0.001 to scientific notation.)

62. To convert square kilometers to square miles, multiply the number of square kilometers by 3.86×10^{-1} square miles per square kilometer. How many square miles in 0.0067 square kilometers?

63. A typed period in a standard textbook is about 500,000 nanometers in diameter. If a nanometer is 1×10^{-9} meters, how many meters long is a typed period in a textbook?

64. A glucose molecule is about 5×10^{-1} nanometers in diameter. How many meters long is a glucose molecule? (A nanometer is 1×10^{-9} meters.)

65. To convert inches to millimeters, divide the number of inches by 3.937×10^{-2} inches per millimeter. Convert 1.022×10^{-9} inches to millimeters.

66. To convert liters to quarts, divide the number of liters by 9.46×10^{-1} liters per quart. Covert 1.8×10^{-1} liters to quarts.

67. One nanometer is 3.97×10^{-8} inches. How many nanometers are there in one mile? (Write the number of inches in a mile in scientific notation.)

68. To convert square miles to square kilometers, divide the number of square miles by 3.86×10^{-1} square miles per square kilometer. How many square kilometers in 0.000001 square miles?

69. The state of Arizona produced 3384 million eggs in 2003 for a total production value of 3.4404×10^{8} dollars. What was the average price per egg in dollars? What was the average price per dozen?

70. According to the Food and Nutrition Board of the National Academy of Sciences, growing children need, on average, 8×10^{-4} kilograms of calcium each day. In a 30-day month, an eight-year-old boy consumed 2.6×10^{-2} kilograms of calcium as a part of his diet. Is he meeting the recommended daily amount of calcium?

71. The calculated atomic radius of a gold atom is 1.3×10^{-10} meters. Estimate the volume of the atom, assuming it is a sphere.

72. The calculated nuclear radius of a gold atom is 7.3×10^{-15} meters. Estimate the volume of the nucleus of a gold atom, assuming it is a sphere.

In exercises 73–76, answer the question based on this information. A protein is 5×10^{-9} meters in diameter. A bacterium is about 5×10^{-6} meters in diameter.

73. What is the ratio of the diameter of a bacterium to the diameter of a protein?

74. What is the ratio of the diameter of a protein to the diameter of a bacterium?

75. Assume a protein is spherical in shape; determine the volume of a protein.

76. Assume a bacterium is spherical in shape; determine the volume of a bacterium.

 7.2 Calculator Exercises

If you make a mistake when you are simplifying an exponential expression that has several steps, you may have difficulty finding the mistake. In 7.1 Calculator Exercises, you were shown how to

check that your simplified expression was equivalent to the original expression. If you made a mistake, you can check for equivalence step-by-step to find where the mistake was made.

For example, consider the following simplification, which has a mistake:

$$\left[\left(\frac{-2x^{-1}}{3x^{-2}}\right)^2\right]^{-3} = \left(\frac{-2x^{-1}}{3x^{-2}}\right)^{-6} =$$

$$\left(\frac{3x^{-2}}{-2x^{-1}}\right)^6 = \left(\frac{-2x}{3x^2}\right)^6 = \frac{64x^6}{729x^8} = \frac{64}{729x^2}$$

If you check the original expression against the rightmost simplification, you will see that the two aren't equivalent.

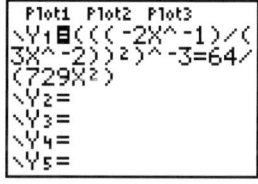
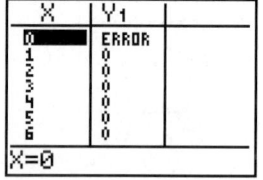

However, if you check step-by-step, you can see that the mistake occurred in the third step.

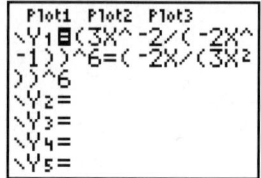
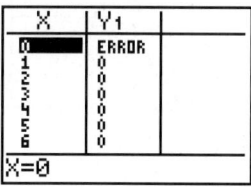

When you recheck your work, you see that

$$\left(\frac{3x^{-2}}{-2x^{-1}}\right)^6 = \left(\frac{-3x}{2x^2}\right)^6 = \frac{729x^6}{64x^{12}} = \frac{729}{64x^6}$$

and this simplification is equivalent to the original expression.

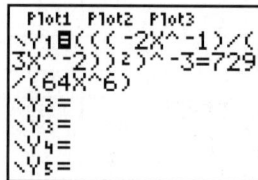
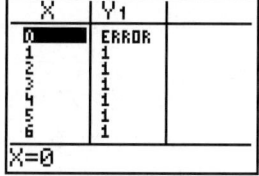

Use the preceding method to determine whether there is an error in each of the following exercises and in which step the error occurs:

1. $\left(\frac{3}{5}x^3\right)\left(\frac{5}{7}x^{-2}\right) = \left(\frac{3}{5}\cdot\frac{5}{7}\right)(x^3\cdot x^{-2}) = \left(\frac{3}{7}\right)(x^{-6}) = \frac{3}{7x^6}$

2. $(2x^{-3})^{-4} = 2^{-4}(x^{-3})^{-4} = \left(\frac{1}{2^4}\right)(x^{-7}) = \frac{1}{16x^7}$

3. $\left(\frac{x^{-4}}{3x}\right)^{-2} = \frac{(x^{-4})^{-2}}{3^{-2}x^{-2}} = \frac{x^8}{-6x^{-2}} = \frac{x^8x^2}{-6} = -\frac{x^{10}}{6}$

7.2 Writing Exercise

In the preceding calculator exercises, the TABLE check displays an error message when x is equal to zero. Explain why this is so.

7.3 POLYNOMIAL ADDITION AND SUBTRACTION

OBJECTIVES
1 Add polynomials.
2 Subtract polynomials.
3 Model real-world situations by using polynomials.

APPLICATION

Pyrotechnicians for the famous Boom's Day festival plan the grand finale with a large display of aerial shell fireworks. Assuming that only gravity has an effect on the shells, the height above ground level for an 8-inch shell shot at a velocity of 235 feet per second from a height of 5 feet is given by the function $s(t) = -16t^2 + 235t + 5$, where t is time in seconds. The height above ground level for a 10-inch shell shot at a velocity of 263 feet per second from a height of 5 feet is given by the function $s(t) = -16t^2 + 263t + 5$, where t is again time in seconds. Determine the difference in the height of the two shells after t seconds if the shells are shot at the same time.

After completing this section, we will discuss this application further. See page 565.

Objective 7.3.1 **Adding Polynomials**

To add two algebraic expressions, we used the distributive law to remove the parentheses and combined like terms. We will do the same for polynomials.

ADDITION OF POLYNOMIALS

To add polynomials enclosed in a set of parentheses,

- Use the distributive law to remove the parentheses.
- Combine like terms.

EXAMPLE 1   Add the polynomials $(2x^3 - 3x^2 + x - 5)$ and $(5x^3 - 3x^2 + 7)$.

Solution

$(2x^3 - 3x^2 + x - 5) + (5x^3 - 3x^2 + 7)$

$= 2x^3 - 3x^2 + x - 5 + 5x^3 - 3x^2 + 7$ Use the distributive law to remove the parentheses.

$= 7x^3 - 6x^2 + x + 2$ Combine like terms.

Sometimes it is easier to see the like terms if we align the polynomials in columns with like terms aligned. We can write missing addends with a coefficient of 0 to keep the columns complete.

$$
\begin{array}{r}
2x^3 - 3x^2 + x - 5 \\
+ \ 5x^3 - 3x^2 + 0x + 7 \\
\hline
7x^3 - 6x^2 + x + 2
\end{array}
$$

Numeric Check

X	Y1	Y2
0	2	2
1	4	4
2	36	36
3	140	140
4	358	358
5	732	732
6	1304	1304

X=0

$Y1 = (2x^3 - 3x^2 + x - 5) + (5x^3 - 3x^2 + 7)$
$Y2 = 7x^3 - 6x^2 + x + 2$
The values for Y1 = Y2.

Graphic Check

$Y1 = (2x^3 - 3x^2 + x - 5) + (5x^3 - 3x^2 + 7)$
$Y2 = 7x^3 - 6x^2 + x + 2$

$(-10, 10, -10, 10)$
The graphs of Y1 and Y2 are the same.

EXAMPLE 2   Add.

$$(6x^2y + 4x^2 - xy^2 + xy) + (5xy + 6x^2 - x^2y^3)$$

Solution

$(6x^2y + 4x^2 - xy^2 + xy) + (5xy + 6x^2 - x^2y^3)$

$= 6x^2y + 4x^2 - xy^2 + xy + 5xy + 6x^2 - x^2y^3$ Use the distributive law to remove the parentheses.

$= 6x^2y - x^2y^3 - xy^2 + 6xy + 10x^2$ Combine like terms.

Aligned in columns, the result is as follows:

$$
\begin{array}{r}
6x^2y + \ 4x^2 - xy^2 + \ xy \\
+ \qquad\quad 6x^2 \qquad\quad + 5xy - x^2y^3 \\
\hline
6x^2y + 10x^2 - xy^2 + 6xy - x^2y^3
\end{array}
$$

Align like terms.

✓ Objective 7.3.1 **CHECKUP**

In exercises 1 and 2, add as indicated.

1. Add $(3x^3 + 2x^2 - 5x + 7)$ and $(5x^3 - 5x^2 + 2 + 4x)$.

2. $(3x^3 + 2x^2y - 4xy^2 + y^3) + (4y^3 - 3xy^2 - 3x^2y + 4x^3)$

3. Explain what is meant by "combining like terms."

Objective 7.3.2 Subtracting Polynomials

To subtract algebraic expressions, we used the distributive law to remove the parentheses by taking the opposite of the subtrahend, added the opposite of the subtrahend to the minuend, and combined like terms. We will do the same for polynomials.

SUBTRACTION OF POLYNOMIALS

To subtract polynomials enclosed in a set of parentheses,

- Remove the parentheses. Use the distributive property and take the opposite of the terms within the subtrahend.
- Combine like terms.

EXAMPLE 3 Subtract the polynomial $(5x^3 - 3x^2 + 7)$ from the polynomial $(2x^3 - 3x^2 + x - 5)$.

Solution

$$(2x^3 - 3x^2 + x - 5) - (5x^3 - 3x^2 + 7)$$

$$= 2x^3 - 3x^2 + x - 5 - 5x^3 + 3x^2 - 7 \quad \text{Remove the parentheses. (Take the opposite of the subtrahend.)}$$

$$= -3x^3 + x - 12 \quad \text{Combine like terms.}$$

To use columnar subtraction, align like terms. However, remember to take the opposite of the subtrahend before adding.

$$
\begin{array}{r}
2x^3 - 3x^2 + x - 5 \\
-(5x^3 - 3x^2 + 0x + 7) \\
\end{array}
\quad \text{or} \quad
\begin{array}{r}
2x^3 - 3x^2 + x - 5 \\
-5x^3 + 3x^2 - 0x - 7 \\
\hline
-3x^3 + x - 12 \\
\end{array}
\quad \text{Change signs and add.}
$$

Numeric Check

X	Y1	Y2
0	-12	-12
1	-14	-14
2	-34	-34
3	-90	-90
4	-200	-200
5	-382	-382
6	-654	-654

X=0

$Y1 = (2x^3 - 3x^2 + x - 5) - (5x^3 - 3x^2 + 7)$
$Y2 = -3x^3 + x - 12$
The values for Y1 = Y2.

Graphic Check

$Y1 = (2x^3 - 3x^2 + x - 5) - (5x^3 - 3x^2 + 7)$
$Y2 = -3x^3 + x - 12$

$(-47, 47, -31, 31)$
The graphs of Y1 and Y2 are the same.

EXAMPLE 4 Subtract.

$$(6x^2y + 4x^2 - xy^2 + xy) - (5xy + 6x^2 - x^2y^3)$$

Solution

$$(6x^2y + 4x^2 - xy^2 + xy) - (5xy + 6x^2 - x^2y^3)$$

$$= 6x^2y + 4x^2 - xy^2 + xy - 5xy - 6x^2 + x^2y^3 \quad \text{Take the opposite of the subtrahend.}$$

$$= 6x^2y - 2x^2 + x^2y^3 - xy^2 - 4xy \quad \text{Combine like terms.}$$

Aligned in columns, the result is as follows:

$$
\begin{array}{r}
6x^2y + 4x^2 - xy^2 + xy \\
-(6x^2 + 5xy - x^2y^3) \\
\end{array}
\quad \text{or} \quad
\begin{array}{r}
6x^2y + 4x^2 - xy^2 + xy \\
- 6x^2 - 5xy + x^2y^3 \\
\hline
6x^2y - 2x^2 - xy^2 - 4xy + x^2y^3 \\
\end{array}
$$

Objective 7.3.2 CHECKUP

In exercises 1 and 2, subtract as indicated.

1. Subtract $(5a^2 - 2 + 6a)$ from $(6a + 13 - 2a^2 + a^3)$.

2. $(4a^4 + 3a^3b - 7a^2b^2 + 9ab^3 - 3b^4) - (2a^2b^2 + 4ab^3 - 5b^4)$

3. In subtracting polynomials, which polynomial is the subtrahend, and why must you take the opposite of each term of the subtrahend when removing its parentheses? Why do you not have to perform this operation in adding two polynomials? ◼

Objective 7.3.3   Modeling the Real World

Many business relations may be defined as a polynomial. Three such relations are the revenue function, the total cost function, and the profit function. We discussed the relationship of these functions to one another in previous chapters. We know that the total cost is found by adding all of the costs of manufacturing and advertising the product. We also know that the profit may be found by subtracting the total cost of an item from the revenue received from the same number of items. Therefore, it is very important to know how to perform the operations of addition and subtraction of polynomials to be able to work with these functions.

EXAMPLE 5

The cost of manufacturing x items is given by the function $m(x) = 4.95x + 231$. The cost of advertising and distributing for the same x items is given by the function $a(x) = 0.50x + 125$. Write a total cost function for x items. Each item sells for $12.00. Write a revenue function, $R(x)$. Write a profit function for x items.

Solution

The total cost of x items, $C(x)$, is the sum of the manufacturing costs and the advertising and distributing costs.

$$C(x) = m(x) + a(x)$$
$$C(x) = (4.95x + 231) + (0.50x + 125)$$
$$C(x) = 5.45x + 356$$

The revenue received for x items, $R(x)$, is the product of the selling price and the number of items, x.

$$R(x) = 12.00x$$

The profit on x items, $P(x)$, is the difference of the revenue and the total cost.

$$P(x) = R(x) - C(x)$$
$$P(x) = 12.00x - (5.45x + 356)$$
$$P(x) = 12.00x - 5.45x - 356 \qquad \text{Change the signs to subtract.}$$
$$P(x) = 6.55x - 356$$

◼

APPLICATION

Pyrotechnicians for the famous Boom's Day festival plan the grand finale with a large display of aerial shell fireworks. Assuming that only gravity has an effect on the shells, the height above ground level for an 8-inch shell shot at a velocity of 235 feet per second from a height of 5 feet is given by the function $s(t) = -16t^2 + 235t + 5$, where t is time in seconds. The height above ground level for a 10-inch shell shot at a velocity of 263 feet per second from a height of 5 feet is given by the function $s(t) = -16t^2 + 263t + 5$, where t is again time in seconds. Determine the difference in the height of the two shells after t seconds if the shells are shot at the same time.

(continued on page 566)

Discussion

The difference in height of the two shells is

$$(-16t^2 + 263t + 5) - (-16t^2 + 235t + 5)$$
$$= -16t^2 + 263t + 5 + 16t^2 - 235t - 5 \quad \text{Change the signs to subtract.}$$
$$= 28t$$

The difference in the height is $28t$ feet, within the domains of the two functions.

 Objective 7.3.3 **CHECKUP**

1. Sybil sells box lunches from a booth in the town square. She pays the town council $15.00 per day to use the booth and $0.25 per box lunch for permission to sell on the square. Her box lunches cost $1.25 each to prepare. She sells the box lunches for $4.50 each.
   a. Write a daily total cost function, $C(x)$.
   b. Write a daily revenue function, $R(x)$.
   c. Write a daily profit function, $P(x)$.

2. A projectile is shot upwards with an initial velocity of 220 feet per second from a tower that is 60 feet above ground. The distance of the projectile from the ground is given by the polynomial function $s(t) = -16t^2 + 220t + 60$, where t is the number of seconds after launch. Another projectile is shot upwards at the same time from ground level with an initial velocity of 200 feet per second. The distance of this projectile from the ground is given by the polynomial function $s(t) = -16t^2 + 200t$. Determine the difference in heights of the two projectiles after t seconds.

7.3 EXERCISES

 Student Solutions Manual    PH Math/Tutor Center   CD Video   *Math*XL MathXL®   **MyMathLab** MyMathLab   Interactmath.com

In exercises 1 and 2, add. Complete the following screens to check numerically and graphically.

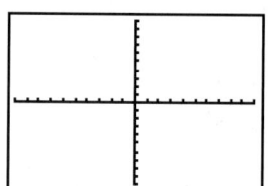

1. Add $(2x^2 - 2x + 3)$ and $(x^4 + 3x^2 + 1)$.

2. Add $(b^3 + 2b^2 + 5b)$ and $(b^2 - b + 2)$.

Add the polynomials as indicated.

3. $(5x^4 + 6x + 3x^3 - 2x^2 - 12) + (4x^4 + 21 - 8x^2 - 9x)$

4. $(-z^3 + z + z^2 + 1) + (2z^3 + 5 + 4z)$

5. Add $(5x^2y - 3xy^2 + 6y^3)$ and $(15x^3 - 8x^2y + 3xy^2)$.

6. Add $(3a^3 + 5a^2b - 2ab^2 + 6b^3)$ and $(b^3 + ab^2 + a^2b + a^3)$.

7. Add $(6 - 7a^3 + 3a^2 - 5a)$, $(6a + 8a^3 + 2)$, and $(5a^2 - 8a - 9)$.

8. Add $(x + 5 + x^2)$, $(2x^2 - 4x)$, and $(3x + 7)$.

9. $\left(\frac{2}{3}y^4 + \frac{1}{6}y^3 + 3y^2 - \frac{1}{3}y + \frac{5}{9}\right) + \left(\frac{7}{3}y^3 - \frac{8}{9}y^2 + \frac{5}{6}y - 3\right)$

10. $\left(\frac{5}{6}x^3 + \frac{17}{24} - \frac{1}{2}x^2 - \frac{3}{4}x\right) + \left(\frac{7}{8} + \frac{1}{4}x^3 - \frac{1}{6}x^2 + \frac{1}{2}x\right)$

11. $(12.07x^3 + 8.6x^2 - 3.19x + 14) + (6.7x^3 - 9.83x^2 + 7x - 4.265)$

12. $(5.1y^2 - 3.6y + 0.8y^3 - 3.7) + (4 - 0.8y - 0.1y^3 + 1.1y^2)$

13. Add $(4756a^3 - 3219a^2 - 1816a + 2083)$ and $(361a^3 + 54217a^2 + 12)$.

14. Add $(509b - 471b^3 + 211 + 54b^2)$ and $(471b^3 - 509b - 4b^2 - 11)$.

15. $(3a + 4b) + (5b + 6c)$

16. $(5x + 7y) + (-6y + 11z)$

In exercises 17 and 18, subtract. Complete the following screens to check numerically and graphically.

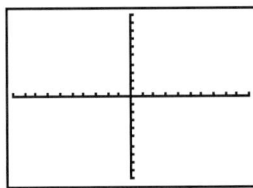

17. $(5z^3 + 2z^2 - 3z + 4) - (3z^3 + z - 2)$

18. $(a^3 - 5a^2 - 4a + 1) - (a^3 - 2a^2 + a - 5)$

Subtract the polynomials as indicated.

19. $(a^5 - 9) - (a^5 - a^4 + a^3 - a^2 + a - 9)$

20. $(b^9 + b^7 + b^5 + b^3 + b + 15) - (b^9 + 15)$

21. Subtract $(12x + 7 + 9x^2)$ from $(16x^2 - 32 + 9x)$.

22. Subtract $(11y^3 + 3 + y^2 - 6y)$ from $(6y^3 - 8 + 2y + y^2)$.

23. $(13a^3 - 6a^2 + 11)$ minus $(12a - 3 + 18a^3)$

24. $(15 + 3x + 6x^3)$ minus $(5x^3 + 2x^2 + 6)$

25. $(42x^3 + 17x^2y + 3xy^2 + 23y^3)$ decreased by $(47x^2y + 12y^3)$

26. $(51p^3 + 18p^2q - 7pq^2 + 41q^3)$ decreased by $(9pq^2 - 8p^2q - 10)$

27. $(4a + 7c)$ decreased by $(2b + 6d)$

28. $(12x + 17y)$ decreased by $(12y - 8z)$

29. $\left(\frac{5}{7}x^2 + \frac{8}{21}x - \frac{11}{14}\right) - \left(\frac{1}{2}x^2 + \frac{5}{6}x + \frac{19}{42}\right)$

30. $\left(\frac{2}{3}x^3 - \frac{17}{24}x + \frac{5}{8}x^2\right) - \left(\frac{3}{8}x^3 + \frac{1}{6}x^2 - \frac{11}{24}x + \frac{1}{3}\right)$

31. Subtract $(12.2x^3 - 0.1x^2y + 0.78xy^2 + 13.07y^3)$ from $(21.2x^3 + 0.9x^2y - 13.22xy^2 + 81.07y^3)$.

32. Subtract $(4.6x^2 + 9.3xy + 17.02y^2)$ from $(7.08x^2 - 3.21xy + 8.27y^2)$.

33. $(5062z^2 - 106z + 8295)$ minus $(379z^2 + 4297z + 1108)$

34. $(476b^3 + 178b^2 - 471b + 972)$ minus $(562b^3 + 873b - 619)$

Business

35. Philbert's Pots has a production process with a fixed setup cost of $200.00 each time a production run is made. It costs $2.50 for the labor to produce a single pot. The cost of materials is $2.00 per pot.

a. Determine the cost function $C(x)$ for producing a run of x pots.
b. If the pots can be sold for $13.50 each, determine the revenue function $R(x)$ for selling x pots.
c. Determine the profit function, $P(x)$.

d. What is the profit if 20 pots are produced and sold? What if 30 pots are produced and sold?

36. America's Best Cellular, Incorporated, has a production process to manufacture ABC cellular phones with a setup cost of $500. The cost of labor and materials for each phone is $20.
a. Determine the cost function for producing a run of x cellular phones.
b. The cellular phones sell for a price of $50. Determine the revenue function for selling x phones.
c. Determine the profit function.
d. What is the profit if 75 phones are sold? What is it if 100 phones are sold?

37. Shonda bakes gourmet cakes and sells them as a business venture. Her records show that the cost of baking x cakes is given by the function $b(x) = 3.50x + 25$. The cost of delivering x cakes to the customer is given by $d(x) = 1.50x + 5$. Write a total cost function for x cakes. The cakes sell for $28.50 each. Write a revenue function, $R(x)$. Write a profit function for x cakes baked and sold.

38. Faouzi prints and assembles trivia desk calendars and sells them. The cost of printing and assembling x calendars is given by the function $a(x) = 125 + 1.25x$. The cost of advertising and distributing the calendars is given by $d(x) = 0.55x + 55$. Write a total cost function for printing and distributing x calendars. The calendars sell for $11.95 each. Write the revenue function, $R(x)$. Write a profit function for x calendars distributed and sold.

Geometry

39. The area of an L-shaped room is determined by dividing the room into two rectangles. The areas of the rectangles are $(x^2 + x - 2)$ square feet and $(2x^2 - x - 1)$ square feet. Determine the area of the room.

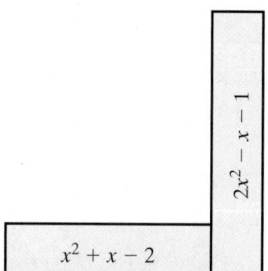

40. The area of a T-shaped room is determined by dividing the room into two rectangles. The areas of the rectangles are $(x^2 + 5x + 6)$ square feet and $(2x^2 + x - 3)$ square feet. Determine the area of the room.

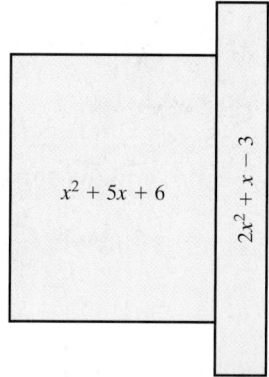

41. Jody's yard is enclosed by a fence with an area of $(2x^2 + 31x + 110)$ square feet. The area of the swimming pool within the yard is $(2x^2 + x)$ square feet. Determine the area enclosed by the fence that is not covered by the pool. (Jody wants to finish this area in concrete.)

42. Cushena purchased a home with a storage building in the corner of his back yard. The area covered by the storage building is $(2x^2 + x)$ square feet. The area of his back yard is $(12x^2 + 19x + 5)$ square feet. Determine the area of his back yard not covered by his storage building. (Cushena needs to buy enough grass seed to sow this area.)

Vertical Distance

43. At a sporting event, a fireworks shell is shot upward with an initial velocity of 240 feet per second from the top of the stadium, a height of 100 feet. At the same time, another shell is shot upward from ground level with an initial velocity of 250 feet per second. After t seconds, the height above ground level for the first shell is given by the function $s(t) = -16t^2 + 240t + 100$, and the height above ground level for the second shell is given by $s(t) = -16t^2 + 250t$. Determine the difference in the height of the shells after t seconds.

44. A signal flare is shot upward at a velocity of 180 feet per second from a tower that is 40 feet above ground. A second flare is shot upward from ground level at a velocity of 150 feet per second. After t seconds, the height above ground-level of the first flare is given by $s(t) = -16t^2 + 180t + 40$, and the height above ground level of the second flare is given by $s(t) = -16t^2 + 150t$. Determine the difference in the height of the flares after t seconds if they are shot at the same time.

Real Data

45. According to statistics published by the U.S. Department of Education, National Center of Education Statistics, the average cost at 2-year institutions of undergraduate tuition, room and board, and fees, $c(x)$, in dollars, can be estimated by the third-degree polynomial function $c(x) = 45.17x^3 - 168x^2 + 239.83x + 5291$, where x is number of years after 1998. The average cost of education at 4-year institutions is also increasing. The cost of undergraduate tuition, room and board, and fees, $c(x)$, in dollars, can be estimated by the third-degree polynomial function $c(x) = 6.83x^3 + 32.5x^2 + 424.67x + 11,888$, where x is number of years after 1998. Determine how much more the average cost of education at a 4-year institution is than the average cost of education at a 2-year institution in year x.

46. The United States has an aging population. Using statistics from the U.S. Bureau of the Census, the percent of the population that is between 45 and 64 years of age can be estimated by the third-degree polynomial function $p(x) = -0.0003x^3 + 0.0313x^2 - 0.3820x + 19.6$, where x is number of years after 1980. The percent of the population 65 and over, $p(x)$, can be estimated by the third-degree polynomial function $p(x) = 0.0003x^3 - 0.003x^2 + 0.137x + 11.3$, where x is number of years after 1980. Determine the difference of the percent of population that is between 45 and 64 years of age less the percent of population that is 65 and over in year x.

47. Based on data from the Bureau of the Census, Foreign Trade Division, the number of passenger cars imported to the United States from Mexico can be estimated by the function $M(t) = -74,147t^2 + 502,360t + 22,099$, where t is the number of years after 1998. The number of passenger cars imported to the United States from Germany can be estimated by the function $G(t) = -46,649t^2 + 406,864t - 306,623$, where t is the number of years after 1998. Find the difference of these two functions, $M(t) - G(t)$, in year t.

48. The number of passenger cars imported to the United States from France can be estimated by the function $F(t) = 45t^2 - 257t + 458$, where t is the number of years after 1998. The number of passenger cars imported to the United States from Sweden can be estimated by the function $S(t) = 18,397t^2 - 133,509t + 327,393$, where t is the number of years after 1998. Find the difference of these two functions, $F(t) - S(t)$, in year t.

49. Data from the Bureau of the Census, U.S. Department of Commerce, indicate that the percentage of foreign-born population in the United States has fluctuated since 1900. The percentage of foreign born for the first part of the century can be estimated by the function $p(x) = -0.013x^2 + 0.24x + 13.6$, where x is the number of years after 1900. The percentage of foreign-born population for the second half of the century can be estimated by the function $p(x) = 0.011x^2 - 1.5x + 55.8$, where x is the number of years after 1900. For a comparison in the middle part of the century, find the difference of the first part of the century less the second half in year x.

50. Statistics from the U.S. Bureau of the Census indicate that some states are experiencing a population shift. The population density of Florida, in people per square mile, can be estimated by the function $P(x) = -0.014x^2 + 6.1x + 180$, where x is the number of years after 1980. The population density of North Dakota, in people per square mile, can be estimated by the function $P(x) = 0.0005x^2 - 0.015x + 9.4$, where x is the number of years after 1980. Find the difference of the population density of Florida minus the population density of North Dakota in year x.

51. Use the following table of data from the U.S. Department of Commerce to generate quadratic polynomials for the number of males, $m(x)$, and the number of females, $f(x)$, in the United States, where x is the number of years after 2000. Find the difference of the functions, $f(x) - m(x)$, in year x.

Year	Number of Males (in thousands)	Number of Females (in thousands)
2001	140,009	145,085
2002	141,533	146,441
2003	143,037	147,773

52. The averages of the batting champions of the National League, $N(x)$, and American League, $A(x)$, are summarized in the table below. Create quadratic functions for each league in which the batting average is given for x years after 2002. Find the difference of the functions, $N(x) - A(x)$, in year x.

Year	National League	American League
2002	.370	.349
2003	.359	.326
2004	.362	.372

7.3 Calculator Exercises

When you are checking your addition and subtraction of polynomials on the calculator, you may want to store the original polynomial in Y1 and the resulting polynomial in Y2. Rather than checking that the TABLE values are equal for Y1 and Y2 or checking that the graphs coincide, you can store Y1 = Y2 in Y3 instead and check to see whether the TABLE values of Y3 are always equal to 1. Likewise, you can check to see that tracing the graph of Y3 is a horizontal line, where Y3 = 1. An example follows.

Is $(3x^3 - x^2 + 4x - 5) + (3x^2 - 5x + 7) = 3x^3 + 2x^2 - x + 2$?

The screens for this method of checking follow.

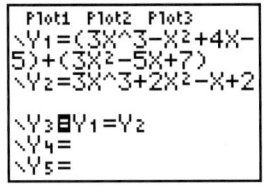
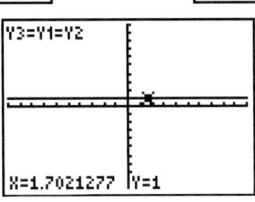

$(-10, 10, 1, -10, 10, 1)$

Note that the expressions in Y1 and Y2 have been "turned off" so that they will not be displayed on the table or graph. To turn them off, move the cursor over the equals sign for Y1 and for Y2, and press ENTER . This will remove the black box around the equals sign, which indicates that it is turned off.

Note also that, to type the expression into Y3, you will need to press the VARS key, move the cursor rightwards to Y-VARS, press 1 for Function, and then press 1 for Y1 or 2 for Y2.

Perform the following additions and subtractions of polynomials, and then check your results on the calculator, using the method just set out.

1. Add $(2x^4 + 4x^2 - 3x + 12)$ and $(3x^3 - 5x^2 + 7x - 9)$.

2. Add $(5.6x^3 + 1.17x^2 - 0.45x + 2.6)$ and $(4.1x^4 - 0.3x^2 + 1.9x + 2.33)$.

3. Subtract $(5x^5 - 3x^2 + 7x - 4)$ from $(3x^4 + 2x^3 - 3x^2 - 2x + 8)$.

4. Subtract $\left(\dfrac{2}{3}x^2 + \dfrac{5}{6}x - \dfrac{4}{9}\right)$ from $\left(\dfrac{5}{6}x^3 + \dfrac{1}{2}x^2 - \dfrac{7}{9}x + 4\right)$.

7.3 Writing Exercises

In this section, you were asked to subtract polynomials. The directions were stated several different ways. You must be careful that you correctly determine which polynomial is being subtracted from which. For example, if you are asked to subtract $(5x^2 - 6)$ from $(11x^2 - 2x + 3)$, which of the following expressions is the correct one?

1. $5x^2 - 6 - 11x^2 - 2x + 3$

2. $11x^2 - 2x + 3 - 5x^2 - 6$

3. $(5x^2 - 6) - (11x^2 - 2x + 3)$

4. $(11x^2 - 2x + 3) - (5x^2 - 6)$

Explain why you think a particular expression is the correct one. Then describe the error(s) in the other three expressions.

7.4 POLYNOMIAL MULTIPLICATION

OBJECTIVES
1. Multiply by a monomial.
2. Multiply two binomials.
3. Multiply polynomials of two or more terms.
4. Multiply polynomials, resulting in special products.
5. Simplify polynomials involving addition, subtraction, and multiplication.
6. Model real-world situations by using polynomials.

APPLICATION

The design of a swimming pool calls for its length to be twice its width. A 5-foot concrete walkway surrounds the pool. Determine a function, $A(w)$, for the area covered by the walkway.

After completing this section, we will discuss this application further. See page 577.

Objective 7.4.1 Multiplying with Monomials

We are ready to begin multiplication of polynomials. We start by multiplying two monomials. Remember that we multiplied algebraic expressions with one term by using the commutative and associative properties to rearrange the factors. We also used the rules for exponents discussed in Section 7.1 to help simplify the products. Recall, too, that we multiplied expressions when one factor had more than one term, using the distributive law. We do the same when multiplying a polynomial by a monomial.

PRODUCTS WITH A MONOMIAL FACTOR

To multiply a monomial by a monomial, use the commutative and associative properties to rearrange factors. Simplify, using the rules of exponents.

To multiply a polynomial with more than one term by a monomial, use the distributive law. Simplify, using the rules of exponents.

EXAMPLE 1

Multiply.

a. $(5x^2y)(-3xy)$ 　　　　　　　　　　　　　　**b.** $2x^2(x - y + 2z)$

Solution

Note that we did monomial multiplication in Section 7.1.

a. $(5x^2y)(-3xy) = 5 \cdot x^2 \cdot y \cdot -3 \cdot x \cdot y$
$$= 5 \cdot -3 \cdot x^2 \cdot x \cdot y \cdot y$$
$$= -15 \cdot x^{2+1} \cdot y^{1+1} \qquad \text{Product rule}$$
$$= -15x^3y^2$$

b. $2x^2(x - y + 2z) = 2x^2 \cdot x - 2x^2 \cdot y + 2x^2 \cdot 2z \qquad \text{Distribute } 2x^2.$
$$= 2x^3 - 2x^2y + 4x^2z \qquad \text{Product rule}$$

or

$$\begin{array}{r} x - y + 2z \\ 2x^2 \\ \hline 2x^3 - 2x^2y + 4x^2z \end{array}$$

Vertical method
Distribute $2x^2$.

✓ Objective 7.4.1 *CHECKUP*

1. Multiply.

   a. $5a^2b^4(-5a^3bc)$ **b.** $-4m^3(m^2n - 5mn^2 + n^3)$

2. When multiplying two polynomials, when would you use only the commutative and associative laws? For what type of polynomial multiplication would you need to use the distributive law?

Objective 7.4.2

Multiplying Binomials

To multiply binomials, we need to use the distributive law. For example,

$$(x + 2)(x + 3) = (x + 2)x + (x + 2)3 \qquad \text{Distribute } (x + 2).$$
$$= x^2 + 2x + 3x + 6 \qquad \text{Distribute } x \text{ and } 3.$$
$$= x^2 + 5x + 6 \qquad \text{Combine like terms.}$$

or

$$(x + 2)(x + 3) = x(x + 3) + 2(x + 3) \qquad \text{Distribute } (x + 3).$$
$$= x^2 + 3x + 2x + 6 \qquad \text{Distribute } x \text{ and } 2.$$
$$= x^2 + 5x + 6 \qquad \text{Combine like terms.}$$

or

$$
\begin{array}{rl}
x + 2 & \text{Vertical method} \\
\underline{x + 3} & \\
3x + 6 & \text{Distribute 3.} \\
\underline{x^2 + 2x} & \text{Distribute } x. \\
x^2 + 5x + 6 & \text{Combine like terms.}
\end{array}
$$

All three methods result in the same polynomial, $x^2 + 5x + 6$.

Numeric Check

X	Y₁	Y₂
-3	0	0
-2	0	0
-1	2	2
0	6	6
1	12	12
2	20	20
3	30	30

X = -3

Y1 = $(x + 2)(x + 3)$
Y2 = $x^2 + 5x + 6$
The values for Y1 = Y2.

Graphic Check

Y1 = $(x + 2)(x + 3)$

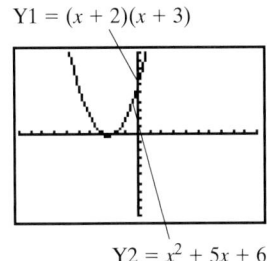

Y2 = $x^2 + 5x + 6$

$(-10, 10, -10, 10)$
The graphs of Y1 and Y2 are the same.

PRODUCTS WITH TWO BINOMIAL FACTORS

$$(a + b)(c + d) = a(c + d) + b(c + d)$$
$$= ac + ad + bc + bd$$

For example,

$$(a + b)(c + d) = a(c + d) + b(c + d)$$
$$\downarrow \quad \downarrow \;\; \downarrow \quad \downarrow \qquad \downarrow \;\; \downarrow \quad \downarrow \qquad \downarrow \;\; \downarrow \quad \downarrow$$
$$(x + 4)(x - 5) = x(x - 5) + 4(x - 5)$$
$$= x^2 - 5x + 4x - 20$$
$$= x^2 - x - 20$$

This process is sometimes called the **FOIL** method. The name comes from the following labels:

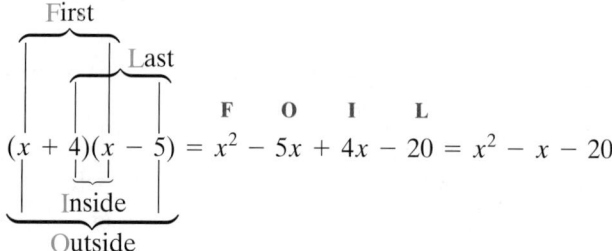

first term	last term	first term	last term	First terms	Outside terms	Inside terms	Last terms
↓	↓	↓	↓	↓	↓	↓	↓

$$(a \;+\; b)(c \;+\; d) = ac \;+\; ad \;+\; bc \;+\; bd$$

↑   ↑   ↑   ↑

outside term   inside term   inside term   outside term

For example,

$$(x + 4)(x - 5) = x^2 - 5x + 4x - 20 = x^2 - x - 20$$

First, Last, FOIL, Inside, Outside

EXAMPLE 2   Multiply.

a. $(2x + 3)(4x - 1)$ **b.** $(x + 3)(x - 3)$ **c.** $(x + 5)^2$

Solution

$$\overset{\text{F}\quad\ \ \text{O}\quad\ \ \text{I}\quad\ \ \text{L}}{}$$

a. $(2x + 3)(4x - 1) = 8x^2 - 2x + 12x - 3$
$$= 8x^2 + 10x - 3 \qquad \text{Combine like terms.}$$

$$\overset{\text{F}\quad\ \ \text{O}\quad\ \ \text{I}\quad\ \ \text{L}}{}$$

b. $(x + 3)(x - 3) = x^2 - 3x + 3x - 9$
$$= x^2 + 0x - 9 \qquad \text{Combine like terms.}$$
$$= x^2 - 9$$

c. $(x + 5)^2 = (x + 5)(x + 5) \qquad \text{Expand.}$
$$= x^2 + 5x + 5x + 25 \qquad \text{FOIL}$$
$$= x^2 + 10x + 25 \qquad \text{Combine like terms.}$$

✓ Objective 7.4.2 · **CHECKUP**

1. Multiply.

   a. $(a + 7)(7a + 1)$ **b.** $(2y - 1)(2y + 1)$ **c.** $(x - 5)^2$

2. In multiplying one binomial expression by another, you can use the FOIL method or the distributive law. Which do you prefer to use, and why?

Objective 7.4.3   ## Multiplying Polynomials

To multiply two polynomial factors, pick one factor and distribute its terms over all the terms of the second polynomial. We can do this several ways—for example,

$$(x - 4)(x^2 + 2x - 1)$$
$$= x(x^2 + 2x - 1) - 4(x^2 + 2x - 1) \qquad \text{Distribute } (x^2 + 2x - 1).$$
$$= x^3 + 2x^2 - x - 4x^2 - 8x + 4 \qquad \text{Distribute } x \text{ and } -4.$$
$$= x^3 - 2x^2 - 9x + 4 \qquad \text{Combine like terms.}$$

or

$$x^2 + 2x - 1$$ Vertical method

$$\underline{ x - 4}$$

$$- 4x^2 - 8x + 4$$ Distribute −4.

$$\underline{x^3 + 2x^2 - x }$$ Distribute x.

$$x^3 - 2x^2 - 9x + 4$$

Numeric Check

X	Y₁	Y₂
-3	-14	-14
-2	6	6
-1	10	10
0	4	4
1	-6	-6
2	-14	-14
3	-14	-14

X = -3

Y1 = $(x - 4)(x^2 + 2x - 1)$
Y2 = $x^3 - 2x^2 - 9x + 4$
The values for Y1 = Y2.

Graphic Check

Y1 = $(x-4)(x^2 + 2x - 1)$
Y2 = $x^3 - 2x^2 - 9x + 4$

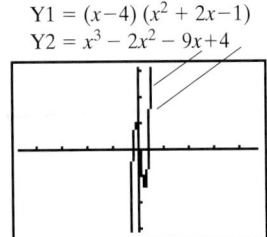

$(-47, 47, -31, 31)$
The graphs of Y1 and Y2 are the same.

PRODUCTS WITH POLYNOMIAL FACTORS

To multiply two polynomial factors, use the distributive law to distribute the terms of one factor over the terms of the second factor.

EXAMPLE 3

Multiply.

a. $(a^2 + 2a + 5)(a^2 - a + 4)$ **b.** $(x - 2)^3$ **c.** $(x - 2)(x^2 + 2x + 4)$

Solution

a. $(a^2 + 2a + 5)(a^2 - a + 4)$
$= a^2(a^2 - a + 4) + 2a(a^2 - a + 4) + 5(a^2 - a + 4)$ Distribute.
$= a^4 - a^3 + 4a^2 + 2a^3 - 2a^2 + 8a + 5a^2 - 5a + 20$ Distribute.
$= a^4 + a^3 + 7a^2 + 3a + 20$ Simplify.

b. $(x - 2)^3 = (x - 2)(x - 2)(x - 2)$ Expand.
$= [x(x - 2) - 2(x - 2)](x - 2)$ Distribute (x − 2).
$= (x^2 - 2x - 2x + 4)(x - 2)$ Distribute x and −2.
$= (x^2 - 4x + 4)(x - 2)$ Combine like terms.
$= x(x^2 - 4x + 4) - 2(x^2 - 4x + 4)$ Distribute (x² − 4x + 4).
$= x^3 - 4x^2 + 4x - 2x^2 + 8x - 8$ Distribute x and −2.
$= x^3 - 6x^2 + 12x - 8$ Combine like terms.

c. $(x - 2)(x^2 + 2x + 4)$
$= x(x^2 + 2x + 4) - 2(x^2 + 2x + 4)$ Distribute (x − 2).
$= x^3 + 2x^2 + 4x - 2x^2 - 4x - 8$ Distribute x and −2.
$= x^3 - 8$ Simplify.

✓ Objective 7.4.3 *CHECKUP*

1. Multiply.
   a. $(x + 2)(3x^2 - 2x - 8)$ **b.** $(x + 1)^3$
   c. $(x + 1)(x^2 - x + 1)$

2. You have seen two methods for multiplying polynomials. One is to use the distributive property repeatedly and the other is to perform vertical multiplication. Which would you choose to use, and why?

Objective 7.4.4   **Special Products**

In previous examples, we determined certain products that we now identify as **special products**.

The **product of a sum and difference of the same two terms** is considered a special product. To determine a rule for this product, complete the following set of exercises.

Guided Discovery 5   Product of the Sum and Difference of the Same Two Terms

Multiply.

1. $(x + 5)(x - 5)$ **2.** $(3x + 1)(3x - 1)$

3. $(x + y)(x - y)$

Write a rule for determining by inspection the product of the sum and difference of the same two terms.

The product of the sum and difference of the same two terms is the difference of the square of the first term and the square of the second term.

> **PRODUCT OF THE SUM AND DIFFERENCE OF THE SAME TWO TERMS**
>
> $$(a + b)(a - b) = a^2 - b^2$$

We know this is true by determining the product algebraically.

$$(a + b)(a - b) = a^2 - ab + ab - b^2$$
$$= a^2 - b^2$$

For example, multiply $(x + 2)(x - 2)$.

$$(a + b)(a - b) = a^2 - b^2$$
$$\downarrow \quad \downarrow \quad \downarrow \quad \downarrow \quad \downarrow \quad \downarrow$$
$$(x + 2)(x - 2) = x^2 - 2^2 = x^2 - 4 \qquad a = x, b = 2$$

The **square of a binomial** is also considered a special product. To determine a rule for this product, complete the following set of exercises.

Guided Discovery 6   Square of a Binomial

Rewrite in expanded form and multiply.

1. $(x + 5)^2$ **2.** $(3x - 1)^2$

3. $(x + y)^2$ **4.** $(x - y)^2$

Write a rule for determining by inspection the square of a binomial.

The square of a binomial that is a sum of two terms is the square of the first term, plus two times the product of the first and last terms, plus the square of the last term. The square of a binomial that is a difference of two terms is the square of the first term, minus two times the product of the first and last terms, plus the square of the last term.

> **SQUARE OF A BINOMIAL**
>
> $$(a + b)^2 = a^2 + 2ab + b^2$$
> $$(a - b)^2 = a^2 - 2ab + b^2$$

We can also determine these products algebraically.

$$(a + b)^2 = (a + b)(a + b) \qquad\qquad (a - b)^2 = (a - b)(a - b)$$
$$= a^2 + ab + ab + b^2 \qquad\qquad\qquad = a^2 - ab - ab + b^2$$
$$= a^2 + 2ab + b^2 \qquad\qquad\qquad\quad = a^2 - 2ab + b^2$$

 TAKE NOTE Remember that $(a + b) \neq a^2 + b^2$ and $(a - b) \neq a^2 - b^2$.

For example, multiply $(x + 2)^2$ and $(x - 2)^2$.

$$(a + b)^2 = a^2 + 2 \ a \ b + b^2$$
$$(x + 2)^2 = x^2 + 2 \cdot x \cdot 2 + 2^2 = x^2 + 4x + 4 \qquad a = x, b = 2$$
$$(a - b)^2 = a^2 - 2 \ a \ b + b^2$$
$$(x - 2)^2 = x^2 - 2 \cdot x \cdot 2 + 2^2 = x^2 - 4x + 4 \qquad a = x, b = 2$$

 TAKE NOTE These special products are helpful to know, but can be found without memorizing the formulas simply by using the FOIL method of multiplying two binomials.

EXAMPLE 4

Multiply.

a. $(2x - 5)(2x + 5)$ 　　　　　　　　**b.** $(2x + 5)^2$

Solution

a. This is the product of the sum and difference of the same two terms. The first term is $2x$ and the second term is 5.

$$(a \ + b)(a \ - b) = a^2 \ - b^2$$
$$(2x - 5)(2x + 5) = (2x)^2 - 5^2 \qquad a = 2x, b = 5$$
$$= 4x^2 \ - 25$$

b. This is the square of a binomial. The binomial is the sum of $2x$ and 5.

$$(a \ + b)^2 = \ a^2 \ + 2 \ a \ b \ + b^2$$
$$(2x + 5)^2 = (2x)^2 + 2(2x)(5) + 5^2 \qquad a = 2x, b = 5$$
$$= 4x^2 + \ 20x \ + 25$$

Objective 7.4.4 CHECKUP

1. Multiply. When using the special-products forms, always state what a and b are.

　a. $(3y - 7)(3y + 7)$ 　　**b.** $(3y - 7)^2$

2. You can choose to learn the forms for special products, or you can choose to obtain the results by just applying the general rules for polynomial multiplication as described in previous sections of this chapter. Which do you prefer? Why?

Objective 7.4.5　Simplifying Using Addition, Subtraction, and Multiplication

In the previous examples, we simplified polynomials involving one operation such as addition, subtraction, or multiplication. We will now expand this simplification to involve more than one operation. In order to complete this simplification, we will follow the order of operations.

EXAMPLE 5

Simplify $(x + 3)^2 - 4x(x + 3)$.

Solution

$$(x + 3)^2 - 4x(x + 3) = (x^2 + 6x + 9) - 4x(x + 3) \qquad \text{Square of a binomial.}$$
$$= x^2 + 6x + 9 - 4x^2 - 12x \qquad \text{Distribuite } -4x.$$
$$= -3x^2 - 6x + 9 \qquad\qquad\qquad \text{Simplify.}$$

EXAMPLE 6   Evaluate $f(x) = x^2 - 3x + 2$ for $f(2 + h)$.

Solution

$f(x) = x^2 - 3x + 2$

$f(2 + h) = (2 + h)^2 - 3(2 + h) + 2$ Substitute $(2 + h)$.

$f(2 + h) = (4 + 4h + h^2) - 3(2 + h) + 2$ Square of a binomial.

$f(2 + h) = 4 + 4h + h^2 - 6 - 3h + 2$ Distribute -3.

$f(2 + h) = h + h^2$ Simplify.

✓ **Objective 7.4.5 CHECKUP**

1. Simplify $(2x - 1)^2 - x(2x - 1)$.

2. Evaluate $g(x) = x^2 - x + 1$ for $g(a + h)$.

Objective 7.4.6   Modeling the Real World

We have seen that many important quantities are expressed as products. Geometric areas are products of the sides of a rectangle, the square of the side of a square, or the product of the base and the height of a parallelogram. Volumes are products of three dimensions, such as the width, length, and height of a rectangular solid or the third power of the side of a cube. Calculations of these kinds of quantities often involve multiplying polynomials.

EXAMPLE 7   A rectangular garden plot has a length that is twice its width. Jay plans to increase the length by 5 feet and decrease the width by 2 feet. Write a polynomial representation of the area of the new garden plot in terms of the original width, w. What is the area of the new garden plot if the garden width was 5 feet?

Solution

Let w = original width (in feet)

$2w$ = original length (in feet)

$w - 2$ = new width (in feet)

$2w + 5$ = new length (in feet)

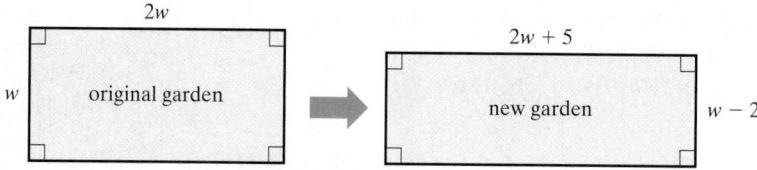

The area is the product of the length and width.

$$(2w + 5)(w - 2) = 2w^2 - 4w + 5w - 10$$
$$= 2w^2 + w - 10$$

The new area is $(2w^2 + w - 10)$ square feet.
Substitute 5 for w to determine the new area.

$$2w^2 + w - 10 = 2(5)^2 + 5 - 10$$
$$= 45$$

The new area is 45 square feet.

EXAMPLE 8   A company that takes people to the hospital by mini bus finds that for every dollar decrease in fare, it can sell two extra tickets. If the standard fare is $12 per ticket and 20 tickets are sold at this rate, write a simplified polynomial function for the bus trip's revenue in terms of the number of dollar decreases, x.

Solution

$$\text{Let } x = \text{the number of dollar decreases}$$
$$R(x) = \text{the total revenue}$$

The fare is the standard fare, $12, minus the decrease amount of $1 times the number of decreases, $1x$ or x.

$$12 - x = \text{the amount of the fare}$$

The number of tickets sold is the original number sold, 20, plus the additional number of tickets sold, 2 tickets per decrease in price, or $2x$.

$$20 + 2x = \text{the number of tickets sold}$$

The revenue is the amount of the fare, $12 - x$, times the number of tickets sold, $20 - 2x$.

$$R(x) = (\text{amount of the fare})(\text{number of tickets})$$
$$R(x) = (12 - x)(20 + 2x)$$
$$R(x) = 240 + 24x - 20x - 2x^2$$
$$R(x) = 240 + 4x - 2x^2$$

A revenue function is $R(x) = 240 + 4x - 2x^2$, where x is the number of dollar discounts. ■

APPLICATION

The design of a swimming pool calls for its length to be twice its width. A 5-foot concrete walkway surrounds the pool. Determine a function, $A(w)$, for the area covered by the walkway.

Discussion

$$\text{Let } w = \text{the width of the pool in feet}$$
$$2w = \text{length of the pool in feet}$$

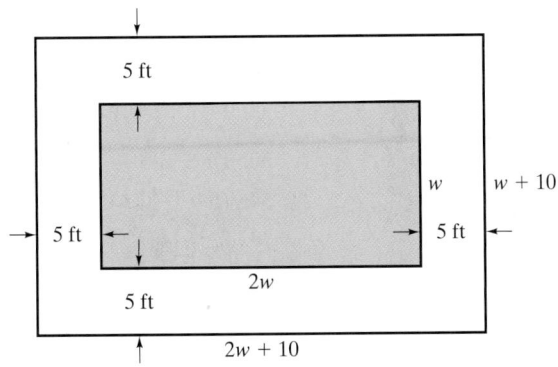

The walkway extends 5 feet on each side of the pool. Therefore, the width of the pool and walkway is $(w + 10)$ feet. The length of the pool and walkway is $(2w + 10)$ feet.

The area of the pool and walkway is the length times the width.

$$(w + 10)(2w + 10) = (2w^2 + 30w + 100) \text{ square feet}$$

The area of the pool is the width times the length, $w(2w)$, or $2w^2$ square feet.

A function for the area of the walkway, in square feet, is the combined area of the pool and walkway minus the area of the pool.

$$A(w) = (2w^2 + 30w + 100) - (2w^2)$$
$$A(w) = 30w + 100$$

✓ Objective 7.4.6 *CHECKUP*

1. Jay has another garden plot for flowers. It is a square garden. He wishes to make it rectangular by increasing one side by 4 feet to become the width and by enlarging the other side to 3 feet more than 2 times its original measure to become the length. Write a polynomial expression to represent the area of the new flower garden in terms of its original side, s. What is the area of the new garden if it measured 5 feet on a side before the increase?

2. A child care center that owns a van transports children to after-school programs. The center finds that for every increase of $0.25 in its fee it will lose a client because parents will provide their own transportation. If the standard fee is $2.50 per trip per child and 15 children travel at this price, write a simplified polynomial function for the van transport's revenue in terms of the number of $0.25 increases, x.

3. A rectangular garden has a length that is three times its width. A brick walkway around the garden measures 2 feet across. Determine a function for the area covered by the walkway.

7.4 EXERCISES

 Student Solutions Manual   PH Math/Tutor Center   CD Video    MathXL®   MyMathLab   Interactmath.com

Multiply.

1. $(8ab^2)(-2a^3b)$
2. $(-5p^3q)(-3p^2q^2)$
3. $-2x(3x - y + 2z)$
4. $-a(4a - 3b + 2c)$
5. $2a^3(3a + 2b - c)$
6. $3x^2(2x - 3y + z)$

In exercises 7 and 8, multiply. Complete the following screens to check numerically and graphically.

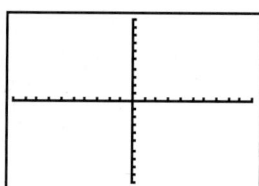

7. $(x - 1)(x + 2)$
8. $(x + 1)(x - 5)$

Multiply

9. $(x + 4)(x + 2)$
10. $(a + 6)(a + 7)$
11. $(5 + x)(3 + 2x)$
12. $(4 + z)(1 + 7z)$
13. $(3y - 2)(2x + 5)$
14. $(5a - 2)(3b + 4)$
15. $(3x + 4y)(x - 2y)$
16. $(2a + 3b)(a - 4b)$
17. $(a - 2.4)(5a + 3.8)$
18. $(p - 1.7)(4p + 2.9)$
19. $\left(a + \dfrac{2}{3}\right)\left(a + \dfrac{1}{3}\right)$
20. $\left(x - \dfrac{1}{5}\right)\left(x + \dfrac{3}{5}\right)$
21. $(2x^2 - 3)(x^2 + 4)$
22. $(4x^2 + 3)(2x + 1)$
23. $(2x + 3y^2)(3x^2 - 5y)$
24. $(4a^2 + 3b)(6a - 5b^2)$
25. $(x + 4)(x^2 - 4x + 16)$
26. $(x - 1)(x^2 + x + 1)$
27. $(3x - 2)(2x^2 - 5x - 3)$
28. $(4x + 3)(x^2 - 5x - 2)$
29. $(x^2 + x + 1)(x^2 + 2x + 3)$
30. $(a^2 + a - 2)(a^2 - 2a + 1)$
31. $(a + b + c)^2$
32. $(a - b - c)^2$
33. $(z + 3)^3$
34. $(r + 2)^3$
35. $(3a - 2b)^3$
36. $(2x - 3y)^3$
37. $(x - 5)(x + 5)$
38. $(y + 12)(y - 12)$
39. $(3m + 7)(3m - 7)$
40. $(5p - 4)(5p + 4)$
41. $(2a + 3b)(2a - 3b)$
42. $(9p - 2q)(9p + 2q)$
43. $(4x - 1.5)(4x + 1.5)$
44. $(3z + 2.5)(3z - 2.5)$
45. $\left(\dfrac{2}{5}x - 1\right)\left(\dfrac{2}{5}x + 1\right)$
46. $\left(\dfrac{4}{7}y - 2\right)\left(\dfrac{4}{7}y + 2\right)$
47. $(x^2 + 7)(x^2 - 7)$
48. $(y^2 - 9)(y^2 + 9)$
49. $(m + 7)^2$
50. $(p + 6)^2$
51. $(x - y)^2$
52. $(u - v)^2$
53. $(2p + 9q)^2$
54. $(5m - 11n)^2$
55. $(6c - 5)^2$
56. $(8d + 3)^2$
57. $(3x^2 + 2)^2$
58. $(2z^2 - 5)^2$

In exercises 59 and 60, simplify.

59. a. $(x - 2)^2 + 3x(x - 2)$ b. $(2x + 1)^2 - x(2x + 1)$
   c. $x(x + 1)(x - 2) + x(x + 1)(x + 2)$
   d. $x(x^2 - 9)(2x) - x(x^2 - 9)(x + 3)$

60. a. $(x - 3)^2 + 2x(x - 3)$ b. $(3x + 1)^2 - x(3x + 1)$
   c. $x(x + 3)(x - 2) + x(x + 3)(x + 2)$
   d. $x(x^2 - 4)(3x) - x(x^2 - 4)(x + 2)$

In exercises 61 and 62, evaluate the function for the given values.

61. $f(x) = x^2 + 2x - 3$
  a. $f(3 + h)$
  b. $f(x + h)$

62. $g(x) = x^2 - 3x + 4$
  a. $g(2 + h)$
  b. $g(a + h)$

Geometry

In exercises 63–70, determine the area of the following figures.

63.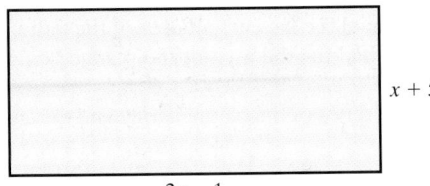
$x + 5$
$2x - 1$

64.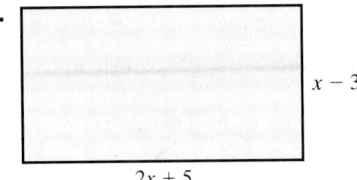
$x - 3$
$2x + 5$

65.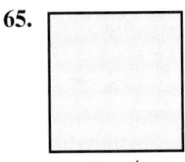
$x - 4$

66.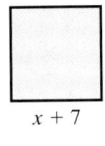
$x + 7$

67.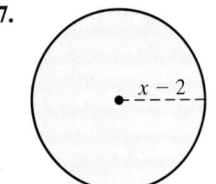
$x - 2$

68.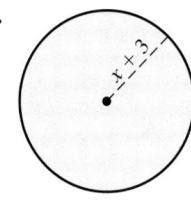
$x + 3$

69.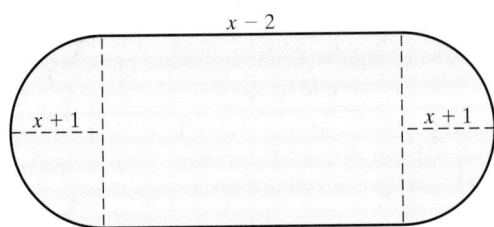
$x - 2$
$x + 1$ $x + 1$

70.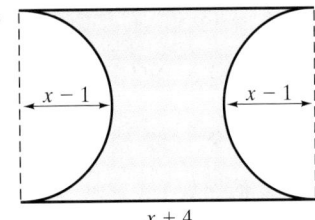
$x - 1$ $x - 1$
$x + 4$

71. A box is to be made out of a rectangular piece of cardboard that is 12 inches wide and 18 inches long. Squares x inches on a side are cut out of the corners, and the sides are bent upward.

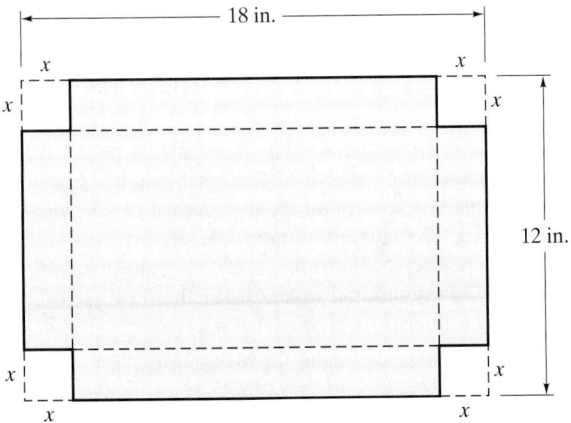
18 in.
12 in.

  a. Write expressions for the length, width, and height of the box.
  b. Write a simplified expression for the volume of the box.
  c. Write a simplified expression for the outside surface area of the box. (Note that the box does not have a top.)

72. A box is to be made out of a square piece of cardboard that is 10 inches on a side. Squares y inches on a side are cut out of the corners, and the sides are then bent upward.

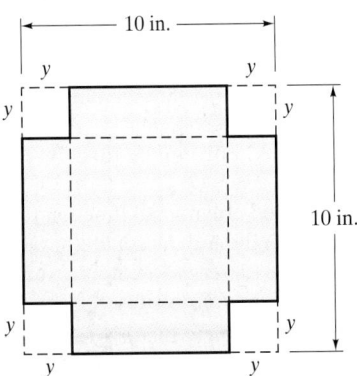
10 in.
10 in.

  a. Write expressions for the length, width, and height of the box.
  b. Write a simplified expression for the volume of the box.
  c. Write a simplified expression for the outside surface area of the box, which does not have a top.

73. Sammy wants to put a circular redwood deck around his circular pool. He wants the deck to be 5 feet wide. If the radius from the center of the pool to the outer edge of the deck is x

feet, write a polynomial to represent the area of the deck by completing the following steps:

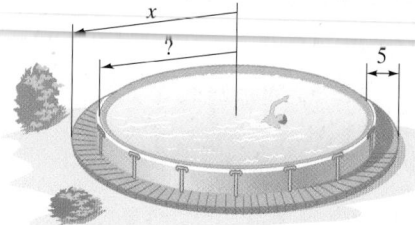

a. Find the area of the outer circle.
b. Find the area of the inner circle.
c. Find the difference of the two areas, which will be the area of the deck.

74. A circular barbecue pit at the Butcher Shop Restaurant is surrounded by a concrete walkway that is x feet wide. The distance from the center of the pit to the outer edge of the walkway is 6 feet.

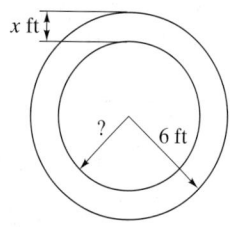

a. Find the area of the outer circle.
b. Find the area of the inner circle.
c. Find the difference of the two areas, which will be the area of the walkway.

75. A triangle has a base that is 5 feet less than four times the height. Find a simplified polynomial function for its area.

76. A triangle has a height that is 2 feet more than seven times the corresponding base. Find a simplified polynomial function for its area.

77. A right triangle has a base that is 2 meters less than its height. The hypotenuse (or the side opposite the right angle) is 2 meters more than the height.
a. Write a simplified polynomial function for the square of the hypotenuse.
b. Write a simplified polynomial function for the sum of the square of the height and the square of the base.
c. If the height is 8 meters, evaluate the functions in parts **a** and **b** and compare your results.

78. A right triangle has a height that is 1 foot more than its base. The hypotenuse (or the side opposite the right angle) is 2 feet more than the base.
a. Write a simplified polynomial function for the square of the hypotenuse.
b. Write a simplified polynomial function for the sum of the square of the height and the square of the base.
c. If the base is 3 feet, evaluate the functions in parts **a** and **b** and compare your results.

79. Pandora plans to enlarge the deck on her house. The current deck is three times as long as it is wide. Pandora plans to double the width and add 10 feet to the length.
a. Write a polynomial for the current area of the deck.
b. Write a polynomial for the area of the planned enlarged deck.
c. What is the difference of the planned area and the current area?
d. The width of the current deck is 10 feet. How many square feet will she be adding?

80. Laurie has a square patio. She plans to enlarge the patio by adding 5 feet to the width and doubling the length.
a. Write a polynomial for the current area of the patio.
b. Write a polynomial for the area of the planned enlarged patio.
c. What is the difference of the planned area and the current area?
d. The length of a side of the current patio is 12 feet. How many square feet will she be adding?

Business

81. A company that takes senior citizens to a casino via mini bus has a standard fare of $15.00 per ticket. A reduction of $0.50 per person is given as an incentive for groups. Determine a revenue function.

82. A movie theater manager gives a reduced ticket price for children's birthday groups. There is a discount of $0.75 for each child. If the regular children's ticket price is $8.75 per child, determine a revenue function.

83. A taxi service that transports children to after school programs gives a discount of $0.25 for each child. If the standard fee is $4.00 per trip, determine a revenue function.

84. An apartment furniture rental agency gives a rental discount of $5 per unit for each item rented. If the standard rental price is $35 per item, determine a revenue function.

85. A car rental agency finds that for every increase of $5 daily, it will rent two fewer units. If 150 vehicles are rented at $45 per day, write a simplified polynomial function for rental revenue in terms of x, the number of increases.

86. A mini-storage business finds that for every fee decrease of $10, it will rent five more units. If 250 storage units are now rented at $40 per month, write a simplified polynomial function for monthly revenue in terms of x, the number of decreases.

87. An orchard grower finds that if he plants peach trees too close together, the trees produce fewer peaches. For every 15 fewer trees per acre planted, an increase of 25 peaches per tree occurs. The current standard at the orchard is to plant 200 trees per acre, which will yield 75 peaches per tree. Write a simplified polynomial function for the total yield in terms of x, the number of 15 tree decreases.

88. A movie theater manager finds that for every extra ticket agent he puts on duty, he can sell 25 more tickets per hour. If he currently has 4 agents on duty who sell 115 tickets per hour, write a polynomial for the total number of tickets sold in terms of x, the number of extra agents.

7.4 Calculator Exercises

In checking the equivalence of simplified expressions graphically, it may be difficult to determine whether the graphs coincide. In Section 7.1, you learned that you can use the "bubble" graphing feature of the calculator to follow the trace of the coinciding graphs. You can also use the graphing features that allow you to graph dotted graphs and boldface graphs. As an example, suppose you want to check the equivalence of the simplification

$$(2x - 3)(4x + 1) = 8x^2 - 10x - 3$$

Store the original expression in Y1 and the simplified expression in Y2. When you do this, move the cursor to the left of the equals sign of Y1, and press ENTER until you see a dotted line. Likewise, move the cursor to the left of the equals sign of Y2, and press ENTER until you see a bold line. Then, when you press GRAPH, you should see a dotted graph first, followed by a bold graph that traces over the dotted graph whenever the simplified

expression is in fact equivalent to the original expression. The screens for this example are as follows:

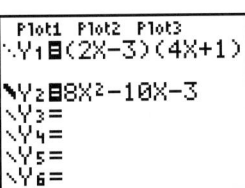

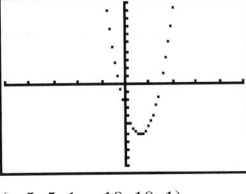

$(-5, 5, 1, -10, 10, 1)$

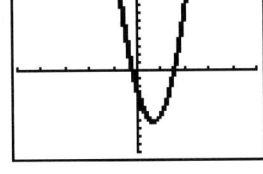

$(-5, 5, 1, -10, 10, 1)$

Try this approach to check the following simplifications:

1. Is $(2x - 1)(2x + 1) = 2x^2 - 1$?

2. Is $(x + 1)(x - 1) = x^2 + x + 2$?

3. Is $(x - 2)(x - 1) = x^2 - 3x + 2$?

4. Is $(0.5x + 1)(4x - 0.8) = 2x^2 + 3.6x - 0.8$?

5. Is $\left(\frac{1}{2}x - 3\right)\left(2x + \frac{1}{3}\right) = x^2 - \frac{35}{6}x + 1$?

6. Is $(x^2 + 4)(x^2 - 1) = x^4 + 3x^2 - 4$?

7. Is $(x^2 + 1)(2x - 1) = 2x^3 - x^2 + 2x - 1$?

8. Is $(x^2 - 1)(0.3x - 1.4) = 0.3x^3 - 1.4x^2 - 0.3x - 1.4$?

7.4 Writing Exercises

More about Special Products

In this section, you have seen some special polynomials that are created by multiplication of binomials or polynomials. Some of these are listed here. Match each product with the correct polynomial.

1. $(A + B)(A - B)$ **a.** $A^2 + 2AB + B^2$

2. $(A + B)^2$ **b.** $A^2 - 2AB + B^2$

3. $(A - B)^2$ **c.** $A^2 - B^2$

4. $(A - 1)(A^2 + A + 1)$ **d.** $A^3 - B^3$

5. $(A + 1)(A^2 - A + 1)$ **e.** $A^3 + 1$

6. $(A - B)(A^2 + AB + B^2)$ **f.** $A^3 - 1$

7. $(A + B)(A^2 - AB + B^2)$ **g.** $A^3 + B^3$

Explain how these matches sometimes can help you when you are multiplying polynomials.

7.5 POLYNOMIAL DIVISION

OBJECTIVES
1 Divide by a monomial.
2 Divide by a polynomial.
3 Model real-world situations by using polynomials.

APPLICATION

Sio signed a contract for her new job. According to the contract, she is to make \$20,000 the first year and receive an increase of 5% per year for the next two years. Sio's total salary for three years is given by the function $s(x) = \dfrac{20{,}000(1 - x^3)}{1 - x}$,

where x is the sum of 1 and the percentage increase, converted to a decimal, or 1.05. Write an equivalent function by simplifying $s(x)$. Determine Sio's total salary for three years, using the original function and the simplified function.

After completing this section, we will discuss this application further. See page 587.

Dividing with Monomials

We have already divided algebraic expressions by a single-term expression. To divide two monomials, we use the commutative and associative properties to rearrange the factors. We also use the rules for exponents to help simplify the quotient, as in Section 7.1. *We will assume that variables represent nonzero values, so that the expressions are defined.*

To divide a polynomial of more than one term by a monomial, we use the distributive law, as we did with algebraic expressions.

QUOTIENTS WITH A MONOMIAL DIVISOR

To divide a monomial by a monomial, use the commutative and associative properties to rearrange factors. Simplify by using the rules of exponents.

To divide a polynomial with more than one term by a monomial, use the distributive law. Again, simplify by using the rules of exponents.

EXAMPLE 1

Divide. Express your answer with positive exponents.

a. $\dfrac{6x^5y^4z}{-2xy^2z}$ **b.** $\dfrac{4x^2y^3z - 2xy^2z}{2xyz}$ **c.** $\dfrac{2a^2 + 6a^2b - 4b^2}{2a}$

Solution

a. Note that we simplified this type of example in Section 7.1.

$$\frac{6x^5y^4z}{-2xy^2z} = \frac{6}{-2} \cdot \frac{x^5}{x} \cdot \frac{y^4}{y^2} \cdot \frac{z}{z}$$

$$= -3 \cdot x^{5-1} \cdot y^{4-2} \cdot z^{1-1} \qquad \text{Quotient rule}$$

$$= -3x^4y^2z^0 \qquad\qquad \text{Remember, } z^0 = 1.$$

$$= -3x^4y^2$$

b. $\dfrac{4x^2y^3z - 2xy^2z}{2xyz} = \dfrac{4x^2y^3z}{2xyz} - \dfrac{2xy^2z}{2xyz}$ \qquad Distribute 2xyz.

$$= \frac{4}{2} \cdot \frac{x^2}{x} \cdot \frac{y^3}{y} \cdot \frac{z}{z} - \frac{2}{2} \cdot \frac{x}{x} \cdot \frac{y^2}{y} \cdot \frac{z}{z}$$

$$= 2x^{2-1}y^{3-1}z^{1-1} - 1x^{1-1}y^{2-1}z^{1-1} \qquad \text{Quotient rule}$$

$$= 2x^1y^2z^0 - 1x^0y^1z^0$$

$$= 2xy^2 - y$$

c. $\dfrac{2a^2 + 6a^2b - 4b^2}{2a} = \dfrac{2a^2}{2a} + \dfrac{6a^2b}{2a} - \dfrac{4b^2}{2a}$ \qquad Distribute 2a.

$$= 1a^{2-1} + 3a^{2-1}b - 2a^{-1}b^2 \qquad \text{Rules of exponents}$$

$$= a + 3ab - \frac{2b^2}{a} \qquad\qquad \text{Simplify.}$$

✓ ## Objective 7.5.1 *CHECKUP*

1. Divide. Express your answers with positive exponents.

a. $\dfrac{27a^4b^5c^3}{9a^2b^2c^2}$ **b.** $\dfrac{18x^2y^2 + 3xy^3}{-3xy}$

c. $\dfrac{12x^3 + 6x^2y - 9xy^2 - 2y^3}{4x^2}$

2. In dividing a polynomial by a monomial, when would you need to use the distributive law?

Objective 7.5.2

Dividing Polynomials

To divide a polynomial by a polynomial other than a monomial, we use long division. Polynomial long division follows the same steps as numeric long division. Review the steps of long division, as shown in the following example:

$$
\begin{array}{r}
12 \\
56{\overline{\smash{\big)}\,675}} \\
\underline{-56} \\
115 \\
\\
\underline{-112} \\
3
\end{array}
$$

Divide: $67 \div 56 = 1$. Place 1 in the quotient.

Multiply: $1(56) = 56$.

Subtract: $67 - 56 = 11$. Bring down the 5.

Divide: $115 \div 56 = 2$. Place 2 in the quotient.

Multiply: $2(56) = 112$.

Subtract: $115 - 112 = 3$. The remainder is 3.

The quotient is $12\dfrac{3}{56}\left(\dfrac{\text{remainder}}{\text{divisor}}\right)$. We can check division.

$$56 \cdot 12 + 3 = 675$$

divisor · quotient + remainder = dividend

| **EXAMPLE 2** |

Divide $x^2 + x - 12$ by $x - 3$.

Solution

The dividend is $x^2 + x - 12$. The divisor is $x - 3$.

$$
\begin{array}{r}
x \\
x - 3{\overline{\smash{\big)}\,x^2 + x - 12}}
\end{array}
$$

Divide the first term of the dividend by the first term of the divisor. $\dfrac{x^2}{x} = x$

$$
\begin{array}{r}
x \\
x - 3{\overline{\smash{\big)}\,x^2 + x - 12}} \\
x^2 - 3x
\end{array}
$$

Multiply the partial quotient by the divisor. $x(x - 3) = x^2 - 3x$

$$
\begin{array}{r}
x \\
x - 3{\overline{\smash{\big)}\,x^2 + x - 12}} \\
\underline{-(x^2 - 3x)} \\
4x - 12
\end{array}
$$

Subtract (change signs and add), and bring down the next term. $(x^2 + x) - (x^2 - 3x) = x^2 + x - x^2 + 3x = 4x$

$$
\begin{array}{r}
x + 4 \\
x - 3{\overline{\smash{\big)}\,x^2 + x - 12}} \\
\underline{-(x^2 - 3x)} \\
4x - 12
\end{array}
$$

Divide the first term of the new dividend by the first term of the divisor. $\dfrac{4x}{x} = 4$

$$
\begin{array}{r}
x + 4 \\
x - 3{\overline{\smash{\big)}\,x^2 + x - 12}} \\
\underline{-(x^2 - 3x)} \\
4x - 12 \\
4x - 12
\end{array}
$$

Multiply the partial quotient by the divisor. $4(x - 3) = 4x - 12$

$$
\begin{array}{r}
x + 4 \\
x - 3{\overline{\smash{\big)}\,x^2 + x - 12}} \\
\underline{-(x^2 - 3x)} \\
4x - 12 \\
\underline{-(4x - 12)} \\
0
\end{array}
$$

Subtract (change signs and add). $(4x - 12) - (4x - 12) = 4x - 12 - 4x + 12 = 0$

The quotient is $x + 4$.
The remainder is 0.

We can check by multiplying.

$$(x - 3)(x + 4) = x^2 + 4x - 3x - 12 \qquad \text{divisor · quotient}$$
$$= x^2 + x - 12 \qquad\qquad\qquad = \text{dividend}$$

Numeric Check

X	Y₁	Y₂
-3	1	1
-2	2	2
-1	3	3
0	4	4
1	5	5
2	6	6
3	ERROR	7

X = -3

$Y1 = \dfrac{x^2 + x - 12}{x - 3}$

$Y2 = x + 4$

$Y1 = Y2$ for all values except $x = 3$.

The quotient $\dfrac{x^2 + x - 12}{x - 3}$ is not defined for $x = 3$ (division by zero).

Graphic Check

$Y1 = \dfrac{x^2 + x - 12}{x - 3}$

$Y2 = x + 4$

$(-10, 10, -10, 10)$

Note: Y1 appears to equal Y2.

EXAMPLE 3   Divide $\dfrac{4x^3 + 3x + 5}{2x - 3}$.

Solution

You will need to write any missing addends with 0 coefficients in order to keep the columns aligned. There is no x^2 term, so we need to add $0x^2$ in order to write in decreasing order.

$2x - 3 \overline{)4x^3 + 0x^2 + 3x + 5}$ Write as long division. Write missing addend with 0 coefficient.

$\begin{array}{r} 2x^2 \\ 2x - 3 \overline{)4x^3 + 0x^2 + 3x + 5} \end{array}$ Divide the first term of the dividend by the first term of the divisor. $\frac{4x^3}{2x} = 2x^2$

$\begin{array}{r} 2x^2 \\ 2x - 3 \overline{)4x^3 + 0x^2 + 3x + 5} \\ 4x^3 - 6x^2 \end{array}$ Multiply the partial quotient by the divisor.
$2x^2(2x - 3) = 4x^3 - 6x^2$

$\begin{array}{r} 2x^2 \\ 2x - 3 \overline{)4x^3 + 0x^2 + 3x + 5} \\ -(4x^3 - 6x^2) \\ \hline 6x^2 + 3x \end{array}$ Subtract (change signs and add), and bring down the next term.
$(4x^3 + 0x^2) - (4x^3 - 6x^2) = 4x^3 + 0x^2 - 4x^3 + 6x^2 = 6x^2$

$\begin{array}{r} 2x^2 + 3x \\ 2x - 3 \overline{)4x^3 + 0x^2 + 3x + 5} \\ -(4x^3 - 6x^2) \\ \hline 6x^2 + 3x \end{array}$ Divide the first term of the new dividend by the first term of the divisor. $\frac{6x^2}{2x} = 3x$

$\begin{array}{r} 2x^2 + 3x \\ 2x - 3 \overline{)4x^3 + 0x^2 + 3x + 5} \\ -(4x^3 - 6x^2) \\ \hline 6x^2 + 3x \\ 6x^2 - 9x \end{array}$ Multiply the partial quotient by the divisor.
$3x(2x - 3) = 6x^2 - 9x$

$\begin{array}{r} 2x^2 + 3x \\ 2x - 3 \overline{)4x^3 + 0x^2 + 3x + 5} \\ -(4x^3 - 6x^2) \\ \hline 6x^2 + 3x \\ -(6x^2 - 9x) \\ \hline 12x + 5 \end{array}$ Subtract (change signs and add), and bring down the next term.
$(6x^2 + 3x) - (6x^2 - 9x) = 6x^2 + 3x - 6x^2 + 9x = 12x$

$$
\begin{array}{r}
2x^2 \;+\; 3x \;+\; 6 \\
2x - 3 \overline{)\; 4x^3 + 0x^2 \;+\; 3x \;+\; 5} \\
-(4x^3 - 6x^2) \\
\hline
6x^2 \;+\; 3x \\
-(6x^2 \;-\; 9x) \\
\hline
12x \;+\; 5
\end{array}
$$

Divide the first term of the new dividend by the first term of the divisor. $\frac{12x}{2x} = 6$

$$
\begin{array}{r}
2x^2 \;+\; 3x \;+\; 6 \\
2x - 3 \overline{)\; 4x^3 + 0x^2 \;+\; 3x \;+\; 5} \\
-(4x^3 - 6x^2) \\
\hline
6x^2 \;+\; 3x \\
-(6x^2 \;-\; 9x) \\
\hline
12x \;+\; 5 \\
12x \;-\; 18
\end{array}
$$

Multiply the partial quotient by the divisor, $6(2x - 3) = 12x - 18$

$$
\begin{array}{r}
2x^2 + 3x \;+\; 6 \;+\; \dfrac{23}{2x - 3} \\
2x - 3 \overline{)\; 4x^3 + 0x^2 \;+\; 3x + 5} \\
-(4x^3 - 6x^2) \\
\hline
6x^2 + 3x \\
-(6x^2 - 9x) \\
\hline
12x + \;\;5 \\
-(12x - 18) \\
\hline
23
\end{array}
$$

Subtract (change signs and add). Write the remainder as a fraction in the quotient.

$(12x + 5) - (12x - 18) = 12x + 5 - 12x + 18 = 23$

The quotient is $2x^2 + 3x + 6 + \frac{23}{2x - 3}$.

Check: $\underset{\text{divisor}}{(2x - 3)}\,\underset{\text{quotient}}{(2x^2 + 3x + 6)} + \underset{\text{remainder}}{23}$

$$
\begin{aligned}
&= 2x(2x^2 + 3x + 6) - 3(2x^2 + 3x + 6) + 23 \\
&= 4x^3 + 6x^2 + 12x - 6x^2 - 9x - 18 + 23 \\
&= 4x^3 + 3x + 5
\end{aligned}
$$

dividend

EXAMPLE 4 Divide $\dfrac{27x^3 - 1}{3x - 1}$.

Solution

The coefficients of the x^2 and x terms of the dividend are 0.

$$
\begin{array}{r}
9x^2 \\
3x - 1 \overline{)\; 27x^3 + 0x^2 \;+\; 0x - 1} \\
-(27x^3 - 9x^2) \\
\hline
9x^2 \;+\; 0x
\end{array}
$$

Divide the first term of the dividend by the first term of the divisor. Multiply the partial quotient by the divisor. Subtract, and bring down the next term.

$$
\begin{array}{r}
9x^2 \;+\; 3x \\
3x - 1 \overline{)\; 27x^3 + 0x^2 \;+\; 0x - 1} \\
-(27x^3 - 9x^2) \\
\hline
9x^2 + 0x \\
-(9x^2 - 3x) \\
\hline
3x \;-\; 1
\end{array}
$$

Divide the first term of the new dividend by the first term of the divisor. Multiply the partial quotient by the divisor. Subtract, and bring down the next term.

$$\begin{array}{r} 9x^2 + 3x + 1 \\ 3x - 1 \overline{)\, 27x^3 + 0x^2 + 0x - 1} \\ \underline{-(27x^3 - 9x^2)} \\ 9x^2 + 0x \\ \underline{-(9x^2 - 3x)} \\ 3x - 1 \\ \underline{-(3x - 1)} \\ 0 \end{array}$$

Divide the first term of the new dividend by the first term of the divisor. Multiply the partial quotient by the divisor. Subtract, and bring down the next term.

The quotient is $9x^2 + 3x + 1$. Check: $(3x - 1)(9x^2 + 3x + 1) = 27x^3 - 1$ ■

✓ Objective 7.5.2 **CHECKUP**

1. Divide. Check your answer.

   a. Divide $(10x^2 + 7x - 12)$ by $(2x + 3)$.

   b. $\dfrac{8x^3 + 16x^2 + 27}{2x + 5}$

   c. $\dfrac{8x^3 + 27}{2x + 3}$

2. In dividing one polynomial by another, when will there be a remainder? What does the remainder represent?   ■

Objective 7.5.3   Modeling the Real World

We've already mentioned that polynomial functions and exponential expressions are both very common in modeling real-world situations. Therefore, performing mathematical operations with these functions and expressions becomes an important part of working with applications of mathematics. Any operation you can do with numbers you can also do with polynomials. The only difference is that polynomials don't reduce to simple terms quite as easily as real numbers do.

EXAMPLE 5

Alfredo Travel Company offers a spring tour of Lutz's Gardens. The regular price is $99.95 per package. A reduction of $1.00 per package purchased is given for groups. The bus expenses are estimated to be $105.00, the driver is paid $300.00, and the tickets to the gardens are $19.95 per person. The bus can carry up to 30 people.

a. Determine a total cost function, $C(x)$.

b. Determine a revenue function, $R(x)$.

c. Determine a profit function, $P(x)$.

d. Determine an average profit (profit per package) function, $A(x)$.

e. If 23 members of Springfield Garden Club purchase a tour package, what is the profit per package for Alfredo Travel Company?

Solution

Let x = the number of tour packages purchased

a. The total cost is $105.00, plus $300.00 (that is, $405.00), plus $19.95 per ticket (number of tour packages purchased).

$$C(x) = 19.95x + 405$$

b. The reduction in the package is $1.00 times the number of packages purchased, or $1.00x$. The price of the package is $99.95 minus the reduction, or $(99.95 - 1.00x)$. The revenue is the price of the package times the number of packages purchased, or $(99.95 - 1.00x)x$.

$$R(x) = (99.95 - 1.00x)x$$
$$R(x) = 99.95x - x^2$$

c. The profit is the revenue minus the total cost.

$$P(x) = (99.95x - x^2) - (19.95x + 405)$$
$$P(x) = 99.95x - x^2 - 19.95x - 405$$
$$P(x) = -x^2 + 80x - 405$$

d. The average profit (profit per package) is determined by dividing the profit by the number of packages purchased.

$$A(x) = \frac{-x^2 + 80x - 405}{x}$$

$$A(x) = -x + 80 - \frac{405}{x}$$

e. If $x = 23$, find $A(23)$.

$$A(23) = -(23) + 80 - \frac{405}{(23)}$$

$$A(23) \approx 39.39$$

The average profit for Alfredo Travel Company is $39.39 per package if 23 packages are purchased. ■

APPLICATION

Sio signed a contract for her new job. According to the contract, she is to make $20,000 the first year and receive an increase of 5% per year for the next two years. Sio's total salary for three years is given by the function $s(x) = \dfrac{20{,}000(1 - x^3)}{1 - x}$, where x is the sum of 1 and the percentage increase, converted to a decimal, or 1.05. Write an equivalent function by simplifying $s(x)$. Determine Sio's total salary for three years, using the original function and the simplified function.

Discussion

$$s(x) = \frac{20{,}000(1 - x^3)}{1 - x}$$
$$s(x) = \frac{20{,}000 - 20{,}000x^3}{1 - x}$$

Divide.

Write in descending order:

$$
\require{enclose}
\begin{array}{r}
20{,}000x^2 + 20{,}000x + 20{,}000 \\
-x + 1 \enclose{longdiv}{-20{,}000x^3 + 0x^2 + 0x + 20{,}000} \\
\underline{-(-20{,}000x^3 + 20{,}000x^2)} \\
-20{,}000x^2 + 0x \\
\underline{-(-20{,}000x^2 + 20{,}000x)} \\
-20{,}000x + 20{,}000 \\
\underline{-(-20{,}000x + 20{,}000)} \\
0
\end{array}
$$

Therefore,

$$s(x) = 20{,}000x^2 + 20{,}000x + 20{,}000$$

To determine Sio's total salary for three years, we need to evaluate each function with $x = 1.05$.

(continued on page 588)

original function	simplified function
$s(x) = \dfrac{20{,}000(1 - x^3)}{1 - x}$	$s(x) = 20{,}000x^2 + 20{,}000x + 20{,}000$
$s(1.05) = \dfrac{20{,}000(1 - 1.05^3)}{1 - 1.05}$	$s(1.05) = 20{,}000(1.05)^2 + 20{,}000(1.05) + 20{,}000$
$s(1.05) = 63{,}050$	$s(1.05) = 63{,}050$

Sio will receive \$63,050 over the three-year period.

✓ Objective 7.5.3 **CHECKUP**

1. A hotel offered a package deal for a weekend stay that included tickets to dinner and a touring production of a Broadway play. The price of the package was \$259 per person. A reduction of \$5 per person was offered for group purchases. The hotel incurred a fixed cost of \$200 paid to a travel agent to arrange a group excursion and spent \$25 per person for the dinner and \$50 per person for the tickets to the play. Assume that x people in a group purchase the package.

   a. Determine a total cost function, $C(x)$, for the group's excursion.

   b. Determine a revenue function, $R(x)$, for the group's excursion.

   c. Determine a profit function, $P(x)$, for the group's excursion.

   d. Determine an average profit function, $A(x)$, for the group's excursion.

   e. If 10 people in a group purchased the package, what was the average profit per package for the excursion?

2. At his birth, Benjamin received a gift of \$5000. For the next three years, he received an additional gift on his birthday that was \$5000 increased by 10% per year. The total amount of money Benjamin received from his benefactor is given by the function $g(y) = \dfrac{5000(1 - y^4)}{1 - y}$, where y is the sum of the percentage increase (converted to decimal form) and 1. Write a function equivalent to $g(y)$ by simplifying it. Using the original function and the simplified function, determine the total amount Benjamin received.

7.5 EXERCISES

 Student Solutions Manual　 PH Math/Tutor Center　 CD Video　Math XL MathXL®　MyMathLab MyMathLab　 Interactmath.com

In exercises 1–14, divide as indicated, and express your results with positive exponents only.

1. $\dfrac{20a^4b^2c}{-5a^2bc}$

2. $\dfrac{18x^7y^2z^2}{-9x^3yz^2}$

3. $\dfrac{6x^4y^6z^2 + 18x^2y^3z}{3x^2y^3z}$

4. $\dfrac{15x^5y^5z^3 + 10x^3y^5z^2}{5x^3y^4z^2}$

5. $\dfrac{6x^3 + 12x^2 - 18x}{3x}$

6. $\dfrac{21a^4 - 14a^2 + 42a}{7a}$

7. $\dfrac{12x^4 - 9x^3 + 45x^2 + 15x}{3x}$

8. $\dfrac{25z^4 - 10z^3 + 45z^2 + 15z}{5z}$

9. $\dfrac{3x^2 + 4x - 5}{x}$

10. $\dfrac{2x^2 - 3x + 1}{x}$

11. $\dfrac{3p^3 - 9p^2q + 6pq^2 - 12q^3}{3pq}$

12. $\dfrac{7c^3 - 21c^2d + 14cd^2 - 35d^3}{7cd}$

13. $\dfrac{9x^4 + 6x^3y - 18x^2y^2 - 24xy^3 + 72y^4}{-3xy}$

14. $\dfrac{12a^3 - 30a^2b - 24ab^2 + 6b^3}{6a^2b}$

In exercises 15 and 16, divide. Complete the following screens to check numerically and graphically.

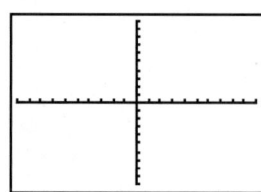

15. $(2x^2 + 9x - 35) \div (x + 7)$

16. $(3x^2 + x - 44) \div (x + 4)$

In exercises 17–40, divide as indicated.

17. Divide $15x^2 - 8x - 12$ by $3x + 2$.

18. Divide $12x^2 - 19x - 21$ by $4x + 3$.

19. $\dfrac{5x^2 - 24x - 36}{x - 6}$

20. $\dfrac{6x^2 - 25x - 25}{x - 5}$

21. $(3y^2 + 19y - 20) \div (y + 8)$

22. $(5z^2 + 3z - 10) \div (z + 2)$

23. $\dfrac{6a^2 - 5a - 30}{2a - 5}$

24. $\dfrac{12b^2 - 13b - 15}{3b - 7}$

25. $(5x^3 - 14x^2 - 3x + 2) \div (5x + 2)$

26. $(12x^3 - 11x^2 + 17x - 10) \div (3x - 2)$

27. $\dfrac{8x^3 + 8x - 5}{2x - 1}$

28. $\dfrac{9x^3 + 17x - 14}{3x - 2}$

29. $(9a^2 - 49) \div (3a + 7)$ **30.** $(49b^2 - 121) \div (7b + 11)$

31. $\dfrac{5x^2 + 30x + 9}{5x + 3}$ **32.** $\dfrac{36y^2 + 60y + 25}{6y + 5}$

33. $(16z^2 - 88z + 121) \div (4z - 11)$

34. $(64p^2 - 112p + 49) \div (8p - 7)$

35. $\dfrac{x^3 + 27}{x + 3}$ **36.** $\dfrac{y^3 + 343}{y + 7}$

37. $\dfrac{a^3 - 125}{a - 5}$ **38.** $\dfrac{b^3 - 27}{b - 3}$

39. Divide $64x^3 + 27$ by $4x + 3$.

40. Divide $125z^3 - 8$ by $5z - 2$.

In exercises 41 and 42, simplify and divide.

41. a. $\dfrac{6x(x - 3) - (3x^2 + 7)}{(x - 3)^2}$

b. $\dfrac{(4x + 1)(x + 1) - (2x^2 + x - 2)}{(x + 1)^2}$

42. a. $\dfrac{8x(x + 2) - (4x^2 - 3)}{(x + 2)^2}$

b. $\dfrac{(6x + 1)(x - 1) - (3x^2 + x + 1)}{(x - 1)^2}$

Geometry

In exercises 43–46, find the missing side.

43.

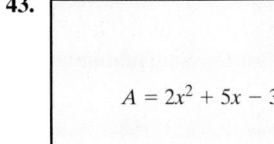

$A = 2x^2 + 5x - 3$?

$x + 3$

44.

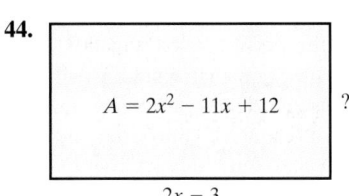

$A = 2x^2 - 11x + 12$?

$2x - 3$

45.

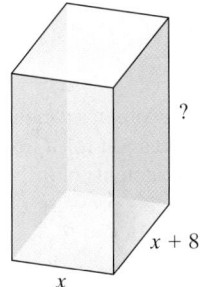

$V = x^3 + 3x^2 - 40x$

?

$x + 8$

x

46.

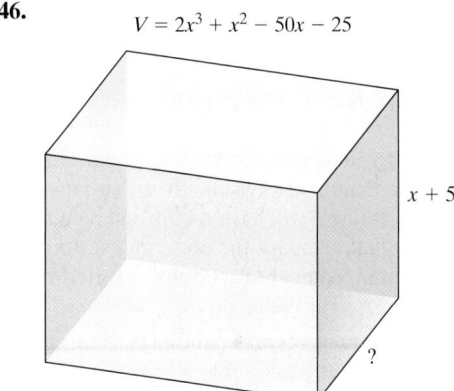

$V = 2x^3 + x^2 - 50x - 25$

$x + 5$

?

$2x + 1$

Business

47. Jennifer established a business that buys and resells used graphing calculators. She advertised in the local paper that she was in the market to buy and sell the calculators. She spent $45 for her advertisement. She bought used calculators for $35 each and resold them for $50 each.

a. Determine a total cost function for Jennifer's operation if she buys x calculators.

b. Determine a revenue function if she sells all the calculators she buys.

c. Determine a profit function.

d. Determine an average profit (per calculator) function.

e. What will be Jennifer's average profit if she sells 30 calculators?

48. Karla formed a company to design Web pages for clients. She spent $1000 to advertise in business journals that she provided such a service. She spent about $75 in labor and materials for each Web page she designed. She charged her clients $350 for each Web page she designed for them.
   a. Determine a total cost function for Karla's operation if she designs x pages.
   b. Determine a revenue function.
   c. Determine a profit function.
   d. Determine an average profit (per Web page) function.
   e. What will be Karla's average profit if she designs 10 Web pages?

49. A bus service that serves a local college campus has a standard fare of $4.50 per ticket and gives a reduction of $0.10 per ticket as an incentive for groups. The company estimates that it pays $200.00 in gas plus overhead expenses of $2.00 per ticket.
   a. Write a simplified polynomial function for the bus service's total cost, $C(x)$, where x is the number of tickets.
   b. Write a simplified polynomial function for the bus service's revenue $R(x)$.
   c. Determine a profit function, $P(x)$.
   d. Determine an average profit (profit per ticket) function, $A(x)$.

50. A local retailer sells homemade candy for $33.50 a box. For corporate clients, he gives a reduction of $0.50 for each box purchased. The retailer has spent $500.00 making the candy and $1.25 per box for packaging.
   a. Write a simplified polynomial function for the retailer's total cost, $C(x)$, where x is the number of boxes sold.
   b. Write a simplified polynomial function for the retailer's revenue from corporate clients, $R(x)$.
   c. Determine a profit function, $P(x)$.
   d. Determine an average profit (profit per box) function, $A(x)$.

51. Scott enrolled in a college program that would give him a bachelor's degree and a master's degree after five years of combined study. To help him through the program, his parents gave him $6000 the first year and increased that amount by 10% each subsequent year. A function for the total amount of money his parents gave Scott is given by $m(t) = \dfrac{6000(1 - t^5)}{1 - t}$, where t is the sum of 1 and the per-

centage increase (converted to decimal form) each year. Write a simplified expression for this function by performing the division. Determine the total amount of money Scott received by first evaluating the original function and then evaluating the simplified function. What would be the total amount if Scott's parents had increased each year's payment by 15%?

52. To encourage her son to do well in high school, Sharon promised to give him $10 for his first A, and double the amount each time he earned another A. She was surprised to see that her son earned six A's during the grading period. She paid him $d(x) = \dfrac{10(1 - x^6)}{1 - x}$ dollars, where x is the factor for increasing the amount. Write a simplified expression for this function by performing the division. Evaluate the original function and the simplified function, given that $x = 2$, since Sharon doubled the amount each time. What would the total amount have been if she had tripled the amount each time?

53. To encourage a client to continue to rent equipment from his company, Randy offers a percentage discount on the charge for each additional week of rental. A client pays $250 to rent a piece of equipment for the first week, and the amount is reduced 10% each subsequent week of rental. If the client rents the equipment for five weeks, a function for the total rental cost is $c(n) = \dfrac{250(1 - n^5)}{1 - n}$, where n is the difference of 1 and the percent reduction (converted to a decimal). Write a simplified expression for this function by performing the division. Evaluate the original function and the simplified function for the 10% reduction.

54. Nelsy operates a collector basket business out of her home. Recently, she discovered that over the previous six weeks her sales declined steadily at a rate of 8% per week. If Nelsy's first week's sales were $550, a function for the total amount of her sales over the six-week period is $s(w) = \dfrac{550(1 - w^6)}{1 - w}$, where w is the difference of 1 and the percentage decline (converted to decimal form). Write a simplified expression for this function by performing the division. Evaluate the original function and the simplified function for the 8% decline.

 ## 7.5 Calculator Exercises

Using the table feature of your calculator, you easily can examine functions that involve polynomial division to see what effect varying the values of the variable will have on the end result. Following are two exercises that compare the pressure exerted on a floor by a man or a woman, compared with that exerted by an elephant. You will be surprised at the results!

1. Pressure is measured in units of force per unit of area. For example, if an elephant weighs 7 tons and each of its four feet is considered to be a circle with a radius of 8 inches, then the pressure the elephant exerts on the floor would be 14,000 pounds divided by four times the area of one of the elephant's foot-pads, $4(\pi 8^2)$, or approximately 17.4 pounds per square inch. By contrast, a woman weighing 110 pounds and wearing high heels would exert a pressure of 110 divided by two times the area of her heel. (We make the simplifying assumption that her weight is distributed on her heels and not on the soles of her shoes.) Write a polynomial division expression for the

pressure per square inch exerted by the woman's weight. Set up a table of values to evaluate this expression for a heel radius that varies from 0.25 to 1 inch, in increments of 0.25 inch. For what radius of the heel is the woman's pressure on the floor approximately the same as the elephant's?

2. Assuming that a man's weight is fully distributed on his circular heels, the pressure exerted on the floor by a man weighing 175 pounds would be equal to his weight divided by the area of both of his heels. Write a polynomial division expression for the pressure per square inch exerted by the man's weight. Construct a table of values for a heel radius that varies from 1 to 1.5 inches, in increments of 0.05 inch. For what radius of the heel is the man's pressure on the floor approximately the same as the pressure of an elephant, as described in exercise 1?

7.5 Writing Exercises

Refer to the writing exercise in Section 7.4. There you were asked to match various forms of polynomial multiplication operations to the resulting polynomials. For example, if you determined that $(A - B)(A + B) = A^2 - B^2$, then you should see that $\dfrac{A^2 - B^2}{A + B} = A - B$. In this way, division can be related to multiplication.

Write a short summary of how you can use the relationships that you determined from the writing exercise in Section 7.4 to help you perform polynomial divisions. When will these relationships not be useful? See if you can use the relationships to perform the following divisions more easily.

1. $(a^2 + 2ab + b^2) \div (a + b)$
2. $(x^3 - y^3) \div (x - y)$
3. $(x^3 + 1) \div (x^2 - x + 1)$
4. $(a^2 - b^2) \div (a + b)$
5. $(x^2 - 16x + 64) \div (x - 8)$
6. $(z^3 + 125) \div (z + 5)$
7. $(b^3 - 1) \div (b - 1)$
8. $(x^6 - y^6) \div (x^3 - y^3)$
9. $(4p^2 - 9q^2) \div (2p + 3q)$
10. $(8x^3 - 729) \div (2x - 9)$

■ Chapter 7 Summary

Vocabulary Review

After completing this chapter, you should be able to define the following key terms.
FOIL method
power-to-a-power rule
product of the sum and difference of the same two terms
product rule
product-to-a-power rule
quotient rule
quotient-to-a-power rule
square of a binomial

Fill in the blank with one of the words or phrases listed above.

1. $2^3 \cdot 2^4 = 2^7$ is an example of the _____.
2. $\dfrac{3^2}{3^{-1}} = 3^3$ is an example of the _____.
3. $(4^2)^3 = 4^6$ is an example of the _____.
4. $(2x)^3 = 2^3 x^3$ is an example of the _____.
5. $(x - y)(x + y) = x^2 - y^2$ is an example of the _____.
6. $(x - y)^2 = x^2 - 2xy + y^2$ is an example of the _____.
7. $(x - 3)(x + 4) = x^2 + 4x - 3x - 12 = x^2 + x - 12$ is an example of the _____.

Reflections

1. Explain the difference between the expanded form and the exponential form of an algebraic expression.
2. If an algebraic expression has an exponential expression with a positive integer exponent greater than 1, how can you evaluate the exponential expression?
3. If an algebraic expression has an exponential expression with an exponent equal to 1, how can you evaluate the exponential expression?
4. If an algebraic expression has an exponential expression with an exponent equal to 0, how can you evaluate the exponential expression?
5. If an algebraic expression has an exponential expression with a negative integer exponent, how can you evaluate the exponential expression?
6. State the product rule for exponents and the power-to-a-power rule for exponents. How do they differ from one another?
7. In adding two polynomials, what do you do to simplify the result?
8. How does subtracting two polynomials differ from adding two polynomials?

9. What properties and laws of the real-number system are important to the process of multiplying two polynomials?

10. How do you divide a polynomial expression by a monomial expression?

11. How do you divide a polynomial expression by another polynomial expression when neither is a monomial?

■ Chapter 7 Section-by-Section Review

7.1

Recall		Examples
Integer exponents		
$a^n = a \cdot a \cdot a \cdot \cdots \cdot a$ $\quad n$ factors		$t^4 = t \cdot t \cdot t \cdot t$
$a^1 = a$		$t^1 = t$
$a^0 = 1$, where $a \neq 0$		$t^0 = 1$
Rules for exponents		Simplify. Assume that all expressions are defined.
$a^m \cdot a^n = a^{m+n}$	Product rule	$t^3 t^6 = t^{3+6} = t^9$
$\dfrac{a^m}{a^n} = a^{m-n}, a \neq 0$	Quotient rule	$\dfrac{t^6}{t^3} = t^{6-3} = t^3$
$(a^m)^n = a^{mn}$	Power-to-a-power rule	$(t^3)^6 = t^{3\cdot6} = t^{18}$
$(ab)^m = a^m b^m$	Product-to-a-power rule	$(st)^3 = s^3 t^3$
$\left(\dfrac{a}{b}\right)^m = \dfrac{a^m}{b^m}, b \neq 0$	Quotient-to-a-power rule	$\left(\dfrac{s}{t}\right)^2 = \dfrac{s^2}{t^2}$

Write in expanded form.

1. $-5c^2$

2. $(-5c)^2$

3. $4(x + y)^2 z^0$

4. $\left(\dfrac{2}{3}\right)^4 x^2$

Simplify exercises 5–23.

5. $a^2 \cdot a^7$

6. $(p + q)^3 (p + q)$

7. $\dfrac{2}{3} b^3 \cdot b \cdot b^4$

8. $\dfrac{t^{12}}{t^9}$

9. $\dfrac{24a^4}{3a^2}$

10. $\dfrac{(x + 3y)^5}{(x + 3y)^4}$

11. $(cd)^{22}$

12. $(-2a)^4$

13. $(-2a)^5$

14. $(3x^3)^2$

15. $\left[(a + b)^2\right]^5$

16. $(a^3)^0$

17. $\left(\dfrac{-2x}{3z}\right)^3$

18. $\left(\dfrac{-4d}{e}\right)^3$

19. $-2xy^2 \cdot 4x^3 y^5$

20. $\dfrac{72x^4 y^5 z^3}{-24x^2 y^4 z^3}$

21. $\dfrac{(x^2 y^3)^4}{x^3 y^5}$

22. $\left(\dfrac{2p^2 q}{pq^2}\right)^3$

23. $\left[\left(\dfrac{m}{4n}\right)^2\right]^2$

24. A square is decreased in size by reducing each side to one-fourth of its original length. Write expressions for the areas of the original square and the reduced square. Compare the two areas.

25. A circular garden is increased in size by doubling its radius. Write expressions for the area of the original garden and the area of the enlarged garden. Compare the two areas. What is the area of the enlarged garden if the original garden had a radius of 6 feet?

26. The home range of a black bear is different for adult females and adult males and is also dependent on many other factors.

   a. Determine the average home range of an adult female black bear if the average movement (in a straight line) is estimated as x miles.

   b. The average movement for the adult male black bear is 3 times the average movement of an adult female black bear. Determine the average home range of an adult male black bear.

   c. Determine the ratio of the average adult male black bear home range to the average adult female black bear home range.

   d. If the average movement for an adult female black bear is 2 miles, determine the adult female black bear's average home range and the average home range of an adult male black bear.

27. Luxembourg had the highest gross domestic product in 2003 at 5.51×10^4 dollars per capita. The population of Luxembourg is approximately 4.63×10^5. What was this country's total gross domestic product in 2003?

28. Japan's population was about 1.27×10^8 in 2003. Its total gross domestic product was approximately 3.556×10^{12} dollars. What was the per capita gross domestic product in 2003?

29. The star Pollux is 3.37×10^1 light-years away from the Earth. Given that a light-year is about 5.9×10^{12} miles, approximate the distance of Pollux from Earth.

7.2

Recall	Examples
Integer exponents $a^{-n} = \dfrac{1}{a^n}$, where $a \neq 0$ $\dfrac{1}{a^{-n}} = a^n$, where $a \neq 0$	Simplify. Assume that all expressions are defined. $t^{-3} = \dfrac{1}{t^3}$ $\dfrac{1}{t^{-2}} = t^2$ $\dfrac{t^{-3}}{t^{-4}} = \dfrac{t^4}{t^3} = t$
Rules for negative exponents are the same as rules for positive exponents.	Simplify. Write with positive exponents. $t^{-3}t^5 = t^{-3+5} = t^2$ $\dfrac{t^6}{t^{-3}} = t^{6-(-3)} = t^9$ $(t^{-3})^6 = t^{-3 \cdot 6} = t^{-18} = \dfrac{1}{t^{18}}$ $(st)^{-3} = s^{-3}t^{-3} = \dfrac{1}{s^3 t^3}$
Quotient-to-a-negative-power rule $\left(\dfrac{a}{b}\right)^{-m} = \left(\dfrac{b}{a}\right)^{m} = \dfrac{b^m}{a^m}$	Simplify. Write with positive exponents $\left(\dfrac{s}{t}\right)^{-2} = \left(\dfrac{t}{s}\right)^{2} = \dfrac{t^2}{s^2}$

Simplify exercises 30–38. Write with positive exponents.

30. $\dfrac{3^{-2}h^{-4}}{k^{-2}}$

31. $c^8 d^{-5}$

32. $(-b^2)(-3b^{-5})$

33. $\dfrac{5z^{-3}}{15z^{-7}}$

34. $(5a^{-4}b^2)^{-3}$

35. $\dfrac{144x^{-4}y^{-3}}{12x^2 y^{-4}}$

36. $\left(\dfrac{27a^5 b^{-3}}{9a^2 b^7}\right)^2$

37. $\left(\dfrac{a^{-3}}{b^{-4}}\right)^{-2}$

38. $\left(\dfrac{2a^{-2}b}{24a^5 b^{-2}}\right)^{-2}$

39. Point is a measurement used in typography. One point is equal to 1.3837×10^{-2} inches. If a person is word processing a document with a 12-point font (1.2×10^1), determine the length of each character in inches.

40. The atomic radius of a chlorine atom is 9.9×10^{-9} centimeters. The atomic radius of a sodium atom is 1.86×10^{-8} centimeters. What is the ratio of the atomic radius of chlorine to the atomic radius of sodium?

41. To convert meters to miles, multiply the number of meters by 6.215×10^{-4} miles per meter. The equatorial radius of Jupiter is 71,492,000 meters.
a. Convert the equatorial radius to miles.
b. Determine the volume of Jupiter using the radius found in part **a.**

7.3

Recall	Examples
Addition of polynomials • Use the distributive law to remove parentheses. • Combine like terms.	Add. $(x^3 + 2x^2 - x + 4) + (3x^2 - 6x + 2)$ $= x^3 + 2x^2 - x + 4 + 3x^2 - 6x + 2$ $= x^3 + 5x^2 - 7x + 6$
Subtraction of polynomials • Use the distributive law to remove parentheses by taking the opposite of the subtrahend. • Combine like terms.	Subtract. $(x^3 + 2x^2 - x + 4) - (3x^2 - 6x + 2)$ $= x^3 + 2x^2 - x + 4 - 3x^2 + 6x - 2$ $= x^3 - x^2 + 5x + 2$

Add the polynomials.

42. Add $(5x^4 + 3x^3 + 6x - 3)$ and $(4x^3 + 5x^2 + 7)$.

43. $(3.57z^3 - 2.08z^2 + 8.77z - 1.99) + (4.73 - 2.98z + 5.64z^2)$

In exercises 44–46, subtract the polynomials as indicated.

44. Subtract $(a^4 + 2a^3 + 3a^2 + 4a + 5)$ from $(5a^4 + a^3 + a^2 + a + 1)$.

45. $(65z^4 + 27z^2 + 36)$ decreased by $(16z^3 + 8z + 12)$

46. $\left(\dfrac{5}{8}b^4 + \dfrac{7}{8}b^3 - \dfrac{3}{4}b^2 + \dfrac{1}{2}b - \dfrac{1}{4}\right)$ minus $\left(\dfrac{1}{2}b^4 + \dfrac{3}{8}b^2 + \dfrac{1}{8}b\right)$

47. The cost of producing a certain item consists of a fixed cost of $10.00 to set up the run and $3.50 per item for labor and materials. The items sell for $10.00 each.
  a. Write the total cost function for producing x items, $C(x)$.
  b. Write a revenue function for selling x items, $R(x)$.
  c. Write the profit function, $P(x)$.
  d. What is the profit if 10 items are produced and sold? What if 25 items are produced and sold?

48. Danielle produces prints of her watercolor artwork and frames the prints for sale. The cost of printing and framing x copies of a piece of art is given by the function $f(x) = 150 + 25x$. Danielle's cost of packaging and mailing x copies is given by the function $m(x) = 25 + 4.50x$. Write a total cost function for framing and mailing x copies. Danielle charges $125 for each framed print mailed to a customer. Write a revenue function, $R(x)$. Write a profit function for x prints framed and mailed to customers.

49. U.S. per capita annual consumption of poultry and red meat is monitored by the U.S. Department of Agriculture. The amount of red meat consumed per capita, $r(x)$, in pounds, can be estimated by the function $r(x) = 0.063x^2 + 0.023x + 120.2$, where x is the number of years after 2000. The amount of poultry consumed per capita, $p(x)$, in pounds, can be estimated by the function $p(x) = -0.003x^2 + 1.81x + 77.4$, where x is the number of years after 2000. Find the difference of these two functions $r(x) - p(x)$ in year x.

7.4

Recall	Examples
Multiply polynomials • To multiply a monomial by a monomial, use the rules of exponents. • To multiply a polynomial with more than one term by a monomial, use the distributive law and the rules for exponents. • To multiply two binomials, use the FOIL method. • To multiply two polynomials with more than two terms, use the distributive law and the rules for exponents.	Multiply. $2x^3 \cdot 5xy^2 = 10x^4y^2$ $2x^3(x^2 + 3x - 5) = 2x^5 + 6x^4 - 10x^3$ $\begin{aligned}(x + 3)(2x - 1) &= 2x^2 - x + 6x - 3 \\ &= 2x^2 + 5x - 3\end{aligned}$ $\begin{aligned}(x - 2)(x^2 + 3x - 1) &= x(x^2 + 3x - 1) - 2(x^2 + 3x - 1) \\ &= x^3 + 3x^2 - x - 2x^2 - 6x + 2 \\ &= x^3 + x^2 - 7x + 2\end{aligned}$
Product of the sum and difference of the same two terms $(a + b)(a - b) = a^2 - b^2$	Multiply. $\begin{aligned}(x + 3)(x - 3) &= x^2 - 3^2 \\ &= x^2 - 9\end{aligned}$
Square of a binomial $(a + b)^2 = a^2 + 2ab + b^2$ $(a - b)^2 = a^2 - 2ab + b^2$	Multiply. $\begin{aligned}(x + 2)^2 &= x^2 + 2(x)(2) + 2^2 \\ &= x^2 + 4x + 4\end{aligned}$ $\begin{aligned}(x - 3)^2 &= x^2 - 2(x)(3) + 3^2 \\ &= x^2 - 6x + 9\end{aligned}$

In exercises 50–68, multiply as indicated.

50. $-3a^3b(5ab^3)$

51. $(-6.9x^3z^4)(3.4xz^3)$

52. $6x^3(3x^2 + 2x - 7)$

53. $-7a(3a^6 + a^4 - 2a^2)$

54. $4a^2(2a - 3b + c)$

55. $(p + 6)(p - 9)$

56. $(5x - 2)(x + 11)$

57. $(x + y)(2x - y)$

58. $(2x + 1)(3x^2 + 5x - 4)$

59. $(a - 3)(a^2 + 3a + 9)$

60. $(x^2 + 2x + 3)(x^2 - x + 5)$

61. $(z^2 + 2z - 3)^2$

62. $(b - 4)^3$

63. $(2x - 5)(2x + 5)$

64. $\left(\dfrac{4}{5}x - \dfrac{1}{2}\right)\left(\dfrac{4}{5}x + \dfrac{1}{2}\right)$

65. $(z^2 - 10)(z^2 + 10)$

66. $(y + 9)^2$

67. $(3x - 5)^2$

68. $(x^3 + 3)^2$

69. Simplify.
  a. $(x - 1)^2 + 3x(x - 1)$
  b. $x(x + 2)(x - 1) - x(x + 2)(x + 1)$

70. Given $f(x) = x^2 - 4x + 3$, evaluate $f(x + h)$.

71. The length of a box is 3 inches more than the height. The width of the box is 3 inches less than the height.
  a. Write expressions for the length, width, and height of the box.
  b. Write an expression for the volume of the box.

72. Andre plans to enlarge the deck on his house. The current deck is three times as long as it is wide. Andre plans to double the width and add 9 feet to the length.
   a. Write a polynomial for the current area of the deck.
   b. Write a polynomial for the area of the planned enlarged deck.
   c. What is the difference of the planned area and the current area?

73. The width of a rectangle is nine more than twice the length. Write a simplified polynomial function for the square of the width in terms of the length, x.

74. A car rental agency finds that for every increase of $5.00 on its average daily charge of $49.95, there will be two fewer rentals. Determine a daily revenue function if the number of rentals at $49.95 is 75.

75. A bus service that serves a local college campus discovers that for every $0.70 decrease on an all-day ticket it can sell four extra tickets. If the standard fare is $4.50 per ticket and at that price 50 tickets are sold, write a simplified polynomial function for the bus service's revenue, $R(x)$, in terms of the number of $0.70 decreases, x.

7.5

Recall	Examples
Divide polynomials • To divide a monomial by a monomial, use the rules for exponents. • To divide a polynomial with more than one term by a monomial, use the distributive law and the rules for exponents. • To divide two polynomials with more than one term, use the steps of long division.	Divide. $\dfrac{6x^2}{3x} = \dfrac{6}{3} \cdot \dfrac{x^2}{x} = 2x$ $\dfrac{6x^2 + 3x - 2}{3x} = \dfrac{6x^2}{3x} + \dfrac{3x}{3x} - \dfrac{2}{3x} = 2x + 1 - \dfrac{2}{3x}$ $$\begin{array}{r} 2x + 1 - \dfrac{4}{2x+1} \\[4pt] 2x+1\overline{)\,4x^2 + 4x\ - 3} \\ \underline{-(4x^2 + 2x)} \\ 2x - 3 \\ \underline{-(2x + 1)} \\ -4 \end{array}$$

In exercises 76–84, divide as indicated and express the results with positive exponents only.

76. $\dfrac{144x^6 y^3 z^4}{2x^5 y^2 z^6}$

77. $\dfrac{6ab^2 + 18a^2 b}{3a^2 b^2}$

78. $\dfrac{15b^4 - 10b^3 - 25b^2 + 6}{-5b}$

79. Divide $15x^2 + 19x - 56$ by $5x - 7$.

80. $(8x^2 + 2x - 19) \div (2x + 3)$

81. $\dfrac{x^3 - 44x + 35}{x + 7}$

82. $\dfrac{z^3 - 8}{z - 2}$

83. $(16a^2 - 25) \div (4a + 5)$

84. $(4x^2 + 36x + 81) \div (2x + 9)$

85. Simplify and divide.
$$\frac{(12x - 18)(x - 2) - (6x^2 - 18x)}{(x - 2)^2}$$

86. An owner of a produce stand has fixed costs of $35.00 per day to operate the stand. During October, he sells only pumpkins. He purchases the pumpkins from local farmers at a cost of $1.25 each. In turn, he sells the pumpkins for $3.75 each.
   a. Determine a total cost function for the daily operation of the stand if the owner buys x pumpkins to sell.
   b. Determine a revenue function for selling the x pumpkins.
   c. Determine a daily profit function.
   d. Determine an average daily profit (per pumpkin) function.
   e. What will be the average profit if the owner sells 25 pumpkins in a day?

87. The owner of a pumpkin patch decided he was overstocked with pumpkins and must sell them before Halloween. He was selling the large pumpkins for $2.50 each. He advertised a reduction in the cost of $0.25 per pumpkin purchased. He estimates his cost as $0.75 per pumpkin plus $25.00 for advertisements.
   a. Determine a total cost function, $C(x)$, for x pumpkins.
   b. Determine a revenue function, $R(x)$, for selling x pumpkins to an individual.
   c. Determine a profit function, $P(x)$, for selling x pumpkins to an individual.
   d. Determine an average profit function, $A(x)$, for x pumpkins.

88. The charge to rent a piece of machinery was $2000 for the first year. Every year thereafter, the charge was reduced by 15%. The total charge for renting the machinery for four years is given by the function $c(t) = \dfrac{2000(1 - t^4)}{1 - t}$, where t is equal to 1 minus the percent reduction. Determine a simplified function by performing the division. Evaluate the original function and the simplified function to determine the total charge for four years.

■ Chapter 7 Mixed Review

Simplify. Write with only positive exponents.

1. $m^{-7}n^5$

2. $(3a^{-5}b^4)^{-2}$

3. $\left(\dfrac{21x^4y^{-3}}{7x^3y^2}\right)^2$

4. $\dfrac{5^{-3}t^3}{4^{-3}s^4}$

5. $\dfrac{128a^{-3}b^{-2}}{32a^2b^{-5}}$

6. $\left(\dfrac{2}{5}x^2y^{-3}\right)\left(\dfrac{5}{7}x^{-5}y^{-1}\right)$

7. $\left(\dfrac{15h^2k^5}{3h^{-1}k^7}\right)^{-2}$

8. $s^2 \cdot s^8$

9. $(m+n)^5(m+n)$

10. $(3y^2)^3$

11. $\dfrac{c^9}{c^6}$

12. $(x^0)^8$

13. $-5a^2b^3 \cdot 3ab^4$

14. $\dfrac{1}{2}z^4 \cdot z \cdot z^2$

15. $(b^5)^7$

16. $(-3d)^6$

17. $(-3d)^3$

18. $(x^4y^5z)^4$

19. $\dfrac{25b^5}{5b^3}$

20. $\dfrac{(a+2b)^9}{(a+2b)^2}$

21. $\dfrac{64p^5q^7}{-4p^2q}$

22. $[(4x)^2]^3$

23. $\left[\left(\dfrac{c}{2d}\right)^3\right]^2$

24. $\left(\dfrac{-3a^2}{4b}\right)^3$

25. $\dfrac{(3a^3)^3}{54a^7}$

26. $\left(\dfrac{21a^6b^2}{7a^3b^6}\right)^2$

Add the polynomials as indicated.

27. Add $(2y^2 + 4y - 3)$ and $(8y^2 - 12y + 15)$.

28. $\left(\dfrac{3}{8}a^3 + \dfrac{3}{4}a^2 - \dfrac{5}{8}a + \dfrac{1}{4}\right) + \left(\dfrac{3}{4}a^3 + \dfrac{7}{16}a - \dfrac{5}{8}a^2 + \dfrac{11}{16}\right)$

29. Add $(4.9z^3 - 6.82z^2 + 12z - 11.07)$ and $(4.6 - 1.83z + 4.9z^2)$.

Subtract the polynomials as indicated.

30. $(2x^3 + 6x^2 - 9x + 13) - (4x^3 + 17x^2 - x + 6)$

31. Subtract $(5a^4 + 4a^3 + 3a^2 + 2a + 1)$ from $(6a^4 + 3a^2 + 4a + 5)$.

32. $(117z^4 + 43z^2 + 88)$ decreased by $(18z^3 + 50z + 32)$

Multiply.

33. $11x^5y^6(13x^2y^6)$

34. $-6x(2x^4 - 4x^3 + 6x^2 + 8x - 10)$

35. $9a(4a^5 + 2a^3 - 3a)$

36. $(m - 11)(m + 11)$

37. $(z - 8)^2$

38. $(4a - 7)(a + 13)$

39. $(13 - x)(13 + x)$

40. $(b^3 + 4)^2$

41. $(t + 2)^3$

42. $(7x - 2)(x^2 + 4x - 3)$

43. $(p + q + r)^2$

44. $(b - 4)(b^2 + 4b + 16)$

45. $(y + 5)(y - 9)$

46. $(x^2 + 3x + 1)(x^2 - x + 4)$

Divide. Express your results with positive exponents.

47. $\dfrac{81x^5y^7z}{27x^2y^6z^2}$

48. $\dfrac{14b^4 - 21b^3 - 35b^2 + 24b}{-7b}$

49. $\dfrac{16cd^2 + 8c^2d}{4c^2d^2}$

50. $\dfrac{24x^2 - 37x - 5}{3x - 5}$

51. $(2x^2 - 13x - 50) \div (2x + 5)$

52. $\dfrac{27a^3 - 8}{3a - 2}$

53. $(25x^3 + 39x - 8) \div (5x - 1)$

Write exercises 54 and 55 in expanded form.

54. $-3d^4$

55. $(-3d)^4$

In exercises 56 and 57, simplify.

56. $x(x - 2)(x + 3) + x(x - 2)(x - 3)$

57. $\dfrac{4x(x - 4) - (2x^2 + 3)}{(x - 4)^2}$

58. Given $f(x) = x^3 - 3x + 4$, evaluate $f(a + h)$.

59. Shondra opened a day-care center. Her daily cost to operate the center was $35.00. She spent $2.75 per child each day for supplies and snacks. She charged her clients $10.00 per day for each child left with the center.
 a. Write a total cost function for caring for x children on a given day.
 b. Write a revenue function if x children are cared for on a given day.
 c. Write a profit function for the day.
 d. Write the average profit function per child.
 e. What will be the average profit per child if the center has 10 children being cared for on a given day?

60. Reggie tutored math students. To encourage them to hire him in groups, he offered a discount. The price for tutoring one student was $25 per hour. If a second student attended the tutoring session, the price was reduced 5%. Each subsequent student also received the 5% discount. Reggie left it to the students to figure out how they would divide the cost among themselves. The total amount of money Reggie received for each hour of tutoring five students is given by the function
$$m(s) = \frac{25(1 - s^5)}{1 - s},$$ where s is 1 minus the percentage discount (in decimal form). Write a simplified expression for $m(s)$ by performing the division. Evaluate the original function and the simplified function, given that the discount is 5%.

61. Stars that are a distance of more than 300 light-years away from Earth have uncertainty in the measure of their distances. Earlier in the chapter, it was said that the star Deneb would be the brightest star in the sky if all stars were the same distance from the Earth. The accepted distance of Deneb from Earth is 3227.7 light-years. With the uncertainty taken into account, this distance may really be only about 1600 light-years from Earth. Given that a light-year is about 5.9×10^{12} miles, approximate the distance of 1600 light-years in miles.

62. The length of a rectangular box is 3 inches more than twice the height of the box. The width of the box is equal to the height.
 a. Write expressions for the length, width, and height of the box.
 b. Write an expression for the volume of the box.
 c. What is the volume of the box if its height is 8 inches?

63. A triangle has a base that is 5 cm more than twice its height.
 a. Write a polynomial that represents the area of the triangle if its height is x cm.
 b. What is the area of the triangle if its height is 12 cm?

64. A square patio measures x feet on a side. It will be enlarged to a width that is double the length of a current side and a length that is 5 feet more than the new width.
 a. Write a polynomial for the current area of the patio.
 b. Write a polynomial for the enlarged area of the patio.
 c. What is the difference of the enlarged area and the original area?

65. According to data from the U.S. Department of Energy, the price per gallon of unleaded regular gasoline in cents, $r(x)$, can be represented by the function $r(x) = -0.25x^2 + 24.55x + 87.7$, where x is the number of years after 2000. The price per gallon of unleaded premium gasoline in cents, $p(x)$, can be represented by the function $p(x) = 1.3x^2 + 13.4x + 125.8$, where x is the number of years after 2000. Find the difference of these two price functions, $p(x) - r(x)$, in year x.

66. The atomic radius of a fluorine atom is 6.4×10^{-9} centimeters. The atomic radius of a calcium atom is 1.97×10^{-8} centimeters.
 a. What is the ratio of the atomic radius of calcium to the atomic radius of fluorine?
 b. What is the volume of the calcium atom?

67. In chemistry, Avogadro's number is 6.0221×10^{23}, the number of molecules in a mole of any molecular substance. How many moles are equivalent to 2×10^{12} molecules?

68. A mini-storage business gives a decrease of $10 per unit for businesses renting multiple units. If the standard price is $125, determine a revenue function.

69. A health club rents lockers to nonmembers for $2.50 per visit. If the price is decreased by $0.25, it is found that 10 extra lockers are rented for each such decrease. If the usual number of lockers rented at $2.50 is 32 lockers, write a simplified polynomial function for locker rental revenue, $R(x)$, in terms of x, the number of decreases.

■ Chapter 7 Test

TEST-TAKING TIPS

When studying for a test, you should try to improve your notes. Read your notes and textbook with pencil in hand. Identify and label what you read according to categories. This chapter had many different methods for manipulating polynomials. If you organize your notes by the various methods and work examples for each method, you will more likely recall these methods during a test. Try to think of various kinds of exercises to which you would apply each method. Compare the methods to see what the differences are. List key points that dictate the method to use. If something confuses you, place a big question mark next to it, and try to get help with the question before taking the test. Then go back and read the confusing material again to see if the help you got reduced your confusion.

Simplify and write with positive exponents.

1. $(2x - 1)(2x - 1)^8$

2. $3x^2y^0z^{-3}$

3. $m^{-9}n^4$

4. $(-2x^2y^{-1})^{-3}$

5. $\dfrac{a^{12}}{a^5}$

6. $\left[\dfrac{8p^3}{3q}\right]^{-2}$

7. $\dfrac{24a^2b^{-3}c}{3ab^2c^{-2}}$

8. $\dfrac{(a^2b^4)^3}{a^2b^5c}$

9. Add $(3y^2 + 16 - 7y + 5y^3)$ and $(7y + 6y^2 + 4y^4 - 11)$.

10. Subtract $(2x^4 - 4x^2 - 2x - 9)$ from $(7x^5 + 23x^3 + 17x^2 - 39)$.

Multiply.

11. $(-2p^3q^{-5}r^2)(5.7p^6q^7r)$

12. $-4t(2t^3 - 3t^2 - 8t + 6)$

13. $(9 - 5d)(9 + 5d)$

14. $(3x + 4)(5x - 7)$

15. $(4z - 3)(2z^2 - z + 5)$

16. $(x + 3)^2$

In exercises 17–18, divide. Express your results with positive exponents.

17. $\dfrac{15x^6 + 25x^5 - 5x}{5x^2}$

18. $\dfrac{15x^2 + x - 28}{3x - 4}$

In exercises 19–20, simplify.

19. $(x - 5)^2 + 2x(x - 5)$

20. $\dfrac{6x(x + 1) - (3x^2 + 1)}{(x + 1)^2}$

21. Given $g(x) = x^2 - 5x + 6$, evaluate $g(2 + h)$.

22. The width of a box is 4 inches more than the height. The length is twice the height.
   a. Write a polynomial expression for the volume of the box.
   b. What is the volume if the box has a height of 5 inches?

23. Dallie set up a small business providing fruit baskets to customers. The weekly cost for her shop was $235.00. She spent $5.75 per basket for the basket, fruit, and decorations. She charged her customers $25.00 per basket.
   a. Write a total cost function if Dallie produced x baskets per week.
   b. Write a revenue function if she sold x baskets per week.
   c. Write a profit function for the week.
   d. Write the average profit function per basket.
   e. What will be the average profit per basket if Dallie sold 45 baskets in one week?

24. In 2003, the population density of Charlotte, North Carolina was approximately 2.413×10^3 people per square mile. If the area of the city is 2.423×10^2 square miles, estimate the population of Charlotte.

25. Habitat for Humanity is a popular U.S. charity. In 2002, it received private donations of 4.119×10^9 dollars. Its total income was 7.184×10^9 dollars. How many times greater than the number of private donations was the total income of this charity?

26. The Ångstrom (Å) is a unit of length defined as 1×10^{-10} meters. The radius of an oxygen atom is 0.66 Å.
   a. What is the radius of the oxygen atom in meters?
   b. To convert meters to centimeters, divide the number of meters by 1×10^{-2} meters per centimeter. What is the radius in centimeters?
   c. What is the volume of the oxygen atom in cubic centimeters?

27. Garlic and green tea are two of the top-selling medicinal herbs in the United States. The amount of garlic sold, in millions of dollars, can be estimated by the function $g(x) = 3.5x^2 - 14.5x + 188$, where x is the number of years after 2000. The amount of green tea sold, in millions of dollars, can be estimated by the function $t(x) = 15x^2 - 39x + 92$, where x is the number of years after 2000. Find the difference of these two functions, $g(x) - t(x)$, in year x.

28. A pizza parlor gives a reduced rate for ordering multiple pizzas. The regular price is $12.50 per pizza with a discount of $0.25 per pizza for each pizza ordered. Determine a revenue function.

29. A limousine company's weekday business involves transporting customers to the airport. After experimenting with various fee structures, the company finds that for every increase of $3.50 in its fee it will lose two customers. If the standard fee per person for a trip to the airport is $37.50 and 45 such fares are sold at this price, write a simplified polynomial function for the company's revenue, $R(x)$, in terms of x, the number of increases.

30. Explain the difference between $x^5 \cdot x^8$ and $(x^5)^8$. Simplify each expression.

7

Project

PART I How would you simplify $(x + y)^3$? One way would be to multiply the binomial $(x + y)$ by itself three times. That would be very time consuming and prone to error. Surely, there must be an easier way! You will be happy to know that there is. The famous mathematician Blaise Pascal employed such a method in 1653, called his arithmetical triangle. The first account of his method was printed in 1665. To employ the method, you must construct a triangle as follows:

 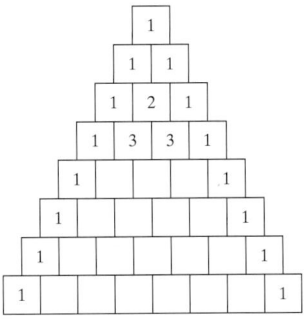

The entry in a particular cell of the triangle is formed by adding the two numbers directly above the cell. Then the numbers along a row are used to determine the coefficients of each term in the simplification of $(x + y)^n$ (that is, any power of a binomial). The top row is the coefficient of $(x + y)^0$, the row below that yields the coefficients for $(x + y)^1$, and so forth. Thus,

$(x + y)^0 = 1$ since the first row contains $\{1\}$.

$(x + y)^1 = x + y$, since the second row contains $\{1, 1\}$

$(x + y)^2 = x^2 + 2xy + y^2$, since the third row contains $\{1, 2, 1\}$

$(x + y)^3 = x^3 + 3x^2y + 3xy^2 + y^3$, since the fourth row contains $\{1, 3, 3, 1\}$

Note that the exponents of x and y in each term sum to the power that you are expanding. So always start with x to that power as the first term, and then reduce the exponent of x by one and increase the exponent of y by one for each subsequent term of the expansion.

One thing you should know for sure:
$(x + y)^n \neq x^n + y^n$!

1. Write the following power expansions, using the remaining rows of the triangle.

   a. $(x + y)^4$ **b.** $(x + y)^5$

   c. $(x + y)^6$ **d.** $(x + y)^7$

2. Now add two more rows to the triangle. Then use these to write the power expansion of $(x + y)^9$.

Pascal's triangle will also work for other binomial power expansions. For example, if we replace y by -1,

$$(x - 1)^4 =$$
$$x^4 + 4x^3(-1)^1 + 6x^2(-1)^2 + 4x^1(-1)^3 + (-1)^4$$
$$= x^4 - 4x^3 + 6x^2 - 4x + 1$$

3. See if you can use Pascal's triangle to determine the following binomial powers:

   a. $(x + 1)^4$ **b.** $(x - 3)^5$

   c. $(2x + 1)^3$ **d.** $(x - 3y)^4$

   e. $(2x - 5y)^6$

PART II Many Internet sites present interesting facts about Pascal's triangle. For example, if you were to take all the cells containing odd numbers and color them one color, and all the cells containing even numbers and color them another color, interesting patterns emerge. Search the Internet for a site that studies Pascal's triangle. Try to find a site that contains a large triangle grid, and print it out. If the cells of the triangle are not completely filled out, complete the calculations for the cells. Then color all the even-numbered cells one color.

1. One of the patterns you should observe is symmetry. Write a short explanation of what this means to you.

2. Another pattern that is present is something called a *fractal*. Research this term, and explain what it means in relation to your triangle.

3. Pascal's triangle is also related to another famous triangle, Sierpinski's triangle. Research this triangle and write a short discussion of the relationship.

PART III Pascal's triangle was studied by others beside Pascal. Omar Khayyám was said to have studied it. Many centuries earlier, it was described by a Chinese mathematician, Yang Hui. Similar triangular arrangements were known to the Arabs about the same time that the Chinese were using it. Find a reference on the history of mathematics, and report on a civilization that was known to use Pascal's triangle. Document your reference. Identify any individuals, and describe what is known about the civilization's use of the triangle.

8

Factoring

I n this chapter, we continue our discussion of polynomials. We will discuss methods of factoring a polynomial—that is, writing the polynomial as a product of factors. This will turn out to be very important for simplifying complicated polynomial expressions and making them easier to work with when we solve equations and inequalities. Factoring is also the basis for working with rational expressions and equations.

Geometric figures often involve areas that can be described by polynomial expressions. Designers and architects must work with these expressions as they draw plans for the efficient use of space in a home, an office, or a manufacturing plant. Engineers and construction workers also use polynomials as a check on the dimensions written on plans and lists of materials. The opening photo shows the Rose Center for Earth and Space, which contains the Hayden Sphere having a diameter of 87 feet enclosed within a cubic-shaped building, 95 feet on each edge. We will describe some of these applications in each section of the chapter. We will conclude the chapter with a project illustrating the use of polynomials in determining the area of rectangular figures.

8.1 GREATEST COMMON FACTORS

OBJECTIVES

1 Determine greatest common factors for sets of monomials.

2 Factor out greatest common monomial factors from polynomials.

3 Factor out greatest common polynomial factors from polynomials.

4 Factor polynomials by grouping.

5 Model real-world situations by factoring out greatest common factors from polynomials.

APPLICATION

The official dimensions of an Olympic-size pool are 50 meters by 21 meters. If the width of a walkway around the pool is x meters on all sides, write a polynomial expression that a designer could use to determine the area of the walkway. Factor the polynomial and discuss the meaning of the factors. If a customer wanted to install a 10-meter walkway around his Olympic-size pool, how many square meters of material would he need?

We will discuss this application further. See page 608.

Objective 8.1.1   ### Determining the Greatest Common Factor

In Chapter P, we stated that two numbers which are multiplied together are called factors of the resulting product. For example, since $2 \cdot 6 = 12$, then 2 and 6 are factors of 12. Also, we may describe a factor of a given number as a number that divides into the given number evenly, or with a remainder of 0. For example, 2 is a factor of 12 because 2 divides into 12 with a remainder of 0.

To determine the integer factors of a number, divide the number by all the integers whose absolute value is less than or equal to the number itself. The integers that divide evenly are factors.

For example, to determine the positive integer factors of 24, we divide 24 by all the positive integers from 1 to 24. The positive integer factors of 24 are 1, 2, 3, 4, 6, 8, 12, and 24. Since we are repeatedly dividing by consecutive integers, the calculator will do this quickly for us by means of a table.

 TAKE NOTE Remember, there is no need to look beyond the numbers whose absolute value is the number itself.

TECHNOLOGY   Integer Factors

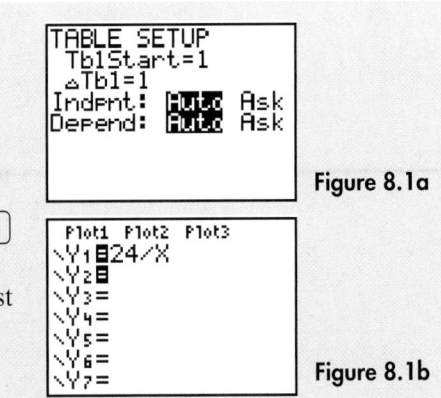

Determine the integer factors of 24.

For **Figure 8.1a**,

Set up the table.

Set the first column for x equal to integer values starting at 1.

[2nd] [WINDOW] (TBLSET) [1] [ENTER] [1] [ENTER] [ENTER] [▼] [ENTER]

For **Figure 8.1b**,

Set the second column for the number, 24, divided by the integer in the first column, x.

[Y=] [2] [4] [÷] [X,T,θ,n]

Figure 8.1a

Figure 8.1b

(continued on page 602)

For **Figure 8.1c**,
View the table to find the integer factors in the first column that correspond to an integer in the second column.

[2nd] [GRAPH] (TABLE)

Move down the table to determine additional positive integer factors of 24.
For **Figure 8.1d**,
Move up the table to determine the negative integer factors of 24.

The integer factors of 24 are $-24, -12, -8, -6, -4, -3, -2, -1, 1, 2, 3, 4, 6, 8, 12$, and 24.

X	Y1
1	24
2	12
3	8
4	6
5	4.8
6	4
7	3.4286

X=1

Figure 8.1c

X	Y1
-7	-3.429
-6	-4
-5	-4.8
-4	-6
-3	-8
-2	-12
-1	-24

X= -7

Figure 8.1d

The **greatest common factor (GCF)** of a set of positive integers is the largest factor common to all the numbers.

To find the GCF of a set of numbers, determine the factors for each number in the set, and then choose the largest factor common to all the sets of factors.

For example, determine the GCF for 24, 36, and 72.

The factors of 24 are 1, 2, 3, 4, 6, 8, 12, and 24.

The factors of 36 are 1, 2, 3, 4, 6, 9, 12, 18, and 36.

The factors of 72 are 1, 2, 3, 4, 6, 8, 9, 12, 18, 24, 36, and 72.

greatest common factor = 12

The GCF of 24, 36, and 72 is 12.

Although we can always determine the GCF of a set of positive integers by this method, an alternative method is needed to find the GCF of a set of monomials with variable factors. In Chapter P, we wrote exponential expressions in expanded form. We use this process for variables. The GCF of a set of variables is the product of the common factors. For example,

$$x^3 y^2 z = x \cdot x \cdot x \cdot y \cdot y \cdot z$$
$$x^2 y^3 z^2 = x \cdot x \cdot y \cdot y \cdot y \cdot z \cdot z$$
$$x^2 y^2 z = x \cdot x \cdot y \cdot y \cdot z$$

$$x \cdot x \cdot y \cdot y \cdot z = x^2 y^2 z$$

The GCF of $x^3 y^2 z$, $x^2 y^3 z^2$, and $x^2 y^2 z$ is $x^2 y^2 z$.

 TAKE NOTE To determine the GCF of a set of variables, we choose the smallest exponent common to that variable.

We expand this process to determine the GCF of the numeric coefficient of the monomials in a set. Before we discuss this method, we need the following definition: A **prime number** is a counting number greater than 1 that has exactly two different counting-number factors, namely, 1 and itself. The prime numbers less than 30 are 2, 3, 5, 7, 11, 13, 17, 19, 23, 29.

To factor a number *completely*, we write the number as a product of prime numbers. For example, factor 24 completely.

$$24 = 2 \cdot 2 \cdot 2 \cdot 3 = 2^3 \cdot 3$$

An alternative method to find the GCF of a set of positive integers is to factor completely each integer in the set and then determine the product of the common prime factors.

For example, determine the GFC for 24, 36, and 72.

$$24 = 2 \cdot 2 \cdot 2 \cdot 3 = 2^3 \cdot 3$$
$$36 = 2 \cdot 2 \cdot 3 \cdot 3 = 2^2 \cdot 3^2$$
$$72 = 2 \cdot 2 \cdot 2 \cdot 3 \cdot 3 = 2^3 \cdot 3^2$$

The GCF of 2^3, 2^2, and 2^3 is 2^2, since 2 is the smallest exponent to which 2 is raised. The GCF of 3, 3^2, and 3^2, is 3^1 or 3, since 1 is the smallest exponent on 3. Thus, the GCF of 24, 36, and 72 is the product $2^2 \cdot 3$ or 12.

DETERMINING THE GREATEST COMMON FACTOR

To find the GCF of a set of monomials, determine the product of

- the GCF of the coefficients;
- the GCF of each variable.

| **EXAMPLE 1** | Determine, for each set of monomials, its greatest common monomial factor. |

a. $12x^2y^4z^3$ and $30xy^3z^2$ **b.** $132a^2b^2c^2$ and $72a^2b^3$

Solution

a. $12x^2y^4z^3$ and $30xy^3z^2$

The GCF of 12 and 30 is 6.
The GCF of x^2 and x is x.
The GCF of y^4 and y^3 is y^3.   *The GCF of the variable factors contains*
The GCF of z^3 and z^2 is z^2.   *the smallest exponent common to each.*

Thus the GCF of $12x^2y^4z^3$ and $30xy^3z^2$ is $6xy^3z^2$.

b. $132a^2b^2c^2$ and $72a^2b^3$

The coefficients 132 and 72 are large, so we will write the coefficients as prime factors.

$$132a^2b^2c^2 = 2^2 \cdot 3^1 \cdot 11a^2b^2c^2$$
$$72a^2b^3 = 2^3 \cdot 3^2a^2b^3$$

The GCF is $2^2 \cdot 3 \cdot a^2b^2 = 12a^2b^2$ *Choose the smallest exponent common to each factor.*

The GCF of $132a^2b^2c^2$ and $72a^2b^3$ is $12a^2b^2$. ■

✓ Objective 8.1.1 *CHECKUP*

1. For each set of monomials, determine its greatest common monomial factor.

a. $12a^2b^3c$; $18a^3bc^2$
b. $84x^3y^5z^2$; $210x^7y^3z^2$

Objective 8.1.2

Factoring Out Greatest Common Monomial Factors

In Chapter P, we reversed the distributive law in order to factor numeric expressions. The distributive law states that

$$a(b + c) = ab + ac, \quad \text{so that} \quad 2(3 + 4) = 2 \cdot 3 + 2 \cdot 4$$

To reverse the law and factor, we write

$$ab + ac = a(b + c), \quad \text{so that} \quad 2 \cdot 3 + 2 \cdot 4 = 2(3 + 4)$$

We are now ready to do the same for polynomials. To factor a polynomial completely, we first determine the greatest common factor (GCF) of its terms and then use the distributive law.

EXAMPLE 2

Factor $2x^2 + 4x + 6$.

Solution

$$2x^2 + 4x + 6 = 2 \cdot x^2 + 2 \cdot 2x + 2 \cdot 3$$
The GCF is 2. Write each term as a product of the GCF and its remaining factor.

$$= 2(x^2 + 2x + 3)$$
Use the distributive law.

We can check all factoring by multiplying the factors and obtaining the original polynomial or by a numeric or graphic check on the calculator if the expression contains only one variable. This will verify that the product of the factors is equivalent to the original polynomial, but it will not verify that the polynomial is factored completely.

Algebraic Check

$2(x^2 + 2x + 3) = 2x^2 + 4x + 6$

Numeric Check

X	Y₁	Y₂
-3	12	12
-2	6	6
-1	4	4
0	6	6
1	12	12
2	22	22
3	36	36

X= -3

Y1 = $2x^2 + 4x + 6$
Y2 = $2(x^2 + 2x + 3)$
The table confirms that Y1 = Y2.

Graphic Check

Y1 = $2x^2 + 4x + 6$

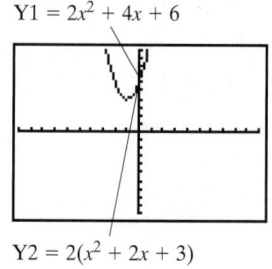

Y2 = $2(x^2 + 2x + 3)$
$(-10, 10, -10, 10)$

The graph confirms that Y1 and Y2 coincide.

 TAKE NOTE A polynomial that is factored completely has no common factors in its terms.

The polynomial $12x - 6y = 2(6x - 3y)$ is not factored completely, because the terms in the polynomial factor $6x - 3y$ have a GCF, 3, and may be factored again. Therefore,

$$12x - 6y = 2(6x - 3y)$$
$$= 2 \cdot 3(2x - y)$$
$$= 6(2x - y)$$

Now $12x - 6y = 6(2x - y)$ is factored completely, because the terms in the binomial $2x - y$ do not have a common factor.

FACTORING OUT THE GCF FROM A POLYNOMIAL

To factor out the GCF from a polynomial,

- Determine the GCF of all the terms. If the GCF is 1, there is no need to continue.
- Write each term as a product of the GCF and another factor.
- Reverse the distributive law, and write a product of the GCF and a polynomial.

 TAKE NOTE If the first term of the polynomial is negative, write a product of the opposite of the GCF and a polynomial.

EXAMPLE 3

Factor completely. Check the factors.

a. $-10x^4y^2 - 15xy^3 - 10x^2y^3$

b. $28a^3b^4 + 42a^4 - 14a^2b^5$

Solution

a. $-10x^4y^2 - 15xy^3 - 10x^2y^3$
$= (-5xy^2) \cdot 2x^3 + (-5xy^2) \cdot 3y + (-5xy^2) \cdot 2xy$ The GCF is $5xy^2$, but the first term is negative, so we factor out $-5xy^2$.
Use the distributive law.

$= -5xy^2(2x^3 + 3y + 2xy)$

The check is left for you.

 TAKE NOTE   When the first term is negative, we factor out a negative GCF.

b. Try to factor out the GCF mentally. Determine the polynomial by asking yourself what factor is needed to determine the original product.

$28a^3b^4 + 42a^4 - 14a^2b^5 = 14a^2(\quad + \quad - \quad)$ The GCF is $14a^2$. Write each term as a product of the GCF and a factor.

$= 14a^2(2ab^4 + 3a^2 - b^5)$ $14a^2 \cdot 2ab^4 = 28a^3b^4$
$14a^2 \cdot 3a^2 = 42a^4$
$14a^2 \cdot -b^5 = -14a^2b^5$

The check is left for you.   ■

✓ Objective 8.1.2 **CHECKUP**

1. Factor completely. Check.
  a. $6a^3b^2 - 12a^2b^3 + 24a^2b^2$
  b. $-8x^2y^3z - 24x^3y^2 + 36xyz$

2. How can you check to see that you have correctly factored out a greatest common factor from a polynomial?

3. After you have factored out a common factor from a polynomial, what should you do to be sure that you have factored out the greatest common factor?

■

Objective 8.1.3   ## Factoring Out Greatest Common Polynomial Factors

A polynomial may have a polynomial other than a monomial as its greatest common factor.

EXAMPLE 4   Factor $2x(x + 1) + 3(x + 1)$.

Solution

$2x(x + 1) + 3(x + 1)$ has two terms, $2x(x + 1)$ and $3(x + 1)$, and a GCF of $(x + 1)$.

$2x(x + 1) + 3(x + 1) = (x + 1)(2x + 3)$ Use the distributive law.

Check to see that the product of the factors is equivalent to the simplification of the original polynomial.

Since the polynomial is in one variable, we can check numerically or graphically as well as algebraically.

Algebraic Check

$(x + 1)(2x + 3) = 2x^2 + 3x + 2x + 3 = 2x^2 + 5x + 3$
is equivalent to the original polynomial,

$2x(x + 1) + 3(x + 1) = 2x^2 + 2x + 3x + 3 = 2x^2 + 5x + 3$

Numeric Check

X	Y1	Y2
-3	6	6
-2	1	1
-1	0	0
0	3	3
1	10	10
2	21	21
3	36	36

X= -3

Y1 = 2x(x + 1) + 3(x + 1)
Y2 = (x + 1)(2x + 3)
The table confirms
Y1 = Y2.

Graphic Check

Y1 = 2x(x + 1) + 3(x + 1)

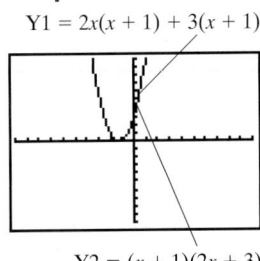

Y2 = (x + 1)(2x + 3)

$(-10, 10, -10, 10)$
The graphs of Y1 and Y2 are coinciding.   ■

EXAMPLE 5 Factor completely and check.

a. $3x(x^2 + 1) + 4(x^2 + 1)$ **b.** $5x^2(2x + 3y) - (2x + 3y)$

Solution

a. $3x(x^2 + 1) + 4(x^2 + 1) = (x^2 + 1)(3x + 4)$ The GCF is $(x^2 + 1)$.
The check is left for you.

b. $5x^2(2x + 3y) - (2x + 3y) = (2x + 3y)(5x^2 - 1)$ The GCF is $(2x + 3y)$.
Remember that $-(2x + 3y)$
is the same as $-1(2x + 3y)$.

The multiplication check is left for you. A numeric or graphic check is not possible, because the polynomial has two variables.

✓ Objective 8.1.3 *CHECKUP*

1. Factor completely and check.
a. $7a(2a + b) + 4b(2a + b)$ **b.** $4x^2(3x - 2) - 3(3x - 2)$

Objective 8.1.4   Factoring by Grouping

A polynomial, such as the polynomial $2ax^2 + 4bx + axy + 2by$, may not appear to have a greatest common factor. However, notice that if we rewrite this polynomial as a sum of two binomials, each binomial has a GCF.

$$2ax^2 + 4bx + axy + 2by$$
$$(2ax^2 + 4bx) + (axy + 2by)$$

The first binomial, $2ax^2 + 4bx$, has a GCF of $2x$. The second binomial, $axy + 2by$, has a GCF of y. Factor out the corresponding GCF from each binomial.

$$2x(ax + 2b) + y(ax + 2b)$$

Now the two terms $2x(ax + 2b)$ and $y(ax + 2b)$ have a GCF of $(ax + 2b)$. Factoring this GCF out of each term, we obtain

$$(ax + 2b)(2x + y)$$

This process is called **factoring by grouping**.
Remember to check your factoring.

FACTORING A POLYNOMIAL WITH FOUR TERMS BY GROUPING
To factor a polynomial with four terms by grouping,

- Factor out the GCF from all of the terms.
- Rewrite the polynomial as a sum of two binomials.
- Factor out the corresponding GCF from each of the two binomials.
- Determine that the binomial in each group is the GCF of the resulting terms.
- Factor out the common binomial.
- If no common factor is found, a different grouping may be needed or the polynomial may not factor.

EXAMPLE 6 Factor completely and check.

a. $2x^2 - 10x + 7x - 35$

b. $3x^4 + 6x^2 - x^2 - 2$

c. $6x^2 - 3x + 12x - 6$

Solution

a. $2x^2 - 10x + 7x - 35$

$= (2x^2 - 10x) + (7x - 35)$ Group the terms.

$= 2x(x - 5) + 7(x - 5)$ Factor out the GCF (2 x and 7) from each group.

$= (x - 5)(2x + 7)$ Factor out (x − 5) from each term.

The check is left for you.

b. $3x^4 + 6x^2 - x^2 - 2$

$= (3x^4 + 6x^2) + (-x^2 - 2)$ Group the terms.

$= 3x^2(x^2 + 2) + (-1)(x^2 + 2)$ Factor out the GCF from each group ($3x^2$ and -1).

$= (x^2 + 2)(3x^2 - 1)$ Factor out (x^2 + 2) from the remaining terms.

The check is left for you.

c. $6x^2 - 3x + 12x - 6$

$= 3(2x^2 - x + 4x - 2)$ Factor out the GCF (3).

$= 3[(2x^2 - x) + (4x - 2)]$ Group the terms.

$= 3[x(2x - 1) + 2(2x - 1)]$ Factor out the GCF of each group.

$= 3(2x - 1)(x + 2)$ Factor out (2x − 1) from the remaining terms.

The check is left for you.

Objective 8.1.4 CHECKUP

1. Factor completely and check.

a. $6x^2 - 10x + 9x - 15$

b. $2y^4 + 2y^2 - 5y^2 - 5$

c. $15a^3 - 20a^2 + 105a^2 - 140a$

Objective 8.1.5   Modeling the Real World

It sometimes happens that the simplest way to model a complicated real-world situation gives rise to a complicated polynomial expression. But once you have the polynomial written down, you should always think about ways to factor it. This will make any operations you need to perform with the polynomial simpler and will help you avoid errors.

EXAMPLE 7   Casey's father decided he would give his son a surprise birthday present. He wrote the following message:

> Every day for a week you will receive a gift of $5 more than you received the day before.

a. Write a polynomial for the total amount Casey will receive if he receives x dollars the first day. Simplify the polynomial.

b. Factor out the GCF from your simplified expression in part **a**.

c. Explain in your own words the meaning of the binomial factor.

Suppose Casey receives $10 the first day from his father.

d. Evaluate the polynomial in part **a** to determine the total amount Casey will receive in a week.

e. Evaluate the binomial factor found in part **b**.

f. Show that the value obtained in part **e** has the meaning given in part **c**.

Solution

a. Let x = amount received the first day

Casey will receive

$$x + (x + 5) + (x + 10) + (x + 15) + (x + 20) + (x + 25)$$
$$+ (x + 30) \text{ or } (7x + 105) \text{ dollars}$$

b. $7x + 105 = 7(x + 15)$

c. The binomial $(x + 15)$ is the average daily amount in dollars that Casey will receive for each of the seven days.

d. $7x + 105 = 7(10) + 105 = 70 + 105 = 175$

If Casey receives $10 on the first day, he will receive $175 in a week from his father.

e. $x + 15 = 10 + 15 = 25$

f. Casey will receive an average of $25 per day for a week. This will amount to

$$\frac{7 \text{ days}}{1 \text{ week}} \cdot \frac{\$25}{1 \text{ day}} = \frac{\$175}{1 \text{ week}}$$

or $175 for the week, the same amount found in part **d**.   ■

EXAMPLE 8

The standard fare for riding a mini bus to the hospital is $13. At this price 20 tickets are sold. The bus company finds that if it decreases the price of the ticket, more people will use the bus service. The revenue function for the bus trip is $R(x) = 260 + 39x - 40x - 6x^2$, where x is the number of decreases.

a. Factor the revenue function.

b. Determine the amount of the decrease in the price of the ticket. Determine the number of additional people per decrease who will use this service if the ticket is discounted this amount.

Solution

a. $R(x) = 260 + 39x - 40x - 6x^2$

$R(x) = (260 + 39x) + (-40x - 6x^2)$ Group the terms.

$R(x) = 13(20 + 3x) - 2x(20 + 3x)$ Factor out the GCF from each group.

$R(x) = (13 - 2x)(20 + 3x)$ Factor out $(20 + 3x)$ from each term.

b. Revenue is the price per ticket times the number of tickets sold.

$$R(x) = (13 - 2x)(20 + 3x)$$

$R(x) = \text{price per ticket} \cdot \text{number of tickets}$

Since $13 is the standard fare and x is the number of the decreases, the price per ticket is $13 - 2x$ or $13 minus $2 per decrease. The price of the ticket is reduced at a rate of $2 per decrease.

The number of tickets is $20 + 3x$ or 20 tickets plus 3 tickets per decrease. For every $2 decrease in the price, the number of tickets sold increases by 3.   ■

 **APPLICATION**

The official dimensions of an Olympic-size pool are 50 meters by 21 meters. If the width of a walkway around the pool is x meters on all sides, write a polynomial expression that a designer could use to determine the area of the walkway. Factor the polynomial and discuss the meaning of the factors. If a customer wanted to install a 10-meter walkway around his Olympic-size pool, how many square meters of material would he need?

Discussion

Pool and walkway:

$21 + 2x = \text{width}$
$50 + 2x = \text{length}$
$(21 + 2x)(50 + 2x) = \text{area}$

Pool:

$21 = \text{width}$
$50 = \text{length}$
$(21)(50) = \text{area}$

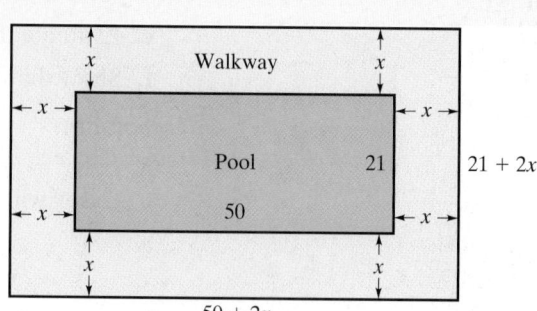

The area of the walkway is the difference of the area of the pool and walkway and the area of the pool.

$$(21 + 2x)(50 + 2x) - (21)(50) = 1050 + 42x + 100x + 4x^2 - 1050$$
$$= 142x + 4x^2$$

The area of the walkway is $142x + 4x^2$ square meters.

$$142x + 4x^2 = 2x(71 + 2x) \qquad \text{Factor.}$$

The area of the walkway is equivalent to a rectangle $2x$ meters by $(71 + 2x)$ meters.

If the walkway is 10 meters wide, the area covered by the walkway is

$$142x + 4x^2 = 142(10) + 4(10)^2 \quad \text{or} \quad 2x(71 + 2x) = (2 \cdot 10)(71 + 2 \cdot 10)$$
$$= 1820 \qquad\qquad\qquad\qquad = 1820$$

The area of the walkway is 1820 square meters.

Objective 8.1.5 **CHECKUP**

1. Katie gave up smoking as her New Year's resolution. Her dad told her that as an incentive, every month for six months he would give her $12 more than he gave her the month before if she continued refraining from smoking.
   a. Write a polynomial for the total amount of money Katie will receive if she receives x dollars after not smoking for the first month and she continues to not smoke for six months.
   b. Factor the polynomial and explain what each factor represents.
   c. If her dad gives her $50 the first month, how much will Katie receive if she doesn't smoke for the six months?
   d. What is her average monthly amount received for not smoking? Does this check with your explanation in part **b**?

2. Many new office buildings have an atrium in the center that opens up to the full height of the building. One such building has an atrium that measures 150 feet long and 100 feet wide.

The atrium is surrounded by offices that add an additional x feet to all sides of the atrium. Write a polynomial for the area of the floor space of the offices. Factor the polynomial and discuss the meaning of the factors. If the offices add an additional 40 feet to all sides of the atrium, how many square feet of area do the offices occupy?

3. The standard rate for a weekend tour is $25 per person. At this price, 20 tickets are sold. The tour company manager finds that if he increases the price of the ticket, fewer people will use the tour company's service. The revenue function for the tour is $R(x) = 500 + 20x - 75x - 3x^2$, where x is the number of increases.
   a. Factor the revenue function.
   b. Determine the amount of the increase in the price of the ticket.
   c. Determine the number of fewer tickets per increase if the ticket is increased by this amount.

8.1 EXERCISES

 Student Solutions Manual   PH Math/Tutor Center   CD Video Math XL MathXL® MyMathLab MyMathLab   Interactmath.com

For each set of monomials, determine the greatest common monomial factor.

1. $60a^2b^4c^3$; $50a^3bc^2$
2. $45x^2yz$; $90x^3yz^2$
3. $252x^3y^4$; $180x^2z$
4. $126u^3v^4$; $315u^5v^2$
5. $45pq^4$; $135r^4s$
6. $80c^5d^2$; $24a^2b^2$
7. $63xyz$; $98xyz$
8. $40a^2bc$; $250a^2bc$
9. $60a^2b^3c^3$; $90ab^2c$; $150a^2b^4c^2$
10. $120x^2y^4z^3$; $270x^2y^2z$; $750xy^2z$

Factor exercises 11–70 completely and check.

11. $4x + 12y$
12. $-7x + 21y$
13. $8x^3 - 4x^2 + 12x - 24$
14. $9d^5 - 12d^3 + 21d + 24$
15. $3a^4 - 5a^3 + 7a^2$
16. $-4p^5 - 9p^4 - 11p^3$
17. $-3x^5 - 9x^4 - 12x^3$
18. $5m^3 - 15m^2 + 30m$
19. $7x^4y^2 - 3x^2y^2 + 9x^2y^4$
20. $-3u^3v + 4u^2v^2 - 8uv^3$
21. $8a^5b^3c + 4a^4b^2 + 16a^3c$
22. $7x^3y^5 - 21x^2y^4 + 63xy^3$
23. $66u^3v^4 - 88u^4v^3$
24. $-39c^2d^3 + 52c^3d^2$
25. $3x^3 + 5y^4$
26. $p^4 + 7q^2$
27. $5x(x + 3) - 4(x + 3)$
28. $3y(y + 7) - 5(y + 7)$
29. $x(2x + y) + 2y(2x + y)$
30. $3a(a + 3b) + b(a + 3b)$
31. $6x^2 + 10x + 21x + 35$

32. $15x^2 + 6x + 10x + 4$

33. $x^2 + 8x + x + 8$

34. $y^2 + 4y + y + 4$

35. $2a^2 + 3a - 2a - 3$

36. $2z^2 + 7z - 2z - 7$

37. $2x^2 + xy + 4xy + 2y^2$

38. $3p^2 + 9pq + pq + 3q^2$

39. $x^2 + xy - xy - y^2$

40. $m^2 + mn - mn - n^2$

41. $10xy - 55y + 24x - 132$

42. $28xy + 21y - 36x - 27$

43. $12ac + 3bc + 4ad + bd$

44. $10mp + 5np + 4mq + 2nq$

45. $2x^2y^2 + 3xy - 8xy - 12$

46. $7a^2b^2 - 2ab + 21ab - 6$

47. $-x^2 - 3x - xy - 3y$

48. $-a^2 - ab - 7a - 7b$

49. $x^4 + x^2y^2 + 2x^2y^2 + 2y^4$

50. $3p^4 - 3p^2q^2 + p^2q^2 - q^4$

51. $ac + bc + ad + bd$

52. $xy + y^2 + zx + zy$

53. $8x^2 + 4x + 24x + 12$

54. $21y^2 + 14y + 84y + 56$

55. $u^4 + u^3v - 2u^3v - 2u^2v^2$

56. $a^4 + a^3b + 2a^3b + 2a^2b^2$

57. $6a^4 + 6a^3b^2 + 6a^3b + 6a^2b^3$

58. $5c^5 + 5c^4d^2 + 5c^3d + 5c^2d^3$

59. $-4x^3 - 12x^2 - 2x^2 - 6x$

60. $-10y^3 + 50y^2 - 15y^2 + 75y$

61. $4x^2 + 6xz + 6xz + 9z^2$

62. $9u^2 + 12uv + 12uv + 16v^2$

63. $36a^2 - 30ab - 30ab + 25b^2$

64. $16x^2 + 12xy + 12xy + 9y^2$

65. $5m^3 + 5m^2n + 5m^2n + 5mn^2$

66. $7p^3 - 7p^2q - 7p^2q + 7pq^2$

67. $2x^3 + 3x + 8x^2 + 12$

68. $5c^4 + 7c - 15c^3 - 21$

69. $5a^2x + 2b^2x + 15a^2y + 6b^2y$

70. $2a^2c + 3b^2c + 14a^2d + 21b^2d$

In exercises 71–74, factor completely.

71. Simple interest amount: $A = P + Prt$

72. Vertical position: $s(t) = -16t^2 + v_0t$

73. Surface area of right circular cylinder: $S = 2\pi r^2 + 2\pi rh$

74. Area of a trapezoid: $A = \frac{1}{2}hb + \frac{1}{2}hB$

Miscellaneous

75. Amy's dad promised her that for each soccer goal she made, he would give her $1 more than he gave her for her last soccer goal. She made nine goals during the season.

a. Write a polynomial for the total amount of money Amy will receive if she receives x dollars for her first goal.

b. Factor out the GCF from the simplified expression in part **a**.

c. Explain what the factors in part **b** represent.

d. If Amy's dad gave her $10 for her first goal, determine the total amount of money Amy received. Check your explanation in part **c**, using $10 for x.

76. Wynona started a program to quit smoking. She decided to limit herself to two fewer cigarettes than her limit from the day before. She was able to hold to the program.

a. Write a polynomial for the total number of cigarettes Wynona smoked during the first week if she smoked c cigarettes the first day.

b. Factor out the GCF from the simplified expression in part **a**.

c. Explain what the factors in part **b** represent.

d. If Wynona smoked 20 cigarettes the first day, determine the total number of cigarettes she smoked the first week. Does your explanation in part **c** check, using that number? How many cigarettes did she smoke on the seventh day of the week?

77. In a sports program with n teams, it can be shown that the number of times each team must play every other team exactly two times in the program is given by $n^2 - n$.

a. Factor the expression completely.

b. Evaluate the original expression and the factored expression for a program that has 21 teams in it.

c. Which expression was easier to evaluate and why?

78. It can be shown that in a sports program with n teams, the number of ways in which you can have three teams finish in the top three positions is given by $n^3 - 2n^2 - n + 2n$.

a. Factor this expression completely.

b. Evaluate the original expression and the factored expression for a program that has 11 teams in it.

c. Which expression was easier to evaluate and why?

Geometry

79. The area of a rectangle is given by the expression $w^2 + 5w$. Factor this expression to determine the dimensions of the rectangle.

80. The area of a parallelogram is given by the expression $b^2 - 3b$. Factor this expression to determine the base and height of the parallelogram.

81. The area of a rectangle is given by the expression $x^2 + 7x - 3x - 21$. Factor this expression, using grouping to determine algebraic expressions for the rectangle's width and length.

82. The area of a square is given by the expression $4x^2 + 6x + 6x + 9$. Factor this expression, using grouping to determine an algebraic expression for the length of the square's sides.

83. An employee parking lot measures 50 feet by 200 feet. It is surrounded by a green strip of grass and shrubs that adds x feet to all of its sides. Write a polynomial for the area of the green strip. Factor the polynomial and discuss the meaning of the factors. If the green strip adds 10 feet to all sides of the parking lot, how many square feet of greenery is there?

84. A painting measures 30 inches in length and 24 inches in width. The painting is surrounded by a frame that adds x inches to each side. Write a polynomial for the area of the frame facing out from the painting. Factor the polynomial and discuss the meaning of the factors. If the frame adds 5 inches to each side of the painting, how many square inches of frame are added to the face of the painting.

Business

85. Nathan's Tours offers a fall tour to the mountains. The regular price is $100 per package. A reduction per package purchased is offered to groups. The revenue for a certain group is $R(x) = 100x - 3x^2$, where x is the number of packages purchased (or reductions). Factor the revenue function. Determine the amount per reduction in the cost of the package.

86. Mountain View Restaurant offers dinner specials to large groups. The regular price for dinner is $25, and the restaurant will reduce the charge per person in the group. The revenue for a certain group is $R(x) = 25x - x^2$, where x is the number of persons in the group (or reductions). Factor the revenue function. Determine the amount per reduction in the cost of dinner.

87. A day-care manager charges $12 per half-day for a child under 3 years of age. At this charge he has 5 children. In order to increase the number of children, he plans to reduce his charge. The revenue will be $R(x) = 60 - 5x + 24x - 2x^2$, where x is the number of decreases. Factor the function. Determine the amount of each decrease and the number of additional children per decrease.

88. A hotel manager determines that if she reduces the nightly charge of a room that rents for $100, she will have more customers than the 50 she has at this price. The revenue will be $R(x) = 5000 + 300x - 50x - 3x^2$, where x is the number of decreases. Factor the revenue function. Determine the amount of each decrease and the number of additional customers per decrease.

89. A theme park has daily revenues of $R(x) = 15,000 + 5000x - 1125x - 375x^2$, where x is the number of 3D theatre shows presented. Use grouping to factor this polynomial completely.

90. A car dealer estimates that his weekly revenues are $R(x) = 460 + 115x + 100x + 25x^2$, where x is the number of cars sold. Use grouping to factor this polynomial completely.

91. After employing a mathematical procedure, a student needs to factor the following function: $6x(2x + 1)^2 + 12x^2(2x + 1)$. Factor completely and check.

92. When working a mathematical example for her students, an instructor of higher math needs to factor the following function: $d(x) = 6x^2(3x - 1)^2 + 12x^3(3x - 1)$. Factor completely and check.

8.1 Calculator Exercises

Part 1. Finding the Greatest Common Factor by Using the Calculator

The Tl-84 Plus has an instruction under the CATALOG key that will find the greatest common divisor (gcd) of two numbers. This will be the greatest common factor of the two numbers. To use the instruction, press [2nd] [0] **(CATALOG)**, which lists the catalog of all instructions. Then scroll down the catalog listing until the cursor is pointed at gcd(, and press [ENTER]. This will place the instruction on the home screen, after which you can type in the two numbers, separated by a comma, for which you want the greatest common factor. Then type an end parenthesis. When you press [ENTER], the calculator will display the GCF. For example, if you wish the GCF of the numbers 56 and 14, the following screens find it:

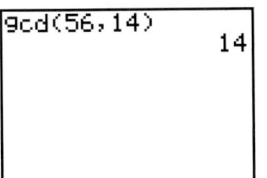

If you need to find the GCF of three or more numbers, enter them in pairs, and find the GCF of each pair. Then select the smallest GCF of all the pairs, which will be the GCF of all the numbers. Can you explain why?

For example, find the GCF of 56, 14, and 24.

```
gcd(56,14)
            14
gcd(56,24)
             8
gcd(14,24)
             2
```

The GCF of 56, 14, and 24 is 2, since that is the largest number that divides all three numbers evenly.
Use this calculator feature to find the greatest common factors in the following exercises.

1. $105x^2yz^3$, $147xy^2z^2$ **2.** $104ab^2c^2$, $65b^3c$, $143a^2c^2$

3. $108x^3$, $96x^2$, $72x^5$ **4.** $64abc$, $128abc^2$, $192ab^2c$, $224a^2bc$

Part 2. Factoring a Number into Prime Factors by Using the Calculator

Graphing calculators can be programmed to perform certain operations. The program[1] that follows will factor a number into a product of prime factors. To place your calculator into a program edit mode, enter [PRGM] [▶] [▶] to New, and then press the [ENTER] key. This will place the calculator into a mode so that you can enter a program. At each step, key in the instructions, and press [ENTER] to move to the next step. If you make a mistake, use the arrow keys to move back up and correct it. Many of the instructions use keys with which you are already familiar. Any other programming instruction can be found by pressing the [PRGM] key, using the arrow keys to find the instruction, and then pressing the [ENTER] key to select the instruction. Enter the following program:

PROGRAM:PRIME
Input N
N→M
1→C
2→D
Lbl 1
M/D→B
If fPart(B)=0

[1]By permission of Nan Burwell, Pellissippi State Technical Community College.

Goto 2
C+2→D
D→C
If D≥($\sqrt{\ }$(M)+1)
Goto 3
Goto 1
Lbl 2
iPart(B)→M
Disp D
Pause
If M=1
Goto 3
Goto 1
Lbl 3
If M≠1
Disp M
If M=N
Disp "PRIME"
Disp "DONE"

Note: fPart(is found in the NUM menu under the [MATH] key.

iPart(is found in the NUM menu under the [MATH] key.

The equation sign and the inequality signs are found under the [2nd] [MATH] (TEST) keys.

To run the program, enter [PRGM] [▼] to go to the appropriate program, and then press [ENTER] once to select the program and again to execute the program. At the question mark prompt, key in the number to be factored, and press [ENTER] repeatedly until the calculator indicates that the factoring is done. If you press [ENTER] again, the program will be restarted so that you can enter another number.

Use the program to factor the following numbers completely:

1. 30   **2.** 108   **3.** 525   **4.** 1287   **5.** 1547   **6.** 4500

8.1 Writing Exercises

Gennifer was asked to completely factor the polynomials listed. In each case, the answer she gave was incorrect. Explain what is wrong with each result.

1. $-8a - 4b = -4(2a - b)$ **2.** $5x^2 + 10x = 5(x^2 + 2x)$

3. $4x^2 + 3x + 4x + 3 = (4x + 3)(x + 0)$

4. $4y^3 - 6y^2 = 2^2 \cdot y^3 - 2 \cdot 3 \cdot y^2$

8.2 FACTORING PERFECT-SQUARE TRINOMIALS, DIFFERENCES OF SQUARES, AND SUMS AND DIFFERENCES OF CUBES

OBJECTIVES

1. Factor a perfect-square trinomial.
2. Factor a difference of two squares.
3. Factor a sum or difference of two cubes.
4. Model real-world situations by factoring special products.

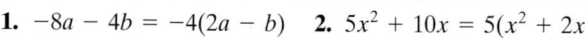

APPLICATION

A certified report for Quality Jewelry reports that an emerald-cut square diamond of 4.22 carats is worth $59,360. To make the diamond more lustrous, two sides of the face are decreased by x millimeters. The surface area of the face, in square millimeters, of this more lustrous diamond is given by the polynomial $88.36 - 19.8x + x^2$. Factor the polynomial, and determine the length of the sides of the original diamond.

After completing this section, we will discuss this application further. See page 617.

In the previous chapter, we determined the product of two polynomials. We identified certain of these products as special products. If we can identify these products, we can determine their factors quickly.

Objective 8.2.1   Factoring a Perfect-Square Trinomial

One special product is the square of a binomial.

$$(a + b)^2 = a^2 + 2ab + b^2$$
$$(a - b)^2 = a^2 - 2ab + b^2$$

We can reverse this operation by factoring the trinomial into a square of a binomial.

FACTORING A PERFECT-SQUARE TRINOMIAL

To factor a perfect-square trinomial, we write

$$a^2 + 2ab + b^2 = (a + b)^2$$
$$a^2 - 2ab + b^2 = (a - b)^2$$

In order to do this factoring, we need to recognize when a polynomial is a perfect-square trinomial. In a perfect-square trinomial, the first and last terms are perfect squares, and the middle term is either positive or negative twice the product of the terms that are squared—that is, $a^2 + 2ab + b^2$ or $a^2 - 2ab + b^2$. The binomial factor of a perfect-square trinomial is $(a + b)^2$ or $(a - b)^2$. For example,

$$a^2 + 2\ a\ b + b^2 = (a + b)^2$$
$$x^2 + 10x + 25 = (x)^2 + 2(x)(5) + (5)^2 = (x + 5)^2$$

$$a^2 - 2\ a\ b + b^2 = (a - b)^2$$
$$x^2 - 10x + 25 = (x)^2 - 2(x)(5) + (5)^2 = (x - 5)^2$$

We can check factoring by multiplying the factors; the result should be the polynomial that was factored. We can also check numerically or graphically on the calculator.

Algebraic Check

$$(x - 5)^2 = (x - 5)(x - 5)$$
$$= x^2 - 5x - 5x + 25$$
$$= x^2 - 10x + 25$$

Numeric Check

X	Y1	Y2
-3	64	64
-2	49	49
-1	36	36
0	25	25
1	16	16
2	9	9
3	4	4

X= -3

$Y1 = x^2 - 10x + 25$
$Y2 = (x - 5)^2$
The table shows Y1 = Y2.

Graphic Check

$Y1 = x^2 - 10x + 25$

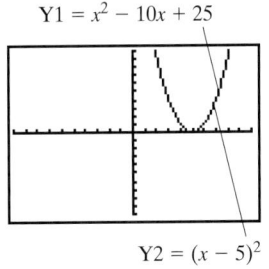

$Y2 = (x - 5)^2$

$(-10, 10, -10, 10)$
The graphs are coinciding.

EXAMPLE 1

Factor completely and check.

a. $4x^2 + 12xy + 9y^2$ **b.** $3x^2 - 24xy + 48y^2$

c. $m^2 + 12m + 144$ **d.** $x^4 + 18x^2 + 81$

Solution

a. $4x^2 + 12xy + 9y^2 = (2x)^2 + 2(2x)(3y) + (3y)^2$ *Determine that $a = 2x$ and $b = 3y$.*
$$= (2x + 3y)^2$$
The check is left for you.

b. $3x^2 - 24xy + 48y^2 = 3(x^2 - 8xy + 16y^2)$ *Factor out a common factor.*
$$= 3[(x)^2 - 2(x)(4y) + (4y)^2]$$ *Determine that $a = x$ and $b = 4y$.*
$$= 3(x - 4y)^2$$

The check is left for you.

c. $m^2 + 12m + 144$ does not factor. The first and last terms are perfect squares: m^2 and 12^2. However, the middle term is not $2(m)(12)$.

d. $x^4 + 18x^2 + 81 = (x^2)^2 + 2(x^2)(9) + (9)^2$ *Determine that $a = x^2$ and $b = 9$.*
$$= (x^2 + 9)^2$$

The check is left for you.

Objective 8.2.1 *CHECKUP*

1. Factor completely and check.

   a. $49a^2 + 42ab + 9b^2$ b. $5x^2 - 60x + 180$

   c. $p^2 - 8p + 64$ d. $y^4 + 8y^2 + 16$

2. What should you look for in a polynomial in order to factor it as a perfect-square trinomial?

■

Objective 8.2.2   Factoring a Difference of Two Squares

One special product consists of two factors, one the sum and the other the difference of the same two terms.

$$(a + b)(a - b) = a^2 - b^2$$

If we reverse this operation, we obtain two binomial factors.

> **FACTORING THE DIFFERENCE OF TWO SQUARES**
>
> To factor the difference of two squares, we write
>
> $$a^2 - b^2 = (a + b)(a - b)$$

In order to do this factoring, we need to recognize a polynomial as the difference of two squares. The difference of two squares is a binomial consisting of the subtraction of two perfect-square terms—that is, $a^2 - b^2$. The factors of a difference of two squares are $(a + b)$ and $(a - b)$.

For example, factor $x^2 - 25$ completely.

$$a^2 \quad - \quad b^2 \quad = \quad (a + b)(a - b)$$
$$\downarrow \qquad \downarrow \qquad \downarrow \quad \downarrow \; \downarrow \qquad \downarrow$$
$$x^2 - 25 = (x)^2 - (5)^2 = (x + 5)(x - 5)$$

The factors may be checked, as with the previous objective.

EXAMPLE 2   Factor completely and check.

a. $4x^2 - 9y^2$ b. $3x^2 - 48$

c. $144 + x^2y^2$ d. $m^4 - 81$

Solution

a. $4x^2 - 9y^2 = (2x)^2 - (3y)^2$ Determine that $a = 2x$ and $b = 3y$.

   $ = (2x + 3y)(2x - 3y)$ Write a product of the sum and difference of a and b.

   The check is left for you.

b. $3x^2 - 48 = 3(x^2 - 16)$ Factor out the common factor.

   $ = 3[(x)^2 - (4)^2]$ Determine that $a = x$ and $b = 4$.

   $ = 3(x + 4)(x - 4)$ Write the special product as a product of the sum and difference of a and b.

   The check is left for you.

c. $144 + x^2y^2$ will not factor. This is not a difference of squares, but a *sum* of squares.

d. Remember that a variable term is a perfect square when its exponent is an even number. That is, x^4 is a perfect square of x^2 because $x^4 = (x^2)^2$, and x^6 is a perfect square of x^3 because $x^6 = (x^3)^2$.

Therefore, we can factor the difference of two squares if the variable terms have even exponents.

$$m^4 - 81 = (m^2)^2 - (9)^2 \qquad \text{Determine that } a = m^2 \text{ and } b = 9.$$
$$= (m^2 + 9)(m^2 - 9) \qquad \text{Write a product of the sum and difference of } a \text{ and } b.$$
$$= (m^2 + 9)[(m)^2 - (3)^2] \qquad \text{Determine the perfect-square terms of the second factor.}$$
$$= (m^2 + 9)(m + 3)(m - 3) \qquad \text{Write the second factor as a product of a sum and a difference.}$$

The check is left for you.

 Objective 8.2.2 CHECKUP

1. Factor completely and check.
   a. $25x^2 - 16y^2$ b. $2z^2 - 18$
   c. $a^2 + b^2$ d. $c^4 - 16$

2. What are the things you should look for in a polynomial in order to factor it as the difference of two squares?

Objective 8.2.3   **Factoring a Sum or Difference of Cubes**

A third type of polynomial that we need to be able to factor results in the product of a binomial and a trinomial. Complete the following set of exercises to determine this product and to discover a pattern you can use to factor it.

 Guided Discovery 1   Factoring a Sum or Difference of Two Cubes

Multiply.

1. $(x + 5)(x^2 - 5x + 25)$

2. $(x - 5)(x^2 + 5x + 25)$

Write a rule to factor the sum or difference of two cubes.

The first product is a sum of two cubes. The second product is a difference of two cubes. In order to factor these polynomials, we turn these results around and write a binomial and trinomial factor.

FACTORING THE SUM OR DIFFERENCE OF TWO CUBES

To factor the sum or difference of two cubes, we write

$$a^3 + b^3 = (a + b)(a^2 - ab + b^2)$$
$$a^3 - b^3 = (a - b)(a^2 + ab + b^2)$$

 TAKE NOTE The binomial factor has the same sign as the polynomial being factored. The middle term of the trinomial has the opposite sign of the polynomial being factored. The last term in the trinomial is always positive.

$$a^3 + b^3 = (a + b)(a^2 - ab + b^2) \qquad \text{Remember SOAP.}$$
$$ S O AP \qquad\qquad S = \text{same}$$

$$a^3 - b^3 = (a - b)(a^2 + ab + b^2) \qquad O = \text{opposite}$$
$$ S O AP \qquad\qquad AP = \text{always positive}$$

If you cannot remember this, divide the sum of two cubes, $a^3 + b^3$, by $a + b$ and the difference of two cubes, $a^3 - b^3$, by $a - b$ to obtain the trinomial factor.

For example, factor $x^3 - 27$ completely.

$$a^3 - b^3 = (a - b)(a^2 + a b + b^2)$$

$$x^3 - 27 = (x)^3 - (3)^3 = (x - 3)[x^2 + x(3) + (3)^2]$$
$$= (x - 3)(x^2 + 3x + 9)$$

The factors may be checked by multiplying, or they may be checked numerically or graphically on your calculator.

EXAMPLE 3 Factor completely and check.

a. $m^3 + 64$ **b.** $27x^3 - 125y^3$

Solution

a. $m^3 + 64 = (m)^3 + (4)^3$ Determine $a = m$ and $b = 4$.
$$= (m + 4)[m^2 - 4m + (4)^2]$$ Write a product of a binomial factor and a trinomial factor.
$$= (m + 4)(m^2 - 4m + 16)$$ Simplify.

The check is left for you.

b. $27x^3 - 125y^3 = (3x)^3 - (5y)^3$ Determine $a = 3x$ and $b = 5y$.
$$= (3x - 5y)[(3x)^2 + (3x)(5y) + (5y)^2]$$ Write a product of a binomial and a trinomial.
$$= (3x - 5y)(9x^2 + 15xy + 25y^2)$$ Simplify.

The check is left for you.

Objective 8.2.3 CHECKUP

1. Factor completely and check.
a. $a^3 - 8$ **b.** $8x^3 + 27y^3$

2. In factoring a polynomial, how would you recognize it to be the sum or difference of two cubes?

Objective 8.2.4 Modeling the Real World

Many applications involving the area of a figure are modeled by polynomials. If the shape of the original figure is a rectangle, then factoring these polynomials will result in the length and the width of the figure. This will enable us to work with figures when the dimensions vary and are written in terms of a variable.

EXAMPLE 4

Lynn wants to redesign the square deck on her house, using as much of the outside railing and all of the usable carpet as possible. However, she cannot use 9 square feet of the outdoor carpet because it has grease stains from the grill.

a. Determine the possible dimensions of Lynn's new deck in terms of the original side of length x feet.

b. If Lynn's original deck was 12 feet by 12 feet, determine the new deck's dimensions.

c. Using the dimensions found in part **b**, draw two possible decks.

d. Determine the amount of railing for each deck in part **c**.

e. If only the original railing is used, determine whether either drawing in part **c** is possible.

Solution

a. Since the length of the original deck (carpet) is x feet, the area of the original square deck is x^2.

The new deck (carpet) area is 9 square feet less than the original area, or $x^2 - 9$.

To determine the dimensions of the new deck, we must factor the area to determine the dimensions that were multiplied together.

$$x^2 - 9 = (x)^2 - (3)^2 = (x + 3)(x - 3)$$

The resulting dimensions are $(x + 3)$ feet and $(x - 3)$ feet.

b. If $x = 12$, then the new deck's dimensions are 15 feet $(x + 3)$ by 9 feet $(x - 3)$.

c.

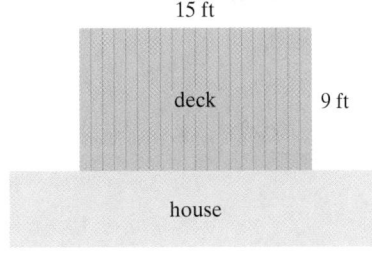

d. The first drawing will need $9 + 15 + 9$, or 33, feet of railing. The second drawing will need $15 + 9 + 15$, or 39, feet of railing.

e. The original deck had $12 + 12 + 12$, or 36, feet of railing. The first drawing in part **c** shows the only possible deck using these conditions. ∎

APPLICATION

A certified report for Quality Jewelry reports that an emerald-cut square diamond of 4.22 carats is worth $59,360. To make the diamond more lustrous, two sides of the face are decreased by x millimeters. The surface area of the face, in square millimeters, of this more lustrous diamond is given by the polynomial $88.36 - 19.8x + x^2$. Factor the polynomial, and determine the length of the sides of the original diamond.

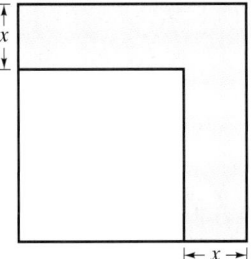

Discussion

The polynomial is a perfect-square trinomial, because $9.4^2 = 88.36$ and $2(9.4) = 19.8$.

$$88.36 - 19.8x + x^2 = (9.4 - x)^2 \quad \text{Factor.}$$

The diamond face is $9.4 - x$ millimeters on a side, or 9.4 millimeters minus x millimeters. Therefore, the original diamond was 9.4 millimeters on a side.

✓ Objective 8.2.4 CHECKUP

1. Lynn has a square plot in her yard, measuring 16 feet on a side, that she wants to make into an outdoor sitting area. She plans to put a square patio in the plot for furniture, with the remainder of the plot landscaped as a garden.

a. Determine a polynomial for the area of the plot available for landscaping if the patio measures p feet on a side.

b. Factor the polynomial for the area. Use the factors to determine the dimensions of an equivalent rectangular garden area if the patio will be 7 feet on a side.

c. Lynn sees an advertisement for garden plants which states that the package contains enough plants for a 10-by-20-foot garden. Will the package be large enough for her garden?

2. Marge decided to salvage an antique quilt that had damage along one side. To maintain the integrity of the design, she had to trim each side of the quilt. The original shape of the quilt was square, and an equal width was trimmed from each side. Given that Marge trimmed x feet from each side, a poly-nomial representing the new area of the quilt is $81 - 18x + x^2$ square feet. Factor the polynomial, and de-termine the length of each side of the original quilt. If 1.25 feet were trimmed from each side, use the factored expres-sion to determine the area of the trimmed quilt.

8.2 EXERCISES

 Student Solutions Manual    PH Math/Tutor Center   CD Video   Math XL MathXL®   MyMathLab MyMathLab   Interactmath.com

In exercises 1–58, factor completely. Check by multiplication, by a table of values, or graphically.

1. $x^2 + 4x + 4$

2. $p^2 + 14p + 49$

3. $16z^2 + 40z + 25$

4. $36x^2 + 84x + 49$

5. $x^2 + 13x + 169$

6. $y^2 + 12y + 144$

7. $x^2 - 10x + 25$

8. $y^2 - 16y + 64$

9. $36z^2 - 60z + 25$

10. $64m^2 - 48m + 9$

11. $c^2 - 16d + 16d^2$

12. $z^2 - 20z + 25$

13. $a^4 - 32a^2 + 256$

14. $b^4 - 98b^2 + 2401$

15. $16x^4 - 72x^2 + 81$

16. $625y^4 - 200y^2 + 16$

17. $3x^2 + 24x + 48$

18. $16x^2 + 32x + 16$

19. $2a^2 - 12a + 18$

20. $5x^2 - 70x + 245$

21. $p^3 + 2p^2q + pq^2$

22. $y^2z^2 + 4yz^3 + 4z^4$

23. $2p^5 - 4p^3q^2 + 2pq^4$

24. $5u^5 - 40u^3v^2 + 80uv^4$

25. $m^5 + 2m^3n^2 + mn^4$

26. $p^7 + 2p^5q^2 + p^3q^4$

27. $x^2 - 100$

28. $y^2 - 64$

29. $121 - c^2$

30. $196 - b^2$

31. $49a^2 - 4$

32. $25z^2 - 9$

33. $25 - 4y^2$

34. $64 - 9x^2$

35. $16u^2 - 9v^2$

36. $36a^2 - 25b^2$

37. $7z^2 - 28$

38. $8x^2 - 8$

39. $25 + 4p^2$

40. $9y^2 + 4$

41. $x^4 - 625$

42. $a^4 - 1296$

43. $256 - z^4$

44. $625 - b^4$

45. $x^8 - 1$

46. $y^8 - 256$

47. $x^3 - 27$

48. $z^3 - 343$

49. $a^3 + 64$

50. $m^3 + 1$

51. $27x^3 + 64y^3$

52. $125p^3 + 27q^3$

53. $8p^3 - 125q^3$

54. $27u^3 - 8v^3$

55. $p^4 + 64pq^3$

56. $125x^3y + y^4$

57. $81u^4 - 3uv^3$

58. $2a^3b - 54b^4$

Determine the area of the shaded region. Factor the area.

59.

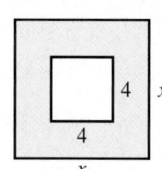

60.

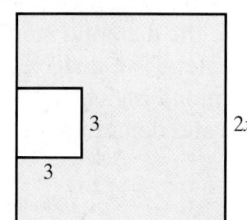

61.

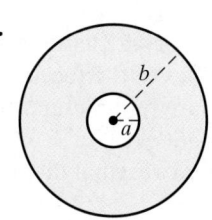

62.

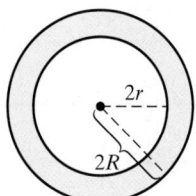

63.

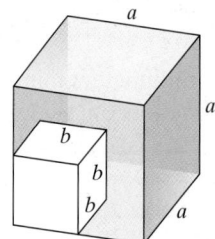

64.

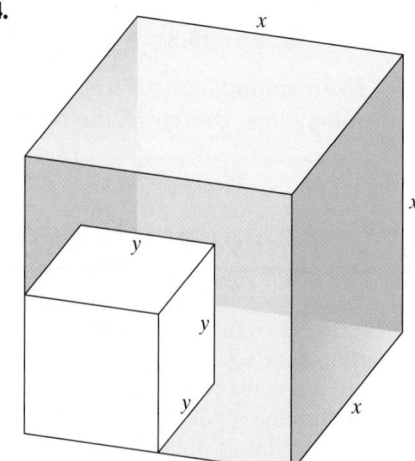

65. A farmer leases you a plot of land for a garden. The plot is square, but it contains a smaller square, 15 feet on a side, that cannot be used.
  a. Write a polynomial for the area of the land you will be able to garden, assuming that the plot is x feet on a side.
  b. Factor the polynomial to find the dimensions of a rectangular plot with an equivalent area.
  c. If the square plot is 100 feet on a side, would you have more garden than another rectangular plot that measures 85 by 100 feet and that is available for the same rental fee? Explain.

66. A machinist must fabricate a square piece of metal that is y inches on a side and that has a triangle cut out of it with a base of x inches and a height of one-half the base.

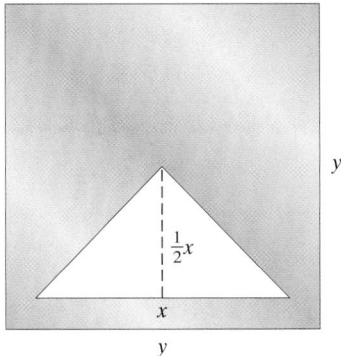

  a. Write a polynomial for the area of the metal square with the triangle removed.
  b. Factor the polynomial to find the dimensions of a rectangular piece of metal that would have an equivalent area.
  c. If the square is 12 inches on a side and the triangle has a base of 4 inches, what are the dimensions of a rectangle with an equivalent area?

67. For a rock concert, promoters built a square stage and surrounded it with a mosh pit that was x feet on each side. A polynomial that represents the area of the stage and mosh pit is $(1225 + 140x + 4x^2)$ square feet. Factor the polynomial and determine the dimensions of the stage. If the mosh pit was 25 feet wide on each side of the stage, use the factored expression to find the area of the stage and mosh pit. Find the area of the stage, and use the two areas to determine the area of the mosh pit.

68. A landscaper is developing a design for a customer's yard that has the shape of a square. She plans to border the yard with a shrub trim that will be x feet wide. A polynomial that represents the central area of the yard not covered with the shrub trim is $(4225 - 260x + 4x^2)$ square feet. Factor the polynomial and determine the dimensions of the yard. If the shrub trim is 5 feet wide, use the factored expression to find the central area. Find the area of the yard, and use the two areas to determine the area of the shrub trim.

69. A handyman makes a square patio of side x feet out of concrete paving blocks. He charges his customer $9 per square foot for installation. His overhead on the job is $100, and his material cost is $5 per square foot. Write a polynomial that represents his profit for the patio installation and then factor it.

70. Evan, a carpenter, constructs a square wooden deck of side x feet for his neighbor. He estimates that his overhead on the job is $49 and the material cost is $15 per square foot. Because the neighbor is a friend, he charges him less than he would on a regular job and charges him only $24 per square foot. Write a polynomial that represents his profit on the deck and then factor it.

71. Damon, a tilesetter, creates a granite design for a customer's foyer. His overhead on the job is $64.00, and the materials cost $6.25 per square foot. He charges the customer $22.25 per square foot for installation. Write a polynomial that represents his profit if the shape of the design is a square with side x feet. Factor the polynomial.

72. Sod is a lawn option offered by most landscapers. For a particular job, overhead is estimated at $30.25, and the landscaper pays for sod by the roll at a cost of $2.05 per square yard. He charges the homeowner $2.30 per square yard for laying and watering the sod. Write a polynomial for the profit on this job if the yard is shaped like a square with side x yards. Factor the polynomial.

73. A glassblower uses oxygen for his torches. A supply company charges $1 per cubic foot for the oxygen, plus a fixed cost of $125 for deposit on the bottle and shipping fee. Write a polynomial for the cost of x^3 cubic feet of oxygen with a one-time deposit and shipment fee. Factor the polynomial.

74. Timber sales are sometimes measured in units of hundreds of cubic feet. A national forest in the Pacific Northwest offered for sale about $\frac{1}{27}$ as many hundreds of cubic feet in 1999 as it did in 1997. The 2000 amount was about 216 units more than in 1999. Write a polynomial for the 2000 amount in units of hundreds of cubic feet if the 1997 amount was x^3 units. Factor the polynomial.

75. A contractor pours a patio of concrete. He charges his customer $107 per cubic yard for installation. It cost him $64 to have the concrete delivered, and the redimix company charges him $80 per cubic yard for the concrete. Write a polynomial that represents his profit for a patio of x^3 cubic yards and then factor it.

76. A standard dry quart is actually measured in cubic inches with one dry quart equivalent to 67.2 cubic inches. A vendor at a farmer's market sells berries for 12 cents per cubic inch, having paid 4 cents per cubic inch from the grower. If his overhead is $270, write a polynomial for his profit in cents of x^3 cubic inches. Factor the polynomial.

8.2 Calculator Exercises

Students often forget that a calculator can help them when they are factoring the difference of two squares or the sum or difference of two cubes. Many times, students are stumped and cannot see that a polynomial has a perfect-square value or a perfect-cube value. Remember, you can always use the square-root function or the cube-root function on your calculator to help recognize these forms. Determine whether the following are perfect squares or cubes by using your calculator (be careful, some may be both):

1. 841   **2.** 42,875   **3.** 361   **4.** 729

Now that you know you can check your calculator for perfect squares and cubes, use the calculator to help you factor the following polynomials:

5. $x^2 - 1225$ **6.** $a^3 - 6859$ **7.** $256y^2 - 441$

8. $343b^3 - 1728$ **9.** $z^2 - 729$ **10.** $z^3 - 729$

8.2 Writing Exercise

Many students make the mistake of believing that $(a + b)^2 = a^2 + b^2$ and that $(a - b)^2 = a^2 - b^2$, both of which are not true for all values of a and b. Based upon what you have learned in this section about special products, explain why these two mistaken beliefs are not true. The mistakes are made so often that they have a special name: Some call them the "Freshman's Dream," because they are usually made by first-year college students just beginning their math studies. Resolve now that you will not be one of those who make these two common mistakes.

8.3 FACTORING TRINOMIALS BY USING THE TRIAL-AND-ERROR METHOD

OBJECTIVES

1 Factor trinomials of the form $ax^2 + bx + c$, $a = 1$.
2 Factor trinomials of the form $ax^2 + bx + c$, $a \neq 1$.
3 Model real-world situations by factoring trinomials.

APPLICATION

According to the *USA Volleyball Rule Book*, the standard playing court must be surrounded by an area (free zone) with a recommended minimum width of 2 meters. The area, in square meters, of the playing court with a free zone of x meters in width is given by the polynomial $162 + 54x + 4x^2$. Factor the polynomial and determine the dimensions of the playing court.

After completing this section, we will discuss this application further. See page 628.

In this section, we continue our discussion of factoring. We will now factor a quadratic trinomial: a trinomial of the form $ax^2 + bx + c$, with $a \neq 0$, $b \neq 0$, and $c \neq 0$. The **leading coefficient** of the quadratic trinomial is a, the coefficient of the quadratic term, x^2.

Objective 8.3.1   **Factoring Quadratic Trinomials with $a = 1$**

To determine a process for factoring a quadratic trinomial, we need to find a pattern. We can see this pattern by using variables instead of numbers and multiplying.

$$\begin{aligned}
& \quad\quad\quad\; \text{F} \quad\; \text{O} \quad\; \text{I} \quad\;\; \text{L} \\
(x + m)(x + n) &= x^2 + nx + mx + mn \quad \text{Use the FOIL method.} \\
&= x^2 + (n + m)x + mn \quad \text{Factor a common factor out of the middle} \\
& \quad\quad\quad\;\; \downarrow \quad\quad\quad\;\; \downarrow \quad\quad \text{two terms.} \\
&= x^2 + \quad bx \quad\;\; + \quad c
\end{aligned}$$

This technique shows that $n + m = b$ and $mn = c$. In other words, look for two numbers whose product is c and whose sum is b.

FACTORING A QUADRATIC TRINOMIAL WITH A LEADING COEFFICIENT OF 1

To factor a quadratic trinomial with a leading coefficient $a = 1$, write

$$x^2 + bx + c = (x + m)(x + n), \text{ where } mn = c \text{ and } n + m = b$$

EXAMPLE 1

Factor $x^2 + x - 6$ completely.

Solution

$$x^2 + x - 6 \qquad a = 1, b = 1, \text{ and } c = -6$$

First, determine the factors of c, -6. Next, add the pairs of factors to determine the sum of b, 1. It is easier to do this in a chart so that we do not omit any possibilities.

Factor	Factor	Sum of Factors
1	−6	−5
−1	6	5
2	−3	−1
−2	3	1

$\leftarrow b$

Choose the last pair of factors, -2 and 3, because their sum is 1 (b).

$$x^2 + x - 6 = (x - 2)(x + 3)$$

We should always check the factors.

Algebraic Check

$$(x - 2)(x + 3) = x^2 + 3x - 2x - 6$$
$$= x^2 + x - 6$$

Numeric Check

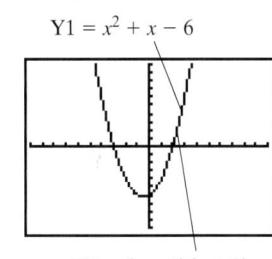

$$Y1 = x^2 + x - 6$$
$$Y2 = (x - 2)(x + 3)$$
The table shows that
$Y1 = Y2$.

Graphic Check

$$Y1 = x^2 + x - 6$$

$$Y2 = (x - 2)(x + 3)$$

$(-10, 10, -10, 10)$
The graph shows that
$Y1$ and $Y2$ coincide. ■

We could set up the previous chart of factors on the calculator as shown in **Figure 8.2b**.

TECHNOLOGY   Chart of Factors

Determine the factors of c (-6) that add to b (1).
For **Figure 8.2a**,
Set up the table.
Set the first column for x equal to integer values starting at 1.

[2nd] [WINDOW] (TBLSET) [1] [ENTER] [1] [ENTER] [ENTER] [▼] [ENTER]

Set the second column, Y1, equal to c, -6, divided by the integer in the first column, x.

[Y=] [(−)] [6] [÷] [X,T,θ,n]

Set the third column, Y2, equal to the sum of the first two columns, x and Y1.

[▼] [X,T,θ,n] [+] [VARS] [▶] [1] [1]

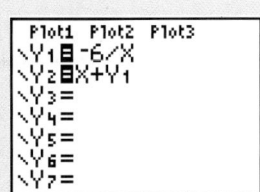

Figure 8.2a

(continued on page 622)

For **Figure 8.2b**,
View the table.

[2nd] [GRAPH] (TABLE)

Find a value in the Y2 column that is equal to b, 1. The factors of c, -6, that have a sum of b, 1, are the integer values of x and Y1 corresponding to that value of b in Y2. The factors of -6 that have a sum of 1 are 3 and -2.

Note that if we move up the table of values [▲] [▲] [▲] we will see that the factors of -6 that have a sum of 1 are also -2 and 3.

X	Y1	Y2
-2	3	1
-1	6	5
0	ERROR	ERROR
1	-6	-5
2	-3	-1
3	-2	1
4	-1.5	2.5

X= -2

Figure 8.2b

To save time in choosing possible factors, we need to see a pattern. Complete the following set of exercises.

Guided Discovery 2   Determining Signs for the Factors of c

Factor the following quadratic trinomials of the form $x^2 + bx + c$.

1. $x^2 + 5x + 6$

If c is positive and b is positive, then the factors of c are both _____.

2. $x^2 - 5x + 6$

If c is positive and b is negative, then the factors of c are both _____.

3. $x^2 + x - 6$

If c is negative and b is positive, then the factors of c have different signs. The factor with the larger absolute value is _____.

4. $x^2 - x - 6$

If c is negative and b is negative, then the factors of c have different signs. The factor with the larger absolute value is _____.

Write a rule to determine when the factors are positive or negative.

SIGNS OF FACTORS

Given $x^2 + bx + c$, the sign of the factors are determined in the following way:

If c is positive, then the factors both have the same sign as b.

If c is negative, then the factors have different signs. (The factor with the larger absolute value has the same sign as b.)

EXAMPLE 2   Factor completely and check.

a. $z^2 + 11z + 24$ **b.** $x^2 + 4x - 7$

c. $2x^2 - 10x + 8$ **d.** $x^4 + 13x^2 + 36$

Solution

a. $z^2 + 11z + 24$ $a = 1, b = 11,$ and $c = 24$

Note: c is positive, so both factors have the sign of b, which is positive.

Write these factors of 24 (c):

Factor	Factor	Sum of Factors
1	24	25
2	12	14
3	8	11
4	6	10

$\leftarrow b$ (next to row with 11)

X	Y₁	Y₂
1	24	25
2	12	14
3	8	11
4	6	10
5	4.8	9.8
6	4	10
7	3.4286	10.429

X=3

$Y1 = 24/x$
$Y2 = x + Y1$

$$z^2 + 11z + 24 = (z + 3)(z + 8)$$

The check is left for you.

Note: The variable z must be changed to x in order to enter the functions on your calculator.

b. $x^2 + 4x - 7$ $a = 1, b = 4,$ and $c = -7$

Note: c is negative, so the factors have different signs. The factor with the larger absolute value must be positive. Write these factors of $-7(c)$:

Factor	Factor	Sum of Factors
−1	7	6

The possible factors of -7 do not add to the desired sum of 4.
 Therefore, $x^2 + 4x - 7$ does not factor.

c. $2x^2 - 10x + 8$

First, factor out the common factor.

$2(x^2 - 5x + 4)$ $a = 1, b = 5,$ and $c = 4$

Note: c is positive, so both factors must have the sign of b, negative.
Write these factors of 4 (c):

Factor	Factor	Sum of Factors
−1	−4	−5
−2	−2	−4

$\leftarrow b$ (next to row with −5)

$$2x^2 - 10x + 8 = 2(x^2 - 5x + 4)$$
$$= 2(x - 1)(x - 4)$$

The check is left for you.

Note: If you multiply, multiply all three factors to check.

d. The process of factoring used in this section can be applied to trinomials that are not quadratic. Any polynomial that can be written in the form $y^2 + by + c$, where y is x^2, x^3, and so forth, can be factored in a similar manner.
 $x^4 + 13x^2 + 36$ is not a quadratic trinomial, because the degree of the polynomial is 4. However, it is a quadratic-like trinomial, with $y = x^2$ and $y^2 = (x^2)^2 = x^4$. Note that $a = 1, b = 13,$ and $c = 36$.

Note: c is positive, so both factors must have the sign of b, which is positive.

Factor	Factor	Sum of Factors
1	36	37
2	18	20
3	12	15
4	9	13

$\leftarrow b$ (next to row with 13)

The first term in the binomials is x^2.

$$x^4 + 13x^2 + 36 = (x^2 + 4)(x^2 + 9)$$

Check by multiplying:

$$(x^2 + 4)(x^2 + 9) = x^4 + 9x^2 + 4x^2 + 36$$
$$= x^4 + 13x^2 + 36 \qquad ■$$

✓ Objective 8.3.1 *CHECKUP*

In exercises 1 and 2, factor completely and check.

1. $x^2 - 4x - 5$

2. a. $b^2 - 12b + 35$ **b.** $c^2 - 5c - 24$
    c. $6d^2 + 60d + 126$ **d.** $y^4 - 2y^2 - 3$

3. If a trinomial is quadratic-like, what must be true about the exponent of each of the three terms?

4. What do we mean by the quadratic term of a trinomial?   ■

Objective 8.3.2

Factoring Quadratic Trinomials with $a \neq 1$

In this section, we factor a quadratic trinomial, $ax^2 + bx + c$, where $a \neq 1$. First, let's review the multiplication problem that results in such a polynomial.

$$\overset{\text{F}\quad\text{O}\quad\text{I}\quad\text{L}}{}$$
$$\downarrow\quad\downarrow\quad\downarrow\quad\downarrow$$
$$(x + 3)(2x - 1) = 2x^2 - x + 6x - 3 = 2x^2 + 5x - 3$$

We want to reverse this multiplication by factoring the trinomial into two binomials. We call this the **trial-and-error method** because we make a guess and check to see whether it is correct.

EXAMPLE 3

Factor $2x^2 + 5x - 3$ completely.

Solution

The product of the first terms in each binomial factor must equal $2x^2$.
The product of the last terms in each binomial factor must equal -3.

$$\overset{2x^2}{\overbrace{}}$$
$$2x^2 + 5x - 3 = (\underline{\quad})(\underline{\quad})$$
$$\underbrace{}_{-3}$$

First, determine the possible factors that result in each binomial factor.

$$2x^2 = x \cdot 2x \qquad -3 = 1 \cdot -3$$
$$= -1 \cdot 3$$

Next, fill in the binomial factors with all the possible combinations, and multiply to find the middle term of the trinomial. Remember that the middle term is the sum of the product of the outer terms and the product of the inner terms.

$$2x^2 + 5x - 3 = (\underline{\quad})(\underline{\quad}) \qquad \text{Middle term}$$
$$(\underline{x + 1})(\underline{2x - 3}) \qquad -3x + 2x = -x$$
$$(\underline{x - 1})(\underline{2x + 3}) \qquad 3x - 2x = x$$
$$(\underline{2x + 1})(\underline{x - 3}) \qquad -6x + x = -5x$$
$$(\underline{2x - 1})(\underline{x + 3}) \qquad 6x - x = 5x$$

The factors $(2x - 1)(x + 3)$ result in the middle term $5x$. Multiply the two binomials to check your factors completely.

$$(2x - 1)(x + 3) = 2x^2 + 6x - x - 3 = 2x^2 + 5x - 3$$

A graphic check will result in equivalent graphs for the two functions $Y1 = 2x^2 + 5x - 3$ and $Y2 = (2x - 1)(x + 3)$.

Therefore, $2x^2 + 5x - 3 = (2x - 1)(x + 3)$.   ■

Graphic Check

$Y1 = 2x^2 + 5x - 3$

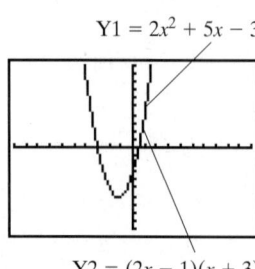

$Y2 = (2x - 1)(x + 3)$

$(10, 10, -10, 10)$
The graphs are coinciding.

FACTORING A QUADRATIC TRINOMIAL WITH A LEADING COEFFICIENT NOT EQUAL TO 1 BY USING THE TRIAL-AND-ERROR METHOD

To factor a quadratic trinomial by using the trial-and-error method,

- Factor out the GCF from all terms.
- Determine the possible factors of the first term and the last term.
- Write a set of binomial factors for each combination of the factors.
- Multiply the factors to determine which set results in the middle term of the trinomial.

Check the factors by multiplying to obtain the original trinomial or by entering into your calculator the original polynomial and the factors as separate functions and determining that the table of values have equivalent Y1 and Y2 columns or the graphs are equivalent.

EXAMPLE 4

Factor completely.

a. $8x^2 - 26x + 15$ **b.** $-6x^2 + 9x + 10$

c. $12x^2 - 14xy - 6y^2$ **d.** $3x^4 + 2x^2 - 8$

Solution

a. $8x^2 - 26x + 15$

First, determine the possible factors of the first and last terms.

$$8x^2 = x \cdot 8x \qquad 15 = 1 \cdot 15$$
$$= 2x \cdot 4x \qquad = -1 \cdot -15$$
$$= 3 \cdot 5$$
$$= -3 \cdot -5$$

Next, fill in the binomial factors with all the possible combinations, and multiply to find the correct middle term in the original trinomial.

Before we begin, observe that the middle term is negative. Therefore, the positive factors of 15 are not possible combinations, as they will result in only positive middle terms. Knowing this reduces the possibilities.

$$8x^2 = x \cdot 8x \qquad 15 = -1 \cdot -15$$
$$= 2x \cdot 4x \qquad = -3 \cdot -5$$

$8x^2 - 26x + 15 = (\underline{\quad}\ \underline{\quad})(\underline{\quad}\ \underline{\quad})$ Middle term

$(\ x\ -\ 1\ )(8x\ -\ 15)$ $-15x - 8x = -23x$

$(\ x\ -\ 3\ )(8x\ -\ 5\ )$ $-5x - 24x = -29x$

$(8x\ -\ 1\ )(\ x\ -\ 15)$ $-120x - x = -121x$

$(8x\ -\ 3\ )(\ x\ -\ 5\ )$ $-40x - 3x = -43x$

$(2x\ -\ 1\ )(4x\ -\ 15)$ $-30x - 4x = -34x$

$(2x\ -\ 3\ )(4x\ -\ 5\ )$ $-10x - 12x = -22x$

$(4x\ -\ 1\ )(2x\ -\ 15)$ $-60x - 2x = -62x$

$(4x\ -\ 3\ )(2x\ -\ 5\ )$ $-20x - 6x = -26x$

The factors $(4x - 3)$ and $(2x - 5)$, when multiplied together, result in the middle term, $-26x$.

$$8x^2 - 26x + 15 = (4x - 3)(2x - 5)$$

A numeric check with $Y1 = 8x^2 - 26x + 15$ and $Y2 = (4x - 3)(2x - 5)$ results in $Y1 = Y2$. Therefore, $8x^2 - 26x + 15 = (4x - 3)(2x - 5)$.

Numeric Check

X	Y1	Y2
-3	165	165
-2	99	99
-1	49	49
0	15	15
1	-3	-3
2	-5	-5
3	9	9

X= -3

The table shows Y1 = Y2.
Y1 = $8x^2 - 26x + 15$
Y2 = $(4x - 3)(2x - 5)$

b. $-6x^2 + 9x + 10$

First, factor out -1 as the greatest common factor because the leading coefficient is negative.

$$-6x^2 + 9x + 10 = -1(6x^2 - 9x - 10)$$

Now determine the possible factors of the first and last terms.

$$
\begin{aligned}
6x^2 &= x \cdot 6x & -10 &= 1 \cdot -10 \\
&= 2x \cdot 3x & &= -1 \cdot 10 \\
& & &= 2 \cdot -5 \\
& & &= -2 \cdot 5
\end{aligned}
$$

Next, fill in the binomial factors with all the possible combinations, and multiply to find the correct middle term in the original trinomial.

$$-1(6x^2 - 9x - 10) = -1(\underline{\quad})(\underline{\quad}) \qquad \text{Middle term}$$

$$
\begin{aligned}
&-1(\ \underline{x} + \underline{1}\ )(6x - 10) \\
&-1(\ \underline{x} - \underline{1}\ )(6x + 10) \\
&-1(\ \underline{x} + \underline{2}\ )(6x - 5\ ) && -5x + 12x = 7x \\
&-1(\ \underline{x} - \underline{2}\ )(6x + 5\ ) && 5x - 12x = -7x \\
&-1(6x + \underline{1}\ )(\ \underline{x} - 10) && -60x + x = -59x \\
&-1(6x - \underline{1}\ )(\ \underline{x} + 10) && 60x - x = 59x \\
&-1(6x + \underline{2}\ )(\ \underline{x} - 5\ ) \\
&-1(6x - \underline{2}\ )(\ \underline{x} + 5\ ) \\
&-1(2x + \underline{1}\ )(3x - 10) && -20x + 3x = -17x \\
&-1(2x - \underline{1}\ )(3x + 10) && 20x - 3x = 17x \\
&-1(2x + \underline{2}\ )(3x - 5\ ) \\
&-1(2x - \underline{2}\ )(3x + 5\ ) \\
&-1(3x + \underline{1}\ )(2x - 10) \\
&-1(3x - \underline{1}\ )(2x + 10) \\
&-1(3x + \underline{2}\ )(2x - 5\ ) && -15x + 4x = -11x \\
&-1(3x - \underline{2}\ )(2x + 5\ ) && 15x - 4x = 11x
\end{aligned}
$$

Note: We did not find the middle term for the binomial factors with common factors.

No factors result in the middle term.
The trinomial $6x^2 - 9x - 10$ does not factor. Therefore,

$$-6x^2 + 9x + 10 = -1(6x^2 - 9x - 10)$$

c. $12x^2 - 14xy - 6y^2$

First, factor out the greatest common factor, 2.

$$12x^2 - 14xy - 6y^2 = 2(6x^2 - 7xy - 3y^2)$$

Now determine the possible factors of the first and last terms.

$$
\begin{aligned}
6x^2 &= x \cdot 6x & -3y^2 &= y \cdot -3y \\
&= 2x \cdot 3x & &= -y \cdot 3y
\end{aligned}
$$

Next, fill in the binomial factors with all the possible combinations, and multiply to find the correct middle term in the original trinomial.

$$2(6x^2 - 7xy - 3y^2) = 2(\underline{\quad}\ \underline{\quad})(\underline{\quad}\ \underline{\quad}) \qquad \text{Middle term}$$

$$2(\underline{\ x\ } + \underline{\ y\ })(6x - 3y)$$
$$2(\underline{\ x\ } - \underline{\ y\ })(6x + 3y)$$
$$2(6x + \underline{\ y\ })(\underline{\ x\ } - 3y) \qquad -18xy + xy = -17xy$$
$$2(6x - \underline{\ y\ })(\underline{\ x\ } + 3y) \qquad 18xy - xy = 17xy$$
$$2(2x + \underline{\ y\ })(3x - 3y)$$
$$2(2x - \underline{\ y\ })(3x + 3y)$$
$$2(\underline{3x} + \underline{\ y\ })(2x - 3y) \qquad -9xy + 2xy = -7xy$$
$$2(\underline{3x} - \underline{\ y\ })(2x + 3y) \qquad 9xy - 2xy = 7xy$$

Note: The binomial factors with common factors are not possible solutions.

The factors $(3x + y)$ and $(2x - 3y)$, when multiplied together, result in the correct middle term.

$$12x^2 - 14xy - 6y^2 = 2(6x^2 - 7xy - 3y^2)$$
$$= 2(3x + y)(2x - 3y)$$

The check is left for you.

d. $3x^4 + 2x^2 - 8$

Quadratic-like trinomials are also found with the leading coefficient not equal to 1. Just as before, we factor them with the same procedure we used for quadratic trinomials.

First, determine the possible factors of the first and last terms. Since the middle term is a factor of x^2, we will need to factor the first term $3x^4$ into factors of x^2.

$$3x^4 = x^2 \cdot 3x^2 \qquad -8 = 1 \cdot -8$$
$$= -1 \cdot 8$$
$$= 2 \cdot -4$$
$$= -2 \cdot 4$$

Next, fill in the binomial factors with all the possible combinations, and multiply to find the correct middle term in the original trinomial.

$$3x^4 + 2x^2 - 8 = (\underline{\quad}\ \underline{\quad})(\underline{\quad}\ \underline{\quad}) \qquad \text{Middle terms}$$
$$(x^2 + \underline{1})(3x^2 - \underline{8}) \qquad -8x^2 + 3x^2 = -5x^2$$
$$(x^2 - \underline{1})(3x^2 + \underline{8}) \qquad 8x^2 - 3x^2 = 5x^2$$
$$(x^2 + \underline{2})(3x^2 - \underline{4}) \qquad -4x^2 + 6x^2 = 2x^2$$

We do not need to continue, since we have found the needed middle term.

The factors $(x^2 + 2)$ and $(3x^2 - 4)$, when multiplied together, result in the correct middle term.

$$3x^4 + 2x^2 - 8 = (x^2 + 2)(3x^2 - 4)$$

The check is left for you.

Objective 8.3.2 *CHECKUP*

In exercises 1 and 2, factor completely and check.

1. $2x^2 - 9x - 5$

2. a. $15x^2 + 7x + 2$ **b.** $-4x^2 + x - 10$
    c. $6x^2 - xy - 2y^2$ **d.** $6x^4 - 23x^2 + 20$

3. In this section, it was stated that if the original trinomial being factored does not have a common factor, then neither of the binomial factors can have a common factor. Explain why this is so.

Objective 8.3.3   **Modeling the Real World**

Trinomials are used to model many real-world situations, such as the equation of motion for a projectile or the equation describing the impact that occurs in some kinds of collisions. In some cases, the trinomial can be factored by using the methods described in this section, enabling us to solve the equations directly. In geometry problems, if the area of a figure is described by a trinomial, factoring it can help us determine the dimensions of the figure.

| EXAMPLE 5 |

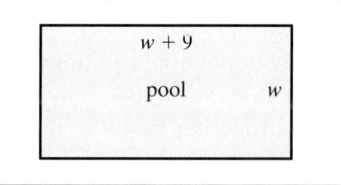

Mandy has designed a swimming pool area for a customer. The length of the pool is to be 9 feet more than the width. The pool is to have a concrete walk around it, with equal width on opposite sides. However, the walk is wider along one set of sides.

Determine the two walk widths if Mandy's figures show that the total area covered by the walk and the pool is $(w^2 + 18w + 56)$ square feet, where w is the pool width.

Solution

To determine the outside dimensions of the walks, find the factors that are multiplied to obtain the total area, $w^2 + 18w + 56$.

$$w^2 + 18w + 56 = (w + 4)(w + 14)$$

The outside dimensions are $(w + 4)$ feet and $(w + 14)$ feet.

The outside width is $(w + 4)$. To determine the width of the walk, we subtract the width of the pool, w, and divide by 2. (The walks along each side are equal.)

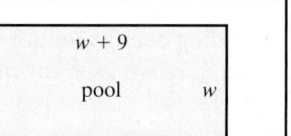

$$\frac{(w + 4) - w}{2} = \frac{4}{2} = 2$$

The walk is 2 feet wide along the pool's length.

The outside length is $(w + 14)$. To determine the width of the walk on this side, we subtract the length of the pool, $w + 9$, and divide by 2.

$$\frac{(w + 14) - (w + 9)}{2} = \frac{5}{2} = 2\frac{1}{2}$$

The walk is $2\frac{1}{2}$ feet along the pool's width.   ■

APPLICATION

According to the *USA Volleyball Rule Book*, the standard playing court must be surrounded by an area (free zone) with a recommended minimum width of 2 meters. The area, in square meters, of the playing court with a free zone of x meters in width is given by the polynomial $162 + 54x + 4x^2$. Factor the polynomial and determine the dimensions of the playing court.

Discussion

The dimensions of the area that includes the playing court and the free zone can be found by factoring.

$$162 + 54x + 4x^2 = (18 + 2x)(9 + 2x)$$

The total area is $(18 + 2x)$ meters by $(9 + 2x)$ meters.

To determine the dimensions of the playing court, we need to subtract $2x$ from the total length and $2x$

from the total width. We must subtract $2x$ because the free zone adds x meters on each side of the playing court, or $2x$.

$$(18 + 2x) - 2x = 18$$
$$(9 + 2x) - 2x = 9$$

The area of the playing court is 18 meters by 9 meters.

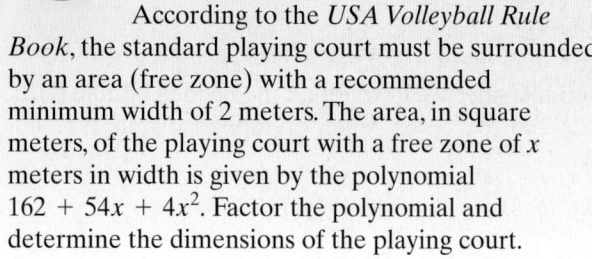

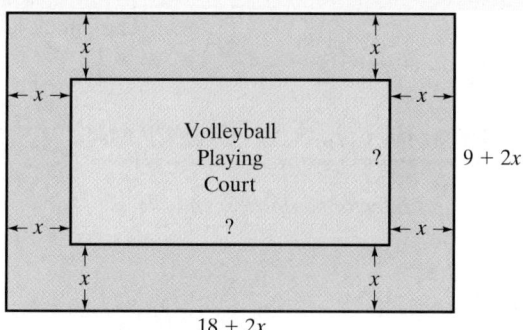

Objective 8.3.3 *CHECKUP*

1. Mandy discovered that she had reversed the numbers on the constant term of the trinomial in Example 5. The trinomial should have been $w^2 + 18w + 65$. Rework the problem to find what the two widths of the walk should then be.

2. The recommended layout for a tennis court on which singles play states that the playing court must be surrounded by a free area such that the baseline at each end is a specified distance from a fixed obstruction and the sideline is a specified distance from a fixed obstruction. The area, in square feet, of the playing area with a free zone of x feet from the baseline and x feet from a sideline is given by the polynomial $4x^2 + 210x + 2106$. Factor the polynomial, and determine the dimensions of the playing area of the tennis court.

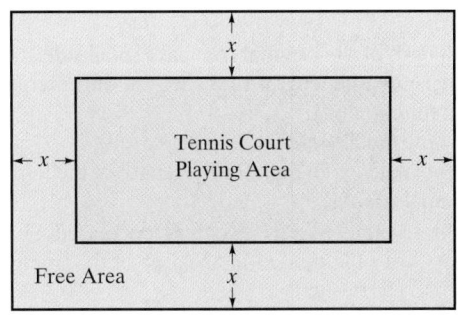

8.3 EXERCISES

Student Solutions Manual   PH Math/Tutor Center   CD Video   Math XL
MathXL®   MyMathLab   Interactmath.com

In exercises 1–64, factor completely and check.

1. $x^2 + 14x + 45$
2. $p^2 + 14p + 48$
3. $y^2 - 15y + 56$
4. $u^2 + 11u - 26$

5. $p^2 - 9p - 36$
6. $v^2 - 12v - 13$
7. $z^2 + 6z + 12$
8. $m^2 - 9m + 15$

9. $x^4 + 25x^2 + 144$
10. $b^4 + 29b^2 + 100$
11. $x^4 - 2x^2 - 3$
12. $d^4 + 18d^2 - 175$

13. $3a^2 + 48a + 165$
14. $7b^2 - 70b + 168$
15. $4c^2 + 44c - 104$
16. $7p^2 - 7p - 140$

17. $x^2 - 11xy + 24y^2$
18. $a^2 - 17ab + 72b^2$
19. $x^2 + 11xy - 12y^2$
20. $a^2 - 9ab - 90b^2$

21. $-3a^2 - 15ab - 18b^2$
22. $-5x^2 + 35xy - 60y^2$
23. $-2x^2 + 14xy + 36y^2$
24. $-6x^2 + 24xy + 126y^2$

25. $3x^2 + 10x + 3$
26. $4x^2 + 12x + 7$
27. $2x^2 - 15x + 7$
28. $3x^2 - 34x + 11$

29. $3x^2 - x - 2$
30. $5x^2 - 2x - 3$
31. $5m^2 + 9m - 2$
32. $7p^2 + 34p - 5$

33. $2m^2 + 7m - 3$
34. $3t^2 - 12t + 4$
35. $4a^2 + 25a + 6$
36. $10c^2 + 41c + 4$

37. $9d^2 - 13d + 4$
38. $8b^2 - 17b + 9$
39. $6x^2 - 23x - 4$
40. $4x^2 - 31x - 8$

41. $8y^2 + 7y - 18$
42. $6z^2 + 19z - 20$
43. $6b^2 + 17b + 12$
44. $15a^2 + 28a + 12$

45. $20x^2 - 31x + 12$
46. $14z^2 + 13z - 12$
47. $18x^2 - 9x - 20$
48. $8x^2 - 22x - 63$

49. $18p^2 - 57p - 21$
50. $-63x^2 - 30x + 48$
51. $2x^4 + 11x^2 + 9$
52. $24x^4 - 22x^2 + 3$

53. $4m^4 + 13m^2 - 12$
54. $5z^4 + 39z^2 - 54$
55. $5x - 6x^2 + 56$
56. $21 - 5b - 4b^2$

57. $6x^2 + 5xy - 6y^2$
58. $14a^2 + 25ab + 6b^2$
59. $4u^2 - 39uv + 56v^2$
60. $3x^2 - 20xy + 32y^2$

61. $9x^4 + 13x^2y^2 + 4y^4$
62. $16x^4 + 41x^2y^2 + 25y^4$
63. $10x^2y^2 + xy - 21$
64. $21p^2q^2 - 2pq - 8$

Geometry

In exercises 65 and 66, factor the area to find the missing side.

65.
$A = 2x^2 + 5x - 12$ $2x - 3$
?

66.
$A = 6x^2 + 5x - 6$?
$3x - 2$

67. The length of a rectangle is 8 inches more than its width. After both the length and width have been increased, the area of the larger rectangle is given by $(w^2 + 14w + 24)$ square inches, where w is the original width.
   a. Factor the polynomial to find the increased width and length.
   b. By how much was the width increased?
   c. By how much was the length increased?

68. A rectangular poster design has a width that is 5 inches less than its length. The width is increased while the length is decreased. The area of the new poster is given by $(x^2 - 4x + 3)$ square inches, where x is the original length.
   a. Factor the polynomial to find the new width and length.
   b. By how much was the width increased?
   c. By how much was the length decreased?

69. A right triangle has its two legs increased by the same amount. After the increase, the area of the triangle is equal to the polynomial $\left(x^2 + \frac{21}{2}x + 20\right)$ square inches, where x is the length of the original triangle's small side.
    a. Determine the lengths of the legs of the enlarged triangle as a function of x.
    b. By how much were the legs increased?
    c. What is the expression for the length of the long leg of the original triangle?

70. A right triangle has its two legs decreased by the same amount. After the reduction, the area of the triangle is equal to the polynomial $\left(\frac{3}{2}x^2 - 12x + 24\right)$ square inches, where x is the length of the original triangle's small leg.
    a. Determine the lengths of the legs of the reduced triangle as a function of x.
    b. By how much were the legs decreased?
    c. What is the expression for the length of the long leg of the original triangle?

71. The recommended layout for a tennis court on which tournament doubles are held states that the playing court must be surrounded by a free area. The free area is defined such that the baseline at each end is a specified distance from a fixed obstruction. Also, the sideline is a specified distance from a fixed obstruction. If the specified distance is x feet, the area, in square feet, of the playing area, including the free zone, is given by the polynomial $4x^2 + 228x + 2808$. Factor the polynomial, and determine the dimensions of the playing area of the tennis court.

72. Requirements for the markings of a football field state that the end zones should be 10 yards long, but can be shortened if the field itself is too short. One football stadium, Sanford Stadium at the University of Georgia, is famous for being surrounded by English privet hedges, and games there are referred to as being played "between the hedges." Suppose this field has end zones that are x yards long and sidelines that are $2x$ yards wide. A polynomial that represents the area of the football field is $8x^2 + 506x + 5300$ square yards. Factor the polynomial, and determine the dimensions of the playing area of the field.

73. The product of the measure of two angles is given by the polynomial $12x^2 - x - 35$. Factor the polynomial to find an expression for the measure of each angle. If $x = 5$, what are the measures of the angles?

74. The product of the measure of two angles is given by the polynomial $6x^2 - x - 15$. Factor the polynomial to find an expression for the measure of each angle. If $x = 5$, what are the measures of the angles?

75. The product of the length of the sides of a rectangle is given by the polynomial $7x^2 + 110x - 32$. Factor the polynomial to find possible expressions for the length of each side. If $x = 3$, is the rectangle a square?

76. The product of the length of the base and height of a parallelogram can be given by the polynomial $9x^2 + 304x + 231$. Factor the polynomial to find possible expressions for the base and height. If $x = 2$, will the base and height be equal?

Business

77. A man who supervises local newspaper delivery estimates paper revenue to be $R(x) = -6x^2 + 66x + 360$, where x is the number of hours he spends on selling subscriptions each week. Factor this polynomial completely.

78. A management agency representing a number of independent bands has revenue $R(x) = -100x^2 + 950x + 3000$, where x is the number of groups represented. Factor this polynomial completely.

79. A men's clothing store estimates weekly revenues on tuxedo rental at $R(x) = 92 + 43x + 5x^2$, where x is the number of tuxedos rented. Factor this polynomial completely.

80. The owner of a franchise sub sandwich shop owns several stores. His total weekly revenue per store is $R(x) = 1350 + 240x + 10x^2$, where x is the number of high school students employed. Factor this polynomial completely.

Vertical Distance

81. A cannon is fired at a Civil War reenactment. The distance above ground of the cannon ball in feet can be given by $d(t) = -16t^2 + 104t + 27$, where t is the time in seconds. Factor this polynomial completely.

82. A hiker at the top of a mountain fires a flare gun into the valley below. The distance above the ground of the flare in feet can be given by $s(t) = -16t^2 - 55t + 125$, where t is the time in seconds. Factor this polynomial completely.

 ## 8.3 Calculator Exercises

It is sometimes difficult to factor a trinomial by using the trial-and-error method if the coefficients are not simple. In these situations, you can use a different calculator technique to find the factors. The technique is based upon the concepts you learned in an earlier chapter concerning the x-intercepts of a graph. You learned that the x-intercepts of a graph represent the points at which the y-coordinate equals zero. You can use this information to help you factor a trinomial.

Suppose you wish to factor the trinomial $40x^2 + 91x - 153$. After trying several combinations of factors that do not work, you decide to use the graphing feature of your calculator to help you. The steps involved are as follows:

1. Define a function with the polynomial.

$$y = 40x^2 + 91x - 153$$

2. Store the function using the $\boxed{\text{Y=}}$ key, and graph the function on the calculator. Note that you will need to adjust the window appropriately to see the graph well.

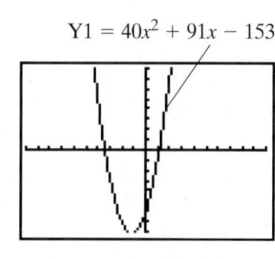

$Y1 = 40x^2 + 91x - 153$

$(-10, 10, 1, -200, 200, 25, 1)$

3. Find the *x*-intercepts of the graph by using the zero option under the [2nd] [TRACE] (CALC) key.

After finding each *x*-intercept, quit the graph and use the Fraction option under the [MATH] key to convert the *x*-values to fractions. (When you key [X,T,θ,n], the intercept value will be stored there.)

Y1 = $40x^2 + 91x - 153$

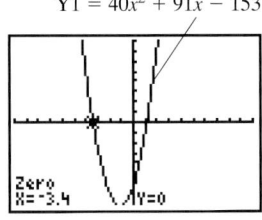
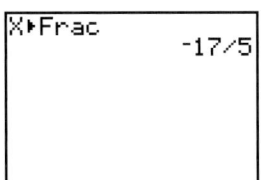

Y1 = $40x^2 + 91x - 153$

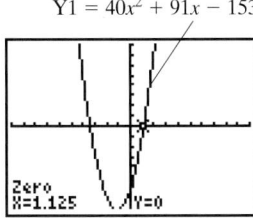
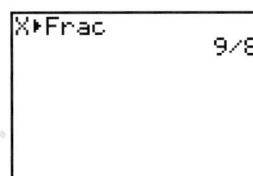

Note that if the trinomial factors into two binomial factors, the *x*-values of the *x*-intercepts must be rational numbers and should always be able to be written as fractions.

$$x = 1.125 \text{ is equivalent to } x = \frac{9}{8}$$

$$x = -3.4 \text{ is equivalent to } x = \frac{-17}{5}$$

4. Take the two equations solved for *x*, and rewrite them in standard form, $ax + b = 0$.

$$x = \frac{9}{8} \qquad\qquad x = \frac{-17}{5}$$
$$8x = 9 \qquad\qquad 5x = -17$$
$$8x - 9 = 0 \quad \text{and} \quad 5x + 17 = 0$$

5. The final two expressions on the left sides of the equations in step 4 are the factors of your original polynomial. Thus, $40x^2 + 91x - 153 = (8x - 9)(5x + 17)$. You can check this answer by multiplication.

Use the preceding method to factor the following trinomials:

1. $40x^2 + 21x - 180$

2. $80x^2 - 232x + 117$

3. $108x^2 - 177x + 55$

4. $180x^2 + 327x + 143$

8.3 Writing Exercise

Ned factored $-3x^2 - 15x + 312$ into $-3(x - 8)(x + 13)$. Lamar factored the same trinomial into $3(13 + x)(8 - x)$. Check to see whether the two answers multiply to the same trinomial. If they do, discuss how the two students may have ob-tained different answers, and try to identify the properties of real numbers that tell us that the two are equivalent expressions. State which answer you prefer and explain why.

8.4 FACTORING TRINOMIALS BY USING THE *ac* METHOD

OBJECTIVES
1 Factor trinomials of the form $ax^2 + bx + c$.
2 Model real-world situations by factoring polynomials.

APPLICATION

Delaware's Fred Rust Arena has an ice surface that is classified as an Olympic-sized surface. The length of the surface is twice its width. If a surrounding area of equal width borders the ice surface, then a polynomial for the area of the enclosed surface is $2x^2 + 15x + 25$ square feet. Factor the polynomial and determine the width of the border. If the width of the ice surface is 100 feet, evaluate the factors to determine the area of the enclosed surface and its dimensions.

After completing this section, we will discuss this application further. See page 636.

Objective 8.4.1

Factoring Quadratic Trinomials by Using the *ac* Method

Sometimes, another method may be easier to use to factor quadratic trinomials when the leading coefficient does not equal 1. This is an algorithm called the *ac* method. The ***ac* method** reverses the FOIL method by rewriting the middle term as a sum, using factors of the product of the coefficients a and c in the trinomial $ax^2 + bx + c$. For example,

$$\begin{array}{cccc} F & O & I & L \\ \downarrow & \downarrow & \downarrow & \downarrow \end{array}$$

$$(x + 3)(2x - 1) = 2x^2 - x + 6x - 3 = 2x^2 + 5x - 3$$

We want to reverse this process entirely and obtain

$$2x^2 + 5x - 3 = 2x^2 - x + 6x - 3 = (x + 3)(2x - 1)$$

To do this, first determine the product of the coefficients a and c. Since $a = 2$ and $c = -3$, the product $ac = 2(-3) = -6$.

Next, determine the factors of $ac(-6)$ whose sum is $b(5)$.

This is similar to the procedure we used in factoring a quadratic trinomial with a leading coefficient of 1.

Factor	Factor	Sum of Factors
1	−6	−5
−1	6	5	← b
2	−3	−1
−2	3	1

We can set up the table in the calculator as we did in the previous section. The only difference is that we set the second column to be the product (ac) divided by x.

We will use the factors -1 and 6, because their sum is the same as b, 5. Rewrite the middle term as a sum, using -1 and 6 as the new coefficients. The order of the two terms does not matter.

X	Y1	Y2
-1	6	5
0	ERROR	ERROR
1	-6	-5
2	-3	-1
3	-2	1
4	-1.5	2.5
5	-1.2	3.8

X= -1

Y1 = $(2 \cdot -3)/x$
Y2 = $x + $ Y1

$$5x \qquad\qquad\qquad\qquad\qquad\qquad 5x$$
$$\downarrow \qquad\qquad\qquad\qquad\qquad\qquad \downarrow$$
$$2x^2 + 5x - 3 = 2x^2 - x + 6x - 3 \text{ or } 2x^2 + 5x - 3 = 2x^2 + 6x - x - 3$$

Factor the resulting polynomial, using grouping.

$$(2x^2 - x) + (6x - 3) = x(2x - 1) + 3(2x - 1) \text{ or } (2x^2 + 6x) + (-x - 3) = 2x(x + 3) - 1(x + 3)$$

Factor a common factor from each group.

$$= (2x - 1)(x + 3) \qquad\qquad\qquad\qquad = (x + 3)(2x - 1)$$

Factor a common binomial from each term.

Check the results.

Algebraic Check

$$(2x - 1)(x + 3) = 2x^2 + 6x - x - 3$$
$$= 2x^2 + 5x - 3$$

Numeric Check

X	Y1	Y2
-3	0	0
-2	-5	-5
-1	-6	-6
0	-3	-3
1	4	4
2	15	15
3	30	30

X= -3

Y1 = $2x^2 + 5x - 3$
Y2 = $(2x - 1)(x + 3)$
The table shows that
Y1 = Y2.

Graphic Check

Y1 = $2x^2 + 5x - 3$

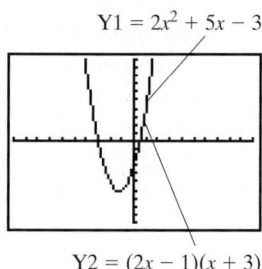

Y2 = $(2x - 1)(x + 3)$

$(-10, 10, -10, 10)$

The graph shows that Y1 and Y2 coincide.

FACTORING A QUADRATIC TRINOMIAL WITH A LEADING COEFFICIENT NOT EQUAL TO 1 BY USING THE *ac* METHOD

To factor a quadratic trinomial by using the *ac* method,

* Factor out the GCF from all terms.
* Determine the product *ac*.
* Determine those factors *m* and *n* of the product *ac* whose sum is *b*.
* Rewrite the trinomial as a four-term polynomial, $ax^2 + mx + nx + c$.
* Factor the resulting polynomial by using grouping.

Check the factors by multiplying to obtain the original trinomial or by entering into your calculator the original polynomial and the product of the factors as separate functions and determining that the table of values have equivalent Y1 and Y2 columns or the graphs are equivalent.

EXAMPLE 1

Factor completely.

a. $8x^2 - 26xy + 15y^2$ **b.** $6x^2 - 9x - 10$

c. $12x^2 - 14x - 6$ **d.** $3x^4 + 2x^2 - 8$

Solution

a. $8x^2 - 26xy + 15y^2$

Since $a = 8, b = -26$, and $c = 15$, it follows that $ac = 8 \cdot 15 = 120$.

Using a table, determine the factors of the product that result in a sum of $-26(b)$. We will need to use only the negative factors of *ac*, because *ac* is positive and *b* is negative.

Note: You may want to use the calculator table.

Factor	Factor	Sum of Factors
−1	−120	−121
−2	−60	−62
−3	−40	−43
−4	−30	−34
−5	−24	−29
−6	−20	−26 ← *b*
−8	−15	−23
−10	−12	−22

X	Y1	Y2
-8	-15	-23
-7	-17.14	-24.14
-6	-20	-26
-5	-24	-29
-4	-30	-34
-3	-40	-43
-2	-60	-62

X= -6

Y1 = $(8 \cdot 15) \div x$
Y2 = $x +$ Y1

The factors −6 and −20 result in a sum of −26. Rewrite the trinomial, using these factors as coefficients of the two new middle terms.

$$
\begin{aligned}
8x^2 - 26xy + 15y^2 &= 8x^2 - 6xy - 20xy + 15y^2 \\
&= (8x^2 - 6xy) + (-20xy + 15y^2) \quad \text{Group.} \\
&= 2x(4x - 3y) + (-5y)(4x - 3y) \quad \text{Factor out common factors.} \\
&= (4x - 3y)(2x - 5y) \quad \text{Factor out a common binomial factor.}
\end{aligned}
$$

The check is left for you.

$$8x^2 - 26xy + 15y^2 = (4x - 3y)(2x - 5y)$$

b. $6x^2 - 9x - 10$

Since $a = 6, b = -9$, and $c = -10$, it follows that $ac = 6 \cdot -10 = -60$.

Using a table, determine the factors of the product that result in a sum of $-9(b)$.

Note: You may want to use the calculator table.

Factor	Factor	Sum of Factors
1	−60	−59
1	60	59
2	−30	−28
−2	30	28
3	−20	−17
−3	20	17
4	−15	−11
−4	15	11
5	−12	−7
−5	12	7
6	−10	−4
−6	10	4

No set of factors results in a sum of −9. The trinomial does not factor.

$$6x^2 - 9x - 10 \text{ does not factor.}$$

c. $12x^2 - 14x - 6$

First, factor out the common factor of 2.

$$12x^2 - 14x - 6 = 2(6x^2 - 7x - 3)$$

Since $a = 6, b = -7$, and $c = -3$, it follows that $ac = 6 \cdot -3 = -18$. Using a table, determine the factors of the product that result in a sum of $-7 (b)$.

Note: You may want to use the calculator table.

Factor	Factor	Sum of Factors	
1	−18	−17	
−1	18	17	
2	−9	−7	← b
−2	9	7	
3	−6	−3	
−3	6	3	

X	Y1	Y2
-3	6	3
-2	9	7
-1	18	17
0	ERR:	ERR:
1	-18	-17
2	-9	-7
3	-6	-3

X=2

Y1 = $(6 \cdot -3) \div x$
Y2 = x + Y1

The factors 2 and −9 result in a sum of −7. Rewrite the trinomial, using these factors as coefficients of the two new middle terms.

$$
\begin{aligned}
12x^2 - 14x - 6 &= 2(6x^2 - 7x - 3) \\
&= 2(6x^2 + 2x - 9x - 3) \\
&= 2[(6x^2 + 2x) + (-9x - 3)] \quad \text{Group.} \\
&= 2[2x(3x + 1) - 3(3x + 1)] \quad \text{Factor out common factors.} \\
&= 2(3x + 1)(2x - 3) \quad \text{Factor out a common binomial factor.}
\end{aligned}
$$

The check is left for you.

$$12x^2 - 14x - 6 = 2(3x + 1)(2x - 3)$$

d. $3x^4 + 2x^2 - 8$ is not a quadratic trinomial. However, the *ac* method may still be used to factor this trinomial.

Since $a = 3, b = 2$, and $c = -8$, it follows that $ac = 3 \cdot -8 = -24$. Using a table, determine the factors of the product that result in a sum of $2 (b)$.

Note: You may want to use the calculator table.

Factor	Factor	Sum of Factors
1	−24	−23
−1	24	23
2	−12	−10
−2	12	10
3	−8	−5
−3	8	5
4	−6	−2
−4	6	2	← *b*

X	Y₁	Y₂
-5	4.8	-.2
-4	6	2
-3	8	5
-2	12	10
-1	24	23
0	ERR:	ERR:
1	-24	-23

X= -4

$Y1 = (3 \cdot -8) \div x$
$Y2 = x + Y1$

The factors −4 and 6 result in a sum of 2. Rewrite the trinomial, using these factors as coefficients of the two new middle terms.

$$3x^4 + 2x^2 - 8 = 3x^4 - 4x^2 + 6x^2 - 8$$
$$= (3x^4 - 4x^2) + (6x^2 - 8) \qquad \text{Group.}$$
$$= x^2(3x^2 - 4) + 2(3x^2 - 4) \qquad \text{Factor out common factors.}$$
$$= (3x^2 - 4)(x^2 + 2) \qquad \text{Factor out a common binomial factor.}$$

The check is left for you.

$$3x^4 + 2x^2 - 8 = (3x^2 - 4)(x^2 + 2) \qquad ■$$

TAKE NOTE Both the trial-and-error method and the *ac* method result in the same factors. As you work exercises, you will develop a sense regarding which method is easier for you to use. Sometimes, one method is shorter than the other. Other times, either method will be about as difficult.

✓ Objective 8.4.1 *CHECKUP*

1. Factor completely, using the *ac* method of factoring a trinomial with a leading coefficient not equal to 1.

  a. $2x^2 - 9x - 5$ **b.** $15x^2 + 7x + 2$
  c. $30x^2 + 65x + 30$ **d.** $6x^4 - 23x^2 + 20$

2. If you had to factor a trinomial whose leading coefficient was not equal to 1, would you first try the trial-and-error method or the *ac* method? Explain your choice.   ■

Objective 8.4.2 ## Modeling the Real World

In previous sections, we factored polynomials representing the area of a rectangle to determine its dimensions. This same procedure may be used to determine the dimensions of other geometric figures as well. However, it may be necessary to factor the polynomial into more than two factors.

EXAMPLE 2

Carri has a triangular flower bed in the corner of her yard where the driveway enters the street at a 90-degree angle. The length of the flower bed along the driveway is twice the length of the flower bed along the street. She plans to increase the length of the sides of her flower bed along the driveway and street by the same number of feet. She has determined that the area of the new flower bed will be $\left(x^2 + \frac{15}{2}x + \frac{25}{2}\right)$ square feet, given that x is the original number of feet on the street side of the flower bed.

a. Determine the lengths of the sides of the new flower bed in terms of x.

b. By how many feet does Carri plan to increase each side?

Solution

a. The area of a triangle is found by the formula $A = \frac{1}{2}bh$. Since the triangle is a right triangle, the base and height are the lengths of the sides along the driveway and the street, respectively. To determine the lengths of these sides, we must factor the area given into the form $\frac{1}{2}bh$.

$$
\begin{array}{ccc}
A & \frac{1}{2} & bh \\
\downarrow & \downarrow & \downarrow
\end{array}
$$

$$
x^2 + \frac{15}{2}x + \frac{25}{2} = \frac{1}{2}(2x^2 + 15x + 25) \qquad \text{Factor out the } \frac{1}{2}.
$$

$$
= \frac{1}{2}(x + 5)(2x + 5) \qquad \text{Factor the } bh \text{ into two binomials.}
$$

The sides of the new triangular bed are $(x + 5)$ feet and $(2x + 5)$ feet.

b. Since the original dimensions of the flower bed were x feet and $2x$ feet, Carri plans to add 5 feet to each side. ∎

APPLICATION

Delaware's Fred Rust Arena has an ice surface that is classified as an Olympic-sized surface. The length of the surface is twice its width. If a surrounding area of equal width borders the ice surface, then a polynomial for the area of the enclosed surface is $2x^2 + 15x + 25$ square feet. Factor the polynomial and determine the width of the border. If the width of the ice surface is 100 feet, evaluate the factors to determine the area of the enclosed surface and its dimensions.

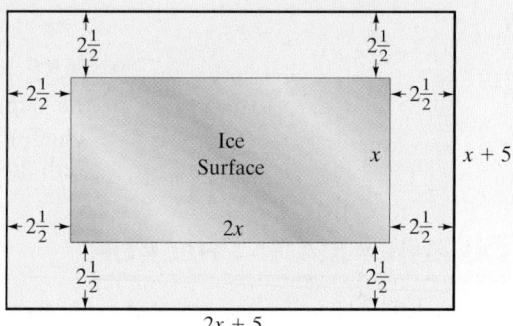

Discussion

$$
ac = 2(25) = 50
$$

10 and 5 are factors of 50 that add to 15.

$$
\begin{aligned}
2x^2 + 15x + 25 &= 2x^2 + 10x + 5x + 25 \\
&= (2x^2 + 10x) + (5x + 25) \\
&= 2x(x + 5) + 5(x + 5) \\
&= (2x + 5)(x + 5)
\end{aligned}
$$

Given the factors, 5 feet is added to the length and width or the walkway is $2\frac{1}{2}$ feet wide.

Let $x = 100$ feet and evaluate the factors.

$$
\begin{aligned}
(2x + 5)(x + 5) &= (2 \cdot 100 + 5)(100 + 5) \\
&= 21{,}525
\end{aligned}
$$

The total area enclosed is 21,525 square feet.

Note that the factors 205 feet and 105 feet are the dimensions of the enclosed surface.

We can check to see that the original polynomial gave us the same value for the area.

$$
\begin{aligned}
2x^2 + 15x + 25 &= 2(100)^2 + 15(100) + 25 \\
&= 21{,}525
\end{aligned}
$$

✓ Objective 8.4.2 CHECKUP

1. Carri has another triangular garden, on the other side of the driveway, that has to be reduced. The length of the flower bed along the drive is three times the length along the street. She cut both sides of the triangle by the same amount. The reduced garden has an area equal to the polynomial $\frac{3}{2}x^2 - 8x + 8$, where x is the length of the small side of the original garden.
   a. Determine the sides of the reduced garden in terms of x.
   b. By how many feet did Carri reduce each side of the garden?

2. Most hockey games are played on a National Hockey League–sized rink. The length of the ice surface for these rinks is 30 feet more than twice the width of the surface. If a surrounding area of equal width borders the ice surface, a polynomial for the total area (border and ice surface) is $2x^2 + 75x + 675$. Factor the polynomial to determine expressions for the width and length of the total area. Determine the width of the border. If the width of the ice surface is 85 feet, evaluate the factors to determine the length and the width of the total area, and determine the total area. ∎

8.4 EXERCISES

In exercises 1–54, use the ac method to factor completely. Check the factors by multiplying, either numerically or graphically.

1. $3x^2 + 19x + 20$

2. $5x^2 + 19x + 12$

3. $6x^2 + 31x + 35$

4. $28x^2 + 29x + 6$

5. $10q^2 + 27q + 11$

6. $8p^2 + 30p + 13$

7. $4x^2 + 14x + 45$

8. $25x^2 + 25x + 16$

9. $20z^2 - 51z + 12$

10. $40y^2 - 31y + 6$

11. $6m^2 - 13m + 6$

12. $10k^2 - 29k + 10$

13. $56p^2 + 13p - 3$

14. $72x^2 + 23x - 4$

15. $15p^2 - 26p + 8$

16. $20q^2 - 49q + 35$

17. $32x^2 - 12x - 5$

18. $24x^2 - 14x - 3$

19. $28k^2 - 19k - 99$

20. $56k^2 - 23k - 45$

21. $24m^2 + 77m - 117$

22. $30x^2 + 47x - 60$

23. $40x^2 - 148x + 28$

24. $54x^2 - 84x + 16$

25. $30x^2 + 87x + 30$

26. $30x^2 + 65x + 30$

27. $16x^2 + 42x - 18$

28. $18x^2 + 64x - 32$

29. $-18x^2 + 75x - 72$

30. $-24x^2 + 76x - 40$

31. $16x^2 - 52x - 80$

32. $24y^2 - 6y - 66$

33. $6x^3 + 25x^2 + 25x$

34. $10y^3 + 29y^2 + 35y$

35. $6x^4 + 7x^2 + 2$

36. $10x^4 + 17x^2 + 3$

37. $8x^4 + 46x^2 + 63$

38. $12y^4 + 28y^2 + 15$

39. $6x^4 - 19x^2 + 15$

40. $12x^4 - 41x^2 + 35$

41. $12x^4 - 17x^2 + 6$

42. $6x^4 - 29x^2 + 35$

43. $8m^4 - 2m^2 - 15$

44. $12p^4 - 8p^2 - 15$

45. $15x^4 + 14x^2 - 16$

46. $18x^4 + 19x^2 - 12$

47. $60y^4 + 57y^2 - 84$

48. $56x^4 + 46x^2 - 30$

49. $-24x^4 + 32x^2 - 10$

50. $-45y^4 - 66y^2 - 24$

51. $6x^2 - 7xy - 20y^2$

52. $21x^2 - 22xy - 8y^2$

53. $40p^2 - 67pq + 28q^2$

54. $54p^2 - 57pq + 10q^2$

Geometry

55. Shannon had a triangular-shaped patio behind her house. The height of the triangle was three-fourths the length of the base. She increased both the height and the base of the triangle by the same amount. As a result, the area of the enlarged patio became $\left(6x^2 + \dfrac{49}{2}x + \dfrac{49}{2}\right)$ square feet, where the base of the original patio was $4x$ feet. Determine the base and the height of the enlarged patio in terms of x. By how many feet did Shannon increase the height and the base?

56. Tyler constructed a walkway along one side of a triangular corner of his yard. Before constructing the walkway, the triangular yard had a base that was five times as large as its height. After Tyler constructed the walkway, the area of the triangular yard was $\left(\dfrac{5}{2}x^2 - 18x + 18\right)$ square feet. Factor this polynomial to determine the dimensions of the yard. By how many feet was each side of the triangular yard reduced?

57. For doubles play in badminton, the recommended free space surrounding the court is at least 2 meters on all four sides. If the length of a badminton court is 1 meter more than twice its width, and the free space on each side is of equal width, the area of the court and the free space can be approximated by the polynomial $(2x^2 + 19x + 42)$ square meters. Factor the polynomial and determine the width of the free space. If the width of the court is approximately 6 meters, evaluate the factors to determine the length and width of the total area, including the free space, and the amount of that area.

58. The recommended playing surface for an English standard billiard table has a length that is twice the width. If the table has a free space of equal width around each side, a polynomial for the total area is $(2x^2 + 21x + 49)$ square meters. Factor the polynomial and determine the width of the free space. If the width of the playing area is 1.8 meters, evaluate the factors to determine the dimensions of the total area, as well as the area itself.

59. The product of the measure of two angles can be given by the polynomial $7x^2 + 195x + 1350$. Factor the polynomial using the *ac* method to find an expression for each angle. If $x = 10$, are the angles supplementary?

60. The product of the length of the sides of a rectangle can be given by the polynomial $15x^2 - 86x + 119$. Use the *ac* method to factor the polynomial and find possible expressions for each side. If $x = 12$, can the rectangle be a square?

Business

61. The cost to provide an art enrichment class to a group of students is estimated to be $C(x) = 18x^2 - 67x - 63$, where x is the number of children. Use the *ac* method to factor this polynomial completely.

62. A furniture company finds that its revenue is $R(x) = 45x^2 + 43x - 28$, where x is the number of sales associates working on a given day. Use the *ac* method to factor this polynomial completely.

63. A builder's total profit on new home sales in thousands of dollars is given by $p(x) = 18x^2 - 3x - 136$, where x is the number of the month of the year. Factor this polynomial completely.

64. A coffee shop estimates its monthly profit in dollars to be $p(x) = 14x^2 + 129x + 61$, where x is the number of the month of the year. Factor this polynomial completely.

65. A children's play facility that offers classes and parties for grade-school students estimates its total profit in dollars to be $p(x) = 21x^2 - 122x - 399$, where x is the number of the week of the year. Factor this polynomial completely.

66. A retail chain estimates company profits in thousands of dollars by $p(x) = 10x^2 - 233x + 1350$, where x is the number of months after February. Factor this polynomial completely.

Vertical Distance

67. A person on a sailboat fires a flare gun at night. The distance above the ground of the flare in feet can be given by $s(t) = -16t^2 + 235t + 75$, where t is the time in seconds. Use the *ac* method to factor this polynomial completely.

68. A police officer fires a gun from the window of a tall building. The distance of the bullet above the ground $s(t) = -9.8t^2 - 89t + 90$ where t is the time in seconds. Use the *ac* method to factor this polynomial completely.

8.4 Calculator Exercises

In using the *ac* method, if you store the values of a, b, and c from the trinomial $ax^2 + bx + c$ in your calculator, you can proceed from one trinomial to another without having to reenter the expressions for Y1 and Y2. The following example illustrates the procedure:

Factor $85x^2 - 91x - 72$ using the *ac* method.

a. Store values for a, b, and c.

b. Set Y1 $= \dfrac{ac}{x}$.

c. Set Y2 to test for the values of m and n that make $m + n = b$ a true statement or Y2 $= x + $ Y1 $= $ B.

| X,T,θ,n | + | VARS | ▶ | 1 | 1 | 2nd |
| MATH | (TEST) | 1 | ALPHA | APPS | (B) |

d. Set your table as before and view the table, scanning for a 1 in the Y2 column.

In this case, Y2 is 1 when the values of m and n are 45 and -136, respectively. Now you can use the grouping method to show that

$$85x^2 - 91x - 72 = 85x^2 - 136x + 45x - 72$$
$$= (85x^2 - 136x) + (45x - 72)$$
$$= 17x(5x - 8) + 9(5x - 8)$$
$$= (17x + 9)(5x - 8)$$

For subsequent problems, you need only store the new values for a, b, and c and go directly to the table to find the new values of m and n.

Note that when you are scanning the table for the pair of numbers, there is some logic to follow in deciding whether to scan in the negative-integer direction or the positive-integer direction. If the coefficient b is negative and c is positive, you will be searching for two negative integers and will want to scan in that direction. If the coefficient c is negative, you may scan in either direction, since one of the integers will be positive and the other negative. If the coefficients b and c are both positive, you need only scan in the positive-integer direction, since the two integers will be positive.

Use this procedure to factor the following polynomials by the *ac* method. Be sure to factor completely.

1. $96x^2 - 16x - 2$ **2.** $24x^2 + 7x - 55$

3. $32x^2 + 102x + 81$ **4.** $72x^2 - 99x + 34$

5. $4p^4 + 109p^2 + 225$

8.4 Writing Exercise

A friend demonstrates to you an alternative way of using the *ac* method in which factoring by grouping is not used to find the final factorization. The method is explained with the following example:

$$8x^2 - 14x - 15$$

Find *ac* and use your calculator to make a table as you would in the *ac* method. Here $ac = -120$, and the factors of the product that result in the sum of -14 are -20 and 6.

Now write the following using the leading coefficient of the original polynomial and the factors of *ac* that were just found:

$$(8x - 20) \quad (8x + 6)$$

Draw a fraction bar under each factor and leave a space for the denominator of each fraction.

Next divide out the greatest common factor out of each factor to get the final factorization.

$$\frac{(8x - 20)}{4} \quad \frac{(8x + 6)}{2}$$
$$(2x - 5)(4x + 3)$$

The factorization can be checked by multiplying.

Use this method to factor these polynomials. Check by multiplying.

1. $15x^2 - 13x - 20$ **2.** $80x^2 - 125x - 70$

3. $24x^2 + 74x + 45$ **4.** $100x^2 + 311x + 99$

Do you think this method always works? If so, can you verify it? If not, tell why.

8.5 GENERAL STRATEGIES FOR FACTORING

OBJECTIVES   1 Factor any given polynomial completely.

2 Model real-world situations by factoring polynomials.

APPLICATION

The first telephone receivers had a cone-shaped mouthpiece. The volume of the mouthpiece was represented by the polynomial $\left(\frac{1}{3}\pi x^3 + \pi x^2\right)$ cubic inches, where x is the length of the radius in inches. Determine a polynomial that expresses the height in terms of the radius.

After completing this section, we will discuss this application further. See page 643.

Objective 8.5.1

Factoring Polynomials

In the previous sections, we discussed methods of factoring polynomials. We now discuss a general strategy to use when any given polynomial is to be factored. The following steps should be employed to factor a polynomial completely.

STEPS TO FACTOR A POLYNOMIAL COMPLETELY

1. Factor out the greatest common factor from all terms. Factor out -1 if the leading coefficient is negative.

   Determine the type of polynomial remaining, and factor as indicated next for each. Repeat steps 2–4 until all polynomial factors (with the exception of a common monomial factor) do not factor.

2. Binomial (two terms)—Difference of two squares:

$$a^2 - b^2 = (a + b)(a - b)$$

   Sum or difference of two cubes:

$$a^3 + b^3 = (a + b)(a^2 - ab + b^2)$$
$$a^3 - b^3 = (a - b)(a^2 + ab + b^2)$$

   Otherwise, the polynomial will not factor.

3. Trinomial (three terms)—Perfect-square trinomial:

$$a^2 + 2ab + b^2 = (a + b)^2$$
$$a^2 - 2ab + b^2 = (a - b)^2$$

   Quadratic trinomial with leading coefficient of 1:

$$x^2 + bx + c = (x + m)(x + n)$$

   where $mn = c$ and $n + m = b$

   Quadratic trinomial with leading coefficient greater than 1: trial-and-error method or ac method

   Otherwise, the polynomial will not factor.

4. Four-term polynomial—Factor by grouping

   Otherwise, the polynomial will not factor.

(continued on page 640)

Check the factors by multiplying to obtain the original polynomial or by entering into your calculator the original polynomial and the product of the factors as separate functions and determining that the tables of values have equivalent Y1 and Y2 columns or the graphs are coincide.

EXAMPLE 1

Factor completely and check.

a. $3y^2 - 243$ **b.** $16y^4 - 200y^2 + 625$

c. $6x^2 + 16x - 70$ **d.** $5x^3 + 12x^2 + 7x$

e. $2a^3b - 8a^2b^2 - 3a^2b^2 + 12ab^3$ **f.** $4x^2 + 14x + 49$

g. $15 + 8x + x^2$

Solution

a. $3y^2 - 243$

The GCF is 3. Therefore, factor out 3 from all terms.

$$3y^2 - 243 = 3(y^2 - 81)$$

The remaining factor is a binomial; in fact, it is a difference of squares: $y^2 - 81 = (y)^2 - (9)^2 = (y + 9)(y - 9)$.

$$3y^2 - 243 = 3(y^2 - 81)$$
$$= 3(y + 9)(y - 9)$$

The remaining factors are binomials. However, neither is a difference of squares or a difference of cubes. The binomials will not factor.

The check is left for you.

$$3y^2 - 243 = 3(y + 9)(y - 9)$$

b. $16y^4 - 200y^2 + 625$

There are no common factors. The polynomial is a trinomial; in fact, it is a perfect-square trinomial: $(4y^2)^2 - 2(4y^2)(25) + (25)^2 = (4y^2 - 25)^2$.

$$16y^4 - 200y^2 + 625 = (4y^2 - 25)^2$$

The remaining polynomial factors are binomials. Both are differences of squares, $4y^2 - 25 = (2y)^2 - (5)^2 = (2y + 5)(2y - 5)$, so we write the factors twice.

$$16y^4 - 200y^2 + 625 = (4y^2 - 25)^2$$
$$= (2y + 5)(2y - 5)(2y + 5)(2y - 5)$$
$$= (2y + 5)^2(2y - 5)^2$$

The remaining factors are binomials that will not factor.

The check is left for you.

$$16y^4 - 200y^2 + 625 = (2y + 5)^2(2y - 5)^2$$

c. $6x^2 + 16x - 70$

The GCF is 2. Therefore, factor 2 out of all terms.

$$6x^2 + 16x - 70 = 2(3x^2 + 8x - 35)$$

The remaining factor is a trinomial with $a > 1$. Since $a = 3$ and $c = -35$ are not both prime, it will be easier to use the ac method: $ac = -105$.

Note: You may want to use the calculator table.

Factor	Factor	Sum of Factors	
1	−105	−104	
−1	105	104	
3	−35	−32	
−3	35	32	
5	−21	−16	
−5	21	16	
7	−15	−8	
−7	15	8	← b

X	Y1	Y2
-7	15	8
-6	17.5	11.5
-5	21	16
-4	26.25	22.25
-3	35	32
-2	52.5	50.5
-1	105	104

X= -7

$Y1 = (3 \cdot -35) \div x$
$Y2 = x + Y1$

Rewrite the middle term of the trinomial, $8x$, as $-7x + 15x$, and factor by grouping.

$$6x^2 + 16x - 70 = 2(3x^2 + 8x - 35)$$
$$= 2(3x^2 - 7x + 15x - 35)$$
$$= 2[(3x^2 - 7x) + (15x - 35)] \quad \text{Group terms.}$$
$$= 2[x(3x - 7) + 5(3x - 7)] \quad \text{Factor out a common factor from each group.}$$
$$= 2(3x - 7)(x + 5) \quad \text{Factor out a common binomial factor from each term.}$$

The remaining binomial factors will not factor.
   The check is left for you.

$$6x^2 + 16x - 70 = 2(3x - 7)(x + 5)$$

d. $5x^3 + 12x^2 + 7x$
   The GCF is x. Factor x out of each term.

$$5x^3 + 12x^2 + 7x = x(5x^2 + 12x + 7)$$

The remaining factor is a trinomial with $a > 1$. Since $a = 5$ and $c = 7$ are prime, we will use the trial-and-error method. Possible factors for the first and last terms are $5x^2 = x \cdot 5x$ and $7 = 1 \cdot 7$. Since $b = 12$ is a positive number, we will use only positive factors of 7. Filling in the blanks with possibilities and checking for the correct middle term will result in the following:

$$x(\underline{}\,\underline{})(\underline{}\,\underline{}) \quad \text{Middle term}$$
$$x(\underline{x} + \underline{1})(\underline{5x} + \underline{7}) \quad 7x + 5x = 12x$$
$$x(\underline{x} + \underline{7})(\underline{5x} + \underline{1}) \quad x + 35x = 36x$$

We choose $x(x + 1)(5x + 7)$, because it results in the correct middle term.

$$5x^3 + 12x^2 + 7x = x(5x^2 + 12x + 7)$$
$$= x(x + 1)(5x + 7)$$

The remaining binomial factors will not factor.
   The check is left for you.

$$5x^3 + 12x^2 + 7x = x(x + 1)(5x + 7)$$

e. $2a^3b - 8a^2b^2 - 3a^2b^2 + 12ab^3$
   The GCF is ab. Factor ab out of each term.

$$2a^3b - 8a^2b^2 - 3a^2b^2 + 12ab^3 = ab(2a^2 - 8ab - 3ab + 12b^2)$$

The remaining polynomial has four terms. We will factor it by grouping.

$$2a^3b - 8a^2b^2 - 3a^2b^2 + 12ab^3 = ab(2a^2 - 8ab - 3ab + 12b^2)$$
$$= ab[(2a^2 - 8ab) + (-3ab + 12b^2)]$$

Group terms.

$$= ab[2a(a - 4b) + (-3b)(a - 4b)]$$

Factor out a common factor from each group.

$$= ab(a - 4b)(2a - 3b)$$

Factor out a common binomial factor from each term.

The remaining binomial factors will not factor.
   The check is left for you.

$$2a^3b - 8^2b^2 - 3a^2b^2 + 12ab^3 = ab(a - 4b)(2a - 3b)$$

f. $4x^2 + 14x + 49$

There are no common factors. The polynomial is a trinomial. It looks similar to a perfect-square trinomial, but upon closer inspection, we see that it is not.

$$4x^2 + 14x + 49 \neq (2x)^2 + 2(2x)(7) + (7)^2$$
$$\uparrow$$
$$28x$$

The polynomial is a trinomial with $a > 1$. Since $a = 4$ and $c = 49$ are not prime, we will use the *ac* method: $ac = 196$. We will use a table to determine the factors, m and n, of the product 196 that will result in a sum of 14(b). Since b is positive, we will only use the positive factors of 196.

Note: You may want to use the calculator table.

Factor	Factor	Sum of Factors
1	196	197
2	98	100
4	49	53
7	28	35
14	14	28

Since no set of factors results in a sum of 14, the trinomial will not factor. $4x^2 + 14x + 49$ will not factor.

g. $15 + 8x + x^2$

There are no common factors. The polynomial is a trinomial that is not written in standard form. We will factor this trinomial by trial and error. Possible factors for the first and last terms are as follows:

$$15 = 1 \cdot 15 \qquad x^2 = x \cdot x$$
$$= 3 \cdot 5$$

Since $b = 8$ is a positive number, we will use only positive factors of 15. Filling in the blanks with possibilities and checking for the correct middle term result in the following:

$$(\underline{\quad} \ \underline{\quad})(\underline{\quad} \ \underline{\quad}) \qquad \text{Middle term}$$
$$(\underline{1} + x)(\underline{15} + x) \qquad x + 15x = 16x$$
$$(\underline{3} + x)(\underline{5} + x) \qquad 3x + 5x = 8x$$

We choose $(3 + x)(5 + x)$, because this results in $8x$ for the middle term.

$$15 + 8x + x^2 = (3 + x)(5 + x)$$

The check is left for you.

$$15 + 8x + x^2 = (3 + x)(5 + x)$$

Objective 8.5.1 *CHECKUP*

1. Factor completely and check.

    a. $10z^2 + 35z - 150$
    b. $6a^3 + 26a^2 + 8a$
    c. $4x^2 + 15x + 25$
    d. $12x^3 - 60x^2y - 6x^2y + 30xy^2$
    e. $-6a^2 + 24$
    f. $81x^4 - 72x^2 + 16$
    g. $12 - 17h - 5h^2$

2. What is the first thing you should always look for in factoring a polynomial?
3. If you are factoring a binomial, for what forms should you be on the lookout?
4. In factoring a trinomial, for what forms should you be looking?
5. In factoring a polynomial with four terms, what method should you try to use?

Objective 8.5.2   Modeling the Real World

Many mathematical relationships cannot be described exactly by polynomials. However, they often can be approximated by polynomials, especially if we are interested in only a small domain of the variable. Because of this capability to approximate, factoring and simplifying polynomials is a very useful technique to learn.

Many business applications involving revenue may be represented by a polynomial having a GCF of the variable representing the number of items sold. When this occurs, the common factor represents the number of items sold, and the second factor represents the cost of each item sold. Therefore, factoring the polynomial allows us to determine the selling price in terms of the number of items sold.

EXAMPLE 2   A tour agency offers special group package rates. One such offer is to give one free ticket if certain conditions are met. Another possibility is to reduce the advertised cost of the ticket. A ticket agent uses a formula to determine that the revenue from a tour is represented by the polynomial $(149.95x - 0.99x^2)$, where x is the number of people participating. Factor the polynomial, and determine whether a free ticket was offered or the advertised cost of the tickets was reduced.

Solution

x = number of people participating

$$149.95x - 0.99x^2 = x(149.95 - x) \qquad \text{Factor out the common factor.}$$

The revenue is the product of x participants and $(149.95 - x)$ dollars, or $(149.95 - 1x)$ dollars.

Therefore, the advertised cost of the ticket ($149.95) is reduced and is $149.95 minus $1 per participant.

APPLICATION

The first telephone receivers had a cone-shaped mouthpiece. The volume of the mouthpiece was represented by the polynomial $\left(\frac{1}{3}\pi x^3 + \pi x^2\right)$ cubic inches, where x is the length of the radius in inches. Determine a polynomial that expresses the height in terms of the radius.

Discussion

x is the length of the radius in inches.

$\frac{1}{3}\pi x^3 + \pi x^2$ is the volume of the mouthpiece.

The formula for the volume of a cone is $\frac{1}{3}\pi r^2 h$.

To determine the height, factor out $\frac{1}{3}\pi x^2$ from the polynomial representing the volume.

$$\frac{1}{3}\pi x^3 + \pi x^2 = \frac{1}{3}\pi x^2(x + 3)$$

Comparing the formula for the volume with the factored polynomial, we have

$$\begin{matrix} \frac{1}{3}\pi r^2 & h \\ \downarrow & \downarrow \end{matrix}$$

$$\frac{1}{3}\pi x^2(x + 3)$$

The radius is x inches and the height is $(x + 3)$ inches.

Objective 8.5.2 *CHECKUP*

1. A supplier of computer software offers a special deal to customers who purchase multiple copies of their software. The total price of purchasing x copies of the software is given as $(349.95x - 8.95x^2)$ dollars. Factor this polynomial. From the factors, explain how the supplier figured the special deal.

2. A tray is made from a rectangular sheet of metal by cutting out squares from each corner and folding up the edges. The volume of the tray is determined to be $(35x - 24x^2 + 4x^3)$ cubic inches, where x is the measure of the side of the squares removed from each corner. Factor the expression for the volume to obtain expressions for the height, width, and length of the tray. What are the dimensions of the tray if the squares cut from the corners measure 1 inch on a side?

8.5 EXERCISES

  Math XL MathXL® MyMathLab MyMathLab Interactmath.com

Student Solutions Manual   PH Math/Tutor Center   CD Video

In exercises 1–32, use the general strategy to factor completely. Check.

1. $3y^3 + 3y^2 + 3y$
2. $10x^3 + 35x^2 - 5x$
3. $10abc^2 + 15abc - 20ab$
4. $6xyz^2 + 10xyz - 6xy$
5. $-40a^2 - 24ab + 48ac$
6. $-28x^2 - 35xy + 21xz$
7. $108x^5 - 75x^3$
8. $32u^3 - 98u$
9. $-200x^3y + 32xy^3$
10. $-18a^3b + 128ab^3$
11. $x^3 - 16x^2 + 64x$
12. $z^3 - 10z^2 + 25z$
13. $12u^2v + 36uv^2 + 27v^3$
14. $50x^3 + 40x^2y + 8xy^2$
15. $3x^4 - 48x^2 + 7x^2 - 112$
16. $2x^4 - 18x^2 + 5x^2 - 45$
17. $4p^4 - 37p^2 + 9$
18. $9z^4 - 40z^2 + 16$
19. $2 + 8y - 42y^2$
20. $3 + 6y - 72y^2$
21. $4u^2v^2 + 36uv + 56$
22. $5a^2b^2 + 35ab + 60$
23. $32x^3 - 64x^2 - 28x^2 + 56x$
24. $15x^3 - 18x^2 - 60x^2 + 72x$
25. $12x^4 + 26x^3 - 30x^2$
26. $15z^4 + 10z^3 - 40z^2$
27. $x^6 - 5x^3y^3 + 3x^3y^3 - 15y^6$
28. $p^6 + 2p^3q^3 - 5p^3q^3 - 10q^6$
29. $x^4 - 5x^3 + 8x^2 - 40x$
30. $2y^4 + 6y^3 + 8y^2 + 24y$
31. $1 - k^8$
32. $256s^8 - 1$

Geometry

In exercises 33–42, factor. Find the missing lengths.

33.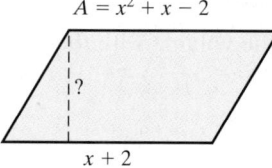
$A = 10x^2 - 13x - 3$?
$5x + 1$

34.
$A = 3x^2 - 5x - 12$?
$3x + 4$

35.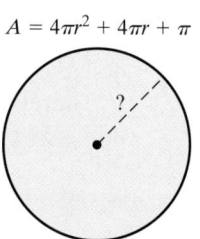
$A = 4\pi r^2 + 4\pi r + \pi$
?

36.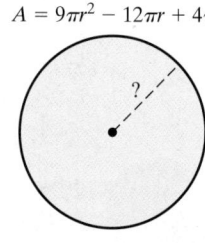
$A = 9\pi r^2 - 12\pi r + 4\pi$
?

37.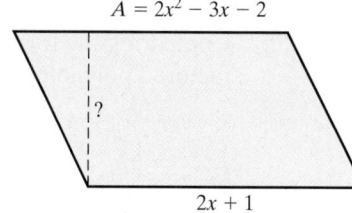
$A = x^2 + x - 2$
?
$x + 2$

38.
$A = 2x^2 - 3x - 2$
?
$2x + 1$

39.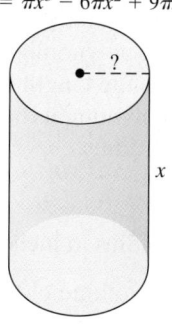
$V = \pi x^3 - 6\pi x^2 + 9\pi x$
?
x

40.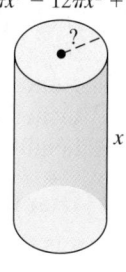
$V = \pi x^3 - 12\pi x^2 + 36\pi x$
?
x

41.

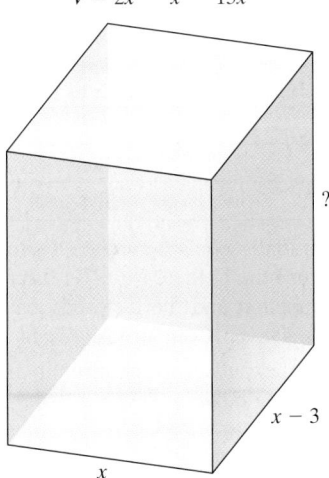

$V = 2x^3 - x^2 - 15x$

?

$x - 3$

x

42.

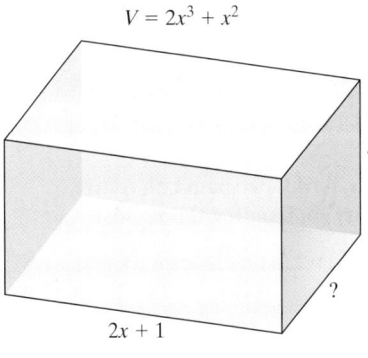

$V = 2x^3 + x^2$

?

?

$2x + 1$

43. A sheet of posterboard has its corners cut out and sides folded up to form an open box. The volume of the box is $(135x - 48x^2 + 4x^3)$ cubic inches, where x is the length of the sides of the squares cut from the corners. Factor the polynomial to determine the length, width, and height of the box. What are the dimensions and volume of the box if x is 2 inches?

44. An open box is formed by cutting out the corners of a piece of tin and folding up the sides. The volume of the box is $(x^3 + 30x^2 + 200x)$ cubic inches, where x is the length of the sides of the squares cut from the corners. Factor the polynomial to determine expressions for the length, width, and height of the box. What are the dimensions and volume of the box if x is 5 inches?

45. The volume of a cylindrical hatbox is $(4\pi x^3 - 20\pi x^2 + 25\pi x)$ cubic inches, where x is the height of the box. Factor the polynomial to determine an expression for the radius of the box. What are the dimensions and volume of the box if x is 8 inches?

46. The volume of a cylindrical waste container is $(\pi x^3 - 16\pi x^2 + 64\pi x)$ cubic inches, where x is the height of the container. Factor the polynomial to determine the radius and diameter of the container. What are the dimensions and volume of the container if x is 15 inches?

47. In his drafting class, Dennis had to draw different perspective views of a cube with a smaller cube carved out of one corner. The original cube measured x inches on a side. Dennis figured that the volume of the remaining object was $(x^3 - 216)$ cubic inches. Factor this polynomial. Do the factors have any interpretation? What are the dimensions of the cube that was carved out of the larger cube?

48. For another project, Dennis had to draw different perspective views of an object that consisted of two different-sized cubes attached on one face. The smaller cube measured x inches on a side. Dennis determined that the total volume of the object was $(x^3 + 13,824)$ cubic inches. Factor this polynomial. Do the factors have any interpretation? What are the dimensions of the larger cube?

Business

49. To encourage sales, Big Ed's Pizza Palace offers discounts on multiple orders. If a person orders x pizzas, the total price is $(14.75x - 0.95x^2)$ dollars. Factor this polynomial. From the factors, explain how Big Ed figured the discount. Should Big

Ed put a limit on the number of pizzas a person may order? Explain.

50. A music club offers its members a special deal on music CDs. If a person orders x CDs from the club, the total price, including shipping and handling, is $(15.70x - 2.24x^2)$ dollars. Factor this polynomial. Explain how the special deal works. Should the music club put a limit on the number of CDs a member may order? Explain.

51. Because of a shortage of fashion dolls for the holiday season, Tallmart stores charge a surcharge on purchases of more than one doll. If a person purchases x dolls, the total price is $(19.95x + 2.99x^2)$ dollars. Factor this polynomial. Explain how Tallmart figured the surcharge.

52. Food Tiger stores have a sale on Thanksgiving turkeys. To discourage excessive purchases by any customer, they charge a surcharge on purchases of more than one turkey. If a customer purchases x turkeys, the total price is $(4.95x + 2x^2)$ dollars. Factor this polynomial and explain how the surcharge is administered.

Vertical Distance

53. An object with no initial velocity falls a distance of $16t^2$ feet in t seconds. The distance fallen between time t_1 and t_2 is $16t_2^2 - 16t_1^2$. Factor this polynomial.

54. An object with no initial velocity falls a distance of $9.8t^2$ meters in t seconds. The distance fallen between time t_1 and t_2 is $9.8t_2^2 - 9.8t_2^2$. Factor this polynomial.

Physics

55. In a resistor of resistance R with voltage V across it, the power is $\dfrac{V^2}{R}$. An electronics calculation involves factoring $\dfrac{V^2}{R} - \dfrac{V_2^2}{R}$. Factor.

56. Hooke's Law states that the work needed to stretch a spring x units is $F = kx$, where k is the spring constant. The work needed to stretch a spring from length x_1 to length x_2 is $\dfrac{kx_2^2 - kx_1^2}{2}$. Factor.

In exercises 57 and 58, write a quadratic function to model the data. Factor the function using any method.

Real Data

57. According to the U.S. Department of Defense, the number of active army personnel has declined since the year 2000.

Years after 2000	U.S. Army Personnel on Active Duty (in hundred thousands)
0	300
1	297
2	288

58. According to the U.S. Department of Education, National Center of Education Statistics, the estimated cost of yearly undergraduate tuition is on the rise since 1998.

Years after 1998	0	1	2
Esimated cost of yearly undergraduate tuition ($)	10,033	10,400	10,773

59. A breeder of pond fish finds that as the weather gets warmer in the summer, his fish breed more quickly. The number of fish as a function of weeks after June 15 can be estimated by following table:

Number of Weeks after June 15	Number of Fish
3	51
4	174
6	504

Write a quadratic function that models these data. Factor the quadratic. Seven weeks after June 15 there were 711 fish. Evaluate both the quadratic function and the factored quadratic when the number of weeks is seven. Compare the results.

60. The estimated yearly school expenses for children in grades K–4 are shown in the following table:

Age of Child	Yearly Expense ($)
5	202
6	318
7	444

Write a quadratic function that models these data. Factor the quadratic. The yearly expense for an 8-year-old child is $580. The yearly expense for a 9-year-old is $726. Evaluate both the quadratic function and the factored quadratic when the age of the child is 8 and 9. Compare the results.

8.5 Calculator Exercises

In 8.3 Calculator Exercises, you were shown how to use the x-intercepts of a graph to help you factor a difficult trinomial. Actually, this method will work for *any* polynomial that can be factored, even when some of the methods we have studied will not. As an example, suppose you wish to factor the polynomial $40x^3 + 122x^2 + 79x - 21$.

Follow these steps:

1. Define a function $y = 40x^3 + 122x^2 + 79x - 21$.

2. Graph the function, using an appropriate window, such as $(-2, 2, 1, -10, 10, 1, 1)$. Note that since we are interested only in finding x-intercepts, the window need not be large enough to show all minima and maxima.

3. Determine the x-values of the x-intercepts.

$$x = 0.2 \qquad\qquad x = -1.5$$

Y1 = 40x³ + 122x² + 79x − 21   Y1 = 40x³ + 122x² + 79x − 21

Zero X=.2 Y=0   Zero X=-1.5 Y=0

$$x = -1.75$$

Y1 = 40x³ + 122x² + 79x − 21

Zero X=-1.75 Y=0

4. Convert the x-values to fractions, and write the resulting equations in standard form.

$$x = \frac{1}{5} \qquad x = -\frac{3}{2} \qquad x = -\frac{7}{4}$$

$$5x - 1 = 0 \qquad 2x + 3 = 0 \qquad 4x + 7 = 0$$

5. The polynomial factors into the product of the expressions on the left of the equations in step 4.

$$40x^3 + 122x^2 + 79x - 21 = (5x - 1)(2x + 3)(4x + 7)$$

Check your results by multiplying, check them numerically with a table of values, or check them graphically.

Try the method on the following polynomials:

1. $16x^3 + 4x^2 - 264x + 189$

2. $50x^3 + 25x^2 - 18x - 9$

3. $90x^3 + 213x^2 - 53x - 140$

4. $18x^3 - 45x^2 - 128x + 320$

8.5 Writing Exercise

Perform the following two multiplications, which involve squares of binomials:

1. $(a^n + b^n)^2$ **2.** $(a^n - b^n)^2$

You should see that the results are two more recognizable forms that could be helpful in factoring. Write a description of how these two results, when turned around, could help you factor some trinomials.

Use your description to factor the trinomials that follow as illustrations of what you have described. Once you do the initial factoring, be sure to check to see whether the factors can be factored further.

3. $x^6 + 2x^3y^3 + y^6$

4. $p^8 - 2p^4q^4 + q^8$

■ Chapter 8 Summary

Vocabulary Review

After completing this chapter, you should be able to define the following key terms.

ac method
factor
factoring by grouping
greatest common factor (GCF)
leading coefficient
prime number
trial-and-error method

Fill in the blank with one of the words or phrases listed above.

1. A _____ of a given number is a number that divides into the given number evenly.

2. The _____ of a set of positive integers is the largest factor common to all of the numbers.

3. An example of the process called _____ is $3x^2 - 6x + x - 2 = (3x^2 - 6x) + (x - 2) = 3x(x - 2) + 1(x - 2) = (x - 2)(3x + 1)$.

4. An example of the _____ of factoring is $6x^2 + 19x + 10 = 6x^2 + 4x + 15x + 10 = 2x(3x + 2) + 5(3x + 2) = (3x + 2)(2x + 5)$.

5. An example of the _____ of factoring is $x^2 - 2x - 15 = (x - 5)(x + 3)$.

Reflections

1. In factoring out a common factor from a polynomial, why do you always seek the greatest common factor?

2. How does a greatest common factor differ from a least common denominator?

3. Explain the difference between a monomial factor and a polynomial factor.

4. Other than a common factor, which can be factored—the difference of two squares or the sum of two squares? Describe the process.

5. Other than a common factor, which can be factored—the difference of two cubes or the sum of two cubes? Describe the process.

6. What is a perfect-square trinomial?

7. Explain what the *ac* method of factoring a trinomial enables you to do.

8. After factoring a polynomial, how can you tell that you factored it correctly?

9. Compare the operation of multiplying polynomials with that of factoring a polynomial.

■ Chapter 8 Section-by-Section Review

8.1

Recall	Examples
Factoring out a GCF • Determine the GCF of all terms. If the leading coefficient is negative, use a negative GCF. • Write each term as a product of the GCF and another factor. • Reverse the distributive law to write a product of the GCF and a polynomial.	Factor. $12x^2 + 4x - 6 = 2(6x^2 + 2x - 3)$ $-24a^2b^3 - 6ab^2 + 12b = -6b(4a^2b^2 + ab - 2)$

(continued on page 648)

Recall	Examples
Factoring by grouping (four terms) • Factor the GCF out of all terms. • Write the polynomial as a sum of two binomials. • Factor each binomial. • Determine the binomial GCF of the resulting terms. • Write a product of the binomial GCF and another binomial.	Factor. $\begin{aligned} 6x^2 - 12x + 10x - 20 &= 2(3x^2 - 6x + 5x - 10) \\ &= 2[(3x^2 - 6x) + (5x - 10)] \\ &= 2[3x(x - 2) + 5(x - 2)] \\ &= 2[(x - 2)(3x + 5)] \\ &= 2(x - 2)(3x + 5) \end{aligned}$

Factor exercises 1–5 completely and check.

1. $20a^6 - 28a^4 + 44a^2$ **2.** $22u^3v^2 + 22u^2v^3$

3. $3x^3 + 3x + x^2 + 1$

4. $7a^4 + 7a^2b^2 + 7a^2b^2 + 7b^4$

5. $15ac + 18ad + 20bc + 24bd$

6. It can be shown that the sum of the natural numbers from 1 to n equals $\frac{1}{2}n^2 + \frac{1}{2}n$.

   a. Factor the expression completely.

   b. Evaluate the original expression and the factored expression for the sum of the natural numbers from 1 to 12.

   c. Which expression was easier to evaluate and why?

7. The area of a rectangle is numerically equal to the polynomial

$$2x^2 - 6x + 5x - 15$$

Factor the expression, using the grouping method to determine algebraic expressions for the rectangle's width and length.

8. Because of a shortage of labor in a resort town, the owners of a fast-food restaurant offered to increase their employees' monthly salary by $10 for each additional month they remain employed. If an employee earns x dollars the first month, write a polynomial for her total pay for seven months. Factor out the GCF from the simplified expression. Interpret what the factors represent. If the employee's beginning salary is $960, determine her total pay for the seven months. Check your interpretation for this beginning salary.

9. A backyard patio design has a rectangular-shaped center made from tiles. The center measures 24 feet by 15 feet. This central section is surrounded by a brick border that adds x feet to each side of the patio. Write a polynomial that represents the area of the brick border. Factor the polynomial and discuss the meaning of the factors. If the brick border adds 3 feet to each side of the patio, how many square feet of brick border are there?

10. A hotel offers a package deal for weekend travelers. The regular price is $300 per package. A reduction per package purchased is offered to groups. The revenue for a certain group is $R(x) = 300x - 7x^2$, where x is the number of packages purchased (or reductions). Factor the revenue function. Determine the amount per reduction in the cost of the package.

11. A hotel manager determines that if he increases the nightly charge of a room that rents for $100, he will have fewer customers than the 50 he has at this rate. The revenue will be $R(x) = 5000 - 300x + 250x - 15x^2$, where x is the number of increases. Factor the revenue function. Determine the amount of each increase and the number of fewer customers per increase.

8.2

Recall	Examples
Factoring a perfect-square trinomial • $a^2 + 2ab + b^2 = (a + b)^2$ • $a^2 - 2ab + b^2 = (a - b)^2$	Factor. $x^2 + 10x + 25 = (x + 5)^2$ $4x^2 - 12x + 9 = (2x - 3)^2$
Factoring the difference of two squares • $a^2 - b^2 = (a + b)(a - b)$	Factor. $9x^2 - 4y^2 = (3x + 2y)(3x - 2y)$
Factoring the difference of two cubes • $a^3 - b^3 = (a - b)(a^2 + ab + b^2)$	Factor. $x^3 - 8 = (x - 2)(x^2 + 2x + 4)$
Factoring the sum of two cubes • $a^3 + b^3 = (a + b)(a^2 - ab + b^2)$	Factor. $27x^3 + y^3 = (3x + y)(9x^2 - 3xy + y^2)$

Factor exercises 12–29 completely and check.

12. $p^2 + 12p + 36$ **13.** $q^2 - 16q + 64$

14. $9x^2 + 30x + 25$ **15.** $49y^2 - 112y + 64$

16. $a^2 - 9a + 81$ **17.** $x^7 + 6x^5y + 9x^3y^2$

18. $x^2 - 169$ **19.** $625 - a^2$

20. $12x^2 - 75$ **21.** $p^2 - q^2$

22. $p^2 + q^2$ **23.** $9x^2 - 25y^2$

24. $16x^4 - 81$ **25.** $x^8 - 1$

26. $c^3 + 27$ **27.** $c^3 - 27$

28. $8z^3 - 125$ **29.** $5h^3 + 40k^3$

30. A design for a school flag is a square with a smaller square 2 feet on a side in its corner. The small square has an icon of the school's mascot in it. The small square is light blue, and the remainder of the large square is navy blue.

   a. Write a polynomial for the area of the flag that is navy blue.

   b. Factor the polynomial to determine the dimensions of a rectangle with the same area as the area in navy blue.

   c. If the large square of the flag is 5 feet on a side, would it require more navy-blue material than a rectangular piece of navy-blue material that is 3 feet by 8 feet? Explain.

31. A circular pond is surrounded by grass and an exercise path that adds x feet to the radius of the circle. A polynomial that represents the area of the pond and exercise space is $(\pi x^2 + 200\pi x + 10,000\pi)$ square feet. Factor the polynomial and determine the radius of the pond. If the grass and exercise path add 20 feet to the radius of the pond and exercise

space, use the factored expression to find the area of the pond and exercise space. Find the area of the pond. Use these two areas to find the area of the exercise space.

32. A flooring contractor sells and installs carpet. He estimates that for a given job his setup cost is $81.00. For a medium-quality carpet that costs him $8.95 per square yard, the customer is charged $17.95 per square yard for padding and installation. Write a polynomial that represents profit on a job involving a square piece of carpet that is x yards on a side. Factor the polynomial.

33. A landscaper buys mulch from a wholesaler and then sells it to customers depending on individual property needs. The landscaper pays $0.60 per cubic foot for the mulch along with a delivery fee of $216.00. He sells the mulch to customers for $0.816 per cubic foot. Write a polynomial for his revenue for x^3 cubic feet of mulch. Factor the polynomial.

8.3

Recall	Examples
Factoring a trinomial with a leading coefficient of 1, using the trial-and-error method • $x^2 + bx + c = (x + m)(x + n)$, where $mn = c$ and $n + m = b$.	Factor. $x^2 + 7x + 12 = (x + 4)(x + 3)$
Factoring a quadratic trinomial with a leading coefficient not equal to 1, using the trial-and-error method • Factor out the GCF from all terms. • Determine the possible factors of the first term and the third term. • Write a set of binomial factors for each combination. • Multiply the factors to determine which set results in the original trinomial.	Factor. $4x^2 + 16x + 15$ $\begin{aligned} 4x^2 &= x \cdot 4x & 15 &= 1 \cdot 15 \\ &= 2x \cdot 2x & &= 3 \cdot 5 \end{aligned}$ Both factors are positive. Check each combination. $4x^2 + 16x + 15 = (2x + 3)(2x + 5)$

Use the trial-and-error method in exercises 34–44 to factor completely. Check.

34. $z^2 + 2z - 99$ **35.** $p^2 + 5pq - 66q^2$ **36.** $6a^2 + 96a + 234$ **37.** $x^4 + 8x^2 + 15$

38. $4q^3 - 28q^2 - 240q$ **39.** $x^2y^2 - 4xy - 117$ **40.** $-7x^2 + 98x - 168$ **41.** $2x^2 - 11x + 5$

42. $6x^2 + 17x + 5$ **43.** $28a^2b^2 + 91ab + 21$ **44.** $-45x^3 - 102x^2 + 48x$

45. The base of a triangle measures twice its height. After the base and the height are increased, the enlarged triangle has an area given by the expression

$$2x^2 + 10x + \frac{21}{2}$$

where x is the height of the original triangle.

   a. Factor the expression to produce expressions for the base and height of the enlarged triangle.

   b. By how much was the base of the original triangle increased?

   c. By how much was the height of the original triangle increased?

46. A rectangle has a width that is 6 inches less than its length. After the width and length are increased, the larger rectangle has an area given by $(x^2 + 17x + 30)$ square inches, where x is the length of the original rectangle.

   a. Factor the polynomial to find the expressions for the increased length and width.

   b. By how much was the length increased?

   c. By how much was the width increased?

47. For Olympic tournaments and world championships, the size of the basketball court is prescribed and must have a minimum clear space on each side. If x meters are allowed on each side, a polynomial for the total area needed is given by $(420 + 86x + 4x^2)$ square meters. Factor the polynomial and determine the dimensions of the basketball court itself.

48. The product of the measure of two angles can be given by the polynomial $12x^2 + 32x + 21$. Factor the polynomial to find possible expressions for the measure of each angle. If $x = 10$, can the angles be complementary?

49. A waterpark has weekly revenues during the summer of $R(x) = 10x^2 + 840x + 6750$, where x is the number of bus groups that take trips to the park. Factor this polynomial completely.

50. A college student throws a ball down from the roof of his dorm building. The distance above ground of the ball in feet can be given by $d(t) = -16t^2 - 64t + 80$, where t is the time in seconds. Factor this polynomial completely.

8.4

Recall	Example
Factoring a quadratic trinomial by using the *ac* method	Factor.
• Factor out the GCF from all terms.	$12x^2 - 2x - 4 = 2(6x^2 - x - 2)$
• Determine the product *ac*.	$ac = (6)(-2) = -12$
• Determine the factors whose sum is the coefficient of the middle term *b*.	The factors of -12 that result in a sum of -1, *b*, are -4 and 3.
• Write the polynomial as a sum of four terms, using the factors as coefficients of the two terms that replace the middle term.	$12x^2 - 2x - 4 = 2(6x^2 - x - 2)$ $= 2[(6x^2 - 4x) + (3x - 2)]$ $= 2[2x(3x - 2) + 1(3x - 2)]$ $= 2[(3x - 2)(2x + 1)]$
• Factor by grouping.	$= 2(3x - 2)(2x + 1)$

In exercises 51–64, use the ac method to factor completely. Check the factors.

51. $3x^2 + 23x + 4$

52. $8x^2 + 22x + 9$

53. $15y^2 - 29y + 12$

54. $10x^2 + 29x + 24$

55. $12y^2 - 13y - 14$

56. $8x^4 + 22x^2 + 15$

57. $10x^4 + 9x^2 - 9$

58. $12x^2 - 35x + 9$

59. $6p^4 - 29p^2 - 28$

60. $24x^2 + 76x + 32$

61. $-40x^4 - 30x^2 + 175$

62. $6x^2 - 7xy - 20y^2$

63. $12x^2 + 40xy + 25y^2$

64. $20x^2 - 27xy + 9y^2$

65. A bowling lane is about 19 times as long as it is wide. Usually, 4.5 meters are added to each end of the lane for an approach and for collecting the pins, and 1.5 meters are added to each side of the lane for ball returns and gutters. A polynomial representing the total area covered by the lane and the added area is $(19x^2 + 66x + 27)$ square meters. Factor the polynomial. If the width of the lane is approximately 1 meter, evaluate the factors to determine the dimensions of the total area and the area itself.

66. The product of the measure of two angles can be given by the polynomial $15x^2 + 38x + 24$. Factor the polynomial using the *ac* method to find an expression for the measure of each angle. If $x = 10$, are the angles supplementary?

67. Quinn has a summer job mowing lawns for people in his subdivision. He estimates his total profit in dollars for the summer to be $p(x) = -2x^2 + 183x + 665$, where x is the number of months after May. Factor this polynomial completely.

68. A missile is fired at an inland target. Its distance above the ground in feet can be given by $s(t) = -16t^2 + 392t + 200$, where t is the time in seconds. Factor this polynomial completely.

8.5

Recall	Examples
Factoring a polynomial	Factor the following polynomials:
• Factor out the GCF from all terms.	$3x^2 - 6x + 6 = 3(x^2 - 2x + 2)$
• Binomials must be the difference of two squares, the difference of two cubes, or the sum of two cubes.	$x^2 - 16 = (x + 4)(x - 4)$ $x^3 - 64 = (x - 4)(x^2 + 4x + 16)$ $x^3 + 64 = (x + 4)(x^2 - 4x + 16)$
• Trinomials may be perfect-square trinomials or may be factored by trial and error or by the *ac* method.	$x^2 + 8x + 16 = (x + 4)^2$ $x^2 + 8x + 15 = (x + 5)(x + 3)$ $2x^2 + x - 15 = 2x^2 - 5x + 6x - 15$ $= (2x^2 - 5x) + (6x - 15)$ $= x(2x - 5) + 3(2x - 5)$ $= (2x - 5)(x + 3)$
• Four-term polynomials may be factored by grouping.	$6x^2 - 15x + 2x - 5 = (6x^2 - 15x) + (2x - 5)$ $= 3x(2x - 5) + 1(2x - 5)$ $= (2x - 5)(3x + 1)$

In exercises 69–76, use the general strategy to factor completely. Check.

69. $-12x^3 + 60x^2y - 75xy^2$

70. $7x^4 + 7x^3 + 7x^2$

71. $12x^3 - 243x$

72. $32x^3 + 32x^2 + 8x$

73. $24x^3 - 14x^2 - 90x$

74. $256x^4 - 288x^2 + 81$

75. $36x^4 - 25x^2 + 4$

76. $2x^4 + 14x^3 - 8x^2 - 56x$

77. The site for a memorial statue is a rectangular piece of land whose length is four times its width. The base of the statue is a square measuring 5 feet on a side.
  a. If x is the width of the site, write a polynomial for the area of land that will not be covered by the statue.
  b. Factor the polynomial to obtain the dimensions of a rectangular plot with an area equivalent to the uncovered area.
  c. If the site has a width of 80 feet, use the factors to find the dimensions of a rectangle with an area equivalent to the uncovered area.

78. A caterer offers a discount for catering a dinner to the planners of a conference for mathematics instructors. If x instructors attend the dinner, the total cost to the planners is $(19.95x - 0.10x^2)$ dollars. Factor this polynomial to determine the price charged for each instructor, and explain how the discount is figured.

79. An object with no initial velocity that falls from a height of 64 feet is $64 - 16t^2$ feet above ground in t seconds. Factor this polynomial.

80. As a part of a computer simulation, a character changes its shape based on pressing the F2 key. Its area changes depending on the number of times the key is pressed. The following table summarizes the area:

Number of Times F2 Key Is Used	Area of Character (sq cm)
2	48
5	375
9	1147

Write a quadratic function to model the data. Factor the function.

■ Chapter 8 Mixed Review

Factor exercises 1–37 completely and check.

1. $z^2 + 9z - 90$

2. $a^2 - 18a + 72$

3. $x^2 + 14xy + 45y^2$

4. $5a^2 + 70a + 245$

5. $2a^2 + 8ab + 12b^2$

6. $x^4 + 10x^2 + 21$

7. $3q^3 - 33q^2 - 126q$

8. $-6x^2 + 42x + 360$

9. $10 + 7x + x^2$

10. $x^2 - 289$

11. $x^3 - 1$

12. $4x^2 - 64$

13. $u^2 + v^2$

14. $36x^2 - 49y^2$

15. $81x^4 - 1$

16. $p^2 + 22p + 121$

17. $q^2 - 30q + 225$

18. $27a^3 + 64b^3$

19. $27a^2b^2 - 72ab + 48$

20. $-50x^3 + 120x^2y - 72xy^2$

21. $8x^4 - 2x^3 + 6x^2 - 12x$

22. $35u^3v^2 + 25u^2v^3$

23. $2x^3 + 10x + x^2 + 5$

24. $m^2 - 2mn - 8mn + 16n^2$

25. $4a^4 + 8a^2b^2 + 8a^2b^2 + 16b^4$

26. $2x^2 - 13x + 11$

27. $24ac + 20ad + 18bc + 15bd$

28. $7x^2 - 19x - 6$

29. $10x^2 - 11x - 6$

30. $36a^2 + 66a + 24$

31. $-30x^2 - 28x + 32$

32. $12x^4 + 13x^2 + 3$

33. $54x^3 + 36x^2 + 6x$

34. $81x^4 - 72x^2 + 16$

35. $4x^4 - 61x^2 + 225$

36. $12x^3 + 18x^2 - 30x^2 - 45x$

37. $3x^4 + 15x^3 - 27x^2 - 135x$

38. The area of a rectangle in square feet is given by the polynomial $8x^2 - 2x - 3$. Factor this polynomial to determine algebraic expressions for the rectangle's width and length.

39. The width of a rectangle is 2 inches less than its length. After the width and length are increased, the larger rectangle has an area given by $(6x^2 - 10x - 4)$ square inches, where x is the length of the original rectangle.
  a. Factor the polynomial to find expressions for the increased length and width.
  b. By how much was the length increased?
  c. By how much was the width increased?

40. The base of a triangle is twice its height. After the base and the height are increased, the enlarged triangle has an area in square feet given by the polynomial

$$x^2 + 12x + 32$$

where x is the height of the original triangle.
  a. Factor the polynomial to produce expressions for the base and height of the enlarged triangle.
  b. By how much was the base of the original triangle increased?
  c. By how much was the height of the original triangle increased?

41. A judge levies a progressively higher penalty each time a person is cited for littering. A person who has been cited x times for littering pays a total penalty of $(50x + 25x^2)$ dollars. Factor this polynomial to determine the penalty paid for a given citation, and explain how the judge determined the penalty.

42. The sheets of a desk calendar are square with a smaller square 3 inches on a side inside. The small square has a daily cartoon in it. The remainder of the large square is white with the day's date on it.
  a. Write a polynomial for the area of the sheet not covered by the cartoon.
  b. Factor the polynomial to determine the dimensions of a rectangle with the same area as that not covered by the cartoon.
  c. If the large square measures 5 inches on a side, is the area not covered by the cartoon larger than the area covered by the cartoon?

43. In the sport of archery, the face of the target is circular. If the face includes a border that is x mm wide around the scoring region, a polynomial for the total area facing the archer is $(372,100\pi + 1220\pi x + \pi x^2)$ square mm. Factor the polynomial to determine the radius of the face of the target. What is the area of the target?

44. A quilt has a central design that is 68 inches wide and 88 inches long. The border around the center adds x inches to each side of the quilt. Write a polynomial that represents the area of the quilt's border. Factor the polynomial and discuss the meaning of the factors. If the border adds 16 inches to each side of the quilt, how many square inches of border are there?

45. A cell phone company offers a package deal for families. The regular price is $35 per package. A reduction per package purchased is offered to families. The revenue for a certain family is $R(x) = 35x - 4x^2$, where x is the number of packages purchased (or reductions). Factor the revenue function. Determine the amount per reduction in the cost of the package.

46. A bookstore owner determines that if he increases the cost of a $100 calculator, he will have fewer purchases than the 50 he has at this price. The revenue will be $R(x) = 5000 + 150x - 100x - 3x^2$, where x is the number of increases. Factor the revenue function. Determine the amount of each increase and the number of fewer purchases per increase.

47. Jose owns an asphalt sealing business. He makes most of his money working on parking lots. For one job at a mall his overhead is $225.00 and materials cost him $0.05 per square foot. He charges the business owner $0.09 per square foot to do the job. Write a polynomial that represents his profit on a job that involves sealing a square parking lot of side x feet. Factor the polynomial.

48. A pharmacy charges $0.027 per cubic centimeter for a prescription medicine. It also charges $8.00 for filling the prescription. Write a polynomial for the cost to fill the prescription of x^3 cubic centimeters of medicine. Factor the polynomial.

49. A gift wrapping service at a local mall finds that the total revenue per day can be estimated by the function $R(x) = 1000 - 70x + 5x^2$, where x is the number of days into the holiday shopping season, which officially starts the day after Thanksgiving. Factor this polynomial completely.

50. An object is thrown downward from a height of 297 feet. The object's distance above the ground in feet can be given by $s(t) = -16t^2 - 6t + 297$, where t is the time in seconds. Factor this polynomial completely.

51. A dental practice estimates its weekly profit in dollars to be $p(x) = 12x^2 - 71x - 116$, where x is the number of weeks after the start of the opening of the practice. Factor this polynomial completely.

52. An object with no initial velocity that falls from a height of 25 feet is $25 - 16t^2$ feet above ground in t seconds. Factor this polynomial.

53. The product of the measure of two angles can be given by the polynomial $50x^2 + 25x + 3$. Factor the polynomial to find possible expressions for the measure of each angle. If $x = 12$, can the angles be supplementary?

54. A florist gives a discount on corsages for graduation. For each dollar decrease in price, she finds that more corsages are sold, but revenue goes down. The following table summarizes the sales:

Number of Discounts	Revenue in Dollars
8	62
5	125
1	153

Write a quadratic function to model the data. Factor the function.

■ Chapter 8 Test

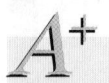

Factor exercises 1–12 completely.

1. $81a^3 + 54a^2 + 9a$

2. $p^3 + 125$

3. $-8a^4b^2 - 36a^3b^3 - 16a^2b^4$

4. $a(a^2 + b^2) - 5b(a^2 + b^2)$

5. $15x^2 - 21xy + 10xy - 14y^2$

6. $64a^2 - 49b^2$

7. $25x^2 - 70x + 49$

8. $3x^3 - 27x^2 + 24x$

9. $x^2 - 4xy - 21y^2$

10. $14x^2 + 25x + 9$

11. $4x^4 + 27x^2 - 7$

12. $x^2 + 8x + 14$

13. A box with a height of x inches has a volume of $(2x^3 + 5x^2 - 3x)$ cubic inches. Factor the polynomial to determine expressions for the width and length of the box.

14. The base of a triangle is 7 inches more than its height. After the base and height are increased by the same amount, the area of the new triangle is $\left(\frac{1}{2}x^2 + \frac{17}{2}x + 30\right)$ square inches.

   a. Factor the polynomial to produce expressions for the base and height of the enlarged triangle.

   b. By how much were the base and height increased?

   c. What was the expression for the base of the original triangle?

15. For a school science project, Reggie designed a packing crate to protect a raw egg that was to be dropped from a height of 20 feet. The objective was to protect the egg so that it would not shatter. Reggie placed the egg in a small box in the shape of a cube 2 inches on a side. This box in turn was placed in a bigger crate that was also shaped like a cube. The larger crate was filled with gelatin to absorb the impact of the drop.

   a. Write a polynomial for the volume of the crate, not including the small cube.

   b. Factor the polynomial. Do the factors have any physical interpretation? Explain.

   c. If the crate measures 12 inches on a side, how many cubic inches of gelatin will it take to fill the crate along with the boxed egg?

16. A potter designs a serving tray that has a circular center surrounded by a border that is x inches wide. The surface area of the tray, including the border, is $(\pi x^2 + 18\pi x + 81\pi)$ square inches. Factor this polynomial to determine the radius of the center of the tray. If the border is 2 inches wide, determine the surface area of the tray, including the border. Then determine the area of the center, and use the two areas to find the area of the border.

17. A cable company offers a package deal for multiple cable connections in one residence. The regular price is $49 per package. A reduction per connection is given. The revenue for a residence is $R(x) = 49x - 2x^2$, where x is the number of connections (or reductions). Factor the revenue function. Determine the amount of reduction per connection in the cost of the package.

18. A cell phone company offers a package deal for multiple cell phones in a family. The regular price of the package is $55. At this price, the company sells 100 packages. The company manager determines that the revenue for the package deal is $R(x) = 5500 - 300x + 55x - 3x^2$, where x is the number of reductions in price. Factor the revenue function. Determine the amount of each reduction and the number of additional packages that will be purchased per reduction.

19. A contractor constructs a square wooden deck of side x feet. He estimates that his overhead on the job is $64 and the material cost is $15 per square foot. He charges $24 per square foot. Write a polynomial that represents his profit on the deck and then factor it.

20. An entertainment company sees a slump in business from the middle of the year until Thanksgiving. The company's profit in thousands of dollars can be represented by the function $p(x) = 6x^2 - 95x + 341$, where x is the number of the month of the year. Factor this polynomial completely.

21. An object with no initial velocity that falls from a height of 81 feet is $81 - 16t^2$ feet above ground in t seconds. Factor this polynomial.

22. The product of the measure of two angles can be given by the polynomial $12x^2 - 16x + 5$. Factor the polynomial to find possible expressions for the measure of each angle. If $x = 12$, can the angles be complementary?

23. David factored the following polynomial as shown:
$$12x^3 + 28x^2 - 27x - 63 = (12x^3 + 28x^2) + (-27x - 63)$$
$$= 4x^2(3x + 7) - 9(3x + 7)$$
$$= (3x + 7)(4x^2 - 9)$$

   a. Identify the method David used to factor the polynomial.
   b. Explain what is wrong with David's solution, and describe how you would correct it.
   c. What is the correct solution?

8

Project

In this chapter, we have used geometric figures as applications of factoring. In this project, we will illustrate some of these applications. In particular, we will explore the special products. To illustrate why the special products factor as they do, we want to visualize the rectangular objects that are formed.*

PART I We know that $a^2 + 2ab + b^2 = (a + b)^2$. We can demonstrate this fact geometrically using the square in the illustration.

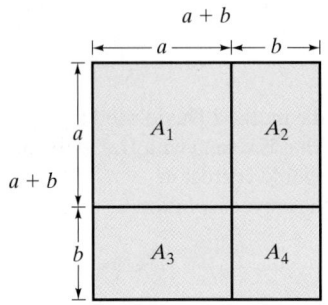

1. Determine the area of the shaded square with sides $(a + b)$.

2. Determine the sum of the areas of the four numbered sections A_1, A_2, A_3, and A_4.

$$A_1 + A_2 + A_3 + A_4$$

3. The areas found in exercises 1 and 2 are equivalent. Write an equation to represent this finding.

4. Choose a small positive integer value for a and a different value for b. Show that these values are solutions of the equation in exercise 3.

5. On graph paper, draw the square in the illustration, using the values chosen for a and b, from exercise 4.

PART II We know that $a^2 - 2ab + b^2 = (a - b)^2$. We can demonstrate this fact geometrically using the square in the illustration.

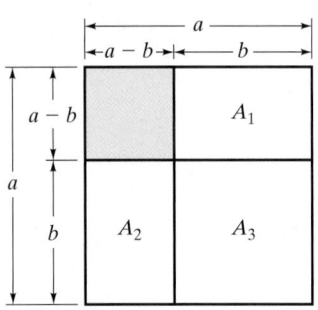

1. Determine the area of the shaded square with sides $(a - b)$.

2. Determine the difference of the entire area of the figure, A, and the sum of the areas of the three numbered sections.

$$A - (A_1 + A_2 + A_3)$$

3. The areas found in exercises 1 and 2 are equivalent. Write an equation to represent this finding.

4. Choose a small positive integer value for a and a different value for b. Show that these values are solutions of the equation in exercise 3.

5. On graph paper, draw the square in the illustration, using the values chosen for a and b, from exercise 4.

PART III We know that $a^2 - b^2 = (a + b)(a - b)$. We can demonstrate this fact geometrically using the rectangle in the illustration.

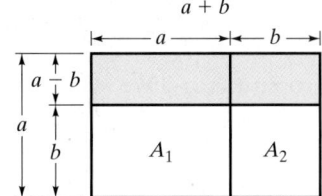

1. Determine the area of the shaded rectangle with sides $(a + b)$ and $(a - b)$.

2. Determine the difference of the entire area of the figure, A, and the sum of the areas of the two numbered sections.

$$A - (A_1 + A_2)$$

3. The areas found in exercises 1 and 2 are equivalent. Write an equation to represent this finding.

4. Choose a small positive integer value for a and a different value for b. Show that these values are solutions of the equation in exercise 3.

5. On graph paper, draw the rectangle in the illustration, using the values chosen for a and b, from exercise 4.

*Instructors may use Cuisinaire® Algebra Tiles for this project.

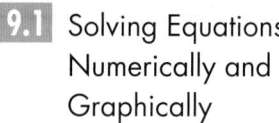
Quadratic and Other Polynomial Equations and Inequalities

Now that we have learned how to work with polynomial expressions, including adding, subtracting, and factoring them, we can proceed to solve polynomial equations and inequalities. In this chapter, we will examine numeric, graphic, and algebraic methods for solving polynomial equations, particularly quadratic equations and inequalities. Because the most precise of these methods is the algebraic approach, we will look at several ways of solving equations algebraically, including factoring, using the principle of square roots, completing the square, and using the quadratic formula.

Economists utilize many types of polynomial equations to model trends in sales and to forecast future sales. In this chapter, we will look at some economic models that involve quadratic equations and show how they illustrate the methods of solution we describe.

Another important application of quadratic equations is the Pythagorean theorem, named after the Greek philosopher and mathematician Pythagoras of Samos. We will explore many different uses for this theorem in the applications and the project for the chapter.

655

9.1 SOLVING EQUATIONS NUMERICALLY AND GRAPHICALLY

OBJECTIVES
1 Identify polynomial equations in one variable.
2 Solve polynomial equations numerically.
3 Solve polynomial equations graphically.
4 Model real-world situations by using polynomial equations, and solve the equations numerically or graphically.

APPLICATION

According to the U.S. Bureau of Economic Analysis, personal income is on the increase. A model estimates the personal income in trillion dollars with the function $i(x) = 0.05x^2 + 0.15x + 8.71$, where x is the number of years after 2001. The 2001 personal income was approximately 8.71 trillion dollars. When will the personal income equal twice this amount?

We will discuss this application further. See page 663.

Objective 9.1.1   **Identifying Polynomial Equations in One Variable**

In this chapter, we will solve polynomial equations in one variable. A **polynomial equation in one variable**, or, simply, a **polynomial equation**, is an equation that relates two polynomials. In an earlier chapter, we discussed polynomial equations in one variable with a degree of 1. These equations were of the form $ax + b = 0$, where $a \neq 0$. We called such equations linear equations in one variable, or, again simply, linear equations.

In this chapter, we discuss other polynomial equations. A polynomial equation with a degree of 2 is called a **quadratic equation in one variable**, or a **quadratic equation**. A polynomial equation with a degree of 3 is called a **cubic equation in one variable**, or a **cubic equation**.

> ### STANDARD FORMS FOR POLYNOMIAL EQUATIONS
>
> Given real numbers $a, b,$ and c, where $a \neq 0$,
>   A linear equation is written in the form
> $$ax + b = 0$$
> A quadratic equation is written in the form
> $$ax^2 + bx + c = 0$$
> A cubic equation is written in the form
> $$ax^3 + bx^2 + cx + d = 0$$
> In general, a polynomial equation in one variable is written in the form
> $$P(x) = 0$$
> where $P(x)$ is a polynomial.

EXAMPLE 1   Determine whether each equation is a polynomial equation. Identify each polynomial equation as quadratic or cubic when applicable.

a. $3x^2 + 5x^6 - 7x^{-3} = 4$ **b.** $6x^2 + 8 - 7x^3 = 12$

c. $3x = 2x^2$ **d.** $\dfrac{1}{4}x^4 = \dfrac{2}{3}x^4 + \dfrac{7}{8}x^6$

Solution

a. $3x^2 + 5x^6 - 7x^{-3} = 4$ is not a polynomial equation, because x has an exponent of -3, which is not a positive integer.

b. $6x^2 + 8 - 7x^3 = 12$, or, equivalently, $7x^3 - 6x^2 + 4 = 0$, is a cubic polynomial equation.

c. $3x = 2x^2$, or, equivalently, $2x^2 - 3x = 0$, is a quadratic polynomial equation.

d. $\frac{1}{4}x^4 = \frac{2}{3}x^4 + \frac{7}{8}x^6$, or, equivalently, $\frac{7}{8}x^6 + \frac{5}{12}x^4 = 0$, is a polynomial equation. ■

Objective 9.1.1 **CHECKUP**

1. Determine whether each equation is a polynomial equation. Identify each polynomial equation as quadratic or cubic when applicable.
   a. $3x^2 - 5 = 4x + 2$ **b.** $x^{-2} + 4x - 7 = 0$
   c. $2\sqrt{x} + 2x - 3 = 0$ **d.** $5x^5 - 2x^2 = 3x + 7$

2. What is the difference between a polynomial expression and a polynomial equation?

3. What is meant by the degree of a polynomial equation?

Objective 9.1.2   Solving Polynomial Equations Numerically

In an earlier chapter, we determined whether a number was a solution of a linear equation by substituting the number into the variable and evaluating the two resulting expressions. If the resulting equation was true, the number substituted was called the solution of the original equation. We use the same procedure for a polynomial equation. The set of all possible solutions of an equation is called the solution set of the equation. For example, given $x^2 - 3 = -x + 3$, determine whether 2 is a solution.

$$
\begin{array}{c|c}
x^2 - 3 & = -x + 3 \\
\hline
(2)^2 - 3 & -(2) + 3 \\
4 - 3 & 1 \\
1 &
\end{array}
$$

The number 2 is thus a solution, because the resulting equation, $1 = 1$, is true.

A linear equation that is not an identity has at most one solution. However, other polynomial equations may have more than one solution and not be identities.

In order to find other solutions of the equation $x^2 - 3 = -x + 3$, continue to substitute values for x and determine whether the resulting equations are true. A table of values is helpful in organizing this method.

SOLVING A POLYNOMIAL EQUATION NUMERICALLY

To solve a polynomial equation numerically,
Set up an extended table of values as follows:

- The first column is labeled with the independent variable.
- The second column is labeled with the expression on the left side of the equation.
- The third column is labeled with the expression on the right side of the equation.

Complete the table:

- Substitute values for the independent variable.
- Evaluate the second and third columns.

(continued on page 658)

• Continue until values for the two expressions (the numbers in the second and third columns) are equal.

The values for the independent variable (the number in the first column) that result in equivalent expressions are the solutions.

For example, a sample table to determine another solution of $x^2 - 3 = -x + 3$ could appear as follows:

x	$x^2 - 3$	$-x + 3$	
-4	$(-4)^2 - 3$ $16 \ - 3$ 13	$-(-4) + 3$ $4 \ + 3$ 7	$13 > 7$, so -4 is not a solution.
-3	$(-3)^2 - 3$ $9 \ - 3$ 6	$-(-3) + 3$ $3 \ + 3$ 6	$6 = 6$, so -3 is a solution.
-2	$(-2)^2 - 3$ $4 \ - 3$ 1	$-(-2) + 3$ $2 \ + 3$ 5	$1 < 5$, so -2 is not a solution.

According to the table, when -3 is substituted for the variable x, the two expressions are equivalent ($6 = 6$). Therefore, -3 is a second solution of the polynomial equation.

To solve $x^2 - 3 = -x + 3$ numerically for integer solutions on your calculator,

$$\text{Let } Y1 = x^2 - 3 \quad \text{and} \quad Y2 = -x + 3$$

The solutions are the x-values that determine equal Y1 and Y2 values. The two solutions from the table are -3 and 2, as shown in **Figure 9.1c**.

Figure 9.1a

Figure 9.1b

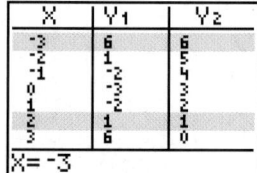

Figure 9.1c

Both linear equations and polynomial equations may have noninteger solutions, no solution, or an infinite number of solutions. However, when solved numerically, certain polynomial equations may have a different result than that found previously with linear equations. To see these different results, complete the following example.

EXAMPLE 2

Solve numerically if possible.

a. $a^3 + a^2 - 4a + 2 = 2a^2 + 2a + 2$

b. $2(x^2 + 3x - 5) = 2x^2 + 2(3x - 5)$

c. $x^3 + 5x^2 + 2x - 7 = x^3 + 5x^2 + 2$

d. $2x^2 + 7x - 4 = 2(x^2 + 3x + 1) + x$

e. $x^2 + 2x + 4 = 3x^2 + 6x + 12$

Calculator Numeric Solution

a. $a^3 + a^2 - 4a + 2 = 2a^2 + 2a + 2$

Rewrite the equation as $x^3 + x^2 - 4x + 2 = 2x^2 + 2x + 2$.

The solutions are -2, 0, and 3, because when -2, 0, and 3 are substituted for the variable in both expressions, the results are equivalent.

a.
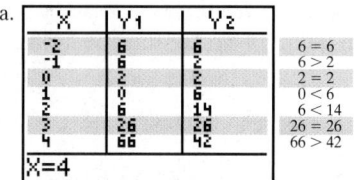

$Y1 = x^3 + x^2 - 4x + 2$
$Y2 = 2x^2 + 2x + 2$

b.

X	Y1	Y2
0	-10	-10
1	-2	-2
2	10	10
3	26	26
4	46	46
5	70	70
6	98	98

$-10 = -10$
$-2 = -2$
$10 = 10$
$26 = 26$
$46 = 46$
$70 = 70$
$98 = 98$

X=0

Y1 = $2(x^2 + 3x - 5)$
Y2 = $2x^2 + 2(3x - 5)$

c.

X	Y1	Y2
0	-7	2
1	1	8
2	25	30
3	71	74
4	145	146
5	253	252
6	401	398

$-7 < 2$
$1 < 8$
$25 < 30$
$71 < 74$
$145 < 146$
$253 > 252$
$401 > 398$

X=0

Y1 = $x^3 + 5x^2 + 2x - 7$
Y2 = $x^3 + 5x^2 + 2$

d.

X	Y1	Y2
0	-4	2
1	5	11
2	18	24
3	35	41
4	56	62
5	81	87
6	110	116

$-4 < 2$
$5 < 11$
$18 < 24$
$35 < 41$
$56 < 62$
$81 < 87$
$110 < 116$

X=0

Y1 = $2x^2 + 7x - 4$
Y2 = $2(x^2 + 3x + 1) + x$

e.

X	Y1	Y2
0	4	12
1	7	21
2	12	36
3	19	57
4	28	84
5	39	117
6	52	156

$4 < 12$
$7 < 21$
$12 < 36$
$19 < 57$
$28 < 84$
$39 < 117$
$52 < 156$

X=0

Y1 = $x^2 + 2x + 4$
Y2 = $3x^2 + 6x + 12$

b. $2(x^2 + 3x - 5) = 2x^2 + 2(3x - 5)$

The expressions are equal for all x-values in the table. If we rewrite this equation in standard form, we obtain an identity, $0 = 0$. The permissible replacements for each expression are all real numbers. The solution set is the set of all real numbers.

c. $x^3 + 5x^2 + 2x - 7 = x^3 + 5x^2 + 2$

The expression on the left is less than the expression on the right for $x = 4$ and greater than the expression on the right for $x = 5$. A noninteger solution lies somewhere between 4 and 5. We will find the exact solution later in this section.

d. $2x^2 + 7x - 4 = 2(x^2 + 3x + 1) + x$

The expression on the left is always less than the expression on the right. Note that the expression on the left is always 6 less than the expression on the right Y2 − Y1 = 6. It appears that the expressions will never be equal. If we rewrite the equation in standard form, we obtain $-6 = 0$, a contradiction. Therefore, the original equation has no solution.

e. $x^2 + 2x + 4 = 3x^2 + 6x + 12$

The expression on the left is always less than the expression on the right. The expressions do not appear to be equal. Note that Y2 − Y1 changes values. If we rewrite the equation in standard form, we obtain $2x^2 + 4x + 8 = 0$. This equation has no real-number solution. We will determine the solution of the equation in Chapter 11. ■

 TAKE NOTE Note that we cannot determine the solutions of the equations in parts **d** and **e**, because in part **d** there is no solution and in part **e** there is no real-number solution. When we write the equations in standard form, we see that an equation with no solution results in a contradiction, whereas an equation with no real-number solution does not result in a contradiction.

NUMERICAL SOLUTIONS OF A POLYNOMIAL EQUATION

To solve a polynomial equation for integer solutions numerically, set up an extended table of values. In analyzing the table, you will find that one of five possibilities will occur.

Integer solutions exist. The solutions are the integers in the first column that correspond to equal values in the second and third columns.

Noninteger solutions exist. In comparing corresponding values in the second and third columns, it is found that the order changes from "less than" to "greater than," or from "greater than" to "less than." A noninteger solution is between the two integers in the first column that indicate this change.

No solution exists. In comparing corresponding values in the second and third columns, it is found that one column is always less than the value in the other column. There is a constant difference between the values in the second column and the third column. The equation is a contradiction.

No real-number solution exists. In comparing corresponding values in the second and third columns, it is found that the value in one column is always less than the value in the other column. There is no constant difference between the values in the second and third column. The equation is not a contradiction.

An infinite number of solutions exist. In comparing corresponding values in the second and third columns, it is found that the values are equal. The equation is an identity. The solution set consists of all numbers for which the equation is defined.

In conclusion, a polynomial equation may be solved numerically by using a table of values. However, if the solution is noninteger, it will be difficult to find by that method. Also, it is difficult to know whether all possible solutions have been found.

✓ Objective 9.1.2 *CHECKUP*

1. Solve numerically.
   a. $b^3 + 3b^2 + 2b = 2b^2 + 6b + 4$
   b. $6x^2 + 3x = 2x + 1$
   c. $(3x - 4)(x + 1) = 3x^2 - x - 1$
   d. $x^2 + 4x + 5 = 2x^2 + 8(x + 1) + 2$
   e. $2(x^2 + 2x - 1) - x(x - 1) =$
      $3x(x + 1) - 2(x^2 - x + 1)$

2. Explain the difference between integer solutions of a polynomial equation and noninteger solutions.

3. What are some of the limitations of the numerical method in solving a polynomial equation?

Objective 9.1.3   ## Solving Polynomial Equations Graphically

A second way to determine a real-number solution of an equation is to graph two functions. The functions to be graphed are written by using each expression in the equation as a rule for one of the functions.

> ### SOLVING A POLYNOMIAL EQUATION GRAPHICALLY
>
> To solve a polynomial equation graphically,
>
> - Write two functions, using each expression in the equation as a rule.
> - Graph both functions on the same coordinate plane by plotting points found in a table of values and connecting the points with a smooth curve to include all values in the domains of the functions.
>
> The solutions of the equation are the x-coordinates of the points of intersection of the two graphs.
> The y-coordinates of the points of intersection of the two graphs are the values obtained for both expressions when the equation is evaluated with the solutions.

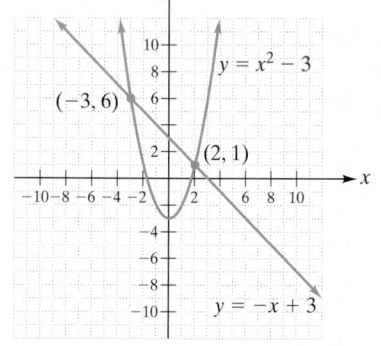

For example, solve $x^2 - 3 = -x + 3$ graphically.
   Set up a table of values for each function.

x	$y = x^2 - 3$	y
-1	$y = (-1)^2 - 3$	-2
0	$y = (0)^2 - 3$	-3
1	$y = (1)^2 - 3$	-2
2	$y = (2)^2 - 3$	1

x	$y = -x + 3$	y
-1	$y = -(-1) + 3$	4
0	$y = -(0) + 3$	3
1	$y = -(1) + 3$	2
2	$y = -(2) + 3$	1

When plotted, the points result in the graph shown at the left.
   The two solutions are the x-coordinates of the intersections, -3 and 2.
   Solve $x^2 - 3 = -x + 3$ graphically on your calculator.
   The intersection of the graphs may be found by using the Intersect option under the CALC menu. The solutions of the equation are the x-coordinates of the points of intersection of the two graphs.
   The y-coordinates of the points of intersection of the two graphs are the values obtained for both expressions when the equation is evaluated with the solutions.
   The two solutions are the x-coordinates of the intersections, -3 and 2, as shown in **Figure 9.2**.
   Remember that polynomial equations may have a finite number of solutions, an infinite number of solutions, no solutions, or no real-number solutions. Thus, solving polynomial equations graphically may yield any of these possibilities.

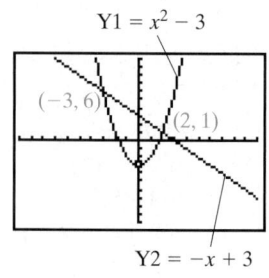

$Y1 = x^2 - 3$

$Y2 = -x + 3$

$(-10, 10, -10, 10)$

Figure 9.2

EXAMPLE 3

Solve graphically if possible.

a. $4x^2 - 3x - 3 = x$

b. $x^3 + x^2 - 4x + 2 = 2x^2 + 2x + 2$

c. $2(x^2 + 3x - 5) = 2x^2 + 2(3x - 5)$

d. $x^2 + 2x + 4 = 3x^2 + 6x + 12$

e. $2x^2 + 7x - 4 = 2(x^2 + 3x + 1) + x$

Calculator Graphic Solution

Define the two expressions as rules for functions, and enter them into your calculator.

a. $4x^2 - 3x - 3 = x$

The two solutions are the x-coordinates of the intersections, -0.5 and 1.5, as shown in **Figure 9.3a** and **Figure 9.3b**. Intersect, under the CALC menu, was used to find the intersection of the graphs.

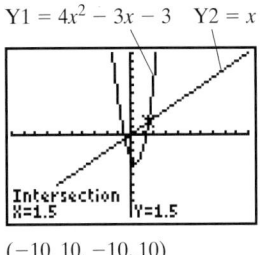

$Y1 = 4x^2 - 3x - 3$ $Y2 = x$

Intersection
X=-.5   Y=-.5

$(-10, 10, -10, 10)$

Figure 9.3a

$Y1 = 4x^2 - 3x - 3$ $Y2 = x$

Intersection
X=1.5   Y=1.5

$(-10, 10, -10, 10)$

Figure 9.3b

b. $x^3 + x^2 - 4x + 2 = 2x^2 + 2x + 2$

The three solutions are the x-coordinates of the intersections: -2, 0, and 3.

c. $2(x^2 + 3x - 5) = 2x^2 + 2(3x - 5)$

The graphs appear to be the same. Rewriting the equation results in $0 = 0$, an identity. The solution set is the set of all real numbers (the common domain of the graphed functions).

d. $x^2 + 2x + 4 = 3x^2 + 6x + 12$

The graphs do not appear to intersect. The standard form of the equation is $2x^2 + 4x + 8 = 0$. The equation is not a contradiction. There is no real-number solution.

e. $2x^2 + 7x - 4 = 2(x^2 + 3x + 1) + x$

The graphs do not appear to intersect. Rewriting the equation results in a contradiction, $-6 = 0$. The equation has no solution.

GRAPHICAL SOLUTIONS OF POLYNOMIAL EQUATIONS

To solve a polynomial equation graphically, graph the two functions defined by the expressions on the left and right sides of the equation. In analyzing the graphs, you will find that one of four possibilities will occur.

One or more solutions exist. The graphs intersect. The solutions are the x-coordinates of the points of intersection.

No solution exists. The graphs do not appear to intersect. The original equation is a contradiction.

No real-number solution exists. The graphs do not appear to intersect. The original equation may be written in standard form and is not a contradiction.

An infinite number of solutions exist. The graphs appear to coincide. The original equation is an identity. The solution set consists of all the numbers in the common domain of the graphed functions.

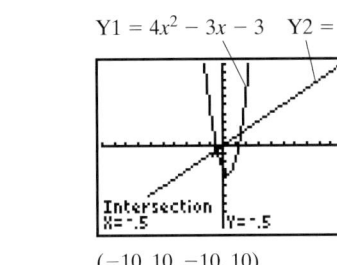

b.

$Y2 = 2x^2 + 2x + 2$

$(3, 26)$

$(-2, 6)$ $(0, 2)$

$Y1 = x^3 + x^2 - 4x + 2$

$(-10, 10, -30, 30)$

c.

$Y1 = 2(x^2 + 3x - 5)$

$Y2 = 2x^2 + 2(3x - 5)$

$(-47, 47, -31, 31)$

d.

$Y2 = 3x^2 + 6x + 12$

$Y1 = x^2 + 2x + 4$

$(-47, 47, -31, 31)$

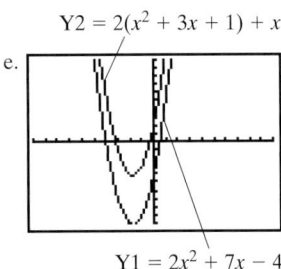

e.

$Y2 = 2(x^2 + 3x + 1) + x$

$Y1 = 2x^2 + 7x - 4$

$(-10, 10, -10, 10)$

In conclusion, we solve a polynomial equation graphically by graphing two functions. On a calculator, this method may be used to find noninteger solutions. Also, with this method we are better able to find all the solutions because we can see the number of points of intersection.

 ## Objective 9.1.3 *CHECKUP*

1. Solve graphically.
   a. $20x^2 + 4x = 15x + 3$ b. $x^3 + 2x^2 = x + 2$
   c. $(3x - 2)(x - 1) = 3x^2 - 5(x + 1)$
   d. $x^2 - 2(3x - 5) = 3(x^2 - 6x) + 30$
   e. $3(2x^3 + 2x^2) - (x + 2) + x^2 = 6x^3 + 7x^2 - x - 2$

2. In solving polynomial equations, we sometimes conclude that there are no solutions of the equation and other times determine that there are no real-number solutions of the equation. What do you think is the difference between these two statements?

3. Once you graphically obtain the solutions of a polynomial equation, how can you check to be sure they are the solutions?

Objective 9.1.4   Modeling the Real World

An application of a quadratic equation is the **vertical-position equation**, used to find the height of an object that was dropped or projected into the air. The height s of the object (in feet) is found by using the equation $s = -16t^2 + v_0t + s_0$, where t is the time (in seconds), v_0 is the initial velocity, and s_0 is the initial height. Galileo discovered this formula in the late 1500s.

> **TAKE NOTE** The initial velocity is 0 feet per second if the object is dropped, is positive if the object is thrown upward, and is negative if the object is thrown downward.

EXAMPLE 4

According to legend, Galileo simultaneously dropped two balls of different weights from the Leaning Tower of Pisa in Italy, to see if they fell at the same rate or different rates. The Greek philosopher Aristotle had said that the heavier object would fall faster, and this was accepted as the truth for 2000 years. Galileo showed that if you neglect air resistance, the balls fall at the same rate. If the balls fell 179 feet, how long did it take them to hit the ground?

Graphic Solution

Substitute values into the vertical-position equation. The balls hit the ground when they are 0 feet above ground level, or when $s = 0$ feet, $v_0 = 0$ feet per second (the objects were dropped from rest), and $s_0 = 179$ feet.

$$s = -16t^2 + v_0t + s_0$$
$$0 = -16t^2 + 0t + 179$$
$$0 = -16t^2 + 179$$

The intersections of Y1 = 0 and Y2 = $-16x^2 + 179$ occur on the x-axis at approximately $(3.34, 0)$ and $(-3.34, 0)$. The negative value of the x-intercept is not valid for this situation, because we cannot have a negative value for time.

The objects were in the air for about 3.34 seconds.

Y2 = $-16x^2 + 179$

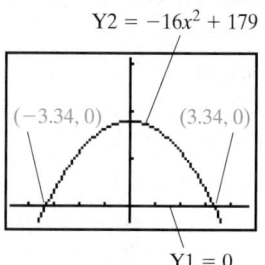

$(-3.34, 0)$ $(3.34, 0)$

Y1 = 0

$(-4.7, 4.7, -31, 310)$

APPLICATION

According to the U.S. Bureau of Economic Analysis, personal income is on the increase. A model estimates the personal income in trillion dollars with the function $i(x) = 0.05x^2 + 0.15x + 8.71$, where x is the number of years after 2001. The 2001 personal income was approximately 8.71 trillion dollars. When will the personal income equal twice this amount?

Discussion

Let x = the number of years after 2001
$\quad i(x)$ = the amount of personal income in trillion dollars
The amount of personal income is twice the 2001 amount or
$8.71 \cdot 2 = 17.42$ trillion dollars, $i(x) = 17.42$.

$i(x) = 0.05x^2 + 0.15x + 8.71$
$17.42 = 0.05x^2 + 0.15x + 8.71$ $\quad$ Substitute 17.42 for $i(x)$.

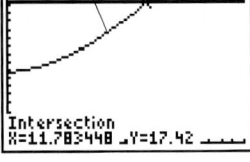

Y1 = $0.05x^2 + 0.15x + 8.71$ $\quad$ Y2 = 17.42

Solve by graphing.
$\quad$ The point of intersection is about (11.78, 17.42). The solution is 11.78. The personal income will be twice the 2001 personal income or 17.42 trillion dollars in 2013 (11.78 years after 2001).

(0, 20, 0, 20)

✓ Objective 9.1.4 **CHECKUP**

1. The Empire State Building is 1250 feet tall. If King Kong dropped a banana from the top of the building, write a vertical-position equation to represent the height, in feet, of the banana with respect to the time, in seconds. How long would it take for the banana to hit the ground?

2. According to the U.S. Bureau of Economic Analysis, although personal income is on the increase, gross savings and investments are on the decline. However, economists predict this decline is only temporary. A model estimates the gross savings and investments in trillion dollars with the function $s(x) = 0.03x^2 - 0.15x + 1.66$, where x is the number of years after 2001. The 2001 gross savings and investments were approximately 1.66 trillion dollars. When will the gross savings and investments return to that amount?

9.1 EXERCISES

 Student Solutions Manual $\quad$ PH Math/Tutor Center $\quad$ CD Video $\quad$ *Math XL* MathXL® $\quad$ **MyMathLab** MyMathLab $\quad$ Interactmath.com

Determine whether each equation is a polynomial equation. Identify each polynomial equation as quadratic or cubic, where applicable.

1. $3x^3 - 2x^2 + x = 5$

2. $3y - 2y^{-1} + 4 = 0$

3. $3\sqrt{y} + y - 4 = 0$

4. $5.7x^3 - 1.9x^2 = 8.6x - 3.5$

5. $\frac{1}{4}x^4 + 3x^2 - \frac{3}{4} = 0$

6. $5(z - 1)^3 = 4(z - 1)^2$

7. $4(x - 2)(x + 7) = 16$

8. $3x + 5\sqrt{x} = 17$

9. $3x^{-2} - 5x = 4x^2$

10. $4a^3 + a^2 - 3a + 2 = 0$

11. $1.7x^2 + 3.2x = 5.7$

12. $\frac{2}{3}x^2 - \frac{5}{9}x = \frac{1}{6}$

Use the calculator screens first to write the equation being solved and then to determine the solution or solutions (if any) of the equation.

13.
```
Plot1 Plot2 Plot3
\Y1■2X²+X
\Y2■M+8
\Y3=
\Y4=
\Y5=
\Y6=
\Y7=
```

14.
```
Plot1 Plot2 Plot3
\Y1■2X(X+1)
\Y2■2X²+2X
\Y3=
\Y4=
\Y5=
\Y6=
\Y7=
```

15.
```
Plot1 Plot2 Plot3
\Y1■X²+4X+8
\Y2■4
\Y3=
\Y4=
\Y5=
\Y6=
\Y7=
```

16.
```
Plot1 Plot2 Plot3
\Y1■X²+2
\Y2■X²−1
\Y3=
\Y4=
\Y5=
\Y6=
\Y7=
```

X	Y1	Y2
-3	15	5
-2	6	6
-1	1	7
0	0	8
1	3	9
2	10	10
3	21	11

X=3

X	Y1	Y2
-3	12	12
-2	4	4
-1	0	0
0	0	0
1	4	4
2	12	12
3	24	24

X=-3

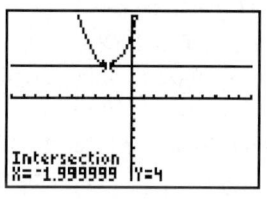

Intersection
X=-1.999999 Y=4

$(-10, 10, -10, 10)$

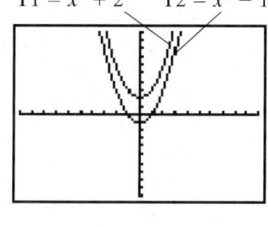

$Y1 = x^2 + 2$ $Y2 = x^2 - 1$

$(-10, 10, -10, 10)$

Solve numerically.

17. $x^2 + 8 = 6x$

18. $x^2 - 6 = -x$

19. $4x^3 = x + 1$

20. $x^2 + x = 15$

21. $x^2 - 7 = x^2 + 3$

22. $x^2 - 3x + 2 = x(x - 3) + 7$

23. $x^2 + 5x + 1 = 1 + x(5 + x)$

24. $x(7 - x^2) + 6 = 6 + 7x - x^3$

25. $x^2 - 2x + 6 = 12 - 4x + 2x^2$

26. $x^2 + 2x + 4 = 1 - (x + 1)^2$

27. $\frac{1}{2}x^2 - x = 6 - 3x$

28. $\frac{1}{2}x^2 + 2x = \frac{3}{2}x + 6$

Solve graphically and check.

29. $x^2 - 3 = 6$

30. $x^2 - 8 = 8$

31. $x^2 - 3 = 2x$

32. $x^2 + 2x + 9 = 1 - 4x$

33. $x^3 = 4x$

34. $\frac{1}{2}x^3 = 4$

35. $x^2 - 3x - 10 = 0$

36. $x^3 + 3x^2 - x - 3 = 0$

37. $x^2 - 2x + 1 = x^2 - 2x - 3$

38. $3 - x^2 = 8 - x$

39. $x^2 + 1 = 3x^2 + 3$

40. $3 - x^2 = 6 - x^2$

41. $x(x + 3) = x^2 + 3x$

42. $(x + 1)^2 = x^2 + 2x + 1$

43. $4x^2 - x^3 = x^2 - 4x$

44. $x^3 - 6x + 2 = 2 - x^2$

45. $x^3 - 2x^2 + 1 = x^3 - 2x^2 + 9$

46. $x^2 - 3 = x^2 - 1$

47. $2x^2 + 10x = -x^2 - x + 4$

48. $2x^2 - x = -x^2 + 2$

49. $9x^2 = 25$

50. $9x^2 = 16$

51. $10x^3 - 7x^2 - 4x = 3x - 4$

52. $4x^3 - 8x^2 = 7x - 5$

53. $x^2 - 0.9x - 10.36 = 0$

54. $x^2 - 5x + 3.36 = 0$

55. $x^3 + 3.7x^2 = 1.74x + 7.56$

56. $x^3 + 0.1x^2 + 5 = 6.02x + 6.2$

Vertical Position

In exercises 57–62, use the position equation, $s = -16t^2 + v_0t + s_0$, to solve the problem presented.

57. A tightrope walker drops her hat from 40 feet above the ground. How many seconds will it take for the hat to hit the ground?

58. A gardener drops his pruning shears while trimming a tree. The gardener is 16 feet above the ground. How long will it take for the shears to hit the ground?

59. A tightrope walker throws a silver dagger vertically downward from 40 feet above the ground. If the initial velocity of the throw is 5 feet per second, how many seconds will it take for the dagger to hit the ground? (**Note:** $v_0 = -5$, since the object is thrown downward. If it had been thrown upward, the initial velocity would have been positive.)

60. A gardener tosses a pruned branch vertically downward to the ground from a height of 16 feet. If the initial velocity of the toss is 2 feet per second, how long will it take for the branch to hit the ground?

61. A tightrope walker throws a baton vertically upward at a velocity of 5 feet per second. If he is 40 feet above the ground, how many seconds will it take for the baton to hit the ground?

62. A gardener tosses a hammer vertically upward to shoo away a squirrel in a tree. The hammer is released at a height of 6 feet above the ground with an initial velocity of 10 feet per second. The gardener misses both the squirrel and the tree. How long will it take for the hammer to hit the ground?

Real Data

63. Using data from the Bureau of Labor Statistics, it is estimated that $p(x)$, the price per gallon of gasoline, can be represented by the function $p(x) = 0.03x^2 - 0.08x + 1.56$, where x is the number of years after 2000. In the spring of 2005, this price was $2.16 per gallon. Use the function to estimate in what year the price will be twice this amount per gallon.

64. The cost of higher education is on the rise. According to statistics published by the U.S. Department of Education, National Center of Education Statistics, the average cost of undergraduate tuition, room and board, and fees, $c(x)$, in dollars, can be estimated by the polynomial function $c(x) = 3x^2 + 365x + 10,076$, where x is number of years after 1998. If the cost is approximately $10,000 in 1998, in what year will it be twice as much?

65. Data from the Bureau of the Census, U.S. Department of Commerce, indicates that the percentage of foreign-born population in the United States has fluctuated since 1900. The percentage of foreign born for the first part of the century can be estimated by the function $p(x) = -0.013x^2 + 0.24x + 13.6$, where x is the number of years after 1900. If 13.6% of the population in 1900 was foreign born, in what year was the foreign-born population about 1% higher than this?

66. The percentage of foreign-born population for the second half of the century can be estimated by the function $p(x) = 0.011x^2 - 1.5x + 55.8$, where x is the number of years after 1900. Use this function to estimate in what year the percent of foreign-born population was 7%.

67. Based on data from the Bureau of the Census, Foreign Trade Division, the number of passenger cars imported to the United States from Mexico can be estimated by the function $M(t) = -74,147t^2 + 502,360t + 22,099$, where t is the number of years after 1998. If the number of cars is 22,099 in 1998, in what year will it be about 30 times that amount?

68. The number of passenger cars imported to the United States, from France can be estimated by the function $F(t) = 45t^2 - 257t + 458$, where t is the number of years after 1998. In 2003 there were approximately 300 cars imported from France. In what year will the amount be about four times as much?

 ## 9.1 Calculator Exercises

In solving a polynomial equation graphically, it is often necessary to experiment with different settings of the window to be able to see the graph clearly. As an example, solve the equation

$$x^3 + 5.2x^2 = 36.9 + 4.49x$$

using the following instructions:

1. Graph the expressions on the left and right sides of the equation, using the decimal window, **ZOOM** **4**. The graph appears to have the shape of a parabola, which is the shape of a quadratic function. But the expressions are cubic and linear, indicating that the decimal window is not a good view.

2. Next, change to a standard window, **ZOOM** **6**. More of the graph appears, but it still does not seem complete.

3. Change to an integer window, **ZOOM** **8** **ENTER**. Much more of the graph appears, but it seems squeezed horizontally.

4. Change Xmin and Xmax by dividing each setting by 10.

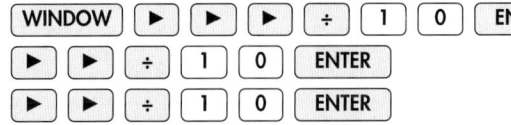

This will spread out the graph. Then view the graph. **GRAPH** This improves the graph, but it looks as if the window is still too small.

5. Change Ymin and Ymax by multiplying each setting by 2.

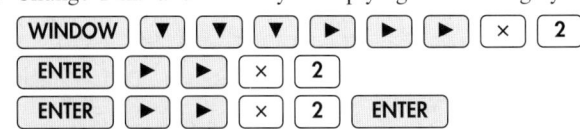

This will expand the graph in the y direction. Then view the graph. **GRAPH** Now you see that the graph consists of a curve that is intersected by a straight line at two or more points.

6. Find the rightmost intersection. One solution of the equation is $x = 2.5$.

7. The leftmost intersection is still not clearly shown. Use ZOOM 1 to box the region where the two graphs meet. Move the cursor to the left upper corner of your desired box and press ENTER. Then use the arrow keys right and down to create the box. Be sure that the box includes the entire portion of the graphs where the intersection occurs. Press ENTER again, and the calculator will enlarge the graph to fit the box.

8. Now you can clearly see that the line intersects the curve at two points. This would be difficult to see otherwise. Find the two intersection points. The other two solutions are $x = -3.6$ and $x = -4.1$. After completing this exercise, restore the calculator window to the standard setting, ZOOM 6.

Use the preceding approach to solve the following equations graphically (you can use multipliers or divisors other than those used in the example you just completed).

1. $x^3 + 5x^2 + 4x + 20 = 5x^2 + 25x$; verify the solutions $x = 1$, $x = 4$, and $x = -5$.

2. $x^3 + 3x^2 - 3x = x^2 - 2x + 2$; verify the solutions $x = -2$, $x = -1$, and $x = 1$.

3. $x^3 - 2x^2 = 30x - x^2$; verify the solutions $x = -5$, $x = 0$, and $x = 6$.

9.1 Writing Exercise

When graphing the expressions on the left and right sides of a polynomial equation as two functions, you can identify both intercepts and intersection points. Define "intercepts" and "intersection points," pointing out the differences and similarities between them. Draw an example of a graph of the expressions on the left and right sides of a polynomial equation, labeling the intercepts and the intersection points. Can the intercepts and the intersection points occur at the same location? Explain.

9.2 SOLVING EQUATIONS ALGEBRAICALLY BY FACTORING

OBJECTIVES
1. Solve polynomial equations by using the zero factor property.
2. Solve polynomial equations by factoring.
3. Model real-world situations by using polynomial equations, and solve the equations by factoring.

APPLICATION

The U.S. Department of Health and Human Services publishes statistics that show that the number of multiple births in the United States is increasing. This is due to increased use of fertility drugs and a greater number of births to older women. More recent data are summarized below:

Number of Years after 2000	Number of Births of Twins (in thousands)
0	119
1	121
2	125

Find the quadratic function that best models these data. If the trends in this table continue, solve by factoring to find the year in which there will be 275,000 sets of twins born.

After completing this section, we will discuss this application further. See page 673.

In the preceding section, we used numeric and graphic methods to solve polynomial equations. While such methods work, they are sometimes limited in their usefulness. Therefore, we need an algebraic method to solve these equations. One such method is to solve by factoring.

Objective 9.2.1   Solving Equations Using the Zero Factor Property

We begin by reviewing a property of real numbers that we discussed in Chapter P. The multiplication property of zero stated that the product of a real number and 0 is 0. We can relate this property to another property called the zero factor property. The *zero factor property* states that if a product is 0, then one or both of the factors must be 0.

For example, $6 \cdot 0 = 0$, $0 \cdot (-5) = 0$, or $0 \cdot 0 = 0$.

ZERO FACTOR PROPERTY

If $ab = 0$, then either $a = 0$, $b = 0$, or both.

We can use this property to solve an equation of the form $P(x) = 0$ when $P(x)$ is in factored form, such as when $P(x) = (x + 5)(x - 2)$.

For example, solve $(x + 5)(x - 1) = 0$.

If $(x + 5)(x - 1) = 0$, then $x + 5 = 0$, $x - 1 = 0$, or both.

We can now determine the solutions by solving the linear equations.

$$
\begin{array}{ccc}
x + 5 = 0 & \text{or} & x - 1 = 0 \\
x + 5 - 5 = 0 - 5 & & x - 1 + 1 = 0 + 1 \\
x = -5 & & x = 1
\end{array}
$$

The solutions of the equation $(x + 5)(x - 1) = 0$ are -5 and 1.

We can check the solutions by substituting them into the original equation or by solving the equation numerically or graphically.

Substitution Check

Let $x = -5$

$$
\frac{(x + 5)(x - 1) = 0}{(-5 + 5)(-5 - 1) \mid 0}
$$

$$
\begin{array}{cc}
(0) & (-6) \\
& 0
\end{array}
$$

Let $x = 1$

$$
\frac{(x + 5)(x - 1) = 0}{(1 + 5)(1 - 1) \mid 0}
$$

$$
\begin{array}{cc}
(6) & (0) \\
& 0
\end{array}
$$

Both values result in true equations. Therefore, the solutions are -5 and 1.

Numeric Check

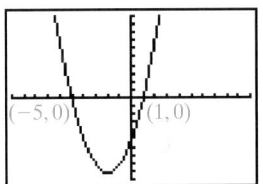

Y1 $= (x + 5)(x - 1)$
Y2 $= 0$
The solutions, -5 and 1, result in equal values for Y1 and Y2.

Graphic Check

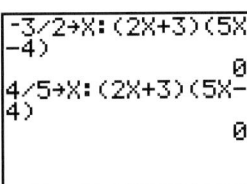

$(-10, 10, -10, 10)$

The solutions, -5 and 1, are the x-coordinates of the intersections of the graphs Y1 and Y2.

EXAMPLE 1   Solve and check. $(2x + 3)(5x - 4) = 0$

Algebraic Solution

$$(2x + 3)(5x - 4) = 0$$

Use the zero factor property.

$$
\begin{array}{ccc}
2x + 3 = 0 & \text{or} & 5x - 4 = 0 \\
2x + 3 - 3 = 0 - 3 & & 5x - 4 + 4 = 0 + 4 \\
2x = -3 & & 5x = 4 \\
x = -\dfrac{3}{2} & & x = \dfrac{4}{5}
\end{array}
$$

The solutions of the equation are $-\frac{3}{2}$ and $\frac{4}{5}$.

Substitution Check

```
-3/2→X:(2X+3)(5X
-4)
                    0
4/5→X:(2X+3)(5X-
4)
                    0
```

Check the solutions on your calculator by substituting the values for the variable in the expression on the left side of the equation. The result should equal 0, the expression on the right side of the equation.

After substituting the solutions into the expression on the left, we find that the results are 0. The solutions check. ■

There is a relationship between the solutions of a polynomial equation and the x-intercepts of its graph. Use your calculator to complete the following set of exercises to determine this relationship.

Guided Discovery 1   Solutions and x-Intercepts

Solve each equation (part **a**). Graph the corresponding equation (part **b**). Label the x-intercepts of each graph. Compare the solution of the equation with the x-intercept of the corresponding equation's graph.

1. a. $(x - 3)(x - 2) = 0$ **b.** $y = (x - 3)(x - 2)$

2. a. $(x + 3)(x - 2) = 0$ **b.** $y = (x + 3)(x - 2)$

3. a. $(x - 3)(x + 2) = 0$ **b.** $y = (x - 3)(x + 2)$

Write a rule for determining the solutions of an equation from the x-intercepts of the graph of its corresponding equation.

4. Use your rule to determine the solutions of the equation $(x + 4)(x - 5) = 0$.

The solutions of these equations are the x-coordinates of the x-intercepts of the graphs of their corresponding equations. This rule is true because when we solve graphically, one of the equations we graph is Y2 $= 0$, the x-axis.

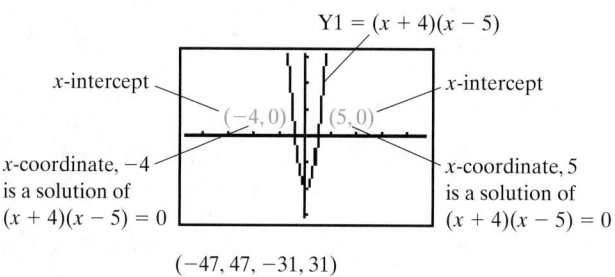

$(-47, 47, -31, 31)$

Using this rule, we determine that the x-intercepts of the graph of $y = (x + 4)(x - 5)$ are $(-4, 0)$ and $(5, 0)$ and the solutions of the equation $(x + 4)(x - 5) = 0$ are $x = -4$ and $x = 5$.

EXAMPLE 2   Graph the equation $y = (x + 2)(2x - 3)$ on your calculator. Determine the x-intercepts of the graph. Write a related equation and determine its solution.

Solution

Graph $y = (x + 2)(2x - 3)$ and determine the x-intercepts of the graph.

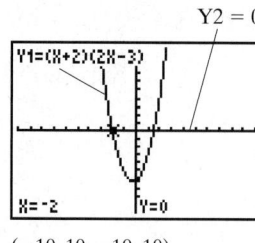

$(-10, 10, -10, 10)$

The x-intercept is $(-2, 0)$.

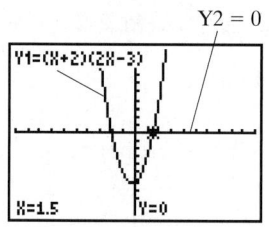

$(-10, 10, -10, 10)$

The x-intercept is $(1.5, 0)$.

The related equation is $(x + 2)(2x - 3) = 0$. The solutions of the equation are -2 and 1.5, the x-coordinates of the x-intercepts of the graph of $y = (x + 2)(2x - 3)$.

EXAMPLE 3   Solve and check graphically. $x(x + 6)(3x - 2) = 0$

Algebraic Solution

$$x(x + 6)(3x - 2) = 0$$

We now have three factors equal to 0. The zero factor property can be expanded to more than two factors. Therefore, we set all three factors equal to 0.

$x = 0$ or $x + 6 = 0$ or $3x - 2 = 0$

$x = -6$ $x = \dfrac{2}{3}$

The solutions of the equation are 0, −6, and $\frac{2}{3}$.
A graphic check on the calculator results in three solutions: 0, −6, and $0.\overline{6}$ $\left(\text{or } \frac{2}{3}\right)$, the x-coordinates of the x-intercepts.

Graphic Check

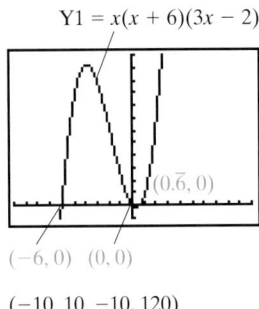

$Y1 = x(x + 6)(3x - 2)$

$(0.\overline{6}, 0)$

$(-6, 0)$ $(0, 0)$

$(-10, 10, -10, 120)$

✓ Objective 9.2.1 *CHECKUP*

1. Solve and check. $(x + 7)(4x - 3) = 0$
2. Graph the equation $y = (x - 1)(2x + 1)$ on your calculator. Determine the x-intercepts of the graph. Write a related equation and determine its solution.

3. Solve and check. $x(4x - 5)(x - 1) = 0$

Objective 9.2.2   Solving Equations by Factoring

As we know, most polynomial equations are not written in the factored form given in examples 1 and 3. We may have to use the algebra skills from previous chapters to manipulate the equation into that form.

SOLVING A POLYNOMIAL EQUATION ALGEBRAICALLY BY FACTORING

To solve a polynomial equation algebraically by factoring,

- Write the equation in the standard form $P(x) = 0$.
- Factor $P(x)$.
- Set each factor equal to 0 and solve for the variable.
- Check the solutions by substitution or by solving numerically or graphically.

In order to check graphically, we can expand the rule we discovered in the last objective. Note that $(x + 4)(x - 5) = 0$ written in standard form is $x^2 - x - 20 = 0$. Therefore, the solutions of $(x + 4)(x - 5) = 0$ or $x^2 - x - 20 = 0$ are $x = -4$ and $x = 5$.

SOLUTIONS OF POLYNOMIAL EQUATIONS

The solutions of a polynomial equation in standard form, $P(x) = 0$, are the x-coordinates of the x-intercepts of the graph of $P(x)$.

For example, solve $x^2 + x - 6 = 0$.

Algebraic Solution

$$x^2 + x - 6 = 0$$ Standard form

$$(x + 3)(x - 2) = 0$$ Factor.

$$x + 3 = 0 \quad \text{or} \quad x - 2 = 0$$ Zero factor property

$$x = -3 \qquad\qquad x = 2$$

The solutions are −3 and 2.

Substitution Check

Substitute the solutions into the original equation

Let $x = -3$

$$\begin{array}{c|c} x^2 + x - 6 = 0 \\ \hline (-3)^2 + (-3) - 6 & 0 \\ 9 - 3 - 6 \\ 0 \end{array}$$

Let $x = 2$

$$\begin{array}{c|c} x^2 + x - 6 = 0 \\ \hline 2^2 + 2 - 6 & 0 \\ 4 + 2 - 6 \\ 0 \end{array}$$

The solutions check.

Numeric Check

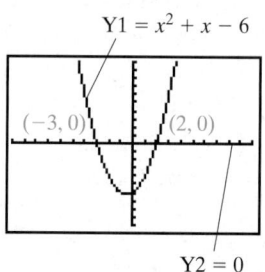

$$Y1 = x^2 + x - 6$$
$$Y2 = 0$$
The solutions, −3 and 2, are the x-values that determine Y1 = Y2.

Graphic Check

Y1 = $x^2 + x - 6$

(−3, 0)   (2, 0)

Y2 = 0

(−10, 10, −10, 10)

The solutions, −3 and 2, are the x-coordinates of the x-intercepts of the graph.

If we cannot trace and find the intersection of the graph with the x-axis, the calculator will calculate it for us. Under the CALC function, choose Zero. Set an interval by choosing a left bound (a point on the graph to the left of the x-intercept) and a right bound (a point on the graph to the right of the x-intercept). Then select a guess between the two bounds. The calculator will display the x-intercept. The solutions (or **roots**) are the x-coordinates of each x-intercept.

EXAMPLE 4   Solve and check.

a. $x^2 - 9 = 0$ **b.** $4x^2 + 20x + 25 = 0$ **c.** $-10x^2 - 41x + 77 = 0$

Algebraic Solution

a.
$$x^2 - 9 = 0$$ Standard form

$$(x + 3)(x - 3) = 0$$ Factor.

$$x + 3 = 0 \quad \text{or} \quad x - 3 = 0$$ Zero factor property

$$x = -3 \qquad\qquad x = 3$$

The solutions are −3 and 3.

Graphic Check

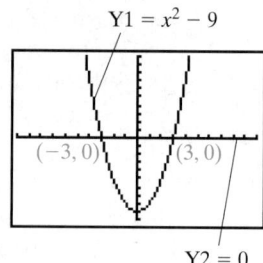

Y1 = $x^2 - 9$

(−3, 0)   (3, 0)

Y2 = 0

(−10, 10, −10, 10)

The graphic check results in the graph of
Y1 = $x^2 - 9$.
The x-coordinates of the x-intercepts are −3 and 3, the solutions.

b. $4x^2 + 20x + 25 = 0$ Standard form

$(2x + 5)^2 = 0$ Factor.

Set each factor equal to 0 and solve. Since the factor is squared, both factors are $2x + 5$. There is no need to solve two equations.

$2x + 5 = 0$

$x = -\dfrac{5}{2}$

The solution is $-\dfrac{5}{2}$. It is called a **double root**.

Graphic Check

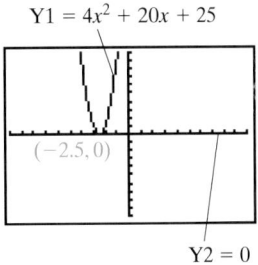

$Y1 = 4x^2 + 20x + 25$

$(-2.5, 0)$

$Y2 = 0$

$(-10, 10, -10, 10)$

The graphic check results in the graph of $Y1 = 4x^2 + 20x + 25$. There is only one x-intercept. The x-coordinate of the x-intercept, -2.5 or $-\dfrac{5}{2}$, is the solution. You need to use Zero under the CALC function to find the intercept.

> **TAKE NOTE** A double root will always occur when the graphic check of a quadratic equation in standard form results in one x-intercept.

c. $-10x^2 - 41x + 77 = 0$ Standard form

$-1(2x + 11)(5x - 7) = 0$ Factor.

Set each factor equal to 0 and solve. The common factor -1 cannot equal 0, because it is a constant.

$2x + 11 = 0$ or $5x - 7 = 0$

$x = -\dfrac{11}{2}$ $x = \dfrac{7}{5}$

The solutions are $-\dfrac{11}{2}$ and $\dfrac{7}{5}$.

Substitution Check

```
-11/2→X: -10X²-41
X+77
                 0
7/5→X: -10X²-41X+
77
                 0
```

Both solutions, $-\dfrac{11}{2}$ and $\dfrac{7}{5}$, when substituted for the variable, result in expressions equal to 0, the second expression value. ■

EXAMPLE 5   Solve and check.

     a. $6x^2 + 14x = 3x + 7$ **b.** $(x + 3)(x - 7) = -9$

Algebraic Solution

a. $6x^2 + 14x = 3x + 7$

Neither side of the equation is 0. Use the properties of equations to write the equation in standard form.

$6x^2 + 14x - 3x - 7 = 3x + 7 - 3x - 7$

$6x^2 + 11x - 7 = 0$ Standard form.

$(3x + 7)(2x - 1) = 0$ Factor.

$3x + 7 = 0$ or $2x - 1 = 0$ Zero factor property

$x = -\dfrac{7}{3}$ $x = \dfrac{1}{2}$

The solutions are $-\dfrac{7}{3}$ and $\dfrac{1}{2}$.

Graphic Check

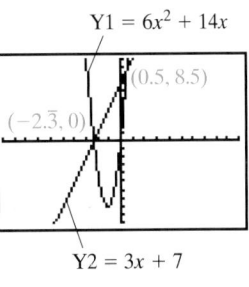

$Y1 = 6x^2 + 14x$

$(0.5, 8.5)$

$(-2.\overline{3}, 0)$

$Y2 = 3x + 7$

$(-10, 10, -10, 10)$

The graphic check shows the intersections of $Y1 = 6x^2 + 14x$ and $Y2 = 3x + 7$ are $(-2.\overline{3}, 0)$ and $(0.5, 8.5)$. The solutions are $-2.\overline{3}$ and 0.5 or $-\dfrac{7}{3}$ and $\dfrac{1}{2}$.

b. $(x + 3)(x - 7) = -9$

Neither side of the equation is 0. Multiply the expression on the left and then use the properties of equations to write the equation in standard form.

$$x^2 - 4x - 21 = -9$$
$$x^2 - 4x - 21 + 9 = -9 + 9$$
$$x^2 - 4x - 12 = 0 \qquad \text{Standard form}$$
$$(x + 2)(x - 6) = 0 \qquad \text{Factor.}$$
$$x + 2 = 0 \quad \text{or} \quad x - 6 = 0 \quad \text{Zero factor property}$$
$$x = -2 \quad \text{or} \qquad x = 6$$

The solutions are -2 and 6.

Graphic Check

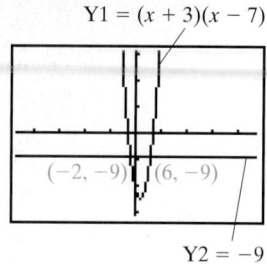

$$Y2 = -9$$

$(-47, 47, -31, 31)$

The graphic check results in the intersection of the graphs $Y1 = (x + 3)(x - 7)$ and $Y2 = -9$. The solutions are -2 and 6. ■

✓ Objective 9.2.2 **CHECKUP**

In exercises 1 and 2, solve and check.

1. a. $a^2 - 81 = 0$ **b.** $16x^2 + 24x + 9 = 0$
   c. $-6x^2 - 7x + 20 = 0$

2. a. $4x^2 - 5x = 12x - 15$ **b.** $(x + 4)(x - 2) = 16$

3. Before you can use the zero factor property to solve a polynomial equation, what must be true about the form of the equation? ■

Objective 9.2.3   Modeling the Real World

Polynomial equations are commonly applied to geometry problems. Use the formulas given to you in earlier chapters, and solve them with the methods of this section. Be careful to evaluate the solutions to see whether they make sense within the constraints of the problem. Solutions of the equation sometimes may not make physical sense.

EXAMPLE 6

LaChung plans to make an open rectangular box from a flat piece of tin. He needs the length to be 5 feet more than the width. He plans to cut out square corners 3 feet on a side for the height of the box. He needs the box to hold 198 cubic feet of mulch.

a. Find the dimensions of the box.

b. Find the dimensions of the piece of tin needed.

Algebraic Solution

a. Let $\quad x = $ width of the box
$\quad x + 5 = $ length of the box

The volume formula for a rectangular solid is $V = LWH$. Substitute values or expressions for the variables $L, W, H,$ and V.

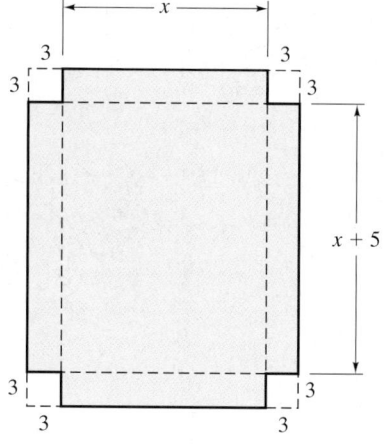

$$V = LWH$$
$$198 = (x + 5)(x)(3)$$
$$198 = 3x^2 + 15x \qquad \text{Simplify.}$$
$$3x^2 + 15x - 198 = 0 \qquad \text{Standard form}$$
$$3(x^2 + 5x - 66) = 0 \qquad \text{Factor out the GCF.}$$
$$3(x - 6)(x + 11) = 0 \qquad \text{Factor the trinomial.}$$
$$x - 6 = 0 \quad \text{or} \quad x + 11 = 0 \qquad \text{Zero factor property}$$
$$x = 6 \quad \text{or} \qquad x = -11 \qquad \text{Solve.}$$

Since x is the width of the box, $x = -11$ is not an appropriate choice. Therefore, the width is 6 feet.

The length is $x + 5 = 6 + 5 = 11$ feet.

The box's dimensions are 11 feet by 6 feet by 3 feet.

b. The length of the tin must be 11 feet plus 6 feet (two 3-foot corner sections), or 17 feet.

The width of the tin must be 6 feet plus 6 feet (again, two 3-foot corner sections), or 12 feet. ■

APPLICATION

The U.S. Department of Health and Human Services publishes statistics that show that the number of multiple births in the United States is increasing. This is due to increased use of fertility drugs and a greater number of births to older women. More recent data are summarized below:

Number of Years after 2000	Number of Births of Twins (in thousands)
0	119
1	121
2	125

Find the quadratic function that best models these data. If the trends in this table continue, solve by factoring to find the year in which there will be 275,000 sets of twins born.

Discussion

Let x = the number of years after 2000
y = the number of births of twins in thousands

The ordered pairs from the table are $(0, 119)$, $(1, 121)$, and $(2, 125)$.

Use the quadratic regression function of your calculator to determine an equation.

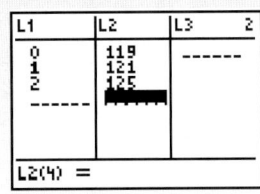 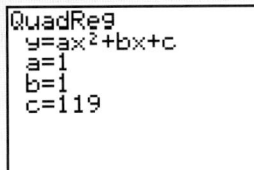

The quadratic function for the number of births of twins is $y = x^2 + x + 119$.

The domain of this function is $x \geq 0$ because x represents the number of years after 2000 and cannot be negative.

To determine when the number of births is 275,000, we set $y = 275$ and solve for x.

$$275 = x^2 + x + 119$$
$$x^2 + x - 156 = 0$$
$$(x - 12)(x + 13) = 0$$
$$x - 12 = 0 \quad \text{or} \quad x + 13 = 0$$
$$x = 12 \qquad\qquad x = -13$$

(***Note:*** $x = -13$ is not in the domain of our function, $x \geq 0$. Therefore, -13 is not a solution.)

There will be 275,000 births of twins 12 years after 2000, or 2012.

 Objective 9.2.3 **CHECKUP**

1. Justin must make a box from balsa wood for a project in his architecture class. He is allowed to use 40 square inches of balsa wood for the project. The height of the box must be the same as its width. The box must have a length that is 2 inches more than the width. What will be the dimensions of the box?

2. The ranking of airports by passenger traffic in 2003 is summarized by the following table:

Ranking	Number of Passengers (in millions)
1	79.1
2	69.5
3	55

Find the quadratic function that best models these data. Round coefficients to the nearest unit. If the trend in this table continues, solve by factoring to find the ranking of the airport with 44 million passengers in 2003. ■

9.2 EXERCISES

In exercises 1–4, graph the equation on your calculator. Determine the x-intercepts of the graph. Write a related equation and determine its solution.

1. $y = (x + 4)(x - 2)$ **2.** $y = (x - 3)(x + 1)$ **3.** $y = (2x - 1)(3x + 5)$ **4.** $y = (2x + 3)(3x - 1)$

Solve exercises 5–44 and check.

5. $(x + 6)(x + 11) = 0$

6. $(p + 9)(p + 13) = 0$

7. $3x(x + 9)(2x - 5) = 0$

8. $9x(x - 4)(6x + 1) = 0$

9. $(4x + 3)(2x - 9)(x + 6) = 0$

10. $(2z + 7)(3z - 8)(z - 7) = 0$

11. $(0.2x + 6.8)(1.3x - 1.69) = 0$

12. $(1.4x + 4.2)(0.7x - 2.8) = 0$

13. $0 = x^2 + 10x + 24$

14. $z^2 + 13z + 40 = 0$

15. $x^2 + 33 = 14x$

16. $52 - 17x + x^2 = 0$

17. $4x^2 + 5x + 24x + 30 = 0$

18. $7x^2 + 8x + 14x + 16 = 0$

19. $5x^2 + 3x = 8$

20. $7x = 3x^2 - 20$

21. $15x^2 = 35x$

22. $63x = 18x^2$

23. $18x^2 - 3x = 5 - 30x$

24. $8x^2 + 12x = 14x + 21$

25. $16x^2 + 72x + 81 = 0$

26. $49x^2 - 28x + 4 = 0$

27. $4x^2 + 25x + 18 = 5x - 7$

28. $9x^2 + 29x + 8 = 5x - 8$

29. $b^2 + 7 = 71$

30. $c^2 - 5 = 139$

31. $9z^2 = 25$

32. $64p^2 = 81$

33. $(x + 1)^2 = 49$

34. $(x - 2)^2 = 36$

35. $(x - 3)(x - 2) = 42$

36. $(x - 5)(x + 4) = 22$

37. $x^2 + (x + 3)^2 = 225$

38. $(x + 5)^2 + x^2 = 625$

39. $x^3 + 7x^2 - 9x - 63 = 0$

40. $z^3 + 5z^2 - 16z - 80 = 0$

41. $18x^3 + 45x^2 - 50x - 125 = 0$

42. $12p^3 + 36p^2 - 147p - 441 = 0$

43. $3x^3 - 3x^2 + 12x - 12 = 0$

44. $2x^3 - 16x^2 + 3x - 24 = 0$

Geometry

45. Phil is designing a water trough for his ranch. The trough will be in the shape of a rectangular box and must hold 72 cubic feet of water. Phil wants it to be 3 feet high, with a width that is 1 foot more than half its length.
  a. If the length is denoted by x, write an expression for the volume of the trough.
  b. Write an equation in terms of the volume, and solve the equation for the dimensions of the trough.

46. A rectangular jewelry box is designed to have a height of 4 centimeters. The length of the box is 1 centimeter more than eight times its width.
  a. If the width is denoted by x, write an expression for the volume of the box.
  b. Write an equation for the volume of the box when it will hold 820 cubic centimeters, and solve the equation for the dimensions of the box.

47. Michelle is designing drawers for a cabinet. She wants each drawer to have a width that is three times its height and a length that is 2 inches more than four times the height. She will need wood for the four sides of the drawer and the bottom.
  a. Write an expression for the surface area of the five sides for which Michelle must obtain wood.
  b. If Michelle figures that she needs 700 square inches of wood for the drawer, what are its dimensions?

48. A cardboard chute in the shape of a rectangular box is constructed with a width that is five times its height and a length

that is 2 units more than seven times its height. The chute is open on its two ends.

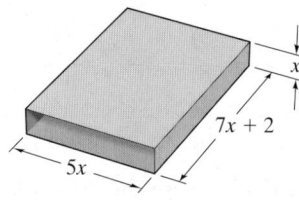

  a. Write an expression for the surface area of the chute.
  b. If the outer surface of the chute has an area of 828 square inches, what are the dimensions of the chute?

49. Steve designs a sail for his sailboat. The sail will be triangular, but not a right triangle. He wants the height to be 4 feet more than the base.
  a. Write an expression for the area of the sail.
  b. If the area of the sail is to be 30 square feet, what are the base and height of the sail?

50. The base of a triangular garden is 2 meters more than five times its height. The garden covers 260 square meters of ground.
  a. Write an expression for the area of the garden.
  b. What do the base and height of the garden measure?

51. The sum of the areas of a rectangle and a triangle can be given by $A(x) = 2x^2 + 5x - 168$, where x is the height of the triangle in feet. For what value of x will the sum of the areas be 180 square feet?

52. Pat has two boxes to be shipped by volume. The sum of the volumes of the boxes can be given by $V(x) = 7x^2 + 9x - 406$, where x is the length of the larger box in inches. If the total volume is 384 cubic inches, what is the length of the larger box?

53. Claims adjusters are concerned with establishing who was at fault in an accident. To help them decide, they use skid marks to determine the speeds of the vehicles. The formula is

$$V^2 = 30FS$$

where V is the velocity of the vehicle (in miles per hour), F is the coefficient of friction of the road in decimal form, and S is the skid length. Write an equation involving velocity if a car skidded 243 feet and the coefficient of friction of the road was 40%. Solve the equation by factoring to determine the velocity of the vehicle.

54. Using the formula from exercise 53, write an equation for the velocity of a car that skidded 250 feet when the coefficient of friction of the road was 27%. Solve the equation by factoring to determine the velocity of the car.

Business

55. A man who supervises pizza delivery for a restaurant estimates daily revenue to be $R(x) = -3x^2 + 66x + 360$, where x is the number of delivery persons on duty. On a particular day revenue was $711. How many delivery staff members worked on this day?

56. A mini golf facility with a game room has weekly revenues of $R(x) = 9x^2 + 480x + 1020$, where x is the number of birthday parties scheduled. During a particular week revenues were $8076. How many birthday parties were scheduled?

57. The owner of a franchise coffee shop owns several city outlets. His total weekly cost for coffee and baked goods is $C(x) = 2000 + 150x + 9x^2$, where x is the number of bakery deliveries. During one week in November his costs were $8600. How many deliveries were made to his shops?

58. A management agency representing a number of athletes has weekly advertising costs per client that can be estimated by the function $C(x) = -80x^2 + 340x + 5700$, where x is the number of television appearances by a given athlete. During one week a particular client cost the agency $2280. How many television appearances were made by this athlete?

59. A car dealership finds that its profit is $P(x) = 45x^2 + 43x - 2$, where x is the number of sales associates working on a given day. If profit on a particular day was $9420, how many salespeople worked on that day?

60. The owner of a French restaurant finds that his weekend profits are $P(x) = -2000 + 135x + 11x^2$, where x is the number of tables served. During one weekend his profit was $5100. How many tables were served?

Real Data

61. According to the U.S. Department of Commerce Bureau of Economic Analysis, personal consumption expenditures for household operations are on the rise. The following table summarizes the data:

Number of Years after 2000	Personal Consumption Expenditures for Household Operations (in billions of dollars)
0	390
2	408
3	429

Find the quadratic function that best models these data. If the trends in this table continue, solve by factoring to find the year in which expenditures reach 800 billion dollars.

62. The Food and Agriculture Organization of the United Nations (FAO) estimates that the world commercial catch of fish, crustaceans, and mollusks in world inland waters is rising. The most recent data are summarized in the following table:

Number of Years after 1990	World Commercial Catch of Fish, Crustaceans, and Mollusks in Inland Waters in Thousands of Metric Tons
9	28,720
10	30,070
11	31,320

Find the quadratic function that best models these data. If the trends in this table continue, solve by factoring to find the year in which there will be 38,520,000 metric tons of fish, crustaceans, and mollusks caught in inland waters worldwide.

9.2 Calculator Exercises

Another helpful technique for solving a polynomial equation graphically is to simplify the equation by placing it in standard form. To do this, move all terms to the left side of the equation, using the properties of equations. The equations will now be of the form

$$ax^2 + bx + c = 0$$
$$ax^3 + bx^2 + cx + d = 0$$

and so on. Then store the left side of the equation in Y1 and set Y2 = 0 (since the right side of the equation is 0). When you graph the equations, their solutions will be the x-coordinates of the points of intersection of the graphs of Y1 and Y2. However, since the graph of Y2 = 0 is the x-axis, the solutions will also be the x-coordinates of the x-intercepts of the graph of Y1. Try this method on the following equations to verify the solutions listed there.

1. $x^3 + 5x^2 + 4x + 20 = 5x^2 + 25x$; verify the solutions $x = 1$, $x = 4$, and $x = -5$.

2. $x^3 + 3x^2 - 3x = x^2 - 2x + 2$; verify the solutions $x = -2$, $x = -1$, and $x = 1$.

3. $x^3 - 2x^2 = 30x - x^2$; verify the solutions $x = -5$, $x = 0$, and $x = 6$.

9.2 Writing Exercise

In solving the equation

$$a^2 - 9a = 0$$

Chantel factored the left side, used the zero factor property, and stated that the solutions of the equation were $a = 0$ and $a = 9$.

In contrast, Holly just divided both sides of the equation by a and solved the resulting equation to get only one solution, $a = 9$. Which do you think is the correct way to solve the equation? Explain.

9.3 PROPERTIES OF SQUARE ROOTS

OBJECTIVES

1 Simplify square-root expressions by using the product rule for square roots.

2 Simplify square-root expressions by using the quotient rule for square roots.

3 Model real-world situations by using multiplication and division of square roots.

APPLICATION

An LCD panel television is sold by its diagonal measurement. Therefore, a 30-inch television has a diagonal measurement of 30 inches. If the width of the screen measures 15 inches, determine the length of the screen.

After completing this section, we will discuss this application further. See page 683.

Objective 9.3.1   ### Simplifying Square Roots by Using the Product Rule

Before we begin, we will review some terminology associated with a square-root expression. A square-root expression is of the form $\sqrt{a}$, where the symbol $\sqrt{}$ is called a radical and a is the radicand. In Chapter P, we defined $\sqrt{a}$ as the principal square root and $-\sqrt{a}$ as the negative square root. Always remember that a square root of a negative number is not defined in the real-number system.

$$\sqrt{36} = 6 \text{ because } (6)^2 = 36$$

$$-\sqrt{36} = -6 \text{ because } (-6)^2 = 36$$

$$\sqrt{-36} \text{ is not a real number.}$$

EVALUATING SQUARE-ROOT EXPRESSIONS

To evaluate a principal square root, observe that $\sqrt{c^2} = |c|$.

To evaluate a negative square root, observe that $-\sqrt{c^2} = -|c|$.

If the radicand cannot be written as the square of a number, we approximate the answer. We use the calculator to do this.

One property of square roots involves multiplication. To discover this product rule, use your calculator to complete the following exercises.

Guided Discovery 2   Multiplication of Square Roots

Evaluate each expression on your calculator, and compare the results obtained in part **a** with the corresponding results in part **b**.

1. **a.** $\sqrt{3} \cdot \sqrt{7} \approx$ _____   **b.** $\sqrt{21} \approx$ _____
2. **a.** $\sqrt{2} \cdot \sqrt{3} \approx$ _____   **b.** $\sqrt{6} \approx$ _____

Write a rule for multiplying square roots.

The value of the expression in part **a** is equivalent to the expression in part **b**. The first value is the product of square roots. The second value is the square root of the product of the radicands in the first expression. Therefore, to multiply square roots, we multiply the radicands and then take the square root of the product. We will show that this rule is true in a later chapter.

PRODUCT RULE FOR SQUARE ROOTS

For any real numbers $\sqrt{a}$ and $\sqrt{b}$,

$$\sqrt{a} \cdot \sqrt{b} = \sqrt{ab}$$

EXAMPLE 1   Multiply.

a. $\sqrt{3} \cdot \sqrt{5}$ **b.** $2\sqrt{3} \cdot 4\sqrt{7}$

Solution

a. $\sqrt{3} \cdot \sqrt{5} = \sqrt{3 \cdot 5} = \sqrt{15}$ *Product rule*

b. $2\sqrt{3} \cdot 4\sqrt{7} = 2 \cdot 4 \cdot \sqrt{3 \cdot 7} = 8\sqrt{21}$ *Product rule*

To simplify square roots, we read the product rule from right to left: $\sqrt{ab} = \sqrt{a} \cdot \sqrt{b}$. For example, to simplify a square root, we rewrite the radicand as a product of a perfect square (preferably the largest possible perfect-square factor) and another factor. We then reverse the product rule by writing a product of square roots. Finally, we simplify the perfect square root. For example,

Check

```
2√(6)
      4.898979486
√(24)
      4.898979486
```

$$\sqrt{24} = \sqrt{4 \cdot 6} = \sqrt{4}\sqrt{6} = \sqrt{2^2}\sqrt{6} = 2\sqrt{6}$$

To check this result on your calculator, first evaluate the square-root expression found algebraically and then evaluate the given square-root expression. The results should be the same.

EXAMPLE 2   Simplify.

a. $\sqrt{48}$ **b.** $\sqrt{128}$ **c.** $-\sqrt{72}$

Solution

a. $\sqrt{48} = \sqrt{16 \cdot 3} = \sqrt{16}\sqrt{3} = 4\sqrt{3}$ $16 = 4^2$

 TAKE NOTE If we had not used the largest perfect-square factor, 16, we would need to simplify the expressions more than once.

For example, if we used the perfect-square factor 4, we would obtain

$$\sqrt{48} = \sqrt{4 \cdot 12} = \sqrt{4}\sqrt{12} = 2\sqrt{12}$$

Notice that the radicand 12 still contains the perfect-square factor 4. We continue simplifying $2\sqrt{12}$.

$$= 2\sqrt{4 \cdot 3} = 2\sqrt{4}\sqrt{3}$$
$$= 2 \cdot 2\sqrt{3} = 4\sqrt{3}$$

b. $\sqrt{128} = \sqrt{64 \cdot 2} = 8\sqrt{2}$ $64 = 8^2$

c. $-\sqrt{72} = -\sqrt{36} \cdot \sqrt{2} = -6\sqrt{2}$ $36 = 6^2$ ■

EXAMPLE 3   Multiply and simplify.

a. $\sqrt{6} \cdot \sqrt{2}$ **b.** $2\sqrt{5} \cdot 3\sqrt{10}$

Solution

a. $\sqrt{6} \cdot \sqrt{2} = \sqrt{12}$ Product rule

$\qquad\qquad = \sqrt{4 \cdot 3}$ $4 = 2^2$

$\qquad\qquad = 2\sqrt{3}$

b. $2\sqrt{5} \cdot 3\sqrt{10} = 6\sqrt{50}$ Product rule

$\qquad\qquad\quad = 6\sqrt{25 \cdot 2}$ $25 = 5^2$

$\qquad\qquad\quad = 6 \cdot 5\sqrt{2}$

$\qquad\qquad\quad = 30\sqrt{2}$ ■

In Chapter 11, we will continue this discussion of simplifying radicals with variables in the radicands.

EXAMPLE 4   Simplify.

a. $-2 + \sqrt{24}$ **b.** $\dfrac{4 + \sqrt{32}}{4}$ **c.** $\dfrac{-6 - \sqrt{28}}{-4}$

Solution

a. $-2 + \sqrt{24} = -2 + \sqrt{4 \cdot 6} = -2 + 2\sqrt{6}$

b. $\dfrac{4 + \sqrt{32}}{4} = \dfrac{4 + \sqrt{16 \cdot 2}}{4} = \dfrac{4 + 4\sqrt{2}}{4}$

$\qquad = \dfrac{\overset{1}{\cancel{4}}\left(1 + \sqrt{2}\right)}{\underset{1}{\cancel{4}}}$ Factor the numerator and divide out the 4.

$\qquad = 1 + \sqrt{2}$

c. $\dfrac{-6 - \sqrt{28}}{-4} = \dfrac{-6 - \sqrt{4 \cdot 7}}{-4} = \dfrac{-6 - 2\sqrt{7}}{-4}$

$\qquad = \dfrac{-\overset{1}{\cancel{2}}\left(3 + \sqrt{7}\right)}{\underset{2}{-\cancel{4}}}$ Factor the numerator and divide out the -2.

$\qquad = \dfrac{3 + \sqrt{7}}{2}$ ■

Objective 9.3.1 *CHECKUP*

1. Multiply. **a.** $\sqrt{2} \cdot \sqrt{3}$ **b.** $2\sqrt{3} \cdot 3\sqrt{5}$
2. Simplify. **a.** $\sqrt{80}$ **b.** $\sqrt{192}$ **c.** $-\sqrt{98}$
3. Multiply and simplify.
   a. $\sqrt{6} \cdot \sqrt{3}$ **b.** $2\sqrt{2} \cdot 3\sqrt{10}$

4. Simplify. **a.** $-3 + \sqrt{32}$ **b.** $\dfrac{5 + \sqrt{75}}{5}$ **c.** $\dfrac{-6 - \sqrt{45}}{-3}$
5. Explain the difference between finding the square root of a number and squaring a number.

Objective 9.3.2   ## Simplifying Square Roots by Using the Quotient Rule

Square roots also have a property involving quotients. To see what it is, complete the following set of exercises.

Guided Discovery 3   Division of Square Roots

Evaluate each expression on your calculator, and compare the results obtained in part **a** with the corresponding results in part **b**.

1. a. $\dfrac{\sqrt{9}}{\sqrt{3}} \approx$ ____ **b.** $\sqrt{3} \approx$ ____

2. a. $\dfrac{\sqrt{6}}{\sqrt{3}} \approx$ ____ **b.** $\sqrt{2} \approx$ ____

Write a rule for dividing square roots.

The value of the expression in part **a** is equivalent to the expression in part **b**. The first value is the quotient of square roots. The second value is the square root of the quotient of the radicands in the first expression. Therefore, to divide square roots, we divide the radicands and then take the square root of the quotient. We will show that this rule is true in a later chapter.

QUOTIENT RULE FOR SQUARE ROOTS

For any real numbers $\sqrt{a}$ and $\sqrt{b}$, where $b \neq 0$,

$$\frac{\sqrt{a}}{\sqrt{b}} = \sqrt{\frac{a}{b}}$$

EXAMPLE 5   Divide.

a. $\dfrac{\sqrt{6}}{\sqrt{2}}$ **b.** $\dfrac{\sqrt{75}}{\sqrt{3}}$ **c.** $\dfrac{\sqrt{256}}{\sqrt{2}}$

Solution

a. $\dfrac{\sqrt{6}}{\sqrt{2}} = \sqrt{\dfrac{6}{2}} = \sqrt{3}$ *Quotient rule*

b. $\dfrac{\sqrt{75}}{\sqrt{3}} = \sqrt{\dfrac{75}{3}} = \sqrt{25} = 5$ *Quotient rule*

c. $\dfrac{\sqrt{256}}{\sqrt{2}} = \sqrt{\dfrac{256}{2}} = \sqrt{128}$ *Quotient rule*

   $= \sqrt{64 \cdot 2}$ *$64 = 8^2$*

   $= 8\sqrt{2}$

In Chapter 11, we will continue this discussion of simplifying radicals with variables in the radicands.

To simplify square roots, we read the quotient rule from right to left: $\sqrt{\dfrac{a}{b}} = \dfrac{\sqrt{a}}{\sqrt{b}}$.

For example, to evaluate a square root having a fractional radicand, we reverse the quotient rule by writing a quotient of square roots. Then we simplify each square root, using the product rule. For example,

$$\sqrt{\frac{5}{36}} = \frac{\sqrt{5}}{\sqrt{36}} = \frac{\sqrt{5}}{6}$$

We must be careful when writing the final result. If the result is a fraction, it is conventional to write the denominator without radicals. The process of changing the fraction to an equivalent form without a radical denominator is called **rationalizing the denominator**. That is, we make the denominator a rational number.

For example, simplify

$$\sqrt{\frac{36}{5}} = \frac{\sqrt{36}}{\sqrt{5}} = \frac{6}{\sqrt{5}}$$

To rationalize the denominator, we use the multiplication property of 1. That is, we multiply the numerator and denominator by the same value. We choose a value that results in the denominator having a perfect-square radicand, so that we can simplify it. Since the denominator is $\sqrt{5}$ and we want a perfect-square radicand, we can multiply the denominator by itself: $\sqrt{5}\,\sqrt{5} = \sqrt{25} = 5$. Therefore, rationalizing the denominator results in

$$\frac{6}{\sqrt{5}} = \frac{6}{\sqrt{5}} \cdot \frac{\sqrt{5}}{\sqrt{5}} = \frac{6\sqrt{5}}{5}$$

EXAMPLE 6

Simplify. Rationalize all denominators. Check your results on your calculator.

a. $\sqrt{\dfrac{3}{4}}$ **b.** $\sqrt{\dfrac{48}{50}}$

Solution

a. $\sqrt{\dfrac{3}{4}} = \dfrac{\sqrt{3}}{\sqrt{4}} = \dfrac{\sqrt{3}}{2}$ Quotient rule

Check

```
√(3)/2
         .8660254038
√(3/4)
         .8660254038
```

The results check.

b. $\sqrt{\dfrac{48}{50}} = \dfrac{\sqrt{48}}{\sqrt{50}} = \dfrac{\sqrt{16}\,\sqrt{3}}{\sqrt{25}\,\sqrt{2}} = \dfrac{4\sqrt{3}}{5\sqrt{2}}$ Quotient rule

$$= \frac{4\sqrt{3}}{5\sqrt{2}} \cdot \frac{\sqrt{2}}{\sqrt{2}} = \frac{4\sqrt{6}}{5\cdot 2}$$ Rationalize the denominator.

$$= \frac{4\sqrt{6}}{10} = \frac{2\sqrt{6}}{5}$$ Simplify.

```
(2√(6))/5
         .9797958971
√(48/50)
         .9797958971
```

The results check.

A second method would be to reduce the fractional radicand before using the quotient rule.

$$\sqrt{\frac{48}{50}} = \sqrt{\frac{24}{25}} = \frac{\sqrt{24}}{\sqrt{25}} = \frac{\sqrt{4}\,\sqrt{6}}{\sqrt{25}} = \frac{2\sqrt{6}}{5}$$

EXAMPLE 7 Multiply and simplify. $\sqrt{\dfrac{1}{2}} \cdot \sqrt{\dfrac{3}{5}}$

Solution

$$\sqrt{\frac{1}{2}} \cdot \sqrt{\frac{3}{5}} = \sqrt{\frac{3}{10}} \qquad \text{Product rule}$$

$$= \frac{\sqrt{3}}{\sqrt{10}} \qquad \text{Quotient rule}$$

$$= \frac{\sqrt{3}}{\sqrt{10}} \cdot \frac{\sqrt{10}}{\sqrt{10}} \qquad \text{Rationalize the denominator.}$$

$$= \frac{\sqrt{30}}{10} \qquad \text{Simplify.}$$

■

Objective 9.3.2 *CHECKUP*

1. Divide.

   a. $\dfrac{\sqrt{6}}{\sqrt{3}}$ b. $\dfrac{\sqrt{48}}{\sqrt{3}}$ c. $\dfrac{\sqrt{90}}{\sqrt{2}}$

2. Simplify. Rationalize all denominators. Check your results on your calculator.

   a. $\sqrt{\dfrac{7}{64}}$ b. $\sqrt{\dfrac{250}{45}}$

3. Multiply and simplify $\sqrt{\dfrac{1}{3}} \cdot \sqrt{\dfrac{2}{5}}$.

4. What does it mean to rationalize the denominator of a quotient?

Objective 9.3.3

Modeling the Real World

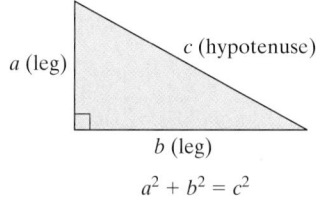

a (leg) c (hypotenuse)

b (leg)

$a^2 + b^2 = c^2$

Another geometric application uses a formula that relates the lengths of three sides of a right triangle. A right triangle is a triangle that contains a 90° angle (**right angle**), denoted by the ⌐ symbol at the angle. The **legs** of a right triangle are the two sides that form the right angle. The **hypotenuse** is the side opposite the right angle.

The **Pythagorean theorem** states that the sum of the squares of the lengths of the legs of a right triangle is equal to the square of the length of the hypotenuse. In other words, $a^2 + b^2 = c^2$, where a and b are the lengths of the legs of a right triangle and c is the length of the hypotenuse.

In the next section we will use equations to determine the length of a side of a right triangle. For this section we will use the equations

$$a = \sqrt{c^2 - b^2}$$
$$b = \sqrt{c^2 - a^2}$$
$$c = \sqrt{a^2 + b^2}$$

 TAKE NOTE The longest length of a side of a right triangle, c, is always the hypotenuse.

EXAMPLE 8 A carpenter uses the Pythagorean theorem to determine if the corner of a room is square (measures 90 degrees). If he measures 3 feet on one wall and 4 feet on the adjacent wall, determine the distance between these two points.

Solution

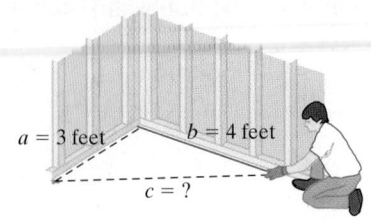

According to the drawing, $a = 3$ (the distance along one wall), $b = 4$ (the distance along the adjacent wall), and $c =$ the distance between the two points.

$$c = \sqrt{a^2 + b^2}$$
$$c = \sqrt{3^2 + 4^2}$$
$$c = \sqrt{9 + 16}$$
$$c = \sqrt{25}$$
$$c = 5$$

The distance between the two points on adjacent walls is 5 feet. ■

An application of a radical expression is used to determine the distance between two points in a rectangular coordinate system.

First, we must determine the distance between two points that lie on the same vertical or horizontal line. To determine the distance between two points that lie on a vertical line, we take the absolute value of the difference between the two y-coordinates of the points. For example, the vertical distance between $(4, 2)$ and $(4, -3)$ is

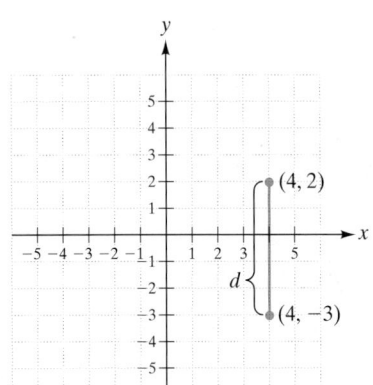

$$|2 - (-3)| = |2 + 3| = |5| = 5$$

The distance between the two points is 5.

To find the distance between two points that lie on a horizontal line, we take the absolute value of the difference between the two x-coordinates of the points. For example, the horizontal distance between $(1, 3)$ and $(4, 3)$ is

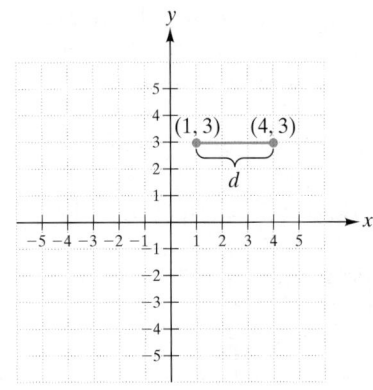

$$|1 - 4| = |-3| = 3$$

The distance between the two points is 3.

Next, to determine the distance between two points that do not lie on a horizontal or vertical line, we apply the Pythagorean theorem. (See **Figure 9.4**.)

$$\text{Let } a = |x_2 - x_1| \text{ and } b = |y_2 - y_1|$$
$$a^2 + b^2 = c^2$$
$$(x_2 - x_1)^2 + (y_2 - y_1)^2 = d^2 \qquad \text{Substitute.}$$

Note: We do not need the absolute-value symbols, because we are squaring the number. It does not matter whether the number is positive or negative; squaring will always result in a nonnegative number.

$$\sqrt{(x_2 - x_1)^2 + (y_2 - y_1)^2} = d \qquad \text{Principle of powers}$$

We do not write the negative square root, because we cannot have a negative distance.

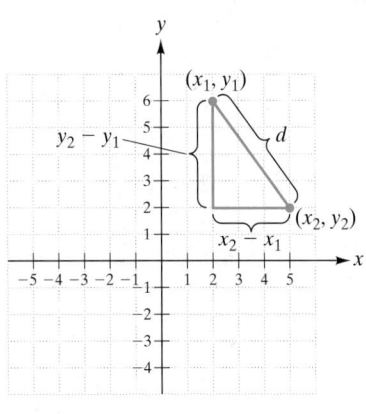

DISTANCE FORMULA

The distance d between any two points on a coordinate plane (x_1, y_1) and (x_2, y_2) is

$$d = \sqrt{(x_2 - x_1)^2 + (y_2 - y_1)^2}$$

Figure 9.4

EXAMPLE 9 Determine the distance between the points $(2, 3)$ and $(5, 1)$.

Solution

Let $x_1 = 2$, $y_1 = 3$, $x_2 = 5$, and $y_2 = 1$

$$d = \sqrt{(x_2 - x_1)^2 + (y_2 - y_1)^2}$$
$$d = \sqrt{(5 - 2)^2 + (1 - 3)^2} \quad \text{Substitute.}$$
$$d = \sqrt{3^2 + (-2)^2}$$
$$d = \sqrt{9 + 4}$$
$$d = \sqrt{13}$$

The distance between the two points is $\sqrt{13}$, or approximately 3.606.

APPLICATION

An LCD panel television is sold by its diagonal measurement. Therefore, a 30-inch television has a diagonal measurement of 30 inches. If the width of the screen measures 15 inches, determine the length of the screen.

Discussion

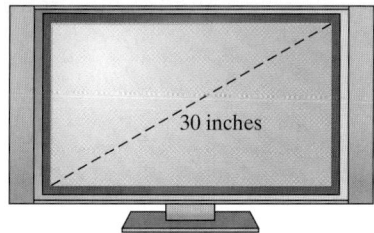

30 inches

According to the drawing, the diagonal is the hypotenuse of a right triangle, c, with length 30 inches. One leg, a, is equal to 15 inches. The other leg, b, is the unknown length of the screen.

$$b = \sqrt{c^2 - a^2}$$
$$b = \sqrt{30^2 - 15^2} \quad \text{Substitute 30 for } c \text{ and 15 for } a.$$
$$b = \sqrt{900 - 225} \quad \text{Simplify.}$$
$$b = \sqrt{675} \quad \text{Simplify:}$$
$$b = \sqrt{225 \cdot 3} \quad 225 = 15^2$$
$$b = 15\sqrt{3}$$

The length of the television screen is $15\sqrt{3}$ inches or about 26 inches.

✓ **Objective 9.3.3 CHECKUP**

1. The lengths of the three sides of a triangle are 3 inches, 5 inches, and 7 inches. Use the Pythagorean theorem to determine if the triangle is a right triangle.
2. Determine the distance between the points $(3, 1)$ and $(4, 2)$.

3. The display screen on a popular pocket pc is 2.125 inches by 2.875 inches. What is the length of the screen's diagonal?

9.3 EXERCISES

 Student Solutions Manual   PH Math/Tutor Center   CD Video *Math* XL MathXL® *MyMathLab* MyMathLab   Interactmath.com

Simplify without using a calculator. Check your results on your calculator.

1. $\sqrt{63}$ 　　　　**2.** $\sqrt{80}$ 　　　　**3.** $\sqrt{243}$ 　　　　**4.** $\sqrt{75}$

5. $\sqrt{147}$ 　　　**6.** $-\sqrt{128}$ 　　　**7.** $-\sqrt{125}$ 　　　**8.** $\sqrt{27}$

9. $-3 + \sqrt{20}$ 　　**10.** $-4 + \sqrt{28}$ 　　**11.** $2 - \sqrt{50}$ 　　**12.** $7 - \sqrt{32}$

13. $\dfrac{4 - \sqrt{48}}{4}$ 　　**14.** $\dfrac{3 - \sqrt{18}}{3}$ 　　**15.** $\dfrac{-6 + \sqrt{45}}{3}$ 　　**16.** $\dfrac{-4 + \sqrt{24}}{2}$

17. $\dfrac{-5 - \sqrt{18}}{-3}$ 　　**18.** $\dfrac{-3 - \sqrt{40}}{-2}$ 　　**19.** $\dfrac{-6 - \sqrt{54}}{-3}$ 　　**20.** $\dfrac{-4 - \sqrt{44}}{-2}$

21. $\sqrt{\dfrac{16}{5}}$ 　　**22.** $\sqrt{\dfrac{9}{7}}$ 　　**23.** $\sqrt{\dfrac{50}{48}}$ 　　**24.** $\sqrt{\dfrac{45}{24}}$

Multiply or divide and simplify.

25. $\sqrt{3}\cdot\sqrt{7}$ **26.** $\sqrt{2}\cdot\sqrt{5}$ **27.** $3\sqrt{2}\cdot4\sqrt{3}$ **28.** $2\sqrt{5}\cdot3\sqrt{3}$

29. $\sqrt{\dfrac{2}{3}}\cdot\sqrt{\dfrac{3}{5}}$ **30.** $\sqrt{\dfrac{3}{4}}\cdot\sqrt{\dfrac{4}{7}}$ **31.** $\sqrt{5}\cdot\sqrt{10}$ **32.** $\sqrt{7}\cdot\sqrt{14}$

33. $4\sqrt{3}\cdot2\sqrt{6}$ **34.** $3\sqrt{5}\cdot2\sqrt{10}$ **35.** $\dfrac{\sqrt{15}}{\sqrt{3}}$ **36.** $\dfrac{\sqrt{10}}{\sqrt{2}}$

37. $\dfrac{\sqrt{50}}{\sqrt{2}}$ **38.** $\dfrac{\sqrt{63}}{\sqrt{7}}$ **39.** $\dfrac{\sqrt{30}}{\sqrt{3}}$ **40.** $\dfrac{\sqrt{105}}{\sqrt{5}}$

Evaluate $\sqrt{b^2-4ac}$ for

41. $a=4, b=3, c=-1$ **42.** $a=2, b=-3, c=1$ **43.** $a=-2, b=3, c=-3$

44. $a=-2, b=-1, c=-3$ **45.** $a=2, b=2, c=-6$ **46.** $a=2, b=-2, c=-1$

Evaluate $2\pi r\sqrt{r^2+h^2}$ for

47. $r=4, h=5$ **48.** $r=3, h=8$ **49.** $r=6, h=2$ **50.** $r=7, h=7$

In exercises 51–60, use the Pythagorean theorem or one of its related equations to answer the given question.

51. A baseball diamond is a square with 90 feet between each base. Determine the distance from home plate to second base.

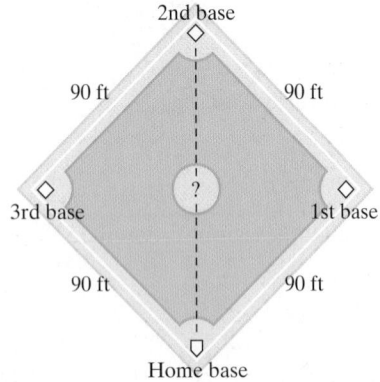

52. A supporting wire is attached to the top of an 80-foot tower. It is anchored to the ground 60 feet from the base of the tower. How long is the supporting wire?

53. A wheelchair ramp has a length of 61 inches. The horizontal distance of the ramp measures 60 inches. What is the vertical distance of the ramp?

54. Trent's kite is flying on 82 feet of string. His dad is standing directly below the kite and is 18 feet away from Trent. How high is the kite?

55. A traffic-control helicopter uses radar to determine that a car on a straight highway is 5000 feet away. The helicopter is 3000 feet above the highway. How far along the ground is the car from the helicopter?

56. A wire supporting a radio tower is attached to the top of the tower and to the ground. The wire is 130 meters long, and it is attached to the ground 50 meters from the base of the tower. How tall is the tower?

57. A bridge that is 1 mile long expands by 1 foot during hot weather. If the bridge did not have adequate expansion joints, how high would the center of the bridge rise?

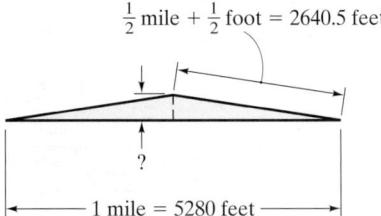

58. A driveway is 50 feet long. During hot weather, it would expand 2 inches. If the driveway did not have expansion joints, how high would the center of the drive rise?

59. A ladder 25 feet long is leaning against the outside wall of a house. If the base of the ladder is 6 feet from the house, estimate how high on the wall the top of the ladder rests.

60. A man who is 5.8 feet tall casts a shadow that is 7 feet long. About how far is it from the top of the man's head to the tip of his shadow?

Distance Formula

In exercises 61–70, find the distance on the coordinate plane between the given points.

61. $(8, -3)$ and $(8, 2)$
62. $(-2, 3)$ and $(-2, 11)$
63. $(-3, 5)$ and $(5, 6)$
64. $(-9, 1)$ and $(-2, -1)$

65. $(-3, -4)$ and $(2, 5)$
66. $(-5, 7)$ and $(3, -4)$
67. $(2.5, 6.1)$ and $(-1.5, 2.1)$
68. $(-3.2, 5.3)$ and $(-6.2, 2.3)$

69. $\left(\dfrac{2}{3}, \dfrac{1}{4}\right)$ and $\left(\dfrac{1}{3}, \dfrac{3}{4}\right)$
70. $\left(\dfrac{3}{5}, \dfrac{3}{4}\right)$ and $\left(\dfrac{1}{5}, \dfrac{1}{4}\right)$

In exercises 71 and 72, find the perimeter of the triangle.

71.

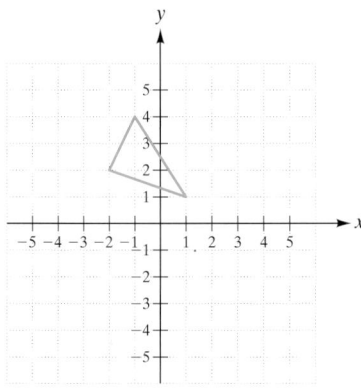

72.

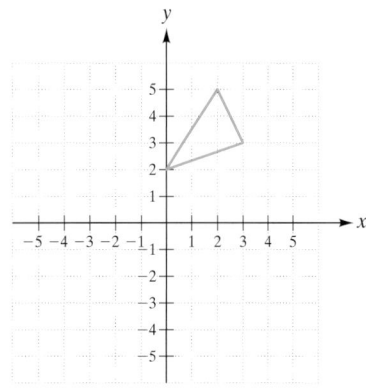

73. Given the points $(1, 0)$, $(3, 2)$, and $(6, -1)$
  a. Verify that the points are the vertices of a right triangle.
  b. Find the area of the triangle.

74. Given the points $(-1, -2)$, $(3, 2)$, and $(6, -1)$
  a. Verify that the points are the vertices of a right triangle.
  b. Find the area of the triangle.

75. Ship B is 236 miles north and 541 miles east of ship A. Assuming that ship A is at the origin of a rectangular coordinate system, write a coordinate pair to represent each of the two ships. What is the distance between the ships to the nearest mile?

76. On a scout camping trip, Chad left the camp site and traveled 3 miles south and 3 miles west. Using the camp site as the origin, write a coordinate pair to represent the location of the camp site and Chad's new location. How far from the camp site is Chad?

77. Dawn and Paul are hiking in a national forest. Dawn travels 3 miles north and 2 miles east. Paul travels 2 miles south and 3 miles west. Write coordinate pairs to represent each location from their origin. If their two-way radios have a range of 5 miles, can they talk to each other?

78. Dawn and Paul are hiking on the Appalachian Trail. Dawn travels 3 miles east and 4 miles south. Paul travels 2 miles west and 5 miles south. Write coordinate pairs to represent each location from their origin. If their two-way radios have a range of 8 miles, can they talk to each other?

9.3 Calculator Exercises

A popular algebra problem deals with sizes of pizza. In order to double the size (area) of a pizza, you must increase its diameter by a factor of $\sqrt{2}$; that is, $d_2 = \sqrt{2}d_1$, where d_2 is the diameter of the pizza with doubled area and d_1 is the diameter of the original pizza. Thus, a pizza that is about twice as large as a 5-inch pizza will be 7 inches in diameter. With this in mind, complete the following table, rounding answers to the nearest inch.

Take the table with you the next time you go out for pizza, and use it for price comparisons!

Original Pizza Diameter	Twice-as-Large Pizza Diameter
5 inches	7 inches
6 inches	
7 inches	
8 inches	
9 inches	
10 inches	
11 inches	
12 inches	

9.3 Writing Exercises

The distance formula finds the length of a line segment given its endpoints as ordered pairs. Another formula, the midpoint formula, finds the midpoint of the segment. A midpoint is a point on a segment that divides the segment into two congruent segments (segments of equal length). For the line segment that has endpoints (x_1, y_1) and (x_2, y_2) the midpoint M has coordinates $\left(\dfrac{x_1 + x_2}{2}, \dfrac{y_1 + y_2}{2}\right)$.

In exercises 1–5, find the midpoint of the segment that has endpoints

1. $(0, 8)$ and $(0, -2)$

2. $(-3, 0)$ and $(9, 0)$

3. $(4, 5)$ and $(6, 7)$

4. $(-2, 15)$ and $(4, -8)$

5. $(-3, -8)$ and $(5, 11)$

6. The segment with endpoints $(x, 7)$ and $(9, y)$ has midpoint $(10, 6.5)$. Find x and y.

7. If the endpoints of the diameter of a circle are $(6, -10)$ and $(-3, 12)$ find the coordinates of the center of the circle.

8. What is the area of the circle in exercise **7**?

9. Explain how you can use the distance formula to prove that the points you have found in the previous exercises are truly midpoints of the given segments.

9.4 SOLVING QUADRATIC EQUATIONS BY COMPLETING THE SQUARE

OBJECTIVES

1 Solve quadratic equations in one variable algebraically by using the principle of square roots.

2 Complete perfect-square trinomials.

3 Solve quadratic equations by completing the square.

4 Model real-world situations by using quadratic equations, and solve the equations by completing the square.

APPLICATION

According to Centers for Medicare and Medicaid Services, national health expenditures are increasing. The following table summarizes this trend:

Year	Health Expenditures in Billion Dollars
2000	1309
2001	1421
2002	1553

a. It is predicted that this trend will continue. Write a quadratic equation for the amount of health expenditures, y, in billion dollars x years after 2000.

b. Using the equation in part **a**, determine when the health expenditures will reach $2,000,000,000,000.

After completing this section, we will discuss this application further. See page 695.

In Section 9.2, an algebraic method for solving polynomial equations was discussed. In Section 9.1, numeric and graphic methods for solving polynomial equations were presented. These methods will work for polynomial equations of any degree. However, quadratic equations are a special type of polynomial equation that have been studied more extensively. In Section 9.2, we learned that some quadratic equations had solutions which we could not find by using the process of factoring. Therefore, we need to identify another algebraic method of finding these solutions.

Objective 9.4.1

Solving Quadratic Equations by Using the Principle of Square Roots

We are now ready to examine a second algebraic method for solving a quadratic equation. In Section 9.2, we found a solution of an equation such as $x^2 = 9$ by factoring. For example,

$$x^2 = 9$$
$$x^2 - 9 = 0$$
$$(x - 3)(x + 3) = 0$$
$$x - 3 = 0 \quad \text{or} \quad x + 3 = 0$$
$$x = 3 \qquad\qquad x = -3$$

The solutions are 3 and −3, which we can combine by writing ±3.

Another way to solve $x^2 = 9$ is to determine values for x that can be squared to equal 9. There are two such numbers: 3 and −3.

We are actually taking the square root of both sides of the equation in order to solve for the variable.

$$x^2 = 9$$
$$\sqrt{x^2} = \sqrt{9} \qquad \text{Take the square root of both sides.}$$
$$|x| = 3 \qquad \text{Evaluate.}$$
$$x = 3 \quad \text{or} \quad x = -3 \qquad \text{Solve the absolute-value equation.}$$

As mentioned previously, this pair of solutions may also be written as $x = \pm 3$.

PRINCIPLE OF SQUARE ROOTS

For any positive number b, if $a^2 = b$, then $a = \sqrt{b}$ or $a = -\sqrt{b}$.

We can also use the principle of square roots to determine solutions of equations such as $x^2 = 5$, in which the squared variable does not equal a perfect square.

$$x^2 = 5$$
$$x = \sqrt{5} \quad \text{or} \quad x = -\sqrt{5}$$

We could not solve, for example, the equivalent equation $x^2 - 5 = 0$ by factoring over the rational numbers.

SOLVING A QUADRATIC EQUATION BY USING THE PRINCIPLE OF SQUARE ROOTS

To solve a quadratic equation of the form $ax^2 + bx + c = 0$ when $b = 0$ (that is, $ax^2 + c = 0$),

- Solve for x^2.
- Apply the principle of square roots.
- Solve the resulting equations.
- Check the solutions by substitution or by solving numerically or graphically.

EXAMPLE 1

Solve and check.

a. $4x^2 - 9 = 0$ **b.** $2x^2 + 4 = 4$

c. $x^2 + 6 = 1$ **d.** $(x + 2)^2 = 9$

e. $(x + 3)^2 - 3 = 2$ **f.** $x^2 - 4x + 4 = 5$

g. $3x^2 - 16 = 0$

Algebraic Solution

a. $4x^2 - 9 = 0$

$$x^2 = \frac{9}{4} \qquad \text{Solve for } x^2.$$

$$x = \sqrt{\frac{9}{4}} \quad \text{or} \quad x = -\sqrt{\frac{9}{4}} \qquad \text{Principle of square roots}$$

$$x = \frac{3}{2} \qquad\qquad x = -\frac{3}{2}$$

The solutions are $\pm\frac{3}{2}$.

Check by substitution.

$4x^2 - 9 = 0$	
$4\left(\dfrac{3}{2}\right)^2 - 9$	0
$4\left(\dfrac{9}{4}\right) - 9$	
$9 - 9$	
0	

$4x^2 - 9 = 0$	
$4\left(-\dfrac{3}{2}\right)^2 - 9$	0
$4\left(\dfrac{9}{4}\right) - 9$	
$9 - 9$	
0	

The solutions are $\pm\frac{3}{2}$.

b. $2x^2 + 4 = 4$ — Solve for x^2.

$$x^2 = 0 \qquad \text{Principle of square roots}$$

$$x = 0$$

The solution is 0, because 0 is neither positive nor negative.

Check

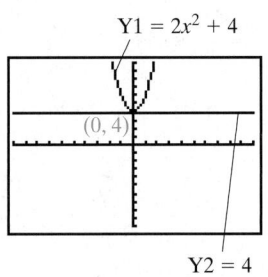

$(-10, 10, -10, 10)$

The solution is 0, the x-coordinate of the intersection.

c. $x^2 + 6 = 1$

$$x^2 = -5 \qquad \text{Solve for } x^2.$$

The solution is not a real number, because there is no real number whose square is negative.

Check by graphing. The graphs do not intersect. In standard form, the equation is $x^2 + 5 = 0$. There is no real-number solution.

Check

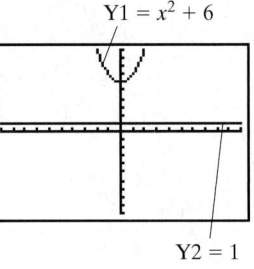

$(-10, 10, -10, 10)$

d. This is a variable expression squared.

$$(x + 2)^2 = 9$$

$$x + 2 = \sqrt{9} \quad \text{or} \quad x + 2 = -\sqrt{9} \qquad \text{Principle of square roots}$$

$$x + 2 = 3 \qquad\qquad x + 2 = -3$$

$$x = 1 \qquad\qquad x = -5$$

The solutions are 1 and -5.

The check is left for you.

e. $(x + 3)^2 - 3 = 2$

$(x + 3)^2 = 5$ Solve for the squared expression $(x + 3)$.

$x + 3 = \sqrt{5}$ or $x + 3 = -\sqrt{5}$ Principle of square roots

$x = -3 + \sqrt{5}$ $x = -3 - \sqrt{5}$

$x \approx -0.764$ $x \approx -5.236$

The solutions are $-3 \pm \sqrt{5}$, or approximately -0.764 and -5.236.

The check is left for you.

f. The expression on the left is a perfect-square trinomial.

$x^2 - 4x + 4 = 5$

$(x - 2)^2 = 5$ Factor.

$x - 2 = \sqrt{5}$ or $x - 2 = -\sqrt{5}$ Principle of square roots

$x = 2 + \sqrt{5}$ $x = 2 - \sqrt{5}$

$x \approx 4.236$ $x \approx -0.236$

The solutions are $2 \pm \sqrt{5}$, or approximately 4.236 and -0.236.

The check is left for you.

g. $3x^2 - 16 = 0$

$3x^2 = 16$

$x^2 = \dfrac{16}{3}$ Solve for x^2.

$x = \pm\sqrt{\dfrac{16}{3}}$ Principle of square roots

$x = \pm\dfrac{4}{\sqrt{3}} \cdot \dfrac{\sqrt{3}}{\sqrt{3}}$ Simplify and rationalize the denominator.

$x = \pm\dfrac{4\sqrt{3}}{3}$

The solutions are $\pm\dfrac{4\sqrt{3}}{3}$, or approximately ± 2.309. The check is left for you. ■

Objective 9.4.1 *CHECKUP*

1. Solve and check.

  a. $9x^2 - 25 = 0$ **b.** $3x^2 - 2 = -2$

  c. $x^2 + 12 = 3$ **d.** $(x - 4)^2 = 16$

  e. $(x - 1)^2 + 5 = 8$ **f.** $x^2 + 2x + 1 = 6$

  g. $2x^2 - 49 = 0$

2. How can you use the principle of square roots to solve a quadratic equation?

Objective 9.4.2 — Completing Perfect-Square Trinomials

As long as a variable expression is a perfect-square trinomial, which can be written as a binomial squared, we can solve an equation by using the principle of square roots. However, we may have an equation, such as $x^2 + 6x = 2$, with a variable expression, $x^2 + 6x$, that is not a perfect-square trinomial. We need to develop a method that will enable us to write an equivalent equation with a perfect-square trinomial.

First, we need to remember that a perfect-square trinomial is in the form $a^2 + 2ab + b^2$. Therefore, using this form to write a trinomial square in terms of x, we substitute x for a.

$a^2 + 2ab + b^2$

$x^2 + 2xb + b^2$ Substitute x for a.

or

$x^2 + 2bx + b^2$ Rewrite the term $2xb$.

The coefficient of x^2 is 1 and the coefficient of x is $2b$. Therefore, to determine a value for b, we divide the coefficient of x by 2. Once we have the value for b, we square it and add it to the trinomial to make the trinomial a perfect square.

EXAMPLE 2   Determine what value must be added to each of the following expressions to obtain a perfect-square trinomial.

a. $x^2 + 6x$ **b.** $x^2 - 3x$ **c.** $x^2 + \dfrac{2}{3}x$

Solution

a. $x^2 + 6x$

The coefficient of x^2 is 1 and the coefficient of x is 6. Dividing 6 by 2, we obtain a value for $b, \dfrac{6}{2} = 3$. Therefore, $b^2 = (3)^2 = 9$. We need to add 9 to the expression to obtain a perfect-square trinomial: $x^2 + 6x + 9$, or $(x + 3)^2$.

b. $x^2 - 3x$

The coefficient of x^2 is 1 and the coefficient of x is -3. Dividing -3 by 2, we obtain a value for b, $-\dfrac{3}{2}$. Therefore, $b^2 = \left(-\dfrac{3}{2}\right)^2 = \dfrac{9}{4}$. We need to add $\dfrac{9}{4}$ to the expression to obtain a perfect-square trinomial: $x^2 - 3x + \dfrac{9}{4}$, or $\left(x - \dfrac{3}{2}\right)^2$.

c. $x^2 + \dfrac{2}{3}x$

The coefficient of x^2 is 1 and the coefficient of x is $\dfrac{2}{3}$. Dividing by 2 $\Big($ or multiplying by $\dfrac{1}{2}\Big)$, we obtain a value for $b, \dfrac{2}{3} \cdot \dfrac{1}{2} = \dfrac{1}{3}$. Therefore, $b^2 = \left(\dfrac{1}{3}\right)^2 = \dfrac{1}{9}$. We need to add $\dfrac{1}{9}$ to the expression to obtain a perfect-square trinomial: $x^2 + \dfrac{2}{3}x + \dfrac{1}{9}$, or $\left(x + \dfrac{1}{3}\right)^2$. ∎

✓ Objective 9.4.2 *CHECKUP*

1. Determine what value must be added to each expression to obtain a perfect-square trinomial.

a. $x^2 + 8x$ **b.** $x^2 - 7x$ **c.** $x^2 - \dfrac{4}{5}x$

2. Explain what is meant by a perfect-square trinomial.

Objective 9.4.3   ## Solving Quadratic Equations by Completing the Square

Now we are ready to solve the equation we introduced in the last objective, $x^2 + 6x = 2$. To do this, we will use a process called completing the square. **Completing the square** is a procedure used to determine a solution of an equation by rewriting the equation as a perfect-square trinomial equal to a rational number. For example, solve $x^2 + 6x = 2$ by completing the square.

$$x^2 + 6x = 2$$
$$x^2 + 6x + 9 = 2 + 9$$

Add 9 to both sides because that is the value of b^2 needed to complete the trinomial square on the left side of the equation.

$$(x + 3)^2 = 11$$

Rewrite the trinomial square as a binomial square.

$$x + 3 = \sqrt{11} \quad \text{or} \quad x + 3 = -\sqrt{11}$$

Principle of square roots

$$x = -3 + \sqrt{11} \qquad x = -3 - \sqrt{11}$$
$$x \approx 0.317 \qquad\qquad x \approx -6.317$$

The solutions are $-3 \pm \sqrt{11}$, or approximately 0.317 and -6.317.

SOLVING A QUADRATIC EQUATION BY COMPLETING THE SQUARE

To solve a quadratic equation by completing the square,

- Isolate the variable terms on one side of the equation.
- Divide both sides of the equation by the coefficient of x^2. (This step is not needed if the coefficient is 1.)
- Determine the value needed to complete the square by dividing the coefficient of x by 2 and squaring the result.
- Add the value obtained to both sides of the equation.
- Rewrite the trinomial as a binomial squared.
- Use the principle of square roots to determine the possible solutions, and solve.
- Check the solutions by substitution or by solving numerically or graphically.

EXAMPLE 3 Solve and check.

a. $x^2 - 5x + 2 = 5$ **b.** $5x^2 + 20x + 30 = 10$ **c.** $x^2 + x + 2 = 0$

Algebraic Solution

a.
$$x^2 - 5x + 2 = 5$$
$$x^2 - 5x = 3 \qquad \text{Isolate the variable terms.}$$
$$x^2 - 5x + \frac{25}{4} = 3 + \frac{25}{4} \qquad \text{Add the value needed to complete the square: } \left(-\frac{5}{2}\right)^2 = \frac{25}{4}.$$
$$\left(x - \frac{5}{2}\right)^2 = \frac{37}{4} \qquad \text{Binomial squared}$$
$$x - \frac{5}{2} = \sqrt{\frac{37}{4}} \quad \text{or} \quad x - \frac{5}{2} = -\sqrt{\frac{37}{4}} \qquad \text{Principle of square roots}$$
$$x - \frac{5}{2} = \frac{\sqrt{37}}{2} \qquad\qquad x - \frac{5}{2} = -\frac{\sqrt{37}}{2}$$
$$x = \frac{5}{2} + \frac{\sqrt{37}}{2} \qquad\qquad x = \frac{5}{2} - \frac{\sqrt{37}}{2}$$
$$x = \frac{5 + \sqrt{37}}{2} \qquad\qquad x = \frac{5 - \sqrt{37}}{2}$$
$$x \approx 5.541 \qquad\qquad x \approx -0.541$$

The solutions are $\dfrac{5 \pm \sqrt{37}}{2}$, or approximately 5.541 and −0.541.

Substitution Check

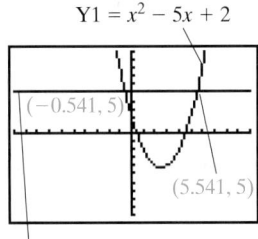

When the solutions are substituted for the variable, the expression equals 5, the expression on the right.

The solutions are $\dfrac{5 \pm \sqrt{37}}{2}$.

Graphic Check

Y1 = $x^2 - 5x + 2$

(−0.541, 5)

(5.541, 5)

Y2 = 5

(−10, 10, −10, 10)

Let Y1 = $x^2 - 5x + 2$ and Y2 = 5. The solutions are approximately 5.541 and −0.541, the x-coordinates of the points of intersection.

b. $5x^2 + 20x + 30 = 10$

$5x^2 + 20x = -20$ *Isolate the variable terms.*

$x^2 + 4x = -4$ *Divide both sides by 5.*

$x^2 + 4x + 4 = -4 + 4$ *Add the value needed to complete the square: $\left(\frac{4}{2}\right)^2 = 2^2 = 4$.*

$(x + 2)^2 = 0$ *Binomial squared*

$x + 2 = 0$ *Principle of square roots*

$x = -2$ *Only one root equals 0.*

The solution is -2 (a double root).

Substitution Check

Let $x = -2$.

$$5x^2 + 20x + 30 - 10$$

$$
\begin{array}{c|c}
5(-2)^2 + 20(-2) + 30 & 10 \\
20 + (-40) + 30 & \\
10 &
\end{array}
$$

The solution is -2.

c. $x^2 + x + 2 = 0$

$x^2 + x = -2$ *Isolate the variable terms.*

$x^2 + x + \dfrac{1}{4} = -2 + \dfrac{1}{4}$ *Add the value needed to complete the square: $\left(\frac{1}{2}\right)^2 = \frac{1}{4}$.*

$\left(x + \dfrac{1}{2}\right)^2 = -\dfrac{7}{4}$

The solution is not a real number, because there is no real number whose square is negative.

Graphic Check

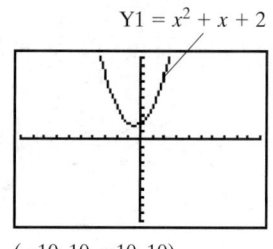

$Y1 = x^2 + x + 2$

$(-10, 10, -10, 10)$

The graph of $Y1 = x^2 + x + 2$ does not intersect the x-axis ($Y2 = 0$). The solution is not a real number. ∎

✓ Objective 9.4.3 **CHECKUP**

1. Solve by completing the square.
   a. $5x^2 - 4x - 5 = 0$
   b. $2x^2 - 32x + 130 = 2$
   c. $x^2 - 2x + 5 = 0$

2. In order to use the method of completing the square to solve a quadratic equation, what must be true of the coefficient of the squared term? Is it always possible to write an equivalent equation that meets this condition? Explain. ∎

Objective 9.4.4   ## Modeling the Real World

In Section 9.3, we discussed the Pythagorean theorem, $c^2 = a^2 + b^2$, where a and b are the lengths of the legs of the right triangle and c is the length of the hypotenuse. At that time, we also gave alternative formulas for the length of each side. It is not necessary to know these formulas. We can solve for the length of a side of a right triangle using the principle of square roots.

EXAMPLE 4   A large boat is towing a smaller boat with a rope that spans 50 feet between hookups. If the rope is attached to the smaller boat at a point 10 feet below the level of attachment to the larger boat (see **Figure 9.5**), what is the distance between the boats?

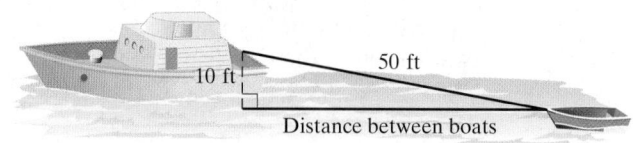

Figure 9.5   10 ft   50 ft   Distance between boats

Algebraic Solution

Let x = the distance between the boats

$$a^2 + b^2 = c^2$$ Pythagorean theorem

$$x^2 + 10^2 = 50^2$$ Substitute x for a, 10 for b, and 50 for c.

$$x^2 + 100 = 2500$$ Simplify.

$$x^2 = 2500 - 100$$ Solve for x².

$$x^2 = 2400$$ Simplify.

$$x = \pm\sqrt{2400}$$ Principle of square roots

$$x = \sqrt{400 \cdot 6}$$ Only the positive root is possible, because we are solving for a distance.

$$x = 20\sqrt{6}$$ Simplify.

$$x \approx 48.99$$

The boats are $20\sqrt{6}$ feet apart, or approximately 49 feet apart.

EXAMPLE 5 One of the most memorable games in World Series history occurred on October 21, 1975. Carlton Fisk of the Boston Red Sox ended Game 6 at Fenway Park with a 12th-inning home run over the wall called the Green Monster. The Green Monster is 315 feet from home plate.

If Carlton hit the baseball at a height of 3 feet and the ball crossed the Green Monster at a point 318 feet away in a straight line from the bat, approximate the height of the ball above the ground as it crossed the wall.

Algebraic Solution

Let x = the height of the ball as it crossed the Green Monster
We see that we have a right triangle.

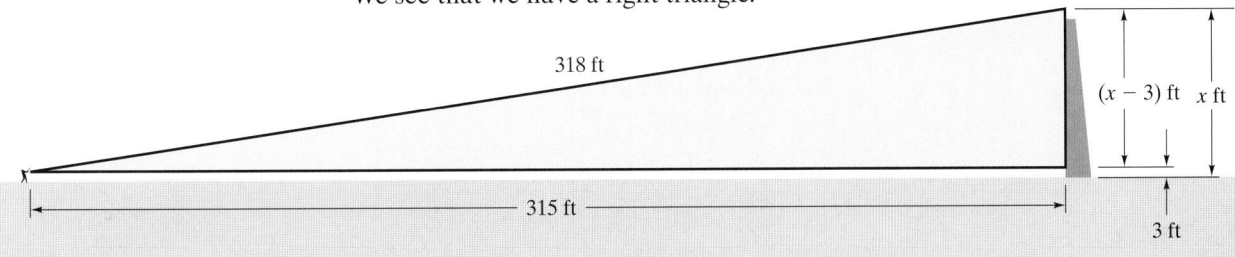

318 ft

$(x - 3)$ ft x ft

315 ft

3 ft

$$a^2 + b^2 = c^2$$ Pythagorean theorem

$$(x - 3)^2 + 315^2 = 318^2$$ Substitute.

$$(x - 3)^2 = 318^2 - 315^2$$ Isolate the squared term.

$$(x - 3)^2 = 1899$$ Simplify.

$$x - 3 = \pm\sqrt{1899}$$ Principle of square roots

$$x = \pm\sqrt{1899} + 3$$

$$x \approx 46.6$$ A negative solution does not represent a height.

The ball crossed the Green Monster at a height of approximately 46.6 feet.

Completing the square is a very good general method for solving quadratic equations. It works with equations that can't be factored and with those that can be factored. Remember that, when using the method of completing the square, you should always start by isolating the terms containing the variable.

EXAMPLE 6

Go Away travel agency is preparing a special sale. The usual cost of a ticket is $150. The agency needs to collect $1000 to break even on the event. The agency wants to offer a special plan by reducing the ticket cost. If Go Away advertises a reduction of $1 per person purchasing a ticket, determine the number of people that need to purchase this special offer so that the travel agency will break even.

Algebraic Solution

Let x = number of people purchasing tickets
The ticket cost is $150 - 1x$, or $150 - x$.

The amount the agency will collect is the product of the number of people purchasing a ticket and the cost per ticket.

$$x(150 - x) = 1000$$
$$150x - x^2 = 1000$$
$$x^2 - 150x = -1000 \qquad \text{Rearrange and divide both sides by } -1.$$
$$x^2 - 150x + (-75)^2 = -1000 + (-75)^2 \qquad \text{Add to both sides.}$$
$$(x - 75)^2 = 4625 \qquad \left(-\tfrac{150}{2}\right)^2 = (-75)^2 \text{ or } 5625$$
$$x - 75 = \pm\sqrt{4625} \qquad \text{Principle of square roots}$$
$$x = 75 \pm \sqrt{4625}$$
$$x \approx 7 \quad \text{or} \quad x \approx 143$$

The agency will break even when 7 or 143 people purchase tickets. It is unlikely that the agency will sell tickets for $150 - $143, or $7 each. The logical answer is that they need to sell 7 tickets. (They most likely will limit the discount so that the cost does not fall below a certain number of dollars.) ■

EXAMPLE 7

The compound-interest formula $A = P(1 + r)^t$ is used to determine the compounded amount A, given a principal P at an interest rate per period r for t periods. This formula can lead to various polynomial equations, including quadratic equations.

Due to the bank policy on education savings accounts, at age 18 Tommy must withdraw his education fund of $7237. He plans to reinvest all of his fund at an annual interest rate such that this money will increase to a total of $8000 in two years. Determine the annual interest rate at which he must reinvest his funds.

Solution

Let x = interest rate
$$A = P(1 + x)^t \qquad \text{Compound-interest formula}$$
$$8000 = 7237(1 + x)^2 \qquad A = 8000, P = 7237, t = 2$$
$$\frac{8000}{7237} = (1 + x)^2 \qquad \text{Solve for the squared term.}$$

$$(1 + x)^2 = \frac{8000}{7237}$$

$$1 + x = \sqrt{\frac{8000}{7237}} \qquad \text{or} \quad 1 + x = -\sqrt{\frac{8000}{7237}} \qquad \text{Principle of square roots}$$

$$x = -1 + \sqrt{\frac{8000}{7237}} \qquad\qquad x = -1 - \sqrt{\frac{8000}{7237}}$$

$$x \approx 0.0514 \qquad\qquad x \approx -2.0514$$

Tommy must reinvest his funds at approximately 5.14%. (Only the positive solution is used; the negative solution is not applicable.) ■

APPLICATION

According to Centers for Medicare and Medicaid Services, national health expenditures are increasing. The following table summarizes this trend:

Year	Health Expenditures in Billion Dollars
2000	1309
2001	1421
2002	1553

a. It is predicted that this trend will continue. Write a quadratic equation for the amount of health expenditures, y, in billion dollars x years after 2000.

b. Using the equation in part **a**, determine when the health expenditures will reach $2,000,000,000,000.

Discussion

a. Let x = the number of years after 2000
   y = the national health expenditures in billion dollars

Use the quadratic regression on your calculator to write a quadratic equation for the data points $(0, 1309)$, $(1, 1421)$, and $(2, 1553)$.

The quadratic equation for the health expenditures, in billion dollars, x years after 2000 is $y = 10x^2 + 102x + 1309$.

b. Substitute $y = 2000$ billion dollars and solve for x.

$$2000 = 10x^2 + 102x + 1309 \quad \text{or}$$
$$10x^2 + 102x + 1309 = 2000$$
$$10x^2 + 102x = 691 \qquad \text{Isolate the variable terms.}$$
$$x^2 + \frac{51}{5}x = \frac{691}{10} \qquad \text{Divide both sides by 10.}$$
$$x^2 + \frac{51}{5}x + \frac{2601}{100} = \frac{691}{10} + \frac{2601}{100} \qquad \text{Add to both sides } \left(\frac{51}{10}\right)^2 \text{ or } \frac{2601}{100}.$$
$$\left(x + \frac{51}{10}\right)^2 = \frac{9511}{100} \qquad \text{Binomial squared}$$

$$x + \frac{51}{10} = \sqrt{\frac{9511}{100}} \qquad \text{or} \qquad x + \frac{51}{10} = -\sqrt{\frac{9511}{100}} \qquad \text{Principle of square roots}$$

$$x = -\frac{51}{10} + \frac{\sqrt{9511}}{10} \qquad\qquad x = -\frac{51}{10} - \frac{\sqrt{9511}}{10}$$

$$x \approx 4.7 \qquad\qquad\qquad x \approx -14.9$$

According to the equation, the national health expenditures would be 2000 billion dollars about 4.7 years after 2000 or 2005.

Objective 9.4.4 CHECKUP

1. A 3.5-foot metal rod is used to hook a disabled vehicle to a tow truck. The two hookups are separated by a horizontal distance of 2.8 feet. What is the vertical distance between the hookups?

2. A Little League player hit a line drive that just barely cleared a fence that was 100 feet away from home plate. If the ball crossed the fence at a point 101 feet away in a straight line from the bat, estimate the height of the fence. Assume that the player hit the ball at a height of 2 feet.

3. A retailer usually sells an item for $60. To promote sales, the price of the item is reduced by $2 times the number of items purchased. The retailer determines that each sale must be $200 to break even on the promotion. Determine the number of items that must be sold to each purchaser in order for the retailer to break even.

4. Tommy is considering investing his money in an aggressive mutual fund instead of in the bank. If he invests the $7237 that he has on hand for two years, what equivalent annual interest rate must he realize in order to have the funds grow to $10,000?

5. According to Centers for Medicare and Medicaid Services, just as national health expenditures are increasing, hospital care expenditures are also increasing. The following table summarizes this trend:

Year	Hospital Care Expenditures in Billion Dollars
2000	413
2001	444
2002	487

a. It is predicted that this trend will continue. Write a quadratic equation for the amount of hospital care expenditures, y, in billion dollars, x years after 2000.

b. Using the equation in part **a**, determine when the hospital care expenditures will reach $500,000,000,000.

9.4 EXERCISES

Student Solutions Manual   PH Math/Tutor Center   CD Video   MathXL®   MyMathLab   Interactmath.com

Solve and check.

1. $x^2 = 144$
2. $x^2 = 121$
3. $a^2 = 13$
4. $b^2 = 15$
5. $q^2 = 98$
6. $p^2 = 200$
7. $2x^2 - 32 = 0$
8. $3x^2 - 27 = 0$
9. $3x^2 + 4 = 6$
10. $5x^2 + 4 = 11$
11. $m^2 + 7 = 5$
12. $12 + v^2 = 5$
13. $(x - 5)^2 = 0$
14. $(2x - 7)^2 = 0$
15. $(z - 7)^2 = 4$
16. $(x + 6)^2 = 9$
17. $(4a - 3)^2 = 4$
18. $(3b - 5)^2 = 1$
19. $(x + 3)^2 - 1 = 3$
20. $(x - 6)^2 - 5 = 20$
21. $2(m - 4)^2 - 6 = 12$
22. $4(n + 9)^2 + 3 = 19$
23. $x^2 + 10x + 25 = 9$
24. $x^2 - 14x + 49 = 100$
25. $9x^2 - 6x + 1 = 144$
26. $25x^2 + 10x + 1 = 64$
27. $(x - 7)^2 - 5 = 1$
28. $(x - 12)^2 + 4 = 9$
29. $(2x + 1)^2 - 3 = 7$
30. $(4x - 5)^2 + 7 = 9$
31. $(x + 3)^2 - 6 = 6$
32. $(x - 15)^2 + 6 = 18$
33. $5x^2 - 4 = 0$
34. $7x^2 - 9 = 0$
35. $2a^2 - 13 = 12$
36. $11b^2 - 8 = 8$

Determine what value must be added to each expression to obtain a trinomial square.

37. $x^2 + 18x$
38. $x^2 - 8x$
39. $x^2 - 9x$
40. $x^2 + 5x$
41. $x^2 + \frac{3}{4}x$
42. $x^2 + \frac{3}{5}x$
43. $x^2 + x$
44. $x^2 - x$

Solve by completing the square.

45. $x^2 + 6x - 20 = 35$
46. $x^2 - 8x - 25 = 40$
47. $x^2 - 3x = 28$
48. $x^2 + 3x = 40$
49. $x^2 + \frac{4}{7}x + \frac{3}{49} = 0$
50. $x^2 + \frac{6}{5}x + \frac{8}{25} = 0$
51. $x^2 + x - 30 = 60$
52. $x^2 - x - 16 = 40$
53. $x^2 - 6x = 2$
54. $x^2 + 8x = 5$
55. $x^2 + 9x = 1$
56. $x^2 - 5x = 2$
57. $x^2 + \frac{8}{9}x = 2$
58. $x^2 + \frac{6}{7}x = 1$
59. $x^2 - x - 5 = 0$
60. $x^2 + x - 10 = 0$
61. $x^2 + x + 10 = 0$
62. $x^2 - x + 6 = 0$
63. $2x^2 + 6x - 1 = 0$
64. $4x^2 + 12x - 3 = 0$
65. $3x^2 + x - 7 = 0$
66. $5x^2 + 2x - 3 = 0$
67. $x^2 - 14x + 55 = 6$
68. $x^2 + 10x + 35 = 10$
69. $4x^2 - 20x + 30 = 5$
70. $9x^2 + 12x + 10 = 6$
71. $\frac{1}{2}x^2 + 5x - 2 = 0$
72. $\frac{1}{3}x^2 - 2x + 1 = 0$

Pythagorean Theorem

73. The Leaning Tower of Pisa is 190 feet tall, but was built on unstable ground. It began to tip while under construction in 1173. By 1990, the tower was 15 feet out of perpendicular. That year, construction began to correct the tilt. In 2001, the construction was complete. The tower is now 13.5 feet out of perpendicular. Determine the vertical distance of the top of the tower above the ground in 1990 and 2001.

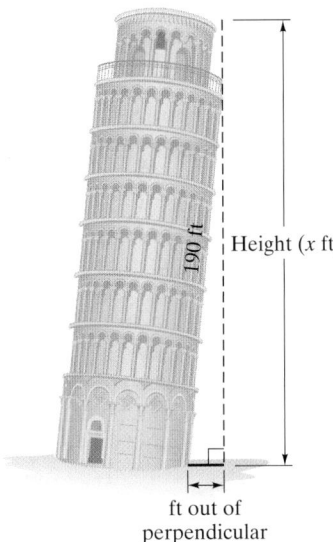

190 ft

Height (x ft)

ft out of perpendicular

74. A flagpole that is 20 feet tall tilts so that it is 1.5 feet out of perpendicular. Determine the pole's height.

75. The gable end of a roof is a right triangle with a span of 50 feet. The distance from the peak of the roof to either eave is the same. Find this distance.

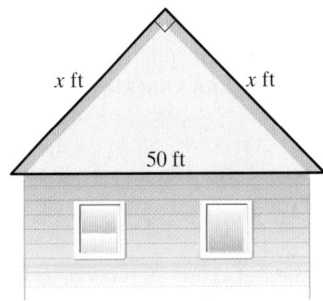

x ft x ft

50 ft

76. The diagonal of a square is 20 cm long. What is the perimeter of the square?

77. A soccer player kicked a goal from a distance of 25 feet along the ground to the goal. The ball entered the goal just below the horizontal bar, and the distance from there to the player's foot was 26 feet. How high was the ball as it crossed the goal line? If the goal was 8 feet high, by how many feet did the ball miss the goal's horizontal bar?

78. A soccer player kicked a ball from a distance of 30 feet along the ground to the goal. The ball missed the goal, crossing just above the horizontal bar, and the distance from there to the player's foot was 31.2 feet. How high was the ball as it crossed over the goal? If the goal was 8 feet high, by how many feet did the ball clear the bar?

Interest

In exercises 79–84, use the compound-interest formula $A = P(1 + r)^t$ to write a quadratic equation, and then solve the equation by using the principle of square roots.

79. If a $4000.00 investment compounded to $4708.90 after two years, determine the annual interest rate of the investment.

80. An investment of $6000.00 compounded to $6678.15 after two years. What was the annual interest rate of the investment?

81. At what annual interest rate must $5000 be invested in order for it to compound to $6000 after two years?

82. In order for $1200 to compound to $1600 in two years, what must be the annual interest rate of the investment?

83. Jean invests $7500 for two years in order to have money to add a sunroom onto her home. If she wants to have $9500 for the sunroom, determine the annual compound interest rate she must seek in order to meet her goal.

84. Brenda inherited $20,000 and invested it in a mutual fund for two years. At the end of that time, her investment had grown to $28,085. Determine the annual compound interest rate that would yield that amount of money.

Business

85. The regular cost of a theater ticket is $36. A discount of $1 per person is offered for group purchases. If the theater wants a breakeven of $250 on a group sale, how many tickets should be sold to a group?

86. A stadium ordinarily charges $18 per person to attend a sporting event. A discount of $1 per person is offered for group purchases. If the stadium wants a breakeven of $50 on a group sale, how many tickets should be sold to a group?

87. A restaurant ordinarily charges $19.50 for a steak dinner. For holiday group parties, the restaurant offers a discount of $0.25 per person from this price. Determine the number of persons needed in a group to realize a breakeven point of $200.00.

88. An accounting firm ordinarily is charged $75.00 licensing fee for each employee that uses a copyrighted accounting software package. The supplier offers a discount of $1.50 per copy for multiple licenses. If the supplier wants a breakeven point of $900.00, how many licenses must the accounting firm purchase?

89. Model cars sell for $20 each. To encourage sales, a discount is given so that the price is reduced by $1 times the number of cars purchased. How many cars can be purchased for $75? The dealer does not intend to sell model cars for less than $12 each.

90. To discourage customers from hoarding Bean Buddies the local store ordinarily sells them for $5 each, but adds a surcharge of $0.50 cents times the number of dolls purchased to the price of each doll. (A purchase of one doll costs $5.50, a purchase of two dolls costs $6.00 each, a purchase of three dolls costs $6.50 each, and so on.) Write a quadratic function for the cost of purchasing x dolls. How many Bean Buddies can be purchased for $100.00?

91. The demand for a product is related to its price, x, by the polynomial function $D(x) = \frac{1}{3}x^2 - 64x + 3100$, where x is any price up to $50. At what value should the price be set in order to have a demand of 2000 units for the product? Round your answer to the nearest dollar.

92. Using the same demand function as in exercise **91**, at what value should the price be set in order to have a demand of 1000 units for the product? Round your answer to the nearest dollar.

93. A large construction company studied the relationship between the size of a contract, x (in millions of dollars), and the cost to the company for preparing the bid for the contract, $C(x)$ (in thousands of dollars). A statistical analysis yielded the mathematical model $C(x) = 0.11x^2 + 3.08x + 11$. If the company spends $55,000 to prepare a bid, what should be the approximate size of the contract?

94. Using the same relationship as in exercise **93**, what should be the approximate size of a contract if the cost of preparing the bid is $40,000?

Geometry

95. The length of a rectangle is 4 inches more than its width. The area of the rectangle is 117 square inches. Find its dimensions.

96. The base of a triangle measures 8 cm more than its height. The area of the triangle is 90 square centimeters. Find the height and base of the triangle.

97. A foundation for a shed is to be rectangular, with a width that is 5 feet less than the length. The area of the foundation is to be approximately 85 square feet. Find the length and width of the foundation to the nearest tenth of a foot.

98. One leg of a right triangle is 8 feet longer than the other leg. The hypotenuse of the triangle is approximately 25 feet long. Find the lengths of the legs of the triangle to the nearest hundredth of a foot.

99. Joby buys two boxes of cereal that are packed by volume. The sum of the volumes of the boxes can be given by $V(x) = 6x^2 + 4x + 8$, where x is the width of the larger box. If the total volume is about 400 cubic units, what is the width of the larger box? Round to the nearest hundredth of a unit.

100. The sum of the areas of two triangles can be given by $A(x) = 3x^2 + 10x - 27$, where x is the height of the smaller triangle. For what value of x will the sum of the areas be approximately 840 square units? Round to the nearest tenth.

Vertical Position

In exercises 101–106, use the vertical-position formula $s = -16t^2 + v_0t + s_0$ to write a quadratic equation.

101. Starting 16 feet above the ground, a ball is thrown upward with an initial velocity of 32 feet per second.
    a. Write a quadratic equation for the time it will take the ball to reach the ground.
       (Note: Since the ball is thrown upward, the velocity will be positive; if the ball had been thrown downward, the velocity would be negative.)
    b. Complete the square to find an exact expression for the time it will take the ball to reach the ground.
    c. Estimate the time to the nearest tenth of a second.

102. From a height of 8 feet, a projectile is fired upward with an initial velocity of 88 feet per second.

a. Write a quadratic equation for the time it will take the projectile to reach the ground.
    b. Complete the square to find an exact expression for the time it will take the projectile to reach the ground.
    c. Estimate the time to the nearest tenth of a second.

103. A water balloon is dropped from a 400-foot tower. How long will it take for the balloon to reach a height of 100 feet?

104. A brick falls from the top ledge of a building that is 576 feet tall. How long will it take for the brick to reach a height of 10 feet?

105. How long will it take a free-falling sky diver to descend from 12,000 feet to 5000 feet?

106. How long will it take a free-falling sky diver to descend from 11,000 feet to 3500 feet?

Real Data

107. According to data from the U.S. Department of Commerce, the number of people below the poverty level is increasing. The following table summarizes this trend:

Year	Number of People below the Poverty Level (in millions)
2001	33
2002	35
2003	36

a. It is predicted that the number would first increase and then decrease. Write a quadratic function to model this data. Let y = the number of people below the poverty level, in millions, x years after 2000.

b. Using the function in part **a**, determine the number of years after 2000 when the number of people below the poverty level will return to the 2001 level of 33 million. Interpret the solutions.

108. The U.S. Department of the Treasury tracks average yields of bonds. The following table gives estimates of the June yield on 30-year treasury bonds:

Year	2002	2003	2004
Yield	5.6	4.25	5.3

a. It is predicted that the yields would first decrease and then increase. Write a quadratic function to model these data. Let y = the yield, x years after 2000.

b. Using the function in part **a**, determine the number of years after 2000 in which the yield will increase to the level of the late 1980s of about 8.75. Interpret the solutions.

109. The city of Bakersfield, California, failed to meet acceptable air-quality standards on several days during the years shown in the following table:

Year	Number of Days Acceptable Air-Quality Standards Not Met
2000	132
2001	125
2002	152

a. Based on global warming predictions, it is suggested that these numbers will continue to rise. Write a quadratic function to model these data. Let y = the number of days that Bakersfield fails to meet air-quality standards, x years after 2000.

b. Using the function in part **a**, determine the number of years after 2000 when the city will fail to meet air-quality standards on 300 days of the year. Interpret the solutions.

110. The number of grandchildren living with their grandparents in the United States without a parent present is summarized in the table below:

Year	Number of Grandchildren Living with Grandparents (no parent present) in Thousands
2000	1360
2001	1350
2002	1270

a. Write a quadratic function to model these data. Let y = the number of grandchildren living with grandparents without parents present in thousands, x years after 2000.

b. Using the function in part **a**, determine the number of years after 2000 when there will be one million grandchildren living with their grandparents without parents present. Interpret the solutions.

9.4 Calculator Exercises

Try to solve the quadratic equations that follow by completing the square. Then graph the equations by storing the left side in Y1 and the right side in Y2. In some cases you can find a real-number solution of the equation, and in other cases you cannot. Do you see a connection between those for which you cannot find a real-number solution and their graphs? Is there a connection between those for which you can find a real-number solution and their graphs? Now study the solutions you obtained by completing the square. Do you see any connection between the graphs when you find a rational real-number solution? between the graphs when you find an irrational real-number solution?

1. $x^2 + 8x + 15 = 0$ **2.** $x^2 + 4x + 7 = 0$

3. $x^2 + x - 1 = 0$ **4.** $2x^2 + 11x + 12 = 0$

5. $2x^2 + 6x + 7 = 0$ **6.** $8x^2 + 8x - 5 = 0$

9.4 Writing Exercise

You have seen that some quadratic equations can be solved by factoring and applying the zero factor property, while others can be solved by completing the square to make a square trinomial. If you are faced with solving a quadratic equation algebraically, discuss which method you would try to apply first, explaining the reasons for your choice. Then discuss a situation in which the factoring method might not be best and you would need to try completing the square. Finally, discuss when completing the square might not be best. You may wish to illustrate each situation with a sample exercise from this section.

9.5 SOLVING QUADRATIC EQUATIONS BY USING THE QUADRATIC FORMULA

OBJECTIVES

1 Solve quadratic equations by using the quadratic formula.
2 Determine the number and type of solutions of quadratic equations by using the discriminant.
3 Model real-world situations by using quadratic equations, and solve the equations by using the quadratic formula.

APPLICATION

Water in a stream moves fastest at the surface and slowest at the bottom. A hydrologist measured the velocity of a 2-meter-deep stream at different depths and determined that the velocity of the stream, in meters per second, could be approximated by the equation $y = -0.058x^2 + 0.206x + 0.063$, where x is the depth of the stream in meters.

a. If the average velocity of the stream was 0.191 meter per second, determine the depth at which this average velocity occurred.

b. Hydrologists use the "four-tenths rule" to determine the average velocity of a stream at a point. That is, the average velocity of a stream is approximately the velocity of the stream at a depth of four-tenths of the stream's depth. Compare the approximation obtained by the four-tenths rule with the approximation obtained in part **a**.

After completing this section, we will discuss this application further. See page 707.

Objective 9.5.1

Solving Quadratic Equations by Using the Quadratic Formula

When we have to repeat a process many times, it often saves time to develop a formula for the process. Therefore, instead of completing the square to solve a quadratic equation, we may want to use a formula. To develop such a formula we begin with the standard form of a quadratic equation in one variable, $ax^2 + bx + c = 0$, and repeat the process of completing the square, using letters instead of numbers and remembering that a, b, and c represent real numbers.

$$ax^2 + bx + c = 0$$
$$ax^2 + bx = -c \qquad \text{Isolate the variable terms.}$$
$$x^2 + \frac{b}{a}x = \frac{-c}{a} \qquad \text{Divide by the coefficient of } x^2.$$

Determine the value needed to complete the square. Multiply the coefficient of x by $\frac{1}{2}$ and square the result.

$$\frac{b}{a} \cdot \frac{1}{2} = \frac{b}{2a}$$
$$\left(\frac{b}{2a}\right)^2 = \frac{b^2}{4a^2}$$

Add $\dfrac{b^2}{4a^2}$ to both sides.

$$x^2 + \frac{b}{a}x + \frac{b^2}{4a^2} = \frac{-c}{a} + \frac{b^2}{4a^2}$$

Simplify the right side.

$$\frac{-c}{a} + \frac{b^2}{4a^2} = \frac{-4ac}{4a^2} + \frac{b^2}{4a^2} = \frac{-4ac + b^2}{4a^2} = \frac{b^2 - 4ac}{4a^2}$$

Write the left side as a binomial squared: $\left(x + \dfrac{b}{2a}\right)^2$.

$$\left(x + \frac{b}{2a}\right)^2 = \frac{b^2 - 4ac}{4a^2} \qquad \text{Binomial squared.}$$

Use the principle of square roots to determine the solutions.

$$x + \frac{b}{2a} = \pm\sqrt{\frac{b^2 - 4ac}{4a^2}} \qquad \text{Principle of square roots}$$

$$x + \frac{b}{2a} = \pm\frac{\sqrt{b^2 - 4ac}}{2a} \qquad 4a^2 = (2a)^2$$

$$x = \frac{-b}{2a} \pm \frac{\sqrt{b^2 - 4ac}}{2a} \qquad \text{Subtract } \frac{b}{2a} \text{ from both sides.}$$

$$x = \frac{-b \pm \sqrt{b^2 - 4ac}}{2a} \qquad \text{Simplify.}$$

In writing this formula, be careful to write just one fraction for the right side of the equation.

We can use the preceding formula to solve any quadratic equation. To do this, first write the quadratic equation in standard form: $ax^2 + bx + c = 0$, with real numbers a, b, and c and $a \neq 0$. Then determine the values to substitute for a, b, and c.

QUADRATIC FORMULA

The quadratic formula used for solving a quadratic equation in standard form, $ax^2 + bx + c = 0$, with real numbers a, b, and c and $a \neq 0$, is

$$x = \frac{-b \pm \sqrt{b^2 - 4ac}}{2a}$$

EXAMPLE 1

Solve and check.

a. $2x^2 + 3x - 5 = 0$ **b.** $2x^2 + 3x - 4 = 0$ **c.** $2x^2 + 4x = -2$

d. $2y^2 - 5y + 4 = 0$ **e.** $x^2 + 6x + 1 = 0$

Algebraic Solution

a. $2x^2 + 3x - 5 = 0$ $a = 2$, $b = 3$, and $c = -5$

$$x = \frac{-b \pm \sqrt{b^2 - 4ac}}{2a} \qquad \text{Quadratic formula}$$

$$x = \frac{-(3) \pm \sqrt{(3)^2 - 4(2)(-5)}}{2(2)} \qquad \text{Substitute values for } a, b, \text{ and } c.$$

$$x = \frac{-3 \pm \sqrt{9 + 40}}{4} \qquad \text{Simplify.}$$

$$x = \frac{-3 \pm \sqrt{49}}{4} \qquad \text{Simplify.}$$

$$x = \frac{-3 \pm 7}{4} \qquad 49 = 7^2$$

$$x = \frac{-3 + 7}{4} \quad \text{or} \quad x = \frac{-3 - 7}{4}$$

$$x = \frac{4}{4} \qquad\qquad x = -\frac{10}{4}$$

$$x = 1 \qquad\qquad x = -\frac{5}{2}$$

The solutions are 1 and $-\frac{5}{2}$.

Note: These solutions could have been determined by factoring.

Graphic Check

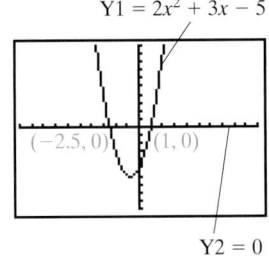

Y1 = $2x^2 + 3x - 5$

$(-2.5, 0)$ $(1, 0)$

Y2 = 0

$(-10, 10, -10, 10)$

The solutions are -2.5 $\left(\text{or } -\dfrac{5}{2}\right)$ and 1.

b. $2x^2 + 3x - 4 = 0$ $a = 2, b = 3,$ and $c = -4$

Substitution Check

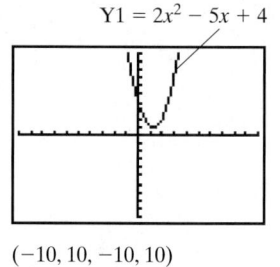

$$x = \frac{-b \pm \sqrt{b^2 - 4ac}}{2a}$$ Quadratic formula

$$x = \frac{-(3) \pm \sqrt{(3)^2 - 4(2)(-4)}}{2(2)}$$ Substitute values for a, b, and c.

$$x = \frac{-3 \pm \sqrt{9 + 32}}{4}$$ Simplify.

$$x = \frac{-3 \pm \sqrt{41}}{4}$$ Simplify.

$$x = \frac{-3 + \sqrt{41}}{4} \quad \text{or} \quad x = \frac{-3 - \sqrt{41}}{4}$$

$$x \approx 0.851 \qquad\qquad x \approx -2.351$$

The solutions are $\dfrac{-3 \pm \sqrt{41}}{4}$, or approximately 0.851 and -2.351.

Note: These solutions could not have been found by factoring. If we substitute the approximate solutions, we will not obtain an exact check, because $0.001402 \neq 0$.

c. $2x^2 + 4x = -2$

$2x^2 + 4x + 2 = 0$ Standard form
                 $a = 2, b = 4,$ and $c = 2$

Substitution Check

Let $x = -1$.

$$x = \frac{-b \pm \sqrt{b^2 - 4ac}}{2a}$$ Quadratic formula

$$x = \frac{-(4) \pm \sqrt{(4)^2 - 4(2)(2)}}{2(2)}$$ Substitute values for a, b, and c.

$$x = \frac{-4 \pm \sqrt{16 - 16}}{4}$$ Simplify.

$$x = \frac{-4 \pm \sqrt{0}}{4}$$ Simplify.

$$x = \frac{-4}{4}$$

$$x = -1$$

The solution is -1.

$$\begin{array}{c|c} 2x^2 + 4x = -2 & \\ \hline 2(-1)^2 + 4(-1) & -2 \\ 2 - 4 & \\ -2 & -2 \end{array}$$

The solution is -1.

d. $2y^2 - 5y + 4 = 0$ This is a quadratic equation in terms of y. $a = 2, b = -5,$ and $c = 4$.

Graphic Check

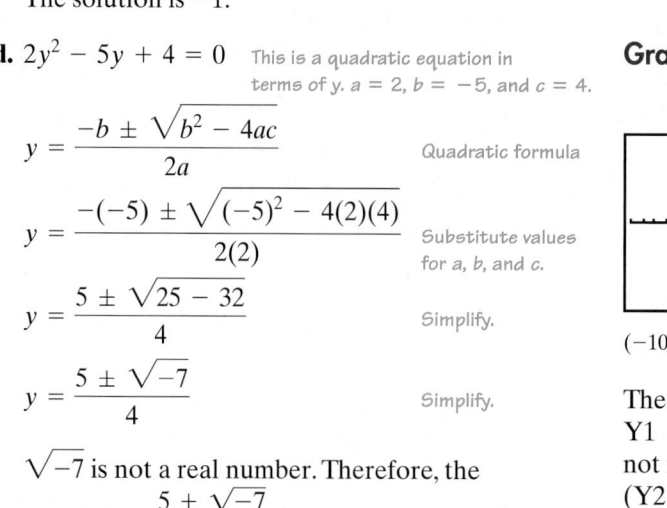

$Y1 = 2x^2 - 5x + 4$

$(-10, 10, -10, 10)$

$$y = \frac{-b \pm \sqrt{b^2 - 4ac}}{2a}$$ Quadratic formula

$$y = \frac{-(-5) \pm \sqrt{(-5)^2 - 4(2)(4)}}{2(2)}$$ Substitute values for a, b, and c.

$$y = \frac{5 \pm \sqrt{25 - 32}}{4}$$ Simplify.

$$y = \frac{5 \pm \sqrt{-7}}{4}$$ Simplify.

$\sqrt{-7}$ is not a real number. Therefore, the expressions $\dfrac{5 \pm \sqrt{-7}}{4}$ do not represent real numbers. The equation has no real-number solution.

The graph of $Y1 = 2x^2 - 5x + 4$ does not intersect the x-axis ($Y2 = 0$). The solution is not a real number.

e. $x^2 + 6x + 1 = 0$ Standard form; $a = 1$, $b = 6$, and $c = 1$

$$x = \frac{-b \pm \sqrt{b^2 - 4ac}}{2a}$$ Quadratic formula

$$x = \frac{-(6) \pm \sqrt{(6)^2 - 4(1)(1)}}{2(1)}$$ Substitute values for a, b, and c.

$$x = \frac{-6 \pm \sqrt{36 - 4}}{2}$$ Simplify.

$$x = \frac{-6 \pm \sqrt{32}}{2}$$ Simplify.

$$x = \frac{-6 \pm \sqrt{16 \cdot 2}}{2}$$ $32 = 16 \cdot 2$

$$x = \frac{-6 \pm 4\sqrt{2}}{2}$$ $16 = 4^2$

$$x = \frac{\overset{1}{\cancel{2}}\left(-3 \pm 2\sqrt{2}\right)}{\underset{1}{\cancel{2}}}$$ Factor the numerator and divide out the 2.

$$x = -3 \pm 2\sqrt{2}$$

Substitution Check

```
-3+2√(2)→X: X²+6X
+1
               0
-3-2√(2)→X: X²+6X
+1
               0
```

The solutions are $-3 \pm 2\sqrt{2}$.

The solutions are $-3 \pm 2\sqrt{2}$, or approximately -0.172 and -5.828.

Objective 9.5.1 **CHECKUP**

1. Solve by using the quadratic formula, and check your solutions.

 a. $2x^2 + x - 6 = 0$ **b.** $x^2 + x - 7 = 0$

 c. $9x^2 - 12x = -4$ **d.** $3k^2 - k + 5 = 0$

 e. $x^2 + 4x - 23 = 0$

2. The quadratic formula appears to be a single rule, yet sometimes there are two separate solutions, sometimes only one double root, and sometimes no real number. Explain how this is possible.

3. What does the symbol $\pm$ mean?

Objective 9.5.2

Determining Characteristics of Solutions by Using the Discriminant

In previous examples, the solutions of a quadratic equation varied in both number (two, one, or none) and type (rational, irrational, or no real number). At times, it is necessary only to determine the type and number of solutions. For example, if it is known that no real-number solution exists, there may not be any reason to attempt to solve the equation. Is there any way to determine the number and kind of solutions of an equation without solving the equation? See if you can find an answer by completing the following set of exercises, using the quadratic formula.

 Guided Discovery 4   Characteristics of the Quadratic-Formula Solution

In Example 1, we obtained the solutions of the given equations. Determine a value for the radicand, $b^2 - 4ac$, of the quadratic formula.

1. $2x^2 + 3x - 5 = 0$

 $x = 1$ or $x = -\dfrac{5}{2}$

 (two rational solutions)

 $b^2 - 4ac =$ _____

2. $2x^2 + 3x - 4 = 0$

 $x = \dfrac{-3 + \sqrt{41}}{4}$ or $x = \dfrac{-3 - \sqrt{41}}{4}$

 (two irrational solutions)

 $b^2 - 4ac =$ _____

3. $2x^2 + 4x + 2 = 0$

 $x = -1$

 (one rational solution)

 $b^2 - 4ac =$ _____

4. $2y^2 - 5y + 4 = 0$

 (no real-number solutions)

 $b^2 - 4ac =$ _____

Write a rule for determining the number of and type of solutions of a quadratic equation by using $b^2 - 4ac$.

The radicand $b^2 - 4ac$ determines the characteristics of the solutions of a quadratic equation. If the radicand is a perfect square ($\neq 0$), the equation has two rational-number solutions. If the radicand is 0, the equation has one rational-number solution. If the radicand is a positive number that is not a perfect square, the equation has two irrational-number solutions. If the radicand is a negative number, the equation has no real-number solutions.

We can understand why this is true if we look at the entire quadratic formula, $x = \dfrac{-b \pm \sqrt{b^2 - 4ac}}{2a}$. The square root simplifies to a positive rational number if the radicand is a perfect square. In the formula, this results in a rational number being added to or subtracted from another rational number and then divided by a second rational number. The result is always two rational numbers.

The square root simplifies to 0 if the radicand is 0. In the formula, this results in 0 being added to or subtracted from another rational number and then divided by a second rational number. The result is always one rational number.

The square root remains if the radicand is a positive number that is not a perfect square. This results in an irrational number being added to or subtracted from a rational number and then divided by a second rational number. The result is always two irrational numbers.

The square root is not defined in the real-number system if the radicand is a negative number. In that case, we cannot obtain a real-number solution of the equation.

We call the radicand $b^2 - 4ac$ the **discriminant** of the quadratic equation $ax^2 + bx + c = 0$.

DETERMINING THE CHARACTERISTICS OF THE SOLUTION OF A QUADRATIC EQUATION BY USING THE DISCRIMINANT

Determine the value of the discriminant $b^2 - 4ac$, of a quadratic equation in standard form, $ax^2 + bx + c = 0$, with rational numbers a, b, and c and $a \neq 0$. One of four possibilities occur.

Discriminant	Number and Type of Real-Number Solutions
0	One rational-number solution
Perfect square, not equal to 0	Two rational-number solutions
Positive number, not a perfect square	Two irrational-number solutions
Negative number	No real-number solution

EXAMPLE 2 Determine the characteristics of the solution of each quadratic equation. Do not solve the equation.

a. $15x^2 + 26x = 12$
b. $\dfrac{3}{4}x^2 - \dfrac{2}{3}x + \dfrac{1}{9} = 0$

c. $0.3x^2 - 0.6x + 0.3 = 0$
d. $3x^2 - 7x + 12 = 0$

Solution

a. $15x^2 + 26x = 12$

$15x^2 + 26x - 12 = 0$ Standard form

$b^2 - 4ac = (26)^2 - 4(15)(-12)$ $a = 15, b = 26,$ and $c = -12$

$= 1396$

The equation has two irrational solutions, because 1396 is positive, but not a perfect square.

b. $\dfrac{3}{4}x^2 - \dfrac{2}{3}x + \dfrac{1}{9} = 0$

$$b^2 - 4ac = \left(-\dfrac{2}{3}\right)^2 - 4\left(\dfrac{3}{4}\right)\left(\dfrac{1}{9}\right) \qquad a = \tfrac{3}{4}, b = -\tfrac{2}{3}, c = \tfrac{1}{9}$$

$$= \dfrac{1}{9}$$

The equation has two rational solutions, because $\dfrac{1}{9}$ is a perfect square.

 TAKE NOTE If you prefer not to work with fractions, write an equivalent equation by multiplying by the LCD of 36. The new equivalent equation, $27x^2 - 24x + 4 = 0$ will have a discriminant value of 144, a perfect square as well.

c. $0.3x^2 - 0.6x + 0.3 = 0$

$$b^2 - 4ac = (-0.6)^2 - 4(0.3)(0.3) \qquad a = 0.3, b = -0.6, c = 0.3$$

$$= 0$$

The equation has one rational solution, because the discriminant is 0.

d. $3x^2 - 7x + 12 = 0$

$$b^2 - 4ac = (-7)^2 - 4(3)(12) \qquad a = 3, b = -7, \text{ and } c = 12$$

$$= 49 - 144$$

$$= -95$$

The equation has no real-number solution, because the discriminant is negative. ■

 Objective 9.5.2 **CHECKUP**

1. Determine the characteristics of the solution(s) of each quadratic equation. Do not solve the equation.

  a. $0.1x^2 + x + 2.3 = 0$ **b.** $25x^2 - 60x + 36 = 0$

  c. $3x^2 - 4x = 32$ **d.** $\dfrac{1}{2}x^2 + 3x + 17 = 0$

2. Under what conditions will a quadratic equation have rational numbers as solutions; irrational numbers as solutions; no real-number solution?

Objective 9.5.3   ## Modeling the Real World

We now have four algebraic methods (factoring, square root principle, completing the square, and quadratic formula), as well as a numeric method and a graphic method, for solving quadratic equations in one variable. First, let's review the strengths and weaknesses of these methods.

Method	Strengths	Weaknesses
Numeric	Easy to set up for integer values on a calculator	Time consuming if completed by hand Will determine solutions only for the input values (usually integers)
Graphic	Easy to set up on a calculator Real-number solutions will always be found if they exist	Appropriate range may be difficult to determine; graph may be hard to read Solution will be rounded for irrational and repeating fraction values
Algebraic	Exact solutions will be found if they exist	Time consuming at times

After reviewing this list, we likely will want to rely more heavily on algebraic methods than on the numeric and graphic methods. Now let us review the steps involved in solving a quadratic equation algebraically.

SOLVING A QUADRATIC EQUATION IN ONE VARIABLE ALGEBRAICALLY

To solve a quadratic equation in one variable, $ax^2 + bx + c = 0$, algebraically, select one of the following methods:

- If $b = 0$—that is, if the quadratic equation has no linear (x) term—solve for x^2 and use the principle of square roots to solve the equation.
- Factor $ax^2 + bx + c$ and, if possible, use the zero factor property to solve the equation.
- If the quadratic expression will not factor, or if it is difficult to factor, use the quadratic formula or complete the square to solve the equation.

EXAMPLE 3

Chloe is planning a Christmas sale. She usually sells doll cradles for $40 per cradle. To encourage customers to purchase more than one cradle, she plans to reduce the price of each cradle by $1 per cradle purchased. In order to make the cradles, she purchased a saw for $150. She estimated that the cost of materials for each cradle is $5.

a. Write a revenue function.

b. Write a total cost function.

c. Write a profit function.

d. Determine the number of doll cradles that Chloe must make and sell to break even, and find the selling price of each cradle for that number of cradles.

Solution

a. Let x = the number of doll cradles sold

$R(x)$ = the total revenue

The selling price of each cradle is $40 minus $1 per cradle sold, or $40 - 1x$. The revenue is the product of the number of cradles sold and the selling price per cradle. Thus,

$$R(x) = x(40 - x)$$
$$R(x) = 40x - x^2$$

b. Let x = the number of cradles made

$C(x)$ = the total cost of making and selling the cradles

The total cost is $5 per cradle, plus $150 for the saw.

$$C(x) = 5x + 150$$

c. Let $P(x)$ = the profit for making and selling the cradles

The profit is the difference of the revenue and the total cost.

$$P(x) = R(x) - C(x)$$
$$P(x) = (40x - x^2) - (5x + 150)$$
$$P(x) = 40x - x^2 - 5x - 150$$
$$P(x) = -x^2 + 35x - 150$$

d. Chloe will break even when the profit is 0 dollars, or $P(x) = 0$.

$$-x^2 + 35x - 150 = 0 \qquad a = -1, b = 35, c = -150$$

$$x = \frac{-b \pm \sqrt{b^2 - 4ac}}{2a} \qquad \text{Quadratic formula}$$

$$x = \frac{-(35) \pm \sqrt{(35)^2 - 4(-1)(-150)}}{2(-1)}$$

$$x = \frac{-35 \pm \sqrt{1225 - 600}}{-2}$$

$$x = \frac{-35 \pm \sqrt{625}}{-2}$$

$$x = \frac{-35 \pm 25}{-2}$$

$$x = \frac{-35 + 25}{-2} \qquad \text{or} \qquad x = \frac{-35 - 25}{-2}$$

$$x = 5 \qquad\qquad\qquad x = 30$$

$$40 - x = 40 - 5 = 35 \qquad 40 - x = 40 - 30 = 10 \qquad \text{Selling price}$$

Chloe will break even when she sells 5 cradles for 35 dollars each or when she sells 30 cradles for 10 dollars each. She would not sell cradles for 10 dollars each, so the correct answer is that the break-even point occurs when Chloe sells 5 cradles.

APPLICATION

Water in a stream moves fastest at the surface and slowest at the bottom. A hydrologist measured the velocity of a 2-meter-deep stream at different depths and determined that the velocity of the stream, in meters per second, could be approximated by the equation $y = -0.058x^2 + 0.206x + 0.063$, where x is the depth of the stream in meters.

a. If the average velocity of the stream was 0.191 meter per second, determine the depth at which this average velocity occurred.

b. Hydrologists use the "four-tenths rule" to determine the average velocity of a stream at a point. That is, the average velocity of a stream is approximately the velocity of the stream at a depth of four-tenths of the stream's depth. Compare the approximation obtained by the four-tenths rule with the approximation obtained in part **a**.

Discussion

a. Let y = the velocity of the stream in meters per second
x = the stream's depth in meters

$$y = -0.058x^2 + 0.206x + 0.063$$
$$0.191 = -0.058x^2 + 0.206x + 0.063 \qquad \text{Let } y = 0.191 \text{ meter per second}$$

Write the equation in standard form and solve using the quadratic formula.

$$-0.058x^2 + 0.206x - 0.128 = 0 \qquad a = -0.058, b = 0.206, c = -0.128$$

$$x = \frac{-b \pm \sqrt{b^2 - 4ac}}{2a} \qquad \text{Quadratic formula}$$

$$x = \frac{-(0.206) \pm \sqrt{(0.206)^2 - 4(-0.058)(-0.128)}}{2(-0.058)}$$

$$x = \frac{-0.206 \pm \sqrt{0.01274}}{-0.116}$$

(continued on page 708)

$$x = \frac{-0.206 + \sqrt{0.01274}}{-0.116} \quad \text{or} \quad x = \frac{-0.206 - \sqrt{0.01274}}{-0.116}$$

$$x \approx 0.8 \qquad\qquad\qquad x \approx 2.7$$

Since the stream is 2 meters deep, the average velocity of the stream occurred at a depth of about 0.8 meter.

b. The four-tenths rule states that the average velocity occurs at 0.4 of the depth (2 m).

$$(0.4)(2) = 0.8$$

The equation in part **a** is a good approximation, because the same value, 0.8 meter, was obtained.

✓ Objective 9.5.3 CHECKUP

Set up a quadratic equation to represent each situation, and then use the quadratic formula to solve the equation.

1. A manufacturer supplies cabinets at wholesale price to a dealer. The price per cabinet depends on the number of cabinets the dealer orders. The listed price of $150 per cabinet will be reduced by $5 per cabinet ordered. It costs the manufacturer $65 to make a cabinet, and there is a fixed delivery cost of $150 for each order.
 a. Write a revenue function for an order of cabinets.
 b. Write a cost function for an order of cabinets.
 c. Write a profit function for an order of cabinets.

d. Determine the number of cabinets that must be ordered to break even on an order. Interpret the break-even point(s).

2. An equation to approximate the velocity of a 2-meter-deep stream, in meters per second, is $y = -0.058x^2 + 0.206x + 0.063$, where x is the depth of the stream in meters. A 2-meter-deep stream has a measured velocity of 0.166 meter per second. Determine the depth at which this measurement was taken.

9.5 EXERCISES

Student Solutions Manual   PH Math/Tutor Center   CD Video   MathXL®   MyMathLab   Interactmath.com

Use the quadratic formula to find the exact solution; then check your solution.

1. $x^2 - 12x + 27 = 0$

2. $x^2 - 12x + 35 = 0$

3. $2x^2 + 3x - 15 = 2x + 6$

4. $3x^2 + 3x - 10 = x + 6$

5. $2z^2 + 11z + 5 = 0$

6. $3y^2 + 31y + 36 = 0$

7. $16p^2 - 8p + 8 = 7$

8. $25q^2 + 20q + 5 = 1$

9. $x^2 + 3x + 4 = 0$

10. $x^2 + x + 5 = 0$

11. $-5a^2 + 4a - 7 = 0$

12. $-3b^2 + b - 5 = 0$

13. $v^2 - 5v + 2 = 0$

14. $t^2 - 3t + 1 = 0$

15. $x(x - 4) + 1 = 0$

16. $x(x + 6) + 7 = 0$

17. $-16t^2 + 5t + 100 = 0$

18. $-16t^2 - 5t + 50 = 0$

19. $3d^2 + 10 = 17$

20. $2r^2 + 4 = 19$

21. $16m = m^2 + 55$

22. $72 = -k^2 - 18k$

23. $x^2 - 6.3x + 7.2 = 0$

24. $x^2 + 3.7x + 1.6 = 0$

25. $1.8 - 5.6x - x^2 = 0$

26. $6.2 + 1.8x - x^2 = 0$

27. $a^2 + 24.01 = 9.8a$

28. $b^2 + 14.2b = -50.41$

29. $1.7z^2 + 1.3z + 5.6 = 0$

30. $2.9t^2 - 5.2t + 8.1 = 0$

31. $-4.9t^2 + 8t + 75 = 0$

32. $-4.9t^2 - 12t + 100 = 0$

Evaluate the discriminant in exercises 33–48 to determine the characteristics of the solution(s) of each quadratic equation. Do not solve the equation.

33. $x^2 - 11x + 24 = 0$

34. $x^2 + 8x + 21 = 0$

35. $a^2 + 12a + 36 = 0$

36. $b^2 - 3b - 8 = 0$

37. $z^2 = 4z - 5$

38. $y^2 + 81 = 18y$

39. $6x^2 - 11x - 7 = 0$

40. $5x^2 - 125 = 0$

41. $7p^2 - 15 = 0$

42. $10q^2 - 7q - 12 = 0$

43. $1 - 5x - 4x^2 = 0$

44. $6x - 5 = 3x^2$

45. $z - 1.25 = 0.2z^2$

46. $2.1 - 1.3t - 4.3t^2 = 0$

47. $0.3x - 2.8 = 1.7x^2$

48. $x^2 = 8.6x - 18.49$

Business

49. A gourmet meat shop that ships frozen steaks to customers charges $9.00 per pound. To encourage larger orders, the shop promises to reduce the price by $0.10 for every pound of steak ordered. The shop spends $6.00 per pound for the steak and spends $7.50 for packaging and shipping each order.
   a. Write a revenue function for an order of steaks.
   b. Write a cost function for an order of steaks.
   c. Write a profit function for an order of steaks.
   d. Determine the number of pounds of steak that must be ordered to break even on an order. Interpret the break-even point(s).

50. Jennah sells hair ribbons through a mail-order business in her home. She ordinarily sells the ribbons for $3.25 each, but reduces this price by $0.05 per ribbon ordered to encourage multiple orders. Her hair ribbons cost $2.00 each to make, and packaging and shipping cost $3.00 per order.
   a. Write a revenue function for an order of hair ribbons.
   b. Write a cost function for an order of hair ribbons.
   c. Write a profit function for an order of hair ribbons.
   d. Determine the number of hair ribbons that must be ordered to break even on an order. Interpret the break-even point(s).

51. A promoter rents and decorates a party hall for $600.00 a night. He charges guests $50.00 per person to attend a New Year's Eve party. He would ordinarily pay a caterer $20.00 per person to provide food and beverages for the party. However, the caterer offers to reduce the price per person by $0.25 for each person attending, to gain the promoter's business.
   a. Write a revenue function for the amount of money the promoter will collect for the party.
   b. Write a cost function for the amount of money the promoter will spend on the party.
   c. Write a profit function for this promotion.
   d. Determine the number of guests that must attend for the promoter to break even on the party. Interpret the break-even point(s).

52. A consulting firm charges customers $250 per day for services. The firm hires freelance consultants and pays them a flat amount of $500 to work a job. In addition, the firm would ordinarily pay the freelancers $75 per day, but because the consultants prefer multiple-day assignments, the firm agrees to reduce this daily payment by $5 for each day the job lasts.
   a. Write a revenue function for the amount of money the firm earns for a consulting job.
   b. Write a cost function for the amount of money the firm pays the freelance consultant to work the job.
   c. Write a profit function for one job that the firm arranges.
   d. Determine the number of days that a job must last for the firm to break even. Interpret the break-even point(s).

53. The Huskie Line, a college bus service, finds that for every $0.10 decrease on an all-day ticket, it can sell four extra tickets. The standard fare is $4.50 per ticket, and at that price 50 tickets per day are sold. The bus service spends $0.75 per ticket for bus maintenance and fees and $200.00 per day on gas. If x is the number of decreases, then the number of tickets sold daily is $50 + 4x$.
   a. Write a revenue function for daily bus revenue.
   b. Write a daily cost function for the bus company.
   c. Write a daily profit function.
   d. Determine the number of decreases for which the bus service will break even on a particular day.

54. A limousine company's weekday business involves transporting customers to the airport. After experimenting with various fee structures, the company finds that for every increase of $3.50 in its fee it will lose two customers. The standard fee per person for a trip to the airport is $37.50, and 145 such fares weekly are sold at this price. The company has weekly expenditures of $15.00 per fare and $5000.00 in overhead. If x is the number of increases, then the number of tickets is $145 - 2x$.
   a. Write a weekly revenue function.
   b. Write a weekly cost function.
   c. Write a weekly profit function.
   d. Determine the number of increases for which the company will break even for a particular week.

55. A school cafeteria sells lunch for $3.45, and at this price sells 300 lunches each day. Past experience has shown that every $0.25 increase in the cost of lunch results in 4 fewer students buying lunch. The cost of ingredients for each meal is estimated to be $2.00 per lunch with overhead costs of $1400.00 per day. If x is the number of increases,
   a. Write a revenue function for daily cafeteria lunch service.
   b. Write a daily cost function for lunch service.
   c. Write a function for daily profit.
   d. Determine the number of increases for which the cafeteria will break even on a particular day.

56. A local retailer sells jars of jam for $33.50 for a box of five jars to 95 customers in his store every week. He finds that for every $1.50 decrease in price he is able to sell 15 more boxes. His cost to make the jam is $23.00 per box, and the labels and packaging of jars and boxes cost him $295.00 each week. If x is the number of decreases,
   a. Write a revenue function for weekly jam sales.
   b. Write a weekly cost function.
   c. Write a function for weekly profit.
   d. Determine the number of decreases for which the retailer will break even for a particular week.

Geometry

57. The length of a rectangle is 9 feet more than three times its width. If its area is 1135 square feet, find its dimensions to the nearest tenth.

58. A parallelogram's base is 5 decimeters less than seven times its corresponding height. If the area is 965 square decimeters, find the length of the base and height to the nearest tenth of a decimeter.

59. The product of an angle's complement and supplement can be given by the function $A(x) = x^2 - 270x + 16,200$, where x is the measure of the angle. If the product is about 900, what is the measure of the angle to the nearest hundredth?

60. The volume of a rectangular prism with height 7 inches can be given by $V(x) = 63x + 42x^2$, where x is its width. If the volume is 600 cubic inches, find the width to the nearest hundredth of an inch.

Pythagorean Theorem

61. A loading ramp is to be built from the ground to the loading dock. The cross section of the ramp is a right triangle with a base that is 6 feet more than the height and a hypotenuse that is 12 feet more than the height. Use the Pythagorean theorem to write a polynomial equation. Find the height, base, and hypotenuse of the ramp.

62. Marge and Gretchen are cutting out right triangles for a quilt they are making. The instructions call for the height of the triangles to be $\frac{3}{4}$ of the base and the hypotenuse to be $\frac{1}{2}$ inch longer than the base. Write a polynomial equation. Find the lengths of the three sides of the triangles.

Vertical Distance

63. An acrobat jumps up from a wire that is 12.5 meters above the ground. Her initial velocity is 5.5 meters per second. Her vertical distance above ground in meters can be determined by the function $s(t) = -4.9t^2 + 5.5t + 12.5$, where t is time in seconds. When will she land in a safety net that is at a height of 3 meters?

64. A coin is thrown down from the top of the Empire State Building, which is 1250 feet tall. It is given an initial velocity of 10 feet per second. The distance above ground in feet can be determined by the function $s(t) = -16t^2 - 10t + 1250$, where t is time in seconds. When will the coin be at a height of 400 feet?

Real Data

65. According to data that summarize American spending on leisure activities, the quadratic function $y = 0.04x^2 + 0.14x + 4.5$ models expenditures on spectator sports, where x is the number of years after 1990 and y is the per capita expenditure in dollars on spectator sports. Use the function and the quadratic formula to determine the year in which per capita expenditure on spectator sports will reach $25.

66. According to data from a communications firm, the number of cable TV systems in the United States can be estimated by the quadratic function $y = 1333x^2 - 6499x + 15,869$, where x is the number of years after 1990 and y is the number of cable TV systems in the United States. Assuming this trend in the numbers continues, use the function and the quadratic formula to determine the year in which the number of cable TV systems in the United States was 130,000.

67. The FBI publishes reports detailing the number of crimes committed by type and year. According to the FBI's data, the quadratic function $y = 6770x^2 - 58,110x + 498,530$ can be used to estimate the number of robberies in the United States, where x is the number of years after 1997 and y is the number of robberies. The number of robberies is predicted to first decrease and then increase after 1997. Use the function and the quadratic formula to determine the year in which there will be 750,000 robberies in the United States.

68. FBI records also support a quadratic function $y = -52,100x^2 - 75,700x + 2,460,500$ that can be used to estimate the number of burglaries in the United States, where x is the number of years after 1997 and y is the number of burglaries. The function suggests that the number of burglaries will first increase and then decrease. Use the function and the quadratic formula to determine the year in which there were one million burglaries in the United States according to this model.

9.5 Calculator Exercises

The calculator can be helpful in applying the quadratic formula to solve a quadratic equation. We will store the formula for the discriminant in Y8 and the two formulas for the solutions in Y9 and Y0. Then we can just store values for a, b, and c in the calculator and view Y8, Y9, and Y0 to see the results for the quadratic formula. The steps to do so follow:

- Store the formula for the discriminant in Y8.

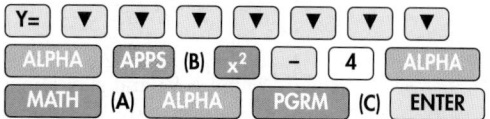

- Store the first solution formula in Y9.

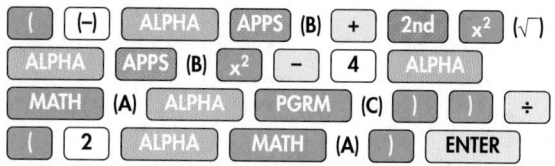

- Store the second solution formula in Y0.

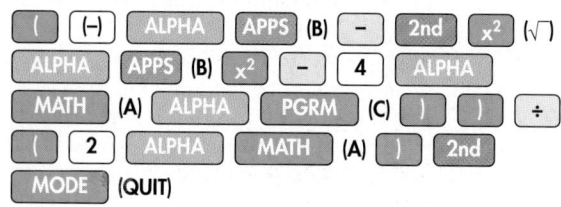

- Store the values for a, b, and c of the quadratic equation in the A, B, and C locations of the calculator. For example, to solve the quadratic equation, $2x^2 + 9x - 35 = 0$, store 2 in A, 9 in B and -35 in C.

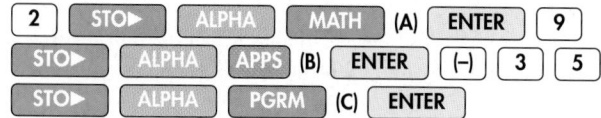

- Recall Y8 to see the value of the discriminant.

  [**VARS**] [▶] [1] [8] [**ENTER**]

  The calculator will display 361, which is a perfect square of 19, indicating that the equation has two rational solutions.

- Recall Y9 and Y0 to see the two solutions of the equation.

  [**VARS**] [▶] [1] [9] [**ENTER**] [**VARS**] [▶]
  [1] [0] [**ENTER**]

  The two solutions are $x = 2.5$ and $x = -7$.

To solve another equation, it is only necessary to store new values for A, B, and C and then recall Y8, Y9, and Y0. The formulas will remain stored in the calculator until you delete them from these three Y locations.

You should make Y8, Y9, and Y0 inactive when you are storing formulas there. Simply move the cursor over the equals sign under [**Y=**] and press [**ENTER**]. The box around the equals sign should disappear, and now these locations will not appear in any tables or graphs that you subsequently create.

Use this method to complete the following table. Remember to place the equation in standard form to determine the values of a, b, and c. When the solution is an irrational number, approximate the solution as a decimal to the nearest thousandth.

	Equation	Value of Discriminant	Types of Roots (Rational, Irrational, Not Real)	Number of Unlike Roots	Roots
1.	$x^2 + 6 = 5x$	1	rational	2	2, 3
2.	$9x^2 + 6x = -1$				
3.	$2x^2 + 1 = 7x$				
4.	$x^2 + 6x = -10$				
5.	$x^2 = 6 - x$				
6.	$5x^2 - 6x = 0$				
7.	$x^2 + 0.36 = 1.2x$				
8.	$1.7x^2 + x + 1.9 = 0$				
9.	$1.5x^2 + 1.2x = 3.6$				
10.	$\frac{1}{4}x^2 + x = \frac{1}{8}$				
11.	$x^2 - \frac{1}{6}x = \frac{1}{6}$				
12.	$\frac{1}{5}x^2 + \frac{2}{3}x = -\frac{7}{8}$				

9.5 Writing Exercises

1. The term *discriminant* is an important term in this section. It is a derivative of the word *discriminate*. Look up this word in a dictionary, and select the definition that most fits its use in this section. Then use the definition to explain why the discriminant is so important to the study of quadratic equations presented here.

2. Although the arithmetic may become more tedious when you solve a quadratic equation whose coefficients are fractions, the quadratic formula still applies. You can choose to solve the equation with the fractions, or you can choose to use the least common denominator to first clear the equation of fractions and then apply the quadratic formula.

   First solve the equations with the fractions. Then clear the equations of fractions before solving. After solving the equations both ways, review your results. Is it better to clear the fractions before solving the equations? Explain.

   a. $\frac{5}{6}x^2 - \frac{4}{9}x - \frac{2}{3} = 0$ **b.** $\frac{1}{4} - \frac{1}{2}x - \frac{1}{9}x^2 = 0$

9.6 MORE REAL-WORLD MODELS

OBJECTIVES 1 Solve formulas for a variable.

2 Model real-world situations by recognizing special triangles.

APPLICATION

We can extend the Pythagorean theorem to three dimensions. The square of the length of the diagonal of a rectangular solid, d, is the sum of the squares of the length of the three sides of the solid, a, b, and c.

a. Determine a formula for the length of the diagonal of a rectangular solid, d.

b. According to the *Guinness Book of World Records*, the smallest video camera was manufactured in the United States by Super Circuits in the year 2000. The camera measures 1.62 centimeters on each side. Use the formula generated in part **a** to determine the length of the diagonal of the camera's interior.

We will discuss this application further in this section. See page 713.

Objective 9.6.1 **Solving Formulas for Variables**

We can use the process for solving polynomial equations to solve formulas for variables.

EXAMPLE 1 Solve the geometric formula for the indicated variable.

a. $A = \pi r^2$ for r

b. $V = \dfrac{1}{3}\pi R^2 + \dfrac{1}{3}\pi r^2$ for r

Solution

a. $A = \pi r^2$ Quadratic equation in terms of r

$\dfrac{A}{\pi} = r^2$ Divide both sides by π.

$r = \sqrt{\dfrac{A}{\pi}}$ Principle of square roots
Use the positive root for length of r.

b. $V = \dfrac{1}{3}\pi R^2 + \dfrac{1}{3}\pi r^2$

$3V = \pi R^2 + \pi r^2$ Multiply both sides by 3.

$3V - \pi R^2 = \pi r^2$ Subtract πR^2 from both sides.

$\dfrac{3V - \pi R^2}{\pi} = r^2$ Divide both sides by π.

$r = \sqrt{\dfrac{3V - \pi R^2}{\pi}}$ Principle of square roots
Use the positive root for length of r.

 TAKE NOTE We do not need to rationalize the denominator when we solve formulas for variables.

EXAMPLE 2 Solve for the indicated variable.

a. Vertical-position formula, $s = -16t^2 + v_0t$, for t.

b. Cylinder surface area formula, $S = 2\pi r^2 + 2\pi rh$, for r.

Solution

a. Solve $s = -16t^2 + v_0t$ for t.

$16t^2 - v_0t + s = 0$ Quadratic equation in terms of t; $a = 16$, $b = -v_0$, $c = s$

$$t = \frac{-b \pm \sqrt{b^2 - 4ac}}{2a}$$ Quadratic formula

$$t = \frac{-(-v_0) \pm \sqrt{(-v_0)^2 - 4(16)(s)}}{2(16)}$$ Substitute values for a, b, and c.

$$t = \frac{v_0 \pm \sqrt{v_0^2 - 64s}}{32}$$

b. Solve $S = 2\pi r^2 + 2\pi rh$ for r.

$2\pi r^2 + 2\pi rh - S = 0$ Quadratic equation in terms of r; $a = 2\pi$, $b = 2\pi h$, $c = -S$

$$r = \frac{-b \pm \sqrt{b^2 - 4ac}}{2a}$$ Quadratic formula

$$r = \frac{-(2\pi h) \pm \sqrt{(2\pi h)^2 - 4(2\pi)(-S)}}{2(2\pi)}$$ Substitute values for a, b, and c.

$$r = \frac{-2\pi h \pm \sqrt{4\pi^2 h^2 + 8\pi S}}{4\pi}$$ Simplify.

$$r = \frac{-2\pi h \pm \sqrt{4(\pi^2 h^2 + 2\pi S)}}{4\pi}$$ Factor out the perfect square of 4.

$$r = \frac{-2\pi h \pm 2\sqrt{\pi^2 h^2 + 2\pi S}}{4\pi}$$ $4 = 2^2$

$$r = \frac{\overset{1}{2}\left(-\pi h \pm \sqrt{\pi^2 h^2 + 2\pi S}\right)}{\underset{2}{4}\pi}$$ Factor out GCF of 2. Divide out factor of 2.

$$r = \frac{-\pi h \pm \sqrt{\pi^2 h^2 + 2\pi S}}{2\pi}$$

APPLICATION

We can extend the Pythagorean theorem to three dimensions. The square of the length of the diagonal of a rectangular solid, d, is the sum of the squares of the lengths of the three sides of the solid, a, b, and c.

a. Determine a formula for the length of the diagonal of a rectangular solid, d. That is, solve the given formula for d.

b. According to the *Guinness Book of World Records*, the smallest video camera was manufactured in the United States by Super Circuits in the year 2000. The camera measures 1.62 centimeters on each side. Use the formula generated in part **a** to determine the length of the diagonal of the camera's interior.

Discussion

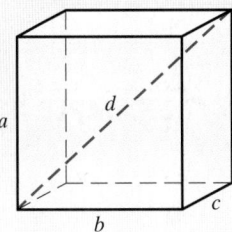

a. $a^2 + b^2 + c^2 = d^2$

$\sqrt{a^2 + b^2 + c^2} = \sqrt{d^2}$ Take the square root of both sides.

$\sqrt{a^2 + b^2 + c^2} = d$

or

$d = \sqrt{a^2 + b^2 + c^2}$

b. Substitute 1.62 for each of sides a, b, and c.

$$d = \sqrt{(1.62)^2 + (1.62)^2 + (1.62)^2}$$

$$d \approx 2.806$$

The diagonal of the tiny camera is about 2.806 centimeters.

Objective 9.6.1   CHECKUP

In exercises 1 and 2, solve each formula for the variable specified.

1. **a.** $A = s^2$ for s

   b. $V = \dfrac{1}{3}\pi R^2 + \dfrac{1}{3}\pi r^2$ for R

2. **a.** Pythagorean theorem, $a^2 + b^2 = c^2$, for the length of side a

   b. Surface area of an open canister, $A = \pi r^2 + 2\pi rh$, for the radius r

3. In August 1998, the world's smallest nightclub was opened by four British men. It was called the "Miniscule of Sound" and had a maximum capacity of 14 people, including the DJ! The nightclub was 8 feet by 4 feet by 8 feet in dimensions. Determine the length of a diagonal from one corner of the ceiling to the opposite corner of the floor.

Objective 9.6.2

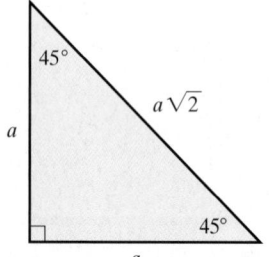

Special Triangles

Now we are ready to apply the Pythagorean theorem to some special triangles. First let's consider an isosceles right triangle. An **isosceles right triangle** has two **congruent** (equal) legs and two congruent (45°) angles opposite the congruent legs.

To determine the length of the hypotenuse in terms of the length of the congruent legs, we solve the Pythagorean theorem for c, substituting a for the length of each leg.

$$a^2 + b^2 = c^2$$
$$a^2 + a^2 = c^2 \qquad \text{Substitute.}$$
$$2a^2 = c^2 \qquad \text{Simplify.}$$
$$\pm\sqrt{2a^2} = c \qquad \text{Principle of square roots}$$
$$\pm a\sqrt{2} = c \qquad \text{Simplify.}$$

Therefore, the hypotenuse of an isosceles right triangle is $a\sqrt{2}$.

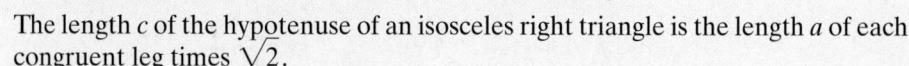
ISOSCELES RIGHT TRIANGLE (45°–45°–90°)

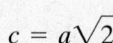
The length c of the hypotenuse of an isosceles right triangle is the length a of each congruent leg times $\sqrt{2}$.

$$c = a\sqrt{2}$$

For example, determine the hypotenuse of an isosceles right triangle if the length of each congruent leg is 5 cm.

$$c = a\sqrt{2}$$
$$c = 5\sqrt{2} \qquad \text{Substitute.}$$

The hypotenuse is $5\sqrt{2}$ cm, or approximately 7.071 cm.

EXAMPLE 3   Determine the length of each congruent leg of an isosceles right triangle if the hypotenuse is 5 cm.

Algebraic Solution

Substitute 5 for c in the formula and solve for a.

$$c = a\sqrt{2}$$
$$5 = a\sqrt{2} \qquad \text{Substitute.}$$
$$\frac{5}{\sqrt{2}} = \frac{a\sqrt{2}}{\sqrt{2}} \qquad \text{Divide both sides by } \sqrt{2}.$$
$$\frac{5}{\sqrt{2}} = a \qquad \text{Simplify.}$$
$$\frac{5}{\sqrt{2}} \cdot \frac{\sqrt{2}}{\sqrt{2}} = a \qquad \text{Rationalize the denominator.}$$
$$\frac{5\sqrt{2}}{2} = a \qquad \text{Simplify.}$$

The congruent legs are $\dfrac{5\sqrt{2}}{2}$ cm, or approximately 3.536 cm.

EXAMPLE 4   A single-engine airplane is flying at a low altitude. The pilot takes a reading on the power lines he is approaching. The angle between the horizontal and the power lines is 45°. The distance reading is 100 feet. If the pilot needs to clear the power lines at a height of 75 feet due to local regulations, will he need to adjust his present course?

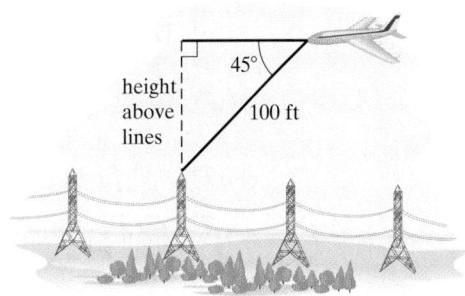

Algebraic Solution

Let x = height above power lines
The hypotenuse is 100 feet.

$$c = a\sqrt{2} \qquad {\scriptstyle c = 100,\ a = x}$$

$$100 = x\sqrt{2}$$

$$\frac{100}{\sqrt{2}} = x$$

$$\frac{100}{\sqrt{2}} \cdot \frac{\sqrt{2}}{\sqrt{2}} = x$$

$$\frac{100\sqrt{2}}{2} = x$$

$$50\sqrt{2} = x$$

$$x \approx 70.71 \text{ feet}$$

The pilot must adjust his altitude in order to clear the power lines at 75 feet. ■

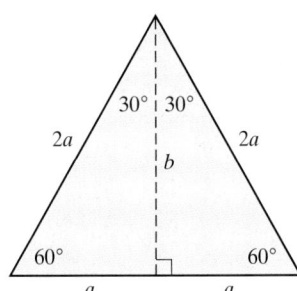

Now let's consider an equilateral triangle. An **equilateral triangle** has three congruent (equal) sides and three congruent (60°) angles. If we draw an altitude for this triangle, it will bisect an angle and the side opposite the angle. Then we will have two congruent right triangles. The angles will measure 30°–60°–90°, and the side opposite the 90° angle will be twice the length of the side opposite the 30° angle.

To determine the length of the second leg (the one opposite the 60° angle), we solve the Pythagorean theorem for b, substituting a for the length of the shorter leg and $2a$ for the length of the hypotenuse.

$$a^2 + b^2 = c^2$$

$$a^2 + b^2 = (2a)^2 \qquad {\scriptstyle \text{Substitute.}}$$

$$a^2 + b^2 = 4a^2 \qquad {\scriptstyle \text{Simplify.}}$$

$$b^2 = 4a^2 - a^2 \qquad {\scriptstyle \text{Subtract } a^2 \text{ from both sides.}}$$

$$b^2 = 3a^2 \qquad {\scriptstyle \text{Simplify.}}$$

$$b = \pm\sqrt{3a^2} \qquad {\scriptstyle \text{Principle of square roots}}$$

$$b = \pm a\sqrt{3} \qquad {\scriptstyle \text{Simplify.}}$$

Therefore, the side opposite the 60° angle of a 30°–60°–90° right triangle is $a\sqrt{3}$.

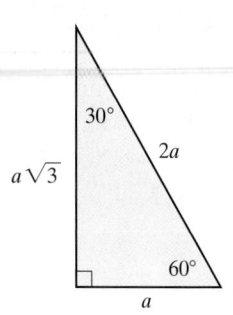

RIGHT TRIANGLE (30°–60°–90°)

The length c of the hypotenuse of a 30°–60°–90° triangle is twice the length a of the shorter side.

$$c = 2a$$

The length b of the longer leg of a 30°–60°–90° triangle is the length a of the shorter leg times $\sqrt{3}$.

$$b = a\sqrt{3}$$

For example, determine the length of the longer leg of a 30°–60°–90° triangle if the shorter leg is 5 inches.

Substitute 5 for a in the formula and solve for b.

$$b = a\sqrt{3}$$
$$b = 5\sqrt{3} \qquad \text{Substitute.}$$

The longer leg is $5\sqrt{3}$ inches, or approximately 8.660 inches.

EXAMPLE 5

Determine the length of the hypotenuse of a 30°–60°–90° triangle if the length of the side opposite the 60° angle is 5 inches.

Algebraic Solution

Use the formula for the longer side, $b = a\sqrt{3}$, substitute 5 for b, and solve for the shorter side, a.

$$b = a\sqrt{3}$$

$$5 = a\sqrt{3} \qquad \text{Substitute.}$$

$$\frac{5}{\sqrt{3}} = \frac{a\sqrt{3}}{\sqrt{3}} \qquad \text{Divide both sides by } \sqrt{3}.$$

$$\frac{5}{\sqrt{3}} = a \qquad \text{Simplify.}$$

$$\frac{5}{\sqrt{3}} \cdot \frac{\sqrt{3}}{\sqrt{3}} = a \qquad \text{Rationalize the denominator.}$$

$$\frac{5\sqrt{3}}{3} = a \qquad \text{Simplify.}$$

Now substitute for a in the formula for the hypotenuse, $c = 2a$.

$$c = 2a$$

$$c = 2\left(\frac{5\sqrt{3}}{3}\right) \qquad \text{Substitute.}$$

$$c = \frac{10\sqrt{3}}{3} \qquad \text{Simplify.}$$

Therefore, the hypotenuse is $\dfrac{10\sqrt{3}}{3}$ inches, or approximately 5.774 inches.   ■

EXAMPLE 6

It is recommended that an amateur diver stay within 30 feet of the surface of the water. An amateur diver carrying a homing device is alone in the water. At an angle from the water surface of 60°, a boat receiving the diver's signal measures the distance to the diver to be 40 feet. Is the diver out of the safety range?

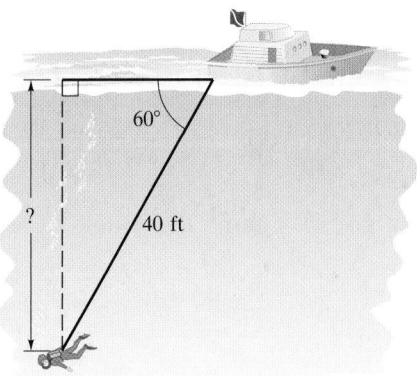

Algebraic Solution

The hypotenuse of the triangle (c) is 40 feet. We are looking for the side opposite the 60° angle (b).

$$c = 2a$$
$$40 = 2a \qquad \text{Substitute.}$$
$$20 = a$$

The shorter side is 20 feet.

$$b = a\sqrt{3}$$
$$b = 20\sqrt{3} \qquad \text{Substitute.}$$
$$b \approx 34.64$$

The diver is approximately 34.64 feet below the water surface. He is below the safety level for amateur divers.

 TAKE NOTE Remember that the special-triangle formulas are derived from the Pythagorean theorem. Therefore, if you do not remember them, you can always use the Pythagorean theorem to solve the problem. It will just take more steps.

✓ Objective 9.6.2 *CHECKUP*

1. Determine the length of each congruent leg of an isosceles right triangle whose hypotenuse measures 6 mm.

2. A ramp makes a 30° angle with the floor. If the vertical distance of the ramp is 3 feet, find the horizontal distance of the ramp and the ramp's length.

3. Describe the features of an isosceles right triangle.

4. Describe the features of an equilateral triangle.

5. Describe the features of a 30°–60°–90° triangle.

9.6 EXERCISES

 Student Solutions Manual    PH Math/Tutor Center   CD Video   *Math*XL MathXL®   *MyMathLab* MyMathLab   Interactmath.com

In exercises 1–32, solve each formula for the specified variable.

1. $E = mc^2$ for c

2. $A = 4\pi r^2$ for r

3. $V = \pi r^2 h$ for r

4. $F = \dfrac{mv^2}{R}$ for v

5. $E = \dfrac{1}{2}mv^2$ for v

6. $A = \dfrac{\pi r^2 S}{360}$ for r

7. $C = \dfrac{n(n-1)}{2}$ for n

8. $S = \dfrac{n(n+1)}{2}$ for n

9. $x^2 - y^2 = c^2$ for x

10. $x^2 + y^2 = r^2$ for x

11. $F = mw^2r$ for w

12. $w = I^2Rt$ for I

13. $w_k = (m - m_0)c^2$ for c

14. $a = -4\pi^2f^2x$ for f

15. $s = \dfrac{1}{2}at^2$ for t

16. $P = \dfrac{1}{3}Nm_1v^2$ for v

17. $v^2 = v_0^2 + 2as$ for v_0

18. $w_1^2 = w_0^2 + 2\alpha\theta$ for w_0

19. $I = \dfrac{c}{r^2}$ for r

20. $E = k\dfrac{q_1}{r^2}$ for r

21. $F = g\dfrac{mM}{r^2}$ for r

22. $e = \dfrac{Em}{B^2r}$ for B

23. $I = m_1r_1^2 + m_2r_2^2$ for r_2

24. $I = I_G + mh^2$ for h

25. $F = \dfrac{1}{2}kx^2 - \dfrac{1}{2}ky^2$ for x

26. $F = \dfrac{1}{2}kx^2 - \dfrac{1}{2}ky^2$ for y

27. $y - 3 = -4(x + 7)^2$ for x

28. $(x + 5)^2 + (y - 3)^2 = 9$ for x

29. $S = 2\pi r^2 + 2\pi rh$ for r

30. $a^2 = b^2 + c^2 - 2bc$ for b

31. $A = P(1 + r)^2$ for r

32. $S = 16t^2 + gt$ for t

Use the properties of an isosceles right triangle to solve. Round your answers to the nearest hundredth.

33. Determine the length of the hypotenuse of an isosceles right triangle whose legs measure 3.75 meters.

34. What is the length of the hypotenuse of an isosceles right triangle whose legs measure 6.55 feet?

35. What will be the lengths of the legs of an isosceles right triangle whose hypotenuse measures 7.6 feet?

36. If the hypotenuse of an isosceles right triangle measures 14.9 centimeters, what are the lengths of its legs?

37. The top of a telephone pole is anchored with a guy wire that makes a 45-degree angle with the ground. If the pole is 20 feet high, how long is the guy wire?

38. A guy wire makes a 45-degree angle from the ground to the top of a pole. The wire is anchored 15 feet away from the base of the pole. How long is the wire?

39. A wire runs from the top of a building to the ground at a 45-degree angle. If the wire is 42.5 feet long, how high is the building?

40. A wire at a boot camp runs from the top of a tower to the ground at a 45-degree angle. If the wire is 145 feet long, how high is the tower?

41. An amateur diver is expected to stay within 30 feet of the surface of the water. His homing device sends a signal back to the boat at an angle of 45° from the water level and from a distance of 40 feet. Is the diver within the expected depth?

42. The amateur diver in exercise **41** moves further in the water and now sends a signal back to the boat at an angle of 45° from the water level, but from a distance of 50 feet. Is the diver within the expected depth?

In exercises 43–52, assume that the right triangles are 30°–60°–90° triangles, and use the properties of such triangles to solve. Round your answers to the nearest tenth.

43. Determine the lengths of the unknown sides of a triangle if the side opposite the 60° angle measures 18.6 inches.

44. In a triangle, if the side opposite the 60° angle measures 2.19 centimeters, find the lengths of the other sides of the triangle.

45. Given that the hypotenuse of a triangle measures 22 inches, what are the lengths of the legs?

46. What are the measures of the legs of a triangle if the hypotenuse measures 34 centimeters?

47. If the short leg of a triangle measures 21 centimeters, what are the lengths of the other sides?

48. What will be the lengths of the other sides when the length of the short leg of a triangle measures 8.2 inches?

49. An airplane is flying at an altitude of 4000 feet and is approaching the runway at a 30-degree angle. Find the horizontal distance to the set-down point on the runway and the slanted distance from the plane to the runway.

50. A kite is 120 feet above the ground. The string to the kite makes a 60-degree angle with the ground. Find the horizontal distance between the kite and its flyer and the length of the string between the kite and its flyer.

51. A guy wire reaches from the top of a pole to the ground at a 60-degree angle. The distance between the base of the pole and the point at which the wire is anchored to the ground measures 8 feet. Find the height of the pole and the length of the wire.

52. A telephone pole is 13 meters high. The pole is anchored with a guy wire that makes a 60-degree angle with the ground. How much wire is needed, and how far from the base of the pole should it be anchored?

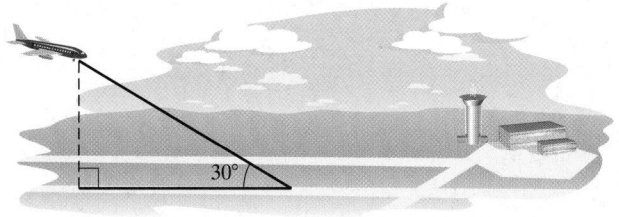

In exercises 53–60, use the properties of right triangles and your knowledge of geometry. Do not round your answers. Give exact measurements.

53. If a square has side 11 meters, find the length of its diagonal.

54. If the diagonal of a square is 7 meters, find the length of a side of the square.

55. If a cube has side 5 centimeters, find the length of its diagonal.

56. If the diagonal of a cube is 9 feet, find the length of a side of the cube.

57. An equilateral triangle has side 6 yards. Find its height. What is the area of the triangle?

58. An equilateral triangle has side 10 feet. Find its height. What is the area of the triangle?

59. An isosceles triangle has base 4 feet and base angles of 45 degrees. Find the length of the corresponding height. What is the area of the triangle? What is the perimeter of the triangle?

60. An isosceles triangle has height 7 meters and base angles of 45 degrees. Find the length of the corresponding base. What is the area of the triangle? What is the perimeter of the triangle?

9.6 Calculator Exercises

Remember that you can check your calculations for special triangles by using the Pythagorean theorem and your calculator. In Example 3 of this section, you determined that if the hypotenuse of an isosceles right triangle was $c = 5$ cm, then the length of each congruent leg was $a = \dfrac{5\sqrt{2}}{2}$ cm. To check this on the calculator, store the values for a and c, and type the Pythagorean theorem when $a = b$. If the calculator displays 1, the theorem holds; if the calculator displays 0, the theorem does not hold and an error has been made. The screen for this example follows:

```
5→C: (5√(2))/2→A:
A²+A²=C²
                     1
```

To check Example 5, store 5 for b, $\dfrac{5\sqrt{3}}{3}$ for a, and $\dfrac{10\sqrt{3}}{3}$ for c. The screen for this example follows:

```
5→B: (5√(3))/3→A:
(10√(3))/3→C: A²+
B²=C²
                     1
```

Use the method to check the following special-triangle calculations:

1. Given an isosceles right triangle with legs of length a and hypotenuse of length c, check the following pairs of values:

   a. $a = 8, c = 8\sqrt{2}$ **b.** $a = 12, c = 12\sqrt{3}$

   c. $a = 6\sqrt{2}, c = 12$ **d.** $a = \dfrac{8\sqrt{3}}{3}, c = 8$

2. Given a 30°–60°–90° triangle with legs of length a and b and hypotenuse of length c, check the following triples of values:

   a. $a = 5, b = 5\sqrt{3}, c = 10$

   b. $a = 10, b = 10\sqrt{3}, c = 5$

   c. $a = 5, b = 5\sqrt{2}, c = 10$

   d. $a = 5, b = 10, c = 5\sqrt{3}$

   e. $a = 10, b = 10\sqrt{3}, c = 20$

9.6 Writing Exercises

In this section, you were given formulas to be used to determine the lengths of the sides of special right triangles. Unless you are very careful, it is easy to make a mistake in trying to recall which formula to use. You may confuse which formula to assign to which side of the triangle, or you may not remember whether to use a factor of $\sqrt{2}$ or of $\sqrt{3}$. However, one of the helping hands in this section suggested that you can always fall back on the Pythagorean theorem to calculate the lengths of the sides of these special triangles. Explain how you would determine all sides of the following triangles:

1. An isosceles right triangle when you know the length of one of the congruent legs.

2. An isosceles right triangle when you know the length of the hypotenuse.

3. A 30°–60°–90° triangle when you know the length of the shortest leg.

4. A 30°–60°–90° triangle when you know the length of the longest leg.

5. A 30°–60°–90° triangle when you know the length of the hypotenuse.

6. An equilateral triangle when you know the height of the triangle.

9.7 MORE QUADRATIC FUNCTIONS AND THEIR GRAPHS

OBJECTIVES

1. Analyze the graph of a quadratic function.
2. Algebraically determine the intercepts of a quadratic function.
3. Algebraically determine the vertex of a parabola.
4. Graph a quadratic function.
5. Write a quadratic function given the x-intercepts of its graph.
6. Analyze the graph of real data modeled by a quadratic function.

APPLICATION

Using data from annual financial reports for Gateway, Inc., a quadratic function for the amount of revenue from sales in millions of dollars is $R(x) = 508x^2 - 1277x + 4171$, where x is the number of years after 2002.

a. Assuming that the equation continues to apply, determine the minimum revenue from sales and in what year it occurred.

b. What was the amount of revenue from sales in 2002?

c. Assuming that the equation continues to apply, in what year will the company rebound to its 2002 revenue from sales?

We will discuss this application further in this section. See page 734.

Objective 9.7.1   **Analyzing Quadratic Function Graphs**

In Chapter 1, we introduced functions and analyzed their graphs. We continued this discussion in Chapter 3, when we discussed linear functions of the form $f(x) = mx + b$. In Chapter 6, we expanded this discussion with polynomial functions. In that chapter, we relied on our calculator to help us analyze the graphs. We are now ready to return to the topic of polynomial functions and analyze the graphs using our algebra skills.

Remember, polynomial functions are classified by their degree.

$f(x) = 2x - 3$	The degree is one, and the function is called a linear function.
$f(x) = x^2 + 6x + 5$	The degree is two, and the function is called a quadratic function.
$f(x) = x^3 - 2x^2 + x + 4$	The degree is three, and the function is called a cubic function.

In this section we will limit our discussion to quadratic functions. However, the graphs of the other polynomial functions may be analyzed using similar techniques.

In Chapter 6, we analyzed the graph of a quadratic function. Each quadratic function graphed as a U-shaped curve called a parabola. Let's analyze the graph of a quadratic function and review what we have previously learned.

EXAMPLE 1   Given the graph, $y = f(x)$,

a. Find the domain and range.

b. Find the x-intercepts and the y-intercept.

c. Determine if the graph is concave upward or concave downward.

d. Find the vertex and determine the axis of symmetry.

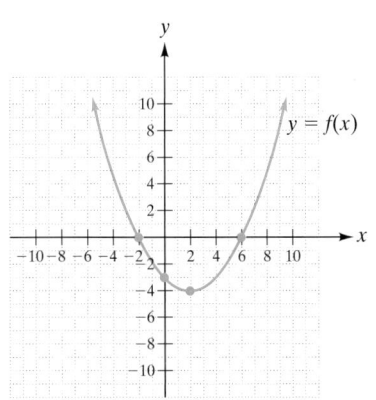

e. Find the relative maximum and relative minimum. Find the absolute maximum and absolute minimum. Find the *x*-values for which the function is increasing and for which it is decreasing.

f. Find the *x*-values for which the *y*-values are equal to zero.

g. Find the solutions of $f(x) = 0$.

Solution

a.

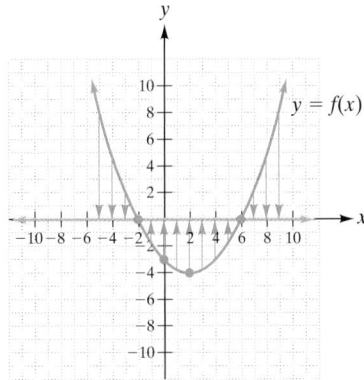

To find the domain, we project the graph onto the *x*-axis. The domain is the set of all real numbers, or $(-\infty, \infty)$.

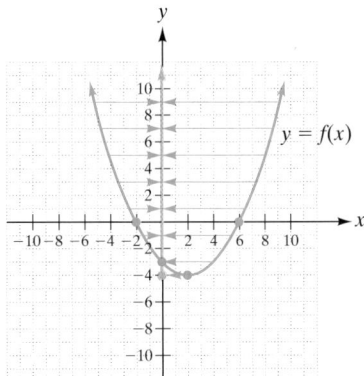

To find the range, we project the graph onto the *y*-axis. The range is the set of all real numbers greater than or equal to −4, or $[-4, \infty)$.

b.

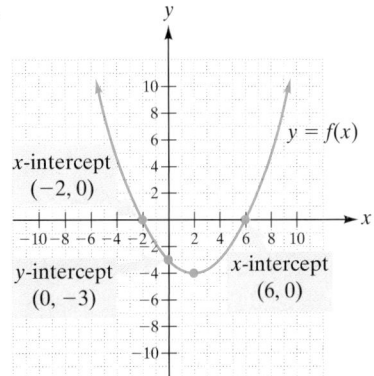

The *x*-intercepts, $(-2, 0)$ and $(6, 0)$, are the ordered pairs where the graph touches or crosses the *x*-axis. The *y*-intercept, $(0, -3)$, is the ordered pair where the graph touches or crosses the *y*-axis. Since the graph of a quadratic is U-shaped, there will be only one *y*-intercept and at most two *x*-intercepts.

c. The graph is concave upward because it opens upward.

d.

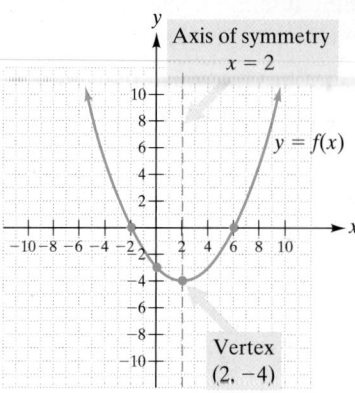

The vertex is the lowest point on a concave upward graph, or the point $(2, -4)$. The axis of symmetry, $x = 2$, is the vertical line through the vertex.

e.

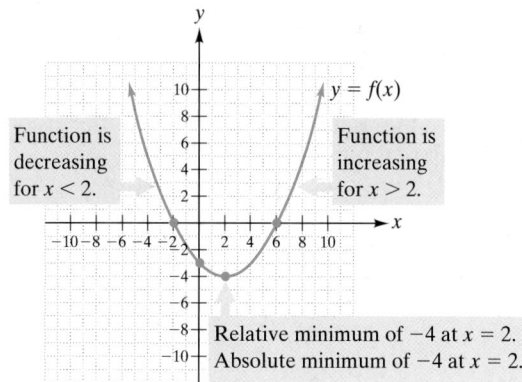

The graph has one low point, $(2, -4)$. This means that the function has a relative minimum of -4 at $x = 2$. The absolute minimum value of the function is also -4 at $x = 2$ because it is the smallest function value. The graph does not have any high points so the function does not have a relative maximum. The function increases without bound so it has no absolute maximum.

The function is decreasing for $x < 2$, $(-\infty, 2)$, (at $x = 2$ the function has attained its absolute minimum value) and increasing for $x > 2$, $(2, \infty)$.

f. The x-values, -2 and 6, for which $y = 0$, are the x-values of the x-intercept.

g. The solutions of $f(x) = 0$ are the x-values for which $y = f(x) = 0$. As stated in part **f**, these values are -2 and 6. ■

✓ Objective 9.7.1 *CHECKUP*

1. Given the following graph, $y = f(x)$,

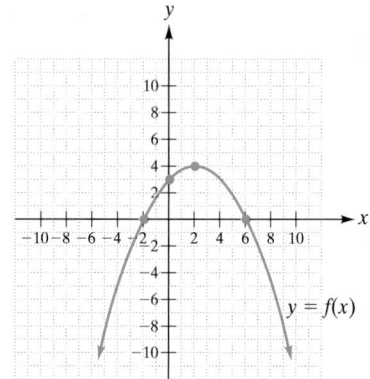

a. Find the domain and range.
b. Find the x-intercepts and the y-intercept.
c. Determine if the graph is concave upward or concave downward.
d. Find the vertex and determine the axis of symmetry.
e. Find the relative maximum and relative minimum. Find the absolute maximum and absolute minimum. Find the x-values for which the function is increasing and for which it is decreasing.
f. Find the x-values for which the y-values are equal to zero.
g. Find the solutions of $f(x) = 0$.

2. An absolute maximum is always a relative maximum but a relative maximum may not be an absolute maximum. Explain. ■

Objective 9.7.2

Determining the Intercepts

Since the y-intercept is the point on a graph where the graph touches or crosses the y-axis, we know that this point has an x-coordinate equal to zero. To determine the y-intercept of a graph algebraically from its equation, let $x = 0$, solve the resulting equation for y, and write an ordered pair.

Since the x-intercept is the point on a graph where the graph touches or crosses the x-axis, we know that this point has a y-coordinate equal to 0. To determine the x-intercept of a graph algebraically from its equation, let $y = 0$, solve the resulting equation for x, and write an ordered pair.

 TAKE NOTE To determine algebraically the intercepts of the graph of a quadratic function, we use the same procedure that we used for linear functions.

EXAMPLE 2

Determine algebraically the x-intercepts and the y-intercept of the graph of the quadratic function, $g(x) = x^2 + 2x - 8$.

Solution

x-intercept

Let $y = g(x) = 0$ and solve for x.

$$g(x) = x^2 + 2x - 8$$
$$0 = x^2 + 2x - 8$$
$$0 = (x + 4)(x - 2)$$
$$x + 4 = 0 \quad \text{or} \quad x - 2 = 0$$
$$x = -4 \qquad\qquad x = 2$$

The x-intercepts of the graph of $g(x) = x^2 + 2x - 8$ are $(-4, 0)$ and $(2, 0)$.

Check

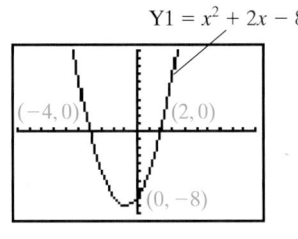

$(-10, 10, -10, 10)$

y-intercept

Let $x = 0$.

$$g(x) = x^2 + 2x - 8$$
$$g(0) = (0)^2 + 2(0) - 8$$
$$g(0) = -8$$

The y-intercept of the graph of $g(x) = x^2 + 2x - 8$ is $(0, -8)$. ◼

 TAKE NOTE Remember, the y-coordinate of the y-intercept is the constant term of the quadratic function. The x-coordinate of the y-intercept is 0. We should be able to determine the y-intercept without using algebra.

Objective 9.7.2 *CHECKUP*

1. Determine algebraically the x-intercepts and the y-intercept of the graph of the polynomial function, $f(x) = x^2 - 2x - 3$. Check your results on your calculator.

2. The graph of a quadratic function will have one y-intercept. Explain.

Objective 9.7.3

Determining the Vertex

In Chapter 6, we defined the standard form for a quadratic function.

STANDARD FORM FOR A QUADRATIC FUNCTION

A quadratic function can be written in the standard form $f(x) = ax^2 + bx + c$, where $a \neq 0$.

In Chapter 6, we also defined the vertex of a parabola as its highest point or lowest point and determined the vertex both graphically and algebraically. To determine the vertex algebraically, we used the vertex formula.

VERTEX FORMULA

The graph of $f(x) = ax^2 + bx + c, a \neq 0$ is a parabola with a vertex of $\left(\dfrac{-b}{2a}, f\left(\dfrac{-b}{2a}\right) \right)$.

In this section we will continue this discussion. In the writing exercise at the end of this section, we will derive the vertex formula.

The vertex of the parabola is important in the analysis of its corresponding quadratic function. The quadratic function, $f(x) = ax^2 + bx + c$, whose graph is concave downward has an absolute maximum value of $f\left(\dfrac{-b}{2a}\right)$ at $x = \dfrac{-b}{2a}$. The quadratic function, $f(x) = ax^2 + bx + c$, whose graph is concave upward has an absolute minimum value of $f\left(\dfrac{-b}{2a}\right)$ at $x = \dfrac{-b}{2a}$.

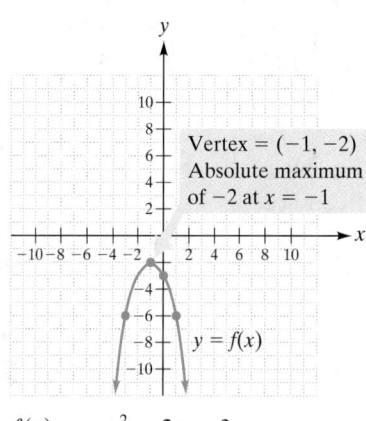

$f(x) = -x^2 - 2x - 3$
concave downward

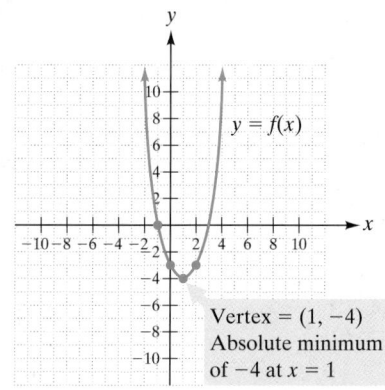

$f(x) = x^2 - 2x - 3$
concave upward

EXAMPLE 3

Algebraically determine the vertex of the quadratic function, $g(x) = x^2 + 2x - 8$.

Solution

The coefficients of $g(x) = x^2 + 2x - 8$ are $a = 1, b = 2$, and $c = -8$.

Use the vertex formula, $\left(\dfrac{-b}{2a}, g\left(\dfrac{-b}{2a}\right) \right)$.

$x = \dfrac{-b}{2a} = \dfrac{-(2)}{2(1)} = -1 \qquad g\left(\dfrac{-b}{2a}\right)$

$g(-1) = (-1)^2 + 2(-1) - 8$

$g(-1) = -9$

The vertex is $\left(\dfrac{-b}{2a}, g\left(\dfrac{-b}{2a}\right) \right)$ or $(-1, -9)$.

Check

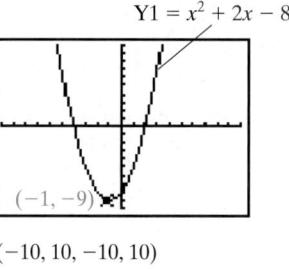

$(-10, 10, -10, 10)$

✓ Objective 9.7.3 *CHECKUP*

1. Algebraically determine the vertex of the quadratic function, $g(x) = x^2 - 2x - 3$.

2. The definition of the standard form of a quadratic function states that $a \neq 0$. Explain.

Graphing Quadratic Functions

In Chapter 6, we also determined that the coefficients, a, b, and c, of a quadratic function written in standard form affect the graph of the function. Now let's combine all that we have discussed to graph a quadratic function.

GRAPHING A QUADRATIC FUNCTION

To graph a quadratic function of the form $y = f(x) = ax^2 + bx + c$,

1. Determine whether the parabola is concave upward ($a > 0$) or concave downward ($a < 0$).

2. Determine the width of the parabola in comparison to the graph of $y = x^2$. The parabola is the same width as $y = x^2$ when $|a| = 1$; the parabola is narrower than the graph of $y = x^2$ when $|a| > 1$; the parabola is wider than the graph of $y = x^2$ when $|a| < 1$.

3. Determine the y-intercept of the parabola. The y-intercept is $(0, c)$.

4. Determine the x-intercept(s). Let $y = f(x) = 0$, and solve for x.

5. Determine the vertex, $\left(\dfrac{-b}{2a}, f\left(\dfrac{-b}{2a} \right) \right)$.

6. Determine the axis of symmetry, $x = \dfrac{-b}{2a}$.

7. Plot the intercepts and the vertex along with the axis of symmetry. Locate additional points as needed to complete the curve. Label all points graphed. Connect the points with a smooth curve to complete the graph.

EXAMPLE 4

Graph the quadratic function, $g(x) = x^2 + 2x - 8$.

Solution

The coefficients of $g(x) = x^2 + 2x - 8$ are $a = 1$, $b = 2$, and $c = -8$.

1. The graph is concave upward, because $1 > 0$ (a is positive).

2. The graph has the same width as the graph of $y = x^2$, because $a = 1$.

3. The $g(x)$-intercept is $(0, -8)$. (The x-coordinate is always 0 and $c = -8$.)

4. The x-intercepts are $(-4, 0)$ and $(2, 0)$. (See Example 2.)

5. The vertex is $(-1, -9)$. (See Example 3.)

6. The axis of symmetry is $x = \dfrac{-b}{2a}$ or $x = -1$.

7. Plot and label the following points.

x	$g(x)$	
0	-8	$g(x)$-intercept
-4	0	x-intercept
2	0	x-intercept
-1	-9	Vertex

Draw the axis of symmetry with a dashed line and label.

The parabola is symmetric about the axis of symmetry. Therefore, an ordered pair, $(-2, -8)$, would be located to the left of the axis the same number of units as the ordered pair $(0, -8)$ is located to the right of the axis of symmetry.

If we determine additional points using $x = 1$ and $x = 3$, we can complete the graph.

$$g(1) = (1)^2 + 2(1) - 8 = -5$$
$$g(3) = (3)^2 + 2(3) - 8 = 7$$

Graph the ordered pairs, $(1, -5)$ and $(3, 7)$, and the two points symmetric about the axis to the ordered pairs, $(-3, -5)$ and $(-5, 7)$.

Draw a smooth curve to complete the graph and label.

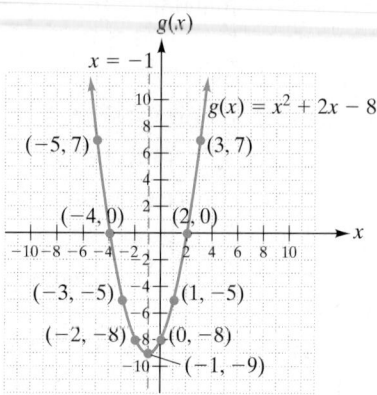

EXAMPLE 5   Graph the quadratic function, $f(x) = -2x^2 - 4x - 3$.

Solution

The coefficients of $f(x) = -2x^2 - 4x - 3$ are $a = -2$, $b = -4$, and $c = -3$.

1. The graph is concave downward, because $-2 < 0$ (a is negative).

2. The graph is narrower than the graph of $y = x^2$, because $|-2| > 1$.

3. The $f(x)$-intercept is $(0, -3)$. (The x-coordinate is always 0 and $c = -3$.)

4. Let $f(x) = 0$ and solve for x to determine the x-intercepts.

$$f(x) = -2x^2 - 4x - 3$$
$$0 = -2x^2 - 4x - 3$$

We will solve by the quadratic formula. Let $a = -2$, $b = -4$, and $c = -3$.

$$x = \frac{-b \pm \sqrt{b^2 - 4ac}}{2a}$$

$$x = \frac{-(-4) \pm \sqrt{(-4)^2 - 4(-2)(-3)}}{2(-2)} \qquad \text{Substitute values for } a, b, \text{ and } c.$$

$$x = \frac{4 \pm \sqrt{16 - 24}}{-4} \qquad \text{Simplify.}$$

$$x = \frac{4 \pm \sqrt{-8}}{-4}$$

There are no real number solutions because the radicand (discriminant) is negative. Therefore, there are no x-intercepts.

5. Use the vertex formula, $\left(\dfrac{-b}{2a}, f\left(\dfrac{-b}{2a} \right) \right)$, to find the vertex.

Substitute values for a and b.

$$x = \frac{-b}{2a} \qquad\qquad f\left(\frac{-b}{2a} \right) = f(-1) = -2(-1)^2 - 4(-1) - 3 = -1$$

$$x = \frac{-(-4)}{2(-2)}$$

$$x = \frac{4}{-4}$$

$$x = -1$$

The vertex is $(-1, -1)$.

6. The axis of symmetry is $x = \dfrac{-b}{2a}$ or $x = -1$.

7. Plot and label the following points.

x	$f(x)$	
0	−3	f(x)-intercept
−1	−1	vertex

Draw the axis of symmetry with a dashed line and label.

The parabola is symmetric about the axis of symmetry. Therefore, an ordered pair, $(-2, -3)$, would be located to the left of the axis the same number of units as the ordered pair $(0, -3)$ is located to the right of the axis of symmetry.

If we determine an additional point for $x = 1$, we can complete the graph.

$$f(1) = -2(1)^2 - 4(1) - 3 = -9$$

Graph the ordered pair, $(1, -9)$, and the point symmetric about the axis to the ordered pair, $(-3, -9)$.

Draw a smooth curve to complete the graph and label.

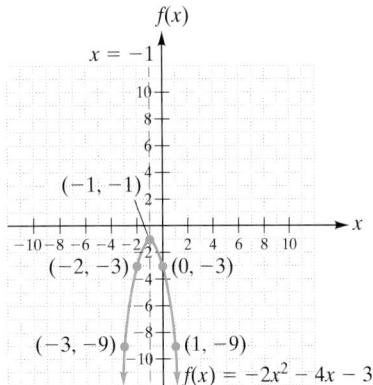

Objective 9.7.4 **CHECKUP**

1. Graph the quadratic function, $g(x) = x^2 - 2x - 3$.

2. Graph the quadratic function, $f(x) = \dfrac{1}{2}x^2 + 2x + 6$.

3. Explain the relationship between the coordinates of the vertex and the equation of the axis of symmetry.

Objective 9.7.5   Writing a Quadratic Function from Its *x*-Intercepts

In this chapter, we discovered that the solutions of a quadratic equation in the form $ax^2 + bx + c = 0$ are the x-coordinates of the x-intercepts of the graph of its corresponding equation, $f(x) = ax^2 + bx + c$. Therefore, if we know the x-coordinates of the x-intercepts, we can write an equation for which they are the solutions and then write its corresponding function. We will reverse the zero factor property.

CONVERSE OF THE ZERO FACTOR PROPERTY

If either $a = 0$ or $b = 0$, or both, then $ab = 0$.

EXAMPLE 6

The x-intercepts of the graph for a quadratic function are $\left(\dfrac{3}{4}, 0\right)$ and $(3, 0)$. Write such a quadratic function.

Solution

The solutions to the corresponding equation, $ax^2 + bx + c = 0$, are $x = \dfrac{3}{4}$ and $x = 3$. If we reverse the process of solving using the zero product property, we will find an original equation.

Rewrite the equations for the solutions as expressions equal to 0.

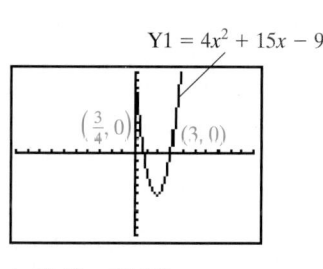

Y1 = $4x^2 + 15x - 9$

$\left(\dfrac{3}{4}, 0\right)$ $(3, 0)$

$(-10, 10, -10, 10)$

$x = \dfrac{3}{4}$ 　　　　　　　　　　　　　　　　　　　　 $x = 3$

$x - \dfrac{3}{4} = 0$ 　Subtract $\dfrac{3}{4}$ from both sides. 　　$x - 3 = 0$ 　Subtract 3 from both sides.

$4x - 3 = 0$ 　Multiply both sides by 4.

$(4x - 3)(x - 3) = 0$ 　Converse of the zero factor property

$4x^2 - 12x - 3x + 9 = 0$ 　Multiply.

$4x^2 - 15x + 9 = 0$

The graph of the function, $f(x) = 4x^2 - 15x + 9$, has two x-intercepts, $\left(\dfrac{3}{4}, 0\right)$ and $(3, 0)$.

 TAKE NOTE The graphs of many other quadratic functions have the same x-intercepts. We can find these functions by multiplying both sides of the equation $4x^2 - 15x + 9 = 0$ by any nonzero real number. For example,

Multiply by -1: 　$-4x^2 + 15x - 9 = 0$ 　results in $f(x) = -4x^2 + 15x - 9$

Multiply by 2: 　$8x^2 - 30x + 18 = 0$ 　results in $f(x) = 8x^2 - 30x + 18$

The graphs of each of these functions have the same x-intercepts.

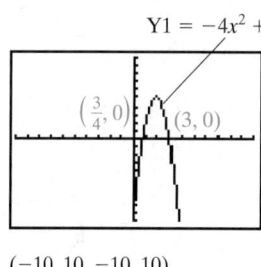

Y1 = $-4x^2 + 15x - 9$

$\left(\dfrac{3}{4}, 0\right)$ $(3, 0)$

$(-10, 10, -10, 10)$

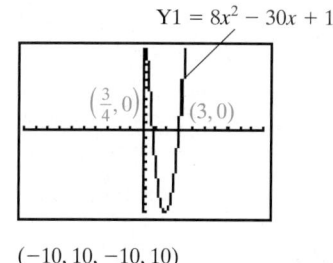

Y1 = $8x^2 - 30x + 18$

$\left(\dfrac{3}{4}, 0\right)$ $(3, 0)$

$(-10, 10, -10, 10)$

✓ Objective 9.7.5 *CHECKUP*

1. The x-intercepts of the graph for a quadratic function are $\left(\dfrac{2}{3}, 0\right)$ and $(-3, 0)$. Write such a quadratic function, $g(x)$.

2. In this section we discussed the converse of the zero factor property. State the zero factor property.

Objective 9.7.6 　### Modeling the Real World

As we have seen in this chapter, many situations may be modeled by a quadratic function. If we graph the quadratic function, we can better describe the relationship between the two variables. For example, we have observed that the vertical height of an object, such as a football, is related to the time after it is released and can be modeled by a quadratic function.

EXAMPLE 7

The height of a football with respect to the time in the air is represented in the accompanying graph.

a. What was the initial height of the football?

b. How high was the football after 1 second?

c. What was the maximum height of the football?

d. When did the maximum height occur?

e. After the football has been in the air a half of a second, a player on the opposing team jumps vertically 10 feet. Can he catch the football?

f. When does the football reach the ground?

Solution

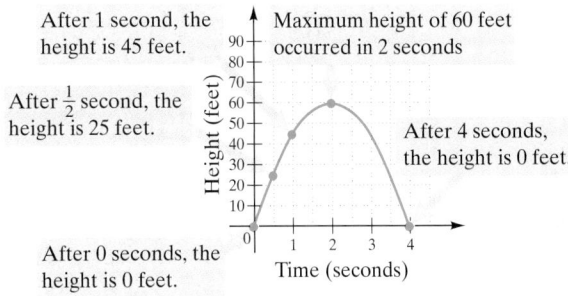

a. At $t = 0$ second, the height is 0 feet. Therefore, the initial height of the football was ground level. (The football was kicked, not thrown.)

b. At $t = 1$ second, the height was approximately 45 feet.

c. The maximum height of the football was 60 feet.

d. The maximum height occurred two seconds after the football was in the air.

e. At $t = \dfrac{1}{2}$ second, the height was approximately 25 feet. Therefore, the opposing player jumping 10 feet vertically could not catch the football.

f. At $t = 4$ seconds, the football returns to the ground. (It originally was at ground level.) ■

EXAMPLE 8

A signal flare is shot upward from a cliff 100 meters high. If the initial velocity of the flare is 91.2 meters per second, a function for the position (in meters) of the flare above ground is $s(t) = -4.9t^2 + 91.2t + 100$, where t is time in seconds.

a. What is the height of the flare after 3 seconds?

b. What is the maximum height of the flare? When did the maximum height occur?

c. When did the flare return to its original height?

d. When did the flare hit the ground below the cliff?

e. Graph the position of the flare in terms of t seconds.

Solution

a. Let $t = 3$ seconds.

$$s(3) = -4.9(3)^2 + 91.2(3) + 100 = 329.5$$

The flare height in 3 seconds is 329.5 meters.

b. The function is concave downward because the coefficient a, -4.9, is negative. Therefore, the function attains a maximum value at its vertex. Use the vertex formula $\left(\dfrac{-b}{2a}, s\left(\dfrac{-b}{2a} \right) \right)$.

$$t = \frac{-b}{2a} = \frac{-91.2}{2 \cdot -4.9} \approx 9.31 \qquad \text{Substitute } a = -4.9 \text{ and } b = 91.2.$$

$$s(9.31) = -4.9(9.31)^2 + 91.2(9.31) + 100 = 524.36$$

After approximately 9.31 seconds, the flare will reach its maximum height of 524.36 meters.

c. Let $s(t) = 100$ meters (the original height)

$$s(t) = -4.9t^2 + 91.2t + 100$$
$$100 = -4.9t^2 + 91.2t + 100 \qquad \text{Substitute } s(t) = 100.$$
$$0 = -4.9t^2 + 91.2t \qquad \text{Subtract 100 from both sides.}$$
$$0 = t(-4.9t + 91.2) \qquad \text{Factor.}$$
$$t = 0 \quad \text{or} \quad -4.9t + 91.2 = 0 \qquad \text{Zero factor property}$$
$$-4.9t = -91.2$$
$$t \approx 18.6$$

The flare will return to its original height of 100 meters in about 18.6 seconds. (Note that $t = 0$ is when the flare was shot.)

d. Let $s(t) = 0$ (meters above ground level)

$$s(t) = -4.9t^2 + 91.2t + 100$$
$$0 = -4.9t^2 + 91.2t + 100 \qquad \text{Substitute } s(t) = 0.$$

Solve for t using the quadratic formula.

$$t = \frac{-b \pm \sqrt{b^2 - 4ac}}{2a} \qquad \text{Quadratic formula}$$

$$t = \frac{-91.2 \pm \sqrt{(91.2)^2 - 4(-4.9)(100)}}{2(-4.9)} \qquad \text{Substitute } a = -4.9, b = 91.2, c = 100.$$

$$t = \frac{-91.2 \pm \sqrt{10277.44}}{-9.8} \qquad \text{Simplify.}$$

$$t \approx -1.04, t \approx 19.65$$

The flare hit the ground in about 19.65 seconds. (We do not use the negative solution.)

e. The function is concave downward with a vertex of $(9.31, 524.36)$. The axis of symmetry is $t = 9.31$. The $s(t)$-intercept is $(0, 100)$, when the flare was shot at $t = 0$ second at a height of 100 meters. The t-intercept is $(19.65, 0)$, when the flare hit the ground. We also have the ordered pairs $(3, 329.5)$ and $(18.6, 100)$.

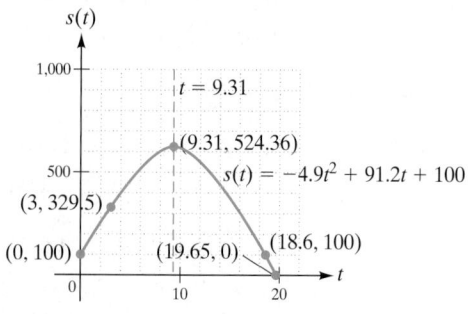

We have also modeled business applications that involve revenue, cost, and profit. Let us discuss these applications and look at the graphs of these functions.

EXAMPLE 9   A manufacturer of chairs determines the revenue, cost, and profit for producing and selling x chairs. Analyze the following graphs.

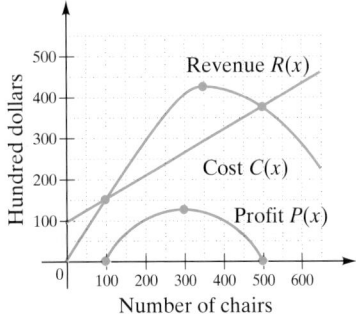

a. Find the manufacturer's break-even points.

b. Find the number of chairs produced and sold that will maximize the revenue. What is the maximum revenue?

c. Find the x-intercepts of the graph of the profit function. Discuss the significance of these points.

d. Find the number of chairs that will maximize the profit. What is the maximum profit?

Solution

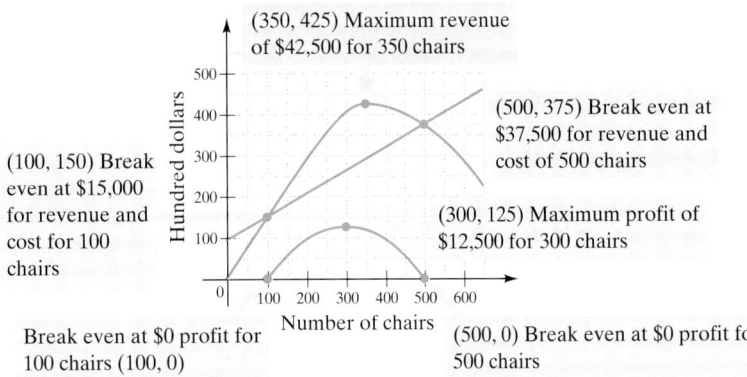

a. The manufacturer breaks even when the revenue is equal to the cost. The points of intersection of the graph of the revenue function and the graph of the cost function are (100, 150) and (500, 375). The manufacturer will break even when 100 chairs are produced and sold for $15,000 and 500 chairs are produced and sold for $37,500.

b. The vertex of the revenue function is (350, 425). Three hundred fifty chairs sold will maximize the revenue at $42,500.

c. The x-intercepts of the profit are (100, 0) and (500, 0). Therefore, the company will break even (have no profit) when 100 and 500 chairs are sold. This is the same answer we obtained in part **a**.

d. The vertex of the profit function is (300, 125). Three hundred chairs will maximize the profit at $12,500. ■

EXAMPLE 10   A manufacturer supplies cabinets at wholesale price to a dealer. The price per cabinet depends on the number of cabinets ordered. The list price is $150 per cabinet and will be reduced by $1 per cabinet ordered. It costs the manufacturer $65 to produce a cabinet, and there is a fixed delivery charge of $150 per order.

a. Write a revenue function for an order of x cabinets.

b. Write a cost function for an order of x cabinets.

c. Write a profit function for an order of x cabinets.

d. Determine the number of cabinets for which there will be no revenue.

e. Determine the number of cabinets that will maximize the revenue. What is the maximum revenue?

f. Determine the number of cabinets for which there will be no profit.

g. Determine the number of cabinets that will maximize the profit. What is the maximum profit?

h. Determine the number of cabinets for which the manufacturer will break even.

i. Graph the revenue, cost, and profit functions on one coordinate system and check the answers to parts **a–h** graphically.

Solution

a. Let x = the number of cabinets
$R(x)$ = the revenue

The price of the cabinets is \$150 minus \$1 per cabinet ordered.

$$150 - 1x = \text{the price of the cabinets}$$

The revenue is the number of cabinets times the price per cabinet.

$$R(x) = x(150 - x) \text{ or } R(x) = 150x - x^2$$

b. Let x = the number of cabinets
$C(x)$ = the cost

The cost is \$65 per cabinet plus the delivery charge of \$150.

$$C(x) = 65x + 150$$

c. Let x = the number of cabinets
$P(x)$ = the profit

The profit is the amount of revenue minus the cost.

$$P(x) = (150x - x^2) - (65x + 150) \text{ or } P(x) = -x^2 + 85x - 150$$

d. There will be no revenue when $R(x) = 0$.

$$R(x) = 150x - x^2$$

$$0 = 150x - x^2 \qquad \text{Substitute } R(x) = 0.$$

$$0 = x(150 - x) \qquad \text{Factor.}$$

$$x = 0 \quad 150 - x = 0 \qquad \text{Zero factor property}$$

$$x = 150$$

There will be no revenue when 0 cabinet or 150 cabinets are sold. (Note that this occurs at the x-intercepts of the graph of the revenue function.)

e. The graph of the revenue function is concave downward because $a = -1$ (a negative number), so the function has an absolute maximum value at the vertex. Use the vertex formula.

$$x = \frac{-b}{2a}$$

$$x = \frac{-150}{2 \cdot -1} \qquad \text{Substitute } a = -1 \text{ and } b = 150.$$

$$x = 75$$

$$R(75) = 150(75) - (75)^2$$

$$R(75) = 5625$$

The maximum revenue of \$5625 is reached when 75 cabinets are sold.

f. There will be no profit when $P(x) = 0$.

$$P(x) = -x^2 + 85x - 150$$

$$0 = -x^2 + 85x - 150 \qquad \text{Substitute } P(x) = 0.$$

$$x^2 - 85x + 150 = 0 \qquad a = 1, b = -85, c = 150$$

$$x = \frac{-b \pm \sqrt{b^2 - 4ac}}{2a}$$

$$x = \frac{-(-85) \pm \sqrt{(-85)^2 - 4(1)(150)}}{2(1)}$$

$$x = \frac{85 \pm \sqrt{6625}}{2}$$

$$x = \frac{85 \pm 5\sqrt{265}}{2} \qquad \sqrt{6625} = \sqrt{25 \cdot 265} = 5\sqrt{265}$$

$$x \approx 1.8 \quad \text{and} \quad x \approx 83.2$$

Note that the x-intercepts are approximately $(1.8, 0)$ and $(83.2, 0)$.

There will be no profit when $x = 1.8$ and $x = 83.2$. When 1 and 84 cabinets are produced and sold, there is a loss of \$66. If we round these numbers to 2 and 83 cabinets produced and sold, there will actually be a slight profit of \$16 because $P(2) = 16$ and $P(83) = 16$.

g. The graph of the profit is concave downward ($a = -1$), so the function has an absolute maximum value at the vertex. Use the vertex formula.

$$x = \frac{-b}{2a}$$

$$x = \frac{-85}{2 \cdot -1} \qquad \text{Substitute } a = -1 \text{ and } b = 85.$$

$$x = 42.5$$

$$P(42.5) = -(42.5)^2 + 85(42.5) - 150$$

$$P(42.5) = 1656.25$$

The function attains an absolute maximum at the vertex, $(42.5, 1656.25)$. However, since x cannot equal a fractional part of a cabinet, we will need to look at a table of values to determine the maximum profit.

X	Y1	
40	1650	
41	1654	
42	1656	
43	1656	
44	1654	
45	1650	
46	1644	
X=40		

According to the table of values, the maximum profit is \$1656 when 42 or 43 cabinets are sold.

h. The manufacturer will break even when the revenue and cost are equal.

$$R(x) = C(x)$$

$$150x - x^2 = 65x + 150$$

$$x^2 - 85x + 150 = 0$$

Use the quadratic formula to solve for x. Let $a = 1$, $b = -85$, and $c = 150$.

$$x = \frac{-b \pm \sqrt{b^2 - 4ac}}{2a}$$

Quadratic formula

$$x = \frac{-(-85) \pm \sqrt{(-85)^2 - 4(1)(150)}}{2(1)}$$

Substitute values for a, b, and c.

$$x = \frac{85 \pm \sqrt{6625}}{2}$$

Simplify.

$$x = \frac{85 \pm \sqrt{25 \cdot 265}}{2}$$

$6625 = 25 \cdot 265$

$$x = \frac{85 \pm 5\sqrt{265}}{2}$$

$25 = 5^2$

$$x \approx 1.8, \; x \approx 83.2$$

The manufacturer will break even (make a slight profit of $16) when approximately 2 cabinets and 83 cabinets are produced and sold. Note that this was also determined in part **f** when the profit was $0.

i.

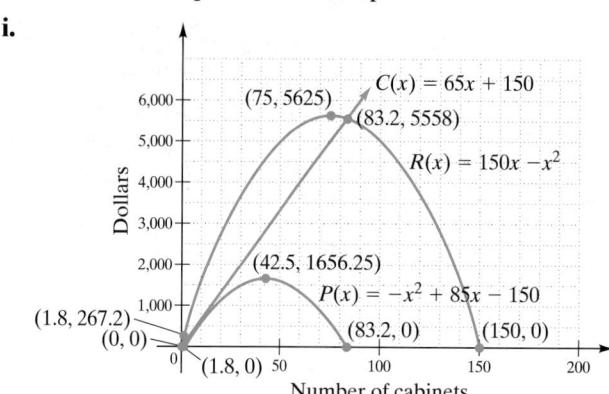

APPLICATION

Using data from annual financial reports for Gateway, Inc., a quadratic function for the amount of revenue from sales in millions of dollars is $R(x) = 508x^2 - 1277x + 4171$, where x is the number of years after 2002.

a. Assuming that the equation continues to apply, determine the minimum revenue from sales and in what year it occurred.

b. What was the amount of revenue from sales in 2002?

c. Assuming that the equation continues to apply, in what year will the company rebound to its 2002 revenue from sales?

Discussion

a. The graph of the revenue function is concave upward because $a = 508$ and is positive. Therefore, a minimum value function value will occur at the vertex. Use the vertex formula, $\left(\frac{-b}{2a}, R\left(\frac{-b}{2a} \right) \right)$.

$$x = \frac{-b}{2a}$$

$$x = \frac{-(-1277)}{2 \cdot 508}$$

Substitute $a = 508$ and $b = -1277$

$$x = \frac{1277}{1016}$$

$$x \approx 1.3$$

$$R(x) = 508x^2 - 1277x + 4171$$
$$R(1.3) = 508(1.3)^2 - 1277(1.3) + 4171$$
$$R(1.3) = 3369.42$$

The vertex is approximately $(1.3, 3369.42)$. The minimum revenue from sales was 3369.42 million dollars in 2004 (1.3 years after 2002).

b. The 2002 revenue from sales is the function value when $x = 0$ or the $R(x)$-intercept. The $R(x)$-intercept is $(0, c)$ or $(0, 4171)$. The 2002 revenue from sales is 4171 million dollars.

c. To determine when the revenue from sales will return to the 2002 amount of 4171 million dollars, let $R(x) = 4171$ and solve for x.

$$R(x) = 508x^2 - 1277x + 4171$$

$$4171 = 508x^2 - 1277x + 4171 \quad \text{Substitute } R(x) = 4171.$$

$$0 = 508x^2 - 1277x \quad \text{Subtract 4171 from both sides.}$$

$$0 = x(508x - 1277) \quad \text{Factor.}$$

$$x = 0 \quad \text{or} \quad 508x - 1277 = 0 \quad \text{Zero factor property}$$

$$x = \frac{1277}{508}$$

$$x \approx 2.5$$

The revenue from sales will reach the 2002 amount of 4171 million dollars in 2.5 years after 2002 or in 2005.

Objective 9.7.6 CHECKUP

1. The height of a baseball with respect to the time in the air is represented in the following graph.

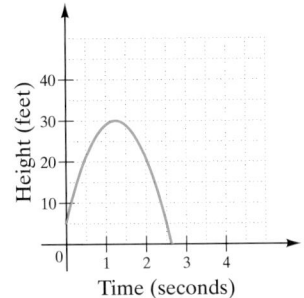
Time (seconds)

   a. What was the initial height of the baseball?
   b. How high was the baseball after 1 second?
   c. What was the maximum height of the baseball?
   d. When did the maximum height occur?
   e. After the baseball is in the air a half of a second, a player on the opposing team jumps vertically 10 feet. Can he catch the baseball?
   f. When does the baseball reach the ground?

2. A projectile is shot upward from a height of 250 feet. If the initial velocity of the projectile is 200 feet per second, a function for the position (in feet) of the projectile above ground is $s(t) = -16t^2 + 200t + 250$, where t is time in seconds.
   a. What is the height of the projectile after 3 seconds?
   b. What is the maximum height of the projectile? When did the maximum height occur?
   c. When did the projectile return to its original height?
   d. When did the projectile hit the ground?
   e. Graph the position of the projectile in terms of t seconds.

3. A manufacturer of tricycles determines the revenue, cost, and profit for producing and selling x tricycles. Analyze the following graphs.

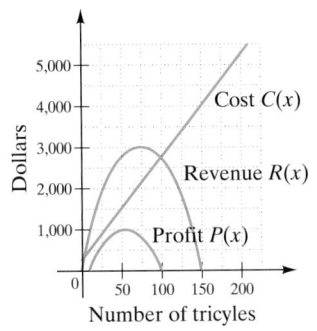
Number of tricycles

   a. Find the manufacturer's break-even points.
   b. Find the number of tricycles produced and sold that will maximize the revenue. What is the maximum revenue?
   c. Find the x-intercepts of the graph of the profit. Discuss the significance of these points.
   d. Find the number of tricycles that will maximize the profit. What is the maximum profit?

4. A manufacturer supplies bikes at wholesale price to a dealer. The price per bike depends on the number of bikes ordered. The list price is $200 per bike and will be reduced by $5 per bike ordered. It costs the manufacturer $75 to produce a bike, and there is a fixed delivery charge of $150 per order.
   a. Write a revenue function for an order of x bikes.
   b. Write a cost function for an order of x bikes.
   c. Write a profit function for an order of x bikes.
   d. Determine the number of bikes for which there will be no revenue.
   e. Determine the number of bikes that will maximize the revenue. What is the maximum revenue?
   f. Determine the number of bikes for which there will be no profit.
   g. Determine the number of bikes that will maximize the profit. What is the maximum profit?
   h. Determine the number of bikes for which the manufacturer will break even.
   i. Graph the revenue, cost, and profit functions on one coordinate system and check the answers to parts **a–h** graphically.

5. Using data from annual financial reports for Gateway, Inc., a quadratic function for the amount of net income in millions of dollars is $I(x) = 82x^2 - 299x - 298$, where x is the number of years after 2002.
   a. Assuming that the equation continues to apply, determine the minimum net income and in what year it occurred.
   b. What was the net income in 2002?
   c. Assuming that the equation continues to apply, in what year will the company rebound to its 2002 net income from sales?

9.7 EXERCISES

Student Solutions Manual   PH Math/Tutor Center   CD Video   Math XL MathXL®   MyMathLab MyMathLab   Interactmath.com

In exercises 1–8, use the given graph of y = f(x) to answer the questions.

a. Find the domain and range.

b. Find the *x*-intercepts and the *y*-intercept.

c. Determine if the graph is concave upward or concave downward.

d. Find the vertex and determine the axis of symmetry.

e. Find the relative maximum and relative minimum. Find the absolute maximum and absolute minimum. Find the *x*-values for which the function is increasing and for which it is decreasing.

f. Find the *x*-values for which the *y*-values are equal to zero.

g. Find the solutions of $f(x) = 0$.

1.

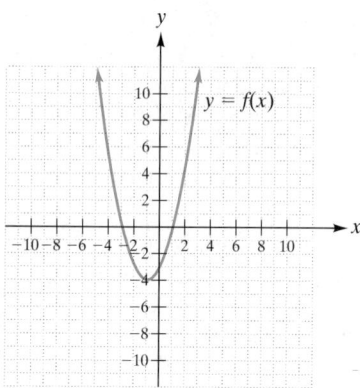

2.

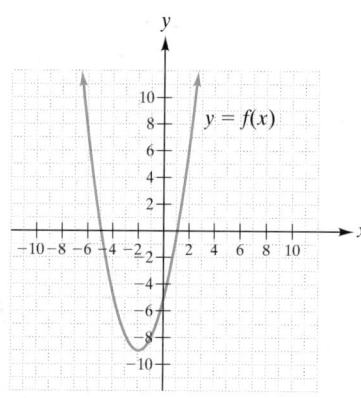

3.

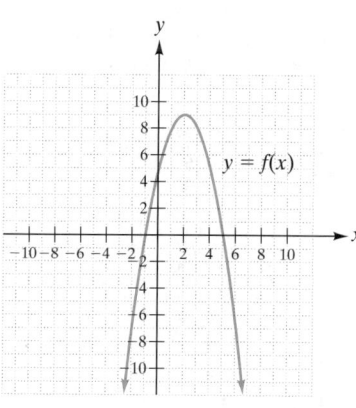

4.

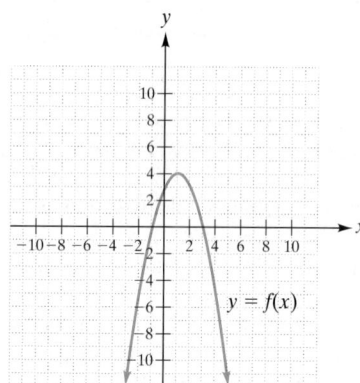

5.

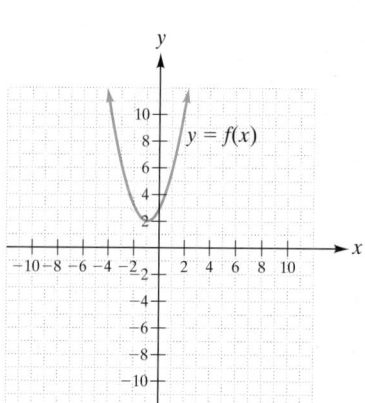

6.

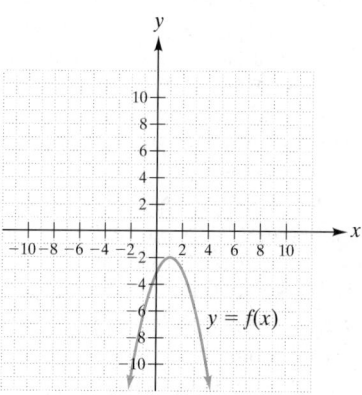

7.

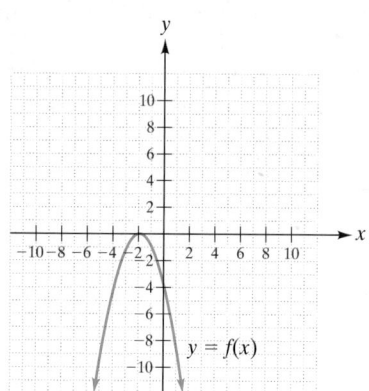

8.

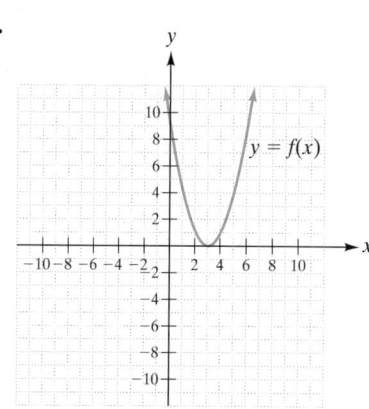

In exercises 9–16, determine the x-intercept and the y-intercept of the graph of the quadratic function without graphing.

9. $f(x) = x^2 + x - 6$ **10.** $f(x) = x^2 - x - 20$ **11.** $g(x) = x^2 - 9$ **12.** $h(x) = x^2 - 16$

13. $y = -x^2 - 6x + 4$ **14.** $y = -x^2 + 4x + 7$ **15.** $y = f(x) = 3x^2 + 2x + 5$ **16.** $y = g(x) = 2x^2 + 4x + 7$

In exercises 17–24, determine the vertex and axis of symmetry of the quadratic function without graphing.

17. $f(x) = x^2 + 4x + 5$ **18.** $f(x) = x^2 - 2x + 4$ **19.** $g(x) = x^2 - 9$ **20.** $h(x) = x^2 - 16$

21. $y = -x^2 + 2x + 1$ **22.** $y = -x^2 - 4x + 1$ **23.** $y = f(x) = 3x^2 + 2x + 1$ **24.** $y = g(x) = 2x^2 + 4x + 5$

In exercises 25–32, graph the quadratic function using the seven steps given in this section.

25. $f(x) = x^2 + 6x + 8$ **26.** $f(x) = x^2 - 2x - 8$ **27.** $y = -2x^2 - 4x$ **28.** $y = -3x^2 + 6x$

29. $w(x) = x^2 - 2x - 4$ **30.** $l(x) = x^2 - 4x - 3$ **31.** $g(x) = 2x^2 - x + 5$ **32.** $h(x) = 3x^2 - x + 4$

In exercises 33–42, write a quadratic function for the given sets of x-intercept(s) of the graphs.

33. $(3, 0); (-4, 0)$ **34.** $(-2, 0); (3, 0)$ **35.** $\left(\frac{1}{4}, 0\right); \left(\frac{2}{3}, 0\right)$ **36.** $\left(\frac{3}{5}, 0\right); \left(\frac{1}{2}, 0\right)$ **37.** $(1.3, 0); (4.2, 0)$

38. $(2.5, 0); (1.1, 0)$ **39.** $(0, 0); (125.50, 0)$ **40.** $(0, 0); (234.75, 0)$ **41.** $(4, 0)$ **42.** $(-2, 0)$

Vertical Position

43. A hockey player strikes a puck. The height of the puck with respect to time is shown in the following graph.

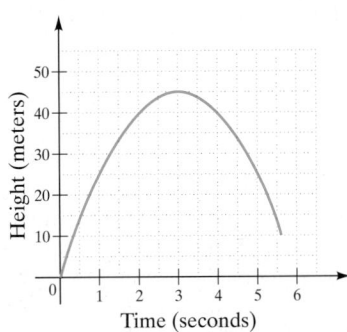

Time (seconds)

a. What was the initial height of the puck?
b. How high was the puck in 2 seconds?
c. What was the maximum height of the puck?
d. When did the maximum height occur?
e. What was the final height of the puck? When does this occur?

44. The height of a diver with respect to time is shown in the following graph.

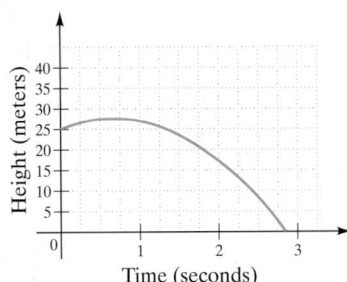

Time (seconds)

a. What was the initial height of the diver?
b. How far above the water was the diver in 1 second?
c. What was the maximum height of the diver?

d. When did the maximum height occur?
e. When did the diver enter the water?

45. As part of a demonstration, a hunter shoots a bullet upward out of a gun from a height of 250 feet. He gives the object an initial velocity of 200 feet per second. The position function for the bullet in feet is $s(t) = -16t^2 + 200t + 250$, where t is the number of seconds.
a. What is the height of the bullet after 2 seconds?
b. What is the maximum height of the bullet? When did the maximum height occur?
c. When did the bullet return to its original height?
d. When did the bullet hit the ground?
e. Graph the position of the bullet in terms of t seconds.

46. A ball is thrown with an upward velocity of 25 feet per second from an upper floor of an apartment building window, 75 feet up. The position function for the ball in feet is $s(t) = -16t^2 + 25t + 75$, where t is the number of seconds.
a. What is the height of the ball after one-half of a second?
b. What is the maximum height of the ball? When did the maximum height occur?
c. When did the ball return to its original height?
d. When did the ball hit the ground?
e. Graph the position of the ball in terms of t seconds.

47. A weight is projected up with a velocity of 8 meters per second from a height of 110 meters. The position function of the weight, in meters above the ground, after t seconds is $s(t) = -4.9t^2 + 8t + 110$.
a. What is the height of the weight after one-tenth of a second?
b. What is the maximum height of the weight? When did the maximum height occur?
c. When did the weight return to its original height?
d. When did it hit the ground?
e. Graph the position of the weight in terms of t seconds.

48. A rocket is shot from a platform 50 meters high and given an initial velocity of 550 meters per second. The position

function of the rocket, in meters above the ground, after t seconds is $s(t) = -4.9t^2 + 550t + 50$.
a. What is the height of the rocket after 6 seconds?
b. What is the maximum height of the rocket? When did the maximum height occur?

c. When did the rocket reach a height of 10,000 meters?
d. When did it hit the ground?
e. Graph the position of the rocket in terms of t seconds.

Business

49. Mrs. Tilley hires a business consultant who determines the daily revenue, cost, and profit for producing and selling x units of pottery. Analyze the following graph.

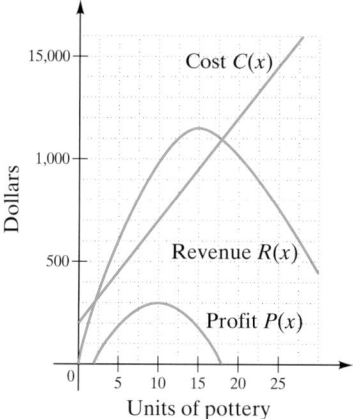

a. Find the manufacturers break-even points.
b. Find the number of units of pottery sold that will maximize the revenue. What is the maximum revenue?
c. Find the x-intercepts of the graph of the profit function. Discuss the significance of these points.
d. Find the number of units of pottery that will maximize the profit. What is the maximum profit?

50. Mr. Tilley hired the same consultant. He was given the daily cost, revenue, and profit for purchasing and selling x go-carts. Analyze the graph.

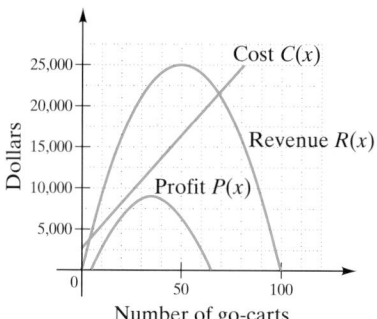

a. Find the manufacturer's break-even points.
b. Find the number of go-carts sold that will maximize the revenue. What is the maximum revenue?
c. Find the x-intercepts of the graph of the profit function. Discuss the significance of these points.
d. Find the number of go-carts that will maximize the profit. What is the maximum profit?

51. A bus service that transports teenagers to athletic events gives a discount of $0.75 for each person transported. The standard fee is $14.00, per trip, and it costs the bus service $3.00, per person with fixed costs of $10.00, for their bus.

a. Write a revenue function for a group of x people.
b. Write a cost function for a group of x people.
c. Write a profit function for a group of x people.
d. Determine the number of people for which there will be no revenue.
e. Determine the number of people that will maximize revenue. What is the maximum revenue?
f. Determine the number of people for which there will be no profit.
g. Determine the number of people that will maximize profit. What is the maximum profit?
h. Determine the number of people for which the bus service will break even.
i. Graph the revenue, cost, and profit functions on one coordinate system.

52. A manager of an amusement park gives a reduced ticket price for children's school groups. There is a discount of $0.80 for each child. The regular children's ticket price is $28.75 per child and it costs the carnival $3.50 per child with fixed costs of $125.00.

a. Write a revenue function for a group of x children.
b. Write a cost function for a group of x children.
c. Write a profit function for a group of x children.
d. Determine the number of children for which there will be no revenue.
e. Determine the number of children that will maximize revenue. What is the maximum revenue?
f. Determine the number of children for which there will be no profit.
g. Determine the number of children that will maximize profit. What is the maximum profit?
h. Determine the number of children for which the park will break even.
i. Graph the revenue, cost, and profit functions on one coordinate system.

53. A courier's business involves delivering documents for a number of city corporations. After experimenting with various fee structures, it decides to decrease the standard fee $0.10 per delivery. The standard fee per delivery is $5.50. The business has daily expenditures of $0.75 per delivery and $25.00 in overhead. If x is the number of decreases and the number of deliveries,

a. Write a revenue function for x deliveries with x decreases.
b. Write a cost function for x deliveries with x decreases.
c. Write a profit function for x deliveries with x decreases.
d. Determine the number of deliveries/decreases for which there will be no revenue.
e. Determine the number of deliveries/decreases that will maximize revenue. What is the maximum revenue?
f. Determine the number of deliveries/decreases for which there will be no profit.
g. Determine the number of deliveries/decreases that will maximize profit. What is the maximum profit?

h. Determine the number of deliveries/decreases for which the business will break even.

i. Graph the revenue, cost, and profit functions on one coordinate system.

54. The office of public transportation for a metropolitan area decides to discount the price of an all-day ticket $0.05 per ticket. The standard fare is $5.50 per ticket. The office spends $0.75 per ticket to provide service and has fixed costs of $50.00. If x is the number of decreases and the number of tickets sold,

a. Write a revenue function for sales of x tickets with x decreases.

b. Write a cost function for sales of x tickets with x decreases.

c. Write a profit function for sales of x tickets with x decreases.

d. Determine the number of tickets/decreases for which there will be no revenue.

e. Determine the number of tickets/decreases that will maximize revenue. What is the maximum revenue?

f. Determine the number of tickets/decreases for which there will be no profit.

g. Determine the number of tickets/decreases that will maximize profit. What is the maximum profit?

Real Data

57. Using data from an Internet finance site, a quadratic function that approximates total monthly revenues for Pepsico Inc., in billions of dollars, is $R(x) = -0.01x^2 + 0.07x + 7.65$, where x is the number of months after September 2004.

a. Assuming that the equation continues to apply, determine the maximum revenue for these sales and in what month it occurred.

b. What was the amount of total revenue in June 2005? In January 2006?

c. Assuming that the equation continues to apply, in what month and year will revenue be 7 billion dollars?

58. Using data from an Internet finance site, a quadratic function that approximates total monthly revenues for American Greeting Corporation, in millions of dollars, is $R(x) = -7.1x^2 + 67.2x + 396.6$, where x is the number of months after August 2004.

a. Assuming that the equation continues to apply, determine the maximum revenue for these sales and in what month it occurred.

b. What was the amount of total revenue in June 2005? In December 2005?

c. Assuming that the equation continues to apply, in what month and year will revenue be 425 million dollars?

Geometry

61. The area of a rectangle with a fixed perimeter can be modeled with the function $A(x) = -x^2 + 450x$, where x is the measure of its width in feet.

a. For what width is the area a maximum?

b. For what width is the area a minimum? Comment on your answer.

c. What is the area for a width of 50 feet?

d. For what widths is the area 34,750 square feet?

h. Determine the number of tickets/decreases for which the office will break even.

i. Graph the revenue, cost, and profit functions on one coordinate system.

55. The owner of a trucking company estimates the yearly depreciation in dollars on his fleet of trucks by $D(x) = 27{,}000x - 1500x^2$, where x is the number of years since 1995.

a. Assuming that the equation continues to apply, determine the maximum yearly depreciation and the year in which it occurred.

b. What will the depreciation be in 2010?

c. Assuming that the equation continues to apply, in what years will the depreciation be $108,000?

56. As part of an adjustable rate mortgage, Darlene's mortgage company uses the function $P(x) = 6000x - 500x^2$ to estimate her yearly mortgage payment in dollars, where x is the number of years after obtaining the loan.

a. In what year will she have her maximum payment? What is her maximum yearly payment?

b. If the equation continues to apply, what will be her yearly payment in the fifth year?

c. If the equation continues to apply, estimate the years in which she will pay $10,000.

59. Using data from an Internet finance site, a quadratic function that approximates gross profit for Pepsico Inc., in billions of dollars, is $P(x) = -0.11x^2 + 0.57x + 3.96$, where x is the number of months after September 2004.

a. Assuming that the equation continues to apply, determine the maximum gross profit and in what month it occurred.

b. What was the amount of gross profit in January 2005? In January 2006?

c. Assuming that the equation continues to apply, in what month and year will the gross profit be 2.6 billion dollars?

60. Using data from an Internet finance site, a quadratic function that approximates gross profits for American Greeting Corporation, in millions of dollars, is $P(x) = -2.08x^2 + 21.29x + 197.38$, where x is the number of months after August 2004.

a. Assuming that the equation continues to apply, determine the maximum gross profit and in what month it occurred.

b. What was the amount of gross profit in December 2004? In December 2005?

c. Assuming that the equation continues to apply, in what month and year will the gross profit be 150 million dollars?

62. The area of a rectangle with a fixed perimeter can be modeled with the function $A(x) = 570x - x^2$, where x is the measure of its length in yards.

a. For what length is the area a maximum?

b. For what length is the area a minimum? Comment on your answer.

c. What is the area for a length of 50 yards?

d. For what length is the area 54,000 square yards?

63. The length and width of a rectangle have a sum of 100 feet. Let x = the width of the rectangle.
  a. Write a function for the area of the rectangle.
  b. For what width is the area a maximum?
  c. For what width is the area a minimum?
  d. What is the area for a width of 25 feet?
  e. For what widths is the area 2000 square feet?

64. The length and width of a rectangle have a sum of 50 feet. Let x = the length of the rectangle.
  a. Write a function for the area of the rectangle.
  b. For what length is the area a maximum?
  c. For what length is the area a minimum?
  d. What is the area for a length of 15 feet?
  e. For what lengths is the area 500 square feet?

 ## 9.7 Calculator Exercises

In this section, we wrote an equation for a quadratic function given the x-intercepts of its graph. We can also write a function for other polynomials given the x-intercepts of their graphs. However, if we want to write a polynomial function and do not know the x-intercepts of its related graph, we can use the regression feature of our calculator as we did for finding quadratic and linear functions. As an example, suppose you wish to find the cubic equation that passes through the points $(0, 0)$, $(1, 2)$, $(-1, -6)$, and $(2, 18)$. To do so, complete the following steps:

• Clear List 1 and List 2 of the calculator.

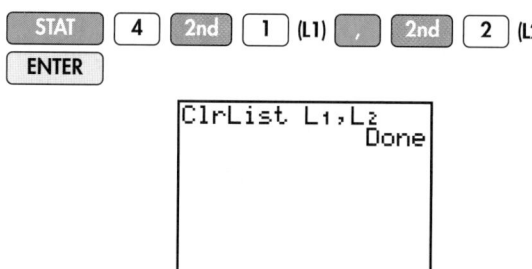

• Store the x-values of the ordered pairs in List 1 and the y-values of the ordered pairs in List 2.

Use the cursor to move to the appropriate list, and then key in the values, pressing ENTER after each, until you have entered the pairs of values into the lists. Be sure the pairs match in the lists.

• Calculate the cubic equation for the points and store the equation in Y1.

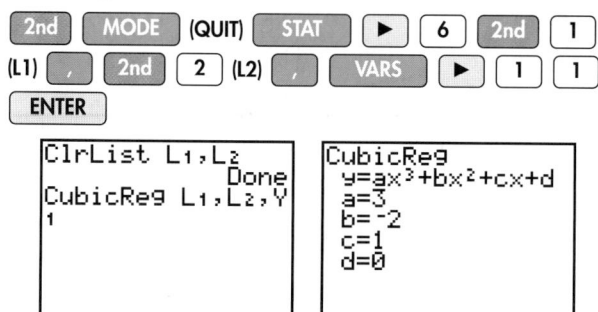

• To view the plotted coordinate pairs and the equation, use the STATPLOT feature of the calculator.

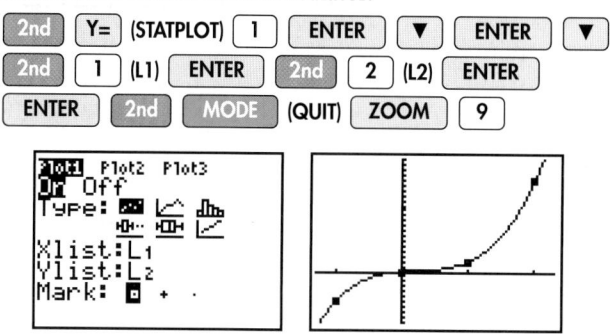

Note that when you use this feature to find a polynomial equation, the number of coordinate pairs through which the function passes must be at least one more than the degree of the polynomial that you are writing. That is, to find a quadratic equation, you must have three coordinate pairs; for a cubic equation, you must have four coordinate pairs; and for a fourth-degree equation, you must have five coordinate pairs. The calculator will accept only up to a fourth-degree equation. To calculate such an equation, you would follow the same steps as you just did, except that when you choose the calculate option, you would choose "QuartReg" instead of "CubicReg."

Use the preceding method to answer the following questions (remember that when you are keying in the values of the coordinate pairs, you can clear the previous set of values stored in Lists L1 and L2 by moving the cursor to the top of the list, pressing CLEAR, and then moving the cursor back down to the location of the first value in the list):

1. Find the cubic equation that passes through $(0, -4)$, $(1, -2)$, $(2, 2)$, and $(-1, -10)$.

2. Find the quartic equation (that is, fourth-degree equation) that passes through $(0, 1)$, $(1, 1)$, $(2, 11)$, $(-1, 5)$, and $(-2, 31)$.

3. Find the cubic equation that passes through $(0, -6)$, $(1, -7)$, $(5, 9)$, and $(-1, 15)$.

4. Find the quartic equation that passes through $(0, 6)$, $(1, -0.7)$, $(2, -1.6)$, $(3, 20.1)$, and $(-1, 13.7)$.

9.7 Writing Exercise

In Section 6.4 writing exercises, we discussed an alternative form of a quadratic function, $y = f(x) = a(x - h)^2 + k$. Using this form, we learned that the vertex of the graph of the function was (h, k). In this section we have used the standard form of a quadratic function, $y = f(x) = ax^2 + bx + c$. If we complete the square, we obtain the following: $y = f(x) = a\left(x + \dfrac{b}{2a}\right)^2 + c - \dfrac{b^2}{4a}$. Determine h from this equation. Determine $f(h)$ in terms of $a, b,$ and c. Write a paragraph discussing the relevance of the values of h and $f(h)$ and the vertex formula.

9.8 SOLVING QUADRATIC INEQUALITIES

OBJECTIVES

1 Identify quadratic inequalities in one variable.
2 Solve quadratic inequalities numerically and graphically.
3 Solve quadratic inequalities algebraically.
4 Model real-world situations by using quadratic inequalities, and solving the inequalities.

APPLICATION

According to the *Apollo 15 Preliminary Science Report*, astronaut David R. Scott conducted a short demonstration experiment. A heavy object, a 1.32-kilogram hammer, and a light object, a 0.03-kilogram feather, were released simultaneously from a height of 1.6 meters to the lunar surface. Both objects were observed to undergo the same acceleration and strike the surface at the same time.

a. Determine the length of time the objects were in free fall.

b. Determine the time interval that the objects were in free fall above 0.8 meter (halfway to the surface).

After completing this section, we will discuss this application further. See page 750.

Earlier in this text, we solved linear inequalities in one variable. Recall that the solution set for a linear inequality contains an infinite number of solutions. Therefore, we describe the set as an inequality or in interval notation. For example, we might have the following descriptions:

Inequality	Interval	Inequality	Interval
$x < 1$	$(-\infty, 1)$	$x \leq 1$	$(-\infty, 1]$
$x > 1$	$(1, \infty)$	$x \geq 1$	$[1, \infty)$
$4 < x < 5$	$(4, 5)$	$4 \leq x < 5$	$[4, 5)$
$4 < x \leq 5$	$(4, 5]$	$4 \leq x \leq 5$	$[4, 5]$

Objective 9.8.1 **Identifying Quadratic Inequalities in One Variable**

In this section, we will be solving quadratic inequalities in one variable. A **quadratic inequality in one variable**, or, simply, a **quadratic inequality**, is written by replacing the equals sign in a quadratic equation in one variable with an order symbol.

STANDARD FORM FOR A QUADRATIC INEQUALITY IN ONE VARIABLE

A quadratic inequality in standard form is written in one of the forms

$$ax^2 + bx + c < 0$$
$$ax^2 + bx + c > 0$$
$$ax^2 + bx + c \leq 0$$
$$ax^2 + bx + c \geq 0$$

where $a, b,$ and c are real numbers and $a \neq 0$.

EXAMPLE 1   Determine whether each inequality is a quadratic inequality.

a. $2x^2 + 3x - 5 < 0$

b. $x^2 + 5x - 7 \leq 2x^2 + 4x + 15$

c. $0.3x^3 + 5.1x^2 > x - 1.2$

d. $6x^{-2} + 5x^{-1} < 0$

Solution

a. $2x^2 + 3x - 5 < 0$ is a quadratic inequality.

b. $x^2 + 5x - 7 \leq 2x^2 + 4x + 15$ is a quadratic inequality, because it simplifies to $-x^2 + x - 22 \leq 0$.

c. $0.3x^3 + 5.1x^2 > x - 1.2$ is not a quadratic inequality, because it has a third-degree term (exponent of 3).

d. $6x^{-2} + 5x^{-1} < 0$ is not a quadratic inequality, because it has variables with negative exponents.

Objective 9.8.1 *CHECKUP*

1. Determine whether each inequality is a quadratic inequality.

   a. $2x + 3 \leq x^2 - 1$ b. $\frac{2}{3}x^2 - 3x \geq \frac{1}{4}$

   c. $3x + 2x^{-2} > 4x^{-1} + 8$ d. $1.2\sqrt{x} - 3.3x^2 \leq 2.5x$

2. Explain the difference between a quadratic equation and a quadratic inequality.

Objective 9.8.2   # Solving Quadratic Inequalities Numerically and Graphically

We solved linear inequalities numerically for integer solutions by using a table of values. We will use the same method to solve a quadratic inequality in one variable for integer solutions.

SOLVING A QUADRATIC INEQUALITY NUMERICALLY

To solve a quadratic inequality numerically for integer solutions, set up an extended table of values.

• The first column is labeled with the name of the independent variable.
• The second column is labeled with the expression on the left side of the inequality.
• The third column is labeled with the expression on the right side of the inequality.

Complete the table.

• Substitute values for the independent variable.
• Evaluate the second and third columns.
• Continue until values for the two expressions (the numbers in the second and third column) result in a true inequality.

The values for the independent variable (the numbers in the first column) that result in a true inequality are solutions of the inequality.

 TAKE NOTE Not all solutions may be found by this method. We are limited to the numbers substituted for the independent variable.

EXAMPLE 2   Solve $x^2 + 2x - 1 \geq 2$ numerically.

Numeric Solution

Set up a table of values.

x	$x^2 + 2x - 1$	2	
-5	14	2	$14 \geq 2$
-4	7	2	$7 \geq 2$
-3	2	2	$2 \geq 2$
-2	-1	2	$-1 \not\geq 2$
-1	-2	2	$-2 \not\geq 2$
0	-1	2	$-1 \not\geq 2$
1	2	2	$2 \geq 2$
2	7	2	$7 \geq 2$
3	14	2	$14 \geq 2$

Calculator Numeric Solution

X	Y1	Y2	
-4	7	2	$7 \geq 2$
-3	2	2	$2 \geq 2$
-2	-1	2	$-1 \not\geq 2$
-1	-2	2	$-2 \not\geq 2$
0	-1	2	$-1 \not\geq 2$
1	2	2	$2 \geq 2$
2	7	2	$7 \geq 2$

X= -4

Y1 $= x^2 + 2x - 1$
Y2 $= 2$

A calculator table will find the integer solutions numerically.

We obtain the same solution set: all integers less than or equal to -3 or all integers greater than or equal to 1, as shown in the figure.

According to the table, when -5, -4, and -3 are substituted into the inequality, the result is a true statement. Also, when 1, 2, and 3 are substituted into the inequality, a true statement results. Therefore, there appear to be two sets of solutions: all integers less than or equal to -3 is the first set, and all integers greater than or equal to 1 is the second set. ■

  TAKE NOTE This method is not recommended, as it does not result in a complete solution set, only an integer solution set. However, as a visualization, it may be used to check other methods.

A second and more inclusive method for determining the solutions of an inequality is to graph two functions, y_1 and y_2. We will use the two expressions in the inequality as the rules of the functions. If we are solving a "less than" $(y_1 < y_2)$ inequality, we choose the x-values that correspond to the portion of the graph for which y_1 is below y_2. If we are solving a "greater than" $(y_1 > y_2)$ inequality, we choose the x-values that correspond to the portion of the graph for which y_1 is above y_2.

SOLVING A QUADRATIC INEQUALITY GRAPHICALLY

To solve a quadratic inequality graphically,

- Write two functions, y_1 and y_2, using the expressions on the left and right sides of the inequality as rules.
- Graph both functions on the same coordinate plane.
- Determine the intersections, if they exist, of the y_1 and y_2 graphs.
- Locate the portion of the y_1 graph below the y_2 graph if the inequality is "less than." Locate the portion of the y_1 graph above the y_2 graph if the inequality is "greater than."
- Determine the x-coordinates for this portion of the graph.
- If the portion is to the left of the intersection, then x is less than the x-coordinate of the intersection.
- If the portion is to the right of the intersection, then x is greater than the x-coordinate of the intersection.
- If the portion is between the left and right intersections, then x is greater than the x-coordinate of the left intersection and less than the x-coordinate of the right intersection.

The solution set of the inequality includes the x-coordinates of the points of intersection of the two graphs if the inequality contains equality.

EXAMPLE 3   Solve graphically $x^2 + 2x - 1 \geq 2$.

Graphic Solution

Let $Y1 = x^2 + 2x - 1$ and $Y2 = 2$

The solution contains the x-coordinates of the points of intersection, -3 and 1, because the inequality contains "equal to." The graph of Y1 is above the graph of Y2 to the left of the intersection point $(-3, 2)$ and to the right of the intersection point $(1, 2)$, as shown in **Figures 9.6a**, **9.6b**, and **9.6c**.

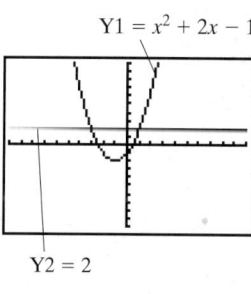

(-10, 10, -10, 10)

Figure 9.6a   **Figure 9.6b**   **Figure 9.6c**

Therefore, the solution is $x \leq -3$ or $x \geq 1$. The solution set may be written in interval notation as $(-\infty, -3]$ or $[1, \infty)$. In mathematics, we write this as $(-\infty, -3] \cup [1, \infty)$, where the symbol $\cup$ is called **union** and means "or." ∎

EXAMPLE 4   Solve graphically.

a. $x^2 + 3x - 4 \leq 2x + 2$ **b.** $3x^2 - x - 2 > 0$ **c.** $-x^2 + 6x > 6$

Graphic Solution

a. $x^2 + 3x - 4 \leq 2x + 2$

Let $Y1 = x^2 + 3x - 4$ and $Y2 = 2x + 2$

The solution contains both x-coordinates of the intersections, because the inequality contains "equal to." Since the inequality also contains "less than," we determine that Y1 is below Y2 between the points of intersection.

Therefore, the solution set is $-3 \leq x \leq 2$, or $[-3, 2]$.

Numeric Check

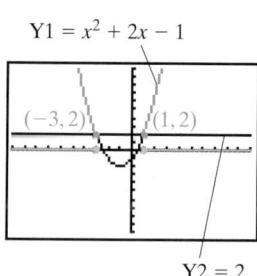

$Y1 = x^2 + 3x - 4$
$Y2 = 2x + 2$

The solution checks.

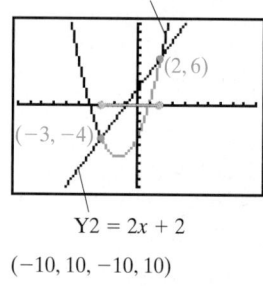

(-10, 10, -10, 10)

b. $3x^2 - x - 2 > 0$

Let $Y1 = 3x^2 - x - 2$ and $Y2 = 0$ (The latter will graph a horizontal line on the x-axis.)

The solution does not contain the x-coordinates of the points of intersection. Since the inequality is "greater than," we determine that Y1 is above Y2 to the left of the intersection point $\left(-\frac{2}{3}, 0\right)$ and to the right of the intersection point $(1, 0)$.

Therefore, the solution set is $x < -\frac{2}{3}$, or $x > 1$. In interval notation, the solution is $\left(-\infty, -\frac{2}{3}\right) \cup (1, \infty)$.

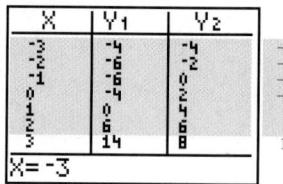

$Y1 = 3x^2 - x - 2$
$Y2 = 0$

The solution checks.

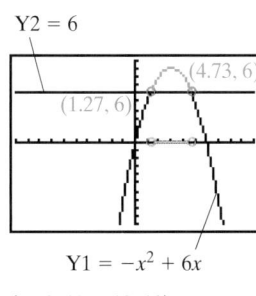

Y2 = 6

(4.73, 6)
(1.27, 6)

Y1 = $-x^2 + 6x$

$(-10, 10, -10, 10)$

c. $-x^2 + 6x > 6$

Let Y1 = $-x^2 + 6x$ and Y2 = 6

The solution does not contain the x-coordinates of the points of intersection. Since the inequality is "greater than," we determine that Y1 is above Y2 between the approximate points of intersection, (1.27, 6) and (4.73, 6).

Therefore, the approximate solution set is $1.27 < x < 4.73$. In interval notation, the solution is approximately $(1.27, 4.73)$.

X	Y1	Y2	
-1	-7	6	-7 ≯ 6
0	0	6	0 ≯ 6
1	5	6	5 ≯ 6
2	8	6	8 > 6
3	9	6	9 > 6
4	8	6	8 > 6
5	5	6	5 ≯ 6

X= -1

Y1 = $-x^2 + 6x$
Y2 = 6

The solution checks.

There are special cases of linear inequalities that have no solution or for which the solution is all real numbers. There are also special cases of quadratic inequalities. In fact, several types of solutions are possible. To see what they are, complete the following set of exercises on your calculator.

💡 Guided Discovery 5   Special Cases of Quadratic Inequalities

Graph the functions that follow. Label points of intersection if possible. Determine the solutions of the given inequalities.

1. $f(x) = -x^2 - 5$
    $g(x) = 0$
a. $-x^2 - 5 > 0$
b. $-x^2 - 5 \geq 0$
c. $-x^2 - 5 < 0$
d. $-x^2 - 5 \leq 0$

2. $h(x) = x^2 + 5x + 8$
    $j(x) = 0$
a. $x^2 + 5x + 8 > 0$
b. $x^2 + 5x + 8 \geq 0$
c. $x^2 + 5x + 8 < 0$
d. $x^2 + 5x + 8 \leq 0$

3. $y_1 = -x^2 - 10x - 25$
    $y_2 = 0$
a. $-x^2 - 10x - 25 > 0$
b. $-x^2 - 10x - 25 \geq 0$
c. $-x^2 - 10x - 25 < 0$
d. $-x^2 - 10x - 25 \leq 0$

4. $y_1 = 2x^2 - 12x + 18$
    $y_2 = 0$
a. $2x^2 - 12x + 18 > 0$
b. $2x^2 - 12x + 18 \geq 0$
c. $2x^2 - 12x + 18 < 0$
d. $2x^2 - 12x + 18 \leq 0$

Guided Discovery 5 illustrates that some quadratic inequalities have no solution, while others have a solution set consisting of all real numbers. Still other solution sets contain only one value or all real numbers except one value.

EXAMPLE 5

Solve graphically.

a. $2x^2 \geq x^2$ **b.** $x^2 - 4x + 7 > -x^2 + 4x - 1$ **c.** $x^2 + 2 \leq 2$

Graphic Solution

a. $2x^2 \geq x^2$

Let Y1 = $2x^2$ and Y2 = x^2

The solution contains the x-coordinate of the intersection point, (0, 0), because the inequality contains equality. Since the inequality is "greater than," we determine that Y1 is above Y2 at all points to the left and to the right of the intersection. Therefore, the solution set is the set of all real numbers.

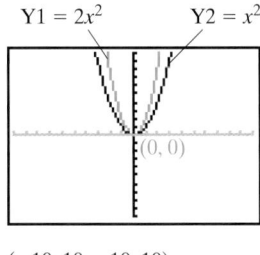

Y1 = $2x^2$ Y2 = x^2

(0, 0)

$(-10, 10, -10, 10)$

Numeric Check

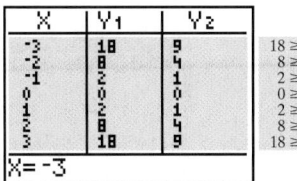

X	Y1	Y2	
-3	18	9	18 ≥ 9
-2	8	4	8 ≥ 4
-1	2	1	2 ≥ 1
0	0	0	0 ≥ 0
1	2	1	2 ≥ 1
2	8	4	8 ≥ 4
3	18	9	18 ≥ 9

X= -3

Y1 = $2x^2$
Y2 = x^2

The values of Y1 are always greater than or equal to their Y2 values.

$Y1 = x^2 - 4x + 7$

(2, 3)

$Y2 = -x^2 + 4x - 1$

$(-10, 10, -10, 10)$

b. $x^2 - 4x + 7 > -x^2 + 4x - 1$

Let $Y1 = x^2 - 4x + 7$ and
$Y2 - -x^2 + 4x - 1$

The solution does not contain the x-coordinate of the intersection point, (2, 3), because the inequality does not contain equality. Since the inequality is "greater than," we determine that Y1 is above Y2 at all points to the left of the intersection point and all points to the right of the intersection point.

Therefore, the solution set is the set of all real numbers except 2, or $x \neq 2$. In interval notation, the solution is $(-\infty, 2) \cup (2, \infty)$.

X	Y1	Y2
-2	19	-13
-1	12	-6
0	7	-1
1	4	2
2	3	3
3	4	2
4	7	-1

$X = -2$

$19 > -13$
$12 > -6$
$7 > -1$
$4 > 2$
$3 \not> 3$
$4 > 2$
$7 > -1$

$Y1 = x^2 - 4x + 7$
$Y2 = -x^2 + 4x - 1$

The values of Y1 are always greater than the corresponding values for Y2 except when $x = 2$. The solution set is all real numbers except 2.

$Y1 = x^2 + 2$ $Y2 = 2$

(0, 2)

$(-10, 10, -10, 10)$

c. $x^2 + 2 \leq 2$

Let $Y1 = x^2 + 2$ and $Y2 = 2$

The solution contains the x-coordinate of the intersection point, (0, 2), because the inequality contains "equal to." Since the inequality is "less than," we determine that Y1 is not below Y2.

Therefore, the only solution is 0.

X	Y1	Y2
-2	6	2
-1	3	2
0	2	2
1	3	2
2	6	2
3	11	2
4	18	2

$X = -2$

$6 \not\leq 2$
$3 \not\leq 2$
$2 \leq 2$
$3 \not\leq 2$
$6 \not\leq 2$
$11 \not\leq 2$
$18 \not\leq 2$

$Y1 = x^2 + 2$
$Y2 = 2$

The solution is 0, the only value with corresponding equal Y1 and Y2 values. ∎

Objective 9.8.2 *CHECKUP*

1. Solve numerically for integer solutions. $2x^2 + 5x - 3 < 0$

In exercises 2–4, solve graphically.

2. $2x^2 + 5x - 3 < 0$

3. a. $x^2 + 2x - 7 \geq 3x + 5$ **b.** $-x^2 + 4 < x$
   c. $x^2 - 2x - 3 < x - 1$

4. a. $x^2 \leq 3x^2$ **b.** $x^2 - 4x + 1 > -3$
   c. $x^2 - 4x + 7 \leq -5 + 8x - 2x^2$

5. Describe what you might see if you graphically solved a quadratic inequality with the following results:
   a. The solution set consists of all real numbers.
   b. The solution set consists of a single value.
   c. The solution set consists of an interval on the number line.
   d. The inequality has no real-number solution.

Objective 9.8.3   Solving Quadratic Inequalities Algebraically

Several methods are available for solving a quadratic inequality algebraically. We will illustrate one of them.

When we solved quadratic inequalities graphically, we first determined the points of intersection of the graphs. Algebraically, we need to determine these points by solving a quadratic equation. Remember, we have several methods available to do this. We call these points of equality **critical points**—endpoints of possible interval solutions. After determining the possible intervals for the solution, we need test only one point in each interval. If one point in an interval is a solution, all points in the interval are solutions.

SOLVING A QUADRATIC INEQUALITY ALGEBRAICALLY

To solve a quadratic inequality in one variable algebraically,

- Determine the critical points (points of equality) by solving a quadratic equation and replacing the inequality symbol with an equals sign. Use the original inequality to determine whether the points of equality are in the solution.
- Determine the possible intervals for the solution by using the critical points as endpoints.
- Test one value in each interval for a true statement. If the inequality is true for the value tested, then the inequality is true for all values in the interval.

Write the solution set as a union of all possible intervals.

EXAMPLE 6   Solve algebraically.

   a. $x^2 + 3x - 4 \le 2x + 2$ **b.** $3x^2 - x - 2 > 0$ **c.** $-x^2 + 6x > 3$

Algebraic Solution

a. $x^2 + 3x - 4 \le 2x + 2$

Determine the critical points.

$$x^2 + 3x - 4 = 2x + 2$$
$$x^2 + x - 6 = 0$$
$$(x + 3)(x - 2) = 0$$
$$x = -3 \quad \text{or} \quad x = 2$$

The inequality contains equality, so the critical points are solutions. We include them in the intervals.

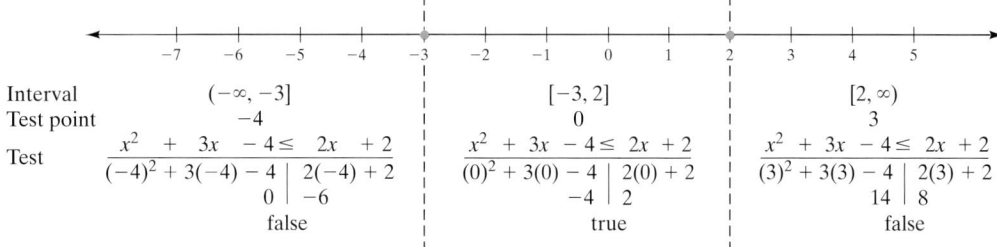

	$(-\infty, -3]$	$[-3, 2]$	$[2, \infty)$
Interval			
Test point	-4	0	3
Test	$\dfrac{x^2 + 3x - 4 \le 2x + 2}{(-4)^2 + 3(-4) - 4 \mid 2(-4) + 2}$	$\dfrac{x^2 + 3x - 4 \le 2x + 2}{(0)^2 + 3(0) - 4 \mid 2(0) + 2}$	$\dfrac{x^2 + 3x - 4 \le 2x + 2}{(3)^2 + 3(3) - 4 \mid 2(3) + 2}$
	$0 \mid -6$	$-4 \mid 2$	$14 \mid 8$
	false	true	false

Therefore, the solution is $[-3, 2]$.

b. $3x^2 - x - 2 > 0$

Determine the critical points.

$$3x^2 - x - 2 = 0$$
$$(3x + 2)(x - 1) = 0$$
$$x = -\frac{2}{3} \quad \text{or} \quad x = 1$$

The inequality does not contain equality. We do not include the critical points as solutions.

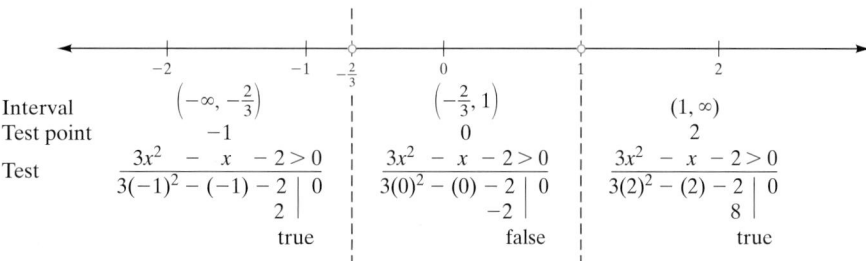

	$\left(-\infty, -\frac{2}{3}\right)$	$\left(-\frac{2}{3}, 1\right)$	$(1, \infty)$
Interval			
Test point	-1	0	2
Test	$\dfrac{3x^2 - x - 2 > 0}{3(-1)^2 - (-1) - 2 \mid 0}$	$\dfrac{3x^2 - x - 2 > 0}{3(0)^2 - (0) - 2 \mid 0}$	$\dfrac{3x^2 - x - 2 > 0}{3(2)^2 - (2) - 2 \mid 0}$
	2	-2	8
	true	false	true

Therefore, the solution is $\left(-\infty, -\frac{2}{3}\right) \cup (1, \infty)$.

c. $-x^2 + 6x > 3$

Determine the critical points.

$$-x^2 + 6x = 3$$
$$-x^2 + 6x - 3 = 0$$

This equation does not factor. We need to use the quadratic formula. Use $a = -1, b = 6,$ and $c = -3$.

$$x = \frac{-b \pm \sqrt{b^2 - 4ac}}{2a}$$

$$x = \frac{-(6) \pm \sqrt{(6)^2 - 4(-1)(-3)}}{2(-1)}$$

$$x = \frac{-6 \pm \sqrt{24}}{-2}$$

$$x = \frac{-6 \pm 2\sqrt{6}}{-2}$$

$$x = \frac{-\overset{1}{\cancel{2}}\left(3 \pm \sqrt{6}\right)}{\underset{1}{-\cancel{2}}}$$

$$x = 3 \pm \sqrt{6}$$
$$x \approx 0.551 \quad \text{or} \quad x \approx 5.450$$

The inequality does not contain equality. We do not include the critical points as solutions.

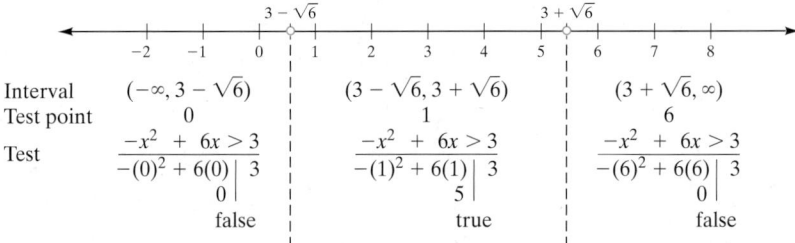

Therefore, the solution is $\left(3 - \sqrt{6}, 3 + \sqrt{6}\right)$. ∎

The special cases of quadratic inequalities solved graphically in Example 5 may also be solved algebraically.

EXAMPLE 7

Solve algebraically.

a. $2x^2 \geq x^2$ **b.** $x^2 - 4x + 7 > -x^2 + 4x - 1$ **c.** $x^2 + 2 \leq 2$

Algebraic Solution

a. $2x^2 \geq x^2$

Determine the critical points.

$$2x^2 = x^2$$
$$x^2 = 0$$
$$x = 0$$

The inequality contains equality. We include the critical point as a solution.

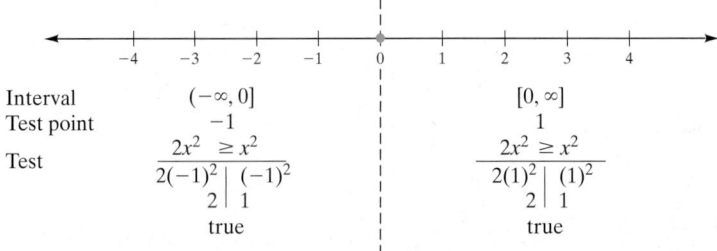

Therefore, the solution is $(-\infty, 0] \cup [0, \infty)$, which is equivalent to $(-\infty, \infty)$, or the set of all real numbers.

b. $x^2 - 4x + 7 > -x^2 + 4x - 1$
Determine the critical points.

$$x^2 - 4x + 7 = -x^2 + 4x - 1$$
$$2x^2 - 8x + 8 = 0$$
$$2(x^2 - 4x + 4) = 0$$
$$2(x - 2)^2 = 0$$
$$x - 2 = 0$$
$$x = 2$$

The inequality does not contain equality. We do not include the critical point as a solution.

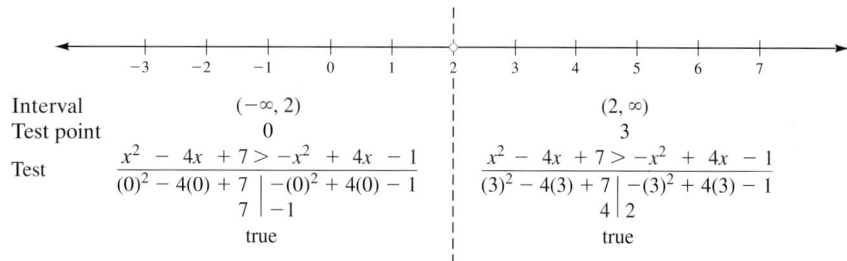

Interval	$(-\infty, 2)$	$(2, \infty)$
Test point	0	3
Test	$\dfrac{x^2 \ - 4x \ + 7 > -x^2 \ + 4x \ - 1}{(0)^2 - 4(0) + 7 \ \mid -(0)^2 + 4(0) - 1}$	$\dfrac{x^2 - 4x \ + 7 > -x^2 \ + 4x \ - 1}{(3)^2 - 4(3) + 7 \ \mid -(3)^2 + 4(3) - 1}$
	$7 \mid -1$	$4 \mid 2$
	true	true

Therefore, the solution is $(-\infty, 2) \cup (2, \infty)$, or $x \neq 2$.

c. $x^2 + 2 \leq 2$
Determine the critical points.

$$x^2 + 2 = 2$$
$$x^2 = 0$$
$$x = 0$$

The inequality contains equality. We include the critical point as a solution.

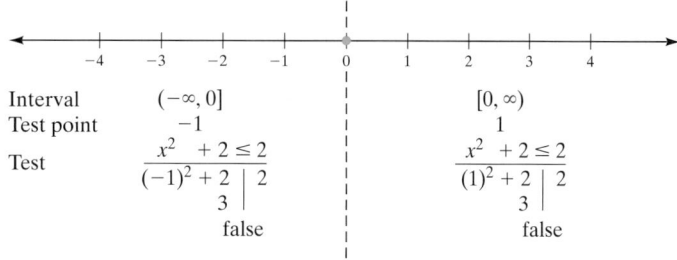

Interval	$(-\infty, 0]$	$[0, \infty)$
Test point	-1	1
Test	$\dfrac{x^2 \ + 2 \leq 2}{(-1)^2 + 2 \ \mid \ 2}$	$\dfrac{x^2 \ + 2 \leq 2}{(1)^2 + 2 \ \mid \ 2}$
	3	3
	false	false

Therefore, the solution is neither possible interval. However, the critical point is a solution. The only solution is 0. ■

✓ Objective 9.8.3 *CHECKUP*

In exercises 1 and 2, solve algebraically.

1. a. $x^2 + 2x - 7 \geq 3x + 5$ **b.** $-x^2 + 4 < x$
 c. $x^2 - 2x - 3 < x - 1$

2. a. $x^2 \leq 3x^2$ **b.** $x^2 - 4x + 1 > -3$
 c. $x^2 - 4x + 7 \leq -5 + 8x - 2x^2$

3. How do you determine the critical points of a quadratic inequality?

4. Why is it important to know the critical points of a quadratic inequality when solving the inequality algebraically?

Objective 9.8.4   Modeling the Real World

Inequalities often give us important information about the quantities related by a quadratic equation. If the equation describes the height of a thrown or falling object, an inequality might tell us when the object is higher or lower than a given height. If the equation describes a cost or sales function, an inequality might tell us the range of numbers of items we need to sell to make a profit. For these reasons, inequalities are very useful in business and science.

EXAMPLE 8

Elisa sells fruit drinks at the local fair. She has determined from past summers that the cost for x days of operation can be estimated by the cost function $C(x) = 2x^2 - 20x + 240$. Determine the number of days she can operate the stand at a cost of no more than $200.

Numeric Solution

We need to determine when the cost function is less than or equal to 200: $C(x) \le 200$.

$$2x^2 - 20x + 240 \le 200$$

Use the inequality $2x^2 - 20x + 240 \le 200$.

Since we need to determine only integer solutions, set up a table of values for x days. Let Y1 = $2x^2 - 20x + 240$ and Y2 = 200.

According to **Figure 9.7**, Elisa should operate her stand for at least three days but not more than seven days, to keep her cost at $200 or less.

X	Y₁	Y₂	
2	208	200	208 ≰ 200
3	198	200	198 ≤ 200
4	192	200	192 ≤ 200
5	190	200	190 ≤ 200
6	192	200	192 ≤ 200
7	198	200	198 ≤ 200
8	208	200	208 ≰ 200

X=2

Figure 9.7

APPLICATION

According to the *Apollo 15 Preliminary Science Report*, astronaut David R. Scott conducted a short demonstration experiment. A heavy object, a 1.32-kilogram hammer, and a light object, a 0.03-kilogram feather, were released simultaneously from a height of 1.6 meters to the lunar surface. Both objects were observed to undergo the same acceleration and strike the surface at the same time.

a. Determine the length of time the objects were in free fall.

b. Determine the time interval that the objects were in free fall above 0.8 meter (halfway to the surface).

Discussion

The vertical-position equation for objects on the moon is different from that for objects on Earth because the moon has only one-sixth of the Earth's gravity. Instead of free-fall acceleration of 9.8 meters per second squared, the acceleration is 1.6 meters per second squared on the moon, which results in vertical-position equation: $s = -0.8t^2 + v_0 t + s_0$, where s is the vertical height in meters, v_0 is the initial velocity, and s_0 is the initial height.

a. Use the vertical-position equation. Let $v_0 = 0$ (the objects were dropped) and $s_0 = 1.6$ (the initial height).

$$s = -0.8t^2 + v_0 t + s_0$$
$$s = -0.8t^2 + 0t + 1.6 \qquad \text{Substitute values.}$$
$$s = -0.8t^2 + 1.6$$

The vertical position when the objects strike the surface is 0 meter. (Let $s = 0$.)

$$s = -0.8t^2 + 1.6$$
$$0 = -0.8t^2 + 1.6 \qquad \text{Substitute } s = 0.$$
$$0 = -0.8(t^2 - 2) \qquad \text{Factor.}$$
$$t^2 - 2 = 0 \qquad \text{Zero factor property}$$
$$t^2 = 2 \qquad \text{Add 2 to both sides.}$$
$$t = \pm\sqrt{2} \qquad \text{Principle of square roots}$$

The objects were in free fall $\sqrt{2}$ seconds or approximately 1.4 seconds.

(*Note:* Search the Web to see a video of this experiment and estimate the time to check our solution.)

b. The length of time in free fall above 0.8 meter is $s > 0.8$ or

$$-0.8t^2 + 1.6 > 0.8$$

Determine the critical points.

$$-0.8t^2 + 1.6 = 0.8$$
$$-0.8t^2 + 0.8 = 0 \qquad \text{Subtract 0.8 from both sides.}$$
$$-0.8(t^2 - 1) = 0 \qquad \text{Factor.}$$
$$-0.8(t - 1)(t + 1) = 0 \qquad \text{Factor.}$$
$$t - 1 = 0 \quad \text{or} \quad t + 1 = 0 \qquad \text{Zero factor property}$$
$$t = 1 \qquad\qquad t = -1$$

The inequality does not contain equality, so the critical points are not solutions. Note that values $t < 0$ are not possible (time is not negative) and $t > \sqrt{2} \approx 1.4$ seconds (time the objects strike the surface).

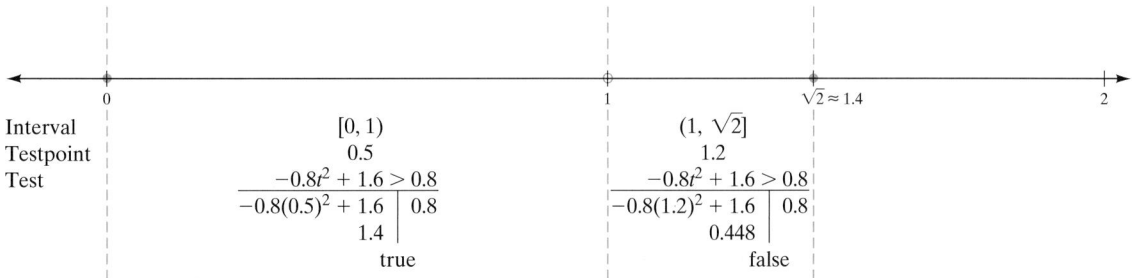

Interval	[0, 1)	(1, √2]
Testpoint	0.5	1.2
Test	$-0.8t^2 + 1.6 > 0.8$	$-0.8t^2 + 1.6 > 0.8$
	$-0.8(0.5)^2 + 1.6 \mid 0.8$	$-0.8(1.2)^2 + 1.6 \mid 0.8$
	1.4	0.448
	true	false

The solution is $[0, 1)$. The objects are dropped at a height above 0.8 meter (0 second) and remain above 0.8 meter from 0 to 1 second.

Objective 9.8.4 *CHECKUP*

1. The wholesale price of a computer is $600. The minimum order a dealer can place is 10 computers. For every additional computer above 10, the price per computer to the dealer is reduced by $20. If x represents the number of computers above 10 that are ordered, the price per computer will be $600 - 20x$, and the number ordered will be $10 + x$. The total revenue from the sale will be $R(x) = (600 - 20x)(10 + x)$. How many computers must be ordered for the revenue to be at least $7500?

2. If astronaut James B. Irwin had thrown a lunar sample upward with an initial velocity of 8 meters per second from a height of 1.6 meters, determine the time interval that the sample would be in flight before it reached its initial height of 4 meters at which David R. Scott caught it.

9.8 EXERCISES

Student Solutions Manual • PH Math/Tutor Center • CD Video • Math XL MathXL® • MyMathLab MyMathLab • Interactmath.com

Determine whether each inequality is a quadratic inequality.

1. $2x^2 - 5 < 4x + 1$

2. $5a - 3 \geq 2a^{-2} + 7$

3. $1.3z - 2.8 > 4.3z^2$

4. $\dfrac{2}{3}x^3 + \dfrac{1}{7}x < \dfrac{5}{7}$

5. $4x^{-2} + 5x^{-1} \geq 2x + 1$

6. $x^2 > 0$

7. $\dfrac{1}{3}x^2 - \dfrac{5}{6}x > \dfrac{3}{4}$

8. $3x - 5 > x^2 + 8$

9. $2x^3 + 4 \leq x^2 + x$

10. $\dfrac{5}{9}x - \dfrac{2}{9}x^2 > \dfrac{2}{3}\sqrt{x} - \dfrac{5}{6}$

11. $3\sqrt{x} + 5x < x^2 - 5$

12. $5.4x^2 + 4.1x - 0.9 \geq 0$

Solve for integer solutions numerically.

13. $x^2 + 3x - 7 \geq x + 8$

14. $x^2 + 4x - 3 \leq 2x + 5$

15. $3x^2 + 9x + 7 < 11 - 2x$

16. $2x^2 + 4x - 8 < 2 + 3x$

17. $4x^2 - 13x - 7 > 18x + 1$

18. $3x^2 + 9x - 5 > 2x + 1$

Solve graphically.

19. $x^2 + 2x + 1 > 4$

20. $x^2 - 8x + 16 \geq 9$

21. $2x^2 + x - 3 < 7$

22. $x^2 - 2x - 8 \leq 2x - 3$

23. $24 + 5x - x^2 < -x + 8$

24. $14 + 5x - x^2 < -2x + 6$

25. $2x^2 - 5 \leq x^2 + 4$

26. $x^2 + 3x - 10 > 10 - 3x - x^2$

27. $\dfrac{1}{4}x^2 - 3 \geq x^2 + 2$

28. $5 - \dfrac{1}{5}x^2 \leq 1 - x^2$

29. $x^2 + 6x + 10 \geq -x^2 - 6x - 8$

30. $-x^2 - 4x \geq 4$

31. $x^2 - 4x + 8 \geq \dfrac{1}{4}x^2 - x + 5$

32. $x^2 - 8x + 15 \geq -x^2 + 8x - 17$

Solve exercises 33–54 algebraically.

33. $x^2 - 2x - 15 \geq 9$

34. $x^2 - 2x - 24 \leq 11$

35. $8 + 2x - x^2 > -7$

36. $10 + 3x - x^2 > -8$

37. $4x^2 - 12x + 9 \leq 4$

38. $4x^2 + 20x + 25 \geq 9$

39. $6 + 5x - x^2 < -8$

40. $20 + x - x^2 > -10$

41. $x^2 + 3 \geq -x + 15$

42. $\frac{1}{2}x^2 + 2 \leq 2x + 8$

43. $10 - 2x^2 < 4x + 4$

44. $7 - x^2 < -2x - 1$

45. $x^2 - x - 6 \leq 12 + 2x - 2x^2$

46. $2x^2 - 11x + 5 \geq -10 + 22x - 4x^2$

47. $x^2 - 3x + \frac{21}{4} \geq 2x^2 - 6x + \frac{15}{2}$

48. $-x^2 - 5x - \frac{17}{4} \leq -\frac{1}{5}x^2 - x + \frac{3}{4}$

49. $x^2 - x - \frac{7}{4} > -2x^2 + 2x - \frac{5}{2}$

50. $x^2 + 6x + 5 < -x^2 - 6x - 13$

51. $x^2 + 4x + 8 \geq 4$

52. $-x^2 + 8x - 14 \geq 2$

53. $2 + 4x - x^2 > 10 - 4x + x^2$

54. $-7 - 4x - \frac{1}{2}x^2 < x^2 + 8x + 17$

Business

55. The mathematics department at a local college estimates that its costs for professional development for faculty can be estimated by the function $C(x) = 0.02x^2 + 300x + 5000$, where x is the number of faculty employed by the department. For what numbers of faculty members will cost exceed $12,500?

56. A bakery's daily costs can be modeled by the function $C(x) = -1.5x^2 + 5x + 70$, where x is the number of hours worked by apprentices. For what numbers of apprentice hours will costs be above $50?

57. An equipment rental company finds that in the category of power tools its weekly repair cost is $C(x) = x^2 - 5x + 17.25$, where x is the number of tools that need repair. For what number of tools will costs be between $11.25 and $14.00?

58. Jenny's monthly expenditures on pet care can be estimated by $C(x) = 2x^2 + 3x + 50$, where x is the number of visits to the groomer by her dogs. For what number of visits will her costs be between $75 and $150?

59. A college student who does private tutoring estimates her monthly revenue to be $R(x) = -0.3x^2 + 15x + 16$, where x is the number of tutoring sessions she leads. For what number of sessions will her revenue be less than $200?

60. A local artist does paintings by commission and has revenue $R(x) = 22x^2 - 36x + 813$, where x is the number of paintings. For what number of paintings will his revenue exceed $15,000?

61. A mailing service estimates its daily revenues to be $R(x) = 1.2x^2 - 3x + 5$, where x is the number of orders handled. For what number of orders will revenue be between $300 and $500?

62. A charitable organization finds that its revenues for a fundraiser can be approximated by the function $R(x) = -0.08x^2 + 1500x + 45$, where x is the number of tables reserved by corporate sponsors. For what number of corporate sponsor tables will revenue be between $20,000 and $30,000?

63. A freelance journalist approximates his monthly business profit by $P(x) = 0.85x^2 + 60x + 100$, where x is the number of works published. For what number of works will his profit be greater than $1000?

64. A telemarketer estimates her profit by $P(x) = 0.085x^2 - 0.3x + 1.2$, where x is the number of calls made. How many calls does she need to make to earn $25 or more?

65. A heating and air-conditioning chain estimates its profits to be $P(x) = 2.3x^2 - 160x + 10,830$, where x is the number of the week of the year. In what weeks are profits less than $9000?

66. A book buyer who buys books from faculty members and then sells them on the Internet estimates his daily profits to be $P(x) = -0.8x^2 + 9x + 5$, where x is the number of Internet sites used. For what number of sites used are profits less than $28?

Vertical Position

67. An egg is thrown upward from a stand that is 25 feet above the ground. The initial speed of the egg is 30 feet per second. For what length of time is the egg higher than the stand?

68. An arrow is projected upward with an initial velocity of 40 feet per second from a height of 220 feet above the ground. Determine the length of time the arrow is higher than the height at which it was released.

69. A skydiver falls downward with an initial velocity of 10 feet per second from a height of 950 feet. During what time period is he between 411 and 500 feet above the ground?

70. A weight is projected downward with an initial velocity of 7 meters per second from a height of 35 meters. During what time period is the weight between 23 and 29 meters above the ground?

As stated in the Application, the vertical-position equation for objects on the moon is different from that for objects on the Earth because the moon has only one-sixth of the Earth's gravity. The vertical position on the lunar surface is $s = -0.8t^2 + v_0t + s_0$, where s is the vertical height in meters, v_0 is the initial velocity, and s_0 is the initial height above the lunar surface.

71. A soccer ball is kicked upward from the surface of the moon with an initial velocity of 3 meters per second. When will it be between 2.2 and 2.7 meters above the moon's surface?

72. A rock on the moon is thrown upward from a height of 6 meters with an initial velocity of 5 meters per second. When will it be between the heights of 12.8 and 13.2 meters?

The vertical-position equation for objects on Mars is different from that for objects on the Earth because Mars has a little more than one-third of the Earth's gravity. The acceleration is 3.7 meters per second squared on Mars, which results in the vertical-position equation $s = -1.85t^2 + v_0t + s_0$, where s is the vertical height in meters, v_0 is the initial velocity, and s_0 is the initial height above the surface.

73. A boulder breaks off of a Martian mountain and drops from a height of 200 meters. During what times is it between 100 and 175 meters above the surface of the planet?

74. A rock is projected upward from a height of 1.7 meters on Mars. It is given an initial velocity of 3.4 meters per second. During what times is it between 2 and 2.5 meters above the Martian surface?

Real Data

75. Using data from the Bureau of Labor Statistics, it is estimated that $p(x)$, the price per gallon of gasoline, can be represented by the function $p(x) = 0.03x^2 - 0.08x + 1.56$, where x is the number of years after 2000. According to this model, in what years will the price of gasoline be between $3 and $5 dollars per gallon?

76. Based on data from the U.S. Department of Labor, the hourly wage in U.S. dollars, $w(t)$, of a production worker in the United States can be estimated by the function $w(t) = 0.01x^2 + 0.63x + 20.07$, where t is the number of years after 2000. For what years will this wage be less than $25 per hour?

77. Compact discs have increasingly replaced cassettes as a means of selling recorded music. Use the method of quadratic regression to find the quadratic function $c(x)$ that best fits the data given in the following table. Let $c(x)$ equal the cassette sales in millions of dollars and x equal the number of years after 1999.

Year	Cassette Sales (net in millions)
1999	123.6
2000	76
2001	45

If the trends in the table continue, for what years will the cassette sales be below 40 million?

78. According to the U.S. Department of Energy, nuclear-based electricity generation has varied in recent years. Use the method of quadratic regression to find the quadratic function $n(x)$ that best fits the data given in the following table. Let $n(x)$ equal nuclear-based electricity generation in million of kilowatt hours and x equal the number of years after 2000.

Year	Nuclear-Based Electricity Generation (millions of kilowatt hours)
2000	769
2001	780
2002	764

If the trends in the table continue, in what years will nuclear-based electricity generation be above 550 million kilowatt hours?

9.8 Calculator Exercises

Part 1. Using the TEST Function to Graphically Solve a Quadratic Inequality

You may use the TEST function of the calculator to determine whether a quadratic inequality is true or false. The calculator denotes a true statement as "1" and a false statement as "0." Using the TEST function, you can graph the number-line solution of an inequality. As an example, suppose you wish to solve the inequality $x^2 + 5x - 6 > 0$.

- Set the screen to integer coordinates for x and tenths coordinates for y.

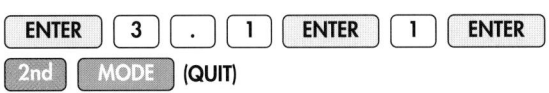

- Enter the inequality in Y1. The inequality symbols are found under the TEST menu.

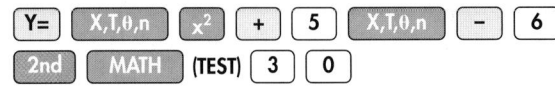

- Graph.

[GRAPH]

The calculator will graph a y-coordinate of 1 for all true statements and a 0 for all false statements. This will appear as a line segment on the screen. You can imagine the graph as a number-line representation of the solution intervals for the inequality. You will have to use your understanding of the endpoints to correctly interpret the graph. Use the procedure to check the solutions of the exercises in 9.8 Exercises.

Part 2. Using the TEST Function to Solve a Quadratic Inequality Numerically

You have been shown how to use the TABLE function to solve a quadratic inequality numerically. Sometimes it is confusing to compare Y1 and Y2 to determine the correct order relation. There is a way to reduce this confusion. As an example, solve $2 - 3x - x^2 > x - 5$ numerically for integer solutions.

- Store the inequality Y2 > Y3 in Y1, the left side of the inequality in Y2, and the right side of the inequality in Y3.

(Doing this will make it easier to scan for values of x that make the inequality true.)

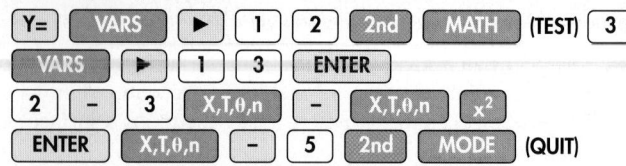

- Set the TBLSET to start at 0 and increment by 1 automatically.
- View the table, scanning up and down for various x-values. Wherever Y1 is equal to 1, the corresponding x-value is an integer solution of the inequality; wherever Y1 is equal to 0, the corresponding x-value is not a solution.

With this method, you no longer have to compare the Y2 and Y3 values to determine whether the x-value makes the inequality true or not. You see this immediately by reading the Y1 value. Use this procedure to check the solutions of exercises 13–18 in 9.8 Exercises.

9.8 Writing Exercise

When the graphical method is used to solve a quadratic inequality, the graph of the expression on the left, stored in Y1, may not intersect the graph of the expression on the right, stored in Y2. However, this does not necessarily mean that the inequality has no solutions. Sketch situations in which this is so, and discuss conditions under which the inequality may still have a solution.

■ Chapter 9 Summary

Vocabulary Review

After completing this chapter, you should be able to define the following key terms.

cubic equation in one variable	isosceles right triangle	quadratic equation in one variable
double root	leg	right angle
equilateral triangle	polynomial equation in one variable	root
hypotenuse	Pythagorean theorem	vertical-position equation

Fill in the blank with one of the words or phrases listed above.

1. The standard form for a _____ is $ax^3 + bx^2 + cx + d = 0$.

2. The standard form for a _____ is $ax^2 + bx + c = 0$.

3. The side opposite the right angle in a right triangle is called the _____.

4. A right triangle with two equal legs is called an _____.

5. A triangle with three equal sides is called an _____.

6. The solution of an equation is also called the _____ of the equation.

Reflections

1. Define what is meant by a polynomial equation. What is the difference between a polynomial equation of degree two and one of degree three?

2. Explain how the zero factor property of real numbers can help you solve a polynomial equation algebraically.

3. Explain how the principle of square roots can help you solve a quadratic equation algebraically.

4. What is the quadratic formula and how is it used?

5. When can the Pythagorean theorem be used in modeling real-world situations?

6. What is the difference between a quadratic equation and a quadratic inequality? How do the solutions to each differ?

■ Chapter 9 Section-by-Section Review

9.1

Recall	Examples
A polynomial equation in one variable is written in the form $P(x) = 0$, where $P(x)$ is a polynomial.	$2x^3 + x^2 - 4x = 0$ Cubic equation $x^2 + x + 5 = 0$ Quadratic equation $-2x^4 + x^2 + 1 = 0$ Polynomial equation
Solving numerically • Complete a three-column table of values: one column for the independent variable, one for the left side of the equation, and one for the right side of the equation. • The solution is the value for the independent variable that results in equal values for the left and right sides of the equation.	Solve $x^2 - 2 = 2x + 1$ numerically. <table><tr><td>x</td><td>$x^2 - 2$</td><td>=</td><td>$2x + 1$</td><td></td></tr><tr><td>−1</td><td>−1</td><td></td><td>−1</td><td>−1 = −1</td></tr><tr><td>0</td><td>−2</td><td></td><td>1</td><td>−2 < 1</td></tr><tr><td>1</td><td>−1</td><td></td><td>3</td><td>−1 < 3</td></tr><tr><td>2</td><td>2</td><td></td><td>5</td><td>2 < 5</td></tr><tr><td>3</td><td>7</td><td></td><td>7</td><td>7 = 7</td></tr></table> The solutions are −1 and 3.
Solving graphically • Graph the two functions defined by the left side of the equation and the right side of the equation. • The solution is the x-coordinate of the point of intersection of the two graphs.	Solve $x^2 - 2 = 2x + 1$ graphically. The solutions are −1 and 3.

Solve numerically for integer solutions.

1. $2x^2 + 5x - 16 = 7x + 8$

2. $\frac{1}{3}x^2 + 5x + 6 = x - 3$

3. $0.7x^2 - 2.5x + 4.6 = 1.7x + 1.1$

Solve exercises 4–9 graphically.

4. $x^2 - 4x + 4 = 9$

5. $x^2 - 6 = \frac{1}{4}x^2 + 6$

6. $x^2 + 3x - 5 = 7 - 2x - x^2$

7. $-0.3x^2 + 4x + 5 = 2.2x - 11.5$

8. $x^2 + 8x + 8 = 0$

9. $2x^3 - 18x = 3x^2 - 27$

10. An amateur scientist drops a lead weight from a platform 96 feet above the ground. How many seconds will it take for the weight to reach the ground?

11. A rocket is shot upward from a stand 15 feet high with initial velocity of 550 feet per second. Write the position function for the rocket. When will the rocket be at a height of 3000 feet?

12. A firework is shot with a downward velocity of 8 feet per second from a hill 40 feet tall. Write its position function. When will the firework be at a height of 25 feet?

13. According to the National Health Interview Survey of the CDC, an increasing number of American adults have mild to severe loss of hearing. One model estimates the percent of people with hearing trouble, $p(x)$, by using the following function, $p(x) = 0.01x^2 - 0.03x - 0.5$, where x is age in years. If, at age 25, 5% of people have hearing trouble, use the function to estimate at what age there will be three times that number of people with hearing trouble.

9.2

Recall	Example
Solving algebraically by factoring • Write the equation in standard form, $P(x) = 0$. • Factor $P(x)$. • Set each factor equal to 0 and solve. • Check the solution(s).	Solve $x^2 - 2 = 2x + 1$ $x^2 - 2x - 3 = 0$ $(x - 3)(x + 1) = 0$ $x - 3 = 0$ or $x + 1 = 0$ $\quad x = 3 \qquad\qquad x = -1$ Check the solutions.

Solve exercises 14–21 algebraically by factoring.

14. $x^2 - 5 = x + 1$

15. $6x^2 - x - 77 = 0$

16. $2x + 10 = x^2 - 5x + 2$

17. $x^2 - 7x - 60 = 0$

18. $3x^2 + 5x - 3 = 1 + 5x + 3x^2$

19. $6x^2 - 8x = 9x - 12$

20. $\dfrac{1}{4}x^2 + \dfrac{3}{2}x - \dfrac{19}{8} = \dfrac{3}{8}x + 2$

21. $9x^2 - 49 = 0$

22. Graph the following equation on your calculator. Determine the x-intercepts of the graph. Write a related equation and determine its solution,
$$y = (x + 2)(x - 1)$$

23. Emma purchased 300 square feet of remnant carpeting to carpet a playroom in the bonus room of her home. She wants to lay the carpet in an area that has a length that is 5 feet more than the width, and she wants to use all of the carpeting. Write a polynomial equation and solve it by factoring to determine the dimensions of the carpeted area.

24. The area of a rectangle can be modeled with the function $A(x) = 6x^2 + 47x + 90$, where x is the width in yards. If the area is 143 square yards, find x.

25. The owner of a fruit stand estimates weekly revenues on sales to be $R(x) = 940 + 50x + 7x^2$, where x is the number of hours beyond 55 that the fruit stand is open. One-week revenues were \$2140. How many hours was the stand open during that week?

26. The ranking of large islands by size is summarized by the following table:

Ranking	Area (thousands of square miles)
2 (New Guinea)	306
6 (Sumatra)	162
8 (Great Britain)	78

Find the quadratic function that best models these data. If the trends in this table continue, find, by factoring, the ranking of the island of Madagascar, which contains roughly 238,000 square miles.

9.3

Recall	Examples
Product Rule for Square Roots For any real numbers $\sqrt{a}$ and $\sqrt{b}$, $\sqrt{a} \cdot \sqrt{b} = \sqrt{ab}$.	Multiply, using the product rule. $3\sqrt{5} \cdot 2\sqrt{2} = 3 \cdot 2 \cdot \sqrt{5 \cdot 2}$ $\qquad\qquad = 6\sqrt{10}$ Simplify, using the product rule. $\sqrt{28} = \sqrt{4 \cdot 7} = \sqrt{4} \cdot \sqrt{7} = 2\sqrt{7}$ $\dfrac{-2 + \sqrt{24}}{4} = \dfrac{-2 + \sqrt{4 \cdot 6}}{4}$ $\qquad\qquad = \dfrac{-2 + 2\sqrt{6}}{4}$ $\qquad\qquad = \dfrac{\overset{1}{\cancel{2}}(-1 + \sqrt{6})}{\underset{2}{\cancel{4}}}$ $\qquad\qquad = \dfrac{-1 + \sqrt{6}}{2}$

(continued on page 757)

Recall	Examples
Quotient Rule for Square Roots For any real numbers $\sqrt{a}$ and $\sqrt{b}$ where $b \neq 0$, $\frac{\sqrt{a}}{\sqrt{b}} = \sqrt{\frac{a}{b}}$.	Divide, using the quotient rule. $$\frac{\sqrt{50}}{\sqrt{2}} = \sqrt{\frac{50}{2}} = \sqrt{25} = 5$$ Simplify, using the quotient rule. $$\sqrt{\frac{49}{2}} = \frac{\sqrt{49}}{\sqrt{2}} = \frac{7}{\sqrt{2}}$$ $$= \frac{7 \cdot \sqrt{2}}{\sqrt{2} \cdot \sqrt{2}} = \frac{7\sqrt{2}}{\sqrt{4}} = \frac{7\sqrt{2}}{2} \quad \textit{Rationalize the denominator.}$$
Distance formula The distance between two points (x_1, y_1) and (x_2, y_2), on a coordinate plane is $d = \sqrt{(x_2 - x_1)^2 + (y_2 - y_1)^2}$.	Determine the distance between the points $(2, 5)$ and $(-1, 3)$. Let $x_1 = 2$, $y_1 = 5$, $x_2 = -1$, and $y_2 = 3$ $d = \sqrt{(x_2 - x_1)^2 + (y_2 - y_1)^2}$ $d = \sqrt{(-1 - 2)^2 + (3 - 5)^2}$ $d = \sqrt{(-3)^2 + (-2)^2}$ $d = \sqrt{13}$

Simplify without using a calculator.

27. $-\sqrt{49}$

28. $\sqrt{200}$

29. $\sqrt{32}$

30. $\sqrt{8}$

31. $-\sqrt{72}$

32. $\dfrac{-6 - \sqrt{50}}{5}$

33. $\dfrac{14 + \sqrt{98}}{14}$

34. $\dfrac{3 - \sqrt{27}}{6}$

35. $\dfrac{-4 + \sqrt{20}}{-2}$

36. $\sqrt{\dfrac{36}{5}}$

37. $\sqrt{\dfrac{40}{32}}$

Multiply or divide and simplify.

38. $\sqrt{6} \cdot \sqrt{10}$

39. $3\sqrt{3} \cdot 2\sqrt{6}$

40. $\dfrac{\sqrt{75}}{\sqrt{3}}$

41. $\dfrac{\sqrt{105}}{\sqrt{5}}$

42. Evaluate $-b + \sqrt{b^2 - 4ac}$ for $a = 2$, $b = -3$, $c = -6$

In exercises 43 and 44, find the distance between the green points.

43. $(3, -1)$ and $(2, 4)$

44. $(2, -3)$ and $(4, 1)$

45. Find the perimeter of the triangle.

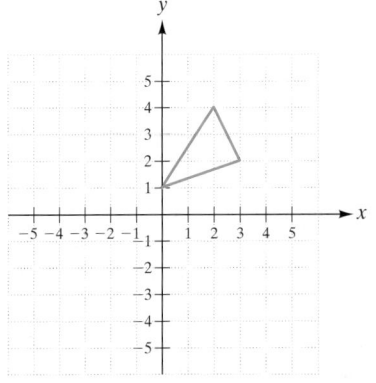

46. A boat ramp has a length of 35 feet. If the vertical distance of the ramp is 15 feet, what is the horizontal distance?

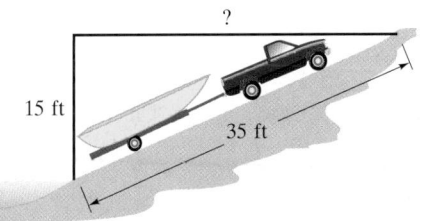

15 ft   35 ft

47. Trever is hiking in the mountains. According to his GPS, he has traveled 5 miles north and 5 miles east of his camp site. Using the camp site as the origin, write a coordinate pair to represent the location of the camp site and Trever's new location. How far from the camp site is Trever?

9.4

Recall	Example
Solving algebraically, using the principle of square roots, when $ax^2 + c = 0$ • Solve for x^2. • Apply the principle of square roots. • Solve the resulting equations. • Check the solution(s).	Solve. $2x^2 - 9 = 7$ $2x^2 - 9 = 7$ $2x^2 = 16$ $x^2 = 8$ $x = \sqrt{8}$　or　$x = -\sqrt{8}$ $x = 2\sqrt{2}$　　$x = -2\sqrt{2}$ Check the solutions.
Solving algebraically by completing the square • Isolate the variable terms • Divide both sides by the leading coefficient. • Add the square of one-half of the coefficient of the x term to both sides. • Rewrite the trinomial as a binomial squared. • Use the principle of square roots to solve the resulting equations. • Check the solution(s).	Solve. $2x^2 + 5x - 1 = 0$ $2x^2 + 5x - 1 = 0$ $2x^2 + 5x = 1$ $x^2 + \dfrac{5}{2}x = \dfrac{1}{2}$ $x^2 + \dfrac{5}{2}x + \dfrac{25}{16} = \dfrac{1}{2} + \dfrac{25}{16}$ $\left(x + \dfrac{5}{4}\right)^2 = \dfrac{33}{16}$ $x + \dfrac{5}{4} = \sqrt{\dfrac{33}{16}}$　or　$x + \dfrac{5}{4} = -\sqrt{\dfrac{33}{16}}$ $x + \dfrac{5}{4} = \dfrac{\sqrt{33}}{4}$　　$x + \dfrac{5}{4} = -\dfrac{\sqrt{33}}{4}$ $x = -\dfrac{5}{4} + \dfrac{\sqrt{33}}{4}$　　$x = -\dfrac{5}{4} - \dfrac{\sqrt{33}}{4}$ $x = \dfrac{-5 + \sqrt{33}}{4}$　　$x = \dfrac{-5 - \sqrt{33}}{4}$ Check the solutions.

Solve exercises 48–54 by using the principle of square roots.

48. $4x^2 - 100 = 0$　　　**49.** $a^2 + 5 = 9$　　　**50.** $x^2 + 3 = 15$　　　**51.** $15 + b^2 = 7$

52. $(x - 4)^2 = 9$　　　**53.** $x^2 + 18x + 81 = 16$　　　**54.** $(z - 2)^2 + 5 = 7$

Solve exercises 55–57 by completing the square.

55. $p^2 - 4p - 96 = 0$　　　**56.** $2x^2 - 5x - 12 = 0$　　　**57.** $x^2 + \dfrac{1}{2}x = 1$

58. A retailer sells figurines for $20 each. In order to promote sales, the price of each figurine is reduced by $1 times the number of figurines purchased. The retailer determines that each sale must be for $100 in order for her to break even on the promotion. Determine the number of figurines that must be sold to each purchaser in order for the retailer to break even.

59. The length of a rectangle is 8 inches more than twice its width. The area of the rectangle is 90 square inches. Write a quadratic equation and solve it by completing the square, to find the dimensions of the rectangle.

60. Stephanie received a length-of-service bonus of $2000 from her employer and invested it in a money market fund for two years. At the end of that period, her investment had grown to $2332.80. Use the compound-interest formula to write a quadratic equation, and then solve the equation, using the principle of square roots, to determine the annual compound-interest rate that resulted in the growth of Stephanie's investment.

61. Modern sky divers typically free-fall from 12,000 feet above the ground until 2500 feet, when they open their parachutes. They can maneuver in free fall by controlling the position of their bodies. Use the vertical-position formula to write an equation, and then solve the equation, using the principle of square roots, to determine the maximum length of time the sky divers would be free-falling.

62. Rap and hip/hop music have represented a varying percentage of sales revenue for all recorded music sold as summarized in the following table:

Year	Percent of Sales Revenue for All Recorded Music Sold
2001	11.4
2002	13.8
2003	13.3

a. As shown in the table, the percent of sales increases and decreases. Write a quadratic equation for the percent of sales revenue of rap and hip/hop music, y, x years after 2000.

b. Using the equation in part **a**, determine the number of years after 2000 when the percent of sales revenue will drop to the 1997 level of 9.7. Interpret the solutions.

9.5

Recall	Example
Solving algebraically by using the quadratic formula • Write the equation in standard form, $ax^2 + bx + c = 0$. • Use the quadratic formula, $x = \dfrac{-b \pm \sqrt{b^2 - 4ac}}{2a}$ • Check the solution(s).	Solve. $2x^2 + 5x - 1 = 0$ $a = 2, b = 5, c = -1$ $x = \dfrac{-b \pm \sqrt{b^2 - 4ac}}{2a}$ $x = \dfrac{-(5) \pm \sqrt{(5)^2 - 4(2)(-1)}}{2(2)}$ $x = \dfrac{-5 \pm \sqrt{25 + 8}}{4}$ $x = \dfrac{-5 \pm \sqrt{33}}{4}$ Check the solutions.
Determining the characteristics of the solution of a quadratic equation by using the discriminant First, determine the value of the discriminant, $b^2 - 4ac$, for the quadratic equation in standard form. • If the discriminant is 0, the equation has one rational solution. • If the discriminant is a perfect square not equal to 0, the equation has two rational solutions. • If the discriminant is a positive number that is not a perfect square, the equation has two irrational solutions. • If the discriminant is a negative number, the equation has no real-number solution.	Determine the characteristics of the solution of the given quadratic equation by using the discriminant. $x^2 + 2x + 1 = 0$ $\quad b^2 - 4ac = (2)^2 - 4(1)(1) = 0$ The equation has one rational solution. $x^2 - x - 2 = 0$ $\quad b^2 - 4ac = (-1)^2 - 4(1)(-2) = 9$ The equation has two rational solutions. $x^2 + 3x + 1 = 0$ $\quad b^2 - 4ac = (3)^2 - 4(1)(1) = 5$ The equation has two irrational solutions. $x^2 - 2x + 3 = 0$ $\quad b^2 - 4ac = (-2)^2 - 4(1)(3) = -8$ The equation has no real-number solution.

Use the quadratic formula to find exact solutions.

63. $x^2 - 2x - 63 = 0$ **64.** $x^2 = 3x + 3$

65. $25x^2 + 1 = 10x$ **66.** $z^2 + \dfrac{7}{20}z - \dfrac{3}{10} = 0$

67. $x^2 + 2.1x - 10.8 = 0$ **68.** $y^2 - 5y + 12 = 0$

69. $x^2 - 10x + 6 = 0$ **70.** $3a^2 - 4a - 12 = 0$

In exercises 71–74, evaluate the discriminant to determine the characteristics of the solution(s) of each quadratic equation. Do not solve the equation.

71. $x^2 + 2x + 10 = 0$ **72.** $x^2 + 20x + 55 = 2x - 26$ **73.** $x^2 = 10x + 75$ **74.** $x = x^2 - 11$

75. Mary Claus sells Christmas Rum Cakes out of her home. Ordinarily, she charges a customer $6.50 for each cake, but to encourage multiple purchases, Mary reduces the price per cake by $0.50 for each cake ordered. She spends $2.50 to make a cake and $3.95 to package and ship an order to the customer.
   a. Write a revenue function for an order of x cakes.
   b. Write a cost function for an order of x cakes.
   c. Write a profit function for an order of x cakes.
   d. Determine the number of cakes that must be ordered for Mary to break even on an order. Interpret the break-even point(s).

76. The length of a rectangle is 8 meters more than three times the width. If its area is 528 square meters, find its dimensions.

77. Information on deaths by heart disease suggests that this number is decreasing and can be estimated by the quadratic function $y = -0.05x^2 - 7.75x + 296.1$, where x is the number of years after 1995 and y is the number of deaths per 100,000 from heart disease. Use the function and the quadratic formula to find the year in which death due to heart disease will decrease to 150 per 100,000.

9.6

Recall	Examples
To solve formulas for a specified variable, use any of the algebraic methods.	Solve $s = 4.9t^2 + 10$ for t $s = 4.9t^2 + 10$ $s - 10 = 4.9t^2$ $\dfrac{s - 10}{4.9} = t^2$ $t = \pm\sqrt{\dfrac{s - 10}{4.9}}$
The length c of the hypotenuse of an isosceles right triangle is the length a of a congruent leg times $\sqrt{2}$. $c = a\sqrt{2}$	Determine the length of the hypotenuse of an isosceles triangle, given that each of the congruent legs measures 4 centimeters. $c = a\sqrt{2}$ $c = 4\sqrt{2}$ The hypotenuse is $4\sqrt{2}$ centimeters.
The length c of the hypotenuse of a $30°-60°-90°$ triangle is twice the length a of the smaller leg. $c = 2a$	Determine the length of the hypotenuse of a $30°-60°-90°$ triangle, given that the smaller leg measures 3 centimeters. $c = 2a$ $c = 2(3)$ $c = 6$ The hypotenuse is 6 centimeters.
The length b of the longer leg of a $30°-60°-90°$ triangle is the length a of the shorter leg times $\sqrt{3}$. $b = a\sqrt{3}$	Determine the length of the longer leg of a $30°-60°-90°$ triangle, given that the shorter leg measures 3 centimeters. $b = a\sqrt{3}$ $b = 3\sqrt{3}$ The longer leg is $3\sqrt{3}$ centimeters.

In exercises 78–81, solve for the variable specified.

78. $s = -16t^2 + 50$ for t

79. $A = \dfrac{1}{4}\pi d^2$ for d

80. $a = bx^2 + c$ for x

81. $s = -16t^2 + v_0t + s_0$ for t

82. The length D of a diagonal inside a rectangular box is related to the dimensions of the box by the Pythagorean theorem, $D^2 = L^2 + W^2 + H^2$, where L, W, and H are, respectively, the length, width, and height of the box. Solve this equation for H. Use the equation to find the height of a box that is 8 inches long, is 4 inches wide, and has a diagonal that is 12 inches long.

83. A rope attached to the top of a pole makes a 45-degree angle with the ground. If the pole is 7 feet high, how long is the rope?

84. Assume that a right triangle is a $30°-60°-90°$ triangle. Determine the lengths of the sides of the triangle if the hypotenuse measures 20 inches.

85. An equilateral triangle has side 8 feet. Find the height. What is the area of the triangle?

9.7

Recall	Examples
Intercepts of the graph of a quadratic function, $y = f(x) = ax^2 + bx + c$ • To determine the x-coordinate of the x-intercept algebraically, substitute 0 for y and solve for x. Write an ordered pair with the second coordinate 0 and the first coordinate the value obtained for x. • To determine the y-intercept, write an ordered pair, $(0, c)$.	Determine the x-intercept of the graph of $y = x^2 + x - 6$. Let $y = 0$. Solve for x. $0 = x^2 + x - 6$ $0 = (x + 3)(x - 2)$ $x + 3 = 0 \qquad x - 2 = 0$ $\qquad x = -3 \qquad\quad x = 2$ The x-intercepts are $(-3, 0)$ and $(2, 0)$. Determine the y-intercept of the graph of $y = x^2 + x - 6$. In the quadratic function, $c = -6$. The y-intercept is $(0, -6)$.
Vertex of the graph of a quadratic function, $y = f(x) = ax^2 + bx + c$, is $\left(\dfrac{-b}{2a}, f\left(\dfrac{-b}{2a}\right)\right)$.	Determine the vertex of the graph of $y = x^2 + x - 6$. $a = 1, b = 1,$ and $c = -6$ $\dfrac{-b}{2a} = \dfrac{-(1)}{2(1)} = -\dfrac{1}{2}$ $f\left(\dfrac{-b}{2a}\right) = f\left(-\dfrac{1}{2}\right) = \left(-\dfrac{1}{2}\right)^2 + \left(-\dfrac{1}{2}\right) - 6 = -\dfrac{25}{4}$ The vertex is $\left(-\dfrac{1}{2}, -\dfrac{25}{4}\right)$.
Graph a quadratic function. To graph a quadratic function of the form, $y = f(x) = ax^2 + bx + c$, 1. Determine the concavity. 2. Determine the width of the parabola in comparison to the graph of $y = x^2$. 3. Determine the y-intercept of the parabola. 4. Determine the x-intercepts of the parabola. 5. Determine the vertex. 6. Determine the axis of symmetry. 7. Plot the intercepts and the vertex along with the axis of symmetry. Locate additional points as needed to complete the curve. Label all points graphed. Connect the points with a smooth curve to complete the graph.	Graph $y = x^2 + x - 6$. 1. Since $a = 1$ (positive), the graph is concave upward. 2. Since $a = 1$, the graph is the same width as the graph of $y = x^2$. 3. The y-intercept is $(0, -6)$. (See above.) 4. The x-intercepts are $(-3, 0)$ and $(2, 0)$. (See above.) 5. The vertex is $\left(-\dfrac{1}{2}, -\dfrac{25}{4}\right)$. (See above) 6. The axis of symmetry is $x = -\dfrac{1}{2}$. 7. Let $x = 1$ and $x = 3$ for additional points. $\quad x = 1; y = 1^2 + 1 - 6 = -4$ $\quad x = 3; y = 3^2 + 3 - 6 = 6$

(continued on page 762)

Recall	Examples
Writing a quadratic function given the x-intercepts of its graph • Use the converse of the zero factor property to determine the equation.	The x-intercepts of the graph of a quadratic function, $f(x)$, are $(2, 0)$ and $\left(\dfrac{1}{2}, 0\right)$. Write the function. The solutions to the corresponding equation are $x = 2$ and $x = \dfrac{1}{2}$. Therefore, $\qquad x = 2 \quad$ or $\qquad x = \dfrac{1}{2}$ $\qquad x - 2 = 0 \qquad x - \dfrac{1}{2} = 0$ $\qquad\qquad\qquad\qquad 2x - 1 = 0$ $(x - 2)(2x - 1) = 0$ $2x^2 - 5x + 2 = 0$ The quadratic function is $f(x) = 2x^2 - 5x + 2$.

86. Use the given graph of $y = f(x)$ to answer the questions.

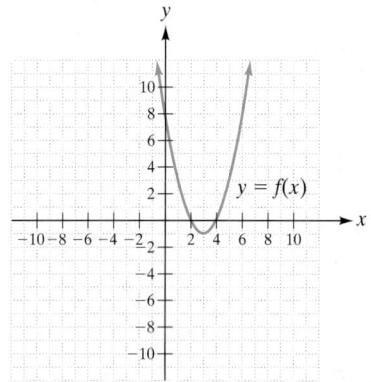

a. Find the domain and range.
b. Find the x-intercepts and the y-intercept.
c. Determine if the graph is concave upward or concave downward.
d. Find the vertex and determine the axis of symmetry.
e. Find the relative maximum and relative minimum. Find the absolute maximum and absolute minimum. Find the x-values for which the function is increasing and for which it is decreasing.
f. Find the x-values for which the y-values are equal to zero.
g. Find the solutions of $f(x) = 0$.

Determine the x-intercept and the y-intercept of the graph of the quadratic function without graphing.

87. $f(x) = x^2 + 3x - 18$ **88.** $g(x) = 2x^2 - 5x + 1$

Determine the vertex and axis of symmetry of the quadratic function without graphing.

89. $f(x) = x^2 + 4x - 12$ **90.** $f(x) = -2x^2 - 4x + 5$

Graph the quadratic function using the seven steps given in this chapter. Show all of your work.

91. $y = -x^2 + 3x + 4$ **92.** $g(x) = 2x^2 - 5x - 12$ **93.** $f(x) = x^2 + 4x - 4$

Write a quadratic function, f(x), for the given sets of x-intercept(s) of the graphs.

94. $(2, 0); (-4, 0)$ **95.** $\left(\dfrac{1}{2}, 0\right); \left(\dfrac{2}{3}, 0\right)$

96. Jim kicked a ball into the air. The height of the ball with respect to time is shown in the following graph.

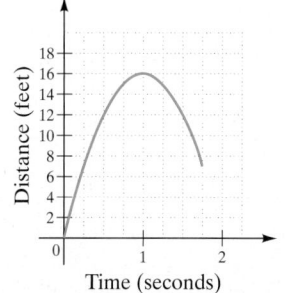

a. What was the initial height of the ball?
b. How high was the ball in $\frac{1}{2}$ second?
c. What was the maximum height of the ball?
d. When did the maximum height occur?
e. What was the final height of the ball? When does this occur?

97. The revenue, cost, and profit for producing and selling x units are shown in the following graphs.

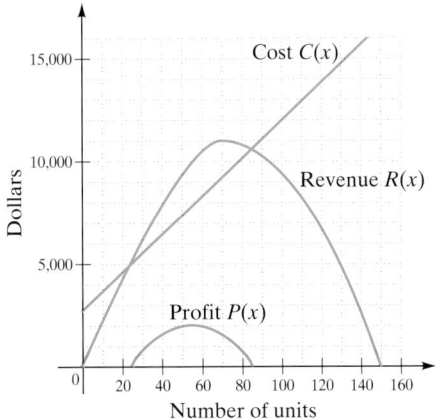

a. Find the manufacturer's break-even points. Discuss.
b. Find the number of units that will maximize the revenue. What is the maximum revenue?
c. Find the x-intercepts of the profit. Discuss the significance of these points.
d. Find the number of units that will maximize the profit. What is the maximum profit?

98. A cliffdiver vaults upward from a cliff 200 meters above a lake with an initial velocity of 7 meters per second. Her position function in meters is $s(t) = -4.9t^2 + 7t + 200$.
a. What is the diver's maximum height?
b. When did the maximum height occur?
c. When did the diver reach a height of 150 meters?
d. When did she hit the surface of the water?
e. If the position function continues below the surface of the water, when was she 4 meters below the surface of the water?
f. Graph the position of the diver in terms of t seconds.

99. A caterer gives a reduced rate for ordering multiple meals for a large wedding. The regular price is $52.50 per plate with a discount of $0.25 per plate for each meal ordered. It costs the caterer $15.00 per plate to create the meal plus staffing costs of $600.00.
a. Write a revenue function for a wedding with x guests (assuming all will eat a meal).
b. Write a cost function for a wedding of x guests.
c. Write a profit function for a wedding of x guests.
d. Determine the number of guests for which there will be no revenue.
e. Determine the number of guests that will maximize revenue. What is the maximum revenue?
f. Determine the number of guests for which there will be no profit.
g. Determine the number of guests that will maximize profit. What is the maximum profit?
h. Determine the number of guests for which the caterer will break even.
i. Graph the revenue, cost, and profit functions on one coordinate system.

9.8

Recall	Examples
Solving quadratic inequalities numerically • Complete a three-column table of values: one column for the independent variable, one for the left side of the inequality, and one for the right side of the inequality. • The solution set consists of all values of the independent variable that result in true inequalities.	Solve $x^2 - 2 \leq 2x + 1$ numerically. <table><tr><td>x</td><td>$x^2 - 2$</td><td>$\leq$</td><td>$2x + 1$</td></tr><tr><td>-1</td><td>-1</td><td></td><td>-1</td></tr><tr><td>0</td><td>-2</td><td></td><td>1</td></tr><tr><td>1</td><td>-1</td><td></td><td>3</td></tr><tr><td>2</td><td>2</td><td></td><td>5</td></tr><tr><td>3</td><td>7</td><td></td><td>7</td></tr></table> The solutions are all integers between -1 and 3, inclusive.
Solving quadratic inequalities graphically • Graph the two functions defined by the left side of the inequality and the right side of the inequality. • Determine the portion of the y_1 graph that lies above the y_2 graph for "greater than" inequalities or the portion of the y_1 graph that lies below the y_2 graph for "less than" inequalities. • Determine the x-coordinates for the appropriate portion of the graph. • The solution set contains the x-coordinate of the intersection if the order relation includes equality.	Solve $x^2 - 2 \leq 2x + 1$ graphically. 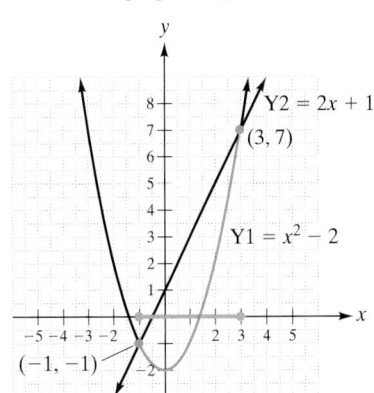 The solution set is the set of all real numbers between -1 and 3, inclusive, or $[-1, 3]$.

(continued on page 764)

Recall	Examples
Solving algebraically • Determine the critical numbers by solving the quadratic equation formed by replacing the inequality sign by an equals sign. • Determine the possible intervals for the solution by using the critical numbers as endpoints. • Test one value in each interval for a true statement. If the inequality is true for the value tested, then the inequality is true for all values in the interval.	Solve $x^2 - 2 < 2x + 1$ algebraically. Solve the associated equation: $x^2 - 2 = 2x + 1$ $x^2 - 2x - 3 = 0$ $(x - 3)(x + 1) = 0$ $x - 3 = 0 \quad \text{or} \quad x + 1 = 0$ $\quad\quad x = 3 \quad\quad\quad\quad\quad x = -1$ The critical points are 3 and -1. The inequality does not include equality, so we do not include 3 and -1 as solutions. 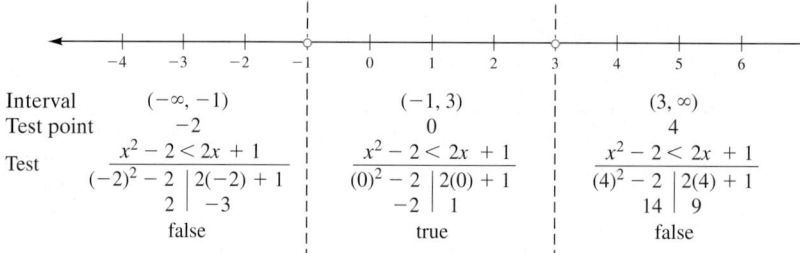 The solution set is $(-1, 3)$. Note that this example differs from the two previous examples in its order relation. Therefore, the solution set is different.

Solve numerically for integer solutions.

100. $x^2 + 6x - 9 \le 4x + 15$

101. $2x^2 + 3x - 8 > 6 + 4x - x^2$

Solve graphically.

102. $x^2 + 2x - 3 \ge 5$ **103.** $5 - x^2 \ge -4$

104. $x^2 - 2x - 1 < x + 3$

105. $x^2 + 3 < 1 - x^2$

106. $x^2 - 6x + 11 > -\dfrac{1}{2}x^2 + 3x - \dfrac{5}{2}$

107. $x^2 - 8x + 18 \le \dfrac{1}{4}x^2 - 2x + 6$

108. $10 - 6x + x^2 < -4 + 6x - x^2$

Solve exercises 109–115 algebraically.

109. $x^2 - 4x + 4 < \dfrac{1}{4}x^2 - x + 3$ **110.** $x^2 + x - 6 \le 12 - 2x - 2x^2$ **111.** $3 - z^2 > -2z$

112. $x^2 + 6x + 11 > -x^2 - 6x - 7$ **113.** $1 - 2x^2 \le 1 - x^2$ **114.** $x^2 + 4x - 2 < -\dfrac{1}{2}x^2 - 2x - 8$

115. $p^2 - 6p - 1 < 0$

116. The cost to rent a booth at a carnival for x days is given by the cost function $C(x) = 3x^2 + 25x + 50$. How many days can the booth be rented for a cost of no more than $200?

117. A dart is shot upward from a height 30 feet above the ground. The initial speed of the dart is 25 feet per second. For what length of time is the dart above the ground?

118. A fast-food business estimates its lunch service profit to be $P(x) = -0.5x^2 + 9x + 160$, where x is the number of staff on duty. For what numbers of staff are profits between $100 and $195?

119. An object's position, $s(t)$, in feet, at time t, in seconds, is given in the following table. Use the method of quadratic regression to find the quadratic function that best fits the data. When is the object at a height of less than 500 feet?

Time in Seconds	Position in Feet
3	806
6	1274
10	1450

■ Chapter 9 Mixed Review

Simplify without using a calculator.

1. $\sqrt{50}$

2. $-\sqrt{48}$

3. $\dfrac{-3 + \sqrt{18}}{3}$

4. $\dfrac{4 - \sqrt{80}}{-2}$

5. $\sqrt{\dfrac{75}{18}}$

Multiply or divide and simplify.

6. $\sqrt{3} \cdot \sqrt{21}$

7. $2\sqrt{5} \cdot 3\sqrt{10}$

8. $\dfrac{\sqrt{65}}{\sqrt{5}}$

9. $\dfrac{\sqrt{96}}{\sqrt{6}}$

10. Find the distance between the points $(2, -5)$ and $(4, 1)$.

Solve graphically.

11. $x^2 - 4 = 2x - 1$

12. $3 - x^2 = -3 - \dfrac{1}{3}x^2$

13. $x^2 + 6x + 9 = 4$

14. $15x^2 + 13x - 72 = 0$

15. $2x + 10 = x^2 + 4x + 7$

16. $x^2 + 9x + 7 = 0$

17. $\dfrac{1}{6}x^2 - 2x + 7 = 9 - \dfrac{1}{4}x^2$

18. $x^2 - 6x - 40 = 0$

Solve numerically for integer solutions.

19. $2x^2 - x - 28 = x^2 + 3x + 17$

20. $3x^2 - 5x - 10 = 7x + 5$

Solve algebraically.

21. $12x^2 + 9x = 8x + 6$

22. $x^2 + 3x - 88 = 0$

23. $5x^2 + 14x - 6 = 8 - 19x$

24. $49x^2 - 16 = 0$

25. $5x^2 - 180 = 0$

26. $11 + b^2 = 2$

27. $(x - 9)^2 = 16$

28. $(p - 7)^2 + 6 = 9$

29. $z^2 + 12z = -33$

30. $m^2 + 7m + 12 = 9$

31. $b^2 + 2.4b - 4.32 = 0$

32. $7q^2 - 7q - 78 = (8q^2 - 3q - 50) - (q^2 + 4q + 28)$

33. $x^2 + 20x + 84 = 0$

34. $2y^2 + 3y - 5 = 0$

35. $4x^2 + 16x - 2 = 0$

Use the quadratic formula to find the exact solution.

36. $4 + 8x + x^2 = 0$

37. $x^2 = 7x + 2$

38. $36q^2 + 25 = 60q$

39. $b^2 - 7b + 16 = 0$

40. $z^2 + 6z - 55 = 0$

41. $4m^2 + 7m = 36$

Solve for the variable specified.

42. $a = \dfrac{x(x + 1)}{2}$ for x

43. $x^2 + y^2 + z^2 = r^2$ for y

44. $A = 4\pi r^2$ for r

Solve numerically for integer solutions.

45. $x^2 + 2x - 7 \le 4x + 8$

46. $x^2 + 9x - 11 \le 4x + 3$

Solve algebraically.

47. $z^2 + 5z - 6 < 12 - 10z - 2z^2$

48. $m^2 - 15 > 2m$

49. $x^2 + 2x - 1 > -x^2 - 2x + 1$

50. $p^2 - 8p - 2 > 0$

51. $2x^2 - 5x - 11 \le 19 + 8x - x^2$

52. $3q^2 + 2q - 17 \ge 5q + 19$

Solve exercises 53–60 graphically.

53. $x^2 - 4x - 1 \ge x + 5$

54. $2 - x^2 > 5 + x^2$

55. $x^2 - 2x - 3 < 12$

56. $7 - x^2 > -9$

57. $x^2 + 4x - 2 > -5 - 4x - x^2$

58. $-x^2 - 10x - 27 < x^2 + 10x + 23$

59. $-x^2 + 6x - 7 > -\dfrac{1}{3}x^2 + 2x - 4$

60. $-x^2 + 6x - 6 \ge -\dfrac{1}{3}x^2 + 2x$

61. Write a quadratic function, $f(x)$, for the given set of x-intercept(s) of the graph.

$$(3, 0); (-5, 0)$$

62. Use the given graph of $y = f(x)$ to answer the questions.

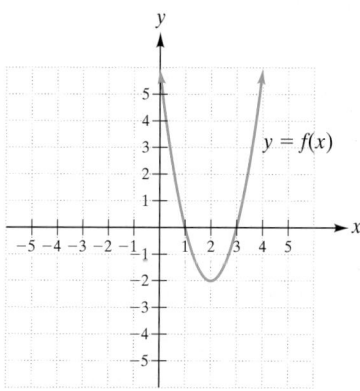

$y = f(x)$

a. Find the domain and range.
b. Find the x-intercepts and the y-intercept.
c. Determine if the graph is concave upward or concave downward.
d. Find the vertex and determine the axis of symmetry.

e. Find the relative maximum and relative minimum. Find the absolute maximum and absolute minimum. Find the x-values for which the function is increasing and for which it is decreasing.
f. Find the x-values for which the y-values are equal to zero.
g. Find the solutions of $f(x) = 0$.

63. Graph the quadratic function using the seven steps given in this chapter. Show all of your work.

$$f(x) = x^2 + 8x + 7$$

64. The cost of producing x items is given by the mathematical model $C(x) = 5x^2 + 75x + 875$. How many items can be produced for approximately $3500?

65. Find the time it will take for a rock to reach the ground if it is shot upward from a slingshot with an initial velocity of $v_0 = 64$ feet per second from a height of $s_0 = 32$ feet.

66. How long will it take a sky diver to free-fall from 11,000 feet to 4000 feet?

67. The hypotenuse of a right triangle measures 42.5 meters, and one of its legs measures 34 meters. What is the measure of the other leg?

68. The area of a rectangle is 144 square cm. Its length measures 6 cm less than three times its width. Find the dimensions of the rectangle.

In exercises 69 and 70, use the compound-interest formula $A = P(1 + r)^t$ to set up a quadratic equation for each situation, and then solve the equation.

69. What must the annual interest rate be for $1200 to compound to a total amount of $1323 after two years?

70. At what annual interest rate must $1200 be invested in order for it to compound to a total amount of $1500 after two years?

71. Angela sells Easter baskets for $10.50 per arrangement. To encourage multiple purchases, she reduces the price per arrangement by $0.50 for each arrangement ordered. She spends $7.50 on each arrangement and $3.00 to deliver an order of the baskets.
a. Write a revenue function for an order of x baskets.
b. Write a cost function for an order of x baskets.
c. Write a profit function for an order of x baskets.
d. Determine the number of baskets that Angela must sell to break even on an order. Interpret the break-even point(s).

72. The two legs of a right triangle measure 20 inches and 48 inches. What is the length of the hypotenuse?

73. What are the lengths of the legs of an isosceles right triangle whose hypotenuse measures 14.21 centimeters?

74. A rope attached to the top of a pole makes a 45-degree angle with the ground. If the pole is 11 feet high, how long is the rope?

75. Assume that a right triangle is a 30°–60°–90° triangle. Determine the lengths of the sides of the triangle if the hypotenuse measures 32 inches.

76. The cost to rent a booth at a carnival for x days is given by the cost function $C(x) = 5x^2 + 20x + 100$. How many days can the booth be rented for a cost of no more than $500?

77. To test the direction of the wind, a bowling ball is dropped from the top of a tower 55 feet tall. Write the position function for the ball. When will it hit the ground?

78. As part of an experiment, a student shoots a projectile upward from a height of 100 feet. He gives the object an initial velocity of 50 feet per second. Write the position function for this projectile. When will it be at a height of 90 feet?

79. An apartment resident throws down a flower pot from his window from a height of 30 meters with an initial velocity of 3 meters per second. Write the position function for the flower pot. When will it be 4 meters above the ground?

80. A target is 10 yards north and 5 yards west of Karla. Using Karla's location as the origin, write a coordinate pair to represent the location of the target and Karla's location. How far from Karla is the target?

81. Based on data from the Bureau of the Census, Foreign Trade Division, the number of passenger cars imported to the United States from Sweden can be estimated by the function $n(t) = 18{,}397t^2 - 133{,}509t + 327{,}393$, where t is the number of years after 1998. In what year was the number about 189,000 cars?

82. The number of grandchildren living with their grandparents in the United States with both parents present can be estimated by the quadratic function $y = -6x^2 - 15x + 531$, where x is the number of years after 2000 and y is, in thousands, the number of grandchildren living with their grandparents and having both parents present. Use the function and the quadratic formula to determine the year in which there were 200,000 grandchildren living with their grandparents and having both parents present.

83. A soccer ball is kicked vertically upward from the surface of the moon with an initial velocity of 3 meters per second. Its vertical position equation is $s(t) = -0.8t^2 + 3t$, where t is the time in seconds.
a. What is the height of the ball after 1.5 seconds?
b. What is the maximum height of the ball? When did the maximum height occur?

c. When was the ball at a height of 2.7 meters?

d. When did the ball hit the surface of the moon?

e. Graph the position of the ball in terms of t seconds.

84. An office computer rental store gives a rental discount of $5 per computer for each unit rented. The standard rental price is $350 per unit. It costs the store $105 per unit with fixed delivery and maintenance costs of $2500.

a. Write a revenue function for a rental of x computers.

b. Write a cost function for a rental of x computers.

c. Write a profit function for a rental of x computers.

d. Determine the number of computers for which there will be no revenue.

e. Determine the number of computers that will maximize revenue. What is the maximum revenue?

f. Determine the number of computers for which there will be no profit.

g. Determine the number of computers that will maximize profit. What is the maximum profit?

h. Determine the number of computers for which the store will break even.

i. Graph the revenue, cost, and profit functions on one coordinate system.

85. A real estate agent approximates her profit to be $P(x) = 2x^2 + 3x + 100$, where x is the number of houses shown. For what numbers of houses shown will her profit be between $2000 and $5000?

86. According to statistics published by the U.S. Department of Education, National Center of Education Statistics, the average cost of undergraduate tuition, room and board, and fees, $c(x)$, in dollars, can be estimated by the polynomial function $c(x) = 3x^2 + 365x + 10{,}076$, where x is number of years after 1998. According to this model in what year will the cost exceed $20,000?

87. An object's position $s(t)$, in meters, at time t, in seconds is given in the following table. Use the method of quadratic regression to find the quadratic function that best fits the data. When is the object at a height that is between 90 and 100 meters above the ground?

Time in Seconds	Position in Meters
1	141
2	124
4	60

■ Chapter 9 Test

A+ TEST-TAKING TIPS

Many students have failed a test at some point in their academic life. It is important that you respond to such a failure properly. Don't blame your teacher, your background, your past performance, your personal deficiencies, or other difficulties in your personal life. These are just excuses for the lack of success. Instead, make up your mind that you will do whatever it takes to master the skills being taught. Learn from your mistakes. If you can, meet with your instructor to review the test, emphasizing the problems you missed. Try to see how you should have approached the problem. If your mistakes are careless ones, think of steps you can take to avoid them in the future. For example, if you make mistakes in transcribing a problem to your paper, make a vow always to check what you transcribe before you begin working the problem. If you make arithmetic mistakes, stop doing the arithmetic in your head. Instead, do the work on paper, and use a calculator whenever you are permitted to do so. Remember that doing your work neatly and in an orderly manner will help you understand the problem. The secret to being successful at mathematics is to be patient and to persevere.

Simplify without using a calculator.

1. $\sqrt{32}$

2. $\dfrac{-2 + \sqrt{20}}{2}$

3. $\sqrt{\dfrac{9}{5}}$

Multiply or divide and simplify.

4. $3\sqrt{7} \cdot 2\sqrt{21}$

5. $\dfrac{\sqrt{45}}{\sqrt{3}}$

6. Find the distance between the points $(-2, 3)$ and $(3, -2)$.

7. Solve. $x^2 - 2 = x + 4$
a. numerically   **b.** graphically   **c.** algebraically

Solve.

8. $x^2 - 4x - 9 = 2x + 7$

9. $2x^3 + 9x^2 - 23x - 66 = 0$

10. $a^2 + 2a - 5 = 2(a^2 + a - 2)$

11. $x^2 - 6x + 13 = 0$

12. $2x^2 - 7x + 3 = 2x - 1$

13. $x^2 - 5x + 4 = 7 - 3x - x^2$

14. $x^2 - x - 6 \le 6$

15. $(x + 3)(x - 2) < 3(x + 3)$

16. $2x^2 + 7x - 9 \ge 4x + 11$

In exercises 17–18, evaluate the discriminant, and then find the exact roots if possible.

17. $x^2 - 9x + 9 = 7x - 5$

18. $x^2 - 3x + 12 = 0$

19. Solve $s = at^2 + c$ for t.

20. Write a quadratic function, $f(x)$, for the given set of x-intercept(s) of the graph.

$$(-3, 0); \left(\frac{1}{2}, 0\right)$$

21. Graph the quadratic function using the seven steps given in this chapter. Show all of your work.

$$f(x) = x^2 + 6x + 5$$

22. Use the given graph of $y = f(x)$ to answer the questions.

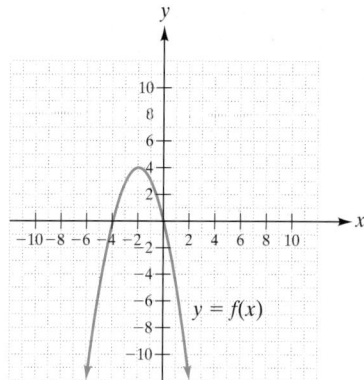

a. Find the domain and range.
b. Find the x-intercepts and the y-intercept.
c. Determine if the graph is concave upward or concave downward.
d. Find the vertex and determine the axis of symmetry.
e. Find the relative maximum and relative minimum. Find the absolute maximum and absolute minimum. Find the x-values for which the function is increasing and for which it is decreasing.
f. Find the x-values for which the y-values are equal to zero.
g. Find the solutions of $f(x) = 0$.

23. The hypotenuse of a 30°–60°–90° triangle measures 28 inches. Find the exact length of the two legs of the triangle. Then approximate the lengths to the nearest tenth of an inch if they are irrational numbers.

24. Use the compound-interest formula, $A = P(1 + r)^t$, to solve the following interest problem: What must the annual interest rate be for $1400 to compound to a total amount of $1573 in two years?

25. Nicole sells Valentine flower arrangements for $12.50 per arrangement. To encourage multiple purchases, she reduces the price per arrangement by $0.50 for each arrangement ordered. She spends $9.50 on each arrangement and $3.95 to package and deliver an order of the arrangements.
a. Write a revenue function for an order of x arrangements.
b. Write a cost function for an order of x arrangements.
c. Write a profit function for an order of x arrangements.
d. Determine the number of arrangements that must be ordered to break even on an order. Interpret the break-even point(s).

26. A gangplank to board a ship is 40 feet long. It touches the ship at a height of 10 feet above the dock. What is the horizontal distance between the ship and the end of the gangplank?

27. An apple orchard finds that revenues can be estimated by $R(x) = -1.2x^2 + 30x + 15$, where x is the number of customers per hour. For what number of customers will revenue be more than $135?

28. Two hikers plan a one-day trip. One hiker travels 3 miles north and 4 miles east. The other travels 2 miles south and 3 miles west. Write coordinate pairs to represent each location from the origin. If their two-way radios have a range of 5 miles, can they talk to each other?

29. An air ball (a shot that completely misses both the backboard and the basket) is shot during a basketball game. The height of release was 2.75 meters with an initial upward velocity of 8 meters per second. Write a position equation for the basketball. When will the basketball be 5 meters above the floor?

30. The Phoenix Shot Tower was used to make lead shot from 1828 to 1892. Molten lead was dropped from a platform at the top of the 234-foot tower through a sieve and into a vat of cold water. Write a position equation for the molten lead. When will the lead reach the surface of the water?

31. A diver leaps upward from the edge of a diving board 30 feet above the water with an initial velocity of 5 feet per second. His position function in feet is $s(t) = -16t^2 + 5t + 30$, where t is the number of seconds.
a. What is the height of the diver after one-half of a second?
b. What is the maximum height of the diver? When did the maximum height occur to the nearest tenth of a second?
c. When did the diver hit the surface of the water?
d. If the position function continues below the surface of the water, at what time was he 3 feet below the surface of the water?
e. Graph the position of the diver in terms of t seconds.

32. A park district that takes children on field trips has a standard fare of $25.00 per child. A reduction of $0.50 per child is given as an incentive for groups. It costs the park district $15.00 per child to take a trip with fixed costs of $25.00.
a. Write a revenue function for a group of x children.
b. Write a cost function for a group of x children.
c. Write a profit function for a group of x children.
d. Determine the number of children for which there will be no revenue.
e. Determine the number of children that will maximize revenue. What is the maximum revenue?
f. Determine the number of children for which there will be no profit.
g. Determine the number of children that will maximize profit. What is the maximum profit?
h. Determine the number of children for which the park district will break even.
i. Graph the revenue, cost, and profit functions on one coordinate system.

33. Explain how to use the value of the discriminant of a quadratic equation to describe the characteristics of the solution(s) of the equation.

9

Project

In this chapter, we have applied the Pythagorean theorem to many different applications that we may encounter in our daily lives. In this project, we will explore other extensions of this very important theorem.

PART I   This activity is designed to illustrate why the Pythagorean theorem is true. It is based on an actual proof attributed to Pythagoras. **Figure 9.8** illustrates the fact that $a^2 + b^2 = c^2$.

1. Determine the area of each of the squares.
2. According to the Pythagorean theorem, the sum of the areas of the smaller two squares is equal to the area of the larger square. Write an equation for this statement, using the areas you found in exercise 1. Your equation should be the Pythagorean theorem.
3. Let $a = 6$, $b = 8$, and $c = 10$. Calculate the area of the squares, and verify that the Pythagorean theorem is correct for these values.
4. Draw **Figure 9.8** on graph paper, using the values $a = 6$, $b = 8$, and $c = 10$. Cut up and reassemble the two small squares to form the larger square.

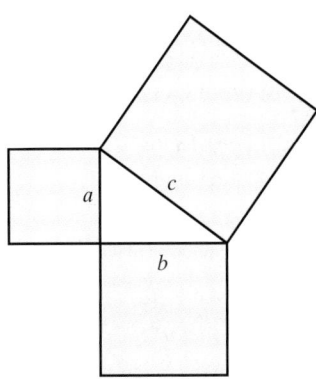

Figure 9.8

PART II   An iterative example of the use of the Pythagorean theorem is demonstrated in the figure to the right.

Determine the exact length of x_1, then x_2, then x_3, and so on, until you get a value for x_6. Do not approximate the lengths.

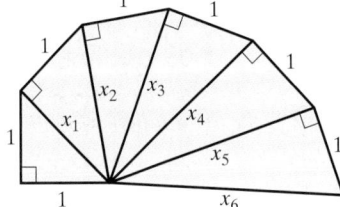

PART III   The equation $x^2 + y^2 = z^2$, where x, y, and z are integers, is called a Diophantine equation. A Greek mathematician, Diophantus of Alexandria, proved that any set of three integers that satisfy this equation has the form $x = a^2 - b^2$, $y = 2ab$, and $z = a^2 + b^2$, where a and b are integers.

This Diophantine equation is a special case of the Pythagorean theorem. We will examine such equations further.

1. Complete the following table.

Case	a	b	$x = a^2 - b^2$	$y = 2ab$	$z = a^2 + b^2$	Diophantine Triple
1.	2	1	3	4	5	3, 4, 5
2.	3	1				
3.	3	2				
4.	4	1				
5.	4	2				
6.	4	3				
7.	5	1				
8.	5	2				
9.	5	3				
10.	5	4				

2. Check each row of the table to be sure that the Diophantine triple does in fact satisfy the Pythagorean theorem. Summarize what your check revealed.
3. Which of the cases have Diophantine triples that are just multiples of a smaller Diophantine triple. What does this observation indicate to you about finding Diophantine triples that satisfy the Pythagorean theorem?
4. How many different Diophantine triples do you think can be found that satisfy the Pythagorean theorem?
5. Substitute the Diophantine expressions for x, y, and z into the Pythagorean theorem to see if they satisfy the theorem.

■ Chapters P–9 Cumulative Review

Simplify exercises 1–12. Write all answers with positive exponents.

1. $(2a^2 + 3ab - 4b^2) + (a^2 + ab - b^2)$

2. $(1.5x^2 + 2.3xy - y^2) - (0.5x^2 + 1.3xy - y^2)$

3. $(3x + 1)(2x - 6)$ **4.** $(5x + 1)^2$

5. $(2x + 3)(2x - 3)$ **6.** $(2.1xy^2z)(3xy^3z^2)$ **7.** $6x^2y^{-1}z^0$

8. $\dfrac{2x^{-1}y}{4xy^2}$ **9.** $\left[\dfrac{(-2a)^3}{5b}\right]^{-2}$ **10.** $(-2p^2q^{-3}r)(4p^3q^5r)$ **11.** $\dfrac{2x^2 + 4x - 6}{2x}$ **12.** $\dfrac{x^2 + 4x - 5}{x + 5}$

13. Given $f(x) = -x^2 + 2x - 1$, evaluate $f(-3)$.

14. Write 5.6×10^{-3} in standard notation.

15. Write -3.4 E6 in standard notation.

16. Solve $A = \frac{1}{2}bh$ for b.   **17.** Solve $s = -16t^2 + 5$ for t.

Factor completely.

18. $x^2 + 2x - 15$ **19.** $10s^2 + 7s - 12$ **20.** $9x^2 - 16$

21. $4x^2 + 12x + 9$ **22.** $a^3 + 27$ **23.** $2a^4 - 32$

24. Solve.
$$2x - 4y = 1$$
$$x + y = 6$$

25. Graph and determine one solution.
$$y < 2x + 5$$
$$y \geq -2x - 1$$

Solve.

26. $x^2 - 4x + 7 = 2x - 1$ **27.** $x^2 - 5x - 12 = 0$ **28.** $3x^2 + 6x = 9$

29. $2x^2 + 4x - 5 = 2x^2 + 4x + 3$ **30.** $2x^2 - 5x + 10 = x^2 - 2$ **31.** $(x - 2)(2x + 1) = 4$

32. $2x + 4 = 5x - 1$ **33.** $2(x + 3) + 4 = (x + 4) + (x + 6)$ **34.** $5x - 2(2.5x - 1) = 4$

35. $|2x - 1| = 4$ **36.** $3|x| - 2 = 7$

Solve exercises 37–39. Write the solution set in interval notation.

37. $2x - 5 > 3x + 4$ **38.** $x^2 - 4x - 5 \geq x + 1$ **39.** $3t^2 - 4t < 2t^2 + 1$

40. Consider the relation $y = -3x + 4$.
   a. Graph the relation.
   b. Is the relation a function? Justify your answer.
   c. Determine the x-values for which the relation is increasing and the x-values for which it is decreasing.
   d. What is the domain of the relation? The range?
   e. Determine the x-intercept and the y-intercept algebraically.

41. Consider the relation $y = x^2 + 4x - 1$.
   a. Determine the x-intercept and the y-intercept algebraically.
   b. Determine the vertex algebraically.
   c. Graph enough points to determine the curve. Label the vertex and the axis of symmetry.
   d. What is the domain of the relation? The range?

42. Write a linear equation that passes through $(3, -2)$ and $(4, 1)$.

43. Write a linear equation that passes through $(-1, 2)$ and is perpendicular to $2x + 3y = 1$.

44. Raynoc plans to sell a mixture of peanuts and cashews at his shop. He usually sells peanuts for $5 per pound and cashews for $12 per pound. How many pounds of each should he mix to sell 7 pounds of the mixture for $10?

45. The crystal ball at Times Square dropped 77 feet in 60 seconds at midnight of the year 2002, through a controlled drop. If the ball were to free-fall 77 feet, how long would it take to drop that distance?

46. An investment opportunity pays 12% simple interest per year. How much should Georgette invest in order to have a total amount of $16,800 at the end of the year to purchase a classic Corvette?

47. Annual reports for a manufacturer of mountain bikes listed the profit for the years 1999–2001 as follows:

Year	1999	2000	2001
Profit in million dollars	9.5	9.8	8.9

   a. An accountant decided that a quadratic function could be used to represent the dwindling profits. Let x = the number of years after 1999 and y = the profit in millions of dollars. Determine a quadratic function for the profit.
   b. Use the quadratic function found in part **a** and the zero factor property to determine the year when the profit will drop to $3.5 million.

48. Sam sells sparklers for the Fourth of July celebration. Ordinarily, the packages sell for $3.50 each. To encourage multiple purchases, Sam reduces the price of each package by $0.25 per package ordered. He spends $2.00 per package on supplies and $1.50 for shipping and handling each order.
   a. Write a revenue function for an order of x packages.
   b. Write a cost function for an order of x packages.
   c. Write a profit function for an order of x packages.
   d. Determine the number of packages that must be ordered to break even on an order. Interpret the break-even point(s).

49. Determine the length of the legs of an isosceles triangle if the hypotenuse measures 8 meters.

50. Janet scored 96, 82, and 94 on the first three tests in her history class. In order to make a B in the course, she must have a test average between 85 and 90, inclusive. Determine the scores she must make on her last test in order to earn a B.

Rational Expressions, Functions, and Equations

In this chapter, we define rational expressions and functions and perform operations on them. Since rational functions are simply ratios of two polynomials, the discussion follows naturally from the preceding chapters on polynomial expressions and functions. Once we've established the basic techniques for working with rational functions, we can show how to use them to help solve equations.

Equations involving rational functions are extremely important in virtually all areas of applied mathematics. They are central to the basic description of electrical circuits, arising in all areas of electronic and computer design. Economic theory and business practice involve rational functions, as do medical practice, biology, and chemistry. We will discuss only the fundamental ideas of rational functions in this chapter, but you should be aware that they underlie the mathematical descriptions of most areas of modern technology. The project concluding this chapter explores two different mathematical models involving rational expressions in the areas of business and psychology.

10.1 RATIONAL EXPRESSIONS AND FUNCTIONS

OBJECTIVES

1 Identify rational expressions.
2 Determine the domain of rational functions.
3 Graph rational functions by using a set of ordered pairs.
4 Model real-world situations by using rational functions.

APPLICATION

According to the U.S. Bureau of the Census, the number of civilians in the labor force who are over 16 years of age and the number in the labor force who are unemployed are as listed in the following table:

Year	Unemployed Labor Force (millions of people)	Labor Force (millions of people)
2001	6.8	143.7
2002	8.4	144.9
2003	8.8	146.5

a. Determine the unemployment rate for each year.

b. The number of people unemployed in the labor force (in millions) may be approximated by $U(x) = -0.6x^2 + 2.2x + 6.8$, where x is the number of years after 2001. The number of people in the labor force (in millions) may be approximated by $L(x) = 1.15x + 143.7$, where x is the number of years after 2001. Determine a function $R(x)$ that approximates the unemployment rate x years after 2001.

c. Use the formula from part **b** to approximate the unemployment rate for the years 2001, 2002, and 2003.

d. Compare the approximations with the actual values in the table. Would you consider this function a good predictor of the unemployment rate?

After completing this section, we will discuss this application further. See page 782.

Objective 10.1.1   **Identifying Rational Expressions**

In Chapter P, we defined a **rational number** to be a number that can be written as a ratio $\frac{a}{b}$, where a and b are integers with $b \neq 0$. For example,

$$\frac{5}{8} \qquad \text{rational number (fraction)}$$

$$0.625 \qquad \text{rational number (decimal)}$$

$$-17 \qquad \text{rational number (integer)}$$

 TAKE NOTE Remember that all integers are rational numbers, because they can be written with a denominator of 1. For example, $-17 = \frac{-17}{1}$.

In this chapter, we discuss rational expressions. A **rational expression** can be written as a ratio $\frac{A}{B}$, where A and B are polynomials with $B \neq 0$. As we continue our discussion of rational expressions with variables in the denominator, we assume that the denominator does not equal 0.

RATIONAL EXPRESSION

A rational expression can be written in the form

$$\frac{A}{B}$$

where A and B are polynomials with $B \neq 0$.

Examples of rational expressions are as follows:

$$\frac{x + y}{2x} \qquad \text{rational expression (algebraic fraction)}$$

$$6x + 4 \qquad \text{rational expression (polynomial)}$$

Other kinds of expressions, such as $x^2 + \dfrac{5}{2z}$, are also rational expressions. To see that this is true, we need to manipulate the expression. Since we do not yet have these skills, we will identify a rational expression as a sum of terms, each of which is a rational expression. The term x^2 can be written as a rational expression in the form $\dfrac{x^2}{1}$, and the term $\dfrac{5}{2z}$ is already in ratio form. Therefore, $x^2 + \dfrac{5}{2z}$ is a rational expression.

EXAMPLE 1

Identify each expression as rational or nonrational.

a. $\dfrac{12 + \sqrt{x}}{x}$ **b.** $x^5 y + 9z$ **c.** $\dfrac{x^3 + x^2 - 3}{x - 5}$ **d.** a^{-3}

Solution

a. $\dfrac{12 + \sqrt{x}}{x}$ is not a rational expression. The expression $12 + \sqrt{x}$ is not a polynomial, because it contains a square-root expression with a variable radicand, $\sqrt{x}$. Therefore, $\dfrac{12 + \sqrt{x}}{x}$ is not a ratio of two polynomials.

b. $x^5 y + 9z$ is a polynomial and a rational expression, because it may be written as $\dfrac{x^5 y + 9z}{1}$, or $\dfrac{x^5 y}{1} + \dfrac{9z}{1}$.

c. $\dfrac{x^3 + x^2 - 3}{x - 5}$ is a rational expression, because $(x^3 + x^2 - 3)$ and $(x - 5)$ are both polynomials.

d. a^{-3} is a rational expression, because it can be written as $\dfrac{1}{a^3}$. ∎

> **TAKE NOTE** Example 1b is a polynomial and also a rational expression. According to the definition of rational expressions, all polynomial expressions are rational expressions. However, since we have already studied polynomial expressions, we will limit our main discussion in this chapter to nonpolynomial rational expressions.

Objective 10.1.1 *CHECKUP*

1. Identify each expression as rational or nonrational.

a. $\dfrac{3\sqrt[5]{x} + 2x}{x + 3}$ **b.** $x^2 + \dfrac{9}{x - 3}$

c. $4x^3 - 2x^2 + x - 5$ **d.** $4x^{-2}$

2. All polynomials are rational expressions, but not all rational expressions are polynomials. Explain why.

Objective 10.1.2   **Determining the Domain of Rational Functions**

A special type of relation called a rational relation equates a rational expression in one independent variable to a dependent variable. Some rational relations are also functions and, therefore, may be written using function notation.

> **RATIONAL FUNCTION**
>
> A rational function can be written in the form
>
> $$f(x) = \frac{A(x)}{B(x)}$$
>
> where $A(x)$ and $B(x)$ are polynomial functions with $B(x) \neq 0$.

Examples of **rational functions** are as follows:

$$f(x) = \frac{6}{x} \qquad\qquad g(x) = \frac{x + 2}{x + 1}$$

$$h(x) = \frac{x^2 + 2x - 15}{x + 5} \qquad\qquad j(x) = \frac{5}{x} + \frac{4}{x^2}$$

The domain of a polynomial function is all real numbers. However, that may not be true for a rational function. Sometimes, substituting certain values for the independent variable in a rational expression results in undefined values for the fractional term. Such numbers must be excluded from the domain. We do this by identifying them as restrictions on the domain, or **restricted values**. We need to be able to determine these restricted values. Complete the following set of exercises to determine a method for finding the restrictions on the domain of a rational function.

Guided Discovery 1   Restricted Values

1. Complete the tables of values for the given rational functions.

a. $f(x) = \dfrac{6}{x}$

x	f(x)
-3	
-2	
-1	
0	
1	
2	
3	

b. $g(x) = \dfrac{x + 2}{x - 1}$

x	g(x)
-3	
-2	
-1	
0	
1	
2	
3	

c. $h(x) = \dfrac{x^2 - x - 2}{x - 2}$

x	h(x)
-3	
-2	
-1	
0	
1	
2	
3	

Determine the restricted values of each function.

2. Graph the given rational functions on a calculator screen $(-9.4, 9.4, 1, -6.2, 6.2, 1, 1)$. Trace each function's graph. What happens when you reach the point on a graph for the restricted x-values found in exercise 1?

Write a rule for determining the restricted values of a rational function by viewing its table of values.

Write a rule for determining the restricted values of a rational function by viewing its graph.

Write a rule for determining the restricted values of a rational function algebraically.

The restrictions on the domain of a rational function are the numbers that result in undefined values for the rational expression. On the function's graph, the restricted values (*x*-values) of the function do not have corresponding function values. This occurs because the function cannot be evaluated when the denominator of the rational expression is 0. Therefore, to determine the restricted values algebraically, we set the expression in the denominator of the rational expression equal to 0 and solve for *x*.

We have discovered three methods—numeric, graphic, and algebraic—of determining the restricted values from the domain of a rational function. The numeric and graphic methods have limitations on their effectiveness, so they should be used only as a check of the algebraic method.

> To determine the restricted values of a rational function, algebraically,
>
> - Set the expression in the denominator equal to 0.
> - Solve for the independent variable.
>
> This method will find all the restricted values.

To determine the restricted integer values of a rational function numerically on your calculator, set up a table of integer values for the function. The restricted integer values are the *x*-values that result in errors in the table. Note that this table does not show all the restricted values.

To determine the restricted values of a rational function graphically on your calculator, graph the function and trace the graph. The *x*-values that have no corresponding *y*-values are restricted values for the rational function. Note that this method will determine only specific *x*-values, depending upon the calculator window setting.

EXAMPLE 2

Determine the restricted values, and then state the domain, of the rational function $f(x) = \dfrac{x^2 - 4}{x - 2}$.

Solution

Algebraic

Set the expression in the denominator equal to 0 and solve.

$$x - 2 = 0$$
$$x = 2$$

Numeric

X	Y1	
0	2	
1	3	
2	ERROR	
3	5	
4	6	
5	7	
6	8	

X=0

$$Y1 = \frac{x^2 - 4}{x - 2}$$

The function is not defined at $x = 2$.

Graphic

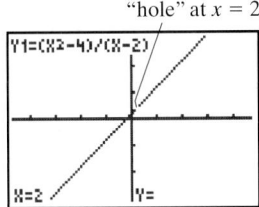
"hole" at $x = 2$

Y1=(X²−4)/(X−2)

X=2   Y=

$(-47, 47, -31, 31)$
Trace the graph and ask for the value of $x = 2$. The graph has a "hole" at $x = 2$.

The restricted value is 2.

Therefore, the domain is the set of all real numbers not equal to 2.

$$x \neq 2 \qquad \text{Inequality notation}$$
$$(-\infty, 2) \cup (2, \infty) \qquad \text{Interval notation}$$

 TAKE NOTE The union symbol ($\cup$) joins the two intervals and is read "or," meaning that the elements in the domain are in the first interval or in the second interval (or both).

EXAMPLE 3   Determine algebraically the restricted values, and then state the domain, of the given rational functions. Check your answer numerically or graphically.

$$\textbf{a. } h(x) = \frac{x + 4}{x^2 - x - 20} \qquad \textbf{b. } j(x) = \frac{6}{x^2 + 12} \qquad \textbf{c. } m(x) = \frac{3x + 1}{5x - 8}$$

Solution

a. $h(x) = \dfrac{x + 4}{x^2 - x - 20}$

Algebraic

To determine the restricted values, set the denominator equal to 0 and solve for x by factoring.

$$x^2 - x - 20 = 0$$
$$(x + 4)(x - 5) = 0$$
$$x + 4 = 0 \quad \text{or} \quad x - 5 = 0$$
$$x = -4 \qquad\qquad x = 5$$

The restricted values are -4 and 5.

Domain: All real numbers not equal to -4 or 5

$$x \neq -4 \quad \text{or} \quad x \neq 5$$
$$(-\infty, -4) \cup (-4, 5) \cup (5, \infty)$$

Numeric Check

Since the restricted values are integers, check the answer numerically. Let $Y1 = \frac{x + 4}{x^2 - x - 20}$ and view the table.

X	Y1
-4	ERROR
-3	-.125
-2	-.1429
-1	-.1667
0	-.2
1	-.25
2	-.3333

X= -4

X	Y1
-1	-.1667
0	-.2
1	-.25
2	-.3333
3	-.5
4	-1
5	ERROR

X=5

The function values for $x = -4$ and $x = 5$ are undefined.
The restricted values are -4 and 5.
The answer checks.

b. $j(x) = \dfrac{6}{x^2 + 12}$

Algebraic

To determine the restricted values, set the denominator equal to 0 and solve for x.

$$x^2 + 12 = 0$$
$$x^2 = -12$$

There is no real number whose square is a negative number. Therefore, the function has no restricted values in the real-number system.

Domain: All real numbers

$$(-\infty, \infty)$$

Graphic Check

The graphed function does not appear to have any "holes" in it and hence likely has no restrictions.

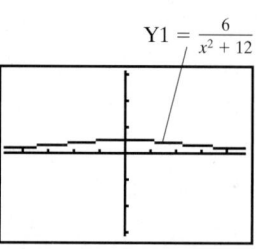

$Y1 = \frac{6}{x^2 + 12}$

$(-4.7, 4.7, -3.1, 3.1)$

c. $m(x) = \dfrac{3x + 1}{5x - 8}$

Algebraic

To determine the restricted values, set the denominator equal to 0 and solve for x.

$$5x - 8 = 0$$
$$5x = 8$$
$$x = \frac{8}{5}$$

The restricted value is $\frac{8}{5}$.

Domain: All real numbers not equal to $\frac{8}{5}$

$$x \neq \frac{8}{5}$$

$$\left(-\infty, \frac{8}{5}\right) \cup \left(\frac{8}{5}, \infty\right)$$

Graphic Check

Since the restricted value is not an integer, we cannot use a table of integer values. Check graphically. Ask for the value of $x = 1.6$.

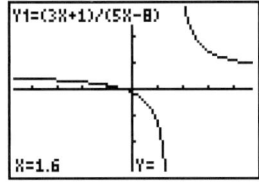

$(-4.7, 4.7, -3.1, 3.1)$

The function is not defined for $x = 1.6$, or $\frac{8}{5}$. The answer checks. ■

✓ Objective 10.1.2 *CHECKUP*

In exercises 1 and 2, determine the restricted values algebraically and then state the domain of the given rational functions. Check your answer numerically or graphically.

1. $s(x) = \dfrac{x^2 + x - 12}{x + 4}$

2. a. $g(x) = \dfrac{x + 8}{x^2 + x - 12}$ **b.** $C(x) = \dfrac{8x}{x^2 + 1}$

c. $a(b) = \dfrac{4}{2b - 3}$

3. What does it mean to say that a rational function has restricted values? ■

Objective 10.1.3   **Graphing Rational Functions**

Rational functions have an infinite number of possible solutions. In order to illustrate these solutions, we use a graph. When we graphed linear functions, we needed two points to determine the linear pattern and one additional point to be used as a check. To graph quadratic functions, we determined the vertex and several points to the left and right of it in order to see the pattern. To graph a rational function, we determine the restricted values. These values will not have corresponding function values. Then we graph several points to the left and right of each restricted value to see a pattern. This may be a very lengthy process by hand.

To help us with this process, we need to be able to determine how the function behaves near the restricted values. Complete the following set of exercises to visualize this behavior.

💡 Guided Discovery 2   Function Behavior Near Its Restricted Value

1. The restricted value for each of the following functions is $x = 1$. Complete the tables of values for the given function.

a. $f(x) = \dfrac{x^2 - 3x + 2}{x - 1}$

x	0	0.9	0.99	0.999	1	1.001	1.01	1.1	2
$f(x)$					undefined				

b. $g(x) = \dfrac{x^2 - x - 2}{x - 1}$

x	0	0.9	0.99	0.999	1	1.001	1.01	1.1	2
$g(x)$					undefined				

Describe each function's behavior as it approaches the restricted value from the left and from the right.

2. Graph the functions on a calculator screen $(-9.4, 9.4, -6.2, 6.2)$. Confirm your description in exercise 1 by tracing the graph from left to right toward the restricted value and then right to left toward the restricted value.

Write a rule for the two possible behaviors.

As the x-values approach 1 from the left, the function $f(x)$ appears to approach a value of -1. As the x-values approach 1 from the right, the function $f(x)$ appears to approach a value of -1. Therefore, our graph showed a "hole" at the $(1, -1)$ location.

However, as the x-values approach 1 from the left, the function $g(x)$ appears to increase without bound. As the x-values approach 1 from the right, the function $g(x)$ appears to decrease without bound. Since x cannot equal 1, the graph of $g(x)$ will never cross the vertical line $x = 1$. This line is called a **vertical asymptote**.

To graph a rational function,

- Determine the restrictions on the domain.
- Determine a table of values by choosing x-values less than and greater than the restricted values. Pay close attention to the x-values that are close to the restricted values.
- Graph the function by plotting the sample set of ordered pairs from the table of values and connecting the points with a smooth curve determined by the pattern seen. Be careful not to cross the vertical line where x is equal to a restricted value, because the restricted values do not have corresponding function values.
- If the graph has a vertical asymptote, graph the line as a dashed line and label.

Note: The calculator TABLE function in Ask mode will set up a table for you.

 TAKE NOTE The calculator window setting is very important in determining the "picture" you receive. You should carefully consider your choices.

EXAMPLE 4

Graph the rational functions.

a. $y = \dfrac{x^2 - x - 15}{x + 3}$ **b.** $y = \dfrac{5}{x} + \dfrac{4}{x^2}$ **c.** $p(x) = \dfrac{x^2 - 4}{x - 2}$

Solution

a. $y = \dfrac{x^2 - x - 15}{x + 3}$

The restricted value is -3. Set up a table of values, using x-values less than and greater than -3.

x	y
-6	-9
-5	-7.5
-4	-5
-3.5	-1.5
-3.1	22.9
-3.01	292.99

x	y
-2.99	-307
-2.9	-36.9
-2.5	-12.5
-2	-9
-1	-6.5
0	-5
1	-3.75
2	-2.6
3	-1.5
4	-0.4286

Graph the ordered pairs found in the table of values, and connect the points with a smooth curve. Graph and label the vertical asymptote, $x = -3$.

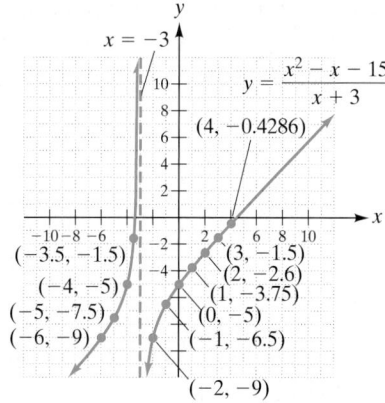

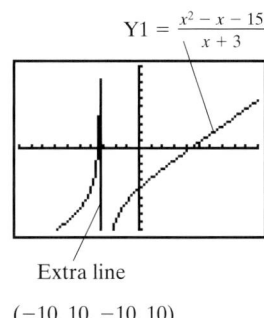

$Y1 = \frac{x^2 - x - 15}{x + 3}$

Extra line

$(-10, 10, -10, 10)$

Calculator Solution

a. Enter the equation in Y1, graph it, and choose the best viewing screen. Note that the standard screen adds an extra line in the graph. Note also that the graph appears to be defined at $x = -3$, a restricted value.

The extra line is due to the fact that the calculator is in connected mode. It connected the two parts of the graph across the vertical line $x = -3$. To graph only points, change the calculator to dot mode, as shown in **Figure 10.1c**.

TECHNOLOGY   Graphing Rational Functions

Graph $y = \dfrac{x^2 - x - 15}{x + 3}$.

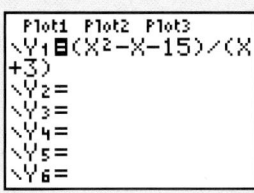

Figure 10.1a

Note: Dot mode

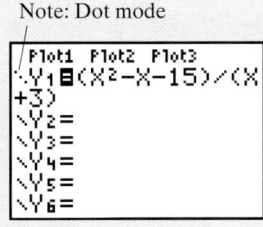

Figure 10.1b

$Y1 = \frac{x^2 - x - 15}{x + 3}$

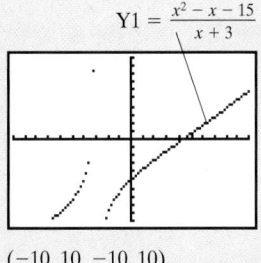

$(-10, 10, -10, 10)$

Figure 10.1c

For **Figure 10.1a**,

Enter the function, $y = \dfrac{x^2 - x - 15}{x + 3}$, in the Y = menu. Remember to group both the numerator and denominator with a set of parentheses.

`Y=` `(` `X,T,θ,n` `x²` `−` `X,T,θ,n` `−` `1` `5` `)` `÷` `(` `X,T,θ,n` `+` `3` `)`

For **Figure 10.1b**,
Set the calculator to dot mode.
Move the arrow to the left of Y1 = and press `ENTER` six times.

For **Figure 10.1c**,
Graph the function on a standard window.

`ZOOM` `6`

Note that the calculator only graphed points on the graph and did not connect them. You will need to connect these points when you draw the graph on paper.

---

b. $y = \dfrac{5}{x} + \dfrac{4}{x^2}$

The restricted value is 0. Therefore, complete a table of values by choosing x-values less than 0 and x-values greater than 0.

x	y	x	y
-6	-0.722	0.01	40500
-5	-0.84	0.1	450
-4	-1	0.5	26
-3	-1.222	1	9
-2	-1.5	2	3.5
-1	-1	3	2.111
-0.5	6	4	1.5
-0.1	350	5	1.16
-0.01	39500	6	0.944

(continued on page 780)

Graph the ordered pairs found in the table of values, and connect the points with a smooth curve. Do *not* connect across the vertical line when *x* is equal to the restricted value. Graph and label the vertical asymptote, $x = 0$.

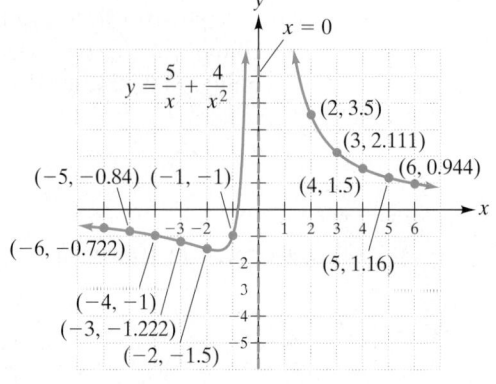

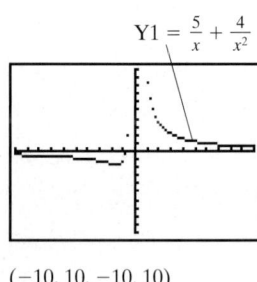

$Y1 = \dfrac{5}{x} + \dfrac{4}{x^2}$

$(-10, 10, -10, 10)$

Calculator Solution

On your calculator, graph in dot mode the rational function $y = \dfrac{5}{x} + \dfrac{4}{x^2}$.

c. $p(x) = \dfrac{x^2 - 4}{x - 2}$

The restricted value is 2. Set up a table of values, using *x*-values less than and greater than 2.

x	p(x)	x	p(x)
−1	1	2.01	4.01
0	2	2.1	4.1
1	3	2.5	4.5
1.5	3.5	3	5
1.9	3.9	4	6
1.99	3.99	5	7

Graph the ordered pairs found in the table of values, and connect the points with a smooth curve. Note that as the *x*-values approach 2 from both the left and the right, values for $p(x)$ approach 4. There is a "hole" in the graph at $(2, 4)$. Thus, this point should be enclosed with an open dot to show that it is not included in the linear graph.

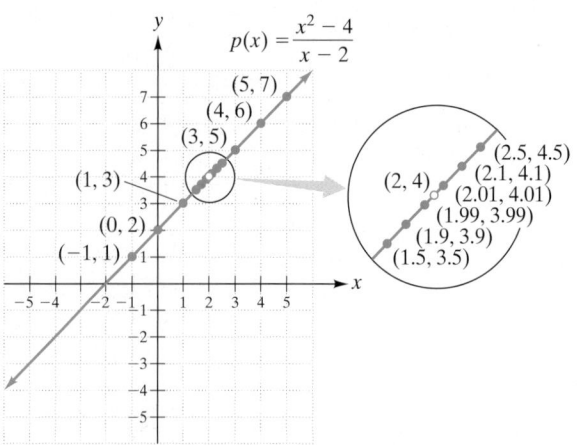

Calculator Solution

Enter the equation in Y1, graph it, and choose the best viewing screen.

Note: The standard screen does not show the "hole," because it is an integer value for x.

$$Y1 = \frac{x^2 - 4}{x - 2}$$

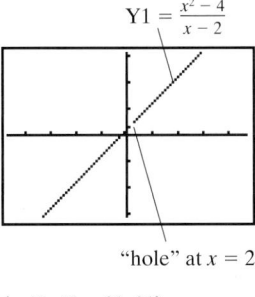

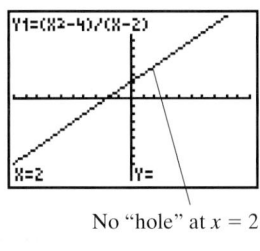

"hole" at $x = 2$	No "hole" at $x = 2$
$(-47, 47, -31, 31)$	$(-10, 10, -10, 10)$

 TAKE NOTE It is always a good idea to look at your table of values as well as your calculator graph. Your calculator graphs may be misleading without proper settings.

 Objective 10.1.3 *CHECKUP*

1. Graph the rational functions. Label the vertical asymptote, if applicable.

   a. $y = \dfrac{8}{x^2} + \dfrac{24}{x^3}$ **b.** $h(x) = \dfrac{x^2 + 8x + 15}{x + 3}$

   c. $g(x) = \dfrac{x^2 - 5x + 8}{x - 2}$

2. Do you think a graph presents a more complete description of the solutions of a rational function than a table of values does? Explain.

3. Describe the relationship between a restricted value for a function and the vertical asymptote of a graph of the function.

Objective 10.1.4   ## Modeling the Real World

Many business and economic applications are modeled by rational functions. Tables of values and graphs of these functions help us analyze the situations modeled and make appropriate business decisions.

EXAMPLE 5

A printer is purchased for $5000 with an additional service contract that costs $400 the first year and increases $100 per year thereafter. The total cost of the copier for x years is given by $C(x) = 5000 + 350x + 50x^2$.

a. Determine a function for the average cost per year for x years.

b. Graph the average-cost function for the domain $[1, 20]$. Determine the minimum average cost per year.

Solution

a. The average cost per year for x years is calculated by dividing the total cost by the number of years.

Let $x =$ the number of years

$$C(x) = \text{the total cost}$$

$$C_{\text{ave}}(x) = \text{the average cost per year}$$

$$C_{\text{ave}}(x) = \frac{C(x)}{x}$$

$$C_{\text{ave}}(x) = \frac{5000 + 350x + 50x^2}{x}$$

b.

$$Y1 = \frac{5000 + 350x + 50x^2}{x}$$

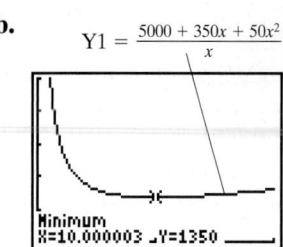

Minimum
X=10.000003 Y=1350

$(0, 20, 0, 5000)$

Note that the function is decreasing and then increasing. The relative minimum of the graph is located at (10, 1350). The minimum average cost per year is $1350. This minimum value occurs when the printer has been in use 10 years.

In business analysis, the year in which the average cost per year is at its minimum is referred to as the replacement time. Therefore, the printer should be replaced when it has been in use 10 years.   ∎

APPLICATION

According to the U.S. Bureau of the Census, the number of civilians in the labor force who are over 16 years of age and the number in the labor force who are unemployed are as listed in the following table:

Year	Unemployed Labor Force (millions of people)	Labor Force (millions of people)
2001	6.8	143.7
2002	8.4	144.9
2003	8.8	146.5

a. Determine the unemployment rate for each year.

b. The number of people unemployed in the labor force (in millions) may be approximated by $U(x) = -0.6x^2 + 2.2x + 6.8$, where x is the number of years after 2001. The number of people in the labor force (in millions) may be approximated by $L(x) = 1.15x + 143.7$, where x is the number of years after 2001. Determine

a function $R(x)$ that approximates the unemployment rate x years after 2001.

c. Use the formula from part **b** to approximate the unemployment rate for the years 2001, 2002, and 2003.

d. Compare the approximations with the actual values in the table. Would you consider this function a good predictor of the unemployment rate?

Discussion

a. In order to determine the unemployment rate, we divide the number of people unemployed by the total number in the labor force.

2001: $\dfrac{6.8}{143.7} \approx 0.047 = 4.7\%$

2002: $\dfrac{8.4}{144.9} \approx 0.058 = 5.8\%$

2003: $\dfrac{8.8}{146.5} \approx 0.060 = 6.0\%$

b. $R(x) = \dfrac{U(x)}{L(x)}$

$R(x) = \dfrac{-0.6x^2 + 2.2x + 6.8}{1.15x + 143.7}$

c.

X	Y1
0	.04732
1	.05799
2	.06027
3	.05437
4	.04046
5	.01874
6	-.0106

X=0

$x = 0$: 2001: $0.047 = 4.7\%$
$x = 1$: 2002: $0.058 = 5.8\%$
$x = 2$: 2003: $0.060 = 6.0\%$

d. The approximate unemployment rates found in part **c** are very close to the rates determined in part **a**. The function is a good predictor.

$Y1 = (-0.6x^2 + 2.2x + 6.8)/(1.15x + 143.7)$

✓ Objective 10.1.4 *CHECKUP*

1. Paul purchased an LCD television panel for $2500. He also purchased a maintenance agreement for the panel that costs $75 for the first year and increases $50 per year thereafter. The total cost of the television and maintenance agreement is $C(x) = 2500 + 50x + 25x^2$ for x years.

a. Determine a function for the average cost per year if Paul keeps the panel and the agreement for x years.
b. Graph the average-cost function for the domain $[1, 20]$. Determine the minimum average cost per year.
c. What advice would you give to Paul?

2. Using data from the U.S. Bureau of the Census, the following table shows the national health expenditures in billions of dollars and the expenditure for Medicare in billions of dollars:

Year	National Health Expenditures (billions of dollars)	Medicare Expenditures (billions of dollars)
2001	1426	249
2002	1559	268
2003	1679	283

a. Calculate the percentage of Medicare expenditures in relation to the national health expenditures for each year.
b. The national health expenditures (in billions of dollars) can be approximated by $N(x) = 126.5x + 1428.2$, where x is the number of years after 2001. Medicare expenditures (in billions of dollars) can be approximated by $M(x) = 17x + 249.7$, where x is the number of years after 2001. Write a rational function, $P(x)$, that approximates the ratio of Medicare expenditures to the national health expenditures, x years after 2001.

c. Use the function, $P(x)$, to approximate the percentage of Medicare expenditures in relation to the national health expenditures for the years 2001, 2002, and 2003.
d. Compare the approximations with the percentages found in part **a**. Is the function from part **b** a good predictor of the percentage of Medicare expenditures in relation to the national health expenditures?

10.1 EXERCISES

 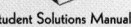

Student Solutions Manual   PH Math/Tutor Center   CD Video   MathXL®   MyMathLab   Interactmath.com

Determine whether each expression is rational or nonrational.

1. $\dfrac{x^2 + 10x + 25}{x + 5}$

2. $\dfrac{x + 4\sqrt{x} + 7}{x - 2}$

3. $z - 4 - \dfrac{25}{z - 4}$

4. $0.8a^2 - 0.2a + 1.2$

5. $\dfrac{x + 3}{\sqrt{x} - 2}$

6. $6x - 3x^{-1}$

7. $6x^2 + 17x - 3$

8. $\dfrac{\sqrt{x} + 3}{5x}$

9. $\dfrac{11}{3xy}$

10. $\dfrac{\sqrt{x^2 + 4}}{x - 6}$

11. $3x^{-2} + 4x^{-1} + 3 - x$

12. $\dfrac{1}{2}x^2 - \dfrac{3}{4}x + \dfrac{7}{8}$

13. $\dfrac{0.5x + 7}{1.2x - 4}$

14. $a + 7 - \dfrac{6}{a + 1}$

15. $\dfrac{2 - 3\sqrt{x}}{2x}$

16. $\dfrac{4}{7 - xy}$

In exercises 17–42, determine the restricted values algebraically, and then state the domain of each rational function. Check your answer numerically or graphically.

17. $y = \dfrac{3 - x}{x}$

18. $y = \dfrac{1 - x}{x^2 + 8x + 15}$

19. $h(x) = \dfrac{x - 5}{x^2 - 11x + 30}$

20. $g(x) = \dfrac{4x^2 + 1}{2x^2 + 6x}$

21. $C(x) = \dfrac{x + 7}{x^2 - 4}$

22. $y = \dfrac{5x^2 - 2}{x^3 - 4x^2 - x + 4}$

23. $y = \dfrac{2x^2 + 7}{x^2 - 5x}$

24. $b(x) = \dfrac{x + 7}{5x}$

25. $f(x) = \dfrac{x + 2}{x^3 - 2x^2 + 4x - 8}$

26. $y = \dfrac{55}{x^2 + 4x + 4}$

27. $f(x) = \dfrac{7}{2x^2 + 17x + 35}$

28. $y = \dfrac{12}{25x^2 + 30x + 9}$

29. $y = \dfrac{x^2 - 3x}{8x^2 + 6x - 9}$

30. $F(x) = \dfrac{x^3 - 8}{4x^3 + 20x^2 - 64x - 320}$

31. $y = \dfrac{4x}{4x^2 + 36x + 81}$

32. $g(x) = \dfrac{7x - 3}{14x^2 + 25x + 9}$

33. $h(x) = \dfrac{6 - x}{x^2 - 22x + 121}$

34. $y = \dfrac{5x + 2}{x^2 + 3x + 4}$

35. $y = \dfrac{3x^2}{9x^2 - 25}$

36. $y = \dfrac{9x^3}{6x^2 + 13x - 15}$

37. $C(x) = \dfrac{5x^3 + 1}{2x^3 + 4x^2 - 18x - 36}$

38. $y = \dfrac{2x^2 + 1}{16x^2 - 49}$

39. $y = \dfrac{3x + 8}{2x^2 + 5x + 7}$

40. $f(x) = \dfrac{9 - 2x}{9x^2 - 24x + 16}$

41. $y = \dfrac{x + 4}{2x + 3}$

42. $g(x) = \dfrac{8x^2 + 19}{10x^2 + 3x - 18}$

In exercises 43–62, graph each rational function. Label the vertical asymptote, if applicable.

43. $y = \dfrac{8}{x}$

44. $y = -\dfrac{4}{x}$

45. $y = \dfrac{6}{x} + \dfrac{9}{x^2}$

46. $y = \dfrac{9}{x} - \dfrac{36}{x^2}$

47. $y = \dfrac{x - 5}{x + 3}$

48. $y = \dfrac{1 - x}{x + 1}$

49. $f(x) = \dfrac{x^2 + 1}{x - 1}$

50. $g(x) = \dfrac{2x^2 + 5}{3x + 1}$

51. $y = \dfrac{x^2 - 9}{x - 3}$

52. $y = \dfrac{x^2 - 4}{x + 2}$

53. $g(x) = \dfrac{2x^2 - 5x + 2}{x - 2}$

54. $c(x) = \dfrac{x^2 + x - 2}{x + 2}$

55. $R(x) = \dfrac{2x^2 + 7x + 6}{x + 2}$

56. $z(x) = \dfrac{2x^2 + 5x - 3}{x + 3}$

57. $y = \dfrac{6x}{x^3 + 8}$

58. $y = \dfrac{4x}{x^3 + 1}$

59. $y = \dfrac{2x}{x^2 + 3}$

60. $y = \dfrac{x}{x^2 + 1}$

61. $f(x) = \dfrac{2x + 3}{x^2 - 2x - 3}$

62. $g(x) = \dfrac{x^2 + 3}{x^2 + x - 2}$

63. Analyze the function $f(x) = \dfrac{x^2 + 1}{x^2 - 4}$.

   a. What is the domain of the function?
   b. Graph the function $f(x)$.
   c. Identify the relative maximum or relative minimum for this function.

64. Analyze the function $f(x) = \dfrac{-10x}{(x^2 - 4)^2}$.

   a. What is the domain of the function?
   b. Graph the function $f(x)$.
   c. Identify the relative maximum or relative minimum for this function.

Business

65. The purchase price of a new heating-and-cooling system is $6500. The manufacturer offers a maintenance agreement for the system that can be purchased for $125 the first year and that increases by $50 per year thereafter. The total cost of the system and maintenance agreement is $C(x) = 6500 + 100x + 25x^2$ for x years.

   a. Determine a function for the average cost per year if the system is kept for x years.
   b. Graph the average-cost function for the domain [1, 40]. Determine the minimum average cost per year.
   c. What advice would you give the customer?

66. Acme Machines sells a high-speed copy machine for $10,000. The maintenance agreement for the machine costs $1200 for the first year and increases by $600 per year thereafter. The total cost of the copier and maintenance agreement is $C(x) = 10,000 + 900x + 300x^2$ for x years of use.

   a. Determine a function for the average cost per year if the copier is kept for x years.
   b. Graph the average-cost function for the domain [1, 20]. Determine the minimum average cost per year.
   c. What recommendation would you make to the customer?

67. The total profit (in dollars) from the sale of x compact disc players is $P(x) = -0.02x^2 + 12x - 100$.

   a. Determine a function for the average profit per player.
   b. Graph the average-profit function for the domain [1, 200].
   c. Determine the maximum average profit per player.

68. The total profit (in dollars) from the sale of x lawn mowers is $P(x) = 20x - 0.02x^2 - 320$.

   a. Determine a function for the average profit per lawn mower.
   b. Graph the average-profit function for the domain [1, 200].
   c. Determine the maximum average profit per lawn mower.

Geometry

69. A designer wants to construct an open box having a square base and surface area of 100 square inches. A function for the volume of the box is $V(x) = \dfrac{x^2(100 - x^2)}{4x}$, where x is the side of the square base. What is the domain of the function? Graph the volume function to determine the maximum volume.

70. A manufacturer needs to construct an open box having a rectangular base in which the length is three times the width and the surface area is 144 square inches. A function for the volume of the box is $V(x) = \dfrac{3x^2(144 - 3x^2)}{8x}$, where x is the width of the rectangular base. What is the domain of the function? Graph the volume function to determine the maximum volume.

Real Data

71. The number of workers in thousands involved in work stoppages (strikes, lockouts) in the United States can be estimated by the function $N(x) = 68x^2 - 257x + 288$, where x is the number of years after 2000. The number of work days idle by such workers, in thousands, can be estimated by $D(x) = 1961x^2 - 6374x + 5564$.

  a. Determine a function, $A(x)$, for the average days idle per worker, where x is the number of years after 2000.

  b. Assuming the trends continue, graph $A(x)$ for the domain $[0, 15]$. In what year will the average number of missed days per worker be a maximum? What is the maximum average number of missed days per worker? In what year will the average number of missed days per worker be a minimum? What is the minimum average number of missed days?

72. The weekly earnings of U.S. production workers can be estimated by the function $E(x) = -0.79x^2 + 15.24x + 478.75$, where x is the number of years after 2000. The weekly number of hours worked by these production workers can be estimated by $N(x) = -0.15x + 34.17$.

  a. Determine a function, $A(x)$, for the average earnings per hour, where x is the number of years after 2000.

  b. Assuming the trends continue, graph $A(x)$ for the domain $[0, 20]$. In what year will average earnings per hour be a maximum? What is the maximum average earnings per hour? In what year will average earnings per hour be a minimum? What is the minimum average earnings per hour?

73. According to the U.S. Environmental Protection Agency, greenhouse gas emissions from human activities are as listed in the table below:

Year	Carbon Dioxide (in teragrams of CO_2)	Total Emissions (in teragrams of CO_2)
2000	5859	7038
2001	5732	6884
2002	5782	6935

  a. Find a quadratic function that estimates carbon dioxide emissions $C(x)$, in teragrams of CO_2, where x is the number of years after 2000.

  b. Find a quadratic function that estimates total emissions $T(x)$, in teragrams of CO_2, where x is the number of years after 2000.

  c. Determine a function, $R(x)$, for the ratio of carbon dioxide emissions to total emissions, where x is the number of years after 2000.

  d. Assuming the trends continue, graph $R(x)$ on the domain $[0, 25]$, where x is the number of years after 2000. In what year will the ratio be 0.836 or the percentage equal 83.6%? What are the minimum and maximum percent from carbon dioxide on this domain, and in what year does each occur?

74. According to the U.S. Environmental Protection Agency, Office of Air Quality Planning and Standards, carbon monoxide emissions are as listed in the table below:

Year	Emissions from Transportation (in thousand tons)	Total Emissions (in thousand tons)
2001	88,153	106,262
2002	86,611	112,054
2003	83,252	106,886

  a. Find a quadratic function that estimates carbon monoxide emissions from transportation $T(x)$, in thousand tons, where x is the number of years after 2001.

  b. Find a quadratic function that estimates total carbon monoxide emissions $E(x)$, in thousand tons, where x is the number of years after 2001.

  c. Determine a function, $R(x)$, for the ratio of emissions from transportation to the total emissions, where x is the number of years after 2001.

  d. Assuming the trends continue, graph $R(x)$ on the domain $[0, 4]$, where x is the number of years after 2001. What is the minimum percent from transportation on this domain and in what year does it occur? Discuss what the function suggests for the year 2005.

10.1 Calculator Exercises

When graphing rational functions with your calculator, you must carefully choose a window that provides a good picture of the graph. To do so, you may need to use a window setting other than the options available under the [ZOOM] key. Remember that you can choose any window you wish by using the [WINDOW] key.

As an example, graph $y = \dfrac{6x + 13}{x + 1}$. First, store the function in Y1 and set Y1 to graph in dot mode. The first screen shows the graph in the decimal window, [ZOOM] [4]. Not much of the graph is visible. The second screen is the integer screen, [ZOOM] [8] [ENTER]. Here, the graph is too compressed,

with much of that part of it near the origin unclear. The third screen is the standard screen, [ZOOM] [6]. This screen is more revealing around the origin, but the y-axis needs to be extended. Do this by pressing [WINDOW] and changing Ymin and Ymax to double their size. At the same time, set Yscl to 0 so that tick marks on the y-axis won't interfere with your view. This is the fourth screen. With it, you can more clearly discern the behavior of the function, particularly around the y-axis. Finally, remember that you can always press [ZOOM] [1] to use the **ZBOX** option to enlarge a particular area of the graph that you need to see in more detail. The four screens are as follows:

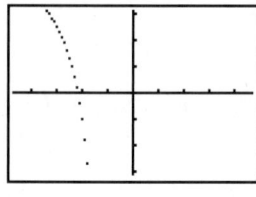
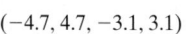

$(-4.7, 4.7, -3.1, 3.1)$

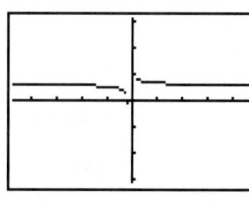

$(-47, 47, -31, 31)$

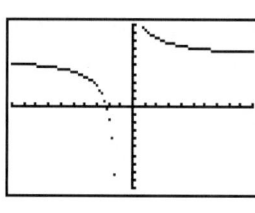

$(-10, 10, -10, 10)$

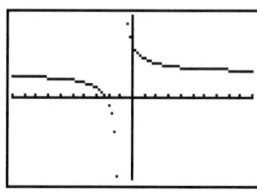

$(-10, 10, -20, 20)$

Find an appropriate window for the following functions:

1. $f(x) = \dfrac{x^3 + 5}{x^2 - 3}$ **2.** $y = \dfrac{1}{x^3 - 1} + \dfrac{1}{x^2}$ **3.** $g(x) = \dfrac{3}{x - 2} + \dfrac{5}{x^2 + 1}$

10.1 Writing Exercise

In the study of statistics, the *average* of a set of observations (that is, numbers) is calculated as the total of the observations divided by the number of observations in the set. Symbolically,

$$\text{ave} = \frac{\text{total}}{n}$$

where n is the number of observations in the set. Consider the restrictions on the divisor in this rational expression. Obviously, n cannot equal 0. What does this mean in terms of collecting observations and calculating averages? Does it make sense that zero should be a restricted value? What minimum number of observations is required to calculate an average?

Also in the study of statistics, the *variability* in a set of observations is calculated as the total of squared deviations from the

average, divided by the number of observations less 1. Don't be concerned if you don't understand all the terminology in this definition. We are really interested only in what is happening with the divisor. Symbolically,

$$\text{var} = \frac{\text{total of squares}}{n - 1}$$

What values are restricted on the divisor in this rational expression? Can you measure variability in numbers if you have zero observations? What if you have only one observation? Again, do the restrictions make sense in the context of the application? Write a short summary of your understanding of the questions raised in this application.

10.2 MULTIPLICATION AND DIVISION OF RATIONAL EXPRESSIONS

OBJECTIVES
1 Simplify rational expressions.
2 Multiply rational expressions.
3 Divide rational expressions.
4 Model real-world situations by using multiplication and division of rational expressions.

APPLICATION

Sio signed a contract for her new job. According to the contract, she is to make $20,000 the first year and receive an increase of 5% per year for the next two years. Sio's total salary for three years is given by the function

$$s(x) = \frac{20{,}000 - 20{,}000x^3}{1 - x},$$

where x is the sum of 1 and the percentage increase converted to a decimal, or 1.05. Write an equivalent function by simplifying $s(x)$. Determine Sio's total salary for three years, using the original function and the simplified function.

After completing this section, we will discuss this application further. See page 795.

Objective 10.2.1 | **Simplifying Rational Expressions**

We are now ready to simplify rational expressions that are algebraic fractions. We simplify these expressions by means of the same procedures we use with numeric fractions.

To write equivalent rational expressions, we need to review a property of real numbers discussed in Chapter P. The multiplication identity property states that the product of a real number and 1 is the real number itself. We use this property to write equivalent rational numbers, which are numbers that have the same value.

To write an equivalent numeric fraction in simplest form, we factor out the greatest common factor (GCF) of the numerator and denominator, rewrite the GCF as 1, and eliminate the factor of 1 by using the identity property. For example, simplify $\frac{6}{14}$.

$$\frac{6}{14} = \frac{2 \cdot 3}{2 \cdot 7} \qquad \text{Factor out the GCF, 2.}$$

$$= \frac{2}{2} \cdot \frac{3}{7}$$

$$= 1 \cdot \frac{3}{7} \qquad \text{Rewrite the GCF as 1.}$$

$$= \frac{3}{7}$$

The multiplication identity property also holds for rational expressions. It allows us to write equivalent rational expressions, using the same procedure as with numeric fractions. **Equivalent rational expressions** have the same value for any permissible replacement of the independent variable. Complete the set of exercises on the next page to see the meaning of this definition.

Guided Discovery 3 | Simplified Expressions and Restricted Values

To simplify $\dfrac{6x^2}{14x}$, complete the following steps:

$$\dfrac{6x^2}{14x} = \dfrac{2x \cdot 3x}{2x \cdot 7} \quad \text{Factor out the GCF, 2x.}$$

$$= \dfrac{2x}{2x} \cdot \dfrac{3x}{7}$$

$$= 1 \cdot \dfrac{3x}{7} \quad \text{Rewrite the GCF as 1.}$$

$$= \dfrac{3x}{7}$$

Check the equivalence of the expressions $\dfrac{6x^2}{14x}$ and $\dfrac{3x}{7}$ by graphing. Let Y1 = $\dfrac{6x^2}{14x}$ and Y2 = $\dfrac{3x}{7}$.

1. Both graphs appear to be coinciding. However, look at a table of values for $x = -3, -2, -1, 0, 1, 2,$ and 3. What do you see?

2. Determine the restricted values for each expression.

3. Explain why the two expressions are equivalent for all values except when $x = 0$.

Note that the original expression to be simplified had a restricted value of $x = 0$, but the simplified expression did not have a restricted value. The permissible values for x in the original expression are all real numbers except 0. The permissible values for x in the simplified expression are all real numbers. Therefore, the two expressions are said to be equivalent expressions for their permissible values.

Another property of multiplication that is often useful in simplifying rational expressions is the multiplication property of -1. The multiplication property of -1 states that the product of a real number and -1 is the opposite of the number itself. This is useful in simplifying rational expressions when the numerator and denominator are opposites.

 TAKE NOTE Two polynomials are opposites if every term of one polynomial corresponds to an opposite term in the second polynomial.

For example, simplify $\dfrac{x-1}{1-x}$.

The numerator and denominator are opposites because x and $-x$ are corresponding terms, as are 1 and -1. Therefore, if we rewrite the denominator as a product of -1 and its opposite, we can factor out a 1 from the expression.

$$\dfrac{x-1}{1-x} = \dfrac{x-1}{-1(-1+x)} \quad \text{Rewrite the denominator as a product of } -1 \text{ and its opposite.}$$

$$= \dfrac{x-1}{-1(x-1)} \quad \text{Rearrange the binomial factor in the denominator.}$$

$$= \dfrac{x-1}{x-1} \cdot \dfrac{1}{-1}$$

$$= 1 \cdot -1 \quad \text{Rewrite the GCF as 1.}$$

$$= -1$$

If the numerator or denominator polynomials contain more than one term, it is necessary to factor them in order to find the GCF.

SIMPLIFYING RATIONAL EXPRESSIONS

To simplify rational expressions,

- Factor the numerator and denominator.
- Write a product of two rational expressions, with one factor containing the GCF of the numerator and denominator and the other containing the remaining factors.
- Rewrite the factor containing the GCF as 1.
- Multiply, obtaining

$$\dfrac{A}{B} = \dfrac{k \cdot C}{k \cdot D} = \dfrac{k}{k} \cdot \dfrac{C}{D} = 1 \cdot \dfrac{C}{D} = \dfrac{C}{D}$$

where $A, B, C,$ and D are polynomials, $B \neq 0$, $D \neq 0$, and k is the GCF of A and B.

TAKE NOTE As in previous chapters, we can check the simplification of one variable expressions numerically or graphically.

| **EXAMPLE 1** | Simplify. |

$$\textbf{a.} \ \frac{5x + 15}{10x - 25} \qquad \textbf{b.} \ \frac{x^2 - 5x - 14}{x^2 - 8x + 7} \qquad \textbf{c.} \ \frac{16 - x^4}{x^3 - 2x^2 + 4x - 8}$$

Solution

a.
$$\frac{5x + 15}{10x - 25} = \frac{5(x + 3)}{5(2x - 5)} \qquad \text{Factor the numerator and denominator.}$$

$$= \frac{5}{5} \cdot \frac{x + 3}{2x - 5} \qquad \text{Write a product, with one factor containing the GCF of the numerator and denominator and the other containing the remaining factors.}$$

$$= 1 \cdot \frac{x + 3}{2x - 5} \qquad \text{Rewrite the GCF as 1.}$$

$$= \frac{x + 3}{2x - 5}$$

Numeric Check

As in previous chapters, we can check our simplification on the calculator by entering the simplified expression and the original expression. All Y1 and Y2 values should be equal.

X	Y₁	Y₂
0	-.6	-.6
1	-1.333	-1.333
2	-5	-5
3	6	6
4	2.3333	2.3333
5	1.6	1.6
6	1.2857	1.2857

X=0

$$Y1 = \frac{x + 3}{2x - 5}$$

$$Y2 = \frac{5x + 15}{10x - 25}$$

b.
$$\frac{x^2 - 5x - 14}{x^2 - 8x + 7} = \frac{(x + 2)(x - 7)}{(x - 1)(x - 7)} \qquad \text{Factor the numerator and denominator.}$$

$$= \frac{x - 7}{x - 7} \cdot \frac{x + 2}{x - 1} \qquad \text{Write a product, with one factor containing the GCF of the numerator and denominator and the other containing the remaining factors.}$$

$$= 1 \cdot \frac{x + 2}{x - 1} \qquad \text{Rewrite the GCF as 1.}$$

$$= \frac{x + 2}{x - 1} \qquad \text{Multiply.}$$

Graphic Check

We can check our simplification graphically by entering Y1 = the simplified expression and Y2 = the original expression. The graphs should coincide.

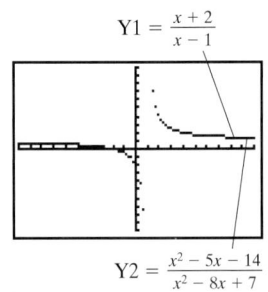

$$Y1 = \frac{x + 2}{x - 1}$$

$$Y2 = \frac{x^2 - 5x - 14}{x^2 - 8x + 7}$$

$(-10, 10, -10, 10)$

c.
$$\frac{16 - x^4}{x^3 - 2x^2 + 4x - 8} = \frac{(2 - x)(2 + x)(4 + x^2)}{(x - 2)(x^2 + 4)} \qquad \text{Factor the numerator and denominator.}$$

$$= \frac{-1(x - 2)(2 + x)(4 + x^2)}{(x - 2)(x^2 + 4)} \qquad \text{Rewrite the factor } 2 - x \text{ as } -1(x - 2).$$

$$= \frac{(x - 2)(4 + x^2)}{(x - 2)(x^2 + 4)} \cdot \frac{-1(2 + x)}{1} \qquad \text{Write a product, with one factor containing the GCF of the numerator and denominator and the other containing the remaining factors. Note: } 4 + x^2 = x^2 + 4.$$

$$= 1 \cdot \frac{-1(2 + x)}{1} \qquad \text{Rewrite the GCF as 1.}$$

$$= -1(2 + x) \quad \text{or} \quad -2 - x \qquad \text{Multiply.}$$

The check is left for you.

Note: You may be aware of a process called **cancellation** that may be used to reduce the number of steps in simplifying rational expressions. However, cancellation must be used properly and with great care. The process involves dividing out common *factors* from the numerator and denominator. For example, Example 1b could have been worked as follows:

$$\frac{x^2 - 5x - 14}{x^2 - 8x + 7} = \frac{(x + 2)(x - 7)}{(x - 1)(x - 7)}$$ *Factor the numerator and denominator.*

$$= \frac{(x + 2)\overset{1}{\cancel{(x - 7)}}}{(x - 1)\underset{1}{\cancel{(x - 7)}}}$$ *Cancel or divide out a common factor of (x − 7).*

Note: $\frac{x - 7}{x - 7} = 1$.

$$= \frac{x + 2}{x - 1}$$

 TAKE NOTE The remaining *x-terms* cannot be canceled. We can cancel or divide out *factors* only. We cannot cancel terms.

CAUTION

To simplify a rational expression by cancellation, the numerator and denominator must be factored. Only factors can be canceled or divided out.

 Objective 10.2.1 CHECKUP

1. Simplify

   a. $\dfrac{3a - 6}{9a + 12}$ b. $\dfrac{x^2 - 6x + 8}{x^2 - 10x + 24}$

   c. $\dfrac{25 - x^2}{x^3 - 5x^2 + 7x - 35}$

2. What is the difference between a factor and a term of a polynomial?

3. When simplifying a rational expression, you can cancel only factors, not terms. Why?

Objective 10.2.2   Multiplying Rational Expressions

To multiply numeric fractions, we multiply the numerators together, multiply the denominators together, and, if necessary, simplify the resulting fraction. For example,

$$\frac{3}{4} \cdot \frac{5}{6} = \frac{3 \cdot 5}{4 \cdot 6} = \frac{15}{24} = \frac{3}{3} \cdot \frac{5}{8} = 1 \cdot \frac{5}{8} = \frac{5}{8}$$

We use the same procedure for multiplication of rational expressions.

$$\frac{6x}{5} \cdot \frac{3y}{4x} = \frac{6x \cdot 3y}{5 \cdot 4x} = \frac{18xy}{20x} = \frac{2x}{2x} \cdot \frac{9y}{10} = 1 \cdot \frac{9y}{10} = \frac{9y}{10}$$

MULTIPLYING RATIONAL EXPRESSIONS

To multiply rational expressions,

• Multiply the numerators.
• Multiply the denominators.
• Factor the numerator and denominator.
• Simplify the resulting rational expression, as in

$$\frac{A}{B} \cdot \frac{C}{D} = \frac{AC}{BD}$$

where A, B, C, and D are polynomials with $B \neq 0$ and $D \neq 0$.

EXAMPLE 2

Multiply and simplify.

a. $\dfrac{x+4}{x-5} \cdot \dfrac{x}{x+1}$

b. $\dfrac{2x-3}{x^2-9} \cdot \dfrac{x-3}{6x^2-7x-3}$

Solution

a. $\dfrac{x+4}{x-5} \cdot \dfrac{x}{x+1} = \dfrac{(x+4)x}{(x-5)(x+1)}$ Multiply numerators and denominators.

$\qquad\qquad\quad = \dfrac{x^2+4x}{x^2-4x-5}$

After multiplying and simplifying, the result may have a product of factors in the numerator and denominator. It is not necessary to complete the multiplication of these factors.

Numeric Check

X	Y₁	Y₂
-1	ERROR	ERROR
0	0	0
1	-.625	-.625
2	-1.333	-1.333
3	-2.625	-2.625
4	-6.4	-6.4
5	ERROR	ERROR

X = -1

$Y1 = \dfrac{x^2+4x}{x^2-4x-5}$

$Y2 = \dfrac{x+4}{x-5} \cdot \dfrac{x}{x+1}$

Note that for all x-values, the corresponding Y1 and Y2 are equal.

 TAKE NOTE For ease in reading and to ensure that the calculator performs the operations correctly, place fractions in parentheses.

b. $\dfrac{2x-3}{x^2-9} \cdot \dfrac{x-3}{6x^2-7x-3}$

$\quad = \dfrac{(2x-3)(x-3)}{(x^2-9)(6x^2-7x-3)}$ Multiply numerators and denominators.

$\quad = \dfrac{(2x-3)(x-3)}{(x-3)(x+3)(2x-3)(3x+1)}$ Factor.

$\quad = \dfrac{(2x-3)(x-3)}{(2x-3)(x-3)} \cdot \dfrac{1}{(x+3)(3x+1)}$ Factor out the GCF.

$\quad = \dfrac{1}{(x+3)(3x+1)}$ Multiply.

The check is left for you.

Just as we may cancel when simplifying algebraic fractions, we may cancel with care when multiplying algebraic fractions. To do this, we simplify by cancellation before we multiply.

To multiply rational expressions by canceling,

- Factor the numerators and denominators.
- Cancel, or divide out, common factors in pairs—one from the numerator and one from the denominator.
- Multiply the remaining factors.

The product will not need to be simplified after all common factors are canceled. For example, the product in Example 2b may be found by this method.

$$\frac{2x - 3}{x^2 - 9} \cdot \frac{x - 3}{6x^2 - 7x - 3}$$

$$= \frac{2x - 3}{(x + 3)(x - 3)} \cdot \frac{x - 3}{(2x - 3)(3x + 1)} \qquad \text{Factor.}$$

$$= \frac{2x - 3}{(x + 3)(x - 3)} \cdot \frac{x - 3}{(2x - 3)(3x + 1)} \qquad \text{Cancel out factors.}$$

$$= \frac{1}{(x + 3)(3x + 1)} \qquad \text{Multiply.}$$

The check is left for you.

✓ Objective 10.2.2 **CHECKUP**

1. Multiply and simplify.

a. $\dfrac{x - 1}{x + 1} \cdot \dfrac{x + 4}{x^2}$ b. $\dfrac{10x + 4}{x^2 - 16} \cdot \dfrac{x + 4}{5x^2 - 18x - 8}$

Objective 10.2.3   **Dividing Rational Expressions**

To divide numeric fractions, we multiply by the reciprocal of the divisor and, if necessary, simplify the resulting fraction. For example,

$$\frac{3}{4} \div \frac{5}{6} = \frac{3}{4} \cdot \frac{6}{5} = \frac{18}{20} = \frac{2}{2} \cdot \frac{9}{10} = 1 \cdot \frac{9}{10} = \frac{9}{10}$$

We use the same procedure to divide rational expressions.

$$\frac{15a^3b}{2cd} \div \frac{20ac^2}{3d} = \frac{15a^3b}{2cd} \cdot \frac{3d}{20ac^2} = \frac{45a^3bd}{40ac^3d} = \frac{5ad}{5ad} \cdot \frac{9a^2b}{8c^3} = 1 \cdot \frac{9a^2b}{8c^3} = \frac{9a^2b}{8c^3}$$

DIVIDING RATIONAL EXPRESSIONS

To divide rational expressions,

- Multiply by the reciprocal of the divisor.
- Factor the numerator and denominator.
- Simplify the resulting rational expression, as in

$$\frac{A}{B} \div \frac{C}{D} = \frac{A}{B} \cdot \frac{D}{C} = \frac{AD}{BC}$$

where A, B, C, and D are polynomials with $B \neq 0$, $D \neq 0$, and $C \neq 0$.

EXAMPLE 3   Divide and simplify.

a. $\dfrac{2x + 1}{2x^2 - 8} \div \dfrac{2x + 1}{x^4 - 16}$ b. $\dfrac{x^2 + 8x + 12}{x^2 + 12} \div (x + 6)$

Solution

a. $\dfrac{2x+1}{2x^2-8} \div \dfrac{2x+1}{x^4-16}$

$= \dfrac{2x+1}{2x^2-8} \cdot \dfrac{x^4-16}{2x+1}$ Rewrite as multiplication by reciprocal of divisor.

$= \dfrac{(2x+1)(x^4-16)}{(2x^2-8)(2x+1)}$ Multiply numerators and denominators.

$= \dfrac{(2x+1)(x^2+4)(x+2)(x-2)}{2(x+2)(x-2)(2x+1)}$ Factor.

$= \dfrac{(2x+1)(x+2)(x-2)}{(2x+1)(x+2)(x-2)} \cdot \dfrac{x^2+4}{2}$ Factor out the GCF.

$= \dfrac{x^2+4}{2}$ Multiply.

b. $\dfrac{x^2+8x+12}{x^2+12} \div (x+6)$

$= \dfrac{x^2+8x+12}{x^2+12} \cdot \dfrac{1}{x+6}$ Rewrite as multiplication by the reciprocal of the divisor.

$= \dfrac{x^2+8x+12}{(x^2+12)(x+6)}$ Multiply numerators and denominators.

$= \dfrac{(x+6)(x+2)}{(x^2+12)(x+6)}$ Factor.

$= \dfrac{x+6}{x+6} \cdot \dfrac{x+2}{x^2+12}$ Factor out the GCF.

$= \dfrac{x+2}{x^2+12}$ Multiply.

The check is left for you.

Numeric Check

X	Y1	Y2
-1	2.5	2.5
0	2	2
1	2.5	2.5
2	4	ERROR
3	6.5	6.5
4	10	10
5	14.5	14.5

X= -1

$Y1 = \dfrac{x^2+4}{2}$

$Y2 = \dfrac{2x+1}{2x^2-8} \div \dfrac{2x+1}{x^4-16}$

Note that Y1 and Y2 values are equal for all values in the domain of the functions.

We may also cancel, with care, when dividing rational expressions.

To divide rational expressions by canceling,

- Multiply by the reciprocal of the divisor.
- Factor the numerators and denominators.
- Cancel, or divide out, common factors in pairs—one from the numerator and one from the denominator.
- Multiply the remaining factors.

The product will not need to be simplified after all common factors are canceled.

For Example 3a,

$$\frac{2x + 1}{2x^2 - 8} \div \frac{2x + 1}{x^4 - 16}$$

$$= \frac{2x + 1}{2x^2 - 8} \cdot \frac{x^4 - 16}{2x + 1}$$ Rewrite as multiplication.

$$= \frac{2x + 1}{2(x + 2)(x - 2)} \cdot \frac{(x^2 + 4)(x + 2)(x - 2)}{2x + 1}$$ Factor.

$$= \frac{\overset{1}{\cancel{2x + 1}}}{2\cancel{(x + 2)}\cancel{(x - 2)}} \cdot \frac{(x^2 + 4)\overset{1}{\cancel{(x + 2)}}\overset{1}{\cancel{(x - 2)}}}{\underset{1}{\cancel{2x + 1}}}$$ Cancel out common factors.

$$= \frac{x^2 + 4}{2}$$ Multiply.

> ✎ **TAKE NOTE** Remember, we cancel common factors. This means that we must be canceling in a *multiplication* problem. Therefore, *always* change the division problem to multiplication *before* canceling factors.

✓ Objective 10.2.3 *CHECKUP*

1. Divide and simplify.

a. $\dfrac{5a + 7}{3x^2 - 3} \div \dfrac{10a + 14}{9x^4 - 9}$ **b.** $\dfrac{5x^2 + 19x - 4}{x^2 - 4} \div (5x - 1)$

2. Why must you first change a division problem to a multiplication problem before performing any cancellation of factors?   ■

Objective 10.2.4   Modeling the Real World

Rational expressions occur in many models of real-world problems. One common example comes from the distance-traveled formula, $d = rt$, where d is the distance traveled by a moving object, r is the average rate, or speed, of the object (which we assume to be constant), and t is the time of travel. If we solve this equation for the time t, we get the rational expression $t = \dfrac{d}{r}$.

EXAMPLE 4   Balto the rescue dog traveled a distance of 125 miles.

a. Write an expression for the time traveled if Balto traveled at a speed of x mph.

b. Write an expression for the new distance Balto traveled if he kept the time constant, but increased his average speed by 10 mph.

c. Use the expression for distance traveled at the increased speed in part **b** to determine the distance Balto traveled if his original speed was 5 miles per hour.

d. Use the expression for time traveled in part **a** to determine the time Balto traveled if his original speed was 5 miles per hour. Use this time to determine the distance Balto traveled at 15 miles per hour (an increase of 10 miles per hour).

e. Compare the answer you obtained in part **c** to that obtained in part **d**.

Solution

a. Let x = rate in miles per hour

$$t = \frac{d}{r}$$ Distance-traveled formula, solved for t

$$t = \frac{125}{x}$$ Substitute 125 for d and x for r.

An expression for the time Balto traveled is $\dfrac{125}{x}$ hours.

b. Since Balto increased his average speed by 10 mph, his new speed (rate) is $x + 10$. The time is still $\dfrac{125}{x}$.

$$d = rt \qquad \text{Distance-traveled formula}$$

$$d = (x + 10)\left(\frac{125}{x}\right)$$

$$d = \left(\frac{x + 10}{1}\right)\left(\frac{125}{x}\right)$$

$$d = \frac{125(x + 10)}{x}$$

An expression for the new distance Balto traveled is $\dfrac{125(x + 10)}{x}$ miles.

c. Let $x = 5$ mph.

$$d = \frac{125(x + 10)}{x}$$

$$d = \frac{125(5 + 10)}{5} \qquad \text{Substitute 5 for x.}$$

$$d = 375$$

If Balto's original speed was 5 mph, he traveled 375 miles when he increased his average speed by 10 mph.

d. Let $x = 5$.

$$t = \frac{125}{x} \qquad\qquad d = rt$$

$$t = \frac{125}{5} \qquad\qquad d = 15(25) \qquad r = 15, t = 25$$

$$t = 25 \quad \text{Substitute 5 for x.} \qquad d = 375$$

Balto traveled 375 miles.

e. The distance Balto traveled was 375 miles in both calculations. ■

APPLICATION

Sio signed a contract for her new job. According to the contract, she is to make $20,000 the first year and receive an increase of 5% per year for the next two years. Sio's total salary for three years is given by the function $s(x) = \dfrac{20{,}000 - 20{,}000x^3}{1 - x}$, where x is the sum of 1 and the percentage increase converted to a decimal, or 1.05. Write an equivalent function by simplifying $s(x)$. Determine Sio's total salary for three years, using the original function and the simplified function.

Discussion

$$s(x) = \frac{20{,}000 - 20{,}000x^3}{1 - x}$$

$$s(x) = \frac{20{,}000(1 - x^3)}{1 - x}$$

$$s(x) = \frac{20{,}000(\overset{1}{\cancel{1 - x}})(1 + x + x^2)}{\underset{1}{\cancel{1 - x}}}$$

$$s(x) = 20{,}000(1 + x + x^2)$$

$$s(x) = 20{,}000 + 20{,}000x + 20{,}000x^2$$

Evaluate each function for $x = 1.05$.

Original function

$$s(x) = \frac{20{,}000 - 20{,}000x^3}{1 - x}$$

$$s(1.05) = \frac{20{,}000 - 20{,}000(1.05)^3}{1 - 1.05}$$

$$s(1.05) = 63{,}050$$

Simplified function

$$s(x) = 20{,}000 + 20{,}000x + 20{,}000x^2$$

$$s(1.05) = 20{,}000 + 20{,}000(1.05) + 20{,}000(1.05)^2$$

$$s(1.05) = 63{,}050$$

Sio will receive $63,050 over the three-year period. (This simplified function was determined in Section 7.5 by division.)

Objective 10.2.4 CHECKUP

1. Reza traveled 150 miles.

   a. Write an expression for his average rate of speed if it took x hours for the trip.

   b. If Reza were to increase his time by 2 hours, write an expression for the new distance he would travel.

   c. Use the expression for distance traveled for the longer period of time in part **b** to determine the distance Reza traveled if his original time was 3 hours.

   d. Use the expression for speed in part **a** to determine the average speed Reza traveled if his original time was 3 hours. Use this speed to determine the distance Reza traveled for 5 hours (an increase of 2 hours).

   e. Compare the answer you obtained in part **c** to that obtained in part **d**.

2. When Benjamin enrolled at a community college, he received a scholarship of $1500. The following year, the scholarship was increased by 20%. The total amount of money Benjamin received for his two years of study is given by $s(y) = \dfrac{1500 - 1500y^2}{1 - y}$, where y is the sum of the percentage increase (converted to decimal form) and 1. Write an equivalent function by simplifying. Using the original function and the simplified function, determine the total amount Benjamin received.

10.2 EXERCISES

 Student Solutions Manual   PH Math/Tutor Center    CD Video   Math XL MathXL®   MyMathLab MyMathLab   Interactmath.com

Simplify.

1. $\dfrac{36x^3y^2z}{54x^2y^5}$

2. $\dfrac{21x^3y^4}{35x^5yz^2}$

3. $\dfrac{-56a^3b^2}{84a^2b^2c}$

4. $\dfrac{99ab^5c}{-72a^3b^2}$

5. $\dfrac{9x - 27}{18x - 6}$

6. $\dfrac{8x + 16}{24x + 12}$

7. $\dfrac{8 - z}{z - 8}$

8. $\dfrac{x - y}{y - x}$

9. $\dfrac{5x^2y^3 + 10xy^4}{15xy^2 - 20x^2y^2}$

10. $\dfrac{15x^2y - 9x^3y}{6x^2y^2 + 3xy^3}$

11. $\dfrac{-6x + 9y - 3z}{3x - 21y + 3z}$

12. $\dfrac{-7x + 28y - 14z}{14x - 7y + 7z}$

13. $\dfrac{x^2 - 8x + 12}{x^2 - 10x + 24}$

14. $\dfrac{x^2 - 6x + 9}{x^2 - 10x + 21}$

15. $\dfrac{x^2 - x - 6}{x^2 + 9x + 14}$

16. $\dfrac{x^2 + 12x + 32}{x^2 - x - 20}$

17. $\dfrac{3x^2 + 7x + 2}{3x^2 - 11x - 4}$

18. $\dfrac{2x^2 + 11x + 5}{2x^2 - 17x - 9}$

19. $\dfrac{6x^2 - x - 2}{4x^2 - 4x - 3}$

20. $\dfrac{10x^2 + 7x - 12}{8x^2 + 2x - 15}$

21. $\dfrac{8x^2 + 12x + 4}{24x^2 - 40x - 16}$

22. $\dfrac{12x^2 + 6x - 6}{27x^2 + 45x - 18}$

23. $\dfrac{2x^2 + xy - y^2}{3x^2 + 4xy + y^2}$

24. $\dfrac{5x^2 - 6xy + y^2}{4x^2 - 3xy - y^2}$

25. $\dfrac{64 - x^2}{x^3 + 2x^2 - 64x - 128}$

26. $\dfrac{25 - x^2}{x^3 + 3x^2 - 25x - 75}$

27. $\dfrac{2x^2 - 7x - 15}{x^3 - 5x^2 + 11x - 55}$

28. $\dfrac{3x^2 - 17x - 28}{x^3 - 7x^2 + 9x - 63}$

Multiply and simplify.

29. $\dfrac{12a^2b^2}{35cd^2} \cdot \dfrac{49c^2d^2}{27ab^3}$

30. $\dfrac{15a^3b^2}{16c^3d^5} \cdot \dfrac{24c^3d^3}{25ab^4}$

31. $\dfrac{-2x^3}{5y^2} \cdot \dfrac{15xy^2}{8x^2}$

32. $\dfrac{12x}{15y^3} \cdot \dfrac{-5xy^5}{26x^4}$

33. $(2.6x^2) \cdot \dfrac{3.1x}{y^2}$

34. $\dfrac{7x^2y}{6z} \cdot 9$

35. $\dfrac{1}{3} \cdot \dfrac{2a^2}{3b}$

36. $\dfrac{7a^3}{3b^2} \cdot \dfrac{2}{5}$

37. $\dfrac{x + 5}{x} \cdot \dfrac{x^3}{x + 4}$

38. $\dfrac{x^3}{x - 11} \cdot \dfrac{x + 15}{x^2}$

39. $\dfrac{3x + 2}{x + 4} \cdot \dfrac{x - 4}{3x + 2}$

40. $\dfrac{x + 7}{4x + 3} \cdot \dfrac{4x + 3}{x - 7}$

41. $\dfrac{x + 7}{2x + 1} \cdot \dfrac{5x + 2}{x}$

42. $\dfrac{3x + 5}{x} \cdot \dfrac{x + 4}{2x + 9}$

43. $\dfrac{x^2 - x - 6}{2x^2 + 3x + 1} \cdot \dfrac{2x^2 - x - 1}{x^2 + 5x + 6}$

44. $\dfrac{x^2 + 8x + 15}{3x^2 - 5x - 2} \cdot \dfrac{3x^2 + 7x + 2}{x^2 - 2x - 15}$

45. $\dfrac{x^2 - xy - 2y^2}{x^2 - 9y^2} \cdot \dfrac{x^2 - 3xy}{x^2 - y^2}$

46. $\dfrac{xy - 5y^2}{x^2 - 4y^2} \cdot \dfrac{x^2 - xy - 2y^2}{x^2 - 25y^2}$

Divide and simplify exercises 47–70.

47. $\dfrac{54a^3b^2}{c} \div \dfrac{36ab^2}{c}$

48. $\dfrac{49a^4b^2}{c^2} \div \dfrac{56a^3b^3}{c^2}$

49. $\dfrac{-21x^2y^3}{z} \div \dfrac{7xy^2}{z^2}$

50. $\dfrac{33x^3y}{z^3} \div \dfrac{-11x^5y^3}{z^2}$

51. $(32ab^2) \div \dfrac{8ab^3}{c}$

52. $(21a^2b^4) \div \dfrac{7ab^2}{c^2}$

53. $\dfrac{21x^2y^2}{z^3} \div (-3xy^3)$

54. $\dfrac{-34x^3y}{z^2} \div (17x^2y^4)$

55. $\dfrac{a+4}{9a^2-1} \div \dfrac{5a+20}{3a+1}$

56. $\dfrac{7a+21}{36a^2-1} \div \dfrac{a+3}{6a-1}$

57. $\dfrac{x^2-16}{5y-2} \div \dfrac{x+4}{25y^2-4}$

58. $\dfrac{x^2-49}{4y+3} \div \dfrac{x+7}{16y^2-9}$

59. $\dfrac{2x^2-5x-3}{x^2-5x-14} \div \dfrac{3x^2+10x+3}{x^2-4x-21}$

60. $\dfrac{x^2-2x-8}{2x^2+x-3} \div \dfrac{3x^2+8x+4}{2x^2-5x-12}$

61. $\dfrac{8x^2+2x-3}{4x^2-1} \div (4x+3)$

62. $\dfrac{15x^2+16x+4}{9x^2-4} \div (5x+2)$

63. $(x+9) \div \dfrac{2x^2+19x+9}{3x+4}$

64. $(x+11) \div \dfrac{2x^2+17x-55}{5x-2}$

65. $\dfrac{1}{3x-5} \div \dfrac{1}{x+7}$

66. $\dfrac{5}{4x+3} \div \dfrac{7}{2x+1}$

67. $\dfrac{x^2+3xy}{7xy+2y^2} \div \dfrac{x^2+4xy+3y^2}{7x^2-5xy-2y^2}$

68. $\dfrac{x^2+7xy+10y^2}{3x^2-4xy-4y^2} \div \dfrac{x^2+5xy}{3xy+2y^2}$

69. $\dfrac{4x+8y}{3x-12y} \div \dfrac{4x+4y}{6x+6y}$

70. $\dfrac{5x+35y}{6x+18y} \div \dfrac{5x-10y}{8x+24y}$

Distance

71. Katarina drove a distance of 170 miles. If her average rate of travel (speed) was x miles per hour, write a rational expression for her time of travel. If she had traveled for the same amount of time, but had decreased her average speed by 10 mph, write an expression for the distance she would have traveled. How far would she have traveled at the reduced speed if her original speed was 50 miles per hour?

72. Brian traveled 155 miles. Write an expression for his time of travel if his average speed was x mph. If he travels the same length of time, but increases his speed by 8 mph, write an expression for the distance he would travel. How far would he travel at the increased speed if his original speed was 45 miles per hour?

Geometry

73. A rectangle has area $A(x) = 10x^3 - 11x^2 - 6x$. Its length is $2x - 3$. Write a function, $w(x)$, for the width of the rectangle. Simplify this function. If the length is 11 yards, what is the width?

74. A parallelogram has area $A(x) = 18x^3 + 39x^2 + 15x$. Its height is $3x + 5$. Write a function, $b(x)$, for the corresponding base. Simplify this function. If the height is 26 feet, what is the base?

75. A box has a volume given by the formula $V = LWH$. Solve this formula for L. If the volume of the box is $15x^3 + 7x^2 - 2x$ cubic inches, its height is x inches, and its width is $3x + 2$ inches, use the new formula to determine an expression for the length in terms of the height x. If the height of the box measures 4 inches, what are the box's other dimensions?

76. A cylindrical can has a volume given by the formula $V = \pi r^2 h$. Solve this formula for h. If a can has a volume of $6\pi x^3 - 5\pi x^2$ cubic inches and its radius is x inches, use the new formula to determine an expression for the height of the can in terms of the radius x. If the radius of the can measures 1.5 inches, what is its height?

Business

77. To encourage her grandson to do well in college, Sharon promised him $500 for completing his first semester of a full-time course load. She promised to increase the amount by 20% for each subsequent semester of a full-time course load that he completed. The total amount that the grandson received was $m(x) = \dfrac{500 - 500x^3}{1 - x}$, where x is the sum of 1 and the percentage increase (converted to decimal form). Write an equivalent function by simplifying this rational function. Using the original function and the simplified function, determine the total amount that the grandson received.

78. Alexandra is a sales representative for a pharmaceutical company. Her sales during the first week of the month totaled $50,000 and increased by 25% each week for the next two weeks. Her total sales for the three-week period were $s(x) = \dfrac{50{,}000 - 50{,}000x^3}{1 - x}$, where x is the sum of 1 and the percentage increase (converted to decimal form). Write an equivalent function by simplifying this rational function.

Using the original function and the simplified function, determine the total amount of Alexandra's sales.

79. The fixed cost of producing an item is $300, and the variable cost is $5 per item produced. The revenue received for selling the item is $25 per item.
  a. Write a cost function and a revenue function for producing and selling x items.
  b. Write an expression for the ratio of revenue to cost for x items, and simplify the expression.
  c. If a production run produces 40 items, what is the value of the revenue-to-cost ratio?

80. The fixed cost of producing an item is $175, and the variable cost is $25 per item produced. The revenue received for selling the item is $75 per item.
  a. Write a cost function and a revenue function for producing and selling x items.
  b. Write an expression for the ratio of cost to revenue for x items, and simplify the expression.
  c. If a production run produces 50 items, what is the value of the cost-to-revenue ratio?

Physics

81. When an object moves around a circle with its acceleration directed toward the center of the circle, this centripetal acceleration can be given by the formula $a = \dfrac{v^2}{r}$, where v is velocity and r is the radius of the circle. Find the product of accelerations of two bodies in which the first has velocity 7 meters per second on circle of radius r, and the second has velocity 5 meters per second on a circle with radius two more than five times the radius of the smaller circle.

82. Centripetal force is related to centripetal acceleration and is given by the formula $F = m\dfrac{v^2}{r}$, where m is mass, v is velocity, and r is the radius of the circle. Find the quotient of the force of an object with mass 0.75 kilogram, velocity 12 meters per second, on a circle of radius r divided by the force of a second object with mass 0.45 kilogram, velocity 15 meters

per second, on a circle with radius two less than that of the first circle.

83. Mass of a body refers to its inertia, while weight of a body is the force due to gravity and can vary with location. The two are related by the formula $w = \dfrac{m}{g}$, where g is acceleration due to gravity. The weight for one body of mass 16 kilograms and acceleration due to gravity of g is divided by the weight for another body whose mass is 27 kilograms at a place where acceleration due to gravity is two more than three times g. What is the quotient?

84. Angular acceleration is defined to be the change in angular velocity over time. If the change of angular velocity for one body is $(w - 4)$ in time t and the change of angular velocity for another body is 11 in time $(t + 7)$, find the quotient of the angular acceleration of the first body divided by the angular acceleration of the second body.

 ## 10.2 Calculator Exercises

In this section, you have used functions of the form $f(x) = \dfrac{k(1 - x^n)}{1 - x}$, where k is a constant and n is the integer 2 or 3. This function was also used in earlier chapters. It is an interesting function, as you have seen. When n equals 2 or 3, you can factor the numerator, and one of the factors is the denominator, so you can simplify the function after factoring.

Let's explore the function on the calculator. To make the exploration easier, we will set k equal to 1 and $f(x)$ equal to y. Then the function becomes $y = \dfrac{1 - x^n}{1 - x}$.

One property of this function is that when you specify a value for n, the denominator always divides evenly into the numerator. The resulting function has degree that is one less than n.

Complete the table that follows. Use your calculator to sketch a graph of the original function and the simplified function for each value of n. To expedite the graphing, store the function as $Y1 = (1 - X \wedge N)/(1 - X)$, and store the various values for

N before viewing each graph. The graphs can best be viewed with a window of $(-4.7, 4.7, 1, -31, 31, 10, 1)$. When sketching the graphs, be sure to show the restricted values as holes or asymptotes. Use long division to find the simplified functions. Can you discern a pattern?

Value for n	Original Function	Simplified Function
2	$y = \dfrac{1 - x^2}{1 - x}$	$y = 1 + x$
3	$y = \dfrac{1 - x^3}{1 - x}$	$y = 1 + x + x^2$
4	$y = \dfrac{1 - x^4}{1 - x}$	
5		
6		

 ## 10.2 Writing Exercise

The rational expression $\dfrac{x^3 + 3x^2 - 4x - 12}{x^3 + 2x^2 - 9x - 18}$ simplifies to $\dfrac{x - 2}{x - 3}$. Prove to yourself that this is so. The original expression has more restricted values than the simplified expression. Determine what the restricted values are for both expressions. Finally, discuss the implications of this difference in restricted values for the two ex-

pressions. If you simplify a rational expression, which should you use as the restricted values in the domain of the function, those from the simplified expression or those from the original expression? Explain the reasons for your answer.

10.3 ADDITION AND SUBTRACTION OF RATIONAL EXPRESSIONS

OBJECTIVES

1 Add and subtract rational expressions with like denominators.

2 Determine the least common denominator for a set of rational expressions.

3 Write equivalent rational expressions, using the least common denominator as the new denominator.

4 Add and subtract rational expressions with unlike denominators.

5 Model real-world situations by using expressions involving addition and subtraction of rational expressions.

APPLICATION

Julio travels from City A to City B at an average rate of 40 miles per hour. He makes the return trip at an average rate of 60 miles per hour. Determine his average rate for the round-trip.

After completing this section, we will discuss this application further. See page 809.

Objective 10.3.1   Adding and Subtracting Rational Expressions with Like Denominators

Now that we can multiply rational expressions, we are ready to add and subtract them. To add or subtract numeric fractions with like denominators, we add or subtract the numerators in order to obtain the numerator of the answer. The denominator of the answer is the like denominator. We simplify the result if necessary. For example,

$$\frac{3}{10} + \frac{1}{10} = \frac{3+1}{10} = \frac{4}{10} = \frac{2}{2} \cdot \frac{2}{5} = 1 \cdot \frac{2}{5} = \frac{2}{5}$$

$$\frac{3}{10} - \frac{1}{10} = \frac{3-1}{10} = \frac{2}{10} = \frac{2}{2} \cdot \frac{1}{5} = 1 \cdot \frac{1}{5} = \frac{1}{5}$$

We use the same procedure for adding and subtracting rational expressions.

$$\frac{2x}{5y} + \frac{x^2}{5y} = \frac{2x+x^2}{5y} = \frac{x(2+x)}{5y}$$

$$\frac{7ab}{2a} - \frac{-3a^2}{2a} = \frac{7ab-(-3a^2)}{2a} = \frac{7ab+3a^2}{2a}$$

$$= \frac{a(7b+3a)}{2a} = \frac{a}{a} \cdot \frac{7b+3a}{2} = \frac{7b+3a}{2}$$

ADDING AND SUBTRACTING RATIONAL EXPRESSIONS WITH LIKE DENOMINATORS

To add rational expressions,

- Add the numerators.
- Use the like denominator for the denominator of the sum, as in

$$\frac{A}{B} + \frac{C}{B} = \frac{A + C}{B}$$

where A, B, and C are polynomials with $B \neq 0$.

To subtract rational expressions,

- Subtract the numerators.
- Use the like denominator for the denominator of the difference, as in

$$\frac{A}{B} - \frac{C}{B} = \frac{A - C}{B}$$

where A, B, and C are polynomials with $B \neq 0$.

Remember to simplify the answer if possible.

EXAMPLE 1

Add or subtract and simplify.

a. $\dfrac{2x}{x + 3} + \dfrac{6}{x + 3}$ **b.** $\dfrac{3x}{3x^2 - 13x + 14} - \dfrac{7}{3x^2 - 13x + 14}$

c. $\dfrac{x + 4}{x^2 + 3x - 4} - \dfrac{x - 1}{x^2 + 3x - 4}$

Solution

a. $\dfrac{2x}{x + 3} + \dfrac{6}{x + 3} = \dfrac{2x + 6}{x + 3}$ Add numerators.

$$= \frac{2(x + 3)}{x + 3}$$ Factor.

$$= 2$$ Simplify.

b. $\dfrac{3x}{3x^2 - 13x + 14} - \dfrac{7}{3x^2 - 13x + 14}$

$$= \frac{3x - 7}{3x^2 - 13x + 14}$$ Subtract numerators.

$$= \frac{3x - 7}{(3x - 7)(x - 2)}$$ Factor.

$$= \frac{1}{x - 2}$$ Simplify.

The check is left for you.

c. $\dfrac{x + 4}{x^2 + 3x - 4} - \dfrac{x - 1}{x^2 + 3x - 4}$

$$= \frac{(x + 4) - (x - 1)}{x^2 + 3x - 4}$$ Subtract numerators.

$$= \frac{5}{x^2 + 3x - 4}$$

The check is left for you.

Numeric Check

X	Y₁	Y₂
-3	2	ERROR
-2	2	2
-1	2	2
0	2	2
1	2	2
2	2	2
3	2	2

X = -3

$Y1 = 2$

$Y2 = \dfrac{2x}{x + 3} + \dfrac{6}{x + 3}$

Note that all Y1 and Y2 values are equal for the x-values in the domain of the functions.

TAKE NOTE Be careful when subtracting numerators with more than one term. It is helpful to use parentheses to group the numerators, as in Example 1c.

✓ Objective 10.3.1 *CHECKUP*

1. Add or subtract and simplify.

a. $\dfrac{3x}{x+7} + \dfrac{21}{x+7}$

b. $\dfrac{x+5}{2x^2+5x-12} + \dfrac{x-8}{2x^2+5x-12}$

c. $\dfrac{2x+7}{x^2+3x-18} - \dfrac{x+7}{x^2+3x-18}$

2. What must be true before you can add or subtract rational expressions?

3. After adding or subtracting rational expressions, what should you do to the result (in addition to checking your work)?

Objective 10.3.2 **Determining the Least Common Denominator**

In order to add or subtract numeric fractions, we must verify that the fractions have like denominators. If they do not, we must change them to equivalent fractions with a common denominator. The **least common denominator (LCD)** is the smallest number of which each denominator is a factor. That is, the LCD is the smallest number divisible by each of the denominators.

To determine the least common denominator of a set of fractions, first factor each of the denominators into its prime factors. Next, write a product consisting of each different denominator factor, using the largest exponent that occurred for each factor.

For example, determine the LCD of $\frac{7}{12}$ and $\frac{1}{30}$.

Factor the denominators.

$$12 = 2^2 \cdot 3$$
$$30 = 2 \cdot 3 \cdot 5$$

The different denominator factors are 2, 3, and 5; the greatest exponent of 2 is 2, of 3 is 1, and of 5 is 1.

Multiply.

$$LCD = 2^2 \cdot 3 \cdot 5 = 60$$

We use the same procedure for finding the LCD of rational expressions.

For example, determine the least common denominator of $\dfrac{7x}{8xy^3}$ and $\dfrac{3z}{20x^2y}$.

Factor the denominators.

$$8xy^3 = 2^3 \cdot x \cdot y^3$$
$$20x^2y = 2^2 \cdot 5 \cdot x^2 \cdot y$$

The different denominator factors are 2, 5, x, and y. The greatest exponent of 2 is 3, of 5 is 1, of x is 2, and of y is 3.

Multiply.

$$LCD = 2^3 \cdot 5 \cdot x^2 \cdot y^3 = 40x^2y^3$$

DETERMINING THE LEAST COMMON DENOMINATOR

To determine the least common denominator of a set of rational expressions,

- Factor each denominator into its prime factors.
- Write a product consisting of each different factor, using the greatest exponent that occurs for each.

EXAMPLE 2   Determine the least common denominator in each of the following sets of rational expressions:

a. $\dfrac{3x}{x + 3}$ and $\dfrac{2x}{x + 2}$

b. $\dfrac{x + 5}{4x^2 - 9}$ and $\dfrac{3x - 1}{2x^2 - x - 3}$

c. $\dfrac{2}{x - 2}$ and $\dfrac{-2}{-x + 2}$

Solution

a. $\dfrac{3x}{x + 3}$ and $\dfrac{2x}{x + 2}$

The denominators do not factor. Therefore, we use both denominators as factors for the LCD.

$$\text{LCD} = (x + 3)(x + 2)$$

There is no need to multiply these factors.

b. $\dfrac{x + 5}{4x^2 - 9}$ and $\dfrac{3x - 1}{2x^2 - x - 3}$

Factor the denominators.

$$4x^2 - 9 = (2x + 3)(2x - 3)$$
$$2x^2 - x - 3 = (2x - 3)(x + 1)$$
$$\text{LCD} = (2x + 3)(2x - 3)(x + 1)$$

c. $\dfrac{2}{x - 2}$ and $\dfrac{-2}{-x + 2}$

Notice that the denominators are opposites. Therefore, either denominator may be considered the LCD.

$$\text{LCD} = x - 2 \quad \text{or} \quad \text{LCD} = -x + 2 \qquad \blacksquare$$

✓ Objective 10.3.2 *CHECKUP*

1. Determine the least common denominator in each set of rational expressions.

    a. $\dfrac{5}{x + 4}$ and $\dfrac{7x}{x - 5}$

    b. $\dfrac{x - 1}{25x^2 - 1}$ and $\dfrac{2x + 5}{15x^2 - 2x - 1}$

    c. $\dfrac{7}{x - 5}$ and $\dfrac{8}{5 - x}$

2. What is the meaning of the word *least* in relation to finding the least common denominator of a set of rational expressions?

3. To find the least common denominator of a set of rational expressions, you should first factor the expressions into prime factors. What is the meaning of the word *prime*?

Objective 10.3.3

Writing Equivalent Rational Expressions with the LCD

Now that we can determine the LCD of a set of rational expressions, we are ready to change the expressions to equivalent expressions, with the LCD as the new denominator of each. We use the multiplication identity property to do this.

Recall the procedure for writing equivalent numeric fractions. First, we must determine the factor needed to multiply the original denominator in order to obtain the new denominator. Next, we multiply the original numeric fraction by a factor of 1 (using the needed factor as the numerator and denominator).

For example, write a numeric fraction equivalent to $\frac{3}{4}$, but with a denominator of 20.

$$\frac{3}{4} = \frac{?}{20}$$ Since $20 = 4 \cdot 5$, we need a factor of 5.

$$\frac{3}{4} = \frac{3}{4} \cdot \frac{5}{5} = \frac{15}{20}$$ Multiply by a factor of 1, $\frac{5}{5}$.

We use the same procedure to write equivalent rational expressions. For example, write a rational number equivalent to $\frac{7x}{8xy^3}$, but with a denominator of $40x^2y^3$.

$$\frac{7x}{8xy^3} = \frac{?}{40x^2y^3}$$

Factor the denominators.

$$40x^2y^3 = 2^3 \cdot 5 \cdot x^2 \cdot y^3$$
$$8xy^3 = 2^3 \cdot \quad x \cdot y^3$$

 TAKE NOTE It is easier to see the "needed" factors if we arrange the factors in the same order, leaving a space for the missing factors, such as 5.

The given denominator, $8xy^3$, must be multiplied by $5x$ to obtain the desired denominator, $40x^2y^3$.

$$\frac{7x}{8xy^3} \cdot \frac{5x}{5x} = \frac{35x^2}{40x^2y^3}$$

DETERMINING EQUIVALENT RATIONAL EXPRESSIONS

To determine an equivalent rational expression,

- Factor the denominator of the original rational expression and the new desired denominator (LCD).
- Determine the factors needed to multiply the original denominator to obtain the desired denominator.
- Multiply the original rational expression by a factor of 1, using the factors found in the preceding step as the numerator and denominator.

EXAMPLE 3   Write an equivalent rational expression with the given LCD.

a. $\dfrac{3x}{x + 3}$; LCD $= x^2 + 5x + 6$

b. $\dfrac{x + 5}{4x^2 - 9}$; LCD $= 4x^4 + 4x^3 - 9x^2 - 9x$

c. $\dfrac{2}{x - 2}$; LCD $= 2 - x$

Solution

a. $\dfrac{3x}{x+3}$; LCD $= x^2 + 5x + 6$

Factor the denominators.

$$x^2 + 5x + 6 = (x+3)(x+2)$$
$$x + 3 \qquad\quad = x + 3 \qquad\qquad \text{\textit{x + 3 does not factor.}}$$

The given denominator must be multiplied by $(x+2)$ to obtain the desired denominator.

$$\frac{3x}{x+3} \cdot \frac{x+2}{x+2} = \frac{3x^2 + 6x}{x^2 + 5x + 6}$$

b. $\dfrac{x+5}{4x^2-9}$; LCD $= 4x^4 + 4x^3 - 9x^2 - 9x$

Factor the denominators.

$$4x^4 + 4x^3 - 9x^2 - 9x = x(2x+3)(2x-3)(x+1)$$
$$4x^2 - 9 \qquad\qquad = (2x+3)(2x-3)$$

The given denominator must be multiplied by $x(x+1)$ to obtain the desired denominator.

$$\frac{x+5}{4x^2-9} \cdot \frac{x(x+1)}{x(x+1)} = \frac{x^3 + 6x^2 + 5x}{4x^4 + 4x^3 - 9x^2 - 9x}$$

c. $\dfrac{2}{x-2}$; LCD $= 2 - x$

The denominators do not factor. However, they are opposites. Therefore, the given denominator must be multiplied by -1 to obtain the desired denominator.

$$\frac{2}{x-2} \cdot \frac{-1}{-1} = \frac{-2}{-x+2} \quad \text{or} \quad \frac{-2}{2-x} \qquad \blacksquare$$

✓ **Objective 10.3.3 CHECKUP**

1. Write an equivalent rational expression with the given least common denominator.

a. $\dfrac{2x}{x+5}$; LCD $= x^2 + 9x + 20$

b. $\dfrac{2x+1}{x^2-16}$; LCD $= x^3 + 7x^2 - 16x - 112$

c. $\dfrac{7}{x-5}$; LCD $= 5x - x^2$

Objective 10.3.4

Adding and Subtracting Rational Expressions with Unlike Denominators

To add or subtract numeric fractions with unlike denominators, we change the fractions to equivalent fractions with like denominators and add or subtract. For example, to add $\frac{7}{12} + \frac{1}{30}$, we use the LCD, 60, that we found earlier.

$$\frac{7}{12} + \frac{1}{30} = \frac{7}{12} \cdot \frac{5}{5} + \frac{1}{30} \cdot \frac{2}{2} \qquad \text{\textit{Change to like denominators.}}$$

$$= \frac{35}{60} + \frac{2}{60}$$

$$= \frac{37}{60} \qquad\qquad\qquad \text{\textit{Add numerators.}}$$

We use the same procedure to add and subtract rational expressions. For example,

$$\frac{7x}{8xy^3} + \frac{3x^2}{20x^2y} = \frac{7x}{8xy^3} \cdot \frac{5x}{5x} + \frac{3x^2}{20x^2y} \cdot \frac{2y^2}{2y^2} \qquad \text{Change to like denominators. We found the LCD, } 40x^2y^3, \text{ earlier.}$$

$$= \frac{35x^2}{40x^2y^3} + \frac{6x^2y^2}{40x^2y^3}$$

$$= \frac{35x^2 + 6x^2y^2}{40x^2y^3} \qquad \text{Add numerators.}$$

$$= \frac{35 + 6y^2}{40y^3} \cdot \frac{x^2}{x^2} \qquad \text{Simplify.}$$

$$= \frac{35 + 6y^2}{40y^3}$$

ADDING AND SUBTRACTING RATIONAL EXPRESSIONS WITH UNLIKE DENOMINATORS

To add rational expressions,

- Change the rational expressions to equivalent expressions with like denominators.
- Add the numerators.
- Use the like denominator for the denominator of the sum, as in

$$\frac{A}{B} + \frac{C}{B} = \frac{A + C}{B}$$

where A, B, and C are polynomials with $B \neq 0$.

To subtract rational expressions,

- Change the rational expressions to equivalent expressions with like denominators.
- Subtract the numerators.
- Use the like denominator for the denominator of the difference, as in

$$\frac{A}{B} - \frac{C}{B} = \frac{A - C}{B}$$

where A, B, and C are polynomials with $B \neq 0$.

Remember to simplify the answer if possible.

EXAMPLE 4   Add or subtract and simplify.

a. $\dfrac{3x}{x + 3} + \dfrac{2x}{x + 2}$

b. $\dfrac{5}{x + 4} + \dfrac{x - 4}{x^2 + 8x + 16}$

c. $\dfrac{2}{x - 2} + \dfrac{2}{2 - x}$

d. $\dfrac{x + 5}{4x^2 - 9} - \dfrac{x - 1}{2x^2 - x - 3}$

e. $\dfrac{x}{x + 3} - \dfrac{2x}{x - 3} + \dfrac{x^2 + 10x + 3}{x^2 - 9}$

Solution

a. $\dfrac{3x}{x+3} + \dfrac{2x}{x+2}$

Neither denominator factors. LCD $= (x+3)(x+2)$. Multiply the first rational expression by $\frac{x+2}{x+2}$ and the second rational expression by $\frac{x+3}{x+3}$.

$$= \dfrac{3x(x+2)}{(x+3)(x+2)} + \dfrac{2x(x+3)}{(x+2)(x+3)}$$

$$= \dfrac{3x^2 + 6x}{(x+3)(x+2)} + \dfrac{2x^2 + 6x}{(x+2)(x+3)} \qquad \text{Multiply each numerator.}$$
$$\text{Do not multiply the denominator.}$$

$$= \dfrac{5x^2 + 12x}{(x+3)(x+2)} \qquad \text{Add numerators.}$$

$$= \dfrac{x(5x+12)}{(x+3)(x+2)} \qquad \text{Factor.}$$

Numeric Check

X	Y₁	Y₂
-3	ERROR	ERROR
-2	ERROR	ERROR
-1	-3.5	-3.5
0	0	0
1	1.4167	1.4167
2	2.2	2.2
3	2.7	2.7

X= -3

$$Y1 = \dfrac{x(5x+12)}{(x+3)(x+2)}$$

$$Y2 = \dfrac{3x}{x+3} + \dfrac{2x}{x+2}$$

For all x-values in the domain of the functions, Y1 = Y2.

b. $\dfrac{5}{x+4} + \dfrac{x-4}{x^2 + 8x + 16} = \dfrac{5}{x+4} + \dfrac{x-4}{(x+4)^2} \qquad \text{Factor the denominators.}$

The largest power of the common factor, $x+4$, is 2. Therefore, LCD $= (x+4)^2$. Multiply the first expression by $\frac{x+4}{x+4}$.

$$= \dfrac{5(x+4)}{(x+4)(x+4)} + \dfrac{x-4}{(x+4)^2}$$

$$= \dfrac{5x+20}{(x+4)^2} + \dfrac{x-4}{(x+4)^2} \qquad \text{Multiply.}$$

$$= \dfrac{6x+16}{(x+4)^2} \qquad \text{Add numerators.}$$

$$= \dfrac{2(3x+8)}{(x+4)^2} \qquad \text{Factor to simplify.}$$

The check is left for you.

c. $\dfrac{2}{x-2} + \dfrac{2}{2-x}$

The denominators do not factor. However, they are opposites: $x-2$ and $2-x$. Therefore, either denominator may be used as the LCD. We will use $x-2$. Multiply the second expression by $\frac{-1}{-1}$.

$$= \dfrac{2}{x-2} + \dfrac{2(-1)}{(2-x)(-1)}$$

$$= \dfrac{2}{x-2} + \dfrac{-2}{x-2} \qquad \text{Multiply.}$$

$$= \dfrac{2-2}{x-2} \qquad \text{Subtract numerators.}$$

$$= \dfrac{0}{x-2} = 0 \qquad \text{Simplify.}$$

The check is left for you.

d. $\dfrac{x + 5}{4x^2 - 9} - \dfrac{x - 1}{2x^2 - x - 3} = \dfrac{(x + 5)}{(2x + 3)(2x - 3)} - \dfrac{(x - 1)}{(2x - 3)(x + 1)}$

Factor the denominators.

$$4x^2 - 9 = (2x + 3)(2x - 3)$$
$$2x^2 - x - 3 = (2x - 3)(x + 1)$$

LCD $= (2x + 3)(2x - 3)(x + 1)$. Multiply the first expression by $\frac{x + 1}{x + 1}$ and the second expression by $\frac{2x + 3}{2x + 3}$.

$= \dfrac{(x + 5)(x + 1)}{(2x + 3)(2x - 3)(x + 1)} - \dfrac{(x - 1)(2x + 3)}{(2x - 3)(x + 1)(2x + 3)}$

$= \dfrac{x^2 + 6x + 5}{(2x + 3)(2x - 3)(x + 1)} - \dfrac{2x^2 + x - 3}{(2x - 3)(x + 1)(2x + 3)}$ Multiply.

$= \dfrac{(x^2 + 6x + 5) - (2x^2 + x - 3)}{(2x + 3)(2x - 3)(x + 1)}$ Subtract numerators.

$= \dfrac{x^2 + 6x + 5 - 2x^2 - x + 3}{(2x + 3)(2x - 3)(x + 1)}$

$= \dfrac{-x^2 + 5x + 8}{(2x + 3)(2x - 3)(x + 1)}$ Simplify.

The check is left for you.

e. $\dfrac{x}{x + 3} - \dfrac{2x}{x - 3} + \dfrac{x^2 + 10x + 3}{x^2 - 9} = \dfrac{x}{x + 3} - \dfrac{2x}{x - 3} + \dfrac{x^2 + 10x + 3}{(x + 3)(x - 3)}$

Factor the denominators. LCD $= (x + 3)(x - 3)$. Multiply the first expression by $\frac{x - 3}{x - 3}$ and the second expression by $\frac{x + 3}{x + 3}$.

$= \dfrac{x(x - 3)}{(x + 3)(x - 3)} - \dfrac{2x(x + 3)}{(x - 3)(x + 3)} + \dfrac{x^2 + 10x + 3}{(x + 3)(x - 3)}$

$= \dfrac{x^2 - 3x}{(x + 3)(x - 3)} - \dfrac{2x^2 + 6x}{(x - 3)(x + 3)} + \dfrac{x^2 + 10x + 3}{(x + 3)(x - 3)}$ Multiply.

$= \dfrac{(x^2 - 3x) - (2x^2 + 6x) + (x^2 + 10x + 3)}{(x + 3)(x - 3)}$ Subtract and add numerators.

$= \dfrac{x^2 - 3x - 2x^2 - 6x + x^2 + 10x + 3}{(x + 3)(x - 3)}$

$= \dfrac{x + 3}{(x + 3)(x - 3)}$ Simplify.

$= \dfrac{1}{x - 3}$ Simplify.

The check is left for you.

✓ Objective 10.3.4 *CHECKUP*

1. Add or subtract and simplify.

a. $\dfrac{2x}{x - 3} + \dfrac{5x}{x - 8}$ **b.** $\dfrac{5}{x - 4} - \dfrac{3}{4 - x}$

c. $\dfrac{x}{x^2 + 10x + 21} + \dfrac{3}{x^2 + 8x + 15}$

d. $\dfrac{x}{x - 4} - \dfrac{3}{x + 4} + \dfrac{6x}{x^2 - 16}$

Objective 10.3.5   ## Modeling the Real World

Geometric formulas are often written as rational expressions. For example, the area of a rectangle is $A = LW$, where L is the rectangle's length and W is its width. We can solve for L to obtain $L = \dfrac{A}{W}$, which is a rational expression. This formula is useful for modeling practical situations in which you want to determine the dimensions of some rectangular object with a given area.

EXAMPLE 5   Two rectangular bins are arranged side by side, as shown in the figures that follow. The area of the smaller bin is 25 square feet and the area of the larger bin is 36 square feet. Determine the total length of the two bins in terms of the width W using the formula $L = \dfrac{A}{W}$.

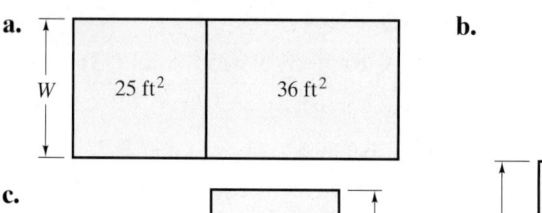

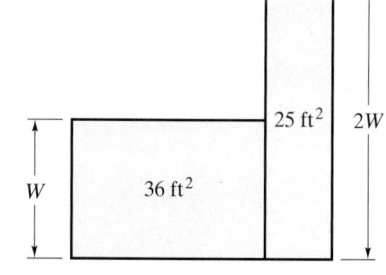

Solution

a. The length of the smaller bin is $\dfrac{25}{W}$ feet. The length of the larger bin is $\dfrac{36}{W}$ feet. The total length is $\dfrac{25}{W} + \dfrac{36}{W} = \dfrac{61}{W}$ feet.

b. The length of the smaller bin is $\dfrac{25}{2W}$ feet. The length of the larger bin is $\dfrac{36}{W}$ feet. The total length is $\dfrac{25}{2W} + \dfrac{36}{W} = \dfrac{25}{2W} + \dfrac{72}{2W} = \dfrac{97}{2W}$ feet.

c. The length of the smaller bin is $\dfrac{25}{W}$ feet. The length of the larger bin is $\dfrac{36}{W + 10}$ feet. The total length is $\dfrac{25}{W} + \dfrac{36}{W + 10} = \dfrac{25W + 250}{W(W + 10)} + \dfrac{36W}{W(W + 10)} = \dfrac{61W + 250}{W(W + 10)}$ feet. ■

EXAMPLE 6   Margaret breaks her leg during her vacation and requires surgery. She wants to have the surgery at home. The hospital she is in is 3 miles from the airport. The flight home is 625 miles. The air attendant states that the average speed of a plane is three times the average speed of ground transportation in an ambulance.

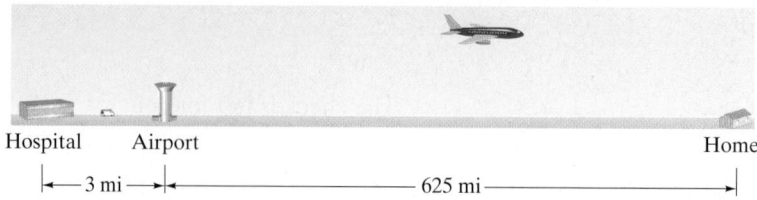

a. Write a function $T(x)$ for the total time traveled to arrive at Margaret's home airport.

b. Graph the function.

c. If the ambulance's speed from the hospital to the airport was 65 mph, estimate, to the nearest hundredth of an hour, the total time traveled to Margaret's home airport.

d. If Margaret travels 4 hours to reach her home airport, estimate, to the nearest mile per hour, the average speed of the ambulance from the hospital to the airport.

Solution

a. Let $x =$ the average speed of the ambulance
$3x =$ the average speed of the plane

Since $t = \dfrac{d}{r}$, we determine the following from the problem:

$$\dfrac{3}{x} = \text{time traveled by the ambulance}$$

$$\dfrac{625}{3x} = \text{time traveled by the plane}$$

The total time traveled is the sum of the two times, or $T(x) = \dfrac{3}{x} + \dfrac{625}{3x}$.

b. $Y1 = \dfrac{3}{x} + \dfrac{625}{3x}$

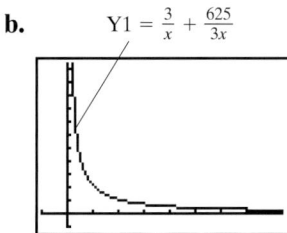

$(-10, 84, -10, 114)$

c. Evaluate $T(65)$. According to the graph, when x is 65, $T(x)$ is approximately 3.25.

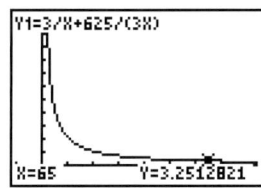

$(-10, 84, -10, 114)$

The total time traveled is approximately 3.25 hours when the ambulance speed is 65 mph.

d. Trace the calculator graph. When $T(x)$ is 3.987 or approximately 4, x is approximately 53.

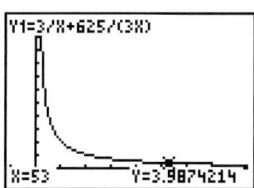

$(-10, 84, -10, 114)$

The average ambulance speed is approximately 53 mph when the total time traveled is 4 hours. ■

APPLICATION

Julio travels from City A to City B at an average rate of 40 miles per hour. He makes the return trip at an average rate of 60 miles per hour. Determine his average rate for the round-trip.

Discussion

Let $x =$ the distance between City A and City B
$x + x = 2x =$ the total distance traveled for the round-trip

Since $t = \dfrac{d}{r}$, we can determine the time traveled.

$$\dfrac{x}{40} = \text{the time traveled from City } A \text{ to City } B$$

$$\dfrac{x}{60} = \text{the time traveled from City } B \text{ to City } A$$

$$\dfrac{x}{40} + \dfrac{x}{60} = \text{the total time traveled}$$

$$\dfrac{x}{40} + \dfrac{x}{60} = \dfrac{3x}{120} + \dfrac{2x}{120} \qquad \text{LCD is 120.}$$

$$= \dfrac{5x}{120}$$

$$= \dfrac{x}{24}$$

The average rate for the entire trip is given by the total distance traveled divided by the total time traveled.

$$2x \div \dfrac{x}{24} = \dfrac{2\overset{1}{\cancel{x}}}{1} \cdot \dfrac{24}{\underset{1}{\cancel{x}}}$$

$$= 48$$

The average rate of travel for the round-trip was 48 miles per hour. Note that this is in contrast to the average of the two speeds, or 50 miles per hour.

Objective 10.3.5 **CHECKUP**

1. a. The width of a rectangle is given by $\dfrac{x-1}{5x}$ yards, and its length is given by $\dfrac{x+1}{3x}$ yards. Find an expression for the perimeter of the rectangle.

b. A second rectangle has a width given by $\dfrac{x+1}{2x}$ yards and a length given by $\dfrac{3x+2}{x}$ yards. Find an expression for its perimeter.

c. Find the difference between the two perimeters.

2. A trucking company makes a delivery 270 miles away. The truck travels 60 miles on rural roads and 210 miles on interstate highways. The average speed of the truck on the interstate is 10 miles per hour less than twice its average speed on the rural roads.

a. Letting x be the average speed on the rural roads, write a function $T(x)$ for the total time of the delivery trip.

b. Graph the function on your calculator.

c. If the average speed on the rural road was 35 mph, use the graph to estimate to the nearest tenth of an hour the total time of the delivery trip.

d. If the total time of the trip was 6 hours, use the graph to find the average speed on the rural roads, and calculate the average speed on the interstate.

3. A plane travels against the wind at an average speed of 200 mph. For the return trip traveling with the wind, the plane averages 300 mph. Determine the average speed of the plane for the round-trip.

10.3 EXERCISES

 Student Solutions Manual   PH Math/Tutor Center   CD Video Math**XL** MathXL® **MyMathLab** MyMathLab   Interactmath.com

In exercises 1–92, add or subtract and simplify.

1. $\dfrac{5}{x} + \dfrac{8}{x}$

2. $\dfrac{3}{x} + \dfrac{9}{x}$

3. $\dfrac{2x}{5xy} + \dfrac{3x}{5xy}$

4. $\dfrac{b}{4ab} + \dfrac{3b}{4ab}$

5. $\dfrac{x-1}{x+6} + \dfrac{x+1}{x+6}$

6. $\dfrac{x-5}{x+12} + \dfrac{2x+5}{x+12}$

7. $\dfrac{2b}{b^2-25} + \dfrac{10}{b^2-25}$

8. $\dfrac{21}{z^2-49} + \dfrac{3z}{z^2-49}$

9. $\dfrac{x-5}{x+3} + \dfrac{x+5}{x+3} + \dfrac{x+9}{x+3}$

10. $\dfrac{x-2}{2x+1} + \dfrac{3x+1}{2x+1} + \dfrac{4x+5}{2x+1}$

11. $\dfrac{4}{d} - \dfrac{9}{d}$

12. $\dfrac{3}{b} - \dfrac{11}{b}$

13. $\dfrac{9xy}{7x^2y} - \dfrac{2xy}{7x^2y}$

14. $\dfrac{2xy}{5xy^2} - \dfrac{7xy}{5xy^2}$

15. $\dfrac{2x-3}{x+9} - \dfrac{x-3}{x+9}$

16. $\dfrac{5x-4}{x+8} - \dfrac{2x-1}{x+8}$

17. $\dfrac{4x-13}{x-5} - \dfrac{2x-3}{x-5}$

18. $\dfrac{3x+5}{x-6} - \dfrac{x+17}{x-6}$

19. $\dfrac{x+3}{x+11} - \dfrac{2x-8}{x+11}$

20. $\dfrac{x+2}{x+13} - \dfrac{3x-7}{x+13}$

21. $\dfrac{z^2}{z+4} - \dfrac{16}{z+4}$

22. $\dfrac{c^2}{c+7} - \dfrac{49}{c+7}$

23. $\dfrac{3c}{c^2-9} - \dfrac{9}{c^2-9}$

24. $\dfrac{5b}{b^2-4} - \dfrac{10}{b^2-4}$

25. $\dfrac{5x+1}{2x+3} - \dfrac{x+2}{2x+3} - \dfrac{2x-5}{2x+3}$

26. $\dfrac{2x+5}{3x-4} - \dfrac{x+4}{3x-4} - \dfrac{3x-2}{3x-4}$

27. $\dfrac{5}{x} + \dfrac{8}{-x}$

28. $\dfrac{3}{-x} + \dfrac{9}{x}$

29. $\dfrac{3x-2}{x-5} + \dfrac{x+8}{5-x}$

30. $\dfrac{x+4}{7-x} + \dfrac{4x-17}{x-7}$

31. $\dfrac{a^2}{a-3} + \dfrac{9}{3-a}$

32. $\dfrac{25}{5-c} + \dfrac{c^2}{c-5}$

33. $\dfrac{5x}{x^2-9} + \dfrac{15}{9-x^2}$

34. $\dfrac{3x-4}{x^2-1} + \dfrac{3-4x}{1-x^2}$

35. $\dfrac{3}{2x} + \dfrac{7}{6x^2}$

36. $\dfrac{9}{5x^2} + \dfrac{3}{10x^3}$

37. $\dfrac{3x+1}{x-6} + \dfrac{x-4}{2x-12}$

38. $\dfrac{2x-3}{x+9} + \dfrac{x+2}{2x+18}$

39. $\dfrac{2x}{2x-3} + \dfrac{6x+9}{4x^2-9}$

40. $\dfrac{2x-1}{5x+2} + \dfrac{4-10x}{25x^2-4}$

41. $\dfrac{7}{3x-5} + \dfrac{4}{3x+5}$

42. $\dfrac{5}{2x-3} + \dfrac{7}{2x+3}$

43. $\dfrac{7}{x-5} + \dfrac{x+1}{x^2-10x+25}$

44. $\dfrac{2}{x-8} + \dfrac{3x+4}{x^2-16x+64}$

45. $\dfrac{b+8}{b} + \dfrac{b}{b+8}$

46. $\dfrac{a-3}{2a} + \dfrac{2a}{a-3}$

47. $\dfrac{x-2}{4x+12} + \dfrac{2x+1}{x^2-9}$

48. $\dfrac{x-1}{x^2-4} + \dfrac{2x-1}{3x+6}$

49. $\dfrac{x+7}{x^2+2x-15} + \dfrac{8-x}{x^2+9x+20}$

50. $\dfrac{3}{x^2+8x+7} + \dfrac{4-x}{x^2+5x-14}$

51. $\dfrac{3a-b}{a^2b} + \dfrac{a+2b}{ab^2}$

52. $\dfrac{p-q}{pq^2} + \dfrac{p+q}{p^2q}$

53. $\dfrac{3x}{x-2y} + \dfrac{4y}{2y-x}$

54. $\dfrac{x}{5x-y} + \dfrac{3y}{y-5x}$

55. $\dfrac{5x+2y}{x^2-9y^2} + \dfrac{6}{x+3y}$

56. $\dfrac{2x+y}{4x^2-9y^2} + \dfrac{7}{2x-3y}$

57. $\dfrac{8}{x^2+6xz+9z^2} + \dfrac{2}{x^2-9z^2}$

58. $\dfrac{5}{x^2-4y^2} + \dfrac{3}{x^2+4xy+4y^2}$

59. $\dfrac{7x+5}{x-2} - \dfrac{x-1}{2-x}$

60. $\dfrac{2x-3}{x-7} - \dfrac{x+4}{7-x}$

61. $\dfrac{3x}{x^2-4} - \dfrac{6}{4-x^2}$

62. $\dfrac{5a}{a^2-36} - \dfrac{30}{36-a^2}$

63. $\dfrac{6x-3}{3x+15} - \dfrac{x-1}{x+5}$

64. $\dfrac{3x+7}{2x+3} - \dfrac{x+4}{6x+9}$

65. $\dfrac{7}{2x-5} - \dfrac{9}{2x+5}$

66. $\dfrac{9}{3x-1} - \dfrac{4}{3x+1}$

67. $\dfrac{6}{x^2+12x+36} - \dfrac{2x+1}{x+6}$

68. $\dfrac{3}{x^2-14x+49} - \dfrac{x-4}{x-7}$

69. $\dfrac{x}{8-x} - \dfrac{8-x}{x}$

70. $\dfrac{x-10}{x} - \dfrac{x}{x-10}$

71. $\dfrac{x+2}{3x+12} - \dfrac{x-4}{x^2-16}$

72. $\dfrac{7}{x^2-9} - \dfrac{9}{x^2+3x}$

73. $\dfrac{11}{b^2-9} - \dfrac{7}{2b^2-b-15}$

74. $\dfrac{14}{a^2-25} - \dfrac{9}{2a^2-9a-5}$

75. $\dfrac{7}{5ab^2} - \dfrac{15}{10a^2b} - \dfrac{3}{2b}$

76. $\dfrac{5}{16x^2y} - \dfrac{2}{24xy} - \dfrac{7}{6xy^2}$

77. $\dfrac{4p-q}{p+3q} - \dfrac{p+2q}{p+3q}$

78. $\dfrac{2x-z}{x+5z} - \dfrac{x-4z}{x+5z}$

79. $\dfrac{7}{x^2+6xy+9y^2} - \dfrac{2}{x^2-9y^2}$

80. $\dfrac{8}{x^2+10xy+25y^2} - \dfrac{3}{x^2-25y^2}$

81. $\dfrac{x}{x+5} - \dfrac{4}{x-5} + \dfrac{10x}{x^2-25}$

82. $\dfrac{6z}{z^2-81} - \dfrac{3}{z-9} + \dfrac{2z}{z+9}$

83. $1 + \dfrac{x-9}{x+10}$

84. $3 + \dfrac{x}{3x+1}$

85. $5 - \dfrac{4}{2x+7}$

86. $1 - \dfrac{x}{x+4}$

87. $\dfrac{2x-3}{x+7} - 1$

88. $\dfrac{5x+8}{9x-2} - 4$

89. $\dfrac{3}{x+3} + x + 5$

90. $x + 3 + \dfrac{2}{x+1}$

91. $2x + 1 - \dfrac{3}{x-4}$

92. $\dfrac{5x}{4x-1} - 5x$

Geometry

93. In **Figure 10.2a**, the smaller rectangle has an area of 20 square feet, and the larger rectangle has an area of 45 square feet. Given the lengths shown, find an expression for the sum of the two widths of the rectangles in terms of L. Repeat the exercise for **Figure 10.2b**.

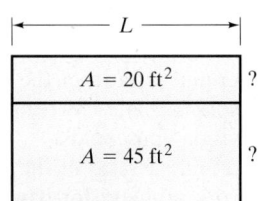

Figure 10.2a   Figure 10.2b

94. In **Figure 10.3a**, the smaller rectangular box has a volume of 60 cubic inches, while the larger rectangular box has a volume of 200 cubic inches. Given the lengths shown, find an expression for the difference in the two widths in terms of L. Repeat the exercise for **Figure 10.3b**.

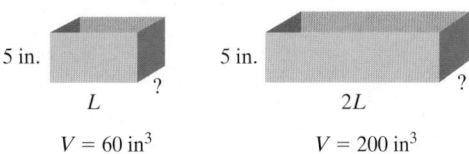

$V = 60 \text{ in}^3$ $V = 200 \text{ in}^3$

Figure 10.3a

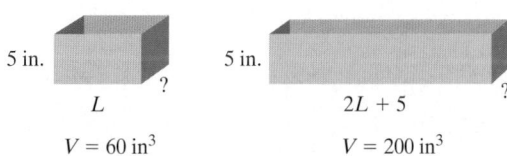

$V = 60 \text{ in}^3$ $V = 200 \text{ in}^3$

Figure 10.3b

95. The width of a rectangle is given by $\dfrac{24}{x-1}$ feet, and its length is given by $\dfrac{72}{x+1}$ feet. Find an expression for the perimeter of the rectangle.

96. The base of a trapezoid measures $\dfrac{60}{x+3}$ inches, its top measures $\dfrac{42}{x+3}$ inches, and its sides measure $\dfrac{9}{x}$ inches and $\dfrac{21+x}{2x}$ inches. Find an expression for the perimeter of the trapezoid.

Distance

97. Joey has entered an amateur triathlon competition. One leg of the race is a 26-mile stretch in which he will run. Another leg of the race is a 110-mile stretch in which he will bicycle. Joey figures that he can bike 20 miles per hour faster than he can run.
  a. Letting x be his average running speed, write a function for the total time it will take Joey to complete the two legs of the race.
  b. Graph the function.
  c. If Joey's average running speed is 9 miles per hour, use the graph to estimate, to the nearest tenth of an hour, the total time to complete the two legs of the race.
  d. If the total time to complete the two legs of the race is 8 hours, use the graph to estimate Joey's average running speed, and then determine his biking speed.

98. In Joey's amateur triathlon competition, another leg of the competition is a swim race. For this competition, he must swim 1 mile upriver and then return. The speed of the river current is 2 miles per hour.
  a. Letting x be Joey's swimming speed in still water, write a function for the total time it will take him to swim up the river and back.
  b. Graph the function in the window $(0, 9.4, 1, 0, 6.2, 1, 1)$.
  c. If Joey's swimming speed in still water is 2.5 mph, how long will it take him to complete this leg of the competition? Round your answer to the nearest tenth of an hour.

  d. If Joey wants to complete the swimming leg of the competition in 1.5 hours, how fast should he be able to swim in still water?

99. A boat travels upriver at an average speed of 25 mph and returns downriver at an average speed of 35 mph. Determine the average speed of the boat for the entire round-trip.

100. One member of a speed ski team averaged 125 mph down the slopes. The other member of the team averaged 100 mph down the slopes. Determine the average speed for the team for both runs down the slopes.

Physics

101. When an object moves around a circle with its acceleration directed toward the center of the circle, this centripetal acceleration can be given by the formula $a = \dfrac{v^2}{r}$, where v is velocity and r is the radius of the circle. Find the sum of accelerations of two bodies in which the first has velocity 5 meters per second on circle of radius r, and the second has velocity 3 meters per second on a circle with radius two more than five times the radius of the smaller circle.

102. Mass of a body, m, refers to its inertia, while weight of a body, w, is the force due to gravity and can vary with location. The two are related by the formula $w = \dfrac{m}{g}$, where g is acceleration due to gravity. The weight for one body of mass 5 kilograms and acceleration due to gravity of g is added to the weight for another body whose mass is 7 kilograms at a place where acceleration due to gravity is three more than twice g. What is the sum?

103. Angular acceleration is defined to be the change in angular velocity over time. If the change of angular velocity for one body is $(w - 5)$ in time t and the change of angular velocity for another body is 9 in time $(t + 7)$, find the difference between these angular accelerations.

104. Centripetal force, F, is related to centripetal acceleration and is given by the formula $F = \dfrac{mv^2}{r}$, where m is mass, v is velocity, and r is the radius of the circle. Find the difference in the forces of two objects in which one has mass 0.8 kilogram, velocity 10 meters per second on circle of radius r, and the other has mass 0.3 kilogram, velocity 20 meters per second on a circle with radius two less than that of the first circle.

Real Data

105. The number of viewing shares for network affiliates for all television households can be estimated by the function $T(x) = -2.5x^2 + 4.5x + 40$, where x is the number of years after 2000. The number of shares for network affiliates for all cable households can be estimated by the function $C(x) = -2.5x^2 + 5.5x + 34$, and the number of shares for network affiliates for all pay cable households by $P(x) = -3x^2 + 7x + 31$, where x is the number of years after 2000.
  a. Determine a ratio of the number of viewing shares for network affiliates for cable households to those for all television households.
  b. Determine a ratio of the number of viewing shares for network affiliates for pay cable households to those for all television households.
  c. Find the sum of the ratios in part **a** and part **b**.

106. The amount of U.S. energy production in quadrillion Btu's can be estimated by $P(x) = -0.105x^2 + 0.065x + 71.22$, where x is the number of years after 2000. The amount of production from coal in quadrillion Btu's can be approximated by $C(x) = -0.39x + 23.48$. The amount of production of nuclear electric power quadrillion Btu's can be approximated by $N(x) = -0.17x + 8.48$.

a. Determine a ratio of the amount of production from coal to the U.S. energy production, where x is the number of years after 2000.

b. Determine a ratio of the amount of production from nuclear electric power to the U.S. energy production, where x is the number of years after 2000.

c. Find the difference in the ratios in part **a** and part **b**.

In exercises 107 and 108, we discuss a PE ratio. The PE ratio (price-earnings ratio) is a measure of valuation of individual stocks. To calculate the PE ratio, divide the price per share (market value) of a stock by its yearly earnings per share.

107. For one particular stock in the toy industry, its price per share can be estimated by the function $P(x) = 9.31x + 27.27$, where x is the number of years after 2004, and its earnings per share can be estimated by $E(x) = 0.35x + 1.9$. For another stock in the same industry, its price per share can be estimated by the function $P(x) = 12.18x + 14.81$, where x is the number of years after 2004, and its earnings per share can be estimated by $E(x) = 0.26x + 0.96$.

a. Write a function for the PE ratio for each of the two stocks.

b. Find the difference between the two PE ratio functions.

108. For one particular stock in the computer industry, its price per share can be estimated by the function $P(x) = 6.38x + 23.82$, where x is the number of years after 2004, and its earnings per share can be estimated by $E(x) = 0.13x + 1.29$. For another stock in the same industry, its price per share can be estimated by the function $P(x) = 30.59x + 14.85$, where x is the number of years after 2004, and its earnings per share can be estimated by $E(x) = 0.21x + 1.41$.

a. Write a function for the PE ratio for each of the two stocks.

b. Find the difference between the two PE ratio functions.

10.3 Calculator Exercise

In this section, you were shown how to check your addition and subtraction of rational functions by using the table (numeric-check) feature of your calculator. One problem that often occurs in doing this is that a student will incorrectly place parentheses when storing the original expressions and the simplified expressions into the calculator.

As an example, suppose you were checking the simplification $\frac{3x + 2}{x + 1} + \frac{2x + 3}{x + 1} = 5$.

When you enter the left expression, be sure to place parentheses around both numerators and both denominators. If you fail to do so, the table will not indicate equivalence. The only time that you can key in a numerator or a denominator without parentheses is when there is no mathematical operation contained within the expression. Even then, it is a safety measure to always enclose

numerators and denominators in parentheses. Also, when the numerator or denominator is a product of expressions in parentheses, you must use an additional pair of parentheses to enclose the entire product.

Practice checking the following equivalent expressions:

1. $\dfrac{x + 4}{2x} + \dfrac{3x - 4}{2x} = 2$

2. $\dfrac{5}{3 - x} - \dfrac{x - 8}{x - 3} = -1$

3. $\dfrac{3x - 5}{2x + 1} + \dfrac{4x + 7}{2x + 1} = \dfrac{7x + 2}{2x + 1}$

4. $\dfrac{4}{x + 3} - \dfrac{5}{x + 2} = \dfrac{-x - 7}{(x + 3)(x + 2)}$

5. $\dfrac{x + 1}{x^2 - x - 6} + \dfrac{2x - 1}{x^2 + 5x + 6} = \dfrac{3x^2 - 3x + 6}{(x - 3)(x + 2)(x + 3)}$

10.3 Writing Exercise

Part 1.

Many mathematical models use rational expressions to explain the behavior of physical objects. Listed here are several simple mathematical models that use rational expressions:

1. If two resistors R_1 and R_2 (measured in ohms) are connected in parallel, then the combined resistance R_T (in ohms) is given by $\dfrac{1}{R_T} = \dfrac{1}{R_1} + \dfrac{1}{R_2}$.

2. The combined capacitance C of two capacitors C_1 and C_2 connected in series is given by $\dfrac{1}{C} = \dfrac{1}{C_1} + \dfrac{1}{C_2}$.

3. If two blood vessels share common endpoints (connected in parallel), and if r_1 and r_2 are the resistances of the two vessels to the flow of blood (measured in dynes), then the combined resistance of the vessels is given by $\dfrac{1}{r} = \dfrac{1}{r_1} + \dfrac{1}{r_2}$.

4. The force F required to stretch a spring is given by $F = kx$, where x is the distance the spring stretches and k is the spring

constant of the spring. If two springs with spring constants k_1 and k_2 are connected in sequence, the spring constant K of the combination is given by $\dfrac{1}{K} = \dfrac{1}{k_1} + \dfrac{1}{k_2}$.

5. The focal length f of a lens is related to the distances q and p from the lens of the object and of the image by the formula $\dfrac{1}{f} = \dfrac{1}{p} + \dfrac{1}{q}$.

6. If two lenses with focal lengths f_1 and f_2 are placed in contact with one another, the focal length of the combination is given by $\dfrac{1}{f} = \dfrac{1}{f_1} + \dfrac{1}{f_2}$.

Search in the library for a reference that discusses one of these applications. Or, if you prefer, find a reference on another mathematical model that involves rational expressions. Describe the model you find. If the reference contains an example that uses the model, summarize the example in a brief written report. Be sure to include the title, author, publisher, and call number of the reference you found.

Part 2.

Now that you know how to add, subtract, multiply, and divide rational expressions, you should be able to figure out the steps needed to simplify a complex rational expression. Suppose you were asked to simplify the expression, $\dfrac{\dfrac{2}{x} + \dfrac{x}{2}}{\dfrac{y}{3} - \dfrac{3}{y}}$. List the steps you would follow to do this.

Hints: Can you simplify the numerator? What about the denominator? Can you rewrite the expression as a division exercise?

Now see if you can use your steps to simplify the following expressions:

1. $\dfrac{\dfrac{3xy}{2z^2}}{\dfrac{9x^3y}{8z}}$

2. $\dfrac{2x + \dfrac{1}{x}}{5x}$

3. $\dfrac{\dfrac{a+b}{a-b}}{\dfrac{a^2 + 2ab + b^2}{a^2 - b^2}}$

4. $\dfrac{\dfrac{2x}{5} - \dfrac{5}{x}}{\dfrac{2x}{5} + \dfrac{1}{15x}}$

5. $\dfrac{\dfrac{1}{a^2} + \dfrac{2}{ab}}{\dfrac{3}{ab^2} + \dfrac{1}{b}}$

10.4 SOLVING RATIONAL EQUATIONS IN ONE VARIABLE

OBJECTIVES

1. Identify rational equations in one variable.
2. Solve rational equations algebraically.
3. Differentiate between a rational equation and a rational expression.
4. Model real-world situations by using rational equations.

APPLICATION

First constructed by the Greek mathematician Euclid, the golden section can be determined by dividing a line segment into two lengths so that the shorter length, s, is to the longer length, l, as the longer length, l, is to the whole, $s + l$. Renaissance writers called this the "divine proportion." A rectangle with sides of s and l, a golden rectangle, is thought to be most pleasing to the eye. The golden rectangle is found in the design of temples, pyramids, and artwork.

a. Write a proportion for a golden rectangle in terms of its shorter side, s, and its longer side, l.

b. Find the dimensions of a golden rectangle if the shorter side is 8 inches.

After completing this section, we will discuss this application further. See page 822.

Objective 10.4.1   Rational Equations in One Variable

A **rational equation in one variable**, or, simply, **rational equation**, is an equation that can be written in the form of a rational expression, containing one variable, that is equal to 0. We are now ready to solve such equations.

STANDARD FORM FOR A RATIONAL EQUATION IN ONE VARIABLE

A rational equation in one variable is written in the form

$$R(x) = 0$$

where $R(x)$ is a rational expression.

For example, the following are rational equations in one variable:

$$\frac{2}{x} = \frac{x}{8} \qquad \text{Standard form, } \frac{2}{x} - \frac{x}{8} = 0$$

$$\frac{x+2}{x+1} = \frac{x+1}{x} \qquad \text{Standard form, } \frac{x+2}{x+1} - \frac{x+1}{x} = 0$$

$$\frac{5}{x} + \frac{x-5}{3x} - \frac{x^2-9}{x+3} = 0 \qquad \text{Standard form}$$

EXAMPLE 1   Determine whether each equation is rational.

a. $3x^2 + 5x^6 - 7x^3 = 0$ **b.** $6x^{-2} + 8 - 7x^{-3} = 12$ **c.** $x^{3/4} = 2x^2$

Solution

a. $3x^2 + 5x^6 - 7x^3 = 0$ is a polynomial equation, but it is also a rational equation, because each term can be written as a rational expression with a denominator of 1.

$$\frac{3x^2}{1} + \frac{5x^6}{1} - \frac{7x^3}{1} = 0$$

b. $6x^{-2} + 8 - 7x^{-3} = 12$ is a rational equation, because an expression that contains a variable with a negative integer exponent can be written as a rational expression.

$$6x^{-2} = \frac{6}{x^2} \quad \text{and} \quad 7x^{-3} = \frac{7}{x^3}$$

Therefore, $\dfrac{6}{x^2} + 8 - \dfrac{7}{x^3} - 12 = 0$.

c. $x^{3/4} = 2x^2$ is not a rational equation, because an expression containing a variable base with a fractional exponent cannot be written as a rational expression. ■

 Objective 10.4.1 CHECKUP

1. Determine whether each equation is rational.
  a. $4z^2 - 3z - 1 = 0$ **b.** $a + 2 = a^{1/2}$
  c. $3m^{-2} + 4m^{-1} = -6$

2. Explain the difference between a rational equation and a rational expression. ■

Objective 10.4.2

Solving Rational Equations Algebraically

In previous chapters, we solved linear and quadratic equations numerically and graphically. The same procedures are used to solve rational equations numerically and graphically. We will use these procedures to check our solutions when we solve rational equations algebraically.

We are now ready to solve rational equations in one variable algebraically. We have already solved linear equations with fractional coefficients. To simplify these equations, we applied the multiplication property of equations. The multiplication property of equations states that if both sides of an equation are multiplied by the same nonzero expression, the result is an equivalent equation. We used this property to clear the fractions by multiplying by the least common denominator of all the fractions. For example, solve $\dfrac{1}{2}x + \dfrac{3}{4}x = \dfrac{2}{3}x + 7$.

$$\frac{1}{2}x + \frac{3}{4}x = \frac{2}{3}x + 7 \qquad \text{\small The LCD is 12.}$$

$$12\left(\frac{1}{2}x + \frac{3}{4}x\right) = 12\left(\frac{2}{3}x + 7\right) \qquad \text{\small Multiply by 12.}$$

$$\overset{6}{\cancel{12}}\left(\frac{1}{2}x\right) + \overset{3}{\cancel{12}}\left(\frac{3}{4}x\right) = \overset{4}{\cancel{12}}\left(\frac{2}{3}x\right) + 12(7) \qquad \text{\small Distribute 12.}$$

$$6x + 9x = 8x + 84$$
$$15x = 8x + 84$$
$$7x = 84 \qquad \text{\small Subtract 8x.}$$
$$x = 12 \qquad \text{\small Divide by 7.}$$

We use the same procedure for rational equations. However, we need to be aware of the restricted values for the equation.

SOLVING A RATIONAL EQUATION ALGEBRAICALLY

To solve a rational equation in one variable algebraically,

- Determine the restricted values for the equation.
- Multiply both sides of the equation by the least common denominator of all the terms.
- Solve the resulting equation.
- Discard any solutions that are restricted values.

Check the solution by substituting or by solving numerically or graphically.

EXAMPLE 2   Solve $\dfrac{2}{x} + \dfrac{4}{2x} = \dfrac{3}{x} + 1$.

Algebraic Solution

$$\frac{2}{x} + \frac{4}{2x} = \frac{3}{x} + 1 \qquad \text{The restricted value is 0. The LCD is 2x.}$$

$$2x\left(\frac{2}{x} + \frac{4}{2x}\right) = 2x\left(\frac{3}{x} + 1\right) \qquad \text{Multiply by 2x.}$$

$$2x\left(\frac{2}{x}\right) + 2x\left(\frac{4}{2x}\right) = 2x\left(\frac{3}{x}\right) + 2x(1) \qquad \text{Distribute 2x.}$$

$$4 + 4 = 6 + 2x$$

$$8 = 6 + 2x$$

$$2 = 2x \qquad \text{Subtract 6.}$$

$$1 = x \qquad \text{Divide by 2.}$$

Substitution Check

$$\frac{2}{x} + \frac{4}{2x} = \frac{3}{x} + 1$$

$$\frac{2}{1} + \frac{4}{2(1)} \;\bigg|\; \frac{3}{1} + 1$$

$$2 + 2 \;\bigg|\; 3 + 1$$

$$4 \;\bigg|\; 4$$

The solution is 1, because when 1 is substituted for x, the resulting expressions are equal.

Numeric Check

X	Y1	Y2
-3	-1.333	0
-2	-2	-.5
-1	-4	-2
0	ERROR	ERROR
1	4	4
2	2	2.5
3	1.3333	2

X= -3

$$Y1 = \frac{2}{x} + \frac{4}{2x}$$

$$Y2 = \frac{3}{x} + 1$$

The solution is 1, because this value results in Y1 = Y2.

Graphic Check

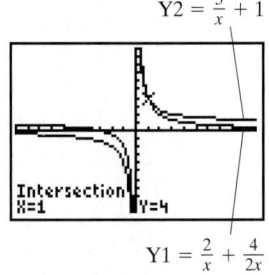

$(-10, 10, -10, 10)$

The intersection is $(1,4)$. The solution is 1.

EXAMPLE 3   Solve.

a. $\dfrac{a}{a-2} = \dfrac{a+1}{a-3}$

b. $x^{-2} - 2 = 2$

c. $1 - \dfrac{4}{x+2} = \dfrac{2x}{x+2}$

d. $\dfrac{2}{x+3} - \dfrac{x+1}{x^2+5x+6} = \dfrac{4}{x^2-4}$

Algebraic Solution

a.
$$\frac{a}{a-2} = \frac{a+1}{a-3}$$

Restricted values are 2 and 3. The LCD is $(a-2)(a-3)$.

$$\cancel{(a-2)}(a-3)\left(\frac{a}{a-2}\right) = (a-2)\cancel{(a-3)}\left(\frac{a+1}{a-3}\right)$$

Multiply by the LCD.

$$(a-3)a = (a-2)(a+1)$$

Simplify.

$$a^2 - 3a = a^2 - a - 2$$

Simplify.

$$-2a = -2$$

Subtract a^2 and add a.

$$a = 1$$

Divide by -2.

Numeric Check

Since the solution is an integer, check by solving numerically. Substitute x for a.

X	Y1	Y2
-3	.6	.33333
-2	.5	.2
-1	.33333	0
0	0	-.3333
1	-1	-1
2	ERROR	-3
3	3	ERROR

X= -3

$$Y1 = \frac{x}{x-2}$$
$$Y2 = \frac{x+1}{x-3}$$

The solution is 1, because this value results in $Y1 = Y2$.

b.
$$x^{-2} - 2 = 2$$

$$\frac{1}{x^2} - 2 = 2$$

Rewrite without the negative exponent. The restricted value is 0. The LCD is x^2.

$$x^2\left(\frac{1}{x^2} - 2\right) = 2x^2$$

Multiply by x^2.

$$\cancel{x^2}\left(\frac{1}{\cancel{x^2}}\right) - 2x^2 = 2x^2$$

Distribute x^2.

$$1 - 4x^2 = 0$$

Subtract $2x^2$.

$$(1 + 2x)(1 - 2x) = 0$$

Factor.

$$1 + 2x = 0 \quad \text{or} \quad 1 - 2x = 0$$

Use the zero factor property.

$$x = -\frac{1}{2} \qquad\qquad x = \frac{1}{2}$$

Solve.

Graphic Check

Check by graphing on a calculator decimal screen.

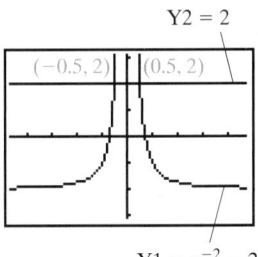

$Y2 = 2$

$(-0.5, 2)$ $(0.5, 2)$

$Y1 = x^{-2} - 2$

$(-4.7, 4.7, -3.1, 3.1)$

The intersections are $(-0.5, 2)$ and $(0.5, 2)$. The solutions are -0.5 and 0.5 or $-\frac{1}{2}$ and $\frac{1}{2}$.

c.
$$1 - \frac{4}{x+2} = \frac{2x}{x+2}$$

The restricted value is -2. The LCD is $(x+2)$.

$$(x+2)\left(1 - \frac{4}{x+2}\right) = (x+2)\left(\frac{2x}{x+2}\right)$$

Multiply by the LCD.

$$(x+2)(1) - \cancel{(x+2)}\left(\frac{4}{\cancel{x+2}}\right) = \cancel{(x+2)}\left(\frac{2x}{\cancel{x+2}}\right)$$

Distribute the LCD.

$$x + 2 - 4 = 2x$$

$$x - 2 = 2x$$

$$-2 = x$$

Subtract x.

Numeric Check

X	Y1	Y2
-3	5	6
-2	ERROR	ERROR
-1	-3	-2
0	-1	0
1	-.3333	.66667
2	0	1
3	.2	1.2

X= -3

$$Y1 = 1 - \frac{4}{x+2}$$

$$Y2 = \frac{2x}{x+2}$$

Note that when $x = -2$, Y1 and Y2 are undefined.

We determined that -2 is a restricted value. Therefore, it cannot be a solution.

We call -2 an **extraneous solution**. This is the reason it is very important to determine the restricted values for the equation first. The given equation has no solution.

d. $\dfrac{2}{x+3} - \dfrac{x+1}{x^2+5x+6} = \dfrac{4}{x^2-4}$

Factor each denominator.
Restricted values are
-3, -2, and 2.

Numeric Check

$X = -3$

$$\frac{2}{x+3} - \frac{x+1}{(x+3)(x+2)} = \frac{4}{(x+2)(x-2)}$$

$$(x+2)(x-2)(x+3)\left(\frac{2}{x+3} - \frac{x+1}{(x+3)(x+2)}\right)$$

$$= (x+2)(x-2)(x+3)\left(\frac{4}{(x+2)(x-2)}\right)$$

Multiply by the LCD,
$(x+2)(x-2)(x+3)$.

$$(x+2)(x-2)\cancel{(x+3)}\left(\frac{2}{\cancel{x+3}}\right) - \cancel{(x+2)}(x-2)\cancel{(x+3)}\left(\frac{x+1}{\cancel{(x+3)}\,\cancel{(x+2)}}\right)$$

$X = 1$

$$= \cancel{(x+2)}\cancel{(x-2)}(x+3)\left(\frac{4}{\cancel{(x+2)}\,\cancel{(x-2)}}\right)$$

Distribute the LCD.

$$Y1 = \frac{2}{x+3} - \frac{x+1}{x^2+5x+6}$$

$$Y2 = \frac{4}{x^2-4}$$

$$(x+2)(x-2)2 - (x-2)(x+1) = (x+3)4$$

$$(2x^2-8) - (x^2-x-2) = 4x+12$$

$$x^2+x-6 = 4x+12$$

$$x^2-3x-18 = 0$$

Subtract 4x and 12.

$$(x-6)(x+3) = 0$$

Factor.

$$x-6 = 0 \quad \text{or} \quad x+3 = 0$$

Use the zero factor property.

$$x = 6 \qquad\qquad x = -3$$

Solve.

Note that when $x = -3$, Y1 is not defined. Therefore -3 is an extraneous solution. When $x = 6$, Y1 = Y2. The solution is 6.

The solution is 6. The value -3 is a restricted value and not a solution. ■

An alternative method may be used to solve Example 3a. The rational equation to be solved, $\dfrac{a}{a-2} = \dfrac{a+1}{a-3}$, consists of two expressions, each of which is an algebraic fraction: $\dfrac{a}{a-2}$ and $\dfrac{a+1}{a-3}$. This special type of rational equation is called a **proportion**. To solve a proportion, we can equate the cross products; that is, we multiply the numerator of one fraction and the denominator of the other fraction and solve the remaining equation.

$$\frac{a}{a-2} \bowtie \frac{a+1}{a-3}$$

$$a(a-3) = (a+1)(a-2)$$

Equate the cross products.

$$a^2-3a = a^2-a-2$$

Note: This is the same as the equation in the previous solution.

$$-3a = -a-2$$

Subtract a^2 from both sides.

$$-2a = -2$$

Add a to both sides.

$$a = 1$$

Divide both sides by -2.

Some rational equations are contradictions and have no solution. Other rational equations are identities and have an infinite number of solutions. We determine these situations algebraically the same way as we did for linear and quadratic equations.

EXAMPLE 4 Solve.

a. $\dfrac{3x-15}{6+3x} = \dfrac{x-10}{x+2}$

b. $\dfrac{3}{x} = \dfrac{6}{2x}$

Algebraic Solution

a.
$$\frac{3x - 15}{6 + 3x} = \frac{x - 10}{x + 2}$$ The restricted value is -2.

$$\frac{3x - 15}{3(2 + x)} = \frac{x - 10}{x + 2}$$ Factor the denominators.

$$3(x + 2)\left(\frac{3x - 15}{3(2 + x)}\right) = 3(x + 2)\left(\frac{x - 10}{x + 2}\right)$$ Multiply by the LCD, $3(x + 2)$.

$$3x - 15 = 3x - 30$$

$$-15 = -30$$ Subtract 3x.

Since $-15 \neq -30$, the equation is a contradiction. It has no solution.

b.
$$\frac{3}{x} = \frac{6}{2x}$$ The restricted value is 0.

$$3(2x) = 6x$$ Equate the cross products.

$$6x = 6x$$ Subtract 6x.

$$0 = 0$$

Since $0 = 0$, the equation is an identity. The solution set is the set of all real numbers not equal to 0. (0 is the restricted value for the equation.)   ■

ALGEBRAIC SOLUTIONS OF RATIONAL EQUATIONS

To solve a rational equation algebraically, determine the restricted values, multiply both sides of the equation by the LCD of all fractional terms, and solve the resulting equation. One of three possibilities will occur.

One or more solutions exist.

No solution exists. The solution process results in a contradiction.

An infinite number of solutions exist. The solution set is the set of all real numbers not equal to the restricted values. The solution process results in an identity.

Objective 10.4.2 *CHECKUP*

Solve exercises 1–3 and check.

1. $\dfrac{7}{2x} + \dfrac{3}{x} = 2 - \dfrac{3}{2x}$

2. a. $\dfrac{2x}{x - 3} = \dfrac{6}{x - 3} + 1$ **b.** $\dfrac{x + 2}{x - 3} - \dfrac{15}{x^2 - x - 6} = \dfrac{2}{x - 3}$

   c. $\dfrac{m}{m - 3} = \dfrac{m + 2}{m + 1}$ **d.** $2x^{-2} - 1 = 1$

3. a. $\dfrac{x - 10}{x - 1} = \dfrac{10 - 2x}{2 - 2x}$ **b.** $\dfrac{6}{3x + 3} = \dfrac{2}{x + 1}$

4. How can you tell whether a rational equation has extraneous solutions?

5. In solving a rational equation algebraically, how can you tell whether the equation has no solutions?

6. In solving a rational equation algebraically, how can you tell whether the equation has all real numbers as solutions, excluding restricted values?

■

Objective 10.4.3   Differentiating between Expressions and Equations

One of the most common mistakes made in dealing with the topics of this chapter is a student becoming confused between simplifying a rational expression and solving a rational equation.

$$\text{Equation}\quad \frac{2}{x} + \frac{3}{x} = 1$$

$$\text{Expression}\quad \frac{2}{x} + \frac{3}{x} - 1$$

Solve equation.	Simplify expression.

$$x\left(\frac{2}{x} + \frac{3}{x}\right) = x(1)$$

$$x\left(\frac{2}{x}\right) + x\left(\frac{3}{x}\right) = x$$

$$2 + 3 = x$$

$$5 = x$$

$$\frac{2}{x} + \frac{3}{x} - 1 = \frac{2}{x} + \frac{3}{x} - \frac{x}{x}$$

$$= \frac{5 - x}{x}$$

The solution of the equation is 5.

The simplification of the expression is $\dfrac{5 - x}{x}$.

Caution: Expressions multiplied by the LCD will not result in equivalent expressions.

$$\frac{2}{x} + \frac{3}{x} - 1 \neq x\left(\frac{2}{x} + \frac{3}{x} - 1\right)$$

$$\neq x\left(\frac{2}{x}\right) + x\left(\frac{3}{x}\right) - x(1)$$

$$\neq 2 + 3 - x$$

$$\neq 5 - x$$

This result is not equivalent to the simplification $\dfrac{5 - x}{x}$ previously found. Therefore, we cannot simplify a rational expression by multiplying it by the LCD.

 TAKE NOTE You can *solve* a rational *equation* by multiplying both sides by the LCD. However, you cannot *simplify* a rational *expression* by multiplying it by the LCD.

EXAMPLE 5   Determine which of the following is an equation and which an expression. Solve the given equation and simplify the given expression.

a. $\dfrac{x + 1}{x - 5} - \dfrac{x - 5}{x - 1}$ **b.** $\dfrac{x + 1}{x - 5} = \dfrac{x - 5}{x - 1}$

Solution

a. $\dfrac{x + 1}{x - 5} - \dfrac{x - 5}{x - 1}$ is an expression.

Simplify.

$$\frac{x + 1}{x - 5} - \frac{x - 5}{x - 1} = \frac{(x + 1)(x - 1)}{(x - 5)(x - 1)} - \frac{(x - 5)(x - 5)}{(x - 1)(x - 5)} \quad \text{LCD is } (x - 5)(x - 1).$$

$$= \frac{x^2 - 1}{(x - 5)(x - 1)} - \frac{x^2 - 10x + 25}{(x - 1)(x - 5)}$$

$$= \frac{(x^2 - 1) - (x^2 - 10x + 25)}{(x - 5)(x - 1)}$$

$$= \frac{x^2 - 1 - x^2 + 10x - 25}{(x - 5)(x - 1)}$$

$$= \frac{10x - 26}{(x - 5)(x - 1)}$$

$$= \frac{2(5x - 13)}{(x - 5)(x - 1)}$$

b. $\dfrac{x+1}{x-5} = \dfrac{x-5}{x-1}$ is an equation.

Solve.

$$\dfrac{x+1}{x-5} \overset{\text{?}}{=} \dfrac{x-5}{x-1}$$ The restricted values are 5 and 1.

$$(x+1)(x-1) = (x-5)(x-5)$$ Equate the cross products.

$$x^2 - 1 = x^2 - 10x + 25$$

$$-1 = -10x + 25$$

$$-26 = -10x$$

$$x = \dfrac{26}{10}$$

$$x = \dfrac{13}{5}$$

 Objective 10.4.3 CHECKUP

1. Determine which of the following is an equation and which an expression. Solve the given equation and simplify the given expression.

   a. $\dfrac{2x}{x-4} - 1 + \dfrac{9}{x-4}$ **b.** $\dfrac{2x}{x-4} - 1 = \dfrac{9}{x-4}$

2. Explain how you can tell the difference between a rational equation and a rational expression.

3. What mathematical operations can you perform on a rational expression?

4. What mathematical operations can you perform on a rational equation?

Objective 10.4.4

Modeling the Real World

Recall the simple-interest formula $I = PRT$, where I is the amount of simple interest, P is the amount of principal, R is the rate of interest, and T is the amount of time. When this formula is solved for the principal, it gives rise to the rational equation $P = \dfrac{I}{RT}$. This relationship is another example of writing rational expressions to model real-world situations.

EXAMPLE 6

At the end of a two-year investment of $2000, Chantell had earned simple interest of $125 on one investment and $130 on a second investment. She remembered that the second investment earned 0.25% higher interest than the first investment. What were the two simple-interest rates?

Algebraic Solution

Let x = interest rate of the first investment (in decimal form)

$x + 0.0025$ = interest rate of the second investment

The time T is two years.

The first investment interest was $125.

The second investment interest was $130.

Since $P = \dfrac{I}{RT}$,

$$P_1 = \dfrac{125}{x(2)}$$ First investment principal

$$P_2 = \dfrac{130}{(x+0.0025)2}$$ Second investment principal

The total principal was $2000. Therefore, $P_1 + P_2 = 2000$.

$$\frac{125}{x(2)} + \frac{130}{(x + 0.0025)2} = 2000$$

$$\frac{125}{2x} + \frac{130}{2x + 0.005} = 2000$$

$125(2x + 0.005) + 130(2x) = 2000(2x)(2x + 0.005)$ LCD $= 2x(2x + 0.005)$

$$250x + 0.625 + 260x = 8000x^2 + 20x$$

$$8000x^2 - 490x - 0.625 = 0$$ Write in standard form.

Use the quadratic formula to solve for x.
Let $a = 8000$, $b = -490$, and $c = -0.625$.

$$x = \frac{-b \pm \sqrt{b^2 - 4ac}}{2a}$$ Quadratic formula.

$$x = \frac{-(-490) \pm \sqrt{(-490)^2 - 4(8000)(-0.625)}}{2(8000)}$$

$$x = \frac{490 \pm \sqrt{240{,}100 + 20{,}000}}{16{,}000}$$

$$x = \frac{490 \pm \sqrt{260{,}100}}{16{,}000}$$

$$x = \frac{490 \pm 510}{16{,}000}$$

$$x = \frac{1000}{16{,}000} \quad \text{or} \quad x = \frac{-20}{16{,}000}$$

$$x = 0.0625 \quad \text{or} \quad x = -0.00125$$

Check these possible solutions graphically by using a window of $(0, 1.175, 0.1, 0, 3100, 100, 1)$.

The x-coordinate of the point of intersection of the graphs is the solution: 0.0625. The value -0.00125 is not a realistic solution.

Chantell earned an interest rate of 0.0625, or 6.25%, on the first investment and an interest rate of $0.0625 + 0.0025 = 0.65$, or 6.5%, on the second investment. ▪

Graphic Solution

Check graphically.

$Y2 = 2000$

Intersection
X=.0625   Y=2000

$$Y1 = \frac{125}{2x} + \frac{130}{2(x + 0.0025)}$$

$(0, 1.175, 0, 3100)$

The x-coordinate of the point of intersection of the graphs is the solution: 0.0625.

APPLICATION

First constructed by the Greek mathematician Euclid, the golden section can be determined by dividing a line segment into two lengths so that the shorter length, s, is to the longer length, l, as the longer length, l, is to the whole, $s + l$. Renaissance writers called this the "divine proportion." A rectangle with sides of s and l, a golden rectangle, is thought to be most pleasing to the eye. The golden rectangle is found in the designs of temples, pyramids, and artwork.

a. Write a proportion for a golden rectangle in terms of its shorter side, s, and its longer side, l.

b. Find the dimensions of a golden rectangle if the shorter side is 8 inches.

Discussion

a. The proportion is the shorter length, s, is to the longer length, l, as the longer length, l, is to the sum of the shorter length and the longer length, $s + l$.

$$\frac{\text{shorter length}}{\text{longer length}} = \frac{\text{longer length}}{\text{sum of the shorter and longer lengths}}$$

$$\frac{s}{l} = \frac{l}{s + 1}$$

b. Substitute 8 for s and solve for l.

$$\frac{s}{l} = \frac{l}{s + l}$$

$$\frac{8}{l} = \frac{l}{8 + l}$$ Substitute.

$$l \cdot l = 8(8 + l)$$ Equate cross products.

$$l^2 = 64 + 8l$$ Simplify.

$$l^2 - 8l - 64 = 0$$ Write in standard form.

$$l = \frac{-b \pm \sqrt{b^2 - 4ac}}{2a}$$ Quadratic formula

$$l = \frac{-(-8) \pm \sqrt{(-8)^2 - 4(1)(-64)}}{2(1)}$$ Substitute $a = 1$, $b = -8$, and $c = -64$.

$$l = \frac{8 \pm \sqrt{320}}{2}$$ Simplify.

$$l = \frac{8 \pm 8\sqrt{5}}{2}$$ $\sqrt{320} = \sqrt{64 \cdot 5} = 8\sqrt{5}$

$$l = \frac{2(4 \pm 4\sqrt{5})}{2}$$ Factor.

$$l = 4 \pm 4\sqrt{5}$$ Simplify.

$$l \approx 12.9, -4.9$$

The golden rectangle is 8 inches by $4 + 4\sqrt{5}$ inches (about 12.9 inches).

 Objective 10.4.4 **CHECKUP**

1. At the end of a three-year investment period, Akim earned $225 in simple interest. He also earned $225 on a second investment for a two-year period. The second investment offered a reduced interest rate, since the investment period was shorter. The simple-interest rate was 0.5% less than that for the longer period. If Akim invested a total of $4000 in the two investments, what were the two simple-interest rates?

2. The relationship between the sides of a golden rectangle is defined by the proportion $\frac{s}{l} = \frac{l}{s + l}$, where s is the length of the short side and l is the length of the long side. Find the dimensions of a golden rectangle if the longer side is 10 inches.

10.4 EXERCISES

 Student Solutions Manual   PH Math/Tutor Center   CD Video    MathXL®    MyMathLab   Interactmath.com

Determine whether each equation is rational.

1. $x^{-3} + 2x^{-2} - x^{-1} = 5$

2. $c^{-1/3} + 5 = 2c$

3. $\dfrac{1}{x + 7} + \dfrac{1}{x} = 5$

4. $\dfrac{1}{5 + x} = \dfrac{\sqrt{2x - 1}}{x^2}$

5. $v^{1/2} + 3v = 10$

6. $\dfrac{4.7}{x} - \dfrac{1.2}{x^2} = 2.6$

7. $\dfrac{\sqrt{2x + 7}}{x} = \dfrac{1}{3 - x}$

8. $\dfrac{\sqrt{5}}{2h^2} = 4 - \dfrac{\sqrt{3}}{h}$

9. $\dfrac{1}{3x^2} + \dfrac{5}{6x} = \dfrac{8}{9}$

10. $3x^{-2} = 5 + x^{-1}$

11. $\dfrac{\sqrt{3}}{x^2} + \dfrac{\sqrt{2}}{x} = 7$

12. $\dfrac{1}{4x + 1} + \dfrac{4}{3x} = 7$

Solve exercises 13–84 algebraically and check numerically, graphically, or by substitution.

13. $\dfrac{1}{a} = \dfrac{5}{9} + \dfrac{2}{3}$

14. $\dfrac{5}{7} - \dfrac{3}{b} = \dfrac{1}{3}$

15. $\dfrac{11}{x} - \dfrac{3}{4} = \dfrac{5}{8}$

16. $\dfrac{3}{x} = \dfrac{5}{8} - \dfrac{3}{4}$

17. $1 - \dfrac{8}{x} = \dfrac{10}{x}$

18. $1 - \dfrac{12}{x} = \dfrac{2}{x}$

19. $\dfrac{1}{2} = \dfrac{5}{2x} - \dfrac{6}{x}$

20. $\dfrac{1}{3} = \dfrac{3}{2x} - \dfrac{1}{x}$

21. $2 = \dfrac{6}{x-2}$

22. $3 = \dfrac{4}{x-5}$

23. $\dfrac{x-4}{2x+3} = \dfrac{5}{21}$

24. $\dfrac{x-1}{3x+2} = \dfrac{6}{13}$

25. $\dfrac{1}{x-6} = \dfrac{17}{2x+3}$

26. $\dfrac{17}{2x-5} = \dfrac{47}{4x+3}$

27. $\dfrac{8}{2x-3} + \dfrac{4}{x} = 0$

28. $\dfrac{17}{5x+2} - \dfrac{2}{x} = 0$

29. $\dfrac{2x+3}{x+4} = \dfrac{5}{x+4}$

30. $\dfrac{3x+1}{x+7} = \dfrac{4}{x-2}$

31. $\dfrac{16}{x} = x$

32. $\dfrac{81}{x} = x$

33. $\dfrac{z}{7} - \dfrac{7}{z} = 0$

34. $\dfrac{2}{y} = \dfrac{y}{32}$

35. $\dfrac{10}{k} + 3 = k$

36. $m = \dfrac{28}{m} - 3$

37. $\dfrac{x}{4} + \dfrac{4}{x} = 3 - \dfrac{4}{x}$

38. $\dfrac{x}{4} + \dfrac{1}{2x} = \dfrac{7}{4} \cdot \dfrac{1}{x}$

39. $\dfrac{y}{5} - \dfrac{21}{5y} = 1 + \dfrac{3}{y}$

40. $\dfrac{z}{5} - \dfrac{2}{z} = \dfrac{2}{5} + \dfrac{1}{z}$

41. $\dfrac{x+7}{x+9} = \dfrac{x}{x+1}$

42. $\dfrac{x+8}{x+4} = \dfrac{x+1}{x-1}$

43. $\dfrac{x-6}{x+5} = \dfrac{x-4}{3x+2}$

44. $\dfrac{x+3}{4x-1} = \dfrac{x+7}{1-4x}$

45. $x^{-1} + \dfrac{2}{3} = \dfrac{3}{5}$

46. $x^{-1} + \dfrac{3}{7} = \dfrac{5}{8}$

47. $x^{-2} - 6 = 3$

48. $x^{-2} + 3 = 19$

49. $1 - 4x^{-1} = 60x^{-2}$

50. $14x^{-2} = 1 + 5x^{-1}$

51. $\dfrac{9}{x-7} + 3 = \dfrac{2x-5}{x-7}$

52. $\dfrac{5}{x-5} + 4 = \dfrac{3x-10}{x-5}$

53. $\dfrac{x+2}{3} = \dfrac{x^2-x+7}{3x-6}$

54. $\dfrac{5x-2}{3} = \dfrac{5x^2+14x+2}{3x+9}$

55. $\dfrac{x-3}{x+4} = \dfrac{14}{x^2+6x+8}$

56. $\dfrac{z+4}{z+1} = \dfrac{30}{z^2-2z-3}$

57. $\dfrac{25}{p^2+p-12} = \dfrac{p+4}{p-3}$

58. $\dfrac{q+3}{q-4} = \dfrac{42}{q^2-2q-8}$

59. $\dfrac{m-2}{m+1} = \dfrac{7m+22}{m^2+6m+5}$

60. $\dfrac{x+6}{x-4} = \dfrac{5x-3}{x^2-7x+12}$

61. $\dfrac{1-4x}{1-x} + 2 = \dfrac{6x-3}{x-1}$

62. $\dfrac{2x-1}{x-1} - 1 = \dfrac{5x-7}{x-1} - 4$

63. $2 + \dfrac{z+2}{2z+1} = \dfrac{3z+6}{2z+1} + 1$

64. $\dfrac{x+5}{x-6} + \dfrac{1}{2} = \dfrac{3x+4}{2x-12}$

65. $\dfrac{1}{x+5} + \dfrac{21}{x^2-25} = 2$

66. $\dfrac{1}{x-9} + \dfrac{1}{8} = \dfrac{3}{x^2-81}$

67. $\dfrac{x+5}{x-3} = \dfrac{1+x}{2-x}$

68. $\dfrac{x+9}{x-2} = \dfrac{3+x}{7-x}$

69. $\dfrac{1}{x+3} + \dfrac{1}{x} = 2$

70. $\dfrac{1}{x+2} - \dfrac{1}{x} = 3$

71. $2w^{-3} + 2w^{-2} - w^{-1} = 1$

72. $15v^{-3} - 5v^{-2} + 1 = 3v^{-1}$

73. $\dfrac{1}{3u^2} + \dfrac{5}{6u} = \dfrac{8}{9}$

74. $\dfrac{3}{5x^2} + \dfrac{2}{x} = \dfrac{7}{11}$

75. $\dfrac{3}{x-5} + \dfrac{3}{x^2-25} = \dfrac{3x+1}{x^2-25}$

76. $\dfrac{3}{x+4} + \dfrac{2}{x+2} = \dfrac{5x+9}{x^2+6x+8}$

77. $\dfrac{3x+7}{x-1} = \dfrac{3x-3}{x-1}$

78. $\dfrac{1}{t+5} - \dfrac{1}{t+3} = \dfrac{-6}{t^2+8t+15}$

79. $\dfrac{b+4}{b-2} = \dfrac{b^2+3b-4}{b^2-3b+2}$

80. $\dfrac{x-5}{2x+3} = \dfrac{x^2-7x+10}{2x^2-x-6}$

81. $\dfrac{a-3}{a-1} + \dfrac{3}{a+1} = \dfrac{(a+3)(a-2)}{a^2-1}$

82. $\dfrac{5}{b-3} - \dfrac{2}{b^2-9} = \dfrac{5b+13}{b^2-9}$

83. $\dfrac{x}{2} - 1 + \dfrac{4}{x} = \dfrac{3}{2x} - \dfrac{1}{2}$

84. $x - 1 + \dfrac{2}{x} = \dfrac{1}{2} - \dfrac{1}{2x}$

85. To diversify her savings, Marianne placed part of her money into one account that paid her $286 simple interest for two years and the remainder in another account that paid her $117 simple interest for two years. The first account was able to offer her 2% more simple interest than the second account could. If she invested a total of $3500, what were the annual interest rates she received?

86. Roger invested some of his savings in an account that paid him 6% simple interest annually, amounting to $420. He invested other savings in an account that paid him 5% simple interest annually, amounting to $367.50. The money in the second account was invested for 18 months longer than that for the first account. What were the two time periods for the investments if the total invested in both accounts was $5600?

87. The maximum variable height (in feet) of an object viewed at a distance of 100 feet from a $\frac{1}{3}$-inch (3.6-millimeter) camera lens combined with an $x =$ millimeter focal length is given by $h(x) = \dfrac{360}{x}$. Determine the focal length needed to take a picture of a 6-foot-tall man.

88. The maximum variable height (in feet) of an object viewed at a distance of 200 feet from a $\frac{1}{4}$-inch (2.7-millimeter) camera lens combined with an $x =$ millimeter focal length is given by $h(x) = \dfrac{540}{x}$. Determine the focal length needed to take a picture of a billboard that is 18 feet high.

89. The relationship between the sides of a golden rectangle is defined by the proportion $\dfrac{s}{l} = \dfrac{l}{s + l}$, where s is the length of the short side and l is the length of the long side. Find the dimensions of the golden rectangle for the following:

a. $s = 7$ feet   **b.** $l = 13$ centimeters

90. An alternative definition for a golden rectangle with sides b and h is $\dfrac{b}{h} = \dfrac{h}{b - h}$. Find the dimensions of the golden rectangle for the following:

a. $h = 7$ feet   **b.** $b = 5$ inches

91. Another proportion for a golden rectangle is $\dfrac{a}{b} = \dfrac{a + b}{a}$, where the dimensions of the rectangle are $(a + b)$ and a. Find the dimensions of the golden rectangle for the following:

a. $a = 7$ feet   **b.** $b = 3$ meters

92. Still another proportion for a golden rectangle is $\dfrac{b}{a} = \dfrac{a}{a + b}$, where the dimensions of the rectangle are $(a + b)$ and a. Find the dimensions of the golden rectangle for the following:

a. $a = 7$ feet   **b.** $b = 3$ meters

In exercises 93 and 94, we discuss a PE ratio. The PE ratio (price-earnings ratio) is a measure of valuation of individual stocks. To calculate the PE ratio, divide the price per share (market value) of a stock by its yearly earnings per share.

93. The PE ratio for a toy manufacturer is given by the function $PE(x) = \dfrac{12.18x + 14.81}{0.26x + 0.96}$, where x is the number of years after 2004. Assuming trends continue, in what year will the ratio be 33.5?

94. The PE ratio for a computer company is given by the function $PE(x) = \dfrac{6.38x + 23.82}{0.13x + 1.29}$, where x is the number of years after 2004. Assuming trends continue, in what year will the ratio be 30?

95. Two blood vessels in a human body are connected in parallel. The combined resistance R of the blood vessels to the flow of blood is related to the resistances r_1 and r_2 of the individual vessels by the mathematical model $\dfrac{1}{R} = \dfrac{1}{r_1} + \dfrac{1}{r_2}$. If the combined resistance is 11.5 dynes and the resistance of the first vessel is 20.5 dynes, what is the resistance of the second vessel, to the nearest tenth of a dyne?

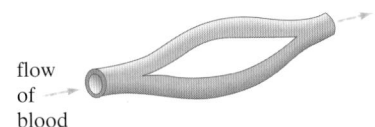

flow of blood

96. When two springs are connected in sequence, the spring constant of the combination K is related to the spring constants k_1 and k_2 of the individual springs by the mathematical model $\dfrac{1}{K} = \dfrac{1}{k_1} + \dfrac{1}{k_2}$. If the constant for the combination is 1.5 pounds per inch and the constant for the first spring is 6 pounds per inch, what is the constant for the second spring?

k_1

k_2

97. When an object moves around a circle with its acceleration directed toward the center of the circle, this centripetal acceleration can be given by the formula $a = \dfrac{v^2}{r}$, where v is velocity and r is the radius of the circle. Suppose that one body has velocity 5 meters per second on a circle of radius r and a second has velocity 3 meters per second on a circle with radius two more than five times the radius of the smaller circle. If the sum of the accelerations is 13.25, find each radius.

98. Centripetal force is related to centripetal acceleration and is given by the formula $F = m\dfrac{v^2}{r}$, where m is mass, v is velocity, and r is the radius of the circle. One object has mass 0.8 kilogram, velocity 10 meters per second on a circle of radius r, and the other has mass 0.3 kilogram, velocity 20 meters per second on a circle with radius two less than that of the first circle. If the sum of the forces is 6.5, find each radius.

99. The number of crimes committed in the United States can be estimated by $C(x) = 549x + 11{,}876{,}120$, where x is the number of years after 2000. The number of murders can be estimated by $M(x) = 167x + 15{,}870$. The number of robberies can be estimated by $R(x) = -2920x + 426{,}477$.

a. Determine the ratio of murders to the number of crimes committed, where x is the number of years after 2000.

b. Determine the ratio of robberies to the number of crimes committed, where x is the number of years after 2000.

c. In what year will the sum of these ratios be equal to 0.031?

100. The number of crimes committed in the United States can be estimated by $C(x) = 549x + 11{,}876{,}120$, where x is the number of years after 2000. The number of burglaries can be estimated by $B(x) = 35{,}344x + 2{,}081{,}187$. The number of property crimes can be estimated by $P(x) = 13{,}704x + 10{,}423{,}485$.

a. Determine the ratio of burglaries to the number of crimes committed, where x is the number of years after 2000.

b. Determine the ratio of property crimes to the number of crimes committed, where x is the number of years after 2000.

c. In what year will the ratio of property crimes to the number of crimes committed be 0.671 more than the ratio of burglaries to the number of crimes committed?

10.4 Calculator Exercises

The calculator contains a "solve" feature that can be used to find solutions of rational equations. To use this feature, first store the left side of the equation in Y1 and the right side of the equation in Y2. Then key in the expression

solve (Y1 − Y2, x, n)

where n is an initial guess close to where you might expect the solution to be, and "solve" is a function selected from the calculator's catalog of functions. The keystrokes used to solve the equation $\frac{7}{2x} + \frac{3}{x} = 2 - \frac{3}{2x}$ are as follows:

1. Store the two sides of the equation in Y1 and Y2.
   Press 2nd MODE (QUIT).
2. Enter 2nd 0 (CATALOG) and move the arrow down to the "solve(" line. Press ENTER .
3. Complete the parentheses by entering Y1 − Y2, x, n, and).

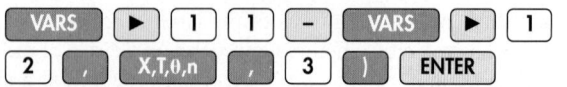

   Here, 3 is our initial guess at the solution. The calculator returns a 4, which is the actual solution.

Once you have entered these keystrokes, you can reuse them for a new equation without having to repeat them.

4. Change what you have stored in Y1 and Y2, using the new left-hand and right-hand expressions of the new equation. Press 2nd MODE (QUIT).
5. Press 2nd ENTER (ENTRY), which will repeat the "solve" instruction, and change the initial guess appropriately. Press ENTER , and the calculator will yield a solution of the new equation.

Try this approach on the exercises that follow. The shortcomings of the method are that you must know how many solutions to seek and you must know approximately where the solutions are. If your initial guess is far from the actual solution, the calculator will time out and give you an error message, since it uses an iterative approach to find the solution. These shortcomings underscore the need to know how to solve a rational equation algebraically.

1. $\frac{4x + 3}{3x - 1} - \frac{3}{4} = \frac{4}{5}$ 2. $\frac{5}{c} + c = \frac{21}{2}$ 3. $\frac{17}{x} = 6 + \frac{5}{x}$

4. $\frac{3}{k} = \frac{17}{4} - \frac{2}{5k}$ 5. $\frac{h}{7} = \frac{3h}{5} - \frac{16}{21}$ 6. $\frac{18}{5 - z} = \frac{8 - z}{2 - z}$

10.4 Writing Exercises

1. In solving a rational equation algebraically, sometimes the result is an identity. You might assume that the set of all real numbers would then be the solution set of the equation. However, that is not always true; there may be numbers that do not satisfy the equation. Write a short paragraph describing what you must consider when a rational equation results in an identity. Describe what qualifications you must make on your statement of the solutions in this situation.
2. In this section, you were cautioned to not confuse a rational equation with a rational expression. Define what we mean by

these two terms. Explain what mathematical operations can be performed on each. Describe how you distinguish one from the other.
3. As stated earlier, the golden rectangle has a long history of use because of its aesthetic properties. The ratio of the length of the shorter side to the length of the longer side of a golden rectangle is referred to as the golden ratio. Go to the library to search, or use the Internet to find a reference on the golden ratio or golden rectangle. Write a short summary of your findings. Be sure to document your reference sources.

10.5 MORE REAL-WORLD MODELS

OBJECTIVES
1 Solve real-world models involving rates.
2 Solve real-world models involving proportions.
3 Solve real-world models involving geometric proportions.
4 Solve formulas for a specified variable.

APPLICATION

A formula for the total resistance R in a parallel circuit is $R^{-1} = r_1^{-1} + r_2^{-1}$, where R is the total resistance, r_1 is the resistance of the first resistor, and r_2 is the resistance of the second resistor.

   a. Solve the formula for R.

   b. A typical lightbulb has a resistance of about 100 ohms. An iron has a resistance of 15 ohms. If a lightbulb and an iron are connected in a parallel circuit, determine the total resistance.

After completing this section, we will discuss this application further. See page 833.

We now know three methods for solving a rational equation: numeric, graphic, and algebraic. We have also solved several types of real-world models with each of these methods. Many other types of models also can be solved with the methods.

In this section, we discuss some common types of real-world models involving rational equations. Remember, there is no set way to work all problems. Also, once a rational equation is written for the problem, it may be solved with any of the methods we have learned.

Let's review the method we have been using to answer a question about a real-world model.

SOLVING REAL-WORLD MODELS

To solve an application problem,

- Read and understand the problem.
- Define a variable for the unknown quantity, and define other quantities in terms of the variable if possible.
- Write an equation with the given information.
- Solve the equation either numerically, graphically, or algebraically.
- Check the solution.
- Write an answer to the question in a complete sentence.

Objective 10.5.1

Solving Rate Problems

A ratio is the quotient of two quantities. A **rate** is a ratio (such as miles per hour) used to compare different kinds of measurements. Rate of work is one type of problem that leads to solving a rational equation. This type of problem is usually referred to as a work problem.

Before we begin, we need to be able to determine a rate of work. We know that if a painter needs four hours to paint a room, then $\frac{1}{4}$ of the job is completed in one hour. In two hours, $\frac{2}{4} = \frac{1}{2}$ of the job is completed. If we use this information, we determine the rate of work by solving any one of the following equations:

Let $\quad x =$ the rate of work

time $\cdot$ rate $=$ amount of job completed

$$1 \cdot x = \frac{1}{4} \qquad \text{\small $\frac{1}{4}$ of job completed}$$

$$2 \cdot x = \frac{1}{2} \qquad \text{\small $\frac{1}{2}$ of job completed}$$

$$3 \cdot x = \frac{3}{4} \qquad \text{\small $\frac{3}{4}$ of job completed}$$

$$4 \cdot x = 1 \qquad \text{\small Entire job completed}$$

All of the equations solved for x result in $x = \frac{1}{4}$. Therefore, the rate of work is $\frac{1}{4}$ job per hour.

RATE OF WORK

If a task can be completed in x hours, then the rate of work is $\frac{1}{x}$ of the task per hour.

Next, we need to understand that if more than one person or machine is working on a task, the total rate of work is the sum of the individual rates. For example, suppose two painters are painting a room. The first painter paints at a rate of $\frac{1}{4}$ room per hour, and his helper paints at a rate of $\frac{1}{6}$ room per hour. Determine the total rate of work.

The sum of the two rates is

$$\frac{1}{4} + \frac{1}{6} = \frac{3}{12} + \frac{2}{12} = \frac{5}{12}$$

Therefore, the total rate of work is $\frac{5}{12}$ room per hour.

EXAMPLE 1   Michelangelo working alone can paint a room in four hours. His helper, Leonardo, would need six hours to do the job alone. Determine the number of hours required for the two painters to paint the room together.

Algebraic Solution

Let x = number of hours needed to paint the room together

$\frac{1}{4}$ is the rate of work for Michelangelo.

$\frac{1}{6}$ is the rate of work for Leonardo.

$\frac{1}{x}$ is the rate of work for both painters working together.

Graphic Check

Check your solution graphically.

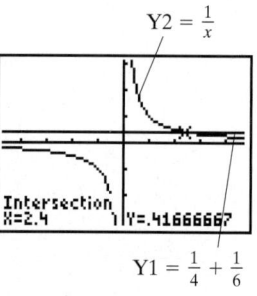

$Y2 = \frac{1}{x}$

$Y1 = \frac{1}{4} + \frac{1}{6}$

$(-4.7, 4.7, -3.1, 3.1)$

The solution is 2.4.

The sum of the individual rates equals the total rate.

$$\frac{1}{4} + \frac{1}{6} = \frac{1}{x} \qquad \text{The restricted value is 0.}$$

$$12x\left(\frac{1}{4} + \frac{1}{6}\right) = 12x\left(\frac{1}{x}\right) \qquad \text{Multiply by the LCD.}$$

$$12x\left(\frac{1}{4}\right) + 12x\left(\frac{1}{6}\right) = 12x\left(\frac{1}{x}\right) \qquad \text{Distribute the LCD.}$$

$$3x + 2x = 12$$

$$5x = 12$$

$$x = \frac{12}{5} \quad \text{or} \quad 2\frac{2}{5}$$

It would take $2\frac{2}{5}$ hours for the painters to paint the room if they work together. Check your solution graphically on your calculator. The solution is 2.4 or $2\frac{2}{5}$. ■

EXAMPLE 2   Normally, it takes three minutes to fill a sink. However, today the drain does not close properly and allows water to drain as it is being filled. Therefore, the sink is filled at the end of five minutes. If the water is turned off, determine the number of minutes that water will remain in the sink.

Algebraic Solution

Let x = number of minutes it takes to drain the sink

$\frac{1}{3}$ is the rate of work for filling the sink.

$\frac{1}{x}$ is the rate of work for draining the sink.

$\frac{1}{5}$ is the rate of work for filling and draining at the same time.

Graphic Check

Check your solution graphically.

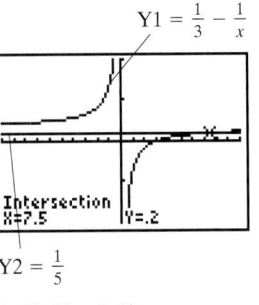

$Y2 = \frac{1}{5}$

$(-10, 10, -2, 2)$

The solution is 7.5.

The difference of the individual rates equals the combined rate.

$$\frac{1}{3} - \frac{1}{x} = \frac{1}{5}$$ The restricted value is 0.

$$15x\left(\frac{1}{3} - \frac{1}{x}\right) = 15x\left(\frac{1}{5}\right)$$ Multiply by the LCD.

$$15x\left(\frac{1}{3}\right) - 15x\left(\frac{1}{x}\right) = 15x\left(\frac{1}{5}\right)$$ Distribute the LCD.

$$5x - 15 = 3x$$

$$2x = 15$$

$$x = \frac{15}{2} \quad \text{or} \quad 7\frac{1}{2}$$

It takes $7\frac{1}{2}$ minutes to drain the sink. Therefore, water will remain in the sink for $7\frac{1}{2}$ minutes. ■

 Objective 10.5.1 **CHECKUP**

1. Merle can mow the lawn around his farmhouse in 2 hours. His wife, Glenna, can do the same job in 1.6 hours. Assuming that they have two lawn mowers and can work together without getting in each other's way, how long will it take them to mow the lawn together?

2. Water is being pumped out of a storage tank at a rate that would empty the tank in two hours. At the same time, water is being pumped into the tank at an unknown rate. If an empty tank can be filled in five hours while water is simultaneously being pumped out, how long would it take to fill an empty tank if no water is pumped out? ■

Objective 10.5.2   ## Solving Proportion Problems

Two ratios (rates) that are equal in value may be written as a rational equation called a proportion. In order for the two ratios to be equal, the numerator and the denominator of each must be written in the same order. For example,

$$\frac{\text{cost}}{\text{weight}} = \frac{\text{cost}}{\text{weight}}, \text{ but } \frac{\text{cost}}{\text{weight}} \neq \frac{\text{weight}}{\text{cost}}.$$

EXAMPLE 3   Justin is practicing batting a baseball with his mother. He has hit 10 out of 20 pitches. His goal is to hit 60% of the pitches. How many consecutive pitches must he hit to raise his average to 60%?

Algebraic Solution

Let x = number of consecutive pitches he must hit

The current ratio of hits to pitches $\left(\dfrac{\text{hits}}{\text{pitches}}\right)$ is $\dfrac{10}{20}$.

The ratio after x consecutive hits $\left(\dfrac{\text{hits}}{\text{pitches}}\right)$ is $\dfrac{10 + x}{20 + x}$.

The desired ratio of hits to pitches is 60%, or $\dfrac{60}{100}$.

The proportion is as follows:

$$\frac{10 + x}{20 + x} = \frac{60}{100}$$

The restricted value is -20.

$$1000 + 100x = 1200 + 60x$$ Equate the cross products.

$$40x = 200$$

$$x = 5$$

Justin must hit five consecutive pitches to raise his average to 60%.
   Check your solution numerically on your calculator. The solution is 5.

Numeric Check

Check your solution numerically.

X	Y1	Y2
0	.5	.6
1	.52381	.6
2	.54545	.6
3	.56522	.6
4	.58333	.6
5	.6	.6
6	.61538	.6

X=6

$Y1 = \dfrac{10 + x}{20 + x}$

$Y2 = \dfrac{60}{100}$

The solution is 5.

c is the harmonic mean of positive numbers a and b if $\dfrac{1}{c} = \dfrac{1}{2}\left(\dfrac{1}{a} + \dfrac{1}{b}\right)$. The harmonic mean can be used to find average rate. c is the average rate of rates a and b. If we use this formula and know the two rates a and b, we must solve a proportion to determine c.

In Section 10.3, we found the average rate of travel for two trips of the same distance but with different average rates of travel (speed). To do this, we found the total distance traveled and divided by the total time traveled. It was a rather complicated procedure. However, we will now return to this application and use the harmonic mean to determine the average rate.

EXAMPLE 4   Julio travels form City A to City B at an average rate of 40 miles per hour. He makes the return trip at an average rate of 60 miles per hour. Determine his average rate for the round-trip.

Solution

Let c = the average rate for the round-trip

$$\frac{1}{c} = \frac{1}{2}\left(\frac{1}{a} + \frac{1}{b}\right)$$

$$\frac{1}{c} = \frac{1}{2}\left(\frac{1}{40} + \frac{1}{60}\right)$$ Substitute 40 for a and 60 for b.

$$\frac{1}{c} = \frac{1}{2}\left(\frac{3}{120} + \frac{2}{120}\right)$$ LCD = 120

$$\frac{1}{c} = \frac{1}{2}\left(\frac{5}{120}\right)$$ Simplify.

$$\frac{1}{c} = \frac{5}{240}$$

$$5c = 240$$ Equate cross products.

$$c = 48$$

Julio's average round-trip rate was 48 miles per hour.

Objective 10.5.2 *CHECKUP*

1. Michelle has scored 6 out of 10 baskets from the free-throw line. How many more consecutive baskets must she make in order to bring her average up to 75%?

2. J.J. walked 1.3 miles per hour for his morning walk to work. Returning in the evening, he walked 0.9 mile per hour. What was his average rate for the two walks?

Objective 10.5.3

Solving Geometric Proportions

Geometric figures can be proportional. One example of proportional figures is similar triangles. **Similar triangles** are triangles with congruent corresponding angles and proportional corresponding sides. The symbol for similar is ~. For example,

$$\triangle ABC \sim \triangle DEF \text{ is read "triangle } ABC \text{ is similar to triangle } DEF."$$

In **Figure 10.4**, sides AB and DE, BC and EF, and AC and DF are corresponding sides. **Corresponding sides** are in the same position in the figure. **Corresponding angles** are A and D, B and E, and C and F.

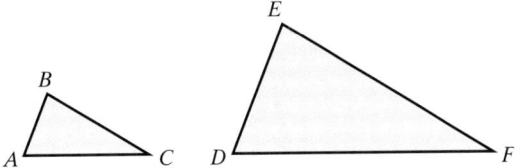

Figure 10.4

The ratio of the measure of any side of one triangle and the measure of the corresponding side on the second triangle are always constant. For example,

$$\frac{AB}{DE} = \frac{BC}{EF} = \frac{AC}{DF}$$

 TAKE NOTE Compare sides from the same triangle in the same order in the ratio $\dfrac{\triangle ABC}{\triangle DEF}$.

Therefore, if two sides of one triangle and one corresponding side of a second triangle are known, the second corresponding side may be found by using a proportion.

EXAMPLE 5

Given that $\triangle ABC \sim \triangle DEF$, determine the length of the unknown labeled side.

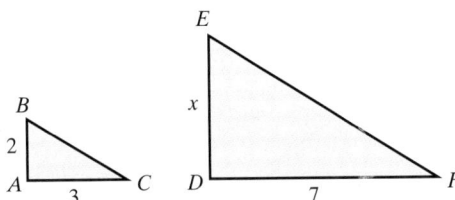

Algebraic Solution

Since $\triangle ABC \sim \triangle DEF$, we have three pairs of corresponding sides that are proportional. However, only two pairs of corresponding sides have their dimensions labeled.

$$\frac{AB}{DE} = \frac{AC}{DF}$$ Compare corresponding sides $\left(\frac{\triangle ABC}{\triangle DEF}\right)$.

$$\frac{2}{x} = \frac{3}{7}$$ Substitute values.

$$3x = 14$$

$$x = \frac{14}{3}$$

The length of the unknown side is $\frac{14}{3}$.

Graphic Check

$$Y1 = \frac{2}{x}$$

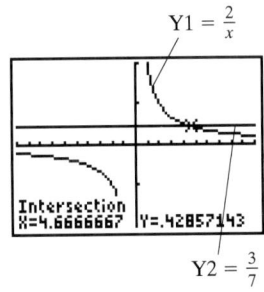

$$Y2 = \frac{3}{7}$$

$(-10, 10, -2, 2)$

Graphing the problem on a calculator results in the solution of approximately 4.667.

EXAMPLE 6

To determine the height of a tree, Sam stood next to it and had Kyle measure the length of his shadow and the tree's shadow. Use **Figure 10.5** to determine the height of the tree.

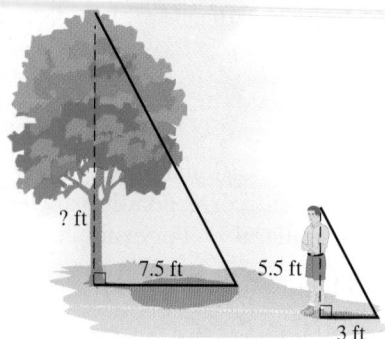

? ft
7.5 ft
5.5 ft
3 ft

Figure 10.5

Algebraic Solution

We first must determine whether the triangles formed are similar—that is, whether the measures of corresponding angles are equal.

We know that the tree and Sam both form right angles with the ground. From geometry, we know that the angles formed by the sun striking the tree and Sam are equal. From geometry, we also know that the sum of the angles of a triangle is 180 degrees and the sums of the two known angles are equal. Hence, the third angles must be equal.

The corresponding sides are therefore proportional, because the corresponding angles are congruent. Let x equal the height of the tree.

$$\frac{7.5}{3} = \frac{x}{5.5} \qquad \text{Compare corresponding sides}$$

$$3x = 41.25$$

$$x = 13.75$$

The height of the tree is 13.75 feet.

Graphic Check

Graphing the problem on a calculator results in the solution 13.75. Note that the equation is actually a linear equation.

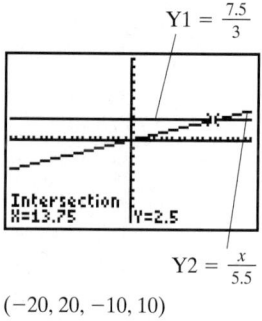

$Y1 = \frac{7.5}{3}$

Intersection
X=13.75   Y=2.5

$Y2 = \frac{x}{5.5}$

$(-20, 20, -10, 10)$

Objective 10.5.3 **CHECKUP**

1. $\triangle ABC \sim \triangle DEF$. Use proportions to find the lengths of the unknown sides.

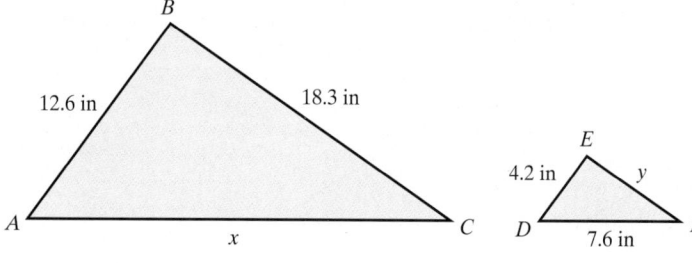

B

12.6 in   18.3 in

E
4.2 in   y

A   x   C   D   7.6 in   F

2. A tower stands 20 feet high and casts a shadow of 18 feet. The combined shadow cast by the tower and an antenna mounted on its top is 27 feet. Find the height of the antenna.

Objective 10.5.4   ## Solving Formulas

Many applications involve the use of formulas, which frequently are rational equations with several variables. Often, we must solve the formula for the variable of interest. We use the same procedure to solve formulas that we use to solve a rational equation.

EXAMPLE 7

a. The ideal-gas law states that, given the initial pressure P_1, initial volume V_1, initial temperature T_1, final pressure P_2, final volume V_2, and final temperature T_2, $\frac{P_1 V_1}{T_1} = \frac{P_2 V_2}{T_2}$. Solve for the initial temperature T_1.

b. Coulomb's law is used to determine the force F between two particles, given the net charge q_1 and q_2 on the particles, the distance d between the particles, and a proportional constant k. Solve $F = \dfrac{kq_1q_2}{d^2}$ for d.

Solution

a. $\dfrac{P_1V_1}{T_1} = \dfrac{P_2V_2}{T_2}$

$\dfrac{P_1V_1T_2}{P_2V_2} = \dfrac{P_2V_2T_1}{P_2V_2}$ Equate cross products.
Divide by P_2V_2.

$\dfrac{P_1V_1T_2}{P_2V_2} = T_1$ Simplify.

or

$T_1 = \dfrac{P_1V_1T_2}{P_2V_2}$

b. $F = \dfrac{kq_1q_2}{d^2}$

$d^2(F) = d^2\left(\dfrac{kq_1q_2}{d^2}\right)$ Multiply by the LCD, d^2.

$\dfrac{d^2F}{F} = \dfrac{kq_1q_2}{F}$ Divide by F.

$d^2 = \dfrac{kq_1q_2}{F}$

$\sqrt{d^2} = \sqrt{\dfrac{kq_1q_2}{F}}$ Take the square root.

$d = \pm\sqrt{\dfrac{kq_1q_2}{F}}$

APPLICATION

A formula for the total resistance R in a parallel circuit is $R^{-1} = r_1^{-1} + r_2^{-1}$, where R is the total resistance, r_1 is the resistance of the first resistor, and r_2 is the resistance of the second resistor.

a. Solve the formula for R.

b. A typical lightbulb has a resistance of about 100 ohms. An iron has a resistance of 15 ohms. If a lightbulb and an iron are connected in a parallel circuit, determine the total resistance.

Discussion

a. $R^{-1} = r_1^{-1} + r_2^{-1}$

$\dfrac{1}{R} = \dfrac{1}{r_1} + \dfrac{1}{r_2}$ Write as a rational equation.

$\dfrac{1}{R}(Rr_1r_2) = \left(\dfrac{1}{r_1} + \dfrac{1}{r_2}\right)(Rr_1r_2)$ Multiply by the LCD, Rr_1r_2.

$\dfrac{1}{R}(\cancel{R}r_1r_2) = \left(\dfrac{1}{\cancel{r_1}}\right)(R\cancel{r_1}r_2) + \left(\dfrac{1}{\cancel{r_2}}\right)(Rr_1\cancel{r_2})$ Distributive property

$r_1r_2 = Rr_2 + Rr_1$

$r_1r_2 = R(r_2 + r_1)$ Factor.

$R = \dfrac{r_1r_2}{r_1 + r_2}$ Divide both sides by $(r_1 + r_2)$.

(continued on page 834)

b. $R = \dfrac{r_1 r_2}{r_1 + r_2}$

$R = \dfrac{(100)(15)}{100 + 15}$ Substitute 100 for r_1 and 15 for r_2.

$R = \dfrac{1500}{115}$

$R = \dfrac{300}{23}$

The total resistance is $\frac{300}{23}$ ohms.

Objective 10.5.4 **CHECKUP**

1. In physics, the gravitational attraction between two spheres is given by $F = \dfrac{Gm_1 m_2}{D^2}$, where G is the universal gravitational constant, D is the distance between the centers of the spheres, and m_1 and m_2 are the masses of the two spheres. Solve this formula for D.

2. Centrifugal force of an object moving in a circle can be given by the formula $C = \dfrac{krm}{t^2}$, where k is a constant, r is the radius of the circle, m is the object's mass, and t is the time. Solve this formula for t.

3. If two springs with spring constants k_1 and k_2 are connected in sequence, the spring constant K of the combination is given by the formula $\dfrac{1}{K} = \dfrac{1}{k_1} + \dfrac{1}{k_2}$.

a. Solve for k_1.

b. If the constant for K is 1.5 pounds per inch and the constant for the second spring is 6 pounds per inch, what is the constant for the first spring?

10.5 EXERCISES

 Student Solutions Manual   PH Math/Tutor Center   CD Video   Math XL MathXL®   MyMathLab MyMathLab   Interactmath.com

Rate Problems

1. Miriam can type a report in 3 hours. Saul can type the same report in 4.2 hours. Assuming that they can work together to get the report done, how long will it take them?

2. Paul can wax his car in 45 minutes. His big brother John can do the job in 30 minutes. If they work together, how long will it take them to wax Paul's car?

3. It takes Jacques twice as long to clean the house as it does his wife, Simone. When they work together, they can clean the house in $3\frac{1}{3}$ hours. How long does it take each of them to do the job alone?

4. When Mary Lynn cleans the pool, it takes her an hour longer than it does when Joe cleans the pool. If they can clean the pool in $1\frac{1}{2}$ hours when they work together, how long does it take each of them working alone?

5. Work records show that Felix averages nine hours to do a certain plumbing job, while Oscar averages six hours to do the same job. How long would you expect them to take to do the job together?

6. JoAnne can grade a set of test papers in 15 minutes. Bob can grade the same number of test papers in 25 minutes. How long will it take them to grade the set of papers working together?

7. A tank is filled by two separate pipelines. When the red pipeline is used alone to fill the tank, it takes four hours. When the blue pipeline is used alone to fill the tank, it takes seven hours. How long would it take if both pipelines were used together to fill the tank?

8. A tank can be drained by two separate drains. When the large drain is used alone, it takes 5 hours to drain the tank. When the smaller drain is used alone, it takes 7.5 hours to drain the tank. If both drains are used together, how long will it take to drain the tank?

9. A gas supply line is used to fill storage tanks. Gas line A can fill the tank in $\frac{2}{3}$ of the time it takes gas line B to fill the tank. Together, the lines can fill the tank in $4\frac{4}{5}$ hours. How long does it take each line alone to fill the tank?

10. Two water supply lines can be used to fill the neighborhood pool. Used alone, the second line takes an hour and a half longer than the first line to fill the pool. Together, they can fill the pool in $4\frac{1}{2}$ hours. How long does it take each line used alone to fill the pool?

Proportion Problems

11. Ricki has earned 45 points out of 60 extra-credit points in her math class. If she completes all of the additional assignments for full credit, how many additional extra-credit points must there be if she wants her average for extra credit to be 80%?

12. A 2.5-liter mixture of diluted vinegar was made by combining 0.8 liter of vinegar with distilled water. How much more pure vinegar must be added to the mixture to bring the percent of vinegar in the mixture up to 40%?

13. The student nature club has spent $120 of its $300 in funds preparing for an Earth Day celebration. The club's budget allocated 45% of all funds to be spent on the celebration. If the club does not want to touch its remaining funds, but instead has a fund-raiser to raise additional funds, how much money should be raised and spent on the celebration to bring the percentage up to 45% of all funds?

14. Felix has raised $75 for his club's fund-raiser. So far, all the members have raised a total of $200, including Felix's contri-

bution. Felix wants to make a last-ditch effort to raise enough additional money so that his contribution will be 50% of the total raised. If no other members raise additional funds, how much more must Felix raise to bring his percentage up to 50% of the total?

15. Billy traveled to work at 23 miles per hour in the morning and 14 miles per hour on the way home in the evening. What was his average rate?

16. Becky drove to the city at 45 miles per hour on Monday. On Tuesday she drove to the city at 34 miles per hour. What was her average rate for the two days?

17. A horse did one lap around a racetrack at 3.2 miles per hour and another lap at 2.1 miles per hour. What was its average rate for the two laps?

18. Gillian walked to the bus stop from home at 1.2 miles per hour. When she returned she walked 0.9 mile per hour. What was her average rate for the walks?

Geometric Proportions

In **Figure 10.6**, $\triangle PQR \sim \triangle XYZ$. *Use these triangles for exercises 19 and 21, and find the measures of the unknown sides of the similar triangles from the information provided. In* **Figure 10.7**, $\triangle JKL \sim \triangle MNO$. *Use these triangles for exercises 20 and 22, and find the measures of the unknown sides of the similar triangles from the information given.*

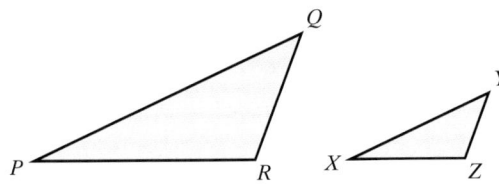

Figure 10.6

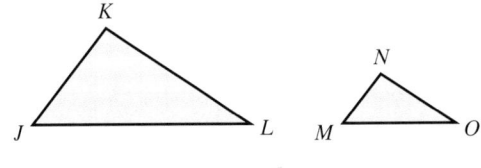

Figure 10.7

19. PQ measures 24 inches, QR measures 12 inches, XZ measures 3 inches, and YZ measures 2 inches.

20. JK measures 7 mm, JL measures 35 mm, NO measures 8 mm, and MO measures 10 mm.

21. QR measures 4.4 cm, PR measures 5.875 cm, XY measures 4.03 cm, and XZ measures 2.35 cm.

22. KL measures 32.4 yards, JL measures 43.92 yards, MN measures 6.9 yards, and NO measures 13.5 yards.

23. Triangle LMN is similar to triangle ABC. If $LM = 8$, $MN = x$, $AB = x + 4$, and $BC = 24$, find MN and AB.

24. Triangle ABC is similar to triangle XYZ and $AB = p$, $XY = 9$, $AC = 2p - 5$, and $XZ = 10$. Find AB and AC.

25. Triangle CAR is similar to triangle BUG. $CA = x + 6$, $BU = 2x - 3$, $CR = x + 4$, and $BG = x$. Find CA, BU, CR, and BG.

26. Triangle CAT is similar to triangle DOG with $CA = 3x + 1$, $DO = x + 2$, $AT = x + 3$, and $OG = x$. Find CA, DO, AT, and OG.

27. Bridgette was walking along a beach edged by a cliff. She wondered how high the cliff was, so she paced the distance from its base to the tip of its shadow. The shadow measured 35 paces, so she estimated it to be 35 feet long. Then she estimated her shadow to be 4 feet long. If Bridgette is 5.5 feet tall, what is the estimated height of the cliff, based on this information?

28. In late afternoon, a 6-foot lamppost casts a 14-foot shadow. How high is a flagpole if it casts a 35-foot shadow?

Physics

Solve the formulas from physics in exercises 29–38 for the indicated variable.

29. $a = \dfrac{v^2}{r}$ for r

30. $a = \dfrac{kF}{m}$ for m

31. $F = m\dfrac{v^2}{r}$ for v

32. $a = \dfrac{2s}{t^2}$ for t

33. $a = \dfrac{w_t - w_0}{t}$ for w_0

34. $m = \dfrac{F_t}{v_t - v_0}$ for v_t

35. $e = \dfrac{v - w}{m - n}$ for w and for n

36. $e = \dfrac{v - w}{m - n}$ for v and for m

37. $T = \dfrac{4\pi^2 a^3}{MG}$ for G

38. $F = \dfrac{kq_1 q_2}{D^2}$ for D

39. A circuit has two resistors wired in parallel. The resistance of one resistor is 5 ohms less than twice the resistance of the other resistor. The total resistance of the circuit is 6 ohms. Find the resistance of each resistor.

40. Two resistors in a circuit are wired in parallel. The resistance of the second resistor is 5 ohms more than three times the resistance of the first resistor. The total resistance of the circuit is 4 ohms. Find the resistance of each resistor.

 **10.5 Calculator Exercises**

While the emphasis of this chapter was on solving rational equations algebraically, you were shown how to check your solutions graphically. To do so, you stored the left expression of the equation in Y1 and the right expression of the equation in Y2, graphed the two equations, and found where the two graphs intersected. With rational equations, the graphs sometimes are difficult to see and the intersection points are not obvious. One remedy for this situation is to define Y3 to be equal to the difference of Y1 and Y2. Then, whenever Y3 equals zero, you have found a value such that Y1 = Y2, which is the solution of the equation. These values will occur wherever the graph of Y3 crosses the x-axis—that is, at x-intercepts.

As an example, solve $\dfrac{6x + 13}{x + 1} = \dfrac{7}{x^2(x + 1)} - \dfrac{4}{x^2}$. Letting

$Y1 = \dfrac{6x + 13}{x + 1}$ and $Y2 = \dfrac{7}{x^2(x + 1)} - \dfrac{4}{x^2}$ define Y3 = Y1 − Y2.

The graph of Y1 and Y2 is shown on the first screen, and the graph of Y3 is shown on the second screen:

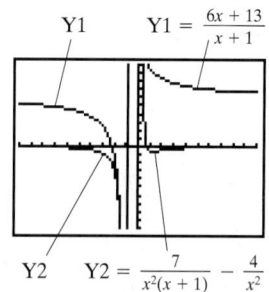
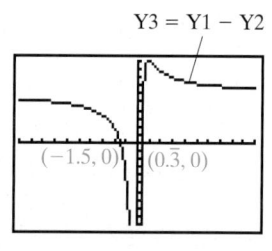

(Remember, you can turn a graph off or on by moving the cursor to the equals sign and pressing [ENTER]. When the box around the equals sign is missing, the graph is turned off. In the first screen, Y3 is turned off; in the second, Y1 and Y2 are turned off.) From the second screen, it is easier to see that there are two x-intercepts, indicating two solutions of the equation. These are found by pressing [2nd] [TRACE] (CALC) [2] for the zero option under the CALC function. Verify that the solutions are $x = 0.333\ldots$ and $x = -1.5$.

Try this method on the following rational equations:

1. $\dfrac{2x + 1}{x} = 1 + \dfrac{12}{x^2}$

2. $\dfrac{x + 1}{x + 3} = \dfrac{8}{2x}$

3. $\dfrac{1}{x} + \dfrac{1}{x + 2} = \dfrac{5}{12}$

 **10.5 Writing Exercises**

In this chapter, you learned that in some instances you can use cross products to solve a rational equation. Consider each of the equations that follow. For which equations can you use cross products? Explain your reasons.

1. $\dfrac{2}{x} = \dfrac{6}{x + 1}$

2. $\dfrac{2}{x} = \dfrac{6}{x} + 1$

3. $x^2 - \dfrac{1}{x} = \dfrac{x + 1}{3}$

4. $\dfrac{x^2 - 1}{x} = \dfrac{x + 1}{3}$

■ Chapter 10 Summary

Vocabulary Review

After completing this chapter, you should be able to define the following key terms.

corresponding angles	rate	restricted values
corresponding sides	rational expression	similar triangles
extraneous solution	rational function	
proportion	rational equation in one variable	

Fill in the blank with one of the words or phrases listed above.

1. A _____ can be written as a ratio $\dfrac{A}{B}$, where A and B are polynomials with $B \neq 0$.

2. A _____ is a number excluded from the domain of a function.

3. A _____ is written in the form $R(x) = 0$, where $R(x)$ is a rational expression.

4. An _____ is a possible solution that is a restricted value.

5. A _____ is a ratio used to compare different kinds of measurements.

6. Similar triangles are triangles with congruent _____ and proportional _____.

Reflections

1. What is the difference between a polynomial expression and a rational expression?

2. What does it mean to cancel when multiplying rational expressions? Can you cancel when dividing rational expressions? Explain.

3. What must be true before you can add or subtract two rational expressions?

4. What is the difference between a rational equation and a rational expression?

5. How do restricted values affect the solutions of a rational equation?

6. In solving a rational equation algebraically, how can you tell when it has no solutions? How can you tell when it has many solutions? How can you tell when it has extraneous solutions?

■ Chapter 10 Section-by-Section Review

10.1

Recall	Examples
A rational function can be written as a ratio of two polynomials.	$f(x) = \dfrac{2x + 1}{x - 5}$ is a rational function.
The domain of a rational function is the set of all real numbers except the function's restricted values. (The restricted values are found by setting the denominator equal to 0 and solving.)	Determine the domain of $f(x) = \dfrac{2x + 1}{x - 5}$. The restricted values are determined when $x - 5 = 0$ $\qquad\qquad\qquad\qquad\qquad\qquad\qquad x = 5$ The domain is the set of all real numbers not equal to 5, or $x \neq 5$, or $(-\infty, 5) \cup (5, \infty)$.
Graph a rational function • Determine the restricted value(s). • Determine a table of values by choosing the x-values less than, and the x-values greater than, the restricted values. • Plot the points and connect them with a smooth curve. Do not cross the vertical line where x equals the restricted value. Label the vertical asymptote.	Graph $f(x) = \dfrac{2x + 1}{x - 5}$. The restricted value is 5. The vertical asymptote is $x = 5$. 表 图

Table of values:

x	$f(x)$	x	$f(x)$
-5	0.9	5.1	112
-2	0.4	5.5	24
0	-0.2	6	13
2	-1.7	7	7.5
4	-9	10	4.2
4.5	-20	15	3.1
4.9	-108		

(continued on page 838)

Recall	Examples
Graph a rational function on a calculator • Determine the restricted value(s). • Set the calculator to Dot MODE. • Enter the function in the Y = menu. • Graph on an appropriate window.	Graph $f(x) = \dfrac{2x + 1}{x - 5}$. $Y1 = \dfrac{2x + 1}{x - 5}$ $(-20, 20, -20, 20)$

Determine whether each expression is rational or nonrational.

1. $3 + \dfrac{x - 5}{x^2 + 6x + 9}$

2. $x^2 - \dfrac{\sqrt{x} + 3x}{x + 1}$

3. $5x^2 - 3x + 2 - 4x^{-1}$

4. $2x + 5$

Determine the restricted values algebraically, and then state the domain of each rational equation.

5. $y = \dfrac{-3}{x^2}$

6. $f(x) = \dfrac{2x + 7}{x^2 + 5x - 24}$

7. $y = \dfrac{5}{4x^2 + 9}$

8. $y = \dfrac{5}{4x^2 - 9}$

In exercises 9–12, graph each rational function.

9. $y = \dfrac{8}{x^2} + \dfrac{3}{x}$

10. $g(x) = \dfrac{x^2 - x - 2}{x - 2}$

11. $p(x) = \dfrac{x + 2}{x + 1}$

12. $y = \dfrac{x^2 + 1}{x^2 + x - 2}$

13. The purchase price of a computerized cash register is $1800. The manufacturer provides a maintenance agreement on the register that is priced at $125 for the first year and that increases by $50 per year each year thereafter. The total cost of the cash register and maintenance agreement is given by $C(x) = 1800 + 100x + 25x^2$ if the cash register is used and maintained for x years.
   a. Determine a function for the average cost per year if the cash register is kept for x years.
   b. Graph the average-cost function for the domain $[0, 20]$. Determine the minimum average cost per year.
   c. What advice on maintaining the cash register would you give this business?

14. A student needs to analyze the function $f(x) = \dfrac{-9}{x^2 - 9}$.
   a. What is the domain of the function?
   b. Graph the function $f(x)$.
   c. Identify any relative maximum or relative minimum for this function.

15. A designer wants to construct an open box having a square base and surface area of 400 square inches. A function for the volume of the box is $V(x) = \dfrac{x^2(400 - x^2)}{4x}$, where x is the side of the square base. What is the domain of the function? Graph the function. What is the maximum volume?

16. The number of union members in thousands in the United States can be estimated by the function $N(x) = -63.5x^2 - 51.5x + 16,502$, where x is the number of years after 2000. The number of people in the labor force in thousands can be estimated by $L(x) = 594x^2 - 2438x + 124,326$.

   a. Determine a function, $R(x)$, for the ratio of the number of union members to the number of people in the labor force, where x is the number of years after 2000.
   b. Assuming the trends continue, graph the function for the domain $[0, 10]$. In what year will the ratio of the union members to the labor force be 0.12 or 12%? What are the minimum and maximum percentages on this domain, and when do they occur?

17. Data regarding the number of commercial radio stations in the United States is summarized in the table below:

Year	Country Format	Total Stations
2002	2131	10,569
2003	2088	10,605
2004	2047	10,649

   a. Find a linear function that estimates the number of country format stations $C(x)$, where x is the number of years after 2000.
   b. Find a quadratic function that estimates the total number of stations $T(x)$, where x is the number of years after 2000.
   c. Determine a function, $R(x)$, for the ratio of the number of country stations to the number of total stations, where x is the number of years after 2000.
   d. Assuming the trends continue, graph $R(x)$ on the domain $[0, 25]$, where x is the number of years after 2000. What are the maximum and minimum percent of country stations on this domain, and in what year does each occur? What does this model suggest regarding the popularity of country music stations?

10.2

Recall	Examples
Simplifying rational expressions • Factor the numerator and denominator. • Simplify the results, as in $\dfrac{A}{B} = \dfrac{\overset{1}{\cancel{k}} \cdot C}{\underset{1}{\cancel{k}} \cdot D} = \dfrac{C}{D}$, where $A, B, C,$ and D are polynomials and $B \neq 0, D \neq 0,$ and k is the GCF of A and B.	Simplify. $\dfrac{x^2 + 2x}{x^2 + x - 2}$ $\dfrac{x^2 + 2x}{x^2 + x - 2} = \dfrac{x(\overset{1}{\cancel{x + 2}})}{(\cancel{x + 2})(x - 1)}$ $= \dfrac{x}{x - 1}$
Multiplying rational expressions • Multiply the numerators and multiply the denominators, as in $\dfrac{A}{B} \cdot \dfrac{C}{D} = \dfrac{AC}{BD}$, where $A, B, C,$ and D are polynomials and B and $D \neq 0$. • Simplify the results.	Multiply. $\dfrac{x}{x - 1} \cdot \dfrac{x^2 - 1}{2x^2 + 3x + 1}$ $\dfrac{x}{x - 1} \cdot \dfrac{x^2 - 1}{2x^2 + 3x + 1} = \dfrac{x}{\underset{1}{\cancel{x - 1}}} \cdot \dfrac{(\overset{1}{\cancel{x - 1}})(\overset{1}{\cancel{x + 1}})}{(2x + 1)(\underset{1}{\cancel{x + 1}})}$ $= \dfrac{x}{2x + 1}$
Dividing rational expressions • Change the division problem to an equivalent multiplication problem, such as $\dfrac{A}{B} \div \dfrac{C}{D} = \dfrac{A}{B} \cdot \dfrac{D}{C} = \dfrac{AD}{BC}$, where $A, B, C,$ and D are polynomials and $B \neq 0, C \neq 0,$ and $D \neq 0$. • Simplify the results.	Divide. $\dfrac{x + 2}{x^2 - 2x + 1} \div \dfrac{x}{x^2 + 3x - 4}$ $\dfrac{x + 2}{x^2 - 2x + 1} \div \dfrac{x}{x^2 + 3x - 4}$ $= \dfrac{x + 2}{x^2 - 2x + 1} \cdot \dfrac{x^2 + 3x - 4}{x}$ $= \dfrac{x + 2}{(\underset{1}{\cancel{x - 1}})(x - 1)} \cdot \dfrac{(\overset{1}{\cancel{x - 1}})(x + 4)}{x}$ $= \dfrac{(x + 2)(x + 4)}{x(x - 1)}$

Simplify.

18. $\dfrac{-56x^3yz}{126x^2y^3z}$
19. $\dfrac{5p - 15}{15p + 25}$
20. $\dfrac{15x - 3x^2}{6x^3 - 30x^2}$
21. $\dfrac{2x^2 + x - 15}{4x^2 + 13x + 3}$
22. $\dfrac{b^2 - 49}{b^3 + 7b^2 + 2b + 14}$

Multiply and simplify.

23. $\dfrac{9x^3}{35y} \cdot \dfrac{-5y^2}{6x^5}$
24. $\dfrac{a + 5}{a - 4} \cdot (a + 1)$
25. $\dfrac{4m - 4}{m^2 - 25} \cdot \dfrac{m - 5}{2m^2 + 5m - 7}$

26. $\dfrac{a - 5}{a + 4} \cdot \dfrac{a + 4}{5 - a}$
27. $\dfrac{7x^2y}{5y - 3x} \cdot \dfrac{3x - 5y}{42xy^3}$
28. $\dfrac{2m + 6}{9m + 45} \cdot \dfrac{-3m - 15}{10m + 30}$

In exercises 29–37, divide and simplify.

29. $\dfrac{14z^5}{25x^2y^3} \div \dfrac{-7z^3}{15xy^4}$
30. $\dfrac{27a^2b}{8cd} \div \dfrac{9c^2d}{16ab^2}$
31. $\dfrac{x^2 + 4x + 3}{5x^2 + 5} \div \dfrac{x^2 - 3x + 2}{x^4 - 1}$

32. $\dfrac{3x^2y}{z^3} \div (2xyz)$
33. $(21a^2bc) \div \dfrac{3ab}{2c}$
34. $\dfrac{x^2 - 4}{x^2 + 4} \div (x - 2)$

35. $(2x^2 - x - 3) \div \dfrac{2x^2 - 7x + 6}{2x^2 - x - 6}$
36. $\dfrac{a + 3}{a + 6} \div \dfrac{a + 2}{a + 4}$
37. $\dfrac{x - 11}{x - 3} \div \dfrac{11 - x}{3 - x}$

38. Mario traveled 220 miles. If the trip took t hours, write an expression for his average rate of speed. If Mario cuts his average speed in half and adds two hours to his time, write an expression for the new distance he would travel.

39. Given the formula for the volume of a box, $V = LWH$, solve for the height H. A box has a volume given by $4x^3 + 12x^2$ cubic inches. The base of the box is a square, with each side measuring $2x$ inches. Use the new formula to find the height of the box.

40. The fixed cost (setup cost) to produce an item is $500, and the variable cost per item produced is $40. The revenue received for selling each item produced is $80 per item.

   a. Write a cost function and a revenue function for producing and selling x items.

   b. Write an expression for the ratio of cost to revenue for x items, and simplify the expression.

41. A rectangle has area $A(x) = 6x^3 - 13x^2 - 5x$. Its length is $(2x - 5)$ feet. Write a function, $w(x)$, for the width of the rectangle. Simplify this function. If the length is 7 feet, what is the width?

42. Acceleration may be given by the formula $a = \dfrac{2s}{t^2}$, where s is position and t is time. Suppose that one body has acceleration in which position is 8 feet and time is t, and another body has acceleration in which position is 13 feet and time is three more seconds than that for the first body.

   a. Find the product of the accelerations.

   b. Find the quotient of the acceleration of the first body divided by the acceleration of the second body.

10.3

Recall	Examples
Adding and subtracting rational expressions with like denominators • Add or subtract the numerators, as in $$\frac{A}{B} + \frac{C}{B} = \frac{A + C}{B}$$ $$\frac{A}{B} - \frac{C}{B} = \frac{A - C}{B}$$ where A, B, and C are polynomials and $B \neq 0$. • Simplify the results.	Add. $\dfrac{5}{x} + \dfrac{x + 2}{x}$ $\dfrac{5}{x} + \dfrac{x + 2}{x} = \dfrac{x + 7}{x}$ Subtract. $\dfrac{x}{x - 3} - \dfrac{x + 1}{x - 3}$ $\dfrac{x}{x - 3} - \dfrac{x + 1}{x - 3} = \dfrac{x - (x + 1)}{x - 3}$ $= \dfrac{x - x - 1}{x - 3}$ $= \dfrac{-1}{x - 3}$
Adding and subtracting rational expressions with unlike denominators • Determine the LCD of the denominators of all the fractions. • Change the fractions to equivalent fractions with the LCD as the denominator. • Add or subtract by using the procedure for like denominators.	Add. $\dfrac{2x}{x - 3} + \dfrac{1}{x + 3}$ $\dfrac{2x}{x - 3} + \dfrac{1}{x + 3} = \dfrac{2x(x + 3)}{(x - 3)(x + 3)} + \dfrac{1(x - 3)}{(x + 3)(x - 3)}$ $= \dfrac{2x^2 + 6x + x - 3}{(x - 3)(x + 3)}$ $= \dfrac{2x^2 + 7x - 3}{(x - 3)(x + 3)}$ Subtract. $\dfrac{2}{x} - \dfrac{x - 1}{x + 4}$ $\dfrac{2}{x} - \dfrac{x - 1}{x + 4} = \dfrac{2(x + 4)}{x(x + 4)} - \dfrac{x(x - 1)}{x(x + 4)}$ $= \dfrac{2x + 8 - x^2 + x}{x(x + 4)}$ $= \dfrac{-x^2 + 3x + 8}{x(x + 4)}$

In exercises 43–56, add or subtract, and simplify.

43. $\dfrac{3y}{5x} + \dfrac{7y^2}{5x}$

44. $\dfrac{5b^3}{7a} - \dfrac{2b}{7a}$

45. $\dfrac{x - 8}{2x - 5} + \dfrac{3x - 2}{2x - 5}$

46. $\dfrac{10x^2 + 3x + 5}{4x^2 - 9} - \dfrac{2 - 7x}{4x^2 - 9}$

47. $\dfrac{4}{5x^3y} + \dfrac{7}{15x^2y^2}$

48. $\dfrac{5x}{x - 8} + \dfrac{2x}{x + 4}$

49. $\dfrac{8}{2x - 1} - \dfrac{4}{x + 5}$

50. $\dfrac{7}{x - y} + \dfrac{4}{y - x}$

51. $\dfrac{4x}{9x^2 - 16} + \dfrac{2}{15x - 20}$

52. $\dfrac{5}{2x^2 - 5x - 3} + \dfrac{7}{3x^2 - 11x + 6}$

53. $\dfrac{7}{2x - 18} - \dfrac{3x + 4}{x^2 - 81}$

54. $\dfrac{8}{2x^2 + x - 6} - \dfrac{2}{3x^2 + 4x - 4}$

55. $\dfrac{7}{x + 5} + \dfrac{6}{x - 5} + \dfrac{8}{5 - x}$

56. $\dfrac{7x}{x + 2} - \dfrac{11}{3x} - \dfrac{5}{6}$

57. The lengths of the sides of a triangle are given by the rational expressions $\dfrac{x-1}{x+1}, \dfrac{x-3}{x}$, and $\dfrac{x+1}{2x}$. Add the lengths to find an expression for the perimeter of the triangle.

58. The perimeter of a rectangle is given by the rational expression $\dfrac{14x^2 + 14x + 6}{x(x+1)}$. If the width of the rectangle is given by the expression $\dfrac{3x}{x+1}$, use subtraction to find an expression for the length of the rectangle.

59. Bob and Gretchen took turns driving on a rural highway. Bob's average speed was 10 miles per hour greater than Gretchen's average speed. Bob drove 125 miles of the trip and Gretchen drove 80 miles of the trip.
   a. Letting x be Gretchen's average speed, write a function $t(x)$ for the total time of the trip.
   b. Graph the function.
   c. If Gretchen's average speed was 30 miles per hour, estimate the total time of the trip, to the nearest tenth of an hour.
   d. If the time of the trip was 4.5 hours, what were Gretchen's average speed and Bob's average speed?

60. Acceleration may also be given by the formula $a = \dfrac{kF}{m}$, where k is a constant, F is force, and m is mass. Suppose that acceleration for one body in which k is 3, F is 7, and mass is m is subtracted from the acceleration for a body in which k is 5, F is 15, and mass is three less than twice the mass of the other body. Subtract to find this difference.

61. The PE ratio (price-earnings ratio) is a measure of valuation of individual stocks. To calculate the PE ratio, divide the price per share (market value) of a stock by its yearly earnings per share. For one particular stock in the broadcasting and entertainment industry, its price per share can be estimated by the function $P(x) = 21.57x + 33$, where x is the number of years after 2004, and its earnings per share can be estimated by the function $E(x) = -0.07x + 1.08$. For another stock in the same industry, its price per share can be estimated by the function $P(x) = 9.11x + 20.88$, where x is the number of years after 2004, and its earnings per share can be estimated by $E(x) = 0.17x + 1.33$.
   a. Write a function for the PE ratio for each of the two stocks.
   b. Find the difference between the two PE ratio functions.

62. The U.S. Department of Commerce, Tourism Industries, keeps track of spending by tourists in the United States. The total amount spent by travelers in the United States, in billions of dollars, can be estimated by the function $T(x) = 4.5x^2 - 23.5x + 570$, where x is the number of years after 2000. The amount spent by domestic travelers in billions can be estimated by the function $D(x) = 2x^2 - 11x + 488$, and the amount spent by international travelers in billions $I(x) = 2.5x^2 - 12.5x + 82$, where x is the number of years after 2000.
   a. Determine a ratio of the amount spent by domestic travelers to the total amount spent by travelers, where x is the number of years after 2000.
   b. Determine a ratio of the amount spent by international travelers to the total amount spent by travelers, where x is the number of years after 2000.
   c. Find the difference in the ratios in part **a** and part **b**.

10.4

Recall	Examples
Rational equation in one variable • A rational equation in one variable is written in the form $R(x) = 0$, where $R(x)$ is a rational expression.	Rational equations in one variable are $\dfrac{2x+1}{x} = 0$ $6 + \dfrac{5}{2x} = \dfrac{x-1}{x+3}$ which can be written as $R(x) = 0$.
Solving a rational equation • Determine the restricted values. • Multiply both sides by the LCD of all of the terms. • Solve the resulting equation. • Discard any solutions that are restricted values. • Check the solution by substituting, solving numerically, or solving graphically.	Solve. $\dfrac{2x^2}{2x+1} + 3 = \dfrac{x}{2x+1}$ Restricted values: $2x + 1 = 0$ $x = -\dfrac{1}{2}$ $\dfrac{2x^2}{2x+1} + 3 = \dfrac{x}{2x+1}$ $(2x+1)\left(\dfrac{2x^2}{2x+1} + 3\right) = (2x+1)\left(\dfrac{x}{2x+1}\right)$ $(2x+1)\left(\dfrac{2x^2}{2x+1}\right) + (2x+1)(3) = (2x+1)\left(\dfrac{x}{2x+1}\right)$ $2x^2 + 6x + 3 = x$ $2x^2 + 5x + 3 = 0$ $(2x+3)(x+1) = 0$ $2x + 3 = 0$ or $x + 1 = 0$ $x = -\dfrac{3}{2}$ $\qquad$ $x = -1$ Check the solutions.

Determine whether each equation is rational.

63. $\dfrac{2x + 3}{6} = \dfrac{5}{\sqrt{x} - 1}$

64. $3x - 7 = 4x^{1/3}$

65. $5x^{-2} + 3x^{-1} + 4 = 18$

66. $\dfrac{2}{x} - \dfrac{5}{x - 3} = 17$

Solve exercises 67–82 algebraically.

67. $x + 3 = \dfrac{3x - 26}{2 - x}$

68. $\dfrac{3}{x + 3} = \dfrac{6}{2x + 6}$

69. $\dfrac{7 - x}{2 - x} = \dfrac{x + 9}{x - 2}$

70. $\dfrac{4}{3x} = 1 - \dfrac{17}{3x}$

71. $\dfrac{5}{2x + 4} = \dfrac{2x + 1}{2}$

72. $\dfrac{3x + 7}{2x - 4} = \dfrac{11}{3}$

73. $\dfrac{z}{50} - \dfrac{2}{z} = 0$

74. $b = 1 + \dfrac{30}{b}$

75. $a + \dfrac{13}{a} = -\dfrac{3}{a} - 8$

76. $1 = 12p^{-2} + p^{-1}$

77. $\dfrac{x - 2}{x - 6} + 3 = \dfrac{3x - 14}{x - 6}$

78. $\dfrac{3}{m + 4} + \dfrac{7}{m^2 - 16} = 2$

79. $\dfrac{2}{(3x + 5) - (2x + 1)} = \dfrac{8}{3(x + 5) + (x + 1)}$

80. $\dfrac{7}{x + 3} + \dfrac{2x - 1}{x^2 + x - 6} = \dfrac{5x - 2}{x^2 - 4}$

81. $1 + \dfrac{1}{x^2} = \dfrac{5}{x}$

82. $\dfrac{5x}{3} + \dfrac{2}{3} = \dfrac{x - 1}{x}$

83. Hope invested part of her annual bonus into one account that paid her $300 simple interest for one year and the remainder in a second account that paid her $560 simple interest for one year. The second account paid her 1% more interest than the first account. If she invested a total of $13,000, what were the annual interest rates that she received?

84. The PE ratio for a broadcasting and entertainment industry is given by the function $PE(x) = \dfrac{9.11x + 20.88}{0.17x + 1.33}$, where x is the number of years after 2004. Assuming trends continue, in what year will the ratio be 30?

85. A rectangle is considered golden and most pleasing to the eye if its sides, b and h, satisfy the equation $\dfrac{b}{h} = \dfrac{h}{b - h}$. Find the dimensions of the golden rectangle if $h = 8$ centimeters.

86. When an object moves around a circle with its acceleration directed toward the center of the circle, this centripetal acceleration can be given by the formula $a = \dfrac{v^2}{r}$, where v is velocity and r is the radius of the circle. Suppose that one body has velocity 5 meters per second on a circle of radius r and a second has velocity 3 meters per second on a circle with radius two more than five times the radius of the smaller circle. The acceleration of the first body is 1.01 more than the acceleration of the second body. Find the radius for each body.

10.5

Recall	Examples
Modeling real-world situations	Jamie has 15 out of 20 questions correct on her computer quiz. How many consecutive questions must she answer correctly to have an average of 80%.
• Define a variable.	Let $x =$ the number of correct consecutive questions The current ratio is $\frac{15}{20}$. The ratio after x correct consecutive questions is $\frac{15 + x}{20 + x}$. The desired ratio is 80%, or $\frac{80}{100} = \frac{4}{5}$.
• Write an equation.	$\dfrac{15 + x}{20 + x} = \dfrac{4}{5}$
• Solve the equation.	$75 + 5x = 80 + 4x$ $5 = x$
• Check the solution.	Check: $\dfrac{15 + x}{20 + x} = \dfrac{4}{5}$ $\dfrac{15 + (5)}{20 + (5)} \;\Big|\; \dfrac{4}{5}$ $\dfrac{20}{25}$ $\dfrac{4}{5}$
• Write a one-sentence answer to the question asked.	Jamie must answer the next five questions correctly in order to have an average of 80%.

87. Norman can install drywall in an average-sized room in six hours. His assistant can do the room in eight hours. How long will it take them to do the room working together?

88. Lucy and Ethel are packaging candy on an assembly line. It takes Lucy 10 minutes longer to pack a crate of candy than it takes Ethel to do the same. If they work together to pack the crate, they can do so in 30 minutes. How long does it take Lucy and Ethel each to do the job alone?

89. One production line can fill a barrel full of chocolate drops in 10 minutes. Another production line can fill the barrel in 15 minutes. How long will it take both lines to fill a barrel working together?

90. One production line takes twice as long to produce widgets as does a high-speed production line. When orders backlog, both production lines must be run. If it takes both lines working together $3\frac{1}{2}$ hours to produce an order, how long would it take each line working alone?

91. Maya and her roommate placed equal amounts of money into their joint account to pay bills. Maya placed $85 into the account, and, upon counting the money, she finds that the total is $210. Her roommate has evidently added money to the account. How much more money must Maya add to the account to make her share 50%?

92. A diluted alcohol solution is made by mixing 1.5 cups of pure grain alcohol with 12 cups of water. How many more cups of pure alcohol should be added to the solution to make it a 25% alcohol solution?

93. Doug ran one lap of a race at 3 miles per hour and the next lap at 2.7 miles per hour. Use the formula for the harmonic mean, $\frac{1}{c} = \frac{1}{2}\left(\frac{1}{a} + \frac{1}{b}\right)$, to find the average rate, c, of the two laps of the rates a and b.

94. Triangle GEO is similar to triangle MTH. If $GE = x - 3$, $MT = 3.5$, $EO = 2$, and $TH = x + 3$, find GE and TH.

95. When an object moves around a circle with its acceleration directed toward the center of the circle, this centripetal acceleration can be given by the formula $a = \dfrac{v^2}{r}$, where v is velocity and r is the radius of the circle. Solve this formula for v.

96. Given $\triangle GHI \sim \triangle JKL$.

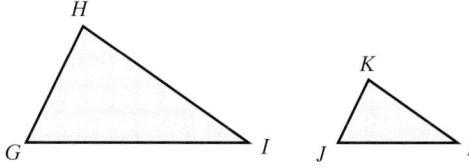

Use the triangles to find the measures of the missing sides of the similar triangles, given the following information:

a. GH measures 4 inches, HI measures 8 inches, JK measures 7 inches, and JL measures 21 inches.

b. HI measures 9.22 cm, GI measures 14.08 cm, KL measures 2.305 cm, and JK measures 1.88 cm.

97. A surveyor sighted along similar triangles to determine the height of a bluff. He was standing 120 feet away from the bluff and 15 feet away from his surveying partner, who was holding the surveyor's rod. The top of the 6-foot rod was in line with the top of the bluff from the partner's point of view. How high was the bluff?

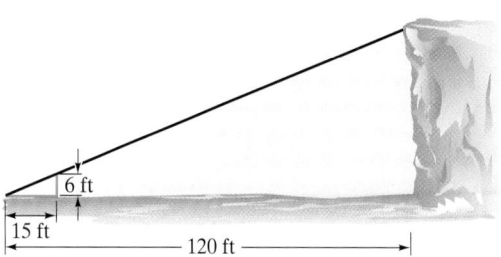

98. In the "Case of the Musgrave Ritual," Sherlock Holmes needs to know where the shadow of an elm tree falls at a certain time of day "when the sun is over the oak tree." However, the tree was struck by lightning and is gone. Fortunately, the owner of the estate knows that the elm was 64 feet tall, because he had used trigonometry to determine that before the tree fell. Holmes quickly fashioned a 6-foot rod and measured its shadow to be 9 feet. He then determined what the length of the shadow of the oak tree would have been. It was elementary, my dear student. What was the length of the tree's shadow?

99. Two resistors are in a parallel circuit. One resistor has a resistance that is 5 ohms more than twice the resistance of the other resistor. The total resistance of the circuit is 30 ohms. Find the resistances of the two resistors, to the nearest ohm.

100. If two lenses with focal lengths f_1 and f_2 are placed in contact with one another, the focal length of the combination is given by $\dfrac{1}{f} = \dfrac{1}{f_1} + \dfrac{1}{f_2}$. Solve for f.

■ Chapter 10 Mixed Review

Graph each rational function.

1. $y = \dfrac{4}{x^2} + \dfrac{1}{x}$

2. $g(x) = \dfrac{x+5}{x^2+5x+4}$

3. $y = \dfrac{2x^2-x-3}{x+1}$

4. $y = \dfrac{x+3}{x+1}$

Determine the restricted values algebraically, and then state the domain of each rational equation.

5. $y = \dfrac{5}{9x^2+25}$

6. $y = \dfrac{5}{9x^2-25}$

7. $g(x) = \dfrac{x+5}{3x}$

8. $h(x) = \dfrac{5x-7}{3x^2+2x-8}$

Simplify.

9. $\dfrac{3x^2+19x+20}{2x^2+13x+15}$

10. $\dfrac{k^2-25}{k^3-5k^2+6k-30}$

11. $\dfrac{-72x^4y^2z}{96xy^6z}$

12. $\dfrac{7q-21}{14q+28}$

13. $\dfrac{12x^2-6x^3}{9x^3-36x}$

Add or subtract, and simplify.

14. $\dfrac{7}{3x+2} - \dfrac{2}{x-3}$

15. $\dfrac{14}{a-b} + \dfrac{9}{b-a}$

16. $\dfrac{7b}{3a} + \dfrac{5b^2}{3a}$

17. $\dfrac{3p^2}{4m} - \dfrac{2p}{4m}$

18. $\dfrac{5}{4x^2y^3} + \dfrac{3}{6x^2y}$

19. $\dfrac{x}{x+3} + \dfrac{4x}{x-5}$

20. $\dfrac{2x}{4x^2-25} + \dfrac{1}{6x-15}$

21. $\dfrac{7}{2x^2+5x-3} + \dfrac{5}{3x^2+11x+6}$

22. $\dfrac{3z-5}{2z-7} + \dfrac{z-9}{2z-7}$

23. $\dfrac{10x^2-8x}{25x^2-16} - \dfrac{5x-4}{25x^2-16}$

24. $\dfrac{3}{x+6} + \dfrac{2}{x-6} + \dfrac{4}{6-x}$

25. $\dfrac{x}{x+1} - \dfrac{3}{2x} - \dfrac{3}{4}$

26. $\dfrac{5}{2x+10} - \dfrac{2x+1}{x^2-25}$

27. $\dfrac{3}{4x^2-17x+15} - \dfrac{2}{5x^2-19x+12}$

Multiply and simplify.

28. $\dfrac{m^2-36}{2m^2+9m+10} \cdot \dfrac{3m+6}{m-6}$

29. $\dfrac{z-3}{z-7} \cdot \dfrac{7-z}{z-3}$

30. $\dfrac{8a^4}{21b} \cdot \dfrac{-35b^3}{12a^7}$

31. $(2c+3) \cdot \dfrac{c+7}{c+3}$

32. $\dfrac{3b-4a}{24ab^3} \cdot \dfrac{8a^2b}{4a-3b}$

33. $\dfrac{5p+20}{12p+96} \cdot \dfrac{-9p-72}{15p+60}$

Divide and simplify.

34. $\dfrac{22g^8}{15h^3k^2} \div \dfrac{-11g^4}{10hk^3}$

35. $\dfrac{18p^2q^2}{25m^2n} \div \dfrac{3mn^3}{5pq^5}$

36. $(15m^3np^2) \div \dfrac{2mn}{5p}$

37. $\dfrac{4x^2-9}{4x^2+9} \div (2x+3)$

38. $\dfrac{x^2-x-6}{2x^2+8} \div \dfrac{x^2-5x+6}{x^4-16}$

39. $\dfrac{5a^2b^3}{c^5} \div (3a^2bc^2)$

40. $\dfrac{z-3}{z-6} \div \dfrac{z+4}{z+8}$

41. $\dfrac{k-7}{k-12} \div \dfrac{7-k}{12-k}$

42. $(2x^2+9x-5) \div \dfrac{2x^2+3x-2}{2x^2+5x+2}$

Solve exercises 43–64 algebraically.

43. $\dfrac{4}{7} - \dfrac{1}{y} = \dfrac{9}{28}$

44. $\dfrac{4}{x-1} = \dfrac{5x-16}{7}$

45. $2 - \dfrac{4}{x+3} = \dfrac{x+2}{x+3}$

46. $\dfrac{5}{m+3} + \dfrac{8}{m^2-9} = \dfrac{3}{5}$

47. $\dfrac{16}{2x+6} = \dfrac{5}{x}$

48. $35 = p^{-2} + 2p^{-1}$

49. $\dfrac{x-6}{x-4} = \dfrac{x+7}{2(x+3)-(x+10)}$

50. $\dfrac{a}{a-7} = \dfrac{a+1}{a-2}$

51. $1 - \dfrac{6}{x} = \dfrac{6}{x} - \dfrac{1}{2} + \dfrac{21}{2x}$

52. $1 + 7x^{-1} = 3$

53. $\dfrac{10}{x+5} - \dfrac{24}{x^2+x-20} = \dfrac{1}{x^2-16}$

54. $\dfrac{2}{(x+3)+(x-9)} = \dfrac{3}{2(x+4)+(x-17)}$

55. $x + 5 = \dfrac{x-11}{2-x}$

56. $5 = \dfrac{3(x+5)}{x+3} + \dfrac{4x}{2x+6}$

57. $\dfrac{1}{2} - \dfrac{3}{2x} = \dfrac{1}{2} + \dfrac{1}{2x} - \dfrac{2}{x}$

58. $5x = \dfrac{9x+4}{x+2}$

59. $\dfrac{x}{3} = \dfrac{27}{x}$

60. $\dfrac{4-x}{3-x} = \dfrac{x+11}{x-3}$

61. $\dfrac{x+8}{2} = \dfrac{2x+11}{x+1}$

62. $x+1 = \dfrac{x^2+5x-12}{3x-1}$

63. $\dfrac{2x}{x+4} = 1 - \dfrac{8}{x+4}$

64. $\dfrac{x-4}{x-8} = \dfrac{6x}{x^2-4x-32}$

65. Dave can hang wallpaper in a room and finish in 10 hours. Joan can do the same room and finish in 7 hours. How long will it take them to paper the room working together?

66. A diluted glue mixture is made by mixing 2 pints of glue with 7 pints of distilled water. How many more pints of glue are needed to bring the mixture up to a 30% glue solution?

67. Antonio drove 120 miles in t hours. Write an expression for his average rate of speed. If he reduces his average speed to $\frac{2}{3}$ of his original speed and adds 1 hour to his time, write an expression for the new distance he could travel.

68. A tree casts a shadow of 18 feet. At the same time of day, a mailbox that is 4 feet high casts a shadow of 3 feet. How high is the tree?

69. Given $V = LWH$ as the volume of a box, solve for H. A box has a width of x inches and a length that is five times the width. If the volume of the box is $10x^3 + 5x^2$ cubic inches, use the new formula to write an expression for the height of the box.

70. One production line takes $1\frac{1}{2}$ hours longer to fill an order than a second production line takes. When both lines are used, the order can be filled in $3\frac{1}{3}$ hours. How long does it take each line working alone to fill the order?

71. The lengths of the sides of a triangle are given by the expressions $\dfrac{6}{x-3}$, 3, and $\dfrac{x-1}{x}$. Find an expression for the perimeter of the triangle.

72. Latoya has two roommates. Each pays one-third of the bills. Latoya has added $70 to the amount her roommates collected, and the total was $250. How much more does Latoya have to add to the money to make her contribution one-third of the total?

73. Two resistors are connected in parallel. The total resistance of the circuit is 25 ohms. If one resistor has a resistance that is 12 ohms more than the resistance of the other resistor, what are the two resistances, to the nearest ohm?

74. The combined capacitance C of two capacitors C_1 and C_2 connected in series is given by $\dfrac{1}{C} = \dfrac{1}{C_1} + \dfrac{1}{C_2}$. Solve for C.

75. The amount of U.S. energy production in quadrillion Btu's can be estimated by $P(x) = -0.105x^2 + 0.065x + 71.22$, where x is the number of years after 2000. The amount of production of coal in quadrillion Btu's can be approximated by $C(x) = -0.39x + 23.48$.
   a. Determine a function, $R(x)$, for the ratio of the amount of production of coal to the U.S. energy production, where x is the number of years after 2000.
   b. Assuming the trends continue, graph $R(x)$ for the domain $[0, 20]$ where x is the number of years after 2000. In what year(s) will the ratio be 0.316 or the percentage be 31.6%? What is the minimum percent from coal and in what year does it occur?

76. Lida purchases a timeshare condominium for $18,000 and management agreement that costs $200 the first year and increases by $75 per year thereafter. The total cost of the condo and management contract is $C(x) = 18{,}000 + 162.5x + 37.5x^2$ for x years.
   a. Determine the average cost for x years.
   b. Graph the average-cost function for the domain $[0, 30]$ to determine the minimum average cost per year.

77. A cylindrical can is to hold 20 cubic inches of a soft drink. Its surface area is $S(x) = 2\pi x^2 + \dfrac{40}{x}$, where x is the radius of the circular base. Graph the function to find the minimum surface area. For what value of x is the surface area a minimum?

78. A parallelogram has area $A(x) = 6x^3 + 7x^2 - 3x$. Its height is $(2x + 3)$ feet. Write a function, $b(x)$, for the corresponding base. Simplify this function. If the height is 15 feet, what is the base?

79. The U.S. Department of Commerce, Bureau of the Census, keeps statistics regarding the types of households in the United States. The total number of U.S. households in thousands can be estimated by the function $T(x) = -1208x^2 + 4712x + 104{,}705$, where x is the number of years after 2000. The number of households headed by married couples can be estimated in thousands by the function $M(x) = -563x^2 + 1844x + 55{,}311$ and the number headed by unmarried couples by $U(x) = -76x^2 + 233x + 4736$, where x is the number of years after 2000.
   a. Determine a ratio for the number of households headed by married couples to the total households, where x is the number of years after 2000.
   b. Determine a ratio for the number of households headed by unmarried couples to the total households, where x is the number of years after 2000.
   c. Find the difference in the ratios in part **a** and part **b**.

80. A definition for a golden rectangle is one in which the proportion $\dfrac{a}{b} = \dfrac{a+b}{a}$ holds true, where the dimensions of the rectangle are $(a + b)$ and a. Find the dimensions of the golden rectangle if $b = 4$ inches.

81. Mass of a body, m, refers to its inertia while weight of a body, w, is the force due to gravity and can vary with location. The two are related by the formula $w = \dfrac{m}{g}$, where g is acceleration due to gravity. Suppose the weight for one body of mass 5 kilograms and acceleration due to gravity of g is added to the weight for another body whose mass is 7 kilograms at a place where acceleration due to gravity is three more than twice g. The sum of these weights is 3.9. Find the two accelerations due to gravity measures.

82. Triangle XYZ is similar to triangle ABC. $XY = AB = c$ and $BC = c + 1$ with $YZ = 4$. Find AB, BC, and XY.

83. Acceleration may also be given by the formula $a = \dfrac{kF}{m}$, where k is a constant, F is force, and m is mass. Solve this formula for m.

■ Chapter 10 Test

Determine the restricted values, and then state the domain of each rational equation.

1. $y = \dfrac{x - 7}{2x^2 + 6x}$

2. $g(x) = \dfrac{x^2 - 4x - 21}{x^2 - 5x - 36}$

3. Graph the rational function $f(x) = \dfrac{x + 4}{x - 2}$.

Simplify.

4. $\dfrac{24x + 56}{9x^2 - 49}$

5. $\dfrac{2z^3 - 18z}{z^3 + 3z^2 + 9z + 27}$

Perform the operations and simplify.

6. $\dfrac{5}{x^2 + 4x} + \dfrac{2}{x^2 + x - 12}$

7. $\dfrac{5x^2 - 40x}{20x^2 + 30x} \div \dfrac{x^2 - 64}{2x^2 + 19x + 24}$

8. $\dfrac{2x + 1}{x^2 + 5x} - \dfrac{x - 4}{x^2 + 10x + 25}$

9. $\dfrac{24x^2 y}{x^2 - xy - 2y^2} \cdot \dfrac{3x^2 - 12xy + 12y^2}{16x^3 y}$

Solve exercises 10–18.

10. $x - 5 = \dfrac{5 - x}{x}$

11. $\dfrac{16}{x - 3} = \dfrac{x - 3}{x}$

12. $\dfrac{b}{5} + \dfrac{1}{2} = \dfrac{1}{5} - \dfrac{11}{10b}$

13. $\dfrac{3}{m} - \dfrac{m}{75} = 0$

14. $6 + 14x^{-1} + 4x^{-2} = 0$

15. $\dfrac{x^2 + 6x + 9}{4x + 20} = \dfrac{x + 6}{x + 5}$

16. $\dfrac{2}{x + 2} = \dfrac{3}{x + 3}$

17. $\dfrac{x - 5}{x + 1} = 1 - \dfrac{6}{x + 1}$

18. $\dfrac{5 - x}{3 - x} = \dfrac{x + 9}{x - 3}$

19. Given $z = \dfrac{x - m}{s}$, solve for s.

20. c is the average rate of the rates a and b and is found by using the formula $\dfrac{1}{c} = \dfrac{1}{2}\left(\dfrac{1}{a} + \dfrac{1}{b}\right)$. Solve for c.

21. A definition for a golden rectangle is the proportion $\dfrac{s}{l} = \dfrac{l}{s + l}$, where s is the length of the short side and l is the length of the long side. Find the dimensions of the golden rectangle if $s = 8$ inches.

22. Acceleration may be given by the formula $a = \dfrac{2s}{t^2}$, where s is position and t is time. Suppose that one body has acceleration in which position is 3 feet and time is t and another body has acceleration in which position is 9 feet and time is two more seconds than that for the first body. Find the difference of the accelerations.

23. Jenny buys a new camper for $17,000 and a maintenance warranty that costs $150 for the first year and increases by $150 per year thereafter. The total cost of the recreational vehicle is $C(x) = 75x^2 + 75x + 17,000$, where x is the number of years after purchase.
   a. Determine a function for the average cost for x years.
   b. Graph the average-cost function for the domain $[0, 20]$ to determine the minimum average cost per year.

24. The amount of U.S. energy production in quadrillion Btu's can be estimated by $P(x) = -0.105x^2 + 0.065x + 71.22$, where x is the number of years after 2000. The amount of production of nuclear electric power quadrillion Btu's can be approximated by $N(x) = -0.17x + 8.48$.
   a. Determine a function, $R(x)$, for the ratio of the amount of production of nuclear electric power to the U.S. energy production, where x is the number of years after 2000.
   b. Assuming the trends continue, graph $R(x)$ for the domain $[0, 18]$, where x is the number of years after 2000. In what year(s) will the ratio be 0.1225 or the percentage be 12.25%? What is the minimum percent from nuclear electric power and in what year does it occur?

25. Chris wants to estimate the height of a tree that casts a shadow measuring 32.5 feet. She knows that a 7-foot pole in the yard casts a shadow of 10.5 feet. What is the height of the tree?

26. Jack can rake the leaves in his yard in 6 hours. When Jill helps him, they can rake the leaves in 2 hours and 24 minutes (that is, $2\frac{2}{5}$ hours). How long would it take Jill to rake the leaves alone?

27. Explain why a rational equation can be solved algebraically by multiplying both sides of the equation by the least common denominator (LCD), but a rational expression cannot be simplified by multiplying by the LCD.

Project

PART 1 In this project, we will first examine rational functions that occur when considering averages. We have seen that we can often express the cost of producing x items as a polynomial function. For example, if there is a setup cost of $500 to prepare for production and a variable cost of $12 per item produced, the cost of producing x items is given by the function $c(x) = 12x + 500$. The average cost of producing x items is determined by dividing this cost function by the number of items produced:

$$c_{ave}(x) = \frac{12x + 500}{x}.$$

1. Graph this function, using a window of $(0, 940, 100, 0, 62, 10, 1)$. Sketch the graph.

2. Answer the following questions:

   a. Does the average cost increase or decrease as the number of items produced increases? Explain what the graph indicates.

   b. As x gets arbitrarily large, what value does the average cost approach? Trace along the curve to explore this.

   c. Do you think there is a limit to how low the average cost will drop as x gets larger? Explain.

3. Complete the second column of the following table of values (the $p_{ave}(x)$ column will be completed later):

x	$c_{ave}(x)$	$p_{ave}(x)$
100		
200		
300		
400		
500		
1000		
1500		
2000		
2500		
3000		

4. Will the average cost of producing x items ever become less than $12? Explain what you think is happening. This is an example of a limit, a concept that you will encounter in many mathematics applications.

5. Next, suppose that all the items produced can be sold for $50 each. Write a revenue function $r(x)$.

6. Use the cost and revenue functions to define a profit function $p(x)$.

7. Finally, write an average-profit function
$$p_{ave}(x) = \frac{p(x)}{x}.$$

8. Graph the average-profit function, using the same window as in step 1, and sketch its graph.

9. Complete the table of values in step 3, using the average-profit function from step 7.

10. Describe the behavior of the average-profit function as the number of items produced and sold increases.

11. Discuss what this project has shown you with regard to using mathematics to model a real-world process and understand how the process behaves.

PART II Another rational function was proposed by L. L. Thurstone to model the number of successful acts per unit of time that one could accomplish after a given number of practice sessions. His model was $f(x) = \frac{a(x + b)}{(x + b) + c}$, where $f(x)$ represents the number of successful attempts after x rehearsals. Using $a = 40$, $b = 1$, and $c = 2$, we can hypothesize an example of Thurstone's model as

$$n(x) = \frac{40(x + 1)}{x + 3}$$

where $n(x)$ is the number of words a particular person can read per minute and x is the number of weeks that the person has been practicing. (Note: This hypothetical example is not based on experimental data.)

Use the latter model to answer the following questions:

1. How does $n(x)$ behave as x increases? Sketch a graph of the function.

2. Is there a practical limit to the number of words per minute that the person can read as the number of weeks of practice grows progressively larger?

3. Interpret what Thurstone's model illustrates in this application.

PART III Sear+ch the literature or the Internet for information on another real-world model that uses rational functions. You may find such an application in areas such as learning theory (L. L. Thurstone's work), physiology (the research of W. O. Fems and J. Marsh on muscle contraction), general business (amortization formulas for repaying a loan), physics (acceleration is a function of force divided by mass), electronics (Ahmdahl's law for determining speedup in computer processing), and so on.

Once you have found an application, write a short description of the model used, explaining what its behavior illustrates, and document your reference source.

Radical Expressions, Functions, and Equations

We have discussed radicals and numbers with exponents in several previous chapters. In this chapter, we examine algebraic expressions that involve radicals and rational exponents. We use the properties of radicals and rational exponents to see how to perform mathematical operations on these expressions. Then we study radical equations in one variable and use standard numerical, graphical, and algebraic methods to solve these equations. We complete our discussion with the topic of imaginary numbers and the complex number system.

Radical equations occur in many common real-life situations. For example, the geometric formulas for determining the dimensions of a square or circular object with a given area involve square roots. The geometric formulas for determining the dimensions of a cubic or spherical object from a given volume involve cube roots. Aside from geometry, many kinds of data from statistical analysis can be described by radical expressions. Also, many relations involving acceleration due to gravity use square roots. We will use these kinds of expressions to illustrate concepts throughout this chapter.

In the project at the end of the chapter, we will discuss a more complicated relation involving rational exponents: "windchill" formulas that meterologists use in their weather forecasts.

11.1 RADICAL EXPRESSIONS, FUNCTIONS, AND GRAPHS

OBJECTIVES
1 Evaluate radical expressions with a real-number radicand.
2 Identify radical functions.
3 Determine the domain of radical functions.
4 Graph radical functions.
5 Model real-world situations with expressions and functions involving radicals.

APPLICATION

During the first year of an infant's life, a baby will grow at an astonishing rate. After the first 12 months, the rate of growth decreases. After age 2, growth is at a fairly steady rate. The National Center for Health Statistics modified its 1977 growth charts in 2000. Using these data, the average length, in inches, of a boy aged 0 to 36 months can be estimated by the function $l(x) = 2.96\sqrt{x} + 19.75$, where x is the number of months after birth.

a. What is the average length of a boy at birth? On his first birthday? On his second birthday? On his third birthday?

b. Graph the function.

c. Use the graph to determine whether the function is increasing or decreasing.

d. Determine the approximate age of a boy 27 inches in length.

We will discuss this application further. See page 859.

Objective 11.1.1   **Evaluating Radical Expressions**

In Chapter P, we defined a radical expression as an expression that can be written in the form $\sqrt[n]{a}$, where n (an integer greater than 1) is the index (the plural is *indices*) and a is the radicand. The symbol $\sqrt{}$ is called the radical sign. If the index is 2, it is conventional not to write it.

We revisited square-root expressions in Chapter 9 and simplified square roots with numerical radicands. Now we will discuss radical expressions having indices of 3 and greater. The process of evaluating radicals with even indices differs from that of evaluating radicals with odd indices. We call radicals with even indices even roots. Radicals with odd indices are called odd roots.

Square roots are examples of even roots. In general, to evaluate even roots, we follow the same rules as for evaluating square roots.

To evaluate even roots,

- The radicand of an even root cannot be a negative number, because all real numbers are positive when raised to an even power. (We discuss the case of a negative radicand of an even root in Section 11.7.)
- The principal root, $\sqrt[n]{a}$, is always a positive value.
- The negative root, $-\sqrt[n]{a}$, is always a negative value.

For example,

$\sqrt[4]{-2}$ does not represent a real number.

$\sqrt{-2}$ does not represent a real number.

The principal root $\sqrt[4]{81} = 3$, because $3^4 = 81$.

The principal square root $\sqrt{81} = 9$, because $9^2 = 81$.

The negative root $-\sqrt[4]{81} = -3$, because $-\sqrt[4]{81}$ is the opposite of the principal root $\sqrt[4]{81}$.

The negative square root $-\sqrt{81} = -9$, because $-\sqrt{81}$ is the opposite of the principal root $\sqrt{81}$.

To evaluate odd roots, we do not have to worry about cases such as principal roots, negative roots, or nonreal numbers. For example,

$\sqrt[3]{64} = 4$, because $4^3 = 64$.

$\sqrt[3]{-64} = -4$, because $(-4)^3 = -64$.

$\sqrt[5]{32} = 2$, because $2^5 = 32$.

$\sqrt[5]{-32} = -2$, because $(-2)^5 = -32$.

EVALUATING RADICAL EXPRESSIONS WITH NUMERICAL RADICANDS

To evaluate a radical expression $\sqrt[n]{a}$,

- If n is an integer >1 and $a = 0$, then the result is 0.
- If n is an even integer >1 and $a < 0$, then the result is not a real number.
- If n is an even integer >1 and $a > 0$, then $\sqrt[n]{a} = |b|$ if $b^n = a$.
- If n is an odd integer >1, then $\sqrt[n]{a} = b$ if $b^n = a$.

```
√(32)
        5.656854249
```

If the radicand cannot be written as a power of the index, we approximate the answer. We can use a calculator to do this. For example, $\sqrt{32} \approx 5.657$, because $(5.657)^2 \approx 32$.

EXAMPLE 1

Evaluate. Round your results to the nearest thousandth if necessary.

a. $\sqrt[3]{-12}$ b. $\sqrt[4]{16}$ c. $-\sqrt[4]{16}$ d. $\sqrt[4]{-16}$

Solution

a. $\sqrt[3]{-12} \approx -2.289$, because $(-2.289)^3 \approx -12$.

b. $\sqrt[4]{16} = 2$, because $2^4 = 16$.

c. $-\sqrt[4]{16} = -2$.

   Since $2^4 = 16$, it follows that $-\sqrt[4]{16} = -(2) = -2$. This is the negative root.

d. $\sqrt[4]{-16}$ is not a real number, because the radicand is negative and the root is even.

See **Figures 11.1a** and **11.1b** for calculator solutions. ■

TECHNOLOGY   Roots with Indices Greater than 2

Evaluate.   a. $\sqrt[3]{-12}$ b. $\sqrt[4]{16}$ c. $-\sqrt[4]{16}$ d. $\sqrt[4]{-16}$

```
a. ³√(-12)
            -2.289428485
b. 4ˣ√(16)
                        2
c. -4ˣ√(16)
                       -2
d. 4ˣ√(-16)
```

```
ERR:NONREAL ANS
1▮Quit
2:Goto
```

Figure 11.1a   **Figure 11.1b**

For **Figure 11.1a**,

The cube root is option 4 under the MATH menu.

a.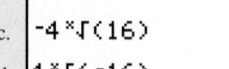

The xth root is option 5 under the MATH menu. Enter the index before the xth root. Enclose the radicand in a set of parentheses.

b. [4] [MATH] [5] [(] [1] [6] [)] [ENTER]

c. [(-)] [4] [MATH] [5] [(] [1] [6] [)] [ENTER]

d. [4] [MATH] [5] [(] [(-)] [1] [6] [)]

For **Figure 11.1b,**

[ENTER]

The error message "NONREAL ANS" means that we are attempting to take an even root of a negative number.

 TAKE NOTE Do not attempt to enter xth roots as a product of the index and the square root $\sqrt[4]{16} \neq 4\sqrt{16}$.

Objective 11.1.1 *CHECKUP*

1. Evaluate. Round results to the nearest thousandth if necessary.
   a. $\sqrt[4]{625}$
   b. $-\sqrt[4]{625}$
   c. $\sqrt[4]{-625}$
   d. $\sqrt[3]{-343}$

2. Explain the difference between finding the square root of a number and squaring a number.

3. When a negative number is multiplied as a factor an even number of times, what will be the sign of the result? Use this fact to explain why the radicand of an even root must be a positive number if the solution is to be a real number.

4. When a negative number is multiplied as a factor an odd number of times, what will be the sign of the result? Use this fact to explain why the radicand of an odd root may be a positive number or a negative number.

Objective 11.1.2 ## Identifying Radical Functions

A **radical relation** equates a radical expression in one independent variable to a dependent variable—for example, $y = \sqrt{x}$ or $y = \sqrt[3]{2x + 5}$.

Some radical relations are also **radical functions** and can be written in function notation, such as $f(x) = \sqrt{x}$ and $g(x) = \sqrt[3]{2x + 5}$.

RADICAL FUNCTION

A radical function can be written in the form

$$f(x) = A(x)$$

where $A(x)$ is a radical expression with the variable x in the radicand.

EXAMPLE 2 State whether each function is a radical function.
   a. $f(x) = \sqrt[3]{5x}$ **b.** $m(x) = 5\sqrt[3]{x}$ **c.** $p(t) = \left(\sqrt{t + 3}\right)^5$

Solution

a. $f(x) = \sqrt[3]{5x}$ is not a radical function, because the radicand does not contain a variable. This is a linear equation.

b. $m(x) = 5\sqrt[3]{x}$ is a radical function, because the radicand contains the independent variable x.

c. $p(t) = \left(\sqrt{t + 3}\right)^5$ is a radical function, because the radicand, $t + 3$, contains the independent variable t.

Objective 11.1.2 *CHECKUP*

1. State whether each function is a radical function.
   a. $f(x) = 2\sqrt{x} + 5$ **b.** $y = \sqrt{2x + 5}$
   c. $y = (\sqrt[3]{x} + 1)^2$

2. How does a radical function differ from a polynomial function?

Objective 11.1.3

Determining the Domain of a Radical Function

In Chapter 10, we saw that rational functions had values excluded from their domains. We called such restrictions on the domain *restricted values*. Radical functions may have values restricted from their domains as well. Sometimes, substituting values for the independent variable in a radical expression results in values that are not real numbers. (In this section, we are concerned with only the real-number system. Another number system is discussed in Section 11.7.) Complete the following set of exercises to determine a method for finding these restricted values.

Guided Discovery 1   Restricted Values

1. Complete the following tables of values for the given radical functions:

   a. $f(x) = \sqrt{x}$

x	$f(x)$
-3	
-2	
-1	
0	
1	

   b. $g(x) = \sqrt[4]{x + 1}$

x	$g(x)$
-3	
-2	
-1	
0	
1	

   c. $h(x) = \sqrt[3]{x}$

x	$h(x)$
-3	
-2	
-1	
0	
1	

   d. $j(x) = \sqrt[5]{x + 1}$

x	$j(x)$
-3	
-2	
-1	
0	
1	

2. Determine the restricted values of each function if possible.

3. The functions in exercises **1a** and **1b** are defined by even roots. The functions in exercises **1c** and **1d** are defined by odd roots. Which functions have restricted values?

4. Graph the given radical functions with restricted values on a decimal calculator screen. Trace each function's graph. What happens when you reach the restricted x-values you found in exercise **2**?

5. Write a rule for determining the restricted values of a radical function by viewing its table of values.

6. Write a rule for determining the restricted values of a radical function by viewing its graph.

7. Write a rule for determining the restricted values of a radical function algebraically.

Only the radical functions defined by even roots have restricted values. In viewing a table of values, the restricted values of a radical function are the numbers that display "ERROR" on a calculator. When we view the function's graph, we see that the restricted values of the function do not have corresponding function values. Since these restricted values occur when the radicand of an even root is less than 0, we can determine the restricted values of even roots algebraically by setting the radicand less than 0 and solving for the independent variable.

We have discovered three methods—numeric, graphic, and algebraic—for determining the restrictions on the domain of a radical function. The numeric and graphic methods have limitations on their effectiveness. They should be used primarily to check the algebraic method.

To determine algebraically the restricted values of a radical function with an even index,

- Set the expression in the radicand less than 0.
- Solve for the independent variable.

This method will find all the restricted values.

To check the restricted integer values of a radical function numerically on your calculator, set up a table of values. Restricted integer values are the x-values that result in nonreal values (ERROR in the table). This method will only determine integer values.

To check the restricted values of a radical function graphically on your calculator, graph the function. The x-values that have no corresponding y-values are restricted values for the radical function. The x-values found by this method will vary according to the window setting of your calculator.

EXAMPLE 3

Determine the restricted values, and then state the domain of the radical function $y = \sqrt[4]{3x} + 1$.

Algebraic Solution

The index, 4, is even. The restricted values occur when the radicand, $3x$, is less than 0.

$$3x < 0$$
$$x < 0$$

The restricted values are all real numbers less than 0.

The domain is all real numbers greater than or equal to 0.

$x \geq 0$ Inequality notation

$[0, \infty)$ Interval notation

Numeric Solution

$Y1 = \sqrt[4]{3x} + 1$

X	Y1
-3	ERROR
-2	ERROR
-1	ERROR
0	1
1	2.3161
2	2.5651
3	2.7321

X=0

The function is not defined for x-values less than 0.

The restricted values are all real numbers less than 0.

The domain is all real numbers greater than or equal to 0.

$x \geq 0$ Inequality notation

$[0, \infty)$ Interval notation

Graphic Solution

$Y1 = \sqrt[4]{3x} + 1$

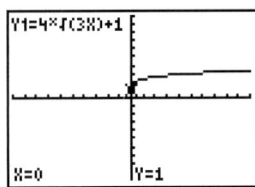

$(-10, 10, -10, 10)$
The graph of the function does not exist for x-values less than 0.

The restricted values are all real numbers less than 0.

The domain is all real numbers greater than or equal to 0.

$x \geq 0$ Inequality notation

$[0, \infty)$ Interval notation

 TAKE NOTE If we want to find the domain directly, without going through the separate step of finding the restricted values, we set the radicand greater than or equal to 0 and solve for the independent variable. For example, $3x \geq 0$, or $x \geq 0$.

EXAMPLE 4 Determine the restricted values algebraically if they exist, and then state the domains of the given radical functions. Check your answers numerically or graphically.

a. $y = \sqrt[3]{x + 5} + \sqrt[3]{x - 8}$ **b.** $f(x) = \sqrt{x + 5} + \sqrt{x - 8}$

c. $g(x) = \sqrt{x^2 + 5x}$

Solution

a. $y = \sqrt[3]{x + 5} + \sqrt[3]{x - 8}$

Algebraic Solution

There are no restricted values, because the index of the radical, 3, is odd.

Domain: All real numbers
$$(-\infty, \infty)$$

Graphic Check

$Y1 = \sqrt[3]{x + 5} + \sqrt[3]{x - 8}$

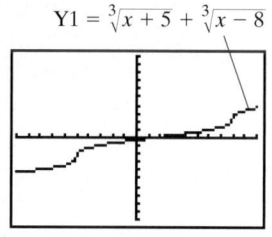

$(-10, 10, -10, 10)$

Since there are no restricted values, check graphically.

The graph appears to be continuous and has no "holes" for restricted values.

b. $f(x) = \sqrt{x + 5} + \sqrt{x - 8}$

Algebraic Solution

There are restricted values, because the index of the radical expressions, 2, is even. To determine the restricted values, set both of the radicands less than 0 and solve for x.

$$x + 5 < 0 \quad \text{or} \quad x - 8 < 0$$
$$x < -5 \qquad\qquad x < 8$$

According to these inequalities, the restricted values are all real numbers less than −5 or all real numbers less than 8. Hence, the restricted values are all real numbers less than 8, since this restriction covers both inequalities.

Domain: All real numbers greater than or equal to 8

$$x \geq 8$$
$$[8, \infty)$$

Numeric Check

X	Y₁	
4	ERROR	
5	ERROR	
6	ERROR	
7	ERROR	
8	3.6056	
9	4.7417	
10	5.2872	

X=8

$Y1 = \sqrt{x + 5} + \sqrt{x - 8}$

The table shows that restricted integer values are less than 8.

c. $g(x) = \sqrt{x^2 + 5x}$

Algebraic Solution

The index, 2, is even. There are restrictions on the domain when the radicand, $x^2 + 5x$, is less than 0 or $x^2 + 5x < 0$. To solve this quadratic inequality, we will first determine the critical points.

$$x^2 + 5x = 0$$

$$x(x + 5) = 0$$

$$x = 0 \quad \text{or} \quad x + 5 = 0$$

$$x = -5$$

We do not include the critical points as a solution because the inequality does not contain equality.

Numeric Check

X	Y1	
-5	0	
-4	ERROR	
-3	ERROR	
-2	ERROR	
-1	ERROR	
0	0	
1	2.4495	

X= -5

$Y1 = \sqrt{x^2 + 5x}$

The table shows the restricted integer values between -5 and 0.

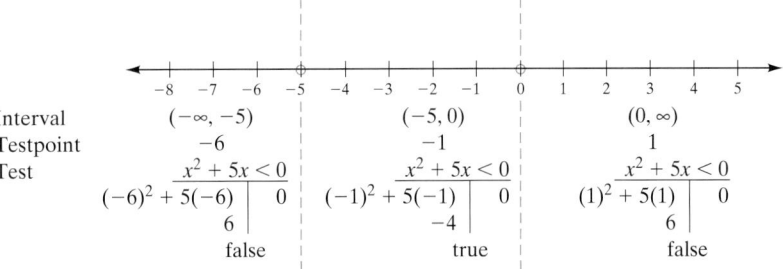

Interval	$(-\infty, -5)$	$(-5, 0)$	$(0, \infty)$
Testpoint	-6	-1	1
Test	$x^2 + 5x < 0$	$x^2 + 5x < 0$	$x^2 + 5x < 0$
	$(-6)^2 + 5(-6) \mid 0$	$(-1)^2 + 5(-1) \mid 0$	$(1)^2 + 5(1) \mid 0$
	6	-4	6
	false	true	false

The restricted values are $(-5, 0)$.
The domain is $(-\infty, -5] \cup [0, \infty)$.

✓ Objective 11.1.3 **CHECKUP**

In exercises 1–2, determine the restricted values and then state the domains of the given functions.

1. $y = \sqrt[4]{3x + 1} - 2$

2. a. $y = \sqrt[3]{x + 2}$ **b.** $g(x) = \sqrt{x + 1} + \sqrt{x - 3}$

     c. $f(x) = \sqrt{x^2 + 3x}$

3. What values must be restricted from the domain of a radical function?

4. When will a radical function have restrictions on its domain?

5. When you graph a radical function on your calculator, how can you tell whether there are restrictions on its domain?

Objective 11.1.4   Graphing Radical Functions

Radical functions have an infinite number of possible solutions. We use a graph to illustrate these solutions. As with any function, to graph a radical function, we determine the domain and then use those values to plot ordered-pair solutions. We need to determine enough ordered pairs so that we can see the pattern. This may be a very lengthy process by hand.

To graph a radical function,

- Determine the restricted values of the domain.
- Determine a table of values by choosing enough x-values in the domain to see a pattern. Pay close attention to the x-values near the restricted values.
- Graph the function by plotting the sample set of ordered pairs from the table of values and connecting the points with a smooth curve determined by the pattern seen. Be careful not to graph a point where x is equal to a restricted value, because the restricted values do not have corresponding function values.

Note: The calculator TABLE function in Ask mode will set up this table.

To graph a radical function on your calculator,

• Enter the equation in Y1.

• Choose an appropriate viewing screen (integer, decimal, standard, or set your own values), and graph the equation.

• Determine individual solutions. Trace and move the cursor, using the left and right arrow keys.

 TAKE NOTE The calculator window setting is very important to the picture you receive. You should consider your choices carefully.

EXAMPLE 5   Graph each radical function.

a. $y = 2\sqrt{3x + 10}$ **b.** $m(x) = \sqrt[3]{2x - 9}$

c. $f(x) = \sqrt{x^2 - x - 6}$

Solution

a. $y = 2\sqrt{3x + 10}$

There are restricted values because the index, 2, is even. The restricted values are

$$3x + 10 < 0$$
$$3x + 10 - 10 < 0 - 10$$
$$3x < -10$$
$$x < -\frac{10}{3}$$

The domain is $\left[-\frac{10}{3}, \infty\right)$.

Complete a table of values by choosing x-values in the domain, which is the set of all real numbers greater than or equal to $-\frac{10}{3}$ or $\left[-\frac{10}{3}, \infty\right)$.

x	y
$-\frac{10}{3}$	0
-3.2	1.2649
-3.1	1.6733
-3	2
-2	4
-1	5.2915
0	6.3246
1	7.2111
2	8
3	8.7178

Graph the ordered pairs found in the table of values, connecting the points with a smooth curve.

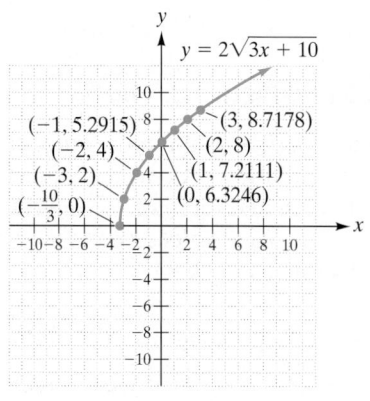

Use your calculator to graph the radical function $y = 2\sqrt{3x + 10}$.

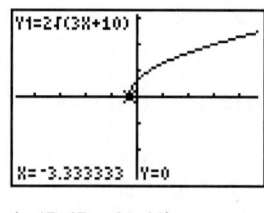

$(-47, 47, -31, 31)$

 TAKE NOTE The endpoint $x = -\frac{10}{3}$ is included in the graph of the function $y = 2\sqrt{3x + 10}$ because it is in the domain.

b. $m(x) = \sqrt[3]{2x - 9}$

There are no restricted values because the index, 3, is odd. The domain of $m(x)$ is the set of all real numbers. Using x-values in the domain, set up a table of values.

x	y
-2	-2.351
-1	-2.224
0	-2.08
1	-1.913
2	-1.71
3	-1.442
4	-1
5	1
6	1.4422
7	1.71
8	1.9129

Graph the ordered pairs found in the table of values, and connect the points with a smooth curve.

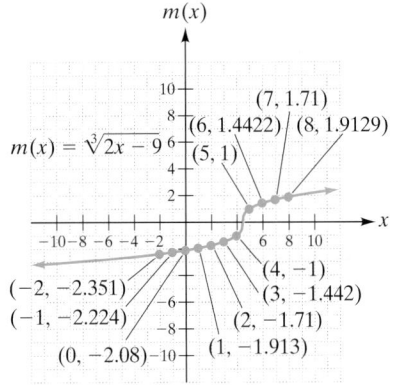

Use your calculator to graph $m(x) = \sqrt[3]{2x - 9}$.

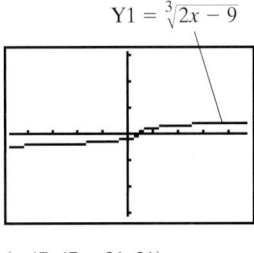

$(-47, 47, -31, 31)$

c. $f(x) = \sqrt{x^2 - x - 6}$

The restricted values are $x^2 - x - 6 < 0$. Determine the critical points.

$$x^2 - x - 6 = 0$$
$$(x - 3)(x + 2) = 0$$
$$x - 3 = 0 \quad \text{or} \quad x + 2 = 0$$
$$x = 3 \qquad\qquad x = -2$$

We do not include the critical points as a solution because the inequality does not contain equality.

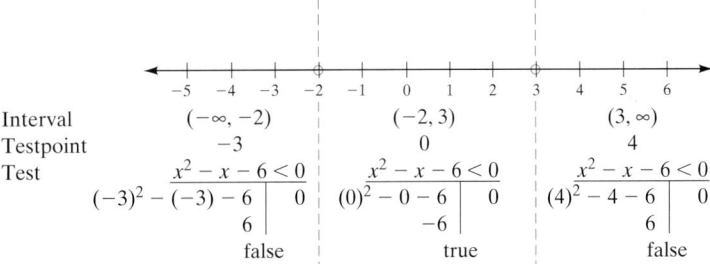

The restricted values are $(-2, 3)$. The domain is $(-\infty, -2] \cup [3, \infty)$. Set up a table of values for each interval.

x	y
-9	9.1652
-6	6
-4	3.7417
-3	2.4495
-2	0
3	0
4	2.4495
5	3.7417
7	6
10	9.1652

Graph the ordered pairs and connect with a smooth curve.

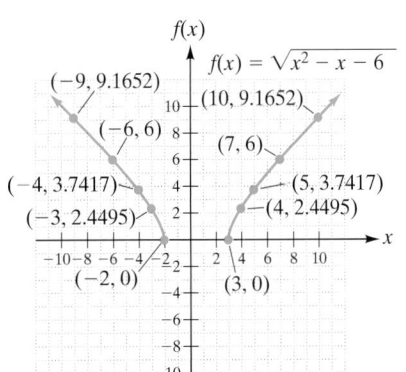

Use your calculator to graph $f(x) = \sqrt{x^2 - x - 6}$.

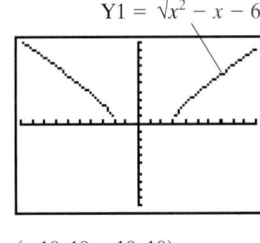

$(-10, 10, -10, 10)$

Objective 11.1.4 *CHECKUP*

1. Graph each radical function.
   a. $y = 2\sqrt{x} + 2$ b. $f(x) = \sqrt[3]{2x - 3}$
   c. $g(x) = \sqrt{x^2 + 2x - 3}$

2. List the steps you would follow to graph a radical function with pencil and paper. What would you do differently if the function had restrictions on its domain?

Objective 11.1.5   Modeling the Real World

In geometry, many area formulas involve squaring a variable. For example, we square the length of a side, s, to obtain the area of a square: $A = s^2$. We can find the exact length of the side by solving the formula for s. When we do, we get $s = \sqrt{A}$. Many volume formulas involve cubing a variable, such as the length of an edge, s. For example, the volume of a cube is $V = s^3$. We can find the exact length of the edge by solving for s. When we do, we obtain $s = \sqrt[3]{V}$.

EXAMPLE 6

A formula for the radius r of a sphere in terms of its volume V is $r = \sqrt[3]{\dfrac{3V}{4\pi}}$.

a. What is the domain of the function?

b. Graph the function.

c. The geodesic dome of the Spaceship Earth at the Epcot Center has a volume of 2.2×10^6 cubic feet. Assuming that the dome is a sphere, what is its diameter?

Solution

a. The function is a cube root with no restrictions on its domain. However, since the function represents the radius of a sphere, it cannot be equal to 0 or less than 0. The domain is $(0, \infty)$.

b. We will set up a table of values using our calculator. Note that 0 is included in the table even though it is not in the domain. We will need the coordinates of this point to determine the endpoint of our graph. The point is plotted as an open dot to show that it is not in the domain of the function.

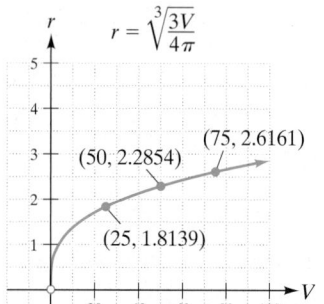

X	Y₁
0	0
25	1.8139
50	2.2854
75	2.6161
100	2.8794
125	3.1018
150	3.2961

X=150

$Y_1 = \sqrt[3]{\dfrac{3x}{4\pi}}$

c. We will use the formula to find the radius of the dome.

$$r = \sqrt[3]{\frac{3V}{4\pi}}$$

$$r = \sqrt[3]{\frac{3(2.2 \times 10^6)}{4\pi}}$$

$$r \approx 80.68$$

```
³√((3(2.2*10^6))
/(4π))
          80.68225425
```

The diameter is twice the radius, or $d = 2r$.

$$d = 2r$$
$$d \approx 2(80.68)$$
$$d \approx 161.36$$

The diameter of the geodesic dome is approximately 161.36 feet.

Every proportion consists of four terms: two means and two extremes.

a—the first term (extreme) $\dfrac{a}{b} = \dfrac{c}{d}$ c—the third term (mean)
b—the second term (mean) d—the fourth term (extreme)

To solve a proportion, we equate the cross products. The product of the extremes will always equal the product of the means.

$$a \cdot d = c \cdot b$$

If a value, m, is repeated in the means and we solve for this value, we obtain

$$\frac{a}{m} = \frac{m}{b}$$
$$m^2 = ab$$
$$m = \pm\sqrt{ab}$$

The positive root of m is the **geometric mean** (mean proportional) of a and b or $m = \sqrt{ab}$.

EXAMPLE 7   If $a = 2$ and $b = 6$, find the geometric mean.

Solution

$$m = \sqrt{ab} \qquad m = \sqrt{4 \cdot 3}$$
$$m = \sqrt{2 \cdot 6} \qquad m = 2\sqrt{3}$$
$$m = \sqrt{12} \qquad m \approx 3.46$$

APPLICATION

During the first year of an infant's life, a baby will grow at an astonishing rate. After the first 12 months, the rate of growth decreases. After age 2, growth is at a fairly steady rate. The National Center for Health Statistics modified its 1977 growth charts in 2000. Using these data, the average length, in inches, of a boy aged 0 to 36 months can be estimated by the function $l(x) = 2.96\sqrt{x} + 19.75$, where x is the number of months after birth.

a. What is the average length of a boy at birth? On his first birthday? On his second birthday? On his third birthday?
b. Graph the function.
c. Use the graph to determine whether the function is increasing or decreasing.
d. Determine the approximate age of a boy 27 inches in length.

Discussion

a. Set up a table of values for $x = 0$ (birth), $x = 12$ (first birthday), $x = 24$ (second birthday), and $x = 36$ (third birthday).

x	$l(x)$	
0	19.75	At 0 months, an average length of a boy is 19.75 inches.
12	30.00	At 12 months, an average length of a boy is 30.00 inches.
24	34.25	At 24 months, an average length of a boy is 34.25 inches.
36	37.51	At 36 months, an average length of a boy is 37.51 inches.

b.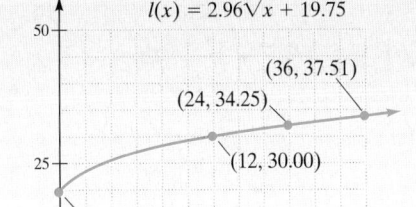

c. The function is increasing. (The graph rises as we trace from left to right.)

d.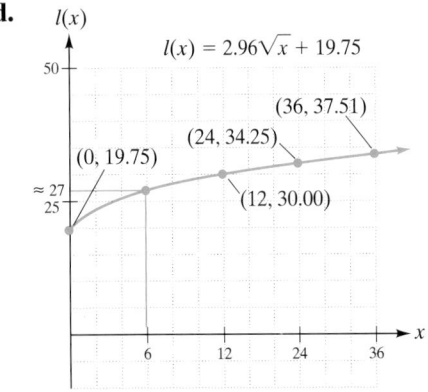

A boy will be approximately 27 inches long at age 6 months.

Objective 11.1.5 *CHECKUP*

1. A formula for the radius r of a circle in terms of its area A is

$$r = \sqrt{\frac{A}{\pi}}.$$

  a. What is the domain of the function?
  b. Graph the function.
  c. The area covered by the dome of Saint Peter's Basilica in Rome is approximately 19,360 square feet. Assuming that the area of the floor space covered by the dome is a circle, what is the dome's diameter?

2. If $a = 5$ and $b = 10$, find the geometric mean, m. (Use the formula $m = \sqrt{ab}$.)

3. The average length, in inches, of a girl aged 0 to 36 months can be estimated by the function $l(x) = 3\sqrt{x} + 19.4$, where x is the number of months after birth.

  a. What is the average length of a girl at birth? On her first birthday? On her second birthday? On her third birthday?
  b. Graph the function.
  c. Determine the approximate age of a girl 28.4 inches in length.

11.1 EXERCISES

Student Solutions Manual PH Math/Tutor Center CD Video *Math*XL MathXL® *MyMathLab* MyMathLab Interactmath.com

Round, to the nearest thousandth if necessary.

1. $-\sqrt[4]{1296}$ **2.** $-\sqrt[4]{2401}$ **3.** $\sqrt[4]{-1296}$ **4.** $\sqrt[4]{-2401}$

5. $\sqrt[3]{216}$ **6.** $\sqrt[3]{1331}$ **7.** $\sqrt[3]{-216}$ **8.** $\sqrt[3]{-1331}$

9. $-\sqrt[3]{216}$ **10.** $-\sqrt[3]{1331}$ **11.** $\sqrt{110}$ **12.** $\sqrt{200}$

13. $-\sqrt{110}$ **14.** $-\sqrt{200}$ **15.** $\sqrt{-110}$ **16.** $\sqrt{-200}$

17. $\sqrt[3]{110}$ **18.** $\sqrt[3]{200}$ **19.** $-\sqrt[3]{110}$ **20.** $-\sqrt[3]{200}$

21. $\sqrt[5]{20}$ **22.** $\sqrt[6]{25}$ **23.** $\sqrt[3]{12.5}$ **24.** $\sqrt[4]{72.8}$

Identify each function as radical or nonradical.

25. $y = \sqrt{5x} + 7$ **26.** $f(x) = 5\sqrt{4x - 7} + 8$ **27.** $f(x) = 2\sqrt{3x + 1} - 5$ **28.** $y = 13 - \sqrt{7x}$

Determine the restricted values, and then state the domain of each function.

29. $y = \sqrt{x - 3}$ **30.** $y = \sqrt{3x + 5}$ **31.** $y = 5 + 4\sqrt{x}$

32. $y = 2\sqrt{x} + 3$ **33.** $y = \sqrt[3]{x - 3}$ **34.** $y = \sqrt[3]{3x + 5}$

35. $f(x) = \sqrt{3x - 1} - \sqrt{x + 2}$ **36.** $f(x) = \sqrt{2x + 1} - \sqrt{x - 3}$ **37.** $y = \sqrt{x^2 + 2x}$

38. $y = \sqrt{x^2 - 5x}$ **39.** $g(x) = \sqrt{x^2 - 6x + 8}$ **40.** $g(x) = \sqrt{x^2 - 3x - 10}$

In exercises 41–50, create a table of values and graph the functions on a Cartesian coordinate plane. Check, using your calculator.

41. $f(x) = \sqrt{x - 5}$ **42.** $h(x) = \sqrt{2x + 5}$ **43.** $y = \sqrt[3]{x} - 5$ **44.** $y = \sqrt[3]{x} + 5$

45. $y = 5\sqrt{x} - 10$ **46.** $y = 6 - 3\sqrt{x}$ **47.** $g(x) = \sqrt[3]{8x}$ **48.** $p(x) = -\sqrt[3]{4x}$

49. $y = \sqrt{x^2 - x - 2}$ **50.** $y = \sqrt{x^2 - x - 12}$

Geometric Mean

In exercises 51–58, recall that the geometric mean, m, of two quantities a and b is defined to be $m = \sqrt{ab}$.

51. Find the geometric mean if $a = 5$ and $b = 13$.

52. Find the geometric mean if $a = 3$ and $b = 17$.

53. Find the geometric mean if $a = 135$ and $b = 495$.

54. Find the geometric mean if $a = -200$ and $b = -500$.

55. Find a function for the geometric mean if $a = x$ and $b = x - 5$. What is the domain of this function? Graph this function.

56. Find a function for the geometric mean if $a = x$ and $b = x + 1$. What is the domain of this function? Graph this function.

57. Find a function for the geometric mean if $a = x + 3$ and $b = x - 7$. What is the domain of this function? Graph this function.

58. Find a function for the geometric mean if $a = x - 5$ and $b = x - 4$. What is the domain of this function? Graph this function.

Geometry

59. A painting is in the shape of a square. Given the area of the painting, write the equation for the length of a side. Find the length of a side in each situation.
   a. The painting is a mural whose area is 289 square feet.
   b. The painting is a canvas whose area is 90.25 square inches.
   c. The painting is a locket whose area is 115 square millimeters.

60. A canvas cover has a square shape. Find the length of a side in each situation.
   a. The canvas covers an area of 529 square yards.
   b. The canvas covers an area of 110.25 square centimeters.
   c. The canvas covers an area of 45 square feet.

61. A puddle of standing water has the shape of a circle. Given the area of the puddle, write the equation for the length of its radius. Find the exact length of the radius of the puddle in each situation. Then approximate the length to the nearest thousandth.
   a. The puddle has an area of 196π square inches.
   b. The puddle has an area of 49 square yards.
   c. The puddle has an area of 108 square meters.

62. Find the exact length of the radius of a circular metal ring that encloses the area cited. Then approximate the length to the nearest thousandth.
   a. The metal ring encloses an area of 225π square decimeters.
   b. The metal ring encloses an area of 361 square feet.
   c. The metal ring encloses an area of 200 square centimeters.

63. The area covered by the dome of St. Paul's Cathedral in London is approximately 8200 square feet. Using the formula for the circular area covered by a dome, write the equation for the length of the radius of the circle. What is the radius of the dome? What is its diameter?

64. The area of the square floor of the central building of the Taj Mahal is approximately 377,000 square feet. Using the formula for the area of a square, write the equation for the length of a side of the floor. What is the length of one of its sides?

Statistics

65. In statistical analyses, data are often summarized in tables called frequency tables. In designing such a table, rules of thumb are used to decide on the number of rows in the table. One such rule is that r, the number of rows in the table, should be equal to the square root of n, the number of pieces of data collected. Graph this relation for values of n ranging from 0 to 400. How many rows should you have in a frequency table for 250 pieces of data?

66. In statistics, if a set of data consists of the integers from 1 to n, the variability of the numbers is given by

$$s = \sqrt{\frac{n(n + 1)}{12}}$$

Graph this relation for values of n ranging from 1 to 250. What is the variability of the integers from 1 to 150?

Business

67. The cost to make x units of a product is $C(x) = 2x + 2\sqrt{x - 5}$, where at least 5 units must be made.
 a. What is the cost to make 10 units? To make 15 units?
 b. Graph the function on its domain.
 c. Use the graph to determine whether the function is increasing or decreasing.
 d. If cost is $122, how many units were made?

68. The cost to make x units of a product is $C(x) = 2x - 3\sqrt{x + 9}$, where at least 7 units must be made.
 a. What is the cost to make 10 units? To make 15 units?
 b. Graph the function on its domain.
 c. Use the graph to determine whether the function is increasing or decreasing.
 d. If cost is $117, how many units were made?

69. The price of a manufacturing unit is $P(x) = 35 - \sqrt{x - 2}$.
 a. Write a function for the revenue, $R(x)$, if x units are sold.

b. What is the revenue if 10 units are sold? If 15 units are sold?
 c. What is the domain of the revenue function?
 d. Graph the function on its domain.
 e. Use the graph to determine whether the function is increasing or decreasing.
 f. If revenue is $1428, how many units were sold?

70. The price of a manufacturing unit is $P(x) = 2.7 + \sqrt{3x + 1}$.
 a. Write a function for the revenue, $R(x)$, if x units are sold.
 b. What is the revenue if 15 units are sold? If 20 units are sold?
 c. What is the domain of the revenue function?
 d. Graph the function on its domain.
 e. Use the graph to determine whether the function is increasing or decreasing.
 f. If revenue is $548, how many units were sold?

Real Data

71. An east coast city's average monthly temperature can be approximated by the function $T(x) = 22\sqrt{x + 1}$ for $0 \le x \le 8$, where x is the number of months after January.
 a. Graph the function on its domain.
 b. Use the graph to determine whether the function is increasing or decreasing.
 c. In what month will the average temperature be 50 degrees?

72. An Alaskan city's average monthly temperature can be approximated by the function $T(x) = \dfrac{44}{\sqrt{x^2 + 1}}$ for $0 \le x \le 5$, where x is the number of months after September.
 a. Graph the function on its domain.
 b. Use the graph to determine whether the function is increasing or decreasing.
 c. In what month will the average temperature be 20 degrees?

73. The percent change in the Consumer Price Index can be estimated by the function $P(x) = \sqrt[3]{\dfrac{110}{x}}$ for $x \ge 1$, where x is the number of years after 2000.
 a. Graph the function.
 b. Use the graph to determine whether the function is increasing or decreasing.
 c. Assuming the trend continues, in what year will the percent change be 2.5%?

74. The amount of money in cents per pound received by U.S. farmers for wool can be estimated by the function $A(t) = \sqrt[3]{47{,}000t - 45{,}000} + 24$ for $t \ge 1$, where t is the number of years after 2000.
 a. Graph the function.
 b. Use the graph to determine whether the function is increasing or decreasing.
 c. Assuming the trend continues, in what year will the amount be 86 cents per pound?

11.1 Calculator Exercises

In graphing a radical function in which the radicand is a perfect square, an interesting result occurs. To see this, first store $f(x) = \sqrt{x^2 + 6x + 9}$ in Y1 on your calculator, and graph $f(x)$. Notice that the graph never drops below the x-axis. Can you explain why?

Now store $g(x) = x + 3$ in Y2 on your calculator, and graph that function. What do you notice about this graph? You should see that the graphs coincide for certain values of x. Determine the interval for which the graphs coincide. Are the two functions equivalent?

Now store $h(x) = |x + 3|$ in Y3, and set Y3 to use the bubble test when it graphs. (To use the bubble, move the cursor to the left of Y3, and press ⟨ **ENTER** ⟩ repeatedly until you see the "−0"

icon.) Does this graph coincide with either $f(x)$ or $g(x)$? Does it suggest how you can simplify $f(x)$?

Next, consider the following simplification of $f(x)$:

$$f(x) = \sqrt{x^2 + 6x + 9} = \sqrt{(x + 3)^2} = x + 3$$

What is wrong with this simplified function? Your calculator graphs should suggest that $f(x)$ does not always simplify as shown. Can you properly state how $f(x)$ simplifies?

Use the same approach to explore the following functions:

1. $f(x) = \sqrt{x^2 - 4x + 4}$
2. $f(x) = \sqrt{4x^2 - 12x + 9}$

11.1 Writing Exercise

For certain values of x, $\sqrt{x^2} = x$, and for certain other values of x, $\sqrt{x^2} = -x$. Identify the values of x that make each statement true. Then explain how you determined your answer.

11.2 RATIONAL EXPONENTS

OBJECTIVES

1 Evaluate expressions of the form $a^{1/n}$, where a is a real number and n is a positive or negative integer.

2 Evaluate expressions of the form $a^{m/n}$, where a is a real number, m is a positive or negative integer, and n is a positive integer.

3 Graph a function defined as an expression having a rational exponent.

4 Model real-world situations by using expressions involving rational exponents.

APPLICATION

A major concern for a person or animal in cold weather is frostbite—damage to body tissue caused by being frozen. Since wind and cold affect the rate of heat lost through exposed skin, knowing the time it takes to become frostbitten is very important.

According to Environment Canada, the time to frostbite in t minutes is related to the wind speed v in km/h at a height of 10 m and the actual air temperature $T°C$ by the formula

$$t = \{[-24.5(0.667v + 4.8)] + 2111\} \cdot (-4.8 - T)^{-1.668}$$

If the wind speed is a constant 40 km/h and the temperature is forecast to drop from $-25°C$ to $-50°C$, determine the time to frostbite at $5°C$ intervals.

After completing this section, we will discuss this application further. See page 870.

Objective 11.2.1   ### Evaluating Expressions Involving $a^{1/n}$

In Chapter P, we evaluated expressions having exponents. In this chapter, we have evaluated expressions involving radicals. There is a relationship between these two types of expressions. Let's see if we can discover the relationship with our calculators.

 Guided Discovery 2   Radical and Rational Exponents

Evaluate each expression, and compare the results obtained in part **a** with the corresponding results in part **b**.

1. a. $\sqrt{3} =$ _____   **b.** $3^{1/2} =$ _____

2. a. $\sqrt[3]{3} =$ _____   **b.** $3^{1/3} =$ _____

3. a. $\sqrt[4]{3} =$ _____   **b.** $3^{1/4} =$ _____

Write a rule for writing a radical expression as an exponential expression.

In part **a**, we evaluate a radical expression. In part **b**, we evaluate an exponential expression consisting of a base that is the same as the radicand of the radical expression in part **a** and an exponent that is the reciprocal of the index of the radical expression in part **a**. The results are the same.

We define an expression with a positive rational exponent having a numerator of 1 to be a radical expression.

EXPRESSIONS WITH RATIONAL EXPONENTS HAVING A NUMERATOR OF 1

$$a^{1/n} = \sqrt[n]{a}$$

In this equation, a is a real number and n is a positive integer >1.

EXAMPLE 1   Write the following expressions as radical expressions, and evaluate them if possible.

a. $625^{1/4}$ b. $-625^{1/4}$ c. $(-625)^{1/4}$

d. $1024^{1/5}$ e. $-1024^{1/5}$ f. $(-1024)^{1/5}$

Solution

a. $625^{1/4} = \sqrt[4]{625} = 5$ $5^4 = 625$

b. $-625^{1/4} = -\sqrt[4]{625} = -5$ The negative sign is not part of the base and therefore indicates a negative root.

c. $(-625)^{1/4} = \sqrt[4]{-625}$, which is not a real number.   The radicand is negative and the index is even.

d. $1024^{1/5} = \sqrt[5]{1024} = 4$ $4^5 = 1024$

e. $-1024^{1/5} = -\sqrt[5]{1024} = -4$ The negative sign is not part of the base and therefore indicates a negative root.

f. $(-1024)^{1/5} = \sqrt[5]{-1024} = -4$ $(-4)^5 = -1024$

Check

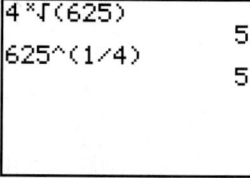

```
4 ˣ√(625)
               5
625^(1/4)
               5
```

Figure 11.2

To check your solution, enter the radical expression and the expression having a rational exponent. The results should be the same. The check for Example 1a is shown in **Figure 11.2.**   ■

We can also define a negative rational exponent as a radical expression.

EXPRESSIONS WITH NEGATIVE RATIONAL EXPONENTS HAVING A NUMERATOR OF 1

$$a^{-1/n} = \frac{1}{a^{1/n}} = \frac{1}{\sqrt[n]{a}}, a \neq 0$$

In these equations, a is a real number and n is a positive integer >1.

EXAMPLE 2   Write the following expressions as radical expressions, and evaluate them if possible. Express your answers as fractions.

a. $625^{-1/4}$ b. $-625^{-1/4}$ c. $(-625)^{-1/4}$

d. $1024^{-1/5}$ e. $-1024^{-1/5}$ f. $(-1024)^{-1/5}$

Solution

a. $625^{-1/4} = \dfrac{1}{625^{1/4}} = \dfrac{1}{\sqrt[4]{625}} = \dfrac{1}{5}$ $5^4 = 625$

b. $-625^{-1/4} = -\dfrac{1}{625^{1/4}} = -\dfrac{1}{\sqrt[4]{625}} = -\dfrac{1}{5}$ $5^4 = 625$

c. $(-625)^{-1/4} = \dfrac{1}{(-625)^{1/4}} = \dfrac{1}{\sqrt[4]{-625}}$, which is not a real number.   The radicand is negative and the index is even.

d. $1024^{-1/5} = \dfrac{1}{1024^{1/5}} = \dfrac{1}{\sqrt[5]{1024}} = \dfrac{1}{4}$ $4^5 = 1024$

e. $-1024^{-1/5} = -\dfrac{1}{1024^{1/5}} = -\dfrac{1}{\sqrt[5]{1024}} = -\dfrac{1}{4}$ $4^5 = 1024$

f. $(-1024)^{-1/5} = \dfrac{1}{(-1024)^{1/5}} = \dfrac{1}{\sqrt[5]{-1024}} = \dfrac{1}{-4} = -\dfrac{1}{4}$ $(-4)^5 = -1024$

Check

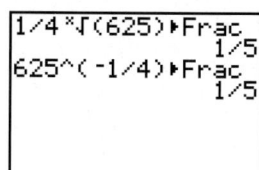

```
1/4 ˣ√(625)▶Frac
               1/5
625^(-1/4)▶Frac
               1/5
```

Figure 11.3

The check for Example 2a is shown in **Figure 11.3.**   ■

If the radicand cannot be written as a power of the index, approximate the answer. Use your calculator to do this.

EXAMPLE 3

```
625^(1/5)
       3.623898318
-1024^(-1/4)
       -.1767766953
```

Evaluate. Round to the nearest thousandth.

a. $625^{1/5}$ **b.** $-1024^{-1/4}$

Calculator Solution

a. $625^{1/5} \approx 3.624$ **b.** $-1024^{-1/4} \approx -0.177$ ■

✓ Objective 11.2.1 **CHECKUP**

1. Write as a radical expression, and evaluate if possible.
   a. $16^{1/4}$ **b.** $-16^{1/4}$ **c.** $(-16)^{1/4}$
   d. $125^{1/3}$ **e.** $-125^{1/3}$ **f.** $(-125)^{1/3}$

2. Write as a radical expression, and evaluate if possible. Express your answer as a fraction.
   a. $125^{-1/3}$ **b.** $-125^{-1/3}$ **c.** $(-125)^{-1/3}$
   d. $16^{-1/4}$ **e.** $-16^{-1/4}$ **f.** $(-16)^{-1/4}$

3. Evaluate. Round to the nearest thousandth.
   a. $16^{1/3}$ **b.** $-125^{1/4}$

4. Describe the relationship between a radical expression and an expression with a rational exponent whose numerator is equal to 1.   ▪

Objective 11.2.2   **Evaluating Expressions Involving $a^{m/n}$**

Some expressions, such as $4^{3/2}$, have a rational exponent with a numerator not equal to 1. We need to be able to evaluate these expressions. Complete the following set of exercises with your calculator to discover a rule for writing an equivalent radical expression from an expression containing a rational exponent.

 Guided Discovery 3   More Radicals and Rational Exponents

Evaluate each expression, and compare the results obtained in each exercise.

1. **a.** $4^{3/2} = $ _____   **b.** $\left(\sqrt{4}\right)^3 = $ _____
   c. $\sqrt{4^3} = $ _____

2. **a.** $64^{2/3} = $ _____   **b.** $\left(\sqrt[3]{64}\right)^2 = $ _____
   c. $\sqrt[3]{64^2} = $ _____

3. **a.** $8^{4/3} = $ _____   **b.** $\left(\sqrt[3]{8}\right)^4 = $ _____
   c. $\sqrt[3]{8^4} = $ _____

4. **a.** $(-8)^{4/3} = $ _____   **b.** $\left(\sqrt[3]{-8}\right)^4 = $ _____
   c. $\sqrt[3]{(-8)^4} = $ _____

Write a rule for converting an expression with a rational exponent to a radical expression.

In each exercise, the two radical expressions have the same value as the expression with a rational exponent. (If you are using a calculator other than the TI-84, this may not be true. If your calculator is one of these, see 11.2 Calculator Exercises.) As we already know, the base of the expression with a rational exponent is the radicand of the radical expression, and the denominator of the rational exponent is the index of the radical expression. The numerator of the rational exponent is the power to which the radical expression is raised, or the power to which the radicand is raised.

We can confirm these statements by rewriting the radical expression as an expression with a rational exponent and simplifying by means of the power-to-a-power rule for exponents. For example, in the first Guided Discovery 3 exercise,

$$\left(\sqrt{4}\right)^3 = (4^{1/2})^3 = 4^{3/2} \quad \text{or} \quad \sqrt{4^3} = (4^3)^{1/2} = 4^{3/2}$$

Therefore, $4^{3/2} = \left(\sqrt{4}\right)^3 = \sqrt{4^3}$.

In general,

$$(\sqrt[n]{a})^m = (a^{1/n})^m = a^{m/n} \quad \text{or} \quad \sqrt[n]{a^m} = (a^m)^{1/n} = a^{m/n}$$

Therefore, $a^{m/n} = (\sqrt[n]{a})^m = \sqrt[n]{a^m}$.

RATIONAL EXPONENTS

$$a^{m/n} = \sqrt[n]{a^m} \quad \text{or} \quad (\sqrt[n]{a})^m$$

In this equation, a is a real number, $a^{1/n}$ is defined, m and n have no common factors other than 1, m is an integer $\neq 0$, and n is a positive integer >1.

 TAKE NOTE Whether one takes the power or the root first does not matter.

EXAMPLE 4 Write as an equivalent radical expression, and evaluate.

   a. $4^{3/2}$ b. $(-32)^{3/5}$ c. $12^{2/5}$
   d. $16^{-3/4}$ e. $-32^{-4/5}$

Solution

a. $4^{3/2} = (\sqrt{4})^3 = 2^3 = 8$ or $4^{3/2} = \sqrt{4^3} = \sqrt{64} = 8$

b. $(-32)^{3/5} = (\sqrt[5]{-32})^3 = (-2)^3 = -8$ or $\sqrt[5]{(-32)^3} = \sqrt[5]{-32,768} = -8$

c. $12^{2/5} = (\sqrt[5]{12})^2 \approx 2.702$ *Calculate on your calculator, because 12 cannot be written as a power of the index 5.*

d. $16^{-3/4} = \dfrac{1}{16^{3/4}} = \dfrac{1}{(\sqrt[4]{16})^3} = \dfrac{1}{(2)^3} = \dfrac{1}{8}$

or

$16^{-3/4} = \dfrac{1}{16^{3/4}} = \dfrac{1}{\sqrt[4]{16^3}} = \dfrac{1}{\sqrt[4]{4096}} = \dfrac{1}{8}$

e. $-32^{-4/5} = -\dfrac{1}{32^{4/5}} = -\dfrac{1}{(\sqrt[5]{32})^4} = -\dfrac{1}{2^4} = -\dfrac{1}{16}$ *Write as a positive exponent first.*

Check

```
(√(4))³
                    8
4^(3/2)
                    8
```

Figure 11.4

To check on your calculator, enter the radical expression and the exponential expression.
The check for Example 4a is shown in **Figure 11.4**. ∎

Objective 11.2.2 *CHECKUP*

1. Write as an equivalent radical expression, and evaluate.
   a. $16^{3/2}$ b. $(-125)^{5/3}$ c. $15^{3/2}$
   d. $81^{-3/4}$ e. $-125^{-5/3}$

2. Explain how the numerator and the denominator of a rational exponent are used to transform an expression into a radical expression. ∎

Objective 11.2.3 **Graphing a Radical Function**

Since a radical expression can be expressed as an expression with a rational exponent, a radical function such as $f(x) = \sqrt{x}$ can also be written as $f(x) = x^{1/2}$. We determine the domain of a function defined by an expression involving a rational exponent as if it were defined by a radical expression. Remember that radical functions with odd indices do not have restricted values. Therefore, if the rational exponent has a denominator that is an odd integer, the function has no restriction on its domain.

To determine algebraically the restricted values of a function defined by an expression involving rational exponents with an even denominator (or an even index),

- Set the base of the expression involving rational exponents less than 0.
- Solve for the independent variable.

EXAMPLE 5   Determine the restricted values algebraically if they exist, and then state the domain of each function. Check your answer numerically or graphically.

a. $y = (x - 7)^{2/5}$ **b.** $g(x) = (3x + 4)^{3/4}$

Solution

a. $y = (x - 7)^{2/5}$

The function has no restricted values, because the denominator of the rational exponent, 5, is odd.

Domain: All real numbers

$$(-\infty, \infty)$$

Graphic Check

Since there are no restricted values, check graphically.

$$Y1 = (x - 7)^{2/5}$$

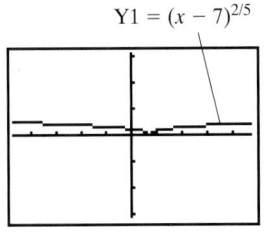

$(-47, 47, -31, 31)$

The graph appears to be continuous and has no "holes" for restricted values.

b. $g(x) = (3x + 4)^{3/4}$

The function has restricted values, because the denominator of the rational exponent is even. To determine the restricted values, set the base of the expression less than 0 and solve for x.

$$3x + 4 < 0$$

$$x < -\frac{4}{3}$$

The restricted values are all real numbers less than $-\frac{4}{3}$.

Domain: All real numbers greater than or equal to $-\frac{4}{3}$

$$x \geq -\frac{4}{3}$$

$$\left[-\frac{4}{3}, \infty\right)$$

Numeric Check

Since the restricted values are less than a fraction, check the solution numerically by selecting x-values close to $-\frac{4}{3}$. This will not be an exact check.

X	Y1
-1.6	ERROR
-1.5	ERROR
-1.4	ERROR
-1.3	.17783
-1.2	.50297
-1.1	.76529
-1	1

X=-1.6

$$Y1 = (3x + 4)^{3/4}$$

Viewing the table, we see that x-values less than -1.3 are restricted. It appears that the restricted values are $x < -1.3$. ■

We graph a radical function defined by an expression involving rational exponents in the same manner as we do other radical functions.

To graph a radical function defined by an expression involving rational exponents,

- Determine the restricted values.
- Determine a table of values by choosing enough points to determine the curve. Pay attention to the x-values that are close to the restricted values.
- Graph the points. Do not graph a point having an x-value equal to a restricted value.

EXAMPLE 6 Graph each radical function.

  a. $y = -3x^{3/4}$ **b.** $g(x) = 5(x + 1)^{2/3}$

Solution

a. $y = -3x^{3/4}$

Set up a table of values by using x-values in the domain, which is the set of all real numbers greater than or equal to 0.

x	y
0	0
0.1	-0.5335
0.5	-1.784
1	-3
2	-5.045
3	-6.839
4	-8.485
5	-10.03
6	-11.5
7	-12.91

Graph the ordered pairs found in the table of values, and connect the points with a smooth curve.

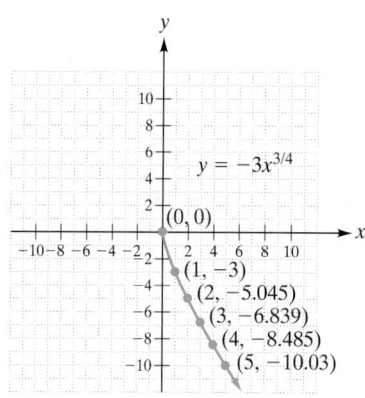

Calculator Check

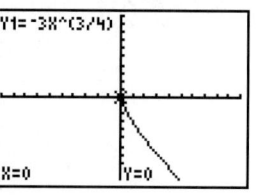

$(-10, 10, -10, 10)$

b. $g(x) = 5(x + 1)^{2/3}$

Set up a table of values by using x-values in the domain, the set of all real numbers.

x	$g(x)$
-3	7.937
-2	5
-1	0
0	5
1	7.937
2	10.4

Graph the ordered pairs found in the table of values, and connect the points with a smooth curve.

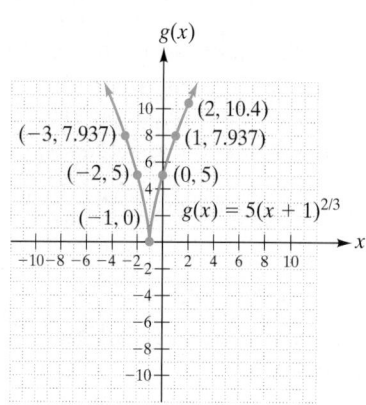

Calculator Check

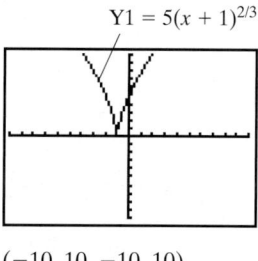

$(-10, 10, -10, 10)$

✓ Objective 11.2.3 CHECKUP

1. Determine the restricted values algebraically if they exist, and then state the domain of each function. Check your answer numerically or graphically.

   a. $y = (x + 2)^{1/2}$ **b.** $f(x) = (2x - 8)^{4/3}$

2. Graph each radical function and check your graphs with your calculator.

   a. $y = -2x^{1/5}$ **b.** $f(x) = 2(x - 1)^{3/2}$

3. List the steps that you should follow if you are graphing a radical function defined by an expression involving rational exponents.

Objective 11.2.4 Modeling the Real World

We have seen that formulas can give rise to radical functions. Often these formulas can be written as expressions involving rational exponents. One such formula is the geometric mean. This formula can be expanded to determine useful averages.

Frequently, a table of values or a graph of the radical function makes it easier to see a bigger "picture" of what is happening.

The geometric mean is a useful average when data vary from very low to very high levels. It can be used to average bacteria levels for water quality standards. It is computed by taking the 1/nth power of the product of n factors.

EXAMPLE 7

A local beach needs to measure bacteria levels for the safety of swimmers. During one hot July month, the readings were as follows:

Week 1—4 fecal bacteria per 100 ml.
Week 2—20 fecal bacteria per 100 ml.
Week 3—1100 fecal bacteria per 100 ml.
Week 4—800 fecal bacteria per 100 ml.

Use the geometric mean to calculate the average bacteria level.

Solution

There are 4 factors given. Therefore, $n = 4$. To calculate the average bacteria level, take the 1/nth or 1/4th power of the product of the 4 factors: 4, 20, 1100, 800.

$$(4 \cdot 20 \cdot 1100 \cdot 800)^{1/4} = 70{,}400{,}000^{1/4} \approx 91.6$$

The average bacteria level was 91.6 fecal bacteria per 100 ml.   ■

EXAMPLE 8

The absolute luminosity (brightness) of a main-sequence star (a star similar to our Sun) is proportional to the 3.5 power of its mass.

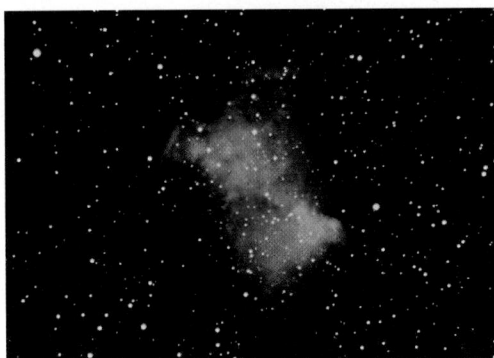

A function, $y = x^{3.5}$, can be used to compare the luminosity of a main-sequence star whose mass is x times that of the Sun with the luminosity of the Sun.

a. Use the comparison function to set up a table of values to compare main-sequence stars whose masses are 1, 10, and 100 times the mass of the Sun ($M_{\odot}$).

b. Graph the comparison function, and specify whether it is increasing or decreasing.

c. If the mass of a star is 10 times the mass of another star, approximately how much brighter (to the nearest thousand units) will the larger star be?

Solution

a. Let Y1 = $x^{3.5}$, and use the Ask mode of TblSet to generate the table of values.

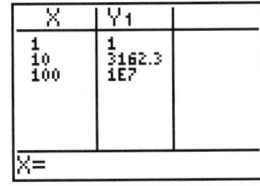

b.

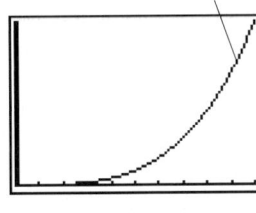

$(0, 100, 0, 1 \times 10^7)$

The function is increasing, because its graph rises from left to right.

c. In comparing the absolute luminosities of two stars of mass $M = 1M_\odot$ and $M = 10M_\odot$, we see that the second star has 10 times more mass than the first. The brightness increases from 1 to about 3162.

$$\frac{3162}{1} = 3162 \approx 3000$$

The star with mass $10M_\odot$ is about 3000 times as bright as the star with $1M_\odot$.

When we compare $M = 10M_\odot$ and $M = 100M_\odot$ (the mass increased 10 times), we find that the luminosity increases from 3162 to 10,000,000.

$$\frac{10,000,000}{3162} \approx 3163 \approx 3000$$

Similarly, the brightness increases about 3000 times.

APPLICATION

A major concern for a person or animal in cold weather is frostbite—damage to body tissue caused by being frozen. Since wind and cold affect the rate of heat lost through exposed skin, knowing the time it takes to become frostbitten is very important.

According to Environment Canada, the time to frostbite in t minutes is related to the wind speed v in km/h at a height of 10 m and the actual air temperature $T°C$ by the formula

$$t = \{[-24.5(0.667v + 4.8)] + 2111\} \cdot (-4.8 - T)^{-1.668}$$

If the wind speed is a constant 40 km/h and the temperature is forecast to drop from $-25°C$ to $-50°C$, determine the time to frostbite at 5°C intervals.

Discussion

Environment Canada states that the time in minutes to frostbite is related to the wind speed and air temperature. If the wind speed is constant, we can simplify the relation by substituting the wind speed of 40 km/h into the equation.

$$t = \{[-24.5(0.667v + 4.8)] + 2111\} \cdot (-4.8 - T)^{-1.668}$$

$$t = \{[-24.5(0.667 \cdot 40 + 4.8)] + 2111\} \cdot (-4.8 - T)^{-1.668} \quad \textit{Use order of operations}$$

$$\textit{to evaluate.}$$

$$t = 1339.74(-4.8 - T)^{-1.668}$$

X	Y1
-25	8.9062
-30	6.1586
-35	4.5537
-40	3.5269
-45	2.826
-50	2.3241

X=

Set up a table of values on your calculator. Use the ASK mode, or set the table difference to -5. (The air temperature is dropping.)

Y1 = $1339.74(-4.8 - x)^{-1.668}$

According to the table, if the wind speed is a constant 40 km/h, then when the air temperature is $-25°C$, exposed skin will become frostbitten in nine minutes, at $-30°C$ in six minutes, at $-35°C$ in five minutes, at $-40°C$ in four minutes, at $-45°C$ in three minutes, and at $-50°C$ in two minutes.

✓ Objective 11.2.4 CHECKUP

1. A sewage treatment plant monitors water quality weekly. During one week its readings for coliform bacteria were (in bacteria per 100 ml): 5, 9, 1300, 200, 700, 350, 90. Use the geometric mean to calculate the average bacteria level.

2. Use the function $y = x^{3.5}$ from Example 8 to compare the absolute luminosities of main-sequence stars with that of the Sun. Assume that the stars have masses of 1, 4, 16, and 64 times the mass of the Sun. Use the results to determine how the absolute brightness of a main-sequence star changes as its mass is increased by a factor of four.

3. Given the formula for the time to frostbite, in minutes, $t = \{[-24.5(0.667v + 4.8)] + 2111\} \cdot (-4.8 - T)^{-1.668}$, assume that the wind speed v is 30 km/h. With this value for v, simplify the equation by using the order of operations. With the simplified equation, set up a table of values on your calculator to determine the time to frostbite for air temperatures varying from $-15°C$ to $-50°C$, in increments of $-5°C$. Interpret the results of your table.

11.2 EXERCISES

Student Solutions Manual

PH Math/Tutor Center

CD Video

MathXL®

MyMathLab
MyMathLab

Interactmath.com

Write as a radical expression, and evaluate if possible.

1. $36^{1/2}$ **2.** $100^{1/2}$ **3.** $216^{1/3}$ **4.** $729^{1/3}$

5. $-81^{1/4}$ **6.** $-625^{1/4}$ **7.** $(-81)^{1/4}$ **8.** $(-625)^{1/4}$

9. $-8^{1/3}$ **10.** $-27^{1/3}$ **11.** $(-8)^{1/3}$ **12.** $(-27)^{1/3}$

Write as a radical expression, and evaluate if possible. Express your answer as a fraction.

13. $36^{-1/2}$ **14.** $100^{-1/2}$ **15.** $216^{-1/3}$ **16.** $729^{-1/3}$

17. $81^{-1/4}$ **18.** $625^{-1/4}$ **19.** $-81^{-1/4}$ **20.** $(-625)^{-1/4}$

21. $8^{-1/3}$ **22.** $27^{-1/3}$ **23.** $(-8)^{-1/3}$ **24.** $(-27)^{-1/3}$

Evaluate to the nearest thousandth.

25. $522^{1/2}$ **26.** $478^{1/3}$ **27.** $522^{1/4}$ **28.** $478^{1/5}$

29. $522^{-1/3}$ **30.** $478^{-1/2}$ **31.** $522^{-1/5}$ **32.** $478^{-1/4}$

Write as a radical expression, and evaluate if possible. Express your results as integers or fractions.

33. $27^{4/3}$ **34.** $25^{3/2}$ **35.** $(-27)^{4/3}$ **36.** $(-25)^{3/2}$

37. $27^{-4/3}$ **38.** $25^{-3/2}$ **39.** $-27^{-4/3}$ **40.** $-25^{-3/2}$

41. $4^{5/2}$ **42.** $9^{3/2}$ **43.** $8^{7/3}$ **44.** $125^{5/3}$

45. $4^{-7/2}$ **46.** $16^{-5/2}$ **47.** $-16^{3/2}$ **48.** $-64^{3/2}$

49. $(-9)^{3/2}$ **50.** $(-4)^{3/2}$ **51.** $-81^{-3/2}$ **52.** $-36^{-3/2}$

Approximate to the nearest thousandth if possible.

53. $28^{5/4}$ **54.** $36^{5/4}$ **55.** $(-21)^{4/3}$ **56.** $(-15)^{2/3}$

57. $5^{-2/3}$ **58.** $7^{-2/3}$ **59.** $-42^{-2/3}$ **60.** $-36^{-2/3}$

61. $(-88)^{3/8}$ **62.** $(-66)^{5/6}$

Determine the restricted values, and then state the domain of each function.

63. $f(x) = (5 - 4x)^{3/4}$ **64.** $f(x) = (7 - 2x)^{2/3}$ **65.** $g(x) = (5 - 4x)^{2/3}$ **66.** $h(x) = (7 - 2x)^{3/4}$

Graph the functions in exercises 67–74 on a Cartesian coordinate system, and check the graphs with your calculator.

67. $y = x^{3/4} + 2$ **68.** $y = 2 - x^{3/4}$ **69.** $y = 3 - x^{2/3}$ **70.** $y = x^{2/3} - 3$

71. $y = x^{4/5} + 1$ **72.** $y = x^{2/5} + 1$ **73.** $y = 5(x - 4)^{2/3}$ **74.** $y = 3(4 - x)^{2/3}$

Geometric Mean

The geometric mean can be used to average bacteria levels for water quality standards. It is computed by taking the $1/n$th power of the product of n factors.

75. An environmental agency measures contamination levels in a shellfish bed. During a five-week period weekly levels were (in number of Enterococci bacteria per 100 ml): 6, 25, 45, 790, 125. Use the geometric mean to calculate the average bacteria level.

76. A waterpark measures water contamination to guide its use of chemicals. During one day it measured bacteria levels (in number of bacteria per 100 ml) to be 5, 10, 23, 45, 78, 23, 89, 120. Use the geometric mean to calculate average bacteria level.

The geometric mean is also used as a financial return instrument. Average return can be computed by the formula:
average return $= ($final value$/$original value$)^{1/\text{number of years}}$.

77. Compute the average return on a stock investment held for 9 years that has final value $4000 and original value $2000.

78. A real estate investment of $255,000 is worth $599,000 after 13 years. What is the average return?

79. Jim invests $105,000 in a business that is worth $180,000 after 5 years. What is his average return?

80. A builder buys waterfront property at $200,000 an acre. After 4 years the value is $245,000. What is her average return?

Real Data

81. The Fish and Wildlife Service of the U.S. Department of the Interior keeps track of endangered and threatened species. For some species recovery plans are in place to help increase population. The number of recovery plans by group can be approximated by $R(x) = 0.85x^{4/5}$, where x is the number of endangered and threatened species.
   a. Graph the function.
   b. Use the graph to determine whether the function is increasing or decreasing.
   c. What is the approximate number of recovery plans for the group mammals which has 346 endangered and threatened species?
   d. If the group fish has 95 recovery plans, how many types of fish are endangered or threatened?

82. The percentage of sales revenue of recorded music and videos in digital download format can be modeled by the function $p(x) = 0.208x^{23/20}$, where p is the percentage and x is the number of years after 2000.
   a. Graph the function.
   b. Use the graph to determine whether the function is increasing or decreasing.
   c. What was the percent of sales in digital download format in 2002?
   d. Assuming trends continue, what will be the percent of sales in digital download format in 2008?

83. At a temperature of 30 degrees, the wind can actually make it seem colder. Wind chill can be estimated by the function $W(x) = 37x^{-1/4}$, where W is the wind chill (the temperature it feels like) and x is the wind speed in miles per hour.
   a. Graph the function.
   b. Use the graph to determine whether the function is increasing or decreasing.
   c. What is the wind chill if the speed of the wind is 20 miles per hour?
   d. For what wind speed is the wind chill 15 degrees?

84. The amount of money earned by the top-grossing North American concert tours in millions of dollars can be estimated by the function $A(x) = 124x^{-4/25}$, where x is the rank of tour's earnings ($x \geq 1$).
   a. Graph the function on its domain.
   b. Use the graph to determine whether the function is increasing or decreasing.
   c. What were the earnings of the concert ranked tenth in earnings (The Backstreet Boys in 2001)?
   d. What is the ranking of the concert that earned about 90 million dollars?

11.2 Calculator Exercises

Consider the exponential expression $(-32)^{3/5}$. Expressions of this type have the following features:

- The base is negative.
- The rational exponent has an odd-numbered denominator.
- The rational exponent has a numerator that is not equal to 1.

   Some calculators are not programmed to correctly evaluate exponential expressions that have these features. You should enter the expression, as given, into your calculator and see whether the calculator returns a result of -8. You can verify that this is the correct result by rewriting the expression as a radical expression and evaluating. If your calculator does not give you this result, you will need to rewrite the expression in one of the following ways and key the new expression into your calculator:

- $[(-32)^{1/5}]^3$
- $[(-32)^3]^{1/5}$
- $\left(\sqrt[5]{-32}\right)^3$
- $\sqrt[5]{(-32)^3}$

You should experiment with your calculator and use the form that returns the correct result.

1. Evaluate $(-27)^{2/3}$.

2. Rewrite the expression in exercise 1 four different ways and check for equivalence with the original expression.

11.2 Writing Exercise

In the definition of rational exponents,
$$a^{m/n} = \sqrt[n]{a^m} = (\sqrt[n]{a})^m$$
it was stated that n is a positive integer greater than 1.

1. Consider what would happen if $n = 1$. Describe what this would do to the expression $a^{m/n}$, and state why the value $n = 1$ is excluded from the definition.

2. Next, consider what would happen if $n = 0$. What would this do to the expression $a^{m/n}$, and why is $n = 0$ excluded from the definition?

3. Explain why we don't need to consider negative integer values for n.

4. Finally, when considering an expression of the form $a^{m/n}$, you should express the exponent $\frac{m}{n}$ in lowest terms. Why?

11.3 PROPERTIES OF RATIONAL EXPONENTS

OBJECTIVES   1 Evaluate exponential expressions with rational exponents by using properties of exponents.

2 Simplify exponential expressions with rational exponents by using properties of exponents.

3 Model real-world situations by using exponential expressions containing rational exponents.

APPLICATION

The Stefan–Boltzmann law states that the temperature of a star is equal to the expression $\left(\dfrac{F}{\sigma}\right)^{1/4}$, where F is the energy flux (amount of energy that leaves the surface) of the star and the Greek letter σ (pronounced *sigma*) is a constant. Write an expression for the total temperature of two stars if one star's energy flux is twice the other.

After completing this section, we will discuss this application further. See page 877.

Objective 11.3.1   ## Evaluating Expressions with Rational Exponents

The properties that we used earlier with integer exponents also apply to rational exponents. Let's review these properties.

PROPERTIES OF RATIONAL EXPONENTS

$$a^{-n} = \frac{1}{a^n}$$ Definition of a negative exponent

$$\frac{1}{a^{-n}} = a^n$$ Definition of a negative exponent

$$a^m \cdot a^n = a^{m+n}$$ Product rule

$$\frac{a^m}{a^n} = a^{m-n}$$ Quotient rule

$$(a^m)^n = a^{mn}$$ Power-to-a-power rule

$$(ab)^m = a^m b^m$$ Product-to-a-power rule

$$\left(\frac{a}{b}\right)^m = \frac{a^m}{b^m}$$ Quotient-to-a-power rule

$$\left(\frac{a}{b}\right)^{-m} = \left(\frac{b}{a}\right)^m$$ Quotient-to-a-negative-power rule

In these expressions, a and b are nonzero real expressions such that both sides of the equation represent real numbers, and m and n are rational expressions.

EXAMPLE 1   Use the properties of exponents to evaluate the given expressions. Check by means of your calculator.

a. $25^{3/4} \cdot 25^{-1/4}$ **b.** $\dfrac{16^{3/8}}{16^{1/8}}$ **c.** $2^{1/2} \cdot 8^{1/2}$ **d.** $\left(\dfrac{3^5}{2^{10}}\right)^{-2/5}$

Solution

a. $25^{3/4} \cdot 25^{-1/4} = 25^{3/4+(-1/4)} = 25^{1/2} = 5$ Product rule

b. $\dfrac{16^{3/8}}{16^{1/8}} = 16^{3/8-1/8} = 16^{1/4} = 2$ Quotient rule

c. $2^{1/2} \cdot 8^{1/2} = (2 \cdot 8)^{1/2} = 16^{1/2} = 4$ Product-to-a-power rule

d. $\left(\dfrac{3^5}{2^{10}}\right)^{-2/5} = \dfrac{(3^5)^{-2/5}}{(2^{10})^{-2/5}}$ Quotient-to-a-power rule

$= \dfrac{3^{(5)(-2/5)}}{2^{(10)(-2/5)}} = \dfrac{3^{-2}}{2^{-4}}$ Power-to-a-power rule

$= \dfrac{2^4}{3^2} = \dfrac{16}{9}$ Definition of a negative exponent

A second way to evaluate this expression is to use the quotient-to-a-negative-power rule first and then use the quotient-to-a-power rule.

$$\left(\frac{3^5}{2^{10}}\right)^{-2/5} = \left(\frac{2^{10}}{3^5}\right)^{2/5} = \frac{2^{10(2/5)}}{3^{5(2/5)}} = \frac{2^4}{3^2} = \frac{16}{9}$$

To check on your calculator, carefully enter the expressions into it. Remember to enclose the rational exponents in parentheses.

a. ```
25^(3/4)*25^(-1/
4)
                5
```

b. ```
16^(3/8)/16^(1/8
)
                2
```

c. ```
2^(1/2)*8^(1/2)
                4
```

d. ```
(3^5/2^10)^(-2/5
)▸Frac
             16/9
```

Objective 11.3.1 **CHECKUP**

1. Use the properties of exponents to evaluate the given expressions Check, using your calculator.

  a. $36^{5/6} \cdot 36^{-1/3}$ **b.** $\dfrac{8^{7/12}}{8^{1/4}}$ **c.** $3^{1/3} \cdot 9^{1/3}$ **d.** $\left(\dfrac{5^2}{3^4}\right)^{-3/2}$

2. Explain the difference between an integer exponent and a rational exponent. Give examples of each.

Objective 11.3.2 Simplifying Expressions with Rational Exponents

To simplify an exponential expression with a rational exponent and a variable base, we use the same rules we used for evaluating an exponential expression with a numerical base.

However, suppose we are evaluating an expression whose exponent has an even-numbered denominator, such as $x^{1/2}$. Then we must be sure that the variable represents only nonnegative numbers, because an even root is not defined for a negative number.

Similarly, suppose we are evaluating an expression whose exponent is negative, such as $x^{-1/3}$. Then we must be sure that the variable represents only nonzero numbers, because we rewrite negative exponents as the reciprocal of the base and a positive power [for example, $\left(\dfrac{1}{x}\right)^{1/3}$]. If the variable x is zero, the reciprocal $\dfrac{1}{x}$ is undefined.

In this text, we will assume that the variable base does not represent values for which the expression is undefined.

EXAMPLE 2

Simplify, using the properties of exponents. Write each result with positive exponents.

a. $x^{1/2}x^{-1/4}$ **b.** $\dfrac{y^{5/8}}{y^{1/4}}$ **c.** $(xy)^{3/4}$ **d.** $\left(\dfrac{x}{y}\right)^{-2/3}$

Solution

a. $x^{1/2}x^{-1/4} = x^{1/2+(-1/4)} = x^{1/4}$ Product rule

b. $\dfrac{y^{5/8}}{y^{1/4}} = y^{5/8-1/4} = y^{3/8}$ Quotient rule

c. $(xy)^{3/4} = x^{3/4}y^{3/4}$ Product-to-a-power rule

d. $\left(\dfrac{x}{y}\right)^{-2/3} = \dfrac{x^{-2/3}}{y^{-2/3}}$ Quotient-to-a-power rule

$\qquad = \dfrac{y^{2/3}}{x^{2/3}}$ Definition of a negative exponent

A second way to evaluate the last expression is to use the quotient-to-a-negative-power rule first and then use the quotient-to-a-power rule.

$$\left(\frac{x}{y}\right)^{-2/3} = \left(\frac{y}{x}\right)^{2/3} = \frac{y^{2/3}}{x^{2/3}}$$

Using combinations of the properties of exponents allows us to simplify more complicated expressions. When we combine the properties of exponents, we may simplify the expression in different orders of steps and still obtain the correct results. Therefore, do not be concerned if you apply the properties of exponents using a different order from what you see in the examples, as long as you obtain the same answers.

EXAMPLE 3

Simplify. Write the result, using positive exponents.

a. $(25x^4y^3)^{1/2}$ **b.** $(2x^{3/4}y)(3x^{2/3}y^{5/8})$ **c.** $\left(\dfrac{5x^{1/10}}{x^{-2/5}}\right)^5$ **d.** $n^{1/3}(n^{2/3} + n^{3/4})$

Solution

a. $(25x^4y^3)^{1/2} = 25^{1/2}(x^4)^{1/2}(y^3)^{1/2}$ Product-to-a-power rule

$\qquad = 25^{1/2}x^{4\cdot1/2}y^{3\cdot1/2}$ Power-to-a-power rule

$\qquad = 5x^2y^{3/2}$

b. $(2x^{3/4}y)(3x^{2/3}y^{5/8}) = (2\cdot3)x^{3/4+2/3}y^{1+5/8}$ Product rule

$\qquad = 6x^{17/12}y^{13/8}$

c. $\left(\dfrac{5x^{1/10}}{x^{-2/5}}\right)^5 = \dfrac{(5x^{1/10})^5}{(x^{-2/5})^5}$ Quotient-to-a-power rule

$\qquad = \dfrac{5^5x^{(1/10)5}}{x^{(-2/5)5}}$ Product-to-a-power rule, power-to-a-power rule

$\qquad = \dfrac{5^5x^{1/2}}{x^{-2}}$

$\qquad = 5^5x^{1/2-(-2)}$ Quotient rule

$\qquad = 5^5x^{5/2}$ or $3125x^{5/2}$

d. $n^{1/3}(n^{2/3} + n^{3/4}) = n^{1/3}n^{2/3} + n^{1/3}n^{3/4}$ Distribute $n^{1/3}$.

$\qquad = n^{1/3+2/3} + n^{1/3+3/4}$ Product rule

$\qquad = n + n^{13/12}$

Objective 11.3.2 *CHECKUP*

Simplify exercises 1 and 2. Write each result with positive exponents.

1. a. $(x^9)^{1/3}$

   b. $x^{1/3} \cdot x^{-1/6}$

   c. $\dfrac{z^{2/3}}{z^{1/6}}$

   d. $\left(\dfrac{p}{q}\right)^{-3/5}$

2. a. $(4a^2b^3)^{1/2}$

   b. $(-3x^{2/3}y)(2x^{3/8}y^{3/4})$

   c. $\left(\dfrac{8x^{2/3}}{4x^{-2/3}}\right)^3$

   d. $a^{1/2}(a^{1/4} - a^{2/3})$

3. In the expression $x^{3/4}$, what restrictions are placed on values of x because of the even denominator in the exponent?

4. In the expression $x^{-2/3}$, what restrictions are placed on the values of x because of the negative exponent?

5. Explain why it is important to be aware of restrictions on the base of an expression with rational exponents whenever conditions such as those illustrated in exercises **3** and **4** are present.

Objective 11.3.3   Modeling the Real World

In our daily lives, we often need to increase or decrease the size of objects that are in the shape of geometric figures. For instance, we might want to increase the size of a room or decrease the size of a fenced area for a pet. We may know the desired area and must determine the dimensions. Usually, we need to evaluate exponential expressions in order to determine these lengths.

EXAMPLE 4

The formula $s = A^{1/2}$ is used to determine the length of the side of a square, given the area A.

a. If the area of a square doubles, how is the length of a side affected? (The ratio of the areas is 2 to 1. What is the ratio of the new side to the original side?)

b. If the area of a square triples, how is the length of a side affected? (The ratio of the areas is 3 to 1. What is the ratio of the new side to the original side?)

c. If the area of a square is multiplied by a factor of x, determine the ratio of the length of a new side to the length of the original side.

Solution

a. Let A = the original area of the square

    s_1 = the length of the original side

   Then $2A$ = the area of the new square (the area doubled)

    s_2 = the length of the new side

   Using the formula $s = A^{1/2}$, we have

$$s_1 = A^{1/2} \quad \text{for the original side}$$
$$s_2 = (2A)^{1/2} = 2^{1/2}A^{1/2} \quad \text{for the new side}$$

   The ratio of the new side to the original side is

$$\frac{s_2}{s_1} = \frac{2^{1/2}A^{1/2}}{A^{1/2}} = \frac{2^{1/2}}{1}$$

   or approximately $\frac{1.414}{1}$, when the ratio of the new area to the original area is $\frac{2}{1}$.

b. Let A = the original area of the square

    s_1 = the length of the original side

   Then $3A$ = the area of the new square (the area tripled)

    s_3 = the length of the new side

   Using the formula $s = A^{1/2}$, we have

$$s_1 = A^{1/2} \quad \text{for the original side}$$
$$s_3 = (3A)^{1/2} = 3^{1/2}A^{1/2} \quad \text{for the new side}$$

The ratio of the new side to the original side is

$$\frac{s_3}{s_1} = \frac{3^{1/2}A^{1/2}}{A^{1/2}} = \frac{3^{1/2}}{1}$$

or approximately $\frac{1.732}{1}$, when the ratio of the new area to the original area is $\frac{3}{1}$.

c. Let A = the original area of the square
   s_1 = the length of the original side

Then xA = the area of the new square (the area is multiplied by a factor of x)
   s_4 = the length of the new side

Using the formula $s = A^{1/2}$, we have

$$s_1 = A^{1/2} \quad \text{for the original side}$$
$$s_4 = (xA)^{1/2} = x^{1/2}A^{1/2} \quad \text{for the new side}$$

The ratio of the new side to the original side is

$$\frac{s_4}{s_1} = \frac{x^{1/2}A^{1/2}}{A^{1/2}} = \frac{x^{1/2}}{1}$$

or $\dfrac{\sqrt{x}}{1}$, when the ratio of the new area to the original area is $\dfrac{x}{1}$. ∎

APPLICATION

The Stefan–Boltzmann law states that the temperature of a star is equal to the expression $\left(\dfrac{F}{\sigma}\right)^{1/4}$, where F is the energy flux (amount of energy that leaves the surface) of the star and the Greek letter σ (pronounced *sigma*) is a constant. Write an expression for the total temperature of two stars if one star's energy flux is twice the other.

Discussion

Let x = the amount of energy flux of the first star
   $2x$ = the amount of energy flux of the second star

$$\left(\frac{x}{\sigma}\right)^{1/4} = \text{the temperature of the first star}$$

$$\left(\frac{2x}{\sigma}\right)^{1/4} = \text{the temperature of the second star}$$

The total temperature is the sum of the individual temperatures.

$$\left(\frac{x}{\sigma}\right)^{1/4} + \left(\frac{2x}{\sigma}\right)^{1/4} = \frac{x^{1/4}}{\sigma^{1/4}} + \frac{2^{1/4}x^{1/4}}{\sigma^{1/4}} \qquad \text{\small Quotient-to-a-power rule}$$

$$= \frac{x^{1/4} + 2^{1/4}x^{1/4}}{\sigma^{1/4}} \qquad \text{\small Add rational expressions.}$$

$$= \frac{x^{1/4}(1 + 2^{1/4})}{\sigma^{1/4}} \qquad \text{\small Factor the numerator.}$$

$$= (1 + 2^{1/4})\frac{x^{1/4}}{\sigma^{1/4}} \qquad \text{\small Rewrite product as factors.}$$

$$= (1 + 2^{1/4})\left(\frac{x}{\sigma}\right)^{1/4} \qquad \text{\small Quotient-to-a-power rule}$$

$$\approx 2.189\left(\frac{x}{\sigma}\right)^{1/4} \qquad \text{\small Evaluate.}$$

The total temperature of the two stars is approximately $2.189\left(\dfrac{x}{\sigma}\right)^{1/4}$, or about 2.189 times the temperature of the first star.

Objective 11.3.3 *CHECKUP*

1. The formula $r = \left(\dfrac{A}{\pi}\right)^{1/2}$ is used to determine the length of the radius of a circle whose area is A.

   a. If the area of a circle is doubled, how is the radius of the circle affected? (The ratio of the area is 2 to 1; what is the ratio of the new radius to the original radius?)

   b. If the area of the circle is tripled, how is the radius of the circle affected? (The ratio of the area is 3 to 1; what is the ratio of the new radius to the original radius?)

   c. If the area of the circle is multiplied by a constant C, determine the ratio of the lengths of the radii.

2. A tank of water has an opening near its base. The flow of water from the opening has a velocity (in feet per second) given by the expression $v = (64.4h)^{1/2}$, where h is the height of the water above the opening.

   a. Write an expression for the velocity of the water flow when the height of water in the tank is doubled.

   b. Determine an expression for the difference between the velocities—that is, the velocity of the water flow when its height is doubled, less the velocity of the water flow from the original height.

11.3 EXERCISES

Student Solutions Manual   PH Math/Tutor Center   CD Video   Math XL MathXL®   MyMathLab MyMathLab   Interactmath.com

Evaluate by using the properties of exponents. Check, using a calculator.

1. $9^{-1/2}$

2. $81^{-1/4}$

3. $\dfrac{1}{8^{-1/3}}$

4. $\dfrac{1}{16^{-1/4}}$

5. $27^{1/3} \cdot 27^{4/3}$

6. $64^{1/4} \cdot 64^{5/4}$

7. $\dfrac{32^{4/5}}{32^{1/5}}$

8. $\dfrac{64^{5/6}}{64^{1/3}}$

9. $(125^{1/2})^{2/3}$

10. $(256^{1/3})^{3/4}$

11. $3^{1/2} \cdot 12^{1/2}$

12. $5^{1/3} \cdot 25^{1/3}$

13. $\left(\dfrac{8}{27}\right)^{1/3}$

14. $\left(\dfrac{27}{125}\right)^{2/3}$

15. $\left(\dfrac{9}{16}\right)^{-1/2}$

16. $\left(\dfrac{81}{16}\right)^{-3/4}$

17. $[(2^{1/2})(8^{1/2})]^{-3/2}$

18. $[(2^{1/2})(32^{1/2})]^{-4/3}$

Simplify exercises 19–64. Write the results, using positive exponents.

19. $x^{-2/3}$

20. $x^{-5/6}$

21. $\dfrac{12}{y^{-3/4}}$

22. $\dfrac{2}{y^{-4/7}}$

23. $z^{2/3} \cdot z^{3/4}$

24. $z^{3/4} \cdot z^{7/8}$

25. $\dfrac{p^{5/6}}{p^{2/3}}$

26. $\dfrac{x^{5/9}}{x^{2/3}}$

27. $(b^{3/4})^{8/9}$

28. $(z^{2/5})^{15/16}$

29. $(x^2 y)^{3/4}$

30. $(pq^3)^{5/6}$

31. $\left(\dfrac{x^2}{y^3}\right)^{5/6}$

32. $\left(\dfrac{a^4}{b^3}\right)^{7/12}$

33. $\left(\dfrac{a}{b}\right)^{-1/3}$

34. $\left(\dfrac{m}{n}\right)^{-3/4}$

35. $c^{3/5} \cdot c^{-4/5}$

36. $k^{5/7} \cdot k^{-3/7}$

37. $(8a^5 b^6)^{2/3}$

38. $(16c^{8/9} d^2)^{3/4}$

39. $(5a^{3/4} b^{2/5})(2a^{1/3} b^{2/5})$

40. $(3x^{1/5} y^{1/3})(-2x^{3/5} y^{1/4})$

41. $\left(\dfrac{m^{3/7}}{2m^{-2/7}}\right)^2$

42. $\left(\dfrac{4z^{5/9}}{z^{-2/9}}\right)^3$

43. $(3a^{1/3} b^2 c^{1/6})^{-2} (2a^{4/3} b^{1/4} c^{5/6})^3$

44. $(2x^{4/9} y^{3/4} z)^{-3} (2x^{2/3} y^{1/4} z^3)^2$

45. $x^{1/4}(x^{2/3} - x^{4/5})$

46. $z^{2/3}(z^{1/4} - z^{1/3})$

47. $2x^{2/5}(x^{1/5} + 3y^{2/5})$

48. $5a^{2/7}(3a^{1/7} - b^{4/7})$

49. $a^{1/4} b^{1/3}(3 - a^{1/2} b^{5/6})$

50. $x^{1/4} y^{3/4}(x^{1/2} y^{3/8} - 4)$

51. $(x^{1/2} - y^{1/2})(x^{1/3} + y^{1/3})$

52. $(c^{2/3} - d^{2/3})(c^{1/2} + d^{1/2})$

53. $(x^{1/4} + y^{1/4})(x^{1/4} - y^{1/4})$

54. $(p^{3/4} - q^{3/4})(p^{3/4} + q^{3/4})$

55. $(x^2 + y^2)(x^{1/2} - y^{1/2})$

56. $(a^{2/3} + b^{2/3})(a - b)$

57. $(x^{1/3} + 2)(x^{1/3} - 2)$

58. $(4 - z^{1/4})(4 + z^{1/4})$

59. $(x^{1/4} + 2)^2$

60. $(x^{1/3} + 3)^2$

61. $(x - y^{1/2})^2$

62. $(x^{1/2} - y)^2$

63. $(a^{1/2} + b^{1/2})^2$

64. $(c^{1/2} - d^{1/2})^2$

Geometry

65. The length s of the side of a cube is related to the volume V of the cube by the formula $s = V^{1/3}$. How should you increase the length of a side in order to increase the volume of the cube to eight times its original volume?

66. The length s of the side of a cube is related to the surface area A of the cube by the formula $s = \left(\dfrac{A}{6}\right)^{1/2}$. How should you increase the length of a side in order to increase the surface area of the cube to nine times its original area?

Vertical Distance

67. The time t (in seconds) it would take an object to fall to the ground from a distance d (in feet) above the ground is given by the formula $t = \left(\dfrac{d}{16.1}\right)^{1/2}$. If you triple the height from which you drop the object, how does this change the time it will take the object to fall to the ground? (**Hint:** Determine the ratio of the times at given distances of d and $3d$.)

68. Using the formula from exercise **67**, what will be the change in the time it will take the object to fall to the ground if you quadruple the height from which you drop the object?

69. The time t (in seconds) it would take an object to fall to the ground from a distance d (in meters) above the ground is given by the formula $t = \left(\dfrac{d}{4.9}\right)^{1/2}$. If you triple the height from which you drop the object, how long will it take the object to fall to the ground? How does this answer compare with that of exercise **67**? Does the change of the unit of measure from feet to meters affect the change in time?

70. Using the formula from exercise **69**, what will be the change in the time it will take the object to fall to the ground if you quadruple the height from which you drop the object? How does this answer compare with that of exercise **68**? Does the change of the unit of measure from feet to meters affect the change in time?

Physics

71. In electronics resonance, frequency is defined to be $f = \dfrac{1}{2\pi(LC)^{1/2}}$, where L is the inductance and C is the capacitance. If L is tripled, what is the effect on the resonance frequency?

72. In electronics resonance, frequency is defined to be $f = \dfrac{1}{2\pi(LC)^{1/2}}$, where L is the inductance and C is the capacitance. If capacitance is cut in half, what is the effect on the resonance frequency?

73. The moment of inertia is a measure of the resistance offered by a body to a change in its angular velocity. It depends on mass and distribution of mass. If a body is made up of masses m and n at distances x and y from an axis with moment of inertia I, these quantities are related by the formula
$$y = \left(\frac{I - mx^2}{n}\right)^{1/2}$$

What happens to the value of y if n is quadrupled? What happens to the value of y if n is multiplied by a factor of $\dfrac{1}{100}$?

74. The moment of inertia is a measure of the resistance offered by a body to a change in its angular velocity. It depends on mass and distribution of mass. If a body is made up of masses m and n at distances x and y from an axis with moment of inertia I, these quantities are related by the formula
$$m = \left(\frac{I - ny^2}{x}\right)^{1/2}$$

What happens to the value of m if x is doubled? What happens to the value of m if x is multiplied by a factor of $\dfrac{1}{9}$?

11.3 Calculator Exercises

Remember that the calculator can help you check whether you have simplified expressions with rational exponents correctly when the expressions involve only a single variable. Store the original expression in Y1 and the simplified expression in Y2. You can create a table of values and check for equivalence, as you have seen before. But you can also use the graphing feature along with the bubble test. To do so, after storing the expressions in Y1 and Y2, move the cursor to the extreme left of Y2 and press [ENTER] four times to select the symbol "−0". Doing this will cause a bubble to trace the graph of Y2. Then, when you press [GRAPH], the calculator will first graph Y1, and if Y2 is an equivalent graph, the bubble will trace along the graph for Y1. This indicates that the graphs coincide and the two expressions are equivalent; otherwise, the two expressions are not equivalent.

Simplify the following expressions, using only positive exponents, and check by graphing with the bubble feature just explained.

1. $\left(x^3\right)^{2/3}$

2. $\left(x^3\right)^{-2/3}$

3. $\dfrac{x^4}{x^{9/4}}$

4. $\dfrac{x^2}{x^{7/2}}$

5. $x^{3/4}\left(x^{3/2} - x^{2/3}\right)$

6. $\left(x^{1/3} + 1\right)\left(x^{1/3} - 1\right)$

11.3 Writing Exercise

In the exercises in this section, you were asked to simplify the expression $(a^{1/2} + b^{1/2})^2$. If you simplified this expression correctly, you saw that the result was *not* $(a + b)$. This is an important point to remember. Explain why the result is not $(a + b)$. Would you expect $(c^{1/2} - d^{1/2})^2$ to be equal to $(c - d)$? Explain.

11.4 PROPERTIES OF RADICALS

OBJECTIVES

1 Simplify radical expressions by using the product rule for radicals.

2 Simplify radical expressions by using the quotient rule for radicals.

3 Model real-world situations by using expressions containing radical expressions.

APPLICATION

The most complete fossil (95%) of a *Tyrannosaurus rex*, Sue, is on display at the Field Museum in Chicago, Illinois. Its height at the hips is 13 feet.

a. Model the leg motion as that of a pendulum, and determine the length of time in seconds during which the leg completed one back-and-forth motion.

b. Dinosaur tracks have been uncovered in the roofs of coal mines where peat in the tracks was reduced to coal. The distance between the consecutive prints of the same foot (stride length) measures 9.3 feet. Twice this distance constitutes a back-and-forth movement measuring about 18.6 feet. Use this distance to estimate Sue's walking speed.

c. From observations of modern animals, zoologist R. McNeill Alexander derived a relationship between an animal's speed (v), its hip height (h), and its stride length (SL), which is $v = 0.25 \cdot g^{1/2} \cdot SL^{5/3} \cdot h^{-7/6}$, where g is the acceleration due to gravity. Determine the animal's walking speed using this relationship.

d. Compare the speeds found in part **b** and part **c**.

After completing this section, we will discuss this application further. See page 887.

Since radical expressions are equivalent to exponential expressions with rational exponents, certain properties of radicals correspond to properties of exponents. In Chapter 9, we defined two such properties for square roots: the product rule and the quotient rule. We now extend these definitions to all radical expressions.

Objective 11.4.1 ### Simplifying Radical Expressions by Using the Product Rule

The product rule for square roots states that for any real numbers $\sqrt{a}$ and $\sqrt{b}$, $\sqrt{a} \cdot \sqrt{b} = \sqrt{a \cdot b}$. For example, $\sqrt{3} \cdot \sqrt{2} = \sqrt{3 \cdot 2} = \sqrt{6}$.

This rule holds for all radical expressions.

PRODUCT RULE FOR RADICALS

For any real numbers $\sqrt[n]{a}$ and $\sqrt[n]{b}$ and any integer index n greater than 1,

$$\sqrt[n]{a} \cdot \sqrt[n]{b} = \sqrt[n]{ab}$$

We can show that this statement is true if we rewrite the radical expressions as exponential expressions with rational exponents and apply the product-to-a-power rule for exponents. That is, we would have the following:

$$\sqrt[3]{-3} \cdot \sqrt[3]{8} = (-3)^{1/3} \cdot 8^{1/3} = (-3 \cdot 8)^{1/3} = (-24)^{1/3} = \sqrt[3]{-24}$$
$$\sqrt[4]{6} \cdot \sqrt[4]{8} = 6^{1/4} \cdot 8^{1/4} = (6 \cdot 8)^{1/4} = 48^{1/4} = \sqrt[4]{48}$$

For the general rule, $\sqrt[n]{a} \cdot \sqrt[n]{b} = a^{1/n}b^{1/n} = (ab)^{1/n} = \sqrt[n]{ab}$.

SIMPLIFYING RADICAL EXPRESSIONS—CONDITION 1

If a radical expression has a radicand with a perfect nth factor and an index of n, it can be simplified by using the product rule.

$$\sqrt[n]{ab} = \sqrt[n]{a} \cdot \sqrt[n]{b}$$

To simplify an nth root,

- Factor the radicand. One factor must be a perfect nth power.
- Reverse the product rule to simplify.

EXAMPLE 1

Simplify without a calculator.

a. $\sqrt{48}$ **b.** $\sqrt[4]{80}$ **c.** $\sqrt[5]{-96}$

Solution

a. $\sqrt{48} = \sqrt{16 \cdot 3}$ *16 is the largest perfect-square factor of 48.*

$\quad = \sqrt{16} \cdot \sqrt{3}$ *Product rule*

$\quad = 4\sqrt{3}$

Check

```
4√(3)
            6.92820323
√(48)
            6.92820323
```

Figure 11.5

 TAKE NOTE If we had not used the largest perfect square factor, 16, but instead used a factor of 4, we would need to simplify the expression twice.

$$\sqrt{48} = \sqrt{4 \cdot 12} = \sqrt{4}\sqrt{12} = 2\sqrt{12} = 2\sqrt{4 \cdot 3} = 2\sqrt{4}\sqrt{3}$$
$$= 2 \cdot 2\sqrt{3} = 4\sqrt{3}$$

b. $\sqrt[4]{80} = \sqrt[4]{16 \cdot 5}$ *16 is the largest fourth-power factor of 80, $16 = 2^4$.*

$\quad = \sqrt[4]{16} \cdot \sqrt[4]{5}$ *Product rule*

$\quad = 2\sqrt[4]{5}$

c. $\sqrt[5]{-96} = \sqrt[5]{-32 \cdot 3}$ *Use a negative factor. -32 s a fifth-power factor of -96, $-32 = (-2)^5$.*

$\quad = \sqrt[5]{-32} \cdot \sqrt[5]{3}$ *Product rule*

$\quad = -2\sqrt[5]{3}$

To check these results on your calculator, first evaluate the result found algebraically and then evaluate the given radical expression. The two values should be the same. The check for Example 1a is shown in **Figure 11.5**. ■

Before we expand the preceding method of simplification to variable radicands, we must remember that evaluating even roots always results in a positive number. Therefore, $\sqrt{x^2} = |x|$ and $\sqrt[4]{x^4} = |x|$. If we assume that no radicand is formed by raising negative quantities to even powers, there will be no need to write these results as absolute values.

In this text, we will assume that no radicand is formed by raising negative quantities to even roots. Therefore, the results will not be written as absolute values.

We simplify radical expressions with variable radicands by using the same procedure. In addition to rewriting the numerical coefficient as a product with a perfect power factor, we also rewrite the variables as products with a perfect power factor. (A perfect power factor is a factor whose exponent is a multiple of the index of the radical.)

Perfect squares of variables must have an exponent that is a multiple of 2.

Perfect square

x^2, because $x^2 = (x)^2$

x^4, because $x^4 = (x^2)^2$

x^6, because $x^6 = (x^3)^2$

Likewise, perfect cubes of variables must have an exponent that is a multiple of 3.

Perfect cube

x^3, because $x^3 = (x)^3$

x^6, because $x^6 = (x^2)^3$

x^9, because $x^9 = (x^3)^3$

Therefore, a perfect nth power must have an exponent that is a multiple of n.

EXAMPLE 2   Simplify.

a. $\sqrt{x^5}$ **b.** $\sqrt{x^4 y^7}$ **c.** $\sqrt[3]{a^4 b^8}$

Solution

a. To determine the exponent of the largest perfect-root factor of a variable, determine the largest multiple of the index that is less than or equal to the variable exponent. For example, the largest perfect-square factor for x^5 is x^4, because 4 is the largest multiple of 2 less than the exponent 5. Therefore, $x^5 = x^4 \cdot x$.

$$\sqrt{x^5} = \sqrt{x^4 \cdot x} \qquad \text{\small x^4 is the largest perfect-square factor of x^5, $x^4 = (x^2)^2$.}$$
$$= \sqrt{x^4} \cdot \sqrt{x} \qquad \text{\small Product rule}$$
$$= x^2 \sqrt{x}$$

b. $\sqrt{x^4 \cdot y^7} = \sqrt{x^4 \cdot y^6 \cdot y} \qquad \text{\small $x^4 = (x^2)^2$ and $y^6 = (y^3)^2$}$

$$= \sqrt{x^4 \cdot y^6} \sqrt{y} \qquad \text{\small Product rule}$$
$$= x^2 y^3 \sqrt{y}$$

c. $\sqrt[3]{a^4 b^8} = \sqrt[3]{a^3 \cdot a \cdot b^6 \cdot b^2} \qquad \text{\small $a^3 = (a)^3$ and $b^6 = (b^2)^3$}$

$$= \sqrt[3]{a^3 b^6} \sqrt[3]{ab^2} \qquad \text{\small Product rule}$$
$$= ab^2 \sqrt[3]{ab^2}$$

EXAMPLE 3   Simplify.

a. $\sqrt{50xy^{15}z^4}$ **b.** $\sqrt[3]{64a^3 b^6 c^{14}}$ **c.** $\sqrt{3x^2 + 12x + 12}$

Solution

a. $\sqrt{50xy^{15}z^4} = \sqrt{25 \cdot 2 \cdot x \cdot y^{14} \cdot y \cdot z^4} \qquad \text{\small Find the perfect-square factors of the radicand.}$

$$= \sqrt{25y^{14}z^4} \sqrt{2xy} \qquad \text{\small Product rule}$$
$$= 5y^7 z^2 \sqrt{2xy}$$

b. $\sqrt[3]{64a^3b^6c^{14}} = \sqrt[3]{64 \cdot a^3 \cdot b^6 \cdot c^{12} \cdot c^2}$ Find the perfect-cube factors of the radicand.

$\qquad = \sqrt[3]{64a^3b^6c^{12}}\,\sqrt[3]{c^2}$ Product rule

$\qquad = 4ab^2c^4\sqrt[3]{c^2}$

c. $\sqrt{3x^2 + 12x + 12} = \sqrt{3(x^2 + 4x + 4)}$ This radicand has terms, not factors. To simplify, factor the radicand.

$\qquad = \sqrt{3(x + 2)^2}$

$\qquad = \sqrt{(x + 2)^2}\,\sqrt{3}$

$\qquad = (x + 2)\sqrt{3}$

Note: Our assumption that no radicand is formed by raising negative quantities to even roots allows us to write the result, $|x + 2|\sqrt{3}$, without absolute values.

EXAMPLE 4 Multiply and simplify.

a. $\left(2x\sqrt{3y}\right)\left(4\sqrt{6xy}\right)$ **b.** $\sqrt{2x - 6} \cdot \sqrt{x - 3}$

c. $2\sqrt[3]{4a^2b^5} \cdot 3ab\sqrt[3]{12ab^2}$

Solution

a. $\left(2x\sqrt{3y}\right)\left(4\sqrt{6xy}\right) = 2x \cdot 4\sqrt{3y \cdot 6xy}$ Multiply nonradical factors and radical factors.

$\qquad = 8x\sqrt{18xy^2}$

$\qquad = 8x\sqrt{9 \cdot 2 \cdot x \cdot y^2}$ Factor.

$\qquad = 8x \cdot 3y\sqrt{2x}$ Simplify.

$\qquad = 24xy\sqrt{2x}$

b. $\sqrt{2x - 6} \cdot \sqrt{x - 3} = \sqrt{(2x - 6)(x - 3)}$

$\qquad = \sqrt{2(x - 3)(x - 3)}$ Factor.

$\qquad = \sqrt{2(x - 3)^2}$

$\qquad = (x - 3)\sqrt{2}$ Simplify.

c. $2\sqrt[3]{4a^2b^5} \cdot 3ab\sqrt[3]{12ab^2}$

$\qquad = 2 \cdot 3ab\sqrt[3]{4a^2b^5 \cdot 12ab^2}$ Multiply nonradical factors and radical factors.

$\qquad = 6ab\sqrt[3]{48a^3b^7}$

$\qquad = 6ab\sqrt[3]{8 \cdot 6 \cdot a^3 \cdot b^6 \cdot b}$ Factor.

$\qquad = 6ab \cdot 2ab^2\sqrt[3]{6b}$ Simplify.

$\qquad = 12a^2b^3\sqrt[3]{6b}$

Objective 11.4.1 *CHECKUP*

1. Simplify without a calculator. Check the results on your calculator.

a. $\sqrt{192}$ **b.** $\sqrt[3]{-40}$ **c.** $\sqrt[4]{162}$

2. Simplify.

a. $\sqrt{x^3}$ **b.** $\sqrt{x^5y^4}$ **c.** $\sqrt[3]{x^5y^{12}}$

3. Simplify.

a. $\sqrt{98x^4y^3z^9}$ **b.** $\sqrt[3]{27m^6n^3p^{10}}$

c. $\sqrt{20x^2 + 20x + 5}$

4. Multiply and simplify.

a. $\left(3a\sqrt{5b}\right)\left(2\sqrt{5ab}\right)$ **b.** $\sqrt{5x + 10} \cdot \sqrt{2x + 4}$

c. $4x\sqrt[3]{12xy^7} \cdot 3y\sqrt[3]{36x^2y^4}$

5. What does the term "perfect *n*th-root factor of a radicand" mean?

Objective 11.4.2

Simplifying Radical Expressions by Using the Quotient Rule

The quotient rule for square roots states that for any real numbers $\sqrt{a}$ and $\sqrt{b}$, $\dfrac{\sqrt{a}}{\sqrt{b}} = \sqrt{\dfrac{a}{b}}$. For example, $\dfrac{\sqrt{6}}{\sqrt{2}} = \sqrt{\dfrac{6}{2}} = \sqrt{3}$. We can extend this rule for all radical expressions.

QUOTIENT RULE FOR RADICALS

For any real numbers $\sqrt[n]{a}$ and $\sqrt[n]{b}$ and any integer index n greater than 1,

$$\frac{\sqrt[n]{a}}{\sqrt[n]{b}} = \sqrt[n]{\frac{a}{b}}$$

We can show that this statement is true if we rewrite the radical expressions as exponential expressions with rational exponents and apply the quotient rule for exponents. That is, we would have the following:

$$\frac{\sqrt[3]{8}}{\sqrt[3]{2}} = \frac{8^{1/3}}{2^{1/3}} = \left(\frac{8}{2}\right)^{1/3} = \sqrt[3]{\frac{8}{2}} = \sqrt[3]{4}$$

$$\frac{\sqrt[4]{16}}{\sqrt[4]{2}} = \frac{16^{1/4}}{2^{1/4}} = \left(\frac{16}{2}\right)^{1/4} = \sqrt[4]{\frac{16}{2}} = \sqrt[4]{8}$$

For the general rule,

$$\frac{\sqrt[n]{a}}{\sqrt[n]{b}} = \frac{a^{1/n}}{b^{1/n}} = \left(\frac{a}{b}\right)^{1/n} = \sqrt[n]{\frac{a}{b}}$$

SIMPLIFYING RADICAL EXPRESSIONS—CONDITION 2

If a radical expression has a fractional radicand, it can be simplified.

$$\sqrt[n]{\frac{a}{b}} = \frac{\sqrt[n]{a}}{\sqrt[n]{b}}$$

For example,

$$\sqrt{\frac{3}{4}} = \frac{\sqrt{3}}{\sqrt{4}} = \frac{\sqrt{3}}{2}$$

We must be careful when writing the final result. If the result is a fraction, it is conventional to write the *denominator* without radicals. The process of changing the fraction to an equivalent form without a radical denominator is called **rationalizing the denominator**. That is, we make the denominator a rational number. Rationalizing the denominator makes it easier to add or subtract radical expressions because the denominators are rational numbers and not radicals.

SIMPLIFYING RADICAL EXPRESSIONS—CONDITION 3

If a radical expression has a denominator containing a radical, it can be rationalized.

For example,

$$\sqrt{\frac{4}{3}} = \frac{\sqrt{4}}{\sqrt{3}} = \frac{2}{\sqrt{3}}$$

is not fully simplified. To rationalize the denominator, we use the multiplication property of 1; that is, we multiply the numerator and denominator by the same value. We choose a value that will result in the denominator's being a perfect root, so that we can simplify it. Since the denominator is $\sqrt{3}$ and we want a perfect-square root, we can multiply the numerator and denominator of the fraction by $\sqrt{3}$.

$$\frac{2}{\sqrt{3}} \cdot \frac{\sqrt{3}}{\sqrt{3}} = \frac{2\sqrt{3}}{\sqrt{9}} = \frac{2\sqrt{3}}{3}$$

We evaluate other roots by using the same process.

EXAMPLE 5   Simplify without a calculator. Rationalize all denominators.

a. $\sqrt{\dfrac{63}{50}}$ **b.** $\sqrt[3]{\dfrac{8}{5}}$

Solution

Check

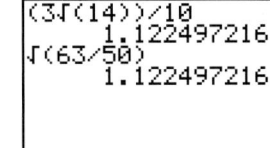

Figure 11.6

a. $\sqrt{\dfrac{63}{50}} = \dfrac{\sqrt{63}}{\sqrt{50}} = \dfrac{\sqrt{9}\sqrt{7}}{\sqrt{25}\sqrt{2}} = \dfrac{3\sqrt{7}}{5\sqrt{2}}$ *Quotient rule*

$\quad = \dfrac{3\sqrt{7}}{5\sqrt{2}} \cdot \dfrac{\sqrt{2}}{\sqrt{2}} = \dfrac{3\sqrt{14}}{5\sqrt{4}} = \dfrac{3\sqrt{14}}{5 \cdot 2} = \dfrac{3\sqrt{14}}{10}$ *Rationalize the denominator.*

b. $\sqrt[3]{\dfrac{8}{5}} = \dfrac{\sqrt[3]{8}}{\sqrt[3]{5}} = \dfrac{2}{\sqrt[3]{5}}$ *Quotient rule*

$\quad = \dfrac{2}{\sqrt[3]{5}} \cdot \dfrac{\sqrt[3]{5^2}}{\sqrt[3]{5^2}} = \dfrac{2\sqrt[3]{5^2}}{\sqrt[3]{5^3}} = \dfrac{2\sqrt[3]{25}}{5}$ *To obtain a perfect-cube root in the denominator, multiply by $\left(\sqrt[3]{5}\right)^2$ or $\sqrt[3]{5^2}$.*

To check these results on your calculator, first evaluate the result found algebraically, and then evaluate the given radical expression. The two values should be the same. The check for Example 5a is shown in **Figure 11.6**.   ■

EXAMPLE 6   Simplify. Rationalize all denominators.

a. $\sqrt{\dfrac{16ab}{3c}}$ **b.** $\sqrt{\dfrac{72x^3y^2}{15xy}}$ **c.** $\sqrt[3]{\dfrac{35m^2}{12np^2}}$

Solution

a. $\sqrt{\dfrac{16ab}{3c}} = \dfrac{\sqrt{16ab}}{\sqrt{3c}} = \dfrac{4\sqrt{ab}}{\sqrt{3c}}$ *Quotient rule*

$\quad = \dfrac{4\sqrt{ab}}{\sqrt{3c}} \cdot \dfrac{\sqrt{3c}}{\sqrt{3c}} = \dfrac{4\sqrt{3abc}}{\sqrt{(3c)^2}} = \dfrac{4\sqrt{3abc}}{3c}$ *Rationalize the denominator.*

b. First, simplify the radicand before applying the quotient rule.

$\quad \sqrt{\dfrac{72x^3y^2}{15xy}} = \sqrt{\dfrac{24x^2y}{5}} = \dfrac{\sqrt{24x^2y}}{\sqrt{5}}$ *Quotient rule*

$\quad = \dfrac{\sqrt{24x^2y}}{\sqrt{5}} \cdot \dfrac{\sqrt{5}}{\sqrt{5}} = \dfrac{\sqrt{120x^2y}}{\sqrt{5^2}} = \dfrac{\sqrt{4x^2 \cdot 30y}}{\sqrt{5^2}} = \dfrac{2x\sqrt{30y}}{5}$

Rationalize the denominator.

c. $\sqrt[3]{\dfrac{35m^2}{12np^2}} = \dfrac{\sqrt[3]{35m^2}}{\sqrt[3]{12np^2}}$ *Quotient rule*

To determine the factor needed to rationalize the denominator, we first determine the smallest perfect cube that is divisible by the numerical factor of the radicand, 12. The smallest perfect cube divisible by 12 is $216 = 6^3$. 216 divided by 12 is 18. Therefore, 18 is the needed numerical factor. Each variable factor must also be a perfect cube. We determine the variable factors needed to be n^2 and p. The cube root of $18n^2p$ is the factor needed to rationalize the denominator.

$$= \frac{\sqrt[3]{35m^2}}{\sqrt[3]{12np^2}} \cdot \frac{\sqrt[3]{18n^2p}}{\sqrt[3]{18n^2p}} = \frac{\sqrt[3]{630m^2n^2p}}{\sqrt[3]{216n^3p^3}} = \frac{\sqrt[3]{630m^2n^2p}}{6np}$$ ■

We also use the quotient rule for radicals to divide radical expressions with the same index.

EXAMPLE 7   Divide and simplify. Rationalize all denominators.

a. $\dfrac{\sqrt{3y}}{\sqrt{6xy}}$ **b.** $\dfrac{2a\sqrt{5a}}{4\sqrt{6ab^2}}$ **c.** $\dfrac{\sqrt[3]{4a^2b^5}}{\sqrt[3]{12ab^2}}$

Solution

a. $\dfrac{\sqrt{3y}}{\sqrt{6xy}} = \sqrt{\dfrac{3y}{6xy}} = \sqrt{\dfrac{1}{2x}}$ *Quotient rule*

$= \sqrt{\dfrac{1}{2x}} \cdot \sqrt{\dfrac{2x}{2x}} = \sqrt{\dfrac{2x}{(2x)^2}} = \dfrac{\sqrt{2x}}{2x}$ *Rationalize the denominator.*

b. $\dfrac{2a\sqrt{5a}}{4\sqrt{6ab^2}} = \dfrac{a\sqrt{5a}}{2\sqrt{6ab^2}} = \dfrac{a\sqrt{5a}}{2b\sqrt{6a}}$ *Simplify.*

$= \dfrac{a}{2b}\sqrt{\dfrac{5a}{6a}} = \dfrac{a}{2b}\sqrt{\dfrac{5}{6}}$ *Quotient rule*

$= \dfrac{a}{2b}\sqrt{\dfrac{5}{6}} \cdot \sqrt{\dfrac{6}{6}} = \dfrac{a}{2b}\sqrt{\dfrac{30}{36}} = \dfrac{a}{2b} \cdot \dfrac{\sqrt{30}}{6} = \dfrac{a\sqrt{30}}{12b}$ *Rationalize the denominator.*

c. $\dfrac{\sqrt[3]{4a^2b^5}}{\sqrt[3]{12ab^2}} = \sqrt[3]{\dfrac{4a^2b^5}{12ab^2}} = \sqrt[3]{\dfrac{ab^3}{3}} = b\sqrt[3]{\dfrac{a}{3}}$ *Quotient rule*

$= b\sqrt[3]{\dfrac{a}{3}} \cdot \sqrt[3]{\dfrac{3^2}{3^2}} = b\sqrt[3]{\dfrac{9a}{3^3}} = \dfrac{b\sqrt[3]{9a}}{3}$ *Rationalize the denominator.*   ■

✓ Objective 11.4.2 *CHECKUP*

1. Simplify without a calculator. Rationalize all denominators. Check your results on your calculator.

a. $\sqrt{\dfrac{27}{20}}$ **b.** $\sqrt[3]{\dfrac{27}{2}}$

2. Simplify. Rationalize all denominators.

a. $\sqrt{\dfrac{25xy}{2z}}$ **b.** $\sqrt{\dfrac{18a^2b^3}{14ab^2}}$ **c.** $\sqrt[3]{\dfrac{6x}{10y^2z}}$

3. Divide and simplify. Rationalize all denominators.

a. $\dfrac{\sqrt{2x}}{\sqrt{10xy}}$ **b.** $\dfrac{4b\sqrt{3ab}}{12\sqrt{15a^2b}}$ **c.** $\dfrac{\sqrt[3]{2c^3d}}{\sqrt[3]{8cd^4}}$

4. What does it mean to rationalize the denominator of a radical expression?

Objective 11.4.3   ## Modeling the Real World

Another example of a radical expression we may encounter is found in a formula for the length of time (in seconds) that it takes for a pendulum to swing from one side of its vertical rest position to the other and back (called the *period* of the pendulum). This time, T, is determined by the acceleration due to gravity, g, and the length of its suspension, L, according to the formula $T = 2\pi\sqrt{\dfrac{L}{g}}$. The acceleration due to gravity is about 32 ft/sec² or 9.8 m/sec². The motion of a pendulum in a grandfather clock can be modeled by this formula. However, with some simplifying assumptions, many other kinds of motion can also be modeled with the formula, such as the swaying of a skyscraper in a strong wind or the swinging of a person's leg while walking.

EXAMPLE 8

Yueling practices daily for a 10-km walk. She swings each arm in a forward-and-back motion as she walks. If the acceleration due to gravity is about 32 ft/sec² and the length of her arm is 2 feet, determine the time it takes Yueling's arm to complete the forward-and-back motion and return to its original starting position, assuming that her arms swing in a pendulum motion and not by her own efforts.

Solution

We will model the motion of Yueling's as a pendulum and use the formula $T = 2\pi\sqrt{\dfrac{L}{g}}$.

$$T = 2\pi\sqrt{\frac{L}{g}}$$

$$T = 2\pi\sqrt{\frac{2}{32}} \qquad \text{Substitute 32 for } g \text{ and 2 for } L.$$

$$T = 2\pi\sqrt{\frac{1}{16}} \qquad \text{Simplify the radicand.}$$

$$T = 2\pi \cdot \frac{1}{4} \qquad \text{Simplify the radical factor.}$$

$$T = \frac{\pi}{2} \qquad \text{Multiply and simplify.}$$

The forward-and-back motion of Yueling's arm takes $\frac{\pi}{2}$ seconds, or approximately 1.57 seconds.

Note that Yueling's arm is not a true pendulum, because it may swing faster or slower due to her own effort. ∎

APPLICATION

The most complete fossil (95%) of a *Tyrannosaurus rex*, Sue, is on display at the Field Museum in Chicago, Illinois. Its height at the hips is 13 feet.

a. Model the leg motion as that of a pendulum, and determine the length of time in seconds during which the leg completed one back-and-forth motion.

b. Dinosaur tracks have been uncovered in the roofs of coal mines where peat in the tracks were reduced to coal. The distance between consecutive prints of the same foot (stride length) measures 9.3 feet. Twice this distance constitutes a back-and-forth movement measuring about 18.6 feet. Use this distance to estimate Sue's walking speed.

c. From observations of modern animals, zoologist R. McNeill Alexander derived a relationship between an animal's speed (v), its hip height (h), and its stride length (SL), which is $v = 0.25 \cdot g^{1/2} \cdot SL^{5/3} \cdot h^{-7/6}$, where g is the acceleration due to gravity. Determine the animal's walking speed using this relationship.

d. Compare the speeds found in part **b** and part **c**.

(continued on page 888)

Discussion

a. $T = 2\pi\sqrt{\dfrac{L}{g}}$ *Pendulum formula*

$T = 2\pi\sqrt{\dfrac{13}{32}}$ *Substitute 32 for g and 13 for L.*

$T = 2\pi\dfrac{\sqrt{13}}{\sqrt{32}}$ *Quotient rule*

$T = 2\pi\dfrac{\sqrt{13}}{\sqrt{16\cdot 2}}$

$T = 2\pi\dfrac{\sqrt{13}}{4\sqrt{2}}$ *Product rule*

$T = 2\pi\dfrac{\sqrt{13}}{4\sqrt{2}}\cdot\dfrac{\sqrt{2}}{\sqrt{2}}$ *Rationalize the denominator.*

$T = 2\pi\dfrac{\sqrt{26}}{4\sqrt{4}}$

$T = 2\pi\dfrac{\sqrt{26}}{4\cdot 2}$

$T = 2\overset{1}{\pi}\dfrac{\sqrt{26}}{\underset{4}{8}}$

$T = \dfrac{\pi\sqrt{26}}{4} \approx 4$

One back-and-forth motion required $\dfrac{\pi\sqrt{26}}{4}$ seconds, or approximately 4 seconds. Sue's leg

is not a true pendulum, because the dinosaur could have swung it faster or slower due to its own effort. However, this model gives us an approximate time that we can use.

b. $r = \dfrac{d}{t}$ *Distance-traveled formula*

$r \approx \dfrac{18.6\text{ ft}}{4\text{ sec}}$ *Substitute.*

$r \approx 4.65\dfrac{\text{ft}}{\text{sec}}$

Sue's approximate walking speed is about 4.65 ft/sec.
Converting this figure to miles per hour yields

$$4.65\dfrac{\overset{1}{\text{feet}}}{\underset{1}{\text{second}}}\cdot 60\dfrac{\overset{1}{\text{second}}}{\underset{1}{\text{minute}}}\cdot 60\dfrac{\overset{1}{\text{minute}}}{\text{hour}}\cdot\dfrac{1}{5280}\dfrac{\text{mile}}{\underset{1}{\text{feet}}}$$

$$\approx 3.17\dfrac{\text{miles}}{\text{hour}}$$

c. $v = 0.25\cdot g^{1/2}\cdot SL^{5/3}\cdot h^{-7/6}$
$v = 0.25(32)^{1/2}\cdot(9.3)^{5/3}\cdot(13)^{-7/6}$
$v \approx 2.9$

The dinosaur's approximate speed is 2.9 feet per second.

d. The dinosaur's motion is not a true pendulum, and our model approximated a faster speed than Alexander's relationship.

✓ Objective 11.4.3 **CHECKUP**

1. The distance from Steve's heel to his hip is about 3 feet. Determine the length of time in seconds during which his leg does one back-and-forth swing, or one stride. The distance between footprints of Steve's same leg is about 6 feet. Determine his walking speed. How does Steve's speed compare with the *Tyrannosaurus rex*'s speed in the application in this section?

2. Evidence of dinosaurs has been found in Queensland, Australia. The *Eubrontes* tracks measure 0.46 meter with a stride length of about 2 meters. Scientists estimate that the hip length of the theropod was 2.25 meters.

a. Model the leg motion as that of a pendulum, and determine the length of time in seconds during which the leg completed one back-and-forth motion.
b. Use the distance formula to approximate the speed of the *Eubrontes*.
c. Use Alexander's relationship $v = 0.25\cdot g^{1/2}\cdot SL^{5/3}\cdot h^{-7/6}$, where g is the acceleration due to gravity, SL is the stride length, and h is the hip length to determine the speed of the *Eubrontes*.

11.4 EXERCISES

Student Solutions Manual   PH Math/Tutor Center   CD Video   Math XL   MathXL®   MyMathLab   MyMathLab   Interactmath.com

Simplify without a calculator. Check your results on your calculator.

1. $\sqrt{28}$ **2.** $\sqrt{75}$ **3.** $\sqrt[3]{-686}$ **4.** $\sqrt[3]{-192}$

5. $\sqrt[4]{112}$ **6.** $\sqrt[4]{7203}$ **7.** $\sqrt[5]{-6250}$ **8.** $\sqrt[5]{-1944}$

Simplify.

9. $\sqrt{20x^4y^3z^2}$ **10.** $\sqrt{12x^3y^9z^8}$ **11.** $\sqrt[3]{72m^5n^9}$ **12.** $\sqrt[3]{108p^7q^8}$

13. $\sqrt[4]{162x^4y^5}$ **14.** $\sqrt[4]{80a^6b^8}$ **15.** $\sqrt[5]{486a^6b^{10}c^2}$ **16.** $\sqrt[5]{729x^2y^8z^{15}}$

17. $\sqrt{5x^2 + 30x + 45}$ **18.** $\sqrt{3x^3 + 6x^2 + 3x}$

Multiply and simplify.

19. $\sqrt{7x} \cdot \sqrt{14y}$

20. $\sqrt{6x} \cdot \sqrt{12y}$

21. $2\sqrt{7xy} \cdot x\sqrt{14y}$

22. $-3\sqrt{7pq} \cdot 2\sqrt{3p^4q}$

23. $\sqrt{7x + 14y} \cdot \sqrt{3x + 6y}$

24. $\sqrt{p^2 + 2pq} \cdot \sqrt{3p + 6q}$

25. $\sqrt{x + 2} \cdot \sqrt{x^2 + 3x + 2}$

26. $\sqrt{x - 7} \cdot \sqrt{x^2 - 6x - 7}$

27. $\sqrt{x^2 + x - 2} \cdot \sqrt{x^2 + 3x - 4}$

28. $\sqrt{x^2 + 6x + 8} \cdot \sqrt{x^2 - 16}$

29. $\sqrt[3]{-4x^4y^2} \cdot \sqrt[3]{6xy}$

30. $\sqrt[3]{-25x^4y} \cdot \sqrt[3]{10x^2y^7}$

Simplify without a calculator. Rationalize all denominators. Check your results on your calculator.

31. $-\sqrt{\dfrac{36}{49}}$

32. $-\sqrt{\dfrac{25}{81}}$

33. $\sqrt{\dfrac{1210}{1440}}$

34. $\sqrt{\dfrac{1690}{1960}}$

35. $-\sqrt{\dfrac{8}{27}}$

36. $-\sqrt{\dfrac{27}{125}}$

37. $\sqrt[3]{\dfrac{4}{125}}$

38. $\sqrt[3]{\dfrac{5}{512}}$

39. $\sqrt[3]{-\dfrac{9}{25}}$

40. $\sqrt[3]{-\dfrac{10}{49}}$

41. $\sqrt[5]{\dfrac{1}{16}}$

42. $\sqrt[3]{\dfrac{1}{81}}$

Simplify. Rationalize all denominators.

43. $\sqrt{\dfrac{4x^2}{9y^2}}$

44. $\sqrt{\dfrac{25x}{49y^2}}$

45. $\sqrt{\dfrac{3x}{25y^2}}$

46. $\sqrt{\dfrac{5p}{49q^2}}$

47. $\sqrt{\dfrac{4xy}{5z}}$

48. $\sqrt{\dfrac{36ab}{7c}}$

49. $\sqrt{\dfrac{2x^2}{6}}$

50. $\sqrt{\dfrac{7z^4}{35}}$

51. $\sqrt[3]{\dfrac{27x^3}{y^6}}$

52. $\sqrt[3]{\dfrac{-64x^6y^3}{z^9}}$

53. $\sqrt[3]{\dfrac{3}{25x^2}}$

54. $\sqrt[3]{\dfrac{7}{36a^2}}$

55. $\sqrt[3]{\dfrac{3x^2y}{5xy^2z}}$

56. $\sqrt[3]{\dfrac{4a^2b^2c}{7ab^2c^2}}$

Divide and simplify. Rationalize all denominators.

57. $\dfrac{\sqrt{5}}{\sqrt{x}}$

58. $\dfrac{\sqrt{10}}{\sqrt{y}}$

59. $\dfrac{\sqrt{4x}}{\sqrt{8xy}}$

60. $\dfrac{\sqrt{5a}}{\sqrt{15ab}}$

61. $\dfrac{\sqrt{z^3}}{\sqrt{8}}$

62. $\dfrac{\sqrt{p^3}}{\sqrt{27}}$

63. $\dfrac{\sqrt{ab^4}}{\sqrt{a^2b}}$

64. $\dfrac{\sqrt{c^2d}}{\sqrt{c^3d^4}}$

65. $\dfrac{3x\sqrt{5x^2y}}{6\sqrt{15x^3y}}$

66. $\dfrac{5p\sqrt{3pq^2}}{15\sqrt{6pq^3}}$

67. $\dfrac{\sqrt[3]{3}}{\sqrt[3]{x^2}}$

68. $\dfrac{\sqrt[3]{7}}{\sqrt[3]{a^2}}$

69. $\dfrac{\sqrt[3]{3x}}{\sqrt[3]{12xy}}$

70. $\dfrac{\sqrt[3]{6b}}{\sqrt[3]{24ab}}$

71. $\dfrac{\sqrt[3]{-8xy^2z^2}}{\sqrt[3]{3x^2y^2z}}$

72. $\dfrac{\sqrt[3]{-27a^2bc^4}}{\sqrt[3]{5a^2b^2c^3}}$

Pendulum

In exercises 73–80, use the formula $T = 2\pi\sqrt{\dfrac{L}{g}}$, where T = the time in seconds for a complete back-and-forth motion of a pendulum,

L = the length of the suspension, and g = the acceleration due to gravity. Let $g = 32$ ft/sec² or 9.8 m/sec².

73. Find the period of a pendulum whose length is 7 feet.

74. Find the period of a pendulum whose length is 12 feet.

75. Find the period of a pendulum whose length is 9 meters.

76. Find the period of a pendulum whose length is 7 meters.

77. Use the pendulum formula to model the motion of a man's leg as he walks. If his leg measures 3 feet from his heel to his hip, determine the time it takes his leg to complete the forward-and-back motion to return to its starting position.

78. A boy's leg measures 1.6 feet from his heel to his hip. Use the pendulum formula to determine the time it takes his leg to complete the forward-and-back motion to return to its starting position as he walks.

79. The hip height of an elephant is approximately 5 feet. Model the leg motion of an elephant as that of a pendulum and determine the amount of time in seconds in which the leg completed one back-and-forth motion. The length of an elephant's stride is about 18 feet. Use this distance to estimate the speed of an elephant.

80. The hip height of a racehorse is approximately 3.6 feet. Model the leg motion of a horse as that of a pendulum and determine the amount of time in seconds in which the leg completed one back-and-forth motion. The length of a racehorse's stride is about 16 feet. Use this distance to estimate the speed of a racehorse.

Geometric Mean

81. Find the geometric mean of a and b if $a = \dfrac{3}{x^2 y^5}$ and $b = \dfrac{2}{xy^2}$. Rationalize the denominator.

82. Find the geometric mean of a and b if $a = \dfrac{2}{x^5 y}$ and $b = \dfrac{7}{x^4 y^6}$. Rationalize the denominator.

Physics

83. In electronics, resonance frequency is defined to be $f = \dfrac{1}{2\pi\sqrt{LC}}$, where L is the inductance and C is the capacitance. If $L = 2x$ and $C = 3x^3$, find a simplified function for f in which the denominator has been rationalized.

84. In electronics, resonance frequency is defined to be $f = \dfrac{1}{2\pi\sqrt{LC}}$, where L is the inductance and C is the capacitance. If $L = 5y$ and $C = 3y^2$, find a simplified function for f in which the denominator has been rationalized.

 ## 11.4 Calculator Exercises

When given a radical expression to simplify, you must be able to determine the largest perfect power factor of the radicand that you can extract from the radical expression. For example, when you simplified $\sqrt[3]{24}$, you had to know that 8 was the largest perfect-cube factor of 24. That was not too difficult to figure out, but suppose you had to simplify $\sqrt[3]{24{,}565}$. It would be very difficult to determine the largest perfect cube factor of 24,565. The table feature of the calculator can be used to help you find this factor. The steps to do so are as follows:

• In Y1, store x^p, where p will be the exponent of the power that you are seeking.

[Y=] [X,T,θ,n] [^] [ALPHA] [8] (P) [ENTER]

• In Y2, store $N/Y1$, where N will be the radicand of the radical expression.

[ALPHA] [LOG] (N) [÷] [VARS] [►] [1] [1]
[2nd] [MODE] (QUIT)

• Store the index of the radicand in P and the radicand in N.

[3] [STO►] [ALPHA] [8] (P) [ENTER] [2] [4]
[5] [6] [5] [STO►] [ALPHA] [LOG] (N) [ENTER]

• Set the table feature to start at 2 and increment by 1 in the Auto mode.

[2nd] [WINDOW] (TBLSET) [2] [ENTER] [1] [ENTER]
[ENTER] [▼] [ENTER] [2nd] [MODE] (QUIT)

• View the table.

[2nd] [GRAPH] (TABLE)

• Scroll down the table until you find the first integer value in the Y2 column. The value in the X column will be the base of the perfect power factor, the value in the Y1 column will be the perfect power factor, and the value in the Y2 column will be the other factor.

X	Y1	Y2
12	1728	14.216
13	2197	11.181
14	2744	8.9523
15	3375	7.2785
16	4096	5.9973
17	4913	5
18	5832	4.2121

X=17

• From the screen, we can see that

$$24{,}565 = 4913 \cdot 5 = 17^3 \cdot 5$$

so

$$\sqrt[3]{24{,}565} = \sqrt[3]{17^3 \cdot 5} = 17\sqrt[3]{5}$$

Use this method to simplify the following radicals:

1. $\sqrt[3]{13{,}718}$ **2.** $\sqrt[4]{199{,}927}$

3. $\sqrt[7]{-1664}$ **4.** $\sqrt{9251}$

 ## 11.4 Writing Exercises

The following examples illustrate the use of rational exponents to simplify radical expressions involving different indices. In each of the examples, an incorrect step has been made, which yields a result that is not equivalent to the original expression. You may use the TABLE feature to see that they are not equivalent to the original expression. Check each step to see where the mistake is made during simplification. Describe the incorrect step.

1. $\sqrt[3]{x^2}\,\sqrt[5]{x^3} = x^{2/3} \cdot x^{3/5} = x^{(2+3)/(3+5)} = x^{5/8} = \sqrt[8]{x^5}$

2. $\sqrt[3]{x^2}\,\sqrt[5]{x^3} = x^{3/2} \cdot x^{5/3} = x^{9/6 + 10/6} = x^{19/6} = \sqrt[6]{x^{19}} = \sqrt[6]{x^{18} \cdot x} = x^3\sqrt[6]{x}$

3. $\dfrac{\sqrt[5]{x^3}}{\sqrt[3]{x^2}} = \dfrac{x^{3/5}}{x^{2/3}} = x^{3/5 - 2/3} = x^{(3-2)/(5-3)} = x^{1/2} = \sqrt{x}$

11.5 OPERATIONS ON RADICALS

OBJECTIVES

1. Add and subtract radical expressions.
2. Multiply radical expressions.
3. Divide radical expressions, and rationalize a denominator having two terms.
4. Model real-world situations by using expressions involving the addition or subtraction of radicals.

APPLICATION

The Hephaesteion was a temple built by the Greeks in the fifth century B.C. The ratio of its width to its height is approximated by the expression $\dfrac{2}{\sqrt{5}-1}$. This number is called the *golden ratio*. Early Greeks believed that rectangles with this ratio were aesthetically pleasing to the eye. Rationalize the denominator of the expression.

After completing this section, we will discuss this application further. See page 897.

Objective 11.5.1   ### Adding and Subtracting Radical Expressions

We are now ready to add and subtract radical expressions. We need to develop a property of radicals that we can use in addition and subtraction. Let's discuss addition and subtraction of like radicals. **Like radicals** have the same index and radicand. The expression $2\sqrt{3} + 5\sqrt{3}$ contains two terms with like radicals, $2\sqrt{3}$ and $5\sqrt{3}$. The coefficients of the radicals in the expression are 2 and 5, respectively.

To add (or subtract) like radicals, we add (or subtract) the coefficients of each like radical.

$$2\sqrt{3} + 5\sqrt{3} = (2 + 5)\sqrt{3} = 7\sqrt{3}$$

ADDITION AND SUBTRACTION OF LIKE RADICALS

To add or subtract like radicals, use the respective formulas

$$a\sqrt[n]{x} + b\sqrt[n]{x} = (a + b)\sqrt[n]{x}$$
$$a\sqrt[n]{x} - b\sqrt[n]{x} = (a - b)\sqrt[n]{x}$$

We can show that this statement is true by using the distributive law, as we did when we combined like terms. For example,

$$2x + x = 2x + 1x = (2 + 1)x = 3x \qquad \text{Like terms}$$
$$2\sqrt{x} + \sqrt{x} = 2\sqrt{x} + 1\sqrt{x} = (2 + 1)\sqrt{x} = 3\sqrt{x} \qquad \text{Like radicals}$$

 TAKE NOTE Just as we cannot add or subtract unlike terms, such as $2x + y$, we cannot add or subtract unlike radicals, such as $2\sqrt{x} + \sqrt{y}$.

EXAMPLE 1   Add or subtract as indicated.

a. $2\sqrt{xy} + 3\sqrt[3]{xy} - 4\sqrt[3]{xy} - \sqrt{xy}$ **b.** $3x\sqrt{y} - 5x\sqrt{y} + 4x\sqrt{y}$

c. $5a\sqrt[3]{abc} + 4\sqrt[3]{abc}$

Solution

a. $2\sqrt{xy} + 3\sqrt[3]{xy} - 4\sqrt[3]{xy} - \sqrt{xy}$

$= 2\sqrt{xy} - \sqrt{xy} + 3\sqrt[3]{xy} - 4\sqrt[3]{xy}$ Rearrange terms.

$= (2 - 1)\sqrt{xy} + (3 - 4)\sqrt[3]{xy}$ Subtract coefficients.

$= \sqrt{xy} - \sqrt[3]{xy}$

b. $3x\sqrt{y} - 5x\sqrt{y} + 4x\sqrt{y}$

$= (3x - 5x + 4x)\sqrt{y}$ Add and subtract coefficients.

$= 2x\sqrt{y}$

c. $5a\sqrt[3]{abc} + 4\sqrt[3]{abc} = (5a + 4)\sqrt[3]{abc}$ Add coefficients. ∎

Sometimes we need to simplify the radical expressions to have like radicals.

EXAMPLE 2   Add or subtract as indicated.

a. $5\sqrt{32} - \sqrt{72}$ **b.** $3ab\sqrt{ab} + 2b\sqrt{a^3b} - a\sqrt{4ab^3}$

c. $\sqrt{2} + \sqrt{\dfrac{1}{2}}$

Solution

a. $5\sqrt{32} - \sqrt{72} = 5\cdot4\sqrt{2} - 6\sqrt{2}$ Simplify radical expressions.

$= 20\sqrt{2} - 6\sqrt{2}$ Subtract coefficients.

$= 14\sqrt{2}$

b. $3ab\sqrt{ab} + 2b\sqrt{a^3b} - a\sqrt{4ab^3}$

$= 3ab\sqrt{ab} + 2ab\sqrt{ab} - 2ab\sqrt{ab}$ Simplify radical expressions.

$= (3ab + 2ab - 2ab)\sqrt{ab}$ Add and subtract coefficients.

$= 3ab\sqrt{ab}$

c. $\sqrt{2} + \sqrt{\dfrac{1}{2}} = \sqrt{2} + \dfrac{\sqrt{1}}{\sqrt{2}}$ Quotient rule

$= \sqrt{2} + \dfrac{\sqrt{1}}{\sqrt{2}}\cdot\dfrac{\sqrt{2}}{\sqrt{2}}$ Rationalize the denominator.

$= \sqrt{2} + \dfrac{\sqrt{2}}{2}$

$= \sqrt{2} + \dfrac{1}{2}\sqrt{2}$

$= \left(1 + \dfrac{1}{2}\right)\sqrt{2}$ Add coefficients.

$= \dfrac{3}{2}\sqrt{2}$ ∎

✓ Objective 11.5.1 *CHECKUP*

In exercises 1 and 2, add or subtract as indicated.

1. a. $3\sqrt{ab} + 5\sqrt[4]{ab} - 4\sqrt{ab} + 2\sqrt[4]{ab}$

    b. $3p\sqrt{q} - 7p\sqrt{q} + 8p\sqrt{q}$

    c. $5m\sqrt[3]{mn} + 2\sqrt[3]{mn}$

2. a. $2\sqrt{48} + \sqrt{75}$ **b.** $6xy\sqrt{xy} + 5y\sqrt{x^3y} - 4x\sqrt{9xy^3}$

    c. $\sqrt{3} - \sqrt{\dfrac{1}{3}}$

3. Define what is meant by the term *like radicals*. Give examples of like radicals and unlike radicals.

4. Explain what a coefficient of a radical term is.

5. What must you do to the radical terms of an addition or subtraction problem before collecting like terms? Why?

Objective 11.5.2 **Multiplying Radicals**

We have already multiplied radical expressions with one term. We use the properties of radicals to simplify these expressions. We are now ready to expand our multiplication of radicals to radical expressions that have more than one term.

To multiply, we use the distributive law, as we did to multiply polynomial expressions with more than one term. For example,

$$2(x + 3) = 2x + 6 \qquad \text{Polynomial expression}$$
$$\sqrt{2}(\sqrt{x} + \sqrt{3}) = \sqrt{2x} + \sqrt{6} \qquad \text{Radical expression}$$
$$(x + 3)(x - 4) = x^2 - 4x + 3x - 12 \qquad \text{Polynomial expression}$$
$$= x^2 - x - 12$$
$$(\sqrt{x} + 3)(\sqrt{x} - 4) = \sqrt{x^2} - 4\sqrt{x} + 3\sqrt{x} - 12 \qquad \text{Radical expression}$$
$$= x - \sqrt{x} - 12$$

EXAMPLE 3 Multiply and simplify.

a. $3\sqrt[3]{x}\left(4\sqrt[3]{x^2} - 2\right)$ **b.** $\left(\sqrt{2} - \sqrt{xy}\right)\left(\sqrt{5} + \sqrt{xy}\right)$

c. $\left(\sqrt{2} + \sqrt{3}\right)^2$ **d.** $(\sqrt{x} - 2)^2$

Solution

a. $3\sqrt[3]{x}\left(4\sqrt[3]{x^2} - 2\right) = 12\sqrt[3]{x^3} - 6\sqrt[3]{x}$ Distributive law
$$= 12x - 6\sqrt[3]{x}$$

b. $\left(\sqrt{2} - \sqrt{xy}\right)\left(\sqrt{5} + \sqrt{xy}\right)$
$$= \sqrt{10} + \sqrt{2xy} - \sqrt{5xy} - \sqrt{(xy)^2} \qquad \text{FOIL method}$$
$$= \sqrt{10} + \sqrt{2xy} - \sqrt{5xy} - xy$$

c. $\left(\sqrt{2} + \sqrt{3}\right)^2$
$$= \left(\sqrt{2} + \sqrt{3}\right)\left(\sqrt{2} + \sqrt{3}\right) \qquad \text{Expand factors.}$$
$$= \sqrt{4} + \sqrt{6} + \sqrt{6} + \sqrt{9} \qquad \text{FOIL method}$$
$$= 2 + 2\sqrt{6} + 3$$
$$= 5 + 2\sqrt{6}$$

We should have noticed that the given expression was a special product, $(a + b)^2 = a^2 + 2ab + b^2$. Then,

$$\left(\sqrt{2} + \sqrt{3}\right)^2 = \left(\sqrt{2}\right)^2 + 2\sqrt{2}\sqrt{3} + \left(\sqrt{3}\right)^2 = 2 + 2\sqrt{6} + 3$$
$$= 5 + 2\sqrt{6}$$

d. $(\sqrt{x} - 2)^2 = (\sqrt{x})^2 - 2 \cdot \sqrt{x} \cdot 2 + 2^2 \qquad (a - b)^2 = a^2 - 2ab + b^2$
$$= x - 4\sqrt{x} + 4$$

The product of the sum and difference of two terms is the difference of their squares.

$$(a + b)(a - b) = a^2 - b^2$$

The expressions $a + b$ and $a - b$ are called **conjugates** of each other. When we multiply conjugates that contain square roots, we obtain an interesting result. Complete the following set of exercises to discover this result.

 Guided Discovery 4   Conjugates

Multiply and simplify.

1. $\left(\sqrt{2} + \sqrt{3}\right)\left(\sqrt{2} - \sqrt{3}\right)$ **2.** $(2 + \sqrt{x})(2 - \sqrt{x})$

What did you notice about the products?

In these exercises, we noticed that the factors contained square roots, but the product did not contain a square root.

We can see why this is true if we multiply $(\sqrt{x} + \sqrt{y})(\sqrt{x} - \sqrt{y})$, using the special product $(a + b)(a - b) = a^2 - b^2$. We obtain

$$(\sqrt{x} + \sqrt{y})(\sqrt{x} - \sqrt{y}) = (\sqrt{x})^2 - (\sqrt{y})^2$$
$$= x - y$$

This kind of simplification works only for radicals involving square roots. We will use conjugates in the next objective to rationalize denominators.

EXAMPLE 4   Multiply. $\left(\sqrt{x} - 2\sqrt{2}\right)\left(\sqrt{x} + 2\sqrt{2}\right)$

Solution

$$\left(\sqrt{x} - 2\sqrt{2}\right)\left(\sqrt{x} + 2\sqrt{2}\right) = (\sqrt{x})^2 - \left(2\sqrt{2}\right)^2 \qquad {\scriptstyle (a - b)(a + b) = a^2 - b^2}$$
$$= x - 8$$

∎

Objective 11.5.2 **CHECKUP**

In exercises 1 and 2, multiply and simplify. Where possible, check for equivalence of your results, using your calculator.

1. **a.** $7\sqrt[3]{x}\left(5\sqrt[3]{x^2} + 4\sqrt[3]{x}\right)$
   b. $\left(\sqrt{3} - \sqrt{ab}\right)\left(\sqrt{7} + \sqrt{ab}\right)$
   c. $\left(\sqrt{10} + \sqrt{5}\right)^2$
   d. $(\sqrt{z} - 5)^2$

2. **a.** $\left(\sqrt{10} + \sqrt{5}\right)\left(\sqrt{10} - \sqrt{5}\right)$
   b. $(11 + 3\sqrt{z})(11 - 3\sqrt{z})$

3. Describe what we mean by a conjugate of a radical expression. Give an example.

4. What special result is obtained when you multiply conjugate expressions?

∎

Objective 11.5.3   **Dividing Radicals**

We have already divided radical expressions with one term. We used the properties of radicals to simplify these expressions. We are now ready to expand our division of radicals to radical expressions that have more than one term.

To divide a radical expression by a radical expression with a single term, we use the distributive law, as we did to divide polynomial expressions. For example,

$$\frac{x + 6}{2} = \frac{x}{2} + \frac{6}{2} \qquad \text{\small Polynomial expression}$$

$$= \frac{1}{2}x + 3 \qquad \text{\small Simplify.}$$

$$\frac{\sqrt{x} + \sqrt{6}}{\sqrt{2}} = \frac{\sqrt{x}}{\sqrt{2}} + \frac{\sqrt{6}}{\sqrt{2}} \qquad \text{\small Radical expression}$$

$$= \frac{\sqrt{x}}{\sqrt{2}} \cdot \frac{\sqrt{2}}{\sqrt{2}} + \sqrt{3} \qquad \text{\small Simplify and rationalize the denominator.}$$

$$= \frac{\sqrt{2x}}{2} + \sqrt{3} \quad \text{or} \quad \frac{1}{2}\sqrt{2x} + \sqrt{3}$$

To divide a radical expression with square roots by a radical expression containing two terms with square roots, we use the multiplication property of 1 and conjugates. Remember that the product of conjugates with at least one square-root term results in an expression without square roots. Therefore, this division process will rationalize the denominator.

EXAMPLE 5   Divide and simplify.

a. $\dfrac{\sqrt{5}}{\sqrt{3} + \sqrt{2}}$ b. $\dfrac{2\sqrt{x} + \sqrt{5}}{\sqrt{x} - 2\sqrt{2}}$ c. $\dfrac{\sqrt{3} + \sqrt{7}}{\sqrt{3} - \sqrt{7}}$

Solution

a. $\dfrac{\sqrt{5}}{\sqrt{3} + \sqrt{2}} = \dfrac{\sqrt{5}}{\sqrt{3} + \sqrt{2}} \cdot \dfrac{\sqrt{3} - \sqrt{2}}{\sqrt{3} - \sqrt{2}}$

Multiplication by 1
Use the conjugate of the denominator as numerator and denominator of the factor of 1.

$= \dfrac{\sqrt{5}\left(\sqrt{3} - \sqrt{2}\right)}{\left(\sqrt{3} + \sqrt{2}\right)\left(\sqrt{3} - \sqrt{2}\right)}$ Multiply.

$= \dfrac{\sqrt{15} - \sqrt{10}}{\left(\sqrt{3}\right)^2 - \left(\sqrt{2}\right)^2}$ Distribute and simplify.

$= \dfrac{\sqrt{15} - \sqrt{10}}{1}$

$= \sqrt{15} - \sqrt{10}$

b. $\dfrac{2\sqrt{x} + \sqrt{5}}{\sqrt{x} - 2\sqrt{2}}$

$= \dfrac{2\sqrt{x} + \sqrt{5}}{\sqrt{x} - 2\sqrt{2}} \cdot \dfrac{\sqrt{x} + 2\sqrt{2}}{\sqrt{x} + 2\sqrt{2}}$

Multiplication by 1
Use the conjugate of the denominator as numerator and denominator of the factor of 1.

$= \dfrac{\left(2\sqrt{x} + \sqrt{5}\right)\left(\sqrt{x} + 2\sqrt{2}\right)}{\left(\sqrt{x} - 2\sqrt{2}\right)\left(\sqrt{x} + 2\sqrt{2}\right)}$ Multiply.

$= \dfrac{2\sqrt{x^2} + 4\sqrt{2x} + \sqrt{5x} + 2\sqrt{10}}{(\sqrt{x})^2 - \left(2\sqrt{2}\right)^2}$

Use the FOIL method and simplify.
See Example 4.

$= \dfrac{2x + 4\sqrt{2x} + \sqrt{5x} + 2\sqrt{10}}{x - 8}$

c. $\dfrac{\sqrt{3} + \sqrt{7}}{\sqrt{3} - \sqrt{7}} = \dfrac{\sqrt{3} + \sqrt{7}}{\sqrt{3} - \sqrt{7}} \cdot \dfrac{\sqrt{3} + \sqrt{7}}{\sqrt{3} + \sqrt{7}}$

Multiplication by 1
Use the conjugate of the denominator as numerator and denominator of the factor of 1.

$= \dfrac{\left(\sqrt{3} + \sqrt{7}\right)\left(\sqrt{3} + \sqrt{7}\right)}{\left(\sqrt{3} - \sqrt{7}\right)\left(\sqrt{3} + \sqrt{7}\right)}$ Multiply.

$= \dfrac{\left(\sqrt{3}\right)^2 + 2\sqrt{21} + \left(\sqrt{7}\right)^2}{\left(\sqrt{3}\right)^2 - \left(\sqrt{7}\right)^2}$ FOIL method

$= \dfrac{3 + 2\sqrt{21} + 7}{3 - 7}$

$= \dfrac{10 + 2\sqrt{21}}{-4}$

$= \dfrac{2\left(5 + \sqrt{21}\right)}{2(-2)}$

Factor the numerator and denominator to simplify the fraction.

$= \dfrac{5 + \sqrt{21}}{-2}$

$= \dfrac{5 + \sqrt{21}}{-2} \cdot \dfrac{-1}{-1}$

Multiplication by 1
Use -1 as the numerator and denominator in order to eliminate a negative denominator.

$= \dfrac{-5 - \sqrt{21}}{2}$

✓ Objective 11.5.3 *CHECKUP*

1. Divide and simplify. Check for equivalence of your result by using your calculator.

   a. $\dfrac{\sqrt{13}}{\sqrt{5} + \sqrt{2}}$ b. $\dfrac{\sqrt{6} + \sqrt{2}}{\sqrt{6} - \sqrt{2}}$ c. $\dfrac{8\sqrt{x} - \sqrt{3}}{\sqrt{x} + 2\sqrt{3}}$

2. Suppose one radical expression involving square roots is being divided by another radical expression with two terms involving square roots. What is accomplished by multiplying both the numerator and the denominator by the conjugate of the denominator? Why would this be desirable? ■

Objective 11.5.4   Modeling the Real World

When we use geometric formulas involving radicals, we encounter values that are not perfect-square radicands, but are irrational numbers instead. Evaluating complicated radical expressions can be tricky, even with a calculator; it is usually a good idea to simplify these radical expressions by using the rules for radicals we've discussed in this section.

EXAMPLE 6   Fernando plans to increase the size of a square fenced area in his yard. The present area is 48 square feet. He plans to increase the fenced area to 108 square feet and keep the shape as a square. Determine the amount of additional fencing that Fernando needs to purchase. (Round your answer to the nearest foot.)

Solution

Determine the length of the sides of the present area and the new area.

Present area: $s = \sqrt{A}$ New area: $s = \sqrt{A}$
$s = \sqrt{48}$ $s = \sqrt{108}$
$s = \sqrt{16 \cdot 3}$ $s = \sqrt{36 \cdot 3}$
$s = 4\sqrt{3}$ $s = 6\sqrt{3}$

Determine the amount of fencing for both areas. Use the perimeter formula.

Present area: $P = 4s$ New area: $P = 4s$
$P = 4 \cdot 4\sqrt{3}$ $P = 4 \cdot 6\sqrt{3}$
$P = 16\sqrt{3}$ $P = 24\sqrt{3}$

The difference in the new perimeter and the present perimeter is the amount of fencing needed.

$$24\sqrt{3} - 16\sqrt{3} = 8\sqrt{3} \approx 14$$

Fernando needs $8\sqrt{3}$ feet of additional fencing, or approximately 14 feet of fencing.

■

EXAMPLE 7   The distance to the horizon in nautical miles is given by the equation $d = 1.17\sqrt{x}$, where x is the height of your eye above the surface of the water in feet.

a. If you are 20 feet above the surface of the water, what is your distance to the horizon?

b. If you are approaching a lighthouse that has a height of 98 feet, and you are on the tower of a fishing boat 18 feet above the surface of the water, determine the distance at which the lighthouse will become visible?

Solution

a. Let $x = 20$.

$$d = 1.17\sqrt{x}$$
$$d = 1.17\sqrt{20}$$
$$d = 1.17\sqrt{4 \cdot 5}$$
$$d = 1.17 \cdot 2\sqrt{5}$$
$$d = 2.34\sqrt{5}$$
$$d \approx 5.23$$

The distance to the horizon is $2.34\sqrt{5}$ or approximately 5.23 nautical miles.

b.

Lighthouse

Foot of ship

The distance at which the lighthouse will become visible is the sum of your distance to horizon and the distance the lighthouse can be seen over the horizon (or the distance to the horizon from the top of the lighthouse).

$$d = 1.17\sqrt{x} \qquad\qquad d = 1.17\sqrt{x}$$
$$d = 1.17\sqrt{18} \qquad\qquad d = 1.17\sqrt{98}$$
$$d = 1.17\sqrt{9 \cdot 2} \qquad\qquad d = 1.17\sqrt{49 \cdot 2}$$
$$d = 1.17 \cdot 3\sqrt{2} \qquad\qquad d = 1.17 \cdot 7\sqrt{2}$$
$$d = 3.51\sqrt{2} \qquad\qquad d = 8.19\sqrt{2}$$
$$3.51\sqrt{2} + 8.19\sqrt{2} = 11.7\sqrt{2}$$

The lighthouse will become visible when you are $11.7\sqrt{2}$ or about 16.55 nautical miles away. ■

APPLICATION

The Hephaesteion was a temple built by the Greeks in the fifth century B.C. The ratio of its width to its height is approximated by the expression $\dfrac{2}{\sqrt{5} - 1}$.

This number is called the *golden ratio*. Early Greeks believed that rectangles with this ratio were aesthetically pleasing to the eye. Rationalize the denominator of the expression.

Discussion

$$\frac{2}{\sqrt{5} - 1} = \frac{2}{\sqrt{5} - 1} \cdot \frac{\sqrt{5} + 1}{\sqrt{5} + 1}$$

Use the conjugate of the denominator as the numerator and denominator of the factor of 1.

$$= \frac{2(\sqrt{5} + 1)}{(\sqrt{5} - 1)(\sqrt{5} + 1)}$$

Multiply.

$$= \frac{2(\sqrt{5} + 1)}{4}$$

$$= \frac{\sqrt{5} + 1}{2}$$

The golden ratio is $\dfrac{\sqrt{5} + 1}{2}$.

Note: The Project in Chapter 2 discusses the golden ratio in more detail.

Objective 11.5.4 CHECKUP

1. Sandra purchased enough baseboard to surround her sunporch floor, which was a square measuring 350 square feet. Julie purchased baseboard for her sunporch, which was also a square, but measuring 224 square feet. What is the difference in the amounts of baseboard the women purchased? Ignore cuts in the baseboard for doors.

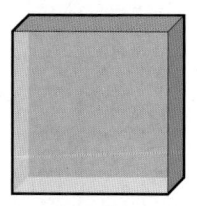 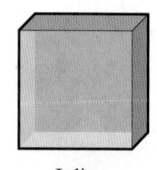

Sandra   Julie

2. The distance to the horizon in nautical miles is given by the equation $d = 1.17\sqrt{x}$, where x is the height of your eye above the surface of the water in feet.
  a. If you are 40 feet above the surface of the water, what is your distance to the horizon?
  b. If you are approaching a lighthouse that has a height of 75 feet and you are on the tower of a fishing boat 12 feet above the surface of the water, determine the distance at which the lighthouse will become visible.

3. The area of a rectangle is $(3\sqrt{5} + \sqrt{10})$ square feet. The length of the rectangle is $(3 + \sqrt{2})$ feet. Find the width.

11.5 EXERCISES

Student Solutions Manual   PH Math/Tutor Center   CD Video   MathXL®   MyMathLab   Interactmath.com

Add or subtract as indicated.

1. $2\sqrt{28} - \sqrt{63}$

2. $5\sqrt{24} - \sqrt{54}$

3. $\sqrt{10} - \sqrt{\dfrac{1}{10}}$

4. $\sqrt{13} + \sqrt{\dfrac{1}{13}}$

5. $\sqrt[3]{24} - 4\sqrt[3]{3}$

6. $2\sqrt[3]{250} + \sqrt[3]{54}$

7. $5\sqrt{75} - 2\sqrt{27} + \sqrt{48}$

8. $4\sqrt{80} - 2\sqrt{45} + \sqrt{20}$

9. $5\sqrt{x} + 9\sqrt{x}$

10. $8\sqrt{bc} - 10\sqrt{bc}$

11. $\sqrt{25x} + \sqrt{36x}$

12. $\sqrt{64p} + \sqrt{144p}$

13. $\sqrt{8x^3} - \sqrt{50x^3}$

14. $\sqrt{48y^5} - \sqrt{75y^5}$

15. $\sqrt{9a} + \sqrt{16a^3}$

16. $\sqrt{121b^3} - \sqrt{16b}$

17. $7a\sqrt{b} + 9a\sqrt{b} - 2a\sqrt{b}$

18. $2x\sqrt{y} - 5x\sqrt{y} + 4x\sqrt{y}$

19. $5\sqrt{pq} - 4\sqrt[3]{pq} + 2\sqrt{pq} + 11\sqrt[3]{pq}$

20. $4\sqrt[3]{ab} - 3\sqrt{ab} - 5\sqrt{ab} + 2\sqrt[3]{ab}$

21. $7y\sqrt{x^3y} + 3x\sqrt{xy^3} - 4xy\sqrt{xy}$

22. $5d\sqrt{c^3d} - 8c\sqrt{cd^3} + 2cd\sqrt{cd}$

23. $2x\sqrt[3]{x^2y^4z} - 3y\sqrt[3]{x^5yz}$

24. $6x\sqrt[4]{xy^5z^2} + y\sqrt[4]{x^5yz^2}$

Multiply and simplify.

25. $\sqrt{7}(\sqrt{5} - \sqrt{7})$

26. $\sqrt{5}(\sqrt{6} + \sqrt{5})$

27. $\sqrt{3}(\sqrt{x} - \sqrt{5})$

28. $2\sqrt{5}(\sqrt{7} + \sqrt{a})$

29. $3\sqrt{a}(2\sqrt{a} - 5)$

30. $8\sqrt{c}(3\sqrt{c} + 4)$

31. $2\sqrt[3]{x}(4\sqrt[3]{x^2} - 6\sqrt[3]{x})$

32. $7\sqrt[3]{a}(5\sqrt[3]{a} - 2\sqrt[3]{a^2})$

33. $(\sqrt{3} - 5\sqrt{6})(2\sqrt{3} + \sqrt{8})$

34. $(3\sqrt{6} + 2)(\sqrt{5} - 4\sqrt{3})$

35. $(\sqrt{3} - \sqrt{x})(\sqrt{2} + \sqrt{x})$

36. $(\sqrt{2} - \sqrt{z})(\sqrt{5} + \sqrt{z})$

37. $(5 - \sqrt{6})(5 + \sqrt{6})$

38. $(\sqrt{11} + \sqrt{12})(\sqrt{11} - \sqrt{12})$

39. $(12 + \sqrt{p})(12 - \sqrt{p})$

40. $(13 - \sqrt{q})(13 + \sqrt{q})$

41. $(\sqrt{2x} + \sqrt{3y})(\sqrt{2x} - \sqrt{3y})$

42. $(\sqrt{6x} + \sqrt{3y})(\sqrt{6x} - \sqrt{3y})$

43. $(\sqrt{a} + 4)^2$

44. $(\sqrt{bc} + 5)^2$

45. $(3\sqrt{b} - 2)^2$

46. $(9\sqrt{c} - 3)^2$

47. $(\sqrt{x} - \sqrt{y})^2$

48. $(\sqrt{2x} - \sqrt{3y})^2$

Divide and simplify.

49. $\dfrac{\sqrt{21x} - \sqrt{14}}{\sqrt{7}}$

50. $\dfrac{\sqrt{10x} + \sqrt{30}}{\sqrt{5}}$

51. $\dfrac{\sqrt{a} - 12}{\sqrt{a}}$

52. $\dfrac{9 + \sqrt{b}}{\sqrt{b}}$

53. $\dfrac{\sqrt{x} + \sqrt{y} + \sqrt{z}}{\sqrt{x}}$

54. $\dfrac{\sqrt{ab} - \sqrt{ac} + \sqrt{bc}}{\sqrt{b}}$

55. $\dfrac{18}{\sqrt{6} + \sqrt{3}}$

56. $\dfrac{24}{\sqrt{10} + \sqrt{2}}$

57. $\dfrac{\sqrt{3} + \sqrt{2}}{\sqrt{3} - \sqrt{2}}$

58. $\dfrac{\sqrt{3} - \sqrt{2}}{\sqrt{3} + \sqrt{2}}$

59. $\dfrac{3x}{\sqrt{x} - 2}$

60. $\dfrac{4w}{3 - \sqrt{w}}$

61. $\dfrac{3b - 4}{\sqrt{3b} - 2}$

62. $\dfrac{ab - 1}{\sqrt{ab} + 1}$

63. $\dfrac{\sqrt{x} + 3}{\sqrt{x} - 3}$

64. $\dfrac{6 - \sqrt{p}}{6 + \sqrt{p}}$

65. $\dfrac{3\sqrt{x} - 4}{4 - 3\sqrt{x}}$

66. $\dfrac{3 - 5\sqrt{x}}{5\sqrt{x} - 3}$

Geometry

67. One painting on a square canvas measures 490 square inches. A second painting on a square canvas measures 810 square inches. How many more inches of frame will the second painting require than that required for the first painting?

68. The footprint of one computer is a square measuring 150 square inches. The footprint of a second computer is also a square, but it measures 216 square inches. By how many inches does the perimeter of the footprint for the second computer exceed that of the first? (**Note:** The footprint of a computer is the base upon which it rests.)

69. A box in the shape of a cube has a volume of 1750 cubic inches. It contains a smaller box shaped like a cube, with a volume of 896 cubic inches. Determine the difference in the perimeters of the bases of the two boxes.

70. A pair of stacking tables in the shapes of cubes consists of one whose volume is 2000 cubic inches and another whose volume is 6750 cubic inches. Determine the difference in the perimeters of the bases of the two tables.

In exercises 71 and 72, recall that the distance to the horizon in nautical miles is given by the equation $d = 1.17\sqrt{x}$, where x is the height of your eye above the surface of the water in feet.

71. If a building has a height of 48 feet and you are 3 feet above the surface of the water, determine the distance at which the building will become visible.

72. If a building has a height of 80 feet and you are 5 feet above the surface of the water, determine the distance at which the building will become visible.

73. The area of a rectangle is $(3\sqrt{2} + \sqrt{6})$ square inches. The width is $\sqrt{2}$ inches. Find the length.

74. The area of a rectangle is $(2\sqrt{3} + \sqrt{6})$ square feet. The length is $\sqrt{3}$ feet. Find the width.

75. The area of a rectangle is $(5 + 3\sqrt{3})$ square inches. The length is $(2 + \sqrt{3})$ inches. Find the width.

76. The area of a rectangle is $(11 + 5\sqrt{5})$ square feet. The width is $(3 + \sqrt{5})$ feet. Find the length.

Distance

In exercises 77 and 78, recall that the distance between two points, (x_1, y_1) and (x_2, y_2), is $d = \sqrt{(x_2 - x_1)^2 + (y_2 - y_1)^2}$.

77. Three times the distance between $(6, 3)$ and $(2, 1)$ is increased by two times the distance between $(3, 4)$ and $(-3, 1)$. Find the sum.

78. Four times the distance between $(5, 6)$ and $(-3, 2)$ is decreased by two times the distance between $(7, 11)$ and $(1, 8)$. Find the difference.

11.5 Calculator Exercises

Operations with radicals represent another situation in which the calculator can be helpful in checking your results if the radical expressions contain only a single variable. By storing the original expression in Y1 and your simplified result in Y2 and comparing the graphs for equivalence, you can see whether your result is correct. Likewise, you can use the TABLE function to explore the equivalence of the two expressions. These methods have already been demonstrated for you in the text.

However, if you store the original expression in Y2 and your simplified result in Y3, then you can define Y1 to be Y2 = Y3, using the TEST key to do so. Then, when you do a TABLE check of your simplification, if the Y1 column contains values of 1, your simplification is equivalent to the original expression. If the column for Y1 contains values of zero, your simplification is not equivalent to the original expression, and you need to check it again.

The screens to check that $\dfrac{x - 4}{\sqrt{x} - 2} = \sqrt{x} + 2$ is the correct simplification are as follows:

As you can see, the two expressions are equivalent, except for restricted values.

Simplify the following expressions, and use the method described to check your results for equivalence.

1. $(3\sqrt[3]{x} + 5\sqrt{x}) + (\sqrt[3]{x} - 3\sqrt{x}) + (4\sqrt{x} + 7)$

2. $(2\sqrt{x} + 7) - (\sqrt{x} + 9)$

3. $2\sqrt[3]{x}(3\sqrt[3]{2x} + 5)$

4. $(2\sqrt{x} + 3\sqrt{2x})(\sqrt{x} + \sqrt{2x})$

5. $\dfrac{x - 16}{\sqrt{x} + 4}$

6. $\dfrac{21}{\sqrt{x} - 7}$

7. $(3\sqrt{x} + 5)(\sqrt{x} - 7) + 3\sqrt{x} - 6$

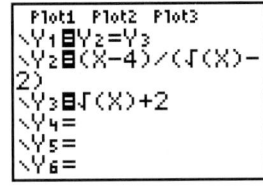

11.5 Writing Exercise

Sometimes, in upper-level mathematics courses, you may be asked to rationalize the numerator of a radical expression. Suppose you had the expression $\dfrac{\sqrt{x} + 5}{\sqrt{x} - 2}$. Explain what it would mean to rationalize the numerator. Then list the steps you would follow to do so. Use your list to rationalize the numerator of the expression presented here.

11.6 SOLVING RADICAL EQUATIONS IN ONE VARIABLE

OBJECTIVES

1 Identify radical equations in one variable.

2 Solve a square-root equation algebraically.

3 Solve a radical equation algebraically.

4 Solve an equation involving rational exponents algebraically.

5 Solve real-world situations that are modeled by radical equations, including those using the distance formula.

APPLICATION

An explosion of energy E (in ft-lb) creates a crater whose diameter d (in feet) is found using the formula $d = kE^{1/3}$, where k is a constant.

a. The explosion of 1 ton of TNT has an energy of 3.1×10^9 ft-lb and creates a crater with a diameter of 30 feet. Determine a value for the constant k.

b. The Barringer meteor crater near Winslow, Arizona, is 4000 feet in diameter. Determine the energy of its explosion. (Use the value for k found in part **a.**)

After completing this section, we will discuss this application further. See page 909.

Objective 11.6.1

Identifying Radical Equations in One Variable

We are now ready to solve radical equations in one variable. A **radical equation in one variable**, or, simply, **radical equation**, can be written in the form of an expression that contains radicals with variables in the radicands and that is equal to 0. Since an exponential expression with a rational exponent is equivalent to a radical expression, a radical equation may also be written in the form of an exponential expression that has a variable base with a rational exponent and that is equal to 0.

STANDARD FORM FOR A RADICAL EQUATION IN ONE VARIABLE

A radical equation in one variable is written in the form

$$D(x) = 0$$

where $D(x)$ is an expression containing radicals with a variable in the radicand or an exponential expression with a variable base and a rational exponent.

EXAMPLE 1 State whether each of the following equations is a radical equation:

a. $\sqrt[5]{x + 3} = 2x$ **b.** $\sqrt{3}x + x = 0$ **c.** $x^{3/4} = 2x^2$

Solution

a. $\sqrt[5]{x + 3} = 2x$ is a radical equation, because $\sqrt[5]{x + 3} - 2x = 0$ and the radicand, $x + 3$, contains a variable.

b. $\sqrt{3}x + x = 0$ is not a radical equation, because the radicand does not contain a variable.

c. $x^{3/4} = 2x^2$ is a radical equation, because $x^{3/4} - 2x^2 = 0$ is equivalent to $\sqrt[4]{x^3} - 2x^2 = 0$ and the radicand, x^3, contains a variable. ■

✓ Objective 11.6.1 *CHECKUP*

1. State whether each of the equations is a radical equation.
   a. $\sqrt{5} + x = 7$ **b.** $\sqrt[3]{2x} = x + 3$
   c. $5x - 3 = x^{2/3}$

2. What is the difference between a radical equation and a radical expression?

Objective 11.6.2   **Solving Square-Root Equations**

In previous chapters, we solved equations numerically and graphically. The same procedures are used to solve radical equations numerically and graphically. We will use these procedures to check our solutions when we solve radical equations algebraically.

To solve algebraically an equation containing a radical expression, we must determine a process that reverses the effect of taking a root of a radicand.

If we begin with an equation that is true and we raise both expressions contained in the equation to the same power, the result is a true equation.

PRINCIPLE OF POWERS
If $a = b$, then $a^n = b^n$.

We use this principle to solve algebraically equations in one variable that contain radicals and rational exponents.

SOLVING A SQUARE-ROOT EQUATION ALGEBRAICALLY
To solve an equation algebraically by using the principle of powers,

- Determine the restricted values of the independent variable for each radical expression.
- Isolate a square-root term on one side of the equation.
- Square both sides of the equation.
- Solve the resulting equation. (If the resulting equation contains a square root, this process must be repeated.)
- Discard any solutions that are restricted values.

Check the solutions numerically, graphically, or by substitution.

EXAMPLE 2

Solve algebraically and check by substitution.

a. $\sqrt{3x + 1} = 4$ **b.** $\sqrt{2x} = -6$ **c.** $\sqrt{x + 6} = x$

Algebraic Solution

a.

$$\sqrt{3x + 1} = 4$$

Restricted values are all real numbers less than $-\frac{1}{3}$.

Square both sides.

$$\left(\sqrt{3x + 1}\right)^2 = 4^2$$
$$3x + 1 = 16$$
$$3x + 1 - 1 = 16 - 1$$
$$3x = 15$$
$$x = 5$$

The solution is 5.

Substitution Check

$$\frac{\sqrt{3x + 1} = 4}{\sqrt{3(5) + 1} \mid 4}$$
$$\sqrt{16}$$
$$4$$

The solution is 5.

b. $\sqrt{2x} = -6$

$\sqrt{2x}$ is a principal root and represents a nonnegative number. Therefore, the expression $\sqrt{2x}$ cannot equal the negative number -6. We say that the equation has no real-number solution.

c.

$$\sqrt{x + 6} = x$$

Restricted values are all real numbers less than -6.

Square both sides.

$$\left(\sqrt{x + 6}\right)^2 = x^2$$
$$x + 6 = x^2$$
$$x^2 - x - 6 = 0 \quad \text{\textit{Standard form for a polynomial equation}}$$
$$(x - 3)(x + 2) = 0 \quad \text{\textit{Factor.}}$$
$$x = 3 \quad \text{or} \quad x = -2$$

Check by substitution.
The solution is 3.

Substitution Check

$$\frac{\sqrt{x + 6} = x}{\sqrt{(3) + 6} \mid 3}$$
$$3$$

A solution is 3.

$$\frac{\sqrt{x + 6} = x}{\sqrt{(-2) + 6} \mid -2}$$
$$2$$

Since $2 \neq -2$, -2 is not a solution.

In Example 1c, applying the principle of powers resulted in a true equation, but one that is not equivalent to the original equation. A simplified example to illustrate this result follows.

$$x = 1 \quad \text{(This equation has one solution, 1.)}$$

Applying the principle of powers, we can square both sides of the equation.

$$x^2 = 1^2 \text{ or } x^2 = 1 \text{ (This equation has two solutions, 1 and } -1.)$$

Not all solutions of the squared equation are solutions of the original equation. However, all solutions of the original equation *are* solutions of the squared equation. This means that we have an *extraneous solution* of -1 after squaring the original equation.

 TAKE NOTE We must always check the final solutions to determine whether they are solutions of the original equation.

EXAMPLE 3

Solve algebraically and check numerically, graphically, or by substitution.

a. $\sqrt{3x + 10} - x = 4$ **b.** $2\sqrt{5x} + 1 = 11$

c. $\sqrt{5a + 4} = \sqrt{4a - 3}$ **d.** $\sqrt{x} + 2 = \sqrt{x + 5}$

Algebraic Solution

a. $\sqrt{3x + 10} - x = 4$ Restricted values of the radical expression
are all real numbers less than $\frac{-10}{3}$.

$\sqrt{3x + 10} = x + 4$ Add x to both sides.

$\left(\sqrt{3x + 10}\right)^2 = (x + 4)^2$ Square both sides.

$3x + 10 = x^2 + 8x + 16$

$x^2 + 5x + 6 = 0$ Set the quadratic expression equal to 0.

$(x + 3)(x + 2) = 0$ Factor.

$x = -3 \quad \text{or} \quad x = -2$ Set each factor equal to 0 and solve.

Since both solutions are integers, check numerically on your calculator.
The solutions are -3 and -2.

b. $2\sqrt{5x} + 1 = 11$ Restricted values of the radical expression are all real
numbers less than 0.

$2\sqrt{5x} = 10$ Subtract 1 from both sides.

$\dfrac{2\sqrt{5x}}{2} = \dfrac{10}{2}$ Divide both sides by 2.

$\sqrt{5x} = 5$

$\left(\sqrt{5x}\right)^2 = 5^2$ Square both sides.

$5x = 25$

$x = 5$

Check by substitution.
The solution is 5.

c. $\sqrt{5a + 4} = \sqrt{4a - 3}$ Restricted values of the radical expressions are
all real numbers less than $\frac{3}{4}$.

$\left(\sqrt{5a + 4}\right)^2 = \left(\sqrt{4a - 3}\right)^2$ Square both sides.

$5a + 4 = 4a - 3$

$a = -7$

The possible solution is a restricted value. The original equation
has no solution.

d. $\sqrt{x} + 2 = \sqrt{x + 5}$ Restricted values of the radical expressions are
all real numbers less than 0.

$(\sqrt{x} + 2)^2 = \left(\sqrt{x + 5}\right)^2$ Square both sides.

$x + 4\sqrt{x} + 4 = x + 5$

$4\sqrt{x} = 1$ Isolate the radical term.

$(4\sqrt{x})^2 = (1)^2$ Square both sides.

$16x = 1$

$x = \dfrac{1}{16}$

Check by substitution.
The solution is $\frac{1}{16}$.

Numeric Check

X	Y₁	Y₂
-4	ERROR	4
-3	4	4
-2	4	4
-1	3.6458	4
0	3.1623	4
1	2.6056	4
2	2	4

X = -3

$Y1 = \sqrt{3x + 10} - x$
$Y2 = 4$

The solutions are -3 and -2.

Substitution Check

$$\dfrac{2\sqrt{5x} + 1 = 11}{}$$

$2\sqrt{5(5)} + 1$	11
$2\sqrt{25} + 1$	
$2 \cdot 5 + 1$	
11	

The solution is 5.

Graphic Check

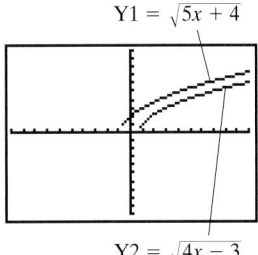

$(-10, 10, -10, 10)$

The graphs do not intersect.
There are no solutions.

Substitution Check

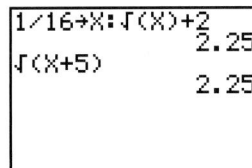

The solution is $\frac{1}{16}$.

Radical equations may have no solution or have infinitely many solutions.

EXAMPLE 4   Solve algebraically and check graphically.

a. $\sqrt{2x} + 3 = \sqrt{2x} - 5$ b. $2\sqrt{2a + 1} = \sqrt{8a + 4}$

Algebraic Solution

a. $\sqrt{2x} + 3 = \sqrt{2x} - 5$ *Restricted values of the radical expressions are all real numbers less than 0.*

$3 = -5$ *Isolate the radical expression by subtracting $\sqrt{2x}$.*

This is a contradiction. There is no solution.

b. $2\sqrt{2a + 1} = \sqrt{8a + 4}$ *Restricted values of the radical expressions are all real numbers less than $-\frac{1}{2}$.*

$\left(2\sqrt{2a + 1}\right)^2 = \left(\sqrt{8a + 4}\right)^2$ *Square both sides.*

$4(2a + 1) = 8a + 4$

$8a + 4 = 8a + 4$

$4 = 4$ *Subtract 8a from both sides.*

This is an identity. The solution set is all real numbers greater than or equal to $-\frac{1}{2}$. (Real numbers less than $-\frac{1}{2}$ are restricted values.)

Graphic Check

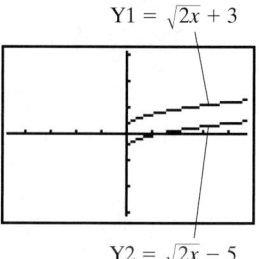

$Y1 = \sqrt{2x} + 3$

$Y2 = \sqrt{2x} - 5$

$(-47, 47, -31, 31)$

The graphs do not appear to intersect. There is no solution.

Graphic Check

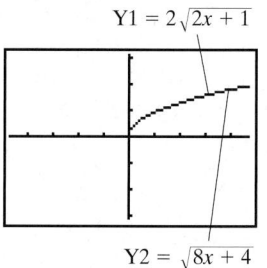

$Y1 = 2\sqrt{2x + 1}$

$Y2 = \sqrt{8x + 4}$

$(-47, 47, -31, 31)$

The graphs are coinciding. The equation has infinitely many solutions. The solution set is all real numbers greater than or equal to $-\frac{1}{2}$. ■

✓ Objective 11.6.2 *CHECKUP*

Solve exercises 1–3 algebraically and check.

1. a. $\sqrt{2x + 1} = 3$ **b.** $\sqrt{5x} = -4$

   c. $\sqrt{x + 12} = x$

2. a. $x - \sqrt{5x - 16} = 2$ **b.** $3\sqrt{2x} + 2 = 8$

   c. $\sqrt{2z + 1} = \sqrt{z - 4}$ **d.** $\sqrt{x} + 1 = \sqrt{x + 3}$

3. a. $\sqrt{x + 1} + 2 = \sqrt{x + 1} - 3$

   b. $3\sqrt{2x - 1} = \sqrt{18x - 9}$

4. The principle of powers states that if an equation is true and if you raise the expressions on the left and right sides of the equation to the same power, you obtain another equation that is true. Does this mean that the new equation has the same solutions as the original equation? Explain your answer.

Objective 11.6.3   ## Solving Other Radical Equations

To solve other radical equations, we use the same procedure as with square-root equations, except we raise each expression to the power of the index.

SOLVING A RADICAL EQUATION ALGEBRAICALLY

To solve an equation algebraically by using the principle of powers,

- Determine the restricted values for the independent variable for each radical expression.
- Isolate a radical term on one side of the equation.
- Raise both sides of the equation to a power that is the same as the index of the isolated radical term—that is, to the second power for square roots, to the third power for cube roots, and so on.
- Solve the resulting equation. (If the resulting equation contains a radical, this process must be repeated.)

Check the solutions numerically, graphically, or by substitution.

EXAMPLE 5   Solve algebraically and check numerically, graphically, or by substitution.

$$\textbf{a.}\ \sqrt[4]{x-5} = 2 \qquad \textbf{b.}\ \sqrt[3]{x^2 + 12x} + 5 = 9$$

Algebraic Solution

a. $\sqrt[4]{x-5} = 2$ Restricted values for the radical expression are all real numbers less than 5.

$\left(\sqrt[4]{x-5}\right)^4 = (2)^4$ Raise to the fourth power on both sides.

$x - 5 = 16$

$x = 21$

The solution is 21.

b. $\sqrt[3]{x^2 + 12x} + 5 = 9$ There are no restricted values. The index, 3, is odd.

$\sqrt[3]{x^2 + 12x} = 4$ Subtract 5 from both sides.

$\left(\sqrt[3]{x^2 + 12x}\right)^3 = (4)^3$ Cube both sides.

$x^2 + 12x = 64$ Simplify.

$x^2 + 12x - 64 = 0$ Standard form of a quadratic equation

$(x + 16)(x - 4) = 0$ Factor.

$x = -16 \quad \text{or} \quad x = 4$ Solve.

The solutions are -16 and 4.

Substitution Check

$$\frac{\sqrt[4]{x-5} = 2}{\sqrt[4]{(21) - 5}\ \Big|\ 2}$$

$$\sqrt[4]{16}$$

$$2 \Big|$$

The solution is 21.

Graphic Check

$$Y1 = \sqrt[3]{x^2 + 12x} + 5$$

$Y2 = 9$

$(-47, 47, -31, 31)$

The x-coordinates of the intersections are -16 and 4.
The solutions are -16 and 4.

✓ Objective 11.6.3 *CHECKUP*

1. Solve algebraically and check.

$\textbf{a.}\ \sqrt[4]{x-3} = 2 \qquad \textbf{b.}\ \sqrt[3]{x^2 + 6x} + 2 = 5$

2. When using the principle of powers to solve a radical equation, how do you decide what power to apply to the expressions on the left and right sides of the original radical equation?

Objective 11.6.4 ## Solving an Equation with Rational Exponents

To solve an equation involving an expression with a rational exponent, we use the principle of powers. To obtain an integer exponent, we raise both expressions in the equation to the denominator of the fractional exponent. That is, if we have $x^{2/3}$, we raise it to a power of 3, $\left(x^{2/3}\right)^3$. By the power-to-a-power property of exponents, we can simplify this expression to $\left(x^{2/3}\right)^3 = x^{(2/3)(3)} = x^2$.

SOLVING AN EQUATION WITH A RATIONAL EXPONENT ALGEBRAICALLY

To solve an equation algebraically by using the principle of powers,
- Determine the restricted values of the independent variable.
- Isolate a term with an exponential expression on one side of the equation.
- Raise both expressions in the equation to the power of the denominator of the exponent.
- Solve the resulting equation. (If the resulting equation contains a rational exponential expression, this process must be repeated.)

Check the solutions numerically, graphically, or by substitution.

For example, solve $x^{2/3} = 4$.

$$x^{2/3} = 4 \qquad \text{There are no restricted values.}$$
$$\left(x^{2/3}\right)^3 = 4^3 \qquad \text{Raise both sides to a power of 3.}$$
$$x^2 = 64$$
$$x = \pm 8 \qquad \text{Principle of square roots}$$

Check by substitution.

$x^{2/3} = 4$	
$(8)^{2/3}$	4
4	

The solution is 8.

$x^{2/3} = 4$	
$(-8)^{2/3}$	4
4	

The solution is -8.

In the example, we used the principle of square roots to solve the equation $x^2 = 64$ and obtain $x = \pm 8$. Before we continue, we need to expand the principle so that it is a rule for all roots. We need to consider two different cases: when the exponent is even and when the exponent is odd.

PRINCIPLE OF ROOTS

Case 1. If n is a positive even integer, b is a positive number, and $a^n = b$, then $a = \sqrt[n]{b}$ or $a = -\sqrt[n]{b}$.

Case 2. If n is a positive even integer, b is a negative number, and $a^n = b$, then a is not a real number.

Case 3. If n is a positive even integer, b is 0, and $a^n = b$, then $a = 0$.

Case 4. If n is a positive odd integer, b is a real number, and $a^n = b$, then $a = \sqrt[n]{b}$.

The principle of roots will allow us to solve equations such as the following:

Case 1. $x^4 = 16$ Case 2. $x^4 = -16$ Case 3. $x^4 = 0$
$\; x = \pm\sqrt[4]{16}$ x is not a real number. $\; x = 0$
$\; x = \pm 2$

Case 4. $x^3 = 8$ or $x^3 = -8$
$\; x = \sqrt[3]{8}$ $\; x = \sqrt[3]{-8}$
$\; x = 2$ $\; x = -2$

EXAMPLE 6   Solve algebraically and check numerically, graphically, or by substitution.

$$\textbf{a. } (x + 2)^{3/4} = 8 \qquad \textbf{b. } (x + 2)^{4/3} = 3 \qquad \textbf{c. } (x + 2)^{2/3} = -3$$

Algebraic Solution

a. $(x + 2)^{3/4} = 8$ *Restricted values are all real numbers less than −2.*

$[(x + 2)^{3/4}]^4 = (8)^4$ *Raise both sides to a power of 4.*

$(x + 2)^3 = 4096$

$x + 2 = \sqrt[3]{4096}$ *Principle of roots*

$x + 2 = 16$

$x = 14$

The solution is 14.

Graphic Check

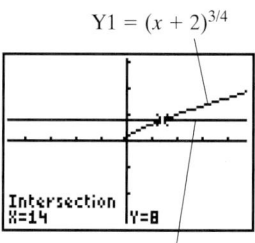

$Y1 = (x + 2)^{3/4}$

$Y2 = 8$

$(-47, 47, -31, 31)$

The x-coordinate of the intersection is 14.
The solution is 14.

b. $(x + 2)^{4/3} = 3$ *There are no restricted values.*

$[(x + 2)^{4/3}]^3 = 3^3$ *Raise both sides to a power of 3.*

$(x + 2)^4 = 27$

$x + 2 = \pm\sqrt[4]{27}$ *Principle of roots*

$x = -2 \pm \sqrt[4]{27}$ *Subtract 2 from both sides.*

The solutions are $-2 \pm \sqrt[4]{27}$.

Substitution Check

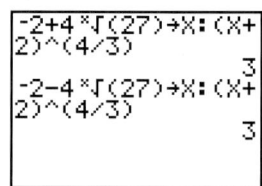

The substitutions of the possible solutions result in 3, the right side of the equation.
The solutions are $-2 \pm \sqrt[4]{27}$.

c. $(x + 2)^{2/3} = -3$ *There are no restricted values.*

$[(x + 2)^{2/3}]^3 = (-3)^3$ *Raise both sides to a power of 3.*

$(x + 2)^2 = -27$

There is no real-number solution of the equation, because, according to the principle of roots, the square of $(x + 2)$ cannot be a negative number.

Graphic Check

$Y1 = (x + 2)^{2/3}$

$Y2 = -3$

$(-10, 10, -10, 10)$

The graphs do not intersect. There is no real-number solution. ■

✓ Objective 11.6.4 **CHECKUP**

1. Solve algebraically and check.

a. $x^{3/5} = 8$ **b.** $(x + 5)^{3/2} = 27$

c. $(3 - x)^{2/3} + 3 = 2$

2. To solve an equation with rational exponents, you may need to use the principle of powers and then the principle of roots. Explain the difference between these two principles. ■

Objective 11.6.5   ## Modeling the Real World

Radical equations are used to describe many situations involving the acceleration due to gravity. In this section, we will discuss one such situation. Dancers and basketball players have great jumping abilities and seem to "hang in the air." The relationship between their hang time t and the vertical height of the jump, d, is given by the equation $t = 2\sqrt{\dfrac{2d}{g}}$, where g is the acceleration due to gravity.

EXAMPLE 7

a. Given that the acceleration due to gravity is 32 feet per second squared, write an equation for the hang time t.

b. According to the *Guinness Book of Records*, Rune Almen of Sweden made the highest high jump on record from a standing position. His hang time was recorded as 1.248 seconds. Determine the vertical height of his jump.

Solution

a. Use the given equation for hang time, substitute 32 for g, and then simplify.

$$t = 2\sqrt{\frac{2d}{g}}$$

$$t = 2\sqrt{\frac{2d}{32}}$$

$$t = 2\sqrt{\frac{d}{16}} \qquad \text{Simplify.}$$

$$t = 2\left(\frac{\sqrt{d}}{\sqrt{16}}\right) \qquad \text{Quotient rule}$$

$$t = 2\left(\frac{\sqrt{d}}{4}\right) \qquad \text{Simplify.}$$

$$t = \frac{\sqrt{d}}{2}$$

An equation for the hang time t (in seconds) is $t = \dfrac{\sqrt{d}}{2}$, where d is the vertical height in feet.

b. Let $x =$ the vertical height in feet

$$1.248 = \frac{\sqrt{x}}{2} \qquad t = 1.248$$

$$2(1.248) = 2\left(\frac{\sqrt{x}}{2}\right) \qquad \text{Multiply both sides by 2.}$$

$$2.496 = \sqrt{x}$$

$$(2.496)^2 = (\sqrt{x})^2 \qquad \text{Square both sides.}$$

$$6.230016 = x$$

Rune's record vertical jump was about 6.23 feet.   ■

EXAMPLE 8

Determine the possible y-coordinates of a point 5 units from $(-1, 4)$ with an x-coordinate of 2.

Solution

Recall that the distance between two points (x_1, y_1) and (x_2, y_2) can be calculated as $d = \sqrt{(x_2 - x_1)^2 + (y_2 - y_1)^2}$.

Let $x_1 = 2$ and $y =$ the missing y-coordinate
Let $x_2 = -1$ and $y_2 = 4$

$$d = \sqrt{(x_2 - x_1)^2 + (y_2 - y_1)^2}$$

$$5 = \sqrt{(-1 - 2)^2 + (4 - y)^2} \qquad \text{Substitute 5 for } d, (2, y) \text{ for } (x_1, y_1), \text{ and}$$
$$\qquad\qquad\qquad\qquad\qquad\qquad\qquad (-1, 4) \text{ for } (x_2, y_2).$$

$$5 = \sqrt{(-3)^2 + (4 - y)^2}$$

$$5 = \sqrt{9 + 16 - 8y + y^2}$$

$$5 = \sqrt{25 - 8y + y^2}$$

$$5^2 = \left(\sqrt{25 - 8y + y^2}\right)^2 \qquad \text{Square both sides.}$$

$$25 = 25 - 8y + y^2$$

$$y^2 - 8y = 0 \qquad \text{Standard form for a quadratic equation}$$

$$y(y - 8) = 0 \qquad \text{Factor.}$$

$$y = 0 \quad \text{or} \quad y = 8 \qquad \text{Solve.}$$

The two possible points are $(2, 0)$ and $(2, 8)$. ■

APPLICATION

An explosion of energy E (in ft-lb) creates a crater whose diameter d (in feet) is found using the formula $d = kE^{1/3}$, where k is a constant.

a. The explosion of 1 ton of TNT has an energy of 3.1×10^9 ft-lb and creates a crater with a diameter of 30 feet. Determine a value for the constant k.

b. The Barringer meteor crater near Winslow, Arizona, is 4000 feet in diameter. Determine the energy of its explosion. (Use the value for k found in part **a**.)

Discussion

a. Use the given formula.

$$d = kE^{1/3}$$

$$30 = k(3.1 \times 10^9)^{1/3} \qquad \text{Substitute 30 for } d \text{ and } 3.1 \times 10^9 \text{ for } E.$$

$$k = \frac{30}{(3.1 \times 10^9)^{1/3}} \qquad \text{Solve for } k.$$

$$k \approx 0.02$$

b.

$$d = kE^{1/3}$$

$$4000 = 0.02E^{1/3} \qquad \text{Substitute 4000 for } d \text{ and 0.02 for } k.$$

$$\frac{4000}{0.02} = E^{1/3} \qquad \text{Divide both sides by 0.02.}$$

$$200{,}000 = E^{1/3}$$

$$(200{,}000)^3 = \left(E^{1/3}\right)^3 \qquad \text{Cube both sides.}$$

$$8{,}000{,}000{,}000{,}000{,}000 = E$$

$$\text{or } E = 8 \times 10^{15}$$

The energy of the meteor explosion that caused the crater near Winslow was approximately 8×10^{15} ft-lb.

✓ Objective 11.6.5 *CHECKUP*

1. According to the *Guinness Book of Records*, Gete Bjordal-shakka (Norway) made the highest high jump on record for women from a standing position. Her hang time was recorded as 1.116 seconds. Determine the vertical height of her jump.

2. Find the possible y-coordinates of a point that is 10 units away from the point $(6, 5)$ and has an x-coordinate of -2.

3. Wolf Creek Crater in Australia is about 2950 feet in diameter. Determine the energy of its explosion. (Use the formula $d = 0.02E^{1/3}$, where d is the diameter in feet and E is the energy in ft-lb.)

■

11.6 EXERCISES

Student Solutions Manual   PH Math/Tutor Center   CD Video   MathXL®   MyMathLab   Interactmath.com

Solve exercises 1–90 algebraically and check.

1. $\sqrt{x} - 3 = 5$

2. $\sqrt{x} - 5 = 2$

3. $\sqrt{x} + 1.7 = 4.5$

4. $\sqrt{x} - 2.4 = 3.8$

5. $\sqrt{x} + 8 = 5$

6. $\sqrt{x} + 11 = 10$

7. $\sqrt{3x} - 4 = 2$

8. $\sqrt{7x} - 2 = 12$

9. $9 - 3\sqrt{2z} = 0$

10. $15 - 5\sqrt{6z} = 0$

11. $3\sqrt{6x} + 1 = 10$

12. $4\sqrt{3x} + 3 = 15$

13. $\sqrt{x + 5} = 3$

14. $\sqrt{3 + x} = 5$

15. $\sqrt{2x + 5} + 4 = 9$

16. $\sqrt{3x + 1} + 2 = 5$

17. $\sqrt{3x + 4} - 2 = 6$

18. $\sqrt{5x + 4} - 3 = 5$

19. $\sqrt{5 - 4x} = x$

20. $\sqrt{x + 30} = x$

21. $\sqrt{6x - 5} = \sqrt{4x + 5}$

22. $\sqrt{3x + 7} = \sqrt{5x - 2}$

23. $3\sqrt{x + 2} = \sqrt{x + 10}$

24. $4\sqrt{x + 3} = \sqrt{x + 18}$

25. $x = 3 + 2\sqrt{x - 4}$

26. $x = 3 + 2\sqrt{2x - 10}$

27. $x = \sqrt{21 - x - x^2} + 3$

28. $\sqrt{(4x + 5)(x + 1)} = 5 + x$

29. $\sqrt{x^2 - 14x + 49} = 7 - x$

30. $\sqrt{4x^2 - 12x + 9} = 3 - 2x$

31. $x = \sqrt{2x + 7}$

32. $\sqrt{8 - 3x} + x = 0$

33. $5 + \sqrt{25 - 2x} = x$

34. $7 + \sqrt{49 - 2x} = x$

35. $\sqrt{x} - 3 = \sqrt{x - 27}$

36. $\sqrt{x} - 8 = \sqrt{x - 64}$

37. $\sqrt{x - 7} = 7 - \sqrt{x}$

38. $\sqrt{x + 15} = 3 + \sqrt{x}$

39. $\sqrt{2x + 5} - 7 = \sqrt{5 + 2x} + 3$

40. $\sqrt{4x + 3} - 5 = \sqrt{3 + 4x} + 9$

41. $\sqrt{2x + 3} = 1 - \sqrt{x + 5}$

42. $\sqrt{3x - 2} = 1 + \sqrt{x + 3}$

43. $\sqrt[3]{3x} = -6$

44. $\sqrt[3]{6x} = -3$

45. $\sqrt[4]{2x} = 10$

46. $\sqrt[4]{2x - 10} = 4$

47. $\sqrt[5]{2x} = -2$

48. $\sqrt[5]{9x} = -3$

49. $\sqrt[3]{x} + 3 = 1$

50. $\sqrt[3]{x} - 7 = -5$

51. $\sqrt[3]{x} + 1 = 5$

52. $\sqrt[4]{x} + 3 = 6$

53. $\sqrt[3]{2x + 1} = 3$

54. $\sqrt[3]{3x + 2} = -4$

55. $\sqrt[4]{x - 5} = 2$

56. $\sqrt[4]{x - 7} = 3$

57. $\sqrt[5]{2x - 5} = 3$

58. $\sqrt[5]{3x - 1} = 2$

59. $\sqrt[3]{x^2 + 7x + 7} = 9$

60. $\sqrt[4]{x^2 + 24x} + 2 = 5$

61. $\sqrt[4]{3x - 5} = \sqrt[4]{2x + 4}$

62. $\sqrt[4]{5x - 7} = \sqrt[4]{x + 5}$

63. $\sqrt[4]{5x - 2} = 2\sqrt[4]{3}$

64. $\sqrt[4]{3x + 6} = 3\sqrt[4]{2}$

65. $x = \sqrt[4]{18x^2 - 81}$

66. $x = \sqrt[4]{8x^2 - 16}$

67. $\sqrt[4]{2x} + \sqrt[4]{3x} = 0$

68. $\sqrt[3]{5x} + \sqrt[3]{x} = 0$

69. $\sqrt[4]{3x - 5} + \sqrt[4]{x - 3} = 0$

70. $\sqrt[4]{x + 3} + \sqrt[4]{2x + 1} = 0$

71. $\sqrt[3]{3x - 5} + \sqrt[3]{x - 3} = 0$

72. $\sqrt[3]{5x - 2} + \sqrt[3]{3x - 2} = 0$

73. $\sqrt[4]{7x - 1} - \sqrt[4]{x + 11} = 0$

74. $\sqrt[4]{8x - 1} - \sqrt[4]{x + 6} = 0$

75. $x^{4/3} = 16$

76. $x^{2/3} = 25$

77. $(x + 6)^{2/5} = 4$

78. $(x + 8)^{2/3} = 16$

79. $(x - 4)^{3/4} = 27$

80. $(x - 9)^{3/2} = 64$

81. $x^{-2/3} = 4$

82. $x^{-3/4} = 27$

83. $(x - 5)^{-3/4} = 27$

84. $(4x + 5)^{3/4} = 125$

85. $(5x - 3)^{-2/3} = \dfrac{1}{25}$

86. $(6x - 1)^{-3/4} = \dfrac{1}{64}$

87. $x^{2/3} + 5 = 3$

88. $x^{4/5} + 6 = 4$

89. $x^{3/4} - 7 = 1$

90. $x^{3/5} - 6 = 21$

In exercises 91–94, recall that hang time is given by the formula, $t = 2\sqrt{\dfrac{2d}{g}}$, where g is the acceleration due to gravity (32 feet per second squared or 9.8 meters per second squared) and d is the vertical distance of the jump.

91. Michael "Wild Thing" Wilson of the Harlem Globetrotters slam-dunked a regulation basketball 12 feet at the Conseco Fieldhouse in Indianapolis, Indiana, in April of 2000. His hang time for the shot was about 1.16 seconds. Determine the vertical distance of his jump. Given that he is 6 feet, 7 inches, tall, does this hang time added to his height equal a 12-foot high basket?

92. If Michael Jordan's hang time for a shot was 0.87 second, what is the vertical distance of the corresponding jump?

93. Determine the distance in meters of Michael "Wild Thing" Wilson's vertical jump if his hang time was about 1.16 seconds.

94. If hang time for a shot by a high school athlete is 0.67 second, what is the vertical distance of the jump?

In exercises 95–100, recall that the distance between two points, (x_1, y_1) and (x_2, y_2), is $d = \sqrt{(x_2 - x_1)^2 + (y_2 - y_1)^2}$.

95. Find the possible y-coordinates of a point that has an x-coordinate of 8 and is 13 units away from (3, 4).

96. Find the possible y-coordinates of a point that has an x-coordinate of -13 and is 17 units away from (2, -3).

97. Find the possible x-coordinates of a point that has a y-coordinate of -1 and is 10 units away from the point $(-2, 5)$.

98. Find the possible x-coordinates of a point that has a y-coordinate of 1 and is 5 units away from (1, -3).

99. Find the possible y-coordinates of a point that has an x-coordinate of 6 and is 5 units away from $(-2, 1)$.

100. Find the possible x-coordinates of a point that has a y-coordinate of 1 and is 2 units away from (1, 9).

In exercises 101–104, recall that the average return can be computed by the formula
average return = (final value/original value)$^{1/\text{number of years}}$.

101. If average return is 1.2, find the original value of a stock investment held for 9 years that has final value $5000.

102. If average return is 1.12, find the original value of a stock investment held for 9 years that has final value $10,000.

103. A real estate investment of $225,000 has average return of 1.078 after 15 years. What was its final value?

104. Meg invests $34,000 in a business that has average return of 1.123 after 15 years. What was the final value of the business?

105. One of the largest known craters believed to have been produced by a meteorite was discovered in northwestern Quebec, Canada. The circular pit is approximately 2.5 miles in diameter, or 13,200 feet. Use the formula presented in this section to determine the energy of the explosion when the meteor struck.

106. Use the formula in this section to determine the energy of the explosion of a meteor that creates a crater having a diameter of 5000 feet.

107. Civil engineers relate the crushing load L (in tons) for a square wooden pillar that has a thickness T (in inches) and a height H (in feet) by using the mathematical model $T = \left(\dfrac{LH^2}{25}\right)^{1/4}$. If a square wooden pillar has a thickness of 4 inches and a height of 8 feet, what is its crushing load?

108. Use the formula in exercise **107** to find the crushing load of a wooden pillar that is 6 inches thick and 10 feet tall.

109. a. The cost in dollars to make x meals is $C(x) = \sqrt{9x - 7}$. If it cost $17.55, how many meals were made?

  b. The revenue in dollars from selling x meals is $R(x) = \sqrt{10x + 1}$. If revenue is $19, how many meals were sold?

  c. Write a function $P(x)$ for the profit in dollars for x meals. How many meals must be sold to make a profit of $2?

110. a. The cost in dollars to make x meals is $C(x) = \sqrt{8x + 6}$. If it cost $19.95, how many meals were made?

  b. The revenue in dollars from selling x meals is $R(x) = \sqrt{10x - 1}$. If revenue is $17, how many meals were sold?

  c. Write a function $P(x)$ for the profit in dollars for x meals. How many meals must be sold to make a profit of $2?

111. a. Randy estimates that it cost him $C(x) = -2x + 10\sqrt{x + 3}$ dollars to make each of x lamps. If the cost is $6, how many lamps did he make?

  b. Randy finds that his revenue from selling each of x lamps is $R(x) = \sqrt{2x + 9}$. If the revenue is $10.44, how many lamps were sold?

  c. Write a function $P(x)$ for profit in dollars for x lamps. What is the break-even point?

112. a. The cost in dollars to make x machine parts is given by $C(x) = 15\sqrt{3x + 11}$. If the cost is $100, how many parts were made?

  b. The total revenue in dollars when x machine parts are sold is $R(x) = 12x - 2\sqrt{x + 9}$. If the revenue is $466, how many parts were made?

  c. Write a function $P(x)$ for the profit in dollars from selling x machine parts. Find the break-even point.

 ## 11.6 Calculator Exercises

Some radical equations may be difficult or impossible to solve algebraically. When this is the case, you can use your calculator to solve the equations graphically. Even so, you will need to be creative in how you do that. First of all, you may have to explore different window settings to get a good picture of what is happening with the graphs. You may have to increase the range of values on the x-axis while reducing the range of values on the y-axis in order to see the graphs well. You can easily do this by adjusting the | WINDOW | settings. Also, you may have to try different strategies for graphing. The following are two strategies to try:

  Strategy 1. Store the left side of the equation in Y1 and the right side of the equation in Y2, and graph the equations to see where the graphs intersect. The x-values of the intersection points will be the solutions of the equations.

  Strategy 2. Store the left side of the equation in Y2 and the right side of the equation in Y3, and turn off these two functions by moving the cursor to the equals sign under | Y= | and pressing

| ENTER |. Then, define Y1 to equal Y2 − Y3, using the | VARS | to key this definition into Y1. Next, graph Y1 and use the zero function under the CALC menu to find the x-intercepts of Y1. The x-values of these intercepts represent solutions of the radical equation.

Use one of the preceding strategies on your calculator to solve the following equations:

1. $\left(\sqrt[4]{2x + 1}\right)\left(\sqrt[3]{x - 13}\right) = 9$

2. $\sqrt[5]{3x + 2} - \sqrt[4]{8x + 1} = -1$

3. $\dfrac{\sqrt{3x + 4}}{\sqrt[4]{x - 4}} = \sqrt[3]{4x - 16}$

4. $\sqrt[3]{2x + 1} = \sqrt[4]{3x^2}$

5. $x^{3/2} + 2x^{1/2} - 7 = 0$

6. $3x^{2/3} - 5x^{1/3} - 9 = 0$

11.6 Writing Exercise

You have learned methods for solving many different types of equations, including the following:

1. linear equations, by isolating the variable;

2. polynomial equations, by factoring and using the zero factor rule;

3. rational equations, by multiplying through by the least common denominator; and

4. radical and exponential equations, by applying the power principle and the root principle.

In some cases, you may have a combination of these types of equations, which you can solve by creatively applying the tech-

niques you have learned. Discuss how you would approach the following exercises, and then try to solve the equations using the foregoing methods.

1. $\sqrt{m + \dfrac{1}{m}} = \dfrac{5\sqrt{2}}{7}$

2. $\dfrac{\sqrt{5k + 1}}{\sqrt{5k - 1}} = \dfrac{\sqrt{51}}{7}$

3. $\dfrac{\sqrt{3}}{\sqrt{2z - 3}} = \sqrt{\dfrac{3}{z}}$

4. $\sqrt{2 + \sqrt{p}} = 4$

5. $\dfrac{\sqrt{a - 7}}{2} = \dfrac{4}{\sqrt{a + 5}}$

6. $\sqrt{\dfrac{1}{t} + \dfrac{1}{t + 2}} = \dfrac{\sqrt{15}}{6}$

11.7 EQUATIONS WITH IMAGINARY-NUMBER SOLUTIONS

OBJECTIVES

1 Write imaginary numbers.

2 Perform operations on imaginary numbers.

3 Perform operations on complex numbers.

4 Solve equations having an imaginary solution.

5 Model real-world situations by using complex numbers.

APPLICATION

The equation $(x^2 + y^2)^2 = 2k^2(x^2 - y^2)$ gives a graph called the Lemniscate of Bernoulli. If $x = 0$ and $k = 3$, find y.

After completing this section, we will discuss this application further. See page 923.

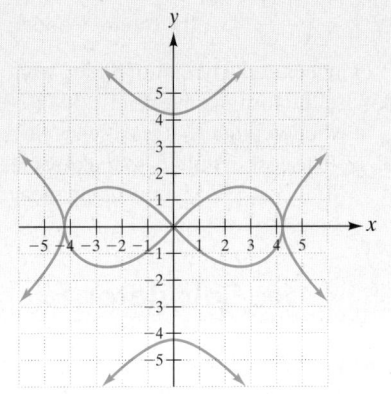

In this section, we complete our discussion of solving equations that have non-real-number solutions.

The key to working with square roots of negative numbers is to isolate the factor -1 in the radicand. Then we can proceed to work with the rest of the number, carrying that factor along as if it were a variable. We illustrate this idea by first introducing and operating with imaginary numbers. Then we combine imaginary numbers with real numbers to form complex numbers and work with them.

Objective 11.7.1   Writing Imaginary Numbers

First, we must define a number to be the principal square root of -1. This number is the **imaginary unit i**.

DEFINITION OF i

The imaginary unit $i = \sqrt{-1}$.
Therefore, $i^2 = -1$.

Using this definition and the product rule for square roots, we can define the square root of any negative real number in terms of i. For example, write $\sqrt{-5}$ in terms of i.

$$\sqrt{-5} = \sqrt{-1 \cdot 5} \qquad \text{Isolate a factor of } -1 \text{ in the radicand.}$$
$$= \sqrt{-1} \cdot \sqrt{5} \qquad \text{Product rule for square roots}$$
$$= i\sqrt{5} \qquad \text{Substitute } i \text{ for } \sqrt{-1}.$$

This process leads us to the definition of the square root of a negative real number in terms of i.

SQUARE ROOT OF A NEGATIVE NUMBER

$\sqrt{-b} = i\sqrt{b}$, where b is any positive real number.

 TAKE NOTE Be careful when writing the expression $\sqrt{b}i$ with the square root first. It can be hard to see that i is not under the square-root symbol. Therefore, we recommend that you write the expression with the i first, as $i\sqrt{b}$.

The calculator can be set to write the square root of a negative number in terms of i. For example, $\sqrt{-5}$ is written in terms of i as shown in **Figures 11.7a** and **11.7b**.

TECHNOLOGY — Imaginary Numbers

Write $\sqrt{-5}$ in terms of i.
For **Figure 11.7a**,
Change the calculator to $a + bi$ mode by highlighting "$a + bi$" under the MODE menu.

[MODE] [▼] [▼] [▼] [▼] [▼] [▼] [►] [ENTER]

Return to the home screen.

[2nd] [MODE] (QUIT)

Enter the square-root expression to be written in terms of i.

[2nd] [x²] (√) [(−)] [5] [ )] [ENTER]

This is an approximate decimal value for $i\sqrt{5}$. Enter this value to check.

[2nd] [.] (i) [2nd] [x²] (√) [5] [ )] [ENTER]

For **Figure 11.7b**,
For ease in reading approximate values, set the calculator to the number of decimal places you want to round to. For example, round to two decimal places the values found in **Figure 11.7a**.
Set the calculator to round to two decimal places.

[MODE] [▼] [►] [►] [►] [ENTER] [2nd] [MODE] (QUIT)

Reenter the square-root expression.

[2nd] [x²] (√) [(−)] [5] [ )] [ENTER]

Reenter $i\sqrt{5}$ to check.

[2nd] [.] (i) [2nd] [x²] (√) [5] [ )] [ENTER]

Note: You could recall the previous entries by using [2nd] [ENTER] (ENTRY).

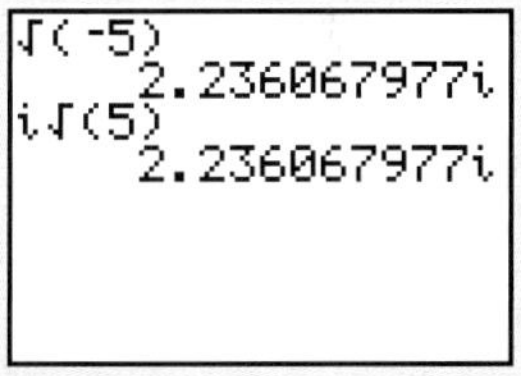

```
√(-5)
          2.236067977i
i√(5)
          2.236067977i
```
Figure 11.7a

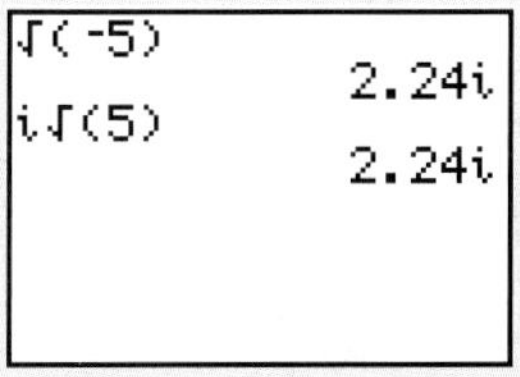

```
√(-5)
               2.24i
i√(5)
               2.24i
```
Figure 11.7b

EXAMPLE 1 Write in terms of i.

a. $\sqrt{-36}$ b. $\sqrt{-\dfrac{9}{16}}$ c. $\sqrt{-8}$

Solution

a. $\sqrt{-36} = i\sqrt{36}$ *Write the square root of a negative number in terms of i.*

   $\quad\quad\;\; = 6i$ $\sqrt{36} = 6$

b. $\sqrt{-\dfrac{9}{16}} = i\sqrt{\dfrac{9}{16}}$ *Write the square root of a negative number in terms of i.*

   $\quad\quad\quad\; = \dfrac{3}{4}i$ $\sqrt{\frac{9}{16}} = \frac{3}{4}$

c. $\sqrt{-8} = i\sqrt{8}$ *Write the square root of a negative number in terms of i.*

   $\quad\quad\; = 2i\sqrt{2}$ $\sqrt{8} = 2\sqrt{2}$

Check these solutions with your calculator. Round approximate values to two decimal places, as shown in **Figures 11.8a** and **11.8b.**

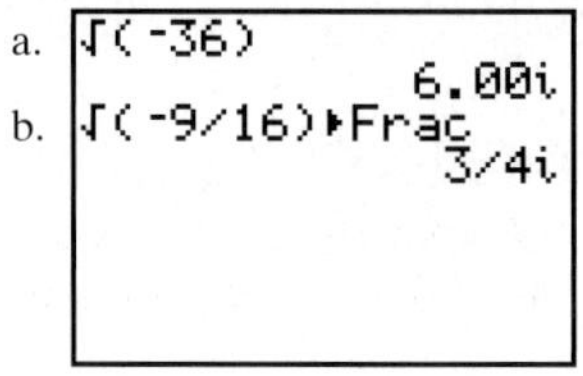

a. √(-36)
                    6.00i
b. √(-9/16)▸Frac
                    3/4i

c. √(-8)
                    2.83i
   2i√(2)
                    2.83i

Figure 11.8a 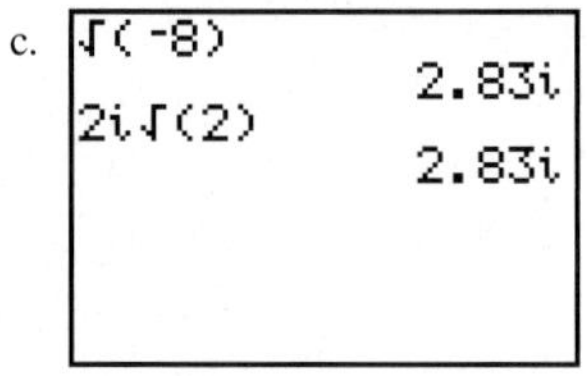   **Figure 11.8b**

✓ Objective 11.7.1 *CHECKUP*

1. Write the expressions in terms of i.

   a. $\sqrt{-49}$ b. $\sqrt{-\dfrac{4}{81}}$ c. $\sqrt{-27}$

2. Explain the difference between the following two radicals:
   a. $-\sqrt{16}$ b. $\sqrt{-16}$
3. What is an imaginary number?

Objective 11.7.2   Operations on Imaginary Numbers

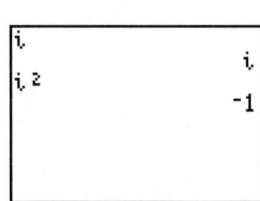

Figure 11.9

When we perform operations with imaginary numbers, we must first write all square roots of negative numbers in terms of i. Even though the symbol i is *not* a variable, we can then treat it as a variable when performing operations.

Before we begin, we need to evaluate i raised to powers greater than 2. For example, evaluate i^1 and i^2 on your calculator, as shown in **Figure 11.9**.

Complete the following set of exercises with your calculator to discover the results of raising i to powers greater than 2.

💡 Guided Discovery 5   Powers of i

1. Evaluate the following expressions:

   $i^1 = \underline{\;\;i\;\;}$ $i^2 = \underline{\;\;-1\;\;}$

   a. $i^3 = $ _____   b. $i^4 = $ _____

   c. $i^5 = $ _____   d. $i^6 = $ _____

2. Look for a pattern and predict the following:

   $i^7 = $ _____

Check your prediction on your calculator. Were you correct? The calculator value is written in scientific notation. If you evaluate the calculator value, it should be approximately $-i$.

3. Predict a value for i^8 and check your results again.

   $i^8 = $ _____

Look for a pattern and then write a rule for evaluating i to any power.

The values for the powers of i repeat the pattern $i, -1, -i, 1, i, \ldots$.

POWERS OF i

To determine the value of i raised to a power, divide the power by 4.

- If the remainder is 1, the value of the expression is i.
- If the remainder is 2, the value of the expression is -1.
- If the remainder is 3, the value of the expression is $-i$.
- If the remainder is 0, the value of the expression is 1.

We can see algebraically that this pattern holds:

$$i^1 = i$$
$$i^2 = -1$$
$$i^3 = (i^2)(i) = (-1)(i) = -i$$
$$i^4 = (i^3)(i) = (-i)(i) = -i^2 = -(-1) = 1$$
$$i^5 = (i^4)(i) = (1)(i) = i$$
$$\vdots$$

We can add, subtract, multiply, and divide imaginary numbers.

Addition	$ai + bi = (a + b)i$	Add the coefficients of i.
Subtraction	$ai - bi = (a - b)i$	Subtract the coefficients of i.
Multiplication	$(ai)(bi) = (ab)i^2$	Multiply the coefficients of i. Remember that $i \cdot i = i^2$.
	$= (ab)(-1)$	Substitute -1 for i^2.
	$= -ab$	Simplify.
Division	$\dfrac{ai}{bi} = \dfrac{a}{b}$	Simplify.

 TAKE NOTE We do not need to memorize these patterns. Simply perform the operations, treating i as a variable.

For example,

$$\sqrt{-2}\,\sqrt{-18} = i\sqrt{2} \cdot i\sqrt{18} \quad \text{Write each square root of a negative number in terms of } i.$$
$$= i^2\sqrt{36} \quad \text{Product rule for radicals}$$
$$= -1 \cdot 6 \quad \text{Substitute } -1 \text{ for } i^2.$$
$$= -6$$

 TAKE NOTE Remember to write the square roots of a negative number in terms of i before you perform operations with imaginary numbers. For example, $\sqrt{-2} \cdot \sqrt{-18} \neq \sqrt{36}$ or 6.

EXAMPLE 2 Perform the indicated operation.

a. $\sqrt{-27} + \sqrt{-12}$ **b.** $2\sqrt{-63} - 3\sqrt{-28}$

c. $\dfrac{\sqrt{-25}}{\sqrt{-16}}$ **d.** $\sqrt{-2}\,\sqrt{-3}\,\sqrt{-5}$

e. $\left(\sqrt{-3} + \sqrt{-4}\right)\left(\sqrt{-2} - \sqrt{-6}\right)$

Solution

a. $\sqrt{-27} + \sqrt{-12} = i\sqrt{27} + i\sqrt{12}$ Write the square root of a negative number in terms of *i*.

$$= 3i\sqrt{3} + 2i\sqrt{3}$$ Simplify the radicals.

$$= 5i\sqrt{3}$$

b. $2\sqrt{-63} - 3\sqrt{-28} = 2i\sqrt{63} - 3i\sqrt{28}$ Write the square root of a negative number in terms of *i*.

$$= 2i \cdot 3\sqrt{7} - 3i \cdot 2\sqrt{7}$$ Simplify the radicals.

$$= 6i\sqrt{7} - 6i\sqrt{7}$$ Multiply.

$$= 0$$

c. $\dfrac{\sqrt{-25}}{\sqrt{-16}} = \dfrac{i\sqrt{25}}{i\sqrt{16}}$ Write the square root of a negative number in terms of *i*.

$$= \frac{5i}{4i}$$ Simplify the radicals.

$$= \frac{5}{4}$$ Simplify.

d. $\sqrt{-2}\,\sqrt{-3}\,\sqrt{-5} = i\sqrt{2} \cdot i\sqrt{3} \cdot i\sqrt{5}$ Write the square root of a negative number in terms of *i*.

$$= i^3\sqrt{30}$$ Product rule for square roots

$$= (-i)(\sqrt{30})$$ Substitute $-i$ for i^3.

$$= -i\sqrt{30}$$

e. $\left(\sqrt{-3} + \sqrt{-4}\right)\left(\sqrt{-2} - \sqrt{-6}\right)$

$$= \left(i\sqrt{3} + i\sqrt{4}\right)\left(i\sqrt{2} - i\sqrt{6}\right)$$ Write the square root of a negative number in terms of *i*.

$$= i^2\sqrt{6} - i^2\sqrt{18} + i^2\sqrt{8} - i^2\sqrt{24}$$ FOIL method

$$= i^2\sqrt{6} - 3i^2\sqrt{2} + 2i^2\sqrt{2} - 2i^2\sqrt{6}$$ Simplify the radicals.

$$= (-1)\sqrt{6} - 3(-1)\sqrt{2} + 2(-1)\sqrt{2} - 2(-1)\sqrt{6}$$ Substitute -1 for i^2.

$$= -\sqrt{6} + 3\sqrt{2} - 2\sqrt{2} + 2\sqrt{6}$$ Multiply.

$$= \sqrt{6} + \sqrt{2}$$

Check

```
√(-27)+√(-12)
              8.66i
5i√(3)
              8.66i
```

Figure 11.10

We can check these operations on the calculator. Set your calculator to round to two decimal places and to $a + bi$ mode, and then enter the expression. Answers with radicals are approximated and can be checked by entering the exact answer and comparing the two results. The check for Example 2a is shown in **Figure 11.10**. ■

✓ Objective 11.7.2 **CHECKUP**

1. Perform the indicated operation.

   a. $\sqrt{-4} + \sqrt{-64}$ **b.** $5\sqrt{-20} - 3\sqrt{-125}$

   c. $\dfrac{\sqrt{-100}}{\sqrt{-121}}$ **d.** $\sqrt{-6}\,\sqrt{-10}\,\sqrt{-15}$

   e. $\left(\sqrt{-5} - \sqrt{-6}\right)\left(\sqrt{-2} - \sqrt{-15}\right)$

2. Is the imaginary number *i* a variable? Explain.

3. How is the imaginary number *i* treated the same as a variable?

Objective 11.7.3   Operations on Complex Numbers

As we performed operations on imaginary numbers in the last section, we obtained values expressed in different forms. For example, some of the results were real numbers, and others were expressions that contained the imaginary number *i*. Together they make up the **complex-number system**.

STANDARD FORM FOR A COMPLEX NUMBER

A complex number is written in the standard form

$$a + bi$$

where a and b are real numbers.

If $b = 0$, then $a + 0i = a$ is a real number.

If $b \neq 0$, then $a + bi$ is an imaginary number.

If $a = 0$ and $b \neq 0$, then $0 + bi = bi$ is a pure imaginary number.

We call a the real part, and b the imaginary part, of the complex number.

In summary, the set of complex numbers consists of two mutually exclusive sub-sets: real numbers and imaginary numbers. Remember that two sets are mutually exclusive when any number that belongs to one set does not belong to the other set. To visualize the set of complex numbers, we add the set of imaginary numbers to the set of real numbers that we viewed on page 44, obtaining the following diagram:

Complex numbers

Real numbers		Imaginary numbers
Rational numbers	Irrational numbers	
Integers		
Whole numbers		
Natural numbers or Counting numbers		

Two complex numbers $a + bi$ and $c + di$ are equal if and only if $a = c$ and $b = d$. For example,

$\sqrt{4} + \sqrt{-3}$ and $2 + i\sqrt{3}$ are equal, because $\sqrt{4} = 2$ and $\sqrt{-3} = i\sqrt{3}$.

We can add and subtract complex numbers by adding the real parts and the imaginary parts separately.

$$(a + bi) + (c + di) = (a + c) + (b + d)i$$

$$(a + bi) - (c + di) = (a - c) + (b - d)i$$

Again, we treat i as a variable and perform the operations in the same manner as adding and subtracting binomials.

EXAMPLE 3

Add or subtract. Write your answer in standard form for a complex number.

a. $(2 + 3i) + (-4 + 5i)$ **b.** $7 - (2 + i)$ **c.** $-2i - (3 - 2i)$

Solution

a. $(2 + 3i) + (-4 + 5i) = [2 + (-4)] + (3 + 5)i$
$$= -2 + 8i$$

b. $7 - (2 + i) = 7 - 2 - i = 5 - i$

c. $-2i - (3 - 2i) = -2i - 3 + 2i = -3$

Check

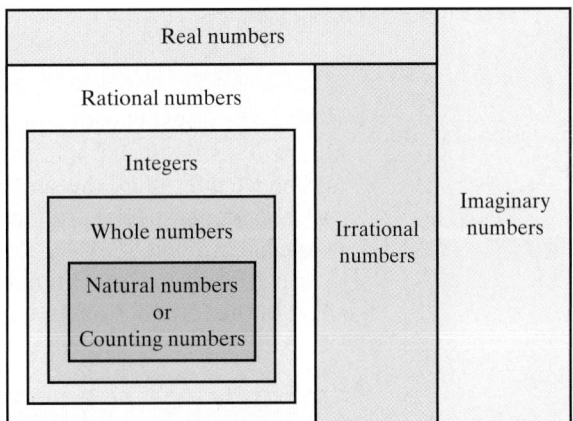

a. (2+3i)+(-4+5i)
    -2+8i
b. 7-(2+i)
    5-i
c. -2i-(3-2i)
    -3

Calculator checks for Examples 3a, 3b, and 3c are shown in the figure.

We multiply complex numbers by using the distributive property. Remember, this leads to the FOIL method for binomials.

 TAKE NOTE Remember to simplify powers of i. Write the products in standard form for complex numbers.

EXAMPLE 4   Multiply. Write your answer in standard form for a complex number.

a. $2(3 - 4i)$ **b.** $3i(6 + i)$ **c.** $(-5 + 2i)(7 - 6i)$

Solution

a. $2(3 - 4i) = 6 - 8i$ Distributive property

b. $3i(6 + i) = 18i + 3i^2$ Distributive property

$$= 18i + 3(-1)$$
$$= 18i - 3$$
$$= -3 + 18i$$

c. $(-5 + 2i)(7 - 6i) = -35 + 30i + 14i - 12i^2$ FOIL method

$$= -35 + 30i + 14i - 12(-1)$$
$$= -35 + 30i + 14i + 12$$
$$= -23 + 44i$$

Check the answers with your calculator, as in Example 3. ■

When we multiplied the sum and difference of the same two terms using binomials, we obtained a special product. Similarly, the product of $a + bi$ and $a - bi$ results in a special product.

The product is a real number, the sum of the squares of a and b. Complex numbers of the form $a + bi$ and $a - bi$ are called **complex conjugates**.

PRODUCT OF COMPLEX CONJUGATES

$$(a + bi)(a - bi) = a^2 + b^2$$

We can verify this result by multiplying $a + bi$ and $a - bi$ algebraically.

$$(a + bi)(a - bi) = a^2 - abi + abi - b^2i^2$$
$$= a^2 - abi + abi - b^2(-1)$$
$$= a^2 - abi + abi + b^2$$
$$= a^2 + b^2$$

 TAKE NOTE Be careful not to confuse this product with the special product for real numbers $(a + b)(a - b) = a^2 - b^2$.

The following pairs of complex numbers are examples of complex conjugates.

$$\begin{array}{lcl} 2 + 3i & \text{and} & 2 - 3i \\ -4 - i & \text{and} & -4 + i \\ 5 \text{ (or } 5 + 0i) & \text{and} & 5 \text{ (or } 5 - 0i) \\ 2i \text{ (or } 0 + 2i) & \text{and} & -2i \text{ (or } 0 - 2i) \end{array}$$

To divide a complex number by a nonzero real number, we use the distributive property, as we did with binomials.

$$\frac{a + bi}{c} = \frac{a}{c} + \frac{bi}{c} = \frac{a}{c} + \frac{b}{c}i$$

However, to divide two complex numbers $\dfrac{a + bi}{c + di}$, we multiply the numerator and denominator by the conjugate of the denominator, $c - di$.

$$\frac{a + bi}{c + di} = \frac{(a + bi)(c - di)}{(c + di)(c - di)}$$

EXAMPLE 5   Divide. Write your answer in standard form for a complex number.

a. $\dfrac{3 + 9i}{3}$ b. $\dfrac{2 - 3i}{4 + i}$ c. $\dfrac{-2 + 4i}{5i}$

Solution

a. $\dfrac{3 + 9i}{3} = \dfrac{3}{3} + \dfrac{9i}{3}$ *Distributive property*

$= 1 + 3i$

Check this answer with your calculator.

b. $\dfrac{2 - 3i}{4 + i} = \dfrac{(2 - 3i)(4 - i)}{(4 + i)(4 - i)}$ *Multiply the numerator and denominator by the conjugate of the denominator.*

$= \dfrac{8 - 2i - 12i + 3i^2}{16 + 1}$ *$(a + bi)(a - bi) = a^2 + b^2$, with $a = 4$ and $b = 1$*

$= \dfrac{8 - 2i - 12i + 3(-1)}{16 + 1}$

$= \dfrac{8 - 2i - 12i - 3}{17}$

$= \dfrac{5 - 14i}{17}$

$= \dfrac{5}{17} - \dfrac{14}{17}i$ *Standard form*

Check this answer with your calculator.

c. $\dfrac{-2 + 4i}{5i} = \dfrac{(-2 + 4i)(-5i)}{(5i)(-5i)}$ *Conjugate of the denominator, 5i, or 0 + 5i, is 0 − 5i, or −5i.*

$= \dfrac{10i - 20i^2}{25}$ *$(5i)(-5i) = -25i^2 = -25(-) = 25$*

$= \dfrac{10i - 20(-1)}{25}$

$= \dfrac{10i + 20}{25}$

$= \dfrac{10}{25}i + \dfrac{20}{25}$

$= \dfrac{2}{5}i + \dfrac{4}{5}$

$= \dfrac{4}{5} + \dfrac{2}{5}i$ *Standard form*

Check this answer with your calculator.   ■

Objective 11.7.3 **CHECKUP**

1. Add or subtract.
   a. $(15 - 12i) + (11 + 7i)$ b. $11 - (5 - 3i)$
   c. $21i - (8 + i)$

2. Multiply.
   a. $i(12 + 3i)$ b. $(8 - 4i)(9 + 2i)$ c. $(7 + 3i)(7 - 3i)$

3. Divide.
   a. $\dfrac{24 - 18i}{6}$ b. $\dfrac{7 - 8i}{2i}$ c. $\dfrac{5}{8 - i}$

4. Explain the difference between the conjugate of a radical expression and the conjugate of a complex number. How are these two kinds of conjugates used?   ■

Objective 11.7.4

Solving Equations Having Imaginary-Number Solutions

Some quadratic equations can be solved by using the principle of square roots. That is,

$$\text{for any positive number } b, \text{ if } a^2 = b, \text{ then } a = \pm\sqrt{b}.$$

This principle limits us to a positive number b in order to obtain real-number solutions. For example, solve $x^2 = 1$.

$$x^2 = 1$$
$$x = \pm 1$$

To solve the equation $x^2 = -1$, we need a new principle.

PRINCIPLE OF SQUARE ROOTS FOR IMAGINARY-NUMBER SOLUTIONS

For any negative number b, if $a^2 = b$, then $a = \pm i\sqrt{b}$.

Now we can solve the equation $x^2 = -1$.

$$x^2 = -1$$
$$x = \pm i\sqrt{1}$$
$$x = \pm i$$

We can check the solutions by substitution.

Let $x = i$

$$\frac{x^2 = -1}{(i)^2 \mid -1}$$
$$-1 \mid$$

Let $x = -i$

$$\frac{x^2 = -1}{(-i)^2 \mid -1}$$
$$i^2 \mid$$
$$-1 \mid$$

Both solutions check. The solutions are $\pm i$.

EXAMPLE 6

Solve.

a. $2x^2 + 16 = 0$ **b.** $(x + 3)^2 + 16 = 0$ **c.** $3(2x - 3)^2 = -15$

Solution

a. $2x^2 + 16 = 0$

$$2x^2 = -16 \quad \text{Subtract 16 from both sides.}$$

$$\frac{2x^2}{2} = -\frac{16}{2} \quad \text{Divide both sides by 2.}$$

$$x^2 = -8 \quad \text{Simplify.}$$

$$x = \pm i\sqrt{8} \quad \text{Principle of square roots for imaginary-number solutions}$$

$$x = \pm 2i\sqrt{2} \quad \text{Simplify.}$$

Substitution Check

```
2i√(2)→X:2X²+16
                0
-2i√(2)→X:2X²+16
                0
```

The substitution of the possible solutions results in 0, the right side of the equation. The solutions are $\pm 2i\sqrt{2}$.

b. $(x + 3)^2 + 16 = 0$

$$(x + 3)^2 = -16 \quad \text{Subtract 16 from both sides.}$$

$$x + 3 = \pm i\sqrt{16} \quad \text{Principle of square roots for imaginary-number solutions}$$

$$x + 3 = \pm 4i \quad \text{Simplify.}$$

$$x = -3 \pm 4i \quad \text{Subtract 3 from both sides.}$$

The check is left for you.

c. $3(2x - 3)^2 = -15$

$\qquad (2x - 3)^2 = -5$ Divide both sides by 3.

$\qquad\quad 2x - 3 = \pm i\sqrt{5}$ Principle of square roots for imaginary-number solutions

$\qquad\qquad 2x = 3 \pm i\sqrt{5}$ Add 3 to both sides.

$\qquad\qquad\quad x = \dfrac{3 \pm i\sqrt{5}}{2}$ Divide both sides by 2.

$\qquad\qquad\quad x = \dfrac{3}{2} \pm \dfrac{\sqrt{5}}{2}i$ Standard form

The check is left for you.   ■

A second method of solving quadratic equations in the standard form, $ax^2 + bx + c = 0$, is to use the quadratic formula,

$$x = \frac{-b \pm \sqrt{b^2 - 4ac}}{2a}$$

When we solved quadratic equations with the use of the quadratic formula, we found that some equations had no real-number solutions. This was the result when the discriminant was a negative number. Now we can see that these solutions are imaginary numbers.

EXAMPLE 7   Solve.

a. $3x^2 + 8x + 15 = 0$ **b.** $\dfrac{y - 2}{y - 5} = \dfrac{4}{y + 4}$

Solution

a. $3x^2 + 8x + 15 = 0$ **Check**

$x = \dfrac{-b \pm \sqrt{b^2 - 4ac}}{2a}$ Quadratic formula

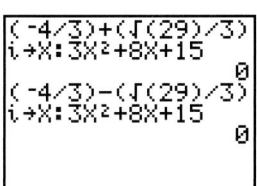

$x = \dfrac{-(8) \pm \sqrt{(8)^2 - 4(3)(15)}}{2(3)}$ $a = 3, b = 8,$ and $c = 15$

$x = \dfrac{-8 \pm \sqrt{64 - 180}}{6}$

$x = \dfrac{-8 \pm \sqrt{-116}}{6}$ Check the two imaginary-number solutions by substitution on your calculator.

$x = \dfrac{-8 \pm i\sqrt{116}}{6}$ Write the square root of a negative number in terms of i.

$x = \dfrac{-8 \pm i\sqrt{4 \cdot 29}}{6}$

$x = \dfrac{-8 \pm 2i\sqrt{29}}{6}$ Simplify the radical.

$x = -\dfrac{8}{6} \pm \dfrac{2i\sqrt{29}}{6}$

$x = -\dfrac{4}{3} \pm \dfrac{\sqrt{29}}{3}i$

b.
$$\frac{y - 2}{y - 5} = \frac{4}{y + 4}$$

$$y^2 + 4y - 2y - 8 = 4y - 20 \qquad \text{Cross multiply.}$$

$$y^2 - 2y + 12 = 0 \qquad \begin{array}{l}\text{Standard form of a}\\ \text{quadratic equation}\\ \text{(in terms of } y)\end{array}$$

$$y = \frac{-b \pm \sqrt{b^2 - 4ac}}{2a} \qquad \text{Quadratic formula}$$

$$y = \frac{-(-2) \pm \sqrt{(-2)^2 - 4(1)(12)}}{2(1)} \qquad \begin{array}{l} a = 1, b = -2, \\ \text{and } c = 12 \end{array}$$

$$y = \frac{2 \pm \sqrt{4 - 48}}{2}$$

$$y = \frac{2 \pm \sqrt{-44}}{2}$$

$$y = \frac{2 \pm i\sqrt{44}}{2} \qquad \begin{array}{l}\text{Write the square root}\\ \text{of a negative number}\\ \text{in terms of } i.\end{array}$$

$$y = \frac{2 \pm i\sqrt{4 \cdot 11}}{2}$$

$$y = \frac{2 \pm 2i\sqrt{11}}{2} \qquad \text{Simplify the radical.}$$

$$y = \frac{2}{2} \pm \frac{2i\sqrt{11}}{2}$$

$$y = 1 \pm i\sqrt{11}$$

Check

```
1+i√(11)→Y:(Y-2)
/(Y-5)
          .56-.37i
4/(Y+4)
          .56-.37i
```

Check the two imaginary-number solutions by substitution on your calculator. The check of $1 + i\sqrt{11}$ is shown.

✓ Objective 11.7.4 CHECKUP

Solve exercises 1 and 2.

1. a. $5x^2 + 20 = 0$ **b.** $(x - 4)^2 + 27 = 0$
  c. $-6(3z + 1)^2 = 12$

2. a. $5x^2 + 3x + 9 = 0$ **b.** $\dfrac{x + 4}{x - 6} = \dfrac{2}{x + 8}$

3. In the quadratic formula, what is the discriminant?

4. If the solutions of a quadratic equation are imaginary numbers, what must be the sign of the discriminant?

Objective 11.7.5 Modeling the Real World

In previous chapters, we examined an important formula called Ohm's law, $V = IR$, which applies to direct-current (DC) circuits, such as the circuit form when you connect a battery. However, there is another kind of electric circuit, called an alternating-current (AC) circuit, which is used to provide the electric power in houses, offices, and industry. The electrical quantities in an AC circuit—for example, voltage and current—can be described by complex numbers.

In an AC circuit, Ohm's law takes on a slightly different form, $V = IZ$. The quantity V is still called the voltage and the quantity I is still called the current, although both may be complex numbers. The quantity Z is called the impedance and includes other electrical properties that we won't discuss, as well as the resistance R, which is the same as in DC circuits. When engineers work with the AC form of Ohm's law, they often have to determine the magnitude of the voltage, which is denoted as $|V|$. If the voltage is given in the complex form $a + bi$, the magnitude of the voltage is the principal square root of the sum of the squares of the real part and the imaginary part, or $|V| = \sqrt{a^2 + b^2}$. We will solve a couple of problems by means of these equations in order to give you practice in working with complex numbers.

EXAMPLE 8

In a particular circuit, the current, I, is $2 - 3i$ amperes and the impedance, Z, is $6 + 2i$ ohms. Find the magnitude of the total voltage, $|V|$, across this part of the circuit.

Solution

The formula for total voltage is $V = IZ$.

$$V = IZ$$
$$V = (2 - 3i)(6 + 2i)$$
$$V = 12 + 4i - 18i - 6i^2$$
$$V = 12 + 4i - 18i - 6(-1)$$
$$V = 12 + 4i - 18i + 6$$
$$V = 18 - 14i$$

The total voltage is $18 - 14i$ volts.

The magnitude of the total voltage is $|V| = \sqrt{a^2 + b^2}$, where $a = 18$ and $b = -14$.

$$|V| = \sqrt{(18)^2 + (-14)^2} \approx 22.8$$ *Use a calculator to approximate to two decimal places.*

The magnitude of the total voltage is approximately 22.8 volts.

APPLICATION

The equation $(x^2 + y^2)^2 = 2k^2(x^2 - y^2)$ gives a graph called the Lemniscate of Bernoulli. If $x = 0$ and $k = 3$, find y.

Discussion

$$(x^2 + y^2)^2 = 2k^2(x^2 - y^2)$$
$$(0^2 + y^2)^2 = 2(3)^2(0^2 - y^2)$$ *x = 0 and k = 3*
$$y^4 = -18y^2$$ *Simplify.*
$$y^4 + 18y^2 = 0$$ *Standard form*
$$y^2(y^2 + 18) = 0$$ *Factor.*
$$y^2 = 0 \quad \text{or} \quad y^2 + 18 = 0$$ *Zero factor property*
$$y = 0 \qquad\qquad y^2 = -18$$
$$y = \pm i\sqrt{18}$$ *Principle of square roots*
$$y = \pm i\sqrt{9 \cdot 2}$$
$$y = \pm 3i\sqrt{2}$$

If $x = 0$ and $k = 3$, then $y = 0$ or $y = \pm 3i\sqrt{2}$.

 Objective 11.7.5 **CHECKUP**

1. Find the magnitude of the total voltage across a circuit when the current is $4 - 2i$ amperes and the impedance is $5 + 3i$ ohms.

2. The equation $(x^2 + y^2)^2 = 2k^2(x^2 - y^2)$ gives a graph called the Lemniscate of Bernoulli. If $x = 0$ and $k = 5$, find y.

11.7 EXERCISES

 Student Solutions Manual  PH Math/Tutor Center   CD Video  MathXL® MyMathLab   Interactmath.com

Write in terms of i.

1. $\sqrt{-100}$

2. $\sqrt{-144}$

3. $\sqrt{-\dfrac{16}{49}}$

4. $\sqrt{-\dfrac{36}{121}}$

5. $\sqrt{-32}$

6. $\sqrt{-75}$

7. $2\sqrt{-50}$

8. $-3\sqrt{-98}$

Perform the indicated operations.

9. $7\sqrt{-36} + 9\sqrt{-4}$ **10.** $5\sqrt{-16} + 2\sqrt{-9}$ **11.** $2\sqrt{-121} - 3\sqrt{-9}$ **12.** $3\sqrt{-144} - 2\sqrt{-25}$

13. $\dfrac{\sqrt{-144}}{\sqrt{-225}}$ **14.** $\dfrac{\sqrt{-64}}{\sqrt{-100}}$ **15.** $\sqrt{-5}\,\sqrt{-8}\,\sqrt{-10}$ **16.** $\sqrt{-3}\,\sqrt{-5}\,\sqrt{-15}$

17. $\left(\sqrt{-6} + \sqrt{-4}\right)\left(\sqrt{-3} - \sqrt{-8}\right)$ **18.** $\left(\sqrt{-3} + \sqrt{-10}\right)\left(\sqrt{-5} - \sqrt{-6}\right)$

19. $\left(\sqrt{-5} - \sqrt{-7}\right)\left(\sqrt{-5} + \sqrt{-7}\right)$ **20.** $\left(\sqrt{-3} + \sqrt{-11}\right)\left(\sqrt{-3} - \sqrt{-11}\right)$

Add or subtract. Write your answer in standard form for a complex number.

21. $(3 + 5i) + (-8 - i)$ **22.** $(9 - 17i) + (-11 + 8i)$ **23.** $(6 + 2i) - (3 + 3i)$ **24.** $(14 + 3i) - (5 - 6i)$

25. $(4 - 5i) - (3 - 5i)$ **26.** $(6 + 8i) - (6 + 2i)$ **27.** $\left(\dfrac{1}{2} + 5i\right) + \left(3 - \dfrac{2}{3}i\right)$ **28.** $\left(\dfrac{3}{8} + 6i\right) + \left(\dfrac{1}{8} - 7i\right)$

29. $(4.5 + 6.7i) - (2.88 - 4.68i)$ **30.** $(12.7 - 3.63i) + (4.6 + 12.7i)$

31. $\left(2\sqrt{3} - i\sqrt{2}\right) + \left(5\sqrt{3} + 2i\sqrt{2}\right)$ **32.** $\left(5\sqrt{5} + i\sqrt{3}\right) - \left(7\sqrt{5} + 8i\sqrt{3}\right)$

Multiply. Write your answer in standard form for a complex number.

33. $(4 - 3i)(6 + 5i)$ **34.** $(9 + 6i)(5 - 4i)$ **35.** $(5 + 7i)(5 - 7i)$

36. $(11 - 3i)(11 + 3i)$ **37.** $(-6 - i)(-6 + i)$ **38.** $(-5 + 2i)(-5 - 2i)$

39. $(0.4 - 3.1i)(5.7 + 0.8i)$ **40.** $(2.5 + 3.4i)(1.2 - 0.6i)$ **41.** $\left(\dfrac{3}{5} + \dfrac{1}{2}i\right)\left(\dfrac{2}{5} - \dfrac{2}{3}i\right)$

42. $\left(\dfrac{3}{4} - \dfrac{2}{3}i\right)\left(\dfrac{3}{5} + \dfrac{1}{3}i\right)$ **43.** $i\sqrt{2}\left(\sqrt{2} + i\sqrt{3}\right)$ **44.** $-3i\sqrt{3}\left(\sqrt{6} - i\sqrt{15}\right)$

45. $\left(\sqrt{3} - i\sqrt{5}\right)\left(\sqrt{3} + i\sqrt{5}\right)$ **46.** $\left(\sqrt{7} + 2i\sqrt{6}\right)\left(\sqrt{7} - 2i\sqrt{6}\right)$

Divide. Write your answer in standard form for a complex number.

47. $\dfrac{7 + 21i}{7}$ **48.** $\dfrac{16 + 48i}{8}$ **49.** $\dfrac{-4 + 7i}{3 - i}$ **50.** $\dfrac{47 + 13i}{5 + 2i}$

51. $\dfrac{6 - 5i}{2i}$ **52.** $\dfrac{12 + 9i}{-6i}$ **53.** $\dfrac{16.2 - 13.5i}{2.7i}$ **54.** $\dfrac{9.03 + 6.45i}{4.3i}$

55. $\dfrac{21.2 - 10.4i}{4.5 + i}$ **56.** $\dfrac{-19.7 + 21.5i}{1 + 7.4i}$ **57.** $\dfrac{\sqrt{6} + i\sqrt{14}}{i\sqrt{2}}$ **58.** $\dfrac{\sqrt{15} - i\sqrt{21}}{i\sqrt{3}}$

59. $\dfrac{2 + 5i\sqrt{6}}{2\sqrt{3} + i\sqrt{2}}$ **60.** $\dfrac{23 + 4i\sqrt{10}}{\sqrt{5} + 2i\sqrt{2}}$

Solve exercises 61–100.

61. $a^2 + 7 = 0$ **62.** $b^2 + 11 = 0$ **63.** $z^2 + 5 = 1$ **64.** $m^2 + 18 = 2$

65. $3p^2 + 75 = 0$ **66.** $4q^2 + 64 = 0$ **67.** $4d^2 + 12 = 0$ **68.** $5c^2 + 10 = 0$

69. $(t + 1)^2 + 9 = 0$ **70.** $(s - 3)^2 + 36 = 0$ **71.** $4(x - 5)^2 + 22 = 2$ **72.** $2(x + 3)^2 + 21 = 5$

73. $4(2x + 5)^2 = -16$ **74.** $3(2y - 1)^2 = -75$ **75.** $2(z + 2.5)^2 + 10.58 = 0$ **76.** $3(y - 1.4)^2 + 7.68 = 0$

77. $\left(b - \dfrac{1}{2}\right)^2 + \dfrac{1}{4} = 0$ **78.** $\left(c + \dfrac{2}{3}\right)^2 + \dfrac{9}{16} = 0$ **79.** $x^2 + 2x + 4 = 0$ **80.** $x^2 - 6x + 14 = 0$

81. $b^2 - 10b + 27 = 0$ **82.** $x^2 + 14x + 51 = 0$ **83.** $4y^2 + 4y + 5 = 0$ **84.** $9x^2 + 24x + 17 = 0$

85. $9p^2 - 12p + 8 = 0$ **86.** $16z^2 - 8z + 7 = 0$ **87.** $x^2 - 2.4x + 3.44 = 0$ **88.** $m^2 + 4.2m + 7.41 = 0$

89. $2y^2 - 2y + 1.22 = 0$ **90.** $3z^2 + 3.6z + 1.35 = 0$ **91.** $x^2 - \dfrac{2}{3}x + \dfrac{13}{36} = 0$ **92.** $x^2 + \dfrac{1}{2}x + \dfrac{25}{144} = 0$

93. $4z^2 + \dfrac{4}{3}z + \dfrac{2}{9} = 0$ **94.** $9x^2 + 3x + \dfrac{13}{16} = 0$ **95.** $\dfrac{x}{x - 2} = \dfrac{5}{x + 3}$ **96.** $\dfrac{a}{a - 9} = \dfrac{4}{a + 7}$

97. $\dfrac{y + 7}{y - 3} = \dfrac{6}{y + 4}$ **98.** $\dfrac{b + 5}{b - 6} = \dfrac{8}{b + 1}$ **99.** $\dfrac{z - 5}{z(z + 3)} = \dfrac{4}{5}$ **100.** $\dfrac{c - 9}{c(c + 3)} = \dfrac{2}{3}$

101. Find the magnitude of the total voltage V across a circuit if the current I is $3 + 5i$ amperes and the impedance Z is $5 + 4i$ ohms. Use the formula $V = IZ$.

102. What is the total voltage V across a circuit when the current I is $5 - i$ amperes and the impedance Z is $8 + 2i$ ohms?

103. Use the formula $I = \dfrac{V}{Z}$ to find the magnitude of the current I across a circuit when the voltage V is $18 + i$ volts and the impedance Z is $2 + 3i$ ohms.

104. Find the magnitude of the current I across a circuit when the voltage V is $40 + 44i$ volts and the impedance Z is $6 + 4i$ ohms.

105. In analyzing the laminar flow of fluids, energy loss is calculated with the use of the quantity $K = 1.00 - 2.67r + r^2$, where r is the ratio of cross-sectional areas of the fluid. Let $K = -1.75$ and solve the resulting equation for r.

106. Using the relation in exercise **105**, let $K = -2.50$, and solve the resulting equation for r.

107. $(x^2 + y^2)^2 = 2k^2(x^2 - y^2)$ gives a graph called the Lemniscate of Bernoulli. If $x = 0$ and $k = 2$, find y.

108. $(x^2 + y^2)^2 = 2k^2(x^2 - y^2)$ gives a graph called the Lemniscate of Bernoulli. If $x = 0$ and $k = 4$, find y.

109. The equation $x^4 + y^4 = 2axy^2$ gives a graph called a bifoliate. If $y = \sqrt{x}$ and $a = -2$, find x.

110. The equation $x^4 + y^4 = 2axy^2$ gives a graph called a bifoliate. If $y = \sqrt{x}$ and $a = -8$, find x.

111. The curve $x(x^2 + y^2) = 2ky^2$ is called the Cissoid of Diocles. If $x = -1$ and $k = 1$, find y.

112. The curve $x(x^2 + y^2) = 2ky^2$ is called the Cissoid of Diocles. If $x = -2$ and $k = 3$, find y.

As a part of a branch of mathematics called differential equations, one is often asked to solve what are called characteristic equations. These solutions are then used to solve more complicated equations.

In exercises 113–116, solve the following characteristic equations.

113. $m^2 + 48 = 0$ **114.** $m^2 + 80 = 0$

115. $m^2 + 7m + 15 = 0$ **116.** $m^2 + m + 1 = 0$

117. Show that the square root of $5 - 12i$ is $3 - 2i$.

118. Show that the square root of $48 - 14i$ is $7 - i$.

The complex modulus of a complex number $a + bi$ is defined to be $\sqrt{a^2 + b^2}$.

119. Given the number $5 + 3i$,
   a. Write the complex modulus of the number.
   b. Square the complex modulus.
   c. Write the complex conjugate of the number.
   d. Find the product of the number and the complex conjugate.
   e. Compare your answers in part **b** and part **d**.

120. Given the number $11 + 6i$,
   a. Write the complex modulus of the number.
   b. Square the complex modulus.
   c. Write the complex conjugate of the number.
   d. Find the product of the number and the complex conjugate.
   e. Compare your answers in part **b** and part **d**.

121. Consider the function $f(x) = 2x^2 - 12x + 23$.
   a. Graph the function.
   b. Use the graph to tell where the function value is equal to zero.
   c. Solve the equation $2x^2 - 12x + 23 = 0$ algebraically.
   d. For what values of x is $f(x) = 0$?
   e. Explain the difference in your answers to parts **b** and **d**.

122. Consider the function $g(x) = -3x^2 + x - 5$.
   a. Graph the function.
   b. Use the graph to tell where the function value is equal to zero.
   c. Solve the equation $-3x^2 + x - 5 = 0$ algebraically.
   d. For what values of x is $g(x) = 0$?
   e. Explain the difference in your answers to parts **b** and **d**.

 11.7 Calculator Exercises

Now that you have learned to set your calculator to complex-number mode, you can investigate how the calculator handles roots of negative numbers when the index of the radical is something other than 2. Use the complex-number setting for the following exercises:

Simplify.

1. $\sqrt{-25}$ **2.** $\sqrt[3]{-27}$ **3.** $\sqrt[4]{-64}$

4. $\sqrt[5]{-32}$ **5.** $\sqrt[4]{-324}$ **6.** $\sqrt[4]{-40{,}000}$

When you have your calculator in complex-number mode, you can use the fraction key to change decimal values to fractions. For example, convert $0.25 - 0.8i$ to fractional notation by entering the expression, followed by

  MATH **1** **ENTER**

which results in the expression $\frac{1}{4} - \frac{4}{5}i$.

Convert the following complex numbers to fractional notation:

7. $1.5 - 3.5i$ **8.** $0.4 + 3.2i$ **9.** $-1.8i$

The calculator also can determine the magnitude of a complex number, as required in Example 8 in this section. Remember that

the magnitude of $a + bi$ is calculated as $\sqrt{a^2 + b^2}$. For example, to find the magnitude of $3 + 4i$, enter

 **MATH** ▶ ▶ **5** **3** **+** **4** **2nd** **.** (i) **)**

ENTER

The calculator returns a value of 5 for the magnitude of $3 + 4i$. Use this feature to find the magnitude of the following complex numbers:

10. $6 + 8i$ **11.** $6 - 8i$ **12.** $2 - 5i$

13. 22 **14.** $-7i$ **15.** $i\sqrt{3}$

11.7 Writing Exercise

Fractal geometry is an area of mathematics that uses complex numbers to draw extraordinary pictures called fractals. While you may not have the math skills to fully understand the principles that underlie the process, you can still enjoy the amazing pictures obtained. In the library, find a reference on fractals. You may want to search for some of the most popular drawings, such as the Mandelbrot set or the Sierpinski triangle.

Write a short description of what you have found. Include the title, author, and library call number of the text you reference. Some texts provide programs that can be entered into a graphing calculator to reproduce the designs. You may want to try to do so.

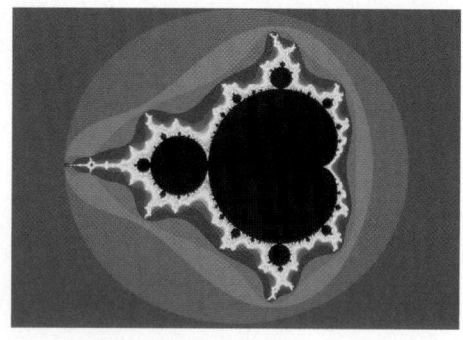

■ Chapter 11 Summary

Vocabulary Review

After completing this chapter, you should be able to define the following key terms.

complex conjugate
complex-number system
conjugate

extraneous solution
imaginary unit *i*
like radicals

radical equation in one variable
radical function
radical relation

Fill in the blank with one of the words or phrases listed above.

1. A _____ can be written in the form $f(x) = A(x)$, where $A(x)$ is a radical expression with the variable x in the radicand.

2. The _____ of the expression $a + b$ is the expression $a - b$.

3. A _____ can be written in the form $A(x) = 0$, where $A(x)$ is a radical expression with the variable x in the radicand.

4. The principal square root of -1 is the _____.

5. The _____ consists of the set of real numbers and the set of imaginary numbers.

Reflections

1. What is the relationship between a radical expression with a variable in its radicand and a variable expression with a rational exponent?

2. How can you determine the restricted values of a radical function?

3. What does it mean to "rationalize a radical expression"?

4. In operating with radical expressions involving square roots, it is sometimes important to be able to determine the conjugate of an expression. What is the conjugate of a radical expression? When is it necessary to work with the conjugate of a radical expression?

5. When solving a radical equation algebraically, how can you tell whether a solution is extraneous?

6. What is the difference between the real-number system and the complex-number system?

7. Explain the process of adding and subtracting two complex numbers.

8. Can you use the FOIL method to multiply two complex numbers? If so, explain how.

9. How can you form the conjugate of a complex number?

10. How is the conjugate of a complex number used to perform division of complex numbers?

11. When you use the quadratic formula to solve a quadratic equation, how can you tell from the nature of the discriminant that the solutions will be imaginary numbers?

■ Chapter 11 Section-by-Section Review

In these exercises, we will assume that the variable base of an exponential expression or a variable radicand does not represent values for which the expression is not defined.

11.1

Recall	Examples
A radical function can be written in the form $f(x) = A(x)$, where $A(x)$ is a radical expression with the variable x in the radicand.	Some radical functions are $f(x) = \sqrt{x + 4}$　　$g(x) = \sqrt[3]{2x - 1}$ $y = \sqrt[4]{x} - 2$　　$y = (\sqrt[3]{x})^2$
The domain of a radical function having an odd index is the set of all real numbers. The domain of a radical function having an even index is the set of all real numbers except the values restricted from the domain. The radicand cannot be negative.	Determine the domain of $f(x) = \sqrt{2x + 1}$. The restricted values are determined by $2x + 1 < 0$ $2x < -1$ $x < -\dfrac{1}{2}$ The domain is the set of all real numbers greater than or equal to $-\frac{1}{2}$, $x \geq -\frac{1}{2}$, or $\left[-\frac{1}{2}, \infty\right)$.
Graph of a radical function • Determine the restricted values. • Determine a table of values by choosing the x-values in the domain of the function. • Plot the points and connect them with a smooth curve.	Graph $f(x) = \sqrt{2x + 1}$. The restricted values are $x < -\frac{1}{2}$. Table of values | x	$f(x) = \sqrt{2x + 1}$	$f(x)$
---	---	---
$-\dfrac{1}{2}$	$f\left(-\dfrac{1}{2}\right) = \sqrt{2\left(-\dfrac{1}{2}\right) + 1}$	0
0	$f(0) = \sqrt{2(0) + 1}$	1
4	$f(4) = \sqrt{2(4) + 1}$	3
5	$f(5) = \sqrt{2(5) + 1}$	$\sqrt{11}$	

Evaluate. Round to the nearest thousandth if necessary.

1. $\sqrt{225}$ **2.** $\sqrt{2.89}$ **3.** $\sqrt{\dfrac{49}{64}}$ **4.** $\sqrt[3]{-\dfrac{27}{125}}$ **5.** $-\sqrt[4]{1296}$

6. $\sqrt[4]{-1296}$ **7.** $\sqrt{150}$ **8.** $\sqrt[3]{-35}$ **9.** $\sqrt[5]{125}$

Determine the restricted values and then state the domain of each radical function in exercises 10 and 11.

10. $y = \sqrt{2x - 7}$ **11.** $y = \sqrt[3]{2x - 7}$

14. In statistics, the variability of the integers 1 to n is calculated as $s = \sqrt{\dfrac{n(n + 1)}{12}}$. Calculate the variability of the integers from 1 to 23.

15. Find the length of a side of a square picture frame that encloses an area of 121 square inches.

16. Find the length of the side of a cube-shaped box whose volume is $\frac{125}{216}$ cubic yards.

17. Find the radius and diameter of a rubber ball whose volume is 65.45 cubic centimeters.

18. Find a function, $f(x)$, for the geometric mean $m = \sqrt{ab}$, if $a = x$ and $b = x + 5$. What is the domain of this function? Graph this function.

Use a table of values to graph each radical function in exercises 12 and 13.

12. $f(x) = 2\sqrt{x}$ **13.** $y = \sqrt[3]{3x - 4}$

19. The amount of money in dollars received by U.S. farmers for a bushel of barley can be estimated by the function $A(t) = \sqrt{1.2t + 2} + 0.8$, where t is the number of years after 2001.
 a. Graph the function.
 b. Use the graph to determine whether the function is increasing or decreasing.
 c. Assuming the trend continues, in what year will the amount be $4 per bushel?

20. The price of a manufacturing unit is $p(x) = \sqrt{x^2 + 20x + 200} - x$, where x is the number of units sold.
 a. What is the price if 25 units are sold? If 35 units are sold?
 b. What is the domain of the price function?
 c. Graph the function on its domain.
 d. Use the graph to determine where the function is increasing and where it is decreasing.
 e. If price is $10.60, how many units were sold?

11.2

Recall	Examples
Expressions with rational exponents can be written as radical expressions. $a^{1/n} = \sqrt[n]{a}$ $a^{-1/n} = \dfrac{1}{a^{1/n}} = \dfrac{1}{\sqrt[n]{a}}$ $a^{m/n} = \sqrt[n]{a^m} = \left(\sqrt[n]{a}\right)^m$	Write as an equivalent radical expression. $x^{1/3} = \sqrt[3]{x}$ $x^{-1/2} = \dfrac{1}{x^{1/2}} = \dfrac{1}{\sqrt{x}}$ $x^{3/4} = \sqrt[4]{x^3} = \left(\sqrt[4]{x}\right)^3$
Graph of a function having a rational exponent • Determine the restricted values. • Determine a table of values by choosing the x-values in the domain of the function. • Plot the points and connect them with a smooth curve.	Graph. $g(x) = (x - 1)^{3/4}$ The restricted values are determined by $x - 1 < 0$ $\quad x < 1$ The domain is the set of all real numbers greater than or equal to 1, $x \geq 1$, or $[1, \infty)$.

x	$g(x) = (x - 1)^{3/4}$	$g(x)$
1	$g(1) = (1 - 1)^{3/4}$	0
2	$g(2) = (2 - 1)^{3/4}$	1
6	$g(6) = (6 - 1)^{3/4}$	3.3
17	$g(17) = (17 - 1)^{3/4}$	8

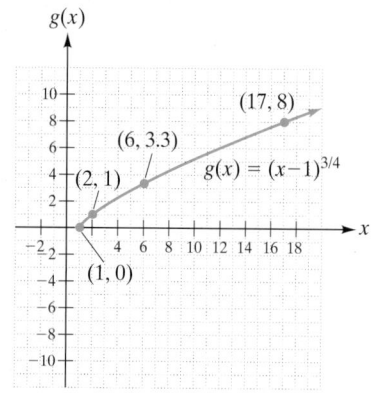

In exercises 21–28, write each expression as a radical expression, and evaluate if possible.

21. $(-64)^{1/3}$ **22.** $-16^{1/4}$ **23.** $(-16)^{1/4}$ **24.** $-64^{-1/3}$

25. $-64^{4/3}$ **26.** $(-64)^{3/2}$ **27.** $16^{-3/4}$ **28.** $(-16)^{-3/4}$

Determine the restricted values and then state the domain of each radical function in exercises 29 and 30.

29. $y = (4x + 9)^{3/4}$ **30.** $f(x) = 2x^{1/3} + 2$

Use a table of values to graph each radical function in exercises 31 and 32.

31. $g(x) = x^{3/2} + 1$ **32.** $y = (2x + 1)^{1/3}$

33. When the coefficient of friction on a road is 30%, the velocity V, in miles per hour, of a car that leaves a skid mark of S feet is given by the mathematical model $V = (9S)^{1/2}$. Graph this function for values of S between 0 and 200 feet. What would you estimate the speed of a car to be if it leaves a skid mark that is 150 feet long?

34. Chad invests $10,000 for his daughter's college fund when she is five years old. When she is 18, this investment has grown in value to $39,000. What is the average return? (Average return can be computed by the formula average return = (final value/original value)$^{1/\text{number of years}}$).

35. World motor vehicle production in millions can be estimated by the function $P(t) = 58t^{3/50}$, where t is the number of years after 2000.
  a. Graph the function.
  b. Use the graph to determine whether the function is increasing or decreasing.
  c. What is the production for the year 2007?
  d. Assuming trends continue, in what year will production be 70 million?

11.3

Recall	Examples
All the properties of integer exponents apply to rational exponents. • Product rule • Quotient rule • Power-to-a-power rule • Product-to-a-power rule • Quotient-to-a-power rule	Simplify, using the properties of exponents. $x^{-1/3}x^{2/3} = x^{-1/3+2/3} = x^{1/3}$ $\dfrac{y^{3/4}}{y^{1/2}} = y^{3/4-1/2} = y^{3/4-2/4} = y^{1/4}$ $(x^{1/3})^{1/2} = x^{1/3 \cdot 1/2} = x^{1/6}$ $(9ab)^{1/2} = 9^{1/2}a^{1/2}b^{1/2} = 3a^{1/2}b^{1/2}$ $\left(\dfrac{x}{y}\right)^{-3/5} = \dfrac{x^{-3/5}}{y^{-3/5}} = \dfrac{y^{3/5}}{x^{3/5}}$

Evaluate, using the properties of exponents.

36. $\dfrac{1}{4^{-1/2}}$ **37.** $8^{2/3} \cdot 8^{5/3}$ **38.** $\dfrac{9^{7/3}}{9^{2/3}}$

39. $\left(\dfrac{4}{9}\right)^{-3/2}$ **40.** $[(3^{1/2})(27^{1/2})]^{-3/2}$ **41.** $(64^{2/3})^{3/4}$

Simplify exercises 42–48. Write your results using positive exponents.

42. $\dfrac{x^{2/3}}{x^{5/6}}$ **43.** $y^{2/5} \cdot y^{-3/10}$ **44.** $(z^{3/5})^{5/9}$

45. $\left(\dfrac{a^3}{b^6}\right)^{-5/12}$ **46.** $(8x^6y^9)^{4/3}$ **47.** $(2a^{3/4}b^{1/3})(3a^{1/3}b^{2/3})$ **48.** $x^{1/3}(x^{2/3} - x^{1/3})$

49. How should the length of the side of a square be changed to increase the area of the square to five times its original size?

11.4

Recall	Examples
Product rule for radicals $\sqrt[n]{a} \cdot \sqrt[n]{b} = \sqrt[n]{ab}$	Simplify, using the product rule. $\sqrt{18xy^3z^5} = \sqrt{9 \cdot 2 \cdot x \cdot y^2 \cdot y \cdot z^4 \cdot z}$ $\phantom{\sqrt{18xy^3z^5}} = \sqrt{9y^2z^4} \sqrt{2xyz}$ $\phantom{\sqrt{18xy^3z^5}} = 3yz^2\sqrt{2xyz}$

(continued on page 930)

Recall	Examples
Quotient rule for radicals $$\frac{\sqrt[n]{a}}{\sqrt[n]{b}} = \sqrt[n]{\frac{a}{b}}$$	Simplify, using the quotient rule. $$\sqrt[3]{\frac{27x^3y}{z^3}} = \frac{\sqrt[3]{27x^3y}}{\sqrt[3]{z^3}} = \frac{3x\sqrt[3]{y}}{z}$$
Rationalize the denominators • If the denominator is one term, multiply the numerator and denominator by the value needed to make the denominator a perfect root.	Rationalize the denominator. $$\frac{2\sqrt{xy}}{\sqrt{5}} \cdot \frac{\sqrt{5}}{\sqrt{5}} = \frac{2\sqrt{5xy}}{5}$$

Simplify without a calculator. Check the results with your calculator.

50. $\sqrt{6300}$ **51.** $\sqrt[3]{-320}$ **52.** $\sqrt[4]{162}$

Simplify.

53. $\sqrt{45x^4y^7z^2}$ **54.** $\sqrt[3]{-64x^2y^7}$ **55.** $\sqrt{12x^2 - 36x + 27}$

Multiply and simplify.

56. $\sqrt{2x} \cdot \sqrt{8x^3}$ **57.** $\sqrt[3]{-2a^2b} \cdot \sqrt[3]{20a^2b^5}$ **58.** $\sqrt{x^2 - 2xy} \cdot \sqrt{3x - 6y}$

Simplify without a calculator, rationalizing all denominators.

59. $\sqrt{\frac{25}{64}}$ **60.** $\sqrt{\frac{13}{289}}$ **61.** $\sqrt{\frac{27}{343}}$ **62.** $\sqrt[3]{\frac{6}{25}}$ **63.** $\frac{\sqrt{50}}{\sqrt{60}}$

Simplify and rationalize in exercises 64–67.

64. $\sqrt{\frac{25a^2}{64b^4}}$ **65.** $\sqrt{\frac{16m}{5}}$ **66.** $\sqrt[3]{\frac{3z^3}{4x^2y}}$ **67.** $\frac{4a\sqrt{5ab^2}}{12\sqrt{10ab^3}}$

68. Find the period of a pendulum whose length is 3 feet.

69. The hip height of a chicken is approximately 0.5 feet. Model the leg motion of a chicken as that of a pendulum and deter- mine the amount of time in seconds in which the leg completed one back-and-forth motion. The length of a chicken's stride is about 1.75 feet. Use this distance to estimate the speed of a chicken.

11.5

Recall	Examples
Addition and subtraction $$a\sqrt[n]{x} + b\sqrt[n]{x} = (a+b)\sqrt[n]{x}$$ $$a\sqrt[n]{x} - b\sqrt[n]{x} = (a-b)\sqrt[n]{x}$$	Add or subtract. $$2\sqrt[3]{x} + 3\sqrt[3]{x} = (2+3)\sqrt[3]{x} = 5\sqrt[3]{x}$$ $$\sqrt{x} - 3\sqrt{x} = (1-3)\sqrt{x} = -2\sqrt{x}$$
Multiplication • Use the distributive property. • If the factors are like roots, use the product rule to simplify.	Multiply. $$2\sqrt[3]{x}(3\sqrt[3]{x} - 1) = 6\sqrt[3]{x^2} - 2\sqrt[3]{x}$$ $$\left(\sqrt{2} + \sqrt{x}\right)\left(3\sqrt{5} - \sqrt{x}\right) = 3\sqrt{10} - \sqrt{2x} + 3\sqrt{5x} - x$$
Division • If the divisor (denominator) is one term, distribute it over the terms of the numerator. • If the divisor (denominator) is two terms containing square roots, multiply the numerator and denominator by the conjugate of the denominator.	Divide. $$\frac{2 + \sqrt{xy}}{\sqrt{x}} = \frac{2}{\sqrt{x}} + \frac{\sqrt{xy}}{\sqrt{x}}$$ $$= \frac{2}{\sqrt{x}} \cdot \frac{\sqrt{x}}{\sqrt{x}} + \frac{\sqrt{y}}{1}$$ $$= \frac{2\sqrt{x}}{x} + \sqrt{y}$$ $$\frac{2 + \sqrt{x}}{3 - \sqrt{x}} = \frac{2 + \sqrt{x}}{3 - \sqrt{x}} \cdot \frac{3 + \sqrt{x}}{3 + \sqrt{x}}$$ $$= \frac{6 + 5\sqrt{x} + x}{9 - x}$$

Add or subtract as indicated.

70. $3\sqrt{5} - 2\sqrt{5} + 7\sqrt{5} - \sqrt{5}$

71. $7\sqrt{11} + 2\sqrt{44}$

72. $\sqrt{15} + \sqrt{\dfrac{1}{15}}$

73. $5\sqrt[3]{16} - \sqrt[3]{54}$

74. $\sqrt{49x} - \sqrt{25x}$

75. $4b\sqrt{a^3 b} - 7a\sqrt{ab^3} + 8ab\sqrt{ab}$

Multiply and simplify.

76. $\sqrt{7}\left(\sqrt{14} - \sqrt{7}\right)$

77. $\sqrt{2a}\left(6 + \sqrt{2a}\right)$

78. $\left(2 - \sqrt{5}\right)\left(4 + \sqrt{5}\right)$

79. $\left(\sqrt{5x} + \sqrt{7y}\right)\left(\sqrt{5x} - \sqrt{7y}\right)$

80. $\left(\sqrt{x} + 8\right)^2$

81. $3\sqrt[3]{x}\left(2\sqrt[3]{x^2} + \sqrt[3]{x}\right)$

Divide exercises 82–87 and simplify.

82. $\dfrac{\sqrt{15x} - \sqrt{30}}{\sqrt{5}}$

83. $\dfrac{\sqrt{z} - 5}{\sqrt{z}}$

84. $\dfrac{24}{\sqrt{5} + 2}$

85. $\dfrac{\sqrt{x} + 2}{\sqrt{x} - 2}$

86. $\dfrac{2\sqrt{x} - 5}{5 - 2\sqrt{x}}$

87. $\dfrac{2x - 9}{\sqrt{2x} - 3}$

88. One square mirror measures 720 square inches. A larger square mirror measures 1620 square inches. How much more framing material will the second mirror require than that required for the first mirror?

89. The area of a rectangle is $(8 + 4\sqrt{5})$ square feet. The width is $(1 + \sqrt{5})$ feet. Find the length.

90. Two times the distance between $(6, 3)$ and $(2, 1)$ is increased by three times the distance between $(3, 4)$ and $(-3, 1)$. Find the sum.

11.6

Recall	Examples
Solving a radical equation algebraically • Determine the restricted values. • Isolate the radical term to one side of the equation. • Raise both sides of the equation to the power of the index. • Solve the resulting equation. • Check the solution(s) numerically, graphically, or by substitution.	Solve. $4 + \sqrt{x + 2} = x$ The restricted values are determined by $x + 2 < 0$ $$x < -2$$ Solve. $$4 + \sqrt{x + 2} = x$$ $$\sqrt{x + 2} = x - 4$$ $$\left(\sqrt{x + 2}\right)^2 = (x - 4)^2$$ $$x + 2 = x^2 - 8x + 16$$ $$x^2 - 9x + 14 = 0$$ $$x = \frac{-b \pm \sqrt{b^2 - 4ac}}{2a}$$ $$x = \frac{-(-9) \pm \sqrt{(-9)^2 - 4(1)(14)}}{2(1)}$$ $$x = \frac{9 \pm \sqrt{25}}{2}$$ $$x = \frac{9 \pm 5}{2}$$ $$x = 7, x = 2$$ Every solution must be checked. See the following check. Graphic check $Y1 = 4 + \sqrt{x + 2}$ $Y2 = x$ 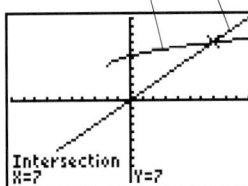 $(-10, 10, -10, 10)$ The intersection is $(7, 7)$. The solution is 7. Note that $x = 2$ is an extraneous solution.

(continued on page 932)

Recall	Examples
| Solving algebraically a radical equation having a rational exponent<br><br>• Determine the restricted values.<br>• Isolate the term having the rational exponent to one side of the equation.<br>• Raise both sides of the equation to the power of the denominator.<br>• Solve the resulting equation.<br>• Check the solution(s) numerically, graphically, or by substitution. | Solve. $(x + 1)^{2/3} = 2$<br>There are no restricted values, because the power has an odd denominator, 3.<br><br>Solve.<br>$(x + 1)^{2/3} = 2$<br>$((x + 1)^{2/3})^3 = 2^3$<br>$(x + 1)^2 = 8$<br>$\sqrt{(x + 1)^2} = \sqrt{8}$<br>$x + 1 = \pm 2\sqrt{2}$<br>$x = -1 \pm 2\sqrt{2}$<br>Check by substitution.<br><br>```
-1+2√(2)→X:(X+1)
^(2/3)
                    2
-1-2√(2)→X:(X+1)
^(2/3)
                    2
```<br><br>The solutions are $-1 \pm 2\sqrt{2}$. |

In exercises 91–100, solve algebraically and check.

91. $2\sqrt{3x} + 3 = 15$ **92.** $\sqrt{4x - 3} = x - 2$ **93.** $2\sqrt{x + 5} = \sqrt{5x + 9}$

94. $\sqrt{x + 6} + 3 = \sqrt{5x - 1}$ **95.** $\sqrt{x + 8} = \sqrt{x - 2}$ **96.** $\sqrt[3]{2x} = -4$

97. $\sqrt[4]{x + 3} = 3$ **98.** $(x + 7)^{2/5} = 4$ **99.** $x^{-3/2} = 8$

100. $2x^{2/3} - 5 = 1$

101. Find the possible y-coordinates of a point that is 5 units away from the point $(3, -2)$ and that has an x-coordinate of 6.

102. If the coefficient of friction on a road is 35%, the velocity V, in miles per hour, of a car that leaves a skid mark of S feet is given by the mathematical model $V = \sqrt{10.5S}$. What would be the length of the skid mark of a car traveling 40 miles per hour if the car had to stop suddenly?

103. The time t in seconds that it would take an object to fall a distance d in feet is given by the expression $t = \sqrt{\dfrac{2d}{32.2}}$.

From what height did a peach drop if it took 6 seconds to fall to the ground?

104. a. The cost in dollars to make x cakes is $C(x) = \sqrt{9x + 6}$. If it cost \$14.90, how many cakes were made?

   b. The revenue in dollars from selling x cakes is $R(x) = \sqrt{10x + 3}$. If revenue is \$22, how many cakes were sold?

   c. Write a function $P(x)$ for the profit in dollars for x cakes. Find the break-even point.

105. A builder buys farmland at \$1800 an acre. After ten years the average return is 1.039. What is the final value?

11.7

Recall	Examples
Square root of a negative number, $\sqrt{-b} = i\sqrt{b}$.	Write in terms of i. $\sqrt{-72} = i\sqrt{72} = i\sqrt{36 \cdot 2} = 6i\sqrt{2}$
Addition and subtraction of complex numbers $(a + bi) + (c + di) = (a + c) + (b + d)i$ $(a + bi) - (c + di) = (a - c) + (b - d)i$	Add or subtract. $(-1 + 3i) + (2 + 4i) = (-1 + 2) + (3 + 4)i$ $\qquad\qquad\qquad\qquad = 1 + 7i$ $(-2 - 3i) - (4 + i) = (-2 - 4) + (-3 - 1)i$ $\qquad\qquad\qquad\qquad = -6 - 4i$

(continued on page 933)
```

Recall	Examples
Multiplication of complex numbers • Use the distributive property to simplify.	Multiply. $$3i(-2 + 4i) = -6i + 12i^2$$ $$= -6i + 12(-1)$$ $$= -6i - 12$$ $$= -12 - 6i$$ $$(2 + i)(-2 - i) = -4 - 2i - 2i - i^2$$ $$= -4 - 4i - (-1)$$ $$= -4 - 4i + 1$$ $$= -3 - 4i$$
Division of complex numbers • If the divisor (denominator) is one term, distribute it over the terms of the numerator. • If the divisor (denominator) is two terms, multiply the numerator and denominator by the conjugate of the denominator.	Divide. $$\frac{2 - 5i}{2} = \frac{2}{2} - \frac{5i}{2}$$ $$= 1 - \frac{5}{2}i$$ $$\frac{2 + i}{3 - i} = \frac{2 + i}{3 - i} \cdot \frac{3 + i}{3 + i}$$ $$= \frac{6 + 5i + i^2}{9 - i^2}$$ $$= \frac{6 + 5i - 1}{9 - (-1)}$$ $$= \frac{5 + 5i}{10}$$ $$= \frac{5}{10} + \frac{5i}{10}$$ $$= \frac{1}{2} + \frac{1}{2}i$$

Solve an equation involving imaginary-number roots
• Use the quadratic formula to solve.
• Check the solution(s) numerically or by substitution.
	Solve $x^2 + 2x + 3 = 0$.
	$a = 1, b = 2,$ and $c = 3$
	$$x = \frac{-b \pm \sqrt{b^2 - 4ac}}{2a}$$
	$$x = \frac{-(2) \pm \sqrt{(2)^2 - 4(1)(3)}}{2(1)}$$
	$$x = \frac{-2 \pm \sqrt{-8}}{2}$$
	$$x = \frac{-2 \pm 2i\sqrt{2}}{2}$$
	$$x = -\frac{2}{2} \pm \frac{2i\sqrt{2}}{2}$$
	$$x = -1 \pm i\sqrt{2}$$
	Check by substitution.
	
	```-1+i√(2)→X:X²+2X```
	```+3```
	``` 0```
	```-1-i√(2)→X:X²+2X```
	```+3```
	``` 0```
	
	The solutions are $-1 \pm i\sqrt{2}$.

Write in terms of i.

106. $\sqrt{-64}$

107. $\sqrt{-\dfrac{25}{49}}$

108. $\sqrt{-6.25}$

109. $\sqrt{-50}$

110. $\sqrt{-\dfrac{81}{2}}$

111. $-5\sqrt{-32}$

Perform the indicated operations.

112. $\sqrt{-25} + \sqrt{-49}$

113. $\sqrt{-144} - \sqrt{-64}$

114. $2\sqrt{-36} + 6\sqrt{-81}$

115. $11\sqrt{4} - 3\sqrt{-36}$

116. $\dfrac{\sqrt{-169}}{\sqrt{-225}}$

117. $\sqrt{-2}\,\sqrt{-6}\,\sqrt{-75}$

118. $\sqrt{-2}\left(\sqrt{-6} + \sqrt{75}\right)$

119. $\left(\sqrt{-2} + \sqrt{-18}\right)\left(\sqrt{-4} - \sqrt{-9}\right)$

120. $\left(\sqrt{-7} + \sqrt{-11}\right)\left(\sqrt{-7} - \sqrt{-11}\right)$

Perform the indicated operations. Write your answer in standard form.

121. $(17 + 4i) + (12 - 6i)$

122. $(12 - 3i) - (1 + i)$

123. $(2 + 5i)(-3 + 4i)$

124. $(3 + 11i)(3 - 11i)$

125. $\dfrac{12 + 15i}{3}$

126. $\dfrac{14 - 21i}{-7i}$

127. $\dfrac{41 + i}{5 - 2i}$

128. $\left(5\sqrt{7} + 8i\sqrt{13}\right) + \left(3\sqrt{7} - 2i\sqrt{13}\right)$

129. $i\sqrt{6}\left(\sqrt{3} - i\sqrt{6}\right)$

130. $\left(\dfrac{2}{3} - \dfrac{3}{5}i\right)\left(\dfrac{1}{2} + \dfrac{1}{3}i\right)$

131. $\dfrac{18 - 11i\sqrt{6}}{3\sqrt{2} + i\sqrt{3}}$

Solve exercises 132–147.

132. $z^2 + 10 = 1$

133. $5t^2 + 125 = 0$

134. $3a^2 + 33 = 0$

135. $(r - 5)^2 + 36 = 0$

136. $7(x + 2)^2 + 23 = 2$

137. $3(4x + 1)^2 = -27$

138. $\left(m + \dfrac{2}{5}\right)^2 + \dfrac{16}{25} = 0$

139. $x^2 - 10x + 29 = 0$

140. $4y^2 + 4y + 10 = 0$

141. $z^2 + 16z + 17 = 0$

142. $9x^2 - 12x + 40 = 0$

143. $4x^2 + 4x + 5.84 = 0$

144. $x^2 - \dfrac{3}{2}x + \dfrac{5}{8} = 0$

145. $\dfrac{x}{x - 5} = \dfrac{10}{x + 1}$

146. $\dfrac{y + 4}{y - 8} = \dfrac{9}{y + 6}$

147. $\dfrac{b - 8}{b(b + 7)} = \dfrac{2}{3}$

148. What is the magnitude of the total voltage V across a circuit if the current I is $5 + 4i$ amperes and the impedance Z is $9 - 2i$ ohms? Use the formula $V = IZ$. Round your answer to the nearest tenth of a volt.

149. Use the formula $Z = \dfrac{V}{I}$ to find the magnitude of the impedance Z when the voltage V is $33 + 19i$ volts and the current I is $5 + 2i$ amperes. Express your answer as a simplified radical.

150. The Conchoid of de Sluze curve is given by $(x - 1)(x^2 + y^2) = ax^2$. If $x = 4$ and $a = 1$, solve for y.

◼ Chapter 11 Mixed Review

Evaluate. Round to the nearest thousandth if necessary.

1. $\sqrt{196}$

2. $\sqrt{4.41}$

3. $\sqrt[3]{-\dfrac{27}{64}}$

4. $\sqrt[4]{256}$

5. $\sqrt[4]{-256}$

6. $\sqrt[3]{-29}$

Write as a radical expression, and evaluate if possible.

7. $121^{1/2}$

8. $(-125)^{1/3}$

9. $-81^{1/4}$

10. $(-81)^{1/4}$

11. $729^{5/6}$

12. $(-729)^{5/6}$

13. $(-8)^{-2/3}$

14. $(-81)^{-3/4}$

Use the properties of exponents to evaluate.

15. $\dfrac{1}{9^{-1/2}}$

16. $27^{2/3} \cdot 27^{5/3}$

17. $\dfrac{6^{7/3}}{6^{2/3}}$

18. $(36^{2/3})^{3/4}$

19. $\left(\dfrac{9}{16}\right)^{-3/2}$

20. $\left[(3^{1/2})(12^{1/2})\right]^{-3/2}$

Simplify without a calculator, rationalizing all denominators.

21. $-\sqrt{\dfrac{72}{98}}$

22. $\sqrt{\dfrac{15}{144}}$

23. $\sqrt{\dfrac{50}{338}}$

24. $\sqrt[3]{-\dfrac{64}{125}}$

25. $\sqrt{150}$

26. $\sqrt[3]{-448}$

27. $\sqrt[4]{48}$

28. $\sqrt[5]{-486}$

Perform the indicated operations and simplify.

29. $\sqrt{15} \cdot \sqrt{35}$

30. $\sqrt{\dfrac{3}{7}} - \sqrt{\dfrac{7}{3}}$

31. $6\sqrt{13} + 3\sqrt{52}$

32. $4\sqrt{7} - 3\sqrt{7} + 11\sqrt{7} - \sqrt{7}$

33. $\sqrt{3}\left(\sqrt{6} - \sqrt{3}\right)$

34. $\left(7 - \sqrt{3}\right)\left(9 + \sqrt{3}\right)$

35. $\left(\sqrt{10} - \sqrt{5}\right)\left(\sqrt{10} + \sqrt{5}\right)$

36. $6\sqrt[3]{375} + 2\sqrt[3]{24}$

Simplify. Write your results using positive exponents.

37. $\dfrac{x^{2/3}}{x^{3/4}}$

38. $z^{3/5} \cdot z^{-3/2}$

39. $\left(\dfrac{p^4}{q^8}\right)^{-5/16}$

40. $(27x^9 y^{12})^{4/3}$

41. $\sqrt{72x^6 y^3 z^4}$

42. $\sqrt[3]{-64x^2 y^7}$

43. $2\sqrt{3xy} \cdot y\sqrt{6x}$

44. $\sqrt[3]{-3a^5 b^5} \cdot \sqrt[3]{18ab^2}$

45. $\sqrt{10x + 35y} \cdot \sqrt{2x + 7y}$

46. $\sqrt{\dfrac{36x^2}{49y^4}}$

47. $\sqrt{\dfrac{25z}{3}}$

48. $\sqrt[3]{\dfrac{-27a}{b^3}}$

49. $\dfrac{\sqrt{6a}}{\sqrt{12ab}}$

50. $\dfrac{\sqrt{x^3 y^2}}{\sqrt{x^4 y^5}}$

51. $\sqrt{121x} - \sqrt{81x}$

52. $16d\sqrt{c^3 d} - 11c\sqrt{cd^3} + 9cd\sqrt{cd}$

53. $\left(\sqrt{a} + 9\right)^2$

54. $\sqrt{6a}\left(3 + \sqrt{6a}\right)$

55. $\left(\sqrt{3x} + \sqrt{2y}\right)\left(\sqrt{3x} - \sqrt{2y}\right)$

56. $2\sqrt[3]{x^2}\left(3\sqrt[3]{x} + 5\sqrt[3]{x^2}\right)$

57. $\dfrac{\sqrt{18x} - \sqrt{42}}{\sqrt{6}}$

58. $\dfrac{\sqrt{m} - 9}{\sqrt{m}}$

59. $\dfrac{18}{\sqrt{7} + 2}$

60. $\dfrac{3 + \sqrt{x}}{3 - \sqrt{x}}$

61. $\dfrac{7 - 3\sqrt{a}}{3\sqrt{a} - 7}$

62. $\dfrac{25 - 7x}{5 - \sqrt{7x}}$

Graph each radical function. State the restricted values on the domain.

63. $f(x) = 5 - \sqrt{x}$

64. $y = x^{3/2} - 3$

Solve.

65. $(x - 1)^{3/2} = \sqrt[3]{2x + 5}$

66. $(x + 4)^{3/5} = (5x - 1)^{2/3}$

67. $\sqrt{x} + 2 = 11$

68. $3\sqrt{5x} + 7 = 52$

69. $\sqrt{3x + 1} = x - 3$

70. $2\sqrt{x + 9} = \sqrt{9x + 1}$

71. $\sqrt{2x + 1} + 2 = \sqrt{6x + 1}$

72. $\sqrt{10 - x} = \sqrt{3 - x}$

73. $\sqrt[3]{3x} = -6$

74. $\sqrt[4]{x + 2} = 3$

75. $(x + 5)^{2/5} = 9$

76. $x^{-3/2} = 27$

77. $3x^{2/3} - 7 = 2$

Write in terms of i.

78. $\sqrt{-169}$

79. $\sqrt{-\dfrac{64}{81}}$

80. $\sqrt{-\dfrac{25}{6}}$

81. $10\sqrt{-80}$

82. $\sqrt{-6.25}$

83. $-\sqrt{-108}$

Perform the indicated operations. Write your answer in standard form.

84. $(22.3 - 1.33i) + (8.55 - 2.9i)$

85. $\sqrt{-64} + \sqrt{-4}$

86. $\sqrt{-196} - \sqrt{-100}$

87. $\left(\dfrac{3}{4} + \dfrac{1}{2}i\right)\left(\dfrac{4}{9} - 2i\right)$

88. $-1.5i(2.9 - 4i)$

89. $7\sqrt{-25} + 3\sqrt{-64}$

90. $\sqrt{-2}\,\sqrt{-6}\,\sqrt{-48}$

91. $\left(\sqrt{-3} - \sqrt{-10}\right)\left(\sqrt{-5} + \sqrt{-6}\right)$

92. $\left(\sqrt{-13} + \sqrt{-17}\right)\left(\sqrt{-13} - \sqrt{-17}\right)$

93. $(21 - i) - (7 + i)$

94. $(9 - 3i)(-9 + 3i)$

95. $\dfrac{18 - 27i}{9i}$

96. $\dfrac{32 - 9i}{2 - 3i}$

97. $\left(\dfrac{5}{6} - 7i\right) + \left(\dfrac{5}{6} + i\right)$

98. $\dfrac{12i + \sqrt{10}}{2\sqrt{5} + i\sqrt{2}}$

99. $\dfrac{\sqrt{-289}}{\sqrt{-841}}$

Solve exercises 100–107.

100. $\dfrac{d - 11}{d(d + 9)} = \dfrac{5}{8}$

101. $(m + 7)^2 + 25 = 0$

102. $4(y - 3)^2 + 29 = 5$

103. $x^2 - 16x + 67 = 0$

104. $9y^2 + 30y + 32 = 0$

105. $a^2 + 100 = 19$

106. $6b^2 + 78 = 0$

107. $\dfrac{y + 9}{y + 1} = \dfrac{5}{y - 7}$

108. Find the length of a side of a square napkin whose area is 529 square inches.

109. In statistics, the variability of the integers 1 to n is calculated as $s = \sqrt{\dfrac{n(n + 1)}{12}}$. Calculate the variability of the integers from 1 to 27.

110. The time t in seconds it would take a pear to fall a distance d in feet is given by the expression $t = \sqrt{\dfrac{2d}{32.2}}$. From what height did the pear fall if it took 4 seconds to reach the ground?

111. Using the formula for the period T of a pendulum of length L, $T = 2\pi\sqrt{\dfrac{L}{32}}$, find the period of a pendulum whose length is 3.5 feet.

112. Find a function, $f(x)$, for the geometric mean $m = \sqrt{ab}$, if $a = x + 6$ and $b = x + 2$. What is the domain of this function? Graph this function.

113. When the temperature is high, the relative humidity can make the temperature feel even warmer because the combination of high temperature and high relative humidity reduces the body's ability to cool itself. The function $T(x) = 75 + 7\sqrt{x - 0.5}, 0.5 \leq x \leq 1$, where x is the amount of relative humidity, gives the temperature of the "heat index" (temperature it feels like) for a temperature range of 75 degrees to 80 degrees.
  a. Graph the function on its domain.
  b. Use the graph to determine whether the function is increasing or decreasing.
  c. At what percent humidity will it feel like a temperature of 78 degrees?

114. The price of a manufacturing unit is $p(x) = -\sqrt{x^2 - 5x - 14} + x$.
  a. Write a function, $R(x)$, for the revenue if x units are sold.
  b. What is the revenue if 100 units are sold? If 150 units are sold?

  c. What is the domain of the revenue function?
  d. Graph the function on its domain.
  e. Use the graph to determine where the function is increasing and where it is decreasing.
  f. If revenue is $115.80, how many units were sold?

115. The number of branches of the nation's top libraries is related to circulation by the function $C(b) = 0.377b^{87/100}$, where C is the circulation in millions and b is the number of branches.
  a. Graph the function.
  b. Use the graph to determine whether the function is increasing or decreasing.
  c. What is the approximate circulation for a library with 65 branches?
  d. If a library has circulation of 5 million, what is its number of branches?

116. The area of a rectangle is $(9 + 5\sqrt{3})$ square feet. The width is $(3 + \sqrt{3})$ feet. Find the length.

117. a. The cost in dollars to make x meals is $C(x) = \sqrt{9x + 8}$. If it cost $10.77, how many meals were made?
  b. The revenue in dollars from selling x meals is $R(x) = \sqrt{10x + 3}$. If revenue is $20, how many meals were sold?
  c. Write a function $P(x)$ for the profit in dollars for x meals. Find the break-even point.

118. Carter invests $50,000 in a business that has average return of 1.123 after 10 years. What was the final value of the business?

119. Find the possible y-coordinates of a point that has an x-coordinate of 7 and is 5 units away from $(3, 2)$.

120. Use the formula $Z = \dfrac{V}{I}$ to find the magnitude of the current I when the voltage V is $30 + 52i$ volts and the impedance Z is $9 + 5i$ ohms. Round your answer to the nearest tenth of an ampere.

121. The Conchoid of de Sluze curve is given by $(x - 1)(x^2 + y^2) = ax^2$. If $x = 3$ and $a = 1$, solve for y.

■ Chapter 11 Test

A^{+}

TEST-TAKING TIPS

Evaluate if possible. Round decimal answers to the nearest thousandth.

1. $\sqrt{196}$
2. $\sqrt[4]{21}$
3. $\sqrt{-25}$
4. $\sqrt[3]{\dfrac{-8}{125}}$

Use the properties of exponents to evaluate the given expressions.

5. $16^{5/2} \cdot 16^{-1/4}$
6. $(81^{4/3})^{3/8}$
7. $\left(\dfrac{8}{27}\right)^{-2/3}$

In exercises 8–15, simplify. Express your results as a single radical expression whenever possible. Rationalize all denominators. (Assume that the variable base of an exponential expression or a variable radicand does not represent values for which the expression is not defined.)

8. $\dfrac{x^{4/5}}{x^{3/10}}$
9. $\left(\sqrt{2x} - \sqrt{5y}\right)\left(\sqrt{2x} + \sqrt{5y}\right)$
10. $\sqrt{6x^3y} \cdot \sqrt{15xy^2}$

11. $\sqrt{\dfrac{3z^3}{2xy^2}}$

12. $\dfrac{\sqrt{50xy^3}}{\sqrt{98x^3y^2}}$

13. $\sqrt{81x} + 2\sqrt{25x} - 3\sqrt{16x}$

14. $5\sqrt[3]{x}\left(2\sqrt[3]{x^2} + 3\sqrt[3]{x}\right)$

15. $\dfrac{\sqrt{x} + 4}{\sqrt{x} + 1}$

Solve exercises 16–19.

16. $(x + 4)^{1/3} + 3 = 2$ **17.** $3\sqrt{x} - 5 = 13$ **18.** $\sqrt{3x + 1} = x - 1$ **19.** $\sqrt{5x + 1} - 2 = \sqrt{x + 1}$

20. Graph the radical function $f(x) = \sqrt{x + 7} - 3$, and state the restricted values on the domain.

Perform the indicated operations. Write your answer in standard form.

21. $3\sqrt{-100} - 2\sqrt{-49}$

22. $\sqrt{-2}\,\sqrt{-7}\,\sqrt{-56}$

23. $\sqrt{-2}\left(\sqrt{-7} - \sqrt{56}\right)$

24. $\dfrac{\sqrt{-225}}{\sqrt{-289}}$

25. $\left(\sqrt{-6} - \sqrt{-13}\right)\left(\sqrt{-6} + \sqrt{-13}\right)$

26. $(8 + 2i)(-5 + i)$

27. $\dfrac{29 + 29i}{5 - 2i}$

28. $(22.47 - 13.6i) - (12.2 - 7.32i)$

29. $i\sqrt{15}\left(\sqrt{3} + i\sqrt{5}\right)$

30. $\dfrac{44 + 16i}{2i}$

Solve exercises 31–36.

31. $x^2 + 196 = 0$

32. $(t + 2)^2 + 15 = 0$

33. $2z^2 + 5 = 2.12$

34. $x^2 - 6x + 17 = 0$

35. $9x^2 - 6x + 7 = 0$

36. $\dfrac{y - 2}{y(y + 1)} = \dfrac{4}{7}$

37. A square tablecloth measures 2000 square inches. A larger square tablecloth measures 3125 square inches. How much more border will the larger tablecloth require over that required by the smaller tablecloth?

38. Find a function, $f(x)$, for the geometric mean $m = \sqrt{ab}$, if $a = x$ and $b = x + 1$. What is the domain of this function? Graph this function.

39. The number of Mexican pesos per U.S. dollar can be approximated by the function $V(x) = \sqrt{80 + 10x}$, where x is the number of years after 2000.
   a. Graph the function.
   b. Use the graph to determine whether the function is increasing or decreasing.
   c. Assuming the trend continues, in what year will one dollar be equal to 13 pesos?

40. The number of deaths due to earthquakes relates to population at the site of the quake and its intensity. The magnitude of an earthquake is related to number of deaths by $M(n) = 3.8n^{7/100}$, where n is the number of deaths.
   a. Graph the function.
   b. Use the graph to determine whether the function is increasing or decreasing.
   c. What was the magnitude if the approximate number of deaths was 13,000?
   d. If the magnitude of an earthquake is 8.0 as it was in China in 1976, what is the expected number of deaths?

41. The hip height of a cross-country runner is approximately 2.8 feet. Model the leg motion of the person as that of a pendulum and determine the amount of time in seconds in which the leg completed one back-and-forth motion. The length of the runner's stride is about 3 feet. Use this distance to estimate the speed of the runner.

42. The area of a rectangle is $(8 + 5\sqrt{2})$ square feet. The width is $(2 + \sqrt{2})$ feet. Find the length.

43. a. The cost in dollars to make x wedding cakes is $C(x) = \sqrt{9x + 6}$. If it cost \$14.90, how many cakes were made?
   b. The revenue in dollars from selling x wedding cakes is $R(x) = \sqrt{10x - 3}$. If revenue is \$15, how many cakes were sold?
   c. Write a function $P(x)$ for the profit in dollars for x wedding cakes. Find the break-even point.

44. A builder buys farmland at \$1500 an acre. After 10 years the average return is 1.039. What is the final value?

45. Explain how you would determine the restricted values in the domain of a radical function in which the index of the radical is an even number. Use an example to illustrate your explanation. Then explain how you would describe the domain of a radical function.

46. The Conchoid of de Sluze curve is given by $(x - 1)(x^2 + y^2) = ax^2$. If $x = 2$ and $a = -3$, solve for y.

47. What is the magnitude of the total voltage V across a circuit if the current I is $8 + 3i$ amperes and the impedance Z is $11 - 3i$ ohms? Use the formula $V = IZ$, and round your answer to the nearest tenth of a volt.

48. Explain the difference between the real-number system and the complex-number system.

11

Project

Many mathematical equations—or models, as they are sometimes referred to—involve radical expressions. In this project, we will investigate one of these models. The model helps us understand the calculation of windchill factors. We will investigate the model using English and metric systems of measurement.

PART I The term *wind chill* was first used by an Antarctic explorer, Paul Siple, in 1939. He described the chilling effect of the wind when combined with a low air temperature on the human skin. Siple and Charles Passel were responsible for the first wind chill formulas, which were used until the winter of 2001. At that time, the United States and Canada revised the formulas after extensive experimentation revealed some of their shortcomings.

One form of the Siple–Passel wind chill formula is

$$T = 0.0817(3.71v^{1/2} + 5.81 - 0.25v)(t - 91.4) + 91.4$$

where t is the actual temperature in Fahrenheit degrees and v is the wind velocity in miles per hour.

One form of the revised wind chill formula is

$$T = 35.74 + 0.6215t - 35.75v^{0.16} + 0.4275v^{0.16}$$

where t is the actual temperature in Fahrenheit degrees and v is the wind velocity in miles per hour.

1. Write both formulas for the wind chill factor, given an air temperature of 32°F.

2. Complete the following table, which calculates the wind chill factor for both formulas if the temperature measures 32°F and the wind velocity, in miles per hour, is as shown in the table:

Wind Speed v, mph	10	15	20	25	30	35	40
Siple–Passel wind chill factor T, °F							
Revised wind chill factor T, °F							

3. Describe what happens to the measured temperature of 32°F as the wind speed increases. That is, what do you "feel" is happening to the temperature?

4. Graph both equations in step 1 on the same coordinate plane.

5. Describe the difference in the wind chill factor obtained by the two equations.

6. Repeat the first five steps for a measured air temperature of 0°F.

7. Compare the tables and graphs you have produced, and describe what happens when the wind speed is held constant and the temperature is dropping.

PART II Canada uses the metric system of measurement. Therefore, a metric version of the Siple–Passel formulas is also available.

One form of the Siple–Passel wind chill formula is given by the equation

$$T = 0.045(5.27v^{1/2} + 10.45 - 0.28v)(t - 33) + 33$$

where t is the actual temperature in Celsius degrees and v is the wind velocity in kilometers per hour.

One form of the revised wind chill formula is given by the equation

$$T = 13.12 + 0.6215t - 11.37v^{0.16} + 0.3965v^{0.16}$$

where t is the actual temperature in Celsius degrees and v is the wind velocity in kilometers per hour.

Repeat steps 1 through 7, using 0°C and −10°C as the air temperature. Compare your findings from Part I and Part II.

PART III Additional adjustments are being proposed to the revised Siple–Passel formulas in order to take account of factors that reflect one's comfort level with the temperature and humidity. Find a reference that discusses one of these concepts, and write a short summary of your findings. Be sure to document your source.

■ Chapters P–11 Cumulative Review

Simplify and write with positive exponents.

1. $2^0 x^{-1} y^2$

2. $(3x^{1/2} y^{3/4})^2$

3. $\left(\dfrac{(2s)^2}{3t} \right)^{-3}$

Simplify.

4. $(2x^3 + 6x^2 y - 2xy^2 + y^3) + (3x^3 + 4xy^2 - y^3)$

5. $(1.2a^2 - 3.6ab + b^2) - (4a^2 + 2.71ab - 3.4b^2)$

6. $(6.8m^2 n)(-2mn^2 p)$

7. $(3a - b)(2a + 4b)$

8. $(2x + 3)(2x - 3)$

9. $(2x + 3)^2$

10. $\dfrac{-15x^2 y^3 z}{3xyz}$

11. $\dfrac{2m^2 n + 4mn - 8n^2}{2m^2 n}$

12. $\dfrac{x^2 + 2x - 3}{x^2 - 9}$

13. $\dfrac{x}{x + 2} + \dfrac{3}{x - 2}$

14. $\dfrac{1}{x + 2} - \dfrac{3}{x - 3} - \dfrac{x + 3}{x^2 + x - 12}$

15. $\dfrac{2a - 5}{a + 2} \cdot \dfrac{2a^2 + 3a - 2}{4a^2 - 25}$

16. $\dfrac{2x}{2x^2 + 9x + 4} \div \dfrac{4x^2 y}{x^2 + 9x + 20}$

17. $\sqrt{8y} + \sqrt{2y} - 2\sqrt{18y}$

18. $\sqrt[3]{25a^4 b} \cdot \sqrt[3]{5ab}$

19. $\left(\sqrt{3} - \sqrt{5} \right)\left(\sqrt{3} + \sqrt{5} \right)$

20. $\dfrac{\sqrt{21abc^3}}{\sqrt{7a^3 b}}$

21. $\dfrac{\sqrt{x} + 2}{\sqrt{x} - 1}$

22. $x^{1/2}(x^{2/3} - x^{3/4})$

Factor exercises 23–25 completely if possible.

23. $16a^2 - 25b^2$

24. $x^2 - 2x - 8$

25. $3x^2 - 9x - 30$

26. Given $f(x) = -x^2 + 3x - 1$, find $f(-2)$.

Graph and label as indicated. Determine the domain and range of each function.

27. $f(x) = -3.2x + 1$; three points on the graph

28. $y = x^2 + 4x + 6$; vertex, y-intercept, enough points to determine the curve, and the axis of symmetry

29. $g(x) = -2x^2 + x + 1$;   vertex, x-intercept, y-intercept, enough points to determine the curve, and the axis of symmetry

30. $y = \dfrac{x^2 - 4}{x + 2}$; enough points to determine the curve

31. $h(x) = \dfrac{2}{x}$; enough points to determine the curve

32. $y = 2\sqrt{x}$; enough points to determine the curve

33. $a(x) = x^{2/3} + 2$; enough points to determine the curve

Solve.

34. $2(x + 3) - 4(x - 1) = x - 2$

35. $x^2 - 3x + 9 = 0$

36. $x^2 + 2x - 15 = 0$

37. $2t^2 + 3t = 4$

38. $\dfrac{x + 1}{x - 1} = \dfrac{x + 3}{x + 2}$

39. $\dfrac{2}{x^2} + \dfrac{3}{2x^2} = \dfrac{1}{8}$

40. $\sqrt{2x - 3} + 5 = 9$

Solve. Write the solution set in interval notation.

41. $2x^2 - 9x - 18 < 0$

Solve.

42. $3x - 4y = 3$
   $x + y = 8$

In exercises 43 and 44, write an equation of the line that satisfies the given conditions.

43. Passes through the points $(3, -5)$ and $(-4, 2)$

44. Perpendicular to $2x + 3y = 5$ and passes through $(-2, 1)$

45. Write a quadratic equation for a curve that passes through the points $(0, -4)$, $(-4, 0)$, and $(1, 0)$.

46. The diagonal of a rectangle measures 20 feet. The length of the rectangle is 4 feet more than the width. Find the dimensions of the rectangle.

47. Determine the possible y-coordinates of a point 5 units from $(-3, 4)$ with an x-coordinate of 0.

48. Kevin can rake the leaves in his yard in 5 hours. His sister Elizabeth can rake the leaves in her yard in 4 hours. It is

12:00 noon. Can Kevin and Elizabeth, working together, be through raking leaves before their mother arrives home at 2:30 P.M.?

49. A small business spends $1000.00 on production equipment. Each item produced costs $0.55 to produce and is sold for $1.25. How many items must be sold before the business breaks even?

50. A sky diver free-falls from a height of 10,000 feet above the ground. He opens his parachute at a height of 2500 feet. Use the vertical-position equation to determine the length of time the sky diver is free-falling.

Exponential and Logarithmic Functions and Equations

In this chapter, we introduce two new types of functions: the exponential function and the logarithmic function. We show how to use the properties of exponents to perform operations with these functions and how to solve equations involving them. Exponential and logarithmic functions have a special relationship: Each is the inverse function of the other. We begin the chapter by discussing what inverse functions are, when they exist, and how we can find them.

Exponential and logarithmic functions are used to model many important real-world situations in business and science. Exponential models of growth and decay describe situations as varied as compound interest, population growth, and radioactive decay. Logarithms are used to describe the magnitudes of earthquakes, sound levels, and the acidity of a chemical solution. We discuss some of these applications throughout the chapter. We conclude with projects illustrating exponential and logarithmic models.

12.1 INVERSE FUNCTIONS

OBJECTIVES
1 Determine the inverse of a relation.
2 Determine whether a function is a one-to-one function.
3 Graph inverse functions.
4 Determine the inverse of a function.
5 Model real-world situations by using inverse functions.

APPLICATION

Currency exchange rates vary daily. According to a recent report, a function for determining the number of European euros given x United States dollars was $f(x) = 0.7787x$. Determine the inverse function $f^{-1}(x)$ and explain its meaning.

We will discuss this application further. See page 949.

Objective 12.1.1

Determining the Inverse of a Relation

In Chapter 1, we defined a relation as a set of ordered pairs. For example, the set of ordered pairs a biologist obtains when Celsius temperatures are converted to Fahrenheit temperatures,

$$T = \{(20, 68), (21, 69.8), (22, 71.6), (23, 73.4)\}$$

is a relation.

If we reverse the order in each ordered pair, another useful relation results. For example, the set of ordered pairs a biologist obtains when Fahrenheit temperatures are converted to Celsius temperatures,

$$\{(68, 20), (69.8, 21), (71.6, 22), (73.4, 23)\}$$

is also a relation.

This second relation is called the **inverse** of the relation T and is denoted T^{-1}.

$$T = \{(20, 68), (21, 69.8), (22, 71.6), (23, 73.4)\}$$
$$T^{-1} = \{(68, 20), (69.8, 21), (71.6, 22), (73.4, 23)\}$$

TAKE NOTE Do *not* confuse the inverse notation T^{-1} with exponential notation. The -1 is *not* an exponent.

INVERSE OF A RELATION WRITTEN AS A SET OF ORDERED PAIRS

To determine the inverse of a relation written as a set of ordered pairs, interchange the coordinates of the independent and dependent variables in the original relation.

EXAMPLE 1

Determine the inverses of the following relations:

a. $f = \{(3, 6), (5, 10), (4, 8), (0, 0)\}$ **b.** $A = \{(1, 2), (\ 2, 3), (4, -5), (0, 2)\}$

Solution

a. $f = \{(3, 6), (5, 10), (4, 8), (0, 0)\}$
$f^{-1} = \{(6, 3), (10, 5), (8, 4), (0, 0)\}$

b. $A = \{(1, 2), (-2, 3), (4, -5), (0, 2)\}$
$A^{-1} = \{(2, 1), (3, -2), (-5, 4), (2, 0)\}$

Recall that a relation can also be written as an equation in two variables. To determine the inverse of a relation expressed in this form, we follow the same procedure as with ordered pairs: Interchange the independent and dependent variables. For example, given $x =$ Celsius temperature, $y =$ Fahrenheit temperature, and the relation $y = \dfrac{9}{5}x + 32$, determine the inverse relation.

Interchange the variables. Let $x =$ Fahrenheit temperature and $y =$ Celsius temperature.

$$x = \frac{9}{5}y + 32$$

Solve for y.

$$x - 32 = \frac{9}{5}y$$

$$\frac{5}{9}(x - 32) = y \quad \text{or} \quad y = \frac{5}{9}(x - 32)$$

INVERSE OF A RELATION WRITTEN AS AN EQUATION

To determine the inverse of a relation written as an equation, interchange the independent and dependent variables in the original equation and solve for the new dependent variable.

EXAMPLE 2   Determine the inverse relations.

a. $y = 3x + 5$ **b.** $y = x^2 - 2$

Solution
a. $y = 3x + 5$

$\qquad x = 3y + 5$ Interchange the variables.

$\qquad x - 5 = 3y$ Solve for y.

$\qquad \dfrac{x - 5}{3} = y \quad \text{or} \quad y = \dfrac{1}{3}x - \dfrac{5}{3}$

b. $y = x^2 - 2$

$\qquad x = y^2 - 2$ Interchange the variables.

$\qquad x + 2 = y^2$ Solve for y.

$\qquad \pm\sqrt{x + 2} = y \quad \text{or} \quad y = \pm\sqrt{x + 2}$ ■

✓ Objective 12.1.1 *CHECKUP*

In exercises 1 and 2, determine the inverse of each relation.

1. a. $g = \{(1, 0.5), (2, 1), (3, 1.5), (4, 2), (5, 2.5), (6, 3)\}$

    b. $K = \left\{\left(\dfrac{1}{2}, 3\right), \left(\dfrac{2}{3}, 4\right), \left(\dfrac{3}{4}, 5\right), \left(\dfrac{4}{5}, 4\right), \left(\dfrac{5}{6}, 3\right)\right\}$

2. a. $y = -4x + 1$ **b.** $y = 3x^2 + 6$

3. The inverse of the function $f(x)$ is denoted by $f^{-1}(x)$. What does the notation $[f(x)]^{-1}$ indicate? Describe the differences in the two notations.   ■

Objective 12.1.2

Determining One-to-One Functions

In Chapter 1, we also defined a function. A function is a relation such that every element in the domain corresponds to only one element in the range. In Example 1, we determined the inverse relation of the two functions f and A.

$$f = \{(3, 6), (5, 10), (4, 8), (0, 0)\}$$
$$A = \{(1, 2), (-2, 3), (4, -5), (0, 2)\}$$

The inverse of the function f is a function.

$$f^{-1} = \{(6, 3), (10, 5), (8, 4), (0, 0)\}$$

However, the inverse of the function A is not a function, because an element in the domain of the inverse relation, 2, is paired with two different elements in the range, 1 and 0.

$$A^{-1} = \{(2, 1), (3, -2), (-5, 4), (2, 0)\}$$

In order for each element in the domain of the inverse to be paired with only one element in the range, each element in the range of the function must be paired with only one element in the domain. The function is then called a **one-to-one function**. The inverse of a one-to-one function is a function.

ONE-TO-ONE FUNCTION

A function is a one-to-one function if no two different ordered pairs have the same second coordinate.

 TAKE NOTE A one-to-one function is a set of ordered pairs in which no two different ordered pairs have the same first coordinate or the same second coordinate.

EXAMPLE 3

Determine whether the following relations are functions. If so, is the function one-to-one?

a. $h = \{(2.75, 3.25), (0.5, 3.25), (-2.25, 2.75)\}$
b. $R = \{(0, 1.5), (1, 2.5), (3, 4.5)\}$
c. $j = \{(3, 5), (3, -5), (2, 6), (2, -6)\}$

Solution

a. $h = \{(2.75, 3.25), (0.5, 3.25), (-2.25, 2.75)\}$
The relation h is a function, because each ordered pair has a different first coordinate.
   The function h is not one-to-one, because the second coordinate, 3.25, is repeated in two ordered pairs. The inverse of h is not a function.

b. $R = \{(0, 1.5), (1, 2.5), (3, 4.5)\}$
The relation R is a function because each ordered pair has a different first coordinate.
   The function R is one-to-one, because no two ordered pairs have the same second coordinate. The inverse of R is a function.

c. $j = \{(3, 5), (3, -5), (2, 6), (2, -6)\}$
The relation j is not a function, because the first coordinates, 3 and 2, are repeated in two different ordered pairs. ■

In Example 2, we determined the inverse of two functions written in equation form:

   a. $y = 3x + 5$ **b.** $y = x^2 - 2$

The inverse of the first function, $y = \frac{1}{3}x - \frac{5}{3}$, is a function. However, the inverse of the second function, $y = \pm\sqrt{x + 2}$, is not a function. If we graph each of the inverses, we can see that one is a function and that one is not a function by using the vertical-line test.

a.

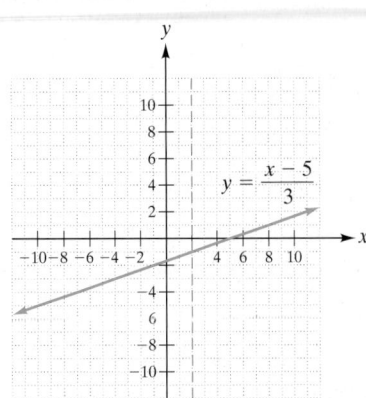

b.

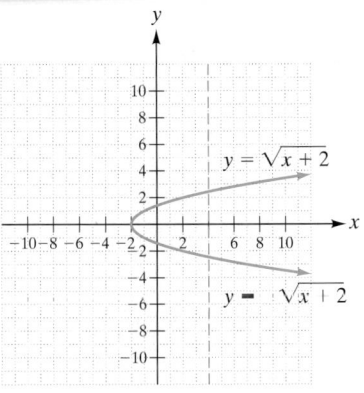

Note: In part **a**, all possible vertical lines intersect the graph once. A sample line is shown. A sample vertical line is drawn for part **b** that intersects the graph more than once.

We can also determine whether the inverse of a function is a function from the graph of the function itself. Complete the following set of exercises to see when a function is one-to-one, or has an inverse that is a function.

Guided Discovery 1   Graphs of One-to-One Functions

In the following graphs of one-to-one functions, draw a horizontal line through more than one point on the graph if possible:

1.

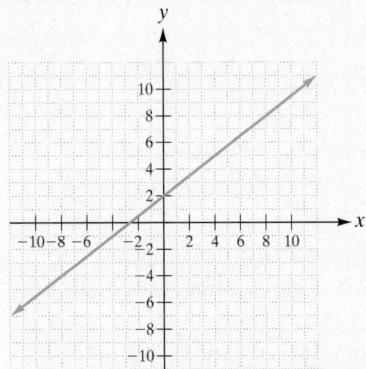

2.

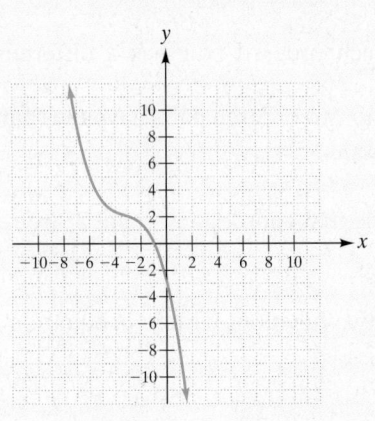

Write a rule for determining a one-to-one function from the graph of a function by drawing a horizontal line through points on the graph.

Check your rule on the following graph of a function, which is not one-to-one:

3.

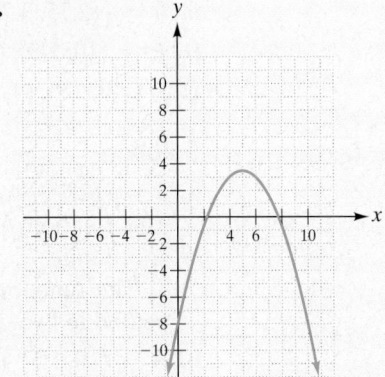

All possible horizontal lines cross the graphs of the one-to-one functions only once. It is possible to draw a horizontal line that crosses the function more than once if that function is not one-to-one.

HORIZONTAL-LINE TEST

If a horizontal line can be drawn such that it intersects the graph of a function more than once, the graph does not represent a one-to-one function. If all horizontal lines intersect the graph at most once, then the graph represents a one-to-one function.

We know that this rule is true because if we graph two distinct ordered pairs with the same y-coordinate, they will lie on the same horizontal line. However, a one-to-one function does not have two ordered pairs with the same y-coordinate.

 TAKE NOTE According to the vertical-line test for functions, it is not possible to draw a vertical line that intersects the graph of a function more than once. According to the horizontal-line test for one-to-one functions, it is not possible to draw a horizontal line that intersects the graph of a one-to-one function more than once. Therefore, it is not possible to draw a vertical or a horizontal line that intersects the graph of a one-to-one function more than once.

EXAMPLE 4   Determine whether the following graphs represent one-to-one functions:

a.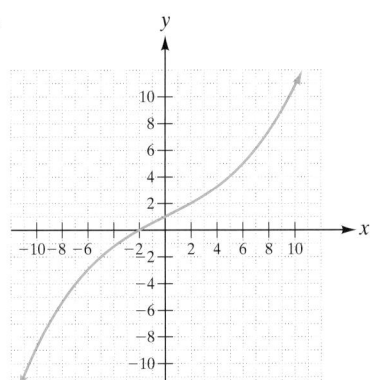

b.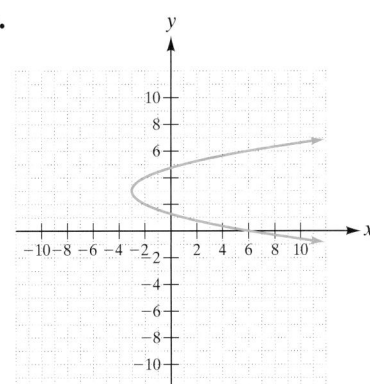

c.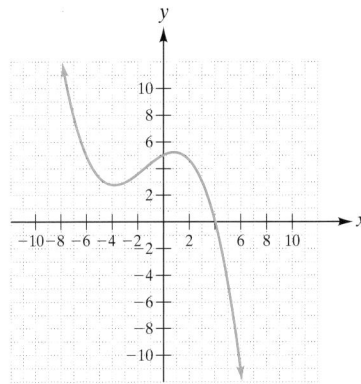

Solution

a. The graph represents a one-to-one function, because all possible vertical and horizontal lines cross the graph only once.

b.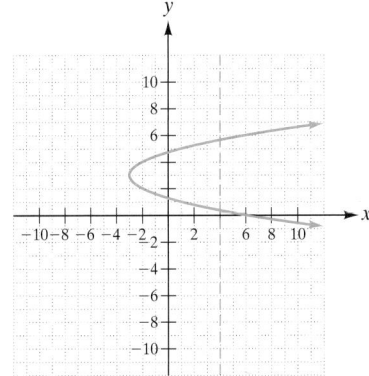

The graph does not represent a function, because a vertical line can be drawn that intersects the graph more than once.

c.

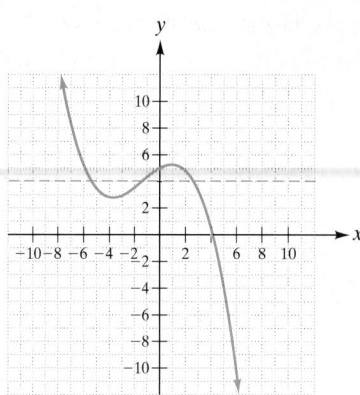

The graph is a function, because it passes the vertical-line test, but a horizontal line can be drawn that intersects the graph more than once. Therefore, it is not a one-to-one function. ∎

Objective 12.1.2 *CHECKUP*

1. Determine whether the relations are functions. If so, is the function one-to-one?
   a. $B = \{(0, -3), (2, 1), (4, 5), (6, 9), (8, 13)\}$ **b.** $G = \{(-2, 5), (-1, 2), (0, 1), (1, 2), (2, 5)\}$
   c. $K = \{(2.1, 4.2), (-2.1, 4.2), (2.1, 6.3)\}$

2. Determine whether the graphs represent one-to-one functions.

   a. 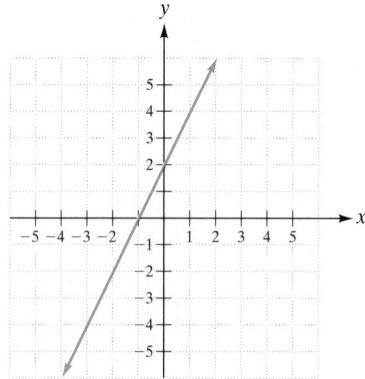   **b.** 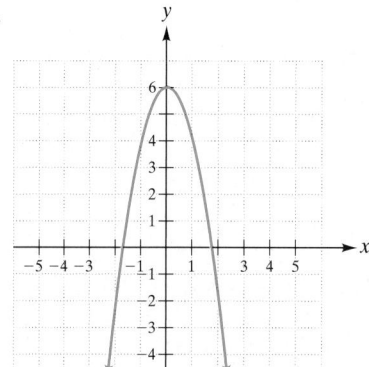   **c.**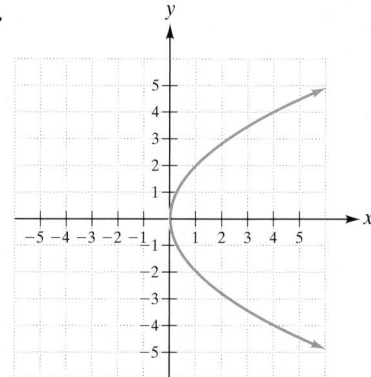

3. For what purpose is the vertical-line test used?
4. For what purpose is the horizontal-line test used?

5. Every one-to-one function is a relation, but not every relation is a one-to-one function. Explain why this is so. ∎

Objective 12.1.3   Graphing Inverse Functions

We interchange the coordinates of the ordered pairs of a one-to-one function to obtain its inverse function. Therefore, the domain and range of a one-to-one function interchange, as do the domain and range of its inverse function. If we graph a one-to-one function and its inverse function on the same coordinate plane, as well as graph the line $y = x$, we obtain an interesting picture. For example,

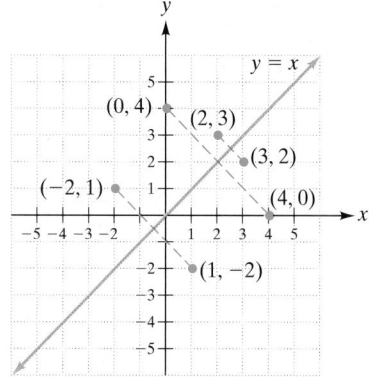

Graph the function $f = \{(2, 3), (0, 4), (-2, 1)\}$.

Graph the inverse function $f^{-1} = \{(3, 2), (4, 0), (1, -2)\}$.

Graph the equation $y = x$.

When we graph the function f and its inverse function f^{-1} on the same coordinate plane, we see that the points graphed are the same distance, on either side, from the line representing the equation $y = x$. This line is called the **line of symmetry**. Visualizing the line of symmetry can help us determine whether we have graphed a function and its inverse function correctly.

TAKE NOTE If you fold your graph paper along the line of symmetry, the graph of the function and the graph of its inverse should match.

EXAMPLE 5

On your calculator, graph the following function and its inverse, as well as the line of symmetry $y = x$:

$$f(x) = x + 4$$
$$f^{-1}(x) = x - 4$$

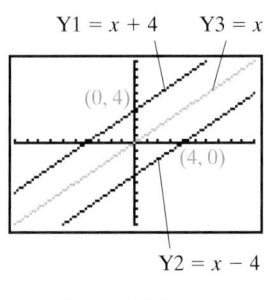

Y1 = x + 4   Y3 = x
(0, 4)
(4, 0)
Y2 = x − 4
$(-10, 10, -10, 10)$

Solution

Note that the graphs for $y = x + 4$ and $y = x - 4$ appear to be symmetric about the line $y = x$. ◼

 TAKE NOTE You need to be careful, because looks are sometimes deceiving. However, you can trace the two lines to determine that the coordinates of the ordered pairs interchange. For example, the ordered pair $(0, 4)$ lies on the graph of $y = x + 4$ and the ordered pair $(4, 0)$ lies on the graph of the inverse $y = x - 4$.

Objective 12.1.3 CHECKUP

1. On your calculator, graph the following function, its inverse, and the line of symmetry $y = x$:

$$f(x) = 2x - 4 \quad \text{and} \quad f^{-1}(x) = \frac{1}{2}x + 2$$

2. What does the line of symmetry $y = x$ mean to you?

Objective 12.1.4 Determining an Inverse Function

If a one-to-one function $f(x)$ is defined by an equation, we can determine the inverse function $f^{-1}(x)$ in the same way we obtained an inverse for a relation.

To determine the inverse of a function $f(x)$,

- Replace $f(x)$ with y.
- Interchange x and y.
- Solve the resulting equation for y.
- Replace y with $f^{-1}(x)$.

EXAMPLE 6

Determine the inverse function $f^{-1}(x)$. Check the inverse with your calculator.

a. $f(x) = \sqrt[3]{2x}$

b. $f(x) = \dfrac{2}{3x} + 4$

Solution

a. $f(x) = \sqrt[3]{2x}$

$y = \sqrt[3]{2x}$ Replace f(x) with y.

$x = \sqrt[3]{2y}$ Interchange x and y.

$x^3 = 2y$ Solve for y.

$y = \dfrac{1}{2}x^3$

$f^{-1}(x) = \dfrac{1}{2}x^3$ Replace y with f⁻¹(x).

Calculator Check

Graph the function, its inverse, and the line of symmetry to check visually.

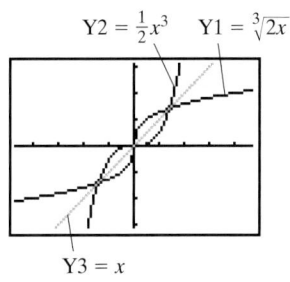

Y2 = ½x³   Y1 = ∛2x

Y3 = x

$(-4.7, 4.7, -3.1, 3.1)$

b.

$$f(x) = \frac{2}{3x} + 4$$

$$y = \frac{2}{3x} + 4 \qquad \text{Replace f(x) with y.}$$

$$x = \frac{2}{3y} + 4 \qquad \text{Interchange x and y.}$$

$$x - 4 = \frac{2}{3y} \qquad \text{Subtract 4 from both sides.}$$

$$3y(x - 4) = 3y\left(\frac{2}{3y}\right) \qquad \text{Multiply both sides by 3y.}$$

$$3xy - 12y = 2 \qquad \text{Simplify.}$$

$$y(3x - 12) = 2 \qquad \text{Factor out a common factor of y.}$$

$$\frac{y(3x - 12)}{3x - 12} = \frac{2}{3x - 12} \qquad \text{Divide both sides by (3x − 12).}$$

$$y = \frac{2}{3x - 12} \qquad \text{Simplify.}$$

Calculator Check

The calculator check is very difficult to visualize. Check to see whether the coordinates are reversed in the ordered pairs of the two functions.

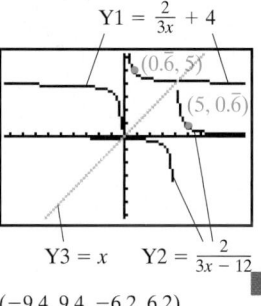

$$Y1 = \frac{2}{3x} + 4$$
$(0.6, 5)$
$(5, 0.\overline{6})$

$$Y3 = x \qquad Y2 = \frac{2}{3x - 12}$$

$$(-9.4, 9.4, -6.2, 6.2)$$

✓ Objective 12.1.4 **CHECKUP**

1. Determine the inverse of each function. Then graph the function, its inverse, and the line of symmetry.
   a. $f(x) = -2x + 6$ **b.** $g(x) = x^3$

2. When is the inverse of a function not a function?
3. How can you test to find whether a given function has an inverse that is a function?

Objective 12.1.5   Modeling the Real World

We have seen many times in this text that important relations in business, science, and social studies are functions. We can write inverse functions for many of them, just as we've learned to do in this section. It is often helpful to interpret the meaning of these inverse functions in terms of the original situation.

This change in your point of view can sometimes provide new insights into your mathematical model.

EXAMPLE 7

Marvin is paid a salary of $300 per week, plus a commission of 6% of his total sales.
a. Write a function $I(x)$ that represents Marvin's weekly income.
b. Determine the inverse function $I^{-1}(x)$.
c. Interpret the meaning of the inverse function $I^{-1}(x)$.

Solution

a. Marvin's income is $300, plus 6% of his weekly sales.
Let x = the amount of Marvin's weekly sales
$I(x)$ = weekly income
$I(x) = 300 + 0.06x$

b.

$$I(x) = 300 + 0.06x$$

$$y = 300 + 0.06x \qquad \text{Let y = I(x).}$$

$$x = 300 + 0.06y \qquad \text{Interchange x and y.}$$

$$x - 300 = 0.06y \qquad \text{Solve for y.}$$

$$\frac{x - 300}{0.06} = y \qquad \text{Divide both sides by 0.06.}$$

$$\frac{50}{3}x - 5000 = y$$

$$I^{-1}(x) = \frac{50}{3}x - 5000 \qquad \text{Replace y with } I^{-1}(x).$$

c. The inverse function $I^{-1}(x)$ represents the amount of Marvin's weekly sales in terms of his total weekly income.

APPLICATION

Currency exchange rates vary daily. According to a recent report, a function for determining the number of European euros, given x U.S. dollars, was $f(x) = 0.7787x$. Determine the inverse function $f^{-1}(x)$ and explain its meaning.

Discussion

$$f(x) = 0.7787x$$

$$y = 0.7787x \quad \text{Substitute y for f(x).}$$

$$x = 0.7787y \quad \text{Interchange x and y.}$$

$$\frac{x}{0.7787} = \frac{0.7787y}{0.7787} \quad \text{Solve for y.}$$

$$\frac{1}{0.7787}x = y$$

$$1.2842x \approx y$$

$$y \approx 1.2842x$$

$$f^{-1}(x) \approx 1.2842x \quad \text{Substitute } f^{-1}(x) \text{ for y.}$$

The inverse function is used to determine the number of U.S. dollars, given x European euros.

 ## Objective 12.1.5 *CHECKUP*

1. Dimitri invests $1200 in a fund that pays 5% simple interest per year.
   a. Write a function $I(x)$ that represents the interest the fund will earn after x years.
   b. Determine the inverse function $I^{-1}(x)$.
   c. Interpret the meaning of the inverse function.

2. A function for determining the number of British pounds, given x U.S. dollars is $f(x) = 0.5327x$. Determine the inverse function and explain its meaning.

12.1 EXERCISES

Student Solutions Manual

PH Math/Tutor Center

CD Video

MathXL®

MyMathLab

Interactmath.com

Determine the inverse of each relation.

1. $h = \{(-3, 5), (-2, 4), (-1, 3), (0, 2), (1, 1), (2, 0)\}$

2. $d = \{(5, 25), (4, 16), (3, 9), (2, 4), (1, 1), (0, 0)\}$

3. $A = \{(3, 6), (2, 7), (1, 8), (0, 8), (-1, 7), (-2, 6)\}$

4. $J = \{(-4, 1), (3, 2), (-2, 1), (1, 2), (0, 1), (-1, 2)\}$

5. $y = 2x - 8$
6. $y = 3x + 6$
7. $y = -3x + 2$
8. $y = 5 - 2x$
9. $y = \frac{3}{4}x + 9$
10. $y = -\frac{2}{3}x + \frac{4}{3}$
11. $y = 0.125x - 2.5$
12. $y = 1.8 - 0.4x$
13. $y = x^2 - 2$
14. $y = x^3 + 1$

Determine whether the given relations are functions. If so, is the function one-to-one?

15. $k = \{(5, 2), (10, 4), (15, 8), (20, 16), (25, 32)\}$

16. $j = \{(-8, 3), (-9, 4), (-10, 5), (-11, 4), (-12, 3)\}$

17. $Q = \{(-2, 0), (-4, 2), (-6, 4), (-8, 2), (-10, 0)\}$

18. $P = \{(1, 16), (2, 15), (3, 14), (4, 13), (5, 12)\}$

19. $A = \{(-1, 0), (0, 1), (-1, 2), (0, 3)\}$

20. $B = \{(6, 5), (-6, 3), (6, 7), (-6, 4)\}$

In exercises 21–26, determine whether each graph represents a one-to-one function.

21.

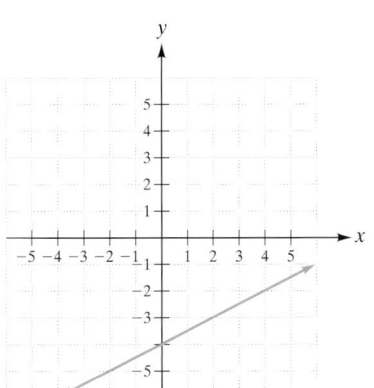

22.

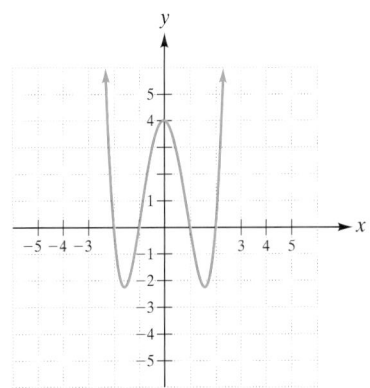

23.

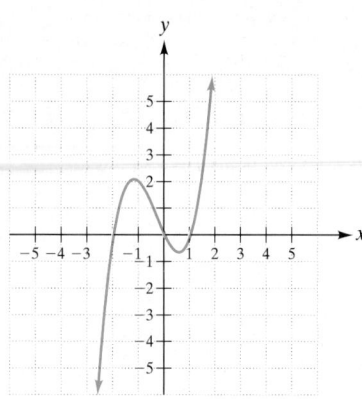

24.

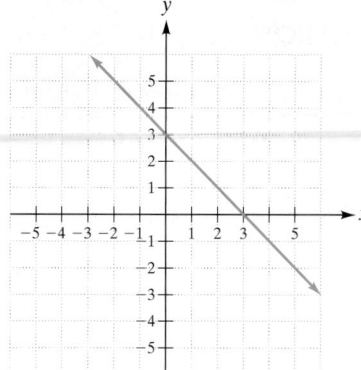

25.

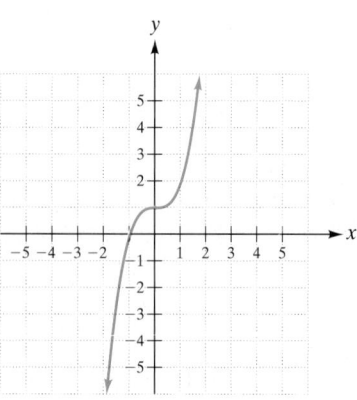

26.

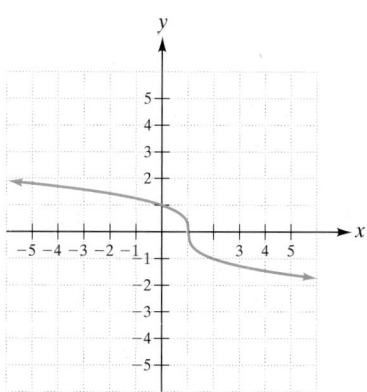

Complete the tables of values to determine whether the following are inverse functions. Explain your answer.

27. $f(x) = 7x - 3$ $g(x) = \dfrac{1}{7}x + \dfrac{3}{7}$

x	$f(x)$
0	
1	

x	$g(x)$
0	
1	

28. $f(x) = -9x + 18$ $g(x) = -\dfrac{1}{9}x + 2$

x	$f(x)$
2	
1	

x	$g(x)$
2	
1	

29. $f(x) = \dfrac{9}{x} + 12$ $g(x) = \dfrac{9}{x - 12}$

x	$f(x)$
-1	
1	

x	$g(x)$
-1	
1	

30. $f(x) = \dfrac{6}{x} - 12$ $g(x) = \dfrac{12}{x - 6}$

x	$f(x)$
1	
2	

x	$g(x)$
1	
2	

31. $f(x) = 8x^3$ $g(x) = \sqrt[3]{x + 2}$

x	$f(x)$
0	
2	

x	$g(x)$
0	
2	

32. $f(x) = \sqrt[3]{3x - 5}$ $g(x) = \dfrac{x^3 + 5}{3}$

x	$f(x)$
-1	
2	

x	$g(x)$
-1	
2	

In exercises 33–38, use calculator graphs to determine whether or not the following are inverse functions. Also graph the line $y = x$. Explain your answer.

33. $f(x) = 6x - 4$

$g(x) = \dfrac{1}{4}x + \dfrac{1}{6}$

34. $f(x) = -3x + 6$

$g(x) = -\dfrac{1}{3}x + 2$

35. $f(x) = \dfrac{4}{x} + 11$

$g(x) = \dfrac{4}{x - 11}$

36. $f(x) = \dfrac{2}{x} - 7$

$g(x) = \dfrac{7}{x - 2}$

37. $f(x) = \sqrt[3]{2x - 9}$

$g(x) = \dfrac{x^3 + 9}{2}$

38. $f(x) = 12x^3$

$g(x) = \sqrt[3]{x + 12}$

Determine the inverse of each function. Then use your calculator to graph the function, its inverse, and the line of symmetry, $y = x$.

39. $g(x) = 3x - 6$

40. $f(x) = -4x + 2$

41. $y = \dfrac{2}{3}x - 4$

42. $y = -\dfrac{2}{5}x + 4$

43. $h(x) = x^2 - 1$

44. $r(x) = 2 - x^2$

45. $y = \dfrac{1}{3}x^3 - 4$

46. $y = \dfrac{1}{4}x^3 + 2$

Write a function that represents each situation. Then determine the inverse of the function. Intepret what the inverse of the function represents.

47. Julia is paid $1500 per month, plus a commission of 2% of the value of all stock transactions she handles. What is Julia's monthly income?

48. Harvey earns $125 per week, plus an average of 15% of his sales in tips waiting tables. What are his weekly earnings?

49. Antonio drives at an average speed of 55 miles per hour. What distance does he travel in a given amount of time?

50. Grace operates a machine that cuts 30 pairs of jeans per hour. How many pairs of jeans can she cut in a given amount of time?

51. Priscilla borrowed $2000 from her parents. They agreed that until she repays the loan, they will charge her 0.5% simple interest per month. What is the total amount Priscilla will repay?

52. Kimberly purchased a bond for $1500. The bond pays 0.4% simple interest per month. What is the total value of the bond?

53. An Internet music provider charges $9.95 per month to use its service. In addition, it charges a fee of $0.60 to burn a song. What is the monthly cost?

54. A discount warehouse offers its customers a membership deal. It costs $100, but they receive 2% cash back on all purchases. What is the membership fee?

55. Automobiles lose value quickly. A particular vehicle that cost $15,000 loses $1750 of its value each year. What is its value?

56. Catalina has an international student loan. At graduation she owes $10,000 and will pay it off $83 each month. What is the amount she owes?

In each of the following exercises, write an equation of a line for each data set. Comment on the domain and range values shown in each table. Graph each line. Determine whether the linear functions are inverse functions. Explain your answer.

57.

x	y
2	−1
14	3
20	5

x	y
−1	2
3	14
5	20

58.

x	y
0	15
6	−39
10	−75

x	y
15	0
−39	6
−75	10

59.

x	y
0	4
5	7
10	10

x	y
4	0
7	5
10	10

60.

x	y
5	8.4
11	22.2
20	42.9

x	y
8.4	5
22.2	11
42.9	20

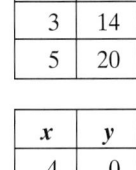 ## 12.1 Calculator Exercises

The calculator can draw the inverse of a function without your having to derive the inverse algebraically. As an example, graph the function $y = \frac{1}{2}x^3 + 3$. Do so by storing the function in Y1, and graph it with the standard window setting. Now draw the inverse by entering the following:

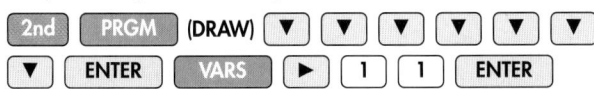

The calculator will draw the inverse of the function on the same graph as the function. Once you have algebraically determined the inverse, you can check it by first graphing the function (stored in Y1), then graphing your algebraically derived inverse (stored in Y2), and finally instructing the calculator to draw the inverse of the original function. If the graph of your inverse and the calculator's inverse coincide, you have correctly determined the inverse. (*Note:* You will not be able to trace the two graphs to verify that they coincide, but you can check visually.) In the following exercises, find the inverse algebraically, graph the function and its inverse, and then check, using this feature of your calculator just discussed:

1. $y = 0.3x^2 - 4$

2. $f(x) = 0.1x^3 + 2$

3. $g(x) = 5\sqrt{x} - 1.5$

4. $y = \dfrac{1}{x} + 2$

12.1 Writing Exercise

In this section, you were cautioned not to confuse the notation $f^{-1}(x)$ with the notation $[f(x)]^{-1}$. Discuss what each notation means, using an example for each. Then consult a dictionary to find definitions for the words *inverse* and *reciprocal*, and relate these definitions to what you have studied.

12.2   EXPONENTIAL FUNCTIONS

OBJECTIVES

1 Identify exponential functions.
2 Evaluate exponential functions.
3 Graph exponential functions.
4 Graph the natural exponential function.
5 Model real-world situations by using exponential functions.

APPLICATION

According to the U.S. Bureau of the Census, the population of the United States (in millions) may be approximated by the exponential function $f(x) = 280(1.01)^x$, where x is the number of years after 2000.

a. Graph this function.

b. According to the graph, what is the estimated population of the United States in the year 2010?

c. In what year does the model predict the population will be 325 million?

After completing this section, we will discuss this application further. See page 959.

Objective 12.2.1   Identifying Exponential Functions

In previous chapters, we studied polynomial functions, rational functions, and radical functions. Each of these functions can be written as a term with a variable base and a rational-number exponent.

$$f(x) = x^2 \qquad\qquad g(x) = x^{-2} \qquad\qquad h(x) = x^{1/2}$$

Polynomial function   Rational function   Radical function

In this section, we examine a function that has a term with a rational-number base and a variable exponent, the reverse of what we previously studied.

$$f(x) = 2^x \qquad\qquad g(x) = 2^{-x} \qquad\qquad h(x) = \left(\frac{1}{2}\right)^x$$

We call each of these functions an **exponential function**.

EXPONENTIAL FUNCTION

An exponential function f can be written in the form

$$f(x) = a^x$$

where $a > 0$, $a \neq 1$, and x is any real number.

Note the restrictions on the base a. The base must be positive and not equal to 1. A base of 1 results in the function $f(x) = 1^x$ or $f(x) = 1$, a constant function.

EXAMPLE 1

For each function, state whether or not it is an exponential function.

a. $y = 5^x$ **b.** $f(x) = x^{-5/3}$ **c.** $g(x) = 0^x$

Solution

a. $y = 5^x$ is an exponential function, because it has a rational-number base and a variable exponent.

b. $f(x) = x^{-5/3}$ is not an exponential function, because the base is a variable. In fact, this is a radical function.

c. $g(x) = 0^x$ is not an exponential function, because it has a base of 0. ■

Objective 12.2.1 *CHECKUP*

1. For each function, state whether or not it is an exponential function.

a. $h(x) = x^{2/3}$ **b.** $k(x) = \left(\dfrac{2}{3}\right)^x$ **c.** $y = 1^x$

Objective 12.2.2   Evaluating Exponential Functions

To evaluate an exponential function, we substitute the value of the independent variable and evaluate the resulting numeric expression. This expression will be an exponential expression containing a real-number exponent. We already know how to evaluate an exponential expression with a rational exponent. For example,

$$a^3 = a \cdot a \cdot a \qquad\qquad a^{-2} = \frac{1}{a^2} \qquad\qquad a^{3/4} = (\sqrt[4]{a})^3$$

Therefore,

$$2^3 = 2 \cdot 2 \cdot 2 = 8 \qquad 5^{-2} = \frac{1}{5^2} = \frac{1}{25} \qquad 16^{3/4} = \left(\sqrt[4]{16}\right)^3 = 2^3 = 8$$

```
2^1.7
         3.249009585
2^1.73
         3.317278183
2^1.732
         3.321880096
```

```
2^√(3)
         3.321997085
```

We also may need to evaluate an exponential expression with an irrational exponent, such as $a^{\sqrt{3}}$. For example, evaluate $2^{\sqrt{3}}$.

Since $\sqrt{3} \approx 1.732$, we can approximate $2^{\sqrt{3}}$ by evaluating $2^{1.7}$, $2^{1.73}$, or $2^{1.732}$, and so on, depending on the accuracy we require.

However, since we are using a calculator to perform these operations, we can also enter the expression with an irrational exponent and obtain an approximation with the accuracy of our calculator display.

EXAMPLE 2   Evaluate the function $g(x) = 8^x$ at the given values.

a. $g(2)$ **b.** $g(-2)$ **c.** $g\left(\dfrac{2}{3}\right)$ **d.** $g\left(\sqrt{2}\right)$

d.

Solution

a. $g(2) = 8^2 = 64$

b. $g(-2) = 8^{-2} = \dfrac{1}{8^2} = \dfrac{1}{64}$

c. $g\left(\dfrac{2}{3}\right) = 8^{2/3} = \left(\sqrt[3]{8}\right)^2 = 2^2 = 4$

d. $g\left(\sqrt{2}\right) = 8^{\sqrt{2}} \approx 18.93$ ■

✓ Objective 12.2.2 **CHECKUP**

1. Evaluate the function $h(x) = 4^x$ at the given values.

   a. $h(3)$ **b.** $h(-3)$

   c. $h\left(\dfrac{3}{2}\right)$ **d.** $h\left(\sqrt{3}\right)$

2. Are there any real-number values of x for which the function $h(x) = 4^x$ cannot be evaluated? (*Hint:* Consider each of the subsets of numbers that make up the real-number system.)

Objective 12.2.3   ## Graphing Exponential Functions

We graph a function by first determining the domain of the function and then evaluating the function for values in its domain. We do not need to determine the domain of an exponential function, because it is given to us in the definition; that is, x is a real number. Therefore, the domain is the set of all real numbers.

To graph an exponential function in the form $f(x) = a^x$, set up a table of values with real-number values for x, plot the points, and connect them with a smooth curve.

EXAMPLE 3   Graph $f(x) = 8^x$. Determine the function's domain and range, the graph's y-intercept and x-intercept, and whether the function is increasing or decreasing.

Solution   **Calculator Check**

Set up a table   Plot the points and connect them
of values.   with a smooth curve.

x	$f(x)$
-3	$\dfrac{1}{512}$
-2	$\dfrac{1}{64}$
-1	$\dfrac{1}{8}$
0	1
1	8
2	64
3	512

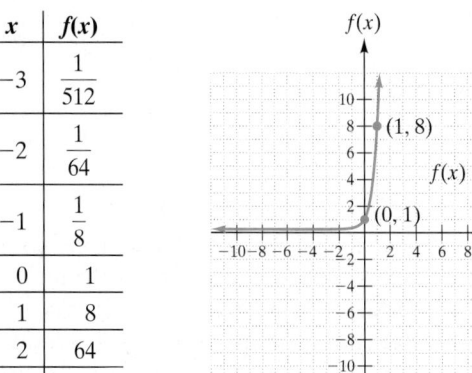

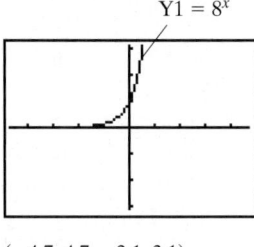

$(-4.7, 4.7, -3.1, 3.1)$

The domain of $f(x)$ is the set of all real numbers. The range of $f(x)$ is the set of all real numbers greater than 0. The graph's y-intercept is $(0, 1)$. The graph does not have an x-intercept. The function is increasing.   ■

Exponential functions can also be written in the form $f(x) = a^{-x}$, where $a > 0$ and $a \neq 1$. These functions are equivalent to other functions written in the form $f(x) = a^x$, where $a > 0$ and $a \neq 1$. Complete the following set of exercises on your calculator to determine the relationship between the two forms.

 Guided Discovery 2   Equivalent Exponential Functions

1. Graph each exponential function on a decimal window.

   a. $f(x) = 2^x$ **b.** $f(x) = 2^{-x}$

   c. $f(x) = \left(\dfrac{1}{2}\right)^x$ **d.** $f(x) = \left(\dfrac{1}{2}\right)^{-x}$

2. Match the graphs of the functions.

Write a rule for determining equivalent functions.

The functions $f(x) = 2^{-x}$ and $f(x) = \left(\dfrac{1}{2}\right)^x$ are equivalent. The functions $f(x) = 2^x$ and $f(x) = \left(\dfrac{1}{2}\right)^{-x}$ are also equivalent.

Using the properties of exponents, we can show algebraically that $a^{-x} = \left(\dfrac{1}{a}\right)^x$ and $a^x = \left(\dfrac{1}{a}\right)^{-x}$, where $a > 0$, $a \neq 1$, and x is a rational number.

$$a^{-x} = (a^{-1})^x \qquad \textit{Power-to-a-power rule}$$
$$= \left(\dfrac{1}{a}\right)^x \qquad \textit{Definition of a negative exponent}$$

$$a^x = (a^{-1})^{-x} \qquad \textit{Power-to-a-power rule}$$
$$= \left(\dfrac{1}{a}\right)^{-x} \qquad \textit{Definition of a negative exponent}$$

EXAMPLE 4   Graph the function $f(x) = \left(\dfrac{1}{8}\right)^x = 8^{-x}$. Determine the function's domain and range, the graph's y-intercept and x-intercept, and whether the function is increasing or decreasing.

Solution

Set up a table of values.

x	$f(x)$
-3	512
-2	64
-1	8
0	1
1	$\dfrac{1}{8}$
2	$\dfrac{1}{64}$
3	$\dfrac{1}{512}$

Plot the points and connect them with a smooth curve.

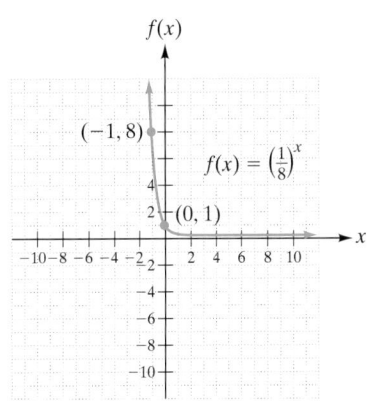

Calculator Check

$Y1 = \left(\dfrac{1}{8}\right)^x = 8^{-x}$

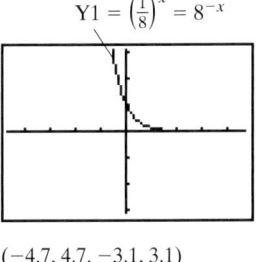

$(-4.7, 4.7, -3.1, 3.1)$

The domain of $f(x)$ is the set of all real numbers. The range of $f(x)$ is the set of all real numbers greater than 0. The graph's y-intercept is $(0, 1)$. The graph does not have an x-intercept. The function is decreasing. ■

Exponential functions and their graphs have several common characteristics. Some of these characteristics are common to all exponential functions, and others are common to certain sets of functions. Two such characteristics are determined by the value of the base a. Complete the following set of exercises to discover the common characteristics of exponential functions and their graphs.

Guided Discovery 3   Effect of the Base a on an Exponential Graph

1. Sketch the graphs of the given exponential functions of the form $f(x) = a^x$, where $a > 0$, on the same coordinate plane. Use the decimal window.

   a. $f(x) = 2^x$ **b.** $f(x) = 5^x$

   c. $f(x) = 10^x$ **d.** $f(x) = \left(\dfrac{1}{2}\right)^x$

   e. $f(x) = \left(\dfrac{1}{5}\right)^x$ **f.** $f(x) = \left(\dfrac{1}{10}\right)^x$

Use your graphs to complete the following exercises:

2. Determine the domain of each function.

3. Determine the range of each function.
4. Are all the functions one-to-one?
5. Determine the y-intercept of each function.
6. Determine the x-intercept of each function.

Choose the correct answer.

7. In exercises **1a–1c**, $a > 1$. The function is *increasing/decreasing*. The larger the value of a, the *steeper/shallower* the graph.

8. In exercises **1d–1f**, $0 < a < 1$. The function is *increasing/decreasing*. The smaller the value of a (as a approaches 0), the *steeper/shallower* the graph.

The exponential function $y = a^x$, where $a > 1$, is always increasing. The larger the value of a, the steeper is the function's graph. The exponential function $y = a^x$, where $0 < a < 1$, is always decreasing. The smaller the value of a, the steeper is the function's graph. All exponential functions are one-to-one and have a domain of the set of all real numbers and a range of the set of all positive real numbers, and their graphs have a y-intercept of $(0, 1)$. Exponential functions have no x-intercept.

Let's summarize what we have learned about the exponential function $f(x) = a^x$ and its corresponding graph.

CHARACTERISTICS OF AN EXPONENTIAL FUNCTION AND ITS GRAPH

For the exponential function $f(x) = a^x$ and its graph, we have the following characteristics:

Domain	The set of all real numbers
Range	The set of all positive real numbers

The function is one-to-one.

y-intercept	$(0, 1)$
x-intercept	There is no x-intercept. The graph of the function approaches, but does not reach, the x-axis.

If $a > 1$, then the function is always increasing.

If $0 < a < 1$, then the function is always decreasing.

 Objective 12.2.3 CHECKUP

In exercises 1 and 2, graph each exponential function.

1. $y = 8^{2x}$ **2.** $y = 8^{-2x}$

3. Why are negative numbers excluded from the range of the exponential function $y = a^x$, $a > 0$?

Objective 12.2.4   The Natural Exponential Function

In all of the examples of exponential functions we have discussed, we chose to use a rational-number base. However, we could have chosen an irrational-number base. In fact, many applications of exponential functions involve a special irrational number as the base. This number occurs often in nature and in human activity, showing up in the description of continuously compounded interest, the decay rates of radioactive elements, and even the growth rates of bacterial populations.

The irrational number is denoted by the symbol e and is called the **natural base**. Rounded to five decimal places, the value of e is 2.71828. The calculator gives us a more accurate value to nine decimal places, as shown in **Figure 12.1**.

TECHNOLOGY Natural Base, e

Calculate the natural base e to nine decimal places.

```
e
        2.718281828
e^(1)
        2.718281828
```

Figure 12.1

For **Figure 12.1**,
Enter e.

[2nd] [÷] (e) [ENTER]

If e is a base of an expression, the calculator allows a more convenient method. Enter e^x followed by the exponent. Remember to close the parentheses. To evaluate e, enter e^1.

[2nd] [LN] (eˣ) [1] [ )] [ENTER]

The irrational number e is used to describe the **natural exponential function** $f(x) = e^x$. Remember, the base e is a positive number greater than 1. Therefore, the domain of the function is the set of all real numbers. The range is the set of all positive real numbers. The graph of the function has a y-intercept at $(0, 1)$ and is always increasing. Calculate a table of values on your calculator, and use the coordinates to graph the function. Check your graph with your calculator.

X	Y1
-3	.04979
-2	.13534
-1	.36788
0	1
1	2.7183
2	7.3891
3	20.086

X = -3

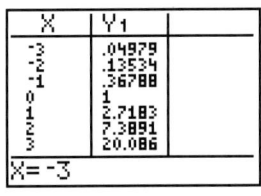

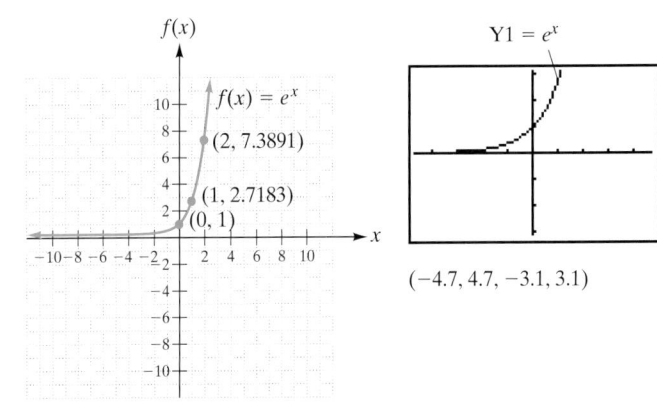

$(-4.7, 4.7, -3.1, 3.1)$

NATURAL EXPONENTIAL FUNCTION

The natural exponential function is defined as

$$f(x) = e^x$$

where x is a real number.

EXAMPLE 5   Graph the function $f(x) = 2e^x$.

Solution

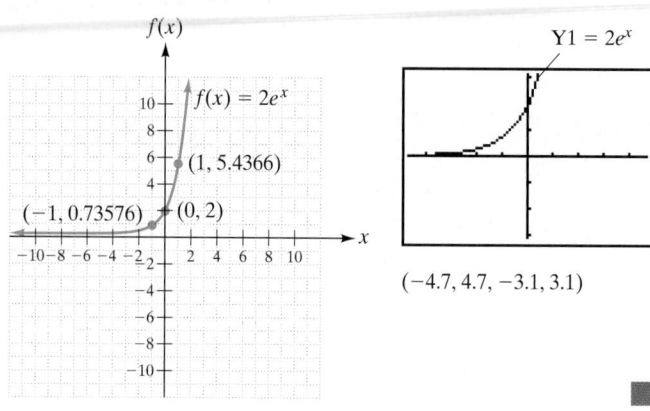

$(-4.7, 4.7, -3.1, 3.1)$

Objective 12.2.4 **CHECKUP**

1. Graph the function $y = 0.5e^x$.

2. The number e is an irrational number. What does this mean?

Objective 12.2.5   ## Modeling the Real World

In Objective 12.2.1, we explained that an exponential function $y = a^x$ is different from a polynomial function $y = x^a$.

As an example, the exponential function $y = 2^x$ increases at a faster rate than the polynomial function $y = x^2$. Therefore, we use an exponential function to describe situations that change quickly over a large range of values of the domain.

Exponential functions model many types of phenomena in the real world. These phenomena range from the calculation of one's balance in a savings account, to the determination of the amount owed on a loan, to the prediction of numbers of individuals in a population.

In Chapter P, we first discussed the calculation of interest. Remember the formula for simple interest, $I = Prt$, where P is the amount of principal, r is the rate of interest per period, and t is the number of periods. Compound interest is based on taking the interest accumulated in one period and adding it to the principal before determining the interest received the next period.

Let $t = 1$ year. At the end of one year, the amount is the principal plus the interest.

$$P + Prt = P + Pr(1)$$
$$= P + Pr$$
$$= P(1 + r)$$

If this amount is left at the same interest rate for one more year, the total amount is the last amount plus the interest.

$$P(1 + r) + [P(1 + r)]rt = P(1 + r) + [P(1 + r)]r(1)$$
$$= P(1 + r) + Pr(1 + r)$$
$$= P(1 + r)(1 + r)$$
$$= P(1 + r)^2$$

If we continue the pattern, we see that at the end of three years the amount is $P(1 + r)^3$. Therefore, we can arrive at the formula given for the compounded amount

$$A = P(1 + r)^t$$

where P = principal, r = interest per period, and t = number of periods.

EXAMPLE 6   Alex plans to invest $10,000 at an annual compounded rate of 8%. Determine the amount of his investment at the end of two years.

Solution

Use the compound-interest formula with $P = 10,000$, $r = 0.08$, and $t = 2$.

$$A = P(1 + r)^t$$
$$A = 10,000(1 + 0.08)^2$$
$$A = 10,000(1.08)^2$$
$$A = 11,664$$

Alex will have $11,664 in his account at the end of two years.   ■

```
10000(1.08)²
          11664
```

Continuously compounded interest is compound interest with very short periods, so that the addition of interest occurs on a continuous basis. A formula for the continuously compounded amount is

$$A = Pe^{rt}$$

where P = principal, t = number of years, and r = annual interest rate compounded continuously.

EXAMPLE 7   Alex plans to invest $10,000 at a rate of 8% compounded continuously. Determine the amount of his investment at the end of two years.

Solution

Use the continuously compounded interest formula with $P = 10,000$, $r = 0.08$, and $t = 2$.

$$A = Pe^{rt}$$
$$A = 10,000e^{(0.08)(2)}$$
$$A = 10,000e^{0.16}$$
$$A \approx 11735.11$$

Alex will have approximately $11,735.11 in his account at the end of two years.   ■

```
10000→P:0.08→R:2
→T:Pe^(RT)
          11735.10871
```

APPLICATION

According to the U.S. Bureau of the Census, the population of the United States (in millions) may be approximated by the exponential function $f(x) = 280(1.01)^x$, where x is the number of years after 2000.

a. Graph this function.

b. According to the graph, what is the estimated population of the United States in the year 2010?

c. In what year does the model predict the population will be 325 million?

Discussion

a. $Y1 = 280(1.01)^x$

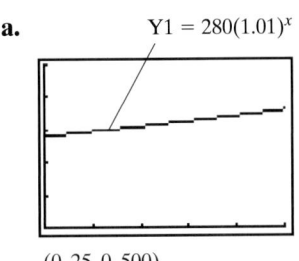

$(0, 25, 0, 500)$

b. Let $x = 2010 - 2000 = 10$

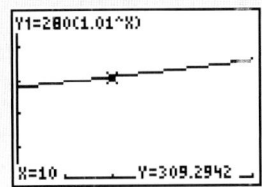

$(0, 25, 0, 500)$

According to the model, the population of the United States will be approximately 309 million in the year 2010.

c. In 2015, 15 years after 2000, the population will be approximately 325 million.

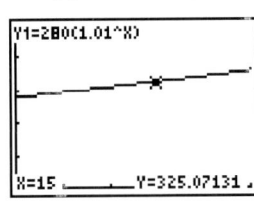

$(0, 25, 0, 500)$

Objective 12.2.5 *CHECKUP*

1. Cindy invests $5000 at an annual compounded interest rate of 6%. How much will she have after four years?

2. If Cindy had invested the $5000 at a continuously compounded rate of 6%, how much would she have after four years?

3. According to data from the U.S. Bureau of the Census, the U.S. unemployment rate may be estimated by the function

$R(x) = 4.84(1.13)^x$, where x is the number of years after 2000.

a. Graph this function.

b. What will the unemployment rate be in 2010?

c. In what year will the rate be 10%?

12.2 EXERCISES

 Student Solutions Manual  PH Math/Tutor Center   CD Video Math XL MathXL® MyMathLab MyMathLab Interactmath.com

For each function, state whether or not it is an exponential function.

1. $y = 7^x$
2. $d(x) = x^{1.5}$
3. $f(x) = 0.3^x$
4. $y = 22.3^x$
5. $g(x) = x^{0.3}$
6. $y = x^4$
7. $y = 1.57^x$
8. $y = 12^x$
9. $y = x^{-3}$
10. $T(x) = \left(\frac{5}{8}\right)^x$
11. $R(x) = \left(\frac{2}{3}\right)^x$
12. $b(x) = 1.5^x$

Evaluate the function $g(x) = 16^x$ at the given values.

13. $g(3)$
14. $g(4)$
15. $g(-2)$
16. $g(-1)$
17. $g\left(\frac{1}{2}\right)$
18. $g\left(\frac{3}{4}\right)$
19. $g(\sqrt{2})$
20. $g(0)$

Evaluate the function $h(x) = 0.64^x$ at the given values.

21. $h(0.3)$
22. $h(1.5)$
23. $h\left(-\frac{1}{3}\right)$
24. $h\left(\frac{5}{6}\right)$
25. $h(-\sqrt{2})$
26. $h(\sqrt{5})$

Graph each exponential function.

27. $f(x) = 4^x$
28. $C(x) = 3^x$
29. $g(x) = 4^{-x}$
30. $D(x) = 3^{-2x}$
31. $h(x) = 4^{2x}$
32. $F(x) = 3^{2x-1}$
33. $j(x) = 4^{(1/2)x}$
34. $K(x) = 3^{x/4}$
35. $k(x) = 4^{x-1}$
36. $L(x) = 3^x + 1$
37. $m(x) = 4^x - 1$
38. $M(x) = 3^{x+1} - 1$
39. $y = e^{(1/2)x}$
40. $y = e^{0.2x}$
41. $y = \frac{1}{2}e^x$
42. $y = 0.2e^x$
43. $y = e^{(-1/2)x}$
44. $y = e^{-0.2x}$
45. $y = e^x + \frac{1}{2}$
46. $y = e^{0.2x} + 0.2$
47. $y = \frac{1}{2}e^{(1/2)x}$
48. $y = 0.2e^{0.2x}$

Graph the following functions. Determine the domain and range. Where is each function increasing or decreasing? Identify any maximum or minimum values.

49. $f(x) = e^{-x^2}$
50. $f(x) = (2^x)^x$
51. $f(x) = e^x - e^{-x}$
52. $f(x) = e^x + e^{-x}$

In exercises 53–56, write a function for the total value of the investment. Graph the function and answer the question.

53. Jerome received his annual bonus of $6000, which he invested at an annually compounded interest rate of 5.5%. How much money was invested after seven years?

54. Marissa received a $3000 commission for landing a book adoption with a major school. She invested the money at an interest rate of 6.2%, compounded annually. What was her investment worth after four years?

55. Jolene inherited $8000, which she invested at a continuously compounded interest rate of 4.8%. How much did she earn after five years?

56. Marty's regional sales netted her a commission of $4500. If she invests the money at a continuously compounded interest rate of 7.5%, how much will the investment be worth after 10 years?

57. The "present value" of an investment desired to be worth $750 after n years at 5% can be given by $A(n) = 750(1.05)^{-n}$, where n is the number of years. Graph this function. What amount needs to be deposited to be worth $750 after one year? After 5 years? After 20 years?

58. The "present value" of an investment desired to be worth $1000 after n years at 9% can be given by $A(n) = 1000(1.09)^{-n}$, where n is the number of years. Graph this function. What amount needs to be deposited to be worth $1000 after one year? After 5 years? After 20 years?

59. The effective annual rate is the amount of simple interest that is equal to an interest rate compounded during a given year. The effective annual rate for an investment with a nominal rate of 7% can be computed by $r(m) = \left(1 + \dfrac{0.07}{m}\right)^m - 1$, where m is the number of compounding periods per year. Graph this function. What is the effective annual rate for an investment of this type which is compounded semiannually? Quarterly? Monthly?

60. The effective annual rate is the amount of simple interest that is equal to an interest rate compounded during a given year. The effective annual rate for an investment with a nominal rate of 10% can be computed by $r(m) = \left(1 + \dfrac{0.1}{m}\right)^m - 1$, where m is the number of compounding periods per year. Graph this function. What is the effective annual rate for an investment of this type which is compounded quarterly? Monthly? Daily?

61. The amount of carbon dioxide emissions worldwide may be estimated by the function $E(x) = 6517(1.013)^x$, where x is the number of years after 2000 and $E(x)$ is measured in millions of metric tons of carbon equivalent. Graph this function. What does the model predict the emissions will be in 2010?

62. According to data from the National Center for Health Statistics, the number of new AIDS cases in the United States can be estimated by the function $C(x) = 40{,}267(1.03)^x$, where $C(x)$ is the number of new cases and x is the number of years after 2000. Graph this function. What does the model predict the number of new cases to be in 2010?

 **12.2 Calculator Exercises**

Part 1. Exploring exponential models

The calculator allows you to easily explore more complicated mathematical models that involve exponential expressions. Graph the following functions and study the effects of the operations indicated:

1. a. $f(x) = e^x$ **b.** $g(x) = e^{-x}$

2. a. $h(x) = e^x + e^{-x}$ **b.** $j(x) = e^x - e^{-x}$

3. a. $k(x) = (e^x)(e^{-x})$ **b.** $m(x) = e^x \div e^{-x}$

4. a. $F(x) = e^{(1/2)x}$ **b.** $G(x) = e^{(-1/2)x}$

5. a. $H(x) = e^{(1/2)x} + e^{(-1/2)x}$ **b.** $J(x) = e^{(1/2)x} - e^{(-1/2)x}$

6. a. $K(x) = (e^{(1/2)x})(e^{(-1/2)x})$ **b.** $M(x) = (e^{(1/2)x}) \div (e^{(-1/2)x})$

Could you have predicted any of the results you obtained? Which rules of exponents apply to these exercises? See if you can use the rules of exponents to write a simplified form of some of the functions listed. Then check your results by graphing.

Part 2. Exponential regression

In Chapter 3 and Chapter 6, we used a technique called regression analysis to analyze data to find an equation of a line and the equation for a parabola. In this section we will utilize this feature to find an equation for an exponential curve. We enter the data points in the same manner as in previous chapters using the STAT EDIT menu. We will then choose ExpReg (Exponential Regression) under the STAT CALC menu. The form of the equation generated will be $y = a(b)^x$, and the values for a and b will be given.

Use the method of exponential regression to find the exponential function that best fits the following data sets. Assuming trends continue, use your model to answer the questions.

1.

Year	Percent of U.S. Population Enrolled in HMOs
2000	30
2001	28.3
2002	26.4

What percent of the population will be enrolled in HMOs in 2008? In what year will 13% of the population be enrolled in HMOs?

2.

Year	U.S. Gold Production in Thousands of Troy Ounces
2001	10,800
2002	9580
2003	8910

What will production be in 2010? In what year will production be about 3050 thousand troy ounces?

3.

Year	Total Retail Car Sales
2001	8,422,625
2002	8,103,229
2003	7,610,481

What will sales be in 2010? In what year will sales be about 4.4 million?

12.2 Writing Exercise

The definition of an exponential function $f(x) = a^x$ specifies that a must be positive and must not equal 1. Consider an exponential equation with a negative base, such as $y = (-2)^x$. Set up a table of values, using integer values of x. What do you notice about the values of y? Does this equation behave like an exponential function? Can you understand why the base of an exponential expression cannot be negative? Explain.

Next, consider an exponential function with a base of 1, for example, $y = 1^x$. What does the table of values look like for this equation? Can you see why it is excluded from the discussion of exponential functions? Explain.

Finally, consider the functions $f(x) = -2^x$, $g(x) = (-2)^x$, and $h(x) = 2^x$. Are any of these functions the same? Which of the functions is an exponential function? Graph each function separately, using a decimal window. Trace the graphs. What do the graphs show? Does this example further confirm the rule that the base of an exponential function must be positive? Explain.

12.3 LOGARITHMIC FUNCTIONS

OBJECTIVES

1. Identify logarithmic functions.
2. Evaluate logarithms.
3. Graph logarithmic functions.
4. Model real-world situations by using logarithmic functions.

APPLICATION

The magnitude R, measured on the Richter scale, of an earthquake of intensity I is defined by the function $R = \log \dfrac{I}{I_0}$, where I_0 is the intensity of a very small vibration in the Earth used as a standard. The San Francisco earthquake of 1906 had a magnitude of 8.3 on the Richter scale. Eighty-three years later, in 1989, San Francisco had another earthquake, this time measuring 7.1.

a. Determine the intensity of each earthquake.

b. The difference on the Richter scale of the 1906 and 1989 earthquakes is 1.2. Determine the ratio of the intensity of the 1906 earthquake to the 1989 earthquake.

After completing this section, we will discuss this application further. See page 971.

Objective 12.3.1 ### Identifying Logarithmic Functions

In Section 12.1, we introduced the concept of the inverse of a function. The horizontal-line test states that if it is not possible to draw a horizontal line which intersects the graph of a function more than once, then the graph represents a one-to-one function. A one-to-one function has an inverse function.

According to the horizontal-line test, all exponential functions are one-to-one and, therefore, have inverse functions.

Let's determine the inverse function of the exponential function.

$$f(x) = a^x \qquad \text{Exponential function}$$
$$y = a^x \qquad \text{Replace } f(x) \text{ with } y.$$
$$x = a^y \qquad \text{Interchange } x \text{ and } y.$$
$$y = \text{the power to which we raise } a \text{ to obtain } x \qquad \text{Solve for } y.$$

In order to write this relationship mathematically, we define the **logarithm of x with base a** to be the power to which we raise a to get x.

LOGARITHM OF x WITH BASE a

The logarithm of x with base a is written in the form $\log_a x$ and is defined as

$$y = \log_a x \quad \text{if and only if } x = a^y$$

where a and x are positive real numbers and $a \neq 1$.

Now we can write the inverse function of the exponential function $f(x) = a^x$ as

$$y = \log_a x$$

or

$$f^{-1}(x) = \log_a x$$

One example of an exponential function and its inverse function is

$$g(x) = 2^x \quad \text{and} \quad g^{-1}(x) = \log_2 x$$

We have now identified a new function called the **logarithmic function**, which is the inverse of the exponential function.

LOGARITHMIC FUNCTION WITH BASE a

The logarithmic function with base a can be written in the form

$$f(x) = \log_a x$$

where a and x are positive real numbers and $a \neq 0$.

EXAMPLE 1

Determine the logarithmic function that is the inverse of the given exponential function.

a. $f(x) = 5^x$ **b.** $g(x) = 10^x$

Solution

a. Given $f(x) = 5^x$, $f^{-1}(x) = \log_5 x$.   *a = 5*

b. Given $g(x) = 10^x$, $g^{-1}(x) = \log_{10} x$.   *a = 10*

Objective 12.3.1 CHECKUP

1. Determine the logarithmic function that is the inverse of the given exponential function.

   a. $f(x) = 3^x$ **b.** $h(x) = 13^x$

2. What is wrong with the statement, "The inverse function of the exponential function $F(x) = 7^x$ is the logarithmic function $F^{-1}(x) = \log_x 7$"? How can you guard against making this mistake?

Objective 12.3.2   Evaluating Logarithms

According to the definition of the logarithm of x with base a, the two equations $y = \log_a x$ and $x = a^y$ are equivalent. For example,

$$y = \log_a x \qquad x = a^y$$

$$3 = \log_2 8 \qquad 8 = 2^3 \qquad \textit{y = 3}$$

Therefore, by definition, *a logarithm is an exponent.*

To evaluate a logarithm $\log_a x$, ask the question, "To what power must a be raised to obtain x?" For example, evaluate $\log_3 9$.

The power to which 3 must be raised to obtain 9 is 2. Therefore, since $3^2 = 9$, then $\log_3 9 = 2$.

EXAMPLE 2   Evaluate.

    a. $\log_2 32$ **b.** $\log_4 2$ **c.** $\log_3 \dfrac{1}{3}$

Solution

a. $\log_2 32$

The power to which 2 must be raised to obtain 32 is 5. Therefore, since $2^5 = 32$, it follows that $\log_2 32 = 5$.

b. $\log_4 2$

The power to which 4 must be raised to obtain 2 is $\frac{1}{2}$. Therefore, since $4^{1/2} = 2$, it follows that $\log_4 2 = \frac{1}{2}$.

c. $\log_3 \dfrac{1}{3}$

The power to which 3 must be raised to obtain $\frac{1}{3}$ is -1. Therefore, since $3^{-1} = \frac{1}{3}$, it follows that $\log_3 \frac{1}{3} = -1$.   ■

When evaluating logarithms, we sometimes encounter certain special cases that are properties of all logarithms. Complete the following set of exercises to identify these properties.

Guided Discovery 4   Properties of Logarithms

Determine the following logarithms in the form $\log_a x$:

1. a. $\log_3 1$ **b.** $\log_5 1$

2. a. $\log_3 3$ **b.** $\log_5 5$

3. a. $\log_3(3^2)$ **b.** $\log_5(5^2)$

4. a. $\log_3(-1)$ **b.** $\log_5(-1)$

5. a. $\log_3 0$ **b.** $\log_5 0$

6. In exercise 1, $x = 1$. The logarithms are _____.

7. In exercise 2, $x = a$, the base. The logarithms are _____.

8. In exercise 3, $x = a^2$, the base squared. The logarithms are _____.

9. In exercise 4, $x = -1$. The logarithms are _____.

10. In exercise 5, $x = 0$. The logarithms are _____.

The properties discovered in these exercises come directly from the definition of a logarithm.

PROPERTIES OF LOGARITHMS

For any positive real numbers a and x, where $a \neq 1$, logarithms have the following properties.

    $\log_a 1 = 0$ because $a^0 = 1$.

    $\log_a a = 1$ because $a^1 = a$.

    $\log_a a^m = m$ because $a^m = a^m$.

    $\log_a(-1)$ is undefined   because a is a positive number and there is no power to which a can be raised to obtain a negative number.

    $\log_a 0$ is undefined   because a is a positive number and there is no power to which a can be raised to obtain 0.

The base of a logarithm can be any positive real number except 1. However, one base that appears more often than other rational numbers is the base 10. A base-10 logarithm is called the **common logarithm**.

COMMON LOGARITHM

The common logarithm of a number x is $\log_{10} x$ or $\log x$.

 TAKE NOTE When we write $\log x$, the base is understood to be 10.

The calculator has a special key for evaluating the common logarithm. For example, evaluate $\log_{10} 100$, and check your results on your calculator.

$$\log_{10} 100 = 2, \text{ because } 10^2 = 100,$$

as shown in **Figure 12.2**.

TECHNOLOGY   The Common Logarithm

Evaluate $\log_{10} 100$.

```
log(100)
            2
```

Figure 12.2

For **Figure 12.2**,
Enter the common-logarithm function, log, followed by 100. Remember to close the set of parentheses.

EXAMPLE 3   Evaluate and check on your calculator.

a. $\log 1$ **b.** $\log 0.01$ **c.** $\log 20$ **d.** $\log 0$

Solution

a. $\log 1 = 0$ *Because $10^0 = 1$.*

b. $\log 0.01 = -2$ *Because $10^{-2} = \frac{1}{10^2} = \frac{1}{100} = 0.01$.*

c. $\log 20 \approx 1.301$ *You must evaluate this on your calculator, because 10 cannot easily be raised to a power to obtain 20.*

d. $\log 0$ is undefined.

Calculator Check

a.
```
log(1)
            0
```
b.
```
log(0.01)
           -2
```
c.
```
log(20)
   1.301029996
```
d.
```
log(0)
```

d.
```
ERR:DOMAIN
1:Quit
2:Goto
```

 TAKE NOTE The calculator will return an error message when the logarithm is undefined.

The logarithm with base e is called the **natural logarithm**. It is written using the special symbol ln x, and is read "el en of x."

NATURAL LOGARITHM

The natural logarithm of a number x is $\log_e x$ or $\ln x$.

All the properties of logarithms listed in this section also hold for natural logarithms.

PROPERTIES OF NATURAL LOGARITHMS

For any positive real number x, natural logarithms have the following properties:

$\ln 1 = 0$	because $e^0 = 1$.
$\ln e = 1$	because $e^1 = e$.
$\ln e^m = m$	because $e^m = e^m$.
$\ln(-1)$ is undefined	because e is a positive number and there is no power to which e can be raised to obtain a negative number.
$\ln 0$ is undefined	because e is a positive number and there is no power to which e can be raised to obtain 0.

The calculator has a special key for evaluating the natural logarithm. For example, evaluate $\ln e^2$, and check your results on your calculator.

$\ln e^2 = 2$, because a property of logarithms states that $\ln e^m = m$ and in this case $m = 2$, as shown in **Figure 12.3**.

TECHNOLOGY The Natural Logarithm

Evaluate $\ln e^2$.

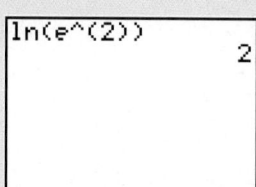

Figure 12.3

For **Figure 12.3**,
Enter the natural logarithm, ln, followed by e^x and the value of the exponent, 2. Remember to close both sets of parentheses.

    2   ENTER

EXAMPLE 4 Evaluate $\ln \dfrac{1}{e^2}$ and check on your calculator.

Solution

$$\ln \frac{1}{e^2} = \ln e^{-2} = -2$$

Calculator Check

```
ln(1/e^(2))
              -2
ln(e^(-2))
              -2
```

To evaluate logarithms with bases other than 10 and e on the calculator, we need to introduce the **change-of-base formula**. It can be shown that $\log_a x$ can be written as a quotient of logarithms with a base other than a.

CHANGE-OF-BASE FORMULA

For any positive real numbers $a, b,$ and x, where $a \neq 1$ and $b \neq 1$,

$$\log_a x = \frac{\log_b x}{\log_b a} \quad \text{or} \quad \log_a x = \frac{\ln x}{\ln a}$$

To evaluate logarithms with bases other than 10 and e,

- Use the change-of-base formula with common logarithms.

$$\log_a x = \frac{\log_{10} x}{\log_{10} a}$$

- Use the change-of-base formula with natural logarithms.

$$\log_a x = \frac{\ln x}{\ln a}$$

TAKE NOTE Note that the original logarithm has base a and the quotient has $\log a$ or $\ln a$ in the denominator (base). This will help you to remember the location of a in the quotient.

EXAMPLE 5 Evaluate $\log_5 12$.

a. Use the change-of-base formula and natural logarithms.

b. Use the change-of-base formula and common logarithms.

Solution

a. $\log_5 12 = \dfrac{\ln 12}{\ln 5} \approx 1.544$

b. $\log_5 12 = \dfrac{\log 12}{\log 5} \approx 1.544$

Calculator Check

```
ln(12)/ln(5)
           1.543959311
log(12)/log(5)
           1.543959311
```

Note: We obtain the same value in **5a** and **5b**.

 Objective 12.3.2 **CHECKUP**

1. Evaluate.

    a. $\log_2 16$ **b.** $\log_8 2$ **c.** $\log_4 \dfrac{1}{64}$

Evaluate exercises 2 and 3. Check with your calculator.

2. a. $\log 1000$ **b.** $\log 0.001$ **c.** $\log(-1)$ **d.** $\log 30$

3. $\ln \dfrac{1}{e^4}$

4. Evaluate $\log_8 24$, using
    a. natural logarithms.   **b.** common logarithms.

5. Explain the difference between the common logarithm of a number and the natural logarithm of a number. Are these the only two forms of logarithms we can use?

Objective 12.3.3 **Graphing Logarithmic Functions**

We are now ready to graph a logarithmic function. We illustrate two methods of setting up a table of values for the function.

The first method involves setting up a table of values for the inverse of the logarithmic function (the exponential function), which is usually easier to evaluate than the logarithmic function. Reversing the coordinates will then determine the table of values for the logarithmic function.

To set up a table of values for a logarithmic function,

- Identify the inverse function (the exponential function).
- Set up a table of values for the exponential function.
- Reverse the coordinates in the ordered pairs to determine the ordered pairs of the logarithmic function.

EXAMPLE 6

Graph the logarithmic function $f(x) = \log_8 x$.

Solution

The inverse function is the exponential function $f^{-1}(x) = 8^x$. The domain of this inverse function is the set of all real numbers. (We set up a table of values for this function in Section 12.2.)

$f^{-1}(x) = 8^x$

x	$f^{-1}(x)$
-3	$\dfrac{1}{512}$
-2	$\dfrac{1}{64}$
-1	$\dfrac{1}{8}$
0	1
1	8
2	64
3	512

Reverse coordinates $\longrightarrow$

$f(x) = \log_8 x$

x	$f(x)$
$\dfrac{1}{512}$	-3
$\dfrac{1}{64}$	-2
$\dfrac{1}{8}$	-1
1	0
8	1
64	2
512	3

Note: We graph both the exponential function and the logarithmic function. We also graph $y = x$, the line of symmetry, to illustrate that the graphs represent inverse functions.

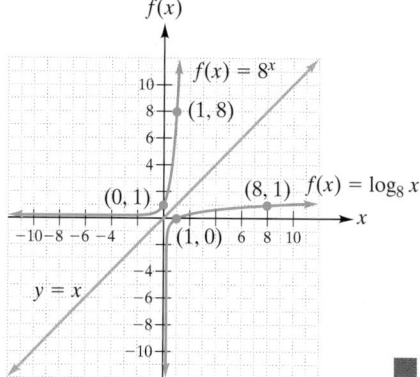

The second method of completing a table of values for the logarithmic function involves substituting values for the independent variable and evaluating the function. First, we determine the domain of the logarithmic function. Since it is the inverse of an exponential function, we reverse the domain and range of the two functions.

Exponential Function		**Logarithmic Function**
Domain ←	all real numbers	→ Range
Range ←	all positive real numbers	→ Domain

Therefore, the domain of a logarithmic function is the set of all positive real numbers.

To complete the table of values, we may need to use a calculator. Also, remember to use the change-of-base formula when needed.

To set up a table of values for a logarithmic function,

- Substitute positive real-number values from the domain of the function for the independent variable.
- Determine values of the dependent variable by evaluating the resulting expression.

EXAMPLE 7 Graph the logarithmic function $f(x) = \log_8 x$.

Solution

Use your calculator and the change-of-base formula to determine a table of values for the function. Let $f(x) = \log_8 x = \dfrac{\ln x}{\ln 8}$.

x	f(x)
0.001	−3.322
0.01	−2.215
0.1	−1.107
0.5	−0.333
1	0
2	0.333
3	0.528
4	0.667
5	0.774
6	0.862

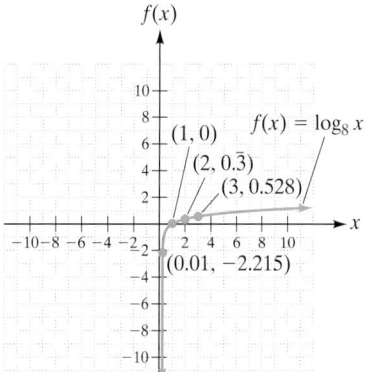

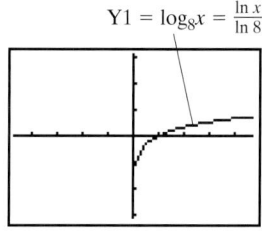

$(-4.7, 4.7, -3.1, 3.1)$

We also have logarithmic functions identified by a common logarithm and a natural logarithm.

COMMON LOGARITHMIC FUNCTION

The common logarithmic function is written in the form

$$f(x) = \log_{10} x \quad \text{or} \quad f(x) = \log x$$

where x is a positive real number.

NATURAL LOGARITHMIC FUNCTION

The natural logarithmic function is defined as $f(x) = \log_e x$ and is written in the form

$$f(x) = \ln x$$

where x is a positive real number.

EXAMPLE 8 Graph.

a. $y = \log x$ **b.** $g(x) = \ln x$

Solution

a. For $y = \log x$ we illustrate the first graphical method.

$$f^{-1}(x) = 10^x \qquad f(x) = \log x$$

x	$f^{-1}(x)$
−3	0.001
−2	0.01
−1	0.1
0	1
1	10
2	100
3	1000

Reverse coordinates ⟶

x	f(x)
0.001	−3
0.01	−2
0.1	−1
1	0
10	1
100	2
1000	3

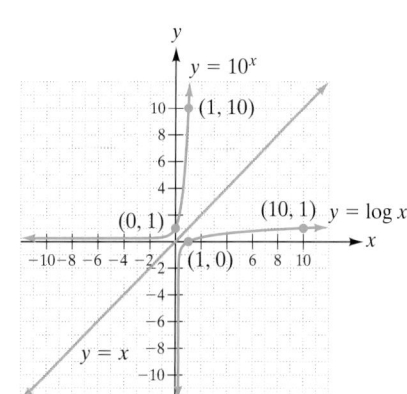

Calculator Check

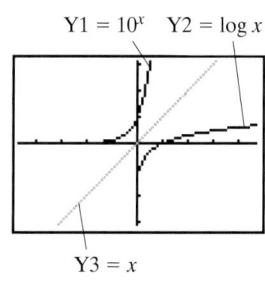

$(-4.7, 4.7, -3.1, 3.1)$

b. For $g(x) = \ln x$, we illustrate the second graphical method.

x	g(x)
0.001	−6.908
0.01	−4.605
0.1	−2.303
0.5	−0.693
1	0
2	0.693
3	1.099
4	1.386
5	1.609
6	1.792

$g(x) = \ln x$

(3, 1.099) (5, 1.609)

(1, 0)

(0.1, −2.303)

Calculator Check

Y1 = ln x

(−4.7, 4.7, −3.1, 3.1)

We can summarize the characteristics of a logarithmic function and its graph by remembering that a logarithmic function is an inverse of an exponential function. Therefore, the domain and range are interchanged.

CHARACTERISTICS OF A LOGARITHMIC FUNCTION AND ITS GRAPH

Given the logarithmic function $f(x) = \log_a x$ and its graph, we have the following characteristics:

Domain	The set of all positive real numbers
Range	The set of all real numbers

The function is one-to-one.

y-intercept	There is no y-intercept. The graph of the function approaches, but does not reach, the y-axis.
x-intercept	$(1, 0)$

If $a > 1$, then the function is always increasing.
If $0 < a < 1$, then the function is always decreasing.

 Objective 12.3.3 CHECKUP

In exercises 1 and 2, use a table of values to graph each logarithmic function.

1. $f(x) = \log_3 x$

2. a. $g(x) = \log(3x)$ **b.** $h(x) = \ln(3x)$

3. Explain the relationship between the domain and the range of an exponential function and the domain and the range of its inverse function—that is, the corresponding logarithmic function.

Objective 12.3.4   Modeling the Real World

Logarithmic functions are used to model many different real-world situations, especially when the independent variable can take a wide range of values. The reason for this is that the values of the logarithmic function change slowly over a large range of values of the domain. Examples of logarithmic functions are found in many of the sciences. For instance, the magnitude of an earthquake is measured on a Richter scale, which uses a logarithmic function to describe motion from millionths of an inch to tens of feet. The loudness of a sound, from the merest whisper to the roar of thunder, is measured in decibels, which are defined by a logarithmic function.

Another important application of common logarithms is found in chemistry. The pH value of a substance is its measure of acidity or alkalinity. Pure water has a pH of

7.0. A pH greater than 7.0 represents an alkaline substance, and a pH value less than 7.0 represents an acidic substance.

The pH of a substance is defined by the function

$$pH = -\log[H^+]$$

where $[H^+]$ is the hydrogen ion concentration in moles per liter.

EXAMPLE 9   Orange juice has a hydrogen ion concentration of 6.3×10^{-4} moles per liter. Determine the pH of orange juice.

```
-log(6.3*10^-4)
      3.200659451
```

Calculator Solution

Substitute 6.3×10^{-4} for $[H^+]$ in the pH formula.

$$pH = -\log[H^+]$$
$$pH = -\log(6.3 \times 10^{-4})$$
$$pH \approx 3.2$$

EXAMPLE 10   Crackers have a pH of 8.4. Determine their hydrogen ion concentration.

Solution

Substitute 8.4 into the formula for pH.

```
10^(-8.4)
    3.981071706E-9
```

$$pH = -\log[H^+]$$
$$8.4 = -\log[H^+]$$
$$-8.4 = \log[H^+] \quad \text{Divide both sides by } -1.$$
$$10^{-8.4} = [H^+] \quad \text{Write as an exponential equation.}$$
$$4.0 \times 10^{-9} \approx [H^+]$$

Note: This calculator value is rounded to one decimal place.

APPLICATION

The magnitude R, measured on the Richter scale, of an earthquake of intensity I is defined by the function $R = \log\dfrac{I}{I_0}$, where I_0 is the intensity of a very small vibration in the Earth used as a standard. The San Francisco earthquake of 1906 had a magnitude of 8.3 on the Richter scale. Eighty-three years later, in 1989, San Francisco had another earthquake, this time measuring 7.1.

  a. Determine the intensity of each earthquake.
  b. The difference on the Richter scale of the 1906 and 1989 earthquakes is 1.2. Determine the ratio of the intensity of the 1906 earthquake to the 1989 earthquake.

Discussion

a. Use the formula $R = \log\dfrac{I}{I_0}$ with $R = 8.3$ and $R = 7.1$.

$$R = \log\frac{I}{I_0} \qquad\qquad R = \log\frac{I}{I_0}$$

$$8.3 = \log\frac{I}{I_0} \qquad 7.1 = \log\frac{I}{I_0} \quad \text{Substitute values.}$$

$$10^{8.3} = \frac{I}{I_0} \qquad 10^{7.1} = \frac{I}{I_0} \quad \text{Write exponential equations.}$$

$$I = 10^{8.3}I_0 \qquad I = 10^{7.1}I_0$$

The intensity of the 1906 earthquake was $10^{8.3}I_0$, and the intensity of the 1989 earthquake was $10^{7.1}I_0$.

(continued on page 972)

b. The ratio of the intensity of the 1906 earthquake to the intensity of the 1989

earthquake is $\dfrac{10^{8.3}I_0}{10^{7.1}I_0} = \dfrac{10^{8.3}}{10^{7.1}} \approx 15.8$.

The intensity of the 1906 earthquake was

approximately 15.8 times as great as that of the 1989 earthquake.

Note: These magnitudes have been revised. See the 12.3.4 Checkup for additional information.

✓ Objective 12.3.4 *CHECKUP*

1. Pure water has a pH of 7.0. What is its hydrogen ion concentration?
2. Until 1979, an earthquake of magnitude 8.5 on the Richter scale was thought to be the most powerful possible. Since then, improvements in seismic measuring techniques have enabled scientists to refine the scale. Now 9.5 is considered

to be the practical limit to measuring an earthquake's magnitude. As a result, the magnitude of the Alaskan earthquake of 1964 has been revised upward to 9.2 on the Richter scale. How does its intensity compare with that of the 1989 San Francisco earthquake, which had a magnitude of 7.1 on the Richter scale?

12.3 EXERCISES

 Student Solutions Manual    PH Math/Tutor Center   CD Video   *Math XL* MathXL®   *MyMathLab* MyMathLab   Interactmath.com

Determine the inverse logarithmic function for each exponential function. (Note: k and b are constants.)

1. $f(x) = 11^x$ **2.** $h(x) = 15^x$ **3.** $g(x) = 6^x$ **4.** $p(x) = 29^x$

5. $H(x) = k^x$ **6.** $J(x) = b^x$

Evaluate.

7. $\log_2 64$ **8.** $\log_2 128$ **9.** $\log_3 243$ **10.** $\log_3 729$

11. $\log_4 256$ **12.** $\log_5 125$ **13.** $\log_2 \dfrac{1}{8}$ **14.** $\log_4 \dfrac{1}{16}$

15. $\log_4 0.25$ **16.** $\log_2 0.125$ **17.** $\log_3 \dfrac{1}{81}$ **18.** $\log_5 \dfrac{1}{125}$

Evaluate and check with your calculator.

19. $\log 10$ **20.** $\log 10{,}000$ **21.** $\log 0.0001$ **22.** $\log 0.000001$

23. $\ln e^3$ **24.** $\ln e^7$ **25.** $\ln e^{-5}$ **26.** $\ln e^{-8}$

27. $\ln \dfrac{1}{e^5}$ **28.** $\ln \dfrac{1}{e^7}$

Evaluate, using your calculator.

29. $\log 15$ **30.** $\log 23$ **31.** $\log \dfrac{1}{12}$ **32.** $\log \dfrac{1}{19}$

33. $\log 1.35$ **34.** $\log 12.5$ **35.** $\ln 14$ **36.** $\ln 27$

37. $\ln 2.85$ **38.** $\ln 11.6$ **39.** $\ln \dfrac{1}{5}$ **40.** $\ln \dfrac{1}{15}$

Evaluate each logarithm, using common logarithms to change the base.

41. $\log_4 12$ **42.** $\log_5 28$ **43.** $\log_2 10$ **44.** $\log_4 100$

45. $\log_5 2.88$ **46.** $\log_3 14.7$ **47.** $\log_5 \dfrac{2}{3}$ **48.** $\log_3 \dfrac{3}{5}$

Evaluate each logarithm, using natural logarithms to change the base.

49. $\log_8 15$ **50.** $\log_6 35$ **51.** $\log_3 5.9$ **52.** $\log_7 3.75$

53. $\log_5 \dfrac{1}{7}$ **54.** $\log_{12} \dfrac{1}{3}$

In exercises 55–60, create a table of values and graph the function.

55. $f(x) = \log_5 x$ **56.** $F(x) = \log_7 x$ **57.** $g(x) = \log(x + 2)$ **58.** $G(x) = \log(x - 2)$

59. $h(x) = \ln(x + 2)$ **60.** $H(x) = \ln(x - 2)$

Graph the following functions. Determine the domain and range. Where is each function increasing or decreasing? Identify any maximum or minimum values.

61. $f(x) = \log|x|$ **62.** $g(x) = \ln x^2$ **63.** $f(x) = (\log x)^2$ **64.** $g(x) = |\ln x|$

65. Rainwater typically has a pH of 6.2. Determine its hydrogen ion concentration.

66. Acid rain in many parts of the world has a pH value as low as 3. What is the hydrogen ion concentration of this level of acid rain?

67. Determine the pH value of seawater if its hydrogen ion concentration is 3.2×10^{-9} moles per liter.

68. What is the pH value of milk, whose hydrogen ion concentration is 4×10^{-7} moles per liter?

69. An estimated 50,000 earthquakes of magnitude 3.5 occur worldwide each year. How do these compare in intensity with the 1906 San Francisco earthquake, which had a magnitude of 8.3 (before the revision mentioned in the previous Checkup) on the Richter scale?

70. Every year, there are approximately 800 earthquakes worldwide with a magnitude of 5.5 on the Richter scale. How do these compare in intensity with the 1989 San Francisco earthquake, which had a magnitude of 7.1 on the Richter scale?

71. The number of U.S. commercial radio stations classified as Soft Adult Contemporary may be estimated by the function $S(x) = 348 - 11 \ln x$, where x is the number of years after 2000. How many Soft Adult Contemporary stations will there be in 2007? In what year will there be 315 such stations?

72. The percent of recorded music sales in cassette format may be estimated by the function $R(x) = 3.31 - 1.13 \ln x$, where x is the number of years after 2000. What will be the percent of sales in cassette format in 2007? In what year will cassettes no longer be part of recorded music sales?

12.3 Calculator Exercises

Part 1. Exploring logarithmic models

Use your calculator to graph the following logarithmic functions:

1. $f(x) = \log x$ **2.** $g(x) = \log(x + 1)$ **3.** $h(x) = \log x + \log(x + 1)$

4. $k(x) = \log[x(x + 1)]$ **5.** $j(x) = \log x - \log(x + 1)$ **6.** $m(x) = \log\left(\dfrac{x}{x + 1}\right)$

Compare the graphs of exercises 3 and 4. Then compare the graphs of exercises 5 and 6. In each pair of exercises, do the graphs appear to be the same? How can you check this using your calculator? If the graphs are the same, does that suggest a

relationship to the logarithm of a product or the logarithm of a quotient? How would you state this relationship? Are there any restrictions on the domains of the functions?

Part 2. Natural logarithmic regression

In this section we will again utilize the regression analysis feature of our calculator to find an equation for a curve. We enter the data points in the same manner as in previous chapters using the STAT EDIT menu. We will then choose LnReg (Natural Logarithmic Regression) under the STAT CALC menu. The

form of the equation generated will be $y = a + b \ln x$, and the values for a and b will be given. When we enter the data points, we need to remember that 0 is restricted from the domain of a logarithmic function and therefore we cannot enter $x = 0$ in our set of values.

Use the method of logarithmic regression to find the logarithmic function that best fits the following data sets. Assuming trends continue, use your model to answer the questions.

1.

Year	Percent Unemployment in France
2001	8.5
2002	8.8
2003	9.3

What will the percent unemployment be in 2008? In what year will there be 10% unemployment?

2.

Year	U.S. Production of Sugar Beets in Thousands of Tons
2001	25,764
2002	27,718
2003	30,605

What will production be in 2010? In what year will production be 40,000,000 tons?

3.

Year	U.S. Disposable Personal Income in Billions of Dollars
2001	7486.8
2002	7827.7
2003	8159.9

What will disposable personal income be in 2008? In what year will disposable personal income be about 9 trillion dollars?

12.3 Writing Exercises

1. Explain the difference between $\log_3 5$ and $\log_5 3$. Evaluate these logarithms, and use your calculator to help you see the difference.

2. Explain the difference between the functions $y = \log x + 2$ and $y = \log(x + 2)$. Graph the functions on your calculator to help you see the difference between them.

3. How does the domain of the function $y = \log x + 2$ differ from the domain of the function $y = \log(x + 2)$?

12.4 PROPERTIES OF LOGARITHMS

OBJECTIVES
1. Rewrite logarithmic expressions by using the properties of logarithms.
2. Model real-world situations by using logarithms.

APPLICATION

If you change the speakers in your stereo system, going from large speakers to smaller ones, there will be a peak response.

To determine the peak response, you must evaluate the expression

$$20[\log 2.6 + \log Q_s + 0.35(\log V_a - \log V_b)]$$

where V_a = volume of the larger speaker, V_b = volume of the smaller speaker, and Q_s is the Q of the system (the ratio of the reactance to the resistance of the circuit). Condense this logarithmic expression.

After completing this section, we will discuss this application further. See page 977.

Objective 12.4.1   Using Properties of Logarithms

In Section 12.3, we discussed properties of logarithms that were derived from the definition of logarithms. In order to rewrite logarithmic expressions, we need to expand our list of properties. Since we know that logarithms are exponents, by definition, we should expect to have properties of logarithms that correspond to the properties of exponents that we discussed in Chapter 7. That is,

$$a^m a^n = a^{m+n} \quad \text{Product rule}$$

$$\frac{a^m}{a^n} = a^{m-n} \quad \text{Quotient rule}$$

$$(a^m)^n = a^{mn} \quad \text{Power-to-a-power rule}$$

Complete the following set of exercises on your calculator to discover these properties.

Guided Discovery 5   Product, Quotient, and Power Rules of Logarithms

Approximate each expression, and compare the results obtained in the left column with the corresponding results in the right column.

1. Product rule

   a. $\log(3 \cdot 4) \approx$ _____   **b.** $\log 3 + \log 4 \approx$ _____

   c. $\ln(2 \cdot 5) \approx$ _____   **d.** $\ln 2 + \ln 5 \approx$ _____

2. Quotient rule

   a. $\log \dfrac{3}{4} \approx$ _____   **b.** $\log 3 - \log 4 \approx$ _____

   c. $\ln \dfrac{2}{5} \approx$ _____   **d.** $\ln 2 - \ln 5 \approx$ _____

3. Power rule

   a. $\log 3^4 \approx$ _____   **b.** $4 \log 3 \approx$ _____

   c. $\ln 2^5 \approx$ _____   **d.** $5 \ln 2 \approx$ _____

Write the following rules of logarithms:

4. Product rule

5. Quotient rule

6. Power rule

For the product rule, the logarithm of a product is equal to the sum of the logarithms of the factors. For the quotient rule, the logarithm of a quotient is equal to the difference of the logarithm of the numerator and the logarithm of the denominator. For the power rule, the logarithm of a base raised to a power is equal to the product of the power and the logarithm of the base.

PRODUCT, QUOTIENT, AND POWER RULES OF LOGARITHMS

Assume that m and n are any real number, variable, or expression, where $m > 0$ and $n > 0$. Also, assume that $a > 0$, $a \neq 1$, and c is a real number.

	Logarithm with Base a	Natural Logarithm
Product rule	$\log_a mn = \log_a m + \log_a n$	$\ln mn = \ln m + \ln n$
Quotient rule	$\log_a \dfrac{m}{n} = \log_a m - \log_a n$	$\ln \dfrac{m}{n} = \ln m - \ln n$
Power rule	$\log_a m^c = c \log_a m$	$\ln m^c = c \ln m$

 TAKE NOTE There is no property of logarithms that can be used to simplify the log of a sum, $\log_a(m + n)$, or the log of a difference, $\log_a(m - n)$.

We can use the properties of logarithms stated in this section and Section 12.3 to rewrite logarithms. We will be working with variable expressions as well as numeric ones.

We will assume that the variables do not represent values for which the expression is not defined.

First, we **expand** a logarithm by using the properties stated previously and writing a sum, a difference, or a product.

EXAMPLE 1   Expand each logarithmic expression.

   a. $\log 3x$ **b.** $\log_2 \dfrac{x}{3}$ **c.** $\log_5 x^3$

Solution

a. $\log 3x = \log 3 + \log x$ Product rule

b. $\log_2 \dfrac{x}{3} = \log_2 x - \log_2 3$ Quotient rule

c. $\log_5 x^3 = 3 \log_5 x$ Power rule

We **condense** a logarithm by using the properties stated previously, reading right to left. In other words, we write a product, quotient, or power.

EXAMPLE 2   Condense each logarithmic expression.

a. $\ln 2 - \ln x$ **b.** $\ln 2 + \ln x + \ln y$ **c.** $2 \ln y$

Solution

a. $\ln 2 - \ln x = \ln \dfrac{2}{x}$ Quotient rule

b. $\ln 2 + \ln x + \ln y = \ln 2xy$ Product rule

c. $2 \ln y = \ln y^2$ Power rule

We can combine the rules of exponents to rewrite more complicated expressions. Remember, the logarithms must have the same base in order to apply the rules of logarithms.

EXAMPLE 3   Expand the logarithmic expression $\log_3 \sqrt{3x}$.

Solution

$$\log_3 \sqrt{3x} = \log_3 (3x)^{1/2} \qquad \text{Definition of square root}$$

$$= \frac{1}{2}\log_3 3x \qquad \text{Power rule}$$

$$= \frac{1}{2}(\log_3 3 + \log_3 x) \qquad \text{Product rule}$$

$$= \frac{1}{2}\log_3 3 + \frac{1}{2}\log_3 x \qquad \text{Distribute } \tfrac{1}{2}.$$

$$= \frac{1}{2}(1) + \frac{1}{2}\log_3 x \qquad \log_3 3 = 1$$

$$= \frac{1}{2} + \frac{1}{2}\log_3 x$$

EXAMPLE 4   Condense the logarithmic expression $2 \ln(2x + 3) + \ln(x + 3) - \ln x$.

Solution

$$2 \ln(2x + 3) + \ln(x + 3) - \ln x$$

$$= \ln(2x + 3)^2 + \ln(x + 3) - \ln x \qquad \text{Power rule}$$

$$= \ln(2x + 3)^2(x + 3) - \ln x \qquad \text{Product rule}$$

$$= \ln \frac{(2x + 3)^2(x + 3)}{x} \qquad \text{Quotient rule}$$

✓ Objective 12.4.1 *CHECKUP*

1. Expand each logarithmic expression.

   a. $\log_5 11x$ **b.** $\ln \dfrac{x}{y}$ **c.** $\ln x^2$

2. Condense each logarithmic expression.

   a. $\log 3 - \log y$ **b.** $\log x + \log y - \log z$ **c.** $-3 \ln x$

3. Expand the logarithmic expression $\log_5 5x^2$.

4. Condense $3 \log(2x - 1) - \log x + \log(x + 1)$.

5. What does it mean to expand a logarithmic expression?

6. What does it mean to condense a logarithmic expression?

Objective 12.4.2 **Modeling the Real World**

Condensing logarithmic expressions is an important skill needed to solve logarithmic equations. Condensing logarithms also may simplify the evaluation of expressions by enabling us to calculate a single logarithm instead of calculating more than one logarithm in an expression. The accuracy of our results in evaluating one expression (rounding once) may be greater than when we evaluate an expression in which we round more than one value.

EXAMPLE 5

The power gain, in decibels (dB), of an electronic device is determined by the logarithmic expression $10(\log P_0 - \log P_i)$, where P_0 is the output power, in watts (W), and P_i is the input power, in watts.

a. Condense the expression, using the rules of logarithms.

b. Use the expression found in part **a** to determine the power gain of an amplifier with an output of 25.0 W and an input of 0.625 W.

Solution

a. $10(\log P_0 - \log P_i) = 10\left[\log\left(\dfrac{P_0}{P_i}\right)\right]$ Quotient rule

$$= \log\left(\dfrac{P_0}{P_i}\right)^{10} \qquad \text{Power rule}$$

b. $\log\left(\dfrac{P_0}{P_i}\right)^{10} = \log\left(\dfrac{25.0}{0.625}\right)^{10} \approx 16.021 \text{ dB}$

APPLICATION

  If you change the speakers in your stereo system, going from large speakers to smaller ones, there will be a peak response.
  To determine the peak response, you must evaluate the expression

$$20[\log 2.6 + \log Q_s + 0.35(\log V_a - \log V_b)]$$

where V_a = volume of the larger speaker, V_b = volume of the smaller speaker, and Q_s is the Q of the system (the ratio of the reactance to the resistance of the circuit). Condense this logarithmic expression.

Discussion

$$20[\log 2.6 + \log Q_s + 0.35(\log V_a - \log V_b)]$$

$$= 20\left[\log 2.6 + \log Q_s + 0.35\log\left(\dfrac{V_a}{V_b}\right)\right] \qquad \text{Quotient rule}$$

$$= 20\left[\log 2.6 + \log Q_s + \log\left(\dfrac{V_a}{V_b}\right)^{0.35}\right] \qquad \text{Power rule}$$

$$= 20\log\left[(2.6)(Q_s)\left(\dfrac{V_a}{V_b}\right)^{0.35}\right] \qquad \text{Product rule}$$

$$= \log\left[2.6Q_s\left(\dfrac{V_a}{V_b}\right)^{0.35}\right]^{20} \qquad \text{Power rule}$$

Objective 12.4.2 *CHECKUP*

1. Use the rules of logarithms to expand the right side of each application from geometry.

   a. $\ln A = \ln(\pi r^2)$ **b.** $\log A = \log\left(\frac{1}{2}bh\right)$

2. Light passing through a transparent solution follows the model

   $$y = c(\ln I_0 - \ln I)$$

   where c is a constant related to the solution, I_0 is the intensity of the light striking the solution, and I is the intensity at a depth of y units in the solution.

   a. Use the rules of logarithms to condense the right side of the model.

b. If $c = 8.5$ for a solution, find the depth y when the intensity at the surface is three times the intensity at a depth of y units.

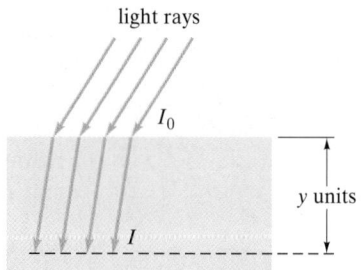

light rays

I_0

y units

I

12.4 EXERCISES

Student Solutions Manual   PH Math/Tutor Center   CD Video   Math XL / MathXL®   MyMathLab / MyMathLab   Interactmath.com

Expand each logarithmic expression.

1. $\log 12a$

2. $\ln 25c$

3. $\ln x^3$

4. $\log z^3$

5. $\log_5 \frac{x}{5}$

6. $\log_7 \frac{7}{y}$

7. $\log \frac{2x^2}{y}$

8. $\log \frac{x^2}{5y^3}$

9. $\log_3 x^3 y^2$

10. $\log_2 a^2 b^4$

11. $\ln \sqrt[3]{xy^2}$

12. $\log \sqrt[4]{x^3 y}$

13. $\log \frac{\sqrt{2x}}{\sqrt[3]{y}}$

14. $\ln \frac{\sqrt[3]{3x^2}}{\sqrt{2y}}$

15. $\log_3 3a$

16. $\log_5 5z$

17. $\log_5 10xy$

18. $\log_3 \frac{xy}{6}$

19. $\log_a(ab^2)$

20. $\log_6(3ab^2)$

Condense each logarithmic expression.

21. $\log x + \log(x + 5)$

22. $\log(x - 1) + \log(x + 1)$

23. $2\ln x + 3\ln y$

24. $3\ln b - 2\ln c$

25. $2\log_3(x + 3) - \log_3(x - 1)$

26. $5\log_5(a - 5) + 2\log_5 a$

27. $\frac{1}{2}\ln x - \frac{1}{5}\ln(x + 1)$

28. $\frac{1}{4}\log z - \frac{1}{3}\log(z + 5)$

29. $\log xy - \log xz$

30. $2\log pq - \log p$

In exercises 31 and 32, use the mathematical model for power gain, $G = \log\left(\frac{P_0}{P_i}\right)^{10}$, where P_0 is the output power in watts and P_i is the input power in watts.

31. Determine the power gain G, in decibels, for an amplifier with an output P_0 of 20 watts and an input P_i of 1.5 watts.

32. What is the power gain G, in decibels, of an amplifier with an output P_0 of 30 watts and an input P_i of 2 watts?

In exercises 33 and 34, use the mathematical model for light passing through a transparent solution, $y = c\ln\frac{I_0}{I}$, where I_0 is the intensity of light striking the solution, I is the intensity at a depth of y units in the solution, and c is a related constant.

33. If $c = 12$ for a liquid, find the depth y when the surface intensity I_0 is 3.5 times the intensity at a depth of y units.

34. If $c = 10$ for a liquid, at what depth y will the surface intensity be six times the intensity at a depth of y units?

If money in an account is compounded continuously, the amount in the account will grow to k times the original investment in $t = \frac{\ln k}{r}$ years when the annual rate of interest is r. Use this model for the following exercises:

35. How long will it take the amount invested to triple if the annual interest rate is 5%?

36. At an annual interest rate of 4.5%, how long will it take an investment to double in value?

37. How long will it take an investment to increase to four times its original value if the annual interest rate is 9%?

38. If the annual interest rate is 10%, how long will it take an investment to increase by a factor of 3.5 times its original value?

12.4 Calculator Exercises

You were told that the log of a sum or a difference does not usually simplify. To investigate this claim, graph the functions in exercises 1–4 on your calculator, using a decimal window.

1. $\log 3x$
2. $\log x + \log 2x$
3. $\log(x^2 - x)$
4. $\log x^2 - \log x$
5. Compare the graphs of exercises 1 and 2. Are they equivalent?

6. Compare the graphs of exercises 3 and 4. Are they equivalent?
7. What is wrong with the statement
$\log(A + B) = \log A + \log B$?
8. What is wrong with the statement
$\log(A - B) = \log A - \log B$?

12.4 Writing Exercise

One of the most useful applications of exponential and logarithmic expressions is the determination of the half-life of chemical elements. Find a library or Internet reference that discusses half-life, and write a short summary of what you find. Be sure to cite your reference.

12.5 SOLVING EXPONENTIAL AND LOGARITHMIC EQUATIONS

OBJECTIVES
1 Identify exponential and logarithmic equations in one variable.
2 Solve exponential and logarithmic equations in one variable algebraically.
3 Model real-world situations by using exponential and logarithmic equations in one variable.

APPLICATION

According to Newton's law of cooling, the temperature T of a body t minutes after it is placed in surroundings having a constant temperature T_0 is determined by the function $T(t) = T_0 + Ce^{-kt}$, where C is the difference between the initial temperature and the surrounding temperature and k is the cooling constant.

a. Boiling water (100°C) is placed in a freezer at 0°C. After 25 minutes, the water temperature is 50°C. Determine the constant of cooling.

b. Determine the temperature of the water after 2 hours.

After completing this section, we will discuss this application further. See page 986.

Objective 12.5.1

Exponential and Logarithmic Equations in One Variable

If we take the logarithm of an expression, we call the expression the **argument** of the logarithm. For example, the expression $(2x + 1)$ is the argument of $\log(2x + 1)$. A **logarithmic equation in one variable**, or, simply, **logarithmic equation**, is an equation with a logarithmic expression having a variable in the argument of the logarithm. For example, the following are logarithmic equations:

$$\log_3 x = 5 \qquad \ln(x + 1) = \ln 5$$

An **exponential equation in one variable**, or, simply, **exponential equation**, is an equation with an exponential expression with a variable exponent. For example, the following are exponential equations:

$$4^x = 26 \qquad e^x = e^{2x-3}$$

EXAMPLE 1	Identify each equation as exponential, logarithmic, or neither.

a. $\ln 3 = x + 4$ **b.** $10e^x = 100$ **c.** $x^5 + 6 = \log 10$

Solution

a. $\ln 3 = x + 4$ is neither a logarithmic nor an exponential equation. The logarithmic argument does not contain a variable; therefore, $\ln 3$ represents a number. The equation is a linear equation.

b. $10e^x = 100$ is an exponential equation, because the exponent of the exponential expression contains a variable.

c. $x^5 + 6 = \log 10$ is neither a logarithmic nor an exponential equation. The exponential expression does not have a variable exponent, and the logarithmic expression is a number. The equation is a polynomial equation. ■

Objective 12.5.1 *CHECKUP*

1. Identify each equation as exponential, logarithmic, or neither.
   a. $8 - x = e^2$ **b.** $2 + \log x = 5$ **c.** $2^x = 4^{x+3}$

2. What is the difference between an exponential equation in one variable and a logarithmic equation in one variable? ▨

Objective 12.5.2   **Solving Equations**

We are now ready to solve exponential and logarithmic equations algebraically. To solve these equations, we need to discuss certain properties. Complete the following set of exercises to discover two such properties.

Guided Discovery 6   Properties of Exponential and Logarithmic Equations

Complete the following statements with "true" or "false":

1. a. If $2 = 2$ is true, then $5^2 = 5^2$ is ____.
   b. If $2 = 2$ is true, then $12^2 = 12^2$ is ____.
   c. If $2 = 2$ is true, then $e^2 = e^2$ is ____.

Write a rule for determining a true equation using exponentials.

2. a. If $2 = 2$ is true, then $\log_5 2 = \log_5 2$ is ____.
   b. If $2 = 2$ is true, then $\log_{12} 2 = \log_{12} 2$ is ____.
   c. If $2 = 2$ is true, then $\ln 2 = \ln 2$ is ____.

Write a rule for determining a true equation using logarithms.

If we begin with an equation that is true and write an exponential expression for each side of the equation, using the same base and the original expressions as exponents, the result is a true equation. If we begin with an equation that is true and take the same logarithm of both expressions contained in the equation, the result is a true equation.

PROPERTIES OF EXPONENTIAL AND LOGARITHMIC EQUATIONS

For a positive real number $a \neq 1$ and real numbers x and y, the following properties hold:

1. a. If $a^x = a^y$, then $x = y$.   **b.** If $x = y$ then $a^x = a^y$.

For positive real numbers x, y, and $a \neq 1$, the following properties hold:

2. a. If $\log_a x = \log_a y$, then $x = y$.   **b.** If $x = y$, then $\log_a x = \log_a y$.

First, we will discuss solving exponential equations. One example is an exponential equation that is written with both sides having exponential expressions with the same base. We use property 1a to solve this exponential equation by equating the exponents. For example, solve $4^x = 4^3$.

$$4^x = 4^3$$
$$x = 3 \qquad \text{Equate the exponents of both sides.}$$

Another example is an exponential equation that cannot be written with both sides having exponential expressions with the same base. To solve this type of equation, we choose a logarithm, usually log or ln, and equate the logarithms of both sides, using property 2b. For example, solve $4^x = 5$.

$$4^x = 5$$
$$\ln 4^x = \ln 5 \qquad \text{Equate the natural logarithms of both sides.}$$
$$x \ln 4 = \ln 5 \qquad \text{Power rule}$$
$$x = \frac{\ln 5}{\ln 4} \qquad \text{Divide both sides by ln 4.}$$
$$x \approx 1.16$$

SOLVING AN EXPONENTIAL EQUATION ALGEBRAICALLY

To solve an exponential equation algebraically,

- Write both sides of the equation as exponential expressions with the same base, equate the exponents, and solve for the variable.

or

- Isolate the exponential expression, take the logarithms of both sides, and solve for the variable.

EXAMPLE 2

Solve algebraically. Check your solution by substitution, numerically, or graphically.

a. $2^x = 32$ **b.** $e^x = 72$ **c.** $5e^{2x} = 8$

Solution

a. $2^x = 32$
$$2^x = 2^5 \qquad \text{Rewrite 32 with the same base as the expression on the left, or 2: } 32 = 2^5.$$
$$x = 5 \qquad \text{Equate the exponents of both sides.}$$

Substitution Check

$$\frac{2^x = 32}{2^5 \,\big|\, 32}$$
$$32 \,\big|$$

Since $32 = 32$, the solution checks.

b. $e^x = 72$
$$\ln e^x = \ln 72 \qquad \text{Equate the natural logarithms of both sides.}$$
$$x = \ln 72 \qquad \text{Property of natural logarithms}$$
$$x \approx 4.277$$

Graphic Check

$Y1 = e^x$ $Y2 = 72$

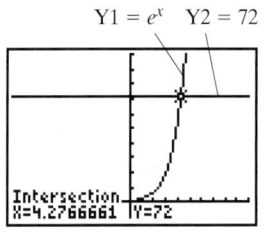

Intersection
X=4.2766661 Y=72

$(-10, 10, -10, 100)$

The solution is about 4.277 because the x-coordinate of the intersection is about 4.277.

c. $5e^{2x} = 8$

$e^{2x} = \dfrac{8}{5}$ Divide both sides by 5.

$\ln e^{2x} = \ln \dfrac{8}{5}$ Equate the natural logarithms of both sides.

$2x = \ln \dfrac{8}{5}$ Property of natural logarithms, $\ln e^{2x} = 2x$.

$x = \dfrac{\ln \dfrac{8}{5}}{2}$ Divide both sides by 2.

$x \approx 0.235$

Graphic Check

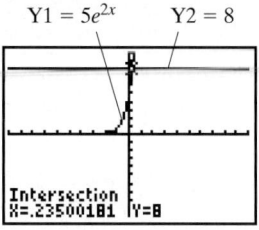

$(-10, 10, -10, 10)$

The solution is about 0.235 because the x-coordinate of the intersection is about 0.235.

We use property 2a to solve logarithmic equations by equating the arguments of logarithms with the same base. For example, solve $\ln(x + 3) = \ln 2$.

$\ln(x + 3) = \ln 2$

$x + 3 = 2$ Equate the arguments of the logarithms of both sides.

$x = -1$ Subtract 3 from both sides.

To solve a logarithmic equation that cannot be written with the same base, we isolate the logarithmic expression, use the definition of logarithms to write an exponential equation, and solve for the variable. For example, solve $\log_7(2x) = 6$.

$\log_7(2x) = 6$

$7^6 = 2x$ Definition of logarithms

$\dfrac{7^6}{2} = x$ Divide both sides by 2.

$x = 58824.5$

SOLVING A LOGARITHMIC EQUATION ALGEBRAICALLY

To solve a logarithmic equation algebraically,

- Determine the restricted values.
- Write both sides of the equation as logarithmic expressions with the same base, equate the arguments, and solve for the variable.

or

- Isolate the logarithmic expression, use the definition of logarithms to write an exponential equation, and solve for the variable.

EXAMPLE 3   Solve algebraically. Check your solution by substitution, numerically, or graphically.

a. $\log x + \log(x - 2) = \log 8$ **b.** $3 \ln 2x = 9$

Algebraic Solution

a. Logarithms are defined for positive values only. Therefore, the restricted values are $x \le 0$ and $x - 2 \le 0$ or $x \le 2$.

$$\log x + \log(x - 2) = \log 8$$
$$\log[x(x - 2)] = \log 8 \qquad \text{Product rule.}$$
$$x(x - 2) = 8 \qquad \text{Equate the arguments of the logarithms of both sides.}$$

$$x^2 - 2x - 8 = 0$$
$$(x - 4)(x + 2) = 0$$
$$x - 4 = 0 \quad \text{or} \quad x + 2 = 0$$
$$x = 4 \qquad\qquad x = -2$$

Since $x = -2$ is a restricted value, the only solution is 4.

b. The restricted values are $2x \le 0$, or $x \le 0$.

$$3 \ln 2x = 9$$
$$\ln 2x = 3 \qquad \text{Divide both sides by 3.}$$
$$e^3 = 2x \qquad \text{Definition of natural logarithms.}$$
$$\frac{e^3}{2} = x \qquad \text{Divide both sides by 2.}$$
$$x \approx 10.043$$

Graphic Check

$Y2 = \log 8 \qquad Y1 = \log x + \log (x - 2)$

Intersection
X=4   Y=.90308999

$(-10, 10, -10, 10)$

According to the graph, there is only one solution, 4. Note that -2 is a restricted value and cannot be a solution.

Graphic Check

$Y2 = 9 \qquad Y1 = 3 \ln 2x$

Intersection
X=10.042768   Y=9

$(-10, 20, -10, 20)$

The solution is about 10.043 because the x-coordinate of the intersection is about 10.043. ■

An exponential equation or a logarithmic equation may not have a solution, or it may have more than one solution. The first of these alternatives occurs if the equation is a contradiction, the second if it is an identity.

EXAMPLE 4

Solve $\log x^4 - \log x = \log x^3$.

Solution

$$\log x^4 - \log x = \log x^3$$
$$\log\left(\frac{x^4}{x}\right) = \log x^3 \qquad \text{Quotient rule}$$
$$\log x^3 = \log x^3 \qquad \text{Simplify.}$$
$$x^3 = x^3 \qquad \text{Equate the arguments of the logarithms of both sides.}$$
$$x^3 - x^3 = x^3 - x^3 \qquad \text{Subtract } x^3 \text{ from both sides.}$$
$$0 = 0$$

This is an identity. The equation thus has an infinite number of solutions. The solution set is the set of all positive real numbers, the permissible values of the variables in the equation. ■

ALGEBRAIC SOLUTIONS OF AN EXPONENTIAL OR LOGARITHMIC EQUATION

To solve an exponential or a logarithmic equation algebraically, determine the restricted values and solve the equation. One of three possibilities will occur.

One or more solutions exist.

No solution exists. The solution process results in a contradiction.

An infinite number of solutions exist. The solution set is the set of all real numbers not equal to the restricted values. The solution process results in an identity.

✓ Objective 12.5.2 *CHECKUP*

In exercises 1–3, solve algebraically.

1. a. $3^x = 81$ **b.** $e^x = 3$ **c.** $2e^x = 7$

2. a. $\ln 2 + 2 \ln x = \ln(6 - x)$ **b.** $5 + \log 3x = 7$

3. $2^{x(x-2)} = 2^{(x-1)^2}$

4. What does it mean to solve an exponential or a logarithmic equation in one variable by the algebraic method?

5. What advantage is there in using the algebraic method over the numerical or graphical method of solving an exponential or a logarithmic equation? ▪

Objective 12.5.3   Modeling the Real World

In Section 12.2, we determined the balance in an account earning continuously compounded interest. This is one example of a quantity that increases over time according to the **exponential growth** model. A similar **exponential decay** model represents a quantity that decreases steadily over time. Examples of these models are found in biology, chemistry, and business, as well as other physical and social sciences.

The exponential growth model is represented by the function $A(t) = A_0 e^{kt}$, where $A(t)$ is the amount of a substance present at time t, A_0 is the initial amount of the substance present, and k represents the growth constant ($k > 0$). The exponential decay model is represented by the same function, except that the growth factor is negative ($k < 0$).

EXAMPLE 5

According to the U.S. Bureau of the Census, the population of the United States in 2005 was 296 million people. The population is projected to increase to 421 million people in 2050.

a. Determine the growth constant.

b. Write an exponential growth function to model the U.S. population.

c. Use the function in part **b** to estimate the U.S. population in 2025.

Solution

a. $A(t) = A_0 e^{kt}$ Exponential growth function; t = number of years after 2005, $A(t) = 421$, $A_0 = 296$, $t = 2050 - 2005 = 45$

$421 = 296 e^{k(45)}$

$\dfrac{421}{296} = e^{45k}$ Divide both sides by 296.

$\ln \dfrac{421}{296} = \ln e^{45k}$ Equate the natural logarithms of both sides.

$\ln \dfrac{421}{296} = 45k$ Property of natural logarithms, $e^{45k} = 45k$

$k = \dfrac{1}{45} \ln \dfrac{421}{296}$ Multiply both sides by $\frac{1}{45}$.

$k \approx 0.008$

The growth constant is about 0.008.

b. $A(t) = A_0 e^{kt}$ Exponential growth function; t = number of years after 2005

$A(t) \approx 296 e^{0.008t}$ $A(t)$ = population in millions, A_0 = 296 million, $k \approx 0.008$, t = number of years after 2005

c. $A(t) \approx 296 e^{0.008t}$

$A(20) \approx 296 e^{0.008(20)}$ Substitute 20 for t(2025 − 2005).

$A(20) \approx 347$

The population of the United States will be approximately 347 million in 2025. ■

EXAMPLE 6

The gross national product has risen exponentially since 2000. The gross national product can be approximated by the exponential growth model $A(t) = A_0 e^{0.0376t}$, where t is the number of years after 2000 and A_0 is the gross national product for 2000. Determine when the 2000 gross national product will double.

Solution

Let A_0 = the gross national product in 2000
  $2A_0$ = double the 2000 gross national product

Therefore, let $A(t) = 2A_0$ and solve for t.

$A(t) = A_0 e^{0.0376t}$

$2A_0 = A_0 e^{0.0376t}$

$2 = e^{0.0376t}$ Divide both sides by A_0.

$\ln 2 = \ln e^{0.0376t}$ Equate the natural logarithms of both sides.

$\ln 2 = 0.0376t$ Property of natural logarithms, $e^{0.0376t} = 0.0376t$

$t = \dfrac{\ln 2}{0.0376}$ Divide both sides by 0.0376.

$t \approx 18.4$

The 2000 gross national product will double in about 18 years. ■

If a quantity grows exponentially, the amount of time it takes to increase to twice its original amount is called the **doubling time**. Note that the amount originally present does not affect this time.

If a quantity decays exponentially, the amount of time it takes to diminish to half of its original amount is called the **half-life**. As with the doubling time, the amount originally present does not affect this time.

EXAMPLE 7

Carbon-14 (C-14) is a radioactive form of carbon found in all living organisms. After an organism dies, the C-14 in it begins to decay. The rate of decay appears to be steady. The half-life of C-14 is about 5730 years. The exponential decay function can be used to approximate the amount of C-14 present t years after an organism dies.

a. Determine the decay factor.

b. If a fossil is found with one-third the C-14 of its living form, determine the time since the organism died.

Solution

a. A_0 = the original amount of C-14 present

$\frac{1}{2}A_0$ = half the original amount of C-14 present

Therefore, let $A(t) = \frac{1}{2}A_0$ and $t = 5730$, and then solve for k.

$$A(t) = A_0 e^{kt}$$

$$\frac{1}{2}A_0 = A_0 e^{k\cdot 5730}$$

$$\frac{1}{2} = e^{5730k} \qquad \text{Divide both sides by } A_0.$$

$$\ln\frac{1}{2} = \ln e^{5730k} \qquad \text{Equate the natural logarithms of both sides.}$$

$$\ln\frac{1}{2} = 5730k \qquad \text{Property of natural logarithms}$$

$$k = \left(\ln\frac{1}{2}\right)\left(\frac{1}{5730}\right) \qquad \text{Multiply both sides by } \frac{1}{5730}.$$

$$k \approx -0.000121$$

The decay constant is about -0.000121.

b. $\frac{1}{3}A_0$ = one-third of the amount of the original C-14

$$A(t) = A_0 e^{kt}$$

$$\frac{1}{3}A_0 \approx A_0 e^{-0.000121t}$$

$$\frac{1}{3} \approx e^{-0.000121t} \qquad \text{Divide both sides by } A_0.$$

$$\ln\frac{1}{3} \approx \ln e^{-0.000121t} \qquad \text{Equate the natural logarithms of both sides.}$$

$$\ln\frac{1}{3} \approx -0.000121t \qquad \text{Property of natural logarithms.}$$

$$t \approx \left(\ln\frac{1}{3}\right)\left(-\frac{1}{0.000121}\right) \qquad \text{Multiply both sides by } -\frac{1}{0.000121}.$$

$$t \approx 9079.44$$

The organism has been dead about 9079 years.   ■

APPLICATION

According to Newton's law of cooling, the temperature T of a body t minutes after it is placed in surroundings having a constant temperature T_0 is determined by the function $T(t) = T_0 + Ce^{-kt}$, where C is the difference between the initial temperature and the surrounding temperature and k is the cooling constant.

a. Boiling water (100°C) is placed in a freezer at 0°C. After 25 minutes, the water temperature is 50°C. Determine the constant of cooling.

b. Determine the temperature of the water after 2 hours.

Discussion

a. $T(t) = T_0 + Ce^{-kt}$

$50 = 0 + 100e^{-k \cdot 25}$ Substitute 50 for $T(t)$, 0 for T_0, 100 for C, and 25 for t.

$50 = 100e^{-25k}$

$\dfrac{1}{2} = e^{-25k}$ Divide both sides by 100.

$\ln\dfrac{1}{2} = \ln e^{-25k}$ Equate the natural logarithms of both sides.

$\ln\dfrac{1}{2} = -25k$ Property of natural logarithms, $e^{-25k} = -25k$

$k = -\dfrac{1}{25}\ln\dfrac{1}{2}$ Multiply both sides by $-\frac{1}{25}$.

$k \approx 0.0277$

The constant of cooling is about 0.0277.

b. $T(120) \approx 0 + 100e^{-0.0277(120)}$ t is measured in minutes, so substitute 120 for t, 0 for T_0, 100 for C, and -0.0277 for k.

$T(120) \approx 3.6$

The temperature is about 3.6°C after 2 hours.

Objective 12.5.3 *CHECKUP*

1. The U.S. Census Bureau determined the total female population of the United States to be about 150 million in 2005. This population is projected to grow to about 157 million in 2010.
   a. Determine the growth constant.
   b. Write an exponential growth function to model the U.S. female population.
   c. Use the function in part **b** to estimate the U.S. female population in 2025.

2. The gross national product growth model is
   $$A(t) = A_0 e^{0.0376t}$$

   where t is the number of years after 2000 and A_0 is the gross national product for 2000. When will the gross national product triple in value?

3. Radium-226 has a half-life of 1620 years. Determine the decay factor of radium-226. How long will it take for a store of radium-226 to diminish to 90 percent of its original amount?

4. Use Newton's law of cooling to determine the time it would take boiling water to cool to 20°C when placed in a freezer at 0°C.

12.5 EXERCISES

 Student Solutions Manual   PH Math/Tutor Center    CD Video   MathXL®    MyMathLab    Interactmath.com

Identify each equation as exponential, logarithmic, or neither.

1. $-3 + \log x^2 = 1$ **2.** $2e^x - 5 = 3$ **3.** $e^3 + x = 2x - 1$ **4.** $\log x^3 + 3 = 5$

5. $e^{2x} - 1 = 5$ **6.** $\log 8 + x = \log 10$ **7.** $x = \log 4 + \log 7$ **8.** $x + e^2 = 1$

Solve exercises 9–70.

9. $5^{2x} = 625$ **10.** $3^{x+2} = 81$ **11.** $e^t = 2$

12. $e^{3t} + 5 = 7$ **13.** $5^x = 1$ **14.** $3^m = 0.5$

15. $3e^{-x} = 2$ **16.** $e^{-2x} + 1 = 5$ **17.** $(2^{3x})(2^5) = 2^8$

18. $(5^x)(5^{x+3}) = 5^4$ **19.** $2^x = 2^{3x-6}$ **20.** $e^{3x-1} = e^{2x+3}$

21. $5^{2x(x-2)} = 5^{3(x-1)}$ **22.** $7^{a^2+4} = 7^{5a}$ **23.** $e^{x(x-2)} = e^{x+10}$

24. $3^{2x(x+6)} = 3^{5(x+3)}$ **25.** $3^{x+x(x-3)} = 3^{(x-1)^2}$ **26.** $5^{(x+3)^2} = 5^{x(x+6)}$

27. $8^{5(x-3)} = 8^{4(x-2)}8^{(x-7)}$ **28.** $e^{a+7} = e^{3a+4}e^{3-2a}$ **29.** $3^{3x} = 9^{x+1}$

30. $5^{x+7} = 25^{x-2}$

31. $5^{2b+5} = 5^4$

32. $7^{3c-1} = 7^{c+9}$

33. $3^{2x^2} \cdot 3^{5x} = 27$

34. $5^{3x^2} \cdot 5^{5x} = 25$

35. $e^{0.5x} = 4$

36. $10^{1.5x} = 8$

37. $(3.5)^x = 12$

38. $(4.3)^z - 5 = 1$

39. $\log_5 c = 5$

40. $3 \log_2 b = 12$

41. $\log x - 0$

42. $\log x = 1$

43. $\ln z = 0$

44. $\ln y = 2$

45. $\log_3 k = 2$

46. $2 \log_5 x = 8$

47. $\log_5 x = -3$

48. $\log_3 k + 5 = 1$

49. $\log_3(a + 2) = 2$

50. $\log_2(3a - 7) = 3$

51. $2 \ln x = 1$

52. $-5 \ln x = 10$

53. $\log x + 4 = 2$

54. $3 \log x - 5 = 1$

55. $5 \ln z + 4 = 4$

56. $\ln x + 2 = 3$

57. $\ln x + \ln(x + 1) = \ln 12$

58. $\ln x + \ln(2x - 5) = \ln 25$

59. $2 \ln(p - 5) = \ln 9$

60. $\ln 16 = 2 \ln(x - 7)$

61. $\log 2x + \log 3x = \log 6 + 2 \log x$

62. $3 \log x - \log x = 2 \log x$

63. $\ln x + \ln(x + 2) = 2 \ln(x + 2)$

64. $2 \ln(x + 2) = \ln(x + 2) + \ln 2$

65. $\log(x + 4) - \log x = \log 2$

66. $\log(x + 3) - \log x = \log 5$

67. $\log x - \log(x + 6) = -1$

68. $\log_7 x - \log_7(x + 6) = -2$

69. $\log_3(x + 16) - \log_3 x = 2$

70. $\ln(x^2 - 3x + 2) - \ln(x - 1) = \ln 5$

71. Expenditures for public elementary and secondary schools totaled $210 billion in 1990 and grew exponentially to $439 billion in 2003. Use the exponential growth function to model the growth in expenditures since 1990. If this growth continues, what will be the estimated expenditures in the year 2010?

72. According to the U.S. Census Bureau, the number of households with cable television in the United States increased exponentially from 52 million in 1990 to 73 million in 2002. Use the exponential growth function to model the number of households with cable television since 1990. If this growth continues, what will be the estimated number of households with cable television in the year 2010?

73. Per capita income in the United States has grown exponentially over the last decade. Per capita income can be estimated by the growth model $A(t) = A_0 e^{0.0195t}$, where t is the number of years after 2000 and A_0 is per capita income for 2000. If the trend continues, in what year will per capita income double its 2000 value?

74. Using the growth model in exercise **73**, in what year will per capita income increase to 1.5 times its value in 2000?

75. Uranium-238 has a half-life of 4.5 billion years. Determine the decay factor of uranium-238. How long will it take for a sample of uranium-238 to diminish to 98% of its original amount?

76. Using the information in exercise **75**, determine how long it will take for a sample of uranium-238 to diminish to 90% of its original amount.

77. In forensics, the temperature of a human body is given by $T(t) = 20 + 17e^{-0.06t}$, where t is the time in hours since death and $T(t)$ is the temperature in degrees Celsius after t hours. How many hours have passed when the temperature is 25 degrees?

78. The temperature of a human body is given by $T(t) = 14 + 23e^{-0.052t}$, where t is the time in hours since death and $T(t)$ is the temperature in degrees Celsius after t hours. How many hours have passed when the temperature is 20 degrees?

79. If a task is done repeatedly, it will be done more efficiently over time. This idea has led to the development of various "learning curves" for production. An assembly-line operation has found that a worker can produce no more than 140 items per week. The learning curve for the number of items, n, produced per week after an employee has worked w weeks is $n(w) = 140(1 - e^{-0.4w})$. The manager of the assembly line would like employees to produce 135 units each week. How long would an employee need to work to reach this level?

80. As part of a psychology experiment, a group of college students is given the same test repeatedly. The percent of correct answers, p, on the xth test is given by the function $p(x) = \dfrac{79}{1 + e^{-0.18x}}$. What was the percent correct on the first test? On the tenth test? On which test will a student score about 75%? What's the highest score a student would ever achieve on the test?

12.5 Calculator Exercises

In this section, we discussed Newton's law of cooling. According to Sir Isaac Newton, objects warmer than their surroundings will eventually cool to a common temperature with the surroundings. The cooling rate depends on how much hotter the object is than its surroundings.

You will need a Calculator Base Laboratory (CBL) with temperature probe, your TI-84 Plus calculator, a cooler with ice, and boiling water in a cup.*

*If boiling water is not available, you may use ice water and measure warming.

1. Connect the TI-84 Plus calculator to the CBL that has a temperature probe in Chan 1.

2. Place the temperature probe in the ice chest and close the lid. Press [MODE] on the CBL to determine the temperature of the surroundings inside the ice chest, and record this temperature as T_0.

3. Place the temperature probe in a cup of boiling water. Allow the temperature probe to warm to the temperature of the water. Place the cup of water with the probe in the ice chest.

4. Run the application, CBL/CBR, and choose DATA LOGGER. Highlight and choose the following options:

5. After entering the given settings, highlight GO and press [ENTER]. Follow the directions on the screen.

    The application will record the temperature, in degrees Celsius, every 60 seconds for 30 minutes. A graph of the results will appear on the screen as the temperatures are recorded (in Real Time).

1. After 15 minutes, trace the graph and record the data points. Enter the values for time in L1 and the values for the temperature in L2. Use STAT CALC ExpReg to determine an exponential regression equation in the form $T = a(b)^x$.

2. Enter the equation from step 1 in Y1, and graph the equation. Does this equation appear in order to "fit" the recorded points?

3. According to Newton's law of cooling, the temperature T of a body in t minutes after it is placed in surroundings having a constant temperature T_0, is determined by the function $T = T_0 + Ce^{-kt}$, where C is the difference between the initial temperature and the surrounding temperature and k is the cooling constant.

    a. Let T_0 equal the temperature inside the ice chest, T equal the temperature of the water after cooling 30 minutes, and t equal 30 minutes. Determine the constant of cooling, k.

    b. Write an equation for T.

    c. Store the equation in Y2, and graph it. Does this equation appear to "fit" the recorded points?

4. Compare the equations found in step 1 and step 3. Which equation appears to be a better model? Can you explain why the equations differ?

12.5 Writing Exercise

In this section, you saw examples of exponential growth models and exponential decay models. Describe the two models and state when it would be appropriate to use either. Then describe a situation that would be an appropriate application of each model.

■ Chapter 12 Summary

Vocabulary Review

After completing this chapter, you should be able to define the following key terms.

argument	exponential function	logarithmic function
change-of-base formula	exponential growth	natural base
common logarithm	half life	natural exponential function
condense	horizontal-line test	natural logarithm
doubling life	inverse	natural logarithmic function
expand	line of symmetry	one-to-one function
exponential decay	logarithm of x with base a	
exponential equation in one variable	logarithmic equation in one variable	

Fill in the blank with one of the words or phrases listed above.

1. An _____ is a function if no two different ordered pairs have the same second coordinate.

2. To determine the _____ of a relation, interchange the coordinates of the independent and dependent variables in the original relation.

3. The _____ is used to determine that a function is one-to-one.

4. An _____ can be written in the form $f(x) = a^x$, where $a > 0$, $a \neq 1$, and x is a real number.

5. A _____ can be written in the form $f(x) = \ln x$, where x is a positive real number.

Reflections

1. What do we mean by the inverse of a relation?

2. How can you construct the inverse of a relation?

3. What is a one-to-one function?

4. What is an exponential function?

5. What is a logarithmic function?

6. What are the two most frequently used bases for a logarithmic function?

7. State the following rules of logarithms:

    a. The product rule

    b The quotient rule

    c. The power rule

■ Chapter 12 Section-by-Section Review

12.1

Recall	Examples
Inverse of a relation • If the relation is a set of ordered pairs, interchange the coordinates of the original ordered pairs. • If the relation is written as an equation, interchange the independent and dependent variables and solve for the new dependent variable.	Determine the inverse of the given relations. $A = \{(1, 2), (3, 5), (-2, 1)\}$ $A^{-1} = \{(2, 1), (5, 3), (1, -2)\}$ $6y = 2x - 4$ $6x = 2y - 4$ $6x + 4 = 2y$ $3x + 2 = y$ or $y = 3x + 2$
One-to-one function • If the relation is a set of ordered pairs, no two different ordered pairs should have the same first coordinate or the same second coordinate. • If the relation is described by a graph, the graph must pass both the vertical-line test and the horizontal-line test.	Determine whether the given relations are one-to-one functions. $A = \{(2, -2), (3, 4), (1, 2)\}$ is a one-to-one function, because no two values are repeated for the first or second coordinates. According to the graph, the relation is not a one-to-one function, because it fails the horizontal-line test.
Graph of a function and its inverse • Determine the inverse of a function. • Graph the function and its inverse. • Graph the line of symmetry, $y = x$.	Graph $f(x) = x^3 - 4$ and its inverse. Determine the inverse. $f(x) = x^3 - 4$ $x = y^3 - 4$ $y = \sqrt[3]{x + 4}$ $f^{-1}(x) = \sqrt[3]{x + 4}$

Determine the inverse of each relation.

1. $h = \{(2, 4.5), (4, 3.5), (6, 2.5), (8, 1.5), (10, 0.5)\}$

2. $y = 3x - 9$

3. $y = x^2 + 1$

4. $y = x^3 - 1$

Determine whether the inverse of each function is a function.

5. $P = \{(9, 1), (8, 2), (7, 3), (6, 1), (5, 2), (4, 3)\}$

6. $Q = \{(1, 9), (2, 8), (3, 7), (4, 6), (5, 5), (6, 4), (7, 3)\}$

Determine whether each graph represents a one-to-one function.

7.

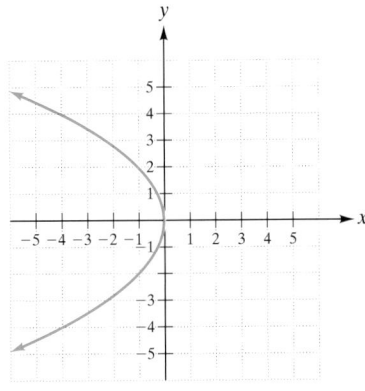

8.

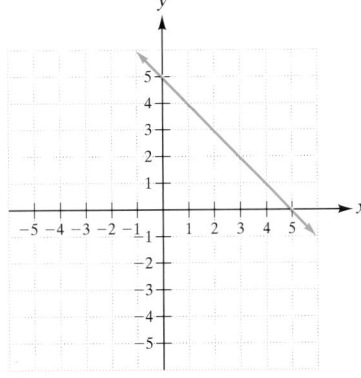

9.

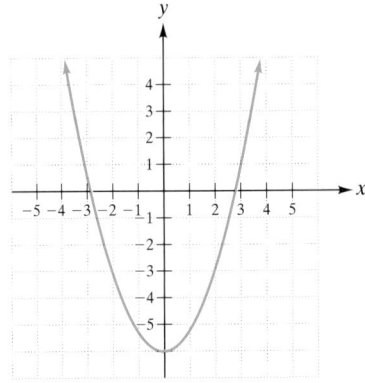

Determine the inverse of each function. Sketch the graph of the function, its inverse, and the line of symmetry.

10. $f(x) = \dfrac{3}{4}x - 3$

11. $y = x^3 + 8$

12. Complete the tables of value to determine whether the following are inverse functions. Explain your answer.

$f(x) = \sqrt[3]{x} + 3$

x	$f(x)$
-2	
5	

$g(x) = x^3 - 3$

x	$g(x)$
	-2
	5

13. Use calculator graphs to determine whether or not the following are inverse functions. Also graph the line $y = x$. Explain your answer.

$$f(x) = 9x - 5$$

$$g(x) = \dfrac{1}{9}x + \dfrac{5}{9}$$

For each situation, write a function that represents it. Determine the inverse of the function and interpret what the inverse function represents.

14. Motomo is paid \$570 per week, plus 3% commission on the value of all sales she handles. What is Motomo's weekly income?

15. Valecia can complete an average of 15 algebra problems in one hour. What is the average number of problems she can complete in a given number of hours?

12.2

Recall	Examples
Exponential functions can be written as $f(x) = a^x$, where $a > 0$ and $a \neq 1$.	Examples of exponential functions are $f(x) = 5^x$ $g(x) = 5^{-x}$

(continued on page 992)

Recall	Examples
Graph an exponential function • Set up a table of values. • Plot the ordered pairs and connect them with a smooth curve. The y-intercept is always $(0, 1)$.	Graph $g(x) = 5^{-x}$.
The natural exponential function is written as $f(x) = e^x$, where e is the natural base.	Examples of natural exponential functions are $f(x) = e^x$ $g(x) = e^{-x}$
Compound interest The compounded amount is $A = P(1 + r)^t$, where P = principal, r = interest rate per period, and t = number of periods.	Determine the amount of an investment of \$5000 at an annual compounded rate of 6% at the end of three years. $A = P(1 + r)^t$ $A = 5000(1 + 0.06)^3$ $A = 5955.08$ There will be \$5955.08 in the account at the end of three years.

Determine whether each function is an exponential function.

16. $f(x) = 2^x$ 　 **17.** $y = x^2$

Evaluate the function $g(x) = 1.21^x$ at the given values.

18. $g(2)$ 　 **19.** $g(-1)$ 　 **20.** $g(0)$

21. $g\left(\dfrac{1}{2}\right)$ 　 **22.** $g(0.3)$ 　 **23.** $g\left(\sqrt{2}\right)$

In exercises 24–26, graph each function.

24. $f(x) = 5^x - 1$ 　 **25.** $g(x) = 9^{(1/2)x}$ 　 **26.** $y = 2e^{0.5x}$

27. Graph the following function. Determine the domain and range. Where is the function increasing or decreasing? Identify any maximum or minimum values.

$$f(x) = -3^{-2x^4}$$

28. Paul invested his holiday bonus of \$1000 into an account that paid 4% interest compounded annually. Write a function for the total value of his investment. Graph the function. How much was the investment worth after four years?

29. The mathematical model $y = 19.6(1.24)^x$, where x is the number of years after 1995 and y is revenue in millions of dollars, predicts the revenue of wireless providers in the United States. What does the model predict that the revenue will be for the year 2010?

30. The "present value" of an investment desired to be worth \$1000 after n years at 8% can be given by $A(n) = 1000(1.08)^{-n}$, where n is the number of years. Graph this function. What amount needs to be deposited to be worth \$1000 after one year? After 5 years? After 20 years?

12.3

Recall	Examples
Logarithm of x with base a $y = \log_a x$ if and only if $x = a^y$	Determine the inverse function of $\quad f(x) = 4^x$ $\quad f^{-1}(x) = \log_4 x$
Change-of-base formula $\log_a x = \dfrac{\log_b x}{\log_b a} = \dfrac{\ln x}{\ln a}$	Evaluate $\log_3 6$. $\log_3 6 = \dfrac{\ln 6}{\ln 3} \approx 1.631$
Graph a logarithmic function Method 1 • Determine the inverse exponential function. • Set up a table of values for the exponential function. • Interchange the coordinates of the exponential function. • Plot the points and connect them with a smooth curve. The x-intercept is always $(1, 0)$.	Graph. $g(x) = \log_2 x$ Method 1 $g^{-1}(x) = 2^x$ <table><tr><th>x</th><th>$g^{-1}(x)$</th></tr><tr><td>-3</td><td>0.125</td></tr><tr><td>-2</td><td>0.25</td></tr><tr><td>-1</td><td>0.5</td></tr><tr><td>0</td><td>1</td></tr><tr><td>1</td><td>2</td></tr><tr><td>2</td><td>4</td></tr><tr><td>3</td><td>8</td></tr></table> Reverse coordinates $\longrightarrow$ <table><tr><th>x</th><th>$g(x)$</th></tr><tr><td>0.125</td><td>-3</td></tr><tr><td>0.25</td><td>-2</td></tr><tr><td>0.5</td><td>-1</td></tr><tr><td>1</td><td>0</td></tr><tr><td>2</td><td>1</td></tr><tr><td>4</td><td>2</td></tr><tr><td>8</td><td>3</td></tr></table>
Graph a logarithmic function Method 2 • Set up a table of values. • Plot the ordered pairs and connect them with a smooth curve. The x-intercept is always $(1, 0)$.	Graph. $g(x) = \log_2 x$ Method 2 <table><tr><th>x</th><th>$g(x)$</th></tr><tr><td>0.125</td><td>-3</td></tr><tr><td>0.25</td><td>-2</td></tr><tr><td>0.5</td><td>-1</td></tr><tr><td>1</td><td>0</td></tr><tr><td>2</td><td>1</td></tr><tr><td>4</td><td>2</td></tr><tr><td>8</td><td>3</td></tr></table>

For each exponential function, determine the logarithmic function that is its inverse.

31. $h(x) = 8^x$ **32.** $A(x) = Ae^{kx}$

Evaluate.

33. $\log 100$ **34.** $\log_2 16$ **35.** $\log_3 \dfrac{1}{27}$ **36.** $\log 1.5$ **37.** $\ln e^4$

38. $\ln 10$ **39.** $\ln e^{-2}$ **40.** $\log \dfrac{3}{5}$ **41.** $\log_5 15$

In exercises 42 and 43, create a table of values for each function and graph.

42. $y = \log_3 x$ **43.** $f(x) = \ln(x - 2)$

44. Graph the following function. Determine the domain and range. Where is the function increasing or decreasing? Identify any maximum or minimum values.

$$h(x) = \log_5(-x)$$

The pH value of a substance is defined by the function $pH = -\log[H^+]$, *where* $[H^+]$ *is the hydrogen ion concentration in moles per liter. Use this relation to answer the following questions:*

45. The hydrogen ion concentration of lemon juice is 6.2×10^{-3} moles per liter. What is the pH of lemon juice?

46. The pH value of blood is typically 7.4. What is the hydrogen ion concentration of blood?

12.4

Recall	Examples
Product rule • $\log_a mn = \log_a m + \log_a n$ • $\ln mn = \ln m + \ln n$	Expand. $\log_3 5x$ $\log_3 5x = \log_3 5 + \log_3 x$ Condense. $\log_3 6 + \log_3 2$ $\log_3 6 + \log_3 2 = \log_3 12$
Quotient rule • $\log_a \dfrac{m}{n} = \log_a m - \log_a n$ • $\ln \dfrac{m}{n} = \ln m - \ln n$	Expand. $\ln \dfrac{2x}{5}$ $\ln \dfrac{2x}{5} = \ln 2x - \ln 5 = \ln 2 + \ln x - \ln 5$ Condense. $\ln 6 - \ln 2$ $\ln 6 - \ln 2 = \ln \frac{6}{2} = \ln 3$
Power rule • $\log_a m^c = c \log_a m$ • $\ln m^c = c \ln m$	Expand. $\log_3 x^5$ $\log_3 x^5 = 5 \log_3 x$ Condense. $4 \ln 3$ $4 \ln 3 = \ln 3^4 = \ln 81$

Write each logarithmic expression in expanded form.

47. $\log 2x^4$ **48.** $\log_7 \dfrac{7x}{y}$ **49.** $\ln 25x^2 y^3 z$ **50.** $\ln \dfrac{\sqrt[3]{2x^2 y}}{\sqrt{yz}}$

In exercises 51–54, write each logarithmic expression in condensed form.

51. $\log(x - 3) + \log(x + 3)$ **52.** $5 \ln x - 3 \ln y$ **53.** $\dfrac{1}{3} \log x - \dfrac{1}{2} \log y$ **54.** $\log ab - \log bc + \log cd$

55. Money invested at a continuously compounded interest rate r will grow to k times the original amount invested in t years, where $t = \dfrac{\ln k}{r}$. How long will it take an investment to triple in value if the annual interest rate is 6%?

12.5

Recall	Examples
Solving an exponential equation • Write both sides of the equation as an exponential with the same base, equate the exponents, and solve for the variable. or • Isolate the exponential expression, take the logarithm of both sides, and solve for the variable.	Solve. $2^x = 32$ $2^x = 32$ $2^x = 2^5$ $x = 5$ Solve. $e^{2x} = 4$ $e^{2x} = 4$ $\ln e^{2x} = \ln 4$ $2x = \ln 4$ $x = \dfrac{\ln 4}{2}$ $x \approx 0.693$
Solving a logarithmic equation • Determine the restricted values. • Write both sides of the equation as a logarithm with the same base, equate the arguments, and solve for the variable. or • Isolate the logarithmic expression, use the definition of logarithms to write an exponential equation, and solve for the variable.	Solve. $\ln x^2 = \ln x + \ln 4$ Restricted values are $x \leq 0$. $\ln x^2 = \ln x + \ln 4$ $\ln x^2 = \ln 4x$ $x^2 = 4x$ $x^2 - 4x = 0$ $x(x - 4) = 0$ $x = 0, x = 4$ The solution is $x = 4$. (0 is a restricted value.) Solve. $\log(x + 3) = 2$ Restricted values are $x + 3 \leq 0$, or $x \leq -3$. $\log(x + 3) = 2$ $x + 3 = 10^2$ $x = 10^2 - 3$ $x = 97$

Identify each equation as exponential, logarithmic, or neither.

56. $e^x + 5 = 7$ **57.** $\ln 7 - x = \ln 3$ **58.** $\log x^2 + 2 = \log x$

59. $x = e^3 - 1$ **60.** $2^x + 7 = 2^{3x}$ **61.** $y = \log_2 5 - e^2$

Solve exercises 62–80.

62. $3^{x+1} = 243$ **63.** $e^{-5t} - 2 = 3$ **64.** $12^a = 1$ **65.** $(3^{2x})(3^5) = 3^8$

66. $e^{2x(x-3)} = e^{2(x-2)(x-1)}$ **67.** $4^{x^2+2x} = 64$ **68.** $5^{2x-3} = 5^{x+9} \cdot 5^{x-12}$ **69.** $10^{2.3x} = 4$

70. $\log_7 a = 49$ **71.** $5 \log_3 x = 45$ **72.** $\ln z = 1$ **73.** $\log b = 0$

74. $\log k = -3$ **75.** $5 + \log_2 x = 3$ **76.** $3 \ln x = 1$ **77.** $\ln(2x^2 + 7x) = \ln 15$

78. $2 \log(x - 2) = \log 9$ **79.** $\log x + \log(x + 4) = 2 \log(x + 2)$ **80.** $7 \ln x - \ln x^3 = 4 \ln x$

81. Census data reported that the resident population 85 years and older was 3.022 million in 1990 and had grown exponentially to 5.120 million in 2005. Use the growth function to model the growth in the resident population 85 years and older since 1990. If this growth continues, what will be the estimated resident population 85 years and older in 2015? The projected resident population 85 years and older that year is 6.822 million. Compare your model's projections with this number.

82. The decay function for carbon-14 (C-14) is approximated as $A(t) = A_0 e^{kt}$, where $k \approx -0.000121$. If skeletal remains are found with two-thirds of the C-14 of the living form, determine the time since the body's demise.

83. In forensics, the number of hours a body has been deceased when exposed to an air temperature of 16 degrees Celsius can be estimated by the function $t(T) = \dfrac{\ln T - 3.611}{-0.089}$, where t is the time in hours and T is the temperature of the body. If the body temperature is 22 degrees, how long has the body been deceased?

■ Chapter 12 Mixed Review

Evaluate.

1. $\log 0.001$ **2.** $\log_7 343$ **3.** $\log_2 \dfrac{1}{64}$ **4.** $\log 5.1$ **5.** $\ln e^{-3}$ **6.** $\ln 100$

7. $\ln e$ **8.** $\ln \dfrac{4}{7}$ **9.** $\log_3 36$

Write each logarithmic expression in expanded form.

10. $\log 3x^2 y$ **11.** $\log_3 \dfrac{9a}{b}$ **12.** $\ln 100p^3 q^2 r$ **13.** $\log \dfrac{\sqrt[5]{6x^3}}{\sqrt{xy}}$

Write each logarithmic expression in condensed form.

14. $\log(x^2 - 9) - \log(x + 3)$ **15.** $2 \log c - 5 \log d$ **16.** $\dfrac{1}{2}\ln x - 3 \ln y$ **17.** $\log 2xy - \log xz + \log 3yz$

Determine the inverse of each relation.

18. $y = 5 - x$ **19.** $y = 1 - x^2$ **20.** $y = 4 - x^3$

21. $y = 2 - \dfrac{4}{5}x$ **22.** $m(x) = 5^x$ **23.** $G(x) = ab^x$, a and b are constants.

Evaluate the function $g(t) = 1 + \left(\dfrac{4}{9}\right)^t$ *at the given values.*

24. $g(3)$ **25.** $g(-1)$ **26.** $g(0)$ **27.** $g\left(\dfrac{1}{2}\right)$ **28.** $g(1.5)$ **29.** $g\left(-\sqrt{3}\right)$

Graph each function.

30. $m(x) = 3^x - 2$ **31.** $k(x) = 8^{(1/3)x}$ **32.** $y = -2e^{0.4x}$ **33.** $y = \log_2 x - 2$ **34.** $g(x) = \ln(x + 1)$

Graph the following functions. Determine the domain and range. Where is each function increasing or decreasing? Identify any maximum or minimum values.

35. $f(x) = -3^{-2x^2}$ **36.** $h(x) = \log_5(x)$

Solve.

37. $\log_6 b = 216$ **38.** $2 \log_3 z = 6$ **39.** $\log z = 1$ **40.** $\ln b = 0$

41. $\log 2m = -4$ **42.** $-1 + \log_3 x = 4$ **43.** $2 \log x = 1$ **44.** $\log(2x^2 + 3x) = \log 9$

45. $2 \ln(x + 3) = \ln 4$ **46.** $\log 4x + \log(x + 1) = 2 \log(2x + 1)$ **47.** $2 \log a + \log a^4 = 6 \log a$

48. $5^{x-3} = 125$ **49.** $e^{-t} + 4 = 5$ **50.** $7^a = e$ **51.** $(6^7)(6^{3x}) = 6^2$

52. $e^{x(x+6)} = e^{(x+5)(x+1)}$ **53.** $2^{x^2} \cdot 2^{-3x} = 16$ **54.** $7^{2x-6} = (7^{3x-11})(7^{5-x})$ **55.** $10^{1.8x} = 9$

In exercises 56 and 57, write a function that represents each situation. Determine the inverse of the function and interpret what the inverse function represents.

56. Diana earns $1200 per month, plus 2.5% commission on all of her sales at a furniture gallery. What is Diana's monthly income?

57. Carlyle is averaging 95 kilometers per hour on his auto trip through Germany. How far can he travel in a given number of hours?

58. Kristin invested her inheritance of $8500 into an account that paid 6.5% interest compounded annually. Write a function for the total value of her investment. Graph the function. How much was the investment worth after 10 years?

59. According to data from the National Center for Health Statistics, the number of people enrolled in HMOs (Health Maintenance Organizations) can be estimated by the function $N(x) = 81.255(0.97)^x$, where $N(x)$ is the number enrolled in millions and x is the number of years after 2000. Graph this function. What does the model predict the number to be in 2012?

The pH value of a substance is defined by the function $\text{pH} = -\log[\text{H}^+]$, *where* $[\text{H}^+]$ *is the hydrogen ion concentration in moles per liter. Use this relation to answer exercises 60 and 61.*

60. The hydrogen ion concentration of apple juice is 1.6×10^{-4} moles per liter. What is the pH of apple juice?

61. The pH value of gastric juice is typically 1.6. What is the hydrogen ion concentration of gastric juice?

62. Money invested at a continuously compounded interest rate r will grow to k times the original amount invested in t years, where $t = \dfrac{\ln k}{r}$. How long will it take an investment to double in value if the annual interest rate is 5.6%?

63. According to the U.S. Census Bureau, the national health expenditures in the United States have increased exponentially from 696 billion dollars in 1990 to 1555 billion dollars in 2002. Use the exponential growth function to model the national health expenditures since 1990. If this growth continues, what will be the estimated national health expenditures in the year 2010?

64. The decay function for carbon-14 (C-14) is approximated as $A(t) = A_0 e^{kt}$, where $k \approx -0.000121$. If the remains of a living organism are found with 40% of the C-14 of its living form, determine the time since the organism died.

65. In forensics, the temperature of a human body is given by $T(t) = 20 + 17e^{-0.06t}$, where t is the time in hours since death and $T(t)$ is the temperature in degrees Celsius after t hours. How many hours have passed when the temperature is 30 degrees?

■ Chapter 12 Test

TEST-TAKING TIPS

If math is your most challenging subject, make sure to study it before you study all other subjects. Do not leave it for last. You must study math when you are most alert and fresh. Then you will do better and you will recall more of what you have studied. It has been shown that a few minutes' break every half-hour while you are studying will refresh you and help you retain more information. Begin each study session with a review of previous material studied. This will keep your math skills polished. Read your text before attempting to do the assigned exercises. Always check your answers with those provided in the text. If you cannot reconcile an answer with that in the text, be sure to mark the exercise so that you can ask about it in class. Try to look ahead at some of the material that will be presented in the next class, so that that material will not be difficult to understand when your instructor presents it.

1. Graph the function $f(x) = x^3$, its inverse, and the line of symmetry.

2. Graph $f(x) = 2^x + 1$.

3. Graph $g(x) = \ln(x + 2)$.

4. Find the inverse of the function $F(x) = 2x - 8$.

5. Evaluate $g(x) = 16^{(1/2)x}$ at the given values.
   a. $g(-1)$ **b.** $g(0)$ **c.** $g(4)$
   c. $g(0.3)$ **d.** $g\left(\sqrt{3}\right)$

Write the expanded form of each expression.

6. $\log 3x^2 y^3 z$

7. $\log_3 \dfrac{9a^2}{b}$

Write the condensed form of each expression.

8. $2 \log x + \log(x - 4)$

9. $\dfrac{1}{2} \ln x - 2 \ln y$

In exercises 10 and 11, graph the following functions. Determine the domain and range. Where is each function increasing or decreasing? Identify any maximum or minimum values.

10. $f(x) = -3^{-x^2}$

11. $g(x) = \log(x^2)$

12. Solve. $9^x = 3^{x+1}$
   a. numerically   **b.** graphically   **c.** algebraically

Solve exercises 13–16.

13. $(2^{3x})(2^{-2}) = 8$

14. $2 \ln a = 3.1$

15. $2 \log x + \log x^4 = 6 \log x$ **16.** $9^x = 5$

17. Pedro earns $400 per week, plus a commission of 3% of all sales he makes at the appliance store.
   a. Write a function for his total weekly income.
   b. Determine the inverse of the function.
   c. Interpret what the inverse of the function represents.

18. Kate discovered a bank deposit book that her deceased grandfather had owned. The bankbook indicated that he had made a single deposit of $2000 into an account that paid 5% interest compounded annually. Write a function for the amount of money that is in the account after x years. What was the investment worth after 20 years?

19. Money invested at a continuously compounded interest rate r will grow to k times the original amount invested in t years, where $t = \dfrac{\ln k}{r}$. How long will it take an investment to double in value if the annual interest rate is 7.5%?

20. According to the U.S. Bureau of Economic Analysis, the personal income per capita was $23,078 in 1995 and had grown exponentially to $31,633 in 2003. Use the growth function to model the growth in personal income. If this growth continues, what will be the estimated personal income per capita in 2015?

21. In forensics, the number of hours a body has been deceased when exposed to an air temperature of 16 degrees Celsius can be estimated by the function $t(T) = \dfrac{\ln T - 3.611}{-0.089}$, where t is the time in hours and T is the temperature of the body. If the body temperature is 20 degrees, how long has the body been deceased?

22. What do we mean by the common logarithm of a number?

12

Project

PART I In this chapter, we used an exponential function to approximate the population of the United States. The world population may also be determined with the use of an exponential function.

1. Search the Internet or your library to find the population of the world every year from 2000 to the present.

2. Enter these data in your calculator. Let L_1 be the number of years after 2000 and L_2 be the world population.

3. Calculate an exponential equation, using the STAT CALC command "ExpReg L_1, L_2."

4. Enter the equation found in step 3 in Y1, and graph it. Does this equation appear to "fit" the recorded points?

5. Use the equation in step 3 to approximate the world population in 2010.

6. Search the Internet or your library to find the projected population of the world in 2010. Compare your results in step 5 with the projections. If the results differ, explain why?

PART II Many situations fit into the exponential growth model. Some of these include the spread of the AIDS virus, the growth of bacteria, sales of compact discs, sales of computers, and values of collectibles such as art or sport cards. Collect data on a variable that may be experiencing exponential growth. You may search the Internet or your library.

1. Develop a mathematical model that represents the growth.

2. Check your model against the data you collected.

3. Use the model to predict a future value of the variable. Write a summary of your findings.

PART III Many situations may fit into a logarithmic model. As you saw in this chapter, the magnitude R of an earthquake of intensity I is defined by the function $R = \log \dfrac{I}{I_0}$, where I_0 is the intensity of a very small vibration in the Earth used as a standard. Collect data on two major earthquakes. You will need to know the magnitude R measured on the Richter scale for each. Place the magnitude data into the model and solve for the intensity of each earthquake, measured in terms of I_0. Then form the ratio of the two intensities and interpret the result. How do the two earthquakes compare in their intensities?

■ Chapters P–12 Cumulative Review

Simplify and write with positive exponents.

1. $5^{-2}x^0y^2$

2. $(-2x^{-3}y^2)^2$

3. $\left(\dfrac{4x^{3/4}}{x^{-1/4}}\right)^2$

Simplify.

4. $(3.2a^2 - 2.6ab + 1.7b^2) - (4a^2 + 2.6ab - b^2)$

5. $(4.5x^2y)(-2y^2z)$

6. $(3x + 2y)(3x - 2y)$

7. $(2x + 6)(2x - 3)$

8. $(x - 4)^2$

9. $\dfrac{25x^2y^4z^2}{-5xyz}$

10. $\dfrac{2r^2s + 4rs - 8s^2}{2rs}$

11. $\dfrac{x^2 - x - 6}{x^2 - 9}$

12. $\dfrac{x}{x + 2} + \dfrac{3}{x - 2} + \dfrac{x - 1}{x^2 - 4}$

13. $\dfrac{1}{x + 4} - \dfrac{x}{x - 2}$

14. $\dfrac{2m - 3}{m + 1} \cdot \dfrac{2m^2 + 5m + 3}{4m^2 - 9}$

15. $\dfrac{16x}{y^3 + y^2 - 12y} \div \dfrac{4x^2y}{y^2 - y - 20}$

16. $\sqrt{18x} - \sqrt{50x} + 4\sqrt{8x}$

17. $\sqrt[3]{16a^2b^2} \cdot \sqrt[3]{8ab^2}$

18. $\left(\sqrt{2} - \sqrt{3}\right)\left(\sqrt{2} + \sqrt{3}\right)$

19. $\dfrac{\sqrt{32xy^2z}}{\sqrt{8x^3y}}$

20. $\dfrac{\sqrt{x} + 4}{\sqrt{x} - 3}$

21. $x^{2/3}(x^{3/4} - x^{1/3})$

Factor completely if possible.

22. $25m^2 - 36n^2$

23. $2x^2 - 4x - 16$

24. $x^2 + 6x - 6$

Graph and label as indicated. Determine the domain and range of each function.

25. $f(x) = \dfrac{2}{3}x + 1$; three points on the graph

26. $y = x^2 + 5x + 4$; vertex, y-intercept, x-intercept, enough points to determine the curve, and the axis of symmetry

27. $y = \dfrac{x^2 + 4}{x + 2}$; enough points to determine the curve

28. $h(x) = \sqrt{x - 5}$; enough points to determine the curve

29. $g(x) = x^{2/3} + 3$; enough points to determine the curve

30. $y = 3^x$; enough points to determine the curve

31. $f(x) = \ln(x - 3)$; enough points to determine the curve

Solve.

32. $2(x - 5) - (x + 4) = 2x - 8$

33. $2(x + 3.1) = (x - 4.2) + (x - 6)$

34. $x^2 - 2x - 12 = 12$

35. $x^2 - 5x + 9 = 0$

36. $\dfrac{x + 1}{x + 2} = \dfrac{x - 1}{x + 3}$

37. $4\sqrt{x + 1} - 14 = -2$

38. $e^{2x-4} = e^{x(x-2)}$

39. $2\log_3 x = \log_3 5$

Solve. Write the solution set in interval notation.

40. $2x - 3 < 3(x - 4)$

41. $x^2 + 2x \geq 2$

Solve.

42. $3x - 2y = 4$
$x + y = 8$

In exercises 43 and 44, write an equation of a line that satisfies the given conditions.

43. Passes through the points $(3, -1)$ and $(-2, 2)$

44. Is perpendicular to $x + 4y = 2.3$ and passes through $(-2, 1)$

45. Write a quadratic equation for a curve that passes through the points $(0, -6)$, $(-4, 0)$, and $(1, 0)$.

46. Given $f(x) = \frac{2}{3}x + 6$, find $f^{-1}(x)$.

47. Happy Recipe Company bought a rebuilt copier for $525 to reproduce its latest recipe book. If it costs $5 per book for materials to print the books and each book sells for $15, determine the break-even point—that is, the point at which the revenue equals the cost of the copies.

48. Nathan has 15 feet of landscaping timbers to place diagonally across his rectangular flower garden. If he wants to use all of the timbers and have the length of the garden be 3 feet more than the width, determine the dimensions of the garden.

49. A tank is drained by two separate drains. When the drain on the left is used alone, it takes 4 hours to drain the tank. When the drain on the right is used alone, it takes 6.5 hours to drain the tank. How long will it take to drain the tank if both drains are used? (Round your answer to the nearest tenth of an hour.)

50. If money is compounded continuously, the amount in the account will grow to k times the original amount invested in $t = \dfrac{\ln k}{r}$ years when the annual rate of interest is r. How long will it take the amount invested to triple if the annual interest rate is 4.5%?

Photo Credits

CHAPTER P **CO** Charles Graham/eStock Photography LLC; **p. 14** Alison Wright/Stock Boston; **p. 33 (top)** NASA Headquarters; **p. 33 (bottom)** James M. McCann/Photo Researchers, Inc; **p. 34** Getty Images, Inc.; **p. 49** Jessica Wecker/Photo Researchers, Inc; **p. 52 (left)** Topham/The Image Works; **p. 52 (right)** Peter French/DRK Photo; **p. 71** Paolo Koch/Photo Researchers, Inc.; **p. 96** SuperStock, Inc.; **p. 104** Getty Images, Inc.; **p. 113** 2001 The Longaberger® Company.

CHAPTER 1 **CO** Bob Daemmrich/The Image Works; **p. 133** Roy Morsch/Corbis/Stock Market; **p. 135** AP Wide World Photos.

CHAPTER 2 **CO** Mary Jelliffe/The Ancient Art & Architecture Collection Ltd.; **p. 205** Susanne Buckler/Getty Images, Inc. - Liaison; **p. 206** John Elk III/Stock Boston; **p. 227** Stacy Pick/Stock Boston; **p. 233** Kent Knudson/Stock Boston; **p. 235** © Alan Schein Photography, Inc./CORBIS; **p. 254** Boyd Norton/The Image Works; **p. 262** W. Cody/Corbis/Bettmann; **p. 266** Chris Bensley/Stock Boston.

CHAPTER 3 **CO** Chad Ehlers/ImageState/International Stock Photography Ltd.; **p. 283** A. Ramey/PhotoEdit Inc.; **p. 312** Paul J. Sutton/Duomo Photography Incorporated; **p. 322** ©Bettmann/CORBIS; **p. 334** Monique Salaber/NASA/The Image Works.

CHAPTER 4 **CO** Eliot Cohen; **p. 367** Michael Ventura/ImageState/International Stock Photography Ltd.; **p. 417** David Young-Wolff/PhotoEdit Inc.

CHAPTER 5 **CO** Matthew Borkoski/Stock Boston; **p. 442** Lee Snider/The Image Works; **p. 452** Elise Amendola/AP Wide World Photos; **p. 463** Chris Takagi; **p. 469** David Young-Wolff/PhotoEdit Inc.

CHAPTER 6 **CO** NASA/Johnson Space Center/The Image Works; **p. 496** A. Gurmankin/M. Morina/Unicorn Stock Photos; **p. 503** Randy Faris/CORBIS/Bettmann; **p. 517** Kyodo News; **p. 523** John Wang/Getty Images, Inc. - Photodisc; **p. 524** E. R. Degginger/Color-Pic, Inc.; **p. 532** Richard Renaldi.

CHAPTER 7 **CO** Gregory Sams/Science Photo Library/Photo Researchers, Inc.; **p. 541** Thomas & Pat Leeson/Photo Researchers, Inc.; **p. 562** Kent Wood/Peter Arnold, Inc.; **p. 567** Paul Griffin/Stock Boston; **p. 590** Jeff Vanuga/Corbis/Bettmann; **p. 599** Salaber/The Image Works.

CHAPTER 8 **CO** Rafael Macia/Photo Researchers, Inc.; **p. 610** Roberto Soncin Gerometta; **p. 620** Curtis Martin/Lonely Planet Images/Photo 20-20; **p. 639** Getty Images Inc. - Hulton Archive Photos.

CHAPTER 9 **CO** Steve Vidler/SuperStock, Inc.; **p. 662** Pictures Colour Library, Ltd./eStock Photography, LLC; **p. 664** Robert Frerck/Odyssey Productions/Chicago; **p. 665** Robert Frerck/Odyssey Productions/Chicago; **p. 684** Ron Sherman/Stock Boston; **p. 693** Bill Horsman/Stock Boston; **p. 698** David Bartruff, Inc.; **p. 712** U.S. Supercircuits; **p. 758** G. Sauvage Vandystadt/Photo Researcher, Inc.

CHAPTER 10 **CO** © Anthony Redpath/CORBIS; **p. 799** Tony Freeman/PhotoEdit Inc. **p. 814** Chris Bensley/Stock Boston.

CHAPTER 11 **CO** Andy Levin/Alamy Images; **p. 858** Eunice Harris/Photo Researchers, Inc.; **p. 860** Romer/Explorer/Photo Researchers, Inc.; **p. 861 (top)** Robert Frerck/Odssey/Chicago; **p. 861 (bottom)** Will and Deni McIntyre/Photo Researchers, Inc.; **p. 863** AP Wide World Photos; **p. 869** Joe Sohm/Chromosohm/Stock Boston; **p. 880** SuperStock, Inc.; **p. 891** Ron Sheridan/The Ancient Art & Architecture Collection Ltd.; **p. 900** Francois Gohier/Photo Researchers, Inc.; **p. 925** Adam Hart-Davis/Science Photo Library/Photo Researchers, Inc.; **p. 926 (left)** Stephen Gerard/Photo Researchers, Inc.; **(right)** Gregory Sams/Science Photo Library/Photo Researchers, Inc.

CHAPTER 12 **CO** Paul Sakuma/AP Wide World Photos; **p. 952** Al Stephenson/Woodfin Camp & Associates; **p. 962** Tom Chargin Photography; **p. 971** Linc Cornell/Stock Boston; **p. 973** Simon Fraser/Science Photo Library/Photo Researchers, Inc.; **p. 985** Sinclair Stammers/Science Photo Library/Photo Researchers, Inc.; **p. 988** Ann States/Corbis/SABA Press Photos, Inc.

Answers to Checkup Exercises

CHAPTER P

SECTION P.1

P.1.1 Checkup   **1. (a)** natural, whole, integer, rational   **(b)** integer, rational   **(c)** whole, integer, rational   **(d)** rational   **(e)** rational   **(f)** rational **(g)** rational   **2. (a)**   **(b)**   **(c)**

P.1.2 Checkup   **1.**

P.1.3 Checkup   **1. (a)** >   **(b)** =   **(c)** >   **2. (a)** $-2 < 6$ **(b)** $\frac{11}{4} = 2.75$ **(c)** $-3 \le 0 < 4$ **P.1.4 Checkup**   **1. (a)** 15   **(b)** 3.3   **(c)** $\frac{2}{7}$

P.1.5 Checkup   **1. (a)** $3\frac{1}{3}$ **(b)** 15   **(c)** $-\frac{4}{7}$ **P.1.6 Checkup**   **1.** $|-80| = 80$ **2.** -1.3%

SECTION P.2

P.2.1 Checkup   **1. (a)** 5   **(b)** -15 **(c)** -6 **2. (a)** -1.58 **(b)** -6.6 **(c)** $\frac{1}{28}$ **(d)** $1\frac{7}{12}$ **3. (a)** 7   **(b)** $-\frac{3}{10}$ **P.2.2 Checkup**   **1. (a)** -2

(b) 1   **(c)** -12 **(d)** 9   **2. (a)** -11.75 **(b)** -4.5 **(c)** $-\frac{41}{28}$ **(d)** 4   **P.2.3 Checkup**   **1. (a)** 32   **(b)** -15 **(c)** -72 **2. (a)** -0.144 **(b)** 0

(c) $\frac{1}{4}$ **(d)** -3 **3. (a)** $-\frac{64}{21}$ **(b)** 0   **P.2.4 Checkup**   **1. (a)** 3   **(b)** -3 **(c)** $\frac{3}{5}$ **2. (a)** -4.1 **(b)** 36   **(c)** 0   **(d)** undefined

(e) indeterminate   **3. (a)** $\frac{4}{9}$ **(b)** $-\frac{27}{16}$ **(c)** $-\frac{1}{10}$ **P.2.5 Checkup**   **1.** $897.63 + 355 + 572 - 120 - 300 - 185.23 - 104.50 -$

$231.97 - (-231.97) - 10$; the current balance in Beverly's account is \$1104.90.   **2.** The number of men enrolled in community colleges in 2004 was 4.368 million.   **3.** The rate is 7.5 cases/nurse. The ward can handle 90 cases.   **4.** Mauna Kea is 33,476 feet high.

SECTION P.3

P.3.1 Checkup   **1. (a)** 1.69   **(b)** 0   **(c)** $\frac{32}{3125}$ **(d)** $\frac{147,008,443}{3125}$ **2. (a)** -2.744 **(b)** $\frac{16}{81}$ **(c)** 1296   **(d)** -1296 **3. (a)** -7 **(b)** -7 **(c)** 1   **(d)** 1

(e) -1 **(f)** indeterminate   **P.3.2 Checkup**   **1. (a)** 7   **(b)** 0.9   **(c)** $\frac{5}{6}$ **(d)** -4 **(e)** not a real number   **(f)** 0   **2. (a)** 4 and 5; 4.123105626

(b) -3 and -4; -3.872983346 **(c)** 8 and 9; 8.366600265   **3. (a)** -4 **(b)** $\frac{2}{5}$ **(c)** 2.080

P.3.3 Checkup   **1.**

P.3.4 Checkup   **1. (a)** $\left(\frac{1}{3}\right)^1 = \frac{1}{3}$ **(b)** $\left(-\frac{1}{3}\right)^1 = -\frac{1}{3}$ **P.3.5 Checkup**   **1. (a)** 7.8345×10^{10} **(b)** -7.3845×10^{10} **(c)** 4.21×10^{-6}

(d) -4.21×10^{-6} **2. (a)** 475,000   **(b)** $-475,000$ **(c)** 0.0000031   **(d)** -0.0000031 **3. (a)** 5.92×10^8; 592,000,000   **(b)** -5.92×10^8; $-592,000,000$
(c) 2.467×10^{-5}; 0.00002467   **(d)** -2.467×10^{-5}; -0.00002467 **P.3.6 Checkup**   **1.** The length of an edge of Rubik's Revenge is about 7.34 centimeters; the length of an edge of the center square is about 3.67 centimeters; the volume of the center cube is 49.375 cubic centimeters.   **2.** The length of the edge is 4.04×10^{-10} meters. The edge is 4.04 Å.   **3.** The length of the edge is about 4.04×10^{-10} meters.

SECTION P.4

P.4.1 Checkup   **1. (a)** $5(3) + 5(7)$ **(b)** $17(5) - 25(5)$ **(c)** $\frac{-46}{2} + \frac{62}{2}$ **(d)** $5 - 9$ **2. (a)** $5(1.2 + 1.8) = 15$ **(b)** $(17 - 23)\frac{1}{3} = -2$

P.4.2 Checkup   **1. (a)** 6   **(b)** 31   **2. (a)** -97 **(b)** 2   **(c)** -65 **(d)** -4 **(e)** -1.3 **P.4.3 Checkup**   **1.** The average high temperature was
1.3 degrees.   **2.** His weight is 170.72 pounds.

SECTION P.5

P.5.1 Checkup   **1. (a)** Let p = previous price; $p + 100$ **(b)** Let l = length; w = width; $2(l + w)$ **(c)** Let n = a number; $8n - 6$

(d) Let b = length of base; h = height; $\frac{1}{2}bh$ **P.5.2 Checkup**   **1. (a)** 5   **(b)** 4   **2. (a)** 12   **(b)** -12 **(c)** 144   **(d)** -144 **3.** -1

P.5.3 Checkup   **1.** Let x = the number of days; y = the number of miles; $29.95x + 0.59y + 5$; the cost of renting a truck for 2 days and 318 miles is $252.52.

2. Let l = length; w = width; $\sqrt{l^2 + w^2}$; $\sqrt{100^2 + \left(\frac{160}{3}\right)^2} = \frac{340}{3} = 113\frac{1}{3}$; the diagonal is $113\frac{1}{3}$ yards.

SECTION P.6

P.6.1 Checkup   **1. (a)** terms: 3; variable terms: $-a^2b$, $4ab$, $-b$; constant terms: none; coefficients: $-1, 4, -1$ **(b)** terms: 2; variable terms:

$3p(p + 8)$, $-5(p + 8)$; constant terms: none; coefficients: 3, -5 **(c)** terms: 3; variable terms: $\frac{2}{5}y$, y^2; constant terms: -2; coefficients: $\frac{2}{5}$, 1, -2

2. (a) 7, -8 **(b)** $3xy$, $-5xy$; $6y$, $7y$ **P.6.2 Checkup**   **1. (a)** $2x^3 + 2x^2 - 4x$ **(b)** $6xy - 2yz$ **(c)** $\frac{25x}{12} + \frac{13y}{12}$

P.6.3 Checkup   **1. (a)** $50p + q$ **(b)** $-18a - 14b - 4c$ **(c)** $20p + 204$ **(d)** $7x + 53$ **P.6.4 Checkup**   **1.** Her profit for the month is $415x - 225$ dollars; her profit for six paintings is $2265.   **2.** Let l = length; w = width; $2(l + w) = 2l + 2w$; the perimeter is 284 inches.

SECTION P.7

P.7.1 Checkup   **1. (a)** equation   **(b)** expression   **(c)** expression   **(d)** inequality   **P.7.2 Checkup**   **1. (a)** yes   **(b)** no

P.7.3 Checkup   **1. (a)**   **(b)**

P.7.4 Checkup   **1. (a)** $(-2, \infty)$ **(b)** $(1, 5)$ **P.7.5 Checkup**   **1.** Let x = number of students moved, $49x = 141$ **2.** $R = \frac{V}{I}$ **3.** Let x = the number of CD's Joseph can order; $6.99x + 5.99 \leq 50.00$ **4.** Let s = systolic pressure, d = diastolic pressure; $130 \leq s \leq 139, 85 \leq d \leq 89, s < 130, d < 85, s < 120, d < 80$.

SECTION P.8

P.8.1 Checkup   **1.** The exact area is 64π square yards, or approximately 201.1 square yards.   **P.8.2 Checkup**   **1.** The surface area is 5329π square feet, or approximately 16,741.5 square feet.   **P.8.3 Checkup**   **1.** The third angle measures 55°.   **2.** The second angle measures 31°.   **P.8.4 Checkup**   **1.** The temperature at the center of the Earth's core could be 3982°C.   **2.** The simple interest is $1700.   **3.** The distance is equal to 8760 ft, or 1.66 miles.   **P.8.5 Checkup**   **1.** The equatorial circumference of Mercury is approximately 15,331 km.   **2.** The volume is equal to 1537.7 ft³, and the surface area is equal to 885.4 ft².

CHAPTER 1

SECTION 1.1

1.1.1 Checkup   **1. (a)**

F	86	77	68	59	50	41	32
C	30	25	20	15	10	5	0

(b)

b	-3	-2	-1	0	1	2	3
a	25	19	13	7	1	-5	-11

1.1.2 Checkup   **1.** Temperature ordered pairs: $(86, 30)$, $(77, 25)$, $(68, 20)$, $(59, 15)$, $(50, 10)$, $(41, 5)$, $(32, 0)$; ordered pairs for (b, a): $(-3, 25)$, $(-2, 19)$, $(-1, 13)$, $(0, 7)$ $(1, 1)$ $(2, -5)$, $(3, -11)$ **1.1.3 Checkup**   **1. (a)** Domain is $\{5, 10, 15\}$; range is $\{15, 30, 45\}$.   **(b)** Domain is $\{0, 1, 2, 3, \dots\}$, or the set of whole numbers; range is $\{4, 6, 8, 10, \dots\}$, or the set of all even integers 4 or larger.   **(c)** Domain is $\{0.5, 1.5, 2.5\}$; range is $\{15.5, 16.5, 17.5\}$.   **1.1.4 Checkup**   **1. (a)** $r = 410 + 131n$

(b)

n	2	3	4	5
r	672	803	934	1065

(c) $(2, 672)$, $(3, 803)$, $(4, 934)$, $(5, 1065)$

2. The volume is 8142 cubic inches when the height is 29.5 inches. The volume is 10,626 cubic inches when the height is 38.5 inches. The volume is 13,110 cubic inches when the height is 47.5 inches.   **3. (a)** $\{(1996, 16), (1997, 148), (1998, 610), (1999, 1640), (2000, 2762), (2001, 3122), (2002, 3933), (2003, 5264)\}$; domain is $\{1996, 1997, 1998, 1999, 2000, 2001, 2002, 2003\}$; range is $\{16, 148, 610, 1640, 2762, 3122, 3933, 5264\}$ **(b)** $\{(0, 16), (1, 148), (2, 610), (3, 1640), (4, 2762), (5, 3122), (6, 3933), (7, 5264)\}$; domain is $\{0, 1, 2, 3, 4, 5, 6, 7\}$; range is $\{16, 148, 610, 1640, 2762, 3122, 3933, 5264\}$ **(c)** Amazon.com sales for the period of 1996 to 2003 ranged from 16 million dollars to 5264 million dollars

SECTION 1.2

1.2.1 Checkup **1. (a)**

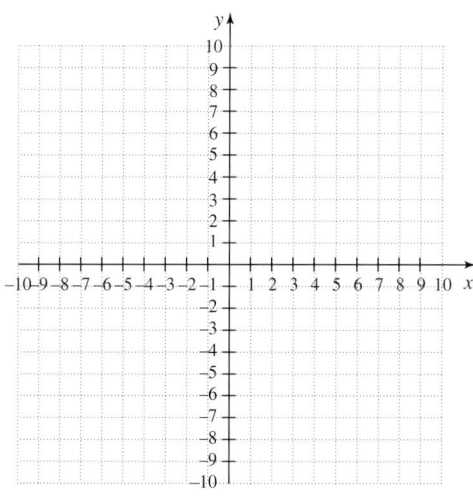

The graph corresponds to the setting of ZStandard.

| ZOOM | 6 |

(b)

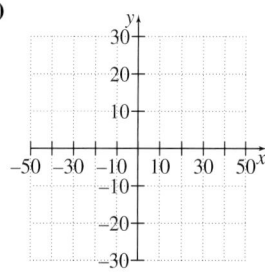

The graph corresponds to the setting of ZInteger.

| ZOOM | 6 | ZOOM | 8 | ENTER |

1.2.2 Checkup **1.**

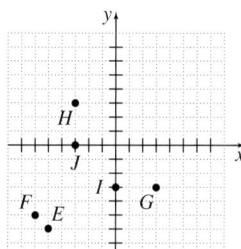

2. $A(-5, -2), B(5, 5), C(-1, 1), D(0, 4), E(4, -3), F(-3, 0)$ **3. (a)** II **(b)** I **(c)** IV **(d)** III **(e)** origin **(f)** x-axis **(g)** y-axis

4. (a)

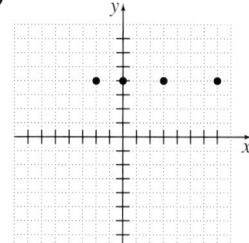

(b)

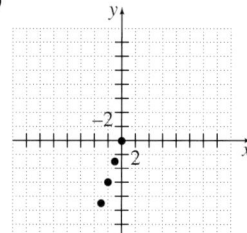

5. (a)

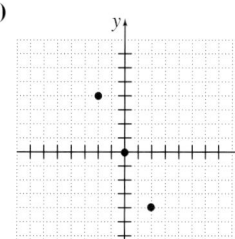

(b)

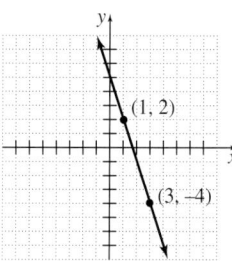

6.

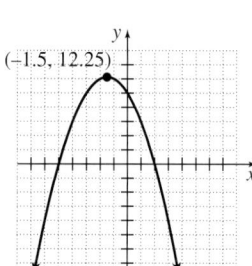

1.2.3 Checkup **1.** Domain is $\{-3\}$; range is the set of all real numbers. **2.** Domain is the set of all real numbers ≥ -4; range is the set of all real numbers. **3.** Domain is the set of all real numbers between -5 and 5 inclusive; range is the set of all real numbers between -5 and 5 inclusive.

1.2.4 Checkup **1. (a)**

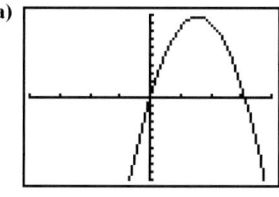

(b) Domain is the set of all real numbers from 0 to 15.625; range is the set of all real numbers between 0 and 977 approximately. **2.** The domain of the revenue, cost, and profit is $\{1998, 1999, 2000, 2001, 2002, 2003\}$. The range of the revenue is the set of all real numbers y such that $550 \leq y \leq 5250$. The range of the cost is the set of all real numbers y such that $450 \leq y \leq 3900$. The range of the profit is the set of all real numbers y such that $100 \leq y \leq 1350$.

SECTION 1.3

1.3.1 Checkup   **1. (a)** function   **(b)** function   **(c)** not a function   **1.3.2 Checkup**   **1. (a)** function   **(b)** not a function   **1.3.3 Checkup**
1. (a) $f(4)$ is not a real number. $f(-4) = -8$ **(b)** $c(-5) = -17; c(5) = -27$ **(c)** $h(1) = -3; h(-1) = -17$ **(d)** $g(b) = 4b - 8; g(b + 1) = 4b - 4$
1.3.4 Checkup   **1. (a)** $c(d) = 5 + 10d$ **(b)** $c(4) - 45$ **2.** The profit for 2003 was $1,348,400,000.

SECTION 1.4

1.4.1 Checkup   **1. (a)** x-intercept is $(5, 0)$; y-intercept is $(0, 3)$.   **(b)** x-intercepts are $(-2, 0), (-1, 0)$, and $(1, 0)$; y-intercept is $(0, -1)$.
2. x-intercepts are $(2, 0)$ and $(-2, 0)$; y-intercept is $(0, -4)$.   **3.** x-intercepts: $(-2, 0), (1, 0), (2.25, 0)$; y-intercept: $(0, 3)$.   **1.4.2 Checkup**
1. (a) relative maximum of 5 at $x = -3$ **(b)** no relative minimum   **(c)** $x < -3$ **(d)** $x > -3$ **2. (a)** relative maximum of 45.9375 at $x = 1.5$
(b) relative minima of -40 at $x = -1$ and 24 at $x = 3$ **(c)** $-1 < x < 1.5$ and $x > 3$ **(d)** $x < -1$ and $1.5 < x < 3$ **1.4.3 Checkup**   **1.** $(1, 0)$
and $(4, 3)$ **2.** $(5, -5)$ **1.4.4 Checkup**   **1. (a)** $C(x) = 0.60x + 35$ **(b)** $R(x) = 1.00x$ **(c)** The break-even point is $x = 87.5$, which means that
with 88 quarters, they will begin to make a profit.

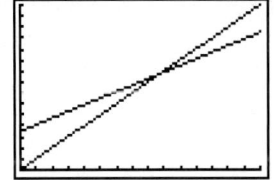

2. (a) The x-intercept is approximately $(6.5, 0)$. About 6.5 years
after 1996 or in the year 2003, the net income is $0
(b) minimum; 4 years after 1996 or in the year 2000, the net income is a loss of $1411.   **(c)** increasing; In the years from 2000
$(x = 4)$ to the year 2003 $(x = 7)$, the net income is increasing.

CHAPTER 2

SECTION 2.1

2.1.1 Checkup   **1. (a)** linear   **(b)** linear   **(c)** nonlinear   **(d)** nonlinear   **2.1.2 Checkup**   **1. (a)** -2 **(b)** 2   **(c)** noninteger between 2 and 3
2.1.3 Checkup   **1. (a)** $x = -2$ **(b)** $x = 2$ **(c)** $b = 2.6$

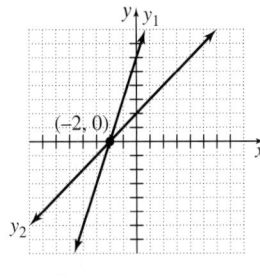

$y_1 = 3x + 6$
$y_2 = x + 2$

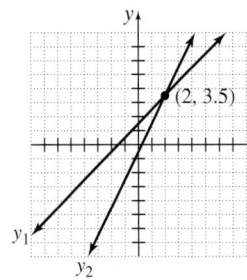

$y_1 = \dfrac{1}{2}(3 + 2x)$

$y_2 = 2x - \dfrac{1}{2}$

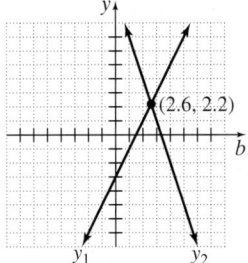

$y_1 = 4b - (2b + 3)$
$y_2 = 10 - 3b$

2.1.4 Checkup   **1. (a)** all real numbers   **(b)** no solution   **2.1.5 Checkup**   **1.** It will take
Gladys 8 hours to complete the job
for $149.   **2.** Phillipe must score
a 96 in order to achieve an average
of 90.

x	y_1	y_2
-3	-10	-10
-2	-8	-8
-1	-6	-6
0	-4	-4
1	-2	-2
2	0	0
3	2	2

$y_1 = y_2$ for all x.

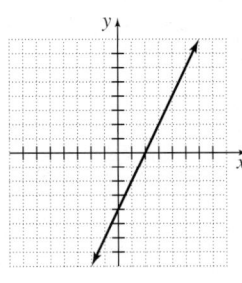

$y_1 = (x - 1) + (x - 3)$
$y_2 = 2(x - 2)$

x	y_1	y_2
-3	-7	-15
-2	-3	-11
-1	1	-7
0	5	-3
1	9	1
2	13	5
3	17	9

$y_1 - y_2 = 8$ for all x.

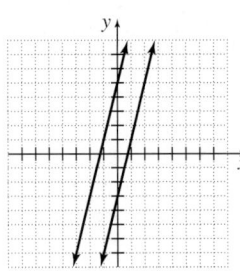

$y_1 = (x + 1) + (3x + 4)$
$y_2 = 3(x - 1) + x$

SECTION 2.2

2.2.1 Checkup   **1. (a)** 22   **(b)** 6   **2.2.2 Checkup**   **1. (a)** $\dfrac{2}{15}$ **(b)** 5   **(c)** -33 **2.2.3 Checkup**   **1.** Big Bird is 98 inches tall.   **2.** Each
side of Cheryl's garden will be 9.5 feet long.   **3.** Five liters of a 20% saline solution contains one liter of salt.   **4.** On Earth, the astronaut and his
suit weigh about 360 pounds.

SECTION 2.3

2.3.1 Checkup   **1. (a)** 6   **(b)** 7   **(c)** $-\dfrac{13}{2}$ **2. (a)** any real number   **(b)** no solution   **3. (a)** $\dfrac{5}{6}$ **(b)** -3 **(c)** 13   **2.3.2 Checkup**   **1.** The break-even point is any real number, since the cost will always equal the revenue.   **2.** The plans will be equal in cost for 204 miles.   **3.** The mixture used 10 cc's of the 40% alcohol solution.   **4.** The number of chirps per minute is 301.

SECTION 2.4

2.4.1 Checkup   **1. (a)** $W = \dfrac{P - 2L}{2}$ **(b)** $a = 4A - b - c - d$ **(c)** $W = \dfrac{S - 2LH}{2L + 2H}$ **2. (a)** $y = 2x - 3$ **(b)** $y = -2x + \dfrac{5}{2}$ **(c)** $y = \dfrac{7}{3}x + 9$

2.4.2 Checkup   **1. (a)** $c = 0.12x + 49.95$ **(b)** $x = \dfrac{25}{3}c - \dfrac{1665}{4}$ **(c)** For \$150, you can drive approximately 834 miles; for \$250, approximately 1667 miles; for \$500, approximately 3750 miles.   **2.** $C = \dfrac{5}{9}(F - 32)$

SECTION 2.5

2.5.1 Checkup   **1.** The integers are 12, 14, and 16.   **2.** The lengths Jim needs to cut are 3 inches, 4 inches, 5 inches, 6 inches, and 7 inches.
2.5.2 Checkup   **1.** \$9389.67 should be invested.   **2.** Zeke will borrow \$4000 at 7% and \$1000 at 8.5%.   **2.5.3 Checkup**   **1.** The room charge before adding the surcharge is \$62.50.   **2.5.4 Checkup**   **1.** The sandbox will have two sides of 3.5 feet and a third side of 5 feet.   **2.** One of the roads must be rotated 34°.

SECTION 2.6

2.6.1 Checkup   **1. (a)** linear   **(b)** nonlinear   **2.6.2 Checkup**   **1. (a)** 1 and -1 **(b)** 5 and -7 **(c)** no solution   **2.6.3 Checkup**   **1. (a)** 9
(b) 6 and 12   **(c)** no solution   **2. (a)** 1 and -1 **(b)** 5 and -7 **(c)** no solution   **2.6.4 Checkup**   **1.** $|72 - h| = 3$; $h = 69$ and $h = 75$; the smallest height for drivers will be 69 inches (or 5 feet, 9 inches), and the largest height will be 75 inches (or 6 feet, 3 inches).   **2.** The scores could be between 66 and 94 or between 66 and 38.

CHAPTER 3

SECTION 3.1

3.1.1 Checkup   **1. (a)** nonlinear   **(b)** linear; $y = -\dfrac{3}{8}$ **(c)** linear; $8x - y = 3$ **(d)** nonlinear   **3.1.2 Checkup**   **1.** Answers will vary: $(0, 4)$, $(2, 2)$, and $(4, 0)$.   **2.**

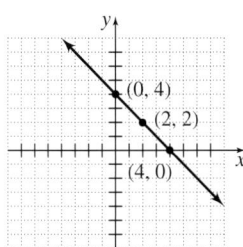

3.

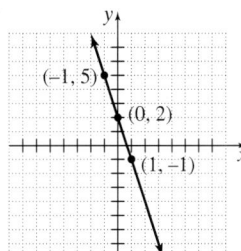

4.

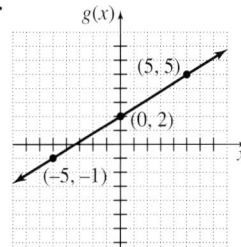

3.1.3 Checkup   **1.** The x-intercept is $(2, 0)$ and the y-intercept is $(0, 12)$.   **3.1.4 Checkup**   **1. (a)** The x-and y-intercepts occur at the origin $(0, 0)$.
(b) The y-intercept is $\left(0, \dfrac{3}{5}\right)$.   **(c)** The x-intercept is $(16, 0)$.

3.1.5 Checkup   **1.**

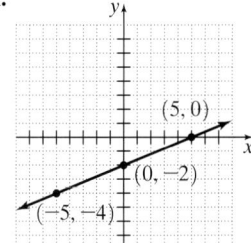

3.1.6 Checkup   **1. (a)** $(1, 3), (3, 7), (5, 11)$
(b)

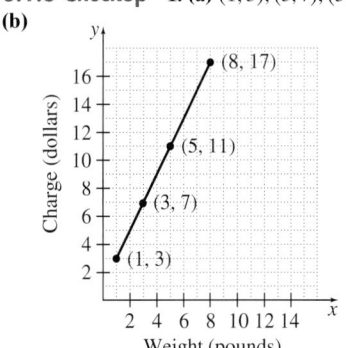

(c) The cost for an 8-pound package is \$17.
(d) Answers may vary.

2. The linear function for the profit that Don will realize is $y = 140x - 700$, with y as profit and x as the number of students in the class. The intercepts are $(0, -700)$ and $(5, 0)$. When there are no students in his class ($x = 0$), Don loses $700. With five students in his class, Don breaks even, or has a profit of 0.

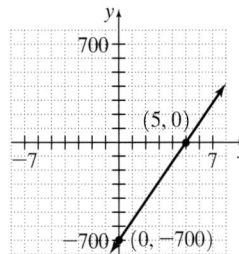

3. The intercepts of the graph are $(0, 5645)$ and $(3.8, 0)$. This means that at $t = 0$ the plane hasn't moved yet, so the distance d is 5645 miles. When the distance is 0, the time is approximately 3 hours and 48 minutes, or 3.8 hours. The time t it takes to fly 3500 miles is approximately 1.44 hours.

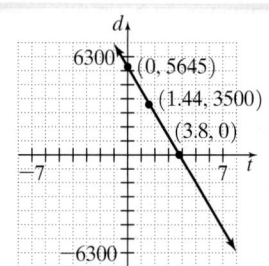

SECTION 3.2

3.2.1 Checkup   1. (a) The slope is 0.   **(b)** The slope is $\frac{2}{5}$.   **(c)** The slope is -3.   **(d)** The slope is undefined.   **2. (a)** The graph represents a function that is constant; the slope is zero.   **(b)** The graph represents a function that is increasing; the slope is positive.   **(c)** The graph represents a function that is decreasing; the slope is negative.   **(d)** The graph does not represent a function; the slope is undefined.

3.2.2 Checkup   1. (a) $m = \frac{3}{2}$ **(b)** $m = 0$ **(c)** $m = $ undefined   **3.2.3 Checkup   1.** The grade is 40%.   **2.** The average rate of change is $9980 per year.   **3.** Graph c. The slope of the third portion is twice that of the first portion. The rest period was 4 minutes.   **4.** The average rate of change of the machine's value is $9000 per year.

SECTION 3.3

3.3.1 Checkup   1. (a) $m = -\frac{7}{11}$; y-intercept is $(0, 13)$.   **(b)** $m = 0$; y-intercept is $(0, -6)$.   **(c)** $m = $ undefined; there is no y-intercept.

3.3.2 Checkup   1. (a)   **(b)**   **(c)**

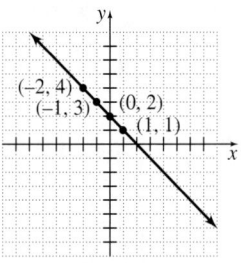   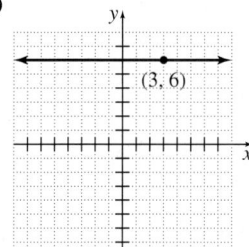

3.3.3 Checkup   1. (a)   **(b)**   **(c)**

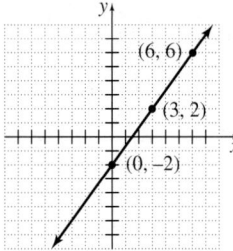   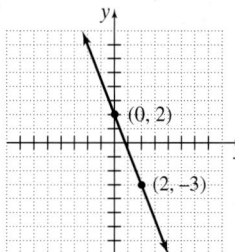   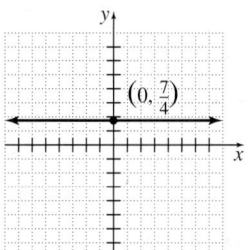

3.3.4 Checkup

1. (a)

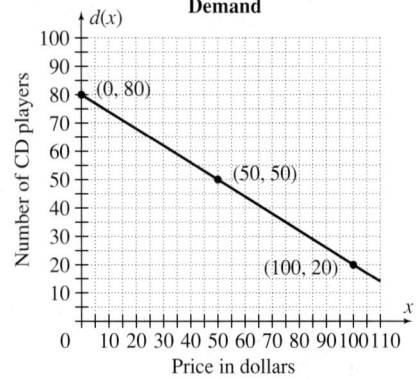

2. (a)

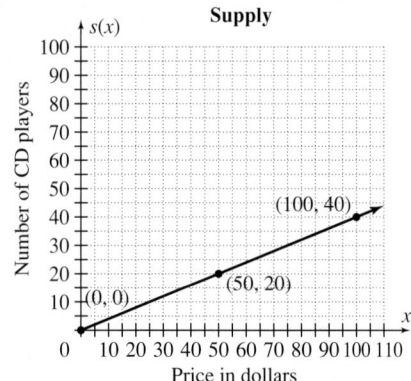

(b) For a demand of 15 videos, the selling price is $108.33.
For a selling price of $59, the demand is about 47 (44.6) videos.

(b) For a supply of 24 videos, the price is $60.
For a selling price of $55, 22 videos are supplied.

3. The depreciation is $5000 per year; $y = 20{,}000 - 5000x$;

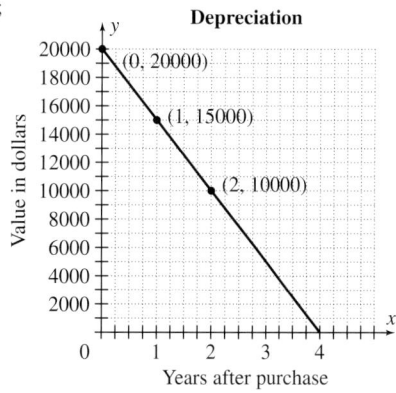

Depreciation

SECTION 3.4

3.4.1 Checkup **1. (a)** intersecting and perpendicular **(b)** parallel **(c)** intersecting **(d)** coinciding   **2. (a)** perpendicular **(b)** parallel

3.

Situation	Relationship between Slopes m_1 and m_2	Relationship between y-Intercept Values b_1 and b_2
Graphs coincide	$m_1 = m_2$	$b_1 = b_2$
Graphs are parallel	$m_1 = m_2$	$b_1 \neq b_2$
Graphs intersect only	$m_1 \neq m_2$ and $m_1 \cdot m_2 \neq -1$	None
Graphs intersect and are perpendicular	$m_1 \cdot m_2 = -1$	None

3.4.2 Checkup **1. (a)** Let x = the number of lawns for which Tim cares. $y = 8.50x + 6.50x + 85$ **(b)** $y = 20x$ **(c)** Since the slopes are different, the lines intersect and there is a break-even point. **(d)** If the revenue function is $y = 15x$, the slopes are the same, but the y-intercepts are different and the lines are parallel. Tim will never break even.   **2.** Yes; $(80, 32)$ is the equilibrium point; when the price is $80, there will be an equal supply and demand of 32 CD players.   **3.** Yes; 48 years after 1990, or 2038, the number of males and the number of females who list their marital status as married will be equal (77.87 million).

SECTION 3.5

3.5.1 Checkup **1.** **(a)** $y = -\dfrac{1}{4}x + 2$ **(b)** $x = 2$ **(c)** $y = -3$ **2. (a)** $y = -2x + 5$ **(b)** $y = 4x - 1$ **(c)** $y = 3$

3.5.2 Checkup **1.** $y = \dfrac{3}{4}x - \dfrac{9}{2}$ **3.5.3 Checkup** **1. (a)** $y = \dfrac{2}{3}x + \dfrac{5}{3}$ **(b)** $y = -3$ **(c)** $x = 5$ **3.5.4 Checkup** **1. (a)** $y = -\dfrac{3}{2}x + \dfrac{13}{2}$ **(b)** $y = -\dfrac{5}{2}x + \dfrac{3}{2}$ **3.5.5 Checkup** **1. (a)** $y = 0.16x + 74.7$ **(b)** In 2000 ($x = 30$), the life expectancy was 79.5 years. This is the exact figure for 2000. **(c)** In 2010 ($x = 40$), the life expectancy will be 81.1 years.   **2. (a)** $m = \dfrac{5}{9}$ **(b)** $C = \dfrac{5}{9}(F - 32)$ **(c)** $24°$ **3.** $y = 1.95x + 28.59$; the height is 66.81 inches.   **4.** $s = 393x + 1606$; in 2008, a family of four will spend $6715 on recreation.

CHAPTER 4

SECTION 4.1

4.1.1 Checkup **1. (a)** The ordered pair is not a solution. **(b)** The ordered pair is a solution.   **4.1.2 Checkup** **1. (a)** $(1, 1)$ **(b)** $(4, -5)$ **2. (a)** No solution **(b)** Infinitely many solutions; all ordered pairs that satisfy $y = 2x + 1$ **(c)** Infinitely many solutions; all ordered pairs that satisfy $y = 2x + 3$ **(d)** No solution   **3.** Answers will vary.   **4.** No; the graphs of two consistent and independent equations will be intersecting lines. The graphs of two independent and inconsistent equations will be parallel lines.   **4.1.3 Checkup** **1.** At 291.5 miles, both offers are equal.   **2.** The monthly car payment is $500, and the monthly insurance payment is $200.   **3.** In the year 2019, the percent of males and females will be equal.

SECTION 4.2

4.2.1 Checkup **1. (a)** $\left(\dfrac{1}{4}, -\dfrac{9}{2}\right)$ **(b)** $\left(\dfrac{2}{11}, -\dfrac{26}{11}\right)$ **2. (a)** infinitely many solutions; all ordered pairs that satisfy $y = 5x - 3$

(b) no solution   **3.** If the system results in an identity, then there will be many solutions, a consistent system, and dependent equations. If the system results in a contradiction, then there will be no solutions, an inconsistent system, and independent equations.   **4.2.2 Checkup** **1.** The two angles measure $125°$ and $55°$.   **2. (a)** $C(x) = 245 + 2.50x$ **(b)** $R(x) = 20x$ **(c)** $y = 245 + 2.5x$; $y = 20x$; Deanna will break even when 14 cakes are produced and sold.   **3.** The number of workers will be equal in the year 2016.

SECTION 4.3

4.3.1 Checkup **1.** **(a)** $(2, -6)$ **(b)** $(1, -1)$ **(c)** $\left(\dfrac{1}{4}, \dfrac{8}{5}\right)$ **2.** **(a)** no solution **(b)** infinitely many solutions; all ordered

pairs that satisfy $y = 5x + 12$ **4.3.2 Checkup** **1.** Let x = the number of cans of cashews sold and y = the number of cans of peanuts sold;

$x + y = 262$; $6.50x + 4.00y = 1240.50$; the solution of the system of equations is $(77, 185)$. The Indian Maidens sold 77 cans of cashews and 185 cans of peanuts.   **2.** Let s = the number of millions of people who speak Spanish; Let c = the number of millions of people who speak Chinese; $s = 18.677c$; $s + c = 29.6$; 1.5 million people speak Chinese; 28.1 million people speak Spanish.

SECTION 4.4

4.4.1 Checkup   1. Let x = Patty's time on the road and y = the distance she traveled when her dad caught up with her. Her dad's distance would also be y, and his time on the road is 0.5 hour less than Patty's time; $y = 55x$; $y = 65(x - 0.5)$; the solution is $(3.25, 178.75)$. Patty's dad must travel for $3.25 - 0.5 = 2.75$ hours before catching up with Patty.   **2.** Let x = average speed of planes in still air, y = average speed of wind; $4(x + y) = 2350$, $5(x - y) = 2350$; the average speed of the planes in still air is 528.75 mph; the average speed of the wind is 58.75 mph.
4.4.2 Checkup   1. Let x = the number of dimes Rosita saved and y = the number of quarters; $x + y + 120 = 498$; $0.05(120) + 0.10x + 0.25y = 63.75$; the solution is $(245, 133)$. Rosita had saved 245 dimes and 133 quarters.   **2.** Let x = the amount of 25% solution and y = the amount of 5% solution in the mix; $x + y = 1$; $0.25x + 0.05y = 0.10(1)$; the solution is $\left(\frac{1}{4}, \frac{3}{4}\right)$. The mix should contain 0.25 liter of the 25% solution and 0.75 liter of the 5% solution.   **3.** Let x = the amount of the 50% glucose solution and y = the amount of the water (0% glucose solution); $0.5x + 0y = 0.2(1)$, $x + y = 1$; She should mix 0.4 liter of the 50% glucose solution with 0.6 liter of water.   **4.** Let x = the amount invested in EE bonds and y = the amount invested in I bonds; $x + y = 30,000$, $0.035x + 0.048y = 1310$; $10,000 should be invested in EE bonds and $20,000 should be invested in I bonds.   **5.** Let x = the amount invested in EE bonds and y = the amount invested in I bonds; $x = 2y$, $0.035x + 0.048y = 11,800$; $200,000 should be invested in EE bonds and $100,000 should be invested in I bonds.

SECTION 4.5

4.5.1 Checkup   1. yes   **2.** yes   **4.5.2 Checkup   1.** $(0.8, 4.5, 1.9)$ **2.** $(-4, 10, -5)$ **3.** no solution   **4.** infinite number of solutions; all ordered triples that satisfy $2x + 4y = 3z + 3$ **4.5.3 Checkup   1.** The three currents are $I_1 = 3$ amperes, $I_2 = \frac{5}{3}$ amperes, and $I_3 = \frac{4}{3}$ amperes.
2. Edgar received 4 ounces of a roast beef sandwich, 3 ounces of french fries, and 12 ounces of milk shake.

CHAPTER 5

SECTION 5.1

5.1.1 Checkup   1.   (a) linear   **(b)** nonlinear   **(c)** nonlinear   **5.1.2 Checkup   1.** $x > -1$ **5.1.3 Checkup   1.** $x < -1$
2. (a) $x \leq -1$ **(b)** $x < 2.5$ **3. (a)** no solution   **(b)** all real numbers   **(c)** all real numbers

5.1.4 Checkup   1. (a) $x > 2$; $(2, \infty)$;   **(b)** $z \geq 3$; $[3, \infty)$;

(c) $x < 7.52$; $(-\infty, 7.52)$;   **2.** $-14 \leq x < -2$; $[-14, -2)$;

3. (a) no solution   **(b)** all real numbers; $(-\infty, \infty)$ **5.1.5 Checkup   1.** The store must buy and sell at least 50 CDs.   **2.** She can have between 1400 and 1750 calories, inclusive.   **3.** The weight must be at least 200 pounds.

SECTION 5.2

5.2.1 Checkup   1. (a) linear; $7x - y < 10$ **(b)** nonlinear   **(c)** linear; $x - y < 0$ **5.2.2 Checkup   1. (a)**

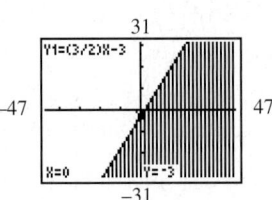

(b)

5.2.3 Checkup   1. (a)

(b)

5.2.4 Checkup   1. (a) Let x = the number of payments Lana makes and y = the number of payments her parents make; $60x + 125y \leq 1500$

(b)

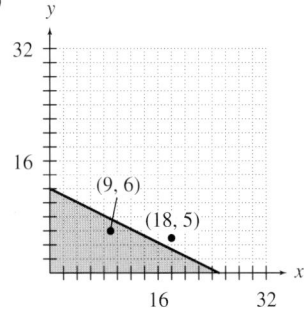

(c) Yes, see the graph.　**(d)** No, see the graph.　**2.** No, Yes.

SECTION 5.3

5.3.1 Checkup　**1.**

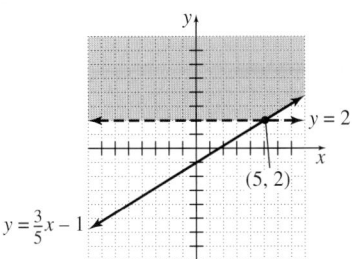

2.

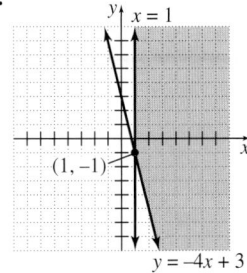

3.

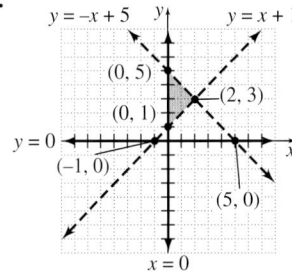

5.3.2 Checkup　**1.** $Y1 = -3x + 4$
$Y2 = -x + 2$

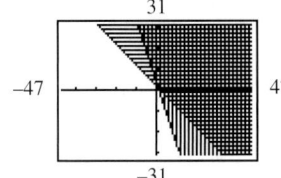

2. *Note:* Set window to first quadrant to achieve last two inequalities.

$Y1 = \dfrac{2}{3}x + 1$

$Y2 = -\dfrac{3}{4}x + 5$

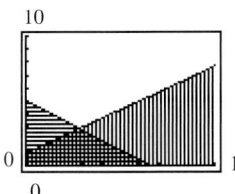

5.3.3 Checkup　**1.** Let x = the number of rag dolls and y = the number of sculptured dolls produced; $1.5x + 4y \le 30$; $1.5x + y \le 24$; possible combinations: $(5, 5)$ indicates that they produce 5 of each doll; $(10, 2)$ indicates that they produce 10 rag dolls and 2 sculptured dolls; see points on figure.
2. Yes, No.

CHAPTER 6

SECTION 6.1

6.1.1 Checkup　**1. (a)** polynomial　**(b)** not a polynomial　**6.1.2 Checkup**　**1. (a)** binomial　**(b)** polynomial　**6.1.3 Checkup**　**1. (a)** The degrees of the terms are 2, 4, and 3; the degree of the polynomial is 4.　**(b)** The polynomial simplifies to $-2x^2 + 5x + 1$; the degrees of the terms are 2, 1, and 0; the degree of the polynomial is 2.　**(c)** The degrees of the terms are 10 and 9; the degree of the polynomial is 10.

6.1.4 Checkup

	descending order	ascending order
1.	$2x^3 - x^2 - 5x + 3$	$3 - 5x - x^2 + 2x^3$
2.	$y^4 + y + 12$	$12 + y + y^4$

6.1.5 Checkup　**1. (a)** 172　**(b)** $\dfrac{3}{4}$　**6.1.6 Checkup**　**1.** Let x = length of a side of the cabin, a = length of the lot, b = width of the lot.

(a) $ab - x^2$　**(b)** $0.05(ab - x^2)$　**(c)** If $x = 35$, $a = 200$, and $b = 150$, then the area not covered by the cabin is 28,775 square feet. The cost of seeding the yard is $1438.75.　**2.** Let x = the length of the side of the square.　**(a)** $8x^2$　**(b)** $6x^2 + 60$　**(c)** $2x^2 - 60$　**(d)** The revenue will be $648; the cost will be $546; the profit will be $102.

SECTION 6.2

6.2.1 Checkup

1. Answers will vary. **(a)**

x	y
−1	−7
0	−2
1	1
2	2
3	1
4	−2

(b)

x	y
−3	0
−2	4
−1	0
0	−6
1	−8
2	0

2. (a) x **(b)** y **(c)** all real numbers

6.2.2 Checkup

1. (a)

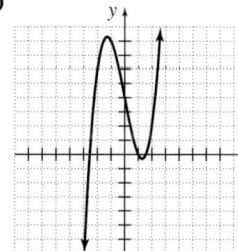

(b)

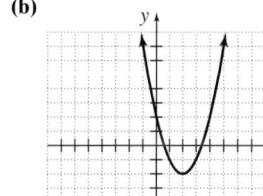

2. (a)

x	y
0	−8
3	7
−1	−9

(b)

x	y
−1	−1
0	1
−2	3

6.2.3 Checkup **1. (a)** all real numbers greater than or equal to 4 **(b)** all real numbers less than or equal to 5 **(c)** all real numbers **2. (a)** all real numbers **(b)** all real numbers less than or equal to 9 **(c)** all real numbers greater than or equal to −2.3 (approx.)

6.2.4 Checkup **1. (a)** −15 **(b)** 60 **2.** $f(5000) \approx 1.255 \times 10^{11}$ or 125,500,000,000 **6.2.5 Checkup** **1. (a)** The domain is the set of all real numbers greater than or equal to 0. **(b)** The absolute maximum is 200 when $x = 20$. The maximum profit is $200 when 20 bikes are sold per week. **(c)** The range is the set of all real numbers less than or equal to 200. The profit ranges from a loss (a negative value) to $200, the maximum profit.

2. (a)

No. Attending	Revenue
5	$650
10	$1100
15	$1350
20	$1400
25	$1250
30	$900
35	$350
40	−$400

(b) The revenue will be at most $1406.25. **(c)** Answers will vary.

3. (a)

1980	1985	1990	2000
19.6	18.4	18.6	22.08

(b) The actual percentage is 0.08% lower than the prediction. **(c)** The projection of 23.7% is about 0.1% higher than the predicted percent.

SECTION 6.3

6.3.1 Checkup **1. (a)** quadratic **(b)** nonquadratic **(c)** nonquadratic **6.3.2 Checkup** **1. (a)** concave upward **(b)** $(−1, 2)$ **(c)** absolute minimum of 2 at $x = −1$ **(d)** $(−1, \infty)$ **(e)** $(−\infty, −1)$ **2.** $(−1, −2)$ **3.** concave upward; graph is wide compared to the graph of $y = x^2$; y-intercept $= (0, 2)$; vertex $= (2, 1)$; axis of symmetry is $x = 2$

6.3.3 Checkup **1.**

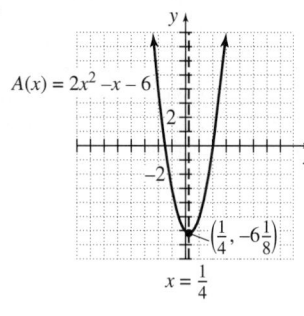

2.

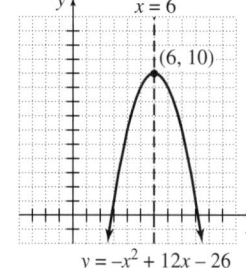

6.3.4 Checkup **1.** The maximum cost of producing the tillers is $40,100 when 2000 tillers are produced. **2. (a)** The vertex is $(9.3, 524)$. **(b)** The maximum height of the signal flare is approximately 524 meters at approximately 9.3 seconds. **(c)** Assuming the flare drops to the ground, the range of the flare's height is between and including 0 meter and 524 meters. **(d)** If the flare died 6 seconds after being shot, the absolute maximum height of the flare was 470.8 meters.

SECTION 6.4

6.4.1 Checkup **1.** $y = 0.75x^2 + 2.75x - 1$

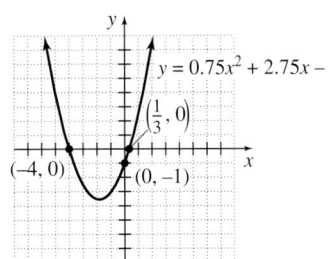

6.4.2 Checkup **1.** $y = x^2 + x - 6$

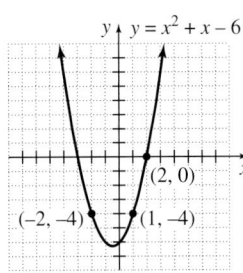

6.4.3 Checkup **1.** Let t = time in seconds after release and $s(t)$ = position of the case in feet above the water. $s(t) = -16t^2 - 30t + 1500$; the case will reach the water in approximately 8.8 seconds.   **2.** $y = 0.000113x^2 - 500$

CHAPTER 7

SECTION 7.1

7.1.1 Checkup **1. (a)** $-5 \cdot y \cdot y \cdot y$ **(b)** $(-5y)(-5y)(-5y)$ **(c)** $3 \cdot 3 \cdot x \cdot x \cdot x$ **(d)** $q \cdot q \cdot q \cdot q$ **(e)** $(a - b)(a - b)(a - b)(a - b)$

7.1.2 Checkup **1. (a)** z^7 **(b)** $(x + y)^8$ **(c)** $\dfrac{a^8}{2}$ **7.1.3 Checkup** **1. (a)** a^4 **(b)** $(x + 5)^2$ **(c)** $\dfrac{2}{11}z^3$ **7.1.4 Checkup** **1. (a)** $-243a^5$

(b) $-64x^{24}$ **(c)** $\dfrac{16p^4}{q^4}$ **7.1.5 Checkup** **1. (a)** $\dfrac{-2a^4b^4}{5}$ **(b)** $3q$ **(c)** $\dfrac{-x^5y^2}{2}$ **(d)** $\dfrac{27a^6}{64b^3}$ **2.** a^{mn}; a^{m+n}

7.1.6 Checkup **1.**

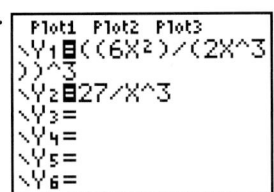 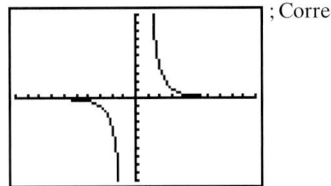 ; Correct

7.1.7 Checkup **1.** The volume of the original box is x^3. The volume of the new box is $\dfrac{1}{8}x^3$. The volume of the new box is one-eighth as large as the volume of the original box. If the original box measures 1.5 meters on a side, its volume is 3.375 cubic meters, and the volume of the new box is 0.421875 cubic meter.   **2. (a)** πx^2 square miles **(b)** $9\pi x^2$ square miles **(c)** 9 to 1 **(d)** The average area was 1444π square miles or about 4536 square miles. The extreme case area was $12,996\pi$ square miles or about 40,828 square miles.   **3.** The distance to the moon is 2.325×10^5 miles or 1.2276×10^9 feet.

SECTION 7.2

7.2.1 Checkup **1. (a)** $\dfrac{y^2}{x^4}$ **(b)** $\dfrac{8a^4b^3}{25}$ **(c)** $\dfrac{q^5}{p^5}$ **7.2.2 Checkup** **1. (a)** $\dfrac{1}{2z^2}$ **(b)** $\dfrac{5}{b}$ **2. (a)** $\dfrac{a}{2b^3}$ **(b)** $\dfrac{a^4}{2b^3}$ **(c)** $\dfrac{125p}{q^2}$ **(d)** $\dfrac{-x^3y^{12}}{125}$ **3. (a)** $\dfrac{h^{12}}{k^6}$

(b) $\dfrac{27c^9}{8d^{12}}$ **7.2.3 Checkup** **1.** A proton is about 1836.645 times as heavy as an electron.   **2.** The volume of the largest atom is about 9.697×10^{-29} m^3.

SECTION 7.3

7.3.1 Checkup **1.** $8x^3 - 3x^2 - x + 9$ **2.** $7x^3 - x^2y - 7xy^2 + 5y^3$ **7.3.2 Checkup** **1.** $a^3 - 7a^2 + 15$ **2.** $4a^4 + 3a^3b - 9a^2b^2 + 5ab^3 + 2b^4$ **7.3.3 Checkup** **1.** Let x = the number of box lunches made and sold in a day.   **(a)** $C(x) = 15 + 1.5x$ **(b)** $R(x) = 4.50x$ **(c)** $P(x) = 3x - 15$ **2.** The difference in the heights is $(20t + 60)$ feet.

SECTION 7.4

7.4.1 Checkup **1. (a)** $-25a^5b^5c$ **(b)** $-4m^5n + 20m^4n^2 - 4m^3n^3$ **7.4.2 Checkup** **1. (a)** $7a^2 + 50a + 7$ **(b)** $4y^2 - 1$ **(c)** $x^2 - 10x + 25$
7.4.3 Checkup **1. (a)** $3x^3 + 4x^2 - 12x - 16$ **(b)** $x^3 + 3x^2 + 3x + 1$ **(c)** $x^3 + 1$ **7.4.4 Checkup** **1. (a)** $9y^2 - 49$ **(b)** $9y^2 - 42y + 49$
7.4.5 Checkup **1.** $2x^2 - 3x + 1$ **2.** $a^2 + 2ah + h^2 - a - h + 1$ **7.4.6 Checkup** **1.** Let $A(s)$ be the area of the new garden.
$A(s) = 2s^2 + 11s + 12$. If the garden measured 5 feet on a side, the area of the new garden will be 117 square feet. **2.** Let $R(x)$ be the revenue.
$R(x) = -0.25x^2 + 1.25x + 37.50$ **3.** Let x be the width of the garden; $3x$ is the length of the garden; $x + 4$ is the width of the garden and walkway,
and $3x + 4$ is the length of the garden and walkway. If $A(x)$ is the area of the walkway, $A(x) = (3x + 4)(x + 4) - 3x(x)$. Thus, $A(x) = 16x + 16$.

SECTION 7.5

7.5.1 Checkup **1. (a)** $3a^2b^3c$ **(b)** $-6xy - y^2$ **(c)** $3x + \dfrac{3y}{2} - \dfrac{9y^2}{4x} - \dfrac{y^3}{2x^2}$ **7.5.2 Checkup** **1. (a)** $5x - 4$ **(b)** $4x^2 - 2x + 5 + \dfrac{2}{2x + 5}$

(c) $4x^2 - 6x + 9$ **7.5.3 Checkup** **1. (a)** $C(x) = 200 + 75x$ **(b)** $R(x) = 259x - 5x^2$ **(c)** $P(x) = -5x^2 + 184x - 200$

(d) $A(x) = -5x + 184 - \dfrac{200}{x}$ **(e)** The average profit is \$114.00 per package. **2.** $g(y) = 5000y^3 + 5000y^2 + 5000y + 5000$; Benjamin received a
total of \$23,205.00.

CHAPTER 8

SECTION 8.1

8.1.1 Checkup **1. (a)** $6a^2bc$ **(b)** $42x^3y^3z^2$ **8.1.2 Checkup** **1. (a)** $6a^2b^2(a - 2b + 4)$ **(b)** $-4xy(2xy^2z + 6x^2y - 9z)$
8.1.3 Checkup **1. (a)** $(2a + b)(7a + 4b)$ **(b)** $(3x - 2)(4x^2 - 3)$ **8.1.4 Checkup** **1. (a)** $(3x - 5)(2x + 3)$ **(b)** $(y^2 + 1)(2y^2 - 5)$
(c) $5a(3a - 4)(a + 7)$ **8.1.5 Checkup** **1. (a)** Let $x =$ the amount Katie received the first month. Let $T(x) =$ the total amount of money Katie
will receive. $T(x) = 6x + 180$. **(b)** $T(x) = 6(x + 30)$; $(x + 30)$ is the average monthly amount Katie will receive if she stops smoking for six months.
(c) $T(50) = 480$; Katie will receive \$480. **(d)** Katie's average monthly receipt is \$80, and this does check with the interpretation from part **b**.
2. (a) $(100 + 2x)(150 + 2x) - (150)(100)$; $4x(125 + x)$; the offices' area is 26,400 ft^2. **3. (a)** $(25 + x)(20 - 3x)$ **(b)** The price of the ticket, \$25,
was increased at a rate of \$1 per increase. **(c)** There were 3 fewer tickets sold per \$1 increase.

SECTION 8.2

8.2.1 Checkup **1. (a)** $(7a + 3b)^2$ **(b)** $5(x - 6)^2$ **(c)** Does not factor. **(d)** $(y^2 + 4)^2$ **8.2.2 Checkup** **1. (a)** $(5x - 4y)(5x + 4y)$
(b) $2(z - 3)(z + 3)$ **(c)** Does not factor. **(d)** $(c - 2)(c + 2)(c^2 + 4)$ **8.2.3 Checkup** **1. (a)** $(a - 2)(a^2 + 2a + 4)$
(b) $(2x + 3y)(4x^2 - 6xy + 9y^2)$ **8.2.4 Checkup** **1. (a)** Let $p =$ the length of a side of the square patio: $A(p) =$ the area to be landscaped.
$A(p) = 16^2 - p^2$. **(b)** $A(p) = (16 - p)(16 + p)$. An equivalent rectangular area will be one that is 9 feet by 23 feet. **(c)** The package covers an
area of 200 square feet. The landscaped area will be 207 square feet. The package is not large enough. **2.** $(9 - x)^2$; the original quilt was 9 feet by 9
feet; the area of the trimmed quilt is 60.0625 ft^2.

SECTION 8.3

8.3.1 Checkup **1.** $(x - 5)(x + 1)$ **2. (a)** $(b - 7)(b - 5)$ **(b)** $(c - 8)(c + 3)$ **(c)** $6(d + 7)(d + 3)$ **(d)** $(y^2 - 3)(y^2 + 1)$
8.3.2 Checkup **1.** $(2x + 1)(x - 5)$ **2. (a)** Does not factor. **(b)** $-1(4x^2 - x + 10)$ **(c)** $(3x - 2y)(2x + y)$ **(d)** $(2x^2 - 5)(3x^2 - 4)$
8.3.3 Checkup **1.** Since the polynomial factors as $(w + 13)(w + 5)$, the outside dimensions are $(w + 5)$ feet wide and $(w + 13)$ feet long. Comparing these dimensions with the inside width of w feet and length of $w + 9$ ft, we find that the walk is 2.5 feet wide along the pool's length and 2 feet
wide along its width. **2.** $2(x + 39)(2x + 27)$ or $(2x + 78)(2x + 27)$; the dimensions of the playing area are 27 feet by 78 feet.

SECTION 8.4

8.4.1 Checkup **1. (a)** $(2x + 1)(x - 5)$ **(b)** Does not factor. **(c)** $5(2x + 3)(3x + 2)$ **(d)** $(2x^2 - 5)(3x^2 - 4)$ **8.4.2 Checkup** **1. (a)** The
polynomial factors as $\dfrac{1}{2}(3x - 4)(x - 4)$. The sides of the reduced garden measure $(3x - 4)$ and $(x - 4)$ feet. **(b)** Carri reduced each of the two
sides of the garden by 4 feet. **2.** $(2x + 45)(x + 15)$; the width is $(x + 15)$ feet and the length is $(2x + 45)$ feet; the border is one-half of 15 or
7.5 feet wide; the width is 100 feet, the length is 215 feet, and the total area is 21,500 square feet.

SECTION 8.5

8.5.1 Checkup **1. (a)** $5(2z - 5)(z + 6)$ **(b)** $2a(3a + 1)(a + 4)$ **(c)** Does not factor. **(d)** $6x(x - 5y)(2x - y)$ **(e)** $-6(a - 2)(a + 2)$
(f) $(3x - 2)^2(3x + 2)^2$ **(g)** $(4 + h)(3 - 5h)$ or $-1(5h - 3)(h + 4)$ **8.5.2 Checkup** **1.** $x(349.95 - 8.95x)$; For every copy of software purchased, a discount of \$8.95 will be given. **2.** The polynomial factors as $x(5 - 2x)(7 - 2x)$. Therefore, the height is x inches, the width is $(5 - 2x)$
inches, and the length is $(7 - 2x)$ inches. If the height is 1 inch, the width is 3 inches and the length is 5 inches.

CHAPTER 9

SECTION 9.1

9.1.1 Checkup **1. (a)** a quadratic polynomial **(b)** not a polynomial **(c)** not a polynomial **(d)** a polynomial **9.1.2 Checkup** **1. (a)** $-2, -1,$
and 2 **(b)** noninteger solutions between -1 and 0 and between 0 and 1 **(c)** contradiction, no solution **(d)** not a contradiction, no real-number
solution **(e)** The solution set is the set of all real numbers. **9.1.3 Checkup** **1. (a)** -0.2 and 0.75 **(b)** $-2, -1,$ and 1 **(c)** no solution, contradiction **(d)** no real-number solution, not a contradiction **(e)** The solution set is the set of all real numbers, identity. **9.1.4 Checkup** **1.** Let
$t =$ time, $s =$ height of banana, $s = -16t^2 + 1250$; the banana would hit the ground after approximately 8.8 seconds. **2.** The gross savings and
investments returned to the 2001 amounts, in 2006.

SECTION 9.2

9.2.1 Checkup **1.** -7 and $\dfrac{3}{4}$ **2.** The x-intercepts are $(1,0)$ and $\left(-\dfrac{1}{2},0\right)$; $(x-1)(2x+1) = 0$; $x = 1$ and $x = -\dfrac{1}{2}$ **3.** 0, 1, and $\dfrac{5}{4}$

9.2.2 Checkup **1. (a)** -9 and 9 **(b)** $-\dfrac{3}{4}$ **(c)** $\dfrac{4}{3}$ and $-\dfrac{5}{2}$ **2. (a)** $\dfrac{5}{4}$ and 3 **(b)** -6 and 4 **9.2.3 Checkup** **1.** The dimensions of the box are 2 inches by 2 inches by 4 inches. **2.** Let $x = $ ranking, $y = $ number of passengers in millions; $y = -2x^2 - 2x + 84$; The airport ranking is 4.

SECTION 9.3

9.3.1 Checkup **1. (a)** $\sqrt{6}$ **(b)** $6\sqrt{15}$ **2. (a)** $4\sqrt{5}$ **(b)** $8\sqrt{3}$ **(c)** $-7\sqrt{2}$ **3. (a)** $3\sqrt{2}$ **(b)** $12\sqrt{5}$ **4. (a)** $-3 + 4\sqrt{2}$ **(b)** $1 + \sqrt{3}$
(c) $2 + \sqrt{5}$ **9.3.2 Checkup** **1. (a)** $\sqrt{2}$ **(b)** 4 **(c)** $3\sqrt{5}$ **2. (a)** $\dfrac{\sqrt{7}}{8}$ **(b)** $\dfrac{5\sqrt{2}}{3}$ **3.** $\dfrac{\sqrt{30}}{15}$ **9.3.3 Checkup** **1.** $7^2 \overset{?}{=} 3^2 + 5^2$; no
2. $\sqrt{2}$ **3.** The diagonal is approximately 3.575 inches.

SECTION 9.4

9.4.1 Checkup **1. (a)** $\pm\dfrac{5}{3}$ **(b)** 0 **(c)** No real number. **(d)** 0 and 8 **(e)** $1 \pm \sqrt{3}$ **(f)** $-1 \pm \sqrt{6}$ **(g)** $\pm\dfrac{7\sqrt{2}}{2}$ **9.4.2 Checkup** **1. (a)** 16
(b) $\dfrac{49}{4}$ **(c)** $\dfrac{4}{25}$ **9.4.3 Checkup** **1. (a)** $x = \dfrac{2 \pm \sqrt{29}}{5}$ **(b)** $x = 8$ **(c)** no real solution **9.4.4 Checkup** **1.** The vertical distance between the two hookups is 2.1 feet. **2.** The fence is approximately 16.2 feet high. **3.** To break even, the retailer must sell 4 or 26 items. **4.** Tommy must realize an equivalent annual interest rate of 17.5%. **5. (a)** $y = 6x^2 + 25x + 413$ **(b)** The hospital care expenditures will reach \$500 billion in 2002.

SECTION 9.5

9.5.1 Checkup **1. (a)** $x = -2$, $x = 1.5$ **(b)** $x = \dfrac{-1 \pm \sqrt{29}}{2}$ **(c)** $x = \dfrac{2}{3}$ **(d)** no real-number solutions **(e)** $x = -2 \pm 3\sqrt{3}$ **9.5.2 Checkup**
1. (a) Discriminant is 0.08; there are two irrational solutions. **(b)** Discriminant is zero; there is one rational solution. **(c)** Discriminant is 400; there are two rational solutions. **(d)** Discriminant is -25; there is no real-number solution. **9.5.3 Checkup** **1. (a)** $R(x) = x(150 - 5x)$
(b) $C(x) = 150 + 65x$ **(c)** $P(x) = -5x^2 + 85x - 150$ **(d)** They will break even when 2 cabinets are sold for \$140 each or 15 cabinets are sold for \$75 each. **2.** The measurement was taken at a depth of 0.602 meters.

SECTION 9.6

9.6.1 Checkup **1. (a)** $s = \sqrt{A}$ **(b)** $\sqrt{\dfrac{3V - \pi r^2}{\pi}}$ **2.** $a = \sqrt{c^2 - b^2}$ **3.** $r = \dfrac{-\pi h + \sqrt{\pi^2 h^2 + \pi A}}{\pi}$ or $r = -h + \sqrt{h^2 + \dfrac{A}{\pi}}$
4. The diagonal measures 12 ft. **9.6.2 Checkup** **1.** The congruent legs are $3\sqrt{2}$, or approximately 4.2 mm long. **2.** The horizontal distance of the ramp is $3\sqrt{3}$ feet (or approximately 5.2 feet), and the ramp's length is 6 feet.

SECTION 9.7

9.7.1 Checkup **1. (a)** The domain is $(-\infty, \infty)$. The range is $(-\infty, 4]$. **(b)** x-intercepts: $(-2, 0)$ and $(6, 0)$; y-intercept: $(0, 3)$ **(c)** downward
(d) vertex: $(2, 4)$; axis of symmetry: $x = 2$ **(e)** relative maximum and the absolute maximum is 4 at $x = 2$, no relative minimum or absolute minimum; increasing: $(-\infty, 2)$, decreasing: $(2, \infty)$ **(f)** -2 and 6 **(g)** -2 and 6 **9.7.2 Checkup** **1.** x-intercepts: $(-1, 0)$ and $(3, 0)$, y-intercept: $(0, -3)$
9.7.3 Checkup **1.** $(1, -4)$
9.7.4 Checkup **1.**   **2.**   **9.7.5 Checkup** **1.** $g(x) = 3x^2 + 7x - 6$

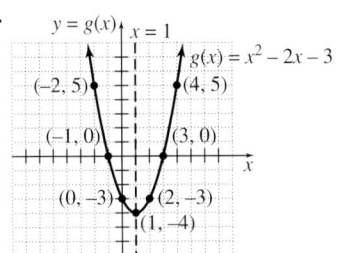

9.7.6 Checkup **1. (a)** 5 feet **(b)** about 29 feet **(c)** 30 feet **(d)** about 1.25 seconds **(e)** no **(f)** about 2.6 seconds
2. (a) 706 feet **(b)** 875 feet at 6.25 seconds **(c)** 12.5 seconds **(d)** about 13.6 seconds **(e)**

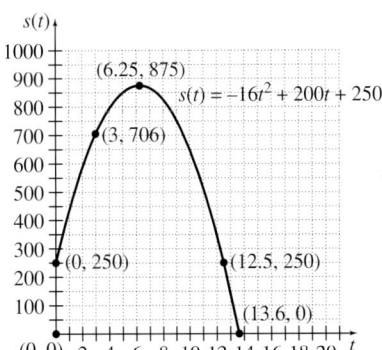

3. (a) $(10, 50)$ and $(100, 2750)$ **(b)** 75 tricycles for $3000 **(c)** $(10, 0)$ and $(100, 0)$; There will be no profit for 10 and 100 tricycles. **(d)** 55 tricycles for $1000 **4. (a)** $R(x) = 200x - 5x^2$ **(b)** $C(x) = 75x + 150$ **(c)** $P(x) = -5x^2 + 125x - 150$ **(d)** 0 and 40 bikes **(e)** 20 bikes for $2000 **(f)** no profit (a loss of $30) for 1 and 24 bikes **(g)** 12 and 13 bikes will have a maximum profit of $630. **(h)** a slight profit ($80) for 2 and 23 bikes **(i)**

5. (a) The minimum net income of -570.52 million dollars occurred in 2004 (1.8 years or about 2 years after 2002). **(b)** The net income in 2002 was -298 million dollars. **(c)** In about 3.6 years, the company will rebound to its 2002 net income from sales.

[Graph showing C(x) = 75x + 150, R(x) = 200x − 5x², and P(x) = −5x² + 125x − 150 with labeled points: (20, 2000), (23.74, 1930.21), (12.5, 631.25), (13, 630), (12, 630), (1.26, 244.79), (40, 0), (0, 0), (1, −30), (24, −30)]

SECTION 9.8

9.8.1 Checkup 1. (a) yes **(b)** yes **(c)** no **(d)** no **9.8.2 Checkup 1.** The integers between -3 and 1 exclusive; that is, $x = -2, -1$, and 0.
2. $-3 < x < \dfrac{1}{2}$ or $\left(-3, \dfrac{1}{2}\right)$ **3. (a)** $x \le -3$ or $x \ge 4$ or $(-\infty, -3] \cup [4, \infty)$ **(b)** $x < -2.562$ or $x > 1.562$ or $(-\infty, -2.562) \cup (1.562, \infty)$
(c) $-0.56 < x < 3.56$ or $(-0.56, 3.56)$ **4. (a)** all real numbers **(b)** $x \ne 2$ or $(-\infty, 2) \cup (2, \infty)$ **(c)** $x = 2$ **9.8.3 Checkup 1. (a)** $x \le -3$ or $x \ge 4$ or $(-\infty, -3] \cup [4, \infty)$ **(b)** $x < -2.562$ or $x > 1.562$ or $(-\infty, -2.562) \cup (1.562, \infty)$ **(c)** $-0.56 < x < 3.56$ or $(-0.56, 3.56)$ **2. (a)** all real numbers **(b)** $x \ne 2$ or $(-\infty, 2) \cup (2, \infty)$ **(c)** $x = 2$

9.8.4 Checkup 1. If the revenue must be at least $7500, then the value of x is between 5 and 15 inclusive. Therefore, the number of computers ordered must be between 15 and 25 inclusive. **2.** The sample is in flight when the time is 0 second up to 0.31 second.

CHAPTER 10

SECTION 10.1

10.1.1 Checkup 1. (a) not a rational expression **(b)** a rational expression **(c)** a rational expression **(d)** a rational expression
10.1.2 Checkup 1. The restricted value is -4. The domain is all real numbers not equal to -4. **2. (a)** The restricted values are -4 and 3. The domain is all real numbers except -4 and 3. **(b)** There are no restricted values. The domain is all real numbers. **(c)** The restricted value is 1.5. The domain is all real numbers except 1.5.
10.1.3 Checkup 1. (a) 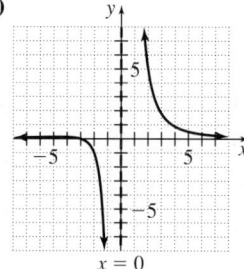 **(b)** 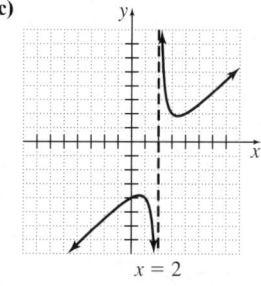 **(c)**

10.1.4 Checkup 1. (a) $C_{\text{ave}}(x) = \dfrac{2500 + 50x + 25x^2}{x}$ **(b)** The minimum average cost per year is $550.00. **(c)** Paul should replace the panel after 10 years.

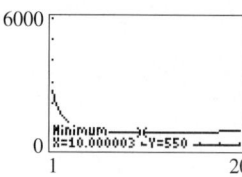

2. (a) 2001: 17.5%
2002: 17.2%
2003: 16.9%
(b) $P(x) = \dfrac{17x + 249.7}{126.5x + 1428.2}$ **(c)** 2001: $x = 0$; $P(x) = 0.175$; 17.5%
2002: $x = 1$; $P(x) = 0.172$; 17.2%
2003: $x = 2$; $P(x) = 0.169$; 16.9% **(d)** The values are equal; yes

SECTION 10.2

10.2.1 Checkup   1. (a) $\dfrac{a-2}{3a+4}$ **(b)** $\dfrac{x-2}{x-6}$ **(c)** $-\dfrac{5+x}{x^2+7}$ **10.2.2 Checkup   1. (a)** $\dfrac{(x-1)(x+4)}{x^2(x+1)} = \dfrac{x^2+3x-4}{x^3+x^2}$

(b) $\dfrac{2}{(x-4)^2} = \dfrac{2}{x^2-8x+16}$ **10.2.3 Checkup   1. (a)** $\dfrac{3(x^2+1)}{2} = \dfrac{3x^2+3}{2}$ **(b)** $\dfrac{x+4}{(x-2)(x+2)} = \dfrac{x+4}{x^2-4}$

10.2.4 Checkup   1. (a) Reza's average speed is $\dfrac{150}{x}$.   **(b)** Reza will travel $\dfrac{150(x+2)}{x}$ miles.   **(c)** Reza traveled 250 miles.   **(d)** Reza traveled 250

miles.   **(e)** The answers are equal.   **2.** $s(y) = 1500(1+y)$; the total amount that Benjamin received was $3300.

SECTION 10.3

10.3.1 Checkup   1. (a) 3   **(b)** $\dfrac{1}{x+4}$ **(c)** $\dfrac{x}{(x+6)(x-3)}$ **10.3.2 Checkup   1. (a)** $(x+4)(x-5)$ **(b)** $(5x-1)(5x+1)(3x-1)$

(c) $-1(x-5)$ or $5-x$ **10.3.3 Checkup   1. (a)** $\dfrac{2x(x+4)}{(x+5)(x+4)}$ or $\dfrac{2x^2+8x}{x^2+9x+20}$ **(b)** $\dfrac{(2x+1)(x+7)}{(x^2-16)(x+7)}$ or $\dfrac{2x^2+15x+7}{x^3+7x^2-16x-112}$

(c) $\dfrac{-7x}{-x(x-5)}$ or $\dfrac{-7x}{5x-x^2}$ **10.3.4 Checkup   1. (a)** $\dfrac{7x^2-31x}{x^2-11x+24}$ or $\dfrac{x(7x-31)}{(x-3)(x-8)}$ **(b)** $\dfrac{8}{x-4}$ **(c)** $\dfrac{x^2+8x+21}{(x+3)(x+5)(x+7)}$ **(d)** $\dfrac{x+3}{x-4}$

10.3.5 Checkup   1. (a) $\dfrac{16x+4}{15x}$ **(b)** $\dfrac{7x+5}{x}$ **(c)** The second perimeter is larger than the first by $\dfrac{89x+71}{15x}$.   **2. (a)** $T(x) = \dfrac{60}{x} + \dfrac{210}{2x-10}$

(b)
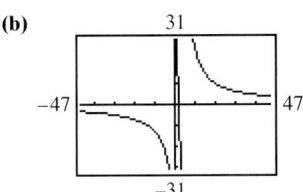

(c)
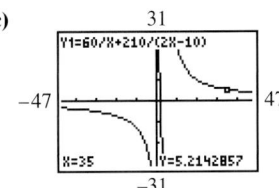

The total time of the delivery trip is approximately 5.2 hours.

(d)
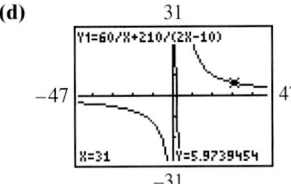

The average speed on the rural roads was 31 mph and on the interstate was 52 mph.

3. The average speed of the plane for the round-trip was 240 mph.

SECTION 10.4

10.4.1 Checkup   1. (a) a rational equation   **(b)** not a rational equation   **(c)** a rational equation   **10.4.2 Checkup   1.** 4   **2. (a)** The solution is extraneous, since it is the same as the restricted value.   **(b)** -5 (3 is an extraneous solution.)   **(c)** -3 **(d)** ±1 **3. (a)** contradiction, no solution

(b) Identity; solution is all real numbers except -1.   **10.4.3 Checkup   1. (a)** expression; $\dfrac{x+13}{x-4}$ **(b)** equation; $x=5$

10.4.4 Checkup   1. Let x = the interest rate for the three-year period. Then $\dfrac{225}{3x} + \dfrac{225}{2(x-0.005)} = 4000$ and $x = 0.05$. The interest rate for

the three-year investment was 5% and for the two-year investment was 4.5%.   **2.** The short side is $-5 + 5\sqrt{5}$ inches or approximately 6.18 inches. The long side is 10 inches.

SECTION 10.5

10.5.1 Checkup   1. Let x = the time it will take to do the lawn together. Then $\dfrac{1}{2} + \dfrac{1}{1.6} = \dfrac{1}{x}$. $x = \dfrac{8}{9}$. It will take them $\dfrac{8}{9}$ of an hour to do the

lawn together.   **2.** Let x = the time to fill an empty tank. Then $\dfrac{1}{5} = \dfrac{1}{x} - \dfrac{1}{2}$. $x = \dfrac{10}{7}$. It will take $1\frac{3}{7}$ hours to fill an empty tank if no water is

pumped out.   **10.5.2 Checkup   1.** Let x = the number of consecutive baskets she must make. Then $\dfrac{6+x}{10+x} = \dfrac{75}{100}$. $x = 6$. Michelle must make six

consecutive baskets to average 75%.   **2.** J.J.'s average rate was approximately 1.1 miles per hour.   **10.5.3 Checkup   1.** Side AC measures

22.8 inches. Side EF measures 6.1 inches.   **2.** The antenna is 10 feet tall.   **10.5.4 Checkup   1.** $D = \sqrt{\dfrac{Gm_1m_2}{F}}$ **2.** $t = \sqrt{\dfrac{krm}{C}}$ or $\dfrac{\sqrt{krmC}}{C}$

3. (a) $k_1 = \dfrac{Kk_2}{k_2 - K}$ **(b)** $k_1 = 2$

CHAPTER 11

SECTION 11.1

11.1.1 Checkup   1. (a) 5   **(b)** -5 **(c)** not a real number   **(d)** -7 **11.1.2 Checkup   1. (a)** radical   **(b)** nonradical   **(c)** radical
11.1.3 Checkup   1. The restricted values are all real numbers less than $-\frac{1}{3}$. The domain is all real numbers greater than or equal to $-\frac{1}{3}$, or
$\left[-\frac{1}{3}, \infty\right)$.   **2. (a)** There are no restricted values. The domain is all real numbers. $(-\infty, \infty)$ **(b)** The restricted values are all real numbers less than

3. The domain is all real numbers greater than or equal to 3, or $[3, \infty)$.   (c) The restricted values are all real numbers between -3 and 0. The domain is all real numbers less than or equal to -3 or greater than or equal to 0 or $(-\infty, -3] \cup [0, \infty)$.

11.1.4 Checkup   **1. (a)** $y = 2\sqrt{x} + 2$ **(b)** $f(x) = \sqrt[3]{2x - 3}$ **(c)** $g(x) = \sqrt{x^2 + 2x - 3}$

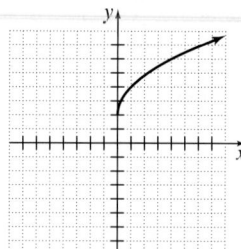
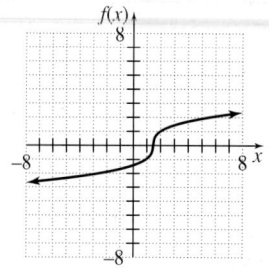
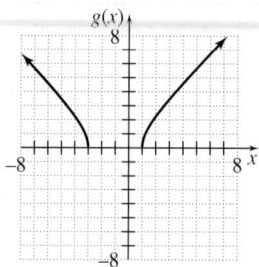

11.1.5 Checkup   **1. (a)** The domain is $(0, \infty)$.

2. $5\sqrt{2}$ **3. (a)** The average length at birth is 19.4 inches; on her first birthday, 29.79 inches; on her second birthday, 34.10 inches; on her third birthday, 37.40 inches.   **(b)**

(b)

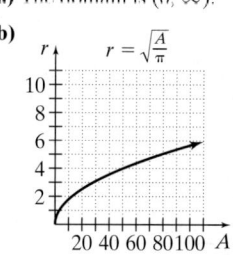

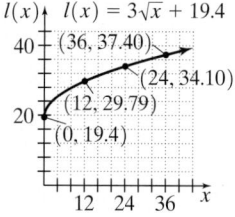

(c) The diameter is approximately 157 feet.   **(c)** A girl will be approximately 28.4 inches long at age 9 months.

SECTION 11.2

11.2.1 Checkup   **1. (a)** $\sqrt[4]{16} = 2$ **(b)** $-\sqrt[4]{16} = -2$ **(c)** $\sqrt[4]{-16}$, not a real number   **(d)** $\sqrt[3]{125} = 5$ **(e)** $-\sqrt[3]{125} = -5$ **(f)** $\sqrt[3]{-125} = -5$

2. (a) $\dfrac{1}{\sqrt[3]{125}} = \dfrac{1}{5}$ **(b)** $-\dfrac{1}{\sqrt[3]{125}} = \dfrac{1}{5}$ **(c)** $\dfrac{1}{\sqrt[3]{-125}} = -\dfrac{1}{5}$ **(d)** $\dfrac{1}{\sqrt[4]{16}} = \dfrac{1}{2}$ **(e)** $\dfrac{1}{-\sqrt[4]{16}} = -\dfrac{1}{2}$ **(f)** $\dfrac{1}{\sqrt[4]{-16}}$, not a real number   **3. (a)** 2.520   **(b)** -3.344

11.2.2 Checkup   **1. (a)** $\left(\sqrt{16}\right)^3$ or $\sqrt{16^3} = 64$ **(b)** $\left(\sqrt[3]{-125}\right)^5$ or $\sqrt[3]{(-125)^5} = -3125$ **(c)** $\left(\sqrt{15}\right)^3$ or $\sqrt{15^3} \approx 58.095$

(d) $\dfrac{1}{\left(\sqrt[4]{81}\right)^3}$ or $\dfrac{1}{\sqrt[4]{81^3}} = \dfrac{1}{27}$ **(e)** $-\dfrac{1}{\left(\sqrt[3]{125}\right)^5}$ or $-\dfrac{1}{\sqrt[3]{125^5}} = -\dfrac{1}{3125}$ **11.2.3 Checkup**   **1. (a)** The restricted values are all real numbers less than

-2. The domain is all real numbers greater than or equal to -2, or $[-2, \infty)$.   **(b)** There are no restricted values. The domain is all real numbers, or $(-\infty, \infty)$.   **2. (a)** $y = -2x^{1/5}$ **(b)** $f(x) = 2(x - 1)^{3/2}$

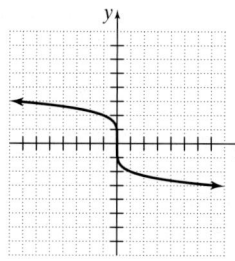
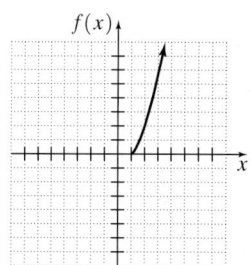

11.2.4 Checkup   **1.** The average bacteria level was 114.5 fecal bacteria per 100 ml.

2.

x	y	
1	1	
		128
4	128	
		128
16	16384	
		128
64	2,097,152	

3.

X	Y1
-50	2.6076
-45	3.1707
-40	3.957
-35	5.1092
-30	6.9098
-25	9.9926
-20	16.058

X=-50

X	Y1
-45	3.1707
-40	3.957
-35	5.1092
-30	6.9098
-25	9.9926
-20	16.058
-15	31.236

X=-15

The absolute brightness increases 128 times as the mass is increased by a factor of 4.

As the temperature decreases by 5°C, the time it takes for frostbite to occur decreases exponentially.

SECTION 11.3

11.3.1 Checkup **1. (a)** 6 **(b)** 2 **(c)** 3 **(d)** $\dfrac{729}{125}$ **11.3.2 Checkup** **1. (a)** x^3 **(b)** $x^{1/6}$ **(c)** $z^{1/2}$ **(d)** $\dfrac{q^{3/5}}{p^{3/5}}$ **2. (a)** $2ab^{3/2}$

(b) $-6x^{25/24}y^{7/4}$ **(c)** $8x^4$ **(d)** $a^{3/4} - a^{7/6}$ **11.3.3 Checkup** **1. (a)** The radius increases by a factor of $\sqrt{2}$. **(b)** The radius increases by a factor of $\sqrt{3}$. **(c)** The ratio is $\sqrt{C}$. **2. (a)** $v = (128.8h)^{1/2}$ **(b)** $v_2 - v_1 = \left(\sqrt{128.8} - \sqrt{64.4}\right)h^{1/2} \approx 3.324\sqrt{h}$

SECTION 11.4

11.4.1 Checkup **1. (a)** $8\sqrt{3}$ **(b)** $-2\sqrt[3]{5}$ **(c)** $3\sqrt[4]{2}$ **2. (a)** $x\sqrt{x}$ **(b)** $x^2y^2\sqrt{x}$ **(c)** $xy^4\sqrt[3]{x^2}$ **3. (a)** $7x^2yz^4\sqrt{2yz}$ **(b)** $3m^2np^3\sqrt[3]{p}$

(c) $(2x + 1)\sqrt{5}$ **4. (a)** $30ab\sqrt{a}$ **(b)** $(x + 2)\sqrt{10}$ **(c)** $72x^2y^4\sqrt[3]{2y^2}$ **11.4.2 Checkup** **1. (a)** $\dfrac{3\sqrt{15}}{10}$ **(b)** $\dfrac{3\sqrt[3]{4}}{2}$ **2. (a)** $\dfrac{5\sqrt{2xyz}}{2z}$

(b) $\dfrac{3\sqrt{7ab}}{7}$ **(c)** $\dfrac{\sqrt[3]{75xyz^2}}{5yz}$ **3. (a)** $\dfrac{\sqrt{5y}}{5y}$ **(b)** $\dfrac{b\sqrt{5a}}{15a}$ **(c)** $\dfrac{\sqrt[3]{2c^2}}{2d}$ **11.4.3 Checkup** **1.** The length of time for one stride is approximately 1.9238 seconds. Steve's walking speed is approximately 6.24 feet per second. **2. (a)** The length of time for one stride is approximately 3.01 seconds. **(b)** The speed is approximately 1.33 meters per second. **(c)** The speed is 0.96 meters per second.

SECTION 11.5

11.5.1 Checkup **1. (a)** $-\sqrt{ab} + 7\sqrt[4]{ab}$ **(b)** $4p\sqrt{q}$ **(c)** $(5m + 2)\sqrt[3]{mn}$ **2. (a)** $13\sqrt{3}$ **(b)** $-xy\sqrt{xy}$ **(c)** $\dfrac{2}{3}\sqrt{3}$

11.5.2 Checkup **1. (a)** $35x + 28\sqrt[3]{x^2}$ **(b)** $\sqrt{21} + \sqrt{3ab} - \sqrt{7ab} - ab$ **(c)** $15 + 10\sqrt{2}$ **(d)** $z - 10\sqrt{z} + 25$ **2. (a)** 5 **(b)** $121 - 9z$

11.5.3 Checkup **1. (a)** $\dfrac{\sqrt{65} - \sqrt{26}}{3}$ **(b)** $2 + \sqrt{3}$ **(c)** $\dfrac{8x - 17\sqrt{3x} + 6}{x - 12}$ **11.5.4 Checkup** **1.** Let $s = $ the length of a side of the square floor and $A = $ the area of the square floor, $s = \sqrt{A}$. The perimeter of the floor is $p = 4s = 4\sqrt{A}$. The perimeter of Sandra's floor is $p_1 = 4\sqrt{350}$ and of Julie's floor is $p_2 = 4\sqrt{224}$. The difference is $d = p_1 - p_2 = 4\sqrt{350} - 4\sqrt{224} = 4\sqrt{14}$. This is approximately 15 feet. **2. (a)** The distance is $2.34\sqrt{10}$ or approximately 7.40 nautical miles. **(b)** The lighthouse will become visible when you are $8.19\sqrt{3}$ or about 14.19 nautical miles away. **3.** The width is $\sqrt{5}$ feet.

SECTION 11.6

11.6.1 Checkup **1. (a)** nonradical **(b)** radical **(c)** radical **11.6.2 Checkup** **1. (a)** 5 **(b)** no real-number solution **(c)** 4. Note: $x = -3$ is an extraneous solution. **2. (a)** 5 and 4 **(b)** 2 **(c)** no real-number solution **(d)** 1 **3. (a)** no real-number solution **(b)** all real numbers greater than or equal to $\dfrac{1}{2}$ **11.6.3 Checkup** **1. (a)** 19 **(b)** -9 and 3 **11.6.4 Checkup** **1. (a)** 32 **(b)** 4 **(c)** There is no real-number solution. **11.6.5 Checkup** **1.** Gete's vertical jump was about 4.98 feet. **2.** $y = -1, y = 11$ **3.** The energy of the Wolf Creek explosion is 3.21×10^{15} ft-lb.

SECTION 11.7

11.7.1 Checkup **1. (a)** $7i$ **(b)** $\dfrac{2}{9}i$ **(c)** $3i\sqrt{3}$ **2. (a)** -4 **(b)** $4i$; answers may vary. **11.7.2 Checkup** **1. (a)** $10i$ **(b)** $-5i\sqrt{5}$ **(c)** $\dfrac{10}{11}$

(d) $-30i$ **(e)** $7\sqrt{3} - 4\sqrt{10}$ **11.7.3 Checkup** **1. (a)** $26 - 5i$ **(b)** $6 + 3i$ **(c)** $-8 + 20i$ **2. (a)** $-3 + 12i$ **(b)** $80 - 20i$ **(c)** 58

3. (a) $4 - 3i$ **(b)** $-4 - \dfrac{7}{2}i$ **(c)** $\dfrac{8}{13} + \dfrac{1}{13}i$ **11.7.4 Checkup** **1. (a)** $x = \pm 2i$ **(b)** $x = 4 \pm 3i\sqrt{3}$ **(c)** $z = -\dfrac{1}{3} \pm \dfrac{i\sqrt{2}}{3}$

2. (a) $-\dfrac{3}{10} \pm \dfrac{3}{10}i\sqrt{19}$ **(b)** $x = -5 \pm i\sqrt{19}$ **11.7.5 Checkup** **1.** The magnitude of the total voltage across the circuit is approximately 26.1 volts. **2.** $y = 0$ or $y = \pm 5i\sqrt{2}$

CHAPTER 12

SECTION 12.1

12.1.1 Checkup **1. (a)** $g^{-1} = \{(0.5, 1), (1, 2), (1.5, 3), (2, 4), (2.5, 5), (3, 6)\}$ **(b)** $K^{-1} = \left\{\left(3, \dfrac{1}{2}\right), \left(4, \dfrac{2}{3}\right), \left(5, \dfrac{3}{4}\right), \left(4, \dfrac{4}{5}\right), \left(3, \dfrac{5}{6}\right)\right\}$

2. (a) $y = -\dfrac{1}{4}x + \dfrac{1}{4}$ **(b)** $y = \pm\sqrt{\dfrac{1}{3}x - 2}$ **12.1.2 Checkup** **1. (a)** This is a one-to-one function. **(b)** This is a function, but it is not one-to-one.

(c) This is not a function. **2. (a)** The graph represents a one-to-one function. **(b)** The graph does not represent a one-to-one function, since it fails the horizontal-line test. **(c)** The graph does not represent a one-to-one function, since it fails the vertical-line test.

12.1.3 Checkup **1.** 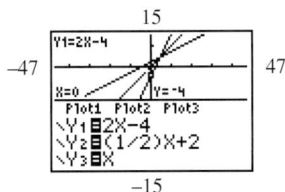 **12.1.4 Checkup** **1. (a)** $f^{-1}(x) = -\dfrac{1}{2}x + 3$ 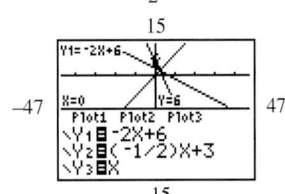 **(b)** $g^{-1}(x) = \sqrt[3]{x}$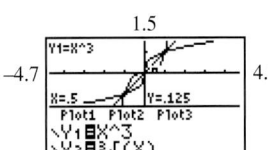

12.1.5 Checkup   **1. (a)** $I(x) = 60x$ **(b)** $I^{-1}(x) = \dfrac{x}{60}$ **(c)** The inverse function represents the number of years over which Dimitri must invest $1200 at 5% simple interest per year in order to earn x dollars in interest.   **2.** $f^{-1}(x) = 1.8772x$, the inverse function represents the number of U.S. dollars, given x number of British pounds.

SECTION 12.2

12.2.1 Checkup   **1. (a)** not an exponential function   **(b)** exponential function   **(c)** not an exponential function   **12.2.2 Checkup**   **1. (a)** 64   **(b)** $\dfrac{1}{64}$ or 0.015625   **(c)** 8   **(d)** approximately 11.036   **12.2.3 Checkup**   **1.** $y = 8^{2x}$ **2.** $y = 8^{-2x}$

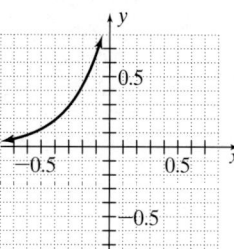

12.2.4 Checkup   **1.** $y = 0.5e^x$

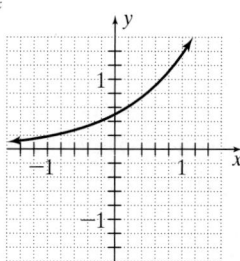

12.2.5 Checkup   **1.** After four years, Cindy will have $6312.38.   **2.** After four years, Cindy would have had $6356.25.   **3. (a)**

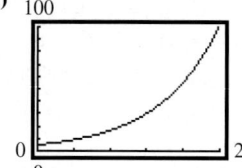

(b) In 2010, the rate will be 16%.
(c) In 2006, the rate was 10%.

SECTION 12.3

12.3.1 Checkup   **1. (a)** $f^{-1}(x) = \log_3 x$ **(b)** $h^{-1}(x) = \log_{13} x$ **12.3.2 Checkup**   **1. (a)** 4   **(b)** $\dfrac{1}{3}$ **(c)** -3 **2. (a)** 3   **(b)** -3 **(c)** undefined   **(d)** ≈ 1.477 **3.** -4 **4. (a)** 1.52832   **(b)** 1.52832

12.3.3 Checkup   **1.**

x	$f(x)$
0.001	−6.288
0.01	−4.192
0.1	−2.096
0.5	−0.6309
1	0
2	0.6309
3	1
4	1.2619
5	1.465

2. (a)

x	$g(x)$
0.001	−2.523
0.01	−1.523
0.1	−0.5229
0.5	0.1761
1	0.4771
2	0.7782
3	0.9542
4	1.0792
5	1.1761

(b)

x	$h(x)$
0.001	−5.809
0.01	3.507
0.1	−1.204
0.5	0.4055
1	1.0986
2	1.7918
3	2.1972
4	2.4849
5	2.7081

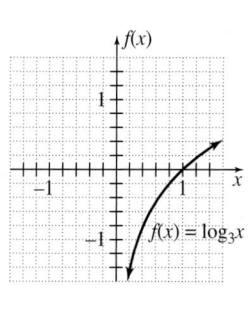

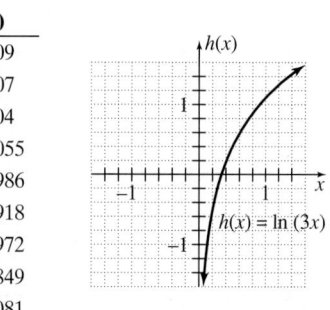

12.3.4 Checkup   1. The concentration of hydrogen in pure water is 10^{-7} mole per liter.   **2.** The ratio of the intensity of the 1964 Alaskan earthquake to the intensity of the 1989 San Francisco earthquake is $\dfrac{10^{9.2}}{10^{7.1}}$, or approximately 126. The Alaskan quake was 126 times as great as the 1989 San Francisco quake.

SECTION 12.4

12.4.1 Checkup   1. (a) $\log_5 11 + \log_5 x$ **(b)** $\ln x - \ln y$ **(c)** $2 \ln x$ **2. (a)** $\log \dfrac{3}{y}$ **(b)** $\log\left(\dfrac{xy}{z}\right)$ **(c)** $\ln(x^{-3}) = \ln\left(\dfrac{1}{x^3}\right)$ **3.** $1 + 2\log_5 x$

4. $\log \dfrac{(2x-1)^3(x+1)}{x}$ **12.4.2 Checkup   1. (a)** $\ln A = \ln \pi + 2 \ln r$ **(b)** $\log A = \log b + \log h - \log 2$ **2. (a)** $y = c \ln\left(\dfrac{I_0}{I}\right)$

(b) The depth is 9.3 units below the surface.

SECTION 12.5

12.5.1 Checkup   1. (a) neither   **(b)** logarithmic   **(c)** exponential   **12.5.2 Checkup   1. (a)** 4   **(b)** $\ln(3)$ **(c)** $\ln\left(\dfrac{7}{2}\right)$ **2. (a)** $\dfrac{3}{2}$

(b) $\dfrac{100}{3}$ **3.** no solution   **12.5.3 Checkup   1. (a)** The growth constant is about 0.009.   **(b)** $A(t) = 150e^{0.009t}$ **(c)** The female population in the United States will be approximately 180 million in 2025.   **2.** The gross national product will triple in value in 29 years or 2029, according to this prediction.   **3.** $A(t) = A_0 e^{-0.000428t}$. When $A(t) = 0.9A_0$, $t = \dfrac{\ln(0.9)}{-0.000428}$, or $t \approx 246$; the radium-226 will diminish to 90% of its original amount in 246 years.   **4.** Let $T(t)$ represent the temperature of the liquid after t minutes in the freezer. The solution is $t = \dfrac{\ln\left(\dfrac{1}{5}\right)}{-0.0277}$, or $t \approx 58.1$. The water will cool to 20°C after 58 minutes.

Instructor Answers to Exercises

CHAPTER P

SECTION P.1 EXERCISES

1. **(a)** integer, rational **(b)** natural, whole, integer, rational **(c)** natural, whole, integer, rational **(d)** rational **(e)** rational **2. (a)** natural, whole, integer, rational **(b)** rational **(c)** natural, whole, integer, rational **(d)** rational **(e)** rational **3. (a)** whole, integer, rational **(b)** rational **(c)** rational **(d)** rational **(e)** rational **4. (a)** natural, whole, integer, rational **(b)** integer, rational **(c)** rational **(d)** rational **(e)** rational
5. 5 and 6 **6.** -2 and -1
7.

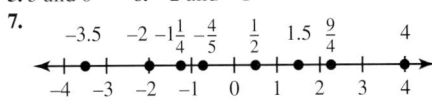

8.

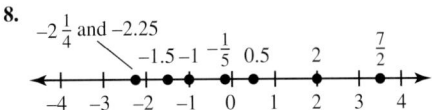

9. $<$ **10.** $<$ **11.** $>$ **12.** $<$ **13.** $>$ **14.** $>$ **15.** $<$ **16.** $<$ **17.** $<$ **18.** $>$ **19.** $>$ **20.** $<$ **21.** $=$
22. $=$ **23.** $>$ **24.** $<$ **25.** $<$ **26.** $>$ **27.** $=$ **28.** $=$ **29.** $>$ **30.** $<$ **31.** $=$ **32.** $=$ **33.** $=$ **34.** $=$

35. $0.295 < 0.7$ **36.** $0.06 > -2.56$ **37.** $-5 < -1 \le 0$ **38.** $20 \le 24 < 25$ **39.** $0.4 = \frac{2}{5}$ **40.** $-\frac{43}{50} = -0.86$ **41.** 15.34 **42.** 25

43. 15.34 **44.** 25 **45.** $3\frac{1}{3}$ **46.** 25 **47.** -23 **48.** -25 **49.** -23 **50.** -25 **51.** -15 **52.** $-\frac{1}{2}$ **53.** 25 **54.** 35 **55.** $-\frac{3}{2}$

56. $-\frac{5}{4}$ **57.** $+45; -115; +200$ **58.** $+1.25; -0.75; -2; +1.75; +1.50$ **59.** -43 **60.** -113 **61.** **(a)** $+5$ **(b)** -5 **(c)** -2

62. **(a)** $+100$ **(b)** -200 **63.**

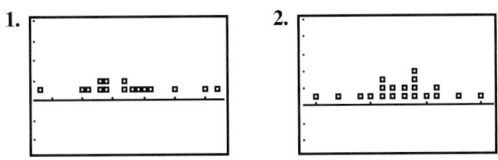

(a) $|3.5|$ **(b)** $|-2.3|$ **(c)** $|3.5| + |-2.3| = 3.5 + 2.3 = 5.8$

64.

(a) $|-3.5|$ **(b)** $|2.3|$ **(c)** $|-3.5| + |2.3| = 3.5 + 2.3 = 5.8$

P.1 CALCULATOR EXERCISES

1.

2.

SECTION P.2 EXERCISES

1. 2 **2.** 1 **3.** -11 **4.** -5 **5.** -2 **6.** -2 **7.** -547 **8.** 682 **9.** 6.66 **10.** 3.16 **11.** -1.3 **12.** -2.8 **13.** 1.37 **14.** 2.09

15. -3.37 **16.** -11.4 **17.** $-\frac{11}{10}$ **18.** $-\frac{19}{28}$ **19.** $-\frac{11}{18}$ **20.** $-\frac{7}{24}$ **21.** $\frac{4}{9}$ **22.** $\frac{1}{2}$ **23.** $\frac{11}{12}$ **24.** $2\frac{13}{15}$ **25.** 7 **26.** 90 **27.** -4

28. 234 **29.** $-\frac{5}{12}$ **30.** $-\frac{17}{20}$ **31.** $-\frac{1}{5}$ **32.** $-\frac{1}{15}$ **33.** -16 **34.** -12 **35.** -7 **36.** -6 **37.** 18 **38.** 16 **39.** 3.7 **40.** 4.4

41. 1.17 **42.** 5.71 **43.** $-\frac{1}{10}$ **44.** $\frac{5}{28}$ **45.** $-\frac{17}{18}$ **46.** $-\frac{11}{24}$ **47.** $-\frac{18}{7}$ **48.** $-\frac{7}{5}$ **49.** $-3\frac{1}{5}$ **50.** $-3\frac{1}{3}$ **51.** $-1\frac{1}{3}$ **52.** $-1\frac{3}{4}$

53. 24 **54.** 28 **55.** -15 **56.** -36 **57.** -20 **58.** -48 **59.** -135 **60.** -224 **61.** 128 **62.** 605 **63.** 0 **64.** 0 **65.** 0.34

66. 68.4 **67.** 7.29 **68.** 5 **69.** -12.5 **70.** -1.083 **71.** $\frac{5}{24}$ **72.** $\frac{22}{51}$ **73.** $-1\frac{1}{4}$ **74.** 1 **75.** $-\frac{3}{28}$ **76.** $-\frac{25}{51}$ **77.** 4800

78. 60,000 **79.** $-\frac{4}{75}$ **80.** $\frac{4}{75}$ **81.** 1.144 **82.** 0.638 **83.** 0 **84.** 0 **85.** -5 **86.** -8 **87.** 8 **88.** 5 **89.** 9 **90.** 8 **91.** 0

92. 0 **93.** -200 **94.** -90 **95.** 8.5 **96.** 0.05 **97.** 1 **98.** -1 **99.** -0.2 **100.** -0.5 **101.** -0.8 **102.** -0.005 **103.** $\frac{7}{9}$

104. $\frac{18}{25}$ **105.** $-\frac{64}{21}$ **106.** $-\frac{27}{17}$ **107.** 1 **108.** $-\frac{4}{9}$ **109.** $\frac{2}{9}$ **110.** $-\frac{7}{16}$ **111.** $-2\frac{2}{9}$ **112.** $-6\frac{3}{5}$

113. 33,872,000 + 1,612,000 = 35,484,000; the projected population is 35,484,000. **114.** 642,000 − 8000 = 634,000; the projected population is 634,000. **115.** 98 − (−90) = 188; the range is 188°F. **116.** 44 − (−56) = 100; the range is 100°F. **117.** 130 − (−180) = 310; the change in the mean surface temperature is 310°C. **118.** 350 − (−170) = 520; the change in the mean surface temperature is 520°C. **119.** 20,320 − (−282) = 20,602; the range is 20,602 feet. **120.** 163 − (−2) = 165; the range is 165 meters.

121. $\frac{1}{2} + \frac{1}{4} + 1 + 1 + \frac{1}{2} = 3\frac{1}{4}$; the recipe requires $3\frac{1}{4}$ cups of dry ingredients. **122.** $1\frac{1}{4} + \frac{3}{4} + \frac{1}{2} + 2\frac{1}{4} - 4\frac{3}{4}$; the pattern uses $4\frac{3}{4}$ yards of material.

123. −255 + 375 + (−575) + 1525 = 1070; Karin is $1070 above her quota because 1070 is a positive number.
124. 385 + 285 + (−555) + (−405) + 265 + 575 = 550; Karin is $550 above her quota.
125. 1500 + 150 + 150 + 150 + (−75) + (−500) + (−200) + 12 = 1187; the net balance in Lindsay's account is $1187.
126. 500 + 75 + 50 + 100 + (−125) + 35 = 635; the balance in the account is $635.
127. 19.95 + 19.95 + 19.95 + (−25) + (−59.27) + (−19.95) = −44.37; Rosie lost $44.37 that morning.
128. 39.95 + 27.95 + 19.99 + (−175) + (−29.95) + (−14.95) = −132.01; Richard lost $132.01 that hour.
129. 8.4 − 0.8 − 0.7 − 1.1 = 5.8; the length of A is 5.8 inches. **130.** 3.4 − 0.3 − 0.3 = 2.8; the length of B is 2.8 inches; 3.4 − 1.4 = 2.0; twice the length of C is 2 inches. C is 1 inch. **131.** (−0.22)(645) = −141.90; Sara has $141.90 deducted every two weeks; (6)(−141.9) = −851.40; this amounts to $851.40 every 12 weeks. **132.** −5 × 9 × 6 = −270; Ron will bet $270 in a week.

133. $(0.05)(40)\left(1\frac{1}{2}\right)(3) = 9$; Sammy earns $9 for his work. **134.** (0.25)(20)(6) = 30; Melanie earns $30 for her troop.

135. $(50)\left(8\frac{1}{2}\right)(4) = 1700$; George drove approximately 1700 miles. **136.** $\left(9\frac{1}{2}\right)\left(1\frac{3}{4}\right)(5) = 83\frac{1}{8}$; Michele will hike $83\frac{1}{8}$ miles.

137. 16,000,000 seconds $\times \dfrac{1\text{ minute}}{60\text{ seconds}} \times \dfrac{1\text{ hour}}{60\text{ minutes}} \times \dfrac{1\text{ day}}{24\text{ hours}} \approx 185.2$; it will take a little over 185 days.

138. 20,000,000 ÷ 60 ÷ 60 ÷ 24 ÷ 7 ≈ 33.1; it will take a little over 33 weeks. **139.** 335 ÷ (3 × 20) ≈ 5.6; Billie will need six CD cabinets to store her collection. **140.** 650 ÷ (3 × 125) = 1.7; Bruce will need two CD cabinets to store his collection. **141.** 770 ÷ 0.17 ≈ 4529.41; The density is about 4529.41 people per square mile. **142.** 56,376 ÷ 839,999 ≈ 0.07; The density is about 0.07 people per square mile.
143. 35,000 ÷ 24 ≈ 1458.3; The anteater eats about 1458.3 ants per hour. 1458.3 × 10 = 14,583; In 10 hours, the anteater will eat 14,583 ants.
144. 45 ÷ 8 = 5.625; A joint has 5.625 rivets per foot. 5.625 × 5 = 28.125; A joint 5 feet long has 28 rivets. **145.** 659 ÷ 38 ≈ 17.34; The gas mileage is about 17.34 miles per gallon. 440 ÷ 17.34 ≈ 25.37; He will need about 25.37 gallons of gas to travel 440 miles. **146.** 403 ÷ 6.5 = 62; The speed was 62 miles per hour. 1065 ÷ 62 ≈ 17.18; A distance of 1065 miles will require about 17.18 hours. **147.** 308,936,000 × 0.793 = 244,986,248; The 2010 projection is a white population of 244,986,248. **148.** 308,936,000 × 0.131 = 40,470,616; The 2010 projection is a black population of 40,470,616.
149. 3,215,000,000 × 0.14 = 450,100,000; 450,100,000 retail prescription drugs were purchased in a supermarket in 2003.
150. 3,215,000,000 × 0.46 = 1,478,900,000; 1,478,900,000 retail prescription drugs were purchased in a traditional chain in 2003.

P.2 CALCULATOR EXERCISES

1. $7\frac{6}{7}$ **2.** $-2\frac{69}{113}$ **3.** $2\frac{253}{487}$ **4.** $-5\frac{13}{19}$

SECTION P.3 EXERCISES

1. $3 \cdot 3 \cdot 3 \cdot 3 = 81$ **2.** $2 \cdot 2 \cdot 2 \cdot 2 \cdot 2 \cdot 2 = 64$ **3.** $(-3)(-3)(-3)(-3) = 81$ **4.** $(-2)(-2)(-2)(-2)(-2)(-2) = 64$ **5.** $-(3 \cdot 3 \cdot 3 \cdot 3) = -81$
6. $-(2 \cdot 2 \cdot 2 \cdot 2 \cdot 2 \cdot 2) = -64$ **7.** $(-4)(-4)(-4) = -64$ **8.** $(-3)(-3)(-3)(-3)(-3) = -243$ **9.** $-(4 \cdot 4 \cdot 4) = -64$
10. $-(3 \cdot 3 \cdot 3 \cdot 3 \cdot 3) = -243$ **11.** 6.25 **12.** 0.16 **13.** $-\frac{9}{49}$ **14.** $-\frac{16}{81}$ **15.** $2\frac{10}{27}$ **16.** $3\frac{3}{8}$ **17.** 102.4947066 **18.** 1,640,401.445

19. 0 **20.** 0 **21.** 1 **22.** 1 **23.** −1 **24.** −1 **25.** 1256 **26.** $-\frac{4}{17}$ **27.** 1 **28.** 1 **29.** −1 **30.** −1 **31.** 1 **32.** 1 **33.** 6

34. 9 **35.** 16 **36.** 18 **37.** −5 **38.** −7 **39.** 0.8 **40.** 0.9 **41.** $-\frac{4}{3}$ **42.** $-\frac{6}{7}$ **43.** 1 **44.** −1 **45.** 0 **46.** 0

47. not a real number **48.** not a real number **49.** between 3 and 4, or approximately 3.162 **50.** between 4 and 5, or approximately 4.690
51. between −2 and −1, or approximately −1.732 **52.** between −4 and −3, or approximately −3.742 **53.** 4 **54.** 2 **55.** 12 **56.** 21

57. 10.726 **58.** 16.288 **59.** −5 **60.** −4 **61.** $\frac{1}{2}$ **62.** $-\frac{9}{11}$ **63.**

64.

65. $\left(\frac{1}{2}\right)^1 = \frac{1}{2}$ **66.** $\left(\frac{1}{5}\right)^1 = \frac{1}{5}$ **67.** $\left(\frac{1}{2}\right)^2 = \frac{1}{4}$ **68.** $\left(\frac{1}{5}\right)^2 = \frac{1}{25}$ **69.** $\left(-\frac{1}{2}\right)^1 = -\frac{1}{2}$

70. $\left(-\frac{1}{5}\right)^1 = -\frac{1}{5}$ **71.** $\left(-\frac{1}{2}\right)^2 = \frac{1}{4}$ **72.** $\left(-\frac{1}{5}\right)^2 = \frac{1}{25}$

	Standard Notation	Scientific Notation	Calculator Notation
73.	23,450,000,000	2.345×10^{10}	2.345 E10
74.	18,300,000,000,000,000,000	1.83×10^{19}	1.83 E19
75.	−0.000006591	-6.591×10^{-6}	−6.591 E−6
76.	−0.00000000072193	-7.2193×10^{-10}	−7.2193 E−10
77.	3.6943	3.6943×10^{0}	3.6943 E0
78.	9.98031	9.98031×10^{0}	9.98031 E0
79.	−711,030	-7.1103×10^{5}	−7.1103 E5
80.	−100,500,000,000	-1.005×10^{11}	−1.005 E11
81.	0.01966	1.966×10^{-2}	1.966 E−2
82.	0.00000555	5.555×10^{-6}	5.555 E−6
83.	−9.95	-9.95×10^{0}	−9.95 E0
84.	−8.103	-8.103×10^{0}	−8.103 E0
85.	27,000,000	2.7×10^{7}	2.7 E7
86.	5,470,000,000	5.47×10^{9}	5.47 E9
87.	−0.00030303	-3.0303×10^{-4}	−3.0303 E−4
88.	−0.00000000511	-5.11×10^{-9}	−5.11 E−9
89.	1.26	1.26×10^{0}	1.26 E0
90.	−8.81	-8.81×10^{0}	−8.81 E0

91. Each side is approximately 3.464 feet.   **92.** The pond is approximately 7.071 feet by 7.071 feet by 2 feet.   **93.** $(755)^2 = 570,025$; the Great Pyramid covers 570,025 ft² of ground.   **94.** Each side is approximately 614 feet.   **95.** Each side is approximately 1.442 feet.   **96.** Each side is approximately 2.466 feet.   **97.** The diagonal is approximately 1067.73 feet.   **98.** The diagonal is approximately 868.332 feet.   **99.** The radius is approximately 78.583 feet.   **100.** The radius is approximately 339.921 feet.   **101.** 1.6722×10^{-2} **102.** 7.8125×10^{-6} **103.** 5×10^2; 2.64×10^6 **104.** 2×10^2; 1.056×10^6 **105.** 42,000,000   **106.** 27,000,000   **107.** 0.00000000000000000000000017   **108.** 0.0000000095   **109.** Each pyramid at Giza would weigh over 1.2×10^{10} pounds.   **110.** 2.36016×10^7; the Great Wall of China is 2.36016×10^7 feet long.   **111.** 59,920,000; The Trans-Alaska Pipeline can carry 59,920,000 barrels of oil in a four-week period.   **112.** Ganymede has a mass of 147,000,000,000,000,000,000,000,000 grams.   **113.** 1.1877×10^7; 2.88205×10^8; 0.041 crimes per person or 4.1 crimes per 100 people.   **114.** 1.426×10^6; 0.0049 crimes per person or 0.49 crimes per 100 people.   **115.** 3.9899×10^7; 2.91049×10^8; 0.137 or 13.7% of the U.S. population is Hispanic.   **116.** 2.448×10^6; 2.88205×10^8; 0.0085 or 0.85% of the U.S. population was reported as deaths.   **117.** 1.628×10^{-9}; the perimeter is 1.628×10^{-9} meters.   **118.** 1.212×10^{-9}; the perimeter is 1.212×10^{-9} meters.   **119.** 3.029×10^{-10}; the length of an edge is 3.029×10^{-10} meters.   **120.** 4.070×10^{-10}; the length of an edge is 4.070×10^{-10} meters.

P.3 CALCULATOR EXERCISES

Part 1

1. 8.949   **2.** −8.225   **3.** 1.331   **4.** $\frac{2}{3}$, or .667   **5.** 1.1399, or 1.140   **6.** −3.3

Part 2

1. 6×10^9 **2.** 6×10^{-4} **3.** 1.963×10^{12} **4.** 1.628×10^{13}

SECTION P.4 EXERCISES

1. $\left(\frac{3}{8}\right)\left(\frac{5}{7}\right) - \left(\frac{3}{8}\right)\left(\frac{1}{9}\right)$ **2.** $-23(31) + (-23)(25)$ **3.** $2.7(-1.5) + 2.7(3.2)$ **4.** $\left(1\frac{1}{4}\right)\left(5\frac{1}{2}\right) - \left(1\frac{1}{4}\right)\left(3\frac{1}{8}\right)$ **5.** $\frac{217}{7} - \frac{175}{7}$

6. $\frac{-78}{6} + \frac{108}{6}$ **7.** $-15 - 19.3$ **8.** $-5.7 - 0.06$ **9.** $\frac{6}{7} + \frac{5}{9}$ **10.** $51 + 19$ **11.** $-1\frac{1}{7} + 2\frac{1}{5}$ **12.** $-89 + 17$ **13.** $-19.37 - 15.043$

14. $-2\frac{1}{4} - 3\frac{5}{8}$ **15.** $15(17 + 23)$ **16.** $81(22 + 8)$ **17.** $-3(14 + 21)$ **18.** $-13(21 + 16)$ **19.** $6(1.2 - 1.3)$ **20.** $5(4.5 - 7)$ **21.** 40

22. −1   **23.** −79   **24.** −129   **25.** 1   **26.** 30   **27.** −5   **28.** −17   **29.** 3   **30.** 2   **31.** −139   **32.** −106   **33.** 121   **34.** −11

35. −22.15   **36.** −3   **37.** 78   **38.** 66   **39.** $\frac{64}{135}$ **40.** $\frac{27}{80}$ **41.** $\frac{73}{72}$ **42.** $\frac{1}{3}$ **43.** −53   **44.** −221   **45.** 24   **46.** 115   **47.** 2

48. 4   **49.** 10   **50.** 8   **51.** 0   **52.** 0   **53.** undefined   **54.** undefined   **55.** The recommended weight is 115.28 pounds.   **56.** The recommended weight is 160.6 pounds.   **57.** The number of units is 360.   **58.** The number of units is 600.   **59.** The student needs $1119.56 a month.   **60.** The student needs $909.56 a month.   **61.** The current will be approximately 0.173 ampere.   **62.** The current will be approximately 0.289 ampere.   **63.** The speed was approximately 32 mph.   **64.** The speed was approximately 49 mph.   **65.** The flow rate is approximately 42 gallons per minute.   **66.** The flow rate is approximately 84 gallons per minute.   **67.** The average change was −0.046.   **68.** The average high temperature was −31°.   **69.** 345.4 square inches of metal is needed.   **70.** 180.55 square inches of cardboard is needed.   **71.** The cone's surface area is about 19.15 square inches.   **72.** The cone's surface area is about 31.71 square inches.

P.4 CALCULATOR EXERCISES

1. 27   **2.** $-\frac{13}{15}$

SECTION P.5 EXERCISES

1. Let p = the total price; $\frac{3}{4}p$ **2.** Let p = the amount invested; $0.06p$ **3.** Let x = the total amount; $\frac{x}{15}$ **4.** Let c = the count; $\frac{55}{c}$

5. Let x = a number; $12x - 25$ **6.** Let x = a number; $8x - 3$ **7.** Let c = the cost of a chair; $3c + 80$ **8.** Let x = a number; $5x + 4$

9. Let L = the length of a rectangle; $\frac{1}{3}(L - 5)$ **10.** Let N = the number of adults; $\frac{1}{3}N + 6$ **11.** Let x = a number; $2.5x - \frac{19.59}{x}$

12. Let x = a number; $3x - \frac{10}{x}$ **13.** Let a = first side; b = second side; c = third side; $\frac{a + b + c}{2}$

14. Let a = the first grade, b = the second grade, c = the third grade; $\frac{a + b + c}{3}$ **15.** Let x = a number; $x^2 + 3x$

16. Let L = the length of a side of a square; $2L - 5$ **17.** Let x = the dollars invested in the first fund; $10{,}000 - x$ **18.** Let a = the number of adults; $456 - a$ **19.** Let x = the number of liters of solution; $0.20x$; $0.80x$ **20.** Let n = the number of nickels; d = number of dimes; $0.05n$; $0.10d$

21. (a) 3 **(b)** -3 **(c)** 9 **(d)** -9 **22. (a)** 1.5 **(b)** -1.5 **(c)** 2.25 **(d)** -2.25 **23.** -10 **24.** -34 **25.** 7   **26.** 13   **27.** -3.1 **28.** 1.82

29. 54.21   **30.** 20.7   **31.** -51 **32.** -81 **33.** $\frac{41}{2}$ **34.** $34\frac{1}{3}$ **35.** 392   **36.** 67.2   **37.** $\frac{64}{15}$ **38.** 66   **39.** 14.28   **40.** $\frac{5}{3}$ **41.** -54

42. -71 **43.** 7.75   **44.** 9.64   **45.** 9   **46.** 13   **47.** 21   **48.** 15   **49.** 1.7   **50.** 4.8   **51.** 10.7   **52.** 13.8   **53.** 5   **54.** 2   **55.** $\frac{3}{2}$

56. $\frac{1}{3}$ **57.** Let a = the number of adult tickets, c = the number of children's tickets; $6a + 2c$; they raised $2170.

58. Let x = the number of hours on the first job, y = the number of hours on the second job; $9.50x + 12.25y$; Katie earned $289.50.

59. Let c = the number of computers sold, a = the number of pieces of ancillary equipment sold; $200c + 50a - 750$; Pablo's profit is $3650.

60. Let T = the number of hours tutoring, A = the number of hours administering tests; $1200 + 8T + 6A$; Shondra earned $2380.

61. Let D = the diameter of a circle; πD; $\pi(12) \approx 37.7$; the circumference is about 37.7 feet.   **62.** Let r = the radius of a circle; $2\pi r$; $2\pi(3) \approx 18.8$; the circumference is about 18.8 feet.   **63.** Let m = the number of miles driven; the rental cost is $19.95 + 0.59m$; the rental cost is $88.39.

64. Let d = the number of days; the rental cost is $145d$; the rental cost is $435.   **65.** Let d = the number of days, m = the number of miles; $64.99d + 0.49m$; the cost is $1132.42.   **66.** Let d = the number of days, m = the number of miles; $76.99d + 0.49m$; the cost is $316.72.

67. Let s = the length of a side of the fan; the area is s^2 and the perimeter is $4s$; the area is 441 square inches and the perimeter is 84 inches.

68. Let b = the base of the triangle, h = the height of the triangle, a and c = the lengths of the other two sides of the triangle; the area is $\frac{1}{2}bh$ and the perimeter is $a + b + c$; the area is 65 square inches and the perimeter is 38 inches.   **69.** Let p = the retail price of the coat; the tax is $0.085p$ and the total price is $p + 0.085p$ or $1.085p$; the tax is $12.67 and the total price is $161.67.   **70.** Let b = the bill; the tip is $0.15b$ and the total bill with tip is $b + 0.15b$ or $1.15b$; the tip is $13.14 and the total bill is $100.72.

P.5 CALCULATOR EXERCISES

1. 130   **2.** 1   **3.** 9   **4.** 61   **5.** 0.25   **6.** $\frac{289}{49}$ **1.** 256   **2.** 1.96   **3.** $\frac{441}{25}$ **4.** 121   **5.** 0.49   **6.** $\frac{529}{49}$

SECTION P.6 EXERCISES

1. (a) 4 **(b)** 12 **(c)** $2x^2, -6x, x$ **(d)** 2, -6, 1, 12 **(e)** $-6x, x$ **2. (a)** 5 **(b)** 1 **(c)** $3y^5, y^3, -y, 4y^3$ **(d)** 3, 1, -1, 1, 4 **(e)** $y^3, 4y^3$

3. (a) 3 **(b)** none **(c)** $3.4a, -11.2b, -0.3a$ **(d)** 3.4, -11.2, -0.3 **(e)** $3.4a, -0.3a$

4. (a) 4 **(b)** none **(c)** $\frac{2}{5}m, \frac{1}{10}n, -\frac{3}{10}m, \frac{1}{5}n$ **(d)** $\frac{2}{5}, \frac{1}{10}, -\frac{3}{10}, \frac{1}{5}$ **(e)** $\frac{2}{5}m$ and $-\frac{3}{10}m$; $\frac{1}{10}n$ and $\frac{1}{5}n$

5. (a) 2 **(b)** none **(c)** $3m(n - 5); 6(n - 5)$ **(d)** 3, 6 **(e)** none   **6. (a)** 2 **(b)** none **(c)** $3p(p + q); -q(p + q)$ **(d)** 3, -1 **(e)** none

7. (a) 4 **(b)** 7 **(c)** $x^2, 3xy, -y^2$ **(d)** 1, 3, -1, 7 **(e)** none   **8. (a)** 4 **(b)** -3 **(c)** $a^2, -b^2, 6ab$ **(d)** 1, -1, 6, -3 **(e)** none   **9.** $x + 14$

10. $-6a + 15$ **11.** $x^3 + x + 6$ **12.** $7h^3 - 2h^2 - 9$ **13.** $1.87a + 6.78b$ **14.** $17.348z - 44.004x$ **15.** $-\frac{1}{2}x + \frac{1}{2}$ **16.** $\frac{13}{8}z + \frac{7}{32}$

17. $7x^3 - 2x^2y - 4xy^2 + 9y^3$ **18.** $10d^5 - 10d^3e^2 + 14d^2e^3 - 16e^5$ **19.** $\frac{3}{2}x + \frac{1}{2}y$ **20.** $-\frac{13}{8}a + \frac{7}{8}b$ **21.** $-2x + 7$ **22.** $13y - 4$

23. $7x + 1$ **24.** $t + 1$ **25.** $-7 - 15y$ **26.** $20z - 19$ **27.** $-x + 6y + 3z$ **28.** $40a + 33b + 14c$ **29.** $2.3y + 0.8z$

30. $-1.92t - 12.8r$ **31.** 0   **32.** $2x - 2y$ **33.** 0   **34.** 0   **35.** $2a$ **36.** $-10m$ **37.** $-30x - 45$ **38.** $-60z - 12$ **39.** $20z + 56$

40. $2a + 410$ **41.** $7.7x - 16.06$ **42.** $3.96a - 2.88$ **43.** $-84m + 49$ **44.** $-12z + 330$ **45.** $20b - 9$ **46.** $-15y + 40$ **47.** $3x + 5$

48. $-6m - 3n$ **49.** $-3b + \frac{1}{2}c$ **50.** $0.3m - n$ **51.** $12a + 3b - \frac{115}{8}c$ **52.** $-15x - \frac{17}{5}y + 25z$ **53.** $-73a + 78b - 60c$

54. $-51x + 252y - 249z$ **55.** $40.3x - 6.7y$ **56.** $65.8p - 18.2q$ **57.** $\frac{5}{12}p - \frac{55}{84}q$ **58.** $-\frac{11}{24}a - \frac{1}{18}b$ **59.** $11 + 4x + 4y$

60. $-51x + 31y - 19$ **61.** $-24a - 30b - 17c + 18$ **62.** $-117x - 77y - 31z + 33$ **63.** $6x + 60y - 132z$ **64.** $4a + 26b - 64c$

65. $7a + 8c$ **66.** $6x - 13y$ **67.** $0.7m - 8.4n$ **68.** $-7.48a + 13.9b$ **69.** $2a + 2b$; The perimeter is 1200 miles.   **70.** $2L + 2W$; The perimeter is 1300 miles.   **71. (a)** Let x = Paul's time; $x + (2x + 10) + (x - 5)$ **(b)** $4x + 5$ **(c)** It takes 85 minutes to mow the yard.   **72. (a)** Let l = the length of the first side; $l + l^2 + 2(l - 1)$ **(b)** $l^2 + 3l - 2$ **(c)** The perimeter is 8 inches.   **73.** The profit is $13.50 + 0.90c$ dollars; the profit is $238.50.   **74.** The profit is $23 + 30h$ dollars; the profit is $128.   **75.** The profit is $2.75 + 1.50w$ dollars; the profit is $8.75.   **76.** The profit is $7 + 1.50p$ dollars; the profit is $175.   **77.** The total cost is $10.7892x$ dollars; Laurie's change is $50 - 10.7892x$ dollars; Laurie's cost is $32.37 and her change is $17.63.   **78.** Mary Lynn's profit is $10.50x - 18.50$ dollars; her profit is $212.50.

P.6 CALCULATOR EXERCISES

1. $-5.342x - 11.8105$ **2.** $1492x - 3996$ **3.** $-\dfrac{21}{260}x - \dfrac{33}{52}y$ **4.** $-1\dfrac{32}{75}x + 2\dfrac{13}{50}$ **5.** $0.91x + 1.0035$ **6.** $-1018.3646x - 119.3616$

7. $x + 3$

SECTION P.7 EXERCISES

1. equation   **2.** expression   **3.** expression   **4.** equation   **5.** inequality   **6.** expression   **7.** inequality   **8.** inequality   **9.** expression
10. inequality   **11.** equation   **12.** equation   **13.** yes   **14.** no   **15.** no   **16.** no   **17.** no   **18.** yes   **19.** yes   **20.** yes   **21.** yes   **22.** no
23. no   **24.** yes   **25.** yes   **26.** no

27. $[6, \infty)$

28. $(-\infty, 9]$

29. $(-\infty, 12)$

30. $(-7, \infty)$

31. $\left(-\dfrac{13}{5}, \infty\right)$

32. $\left(-\infty, 3\dfrac{5}{6}\right)$

33. $\left(-\infty, 4\dfrac{2}{3}\right]$

34. $\left[\dfrac{16}{3}, \infty\right)$

35. $(-\infty, 12.59]$

36. $[5.1, \infty)$

37. $(-6.7, \infty)$

38. $(-\infty, 45.65)$

39. $(5, 13)$

40. $(-2, -1)$

41. $(2, 8)$

42. $[3, 6]$

43. $(-4, 0]$

44. $[0, 5)$

45. $[-1, 6)$

46. $(2, 7]$

47. $[2, 7]$

48. $[15, 30]$

49. $\left(\dfrac{2}{5}, 3\dfrac{1}{3}\right]$

50. $\left[-1\dfrac{3}{4}, \dfrac{2}{3}\right]$

51. $[-2.5, 3.5)$

52. $(-6.5, -1.5)$

53.

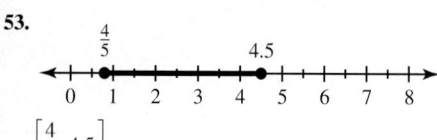

$\left[\dfrac{4}{5}, 4.5\right]$

54.

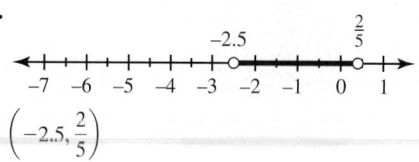

$\left(-2.5, \dfrac{2}{5}\right)$

55. (a) $x < 4.5$;

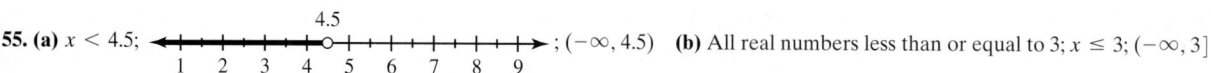

$; (-\infty, 4.5)$ **(b)** All real numbers less than or equal to 3; $x \le 3$; $(-\infty, 3]$

(c) All real numbers less than -2; $x < -2$;

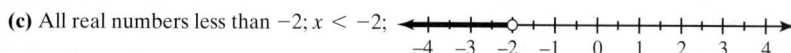

(d) All real numbers greater than or equal to 5.7;

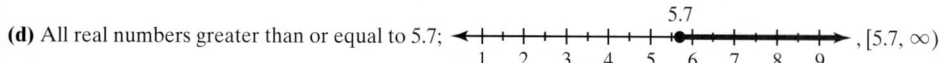

$, [5.7, \infty)$

(e) All real numbers greater than -7; $z > -7$; $(-7, \infty)$ **(f)** All real numbers greater than 2; $z > 2$;

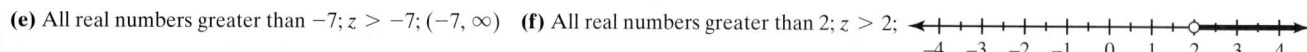

(g) All real numbers between 2 and 8;

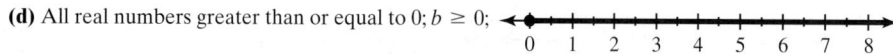

$(2, 8)$

(h) All real numbers between -3 and 2, including -3; $-3 \le y < 2$; $[-3, 2)$

(i) All real numbers between and including 0 and 9; $0 \le y \le 9$;

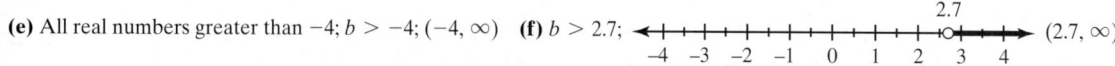

(j) $-1 < x \le 1$;

$(-1, 1]$

56. (a) All real numbers less than -9; $a < -9$;

  (b) All real numbers less than or equal to 5; $a \le 5$; $(-\infty, 5)$

(c) All real numbers less than $\dfrac{1}{2}$;

$; \left(-\infty, \dfrac{1}{2}\right)$

(d) All real numbers greater than or equal to 0; $b \ge 0$;

(e) All real numbers greater than -4; $b > -4$; $(-4, \infty)$ **(f)** $b > 2.7$;

$(2.7, \infty)$

(g) All real numbers between 4 and 11; $4 < c < 11$;

(h) All real numbers between 0 and 5, including 0; $0 \le c < 5$; $(0, 5)$

(i) All real numbers between and including -5 and -1;

$[-5, -1]$

(j) $-3 < x \le 2$;

$(-3, 2)$

57. Let f = the number of flyers; $0.25f + 1650 = 1.25f$ **58.** Let d = the number of days; $35d = 572$

59. Let m = the number of miles; $0.59m + 29.95 = 60.00$ **60.** Let p = the amount of that payment; $12p + 250 = 2500$

61. Let P = the perimeter, d = the diameter, and r = the radius; $P = d + \pi r$

62. Let r = average rate of speed, d = the distance, t = the time; $r = \dfrac{d}{t}$ **63.** $I = A - P$ **64.** $A = P + I$

65. Let n = the number of nickels, d = the number of dimes; $n + d = 2n$ **66.** Let q = the number of quarters; d = the number of dimes; $q = 2d + 5$

67. Let x = the amount invested at 5%, y = the amount invested at 7%; $0.05x + 0.07y = 176$

68. Let x = the amount invested at 8%, y = the amount invested at 10%; $0.08x + 0.10y = 256$

69. Let x = the measure of one angle, y = the measure of a second angle; $x = 3y + 10$

70. Let x = the length of one side of a triangle, y = the length of a second side of a triangle; $x = 2y + 6$ **71.** $H = \dfrac{NI}{L}$ **72.** $n = \dfrac{m}{M}$

73. (a) Let r = the magnitude, $r < 3.5$ **(b)** $3.5 \le r \le 5.4$ **(c)** $r < 6.0$ **74. (a)** Let r = the magnitude, $6.1 \le r \le 6.9$ **(b)** $7.0 \le r \le 7.9$

(c) $r \ge 8.0$ **75.** $39.95 + 0.2x \le 150$ **76.** $300 + 22x < 1000$ **77.** $800 < 450 + 0.05x$ **78.** $15x - 125 \ge 250$

79. $150 \le 25 + 12.5x \le 200$ **80.** $200 \le 4.5x - 350 \le 500$

P.7 CALCULATOR EXERCISES

1. 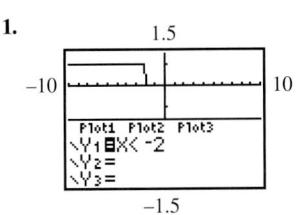   **2.** 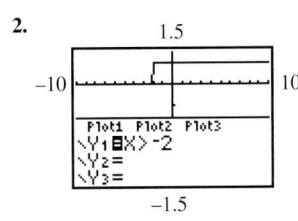   **3.** 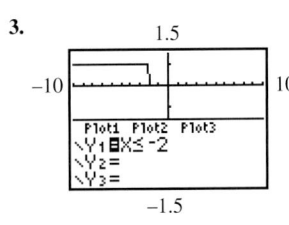   **4.**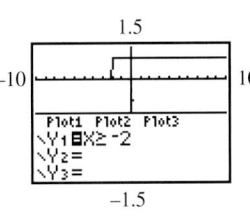

5. 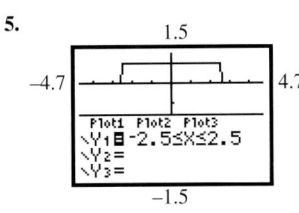   **6.** 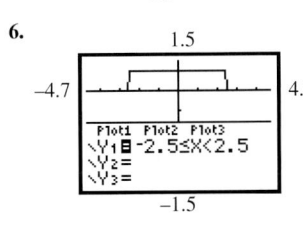   **7.**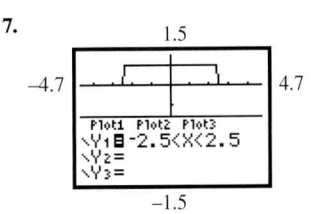

SECTION P.8 EXERCISES

1. 468 in²; 104 in   **2.** 600 mm²; 160 mm   **3.** 24 cm²; 20 cm   **4.** 40 ft²; 26 ft   **5.** $\frac{25}{4}$ ft²; 10 ft   **6.** 31.36 m²; 22.4 m   **7.** 3060 m²; 242 m

8. 3705 in²; 368 in   **9.** 86.6 in²; 33.0 in   **10.** 23.8 ft²; 17.3 ft   **11.** They roam over an area of about 855.3 mi², and the circumference of this area is approximately 103.7 miles.   **12.** They roam over an area of about 20,106.2 mi², and the circumference of this area is approximately 502.7 miles. **13.** The area of the standard lot is 6000 ft², and the perimeter of the lot is 320 ft.   **14.** The square footage of this area is about 78.5 ft², and the border of the area will be 31.4 ft.   **15.** The area of coverage is 2704 in², and the amount of fringe needed for the perimeter is 208 in.   **16.** The deck contained an area of 225 ft², and Marcos will need 56 ft of latticework.   **17.** The area of carpet needed is 20 yd², and the cost will be $139.80. **18.** The flooring cost $1430.40.   **19.** The tile cost $277.20.   **20.** The hardwood flooring cost $451.18.   **21.** 15 ft³; 46 ft²   **22.** 72 ft³; 108 ft² **23.** 421.875 in³; 337.5 in²   **24.** 551.368 cm³; 403.44 cm²   **25.** 35.3 in³; 61.3 in²   **26.** 117.8 in³; 133.5 in²   **27.** 4189 cm³; 1257 cm² **28.** 524 in³; 314 in²   **29.** 0.049 ft³; 0.817 ft²   **30.** 33.51 cm³; 64.38 cm²   **31.** The case contains 5832 in³, with a surface area of 1944 in². **32.** The cube contains 15.625 ft³ of ice. The surface area is 37.5 ft².   **33.** The tank will hold 4188.8 in³ of gas. The surface area is 1256.6 in². **34.** It will take 1005.3 in³ of pellets.; the surface area is 603.2 in².   **35.** The volume of the paperweight is 89.80 in³.   **36.** The volume of the bag is 84.8 in³.   **37.** The box will hold 16 ft³ of toys. Jim painted 40 ft² of surface area, using 1.6 half pints of paint.   **38.** The chest will hold 31.25 ft³ of toys. Lindsay painted 62.5 ft² of surface area using 4 cans of paint.   **39.** The radius of the ball is 47.625 inches, and the volume equals 452,474 cubic inches. The surface area equals 28,502 square inches, and the area covered by the mirrors is 27,600 square inches.   **40.** The volume of the Destiny laboratory is 4310 ft³ and the surface area is 1539 ft².   **41.** 25°   **42.** 19°   **43.** 115°   **44.** 56°   **45.** 79°   **46.** 45°   **47.** The pitch of the roof is 40°.   **48.** The angle formed with the driveway is 20°.   **49.** The other angle is 135°.   **50.** The other angle is 120°.   **51.** The third angle is 85°.

52. The third angle is 60°.   **53.** The temperature is 77°F.   **54.** The temperature is 87.8°F.   **55.** The temperature is $33\frac{1}{3}°$C.

56. The temperature is 18.9°C.   **57.** The temperature is 212°F.   **58.** The temperature is 1945.4°F.   **59.** The temperature is 203°F.   **60.** The temperature is 5370.8°F.   **61.** The temperature is −38.87°C.   **62.** The temperature is 356.58°C.   **63.** The temperature is 28.9°C.   **64.** The temperature is 22.8°C.   **65.** JoAnne paid $162.50 in interest.   **66.** Jack paid $385 in interest.   **67.** $2.92 of interest is earned.   **68.** The interest will be $2 and the total will be $102.   **69.** $48 in interest is paid.   **70.** The simple interest is $144.   **71.** The distance covered was 522.5 miles. **72.** The trip was 511.5 miles.   **73.** He drove 223.806 miles.   **74.** He drove a distance of 315.206 miles.

P.8 CALCULATOR EXERCISES

Students should develop other programs for various formulas.

CHAPTER P SUMMARY

Vocabulary Review

1. set; members   **2.** opposites   **3.** absolute value   **4.** undefined; indeterminate   **5.** base; exponent   **6.** coefficient   **7.** equation **8.** inequality   **9.** order symbols   **10.** perimeter   **11.** area   **12.** circumference   **13.** volume   **14.** right angle   **15.** complementary **16.** supplementary

Reflections

1–16. Answers will vary.

CHAPTER P SECTION-BY-SECTION REVIEW

1. −15: integer, rational; 1000: natural, whole, integer, rational; 0: whole, integer, rational; −2000: integer, rational; 13: natural, whole, integer, rational; $-\frac{15}{17}$: rational; 12.97: rational; $3\frac{5}{8}$: rational; $\frac{12}{4}=3$: natural, whole, integer, rational   **2.**

$$-3\ \ -2\frac{1}{2}\ \ -1.1\ \ \ 0\ \ \frac{3}{4}\ \ 1\frac{1}{2}\ \ 2.5\ \ \ \ 4$$

number line from −4 to 4

3. >   **4.** <   **5.** <   **6.** >   **7.** <   **8.** <   **9.** =   **10.** <   **11.** =   **12.** −100 ≤ −49 < −23   **13.** $\frac{13}{17} > \frac{252}{529}$

14. $-\frac{1729}{50} = -34.58$ **15.** $-\frac{17}{33}$ **16.** 67   **17.** 32.698   **18.** −257   **19.** 2, −6, −7, −1   **20.** −125,000,000   **21.** −14   **22.** −45   **23.** $-\frac{2}{3}$

24. $-\dfrac{1}{12}$ **25.** -0.83 **26.** 14.017 **27.** $\dfrac{62}{63}$ **28.** -44.668 **29.** -123 **30.** 0 **31.** 7.75 **32.** $\dfrac{88}{45}$ **33.** 26 **34.** $-\dfrac{53}{56}$ **35.** -2.4

36. -3.97 **37.** 0 **38.** $-1\dfrac{2}{3}$ **39.** $-\dfrac{11}{9}$ **40.** 124.92 **41.** 78 **42.** -105 **43.** $\dfrac{37}{7}$ **44.** -0.922 **45.** -25 **46.** $\dfrac{9}{35}$ **47.** 8.4048

48. $-\dfrac{4}{9}$ **49.** $-64{,}000$ **50.** 7.04 **51.** $-\dfrac{5}{6}$ **52.** 0 **53.** -55 **54.** $\dfrac{5}{6}$ **55.** -4.59 **56.** 0 **57.** undefined   **58.** 13.7

59. indeterminate   **60.** $\dfrac{3}{4}$ **61.** $735.66 + (-276.12) + (-187.05) + (-68.57) + 75.00 + 185.00 + 50 + (-4.65) + (-12.00) = 497.27$; Cleta has $497.27 left in her account at the end of the month.   **62.** $14{,}494 - (-282) = 14{,}776$; the range of the elevation between these two points is 14,776 feet.   **63.** Of the 1173 community colleges, 997 are public institutions, 141 are private institutions, and 35 are tribal institutions.
64. $345 \div 18.7 \approx 18.45$; Clarence's average mileage is approximately 18.45 mpg. $560 \div 18.45 \approx 30.35$; He will need about 30.35 gallons of gas to travel 560 miles.   **65.** -243 **66.** -81 **67.** 1.44 **68.** 0 **69.** 1 **70.** 1 **71.** -1 **72.** $\dfrac{729}{4096}$ **73.** $\dfrac{16807}{243}$ **74.** 1 **75.** -1 **76.** -15

77. indeterminate   **78.** 0 **79.** 0.8 **80.** $\dfrac{3}{5}$ or 0.6 **81.** -7 **82.** not a real number   **83.** -21.7 **84.** 3.873 **85.** 0.5 **86.** $\dfrac{4}{9}$

87. 30 **88.** 2.154 **89.**   **90.** $\left(\dfrac{1}{4}\right)^1 = \dfrac{1}{4}$ **91.** $4^1 = 4$ **92.** $4^2 = 16$ **93.** $\left(-\dfrac{1}{4}\right)^2 = \dfrac{1}{16}$

$$-\sqrt{68} \quad -\sqrt{16} \quad -\sqrt{7.29} \quad \sqrt{9} \ \sqrt{18} \quad \pi \quad \sqrt[3]{140} \quad 9$$
$$-10\ -8\ -6\ -4\ -2\ 0\ 2\ 4\ 6\ 8\ 10$$

94. 1.89×10^{-7}; $1.89\text{ E}{-7}$ **95.** -2.7085×10^{10}; $-2.7085\text{E}10$ **96.** $589{,}000{,}000{,}000$; $5.89\text{E}11$ **97.** -0.00007093; -7.093×10^{-5}

98. The diamond is 27 meters on a side.   **99.** The box is $4\dfrac{1}{2}$ inches on a side.   **100.** 7.42×10^{11} **101.** $1{,}263{,}200{,}000{,}000$; 5.212×10^{11}; U.S. imports exceed exports by $521,200,000,000.   **102.** 0.000008; 4×10^{-6}; the radius of the blood cell is 4×10^{-6} meters.   **103.** $-2.6(-1.9) + (-2.6)(3.2)$

104. $\dfrac{5}{6}\left(-\dfrac{3}{5}\right) + \dfrac{5}{6}\left(-\dfrac{4}{15}\right)$ **105.** $\dfrac{1687}{7} - \dfrac{1372}{7}$ **106.** $-2.7 - 3.09$ **107.** $21(18 + 42)$ **108.** $5(97 - 17)$ **109.** 16 **110.** -334 **111.** 117
112. -118 **113.** 21 **114.** 0 **115.** undefined   **116.** The lean body weight is 140 pounds.   **117.** The average of the hourly earnings is $14.71.
118. Let $x =$ the number.   **(a)** $55x + 4$ **(b)** $55(x + 4)$ **119.** Let $x =$ the number.   **(a)** $\dfrac{3}{4}(x + 35)$ **(b)** $\dfrac{3}{4}x + 35$ **120.** Let $x =$ the number.

(a) $2x - 20$ **(b)** $20 - 2x$ **121.** $2500 + 275n$ **122.** $\dfrac{650}{h}$ **123.** $200 + 5.5k$ **124.** $0.4x$; $x - 0.4x$ or $0.6x$ **125.** $758 - x$

126. $0.25x$; $x - 0.25x$ or $0.75x$ **127.** $\dfrac{2}{3}$ **128.** $-\dfrac{2}{3}$ **129.** $\dfrac{4}{9}$ **130.** $-\dfrac{4}{9}$ **131.** $\dfrac{2}{3}$ **132.** 15 **133.** 7.5 **134.** $\dfrac{4}{15}$ **135.** undefined

136. 77.48 **137.** 323 **138. (a)** Let $L =$ length, $W =$ width, $H =$ height, $V = LWH$ **(b)** $V = 2{,}491{,}776$ ft^3
139. terms $= 4$; constants $=$ none; variable terms $= 3x, -2y, 4x, 9y$; coefficients $= 3, -2, 4, 9$; like terms $= 3x$ and $4x$, $-2y$ and $9y$
140. terms $= 4$; constants $=$ none; variable terms $= 2a^2, -a, 3a^2, -5a^3$; coefficients $= 2, -1, 3, -5$; like terms $= 2a^2$ and $3a^2$
141. terms $= 3$; constants $= 5.1$; variable terms $= 2.4x, 6.2x$; coefficients $= 2.4, 5.1, 6.2$; like terms $= 2.4x, 6.2x$
142. terms $= 2$; constants $=$ none; variable terms $= 4a(a + b), -b(a + b)$; coefficients $= 4, -1$; like terms $=$ none

143. $0.2z$ **144.** $24x - 42$ **145.** $\dfrac{1}{12}x + \dfrac{7}{8}y$ **146.** $9x^2 + 28xy + 5y^2 - 2$ **147.** $7a + 8b$ **148.** $-7.6a + 9.4b$ **149.** $-90x + 28y$

150. $6x^2 - 34xy$ **151.** $3a - 4b + \dfrac{5}{3}c$ **152.** $129x + 3y$ **153.** $-12x - 21y - 31$ **154.** $10a - 26b - 3c + 15$

155. $x + (2x - 5) + (x + 7)$; $4x + 2$; total number of push-ups is 182.   **156.** $20 - 5.3x$; Katie received $4.10 in change.   **157.** $8.75x - 52.65$; Margaret's net profit is $227.35.   **158.** expression   **159.** inequality   **160.** equation   **161.** yes   **162.** yes   **163.** yes   **164.** no

165.
$$0\ 1\ 2\ 3\ 4\ 5\ 6\ 7\ 8$$
$(-\infty, 3)$

166.
$$-8\ -7\ -6\ -5\ -4\ -3\ -2\ -1\ 0$$
$(-2, \infty)$

167.
$$-8\ -7\ -6\ -5\ -4\ -3\ -2\ -1\ 0$$
$(-\infty, -5]$

168.
$$-3.5$$
$$-8\ -7\ -6\ -5\ -4\ -3\ -2\ -1\ 0$$
$[-3.5, \infty)$

169.
$$-4\ -3\ -2\ -1\ 0\ 1\ 2\ 3\ 4$$
$(-2, 4)$

170.
$$-4\ -3\ -2\ -1\ 0\ 1\ 2\ 3\ 4$$
$(-1, 0]$

171. Let $x =$ the number of pamphlets, $1500 = 1.35x$ **172.** Let $x =$ the dollars invested in one account, $y =$ the dollars invested in another account, $0.06x + 0.08y = 1500$ **173.** Let $x =$ the dollars invested in one account, $y =$ the dollars invested in another account, $x + y = 30{,}000$

174. $f = \dfrac{\sqrt{\frac{T}{m}}}{2L}$ **175.** $(30 + 25)x \geq 300$ **176.** $x + 2x + \dfrac{1}{4}(2x) < 200{,}000$ **177. (a)** F0; $40 \leq f \leq 72$ **(b)** F1; $73 \leq f \leq 112$

(c) F2; $113 \leq f \leq 157$ **178.** 208 m^2; 68 m   **179.** 880 in^2; 128 in.   **180.** 225 cm^2; 60 cm   **181.** 65 m^2; 34 m   **182.** 467.59 ft^2; 76.65 ft
183. 6615 in^3; 2478 in^2 **184.** 3112.136 cm^3; 1278.96 cm^2 **185.** 54,965.3 in^3; 8143.01 in^2 **186.** 145,124.7 cm^3; 13,355.04 cm^2
187. 117.3 cm^3; 151.6 cm^2 **188.** The other angle is 122°.   **189.** The other angle is 32°.   **190.** The third angle is 25°.   **191.** Dan should order 5100 ft^2 of sod and 252 ft of fencing.   **192.** The garden will have about 197.9 ft^2.   **193.** The two 10-in. pizzas are the better deal.   **194.** The truck will hold 80 ft^3.   **195.** The surface area is approximately 113.1 ft^2.   **196.** The total amount of the loan is $956.25   **197.** The temperature is 122°F.

198. The temperature is $26\frac{2}{3}°$C.   **199.** LuAnn traveled 356.5 miles.

CHAPTER P MIXED REVIEW

1. 3.554×10^{17}; 3.554 E17   **2.** -9.2×10^{-5}; -9.2E-5 **3.** 0.00000000000794; 7.94E-12 **4.** $-68,760$; -6.876×10^4 **5.** $42(73 - 23)$

6. $-31(18 + 42)$ **7.** $<$ **8.** $>$ **9.** $<$ **10.** $>$ **11.** $=$ **12.** $<$ **13.** $>$ **14.** $=$ **15.** $-\frac{9}{25}$ **16.** 102   **17.** -0.085

18. -144 **19.** 0.17   **20.** $-1\frac{3}{8}$ **21.** $\frac{1}{18}$ **22.** -182 **23.** -2.48 **24.** $-\frac{3}{11}$ **25.** 1.03   **26.** $-\frac{14}{15}$ **27.** $6\frac{1}{2}$ **28.** $\frac{1}{6}$ **29.** -2 **30.** 88

31. -3.41 **32.** $-\frac{9}{2}$ **33.** $-\frac{1}{3}$ **34.** indeterminate   **35.** undefined   **36.** 8.2   **37.** $-\frac{1}{16}$ **38.** 2.5   **39.** 169   **40.** 2.48832   **41.** -125

42. -625 **43.** $-2\frac{93}{125}$ **44.** 1   **45.** -1 **46.** $-\frac{1}{243}$ **47.** 1   **48.** 1   **49.** -1 **50.** 22   **51.** indeterminate   **52.** $\frac{1}{100}$ **53.** $\frac{1}{100}$

54. 10   **55.** -10 **56.** 50   **57.** not a real number   **58.** -0.112 **59.** -4 **60.** $\frac{9}{4}$ **61.** -2.924 **62.** 1.6   **63.** $\frac{3}{4}$ **64.** $-35,640$

65. $-\frac{2}{5}$ **66.** 0   **67.** -20 **68.** 267   **69.** 50   **70.** 10   **71.** undefined   **72.** $74 \le 75 < 76$ **73.** $\frac{1}{7} > -\frac{2}{5}$ **74.** $\frac{13}{25} = 0.52$

75.

76. terms $= 4$; constants $= 23$; variable terms $= 12x, y, -z$; coefficients $= 12, 1, -1, 23$; like terms $=$ none
77. terms $= 3$; constants $= 75$; variable terms $= 3(a - 2), 5(b - 4)$; coefficients $= 3, 5, 75$; like terms $=$ none
78. terms $= 5$; constants $= 12, -18$; variable terms $= -7x, 14x, x$; coefficients $= 12, -7, 14, -18, 1$; like terms $= 12$ and -18; $-7x, 14x, x$
79. terms $= 5$; constants $=$ none; variable terms $= b^2, 2b, -3b^2, 6b, b^3$; coefficients $= 1, 2, -3, 6, 1$; like terms $= b^2$ and $-3b^2$; $2b$ and $6b$

80. 324   **81.** -324 **82.** 324   **83.** -5.23 **84.** -12 **85.** not a real number   **86.** 2   **87.** $-\frac{5}{4}$ **88.** 3   **89.** equation   **90.** expression

91. inequality   **92.** no   **93.** yes   **94.** no   **95.** no   **96.** $17h$ **97.** $8m + 10$ **98.** $27x - 8 + 15y$ **99.** $15x^4 + x^3 - 7x^2 - 46x - 1$

100. $10.9a + 3.4b$ **101.** $-27y + 15$ **102.** $4g + 4$ **103.** $-x - 2y - 15z$ **104.** $22a + 33b$ **105.** $8x - 12y + \frac{30}{13}z$ **106.** $3x - 4y + 6z$

107. $35.9x - 49.3y$ **108.** $-144a + 132b - 252$ **109.** $-30x + 45$ **110.** $x < -2$;

; $(-\infty, -2)$

111. All real numbers greater than 5; ; $(5, \infty)$

112. All real numbers less than or equal to -1; $x \le -1$; $(-\infty, -1]$
113. All real numbers greater than or equal to -3; $x \ge -3$;

114. All real numbers between -3 and 0, including -3; $[-3, 0)$

115. Approximately 117 credits run per minute.   **116.** $\frac{1}{7}(217,766,000) \approx 31,109,429$; the number of people who could not find the U.S. on a world map is approximately 31,109,429.   **117.** The average of the four indexes is -4.7725.   **118.** The length of each side is 5.070×10^{-10} meters.
119. Let $x =$ the number of hours, $225 + 45x$; Lakeetha will make \$5625 in earnings.   **120.** Chum's pool will hold 1413.7 ft^3 of water.

121. The temperature is $35\frac{5}{9}°$C.   **122.** Randy bicycled 16.25 miles.   **123.** The can's volume is about 12.44 in^3; the can's surface area is about 31.91 in^2.

124. $1.50x - 175$; the profit is \$200.   **125.** $v = \frac{ax}{x + k}$ **126.** The volume is about 0.005 cubic inches.   **127.** The complementary angle is $5°$.

128. The supplementary angle is $137°$.   **129.** The third angle is $91°$.   **130.** The surface area is about 4637.88 square feet.   **131.** Let $x =$ the number of arrangements; $3.50x + 50.00 = 10.50x$ **132.** Let $w =$ weight; $130 \le w \le 165$; $166 \le w \le 190$; $w > 190$

CHAPTER P TEST

1. $<$ **2.** $>$ **3.** $=$ **4.** $\frac{1}{5} \le \frac{1}{4} < \frac{5}{16}$ **5.** $-2.3 > -3.2$ **6.** $0.06 = \frac{3}{50}$ **7.** 13.37   **8.** -20 **9.** -36 **10.** $\frac{3}{95}$ **11.** -3.602

12. $\frac{2}{5}$ **13.** $-\frac{11}{21}$ **14.** -10.81 **15.** indeterminate   **16.** -101.06 **17.** 91   **18.** $-\frac{8}{3}$ **19.** undefined   **20.** 0   **21.** $\frac{34}{3}$ **22.** -14.45

23. 0   **24.** $-\frac{1}{42}$ **25.** 5.1   **26.**   **27.** 5.239×10^{15} **28.** -2.03×10^{-6} **29.** 2.25

30. $\frac{256}{81}$ **31.** 1   **32.** -81 **33.** -64 **34.** -4.008 **35.** indeterminate   **36.** $-\frac{1}{10}$ **37.** 1   **38.** $\frac{6}{11}$ **39.** -1.897 **40.** not a real number

41. 20   **42.** 0   **43.** 9   **44.** −7   **45.** 36   **46.** −36   **47.** 36   **48.** eight terms   **49.** $y^3, -5y^2, 15y, 7y^2, 4y, 6y^3$ **50.** −3, −12

51. 1, −5, 15, −3, 7, −12, 4, 6   **52.** y^3 and $6y^3$, $-5y^2$ and $7y^2$, $15y$ and $4y$, −3 and −12   **53.** $\dfrac{5}{6}x + \dfrac{29}{18}y - \dfrac{5}{9}$ **54.** $6p - q$ **55.** $-5x + 9$

56. $-30x + 10$ **57.** no   **58.** yes   **59.** All numbers greater than or equal to 4; ; $[4, \infty)$

60. All real numbers less than 2; $x < 2$; $(-\infty, 2)$ **61.** All real numbers greater than −1; $x > -1$;

62. $-3 < x < 5$; ; $(-3, 5)$ **63.** The range in temperatures is 94 degrees.

64. The Earth's moon has a mass of 7.3×10^{22} tons.   **65.** The metal needed is 345.4 square inches.   **66.** Let $x =$ the number of birdhouses; $2.00x + 350.00 = 10.50x$ **67.** 0.0378; the milk contains 0.0378 liter of fat; there are 0.004725 liter of fat per serving.   **68.** The toolbox's volume is 12 ft^3; the outside surface area is 34 ft^2 **69.** Tracy's account will have $6400 in 40 years.   **70.** The supplementary angle is 102°.   **71.** The area is 15 square meters. The perimeter is 17 meters.   **72.** The temperature is 77°F.   **73.** F3: $158 \le f \le 206$; F4: $207 \le f \le 260$; F5: $261 \le f \le 318$; F6: $f \ge 319$ **74.** Answer will vary. Possible answer: The area is the space contained within the boundaries, whereas the perimeter is the distance around the boundaries.   **75.** Answers will vary; possible answers: A constant term has no variable. A coefficient is a numeric factor in a variable term.

CHAPTER 1

SECTION 1.1 EXERCISES

1.

x	y
−2	−6
−1	−1
0	4
1	9
2	14
3	19

2.

x	y
−3	18
−2	10
−1	2
0	−6
1	−14

3.

x	y
−15	−11
−10	−8
−5	−5
0	−2
5	1
10	4
15	7

4.

x	y
−18	−11
−9	−4
0	3
9	10
18	17
27	24
36	31

5.

x	y
−2	−3
−1	−0.7
0	1.6
1	3.9
2	6.2

6.

x	y
−3	5.2
−1	−4.4
0	−9.2
1	−14
3	−23.6

7.

x	y
−1	2
−4	1
−7	0
−10	−1
−13	−2

8.

x	y
−10	−2
−4	−1
2	0
8	1
14	2

For problems 9–16, answers will vary. One possibility is given.

9.

x	y
−2	−20
−1	−14
0	−8
1	−2
2	4

10.

x	y
−2	37
−1	26
0	15
1	4
2	−7

11.

x	y
−14	−6
−7	−4
0	−2
7	0
14	2

12.

x	y
−16	11
−8	8
0	5
8	2
16	−1

13.

x	y
−2	11.3
−1	6.7
0	2.1
1	−2.5
2	−7.1

14.

x	y
−2	−22
−1	−11.4
0	−0.8
1	9.8
2	20.4

15.

x	y
−6	−5
−2	−2
0	−½
2	1
6	4

16.

x	y
−11	−6
−3	−3
5	0
13	3
21	6

17.

x	y
−4	−61
−2	−37
0	−13
2	11
4	35

18.

x	y
−3	39
−1	21
1	3
3	−15

19.

y	z
−6	3
−3	4
0	5
3	6
6	7

20.

q	p
−16	−18
−8	−11
0	−4
8	3
16	10

21.

b	a
−2	−22.7
−1	−8.5
0	5.7
1	19.9
2	34.1

22.

n	m
−3	−9.4
−2	−7.5
−1	−5.6
0	−3.7
1	−1.8

23.

x	y
−3	10
−2	3
−1	0
0	1
1	6
2	15
3	28

24.

x	y
−2	−44
−1	−24
0	−10
1	−2
2	0
3	−4
4	−14

25.

x	y
−2	14
−1	−5
0	−12
1	−7
2	10

26.

x	y
5	−63
6	−100
7	−145
8	−198
9	−259

27.

x	y
-3	$\frac{1}{2}$
-1	-2
1	undefined
3	8

28.

x	y
-1	$\frac{7}{4}$
1	$-\frac{3}{2}$
3	undefined
5	$\frac{23}{2}$

29. (a) Let d = distance, t = time, $d = 55t$

(b)

t	d
4	220
8	440
12	660
16	880
20	1100

30. (a) Let C = total cost, p = number of place settings, $C = 15.50p$

(b)

p	C
2	31
4	62
6	93
8	124
10	155
12	186

31. (a) Let d = the number of days, C = the rental cost, $C = 68.99d + 110.00$

(b)

d	C
5	454.95
7	592.93
9	730.91

(c) $(5, 454.95), (7, 592.93), (9, 730.91)$; The cost of renting an intermediate-class automobile is $454.95 for 5 days, $592.93 for 7 days, and $730.91 for 9 days.

32. (a) Let d = the number of days, C = the rental cost; $C = 58.99d + 110.00$

(b)

d	C
7	522.93
14	935.86
21	1348.79

(c) $(7, 522.93), (14, 935.86), (21, 1348.79)$; The cost of renting a minivan is $522.93 for 7 days, $935.86 for 14 days, and $1348.79 for 21 days.

33.

H	V
1	8
3	24
5	40
7	56
9	72

34.

s	V
1	1
2	8
3	27
4	64
5	125
6	216

35.

t	I
1	225
2	450
3	675
4	900
5	1125
6	1350
7	1575
8	1800
9	2025
10	2250
11	2475
12	2700

36.

t	I
1	210
3	630
5	1050
7	1470
9	1890
11	2310
13	2730
15	3150

37.

R	I
1	9
2	4.5
3	3
4	2.25
5	1.8
6	1.5
7	1.286
8	1.125
9	1

38.

R	V
1	5
2	10
3	15
4	20
5	25
6	30
7	35
8	40
9	45
10	50

39. $(-2, 1.6), (-1, 2.8), (0, 4), (1, 5.2), (2, 6.4)$ **40.** $(-4, 7.2), (-2, 6.6), (0, 6), (2, 5.4), (4, 4.8)$ **41.** $\left(\frac{1}{6}, \frac{5}{6}\right), \left(\frac{1}{5}, \frac{4}{5}\right), \left(\frac{1}{4}, \frac{3}{4}\right), \left(\frac{1}{3}, \frac{2}{3}\right), \left(\frac{1}{2}, \frac{1}{2}\right)$

42. $(1, 1), (2, 3), (3, 6), (4, 10), (5, 15)$ **43.** $(2, 8), (4, 16), (6, 24), (8, 32), (10, 40)$ **44.** $(4, 6), (6, 4), (8, 2), (9.5, 0.5)$ **45. (a)** $\{(1994, 56.21),$ $(1995, 51.00), (1996, 47.70), (1997, 42.78), (1998, 39.43), (1999, 41.24), (2000, 45.27), (2001, 47.37), (2002, 48.40), (2003, 49.91)\}$ **(b)** $\{(0, 56.21), (1, 51.00),$ $(2, 47.70), (3, 42.78), (4, 39.43), (5, 41.24), (6, 45.27), (7, 47.37), (8, 48.40), (9, 49.91)\}$ **46. (a)** $\{(1994, 577), (1995, 714), (1996, 806), (1997, 915),$ $(1998, 838), (1999, 929), (2000, 928), (2001, 604)\}$ **(b)** $\{(0, 577), (1, 714), (2, 806), (3, 915), (4, 838), (5, 929), (6, 928), (7, 604)\}$ **47. (a)** $\{(1995, 153.616),$ $(1996, 147.956), (1997, 145.827), (1998, 145.155), (1999, 153.176), (2000, 167.607), (2001, 141.574), (2002, 166.499), (2003, 156.291), (2004, 138.518)\}$ **(b)** $\{(0, 153.616), (1, 147.956), (2, 145.827), (3, 145.155), (4, 153.176), (5, 167.607), (6, 141.574), (7, 166.499), (8, 156.291), (9, 138.518)\}$

48. (a) $\{(1994, 113.6), (1995, 113.8), (1996, 121.7), (1997, 124.1), (1998, 163.1), (1999, 169.1), (2000, 176.0), (2001, 184.0), (2002, 184.4), (2003, 187.0)\}$ **(b)** $\{(0, 113.6), (1, 113.8), (2, 121.7), (3, 124.1), (4, 163.1), (5, 169.1), (6, 176.0), (7, 184.0), (8, 184.4), (9, 187.0)\}$ **49.** domain: $\{3, 5, 7, 9\}$; range: $\{15.8, 17.8, 19.8, 21.8\}$ **50.** domain: $\{11, 15, 19, 23\}$; range: $\{8, 12, 16, 20\}$ **51.** domain: $\{4\}$; range: $\{-3, -1, 1, 3, \ldots\}$ **52.** domain: $\{3, 2, 1, 0, -1, \ldots\}$; range: $\{-1\}$ **53.** domain: $\{2\}$; range: $\{\ldots, -2, -1, 0, 1, 2, \ldots\}$ **54.** domain: $\{\ldots, -2, -1, 0, 1, 2, \ldots\}$; range: $\{0\}$ **55.** domain: $\{2, 4, 6\}$; range: $\{3, 11, 19\}$ **56.** domain: $\{10, 20, 30\}$; range: $\{35, 65, 95\}$ **57.** domain: $\{0, 1, 2, 3, 4, 5, 6\}$; range: $\{0, 1, 2, 3, 4, 5, 6\}$ **58.** domain: $\{-4, -3, -2, -1, 0, 1, 2, 3, 4\}$; range: $\{-12, -11, -10, -9, -8, -7, -6, -5, -4\}$

59. domain: $\{0, 0.5, 1, 1.5, 2, 2.5, 3, 3.5, 4\}$; range: $\{1, 1.25, 2, 3.25, 5, 7.25, 10, 13.25, 17\}$ **60.** domain: $\{0, 0.5, 1, 1.5, 2, 2.5, 3, 3.5, 4\}$; range: $\{-2, -1.75, -1, 0.25, 2, 4.25, 7, 10.25, 14\}$ **61.** domain: $\{2, 3, 6, 11, 18, 27\}$; range: $\{0, 1, 2, 3, 4, 5\}$ **62.** domain: $\{-2, -1, 2, 7, 14, 23\}$; range: $\{0, 1, 2, 3, 4, 5\}$ **63.** domain: $\{-3, -1, 1, 3, 5, 7\}$; range: $\left\{-6, -2, -1\frac{1}{5}, 1\frac{1}{5}, 2, 6\right\}$ **64.** domain: $\{-3, -1, 1, 3, 5, 7\}$;

range: $\left\{-10, -3\frac{1}{3}, 1\frac{3}{7}, 2, 3\frac{1}{3}, 10\right\}$

65.

t	s
0	50
0.5	46
1	34
1.5	14

66.

t	s
0	0
1	209
2	386
3	531
4	644
5	725
6	774
7	791
8	776
9	729
10	650
11	539
12	396
13	221
14	14

67. $(1, 65), (2, 130), (3, 195), (4, 260)$ **68.** $(2.5, 78), (2.75, 71), (3, 65), (3.25, 60), (3.5, 56),$
69. (a) Let n = number of weeks, R = rental cost, $R = 175n + 225$

(b)

n	R($)
1	400
2	575
3	750
4	925

70. (a) Let h = number of hours, R = rental cost, $R = 75h + 300$

(b)

h	R($)
2	450
2.5	487.50
3	525
3.5	562.50
4	600

71. (a) $\{(0, 5206), (5, 7077), (9, 8800), (10, 9206), (11, 9588), (12, 10,076), (13, 10,444), (14, 10,818), (15, 11,380), (16, 12,111)\}$ **(b)** The domain is $\{0, 5, 9, 10, 11, 12, 13, 14, 15, 16\}$. The range is $\{5206, 7077, 8800, 9206, 9588, 10,076, 10,444, 10,818, 11,380, 12,111\}$. For the years 86–87 (0 years after 86–87) to 02–03 (16 years after 86–87) the cost has increased from \$5206 to \$12,111.   **72. (a)** $\{(0, 4.7), (10, 5.4), (20, 6.8), (30, 8.1), (40, 9.2), (50, 9.8), (60, 11.3), (70, 12.5), (80, 12.4)\}$ **(b)** The domain is $\{0, 10, 20, \ldots, 80\}$. The range is $\{4.7, 5.4, 6.8, 8.1, 9.2, 9.8, 11.3, 12.4, 12.5\}$. For the years from 1920 to 2000, the percent over 65 has increased.

SECTION 1.2 EXERCISES

Unless indicated, the scale of each graph is one unit per tick mark.

1.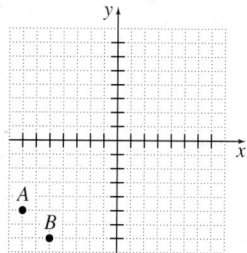

2.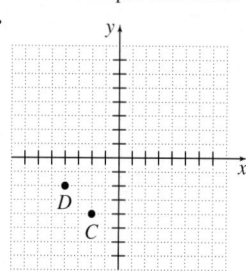

3.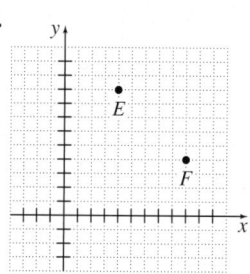

4.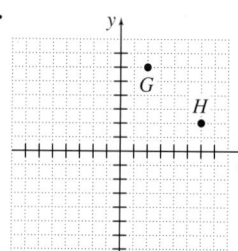

5.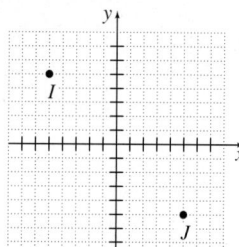

6.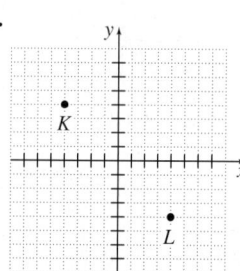

7.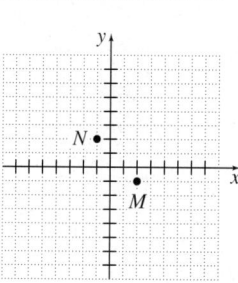

8.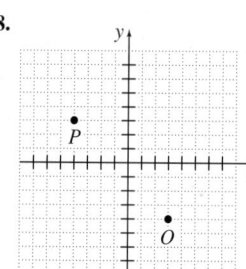

9.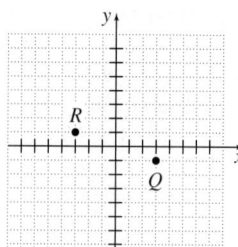

10.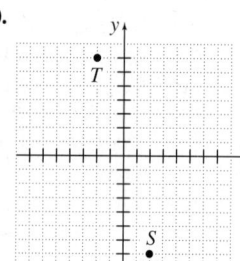

11.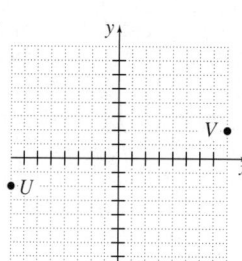

12.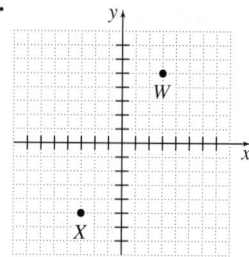

13.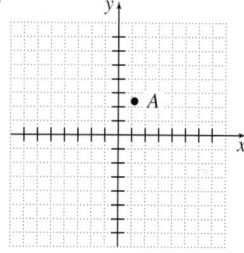

14.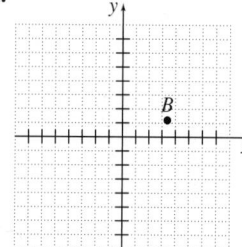

15.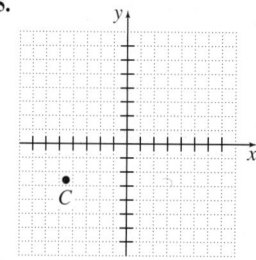

16.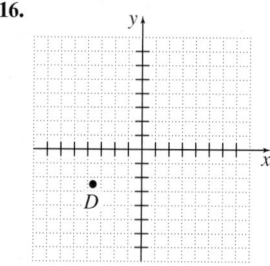

17.

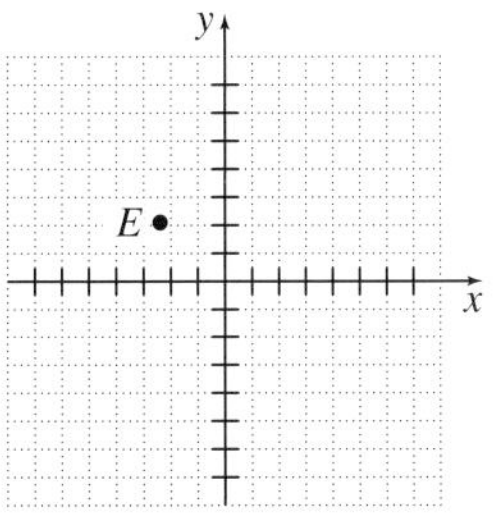

18.

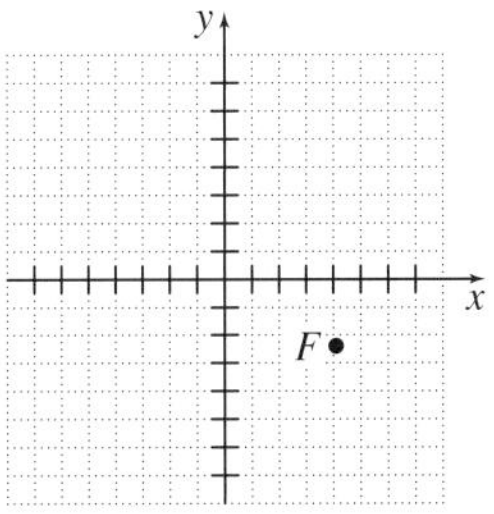

19.

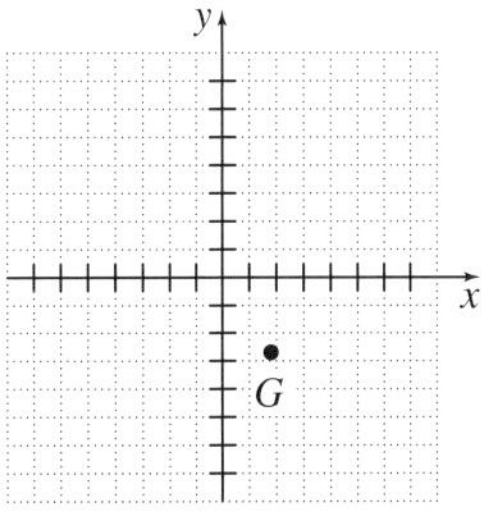

20.

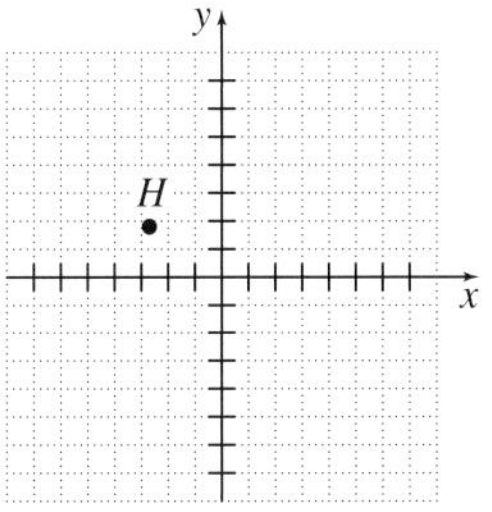

21. quadrant II   **22.** quadrant III   **23.** quadrant I   **24.** quadrant IV   **25.** quadrant III   **26.** quadrant II   **27.** y-axis   **28.** x-axis
29. quadrant IV   **30.** quadrant I   **31.** x-axis   **32.** y-axis   **33.** x-axis   **34.** origin   **35.** quadrant I   **36.** quadrant II   **37.** y-axis
38. x-axis   **39.** quadrant IV   **40.** quadrant III   **41.** quadrant III   **42.** x-axis   **43.** y-axis   **44.** quadrant IV
45. $A(8, 2), B(-9, 7), C(0, 0), D(-2, -3), E(0, 4), F(5, -6), G(-5, 0)$ **46.** $A(-7, -6), B(2, 4), C(-5, 2), D(0, -9), E(5, -5), F(9, -7), G(6, 0)$

47.

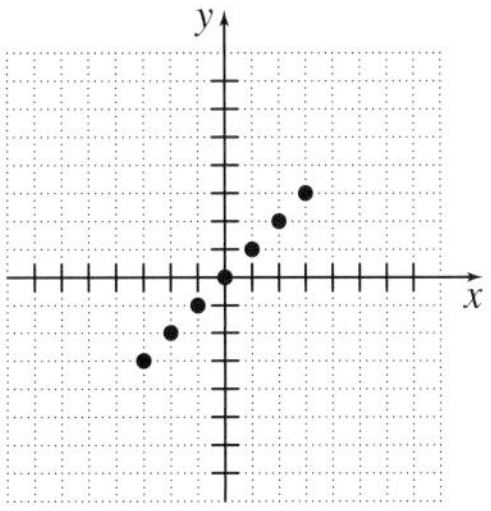

48.

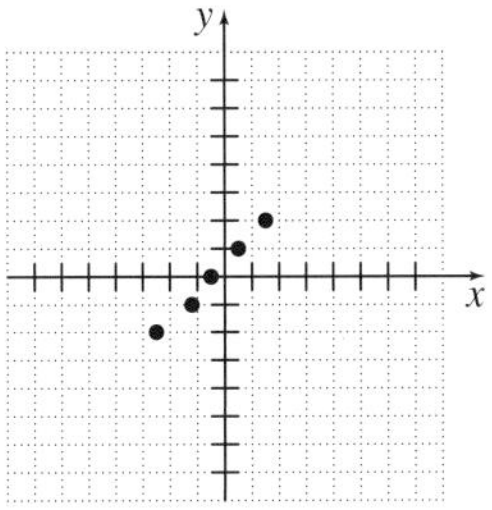

49.

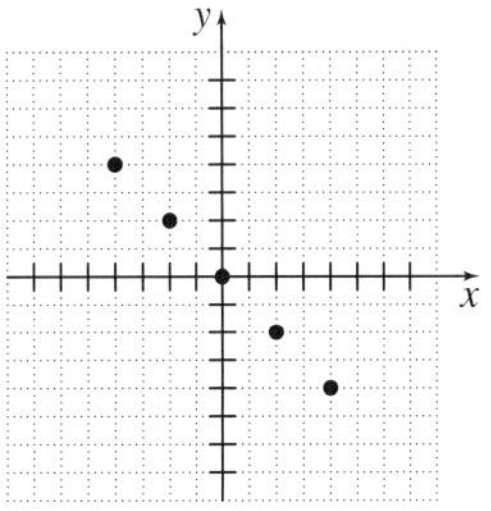

50.

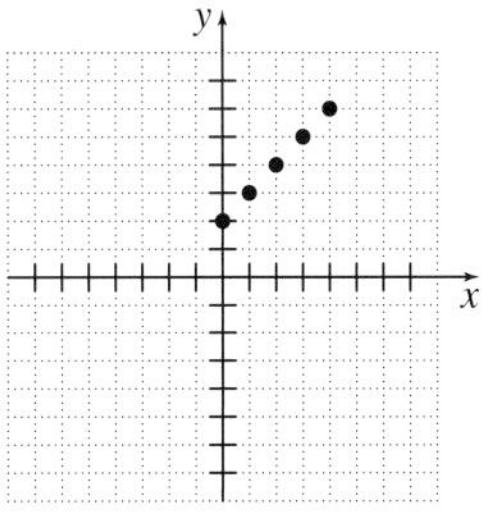

51.

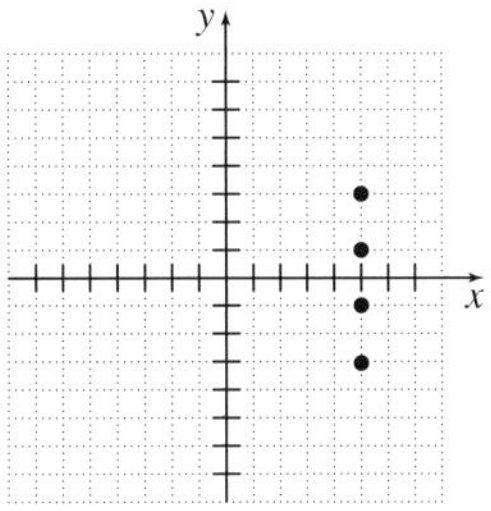

52.

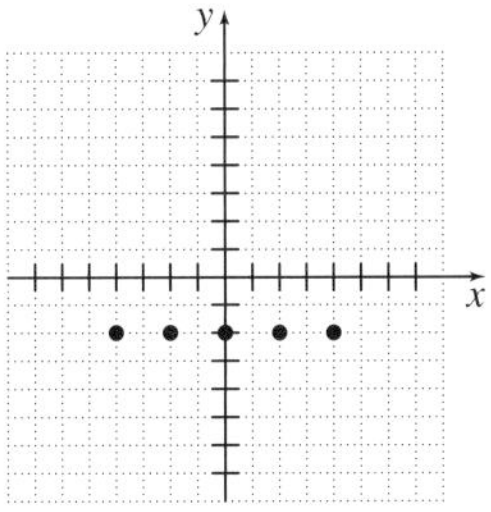

53.

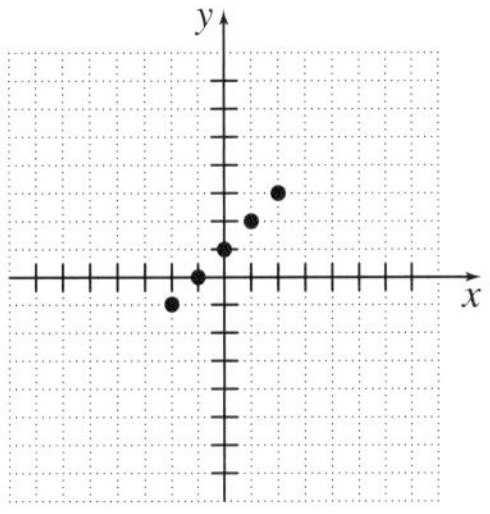

54.

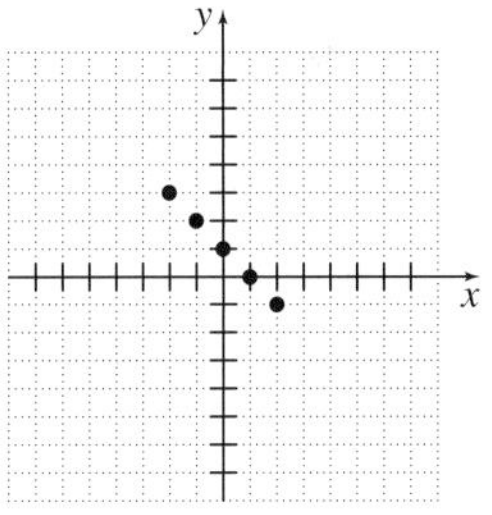

55.

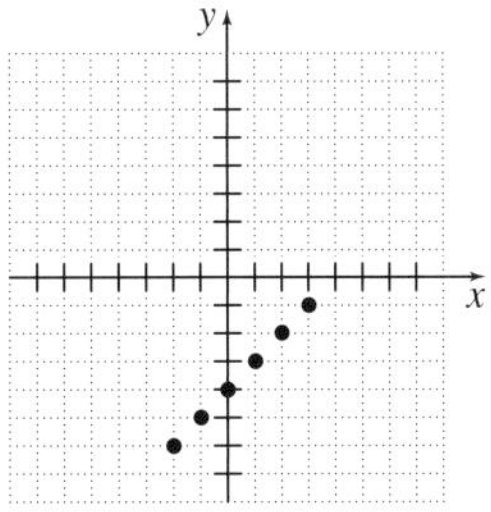

56.

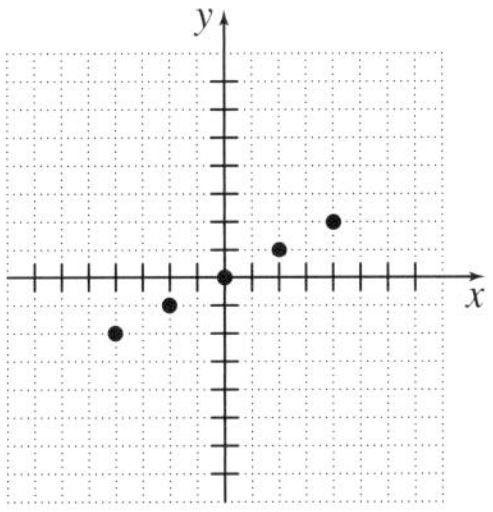

57.

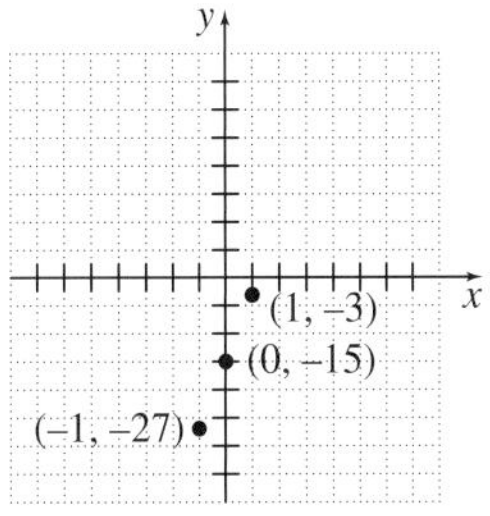

58.

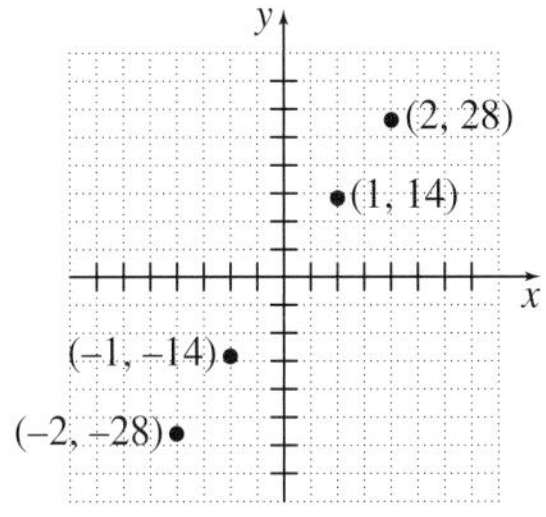

59.

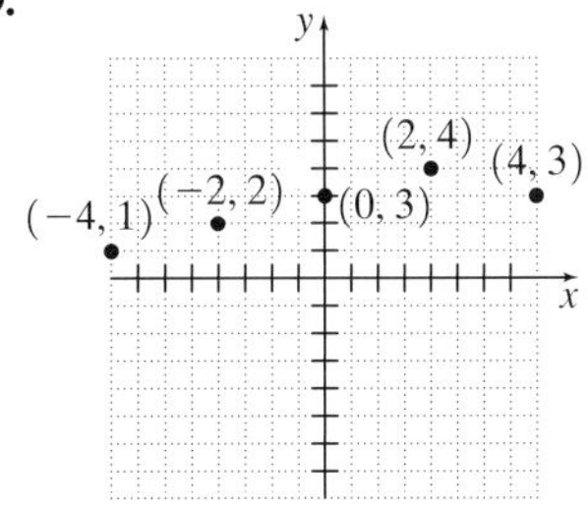

60.

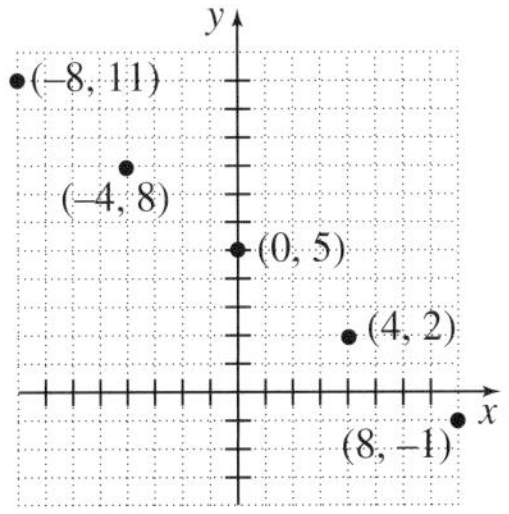

61.

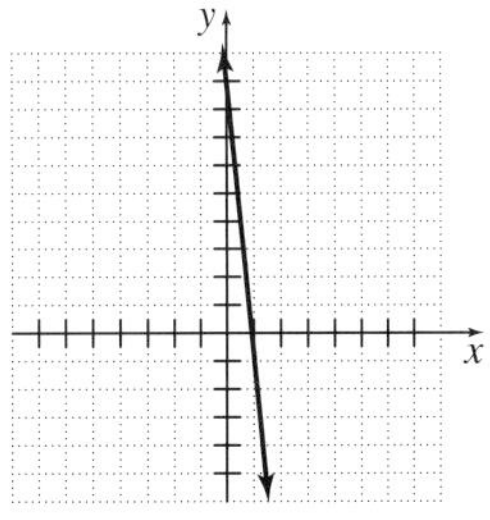

62.

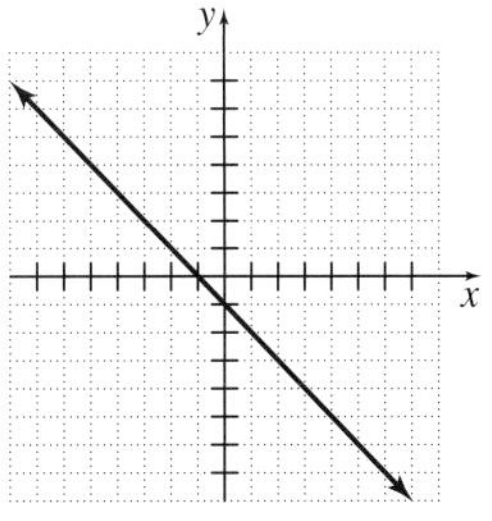

63.

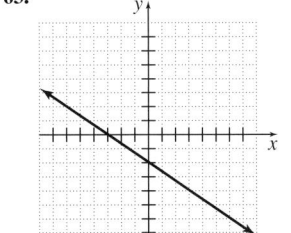

64.

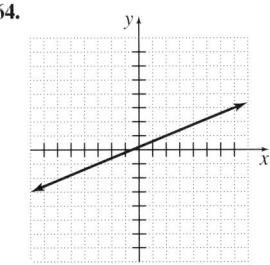

65.

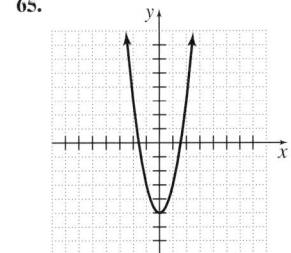

66.

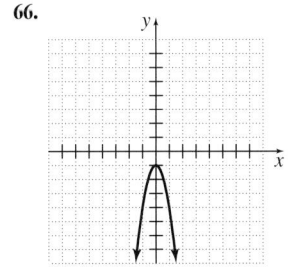

67. 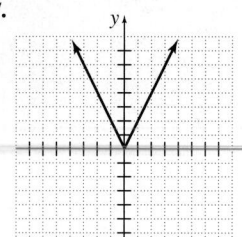 **68.**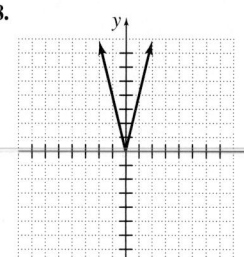

69. domain: the set of all real numbers; range: the set of all real numbers ≤ -1 **70.** domain: the set of all real numbers ≥ 3; range: the set of all real numbers **71.** domain: the set of all real numbers; range: the set of all real numbers ≥ 3 **72.** domain: $\{3\}$; range: the set of all real numbers **73.** domain: $\{1, 2, 3, 4, 5, 6\}$; range (approximately): $\{11, 15.5, 16, 16.5, 18, 23\}$ **74.** domain: $\{1, 2, 3, 4, 5, 6, 7\}$; range: $\{50, 55, 60, 64, 65, 68, 70\}$ **75.** Forcible rape: domain: the set of all real numbers x such that $0 \leq x \leq 9$; range: the set of all real numbers y such that $32 \leq y \leq 41$. Murder: domain: the set of all real numbers x such that $0 \leq x \leq 9$; range: the set of all real numbers y such that $6 \leq y \leq 9$ **76.** Aggravated assault: domain: the set of real numbers x such that $0 \leq x \leq 9$; range: the set of all real numbers y such that $310 \leq y \leq 440$. Robbery: domain: the set of all real numbers x such that $0 \leq x \leq 9$; range: the set of the real numbers y such that $150 \leq y \leq 260$ **77. (a)** domain: the set of all real numbers x such that $0 \leq x \leq 6$; range: the set of all real numbers y such that $10,900 \leq y \leq 14,500$. **(b)** domain: the set of all real numbers x such $0 \leq x \leq 6$; range: the set of all real numbers y such that $4900 \leq y \leq 6200$ **78. (a)** domain: the set of real numbers x such that $0 \leq x \leq 50$; range: the set of all real numbers x such that $19 \leq y \leq 22$ **(b)** domain: the set of real numbers x such that $0 \leq x \leq 50$; range: the set of real numbers x such that $8 \leq y \leq 12.5$

79. (a) 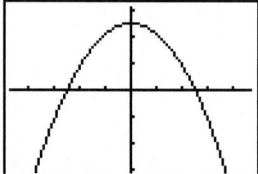   **80. (a)**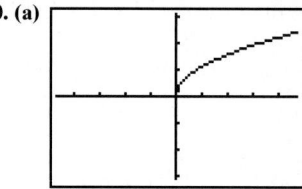

(b) domain: $0 \leq x \leq 2.5$; range: $0 \leq y \leq 100$ **(b)** domain: $x \geq 0$; range: $y \geq 0$

1.2 CALCULATOR EXERCISES

Part 1

1. Integer setting **2.** Decimal setting **3.** Standard setting

Part 2

1. Y1 $= 0.6x - 1.2$

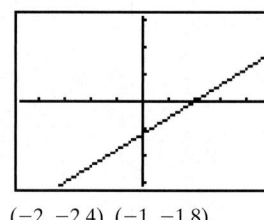

$(-2, -2.4), (-1, -1.8),$
$(0, -1.2), (1, -0.6), (2, 0)$

2. Y1 $= -0.5x + 2.2$

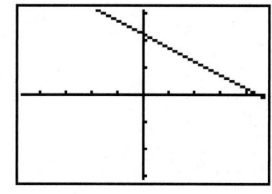

$(-2, 3.2), (-1, 2.7),$
$(0, 2.2), (1, 1.7), (2, 1.2)$

3. Y1 $= |x| - 2$

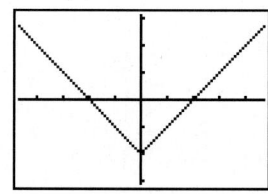

$(-2, 0), (-1, -1),$
$(0, -2), (1, -1), (2, 0)$

4. Y1 $= |x - 2|$

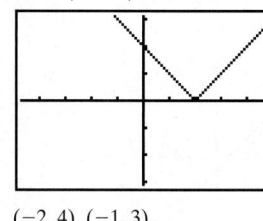

$(-2, 4), (-1, 3),$
$(0, 2), (1, 1), (2, 0)$

5. Y1 $= x - 2$

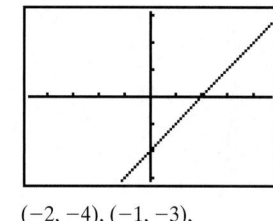

$(-2, -4), (-1, -3),$
$(0, -2), (1, -1), (2, 0)$

6. exercise 3: 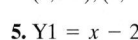 MATH ▶ 1 X,T,θ,n) − 2 ;
exercise 4: MATH ▶ 1 X,T,θ,n − 2) ;
exercise 5: X,T,θ,n − 2

SECTION 1.3 EXERCISES

1. not a function **2.** function **3.** function **4.** function **5.** not a function **6.** not a function **7.** function **8.** function **9.** function
10. not a function **11.** not a function **12.** function **13.** function **14.** not a function **15.** 112 **16.** 1012 **17.** -128 **18.** -328
19. 60 **20.** -36 **21.** 7 **22.** 14 **23.** $20a + 12$ **24.** $-20a + 12$ **25.** $20h + 52$ **26.** $20h - 28$ **27.** $20a - 68$ **28.** $-20a + 92$
29. $20a + 20h + 12$ **30.** $20x + 20h + 12$ **31.** 75 **32.** 3 **33.** 53 **34.** 11 **35.** 11.82 **36.** 4.62 **37.** $\dfrac{173}{25}$ **38.** $\dfrac{93}{25}$ **39.** $\dfrac{203}{25}$
40. $147\dfrac{1}{2}$ **41.** $2b^2 - 4b + 5$ **42.** $2b^2 + 4b + 5$ **43.** 6 **44.** 9 **45.** 24 **46.** 12 **47.** 4.5 **48.** 8.7 **49.** 22.5 **50.** 9.03 **51.** 7
52. 11 **53.** 23 **54.** 5 **55.** 31 **56.** 28 **57.** 24 **58.** 23 **59.** not a real number **60.** not a real number **61.** 25.5 **62.** 25.6
63. 24.5 **64.** 25.2 **65.** $f(x) = 1500 + 35x$; the production run costs $15,500. **66.** $f(x) = 25,000 + 550x$; the cost of production is
$1,675,000. **67.** $f(x) = 125x - 470$; the profit is $49,530. **68.** $f(x) = 1200x - 185$; the profit will be $59,815. **69.** $f(x) = 39 + 25x$; the

charge for renting a truck for three days will be $114. **70.** $f(x) = 475 + 165x$; Susie's week's pay will be $1135. **71.** $f(x) = 2.5 + x$; the charge is $9.50. **72.** $f(x) = 140 + 18.5x$; there will be a $1527.50 charge for a party of 75 guests. **73.** If 22 customers make reservations for the tour, the company will make $2398. **74.** The total monthly rental receipts will be $16,650. **75.** Let x = the number of CD's sold over 5, $f(x) = 25 + 4x$, the cost of 12 used CDs will be $53. **76.** Let x = the number of comics sold over 10, $f(x) = 35 + 1.5x$; the cost of 18 comics will be $47. **77.** Approximately $17,273 will be the cost in 2007. **78.** In 2006, the average benefit will be $1124.54. **79. (a)** In 2007, the price per gallon will be $2.47. **(b)** According to a table of values, when $x = 11(2011)$ the price will be $4.31. **80. (a)** 5% of 25-year-olds have mild to severe loss of hearing. **(b)** According to a table of values, at age 52, 24.98% (about 25%) of this age will have mild to severe loss of hearing.

1.3 CALCULATOR EXERCISES

exercises 1–6

X	Y1
65	278916
-83	-5.6E5
3.1416	45.017
1.4142	7.2426
5634	1.8E11
-3.142	-23.28

Y1◼X^3+X²+X+1

exercises 7–12

X	Y1
-8	4
0	4
-4	0
.8	4.8
-6.3	2.3
.75	4.75

Y1◼√(X²+8X+16)

exercises 13–18

X	Y1
10	1
-5	-.5
20	.33333
5.5	10
5	ERROR
.2	-1.042

Y1◼5/(X-5)

SECTION 1.4 EXERCISES

1. (a) $(-2, 0), (6, 0)$ **(b)** $(0, 3)$ **(c)** 4 **(d)** none **(e)** $x < 2$ **(f)** $x > 2$ **2. (a)** $(-1, 0), (3, 0)$ **(b)** $(0, -3)$ **(c)** none **(d)** -4 **(e)** $x > 1$ **(f)** $x < 1$ **3. (a)** $(3, 0), (-5, 0)$ **(b)** $(0, -3)$ **(c)** none **(d)** -4 **(e)** $x > -1$ **(f)** $x < -1$ **4. (a)** $(4, 0), (-8, 0)$ **(b)** $(0, 4)$ **(c)** 6 **(d)** none **(e)** $x < -2$ **(f)** $x > -2$

Unless indicated, the scale of each graph is one unit per tick mark.

5. $y = 3x - 6$

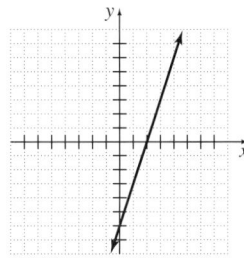

x-intercept: $(2, 0)$
y-intercept: $(0, -6)$

6. $y = 4x + 8$

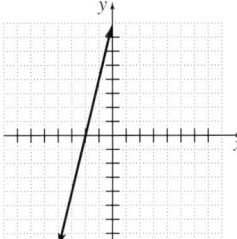

x-intercept: $(-2, 0)$
y-intercept: $(0, 8)$

7. $y = \frac{1}{2}x + 1$

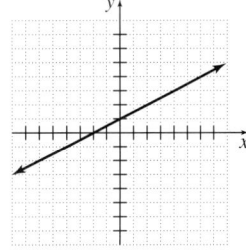

x-intercept: $(-2, 0)$
y-intercept: $(0, 1)$

8. $y = \frac{2}{3}x + 4$

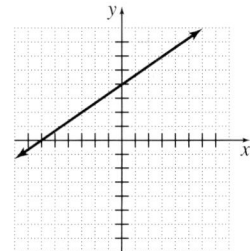

x-intercept: $(-6, 0)$
y-intercept: $(0, 4)$

9. $y = 1.2x - 6$

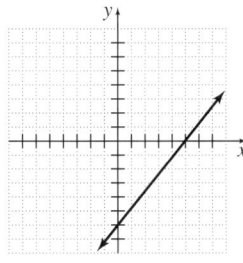

x-intercept: $(5, 0)$
y-intercept: $(0, -6)$

10. $y = 0.2x + 1$

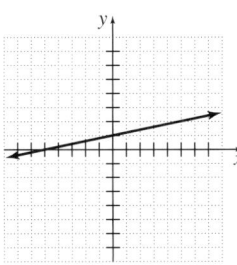

x-intercept: $(-5, 0)$
y-intercept: $(0, 1)$

11. $f(x) = -12x + 24$

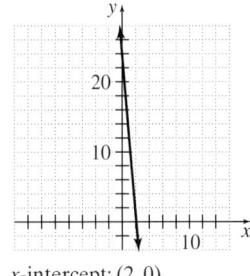

x-intercept: $(2, 0)$
y-intercept: $(0, 24)$

12. $F(x) = 15x - 45$

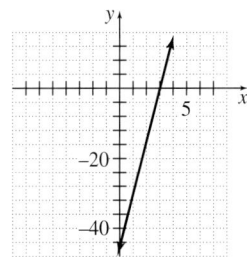

x-intercept: $(3, 0)$
y-intercept: $(0, -45)$

13. $f(x) = 9x + 15$

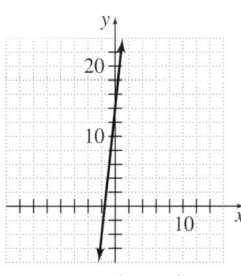

x-intercept: $\left(-\frac{5}{3}, 0\right)$
y-intercept: $(0, 15)$

14. $G(x) = -8x + 36$

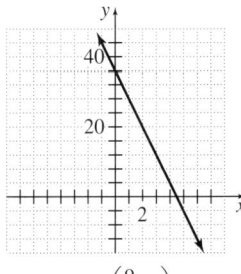

x-intercept: $\left(\frac{9}{2}, 0\right)$
y-intercept: $(0, 36)$

15. $y = x^2 - 9$

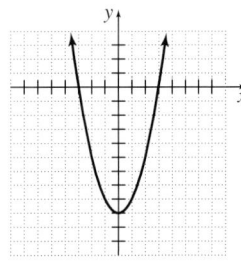

x-intercepts: $(3, 0), (-3, 0)$
y-intercept: $(0, -9)$

16. $y = x^2 - 16$

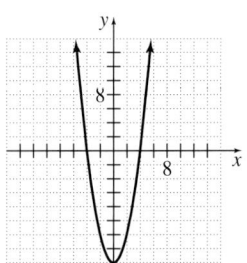

x-intercept: $(4, 0), (-4, 0)$
y-intercept: $(0, -16)$

17. $y = x^2 + 6x + 9$

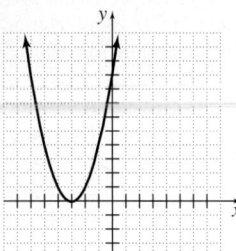

x-intercept: $(-3, 0)$
y-intercept: $(0, 9)$

18. $y = x^2 - 4x + 4$

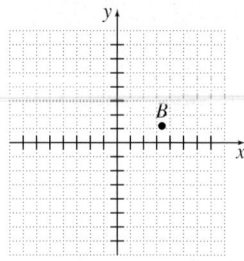

x-intercept: $(2, 0)$
y-intercept: $(0, 4)$

19. $y = 4x^2 + 4x + 1$

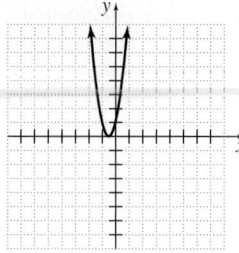

x-intercept: $\left(-\dfrac{1}{2}, 0\right)$
y-intercept: $(0, 1)$

20. $y = 4x^2 - 12x + 9$

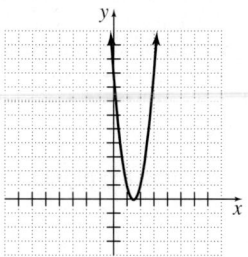

x-intercept: $\left(\dfrac{3}{2}, 0\right)$
y-intercept: $(0, 9)$

21. $g(x) = x^2 + 10x - 3$

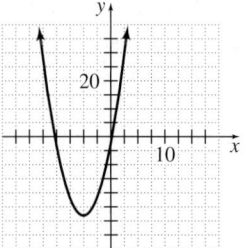

x-intercepts: $(-10.29, 0)$, $(0.29, 0)$
y-intercept: $(0, -3)$

22. $f(x) = 0.4x^2 - 0.4x - 6.5$

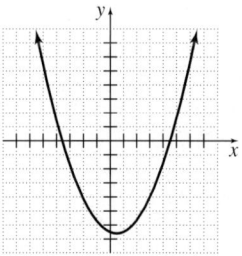

x-intercepts: $(-3.56, 0)$, $(4.56, 0)$
y-intercept: $(0, -6.5)$

23. $H(x) = x^2 - 5x - 24$

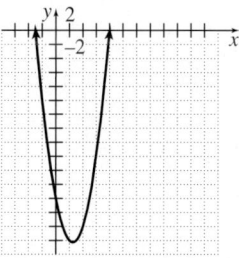

x-intercepts: $(-3, 0)$, $(8, 0)$
y-intercept: $(0, -24)$

24. $g(x) = 2x^2 + 13x - 70$

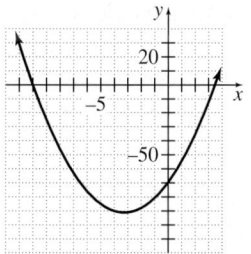

x-intercepts: $(-10, 0)$, $(3.5, 0)$
y-intercept: $(0, -70)$

25. $y = x^3 + x^2 - 2x$

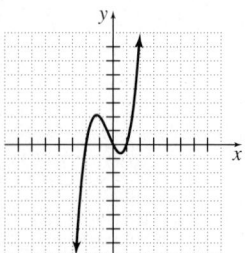

x-intercepts: $(-2, 0)$, $(0, 0)$, $(1, 0)$
y-intercept: $(0, 0)$

26. $y = x^3 + 4x^2 + 3x$

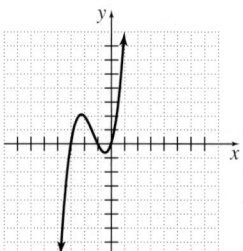

x-intercepts: $(-3, 0)$, $(-1, 0)$, $(0, 0)$
y-intercept: $(0, 0)$

27. $f(x) = x^3 + 2x^2 - x - 2$

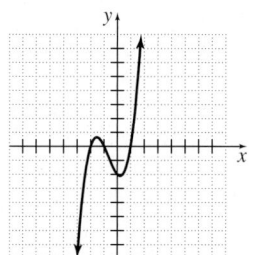

x-intercepts: $(-2, 0)$, $(-1, 0)$, $(1, 0)$
y-intercept: $(0, -2)$

28. $f(x) = x^3 + x^2 - 4x - 4$

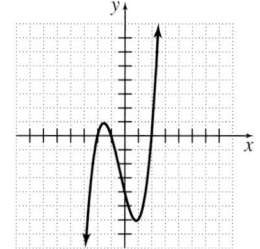

x-intercepts: $(-2, 0)$, $(-1, 0)$, $(2, 0)$
y-intercept: $(0, -4)$

29. $h(x) = |x| - 6$

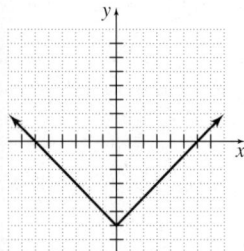

x-intercepts: $(-6, 0)$, $(6, 0)$
y-intercept: $(0, -6)$

30. $f(x) = |2x| - 6$

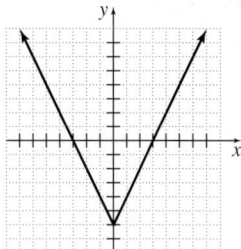

x-intercepts: $(-3, 0)$, $(3, 0)$
y-intercept: $(0, -6)$

31. $y = |2x - 3| - 1$

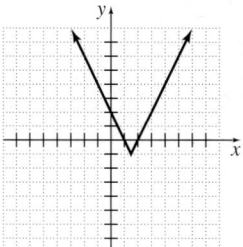

x-intercepts: $(1, 0)$, $(2, 0)$
y-intercept: $(0, 2)$

32. $y = 5 - |3x + 1|$

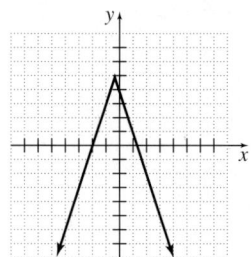

x-intercepts: $(-2, 0)$, $\left(1\dfrac{1}{3}, 0\right)$
y-intercept: $(0, 4)$

33. $y = |x^2 - 2| - 1$

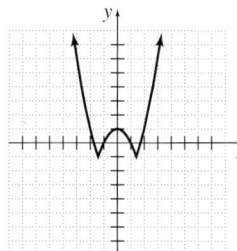

x-intercept: $(-1.73, 0), (-1, 0),$
$(1, 0), (1.73, 0)$
y-intercept: $(0, 1)$

34. $y = |x^2 - 3| - 1$

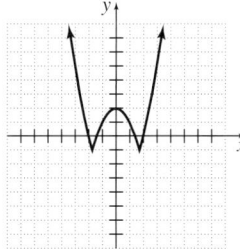

x-intercept:
$(-2, 0), (2, 0), (-1.41, 0), (1.41, 0)$
y-intercept: $(0, 2)$

35. $y = 2x + 8$

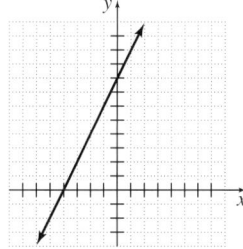

increasing for all x-values

36. $y = 4 - x$

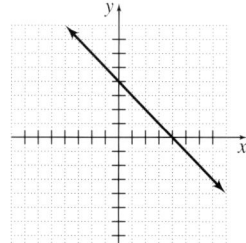

decreasing for all x-values

37. $f(x) = 3 - 2x$

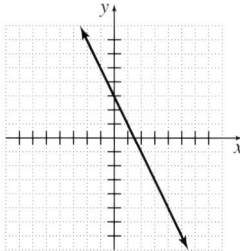

decreasing for all x-values

38. $g(x) = x - 2$

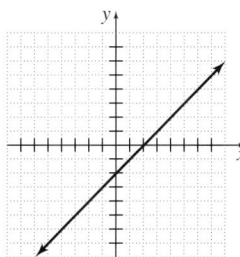

increasing for all x-values

39. $y = 1 - x^2$

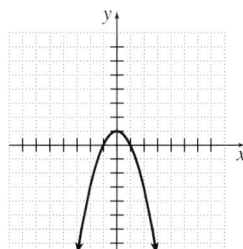

increasing for $x < 0$
decreasing for $x > 0$
relative maximum is 1 at $x = 0$

40. $y = x^2 + 1$

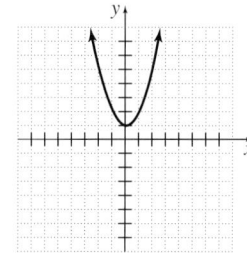

increasing for $x > 0$
decreasing for $x < 0$
relative minimum is 1 at $x = 0$

41. $g(x) = x^2 + 4x + 3$

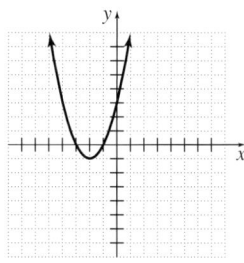

increasing for $x > -2$
decreasing for $x < -2$
relative minimum is -1 at $x = -2$

42. $h(x) = 4x - 5 - x^2$

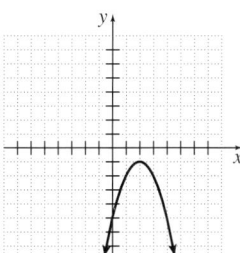

increasing for $x < 2$
decreasing for $x > 2$
relative maximum is -1 at $x = 2$

43. $y = |x + 3|$

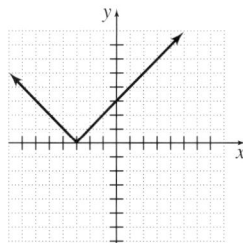

increasing for $x > -3$
decreasing for $x < -3$
relative minimum is 0 at $x = -3$

44. $y = |x| + 3$

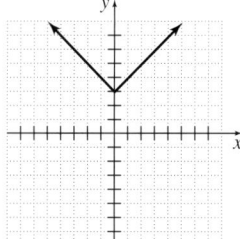

increasing for $x > 0$
decreasing for $x < 0$
relative minimum is 3 at $x = 0$

45. $f(x) = -|x + 3|$

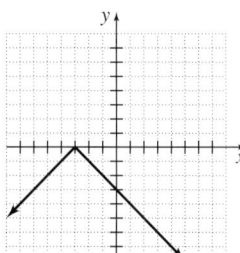

increasing for $x < -3$,
decreasing for $x > -3$
relative maximum is 0 at $x = -3$

46. $p(x) = -|x| + 3$

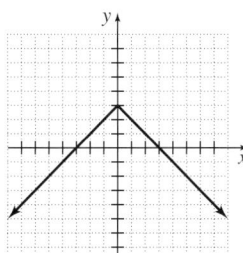

increasing for $x < 0$,
decreasing for $x > 0$
relative maximum is 3 at $x = 0$

47. $(4, 3)$ **48.** $(2, -3)$ **49.** $(-2, -2), (2, 2)$ **50.** $(-2, 5), (0, 1)$
51. $(4, 7)$ **52.** $(8, 1)$ **53.** $(-2, 3)$ **54.** $(-1, -2)$
55. $(-0.75, 5.75)$ **56.** $(-2.\overline{6}, 10.\overline{6})$ **57.** $(3.8, 12)$ **58.** $(3, 5)$
59. $(-1, 3), (1, 3)$ **60.** $(-5, 9), (5, 9)$ **61.** $(1, 3), (3, 11)$
62. $(-4, -2), (-1, 4)$ **63.** $(-2, -1), (4, 2)$ **64.** $(-3, -3), (6, 6)$
65. $(-7, 2), (7, 2)$ **66.** $(4, 4), (-12, 4)$

67. (a)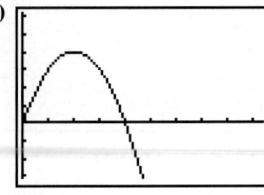

(b) relative maximum is 4000 at $x = 20$
(c) increasing: $0 < x < 20$
    decreasing: $x > 20$

68. (a)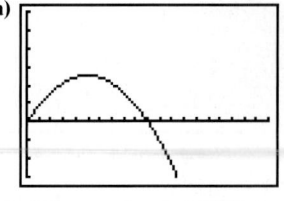

(b) relative maximum is 2500 at $x = 50$
(c) increasing: $0 < x < 50$
    decreasing: $x > 50$

69. (a) Let $p(x) = $ profit $p(x) = 5x - 50$
(b)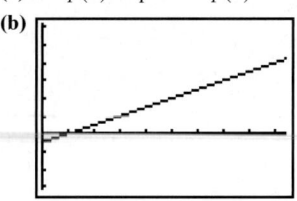

(c) no relative maximum or minimum
(d) no decreasing values increasing for $x > 0$

70. (a) Let $f(x) = $ remaining money
    $f(x) = 50,000 - 5000x$
(b)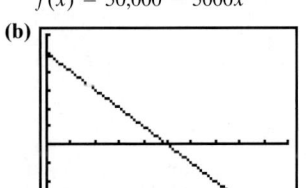

(c) no relative maximum or minimum
(d) decreasing values: $x > 0$
    no increasing values

71. (a) $f(x) = 4x + 50$
(b) $g(x) = 10x$
(c) Y1 $= 4x + 50$
    Y2 $= 10x$

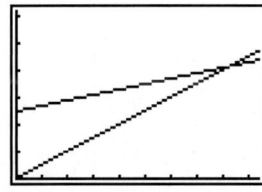

intersection at $(8.\overline{3}, 83.\overline{3})$
(d) At $x = 8.3$ containers, the cost for producing and the cost for selling are the same at $83.33. This means that nine containers must be sold to cover the costs of production.

72. (a) $f(x) = 12x + 100$
(b) $g(x) = 24x$
(c) Y1 $= 12x + 100$
    Y2 $= 24x$

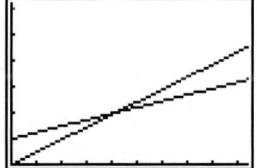

intersection at $(8.\overline{3}, 200)$
(d) At $x = 8.\overline{3}$ carvings, the cost and revenue are equal at $200. This means that nine carvings must be sold to cover the costs of production.

73. (a) $f(x) = 200 + 50x; g(x) = 75x$
(b) Y1 $= 200 + 50x$
    Y2 $= 75x$

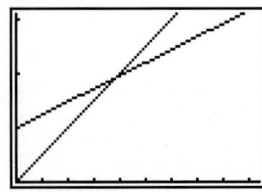

intersection at $(8, 600)$
(c) At eight credit hours, the pay is the same: $600.

74. (a) $f(x) = 25 + 10x; g(x) = 15x$
(b) Y1 $= 25 + 10x$
    Y2 $= 15x$

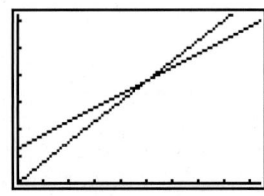

intersection at $(5, 75)$
(c) At five lawns, the pay is the same: $75.

75. (a) constant: $0 < x < 1$ increasing: $1 < x < 6$ decreasing: $6 < x < 11$ **(b)** relative maximum of 83 when $x = 6$; increasing: $0 < x < 6$; decreasing: $6 < x < 11$ **76. (a)** constant: $6 < x < 7$ increasing: $0 < x < 6$ decreasing: $7 < x < 11$ **(b)** relative maximum of 53 when $x = 6$; increasing: $0 < x < 6$; decreasing: $6 < x < 11$ **77.** x-intercepts: $(4, 0)$ and $(6, 0)$; on June 17 $(x = 4)$ and June 19 $(x = 6)$ the intensity of the last flare was 0. y-intercept: $(0, -4)$; on June 13 $(x = 0)$ the intensity of the last flare was -4.   **78.** x-intercepts (approximately): $(4.2, 0)$, $(5.1, 0)$, $(7.5, 0)$, $(9.5, 0)$; on January 25 $(x = 4.2)$, January 26 $(x = 5.1)$, January 28 $(x = 7.5)$, and January 30 $(x = 9.5)$ the customer's account had a $0 balance. y-intercept: $(0, 400)$ on January 20 $(x = 0)$, the account balance was $400.   **79.** x-intercepts are approximately $(2.5, 0)$, $(5.5, 0)$, and $(6.7, 0)$. This means that Yahoo! broke even in 1997, 2000, and 2001.   **80.** x-intercepts are approximately $(0.3, 0)$, $(4.7, 0)$, $(5.4, 0)$, and $(7.4, 0)$. This means that Northwest Airlines broke even in 1993, 1997, 1998, and 2000.

1.4 CALCULATOR EXERCISES

For problems 1–3, graphs will vary.

1. $(-4.\overline{6}, 1.\overline{4})$ and $(6, 5)$ **2.** $(-5, -1)$ and $(5, -1)$ **3.** $(-6, 18)$ and $(6, 18)$

CHAPTER 1 SUMMARY

Vocabulary Review

1. relation   **2.** independent variable   **3.** domain   **4.** range   **5.** coordinate plane   **6.** x-axis; y-axis   **7.** origin   **8.** quadrants
9. function   **10.** x-intercept; y-coordinate   **11.** y-axis; x-coordinate   **12.** increasing   **13.** decreasing   **14.** constant   **15.** relative maximum
16. relative minimum   **17.** intersection

Reflections

1–8. Answers will vary.

CHAPTER 1 SECTION-BY-SECTION REVIEW

1.

a	b
−3	13
−2	11
−1	9
0	7
1	5
2	3
3	1

2.

x	y
9	10
6	8
3	6
0	4
−3	2
−6	0
−9	−2

3.

x	y
−3	−2.4
−2	−2
−1	−1.6
0	−1.2
1	−0.8
2	−0.4
3	0

4.

x	y
−18	−30,190
−7	−1898
0	−22
6	962
21	45,002
22.5	55,457.375

5.

x	y
−2	21
−1	12
0	5
1	0
2	3
3	4

6.

x	y
−2.7	7.994
−1.9	−4.054
−0.6	−13.804
0	−14.2
0.8	−10.696
1.5	−3.85
2.4	10.136

7. Answers will vary.
Possible answer:

x	y
−2	7.7
−1	6.1
0	4.5
1	2.9
2	1.3

8. Answers will vary.
Possible answer:

x	y
−4	−12
−2	−9
0	−6
2	−3
4	0

9. Answers will vary.
Possible answer:

x	y
−4	17
−2	13
0	9
2	5
4	1

10.

x	y
−5	207
−3	91
−1	15
1	−21
3	−17
5	27

11.

x	y
−15	−1
−10	2
−5	5
0	8
5	11
10	14
15	17

12.

x	y
−3	−64.2
−2	−47.1
−1	−30
0	−12.9
1	4.2
2	21.3
3	38.4

13. (a) Let x = gallons of gas
C = total cost
C = 2.099x

(b)

x	C
5	$10.50
10	$20.99
15	$31.49
20	$41.98

14.

r	A
4	50.265
6	113.097
8	201.062
10	314.159

15.

a	b
10	80
20	70
30	60
40	50
45	45

16.

t	I
2	$240
3	$360
4	$480

17.

F	C
−23	−30.6
−14	−25.6
0	−17.8
41	5
50	10
59	15
100	37.8

18. (−10, 37), (−5, 22), (0, 7), (5, −8), (10, −23)   **19.** (−8, 0), (−7, 1), (−4, 2), (1, 3), (8, 4)
20. (−6, −5), (−3, −3), (0, −1), (3, 1), (6, 3)   **21.** (2, 1), (4, 2), (6, 3), (8, 4), (10, 5)   **22. (a)** (0, 0.9), (5, 1.9), (10, 3.2),
(15, 5.0), (20, 5.7), (21, 5.8), (22, 6.2), (23, 6.8)   **(b)** domain: {0, 5, 10, 15, 20, 21, 22, 23};
range {0.9, 1.9, 3.2, 5.0, 5.7, 5.8, 6.2, 6.8}; From 1980 to 2003, the national debt rose from $0.9 trillion to $6.8 trillion.
23. domain: {1, 3, 5, 7, 9}; range: {2, 6, 10, 14, 18}   **24.** domain: { . . . , −6, −4, −2, 0, 2, 4, 6, . . . };
range: { . . . , 6, 4, 2, 0, −2, −4, −6, . . . }   **25.** domain: {−5, −4, −3, −2, −1}; range: {−1, 3, 7, 11, 15}   **26.** domain:
{0, 0.5, 1, 1.5, 2}; range: {2.5, 2.75, 3.5, 4.75, 6.5}   **27.** domain: {−5, −4, −3, −2, −1, 0}; range: $\left\{0, 1, \sqrt{2}, \sqrt{3}, 2, \sqrt{5}\right\}$
28. domain: {−4, −2, 0, 2, 4}; range: {2.4, 4, 12, −12, −4}

29.

L	T
1	1.11
8	3.14
16	4.44
24	5.44
32	6.28

30.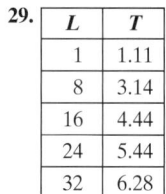

31.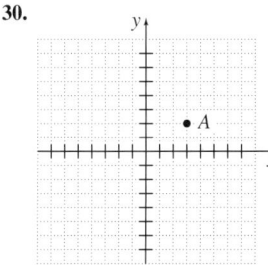

32.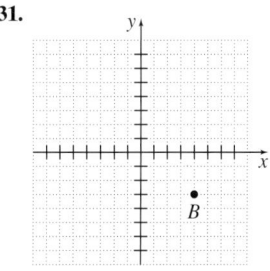

33.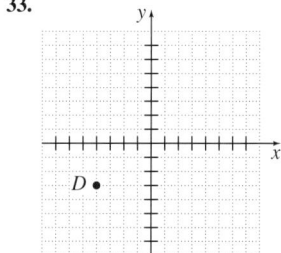

34.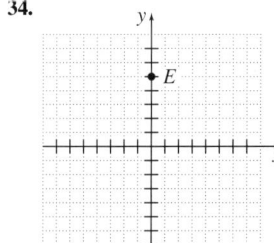

35.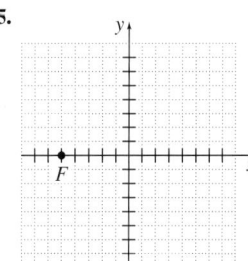

36. A = (5, 3); B = (−2, −5); C = (2, −2);
D = (−3, 5); E = (5, 0); F = (0, −4);
G = (0, 0)
37. quadrant I   **38.** quadrant III
39. quadrant IV   **40.** quadrant II
41. x-axis   **42.** y-axis   **43.** origin

44.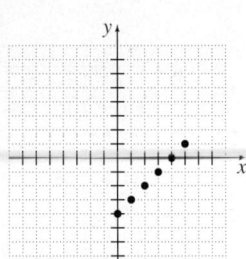

45.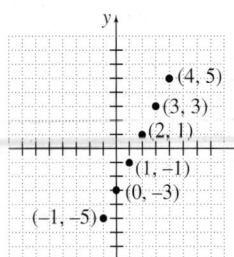

46.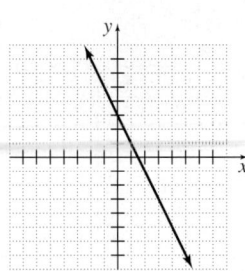

47.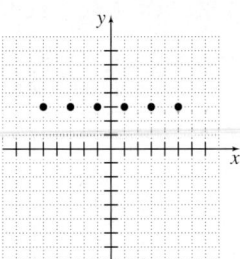

48. domain: the set of all real numbers; range: the set of all real numbers y such that $y \leq 2$ **49.** domain: the set of all real numbers; range: $\{-3\}$
50. domain: the set of all real numbers x such that $0 \leq x \leq 3$; range (approximately): the set of all real numbers y such that $51{,}400 \leq y \leq 56{,}000$

51. (a) $y = 10x + 40$

(b)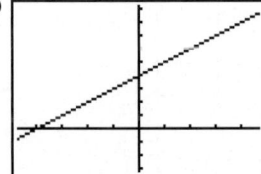

(c) domain: $\{1, 2, 3, 4, \dots\}$
     range: $\{50, 60, 70, 80, \dots\}$

52. (a) $y = x^2$

(b)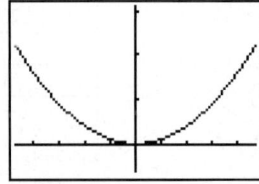

(c) domain: the set of all real numbers x such
     that $x > 0$; range: the set of all real num-
     bers y such that $y > 0$

53. not a function   **54.** function   **55.** not a function   **56.** function   **57.** -39 **58.** 97   **59.** 3   **60.** 27.8   **61.** $1 - 4h$ **62.** $4b + 13$

63. 44   **64.** 14   **65.** -2.25 **66.** $5a^2 + a - 4$ **67.** $5a^2 - a - 4$ **68.** $-\dfrac{63}{16}$ **69.** -2 **70.** 0   **71.** 6

72. Let x = number of widgets, $C(x)$ = cost, $C(x) = 4500 + 17x$; $C(1200) = \$24{,}900$ **73.** Let x = number attending, $T(x)$ = total charge,
$T(x) = 1500 + 125x$; $T(20) = \$4000$ **74.** Let x = number of painted faces, $P(x)$ = profit, $P(x) = 1.50x - 15$; $P(135) = \$187.50$
75. Net sales are $\$319.7$ billion.   **76. (a)** none   **(b)** $(0, 7)$ **(c)** none   **(d)** 1   **(e)** $x > 3$ **(f)** $x < 3$

77. $y = 3x + 9$

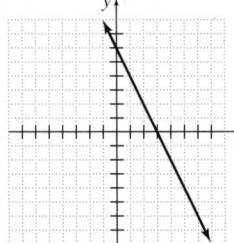

x-intercept: $(-3, 0)$
y-intercept: $(0, 9)$

78. $y = \dfrac{3}{4}x - 9$

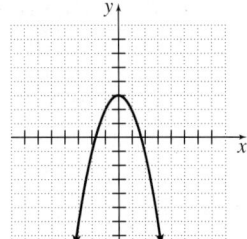

x-intercept: $(12, 0)$
y-intercept: $(0, -9)$

79. $y = x^2 - 0.36$

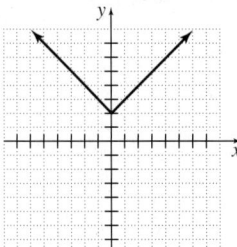

x-intercept: $(-0.6, 0)$, $(0.6, 0)$
y-intercept: $(0, -0.36)$

80. $y = |x| - 4$

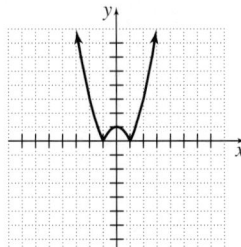

x-intercept: $(-4, 0)$, $(4, 0)$
y-intercept: $(0, -4)$

81. $h(x) = 6 - 2x$

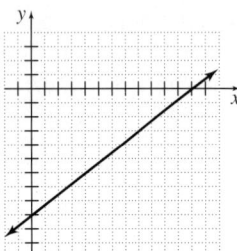

decreasing for all values of x

82. $y = 3 - x^2$

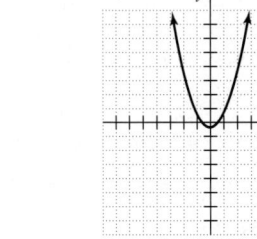

increasing for $x < 0$
decreasing for $x > 0$
relative maximum is 3 at $x = 0$

83. $y = |x| + 2$

increasing for $x > 0$
decreasing for $x < 0$
relative minimum is 2 at $x = 0$

84. $y = |x^2 - 1|$

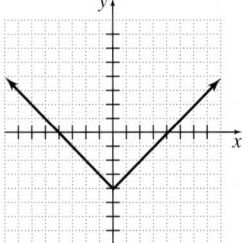

increasing for $-1 < x < 0, x > 1$
decreasing for $x < -1, 0 < x < 1$
relative maximum is 1 at $x = 0$
relative minima are 0 at $x = -1$
and $x = 1$

85. $(3, 4)$ **86.** $(-2, -2), (3, 3)$ **87.** $(-7, 2), (-3, 2)$

88.

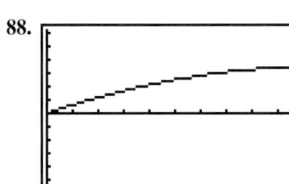

increasing for $x > 0$
no relative maximum or minimum
no decreasing values

89. Let $R(x) =$ revenue, $R(x) = 10.45x$

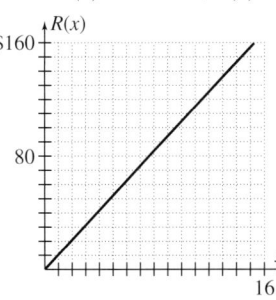

no relative minimum or maximum
increasing for $x > 0$

90. Let $f(x) =$ balance
$f(x) = 216 - 4.5x$

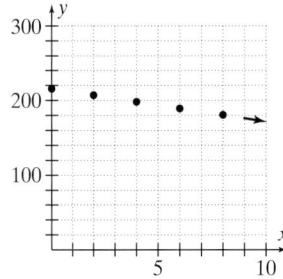

no relative minimum or maximum
decreasing for $x > 0$

91. (a) $f(x) = 400 + 65x$
   $g(x) = 100x$
(b) Y1 $= 400 + 65x$
   Y2 $= 100x$

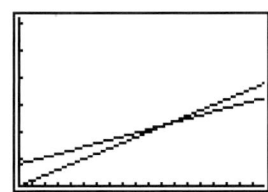

intersect at approximately $(11.4, 1143)$
(c) At about 11.4 credit hours, the stipend is the same at about $1143 for both options.

92. (a) $f(x) = 500 + 12x$
   $g(x) = 25x$
(b) Y1 $= 500 + 12x$
   Y2 $= 25x$

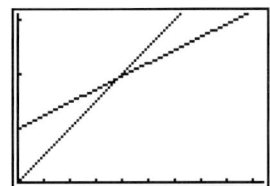

intersect at approximately $(38.5, 961.5)$
(c) At about 38.5 items, the cost to produce and the revenue are equal at about $961.50 each. This means that 39 items must be sold to break even.

93. (a) increasing: $0 < x < 6$, decreasing: $6 < x < 11$ **(b)** relative maximum of 53 when $x = 6$ **(c)** y-intercept: $(0, -11.5)$; In January $(x = 0)$ the average minimum temperature is $-11.5°F$.   **(d)** x-intercepts: $(1.2, 0)$ and $(10.9, 0)$; In March $(x = 1.2)$ and December $(x = 10.9)$ the average minimum temperature is $0°F$.   **94.** y-intercept: $(0, 5)$; When time is 0 (at time of release) the height is 5 feet; x-intercept: $(0.7, 0)$; The ball hit the device 0.7 second after release.

CHAPTER 1 MIXED REVIEW

1. 0   **2.** 18   **3.** 7.2   **4.** 11.7   **5.** $b + 9$ **6.** $-h + 8$ **7.** 0   **8.** 0   **9.** -6.25 **10.** $v^2 - 3v - 4$ **11.** $v^2 + 3v - 4$

12. $-\dfrac{14}{9}$ **13.** 4   **14.** 8   **15.** 16   **16.** function   **17.** not a function

18. $y = 4.8x - 1.2$

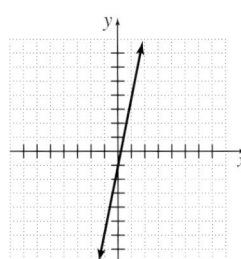

x-intercept at $(0.25, 0)$
y-intercept at $(0, -1.2)$
increasing for all x-values

19. $y = \dfrac{2}{5}x + 4$

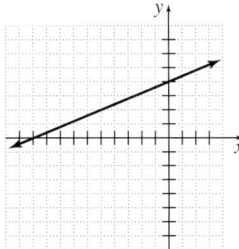

x-intercept at $(-10, 0)$
y-intercept at $(0, 4)$
increasing for all x-values

20. $y = x^2 - 1.21$

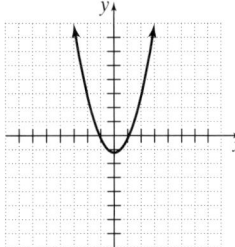

x-intercepts at $(-1.1, 0)$
and $(1.1, 0)$
y-intercepts at $(0, -1.21)$
increasing for $x > 0$
decreasing for $x < 0$
relative minimum is -1.21 at $x = 0$

21. $y = 2 - |x|$

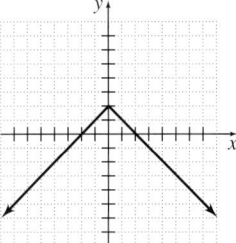

x-intercepts at $(-2, 0), (2, 0)$
y-intercept at $(0, 2)$
increasing for $x < 0$
decreasing for $x > 0$
relative maximum is 2 at $x = 0$

22. $(-3, -4)$ **23.** $(0, 0), (3, 9)$ **24.** $(-1, 2), (3, 6)$ **25.** domain: $\{2, 4, 6, 8, 10\}$; range: $\{1, 2, 3, 4, 5\}$
26. domain: $\{\ldots, -6, -4, -2, 0, 2, 4, 6, \ldots\}$; range: $\{3\}$ **27.** domain: $\{-5, -4, -3, -2, -1\}$; range: $\{25, 16, 9, 4, 1\}$
28. domain: $\{0, 0.5, 1, 1.5, 2\}$; range: $\{-1.5, -1.25, -0.5, 0.75, 2.5\}$ **29.** $(-6, 60), (-3, 36), (0, 12), (3, -12), (6, -36)$
30. $(3, 1), (2, 2), \left(1, \sqrt{7}\right), \left(0, \sqrt{10}\right), \left(-1, \sqrt{13}\right), (-2, 4)$ **31.** $(-7, 1), (0, 5), (7, 9), (14, 13), (21, 17)$

32.

x	y
−4	119
−2	33
0	−5
2	5
4	63

33.

x	y
−12	−14
−8	−11
−4	−8
0	−5
4	−2
8	1
12	4

34.

x	y
−2	25.2
−1	20.5
0	15.8
1	11.1
2	6.4

35.

x	y
−2	35
$-\frac{3}{4}$	0
0	−15
$\frac{3}{4}$	−25.5
5	0

36.

x	y
−6	95
−3	20
0	1
3	32
6	119
9	260

37.

x	y
−3.7	63.014
−2.2	26.504
−0.7	10.694
0	10.4
0.8	15.584
2.3	41.174
3.8	87.464

38. Answers will vary.
Possible answer:

x	y
−1	−6.1
0	−1.6
1	2.9

39. Answers will vary.
Possible answer:

x	y
−4	2
0	3
4	4

40. Answers will vary.
Possible answer:

x	y
−3	19
0	10
3	1

41. $\left(\frac{1}{4}, 1.5708\right), \left(\frac{1}{2}, 3.1416\right), (1, 6.2832), \left(\frac{3}{2}, 9.4248\right), (2, 12.566)$

42.

s	A
3	9
5	25

43.

a	b
30	150
60	120
90	90
120	60
150	30

44.

t	I
2	240
3	360
4	480

45.

C	F
−10	14
−5	23
0	32
5	41
10	50
15	59
20	68
25	77

46. (a) Let x = number of disks, C = cost
$C = 7.95x$

(b)

x	C
1	7.95
2	15.90
3	23.85
4	31.80
5	39.75

47. Let x = number of items, $C(x)$ = total cost, $C(x) = 2500 + 12x$; the cost is \$22,300. **48.** Let x = number of hours, $C(x)$ = cost, $C(x) = 15 + 2x$; the cost is \$35. **49.** Let x = number of people, $C(x)$ = total charges, $C(x) = 275 + 9.50x$; the total charges are \$1557.50. **50.** Let x = number of admissions, $P(x)$ = profit, $P(x) = 4x - 185$; the profit is \$1055.

51. Let $F(x)$ = amount of fluid remaining
$F(x) = 250 - 3.5x$

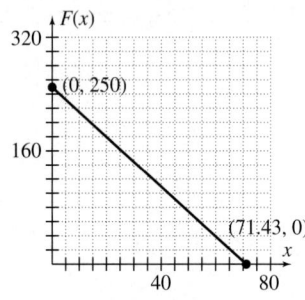

decreasing for $x > 0$

52. Let $F(x)$ = total amount in savings
$F(x) = 1000 + 50x$

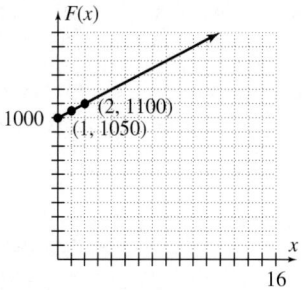

increasing for $x > 0$

53. (a) Let x = number of years
$f(x)$ = first option amount
$g(x)$ = second option amount
$f(x) = 25{,}000 + 5000x$
$g(x) = 6000x$
(b) Y1 = 25,000 + 5000x
Y2 = 6000x

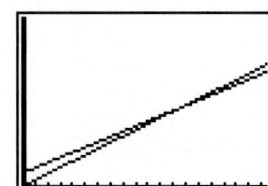

intersect at (25, 150,000)
(c) At 25 years, the money received is the
same: \$150,000.

54. (a) Let $f(x)$ = total acquisition cost
$g(x)$ = revenue
$f(x) = 22x + 600$
$g(x) = 75x$
(b) Y1 = 22x + 600
Y2 = 75x

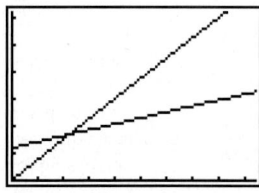

intersect at approximately
(11.32, 849.06)
(c) At about 11.32 appliances, the total acquisition cost and total revenue are equal
at about \$849.06. This means that 12 ap-
pliances must be sold to break even.

55. **(a)** $\{(0, 7.1), (5, 7.2), (10, 5.6), (15, 5.6), (20, 4.0)\}$ **(b)** domain: $\{0, 5, 10, 15, 20\}$; range: $\{4.0, 5.6, 7.1, 7.2\}$ From 1980 ($x = 0$) to 2000 ($x = 20$), the unemployment rate fluctuated from 4.0% to 7.2%. **56.** **(a)** domain: the set of all real numbers x such that $0 \le x \le 5$; range: the set of all real numbers y such that $505 \le y \le 775$ **(b)** domain: the set of all real numbers x such that $0 \le x \le 5$; range: the set of all real numbers y such that $675 \le y \le 835$ **57.** **(a)** A person needs to earn about \$114,000 in 2005 to receive \$35,000 in 2045. **(b)** A person needs to earn about \$114,000 in 2005 to receive \$35,000 in 2045. **58.** **(a)** increasing: $0 < x < 1$; decreasing: $1 < x < 4$ **(b)** relative maximum of 2 when $x = 1$ **(c)** x-intercepts: $(0.5, 0), (1.5, 0)$; In the first quarter and the second quarter after the fourth quarter of 2003, the profit/loss margin was 0%; y-intercept: $(0, -3)$; In the fourth quarter of 2003 ($x = 0$), the loss margin was 3%.

CHAPTER 1 TEST

1.

x	y
-9	0
0	-9
3	60

2. **(a)**

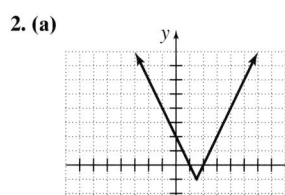

(b) none **(c)** -1 **(d)** $x > 1.5$ **(e)** $x < 1.5$ **(f)** $(2, 0)$ and $(1, 0)$ **(g)** $(0, 2)$
3. **(a)** no, because it does not pass the vertical-line test. **(b)** the set of all real numbers x such that $x \ge -4$ **(c)** the set of all real numbers **4.** $A = (1, 2); B = (-2, -4);$ $C = (-5, 3); D = (2, -5); E = (0, -2)$ **5.** quadrant IV

6.

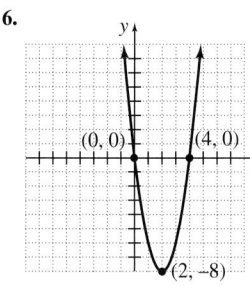

7.

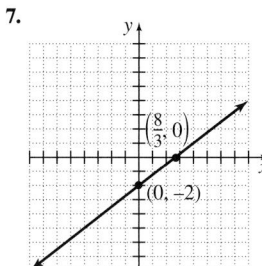

8.

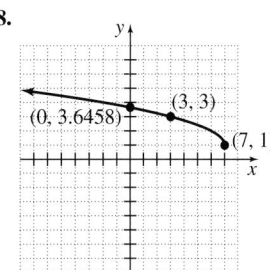

9. 8 **10.** 3 **11.** $\frac{1}{2}a + 6$ **12.** $\frac{1}{2}a + 7$ **13.** **(a)** Let $C(x) = $ cost of production, $C(x) = 450 + 21.50x$ **(b)** Let $R(x) = $ revenue, $R(x) = 30.50x$ **(c)** $(50, 1525)$ **(d)** When 50 items are produced and sold, the company will break even; the revenue and cost of 50 items is \$1525. **14.** The cost is \$5825. **15.** $(2, -4)$ **16.** **(a)** $\{(0, 24.5), (1, 24.5), (2, 24.5), (3, 24.8), (4, 25), (5, 25), (6, 25.1), (7, 25.1), (8, 25.1), (9, 25.3)\}$ **(b)** domain: $\{0, 1, 2, \ldots 9\}$; range: $\{24.5, 24.8, 25, 25.1, 25.3\}$; In 1993 ($x = 0$) the median age of women at their first marriage was 24.5. In 2002 ($x = 9$), the median age was 25.3. This supports the initial statement. **17.** domain: the set of all real numbers x such that $0 \le x \le 9$; range: the set of all real numbers y such that $26.5 \le y \le 27.1$ **18.** In 2008, the median income will be \$65,475. **19.** **(a)** x-intercepts: $(1.8, 0)$ and $(8.2, 0)$; In 1995 ($x = 1.8$) and 2002 ($x = 8.2$), the net income was \$0. **(b)** maximum; Delta's maximum net income was \$1303 million in 2000. **(c)** minimum; Delta's minimum net income was a loss of \$1272 million in 2003. **(d)** decreasing **20.** Answers will vary.

CHAPTERS P–1 CUMULATIVE REVIEW

1. $0, 12$ **2.** $0, 12$ **3.** $-\frac{2}{3}; 0; 12; 1\frac{4}{5}; -0.33$ **4.** $\sqrt{7}$ **5.** $>$ **6.** $>$ **7.** $<$

8.

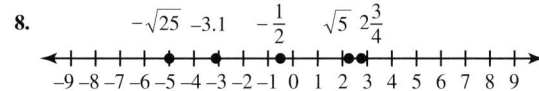

9. -15 **10.** -2.56 **11.** 3 **12.** $-\frac{31}{24}$ **13.** $-1\frac{37}{40}$ **14.** $\frac{63}{640}$ **15.** -62.208 **16.** 0 **17.** 96 **18.** 31 **19.** -6.2 **20.** 0 **21.** -8

22. $\frac{4}{5}$ **23.** -1.095 **24.** not a real number **25.** 1.051 **26.** 1 **27.** 1 **28.** indeterminate **29.** -4096 **30.** 4096 **31.** 100

32. 3.05×10^{-6} **33.** -4.2356×10^6 **34.** 0.0356 **35.** 678,000,000 **36.** 7 **37.** **(a)** 6 **(b)** $a^3, -2a^2, a, -2a^3, 7a$ **(c)** -5

(d) $-a^3 - 2a^2 + 8a - 5$ **38.** $4y + z$ **39.** $\frac{3}{4}y - \frac{43}{48}$ **40.** $-6x - 12$ **41.** No

42.

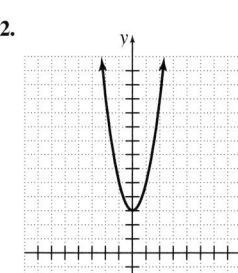

43. domain: the set of all real numbers; range: the set of all real numbers y such that $y \ge 3$ **44.** Yes, since all possible vertical lines cross the graph a maximum of one time. **45.** The relative minimum is 3 when $x = 0$. **46.** $x > 0$

47. **(a)** -2 **(b)** $\frac{1}{3}h - 4$ **48.** The volume is 13.78125 ft^3.

49. Kelsie's interest is \$110; the total investment is \$610.

50. Let $C(x) = $ cost, $C(x) = 35 + 2.80x$; the cost of producing 150 ornaments in one production run is \$455.

CHAPTER 2

SECTION 2.1 EXERCISES

1. linear   **2.** linear   **3.** nonlinear   **4.** linear   **5.** linear   **6.** nonlinear   **7.** nonlinear   **8.** nonlinear   **9.** linear   **10.** linear

11. $2x - 7 = x + 2$; $x = 9$ **12.** $\frac{1}{2}x - 3 = x - 1$; $x = -4$ **13.** $0.5x + 1.25 = 0.5(x + 2.5)$; $x = $ all real numbers

14. $\frac{2}{3}x + 1 = x + 2 - \frac{1}{3}(x + 3)$; $x = $ all real numbers   **15.** $x - (4.5 - 0.5x) = 1.5(x + 2)$; no solution   **16.** $x + 3(x - 5) = 2(2x - 3)$;

no solution   **17.** $\frac{1}{3}x + 1 = \frac{3}{2}x - 1$; noninteger between 1 and 2   **18.** $x - 1 = 3x + 4$; noninteger between -2 and -3 **19.** 14   **20.** 5

21. -6 **22.** -8 **23.** 7   **24.** 0   **25.** all real numbers   **26.** 0.75   **27.** no solution   **28.** no solution   **29.** no solution

30. all real numbers   **31.** 0.5   **32.** all real numbers   **33.** $3x + 2 = 4 - x$; $x = \frac{1}{2}$ **34.** $0.4x - 1.5 = 1 - 0.6x$; $x = 2.5$

35. $\frac{1}{2}x + 5 = 4 - 0.5(6 - x)$; no solution   **36.** $x + \frac{1}{3}(x + 6) = \frac{4}{3}(x + 3)$; no solution   **37.** -3 **38.** all real numbers   **39.** no solution

40. 2   **41.** all real numbers   **42.** -1 **43.** 15   **44.** all real numbers   **45.** no solution   **46.** -8 **47.** 3   **48.** approximately 0.727
49. all real numbers   **50.** no solution   **51.** Mathew can rent the SUV for 10 days.   **52.** Claudette can rent the SUV for 8 days.   **53.** Weston's budget allows him 225 minutes over 500 minutes.   **54.** Weston's budget allows him 200 minutes over 750 minutes.   **55.** The number of pages is 20.
56. The number of miles is 80.   **57.** Any number of rolls will have the same charge for both.   **58.** There is no number of hours for which the fee will be equal.   **59.** The factory should produce 20 pairs of shoes.   **60.** The cost of production will equal the revenue when 10 baskets are produced and sold.   **61.** She can spend $29.   **62.** She should lose 1 pound.   **63.** The seventh day temperature is 78°F.   **64.** The fifth day temperature is 51°F.

2.1 CALCULATOR EXERCISES

Part 1

1. 22   **2.** -12 **3.** 250   **4.** -500

Part 2

Students should experiment with same exercises.

SECTION 2.2 EXERCISES

1. 18   **2.** -104 **3.** 116   **4.** 76   **5.** -7.98 **6.** -4.606 **7.** 0   **8.** $\frac{14}{9}$ **9.** -3 **10.** 50   **11.** -16.85 **12.** 22.6   **13.** -8 **14.** -4

15. 36   **16.** 123   **17.** $-\frac{17}{16}$ **18.** $\frac{17}{30}$ **19.** -90 **20.** 0   **21.** 81   **22.** -62 **23.** -0.02 **24.** -3.7 **25.** $\frac{2}{5}$ **26.** -16 **27.** 4.88

28. -69.2 **29.** -57 **30.** $16\frac{1}{5}$ **31.** 3   **32.** 17   **33.** -2.398 **34.** -10 **35.** $\frac{1}{3}$ **36.** $-\frac{5}{7}$ **37.** 14   **38.** -41 **39.** -1 **40.** 6.3

41. 0   **42.** -1 **43.** His gross pay was $2351.58.   **44.** Her deductions were $387.24.   **45.** It was marked down $41.46.   **46.** The original price was $30.49.   **47.** There was $4.37 sales tax.   **48.** The loan value is $93,000.   **49.** They must sell 580 packets.   **50.** It will take 18 months.
51. The estate was worth $75,400.   **52.** The price was about $5.99.   **53.** Sixteen dogs is the maximum number allowed.   **54.** There are 109 mountains worldwide that are over 24,000 feet high.   **55.** You must place $6400 into savings.   **56.** You borrowed $3500.   **57.** The mechanic needs about 5.7 gallons of solution.   **58.** The gardener needs about 2.5 pints of solution.   **59.** 13,696,000 males were living at home.
60. 13,591,304 females were living at home.   **61.** The average speed was about 65.8 mph.   **62.** The trip had an average of 21 miles per gallon.
63. The quarterly profits were $63,650.   **64.** The jackpot was $45,990,000.   **65.** The height is 17.5 feet.   **66.** The height must be 5 feet.
67. The height must be about 6 feet.   **68.** The radius is about 16 inches.   **69.** The 2000 estimated population is 281,400,000 people.   **70.** The height of the volcano is 19,400 ft.   **71.** A single hair is 100,000 nanometers wide.   **72.** The temperature of the Sun is approximately 3,167,000°F.

2.2 CALCULATOR EXERCISES

1. about 461.2 feet   **2.** about 55.3 inches   **3.** $2\frac{1}{8}$ per share   **4.** 6 pieces   **5.** about 12 gallons   **6.** about 123 square feet   **7.** 62.5 grams

8. 60 grams; does not agree; difference may be round-off error   **9.** about 16.7 feet per second

SECTION 2.3 EXERCISES

1. -2 **2.** 3   **3.** -44 **4.** 12   **5.** 0   **6.** 4.5   **7.** 3.3   **8.** 5   **9.** 7.2   **10.** 1   **11.** $\frac{1}{2}$ **12.** $\frac{2}{3}$ **13.** $\frac{1}{2}$ **14.** -1 **15.** 30

16. -2 **17.** 1   **18.** 0   **19.** 8   **20.** -3 **21.** all real numbers   **22.** all real numbers   **23.** no solution   **24.** no solution   **25.** 2

26. -5 **27.** -6.6 **28.** 2.7   **29.** -1 **30.** 6   **31.** 10   **32.** 8   **33.** 6   **34.** 10   **35.** all real numbers   **36.** no solution   **37.** $\frac{10}{9}$

38. $\frac{28}{3}$ **39.** $-\frac{1}{18}$ **40.** $\frac{9}{5}$ **41.** -120 **42.** -66 **43.** $-\frac{8}{13}$ **44.** $-\frac{3}{8}$ **45.** 107.5   **46.** 3.6   **47.** 0   **48.** 8.8   **49.** -0.05 **50.** 70

51. The monthly payments would be $85.50.   **52.** The monthly charge would be $140.   **53.** He can rent the car for 13 days.   **54.** She can rent the minivan for 9 days.   **55.** The rental plans will cost the same for 74 miles.   **56.** The rental plans will cost the same for 74 miles.   **57.** The rental plans will be the same for 163.53 or about 164 miles.   **58.** The rental plans will be the same for 165 miles.   **59.** The plans will be the same for 1500 minutes.   **60.** The plans will be the same for 2200 minutes.   **61.** The plans will never pay the same.   **62.** There is no number of miles for which the two plans cost the same. **63. (a)** He must type 667 pages to break even. **(b)** He must type 1180 pages to earn a profit of $1000. **64. (a)** He must work 136 hours to break even. **(b)** He must work 163 hours to earn a profit of $1000. **65.** He must mix 0.67 gallon of the 40% mixture and 1.33 gallons of the 70% mixture. **66.** The chemist must mix 1.2 liters of the 40% solution and 0.8 liters of the 65% solution. **67.** There were 12 liters of 30% solution. **68.** There were $2\frac{1}{2}$ gallons of 40% solution. **69.** His project grade must be 91. **70.** Her project grade must be 90. **71.** Christmas Eve should be -56 degrees. **72.** Christmas Eve should be 3 degrees. **73.** Compensation is the same by the two companies for all levels of sales. **74.** The costs are the same for any number of days. **75.** He earned $140.82 in tips. **76.** He worked 6 hours.

2.3 CALCULATOR EXERCISES

1. The sales were $652.80. **2.** She should administer 3.5 tablets. **3.** He needs three sheets.

SECTION 2.4 EXERCISES

1. $s = \dfrac{P}{4}$ **2.** $b = \dfrac{A}{h}$ **3.** $d = \dfrac{C}{\pi}$ **4.** $r = \dfrac{C}{2\pi}$ **5.** $L = \dfrac{V}{WH}$ **6.** $W = \dfrac{V}{LH}$ **7.** $h = \dfrac{2A}{b}$ **8.** $b = \dfrac{2A}{h}$ **9.** $h = \dfrac{V}{\pi r^2}$

10. $h = \dfrac{S - 2\pi r^2}{2\pi r}$ **11.** $P = \dfrac{I}{rt}$ **12.** $r = \dfrac{I}{Pt}$ **13.** $g = \dfrac{v}{t}$ **14.** $t = \dfrac{v}{g}$ **15.** $R = \dfrac{V}{I}$ **16.** $m = \dfrac{E}{c^2}$ **17.** $m = x - zs$ **18.** $s = \dfrac{x - m}{z}$

19. $L = \dfrac{S - 2WH}{2W + 2H}$ **20.** $H = \dfrac{S - 2LW}{2L + 2W}$ **21.** $y = -\dfrac{4}{3}x$ **22.** $y = -\dfrac{1}{3}x$ **23.** $y = \dfrac{1}{2}x$ **24.** $y = \dfrac{1}{3}x$ **25.** $y = -x$ **26.** $y = x$

27. $y = -\dfrac{5}{4}x + 5$ **28.** $y = -x - 3$ **29.** $y = -x - 7$ **30.** $y = 13x - 13$ **31.** $y = \dfrac{1}{2}x + 2$ **32.** $y = -\dfrac{8}{7}x - 8$ **33.** $y = x - 1$

34. $y = 3x - 2$ **35.** $y = 4x - 19$ **36.** $y = -4x + 13$ **37.** $y = -2x + 8$ **38.** $y = 3x + 35$ **39.** $y = -x - 6$ **40.** $y = -5x - 62$

41. $y = \dfrac{2}{3}x + 10$ **42.** $y = -\dfrac{3}{4}x$ **43.** $y = -\dfrac{2}{3}x - \dfrac{1}{3}$ **44.** $y = \dfrac{4}{9}x + \dfrac{1}{6}$ **45. (a)** $P = 200 + 85m$ **(b)** $m = \dfrac{1}{85}P - \dfrac{40}{17}$ **(c)** It will take 24

months to pay off $2240. **(d)** It will take 12 months to pay off $1200. **46. (a)** $c = 75 + 35h$ **(b)** $h = \dfrac{1}{35}c - \dfrac{15}{7}$ **(c)** Richard worked 12 hours for

$495. **(d)** Richard worked 16.5 hours for $652.50. **47. (a)** $T = 22c + 12.50$ **(b)** $c = \dfrac{1}{22}T - \dfrac{25}{44}$ **(c)** She can spend about $1.02 on each student

for a $35 party. **(d)** She can spend about $1.70 on each student for a $50 party. **48. (a)** $T = 175 + 14c$ **(b)** $c = \dfrac{1}{14}T - \dfrac{25}{2}$ **(c)** They can spend

about $35.71 for each member if they raise $675. **(d)** They can spend about $58.92 on each member if they raise $1000.

49. $B = 75 + 3T$; $T = \dfrac{1}{3}B - 25$; Ted's weekly earnings are about $216.67 when his boss averages $725 per week; Ted's weekly earnings are $400 when

his boss averages $1275 per week. **50.** $M = 1.5F - 0.75$; $F = \dfrac{2}{3}M + \dfrac{1}{2}$; females would average $8.80 per hour if males earned $12.45 per hour;

females would average $14.50 per hour if males earned $21 per hour. **51.** $C = 85 + 185d$; $d = \dfrac{C - 85}{185}$. With costs limited to $270, the equipment

can be rented for one day. With costs limited to $825, the equipment can be rented for four days. **52.** $D = 40h + 50$; $h = \dfrac{D - 50}{40}$. If the distance to

Fairbanks is 510 miles, then it will take about 11.5 hours. If the distance to Anchorage is 130 miles, then it will take about 2 hours.

53. $V = 15h$; $h = \dfrac{V}{15}$; the height should be 4 feet for a volume of 60 cubic feet. The height should be $6\dfrac{2}{3}$ feet for a volume of 100 cubic feet.

54. $S = 30 + 16h$; $h = \dfrac{1}{16}S - \dfrac{15}{8}$; the height would be 3.5 feet if the total surface area were 86 square feet; the height would be 5.625 feet if the total

surface area were 120 square feet.

2.4 CALCULATOR EXERCISES

The amount P to invest when $A = $10,000$ at $t = 5, 7, 10$, and 12 is listed in the following table:

t	$P(\$)$
5	7985.20
7	7297.90
10	6376.30
12	5827.50

The amount P to invest when $A = $25,000$ at $t = 5, 7, 10$, and 12 is listed in the following table:

t	$P(\$)$
5	17,617
7	15,316
10	12,415
12	10,793

As more time passes or increases, the amount of money that must be invested decreases.

SECTION 2.5 EXERCISES

1. The integers are 21, 22, and 23. **2.** The integers are 14, 15, and 16. **3.** The integers are 22, 24, and 26. **4.** The integers are 32, 34, and 36. **5.** The integers are 31, 33, and 35. **6.** The integers are 23, 25, and 27. **7.** The doses are 6 grains, 8 grains, and 10 grains. **8.** The doses are 16 cc, 15 cc, 14 cc, 13 cc, and 12 cc. **9.** The number awarded at each stage is three prizes, five prizes, seven prizes, and nine prizes. **10.** The number awarded each day are 2 prizes, 4 prizes, 6 prizes, 8 prizes, and 10 prizes. **11.** The lowest grade was 81 points and the highest grade was 88 points. **12.** The ratings are $-4, -2, 0, 2,$ and 4. **13.** The amount borrowed was \$4000; the interest was \$500. **14.** The amount borrowed was \$1200; the interest was \$108. **15.** You must invest about \$4587.16. **16.** About \$11,160.71 should be invested. **17.** He should invest about \$455,000. **18.** About \$7421.15 should be invested. **19.** \$9500 was invested at 8%; \$5500 was invested at 6.5%. **20.** About \$7494.74 was invested at 9.2%; about \$7505.26 was invested at 3.5%. **21.** He borrowed \$5000 at 5% and \$13,000 at 9.25%. **22.** She borrowed \$3000 at 5% and \$7000 at 6.25%.

23. $A = 1.07P; P = \dfrac{A}{1.07}$; about \$1261.68 should be invested to have \$1350; about \$2336.45 should be invested to have \$2500.

24. $P = 1.11L; L = \dfrac{P}{1.11}$; you will receive \$1200 as a loan if the payback is \$1332; you will receive about \$720.72 as a loan if the payback is \$800.

25. The suggested retail price is \$85.00. **26.** The suggested retail price is \$2300. **27.** The original price was \$85. **28.** The original price was about \$129.99; the amount of the reduction was about \$19.50. **29.** The original cost was about \$12.47. **30.** The dealer paid \$200. **31.** The regular price is \$260. **32.** The regular price is \$73.75. **33.** The SRP should be about \$19,230.77. **34.** The SRP should be about \$10,582.35. **35.** His hourly wage before the increase was about \$13.45. **36.** Her salary before the increase was about \$30,660.38. **37.** The bill before the gratuity was added was about \$124.56. **38.** The bill before the gratuity was added was about \$228.65. The gratuity was \$34.30. **39.** The markup percentage was 80%. **40.** The markup percentage was 40%. **41.** The original price is about \$59.96 if the sale price is \$53.96; the original price is about \$109.94 if the sale price is \$98.95. **42.** The subtotal is about \$25 when the total cost is \$27.19; the subtotal is \$132 when the total cost is \$143.55.

43. Each side measures $9\dfrac{3}{4}$ inches. **44.** The sides measure 2.5 cm, 5 cm, and 4 cm. **45.** The sides measure 6 feet, 6 feet, and 4 feet.

46. The sides measure $15\dfrac{1}{5}$ meters, $15\dfrac{1}{5}$ meters, and $7\dfrac{3}{5}$ meters. **47.** The dimensions are 85 yards by 115 yards. **48.** Each side measures $\dfrac{1}{4}$ inch.

49. The dimensions are 95 cm by 52.25 cm. **50.** The dimensions are 8 inches by 18 inches. **51.** The dimensions should be 8 feet by 40 feet; it will cover 320 square feet of yard. **52.** Each side would be 24 feet; yes, 576 ft² of area is greater than 320 ft² of area. **53.** The supplement is 4.78°. The angles are 4.78°, 90°, and 85.22°. **54.** The supplement of the angle is 15° and the other angles measure 90° and 75°. **55.** The angles are 20°, 40°, and 120°. **56.** The angles are 40°, 80°, and 60°. **57.** The angles are 46°, 56°, and 78°. **58.** The angles are 54.5°, 44.5°, and 81°. **59.** Each angle labeled x is 72 degrees. **60.** Each angle labeled x is 72 degrees and each angle labeled y is 54 degrees.

2.5 CALCULATOR EXERCISES

1. $\{122, 131, 140, 149\}$ **2.** $-17.77777778; -3.888888889; 10; 23.88888889; 37.77777778$ **3.** $\{75, 60, 45, 30\}$ **4.** $\{60, 90, 120, 150\}$

SECTION 2.6 EXERCISES

1. $|-x + 9| + 6 = 9, x = 6, x = 12$ **2.** $|2x + 1| + 2 = 3, x = -1, x = 0$ **3.** -4 and 2 **4.** 2 and 4 **5.** -3 and 1 **6.** 1 and 5 **7.** -2 and 0 **8.** -3 and -1 **9.** -47 and 5 **10.** -10 and 48 **11.** -41 and 3 **12.** -19 and 17 **13.** -3.92 and 8.26 **14.** 21.931 and 23.729 **15.** -1.133 and 0.333 **16.** -7.4375 and 5.6875 **17.** no solution **18.** no solution **19.** 32 **20.** -6 **21.** -8.677 and -1.333 **22.** -0.5 and 5.5 **23.** -138 and 138 **24.** -2400 and 2400 **25.** -41.67 and 41.67 **26.** -0.009 and 0.009 **27.** no solution **28.** no solution

29. $-14\dfrac{5}{9}$ and $14\dfrac{5}{9}$ **30.** $-\dfrac{11}{12}$ and $\dfrac{11}{12}$ **31.** -864 and -292 **32.** -774 and 168 **33.** -1221 and 2663 **34.** 527 and 775 **35.** 5 and 53

36. $-\dfrac{7}{2}$ and $\dfrac{43}{2}$ **37.** no solution **38.** no solution **39.** -42 and 70 **40.** $-\dfrac{73}{2}$ and $\dfrac{67}{2}$ **41.** -6 and 2 **42.** $-\dfrac{33}{2}$ and $\dfrac{1}{2}$ **43.** -16 and -8

44. $\dfrac{3}{2}$ and $\dfrac{13}{2}$ **45.** The maximum depth of Lake Superior is either 513 feet or 1333 feet; the maximum depth is 1333 feet. **46.** The maximum depth of the Caspian Sea is either 3363 feet or 7267 feet; the Caspian Sea is 3363 feet deep. **47.** The minimum and maximum heights the clothes will fit are 5 feet, 3 inches, and 6 feet, 3 inches. **48.** The limits are 5 feet, 9 inches, and 6 feet, 5 inches. **49.** The possible speeds are 823 miles per hour and 661 miles per hour. The speed at a high altitude is 661 miles per hour. **50.** The possible temperatures are -211 degrees and 105 degrees. Crafton's maximum temperature was 105 degrees. **51.** The minimum and maximum percentages are 39% and 45%. **52.** The minimum and maximum percentages are 43.5% and 52.5%. **53.** The range is from 130 pounds to 134 pounds. **54.** The range is from 0.95 pound to 1.05 pounds. **55.** The lengths range from $5\dfrac{1}{4}$ inches to $5\dfrac{3}{4}$ inches. **56.** The lengths range from 25.375 inches 25.625 inches. **57.** The average squirrel lives 8.5 years. **58.** 1,075,000,000 people speak Mandarin Chinese.

2.6 CALCULATOR EXERCISES

1. 0.5 **2.** no solution **3.** 4 and -13 **4.** 1.5 **5.** -7.5 and 7.5

CHAPTER 2 SUMMARY

Vocabulary Review

1. linear equation in one variable **2.** linear absolute value equation in one variable **3.** equivalent equations **4.** contradiction **5.** identity

Reflections

1–8. Answers will vary.

CHAPTER 2 SECTION-BY-SECTION REVIEW

1. nonlinear **2.** linear **3.** linear **4.** nonlinear **5.** linear **6.** nonlinear **7.** $\frac{3}{4}(x + 7) - 5 = \frac{1}{3}(x + 12)$; $x = 9$ **8.** -6 **9.** 6

10. 3 **11.** noninteger between -3 and -2 **12.** all real numbers **13.** no solution **14.** $2.3(x - 5.6) + 4 = 3x - 11.3$; $x = 3.5$ **15.** 2

16. -2 **17.** all real numbers **18.** no solution **19.** 2.4 **20.** The two offers are equivalent at 10 hours. **21.** The fourth-week donation should be \$2165. **22.** The cost of production equals the revenue for 25 items. **23.** 26 **24.** $\frac{32}{39}$ **25.** -2 **26.** 2.933 **27.** -68 **28.** -38.5

29. 105 **30.** $\frac{16}{25}$ **31.** 12 **32.** -2.98 **33.** 3.5 **34.** There were 58 passes given. **35.** There were 280 graduates. **36.** They must sell 5334 books. **37.** The total proceeds were \$42,630. **38.** $1000 = 0.0005c$; $c = 2{,}000{,}000$; the current achieved was 2 million amperes per square centimeter. **39.** He needs approximately 11.43 quarts of solution. **40.** -14 **41.** 2 **42.** -3.4 **43.** $-\frac{11}{6}$ **44.** all real numbers

45. no solution **46.** You can drive 909 miles. **47.** The offers are the same at 15 hours. **48.** Glenda must score 87 on her final. **49.** He must do 7 applications to break even ($x \approx 6.01$). He must do 26.02 or 27 applications to earn a profit of \$500. **50.** $h = \frac{2A}{b + B}$ **51.** $W = \frac{S - 2LH}{2L + 2H}$

52. $y = \frac{6}{5}x - \frac{22}{15}$ **53.** $A = 6000 + 8000n$; $n = \frac{A - 6000}{8000}$; It will last 9 years if the amount is \$78,000; it will last 15 years if the amount is \$126,000.

54. The lengths should be 10 inches, 12 inches, and 14 inches. **55.** The angle behind the fence is $42°$; the other two angles are $90°$ and $48°$.

56. The dimensions are 15 inches by 24 inches. **57.** \$7232.14 should be invested. **58.** He invested \$12,500 at 8.5% and \$2500 at 6.5%.

59. The suit's original price should have been \$262.50. **60.** Casey is paying \$7010.71 this semester. **61.** $3|x + 4| = 6$; $x = -6$, $x = -2$

62. 7 **63.** 8 and 16 **64.** no solution **65.** 1 and 13 **66.** no solution **67.** -16 and 8 **68.** The permissible limits on the part are 62.75 mm and 62.83 mm. **69.** The limits on the percentage of voters are 45% and 53%.

CHAPTER 2 MIXED REVIEW

1. all real numbers **2.** no solution **3.** -4 **4.** 3 **5.** 3.1 **6.** 2 **7.** noninteger between -4 and -3 **8.** -3 **9.** all real numbers

10. -2 **11.** no solution **12.** linear **13.** nonlinear **14.** nonlinear **15.** linear **16.** linear **17.** nonlinear **18.** -348 **19.** $\frac{3}{10}$

20. 32 **21.** -72.3 **22.** -14 **23.** -14.59 **24.** 7 **25.** -444 **26.** $-\frac{2}{3}$ **27.** 7.49 **28.** 8.7 **29.** 6.4 **30.** $-\frac{1}{8}$ **31.** $\frac{11}{7}$ **32.** 6

33. 1.5 **34.** all real numbers **35.** no solution **36.** -3 **37.** 0 and 8 **38.** no solution **39.** $-\frac{14}{5}$ and 2 **40.** 4 and 10 **41.** -21 and 19

42. $y = \frac{2}{3}x + 12$ **43.** $H = \frac{S - 2LW}{2W + 2L}$ **44.** $h = \frac{S - 2\pi r^2}{2\pi r}$ **45.** $P = \frac{I}{RT}$ **46.** Two possible heights are 517 ft and 1023 ft; 1023 ft is the correct height. **47.** The limits on the true percent are 49% and 55%. **48.** The subtotal was about \$65.58; the total bill was about \$70.99. **49.** He expects to receive \$14,125. **50.** An employee needs 120 houses. **51.** The pieces should be 5 inches, 6 inches, 7 inches, and 8 inches. The pieces should be 3 inches, 5 inches, 7 inches, and 9 inches. **52.** The other angles measure $59°$ each. The measure of the supplement is $121°$. **53.** The original price was about \$139.94. **54.** The dimensions are 16.8 feet by 25.2 feet. **55.** The price before tax was about \$299; sales tax was about \$26.16. **56.** The company will break even at 857.14 or 858 packages of cards. A profit of \$500 occurs when 1000 packages of cards are produced and sold. **57.** She should invest \$21,428.57 at 8% and \$28,571.43 at 15%. **58.** One liter of the 30% solution must be mixed. **59.** The plans cost the same for 1.43 or 2 days.

60. In 2004, 510 tornadoes were reported. **61.** $C = 15 + 3.5x$; $x = \frac{C - 15}{3.5}$; She can do 7.14 or 7 tanning sessions. **62. (a)** $A = 40 + 55.5h$

(b) $h = \frac{A - 40}{55.5}$ **(c)** A job that costs \$178.75 lasts 2.5 hours. **63.** The angle made with the width of the rug is $55°$. **64.** The mechanic needs $3\frac{1}{3}$ gallons of the solution.

CHAPTER 2 TEST

1. linear **2.** nonlinear **3.** nonlinear **4.** linear **5.** no solution **6.** -3 **7.** -2.079 **8.** all real numbers **9.** $1\frac{3}{4}$ **10.** -3

11. no solution **12.** -5 and 7 **13.** The pieces should be cut into sections measuring 14 inches, 15 inches, and 16 inches. **14.** The price before it went on sale was about \$239.93. **15.** $W = \frac{P - 2L}{2}$; the width is 7.6 inches. **16.** The other angles measure $69°$ each. The measure of the supplement is $111°$. **17.** 1500 liters of 60% apple juice must be added. **18.** He can burn 14 songs and stay in his budget. **19.** The two plans will cost the same if the job lasts 10 hours. **20.** Cathy will break even when she cleans 240 square yards of carpet ($x \approx 239.13$). She will have a profit of \$600 when she cleans 500 square yards of carpet. **21.** The tuition before increase is \$3281.68. **22.** Kerk must earn a minimum grade of 92. **23.** She invested \$500 at 8% and \$500 at 4.5%. **24.** The minimum percentage was 23.5%. The maximum percentage was 30.5%. **25.** Answers will vary.

CHAPTER 3

SECTION 3.1 EXERCISES

1. linear; $5x + 7y = 35$ **2.** linear; $\sqrt{3}x + 2y = 6$ **3.** nonlinear   **4.** nonlinear   **5.** nonlinear   **6.** nonlinear
7. linear; $2x = 5$ **8.** linear; $5y = 14$

9. Answers will vary.
Possible answer:

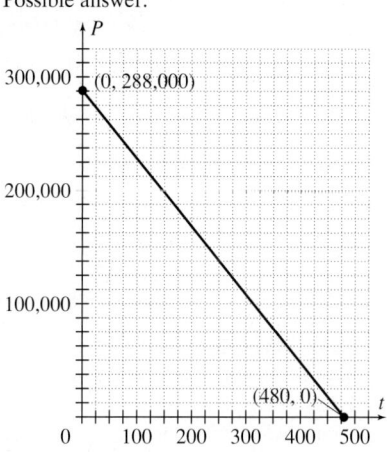

$(0, -2)$, $(12, 0)$, and $(6, -1)$
are three possible solutions.

10. Answers will vary.
Possible answer:

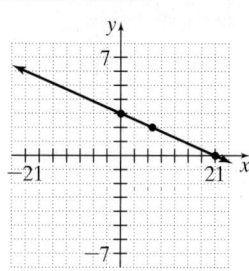

$(0, 3)$, $(21, 0)$, and $(7, 2)$
are three possible solutions.

11. Answers will vary.
Possible answer:

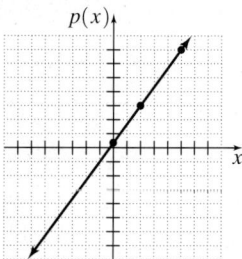

$\left(0, \dfrac{1}{3}\right)$, $(2, 3)$, and $(5, 7)$
are three possible solutions.

12. Answers will vary.
Possible answer:

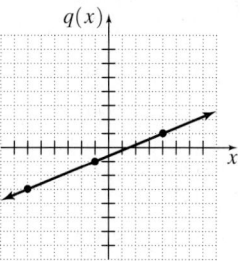

$(-6, -3)$, $(-1, -1)$, and $(4, 1)$
are three possible solutions.

13. Answers will vary.
Possible answer:

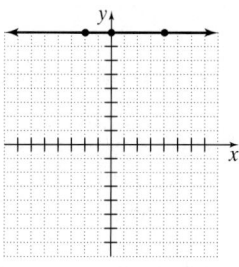

$(0, 8)$, $(4, 8)$, and $(-2, 8)$
are three possible solutions.

14. Answers will vary.
Possible answer:

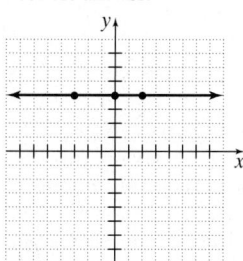

$(0, 4)$, $(2, 4)$, and $(-3, 4)$
are three possible solutions.

15. Answers will vary.
Possible answer:

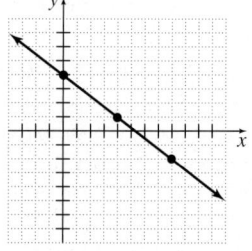

$(0, 4)$, $(4, 1)$, and $(8, -2)$
are three possible solutions.

16. Answers will vary.
Possible answer:

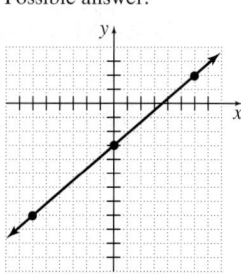

$(-6, -8)$, $(0, -3)$, and $(6, 2)$
are three possible solutions.

17. Answers will vary.
Possible answer:

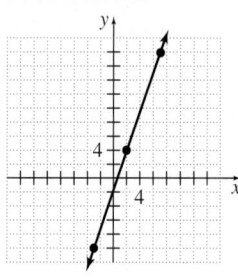

$(-3, -10)$, $(2, 4)$, and $(7, 18)$
are three possible solutions.

18. Answers will vary.
Possible answer:

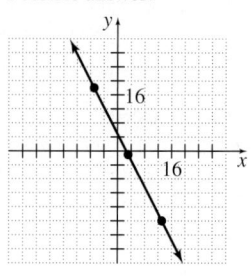

$(-7, 18)$, $(3, -1)$, and $(13, -20)$
are three possible solutions.

19. Answers will vary.
Possible answer:

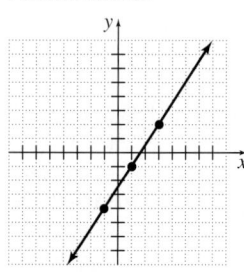

$(-1, -4)$, $(1, -1)$, and $(3, 2)$
are three possible solutions.

20. Answers will vary.
Possible answer:

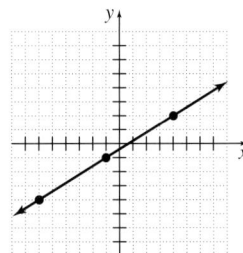

$(-6, -4)$, $(-1, -1)$, and $(4, 2)$
are three possible solutions.

21. Answers will vary.
Possible answer:

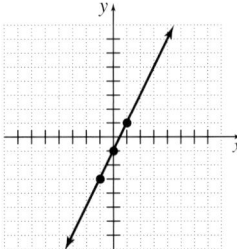

$(-1, -3)$, $(0, -1)$, and $(1, 1)$
are three possible solutions.

22. Answers will vary.
Possible answer:

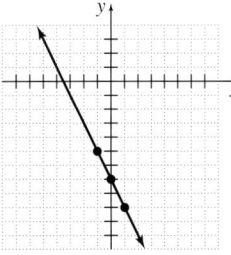

$(-1, -5)$, $(0, -7)$, and $(1, -9)$
are three possible solutions.

23. Answers will vary.
Possible answer:

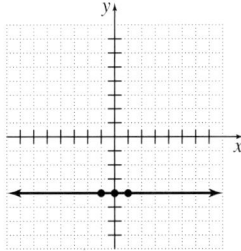

$(-1, -4)$, $(0, -4)$, and $(1, -4)$
are three possible solutions.

24. Answers will vary.
Possible answer:

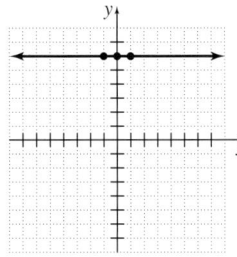

$(-1, 6)$, $(0, 6)$, and $(1, 6)$
are three possible solutions.

25. x-intercept: $(-2, 0)$
y-intercept: $(0, 4)$

26. x-intercept: $(-5, 0)$
y-intercept: $(0, -5)$

27. x-intercept: $(0, 0)$
y-intercept: $(0, 0)$

28. x-intercept: $(0, 0)$
y-intercept: $(0, 0)$

29. x-intercept: $(3, 0)$
y-intercept: none

30. x-intercept: none
y-intercept: $(0, -4)$

31. x-intercept: $(4, 0)$
y-intercept: $\left(0, \dfrac{12}{5}\right)$

32. x-intercept: $(9, 0)$
y-intercept: $(0, 7)$

33. x-intercept: $\left(\dfrac{7}{2}, 0\right)$
y-intercept: $(0, -2)$

34. x-intercept: $(31, 0)$
y-intercept: $(0, -31)$

35. x-intercept: $\left(-\dfrac{27}{2}, 0\right)$
y-intercept: $(0, -3)$

36. x-intercept: $(-3, 0)$
y-intercept: $\left(0, -\dfrac{9}{2}\right)$

37. x-intercept: $(6, 0)$
y-intercept: $(0, 4)$

38. x-intercept: $(-9, 0)$
y-intercept: $(0, -15)$

39. x-intercept: $(0, 0)$
y-intercept: $(0, 0)$

40. x-intercept: $(0, 0)$
y-intercept: $(0, 0)$

41. x-intercept: $(10, 0)$
y-intercept: none

42. x-intercept: $(5, 0)$
y-intercept: none

43. x-intercept: none
y-intercept: $(0, 11)$

44. x-intercept: none
y-intercept: $(0, -5)$

45. $(0, -24)$ **46.** $(0, 2)$ **47.** $(0, -15)$ **48.** $(0, -16)$ **49.** $(0, 0)$ **50.** $(0, 0)$ **51.** $(0, -2)$
52. $(0, 3)$ **53.** $(0, 0)$ **54.** $(0, 0)$ **55.** $(0, 9)$ **56.** $(0, -8)$ **57.** $(0, 0)$ **58.** $(0, 0)$

59.

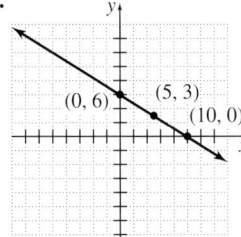

60.

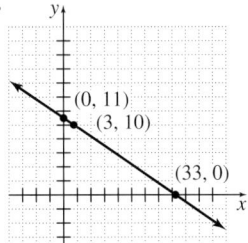

61.

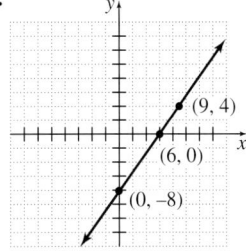

62.

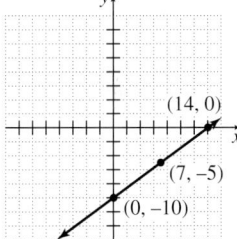

63.

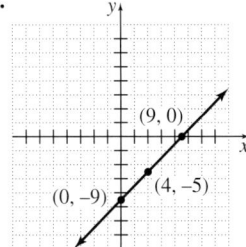

64.

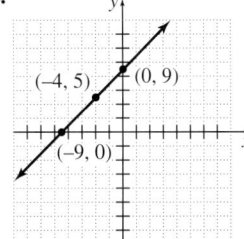

65.

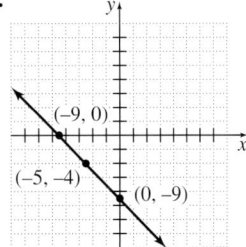

66.

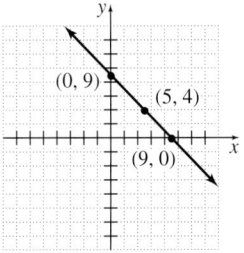

67.

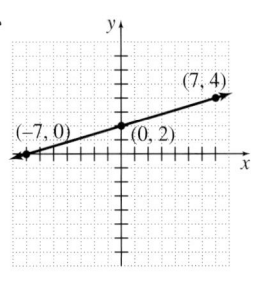

68.

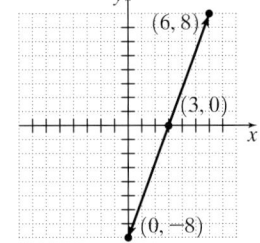

69. (a) $(0, 100), (6, 85), (10, 75)$
(b)

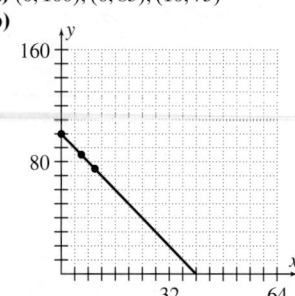

(c) The score for missing 12 questions would be 70.
(d) domain: 0 to 40

70. (a) $(1, 0), (2, 5), (4, 15)$
(b)

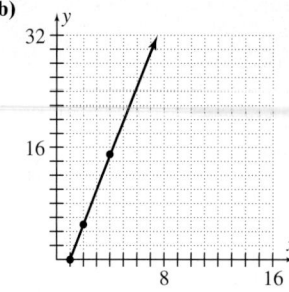

(c) A crew of five people would pack 20 boxes per minute.
(d) Answers will vary. Possible answer: There is probably a maximum number of boxes that can be packed by a large number of people, given the size of the packing plant.

71. (a) $(2, 6), (3.5, 10.5), (10.5, 31.5)$
(b)

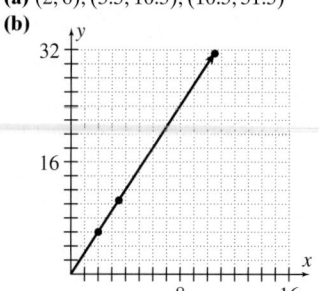

(c) The border would be 12 inches.
(d) Yes, all equilateral triangles have three sides of equal measure.

72. (a) $(15, 50), (25, 70), (10, 40)$
(b)

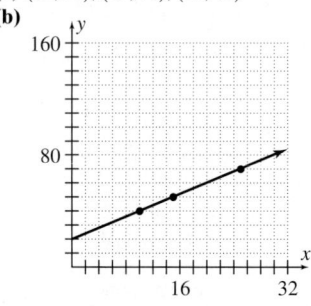

(c) The perimeter would be 60 cm.
(d) Yes, it is a linear equation.

73. (a) $(0, 323.9), (1, 316.3)$
(b)

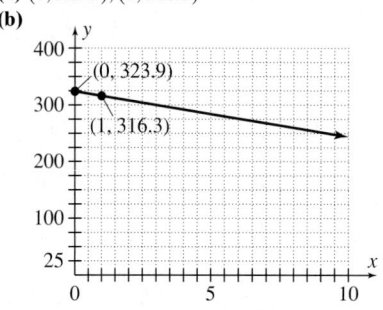

(c) The death rate for 2008 will be 270.7 per 100,000 population.
(d) The death rate will not decrease to 0 per 100,000 population.

74. (a) $(0, 35.7), (1, 35.5)$
(b)

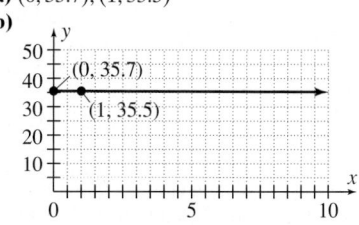

(c) The death rate for 2008 will be 34.3 per 100,000 population.
(d) The death rate will not decrease to 0 per 100,000 population.

75. $y = 50x + 2000$

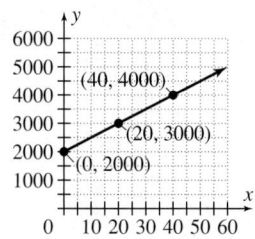

Krista will need to watch all three children 60 days to earn $5000.

76. $c = 10n + 200$

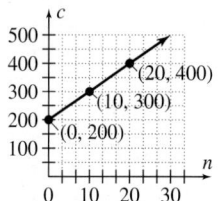

The cost of a party for 10 children is $300. For a budgeted amount of $350, 15 children can attend the party.

77. $c = 2.50w + 300$

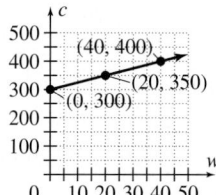

For a budgeted $400, the person can get 40 weeks of recycling service.

78. $c = 3.00n + 11.96$

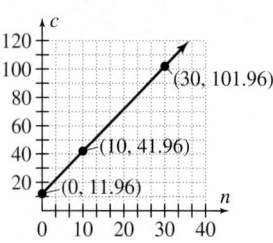

The cost of 9 gallons (18 half gallons) per month is $65.96.
For a budgeted amount of $75 per month, 21 half gallons can be delivered.

79. Let x = number of customers, $P(x)$ = profit, $P(x) = 14.25x - 1000$ Intercepts: $(0, -1000), (70.175, 0)$
If no one goes to the water park, then the park loses $1000.
If 71 people go to the water park, then the park breaks even or makes a small profit of $11.75.

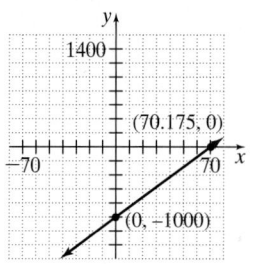

80. Let x = number of games, $P(x)$ = profit, $P(x) = 1.35x - 200$
Intercepts: $(0, -200), (148.15, 0)$
If there are no games bowled, then there is a $200 loss. If 148 games are bowled, then the bowling alley just about breaks even.

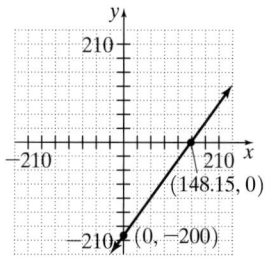

81. (a)

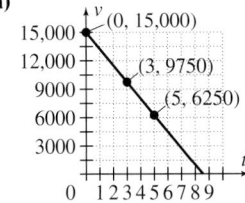

(b) $(0, 15,000)$ and $(8.57, 0)$

(c) The value of the car is $15,000 at purchase.
After 8.57 years the value of the car is $0.

(d) The vehicle will have a value of $7500 after 4.29 years.

82. (a)

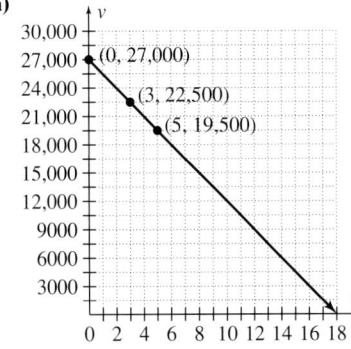

(b) $(0, 27,000)$ and $(18, 0)$

(c) The value of the car is $27,000 at purchase.
After 18 years the value of the car is $0.

(d) The vehicle will have a value of $13,500 after 9 years.

83. (a)

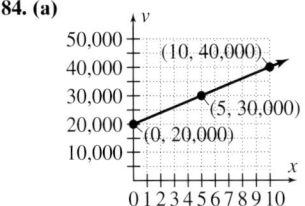

(b) $(0, 3000)$; At the time of purchase the ring was valued at $3000.

(c) After 5.3 years the ring will be worth $5000.

84. (a)

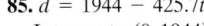

(b) At the time of purchase the property value is $20,000.

(c) The property will be valued at $40,000 after 10 years.

85. $d = 1944 - 425.7t$
Intercepts: $(0, 1944)$, $(4.57, 0)$
At the start of the trip, $t = 0$, the distance between Atlanta and Los Angeles is 1944 miles. At the end of the trip, $d = 0$, the time it took to reach the destination was 4 hours and 0.57 of an hour (equal to 34 minutes). From the graph, it takes just a little over 2 hours to fly 1000 miles from Atlanta.

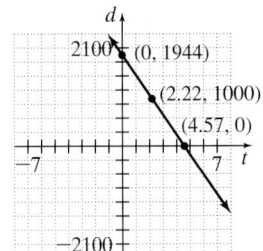

86. $d = 3471 - 389.3t$
Intercepts: $(0, 3471)$ $(8.9, 0)$
At the start of the trip, $t = 0$, the distance between New York City and London is 3471 miles. At the end of the trip, $d = 0$, the time it took to reach the destination was 8 hours and 0.9 of an hour (equal to 54 minutes). From the graph, it takes almost 4 hours to fly 2000 miles from New York City.

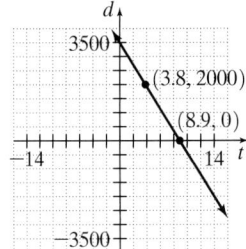

3.1 CALCULATOR EXERCISES

1. $x = \dfrac{1}{3}$

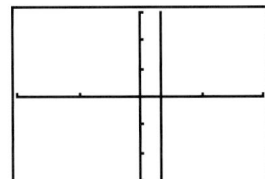

2. $x = 8$

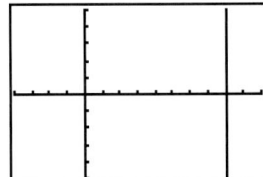

3. $x = -3$

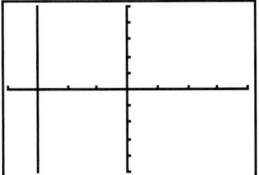

SECTION 3.2 EXERCISES

1. The graph represents a function that is decreasing; the slope is negative; $m = -\dfrac{3}{2}$. **2.** The graph does not represent a function; m is undefined

3. The graph represents a function that is constant; $m = 0$. **4.** The graph represents a function that is increasing; the slope is positive; $m = \dfrac{7}{2}$.

5. The graph represents a function that is increasing; the slope is positive; $m = \dfrac{1}{6}$ **6.** The graph represents a function that is constant; $m = 0$

7. The graph does not represent a function; m is undefined **8.** The graph represents a function that is decreasing; the slope is negative; $m = -\dfrac{5}{2}$ **9.** $\dfrac{2}{3}$

10. $-\dfrac{9}{5}$ **11.** 0 **12.** undefined **13.** undefined **14.** $\dfrac{15}{7}$ **15.** -2 **16.** 0 **17.** $-\dfrac{4}{5}$ **18.** $\dfrac{5}{3}$ **19.** -6 **20.** 0.4 **21.** $\dfrac{19}{12}$ **22.** $-\dfrac{63}{44}$

23. The grade of the advertised terrain is 35%. **24.** The grade of the terrain is 25%. **25.** The pitch of the roof is 27.5%.
26. The pitch of the roof is approximately 42%. **27.** The graph represents a function that is decreasing; $m = -1750$.
28. The graph represents a function that is decreasing; $m = -100$. **29.** The graph represents a function that is increasing; $m = 30$.
30. The graph represents a function that is increasing; $m = 50$. **31.** The graph represents a function that is increasing; $m = 0.545$.
32. The graph represents a function that is decreasing; $m = -0.6$. **33.** The graph represents a function that is constant; $m = 0$.
34. The graph does not represent a function; m is undefined. **35.** Graph b **36.** Graph c **37.** Graph a **38.** Graph a **39.** Graph b
40. Graph c **41.** $3960 per year **42.** $3350 per year **43.** The average rate of change was 71.6 billion dollars per year.
44. The average rate of change was 27.6 billion dollars per year. **45. (a)** 40 miles per hour **(b)** 30 miles per hour **(c)** 31.4 miles per hour
(d) 31.8 miles per hour **46. (a)** $250 per week **(b)** $350 per week **(c)** $280 per week

3.2 CALCULATOR EXERCISES

1–3. Answers will vary.

SECTION 3.3 EXERCISES

1. The slope is 21 and the y-intercept is $(0, 15)$. **2.** The slope is -19 and the y-intercept is $(0, 28)$. **3.** The slope is 5.95 and the y-intercept is
$(0, -2.01)$. **4.** The slope is -3.6 and the y-intercept is $(0, 14.8)$. **5.** The slope is -1255 and the y-intercept is $(0, 85,600)$. **6.** The slope is 45 and
the y-intercept is $(0, 1250)$. **7.** The slope is 4 and the y-intercept is $(0, -16)$. **8.** The slope is -8 and the y-intercept is $(0, 13)$.
9. The slope is 0 and the y-intercept is $(0, -2)$. **10.** The slope is 0 and the y-intercept is $(0, -22)$.
11. The slope is $\frac{5}{2}$ and the y-intercept is $\left(0, -\frac{7}{2}\right)$. **12.** The slope is $\frac{4}{3}$ and the y-intercept is $\left(0, \frac{5}{3}\right)$.
13. The slope is undefined and there is no y-intercept. **14.** The slope is undefined and there is no y-intercept.

15.
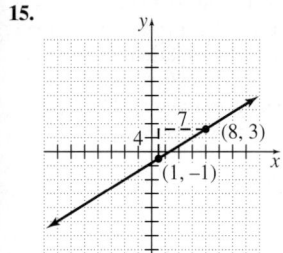

16.
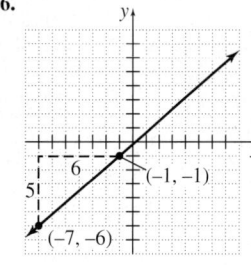

17.
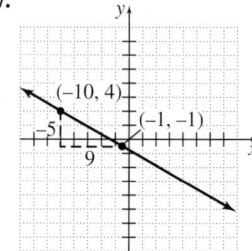

18.
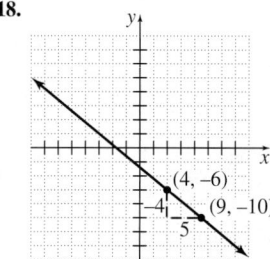

19.
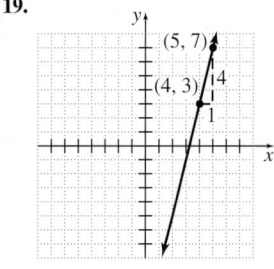

20.
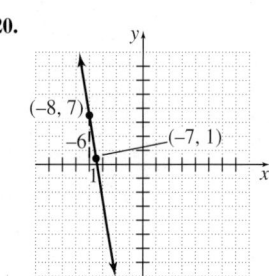

21.
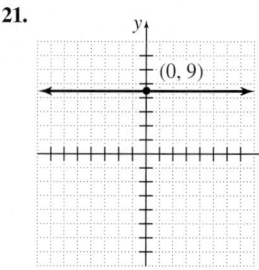

22.
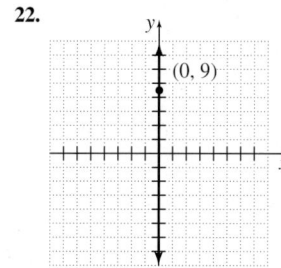

23.
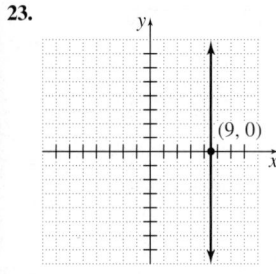

24.
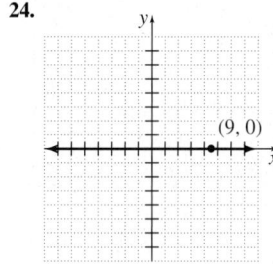

25.
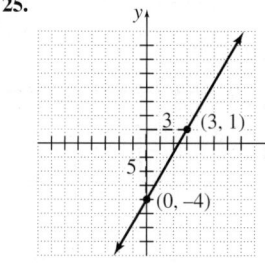

26.
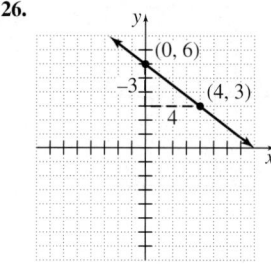

27.
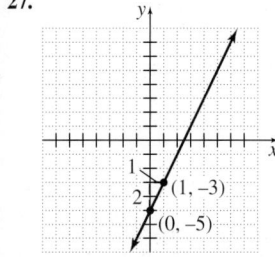

28.
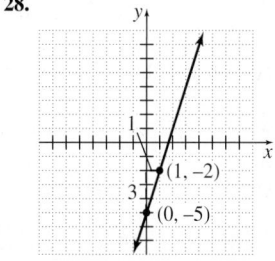

29.
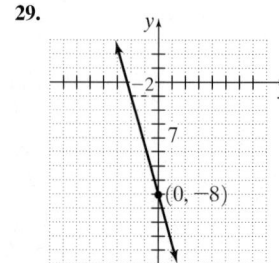

30.
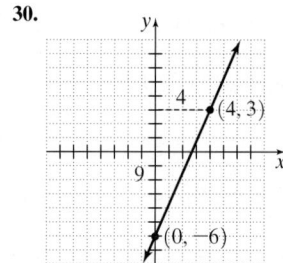

31.

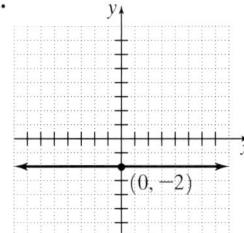

32.

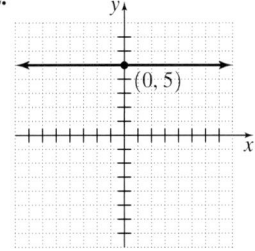

33.

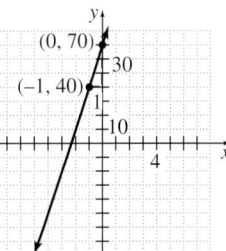

34.

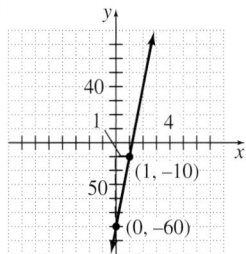

35.

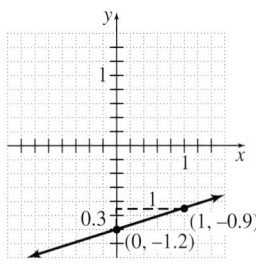

36.

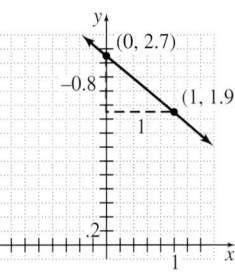

37. (a)

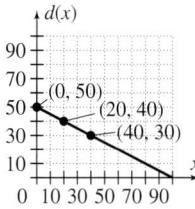

(b) For a demand of 20 packages, the price is $60.
For a price of $50, the demand is 25 packages.

38. (a)

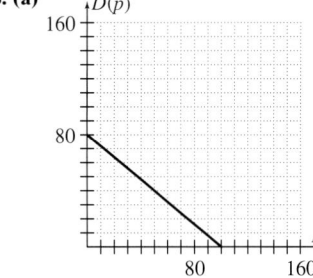

(b) For a price of $10, the demand is 72.
For a price of $20, the demand is 64.
For a price of $40, the demand is 48.
For a price of $64, the demand is 28.8 or 29.
(c) Demand decreases as price increases.
(d) At a price of $100 or more, demand is 0.

39. (a)

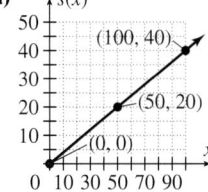

(b) For a supply of 20 calculators, the price is $50.
For a price of $75, the supply is 30 calculators.

40. (a)

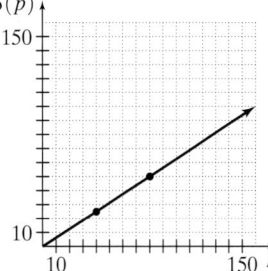

(b) For a price of $10, the supply is 6.25 or 6.
For a price of $20, the supply is 12.5 or 13.
For a price of $40, the supply is 25.
For a price of $64, the supply is 40.
(c) As price increases, supply increases.
(d) No; answers will vary.

41. (a) $c(x) = 0.75x + 50.00$

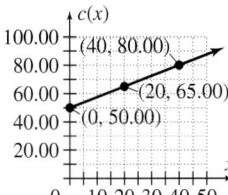

The cost of producing 8 cards is $56.00.
For a cost of $80.00, 40 cards were produced.

(b) $r(x) = 5.00x$

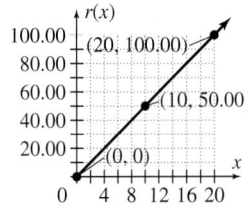

The revenue for selling 8 cards is $40.00.
For a revenue of $80.00, 16 cards were sold.

(c) $p(x) = 4.25x - 50.00$

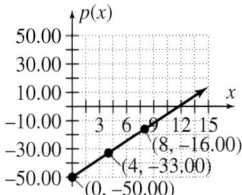

The profit for producing and selling 8 cards is
a loss of $16.00. For a profit of $0.00, 11.76
cards or about 12 cards are produced and sold.

42. (a) $c(x) = 15x + 150$

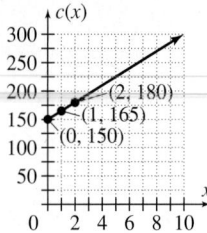

The cost of producing 5 Web pages is $225. For a cost of $300, 10 Web pages were produced.

(b) $r(x) = 50x$

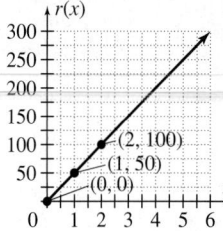

The revenue for selling 5 Web pages is $250. For a revenue of $300, 6 Web pages were sold.

(c) $p(x) = 35x - 150$

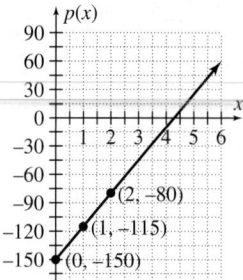

The profit for producing and selling 5 Web pages is $25. For a profit of $0, 4.29 or about 5 Web pages are produced and sold.

43. (a) $c(x) = 4x + 50$

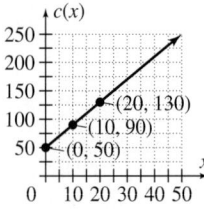

The cost of producing 5 shirts is $70. For a cost of $150, 25 shirts were produced.

(b) $r(x) = 10x$

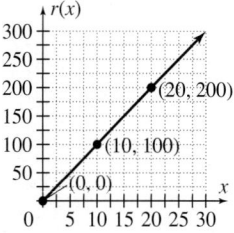

The revenue for selling 5 shirts is $50. For a revenue of $300, 30 shirts were sold.

(c) $p(x) = 6x - 50$

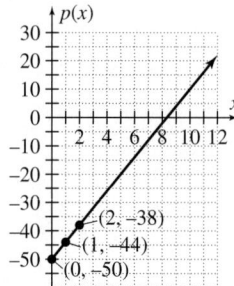

The profit for producing and selling 5 shirts is a loss of $20. For a profit of $0, 8.3 shirts or about 9 shirts are produced and sold.

44. (a) $c(x) = 7x + 50$

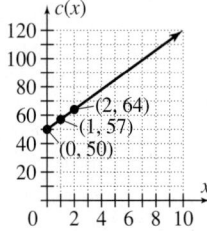

The cost of the service for 2 hours is $64. The cost of 10 hours of service is $120.

(b) $r(x) = 30x$

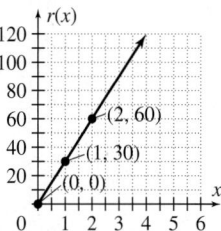

The revenue for 2 hours of service is $60. The revenue of 4 hours of service is $120.

(c) $p(x) = 23x - 50$

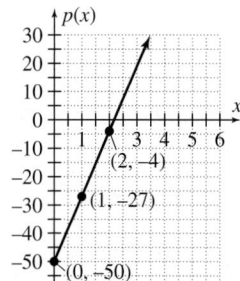

The profit from 5 hours of service is $65. For 2.17 or about 3 hours, the profit is $0.

45. $d = 50t$

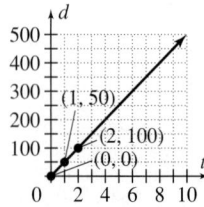

It will take Chloe 8.4 hours to drive the 420 miles to Breanne's home.

46. $d = 55t$

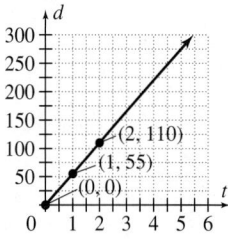

It will take Caitlin 5 hours to drive 275 miles.

47. $y = 350 - 50t$

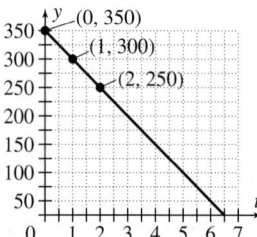

Victoria will be 275 miles from her home after 1.5 hours.

48. $y = 350 + 50t$

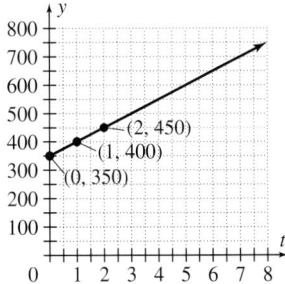

After 1.5 hours, Misty will be 425 miles from home.

3.3 CALCULATOR EXERCISES

	$y = mx + b$		Conclusions	
Equation	m	b	Graph's Inclination, ↑ or ↓	Graph's y-Intercept
$y = 3x + 6$	3	6	↑	$(0, 6)$
$y = -2x + 7$	-2	7	↓	$(0, 7)$
$y = -x - 3$	-1	-3	↓	$(0, -3)$
$y = 4x - 1$	4	-1	↑	$(0, -1)$
$5x - 3y = 9$	$\dfrac{5}{3}$	-3	↑	$(0, -3)$
$4x + 5y = 10$	$-\dfrac{4}{5}$	2	↓	$(0, 2)$
$y = \dfrac{7}{8}x - \dfrac{3}{4}$	$\dfrac{7}{8}$	$-\dfrac{3}{4}$	↑	$\left(0, -\dfrac{3}{4}\right)$
$y = -1.7x + 3.2$	-1.7	3.2	↓	$(0, 3.2)$

SECTION 3.4 EXERCISES

1. intersecting and perpendicular **2.** intersecting and perpendicular **3.** parallel **4.** parallel **5.** only intersecting **6.** only intersecting
7. coinciding **8.** coinciding **9.** only intersecting **10.** only intersecting **11.** parallel **12.** coinciding **13.** intersecting and perpendicular
14. intersecting and perpendicular **15.** parallel **16.** only intersecting **17.** parallel **18.** parallel **19.** coinciding **20.** parallel
21. coinciding **22.** only intersecting **23.** only intersecting **24.** parallel **25.** only intersecting **26.** parallel

27. (a) $y = 0.25x + 3.5$ **(b)** $y = 0.25x$ **(c)** no break-even point **(d)** $y = \dfrac{1}{3}x$ **(e)** At 42 candy bars, Brook will break even.

(f) At 10 candy bars, Brook will break even. **(g)** At about 5.45 candy bars, Brook will break even. At 6 candy bars, Brook will start making a profit.
(h) Answers will vary. **28. (a)** $y = 285 + 200x$ **(b)** $y = 200x$ **(c)** no break-even point **(d)** $y = 300x$ **(e)** At 2.85 radios, Joe will break even. At
3 radios, Joe will make a profit. **(f)** At 3.5 radios, Joe will break even. At 4 radios, Joe will make a profit. **(g)** Answers will vary. **29.** Yes. The
equilibrium point is (55.56, 22.22). When the price is \$55.56, the supply and demand is about 22 packages. **30.** Yes. The equilibrium point is (56.14, 35.09). When the price is \$56.14, the supply and demand is about 35 items.

31. $y_1 = 35 + 0.25x, m = 0.25, b = 35;$
$y_2 = 60; m = 0, b = 60;$
their graphs will intersect because the slopes are not equal;

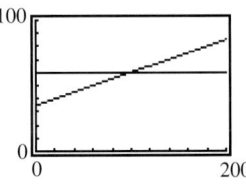

The intersection is $(100, 60)$. At 100 miles,
the prices are equal at \$60 per day.

32. $y_1 = 65, m = 0, b = 65;$
$y_2 = 15 + 10x, m = 10, b = 15;$
their graphs will intersect because the slopes are not equal.;

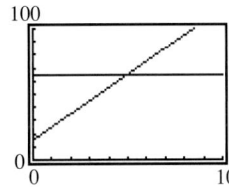

The intersection is $(5, 65)$. At 5 hours,
the costs will be equal at \$65.

33. $y_1 = 10x; m = 10, b = 0; y_2 = 15(x - 4), m = 15, b = -60; y_3 = 150; m = 0, b = 150; y_1$ and y_2 intersect at $(12, 120)$. At 12 seconds, Speedie will
catch Archie at a distance of 120 feet, or before the end zone 150 feet away. **34.** $y_1 = 18x; y_2 = 21.5(x - 0.75)$; at a distance of about 82.9 miles, Tom
will overtake Victor. **35.** Yes; the intersection point is $(2.65, 12,220.59)$; the value of the two vehicles will be equal (or \$12,220.59) 2.65 years after the
year of purchase. **36.** Yes; the intersection point is $(8.20, 23,360.66)$; the value of the two vehicles will be equal (or \$23,360.66) 8.20 years after 2004,
the year of purchase. **37.** Yes; the intersection point is $(22.68, 33.11)$; in 2023 (22.68 years after 2000), the death rate due to heart disease and the
death rate due to homicide will be equal (or 33.11 per 100,000 people). **38.** Yes; the intersection point is $(20.81, 51.55)$; in 2021 (20.81 years after
2000), the death rate due to heart disease and the death rate due to accidents will be equal (or 51.55 per 100,000 people). **39.** Yes; the intersection
point is $(-1024, -518,171)$; this point has no meaning. **40.** Yes; the intersection point is $(-19.46, -15.82)$; this point has no meaning.

3.4 CALCULATOR EXERCISES

Part 1

1. $(-10, 10, 1, -10, 10, 1)$ **2.** $(-47, 47, 10, -31, 31, 10)$ **3.** Yes   **4.** Yes   **5.** intersecting; $(6, 2250)$ **6.** parallel   **7.** intersecting; $(14.4, 1800)$

Part 2

1. 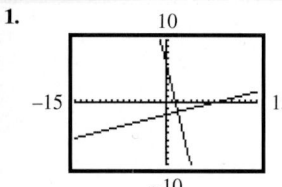   **2.** 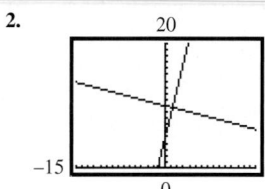   **3.**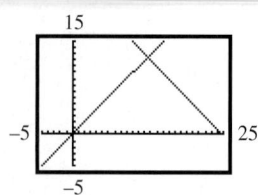

SECTION 3.5 EXERCISES

1. $y = \frac{3}{2}x - 1$ **2.** $y = \frac{1}{2}x + 1$ **3.** $x = -5$ **4.** $x = 4\frac{1}{2}$ **5.** $y = -3x$ **6.** $y = -\frac{1}{5}x - 3$ **7.** $y = -\frac{3}{2}$ **8.** $y = 3\frac{1}{3}$

9. $y = -\frac{2}{5}x + 4$ **10.** $y = -\frac{1}{7}x - 9$ **11.** $y = \frac{5}{9}x$ **12.** $y = \frac{1}{7}x - 1$ **13.** $y = 4x - \frac{3}{4}$ **14.** $y = 11x + \frac{1}{2}$ **15.** $y = -4.1x + 0.5$

16. $y = -6.2x - 2.2$ **17.** $y = -33$ **18.** $y = -4x$ **19.** $y = \frac{2}{3}x - 5$ **20.** $y = -2x + 8$ **21.** $y = -3x + 4$ **22.** $y = \frac{4}{3}x + 5$

23. $y = -1.7x + 3.6$ **24.** $y = 1.4x - 3.3$ **25.** $y = -\frac{3}{2}x - \frac{1}{2}$ **26.** $y = 6$ **27.** $x = -1$ **28.** $y = -5x + 11$ **29.** $y = 2x + 3$

30. $y = \frac{2}{7}x + \frac{20}{7}$ **31.** $y = 2$ **32.** $x = 2$ **33.** $y = \frac{5}{14}x + \frac{51}{14}$ **34.** $y = \frac{14}{27}x - \frac{8}{27}$ **35.** $y = -\frac{3}{2}x$ **36.** $y = -\frac{9}{2}x + \frac{67}{4}$

37. $y = -\frac{42}{13}x + \frac{21}{13}$ **38.** $y = \frac{35}{11}x + \frac{129}{11}$ **39.** $y = x + 0.4$ **40.** $y = -19x + 25$ **41.** $y = \frac{3}{8}x + 4$ **42.** $y = -\frac{5}{3}x + 12$

43. $y = -\frac{1}{2}x + 2$ **44.** $y = 2x - 3$ **45.** $y = 3x - 5$ **46.** $y = -3x + 2$ **47.** $y = 3x - \frac{13}{6}$ **48.** $y = 2x - \frac{3}{2}$ **49.** $y = -1.2x + 2.8$

50. $y = -0.8x + 4.2$ **51.** $y = -\frac{1}{2}x$ **52.** $y = \frac{1}{3}x$ **53.** $y = -\frac{1}{3}x + 7$ **54.** $y = \frac{1}{6}x + 2.4$ **55.** $y = -\frac{1}{5}x - 27$ **56.** $y = -\frac{1}{2}x + 3$

57. $y = \frac{3}{2}x$ **58.** $y = -\frac{4}{5}x$ **59.** $y = \frac{2}{3}x - 2$ **60.** $y = -\frac{4}{5}x - \frac{8}{5}$ **61.** $v(t) = 34{,}000 - 6800t$; in 2.5 years the truck will have lost \$17,000 in value.

62. $v(t) = 24{,}000 + 3600t$; in $3\frac{1}{3}$ years the truck will have lost \$12,000 in value.   **63. (a)** $y = 675x + 26{,}000$ **(b)** According to the equation, the estimated earnings in 2002 were \$30,725 or about \$725, more than the actual value.   **(c)** In 2010, the estimated earnings will be \$36,125.
64. (a) $s = 26.12x + 209$ **(b)** According to the equation, the estimate of gross ticket sales in 2001 was 626.92 million dollars or about 39 million dollars less than the actual value.   **(c)** In 2007, the estimate gross ticket sales will be 783.64 million dollars.   **65.** $s = -1.09x + 543$; according to the equation, in 2001 the average verbal score was about 505, and in 2002 the average verbal score was 504 or 3 points lower than the actual score of 507; in 2015, the equation estimates the average verbal score will be 490.   **66.** $s = 2.5x + 473$; according to the equation, in 2002 the average mathematical score was 528 or 25 points higher than the actual score of 503; in 2010, the equation estimates the average mathematical score will be 548; the pattern cannot continue to increase indefinitely or it would exceed the maximum score allowed on the test.   **67.** $y = -0.005x + 52.5$
68. $y = -0.008x + 55$; answers will vary.   **69.** $K = C + 273$; a Kelvin temperature of 373 corresponds to 100°C.   **70.** $R = F + 460$; the Rankine temperature that corresponds to 75°F is 535.   **71.** $y = 3.14x + 64.98$; the height is approximately 163.11 centimeters.   **72.** $y = 2.99x + 72.93$; the height is approximately 169.42 centimeters.   **73.** Let $x =$ the number of years after 1990, $y =$ the amount spent on reading materials; $y = 0.50x + 150.00$ **74.** Let $x =$ the number of years after 1995, $y =$ the death rate per 100,000 population, $y = 0.50x + 40.5$
75. (a) $y = -0.16x + 11.1$ **(b)** According to the equation, in 1995 the death rate was 10.3 per 100,000 population or 0.3 per 100,000 population greater than the actual value of 10 per 100,000 population.   **(c)** According to the equation, in 2001 the death rate was 9.34 per 100,000 population or 0.16 per 100,000 population less than the actual value of 9.5 per 100,000 population.   **76. (a)** $y = -7.41 + 409.9$ **(b)** According to the equation, in 1982 the death rate was 380.26 per 100,000 population or 8.74 per 100,000 population less than the actual value of 389 per 100,000 population.
(c) According to the equation, in 2001 the death rate was 239.47 per 100,000 population or 8.33 per 100,000 population less than the actual value of 247.8 per 100,000 population.   **77.** $n = 0.54t + 4.3$; in 2010 there will be 25.9 million divorced people; answers will vary
78. $y = 0.9x + 21.4$; in 2010 there will be 57.4 million people that are never married; answers will vary

3.5 CALCULATOR EXERCISES

1. $y = 3.25x + 30.95$ **2.** $y = -9.63x + 727.83$ **3.** $y = 525.375x + 23{,}898.5$ **4.** Let $x =$ the number of years after 1994 and $y =$ the number of deaths per 100,000 population; $y = -7.05x + 301.52$; According to the equation, 252.17 deaths per 100,000 are due to heart disease in 2001, which is 4.37 per 100,000 more than the actual value.   **5.** Let $x =$ the number of years after 1996 and $y =$ the number of deaths per 100,000 population; $y = 0.32x + 23.84$; According to the equation, 25.44 deaths per 100,000 are due to diabetes in 2001, which is 0.14 per 100,000 more than the actual value.

CHAPTER 3 SUMMARY

Vocabulary Review

1. standard form   **2.** slope–intercept form   **3.** point-slope form   **4.** linear function   **5.** coinciding; coincident   **6.** parallel   **7.** intersecting; perpendicular   **8.** perpendicular   **9.** slope, rise, run   **10.** equilibrium point   **11.** break-even point   **12.** average rate of change, grade

Reflections

1–8. Answers will vary.

CHAPTER 3 SECTION-BY-SECTION REVIEW

1. linear; $0.6x - y = -2.3$ **2.** nonlinear   **3.** linear; $6y = 19$

4. Answers will vary.
Possible answer:

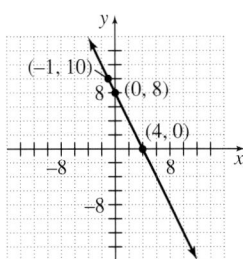

$(-1, 10)$, $(0, 8)$, and $(4, 0)$
are three possible solutions.

5. Answers will vary.
Possible answer:

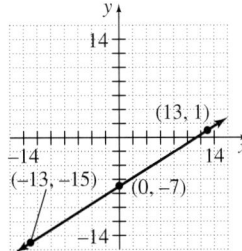

$(0, -7)$, $(13, 1)$, and $(-13, -15)$
are three possible solutions.

6. Answers will vary.
Possible answer:

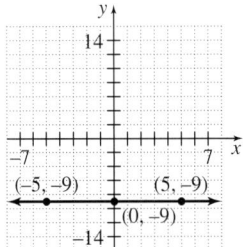

$(0, -9)$, $(5, -9)$, and $(-5, -9)$
are three possible solutions.

7. Answers will vary.
Possible answer:

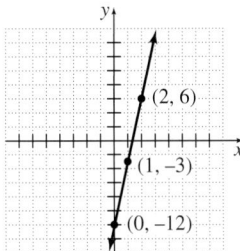

$(0, -12)$, $(1, -3)$, and $(2, 6)$
are three possible solutions.

8. Answers will vary.
Possible answer:

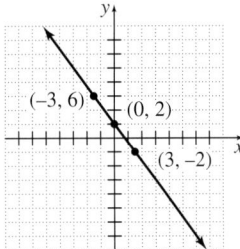

$(-3, 6)$, $(0, 2)$, and $(3, -2)$
are three possible solutions.

9. Answers will vary.
Possible answer:

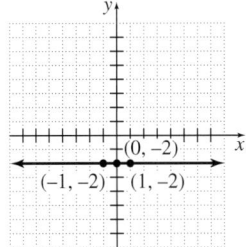

$(-1, -2)$, $(0, -2)$, and $(1, -2)$
are three possible solutions.

10. Answers will vary.
Possible answer:

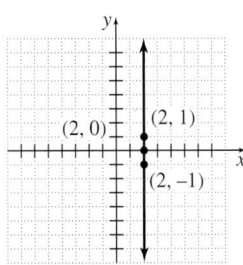

$(2, -1)$, $(2, 0)$, and $(2, 1)$
are three possible solutions.

11. x-intercept: $(-3, 0)$; y-intercept: $(0, -2)$

12. x-intercept: $(-10, 0)$; y-intercept: $(0, 4)$

13. $(0, -3)$

14. $(3, 0)$

15. $(0, 4)$

16. $(0, 0)$

17. $(0, -10)$

18.

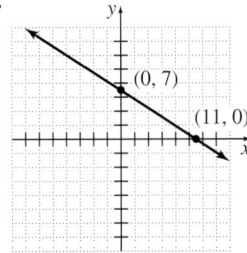

19.

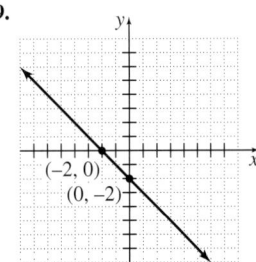

20.

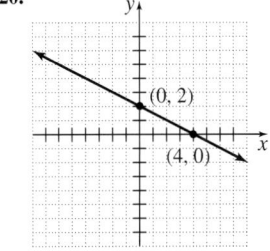

21. (a)

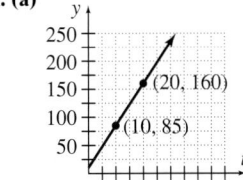

(b) She will receive \$235 for a job that is 30 pages long.

22. Let x = the number of copies,
$P(x)$ = profit, $P(x) = 0.02x - 25$

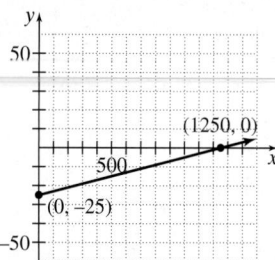

When no copies are made, there
is a loss of $25. When 1250 copies
are made, the center breaks even.

23. (a)

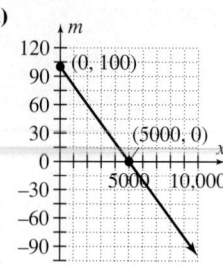

(b) The x-intercept is $(5000, 0)$. The actual membership is $0
for $5000 of yearly purchases. The y-intercept is $(0, 100)$.
The actual membership is $100 before any purchases
are made.

(c) If a customer spends $7500, his membership is $-$50,
or he saves $50.

24. It takes about 1.9 hours
to fly 1000 miles from Chicago.

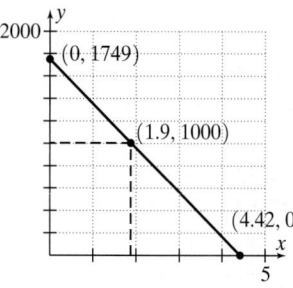

25. (a) $y = 5200 - 100x$

(b) The x-intercept is $(52, 0)$. At 52 weeks, the balance
is $0; the y-intercept is $(0, 5200)$. At 0 weeks,
the balance is $5200.

(c)

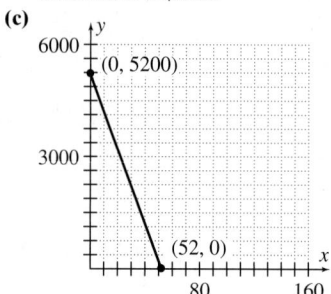

(d) There is $2000 in the account.

26. 0; yes; constant   **27.** $\frac{9}{2}$; yes; increasing   **28.** $-\frac{8}{5}$; yes; decreasing   **29.** undefined; no   **30.** $-\frac{3}{2}$; yes; decreasing   **31.** 50; yes; increasing

32. $\frac{1}{2}$ **33.** $-\frac{5}{3}$ **34.** 0   **35.** undefined   **36.** The grade is 2.5%.   **37.** The depreciation is $121.25 per year.   **38.** Graph a

39. (a) $500 per year   **(b)** $-$4200 per year   **(c)** $3700 per year   **(d)** $-$4250 per year   **40.** The slope is 23 and the y-intercept is $(0, -51)$.

41. The slope is $-\frac{6}{5}$ and the y-intercept is $\left(0, \frac{12}{5}\right)$.   **42.** The slope is 4 and the y-intercept is $(0, 14)$.   **43.** The slope is 0 and the y-intercept is $\left(0, -\frac{9}{2}\right)$.

44.

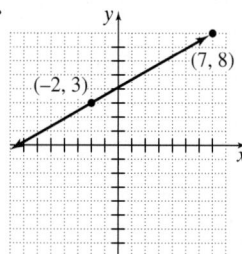

45.

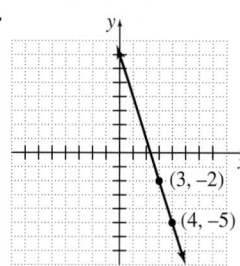

46.

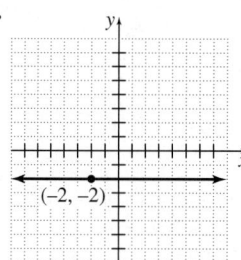

47.

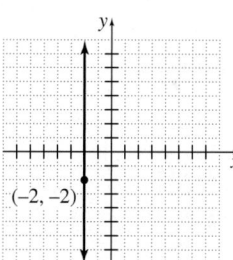

48.

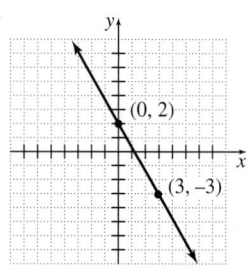

49.

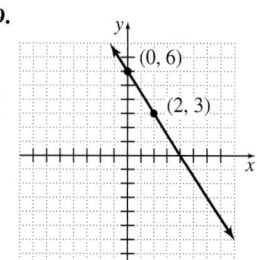

50.

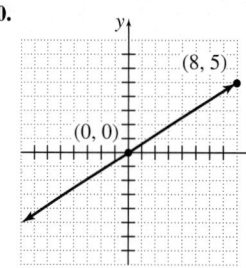

51.

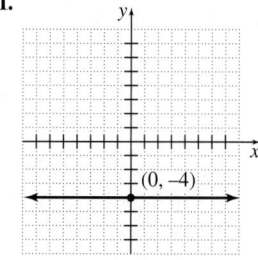

52. (a)

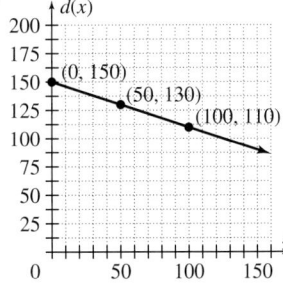

If the demand is 100 players, the price is $125.
If the price is $70, the demand is 122 players.

(b)

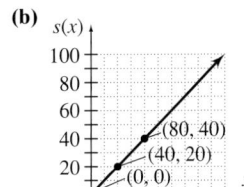

If the supply is 100 players, the price is $200.
If the price is $70, the supply is 35 players.

53. (a) $c(x) = 2x + 100$;

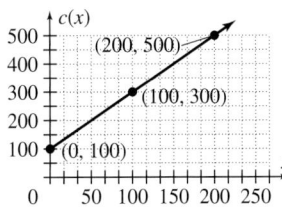

The cost of producing 50 packages is $200.
The number of packages produced for $300 is 100.

(b) $r(x) = 5x$;

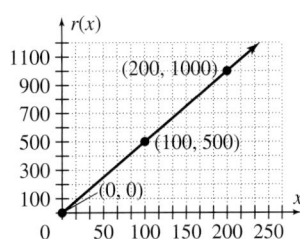

The revenue for selling 50 packages is $250.
To obtain a revenue of $300, 60 packages must be produced and sold.

(c) $p(x) = 3x - 100$;

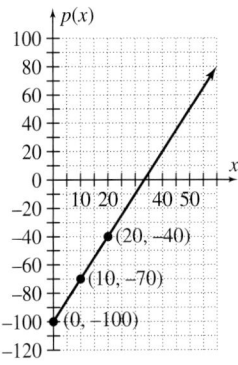

$50 is the profit to produce and sell 50 packages. To obtain a profit of $0, 34 (or 33.3) must be produced and sold.

54. $y = 350 + 50t$;

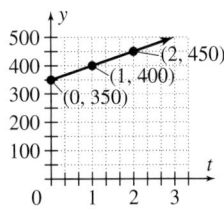

After 1.5 hours of traveling, David will be 425 miles.

55. only intersecting
56. coinciding
57. parallel
58. parallel
59. intersecting and perpendicular
60. only intersecting
61. intersecting and perpendicular
62. intersecting and perpendicular

63. (a) $y = 35x + 85$
(b) $y = 35x$
(c)

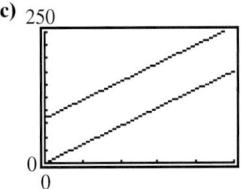

There is no break-even point.
(d) $y = 60x$

(e)

250

The break-even point is at (3.4, 204). He will start making a profit when he sells the fourth calculator.
(f) J. R. should sell the calculators for $60 each.

64. Yes; the point of intersection is (166.67, 83.33). When the price is $166.67, the supply and demand is about 83 DVD players.
65. (a) $y = 3.25x + 16.00$ **(b)** $y = 5.00x$ **(c)** The intersection point is (9.14, 45.71). The break-even point is (9.14, 45.71). When about 9 baskets are produced and sold, the baskets will cost the same amount as the revenue. **66.** Yes; the point of intersection is (2.22, 21,333.33). After about 2.22 years from purchase, the two automobiles will be worth the same (or $21,333.33).

67. Parallel. The slope is 0.9 for both equations. **68.** $y = -\frac{1}{4}x + 1$ **69.** $y = -2x + 3$ **70.** $y = \frac{3}{5}x - 2$ **71.** $y = -3.5$ **72.** $x = 2.6$

73. $y = -5x + 7$ **74.** $y = \frac{3}{11}x + \frac{28}{11}$ **75.** $y = \frac{1}{3}x + \frac{14}{3}$ **76.** $y = 4x - 3$ **77.** $y = -\frac{1}{2}x + 5$

78. $y = 2.23x + 61.41$; The height of the female is about 157.59 centimeters given that the femur is 43.13 centimeters.
79. (a) $y = 535x + 29{,}134$ **(b)** According to the equation, in 2002, the median earnings for women were $30,204 or about $1 more than the actual value. **(c)** In 2010, the median earnings for women will be $34,484. **80.** Let $x =$ the number of years after 1985, $y =$ the expenditure to the nearest hundred dollars; $y = 40x + 1400$. **81.** $y = -79.95x + 3851.00$; According to the equation, in 1995, the cigarette consumption was $2651.75 per capita or about $136.75 per capita more than the actual value. In 2018, the predicted per capita is $812.90. If the trend continues, the cigarette consumption will be a negative number.

CHAPTER 3 MIXED REVIEW

1. $(-1, 8), (0, 8), (1, 8)$ **2.** $(-9, 0), (0, 8), (9, 16)$ **3.** $(-11, -17), (0, -8), (11, 1)$

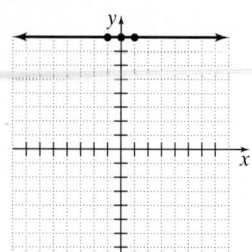 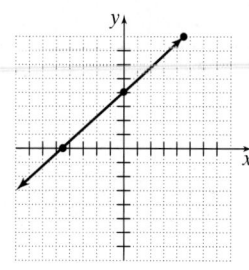 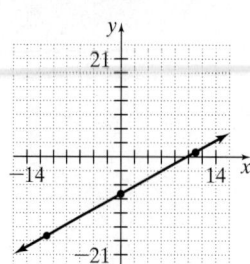

4. **5.** **6.** **7.**

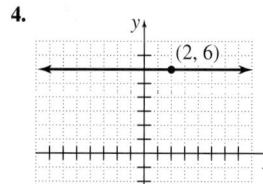 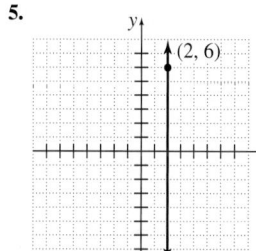 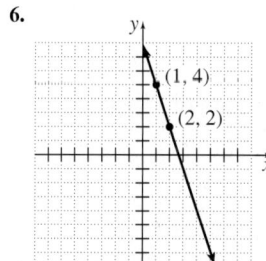 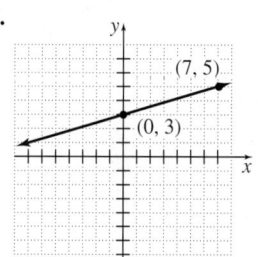

8. **9.** **10.** **11.**

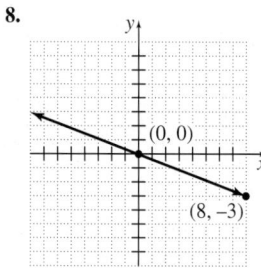 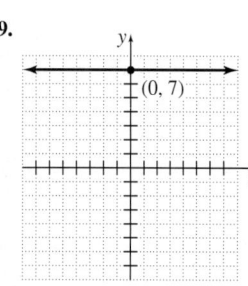 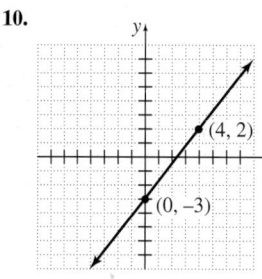 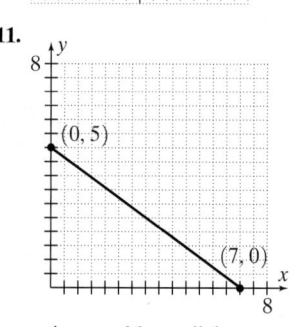

12. **13.**

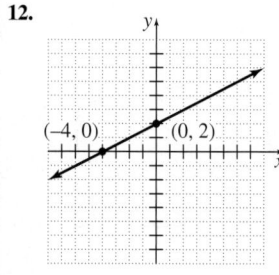 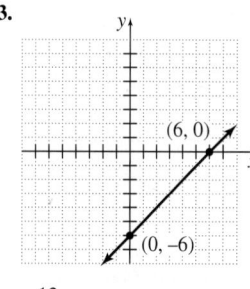

14. only intersecting   **15.** only intersecting   **16.** parallel
17. intersecting and perpendicular   **18.** coinciding
19. intersecting and perpendicular   **20.** parallel   **21.** linear; $x - y = 0$
22. nonlinear   **23.** linear; $5x - 8y = -21$ **24.** nonlinear
25. The slope is undefined; there is no y-intercept.
26. The slope is $-\frac{3}{2}$; the y-intercept is $(0, -5)$.
27. The slope is 3; the y-intercept is $(0, -2)$.
28. The slope is 0; the y-intercept is $(0, 0)$.
29. The slope is 13; the y-intercept is $(0, -15)$.
30. The slope is -5.03; the y-intercept is $(0, 7.92)$.

31. 0   **32.** undefined   **33.** -3 **34.** $\dfrac{13}{6}$ **35.** $(0, 4); m = 1; y = x + 4$; function; increasing

36. $(0, 5); m = -2; y = -2x + 5$; function; decreasing   **37.** $(0, -3); m = 0; y = -3$; function; constant

38. $(0, 10); m = -1; y = -x + 10$; function; decreasing   **39.** $y = 4x - 18$ **40.** $y = -\dfrac{1}{4}x - \dfrac{5}{4}$ **41.** $y = -\dfrac{2}{3}x + 5$ **42.** $x = 4.1$

43. $y = -3x - 8$ **44.** $y = 8$ **45.** $y = 4x + 3.2$ **46.** $y = 3x - 2$ **47.** $y = 2x + 2$

48. (a)

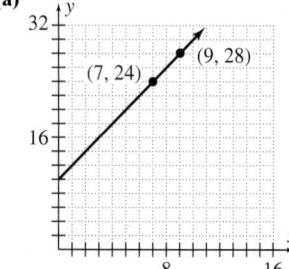

(b) See the graph in part a; Frank would receive $26 for 8 innings. Frank would receive $30 for 10 innings.

49. (a) $y = 20 + 50x$
(b)

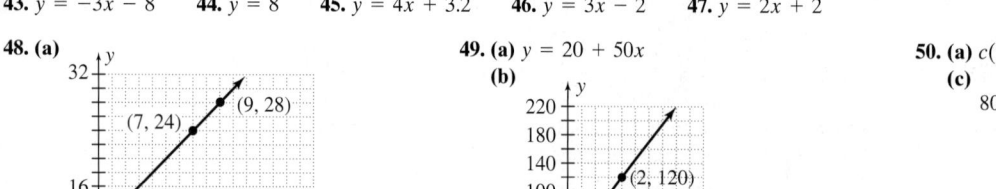

(c) The trainer would earn $120.
(d) He would earn $95.

50. (a) $c(x) = 0.75x + 225$ **(b)** $r(x) = 2x$
(c)

The break-even point is $(180, 360)$.
Revenue equals cost at 180 bows.
(d) No, 150 is less than 180; yes, 200 is greater than 180; she must sell at least 180 bows.

51. The pitch is 16.7%.　　**52.** The average rate of change is $13 per year.　　**53.** Graph a

54. Let x = the number of pictures,
$P(x)$ = profit, $P(x) = 33.50x - 35.00$

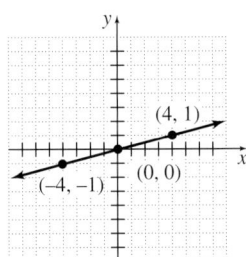

When no pictures are framed, Beckie
lost $35. When 1 picture is framed,
Beckie will almost break even.

55. (a)

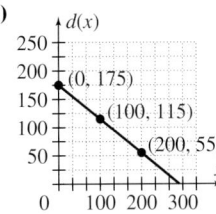

The price is $125 for a demand of
100 cameras. The price is $130 for a
demand of 97 cameras.

(b)

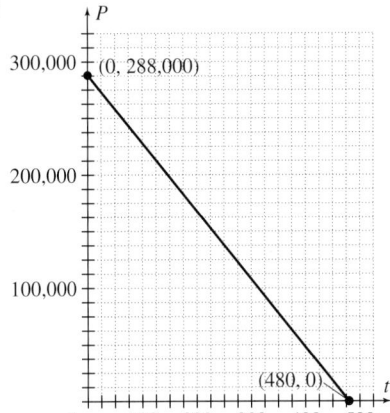

The price is $100 for a supply of
100 cameras.
The price is $130 for a supply of 115 cameras.
(c) Yes; the point of intersection is (113.64,
106.82);
When the price is $113.64, the supply and
demand will be about 107 cameras.

56. $y = 2.24x + 69.09$; the height of the male was about 181.69 centimeters.
57. $y = -2x + 43$; the points will verify.　　**58. (a)** The average rate of change was
$32.62 per capita per year.　**(b)** $y = 32.62x + 401.60$　**(c)** According to the equation, in
2001, $597.32 per capita was spent on recreation, which is $3.42 per capita more than the
actual value.　　**59. (a)** $y = 3.10x + 62.70$　**(b)** According to the equation, in 2001,
$65.80 per capita was spent on toys and sport supplies, which is $0.90 per capita less than
the actual value.

60. (a)

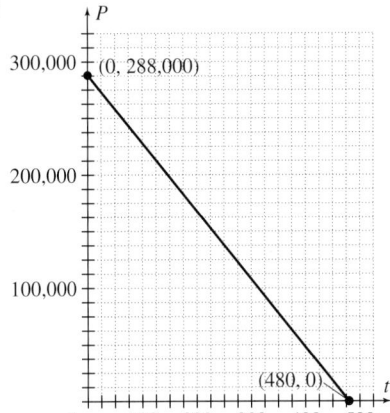

(b) After 0 months of payments, the loan was $288,000,
or the amount of the loan was $288,000. The loan
will be paid (the amount of the loan is $0) after 480
months.
(c) The coefficient -600 represents the amount of payment, $600 per month.

CHAPTER 3 TEST

1. linear　　**2.** linear　　**3.** nonlinear　　**4.** nonlinear

5. Answers will vary.
Possible answer:

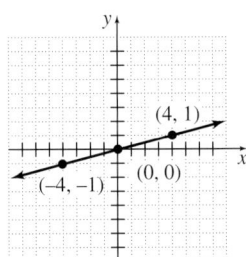

6.

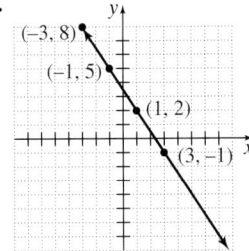

7.

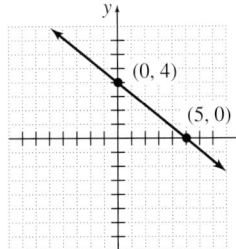

8.

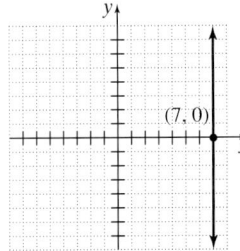

9.

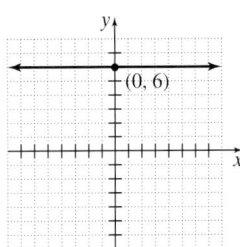

10.

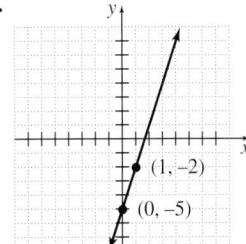

11.

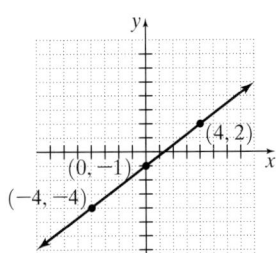

12. 0　　**13.** $-\dfrac{5}{9}$　　**14.** 1　　**15.** undefined　　**16.** only intersecting　　**17.** parallel

18. coinciding　　**19.** intersecting and perpendicular　　**20.** The slope is $\dfrac{3}{4}$; the y-intercept is $(0, 3)$.

21. The slope is -1; the y-intercept is $(0, 3)$.　　**22.** $y = -\dfrac{5}{3}x + \dfrac{13}{3}$　　**23.** $y = 9x + 7$　　**24.** $y = 6x + 8$

25. $y = \dfrac{1}{3}x + \dfrac{7}{3}$　　**26.** y-intercept is $(0, 100)$; $m = -20$; $y = -20x + 100$; decreasing function

27. Graph c　　**28.** The depreciation is about $666.67 per year.
29. The average rate of change was about 6.3 acres per year.

30. (a) $y = 1450 - 150x$

(b)

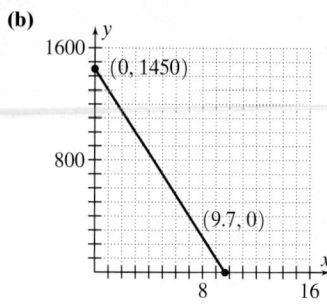

(c) Before any payments, the balance is $1450.
After 10 payments, the balance is zero.
(d) After 5 months ($x \approx 4.8$), half of the loan
($725) will be paid.

32. $y = 2.35x + 83.39$; the male is 182.00 centimeters in height.

33. (a) $c(x) = 2x + 25$;

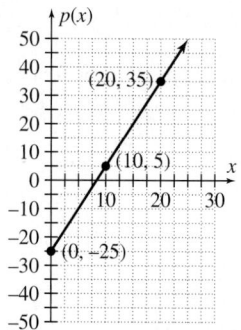

The cost of producing 5 shirts is $35.
The cost of producing 20 shirts is $65.

(c) $p(x) = 3x - 25$;

The profit for producing and selling 5 shirts is a loss of $10;
the profit for producing and selling 8.3 (or 9) shirts will be $0.

(b)

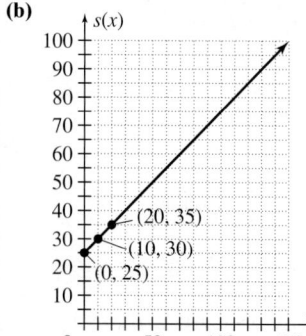

The price is $150 if the supply is 100 printers;
the price is $85 if the supply is 67.5 or 68 printers.

31. Let x = the number of hours, $p(x)$ = the weekly profit,
$p(x) = 15x - 500$;

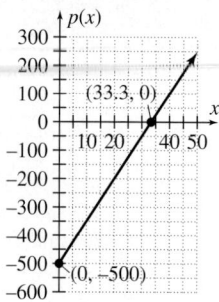

when no one trains (0 hours), the profit is $-$500
or a loss of $500; when 33.3 hours of training have
occurred, the profit is $0 or Alex breaks even.

(b) $r(x) = 5x$;

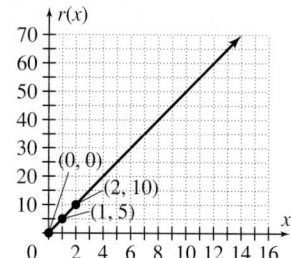

The revenue from selling 5 shirts is $25.
The revenue from selling 13 shirts is $65.

34. (a)

The price is $125 if the demand is 100 printers.
The price is $85 if the demand is 124 printers.

(c) Yes; When the price is $136.35, the supply and demand
is 93.18 or about 93 printers.
35. The grade of the hill is 48%.
36. $c = -10.33t + 487$; in 2010, approximately
332.05 billion cigarettes will be consumed.
37. (a) 1.4% per month   **(b)** -2.3% per month
38. Answers will vary.

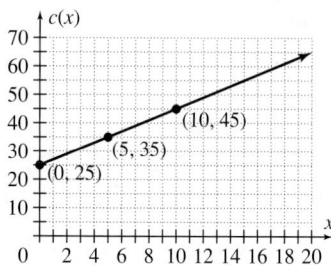

CHAPTERS P–3 CUMULATIVE REVIEW EXERCISES

1. (a) $<$ **(b)** $=$ **(c)** $>$

2.

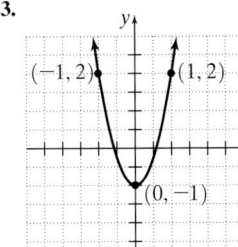

3. 1.02 **4.** -12 **5.** $\dfrac{7}{9}$ **6.** -1.581 **7.** not a real number **8.** 3 **9.** $-\dfrac{43}{35}$ **10.** 392 **11.** 5 **12.** 15 **13.** -16.98

14. $\dfrac{5}{36}$ **15.** 1 **16.** -81 **17.** 81 **18.** $\dfrac{9}{4}$ **19.** $8a - b$ **20.** $11x + 16y$

21. yes **22. (a)** 6 **(b)** $x^3, -2x^2, 7x, -5x^3, 2x$ **(c)** -4 **(d)** $1, -2, 7, -5, 2, -4$ **(e)** $7x, 2x; x^3, -5x^3$

23.

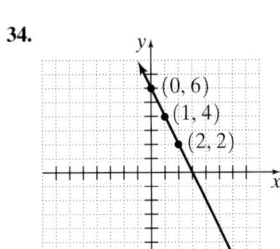

24. Domain is all real numbers; range is all $y \geq -1$. **25.** Yes. It passes the vertical-line test.
26. The relation is increasing for $x > 0$. **27.** The minimum is -1. There is no maximum.
28. (a) -5 **(b)** $-5 + 3h$ **29.** $x = -1$ **30.** $x = -\dfrac{7}{3}$ **31.** $x =$ all real numbers **32.** no solution

33. $x = \dfrac{7}{5}$ or $x = -1$

34.

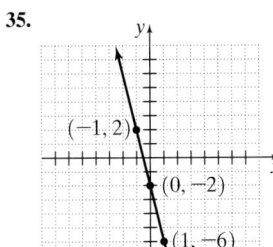

35.

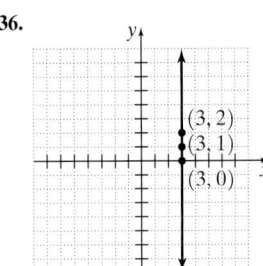

36.

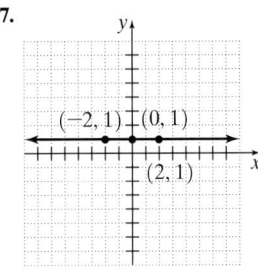

37.

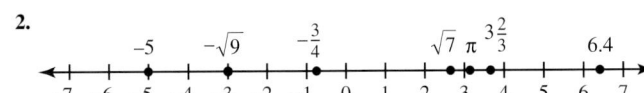

38. parallel **39.** intersecting and perpendicular **40.** 4 **41.** 3 **42.** undefined **43.** $y = -\dfrac{3}{2}x - \dfrac{1}{2}$ **44.** $y = -\dfrac{1}{4}x + \dfrac{7}{2}$

45. $z = 3A - x - y$ **46.** Let $x =$ original price; $0.7x = 87.49$; $x = 124.99$; The original price was \$124.99. **47.** Let $x =$ amount borrowed;
$1612.50 = x + 0.075x$; $x = 1500$; The amount borrowed was \$1500. **48.** Let $x =$ the number of CDs; $300 + 2.50x = 15x$ Break-even point is 24
CDs. If 20 CDs are made, then there will be a loss. If 30 CD's are made, then there will be a profit.
49. (a) 400 **(b)** $y = 400x + 7500$ **(c)** The number of students in 2010 will be about 11,500 students.
(d) The number of students in 2020 will be about 15,500; this seems reasonable for a rapidly growing area.
50. The amount of depreciation is \$6500 per year.

CHAPTER 4

SECTION 4.1 EXERCISES

1. solution **2.** solution **3.** solution **4.** not a solution **5.** not a solution **6.** not a solution **7.** not a solution **8.** solution
9. not a solution **10.** not a solution **11.** $(1, 2)$ **12.** $(1, -3)$ **13.** $\left(3, \dfrac{9}{2}\right)$ **14.** $\left(\dfrac{1}{2}, \dfrac{2}{3}\right)$ **15.** $\left(\dfrac{1}{2}, 4\right)$ **16.** $(-3, -7)$ **17.** $(3, 0)$

18. $(3, 0)$ **19.** $(0, -2)$ **20.** $(0, -2)$ **21.** $(5, -1)$ **22.** $(-4, 4)$ **23.** $\left(-\dfrac{24}{5}, \dfrac{18}{5}\right)$ **24.** $\left(-\dfrac{6}{5}, \dfrac{17}{5}\right)$ **25.** no solution **26.** no solution

27. all ordered pairs (x, y) that satisfy $y = -\dfrac{2}{3}x - 2$ **28.** no solution **29.** $(2, 3)$ **30.** $(2, 3)$ **31.** $\left(\dfrac{1}{6}, -\dfrac{1}{2}\right)$ **32.** $\left(\dfrac{1}{4}, \dfrac{5}{2}\right)$ **33.** $(5, 325)$

34. $(10, 200)$ **35.** no solution **36.** all ordered pairs (x, y) that satisfy $x - y = -1$ **37.** $(-3, -1)$ **38.** $(-4, -3)$
39. (a) $c(x) = 39.95 + 0.59x$, $c(x) = 25.49 + 0.65x$ **(b)** $(241, 182.14)$ **(c)** Budget Rent-A-Truck will be the better plan for a daily trip less than
200 miles. **(d)** U-Haul will be the better plan for a daily trip more than 300 miles. **40. (a)** $c(x) = 29.95 + 0.59x$, $c(x) = 15.49 + 0.65x$
(b) $(241, 172.14)$ **(c)** Jonathan should choose Budget Rent-A-Truck for a daily trip of less than 200 miles. **(d)** Jonathan should choose Penske for a
daily trip of more than 300 miles. **41. (a)** $y = 0.30x$, $y = 49.99 + 0.40(x - 500)$ **(b)** $(1500.1, 450.03)$ **(c)** The phone plans will be equal for approximately 1500 minutes. **42.** **(a)** $y = 42.99$, $y = 38.93 + 0.30(x - 150)$ **(b)** $(163.5, 42.99)$ **(c)** The daily charges will be equal for 163.5 miles.
43. (a) $y = 125 + 0.23x$, $y = 0.34x$; **(b)** The solution is $(1136.36, 386.36)$. **(c)** It will be more cost effective to use presorted mailing for more than
1136 pieces. **(d)** It will be more cost effective to use first class mailing for 1136 or less pieces. **44. (a)** With coupon book: $y = 50 + 13.5x$; without

coupon book: $y = 17.5x$ **(b)** $(12.5, 218.75)$ **(c)** It will be beneficial to purchase the coupon book if you will purchase 13 or more dinners. **(d)** It will be more cost effective not to purchase the coupon book if you will purchase 12 or fewer dinners; the two options are equal at the intersection of 12.5 dinners, with a cost of $218.75. **45.** The cost of renting a nailer is $114, and the cost of renting a drywell lift is $126. **46.** $x + y = 500$; $y = 3x$; the car payment is $125 and the rent payment is $375. **47.** $x + y = 40$; $7x + 8.2y = 298$; she should work 15 hours at the job that pays $8.20 per hour and 25 hours at the job paying $7.00 per hour. **48.** $18x + 22y = 316$; $y = 3 + x$; his wages are $6.25 per hour and $9.25 per hour. **49.** Let x = the number of follow-up visits, y = the total cost, $y = 5000 + 15x$, $y = 3000 + 250x$; $(8.5, 5127.66)$; the two plans will be approximately equal for 9 visits. **50.** Let x = the number of years after purchase, y = the value of the vehicle, $y = 15,000 - 1050x$, $y = 20,000 - 2500x$; $(3.45, 11,379.31)$; the vehicles will have the same value approximately 3.45 years after purchase. **51.** In 2069, the number of males and females will be equal. **52.** In 2000, the number of travelers will be equal. **53.** In 2006, the median earnings will be equal. **54.** In 2005, the number of deaths will be equal. **55. (a)** $m(x) = -2x + 63,586$, $f(x) = -201x + 73,305$ **(b)** $(48.8, 63,488.3)$; In 2049, the number of employed males will equal the number of employed females. **56. (a)** $m(x) = 573x + 63,582$, $f(x) = 810.5x + 72,903$ **(b)** The graphs will intersect prior to the year 2002. After 2002, the number of employed males and females will not be equal.

4.1 CALCULATOR EXERCISES

1. $x = 3$, $y = -5$ **2.** $x = -\dfrac{7}{5}$, $y = 12$ **3.** $x = 8$, $y = 9$ **4.** $x = \dfrac{9}{4}$, $y = -\dfrac{7}{2}$

SECTION 4.2 EXERCISES

1. $(1, 2)$ **2.** $(1, -3)$ **3.** $(16, 13)$ **4.** $(4, -7)$ **5.** $(-2, 2)$ **6.** $(8, 7)$ **7.** $(2, -2)$ **8.** $(-3, -7)$ **9.** $(-8, -1)$ **10.** $(0, 2)$ **11.** $(5, 0)$ **12.** $(-4, -16)$ **13.** $(4, 1)$ **14.** $(-5, -5)$ **15.** $(1, -1)$ **16.** $(4, 9)$ **17.** $(2, 3)$ **18.** $(2, 3)$ **19.** $(0, -2)$ **20.** $(1, -4)$ **21.** $(12, -7)$ **22.** $(4, 11)$ **23.** $(5, -1)$ **24.** $(2, -15)$ **25.** $\left(\dfrac{5}{2}, \dfrac{3}{2}\right)$ **26.** $\left(-\dfrac{13}{5}, -\dfrac{8}{5}\right)$ **27.** no solution **28.** no solution **29.** all ordered pairs (x, y) that satisfy $y = 2x + 3$ **30.** all ordered pairs (x, y) that satisfy $y = -3x + 2$ **31.** $(3, -2)$ **32.** $(2, -1)$ **33.** $(2, 7)$ **34.** $(4, -2)$ **35.** $(232, 68)$ **36.** $(94, 106)$ **37.** $(8, 22)$ **38.** $(10, 3)$ **39.** $(-1, -5)$ **40.** $(2, -1)$ **41.** $(400, 1600)$ **42.** $(400, 2400)$ **43.** $(14, -5)$ **44.** $(9, 2)$ **45.** $x + y = 90$; $y = 4x - 10$; the angles measure 20° and 70°. **46.** $x + y = 90$; $x = 9y + 10$; the angles measure 8° and 82°. **47.** $x + y = 180$; $y - x = 40$; the angles measure 70° and 110°. **48.** $x + y = 180$; $y = 3x + 20$; the angles measure 40° and 140°. **49.** $x + x + y = 180$; $y = x + x + 20$; the angles measure 40°, 40°, and 100°. **50.** $x + x + y = 180$; $y = x + 15$; the angles measure 55°, 55°, and 70°. **51.** The sides measure 10 feet, 10 feet, and 17 feet. **52.** The sides measure 15 inches, 15 inches, and 10 inches. **53.** The dimensions are 45.5 centimeters by 84.5 centimeters. **54.** The dimensions are 12 feet by 18 feet. **55.** The rectangle does not exist because the width cannot be a negative value. **56.** The rectangle does not exist because the width cannot be a negative value. **57.** $R = 2r + 5$; $2\pi R = 283$; the radius of each measures 20 inches and 45 inches. **58.** $2\pi R = 163$; $R = 3r - 10$; the radius of each measures 12 cm and 26 cm. **59.** $x + y = 15$; $y = 25 - x$; there is no solution. **60.** $x + y = 12$; $y = 12 - x$; the solutions are all ordered pairs (x, y) that satisfy $x + y = 12$, where x = acres of alfalfa and y = acres of wheat. **61. (a)** $C(x) = 2500 + 22x$ **(b)** $R(x) = 49x$ **(c)** $C(x) = 2500 + 22x$, $R(x) = 49x$; They must sell 93 ovens to break even. **62. (a)** $R(x) = 89x$ **(b)** $C(x) = 3600 + 35x$ **(c)** $R(x) = 89x$, $C(x) = 3600 + 35x$; They must sell 67 fans to break even. **63.** Elaine will break even when she sells 5 pieces of artwork. **64.** Lowell will break even after 60 hours on the job. **65.** $(55.56, 22.22)$; when the price is $55.56, the demand and the supply will be equal. **66.** $(56.14, 35.09)$; when the price is $56.14, the demand and supply will be equal. **67.** The monthly prices will be equal for 10 visits. **68.** The monthly plans will be equal for 200 minutes. **69.** The charges will be equal for 7 hours. For 5 hours, the better deal is the first plan. For 10 hours, the better deal is the second plan. **70.** The charges will be equal for 7.7 hours. For 6 hours of work, Gary should use Mr. Shire. **71.** The monthly benefits will be equal 11 years after 1990 or in the year 2001. According to the actual values, the monthly benefits will not be equal in 2001. **72.** The currencies will be equal in value when compared to the U.S. dollar 19 years after 1995. According to the actual values, the currencies will be equal in value when compared to the U.S. dollar in 2002. **73. (a)** $e(x) = 5070x + 41,581$, $m(x) = 11,460x + 39,917$ **(b)** $(0.26, 42,901)$; The U.S. exports and U.S. imports to Mexico will be equal in 1994 or 1 year (0.26 year) after 1993. **(c)** The predictions in part **b** appear to be correct. **74. (a)** $s(x) = 0.64x + 26.5$; $m(x) = -0.6x + 49.1$ **(b)** $(18.23, 38.16)$; In 2014 (19 years after 1995), the number of small vehicles and the number of midsize vehicles will be equal. **75.** $x + y = 1.9563 \times 10^{12}$; $y = x + 5.31 \times 10^{10}$; The amounts are 9.516×10^{11} from individual income taxes and 1.0047×10^{12} from other sources. **76.** $\dfrac{x + y}{2} = 2.75 \times 10^{-10}$; $y - x = 4.5 \times 10^{-10}$; the diameters are 5×10^{-11} m for helium and 5×10^{-10} m for cesium.

4.2 CALCULATOR EXERCISES

1. $(153.75, 225.85)$ **2.** $(0.2, 5)$ **3.** $\left(\dfrac{13}{21}, \dfrac{17}{15}\right)$ **4.** $\left(\dfrac{13}{7}, \dfrac{8}{17}\right)$

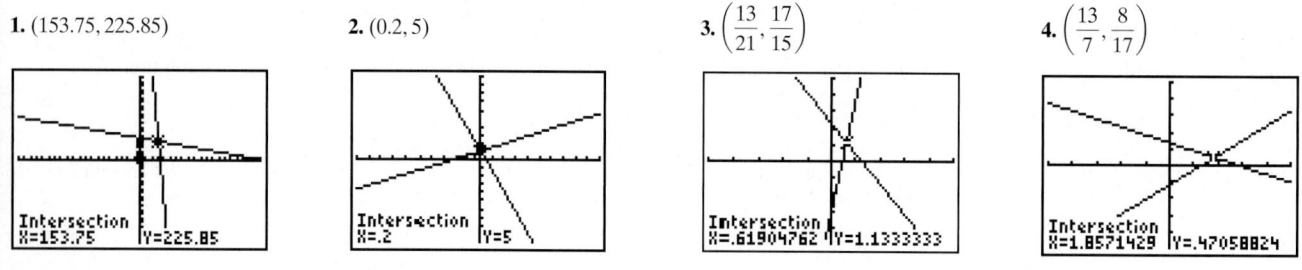

SECTION 4.3 EXERCISES

1. $(-2, 2)$ **2.** $(3, -7)$ **3.** $(5, 2)$ **4.** $(-3, -1)$ **5.** $(-3, -9)$ **6.** $(8, 2)$ **7.** $(8, -2)$ **8.** $(-3, 5)$ **9.** $(4, 3)$ **10.** $(-1, -2)$ **11.** $(7, -9)$ **12.** $(-8, 7)$ **13.** $(-3, 12)$ **14.** $(13, -2)$ **15.** $\left(\dfrac{13}{10}, \dfrac{29}{10}\right)$ **16.** $\left(\dfrac{4}{5}, -\dfrac{7}{5}\right)$ **17.** $\left(-\dfrac{19}{5}, \dfrac{12}{5}\right)$ **18.** $\left(\dfrac{9}{2}, -\dfrac{3}{2}\right)$ **19.** $\left(\dfrac{21}{5}, \dfrac{7}{2}\right)$ **20.** $\left(-\dfrac{9}{5}, -\dfrac{17}{5}\right)$ **21.** $\left(\dfrac{13}{10}, \dfrac{33}{10}\right)$ **22.** $\left(-\dfrac{41}{10}, \dfrac{7}{10}\right)$ **23.** $\left(\dfrac{2}{3}, \dfrac{3}{4}\right)$ **24.** $\left(\dfrac{3}{5}, \dfrac{5}{6}\right)$ **25.** $\left(\dfrac{3}{8}, -\dfrac{3}{4}\right)$ **26.** $\left(\dfrac{7}{9}, -\dfrac{5}{8}\right)$ **27.** all ordered pairs (x, y)

that satisfy $y = \frac{3}{2}x - 9$ **28.** all ordered pairs (x, y) that satisfy $y = \frac{6}{5}x + 2$ **29.** no solution   **30.** no solution   **31.** $(30, -2)$ **32.** $(20, 8)$

33. $(10, 10)$ **34.** $(40, -10)$ **35.** $(-400, -700)$ **36.** $(-250, 550)$ **37.** $\left(\frac{44}{5}, \frac{33}{5}\right)$ **38.** $\left(\frac{43}{10}, -\frac{23}{10}\right)$ **39.** $(52, 48)$ **40.** $(63, 57)$

41. $(7, 4)$ **42.** $(5, 9)$ **43.** $(40, 70)$ **44.** $(80, 20)$ **45.** $(80, 120)$ **46.** $(76, 138)$ **47.** $x + y = 683; 1.5x + 5y = 2645$; there were 220 students who attended the game.   **48.** $x + y = 56; 30x + 45y = 2190$; there were 22 senior citizens and 34 others.   **49.** $x - y = 50; 8.5x + 5y = 3462.5$; they sold 275 cookbooks and 225 calendars.   **50.** $x + y = 5.5; 6x + 4y = 29.5$; they sold her 3.75 pounds of ham and 1.75 pounds of cheese.
51. $x + y = 224.7; y = x - 17.7$; the Rolling Stones grossed \$121.2 million. Pink Floyd grossed \$103.5 million.   **52.** $x + y = 228; y = x + 2$; Michael's time in the 200-meter butterfly was 113 seconds and 115 seconds in the 200-meter medley.   **53.** $x + y = 385; 2x + 2y = 770$; the solution is any number of adults x and any number of children y, where $x + y = 385$.   **54.** $x + y = 8.95; 2x + 2y = 13.95$; there is no solution.
55. $2x + y = 180; y = x + 30$; the three angles measure $50°, 50°$, and $80°$.   **56.** $2x + y = 180; x = y + 30$; the three angles measure $70°, 70°$, and $40°$.
57. $x + y = 180; y - x = 30$; the angles are $75°$ and $105°$.   **58.** $x + y = 90; x = 3y + 7$; the angles measure $20.75°$ and $69.25°$.
59. $x + y = 90; 2y = 150 - 2x$; there are no angles that satisfy the description given.   **60.** $x + y = 180; y = 180 - x$; the angles are any number of

angles x and y, where $x + y = 180$.   **61.** $y = x + 4.864 \times 10^7; \frac{x + y}{2} = 1.1728 \times 10^8$; the distances from the sun are 9.296×10^7 miles for Earth

and 1.416×10^8 miles for Mars.   **62.** $y = 3.6302 \times 10^9 + x; \frac{x + y}{2} = 1.851 \times 10^9$; the distances from the sun are 3.59×10^7 miles for Mercury and

3.661×10^9 miles for Pluto.   **63.** $f + m = 46,050; m = f + 12,426$; the median income for females was \$16,812, and the median income for males was \$29,238.   **64.** $p + i = 762.1; i = 124.6 + 2p$; the out-of-pocket expenditure was 212.5 billion dollars.   **65.** $l + w = 515; l = 2w - 160$; Lucas earned \$290 million; Winfrey earned \$225 million.   **66.** $s + t = 120.4; t = 3s - 13.2$; Tiger earned \$87 million; Shaquille earned \$33.4 million.

4.3 CALCULATOR EXERCISES

1. $(3, -2)$ **2.** $(-2, -3)$ **3.** $(-8, 8)$ **4.** $(0.5, -2.8)$ **5.** $\left(\frac{1}{2}, \frac{2}{3}\right)$ **6.** $\left(\frac{1}{4}, -\frac{2}{3}\right)$

SECTION 4.4 EXERCISES

1. Let x = time driving, y = distance from Nashville; $y = 60x, 220 - y = 65x$; They will meet at a distance of 105.6 miles from Nashville.
2. Let x = time driving, y = distance from Houston; $y = 65x, 240 - y = 55x$; They will meet at a distance of 130 miles from Houston.

3. Let x = time riding, y = distance walking; $y = 6x, 11 - y = 60x$; He walked for $\frac{1}{3}$ hour and rode for $\frac{1}{6}$ hour.   **4.** Let x = time canoeing,

y = distance canoeing; $y = 12x, 30 - y = 3x$; They canoed for 2 hours and hiked for 2 hours. They canoed 24 miles.   **5.** Let x = the time Steve ran and y = the time Steve walked; $x + y = 3.55, 2.3x + 1.2y = 5$; Steve ran approximately 0.67 hour for a distance of approximately 1.5 kilometers and walked approximately 2.88 hours for a distance of approximately 3.5 kilometers.   **6.** Let x = the time on rural roads and y = the time on city

streets; $x + y = \frac{2}{3}, 45x + 35y = 24$; Wei drove $\frac{1}{15}$ hour or 4 minutes on rural roads and $\frac{3}{5}$ hour or 36 minutes on city roads.   **7.** Let x = the

distance Krista drove and y = the time Krista drove; $x = 65y$ and $500 - x = 55(y + 2)$; Krista drove 211.25 miles and her Dad drove 288.75 miles.
8. Let x = the distance Kris drove and y = the time Kris drove; $x = 60y, 600 - x = 50(y + 1)$; Both drove 300 miles.   **9.** Let x = average speed of planes in still air, y = average wind speed; $6(x - y) = 2600, 5(x + y) = 2600$; The average plane speed in still air is about 476.7 miles per hour, and the average wind speed is about 43.3 miles per hour.   **10.** Let x = average speed of planes in still air, y = average wind speed; $4(x - y) = 1750$, $3.5(x + y) = 1750$; The average plane speed in still air is 468.75 mph, and the average wind speed is 31.25 mph.   **11.** Let x = average speed of paddling in still water, y = average current speed; $1.5(x - y) = 6, 0.75(x + y) = 6$; The average speed of paddling was 6 mph, and the average current speed was 2 mph.   **12.** Let x = average speed of the boat in still water, y = average speed of river; $0.75(x + y) = 42, 1(x - y) = 42$; The average speed of the boat in still water is 49 mph, and the average speed of the river is 7 mph.   **13.** Let x = average speed of the boat in still water, y = average speed of the current; $0.25(x + y) = 13.4, 0.3(x - y) = 13.4$; The average speed of the boat in still water is about 49.13 mph, and the average

speed of the current is about 4.47 mph.   **14.** Let x = average speed of the boat in still water and y = average speed of the current; $\frac{1}{3}(x + y) = 14.4$,

$\frac{2}{5}(x - y) = 14.4$; The average speed of the boat in still water is about 39.6 mph, and the average speed of the current was 3.6 mph.

15. Let x = pounds of French vanilla coffee, y = pounds of hazelnut coffee; $x + y = 20, 9.50x + 7.00y = 8.50(20)$; He should use 12 pounds of French vanilla coffee and 8 pounds of hazelnut coffee.   **16.** Let x = pounds of orange spice tea and y = pounds of lemon honey tea; $x + y = 10$, $3.50x + 7.50y = 5.00(10)$; The blend contained 6.25 pounds of orange spice tea and 3.75 pounds of lemon honey tea.   **17.** Let x = the number of azalea plants and y = the number of rhododendron plants; $x + y = 30, 5x + 12y = 250$; She can buy 16 azalea plants and 14 rhododendron plants.
18. Let x = the number of burgers and y = the number of hot dogs; $x + y = 50, 2.50x + 1.00y = 95.00$; She could order 30 burgers and 20 hot dogs.
19. Let x = the number of adults and y = the number of children; $y = 4x, 7.50x + 4.50y = 1938$; There were 76 adults and 304 children.
20. Let x = the number of adults and y = the number of children; $y = 2x, 10.00x + 5.50y = 5355$; There were 255 adults and 510 children.
21. Let x = hourly wage on job 1 and y = hourly wage on job 2; $15x + 20y = 320, 18x + 24y = 384$; Many solutions; any pair of hours (x, y) where $15x + 20y = 320$ will satisfy the system.   **22.** Let x = sale price of shirts and y = sale price of blouses; $2x + 4y = 132, 3x + 6y = 180$; No solution; there are no sale prices that will satisfy this system of equations.   **23.** Let x = number of \$5 bills and y = number of \$10 bills; $x + y = 65, 5x + 10y = 365$; There were 57 \$5 bills and 8 \$10 bills.   **24.** Let x = number of \$20 bills and y = number of \$50 bills; $x + y = 35, 20x + 50y = 1300$; There are 15 \$20 bills and 20 \$50 bills.   **25.** Let x = gallons of grapefruit beverage and y = gallons of orange

beverage; $x + y = 200, 0.45x + 0.75y = 0.55(200)$; They must mix $133\frac{1}{3}$ gallons of grapefruit beverage with $66\frac{2}{3}$ gallons of orange beverage.

26. Let x = pints of 70% solution and y = pints of 40% solution; $x + y = 5, 0.70x + 0.40y = 0.50(5)$; He should mix $1\frac{2}{3}$ pints of 70% solution and

$3\frac{1}{3}$ pints of 40% solution.   **27.** Let x = liters of 60% acid and y = liters of 35% acid; $x + y = 300, 0.60x + 0.35y = 0.50(300)$; He should mix 180

liters of 60% acid with 120 liters of 35% acid.   **28.** Let x = pints of 25% solution and y = pints of 40% solution; $x + y = 8, 0.25x + 0.40y = 0.30(8)$;

She should mix $5\frac{1}{3}$ pints of 25% solution with $2\frac{2}{3}$ pints of 40% solution.   **29.** Let x = the amount of mixing gin and y = the amount of seltzer water; $x + y = 8, 0.36x + 0y = 0.24(8)$; $5\frac{1}{3}$ ounces of mixing gin and $2\frac{2}{3}$ ounces of seltzer water are needed.   **30.** Let x = the amount of the 80% soy solution and y = the amount of the pure dairy formula; 37.5 ounces of the 80% soy solution and 2.5 ounces of the pure dairy formula were mixed. **31.** Let x = gallons of 4.3% milk and y = gallons of skim milk; $x + y = 200, 0.043x + 0y = 0.02(200)$; He should mix about 93 gallons of 4.3% milk with about 107 gallons of skim milk.   **32.** Let x = liters of 45% solution and y = liters of sterile water; $x + y = 25, 0.45x + 0y = 0.35(25)$; Mix $19\frac{4}{9}$ liters of 45% solution with $5\frac{5}{9}$ liters of sterile water.   **33.** Let x = gallons of 45% antifreeze and y = gallons of pure antifreeze; $x + y = 4$, $0.45x + 1.00y = 0.60(4)$; Mabel should drain off about 1.1 gallons and replace with about 1.1 gallons of pure antifreeze.   **34.** Let x = gallons of 35% antifreeze and y = gallons of pure antifreeze; $x + y = 5, 0.35x + 1.00y = 0.50(5)$; The mechanic should drain off about 1.2 gallons and replace with about 1.2 gallons of pure antifreeze.   **35.** Let x = gallons of 12% wine and y = total gallons of 15% wine; $5 + x = y, 0.20(5) + 0.12x = 0.15y$; He should mix $8\frac{1}{3}$ gallons of 12% wine with the 5 gallons of 20% wine to make the 15% wine.   **36.** Let x = ounces of 45% medication and y = ounces of the blended 60% medication; $x + 8 = y, 0.45x + 0.75(8) = 0.60y$; He should mix 8 ounces of the 45% medication with 8 ounces of the 75% to produce 16 ounces of the 60% medication.   **37.** Let x = the amount of the 0.5% solution and y = the total amount; $x + 5 = y, 0.01(5) + 0.005x = 0.0075y$; 5 ounces of the 0.5% solution is needed.   **38.** Let x = the amount of the 90% sandy soil and y = the total amount of soil; $x + 7 = y, 7(0) + 0.90x = 0.10y$; He has 7.875 cubic yards of low-sand dirt.   **39.** Let x = amount invested at 8.5% and y = amount invested at 7%; $x + y = 10,000, 0.085x + 0.07y = 752.50$; She invested $3500 at 8.5% and $6500 at 7%.   **40.** Let x = amount borrowed at 7% and y = amount borrowed at 8.25%; $x + y = 10,000, 0.07x + 0.0825y = 725$; He borrowed $8000 at 7% and $2000 at 8.25%.   **41.** Let x = amount invested at 5% and y = amount invested at 7.25%; $x + y = 16,500, 0.05x + 0.0725y = 1000$; She should invest $8722.22 at 5% and $7777.78 at 7.25%. **42.** Let x = amount invested at 5% and y = amount invested at 7.25%; $x + y = 11,000, 0.05x + 0.0725y = 600$; She should invest $8777.78 at 5% and $2222.22 at 7.25%.   **43.** Let x = the amount invested at 2.5% interest and y = the amount invested at 7.2% interest; $x + y = 7500$, $0.025x + 0.072y = 243.90$; They invested $6300 at 2.5% and $1200 at 7.2%.   **44.** Let x = the value of real estate holdings and y = the value of the stock portfolio; $x + y = 1,500,000, 0.25x + 0.3y = 420,000$; James's real estate was valued at $600,000, and his portfolio was valued at $900,000. **45.** Let x = amount in certificates and y = amount in savings; $x = 2y, 0.0725x + 0.06y = 1230$; She should invest $12,000 in certificates and $6000 in savings.   **46.** Let x = amount in certificates and y = amount in savings; $x = y + 2000, 0.0725x + 0.06y = 1205$; He should invest $10,000 in certificates and $8000 in savings.   **47.** Let x = the balance on the card with 1.6% interest and y = the balance on the card with 2.8% interest; $y = 3x, 0.016x + 0.028y = 200$; the balance on the card with 1.6% interest was $2000, and the balance on the card with 2.8% interest was $6000. **48.** Let x = the amount spent on shoes and y = the amount spent on other items; $x = 2y, 0.20x + 0.30y = 55.50$; She spent $158.57 on shoes and $79.29 on other items.   **49.** Let x = interest rate for $45,000 loan and y = interest rate for $55,000 loan; $x = y + 0.01, 45,000x + 55,000y = 6450$; The interest rate was 7% for the $45,000 loan and 6% for the $55,000 loan.   **50.** Let x = interest rate for $1500 account and y = interest rate for $1200 account; $y = x + 0.003, 1500x + 1200y = 117.90$; The interest rate was about 4.23% for the $1500 investment and about 4.53% for the $1200 investment.

4.4 CALCULATOR EXERCISES

1. Stella is 32 years old, and her son is 12 years old.   **2.** Gulen is 29 years old, and Cecilia is 1 year old.   **3.** Joe is 40 years old, and he will retire at 50 years old.   **4.** Jenny is 15 years old, and Katie is 17 years old.   **5.** On those two birthdays, Mom was 12 and 24 years old. Grandmother was 36 and 48 years old.   **6.** The dresser was 100 years old, and the bed was 48 years old.   **7.** Fric is 21 years old, and Frac is 7 years old.

SECTION 4.5 EXERCISES

1. solution   **2.** not a solution   **3.** solution   **4.** solution   **5.** not a solution   **6.** not a solution   **7.** not a solution   **8.** solution
9. solution   **10.** solution   **11.** not a solution   **12.** solution   **13.** not a solution   **14.** solution   **15.** solution   **16.** not a solution
17. $(4, -3, 7)$ **18.** $(2, -5, -9)$ **19.** $\left(\frac{3}{4}, -\frac{3}{4}, \frac{5}{8}\right)$ **20.** $\left(\frac{1}{3}, \frac{3}{5}, -\frac{2}{3}\right)$ **21.** $\left(0, \frac{9}{5}, -\frac{36}{5}\right)$ **22.** $\left(\frac{9}{2}, -\frac{17}{5}, 0\right)$ **23.** $(573, 471, 283)$
24. $(756, -522, 87)$ **25.** infinite number of solutions; all ordered triples that satisfy $5x - 3y + 7z = 8$ **26.** no solution   **27.** no solution
28. infinite number of solutions; all ordered triples that satisfy $4a - 3b + 7c = -15$

29.
$$12x + 5y + 3.5z = 9547$$
$$x + y + z = 1257$$
$$x - y + z = -87$$
There were 487 adult tickets, 672 child tickets, and 98 resort guest tickets.

30.
$$3.5c + s + 4.25p = 53.5$$
$$c - s - p = 0$$
$$c + s + p = 18$$
Deanna bought nine cups, five saucers, and four dinner plates.

31.
$$x + y + z = 11,200$$
$$x - z = -1400$$
$$0.05x + 0.055y + 0.06z = 623$$
There are an infinite number of solutions.

32.
$$0.015c + 0.0075f + 0.009a = 88.28$$
$$5c - f = 0$$
$$c + f + a = 9850$$
Siegfried's balances are $246.67 on credit card loan, $1233.33 on furniture loan, and $8370 on car loan.

33.
$$x + 5y + 10z = 184$$
$$x - 3y = 0$$
$$x + y + z = 60$$
Ron collected 39 $1 bills, 13 $5 bills, and eight $10 bills.

34.
$$0.32x + 0.03y + 0.35z = 12.25$$
$$x - y = 0$$
$$x + y + z = 50$$
The packet contains 15 $0.32 stamps, 15 $0.03 stamps, and 20 $0.35 stamps.

35.
$$s + m + l = 145$$
$$2.39s + 2.79m + 3.59l = 446.55$$
$$10.8s + 13.5m + 20.4l = 2350 - 4$$
There were 35 small boxes, 40 medium-sized boxes, and 70 large boxes.

36.
$$s + e + t = 77$$
$$6s + 8e + 12t = 60(12) - 4$$
$$3.3s + 4e + 5.4t = 336$$
There is no solution.

37.
$$x + y + z = 15$$
$$z = 3x$$
$$0.02x + 0.03y + 0.07z = 0.055(15)$$
Approximately 3.4 ounces of fragrance 1, 1.4 ounces of fragrance 2, and 10.2 ounces of fragrance 3 should be mixed.

38.
$$o + v + m = 10.5$$
$$0.98o + 0v + 0.67m = 0.5033(10.5)$$
$$o + v = 2m$$
To the nearest tenth of a cup, 3 cups of olive oil, 4 cups of vinegar, and 3.5 cups of mayonnaise should be used.

39.
$$g + l + m = 600$$
$$19.75g + 9.50l + 12m = 7225$$
$$0.50g + 0.10l + 0.90m = 260$$
Tenisha invested $1975 in gold, $2850 in oil, and $2400 in the money market.

40.
$$A + B + C = 65$$
$$18A + 13.2B + 15C = 942$$
$$1.5A + 0.65B + 0.85C = 54.75$$
Hortense purchased 10 units of Ameritag, 35 units of Bankers Fund, and 20 units of Columbia Mutual.

41.
$$1.25x + y + 1.5z = 69.5$$
$$3.5x + 2.5y + 4.5z = 200$$
$$-3x + z = 0$$
Concetta bakes 10 pies, 12 dozen cookies, and 30 cakes.

42.
$$45p + 90s + 15d = 480$$
$$130p + 300s + 55d = 1595$$
$$p - s = 1$$
Gretchen schedules three physicals, two surgeries, and 11 diagnostic treatments.

43.
$$225C + 6.8J + 69.8M = 736$$
$$4.5C + 31.2J + 116.2M = 505$$
$$0.6C + 35.4J + 0.6M = 39$$
The plan should include two servings (2 oz) of cereal, one serving (2 oz) of orange juice, and four servings (8 oz) of milk.

44.
$$6.8H + 2.7B + 2C = 20.3$$
$$11.3H + 28.4B + 6.8C = 64.6$$
$$0.8H + 0.2B + 0.5C = 2.8$$
Chip should have two servings of hot dogs, one serving of beans, and two servings of chips.

45. $A + B + C = 180$
$$C = 2A$$
$$B = \frac{1}{2}(A + C)$$
The angles measure $40°, 60°,$ and $80°$.

46. $x + c + s = 239$
$$x + c = 90$$
$$x + s = 180$$
The angles measure $31°, 59°,$ and $149°$.

4.5 CALCULATOR EXERCISES

1. $(2, 3, -1)$ **2.** $(1, -3, 2)$ **3.** $(0.5, 2, 0.375)$ **4.** $\left(\frac{1}{4}, 3, \frac{2}{3}\right)$ **5.** $(1, 1, 1)$ **6.** $(-1, -1, -1)$ **7.** $(5, 2, -8)$ **8.** $(7, 1, -5)$ **9.** no solution
10. infinite number of solutions; all ordered triples that satisfy $x - y - 4z = 7$.

CHAPTER 4 SUMMARY

Vocabulary Review
1. consistent **2.** inconsistent **3.** dependent **4.** independent **5.** ordered triple

Reflections
1–8. Answers will vary.

CHAPTER 4 SECTION-BY-SECTION REVIEW

1. solution **2.** not a solution **3.** not a solution **4.** not a solution **5.** solution **6.** solution **7.** $(7, 3)$ **8.** $(-4, 2)$ **9.** $(-2, -1)$
10. $\left(\frac{1}{2}, \frac{7}{4}\right)$ **11.** no solution **12.** all ordered pairs (x, y) that satisfy $y = \frac{3}{2}x - 6$ **13.** $(1, -3)$ **14.** $(14, 4)$ **15.** $(25, 400)$ **16.** all ordered

pairs (x, y) that satisfy $y - 1 = 4$ or $y = 5$ **17.** $(-3, 4)$ **18.** $(5, -5)$ **19.** $(-3, -5)$ **20.** $\left(\frac{9}{2}, -\frac{1}{2}\right)$ **21.** $x + y = 5; 125x + 30y = 482.5; 3.5$
hours were spent on the hardware and software, and 1.5 hours were spent on DSL or dial-up lines. **22.** $c(x) = 9.80 + 0.70x; c(x) = 5.00 + x$; if 16 songs are copied, the plans will be equal; the cost is $21.00 per month. **23.** The cost of the nailer and the rental cost will be equal for 47 days of
rental. **24.** $x = 5.26$; the earnings will be the same in 2006. **25.** $\left(-\frac{3}{4}, \frac{5}{8}\right)$ **26.** $(50, 40)$ **27.** no solution **28.** $(-53, -62)$
29. all ordered pairs (x, y) that satisfy $y = 3x + 7$ **30.** $\left(\frac{15}{19}, \frac{10}{19}\right)$ **31.** $(30, 6)$ **32.** $(-10, 2)$ **33.** $(80, 70)$ **34.** $(40, 300)$
35. $x + y = 90; y = 2x + 12$; the difference in the angles is $38°$. **36.** The rectangle is $16\frac{2}{3}$ feet by $41\frac{1}{3}$ feet. **37. (a)** $C(x) = 29x + 450$
(b) $R(x) = 89.95x$ **(c)** $C(x) = 29x + 450, R(x) = 89.95x, x = 7.38$; Therefore, they must acquire and sell eight scooters to break even.
38. When the price is $80, the supply and demand will be equal to 52. **39.** $x = 1.4$ or 2 years after 2001; In 2003, the populations will be equal. The
actual values support this statement. **40.** $(7, -15)$ **41.** $(6, 6)$ **42.** $(-4, 15)$ **43.** $(-3, -4)$ **44.** no solution **45.** $\left(\frac{133}{31}, -\frac{2}{31}\right)$
46. $(4, 8)$ **47.** all ordered pairs (x, y) that satisfy $y = \frac{5}{7}x + 1$ **48.** $\left(\frac{5}{9}, -\frac{7}{9}\right)$ **49.** $\left(\frac{7}{8}, \frac{21}{8}\right)$ **50.** $(10, 5)$ **51.** $(350, -650)$
52. Lucas earned $277.5 million; Gibson earned $197.5 million **53.** She should have 28 small offices and 12 large offices. **54.** The third angle is $90°$.
55. The mass of the Earth is 5.97×10^{24} kg; the mass of Mars is 6.42×10^{23} kg. **56.** $x + y = 150; 0.1x + 0.05y = 0.08(150)$; he should use 90
pounds of 10% nitrogen with 60 pounds of 5% nitrogen. **57.** $0.49x + 0.99y = 0.69(200); x + y = 200$; they should mix 120 pounds of broccoli with
80 pounds of cauliflower. **58.** $x + y = 10; 65x + 45y = 600$; he drove 487.5 miles on the interstate. **59.** $20.5 = (x - y)\frac{7}{20}, 20.5 = (x + y)\frac{1}{3}$;
the boat's speed is about 60.0 mph. The water's speed is about 1.5 mph. **60.** $y = x + 40; 0.25x + 0.30(40) = 0.27y$; the 27% copper alloy contains 60
pounds of the alloy containing 25% copper. **61.** $x + y = 10,000,000; 0.045x + 0.06y = 487,500$; $7,500,000 was invested in the 4.5% interest fund, and
$2,500,000 in the 6% interest fund. **62.** She will need 4 cups of water. She will have 5 cups of the mixture. **63.** Nora traveled $13\frac{1}{3}$ hours.
She traveled 400 miles at 60 miles per hour and 200 miles at 30 miles per hour. **64.** He plans to invest $10,000 in EE bonds and $5000 in I bonds.
65. not a solution **66.** solution **67.** $(11, -15, -22)$ **68.** $\left(\frac{1}{3}, \frac{2}{3}, -2\right)$ **69.** infinite number of solutions; all ordered triples that satisfy
$x + 2y - z = 3$ **70.** infinite number of solutions; all ordered triples that satisfy $x - 3y + 4z = 3$

71.
$$s + t + v = 140$$
$$2.5s + 5t + 7.5v = 637.5$$
$$s - 5t = 0$$
The attendees were 75 students, 15 teachers, and 50 visitors.

72.
$$5C + 3V + 6R = 22$$
$$26C + 0V + 48R = 100$$
$$312C + 237V + 348R = 1446$$
She ate two club sandwiches, two veggie sandwiches, and one roast chicken sandwich.

73.
$$x + y + z = 22$$
$$0.35x + 0.60y + 0.30z = 0.427(22)$$
$$x + y = z$$
2.024 ounces of 35% alloy, 8.976 ounces of 60% alloy, 11 ounces of 30% alloy must be used.

74. The currents are $I_1 = 1$ ampere, $I_2 = 3$ amperes, and $I_3 = 2$ amperes.

CHAPTER 4 MIXED REVIEW

1. $(-14, -6)$ **2.** all ordered pairs (x, y) that satisfy $y = \frac{4}{5}x - 6$ **3.** $(8, -10)$ **4.** $(1200, 900)$ **5.** $(-6, 21)$ **6.** $(-2, -1)$ **7.** no solution

8. $\left(\frac{87}{26}, -\frac{5}{26}\right)$ **9.** $(6, -20)$ **10.** $(3, 7)$ **11.** $\left(-\frac{3}{7}, \frac{6}{7}\right)$ **12.** $\left(\frac{27}{8}, -\frac{21}{8}\right)$ **13.** $(3, -2)$ **14.** no solution   **15.** $(-4, 2)$ **16.** $(3, -3)$

17. no solution   **18.** all ordered pairs (x, y) that satisfy $y = -4x - 3$ **19.** all ordered pairs (x, y) that satisfy $x + 7 = 3$ or $x = -4$

20. all ordered pairs (x, y) that satisfy $y + 9 = 7$ or $y = -2$ **21.** $(6, 5)$ **22.** $(-3, -2)$ **23.** $(5, -2)$ **24.** $(-2, 2)$ **25.** $(1, 1)$ **26.** $(-6, -1)$

27. $(44, -23)$ **28.** $(-12, 5)$ **29.** $(-38, 43)$ **30.** all ordered pairs (x, y) that satisfy $y = 4x - 7$ **31.** $\left(\frac{1}{6}, -\frac{5}{6}\right)$ **32.** $\left(-\frac{3}{5}, -\frac{12}{5}\right)$

33. $\left(\frac{20}{9}, \frac{1}{9}\right)$ **34.** $(723, -491)$ **35.** $\left(\frac{19}{8}, -\frac{21}{8}\right)$ **36.** $\left(180, \frac{5}{9}\right)$ **37.** no solution   **38.** $(120, 180)$ **39.** not a solution   **40.** solution

41. solution   **42.** solution   **43.** not a solution   **44.** solution   **45.** not a solution   **46.** not a solution   **47.** $x + y = 200$; $0.15x + 0.35y = 0.27(200)$; 80 pounds of 15% brass; 120 pounds of 35% brass; 40 pounds more of the 35% alloy will be used.   **48.** $x + 5 = y$; $(1.00)(5) + 0x = 0.98y$; He added 0.10 gallon of oil for a total of 5.10 gallons of fuel.   **49.** $x + y = 180$; $y = x + 10$; the smaller angle measures 85°.   **50.** $x + y = 700$; $0.7x + 0.4y = 400$; there were 100 more women surveyed.   **51.** $x + y = 90$; $y = 3x + 12$; the angles measure 19.5° and 70.5°.   **52.** $x + 18 = y$; $0.15x + 0.25(18) = 0.21y$; she should use 12 cc of the 15% solution to make 30 cc of the mixture.   **53.** $c(x) = 1000 + 200x$; $c(x) = 4000 - 300x$; the cost will be equal for 6 hours.   **54.** $x + y = 50$; $8.5x + 12.5y = 9.5(50)$; the shop should mix 37.5 pounds of gourmet coffee with 12.5 pounds of dutch chocolate.   **55.** $10.75x + 6.5y = 181$; $x + y = 20$; she should work 12 hours at $10.75 per hour and 8 hours at $6.50 per hour.   **56.** $5.75(x - y) = 2600$; $5(x + y) = 2600$; the air speed x equals 486 mph, and the wind speed y is 34 mph.   **57.** $U(x) = 39.95 + 0.15x$; $B(x) = 19.95 + 0.22x$; you must drive at least 286 miles in order for U Rent It to be less costly.   **58.** $C(x) = 7.5 + 2.5x$; $R(x) = 6.5x$; the shopkeeper must produce and sell at least 19 items in order not to lose money.   **59.** $x = 55y$; $545 - x = 60y$; it will take 4.7 hours.   **60.** $x + y = 25,000$; $0.056x + 0.0785y = 1580$; Sharon invested $17,000 at 5.6% and $8000 at 7.85%.   **61.** $y = 2x$; $0.0325x + 0.0367y = 529.50$; she plans to invest $5000 at 3.25% and $10,000 at 3.67%.   **62.** When the price is $65, the supply and demand will equal 36 items.   **63.** $c(x) = 150 + 2x$; $c(x) = 100 + 5(x - 2)$; Nathan can rent the boat for 20 days for the plans to be equal to $190.   **64.** $(-10, 12, 21)$ **65.** $\left(\frac{1}{2}, \frac{3}{4}, -3\right)$ **66.** The three currents are $I_1 = 3.5$ amperes, $I_2 = 2$ amperes, and $I_3 = 1.5$ amperes.

67.
$$4t + 5h + 39b = 92$$
$$19t + 28h + 90b = 255$$
$$289t + 302h + 640b = 2173$$
Matthew ate one turkey sandwich, two ham sandwiches, and two hamburgers.

68.
$$a + h + s = 7.25$$
$$h = 2s - 1$$
$$h = 4a + 1$$
He should use 0.75 pint of algicide, 4 pints of shock, and 2.5 pints of sanitizer.

CHAPTER 4 TEST

1. solution   **2.** all ordered pairs (x, y) that satisfy $y = 4$ **3.** no solution   **4.** $(2, 1)$ **5.** $(-2, 4)$ **6.** no solution   **7.** $\left(\frac{1}{4}, -\frac{3}{8}\right)$

8. no solution   **9.** $(8, 0)$ **10.** $\left(\frac{34}{19}, \frac{13}{19}\right)$ **11. (a)** $C(x) = 5500 + 65x$ **(b)** $R(x) = 125x$ **(c)** $C(x) = 5500 + 65x$
$$R(x) = 125x$$
$$x = 91.67$$
Therefore, 92 items must be produced and sold in order to break even.

12. $y = 3x$; $y = 2(x + 4)$; Kenny's rate was 8 mph and the distance to Dolly was 24 miles.   **13.** $6x + 8y = 58$; $10x + 5y = 55$; the computer takes 3 nanoseconds per addition and 5 nanoseconds per multiplication.   **14.** $x + y = 30$; $1.25x + 2y = 1.5(30)$; he should mix 20 pounds of raisins with 10 pounds of peanuts.   **15.** $c(x) = 50 + 0.50x$; $c(x) = 10 + 3(x - 2)$; the two plans are equal for 18.4 or approximately 18 visits.   **16.** $x + y = 100$; $0.5x + 0.1y = 0.3(100)$; she should mix 50 cc of 50% solution and 50 cc of 10% solution.   **17.** $x + y = 180$; $y = 2x + 15$; the two angles measure 125° and 55°.   **18.** $0.095x + 0.07y = 780$; $x = 2y$; Caitlin invested $6000 in Fund A, and $3000 in Fund B.

19. $36 = \frac{3}{5}(x - y)$; $36 = \frac{1}{2}(x + y)$; the boat's speed is 66 mph; the speed of the current is 6 mph.   **20.** $x + y = 15,000$; $0.0325x + 0.0367y = 500$; she plans to invest $12,024 at 3.25% and $2,976 at 3.67%.   **21.** $x = 60y$; $700 - x = 65y$; they should meet 336 miles from the kennel.

22. $\left(\frac{7}{5}, 2, -\frac{3}{2}\right)$ **23.** infinite number of solutions; all ordered triples that satisfy $x - y - z = 3$.   **24.** Mike makes four bird feeders, eight birdhouses, and three snack tables.   **25.** One solution exists; no solution exists; an infinite number of solutions exist. Answers will vary.

CHAPTER 5

SECTION 5.1 EXERCISES

1. integers less than 24   **2.** integers greater than -2 **3.** no solution   **4.** no solution   **5.** integers greater than $-\dfrac{1}{2}$ **6.** integers less than -6

7. all integers   **8.** all integers   **9.** $x \geq -2$ **10.** $x \leq 2$ **11.** $x > -4$ **12.** $x > 2$ **13.** $x \leq 3$ **14.** $x \geq 2$ **15.** all real numbers

16. all real numbers   **17.** no solution   **18.** no solution   **19.** $x > -3;\ (-3, \infty)$;

20. $x \leq 7;\ (-\infty, 7]$;

21. $x < -6;\ (-\infty, -6)$;

22. $x \leq 0;\ (-\infty, 0]$;

23. $x > 2;\ (2, \infty)$;

24. $x > 7;\ (7, \infty)$;

25. $x > 3.3;\ (3.3, \infty)$;

26. $y > 10.2;\ (10.2, \infty)$;

27. $c \geq 5;\ [5, \infty)$;

28. $a \geq 0;\ [0, \infty)$;

29. $z \geq 6;\ [6, \infty)$;

30. $p \leq 1;\ (-\infty, 1]$;

31. $b > \dfrac{1}{2};\ \left(\dfrac{1}{2}, \infty\right)$;

32. $z < -\dfrac{1}{4};\ \left(-\infty, -\dfrac{1}{4}\right)$;

33. $x \geq 1;\ [1, \infty)$;

34. $x \leq 1;\ (-\infty, 1]$;

35. $x > 8.8;\ (8.8, \infty)$;

36. $x > 0;\ (0, \infty)$;

37. $x \leq \dfrac{1}{2};\ \left(-\infty, \dfrac{1}{2}\right]$;

38. $p \geq -\dfrac{3}{8};\ \left[-\dfrac{3}{8}, \infty\right)$;

39. $b > -120;\ (-120, \infty)$;

40. $x > -66;\ (-66, \infty)$;

41. no solution   **42.** no solution   **43.** all real numbers;

$(-\infty, \infty)$;

44. all real numbers; $(-\infty, \infty)$;

45. $-3 \leq x \leq 7;\ [-3, 7]$;

46. $-2 \leq x \leq 5;\ [-2, 5]$;

47. $-\dfrac{7}{3} \leq x < -\dfrac{1}{3};\ \left[-\dfrac{7}{3}, -\dfrac{1}{3}\right)$;

48. $-1 \leq x < \dfrac{1}{5};\ \left[-1, \dfrac{1}{5}\right)$;

49. $-\dfrac{2}{3} \leq x \leq 3;\ \left[-\dfrac{2}{3}, 3\right]$;

50. $-\dfrac{11}{2} < x < -3;\ \left(-\dfrac{11}{2}, -3\right)$;

51. $350 + 215x \leq 4000$; he can afford no more than 16 appointments.

52. $150 + 70x \le 400$; she can afford no more than 3 hours.   **53.** $15,000 - 1050x > 5500$; his vehicle will be worth more than $5500 for 9 years.
54. $6000 - 200x > 1500$; his balance will be more than $1500 for 22 months.   **55.** $9.75x + 5200 \le 7500$; he can work 235 hours or less.
56. $22 + 3.5x \le 55$; he can use the grinder 9 hours or less.   **57.** $35x + 30(120 - x) \le 4000$; She can order at most 80 meat entreés.
58. $40x + 35(75 - x) \le 2750$; she can order 25 or less meat entrée plates.   **59.** $39.99 + 0.10(x - 500) < 29.99 + 0.05x$; Helen can use less than 800 minutes for the new offer to be less than her current plan.   **60.** $49.99 + 0.59x < 35.99 + 0.75(x - 150)$; the first plan will be less than the second plan for more than 791 miles driven.   **61.** $\dfrac{93 + 97 + 92 + 89 + 95 + x}{6} \ge 93$; Lee must score 92 or better.   **62.** $\dfrac{38 + 62 + 56 + 42 + x}{5} > 50$; she must earn more than $52.   **63.** $2w + 2(2w + 10) \le 300$; the possible widths are $46\frac{2}{3}$ feet or less.   **64.** $2x + 2(2x + 15) \le 240$; the width must be 35 feet or less.   **65.** $x + 2x + (2x + 5) < 25$; the first side is less than 4 inches.   **66.** $x + x + (2x - 7) < 107$; the shorter sides are less than $28\frac{1}{2}$ feet.   **67.** $0.17x - 45 \ge 50$; at least 559 prints must be produced each day.   **68.** $3.55x - (1.25x + 165) \ge 150$; at least 137 orders must be sold each day.   **69.** $0.146x + 1 < 30$; The weight must be less than 198.6 pounds.   **70.** $0.125x + 0.7 < 27$; The weight must be less than 210.4 pounds.
71. $32 < \frac{9}{5}C + 32 < 212$; the degrees Celsius between freezing of water and the boiling of water is 0 degrees and 100 degrees.
72. $0 < \frac{5}{9}(F - 32) < 100$; the degrees Fahrenheit between freezing of water and the boiling of water is 32 degrees and 212 degrees.
73. $82 < \dfrac{82 + 83 + 88 + 92 + x}{5} < 88$; The temperature for the fifth day must be between 65° and 95°.
74. $18 < \dfrac{16.79 + 18.74 + 17.99 + x}{4} < 20$; The closing price must be between $18.48 and $26.48.   **75.** $2000 < 17,500 - 3150x < 10,000$; the value will be between $2000 and $10,000 for 3 and 4 years.   **76.** $60.00 < 28.99 + 0.09x < 75.00$; the monthly bill will be between $60.00 and $75.00 for minutes between 345 and 511.   **77.** $20,730t + 508,604 > 1,000,000$; the population will exceed one million in 2026 and after.   **78.** $-4861t + 338,353 < 250,000$; the population will drop below 250,000 in 2021 and after.   **79.** $27,259 + 2944x > 50,000$; the earnings will exceed $50,000 in 2009 and after.
80. $38,885 + 544x < 50,000$; the earnings will be less than $50,000 for less than 20 years.

5.1 CALCULATOR EXERCISE

Answers will vary.

SECTION 5.2 EXERCISES

1. linear; $x + 1.7y > -4.6$ **2.** nonlinear   **3.** nonlinear   **4.** linear; $-5x + 10y \ge 15$ **5.** nonlinear   **6.** nonlinear   **7.** linear; $6x - 2y > 1$
8. nonlinear   **9.** linear; $4x - y \le -16$ **10.** linear; $-4.2x + 3.5y < -2.8$ **11.** linear; $6x + 15y \le 7$ **12.** linear; $x + 2y < 12$

Unless indicated the scale of each graph is one unit per tick mark.

13. $y < -2x + 3$

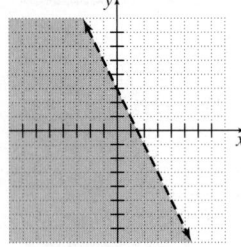

14. $y > 5x - 6$

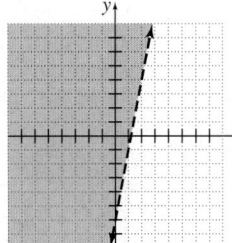

15. $y \le \frac{5}{3}x - 2$

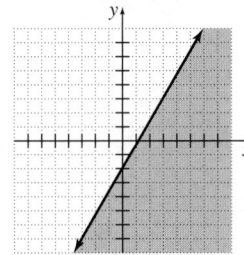

16. $y \ge -\frac{8}{7}x + 2$

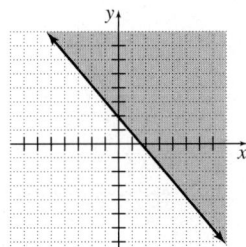

17. $y < -\frac{3}{4}x + 4$

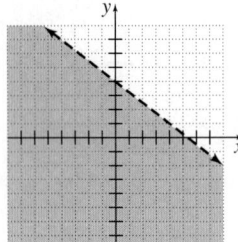

18. $y < \frac{5}{6}x - 3$

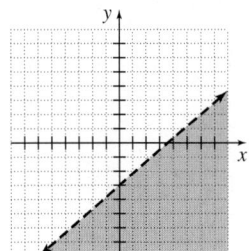

19. $y \ge 2.8x - 1.6$

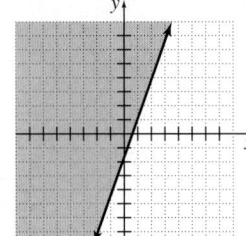

20. $y \ge -1.9x + 4.7$

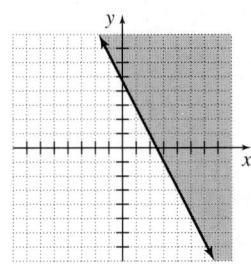

21. $y > \dfrac{3}{2}x - \dfrac{5}{2}$

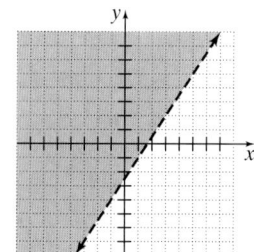

22. $y > \dfrac{3}{5}x - \dfrac{2}{5}$

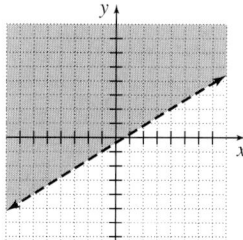

23. $y \geq 2x - 1$

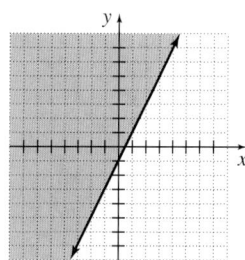

24. $y \leq -2x - 7$

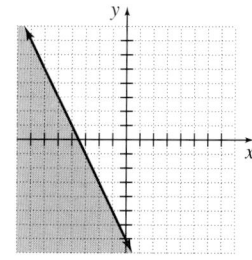

25. $y > -4$

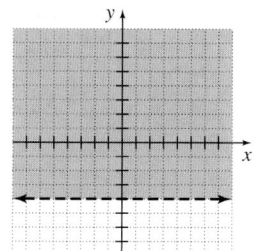

26. $y > 6$

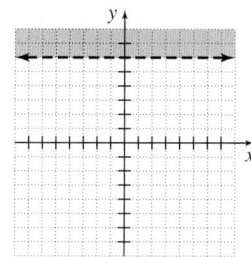

27. $x \leq 1$

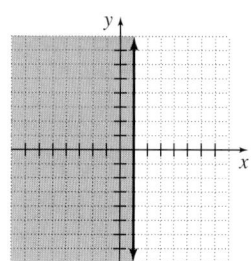

28. $x \leq 5$

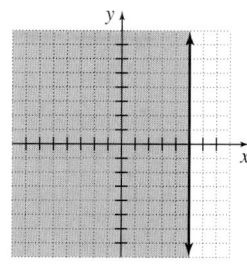

29. $y \geq -\dfrac{3}{5}x + \dfrac{12}{5}$

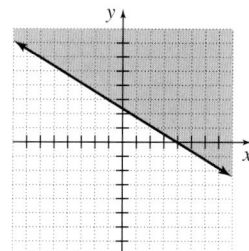

30. $y \geq -\dfrac{7}{9}x + 7$

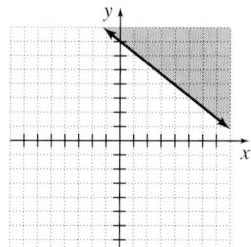

31. $y > -x - 7$

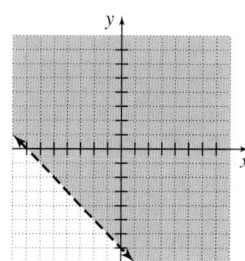

32. $y < x - 3$

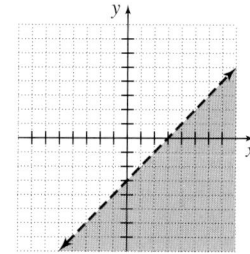

33. $y < -\dfrac{1}{3}x - 3$

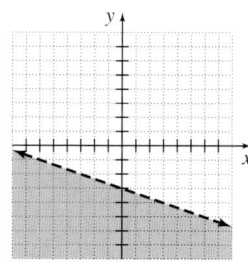

34. $y < -\dfrac{4}{3}x - 4$

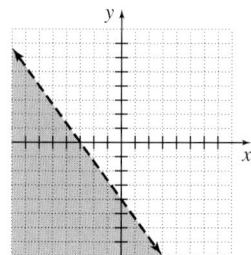

35. $y \leq -\dfrac{3}{8}x + 3$

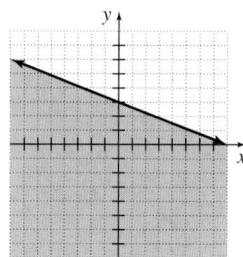

36. $y \geq \dfrac{2}{3}x - 6$

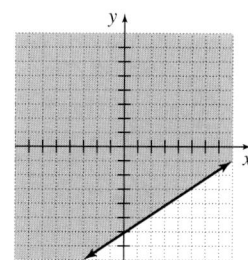

37. $y \geq \dfrac{6}{7}x + \dfrac{5}{7}$

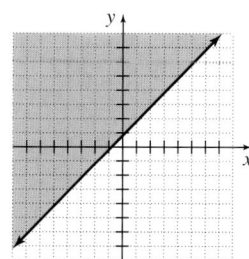

38. $y \leq \dfrac{9}{10}x - \dfrac{13}{20}$

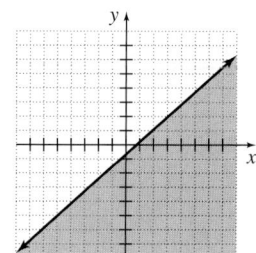

39. $y < 0.5625x$

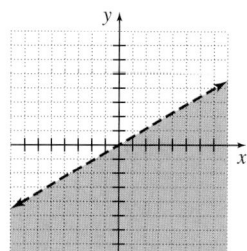

40. $y > -3x$

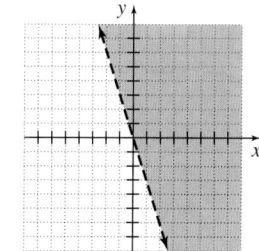

41. $y < 5.4$

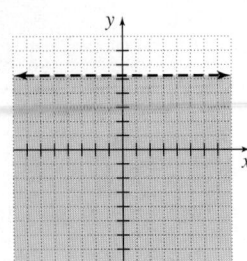

42. $y > 0.25$

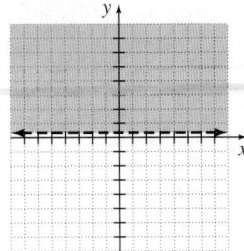

43. $y < x - 9$

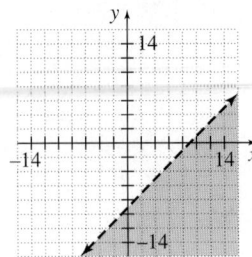

44. $y > x + 9$

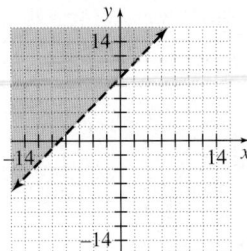

45. $y < -x - 9$

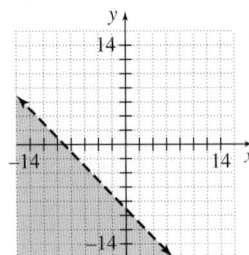

46. $y > -x + 9$

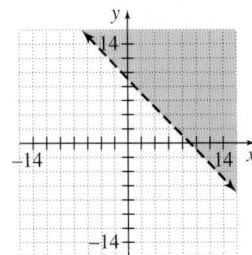

47. $y \leq x$

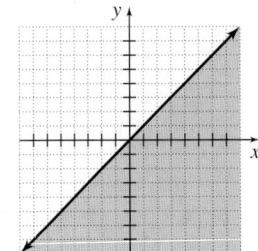

48. $y \geq -x$

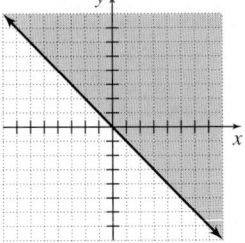

49. $25x + 12y \leq 225$

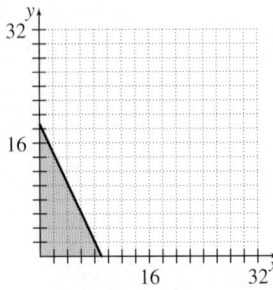

ordered pairs in the shaded region; yes; no

50. $12x + 18y \leq 240$

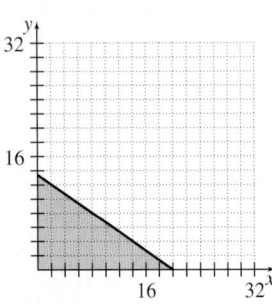

ordered pairs in the shaded region; yes; no

51. $25x + 20y \leq 5100$

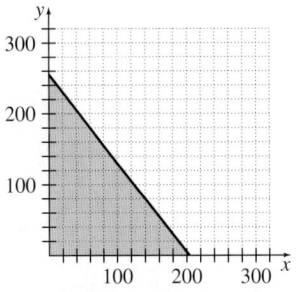

ordered pairs in the shaded region; yes; yes

52. $30x + 20y \leq 600$

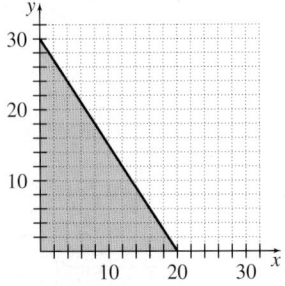

ordered pairs in the shaded region; no; yes

53. $15x + 12y \geq 400$

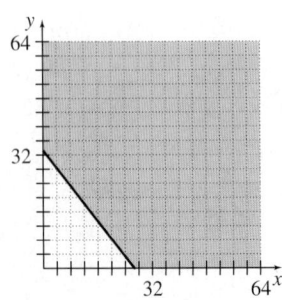

ordered pairs in the shaded region; no; yes

54. $10x - 15y \geq 75$

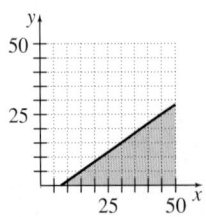

ordered pairs in the shaded region; yes; no

55. $4.5x + 2y \geq 250$

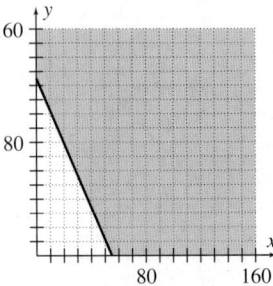

ordered pairs in the shaded region; no; yes

56. $160x + 65y \leq 2000$

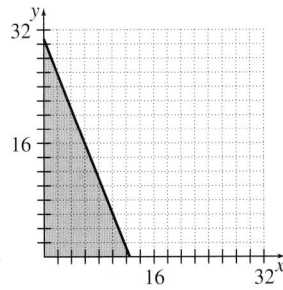

ordered pairs in the shaded region; yes; no

57. $4x + 0.18y \geq 180$

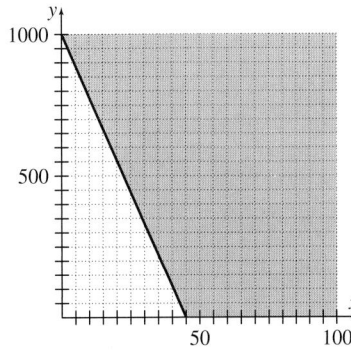

ordered pairs in the shaded region; yes

58. $1.50x + 0.20(y - 5000) \leq 1000$

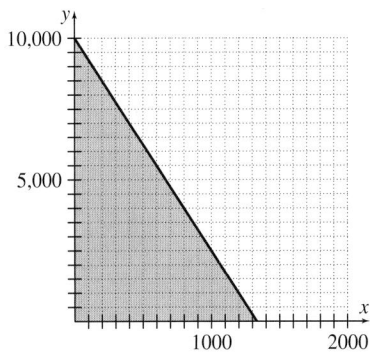

ordered pairs in the shaded region; yes

59. $2x + 2y \leq 220$

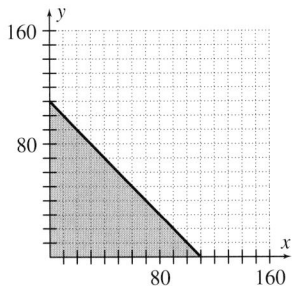

ordered pairs in the shaded region; no; yes

60. $2(10x + 10y) \leq 2400$

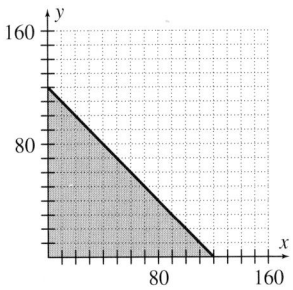

ordered pairs in the shaded region; no; yes

61. $2x + y \leq 107$

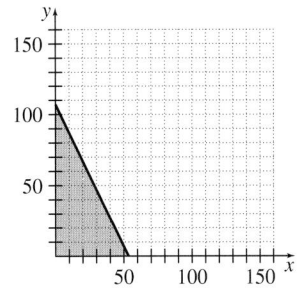

ordered pairs in the shaded region; no; yes

62. $5x + y < 500$

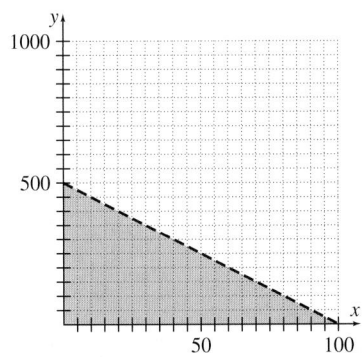

ordered pairs in the shaded region; yes; no

63. $6.85x + 9.30y \leq 160.00$

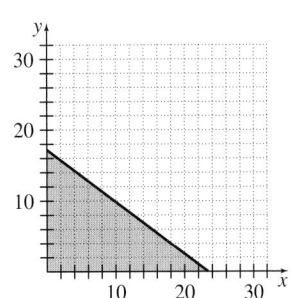

ordered pairs in the shaded region;
a possible combination is fifteen 3-pound packages and six 5-pound packages

64. $5.05x + 9.85y \leq 125.00$

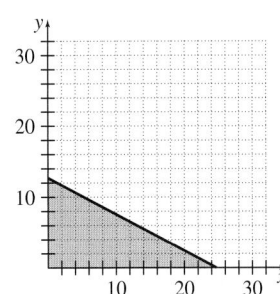

ordered pairs in the shaded region;
a possible combination is twelve 2-pound packages and six 5-pound packages

5.2 CALCULATOR EXERCISES

Answers will vary.

SECTION 5.3 EXERCISES

Unless indicated the scale of each graph is one unit per tick mark.

1.

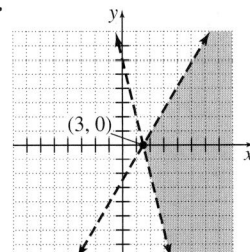

2.

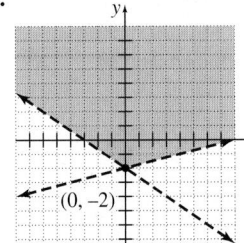

3.

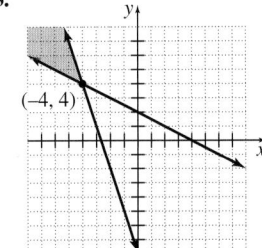

4.

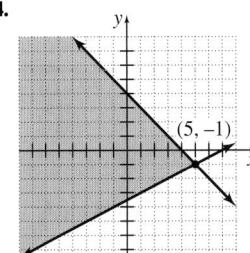

5.
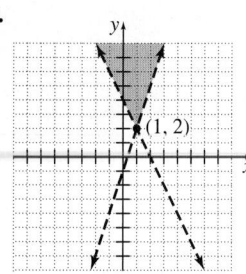
(1, 2)

6.
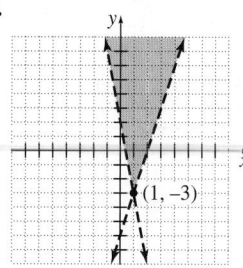
(1, −3)

7.
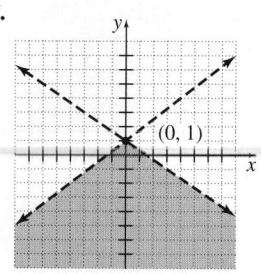
(0, 1)

8.
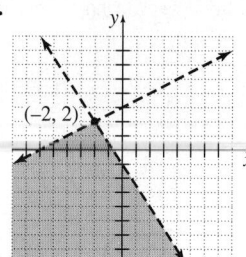
(−2, 2)

9.
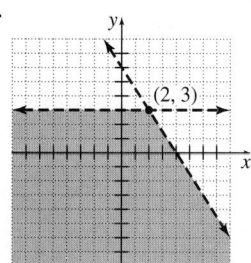
(2, 3)

10.
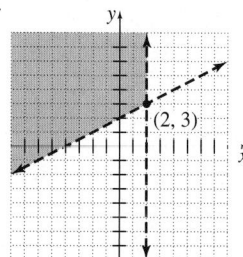
(2, 3)

11.
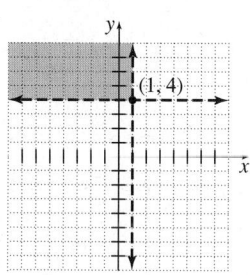
(1, 4)

12.
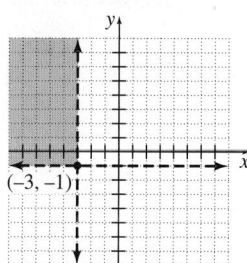
(−3, −1)

13.
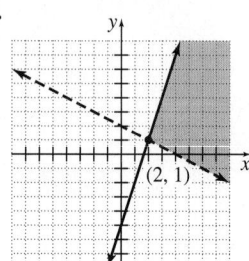
(2, 1)

14.
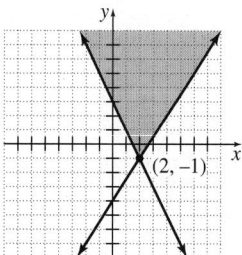
(2, −1)

15.
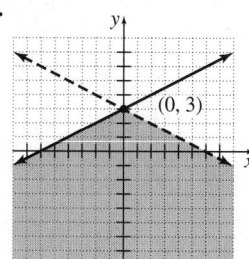
(0, 3)

16.
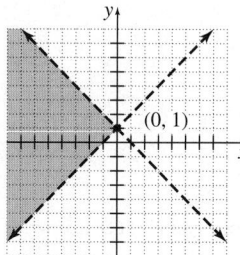
(0, 1)

17.
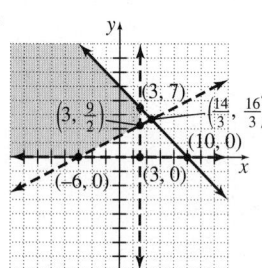
$(3, 7)$; $\left(3, \frac{9}{2}\right)$; $\left(\frac{14}{3}, \frac{16}{3}\right)$; $(10, 0)$; $(3, 0)$; $(-6, 0)$

18.
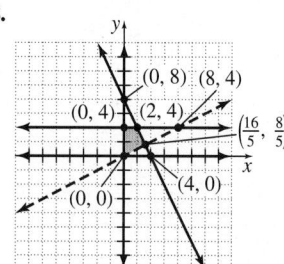
$(0, 8)$; $(8, 4)$; $(0, 4)$; $(2, 4)$; $\left(\frac{16}{5}, \frac{8}{5}\right)$; $(0, 0)$; $(4, 0)$

19.
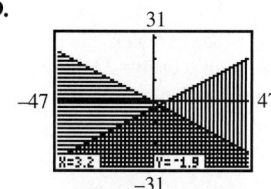

20.
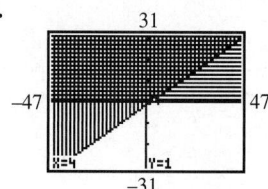

21.
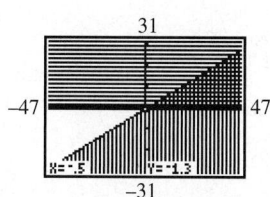

22.
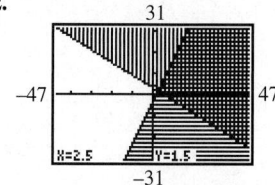

23.
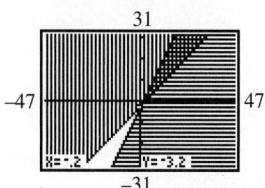

24.
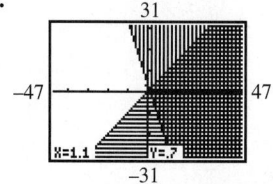

25.
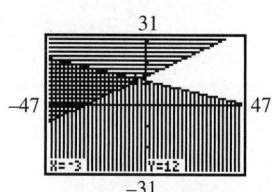

26.
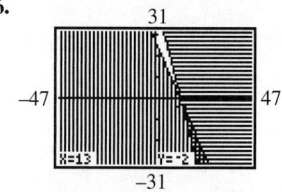

27.
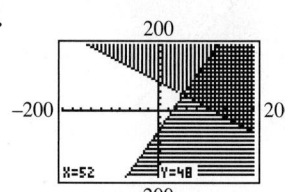

28.
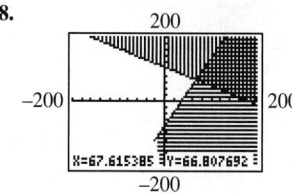

29.
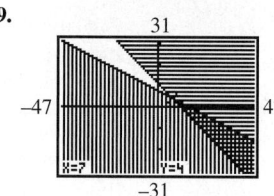

30.
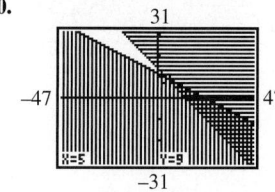

31. $2x + 2y \leq 100$
   $y \geq x + 10$
   $x > 0$
   $y > 0$

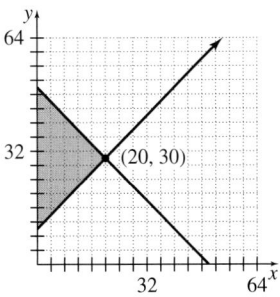

possible answer:
10 feet by 30 feet

32. $2x + 2y \leq 100$
   $y \geq 2x$
   $x > 0$
   $y > 0$

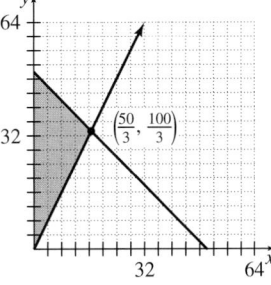

possible answer:
5 feet by 25 feet

33. $x + y \leq 180$
   $x > 10y + 9$
   $x > 0$
   $y > 0$

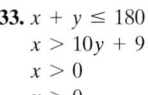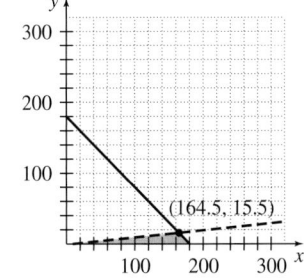

possible measures: 150° and 10°

34. $x + y \geq 90$
   $y \leq 3x - 7$
   $x > 0$
   $y > 0$

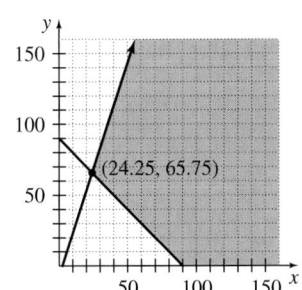

possible measures: 30° and 70°

35. $x + y \leq 3000$
   $0.06x + 0.08y \geq 200$
   $x \geq 0$
   $x \geq 0$

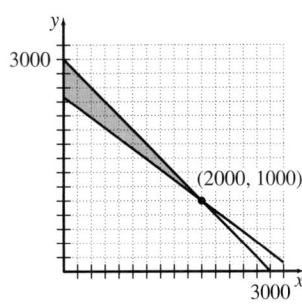

possible answer:
$1000 at 6%; $2000 at 8%

36. $x + y \leq 5000$
   $0.06x + 0.08y \geq 350$
   $x \geq 0$
   $y \geq 0$

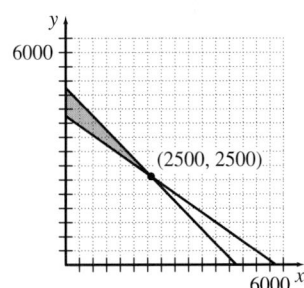

possible answer:
$1000 at 6%; $4000 at 8%

37. $x \geq 5y$
   $0.00525x + 0.00675y \leq 90$
   $x > 0$
   $y > 0$

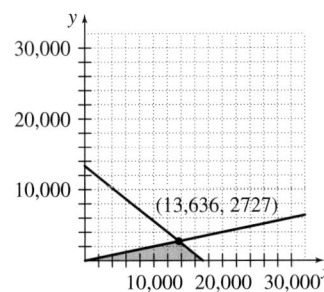

possible combination: $12,000 at 0.525% and
$1000 at 0.675%

38. $y \geq 3x$
   $0.026x + 0.038y > 180$
   $x > 0$
   $y > 0$

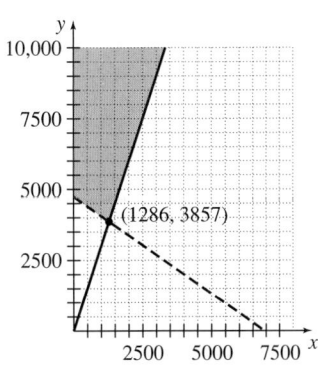

possible combination: $1000 at 2.6% and
$10,000 at 3.8%

39. $0.25x + 0.30y > 25,000$
   $x + y < 500,000$
   $x > 0$
   $y > 0$

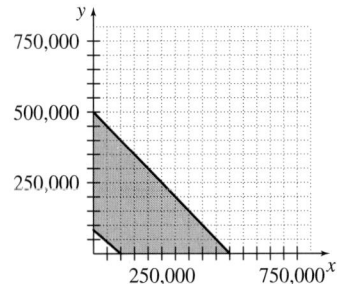

possible values: $250,000 real estate holdings
and $200,000 stock portfolio

40. $0.035x + 0.095y \geq 2500$
$x + y \leq 750{,}000$
$x > 0$
$y > 0$

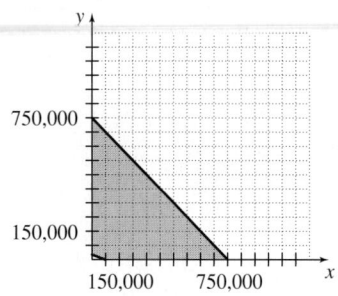

possible amounts: $500,000 with 3.5% gain and $10,000 with 9.5% gain

41. $x + y \leq 20$
$6.5x + 8.25y \geq 150$
$x \geq 0$
$y \geq 0$

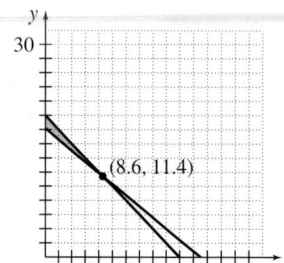

possible answer: He could work 6 hours on the first job and 14 hours on the second job; no; yes

42. $20x + 5y \leq 150$
$x \geq 1.5$
$y \geq 0$

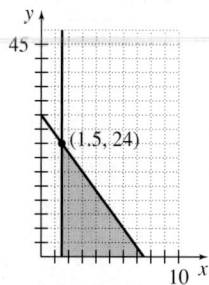

possible answer: One possible combination is three rental hours and 15 guests; yes; no

43. $1.75x + 2.25y \leq 200$
$x \geq 50$
$y \geq 25$

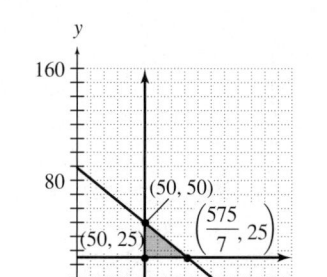

possible answer: 75 servings of lasagna and 30 servings of veal; yes; no

44. $0.05x > 0.01x + y$
$x > 25{,}000$
$y \geq 1399$

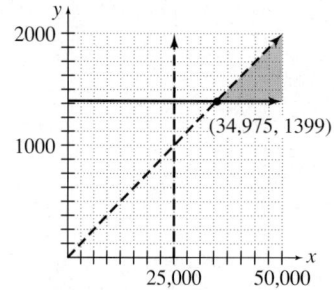

possible answer: 45,000 copies and $1600 machine cost; no; yes

45. $x + y \leq 20$
$6.85x + 9.30y \leq 160.00$
$x \geq 0$
$y \geq 0$

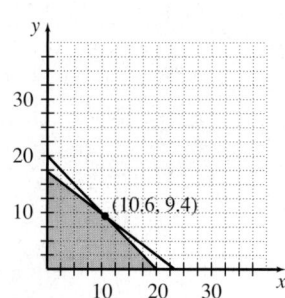

possible combination: ten 3-pound packages and five 5-pound packages

46. $x + y \leq 20$
$5.05x + 9.85y \leq 125.00$
$x \geq 0$
$y \geq 0$

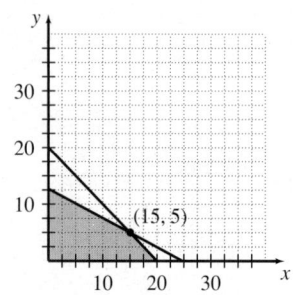

possible combination: fifteen 2-pound packages and two 5-pound packages

5.3 CALCULATOR EXERCISES

1.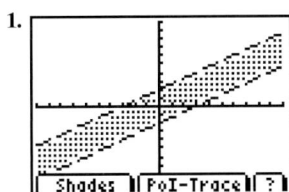

The solution is all ordered pairs contained in the shaded region.

2.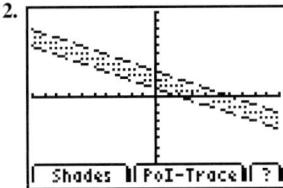

The solution is all ordered pairs contained in the shaded region.

3.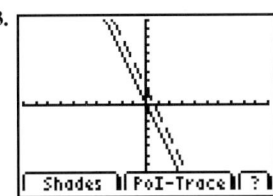

There are no ordered pairs that satisfy this system of linear inequalities.

4.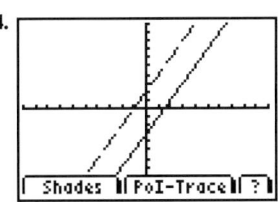

There are no ordered pairs that satisfy this system of linear inequalities.

5.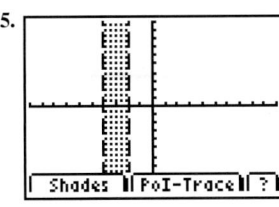

The solution is all ordered pairs contained in the shaded region.

6.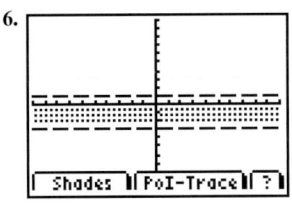

The solution is all ordered pairs contained in the shaded region.

7.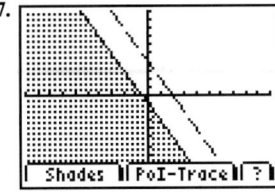

The solution is all ordered pairs below and including the boundary line.

8.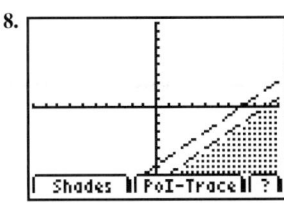

The solution is all ordered pairs below the boundary line $y = x - 9$.

9.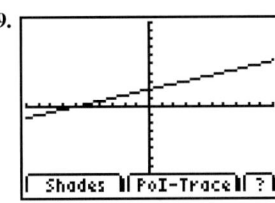

The solution is all ordered pairs on the line $3y = x + 6$ or $y = \frac{1}{3}x + 2$.

10.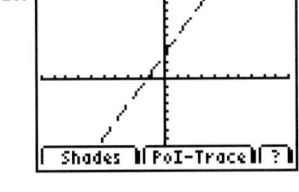

There are no ordered pairs that satisfy this system of linear inequalities.

11.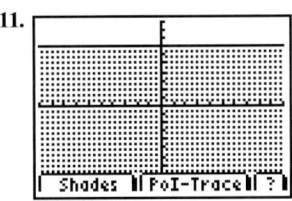

The solution is all ordered pairs below the line $y = 7$. Note, the line is solid but is not part of the solution.

12.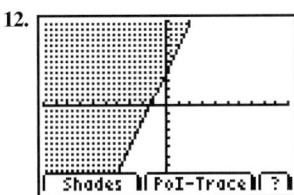

The solution is all ordered pairs above and including the boundary line $y = 3x + 4$.

CHAPTER 5 SUMMARY

Vocabulary Review

1. linear inequality in one variable   **2.** linear inequality in two variables   **3.** system of linear inequalities in two variables   **4.** interval notation

Reflections

1–7. Answers will vary.

CHAPTER 5 SECTION-BY-SECTION REVIEW

1. nonlinear   **2.** linear   **3.** linear   **4.** nonlinear   **5.** linear   **6.** nonlinear   **7.** linear   **8.** linear   **9.** integers less than -6 **10.** integers greater than 6   **11.** integers less than or equal to 3   **12.** integers greater than or equal to -2

13. $x > 2$
$(2, \infty)$

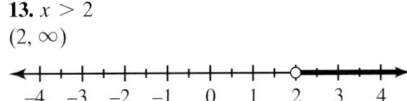

14. $x \leq 2.4$
$(-\infty, 2.4]$

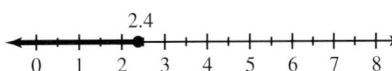

15. no solution

16. all real numbers
$(-\infty, \infty)$

17. $(259, \infty)$ **18.** $\left(-\infty, \frac{32}{39}\right)$ **19.** $(-14, \infty)$ **20.** no solution   **21.** $(-\infty, -3.4]$ **22.** $[1.4, \infty)$ **23.** $(0, \infty)$ **24.** no solution

25. $[2, 3.5)$ **26.** $[8, 12)$ **27.** $49.95 + 0.18x \leq 150$; the number of miles driven should be less than or equal to 555 miles.

28. $\dfrac{2100 + 1300 + 1650 + 1250 + 1725 + x}{6} > 1500$; his sales should be greater than \$975.   **29.** $2x + 2(x + 4) \le 40$; the width can be no more

than 8 feet.   **30.** $35x - (20x + 225) \ge 500$; they must have at least 49 students per day.   **31.** $88 \le \dfrac{89 + 96 + 89 + 80 + 100 + x}{6} \le 92$;

the student must score 74 to 98 on the last test.   **32.** $0.15x + 2 \ge 27$, the weight must be at least $166\frac{2}{3}$ pounds.

33. $49.99 + 0.10(x - 500) < 39.99 + 0.05x$; the second plan will be less than the first plan for less than 800 minutes of long distance per month.
34. $0.3t + 10.4 > 15$; in 2016 and after, the number of deaths by suicide will exceed 15 per 100,000.   **35.** linear; $x + 2y < 12$ **36.** linear;
$6x - 9y > -5$ **37.** nonlinear   **38.** linear; $3x - 14y > -29$ **39.** nonlinear   **40.** nonlinear

41. $y < -2x + 8$

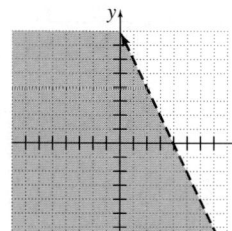

42. $y > \dfrac{3}{5}x - 6$

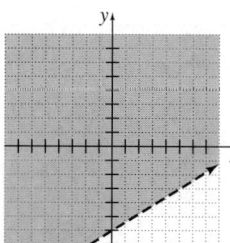

43. $y \le \dfrac{1}{4}x + 3$

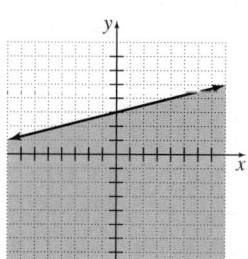

44. $y \ge 3$

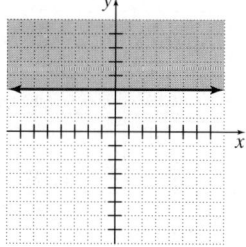

45. $y < -2$

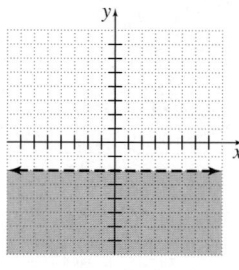

46. $x > 2$

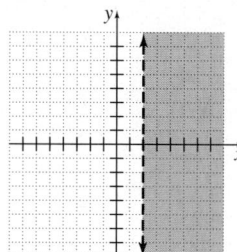

47. $y < \dfrac{2}{3}x - 2$

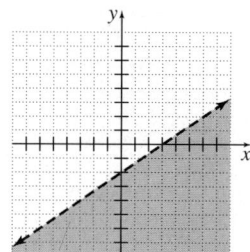
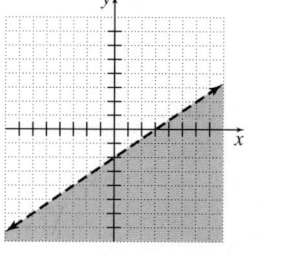
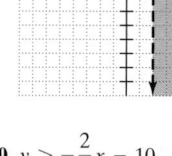

48. $y \ge -4x + 11$

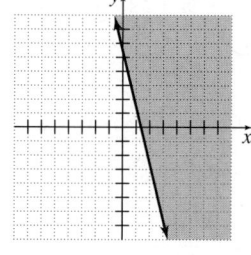

49. $y \ge 0.5x - 2$

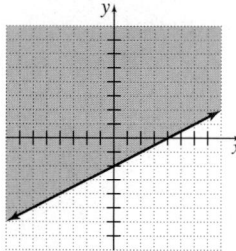

50. $y > -\dfrac{2}{3}x - 10$

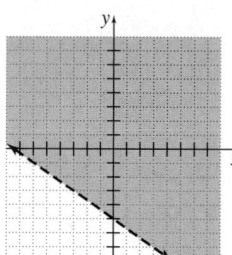

51. $y > -x - 2$

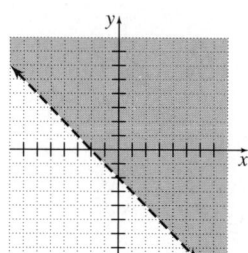

52. $y > -9x + 6$

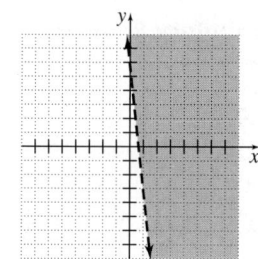

53. $4x + 6y \le 85$

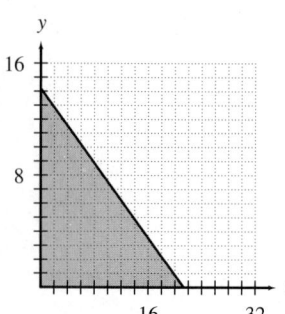

54. $5x - 3y \ge 80$

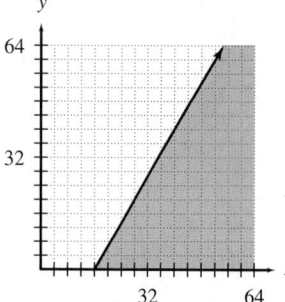

55. $2x + 2y \le 1080$

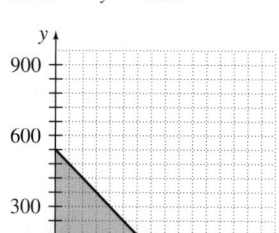

56. $3.50x + 1.50y \le 40.00$

possible answer: 15 rhododendrons and 2 azaleas, or 10 rhododendrons and 5 azaleas

possible answer: 40 correct and 3 incorrect, or 30 correct and 0 incorrect

ordered pairs in the shaded region; yes; a possible dimension is 300 feet by 150 feet.

ordered pairs in the shaded region; no; a possible number of sessions is 7 for a total of 140 minutes.

57.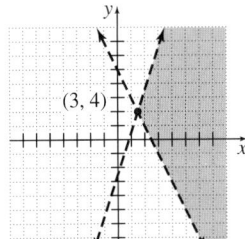

58.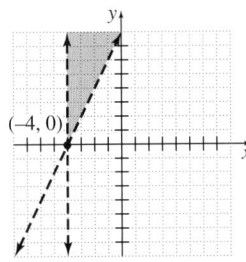

59.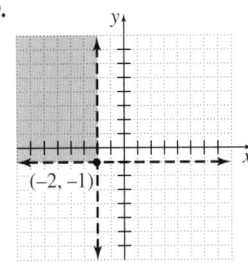

60.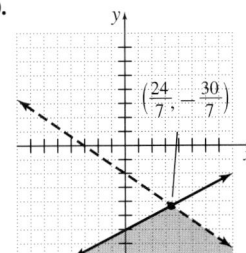

61.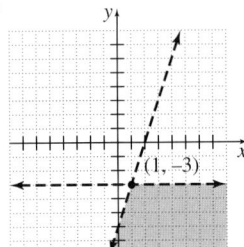

62.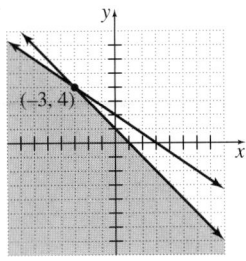

63.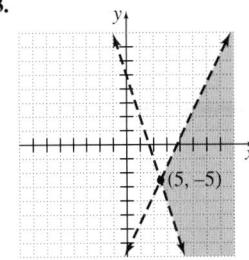

64.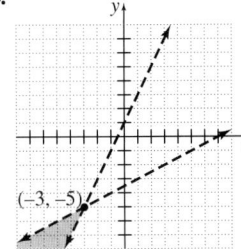

65.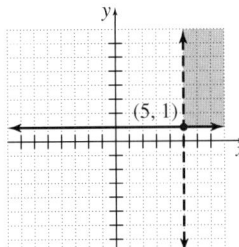

66.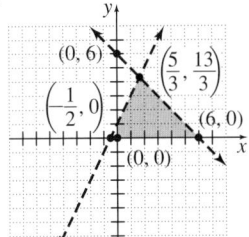

67.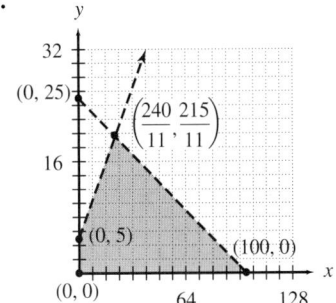

68. $4x + 6y \leq 85$
$y + 4 \leq x$
$x \geq 0$
$y \geq 0$

69. $0.05x + 0.06y \geq 225$
$x + y \leq 4000$
$x \geq 0$
$y \geq 0$

70. $2x + 2y < 175$
$y > x + 15$
$x \geq 0$
$y \geq 0$

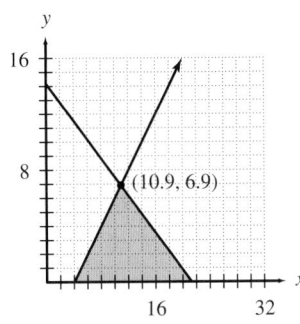

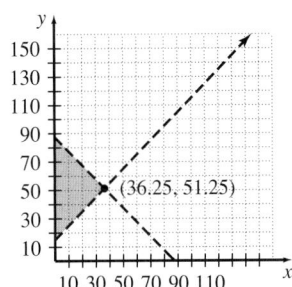

possible dimension: 20 feet by 50 feet

possible answer: 15 rhododendrons and 2 azaleas   possible answer: $200 at 5% and $3800 at 6%

CHAPTER 5 MIXED REVIEW

1. nonlinear   **2.** linear   **3.** nonlinear   **4.** linear   **5.** nonlinear   **6.** $5x + y \leq -18$ **7.** integers less than -4
8. integers greater than 8   **9.** integers less than or equal to -3 **10.** integers less than or equal to 14

11. $x > 2$
$(2, \infty)$

12. $x \leq -4.2$
$(-\infty, -4.2]$

13. all real numbers
$(-\infty, \infty)$

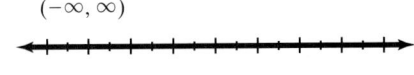

14. no solution **15.** $(-186, \infty)$ **16.** $\left(\dfrac{23}{34}, \infty\right)$ **17.** $(7, \infty)$ **18.** no solution **19.** $[-2.8, \infty)$ **20.** $(-\infty, -3.7]$ **21.** $(-\infty, -1)$ **22.** $(-\infty, \infty)$ **23.** $\left(\dfrac{7}{4}, 3\right]$

24.
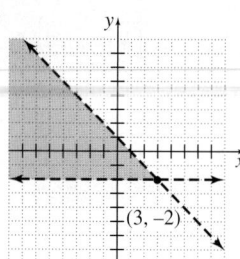

25.
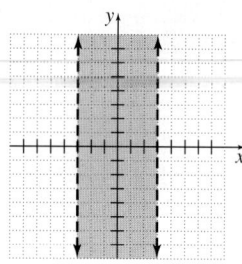

26.
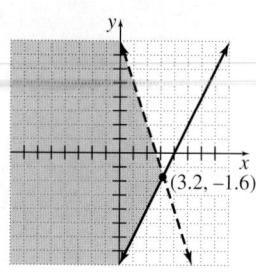

27.
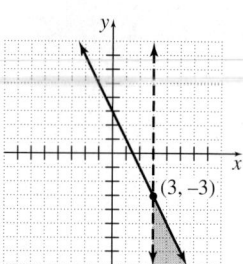

28.
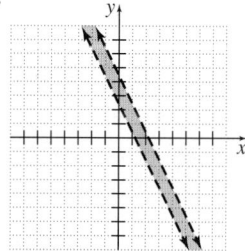

29.
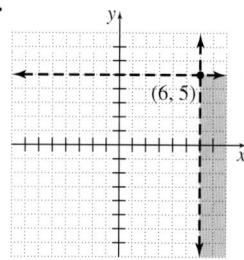

30.
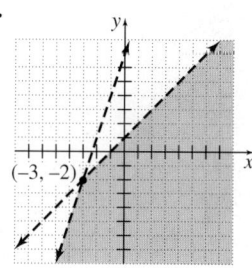

31.
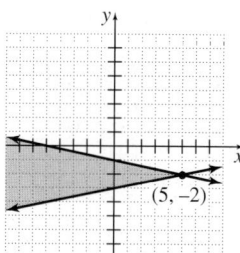

32.
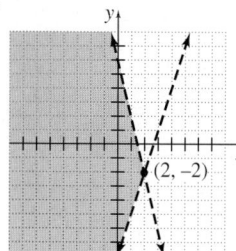

33.
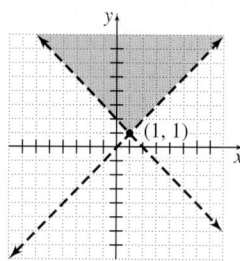

34.
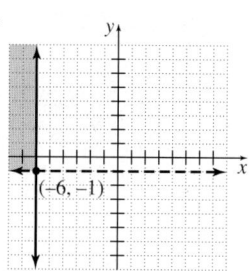

35.
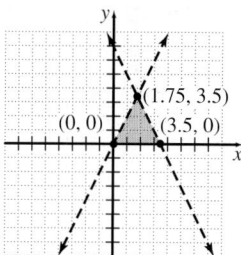

36.
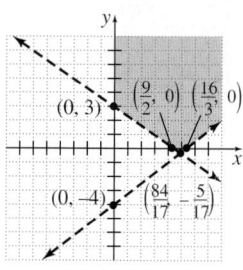

37. $y > \dfrac{9}{5}x - 9$
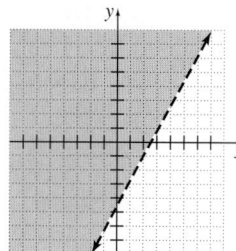

38. $y > \dfrac{4}{3}x - 5$
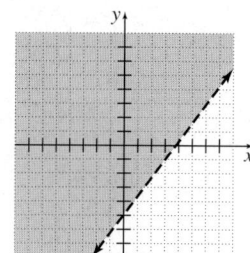

39. $y \le \dfrac{2}{3}x + 3$
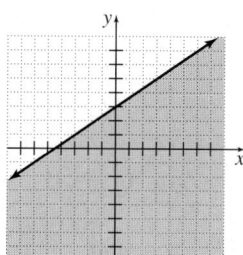

40. $y \ge -5$
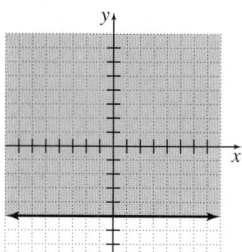

41. $y > \dfrac{5}{3}$
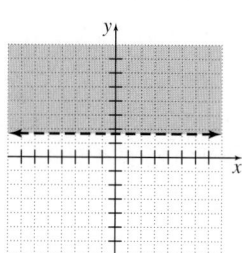

42. $x < -16$
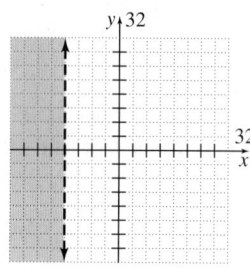

43. $y < \dfrac{1}{7}x - 3$
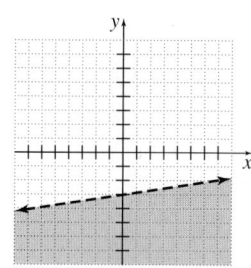

44. $y \geq -0.5x + 3$

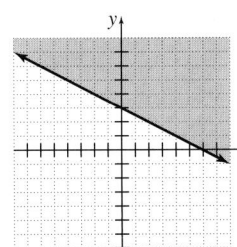

45. $y \geq \frac{8}{3}x - 8$

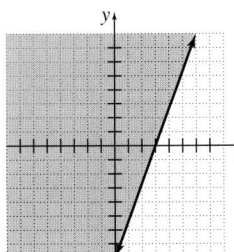

46. $y > -\frac{3}{4}x - 3$

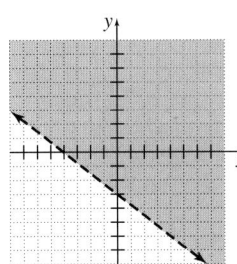

47. $y > x - 7$

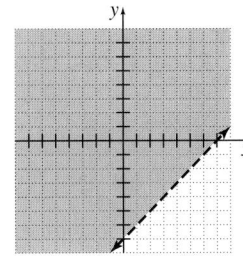

48. $y > -5x + 7$

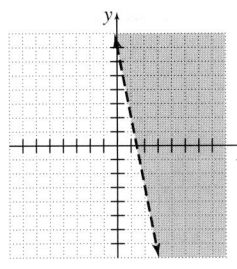

49. $9.99 + 0.75x < 15.00$; Ed can burn less than or equal to 6 songs; possible answer: He can burn 5 songs.

50. $12.5x - (255 + 2.5x) \geq 1200$; to make a profit, at least 146 packs must be sold; possible answer: There were 200 packs sold. **51.** $\frac{45 + 36 + 52 + 48 + 31 + x}{6} < 42$; her sixth phone bill must be less than $40; possible answer: Her phone bill should be $35. **52.** $18x > 600$; the length must be greater than $33\frac{1}{3}$ inches; possible answer: The length is 40 inches. **53.** $19.95x - (1.45x + 17) \geq 600$; he must sell at least 34 packages; possible answer: sell 50 packages. **54.** $500 < \frac{344 + 434 + 254 + 705 + 723 + x}{6} < 600$; the profit should be between $540 and $1140; possible answer: profit of $1000. **55.** $\frac{1}{3}x + 66 > 75$; after 2030, the percent of students at or above basic level will exceed 75%.

56. $3x + y \geq 25$

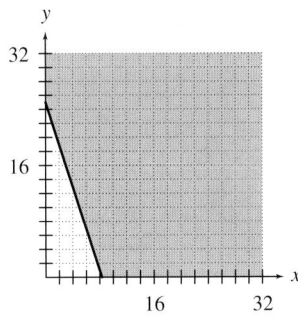

possible answer: 10 wins and five ties

57. $4.14x + 5.50y \leq 90$

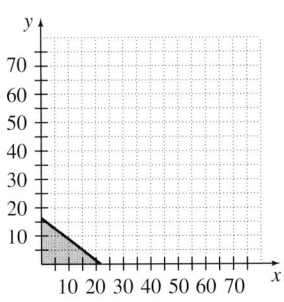

no; yes

58. $x + y < 20,000$
$0.065x + 0.0825y \geq 1400$
$x \geq 0$
$y \geq 0$

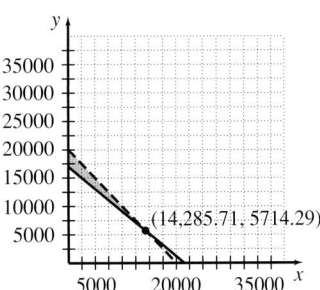

possible combination: $3000 at 6.5% and $15,000 at 8.25%

59. $2x + y \leq 125$
$y \geq 2x$
$x > 0$
$y > 0$

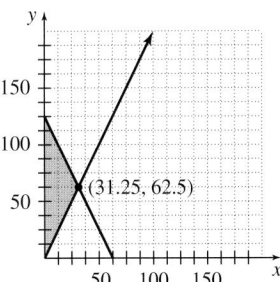

possible answer: 20 meters for the equal sides, 50 meters for the third side, and a perimeter of 90 meters

60. $y \geq 2x$
$x + y \leq 540$
$x \geq 0$
$y \geq 0$

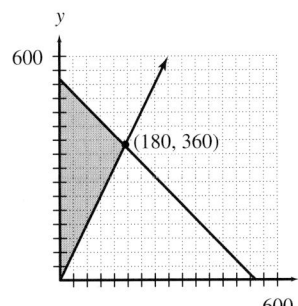

possible answer: 100 acres of oats and 400 acres of wheat

61. $3x + 5y \geq 6000$
$y \geq x + 75$
$x \geq 0$
$y \geq 0$

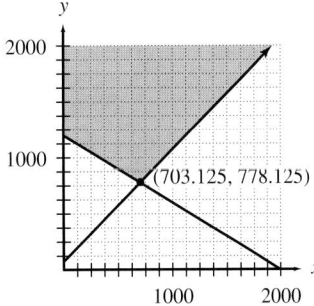

possible answer: $1000 for an efficiency; $1500 for a regular apartment

CHAPTER 5 TEST

1. linear; $x - 3y > 8$ **2.** nonlinear   **3.** linear; $6x - 18 \geq 0$ **4.** linear; $\frac{1}{2}x - y \geq 4\frac{3}{8}$ **5.** no solution

6.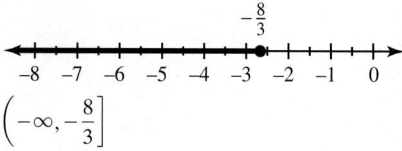

$(-\infty, -4)$

7.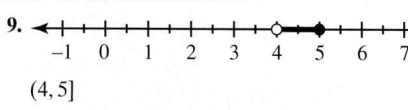

$(-\infty, \infty)$

8.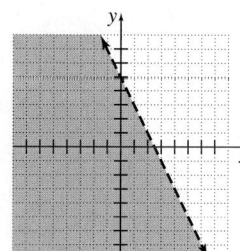

$-\frac{8}{3}$

$\left(-\infty, -\dfrac{8}{3}\right]$

9.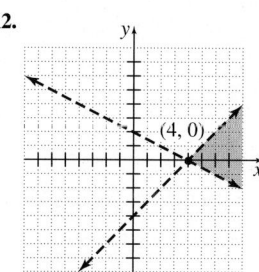

$(4, 5]$

10. $y < -2x + 5$

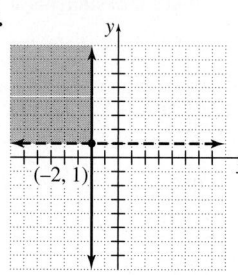

11. $x < 4$

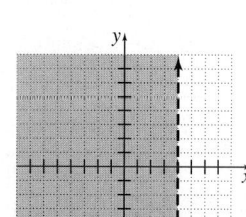

12.

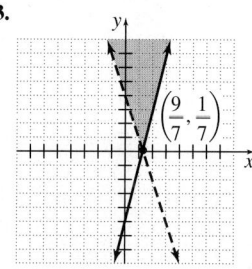

(4, 0)

13.

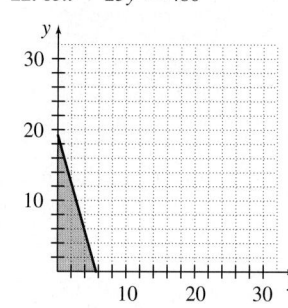

$\left(\dfrac{9}{7}, \dfrac{1}{7}\right)$

14.

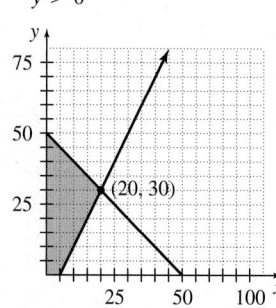

$(-2, 1)$

15. $10,000 - 200x > 5000$; his balance will be more than \$5000 for less than 25 months; possible answer: the balance is more than \$5000 after 5 months.   **16.** $-0.167x + 5.4 < 3$; in 2014 and after, the number of students will be below 3 students per computer; possible answer: in 2015 the number of students per computer will be below 3 students per computer.   **17.** $158 \leq \dfrac{565 + f}{4} \leq 206$; the fourth tornado's wind speed must be between 67 mph and 259 mph inclusive; possible answer: wind speed is 200 mph.   **18.** $49x - (23.5x + 250) \geq 300$; she must sell at least 22 baskets; possible answer: she sells 25 baskets.

19. $7.99x + 12.99y \leq 600.00$

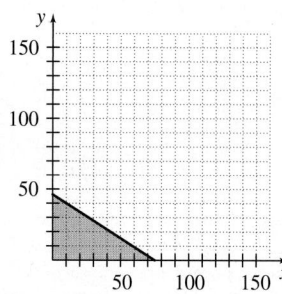

possible answer: 25 pounds of the standard blend and 30 pounds of the special blend.

20. $5x + 2y \geq 20$

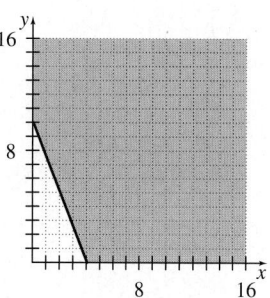

possible answer: five good deeds and five activity sheets

21. $2x + 2y \leq 504$

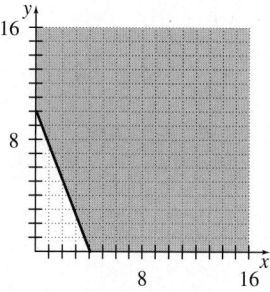

yes; possible dimensions: 100 feet by 50 feet

22. $85x + 25y \leq 480$

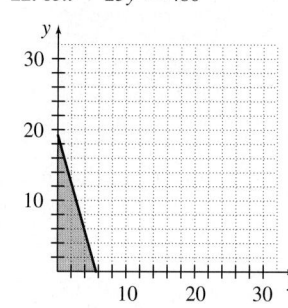

no

23. $2x + 2y \leq 100$
$y \geq 2x - 10$
$x > 0$
$y > 0$

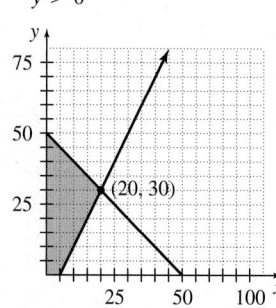

(20, 30)

possible length: 30 feet

24. $0.04x + 0.08y \geq 400$
$x + y \leq 6000$
$x \geq 0$
$y \geq 0$

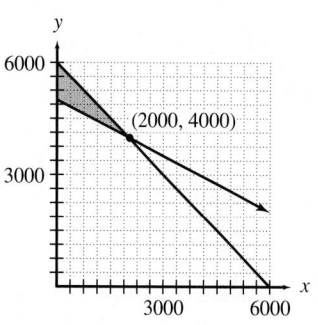

(2000, 4000)

possible answer: \$500 at 4% and \$5500 at 8%

25. Answers will vary.

CUMULATIVE REVIEW CHAPTERS P–5

1. 9   **2.** −9   **3.** $-\dfrac{3}{4}$ **4.** 3.16   **5.** $-\dfrac{3}{2}$ **6.** $\dfrac{9}{40}$ **7.** −6   **8.** 35   **9.** undefined   **10.** $-2x + 2$ **11.** $-2x + 6$

12.

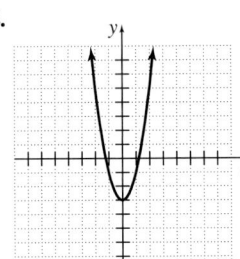

13. The domain of the relation is all real numbers. The range of the relation is all real numbers ≥ -3.
14. The relation is a function, since all possible vertical lines cross the graph a maximum of one time.
15. The relative minimum value is −3 at $x = 0$. There is no relative maximum.
16. The relation is increasing for all $x > 0$ and decreasing for all $x < 0$.
17. The x-intercepts are $(-1.225, 0)$ and $(1.225, 0)$. The y-intercept is $(0, -3)$.

18. $\dfrac{8}{7}$ **19.** −2   **20.** All real numbers   **21.** 2 and −8   **22.** $x = 0$

23. $x \leq -\dfrac{2}{5}$; $\left(-\infty, -\dfrac{2}{5}\right]$

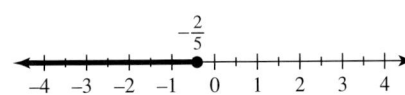

24. no solution

25. $10 < x \leq 30$
$(10, 30]$

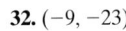

26.

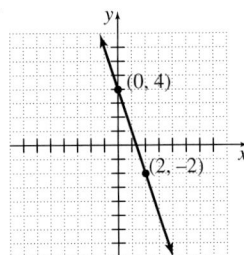

27.

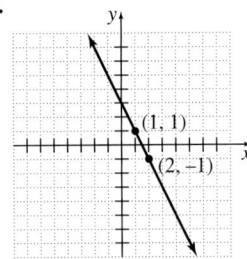

28.

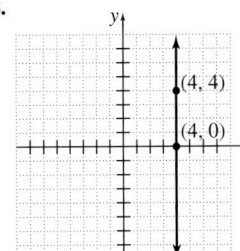

29.

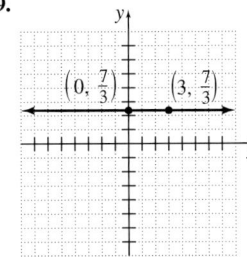

30.

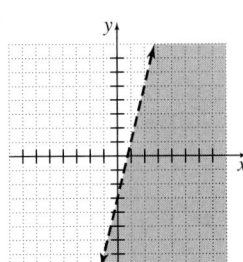

31. intersecting and perpendicular lines   **32.** $(-9, -23)$ **33.** all ordered pairs that satisfy $y = -2x + 4$

34.

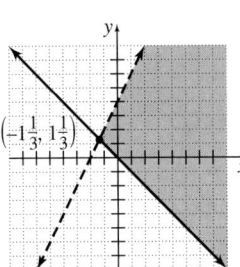

One solution is $(1, 0)$.

35. −5   **36.** undefined   **37.** 2   **38.** 0   **39.** $y = -5x - 7$ **40.** $y = -\dfrac{2}{3}x + \dfrac{22}{3}$ **41.** 5.34×10^6

42. 0.00012   **43.** −0.00004783   **44.** $L = \dfrac{P}{2} - W$ **45.** 2   **46.** Lance should invest $2500.

47. The smaller angle measures $21\frac{2}{3}°$ and the larger angle measures $68\frac{1}{3}°$.   **48.** Mike should mix $3\frac{1}{3}$ pounds of hazelnut coffee and $6\frac{2}{3}$ pounds of cinnamon coffee.   **49.** April must score at least 80 on the last test to get a B in her algebra class.   **50.** $c(x) = 35 + 1.50x$; the cost of renting a chain saw for 12 hours is $53.

CHAPTER 6

SECTION 6.1 EXERCISES

1. yes   **2.** no   **3.** yes   **4.** no   **5.** no   **6.** yes   **7.** yes   **8.** no   **9.** yes   **10.** yes   **11.** no   **12.** yes   **13.** yes
14. no   **15.** no   **16.** yes   **17.** no   **18.** yes   **19.** yes   **20.** yes   **21.** trinomial   **22.** polynomial   **23.** monomial
24. binomial   **25.** binomial   **26.** trinomial   **27.** polynomial   **28.** monomial   **29.** trinomial   **30.** monomial
31. binomial   **32.** binomial   **33.** monomial   **34.** binomial   **35.** trinomial   **36.** binomial   **37.** degrees of terms: 0, 1; degree
of polynomial: 1   **38.** degree of term: 0; degree of polynomial: 0   **39.** degree of term: 0; degree of polynomial: 0
40. degrees of terms: 4, 6, 4; degree of polynomial: 6   **41.** degree of term: 0; degree of polynomial: 0
42. degrees of terms: 2, 2; degree of polynomial: 2   **43.** degrees of terms: 5, 4, 0; degree of polynomial: 5
44. degrees of terms: 1, 0; degree of polynomial: 1   **45.** degrees of terms: 2, 2; degree of polynomial: 2

46. degrees of terms: 9, 6, 5; degree of polynomial: 9   **47.** degrees of terms: 15, 12, 7; degree of polynomial: 15

48. degree of term: 2; degree of polynomial: 2   **49.** $a^3 + 3a^2 - 2a + 5$ **50.** $4a^9 - 2a^6 + 3a^3 - 17$ **51.** $-\frac{8}{15}x^4 + \frac{4}{5}x^3 + \frac{2}{15}x$

52. $-p^5 - p^4 + p^3 + p^2 - p - 1$ **53.** $3.06x^4 + 0.1x^3 + 4.6x^2 - 1.72$ **54.** $23x^9 + 15x^7 + 9x^5 + 5x^3 + 7x + 33$

55. $11 - 2b + 7b^2 - 6b^3$ **56.** $x^2 - 4x^3 + x^4 + 6x^5 - 8x^6$ **57.** $\frac{1}{14}x - \frac{5}{14}x^3 + \frac{1}{7}x^5$ **58.** $1 - q + q^2 + q^3 - q^4 - q^5$

59. $-2.77 + 3.2x^3 + 9.76x^5 + 0.5x^7$ **60.** $4 - 2x + 4x^2 - 2x^3 - 4x^4 + x^5$ **61. (a)** 33   **(b)** 21   **(c)** 1

62. (a) 35   **(b)** -1 **(c)** 1   **63. (a)** 29   **(b)** 29   **(c)** 0   **64. (a)** -1 **(b)** -13 **(c)** 27

65. (a) -2.4 **(b)** 9.0375   **(c)** -20.4625 **66. (a)** 4   **(b)** 21.204   **(c)** -11.3 **67. (a)** 0   **(b)** $-\frac{77}{24}$ **(c)** 0

68. (a) -2 **(b)** 0   **(c)** $34\frac{2}{3}$ **69.** The perimeter measures $(2x^2 + 2x)$ feet; the perimeter is 60 feet.   **70.** The perimeter measures $(4x^2 + 2x)$ meters;
the perimeter is 42 meters.   **71.** The perimeter measures $(x^2 + x + 1)$ inches; the perimeter is 3.64 inches.   **72.** The perimeter measures $(2x^2 + x + 2)$
centimeters; the perimeter is 5 centimeters.   **73.** The surface area measures $(2x^2 + 12x)$ square units; the surface area is 22.5 m². **74.** The surface
area measures $(30h + 100)$ square units; the surface area is 205 in².   **75.** The total area is $(x^2 + 12x + 21)$ m².   **76.** The total area is
$\left(x^2 + \frac{1}{2}xy + y^2\right)$ square units.   **77.** The area not covered by the patio is $(lw \quad 300)$ ft², the area not covered by the patio is 8700 ft².

78. Let l = the length of the yard and w = the width of the yard; $lw - 128$; the area not covered by the strawberry patch is 14,872 square feet.
79. The area not covered by the pool is $(lw - \pi r^2)$ square units; the area not covered by the pool is approximately 811.4 m².   **80.** Let l = the length
of the yard, w = the width of the yard, and r = the radius of the hot tub; $lw - \pi r^2$; the area of the yard not covered by the hot tub is 9921.5 square
feet.   **81.** Let x = the length of the side of the square.   **(a)** $7x^2$ **(b)** $4x^2 + 100$ **(c)** $3x^2 - 100$ **(d)** The revenue is $1575; the cost is $1000; the
profit is $575.   **82.** Let x = the length of the side of the square.   **(a)** $20x^2$ **(b)** $15x^2 + 70$ **(c)** $5x^2 - 70$ **(d)** The revenue is $2880; the cost is
$2230; the profit is $650.   **83.** Let x = the length of the side of the square.   **(a)** $10.25x^2$ **(b)** $3.50x^2 + 225.00$ **(c)** $6.75x^2 - 225.00$ **(d)** The revenue is $2306.25; the cost is $1012.50; the profit is $1293.75.   **84.** Let x = the length of the side of the square.   **(a)** $16.50x^2$ **(b)** $10.25x^2 + 40$
(c) $6.25x^2 - 40$ **(d)** The revenue is $412.50; the cost is $296.25; the profit is $116.25.   **85.** Let x = the radius of the circle.   **(a)** $3.60\pi x^2$
(b) $3.15\pi x^2 + 30.00$ **(c)** $0.45\pi x^2 - 30.00$ **(d)** The revenue is $1130.97; the cost is $1019.60; the profit is $111.37.   **86.** Let x = the radius of the
circle.   **(a)** $3.50\pi x^2$ **(b)** $2.15\pi x^2 + 15.00$ **(c)** $1.35\pi x^2 - 15.00$ **(d)** The revenue is $222.66; the cost is $151.78; the profit is $70.88.   **87.** The ex-
pected mileage is 36,416 miles.   **88.** The expected mileage is 35,968 miles.   **89.** A temperature of -61 degrees was recorded at approximately
5920 feet.   **90.** A temperature of -54 degrees was recorded at approximately 4699 feet.   **91.** The height of the world's tallest building is approximately 1673 feet.   **92.** The AT&T building is approximately 1051 feet.

6.1 CALCULATOR EXERCISES

1. $\{-192, -32, -8, 24\}$ **2.** $\{-432, -108, -24\}$

3. $\{0.229, 0.06725, -32.625, -0.016\}$ or $\left\{\frac{229}{1000}, \frac{269}{4000}, -\frac{261}{8}, -\frac{2}{125}\right\}$

SECTION 6.2 EXERCISES

1.

x	y
-2	4
-1	0
0	-6
1	-8
2	0

2.

x	y
-2	0
-1	8
0	6
1	0
2	-4

3.

x	y
-2	-3
-1	-2
0	1
1	6
2	13

4.

x	y
-2	13
-1	6
0	1
1	-2
2	-3

5. (a)

x	y
-2	6
1	9
-1	5

(b) $y \ge 5$

6. (a)

x	y
-2	-5
3	0
1	4

(b) $y \le 4$

7. (a)

x	y
-1	2
1	4
-2	7

(b) all real
numbers

8. (a)

x	y
1	4
-1	-2
-2	-11

(b) all real
numbers

9. all real numbers   **10.** all real numbers   **11.** $y \le 5$ **12.** $y \le 9$ **13.** $y \ge -5$ **14.** $y \ge -7$ **15.** $y \ge 6$ **16.** $y \ge -4$
17. $y \le 8$ **18.** $y \le 12$ **19.** all real numbers   **20.** all real numbers   **21.** all real numbers   **22.** all real numbers   **23.** all real numbers
24. all real numbers   **25.** all real numbers   **26.** all real numbers   **27.** $y \ge -4$ **28.** $y \ge -2$ **29.** 100   **30.** 81   **31.** 36   **32.** 49
33. 25   **34.** 81   **35.** 4   **36.** 16   **37.** 16   **38.** 49   **39.** 6.25   **40.** 2.56   **41.** 38   **42.** 16   **43.** -14 **44.** -52 **45.** 15.9
46. 156.1   **47.** -217.5 **48.** -41.3 **49.** 2578.3   **50.** 21,063.3   **51.** -2 **52.** -6.7 **53.** $\frac{9}{8}$ **54.** $\frac{167}{8}$ **55.** $-\frac{369}{8}$ **56.** $-\frac{67}{8}$

57. (a) $x \ge 0$ **(b)** The absolute maximum of 700 at $x = 30$. The maximum profit is $700 when 30 items are sold.   **(c)** $p(x) \le 700$; the profit ranges
from a loss (a negative value) to $700, the maximum profit.   **58. (a)** $x \ge 0$ **(b)** The absolute maximum of 800 at $x = 30$.
The maximum profit is $800 when 30 items are sold.   **(c)** $p(x) \le 800$; the profit ranges from a loss (a negative value) to $800, the maximum profit.
59. $0 \le C(x) \le 50$ **60.** $0 \le R(x) \le 15$ **61.** $494.6 \le F(x) \le 1600$ **62.** $400 \le n(t) \le 1175.1$ **63. (a)** When 5, 10, 15, 20, 25, and 30 watches
are ordered, the revenue is $625, $1000, $1125, $1000, $625, and $0, respectively.   **(b)** The range is all non-negative real numbers less than or equal to
1125.   **(c)** This range shows us that the maximum revenue would be $1125.   **64. (a)** When the space is rented for 10, 20, 30, 40, 50, and 60 months,
the cost is $2500, $4000, $4500, $4000, $2500, and $0, respectively.   **(b)** The range is all real numbers less than or equal to 4500.
(c) This range shows us that the maximum cost would be $4500, and there is a value of x for which the cost is $0.

65. $0 < x < 100$

x	$A(x)$
10	900
20	1600
30	2100
40	2400
50	2500
60	2400
70	2100

The maximum possible area is 2500 square feet.

66. $0 < x < 300$

x	$A(x)$
50	12,500
75	16,875
100	20,000
125	21,875
150	22,500
175	21,875
200	20,000

The maximum possible area is 22,500 square feet.

67. $(0, \infty)$; $(0, \infty)$; 60 square feet; 180 square feet; the base is approximately 16.3 feet, and the height is approximately 18.3 feet.

68. $(0, \infty)$; $(0, \infty)$; 108.09 square centimeters; the side is approximately 1.8 centimeters.

69. (a)

Year	Percent Unemployed
1980	7.7
1985	7.9
1990	7.7
1995	7.0
1996	6.8
1997	6.6
1998	6.3

(b) For the years 1980, 1997, and 1998, the percentages are 0.1 apart. However, the values found for the remaining years are not as close. **(c)** Answers will vary.

70. (a)

Year	Number of Recipients
94	14.4
95	13.7
96	12.5
97	11.1
98	9.2
99	7.1

(b) The values are comparable.
(c) The function predicts 4.6 million, and this value is not close to the 2000 number of 5.8 million.

71. (a)

x	30,000	50,000	70,000	90,000	110,000
$b(x)$	17,527	24,247	29,367	32,887	34,807

(b) The function predicts a benefit of $26,634 that is close to the actual amount. **(c)** The function predicts a benefit of $19,921 that is close to the actual amount.

72. (a)

Year	1970	1980	1990
Percent of population 65 and over	9.8	11.3	12.5

(b) The function predicts 13.4% of the population in 2000 was 65 and over, which is 1% higher than the actual percent.
(c) The function predicts 13.6% of the population in 2003 was 65 and over, which is 1.2% higher than the actual percent.

73. (a)

Year	1998	1999	2000	2001
Cost	5291	5408	5460	5718

(b) The function predicts the exact cost of $5718 in 2001.
(c) The function predicts a cost of $6453 in 2002. This amount is over $200 high. **(d)** According to the function, the cost will exceed $10,000 between $x = 5$ and $x = 6$ or between 2003 and 2004. Answers will vary.

74. (a)

Year	1998	1999	2000	2001
Cost	11,888	12,352	12,922	13,639

(b) The function predicts the cost of $13,639 in 2001, which is the same as the actual amount. **(c)** The function predicts a cost of $14,544 in 2002. This amount is close to the amount $14,504. **(d)** According to the function, the cost will exceed $20,000 between $x = 7$ and $x = 8$ or between 2005 and 2006. Answers will vary.

6.2 CALCULATOR EXERCISES

Part 1

1. $y = x$
x int $= (0, 0)$
y int $= (0, 0)$

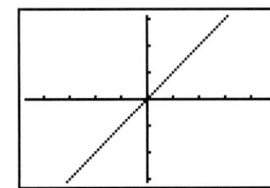

2. $y = x^2 + x$
x int $= (-1, 0)$ and $(0, 0)$
y int $= (0, 0)$

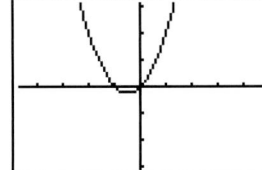

3. $y = x^3 - x$
x int $= (1, 0)(-1, 0)(0, 0)$
y int $= (0, 0)$

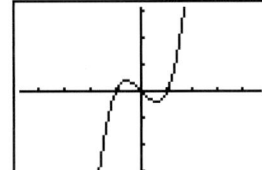

4. $y = x^4 + 2x^3 - x^2 - 2x$
x int $= (1, 0)(0, 0)(-1, 0)(-2, 0)$
y int $= (0, 0)$

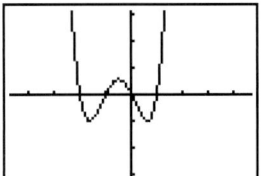

5. $y = x^5 - 5x^3 + 4x$
x int $= (-2, 0)(-1, 0)(0, 0)(1, 0)(2, 0)$
y int $= (0, 0)$

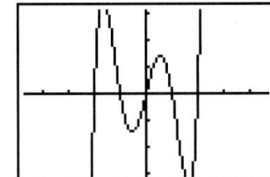

	Degree	# of changes
$y - x$	1	0
$y = x^2 + x$	2	1
$y = x^3 - x$	3	2
$y = x^4 + 2x^3 - x^2 - 2x$	4	3
$y = x^5 - 5x^3 + 4x$	5	4

Part 2

1. -63.156 **2.** 9416390.016 **3.** -4.65793664 **4.** $\dfrac{451}{3}$ **5.** $-\dfrac{29}{48}$ **6.** $-\dfrac{2563}{6}$

SECTION 6.3 EXERCISES

1. nonquadratic   **2.** quadratic   **3.** quadratic   **4.** quadratic   **5.** quadratic   **6.** quadratic   **7.** nonquadratic   **8.** quadratic
9. quadratic   **10.** nonquadratic   **11.** nonquadratic   **12.** quadratic   **13. (a)** concave downward   **(b)** The graph is narrow compared to the
graph of $y = x^2$.   **(c)** $(0, 1)$ **(d)** $(1, 6)$ **(e)** absolute maximum of 6 at $x = 1$ **(f)** increasing $(-\infty, 1)$; decreasing $(1, \infty)$

14. (a) concave upward   **(b)** The graph is narrow compared to the graph of $y = x^2$.   **(c)** $(0, -5)$ **(d)** $\left(\dfrac{1}{2}, -6\dfrac{1}{2}\right)$

(e) absolute minimum of $-6\dfrac{1}{2}$ at $x = \dfrac{1}{2}$ **(f)** increasing $\left(\dfrac{1}{2}, \infty\right)$; decreasing $\left(-\infty, \dfrac{1}{2}\right)$

15–22.

	a	b	c	Graph Wide/Narrow	Graph Concave Upward/Downward	Graph Vertex	Axis of Symmetry	y-Intercept
15.	0.6	6	-2	wide	upward	$(-5, -17)$	$x = -5$	$(0, -2)$
16.	-1	6	-2	neither	downward	$(3, 7)$	$x = 3$	$(0, -2)$
17.	2	3	5	narrow	upward	$(-0.75, 3.875)$	$x = -0.75$	$(0, 5)$
18.	-3	6	-5	narrow	downward	$(1, -2)$	$x = 1$	$(0, -5)$
19.	$-\dfrac{1}{4}$	1	-3	wide	downward	$(2, -2)$	$x = 2$	$(0, -3)$
20.	$\dfrac{1}{3}$	2	-1	wide	upward	$(-3, -4)$	$x = -3$	$(0, -1)$
21.	1	8	1	neither	upward	$(-4, -15)$	$x = -4$	$(0, 1)$
22.	-0.4	2.4	-1.1	wide	downward	$(3, 2.5)$	$x = 3$	$(0, -1.1)$

23.

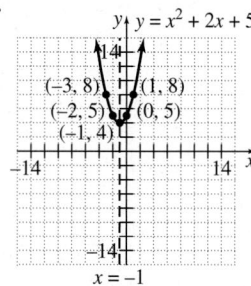

24.

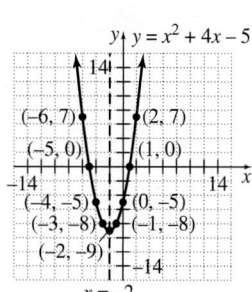

25.

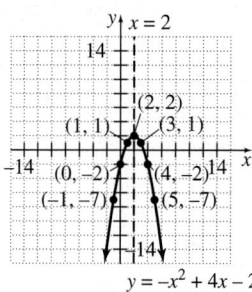

26.

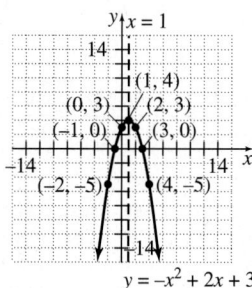

27.

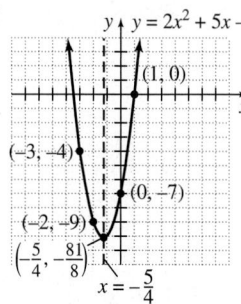

28.

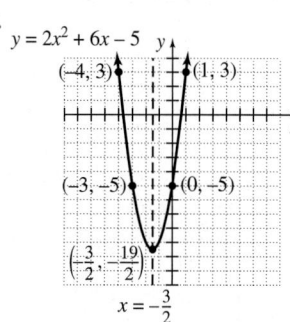

29.

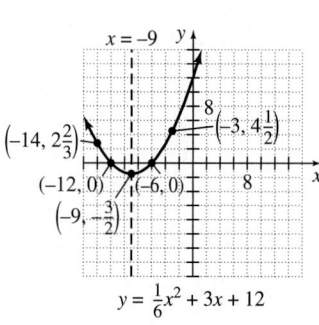

30.

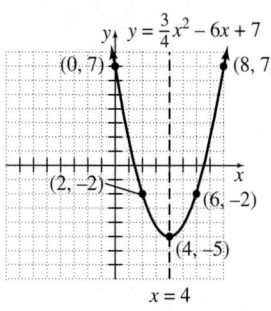

31.

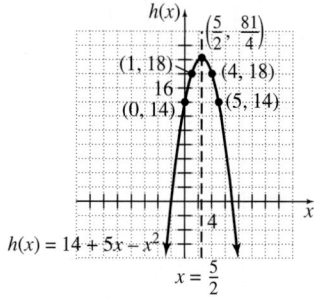

32.

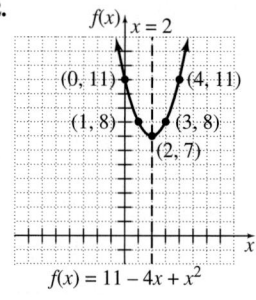

33.

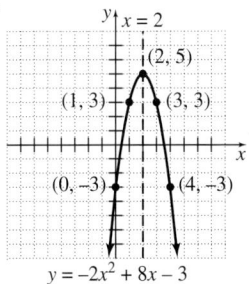

$y = -2x^2 + 8x - 3$

34.

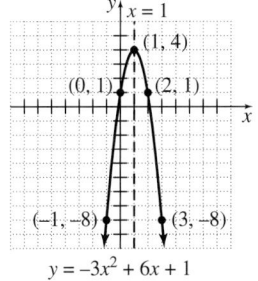

$y = -3x^2 + 6x + 1$

35.

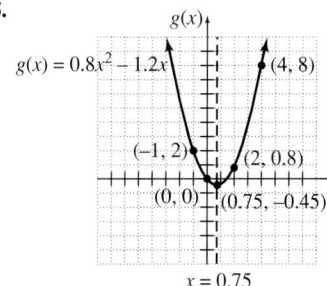

$x = 0.75$

36.

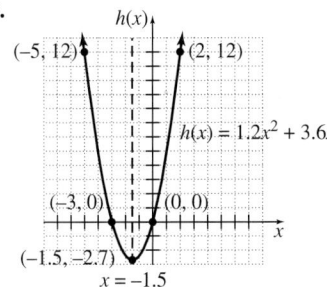

$x = -1.5$

37.

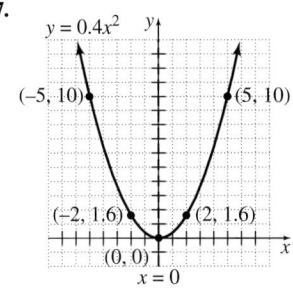

$x = 0$

38.

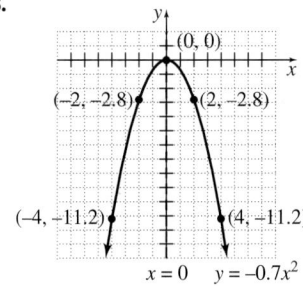

$x = 0$ $y = -0.7x^2$

39.

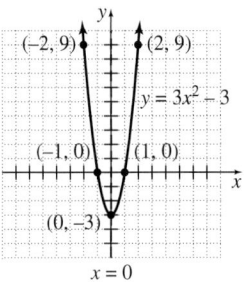

$x = 0$

40.

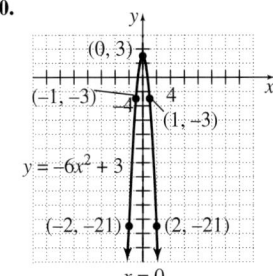

$x = 0$

41.

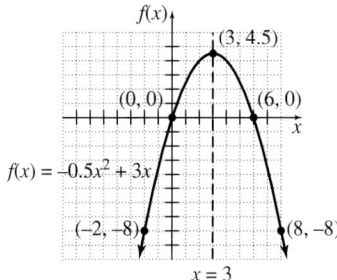

$x = 3$

42.

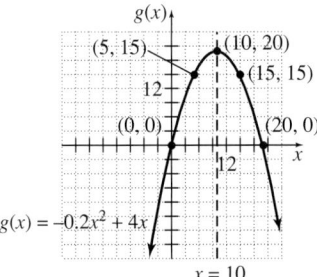

$g(x) = -0.2x^2 + 4x$

$x = 10$

43. (a) concave upward **(b)** $(0, 1.6)$ **(c)** $(1.5, 1.4)$
  (d) absolute minimum of 1.4 when $x = 1.5$
  (e) decreasing $(0, 1.5)$; increasing $(1.5, \infty)$

44. (a) concave upward **(b)** $(0, 5.8)$
  (c) $(3.5, 5.6)$ **(d)** absolute minimum of 5.6 when $x = 3.5$
  (e) decreasing $(0, 3.5)$; increasing $(3.5, \infty)$

45. $Y1 = 140x - x^2$

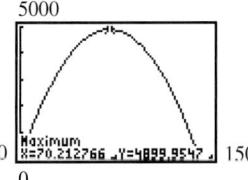

The vertex is $(70, 4900)$; the cottage has a maximum area of 4900 ft^2 when the width is 70 feet.

46. $Y1 = 120x - 2x^2$

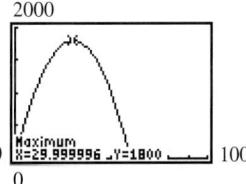

The vertex is $(30, 1800)$; the pen has a maximum area of 1800 ft^2 when the length of two sides are each 30 feet.

47. $Y1 = 10x - x^2$

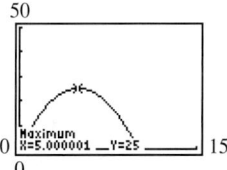

The vertex is $(5, 25)$; the triangle has a maximum area of 25 square inches when the height is 5 inches.

48. $Y1 = x^2 + 10x$

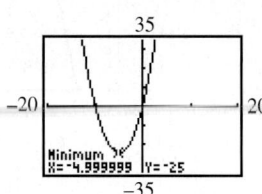

The vertex is $(-5, -25)$; no, the vertex does not have any physical meaning.

49. $Y1 = 46x - x^2$

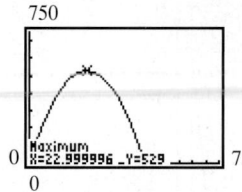

The vertex is $(23, 529)$; at $x = \$23$, the revenue will be at a maximum of $\$529$. Yes, the seller should limit the number of dolls sold.

50. $Y1 = 250x - 25x^2$

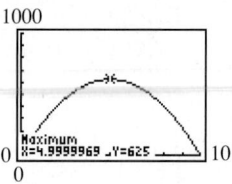

When the number of travelers equals 5, they will maximize their revenue at $\$625$. Yes, they should limit their number.

51. $Y1 = 6x - 0.05x^2 - 5$

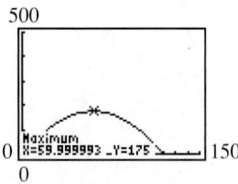

The maximum profit would be $\$175$, when they sell 60 discs.

52. $Y1 = 16000x - 200x^2 - 1000$

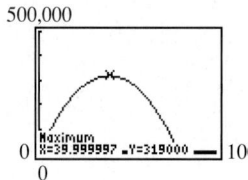

The maximum profit would be $\$319,000$, when they sell 40 pieces of major equipment.

53.

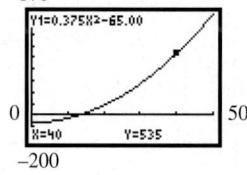

The maximum profit on the given domain $[15, 40]$ is $\$535$ when the base and height measure 40 yards.

54.

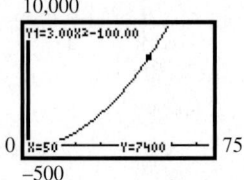

The maximum profit on the given domain $[8, 50]$ is $\$7400$ when the room is 50 feet on a side.

55. $Y1 = -16x^2 + 12x + 24$

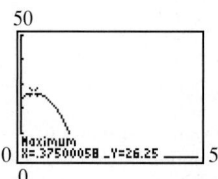

The maximum height the apple will reach is 26.25 feet.

56. $Y1 = -16x^2 + 60x$

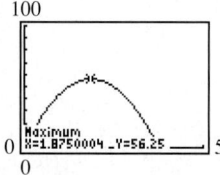

The vertex is $(1.875, 56.25)$; the football will reach a maximum height of 56.25 feet after 1.875 seconds.

57.

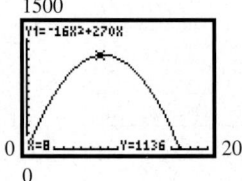

The domain is $[0, 8]$; the rocket is in the air for 8 seconds before it explodes. It explodes before it reaches the maximum value of the function; the maximum height is 1136 feet at 8 seconds. The range is $[0, 1136]$; the rocket ranges from ground level to a height of 1136 feet.

58.

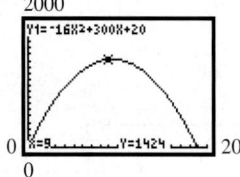

The domain is $[0, 9]$; the rocket is in the air 9 seconds before it explodes. It explodes before it reaches the maximum value of the function; the maximum height is 1424 feet at 9 seconds. The range is $[20, 1424]$; the rocket ranges from 20 feet above ground level to 1424 feet above ground level.

59. $Y1 = -74,147x^2 + 502,360x + 22,099$

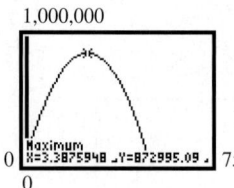

The maximum number of passenger cars imported from Mexico was 872,995 and occurred in 2002 (3.4 years after 1998).

60. $Y1 = -46,649x^2 + 406,864x - 306,623$

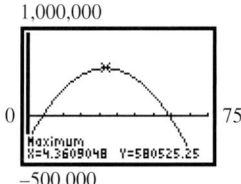

The maximum number of passenger cars imported from Germany was 580,525 and occurred in 2003 (4.4 years after 1998).

6.3 CALCULATOR EXERCISES

1.

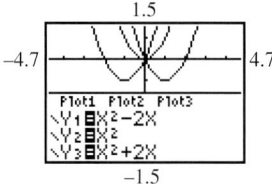

2.

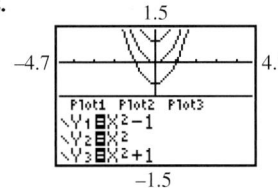

3.

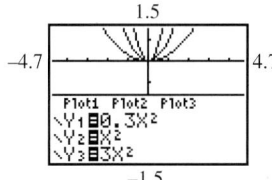

4.

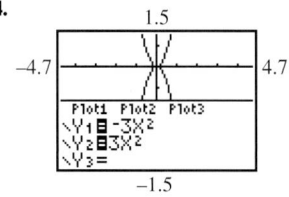

5.

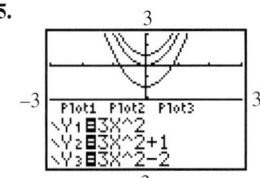

6.

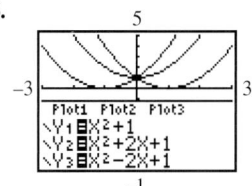

Answers may vary.

SECTION 6.4 EXERCISES

1. $y = x^2 + 2x - 8$

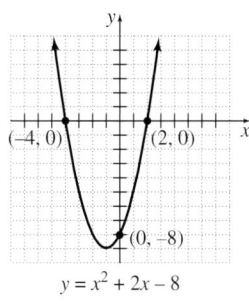

$y = x^2 + 2x - 8$

2. $y = -x^2 + 2x + 3$

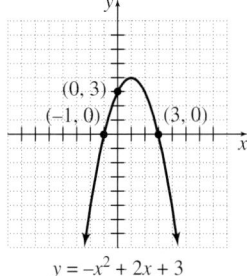

$y = -x^2 + 2x + 3$

3. $y = 2x^2 + 7x - 4$

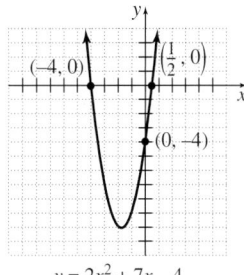

$y = 2x^2 + 7x - 4$

4. $y = 3x^2 + x - 2$

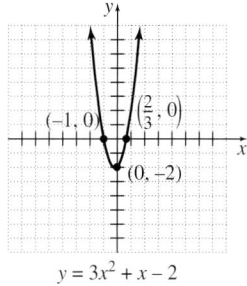

$y = 3x^2 + x - 2$

5. $y = -\frac{1}{3}x^2 + 3$

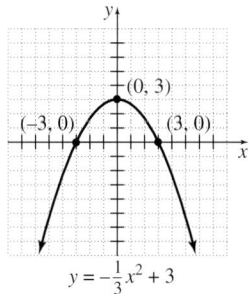

$y = -\frac{1}{3}x^2 + 3$

6. $y = -\frac{1}{16}x^2 + 1$

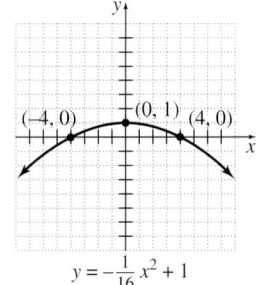

$y = -\frac{1}{16}x^2 + 1$

7. $y = \frac{1}{2}x^2 + x - 4$

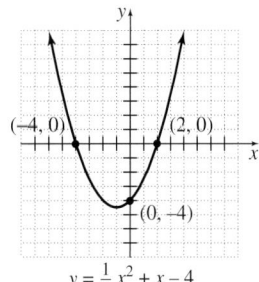

$y = \frac{1}{2}x^2 + x - 4$

8. $y = \frac{1}{3}x^2 - \frac{1}{3}x - 2$

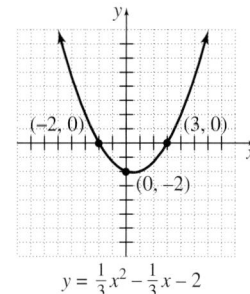

$y = \frac{1}{3}x^2 - \frac{1}{3}x - 2$

9. $y = -\frac{1}{6}x^2 + \frac{2}{3}$

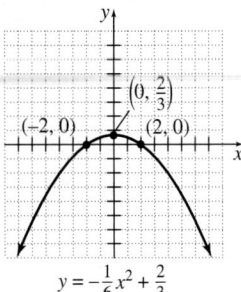

$y = -\frac{1}{6}x^2 + \frac{2}{3}$

10. $y = -\frac{1}{8}x^2 - \frac{1}{8}x + \frac{1}{4}$

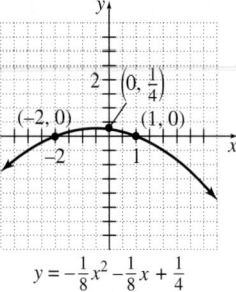

$y = -\frac{1}{8}x^2 - \frac{1}{8}x + \frac{1}{4}$

11. $y = -\frac{8}{9}x^2 + \frac{40}{9}x - 2$

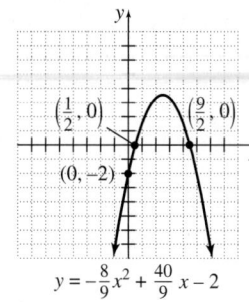

$y = -\frac{8}{9}x^2 + \frac{40}{9}x - 2$

12. $y = -\frac{9}{2}x^2 - \frac{3}{2}x + 1$

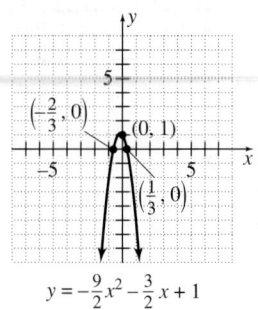

$y = -\frac{9}{2}x^2 - \frac{3}{2}x + 1$

13. $y = x^2 - 2x - 15$

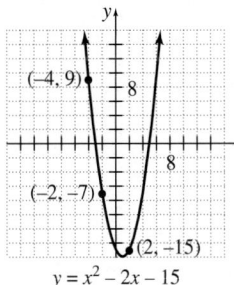

$y = x^2 - 2x - 15$

14. $y = x^2 + 3x - 18$

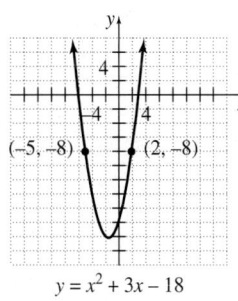

$y = x^2 + 3x - 18$

15. $y = 2x^2 - 3x - 9$

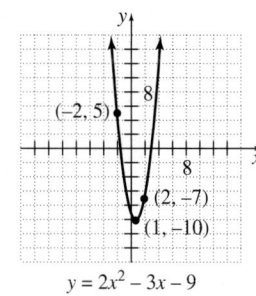

$y = 2x^2 - 3x - 9$

16. $y = 3x^2 - 11x - 4$

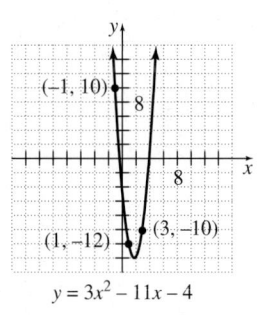

$y = 3x^2 - 11x - 4$

17. $y = \frac{1}{3}x^2 - 2x + 5$

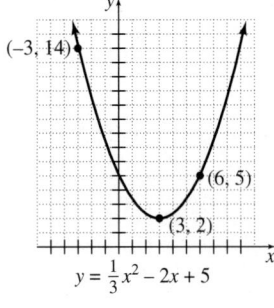

$y = \frac{1}{3}x^2 - 2x + 5$

18. $y = \frac{3}{4}x^2 + x - 4$

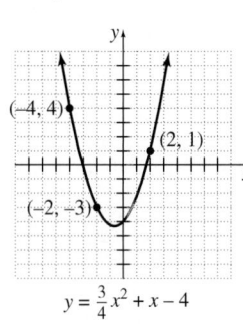

$y = \frac{3}{4}x^2 + x - 4$

19. $y = -x^2 + 4x + 3$

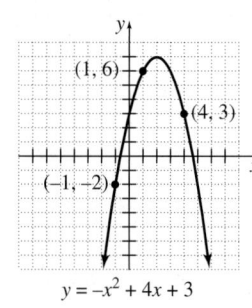

$y = -x^2 + 4x + 3$

20. $y = -x^2 - 2x + 5$

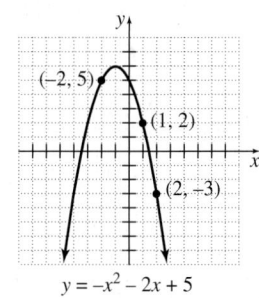

$y = -x^2 - 2x + 5$

21. $y = -2x^2 - 4x - 5$

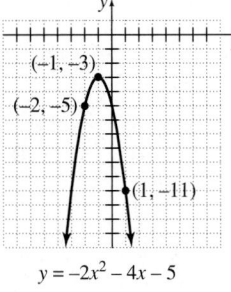

$y = -2x^2 - 4x - 5$

22. $y = -\frac{1}{2}x^2 + 3x - 7$

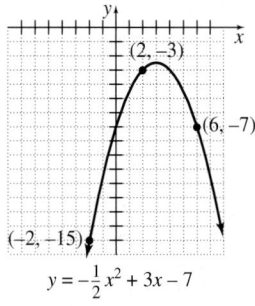

$y = -\frac{1}{2}x^2 + 3x - 7$

23. $y = \frac{1}{2}x^2 + 4x + 10$

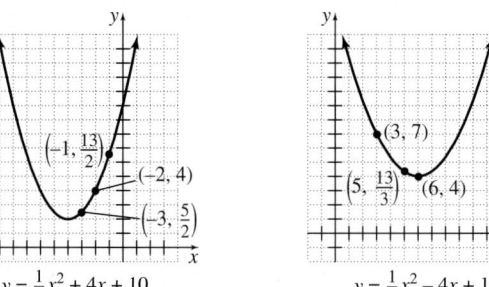

$y = \frac{1}{2}x^2 + 4x + 10$

24. $y = \frac{1}{3}x^2 - 4x + 16$

$y = \frac{1}{3}x^2 - 4x + 16$

25. $s(t) = -16t^2 + 12t + 150$
The ball will hit the ground in approximately 3.5 seconds.

26. $s(t) = -16t^2 + 18t + 220$
The pie will hit the ground in approximately 4.3 seconds.

27. $s(t) = -16t^2 + 400$
The dummy will hit the ground in 5 seconds.

28. $s(t) = -16t^2 + 600$
The toy will hit the ground in approximately 6.1 seconds.

29. $s(t) = -2.7t^2 + 2000$
The cylinder will touch the surface at approximately 27.2 seconds.

30. $s(t) = -2.7t^2 + 25t + 3000$
The probe will reach the surface in approximately 38.3 seconds.

31. $y = 0.0002x^2$ **32.** $y = 0.000097x^2$ **33.** $y = -0.0005x^2 + 360$ **34.** $y = -0.0005x^2 + 185$ **35.** $y = -0.008x^2 + 0.12x + 3.7$; in 2005, the per capita expenditure on radio and television was 3.7.   **36.** $y = 0.036x^2 + 0.14x + 4.5$; in 2005, the per capita expenditure on spectator sports was 14.7.   **37.** $y = 0.8x^2 - 15.4x + 141.8$; in 2000, the function predicts an absolute minimum of 67.7% of U.S. households with TVs have cable television. This is very close to the actual percentage of 67.8%. The function predicts 100% of the U.S. households with TVs would have cable television in 2006. This is not probable.   **38.** $y = -29.9x^2 + 319.3x + 10,414.6$; in 1995, the function predicts an absolute maximum of about 11,267 cable TV systems. This number is close to the value given. The function predicts the number of cable TV systems would fall below 9000 in 2004.   **39.** Let $x =$ the number of years after 2000, $y =$ the number of U.S. Army personnel on active duty, $y = -333.5x^2 + 7618.5x + 471,633$; the function predicts in 2003, there are 491,487 Army personnel (off by approximately 7800); the function predicts in 2004, there are 496,771 Army personnel (off by approximately 3400).   **40.** Let $x =$ the number of years after 1995, $y =$ the number of deaths by heart disease, $y = 0.05x^2 - 8.05x + 296.3$; the function predicts in 1998, 272.6 deaths per 100,000 population due to heart disease (off by 0.2); the function predicts in 2001, 249.8 deaths per 100,000 population due to heart disease (off by 2.0). Answers will vary.

6.4 CALCULATOR EXERCISES

Part 1

1. Let $x =$ the number of years after 1996, $y =$ the number of robberies, $y = -189x^2 - 42,435x + 536,985$.

Year	Number of Robberies
2000	364,221
2001	320,085
2002	275,571

The estimates are significant underestimates.

2. Let $x =$ the number of years after 1998, $y =$ the amount of earnings in dollars, $y = -1,881,525x^2 + 6,830,771x + 2,360,108$.

Year	Earnings ($)
2002	-421,208
2003	-10,524,162

The function fails after 2001 because the values are not negative.

3. Let $x =$ the number of years after 1998, $y =$ the amount of earnings in dollars, $y = -67,549x^2 + 535,072x + 1,100,670$.

Year	Earnings ($)
2002	2,160,174
2003	2,087,305

The estimates are low for 2002 and high for 2003.

4. Let $x =$ the number of years after 1980, $y =$ the energy production in quadrillion Btu, $y = -0.0096x^2 + 0.421x + 66.827$.

Year	Energy Production
2002	70.50
2003	70.68

The estimates are are low for 2002 and high for 2003.

Part 2

1. $(5, 155)$ $(35, 335)$ $(40, 365)$; yes; $C(x) = 6x + 125$ **2.** $(5, 450)$ $(30, 1200)$ $(35, 1050)$; yes; $R(x) = -2x^2 + 100x + 0$

3.

Number of Items Produced and Sold	5	30	35	40
Cost of production	$155	$305	$335	$365
Revenue from sales	$450	$1200	$1050	$800
Profit	$295	$895	$715	$435

Answers in bold

4. $(5, 295)$ $(30, 895)$ $(35, 715)$; yes; $P(x) = -2x^2 + 94x - 125$ **5.** When the value of x is greater than 46, the profit becomes less than zero.
6. $(23.5, 979.5)$ When approximately 23 items are produced, $979.50 profit is achieved.

CHAPTER 6 SUMMARY

Vocabulary Review

1. term   **2.** degree of a term   **3.** degree of a polynomial   **4.** coefficient   **5.** monomial   **6.** binomial   **7.** trinomial   **8.** absolute maximum   **9.** absolute minimum   **10.** vertex

Reflections

1–8. Answers will vary.

CHAPTER 6 SECTION-BY-SECTION REVIEW

1. yes; monomial   **2.** yes; binomial   **3.** no   **4.** yes; polynomial   **5.** no   **6.** yes; trinomial   **7.** The degrees of the terms are 1, 3, 0; the degree of the polynomial is 3.   **8.** The degrees of the terms are 3, 2, 0; the degree of the polynomial is 3.   **9.** The degrees of the terms are 1, 0; the degree of the polynomial is 1.   **10.** The degree of the term is 1; the degree of the polynomial is 1.   **11.** The degrees of the terms are 2, 1, 0; the degree of the polynomial is 2.   **12.** $11y^4 + 9y^3 + 5y^2 - 6y + 12$ **13.** $-p + 5$ **14.** $\frac{1}{4}z^4 + \frac{1}{3}z^3 + \frac{1}{2}z^2 + z + 1$

15. $-2.3b^5 - 9.1b^3 + 0.6b + 1.8$ **16.** 0   **17.** -90 **18.** -98 **19.** 0   **20.** 0   **21.** -1 **22.** -1 **23.** 0   **24.** -1 **25.** 3   **26.** The perimeter is $(2w + 2w^2)$ units; the perimeter is 112 yards.   **27.** The perimeter is $(x^2 + x + 5)$ inches; the perimeter is 11 inches.   **28.** The total area is $(a^2 + 20a)$ in^2.   **29.** The area of the lawn not covered by the garden is $\left(z^2 - \frac{1}{2}xy\right)$ square feet; the area is 6370 ft^2.   **30. (a)** It would take 18.17 minutes.
(b) It would take 16.43 minutes.   **(c)** It would take 13.49 minutes.   **31.** Let $x =$ the length of the side of a square. **(a)** $9.00x^2$ **(b)** $4.75x^2 + 50.00$ **(c)** $4.25x^2 - 50.00$ **(d)** The revenue is $441.00; the cost is $282.75; the profit is $158.25.   **32.** Let $x =$ the length of the side in yards.

(a) $11.95x^2$ **(b)** $8.95x^2 + 80.00$ **(c)** $3.00x^2 - 80.00$ **(d)** The revenue is \$1078.49; the cost is \$887.74; the profit is \$190.75.   **33.** The volume of the dam is approximately 59,506.25 thousand cubic meters.

34.

x	y
-3	18
-2	0
-1	4
0	0
1	-6
2	-8
3	0

35. (a)

x	y
1	3
-1	-5
-2	-6

(b) $y \geq -6$

36. The range is the set of all real numbers.   **37.** $y \geq -12.5$
38. The range is the set of all real numbers.   **39.** $f(-2) = -36$ **40.** $f(0) = -4$
41. (a) $x \geq 0$ **(b)** The absolute maximum of 200 at $x = 20$. The maximum profit is \$200 when 20 items are sold.   **(c)** $p(x) \leq 200$; the profit ranges from a loss (a negative value) to \$200, the maximum profit.   **42. (a)** The revenue for 5, 10, 15, 20, and 25 shirts is \$47.50, \$70, \$67.50, \$40, and $-\$12.50$, respectively. Answers will vary.   **(b)** The cost for 5, 10, 15, and 20 shirts is \$20, \$40, \$60, and \$80, respectively.   **(c)** The profit from 5, 10, 15, and 20 shirts is \$27.50, \$30, \$7.50, and $-\$40$, respectively.   **(d)** Answers will vary.

43.

Hundreds of gallons (x)	900	1000	1100	1200	1300	1400
Cost (y)	16,970	17,000	17,010	17,000	16,970	16,920

; answers will vary.

44. (a)

Year	1980	1985	1990	1995
Cigarette consumption	631.5	593.98	524.7	485.93

(b) The function predicts in 2000, 539.9 billion cigarettes were consumed. This is a high estimate.   **(c)** The function predicts in 2001, 567.3 billion cigarettes were consumed. This is a high estimate.
(d) The function predicts in 2002, 601.4 billion cigarettes were consumed. The function is increasing and the actual number is decreasing.

45. (a)

Year	2006	2007	2008	2009	2010
Price per gallon	2.16	2.47	2.84	3.27	3.76

(b) The function predicts in 2005, the price of gas was \$1.91. This is a close estimate.
(c) Answers will vary.
(d) Answers will vary.

46. quadratic   **47.** nonquadratic   **48.** nonquadratic   **49.** quadratic

50–53.

	a	b	c	Graph Wide/Narrow	Graph Concave Upward/Downward	Graph Vertex	Axis of Symmetry	y-Intercept
50.	$-\frac{1}{4}$	$\frac{1}{2}$	1	wide	downward	$\left(1, \frac{5}{4}\right)$	$x = 1$	$(0, 1)$
51.	-2	4	0	narrow	downward	$(1, 2)$	$x = 1$	$(0, 0)$
52.	$\frac{1}{3}$	1	0	wide	upward	$\left(-\frac{3}{2}, -\frac{3}{4}\right)$	$x = -\frac{3}{2}$	$(0, 0)$
53.	3	-3	1	narrow	upward	$\left(\frac{1}{2}, \frac{1}{4}\right)$	$x = \frac{1}{2}$	$(0, 1)$

54.

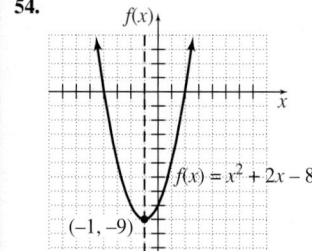

$f(x) = x^2 + 2x - 8$
$(-1, -9)$
$x = -1$

55.

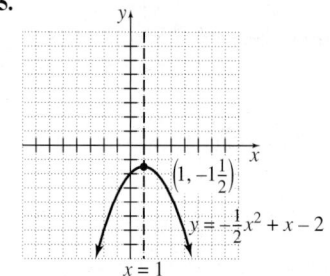

$\left(1, -1\frac{1}{2}\right)$
$y = -\frac{1}{2}x^2 + x - 2$
$x = 1$

56.

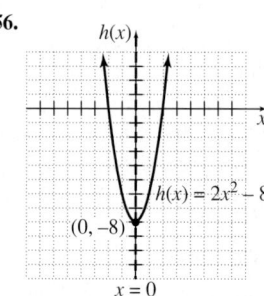

$h(x) = 2x^2 - 8$
$(0, -8)$
$x = 0$

57. (a) concave downward   **(b)** $(0, 0)$ **(c)** $(10, 100)$ **(d)** absolute maximum of 100 when $x = 10$ **(e)** increasing $(0, 10)$; decreasing $(10, \infty)$

58.

$(30, 450)$

The vertex is $(30, 450)$; the revenue is at a maximum of \$450 when 30 photos are ordered.

59. The rock will reach a maximum height of 6025 feet. The range of the rock will be 6025 feet (maximum height) to 0 feet above the river level.
60. The maximum height of the projectile is 850 feet 5 seconds after being shot in the air.
61. The maximum profit is \$965.00 when the patio dimension is 20 feet on a side.
62. The maximum area is 6601.56 square meters when the width is 81.25 meters.
63. The vertex is about $(9.2, 14.7)$; in 1909, the percent of foreign born is at a maximum of about 14.7%.
64. $y = x^2 - 5x - 24$
65. $y = -2x^2 + 9x + 5$
66. $y = x^2 - 7x + 6$
67. $s(t) = -16t^2 + 32t + 160$; the hammer will reach the ground in approximately 4.3 seconds.
68. $f(x) = 0.0109375x^2 + 280$
69. Let $x =$ the number of years after 1960, $y =$ the number of female U.S. Army officers, $y = -18.52x^2 + 330.4x + 3783$; The function predicts that in 1968 the number of female officers will reach a maximum of 5257. This matches the data given. The function predicts that there will be no female officers in 1985.

CHAPTER 6 MIXED REVIEW

1. 0   **2.** −30   **3.** −60   **4.** 0   **5.** 0   **6.** −2   **7.** 5   **8.** 5   **9.** −5

10. (a) binomial; degree of each term is 0, 2; degree of polynomial is 2; $3x^2 + 5$ **(b)** polynomial; degree of each term is 2, 3, 0, 1; degree of polynomial is 3; $-5a^3 + 15a^2 + a + 4$ **(c)** polynomial; degree of each term is 4, 1, 0, 5, 2; degree of polynomial is 5; $x^5 + 5x^4 - 3x^2 + x - 2$

11. (a) trinomial; degree of each term is 2, 1, 0; degree of polynomial is 2.   **(b)** polynomial; degree of each term is 3, 2, 3, 0, 4; degree of polynomial is 4. **(c)** monomial; degree of term is 3; degree of polynomial is 3.

12. 0   **13.** 12   **14.** 0   **15.** 0   **16.** −31.824

17.

x	y
−3	0
−2	16
−1	12
0	0
1	−8
2	0
3	36

18. The range is the set of all real numbers.
19. $y \geq -6$
20. The range is the set of all real numbers.

21. (a)

x	y
0	−2
5	3
3	7

(b) $y \leq 7$

22.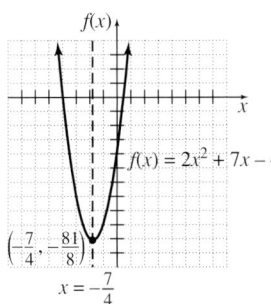

23.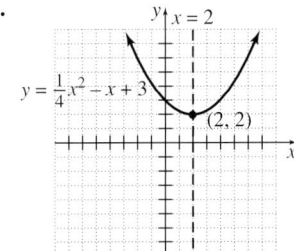

24.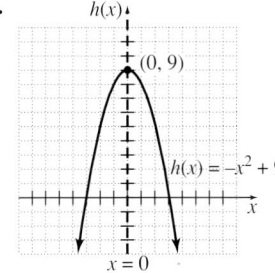

25–28.

	a	b	c	Graph Wide/Narrow	Graph Concave Upward/Downward	Graph Vertex	Axis of Symmetry	y-Intercept
25.	$\frac{1}{3}$	$\frac{2}{3}$	1	wide	upward	$\left(-1, \frac{2}{3}\right)$	$x = -1$	$(0, 1)$
26.	−3	6	0	narrow	downward	$(1, 3)$	$x = 1$	$(0, 0)$
27.	$-\frac{1}{4}$	1	3	wide	downward	$(2, 4)$	$x = 2$	$(0, 3)$
28.	2	4	−6	narrow	upward	$(-1, -8)$	$x = -1$	$(0, -6)$

29. $y = x^2 + 8x + 24$ **30.** $y = x^2 - 5x - 36$

31. (a) concave downward   **(b)** $(0, 200)$ **(c)** $(2, 264)$ **(d)** The absolute maximum of 264 when $t = 2$.   **(e)** increasing $(0, 2)$; decreasing $(2, 6)$ **32.** The polynomial for the perimeter is $(2w^3 + 2w + 10)$ units; the perimeter is 70 feet.   **33.** The polynomial for the total area is $(x^2 + 11x)$ square units.

34. The polynomial is $(xy - \pi z^2)$ square feet; the area measures approximately 3798.9 ft².

35. (a)

x	$P(x)$
0	0
1	12
2	28
3	48
4	72
5	100
6	132
7	168

(b) Answers will vary.

36. (a) The predicted GPA is 3.09375.

(b)

GMAT score, z	500	550	600	650	700	750
GPA in MBA, y	3.575	3.55975	3.504	3.40775	3.271	3.09375

(c) As the entrance exam score goes up, the student's predicted performance goes down.

37. $Y1 = -0.8x^2 + 1500$
     $Y2 = 0$

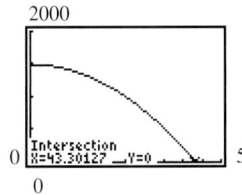

The object will reach the ground in approximately 43.3 seconds.

38. The maximum height is about 9.44 feet above the ground in 0.4 second.
39. Assuming the rock hit ground level, the range is between and including 0 and 19,500 feet. The rock had a maximum height of 19,500 feet.
40. The vertex is at $(7.5, 56.25)$. The maximum revenue is $56 when 7 or 8 books are sold.
41. The absolute maximum profit is $275.00 when the square patio is 10 feet on a side.
42. Let $x =$ the length of a side in feet. **(a)** $11.00x^2$ **(b)** $8.50x^2 + 35.00$ **(c)** $2.50x^2 - 35.00$ **(d)** The revenue is $539.00; the cost is $451.50; the profit is $87.50.
43. Let $x =$ the length of the side in yards. **(a)** $14.25x^2$ **(b)** $10.15x^2 + 80.00$ **(c)** $4.10x^2 - 80.00$ **(d)** The revenue is $1286.06; the cost is $996.04; the profit is $290.03.
44. The volume of the dam is approximately 75,256 thousand cubic meters.

45. (a)

Year	1995	1996	1997	1998	1999	2000
Airline fatalities	711	1549	1433	902	495	749

(b) The function overestimates the number by about 400 fatalities.
(c) The function prediction is a very close estimate.
(d) The function prediction is a very close estimate.
(e) 9/11 occurred in 2001.

46. (a)

Age in years	35	40	45	60	65	70
Percent with hearing trouble	10.7	14.3	18.4	33.7	39.8	46.4

(b) The function prediction is very close.   **(c)** The function predicts approximately 3% to 7% have hearing trouble.   **(d)** The model predicts that 100% of persons 105 years of age have hearing loss. For ages over 105 the percentage is over 100%.

47. The maximum area is 5.0625 square feet when the length of the rectangle is 2.25 feet.   **48.** The absolute minimum percentage of foreign-born population in the second half of the century was about 4.7% in 1968. Answers will vary.   **49.** $y = 8301.7x^2 - 78{,}972.9x + 98{,}029$; there is no absolute maximum or minimum; there will be no male officers in 1961 and 1968. The function cannot be used for predictions.
50. $y = -0.000712x^2 + 170$.

CHAPTER 6 TEST

1. monomial   **2.** polynomial   **3.** binomial   **4.** 5   **5.** 5   **6.** $x^5 + 3x^4 + 9x^2 + 14x + 15$ **7.** $-\dfrac{4}{9} + a - \dfrac{5}{6}a^2 - \dfrac{2}{3}a^3$ **8.** -72 **9.** -224

10. 0   **11.** -6 **12.** 4   **13.**   **(a)** The vertex is $(2, -8)$.   **(b)**

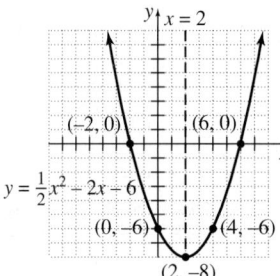

(c) $y \geq -8$
(d) Yes; the graph of the relation passes the vertical line test.
14. (a) concave downward   **(b)** $(0, -100)$
(c) $(30, 800)$ **(d)** The absolute maximum profit is $800 when 30 items are produced and sold.
(e) The profit function is increasing for $(0, 30)$ and decreasing for $(30, \infty)$.

15–16.

	a	b	c	Graph Wide/Narrow	Graph Concave Upward/Downward	Graph Vertex	Axis of Symmetry	y-Intercept
15.	$\frac{1}{2}$	2	3	wide	upward	$(-2, 1)$	$x = -2$	$(0, 3)$
16.	3	-3	$\frac{1}{4}$	narrow	upward	$\left(\frac{1}{2}, -\frac{1}{2}\right)$	$x = \frac{1}{2}$	$\left(0, \frac{1}{4}\right)$

17. $y = x^2 - 6x + 8$ **18.** $y = 2x^2 - x + 3$ **19.** $s(t) \leq 100$. The paper had a maximum height of 100 feet.
20. The vertex is $(18.75, 703.125)$. $703 is the maximum profit earned by selling 19 keyboards.   **21.** $y = -0.000463x^2 + 325$
22. Let x = the length of the side of the square.   **(a)** $0.09x^2$ **(b)** $0.07x^2 + 235.00$ **(c)** $0.02x^2 - 235.00$
(d) The revenue is $8100; the cost is $6535; the profit is $1565.
23. The volume is approximately 2877.45 cubic miles.

24.

Year	1998	1999	2000	2001
Cost	10,076	10,444	10,818	11,198

(a) The function predicts the cost in 2001 to be $11,198, about $200 less than the actual amount.
(b) The function predicts the cost in 2002 to be about $11,584, about $500 less than the actual amount.
(c) Answers will vary.

25. The vertex is approximately $(3.6, 85171)$; in 2002, 85,171 passenger cars were imported from Sweden. This was the minimum number imported from Sweden.   **26.** The vertex is approximately $(2.07, 173)$; in 2002, the lowest sales of garlic were about 173 million dollars.   **27.** The maximum height of the cannon ball was 32.25 meters after 1.5 seconds from being shot.   **28.** Answers will vary.

CHAPTER 7

SECTION 7.1 EXERCISES

1. $-3 \cdot x \cdot x \cdot x \cdot x$ **2.** $-4 \cdot c \cdot c \cdot c$ **3.** $(-3x)(-3x)(-3x)(-3x)$ **4.** $(-4c)(-4c)(-4c)$ **5.** $a \cdot a \cdot a \cdot c \cdot c \cdot c \cdot c \cdot c$ **6.** $x \cdot x \cdot y$ **7.** $\dfrac{3}{4} \cdot \dfrac{3}{4} \cdot \dfrac{3}{4} \cdot x \cdot x$

8. $\left(\dfrac{2}{3}\right)\left(\dfrac{2}{3}\right) \cdot x \cdot x \cdot x$ **9.** $5(x + y)(x + y)$ **10.** $-4(p - q)(p - q)$ **11.** x^{13} **12.** a^{23} **13.** y^{14} **14.** b^{24} **15.** $\dfrac{1}{2}x^8$ **16.** $\dfrac{1}{3}y^6$

17. $(x + y)^6$ **18.** $(x - y)^8$ **19.** $(x + 3)^3$ **20.** $(x + 9)^{13}$ **21.** p^5 **22.** a^2 **23.** $3q^6$ **24.** $3t^7$ **25.** $(2x - 3)^5$ **26.** $(4x + 7)^7$

27. $-\dfrac{1}{3}(p + q)$ **28.** $-\dfrac{1}{2}(xy + 2)^3$ **29.** a^{30} **30.** m^{28} **31.** $81x^4$ **32.** $-125y^3$ **33.** $18a^2$ **34.** $12x^2$ **35.** $a^{21}b^{21}c^{21}$ **36.** $x^9y^9z^9$

37. $125m^9$ **38.** $81k^{16}$ **39.** $(x + y)^6$ **40.** $(a + 2b)^{12}$ **41.** 1   **42.** 1   **43.** $\dfrac{b^4}{d^4}$ **44.** $\dfrac{m^5}{n^5}$ **45.** $\dfrac{81b^4}{c^4}$ **46.** $\dfrac{625y^4}{z^4}$ **47.** $\dfrac{d^6}{64c^6}$

48. $\dfrac{m^4}{81n^4}$ **49.** $-35a^5b^5$ **50.** $-24c^5d^7$ **51.** $5x^2$ **52.** $6b$ **53.** $\dfrac{-9abc^2}{5}$ **54.** $\dfrac{-9p^2q^2}{2}$ **55.** $-2x(4-x)^3$ **56.** $\dfrac{t(15-4t)^4}{3}$

57. p^9q^{20} **58.** k^5m^{11} **59.** $\dfrac{16x^6}{y^4}$ **60.** $\dfrac{25a^4}{49b^2}$ **61.** $-27p^6q^3$ **62.** $25c^2d^2$ **63.** $1024a^{10}$ **64.** $81t^4$ **65.** $\dfrac{x^6}{64y^6}$ **66.** $\dfrac{729z^6}{w^6}$

67. b   **68.** a   **69.** Correct   **70.** Correct   **71.** Correct   **72.** Correct   **73.** Incorrect   **74.** Incorrect   **75.** Correct   **76.** Correct
77. Incorrect   **78.** Incorrect   **79.** The original area is x^2 square units; the enlarged area is $25x^2$ square units; the enlarged area is 25 times the original area; if the original side is 6 feet, the original area and enlarged area are 36 ft^2 and 900 ft^2, respectively.   **80.** The original area is x^2 square units; the enlarged area is $6.25x^2$ square units; the enlarged area is 6.25 times the original area; if the original side is 12 feet, then the original area and enlarged area are 144 ft^2 and 900 ft^2, respectively.   **81.** The volume of the original bin is x^3 cubic units; the volume of the enlarged bin is $64x^3$ cubic units; the volume of the enlarged bin is 64 times the original bin; if the original side measures 1.5 feet, then the volumes of the original bin and enlarged bin are 3.375 ft^3 and 216 ft^3, respectively.   **82.** The volume of the original block is x^3 cubic units; the volume of the smaller block is $0.512x^3$ cubic units; the volume of the smaller block is 0.512 times the volume of the original block; if the original side is 22 inches, then the volume of the original block and smaller block are 10,648 in^3 and 5451.776 in^3, respectively.   **83.** The volume of the original balloon is $\frac{4}{3}\pi x^3$. The volume of the second balloon is $\frac{32}{3}\pi x^3$. The volume of the second one is 8 times the volume of the original balloon. If the radius of the original one is 4 feet, then the volumes of the original balloon and the second balloon are 268.1 ft^3 and 2144.7 ft^3, respectively.   **84.** The surface area of the smaller ball is $4\pi x^2$. The surface area of the larger ball is $9\pi x^2$. The surface area of the larger ball is 2.25 times as large as the surface area of the smaller ball. If the radius of the smaller ball is 27 cm, then the surface areas of the smaller ball and the larger ball are 9160.9 cm^2 and 20,612.0 cm^2, respectively.   **85. (a)** πx^2 square miles   **(b)** $9\pi x^2$ square miles   **(c)** 9 to 1   **(d)** The adult male's home range in an ideal habitat is 3.24π square miles or about 10.18 square miles. The adult male's average home range is 29.16π square miles or about 91.61 square miles.   **86. (a)** πx^2 square miles   **(b)** $3.24\pi x^2$ square miles   **(c)** 3.24 to 1 or 81 to 25   **(d)** The adult female's home range in an ideal habitat is 1.21π square miles or about 3.80 square miles. The adult female's average home range is 3.92π square miles or about 12.32 square miles.   **87.** It will fall $39.2t^2$ meters in twice time t. It will fall about $1.1t^2$ meters in one-third of time t.   **88.** It will fall $144x^2$ feet in triple time x. It will fall $4x^2$ feet in one-half of time x.   **89.** The power will be $\dfrac{9V^2}{R}$ if the voltage V is tripled. The power will be $\dfrac{V^2}{4R}$ if the voltage V is cut in half.   **90.** The kinetic energy is $8mv^2$ if the velocity v is quadrupled. The kinetic energy is $\frac{1}{8}mv^2$ if the velocity v is cut in half.   **91.** The distance is about 1.652×10^{17} miles.   **92.** The distance is about 1.9057×10^{16} miles.   **93.** 275,093,200 milligrams were prescribed in 2002.
94. The total revenues was 1.656×10^{10} dollars or \$16,560,000,000.   **95.** The square of this distance is 7.5625×10^{18} square miles.   **96.** The square of this distance is 2.116×10^{19} square miles.   **97.** The volume of the sun is about 1.412×10^{18} km^3.   **98.** The volume of Jupiter is about 1.225×10^{16} km^3.   **99.** The wavelength is 2.784 meters.   **100.** The wavelength is 2.8966 meters.   **101.** The drug was prescribed about 9118 times.   **102.** The average revenue was about \$107,234.

7.1 CALCULATOR EXERCISES

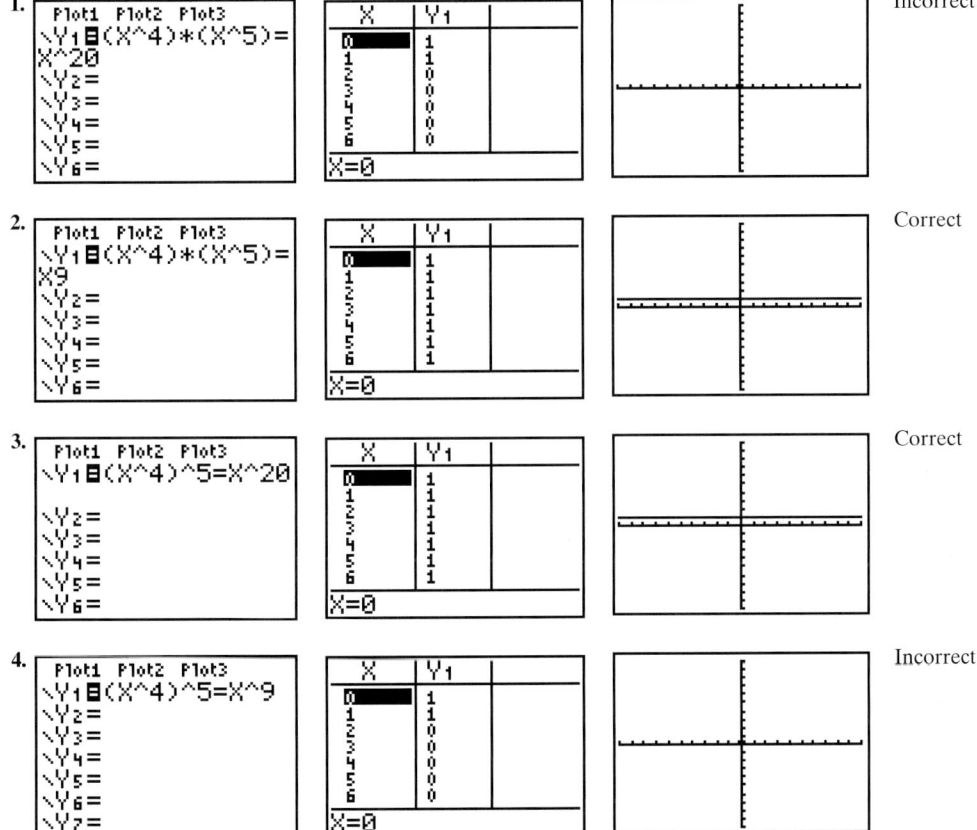

5.
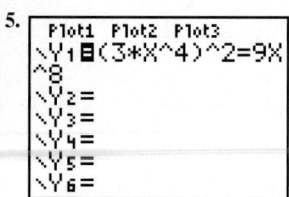
Correct

6.
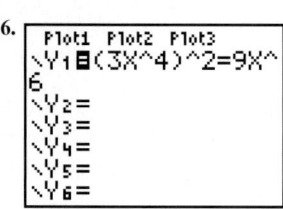
Incorrect

SECTION 7.2 EXERCISES

1. $\dfrac{1}{p^3}$ **2.** $\dfrac{1}{q^2}$ **3.** q^5 **4.** p^3 **5.** $\dfrac{q^5}{p^3}$ **6.** $\dfrac{p^3}{q^2}$ **7.** d^4c^3 **8.** c^2d^5 **9.** $\dfrac{16h^3k^4}{25}$ **10.** $\dfrac{64x^2y^3}{9}$ **11.** $\dfrac{q^5}{p^3}$ **12.** $\dfrac{p^3}{q^2}$ **13.** $-20a^2$

14. $30h^2$ **15.** $\dfrac{m}{4}$ **16.** $\dfrac{y}{6}$ **17.** $\dfrac{81n}{64}$ **18.** $\dfrac{25x}{32}$ **19.** c^8 **20.** p^6 **21.** $\dfrac{a^6}{125b^6}$ **22.** $\dfrac{m^8}{25n^4}$ **23.** $\dfrac{-42}{q^3}$ **24.** $39xy^3$ **25.** $\dfrac{6.02x^5}{y^2}$

26. $15.39y^3$ **27.** $\dfrac{2xy^3}{5}$ **28.** $\dfrac{4a}{15b^2}$ **29.** $\dfrac{-21x^6}{y^3}$ **30.** $-8m^2q^3$ **31.** $\dfrac{1}{m^7}$ **32.** $\dfrac{1}{k^2}$ **33.** $\dfrac{-c^2}{3}$ **34.** $\dfrac{7d^2}{10}$ **35.** $4x^3y^4$ **36.** $3c^2d^5$

37. $\dfrac{k^7}{5h^2}$ **38.** $\dfrac{v^3}{9u^5}$ **39.** $\dfrac{81x^{11}}{5}$ **40.** $\dfrac{4a^{10}}{3}$ **41.** $\dfrac{b^{12}}{8a^{12}}$ **42.** $\dfrac{-c^9}{64d^{12}}$ **43.** $-32p^{10}q^{25}$ **44.** $-32k^{25}m^5$ **45.** $\dfrac{b^3}{a^3}$ **46.** $\dfrac{t}{s}$ **47.** $\dfrac{y^3}{64x^3}$

48. $\dfrac{b^5}{243a^5}$ **49.** $\dfrac{1}{81p^8q^8}$ **50.** $\dfrac{1}{25c^6d^2}$ **51.** $\dfrac{y^3}{z^6}$ **52.** $\dfrac{d^6}{e^8}$ **53.** $\dfrac{125a^9}{b^{12}}$ **54.** $\dfrac{t^{28}}{625s^{12}}$ **55.** a **56.** b

57.
 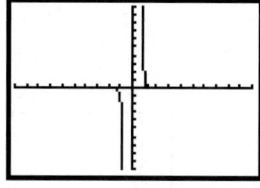

58.
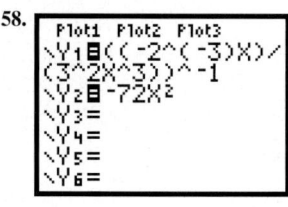 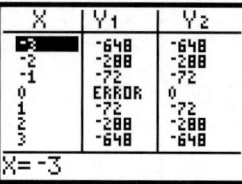 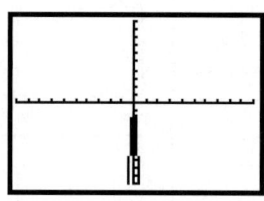

59. 2.677×10^{-5} inch **60.** 2.176×10^{-5} liter **61.** 3.97×10^{-11} inch **62.** 2.59×10^{-3} square mile **63.** A typed period is 5×10^{-4} meter.
64. A glucose molecule is 5×10^{-10} meter. **65.** 2.596×10^{-8} millimeter **66.** 1.9×10^{-1} quart or 0.19 quart **67.** 1.596×10^{12} nanometer
68. 2.591×10^{-6} square kilometer **69.** The average price of an egg was 1.017×10^{-1} dollar (about $0.10). The average cost of a dozen eggs was
1.2204×10^{0} dollars (about $1.22). **70.** Yes; he consumed about 8.7×10^{-4} kilogram. **71.** The volume is about 9.203×10^{-30} cubic meter.
72. The volume is about 1.630×10^{-42} cubic meter. **73.** The ratio is 1000 to 1. **74.** The ratio is 1 to 1000. **75.** The volume of a protein is
about 6.54×10^{-26} cubic meter. **76.** The volume of a bacterium is about 6.54×10^{-17} cubic meter.

7.2 CALCULATOR EXERCISES

1.
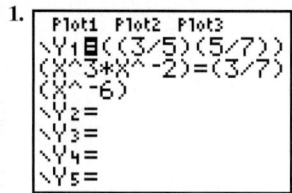
Error in second step

2.
Error in second step

3. 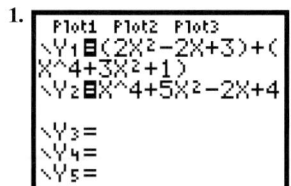 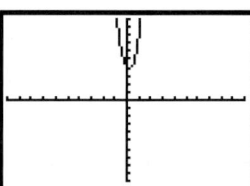 Error in second step

SECTION 7.3 EXERCISES

1.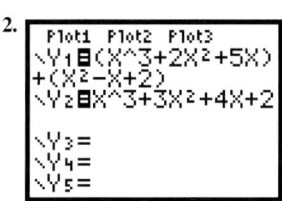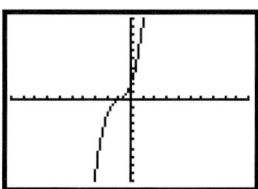

2.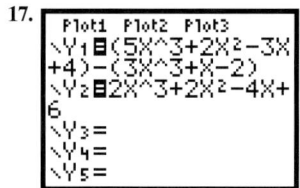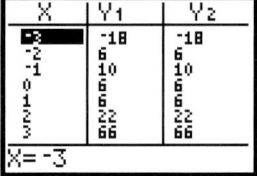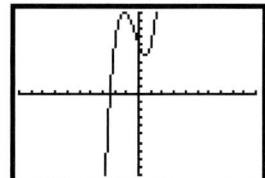

3. $9x^4 + 3x^3 - 10x^2 - 3x + 9$ **4.** $z^3 + z^2 + 5z + 6$ **5.** $-3x^2y + 6y^3 + 15x^3$ **6.** $4a^3 + 6a^2b - ab^2 + 7b^3$ **7.** $a^3 + 8a^2 - 7a - 1$

8. $3x^2 + 12$ **9.** $\frac{2}{3}y^4 + \frac{5}{2}y^3 + \frac{19}{9}y^2 + \frac{1}{2}y - \frac{22}{9}$ **10.** $\frac{13}{12}x^3 - \frac{2}{3}x^2 - \frac{1}{4}x + \frac{19}{12}$ **11.** $18.77x^3 - 1.23x^2 + 3.81x + 9.735$

12. $0.7y^3 + 6.2y^2 - 4.4y + 0.3$ **13.** $5117a^3 + 50998a^2 - 1816a + 2095$ **14.** $50b^2 + 200$ **15.** $3a + 9b + 6c$ **16.** $5x + y + 11z$

17.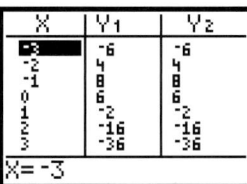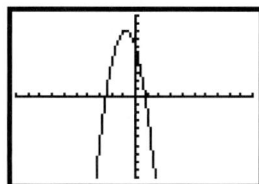

18.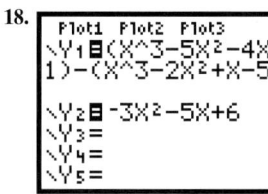

19. $a^4 - a^3 + a^2 - a$ **20.** $b^7 + b^5 + b^3 + b$ **21.** $7x^2 - 3x - 39$ **22.** $-5y^3 + 8y - 11$ **23.** $-5a^3 - 6a^2 - 12a + 14$
24. $x^3 - 2x^2 + 3x + 9$ **25.** $42x^3 - 30x^2y + 3xy^2 + 11y^3$ **26.** $51p^3 + 26p^2q - 16pq^2 + 41q^3 + 10$ **27.** $4a - 2b + 7c - 6d$
28. $12x + 5y + 8z$ **29.** $\frac{3}{14}x^2 - \frac{19}{42}x - \frac{26}{21}$ **30.** $\frac{7}{24}x^3 + \frac{11}{24}x^2 - \frac{1}{4}x - \frac{1}{3}$ **31.** $9x^3 + x^2y - 14xy^2 + 68y^3$ **32.** $2.48x^2 - 12.51xy - 8.75y^2$
33. $4683z^2 - 4403z + 7187$ **34.** $-86b^3 + 178b^2 - 1344b + 1591$ **35. (a)** $C(x) = 200 + 4.5x$ **(b)** $R(x) = 13.5x$ **(c)** $P(x) = 9x - 200$
(d) The profit is $-\$20$ if 20 pots are sold (that is a loss of \$20) and \$70 if 30 pots are sold.   **36. (a)** $C(x) = 500 + 20x$ **(b)** $R(x) = 50x$
(c) $P(x) = 30x - 500$ **(d)** The profit is \$1750 if 75 phones are sold and \$2500 if 100 phones are sold.

37. $C(x) = 5.00x + 30;$ **38.** $C(x) = 180 + 1.80x;$
$R(x) = 28.50x;$ $R(x) = 11.95x;$
$P(x) = 23.50x - 30$ $P(x) = 10.15x - 180$

39. The area is $(3x^2 - 3)$ square feet.   **40.** The area is $(3x^2 + 6x + 3)$ square feet.   **41.** The area enclosed in the fence that is not covered by the pool is $(30x + 110)$ square feet.   **42.** The area of the back yard not covered by the building is $(10x^2 + 18x + 5)$ square feet.   **43.** The difference is $(-10t + 100)$ feet.   **44.** The difference is $(30t + 40)$ feet.   **45.** The average cost at a 4-year institution is $(-38.34x^3 + 200.5x^2 + 184.84x + 6597)$ dollars more than the average cost at a 2-year institution.   **46.** The percent of the population between 45 and 64 is $(-0.0006x^3 + 0.0343x^2 - 0.519x + 8.3)$ more than the percent of population 65 and over.   **47.** The number of passenger cars imported from Mexico is $(-27,498t^2 + 95,496t + 328,722)$ more than the number of passenger cars from Germany.   **48.** The number of passenger cars imported from France is $(-18,352t^2 + 133.252t - 326,935)$ more than the number of passenger cars from Sweden.   **49.** The difference in the percentage of foreign-born population in the first part of the century and the percentage of foreign-born population in the second part of the century is

$(-0.024x^2 + 1.74x - 42.2)$.   **50.** The population density of Florida is $(-0.0145x^2 + 6.115x + 170.6)$ more than the population density of North Dakota.   **51.** The difference in the number of males and the number of females is $(-2x^2 - 162x + 5240)$.   **52.** The difference in the averages of the National League and the American League is $(-0.0275x^2 + 0.0395x + 0.021)$.

7.3 CALCULATOR EXERCISES

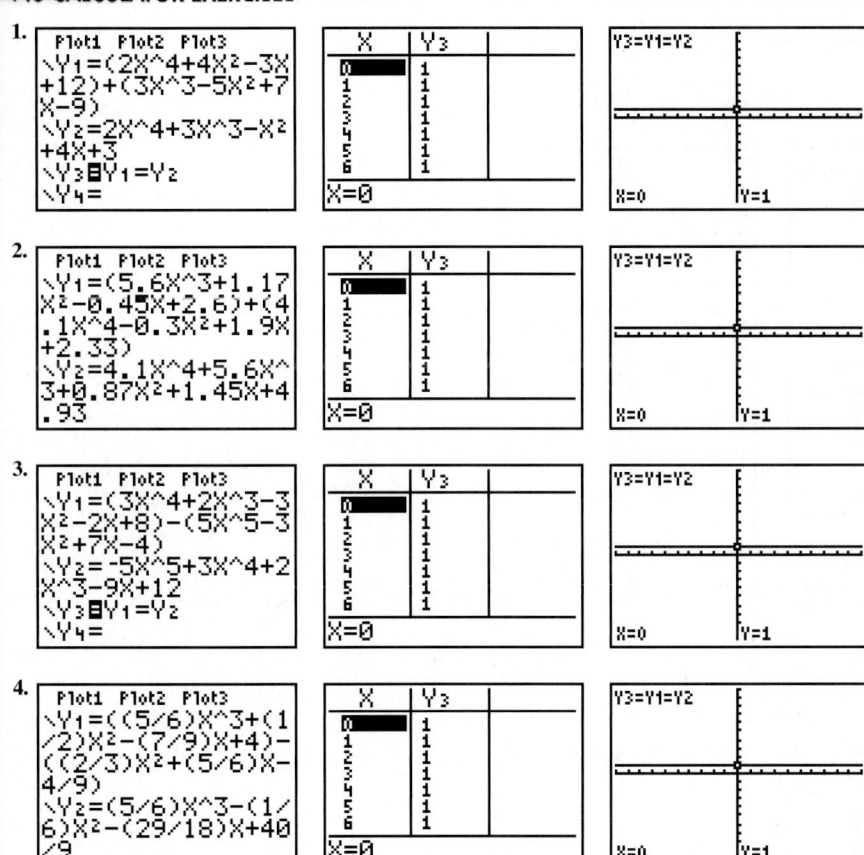

1.

2.

3.

4.

SECTION 7.4 EXERCISES

1. $-16a^4b^3$ **2.** $15p^5q^3$ **3.** $-6x^2 + 2xy - 4xz$ **4.** $-4a^2 + 3ab - 2ac$ **5.** $6a^4 + 4a^3b - 2a^3c$ **6.** $6x^3 - 9x^2y + 3x^2z$

7.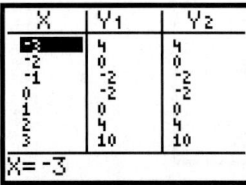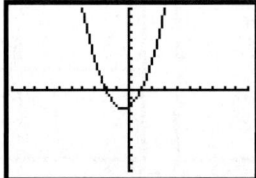

8.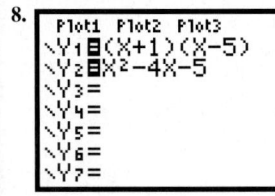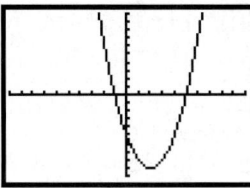

9. $x^2 + 6x + 8$ **10.** $a^2 + 13a + 42$ **11.** $2x^2 + 13x + 15$ **12.** $7z^2 + 29z + 4$ **13.** $6xy - 4x + 15y - 10$ **14.** $15ab + 20a - 6b - 8$

15. $3x^2 - 2xy - 8y^2$ **16.** $2a^2 - 5ab - 12b^2$ **17.** $5a^2 - 8.2a - 9.12$ **18.** $4p^2 - 3.9p - 4.93$ **19.** $a^2 + a + \dfrac{2}{9}$ **20.** $x^2 + \dfrac{2}{5}x - \dfrac{3}{25}$

21. $2x^4 + 5x^2 - 12$ **22.** $8x^3 + 4x^2 + 6x + 3$ **23.** $6x^3 - 10xy + 9x^2y^2 - 15y^3$ **24.** $24a^3 - 20a^2b^2 + 18ab - 15b^3$ **25.** $x^3 + 64$
26. $x^3 - 1$ **27.** $6x^3 - 19x^2 + x + 6$ **28.** $4x^3 - 17x^2 - 23x - 6$ **29.** $x^4 + 3x^3 + 6x^2 + 5x + 3$ **30.** $a^4 - a^3 - 3a^2 + 5a - 2$
31. $a^2 + b^2 + c^2 + 2ab + 2bc + 2ac$ **32.** $a^2 + b^2 + c^2 - 2ab - 2ac + 2bc$ **33.** $z^3 + 9z^2 + 27z + 27$ **34.** $r^3 + 6r^2 + 12r + 8$
35. $27a^3 - 54a^2b + 36ab^2 - 8b^3$ **36.** $8x^3 - 36x^2y + 54xy^2 - 27y^3$ **37.** $x^2 - 25$ **38.** $y^2 - 144$ **39.** $9m^2 - 49$ **40.** $25p^2 - 16$
41. $4a^2 - 9b^2$ **42.** $81p^2 - 4q^2$ **43.** $16x^2 - 2.25$ **44.** $9z^2 - 6.25$ **45.** $\dfrac{4}{25}x^2 - 1$ **46.** $\dfrac{16}{49}y^2 - 4$ **47.** $x^4 - 49$ **48.** $y^4 - 81$
49. $m^2 + 14m + 49$ **50.** $p^2 + 12p + 36$ **51.** $x^2 - 2xy + y^2$ **52.** $u^2 - 2uv + v^2$ **53.** $4p^2 + 36pq + 81q^2$ **54.** $25m^2 - 110mn + 121n^2$

55. $36c^2 - 60c + 25$ **56.** $64d^2 + 48d + 9$ **57.** $9x^4 + 12x^2 + 4$ **58.** $4z^4 - 20z^2 + 25$ **59. (a)** $4x^2 - 10x + 4$ **(b)** $2x^2 + 3x + 1$
(c) $2x^3 + 2x^2$ **(d)** $x^4 - 3x^3 - 9x^2 + 27x$ **60. (a)** $3x^2 - 12x + 9$ **(b)** $6x^2 + 5x + 1$ **(c)** $2x^3 + 6x^2$ **(d)** $2x^4 - 2x^3 - 8x^2 + 8x$
61. (a) $f(3 + h) = h^2 + 8h + 12$ **(b)** $f(x + h) = x^2 + 2xh + h^2 + 2x + 2h - 3$ **62. (a)** $g(2 + h) = h^2 + h + 2$
(b) $g(a + h) = a^2 + 2ah + h^2 - 3a - 3h + 4$ **63.** $2x^2 + 9x - 5$ **64.** $2x^2 - x - 15$ **65.** $x^2 - 8x + 16$ **66.** $x^2 + 14x + 49$
67. $\pi x^2 - 4\pi x + 4\pi$ **68.** $\pi x^2 + 6\pi x + 9\pi$ **69.** $2x^2 - 2x - 4 + \pi x^2 + 2\pi x + \pi$ **70.** $2x^2 + 6x - 8 - \pi x^2 + 2\pi x - \pi$ **71. (a)** length:
$(18 - 2x)$ in.; width: $(12 - 2x)$ in.; height: (x) in.   **(b)** The volume is $(4x^3 - 60x^2 + 216x)$ in^3.   **(c)** The surface area is $(-4x^2 + 216)$ in^2.
72. (a) length: $(10 - 2y)$ in.; width: $(10 - 2y)$ in.; height: y in.   **(b)** The volume is $(4y^3 - 40y^2 + 100y)$ in^3.   **(c)** The surface area is $(-4y^2 + 100)$ in^2.
73. (a) (πx^2) ft^2 **(b)** $\left[\pi(x - 5)^2\right]$ ft^2 **(c)** The area of the deck is $(10\pi x - 25\pi)$ ft^2.   **74. (a)** (36π) ft^2 **(b)** $\left[\pi(6 - x)^2\right]$ ft^2 **(c)** The area of the

deck is $(12\pi x - \pi x^2)$ ft^2.   **75.** Let $x =$ the measure of the height in feet; the area of the triangle is $\left(2x^2 - \dfrac{5}{2}x\right)$ square feet.   **76.** Let $x =$ the

measure of the base in feet; the area of the triangle is $\left(\dfrac{7}{2}x^2 + x\right)$ square feet.   **77. (a)** Let $x =$ the measure of the height in meters, $h(x) =$ the square

of the hypotenuse; $h(x) = x^2 + 4x + 4$ **(b)** Let $x =$ the measure of the height in meters, $s(x) =$ the sum of the square of the height and the square
of the base; $s(x) = 2x^2 - 4x + 4$ **(c)** If the height is 8 meters, then $h(8) = s(8) = 100$. The results are the same.   **78. (a)** Let $x =$ the measure of
the base in feet, $h(x) =$ the square of the hypotenuse, $h(x) = x^2 + 4x + 4$ **(b)** Let $x =$ the measure of the base in feet, $s(x) =$ the sum of the square
of the height and the square of the base; $s(x) = 2x^2 + 2x + 1$ **(c)** If the base is 3 feet, then $h(3) = s(3) = 25$. The results are the same.   **79.** Let
$x =$ the width in feet. **(a)** The current area of the deck is $3x^2$ square feet.   **(b)** The area of the enlarged deck is $(6x^2 + 20x)$ square feet.   **(c)** The difference in the areas is $(3x^2 + 20x)$ square feet.   **(d)** Pandora will be adding 500 square feet.   **80.** Let $x =$ the width in feet. **(a)** The current area of
the patio is x^2 square feet.   **(b)** The area of the enlarged patio is $(2x^2 + 10x)$ square feet.   **(c)** The difference in the areas is $(x^2 + 10x)$ square feet.
(d) Laurie will be adding 264 square feet.   **81.** Let $x =$ the number of persons (reductions), $R(x) =$ the revenue; $R(x) = 15.00x - 0.50x^2$
82. Let $x =$ the number of children (discounts), $R(x) =$ the revenue; $R(x) = 8.75x - 0.75x^2$ **83.** Let $x =$ the number of children (discounts),
$R(x) =$ the revenue; $R(x) = 4.00x - 0.25x^2$ **84.** Let $x =$ the number of items rented (discounts), $R(x) =$ the revenue; $R(x) = 35x - 5x^2$
85. Let $R(x) =$ the revenue; $R(x) = -10x^2 + 660x + 6750$ **86.** Let $R(x) =$ the revenue; $R(x) = -50x^2 - 2300x + 10,000$ **87.** Let $y(x) =$ the
total yield; $y(x) = -375x^2 + 3875x + 15,000$ **88.** Let $t(x) =$ the total number of tickets sold; $t(x) = 25x^2 + 215x + 460$

7.4 CALCULATOR EXERCISES

1. not equivalent; $4x^2 - 1$ **2.** not equivalent; $x^2 - 1$ **3.** equivalent   **4.** equivalent   **5.** not equivalent; $x^2 - \dfrac{35}{6}x - 1$ **6.** equivalent
7. equivalent   **8.** not equivalent; $0.3x^3 - 1.4x^2 - 0.3x + 1.4$

SECTION 7.5 EXERCISES

1. $-4a^2b$ **2.** $-2x^4y$ **3.** $2x^2y^3z + 6$ **4.** $3x^2yz + 2y$ **5.** $2x^2 + 4x - 6$ **6.** $3a^3 - 2a + 6$ **7.** $4x^3 - 3x^2 + 15x + 5$
8. $5z^3 - 2z^2 + 9z + 3$ **9.** $3x + 4 - \dfrac{5}{x}$ **10.** $2x - 3 + \dfrac{1}{x}$ **11.** $\dfrac{p^2}{q} - 3p + 2q - \dfrac{4q^2}{p}$ **12.** $\dfrac{c^2}{d} - 3c + 2d - \dfrac{5d^2}{c}$

13. $\dfrac{-3x^3}{y} - 2x^2 + 6xy + 8y^2 - \dfrac{24y^3}{x}$ **14.** $\dfrac{2a}{b} - 5 - \dfrac{4b}{a} + \dfrac{b^2}{a^2}$

15.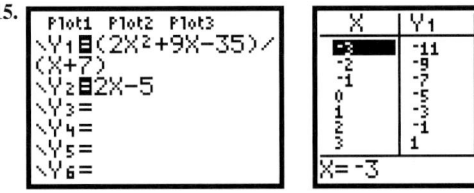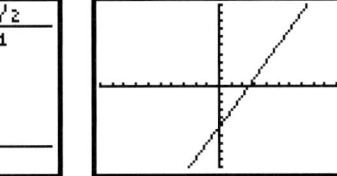

16.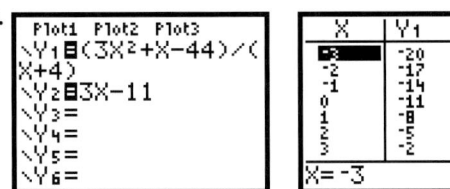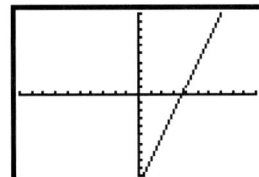

17. $5x - 6$ **18.** $3x - 7$ **19.** $5x + 6$ **20.** $6x + 5$ **21.** $3y - 5 + \dfrac{20}{y + 8}$ **22.** $5z - 7 + \dfrac{4}{z + 2}$ **23.** $3a + 5 - \dfrac{5}{2a - 5}$

24. $4b + 5 + \dfrac{20}{3b - 7}$ **25.** $x^2 - 3.2x + 0.68 + \dfrac{0.64}{5x + 2}$ **26.** $4x^2 - x + 5$ **27.** $4x^2 + 2x + 5$ **28.** $3x^2 + 2x + 7$ **29.** $3a - 7$

30. $7b - 11$ **31.** $x + 5.4 - \dfrac{7.2}{5x + 3}$ **32.** $6y + 5$ **33.** $4z - 11$ **34.** $8p - 7$ **35.** $x^2 - 3x + 9$ **36.** $y^2 - 7y + 49$ **37.** $a^2 + 5a + 25$

38. $b^2 + 3b + 9$ **39.** $16x^2 - 12x + 9$ **40.** $25z^2 + 10z + 4$ **41. (a)** $3 - \dfrac{34}{x^2 - 6x + 9}$ **(b)** $2 + \dfrac{1}{x^2 + 2x + 1}$ **42. (a)** $4 - \dfrac{13}{x^2 + 4x + 4}$

(b) $3 - \dfrac{5}{x^2 - 2x + 1}$ **43.** $2x - 1$ **44.** $x - 4$ **45.** $x - 5$ **46.** $x - 5$ **47. (a)** $C(x) = 35x + 45$ **(b)** $R(x) = 50x$ **(c)** $P(x) = 15x - 45$

(d) $A(x) = 15 - \dfrac{45}{x}$ **(e)** The average profit is $13.50 per calculator.   **48. (a)** $C(x) = 75x + 1000$ **(b)** $R(x) = 350x$ **(c)** $P(x) = 275x - 1000$

(d) $A(x) = 275 - \dfrac{1000}{x}$ **(e)** The average profit is $175 per web page.   **49. (a)** $C(x) = 2.00x + 200.00$ **(b)** $R(x) = 4.50x - 0.10x^2$

(c) $P(x) = -0.10x^2 + 2.50x - 200.00$ **(d)** $A(x) = -0.10x + 2.50 - \dfrac{200.00}{x}$ **50. (a)** $C(x) = 1.25x + 500.00$ **(b)** $R(x) = 33.50x - 0.50x^2$

(c) $P(x) = -0.50x^2 + 32.25x - 500.00$ **(d)** $A(x) = -0.50x + 32.25 - \dfrac{500.00}{x}$ **51.** $6000t^4 + 6000t^3 + 6000t^2 + 6000t + 6000$; he will receive about \$36,631 for a 10% increase and about \$40,454 for a 15% increase. **52.** $10x^5 + 10x^4 + 10x^3 + 10x^2 + 10x + 10$; Sharon paid \$630 when the amount was doubled and \$3640 when the amount was tripled. **53.** $250n^4 + 250n^3 + 250n^2 + 250n + 250$; the total rental cost was about \$1024. **54.** $550w^5 + 550w^4 + 550w^3 + 550w^2 + 550w + 550$; the total sales were about \$2706.

7.5 CALCULATOR EXERCISES

1. $\dfrac{55}{\pi r^2}$ pounds per square inch

2. $\dfrac{175}{2\pi r^2}$ pounds per square inch

r (inch)	Pounds per Square Inch
0.25	280.1
0.50	70.0
0.75	31.1
1.00	17.5

For a radius of 1 inch, the woman's pressure on the floor approximates the elephant's.

r (inches)	Pounds per Square Inch
1.0	27.9
1.05	25.3
1.10	23.0
1.15	21.1
1.20	19.3
1.25	17.8
1.30	16.5
1.35	15.3
1.40	14.2
1.45	13.2
1.50	12.4

For a radius of 1.25 inches, the pressure is approximately the same as the elephant's.

CHAPTER 7 SUMMARY

Vocabulary Review

1. product rule **2.** quotient rule **3.** power-to-a-power rule **4.** product-to-a-power rule **5.** product of the sum and difference of the same two terms **6.** square of a binomial **7.** FOIL method

Reflections

1–11. Answers will vary.

CHAPTER 7 SECTION-BY-SECTION REVIEW

1. $-5 \cdot c \cdot c$ **2.** $(-5c)(-5c)$ **3.** $4 \cdot (x + y) \cdot (x + y)$ **4.** $\dfrac{2}{3} \cdot \dfrac{2}{3} \cdot \dfrac{2}{3} \cdot \dfrac{2}{3} \cdot x \cdot x$ **5.** a^9 **6.** $(p + q)^4$ **7.** $\dfrac{2}{3}b^8$ **8.** t^3 **9.** $8a^2$ **10.** $x + 3y$

11. $c^{22}d^{22}$ **12.** $16a^4$ **13.** $-32a^5$ **14.** $9x^6$ **15.** $(a + b)^{10}$ **16.** 1 **17.** $\dfrac{-8x^3}{27z^3}$ **18.** $\dfrac{-64d^3}{e^3}$ **19.** $-8x^4y^7$ **20.** $-3x^2y$ **21.** x^5y^7

22. $\dfrac{8p^3}{q^3}$ **23.** $\dfrac{m^4}{256n^4}$ **24.** Area of original square: x^2 square units; area of reduced square: $\dfrac{x^2}{16}$ square units; the smaller area is $\dfrac{1}{16}$ of the original area. **25.** Area of original garden: πr^2 square units; area of enlarged garden: $4\pi r^2$ square units; the enlarged garden has an area that is 4 times that of the original garden; the garden has an area of 144π ft^2. **26. (a)** πx^2 square miles **(b)** $9\pi x^2$ square miles **(c)** 9 to 1 **(d)** The adult female's average home range is 4π square miles or about 12.57 square miles. The adult male's average home range is 36π square miles or about 113.10 square miles. **27.** Luxembourg's total gross domestic product in 2003 was approximately 2.55×10^{10} dollars. **28.** Japan's gross domestic product in 2003 was about 2.8×10^4 dollars per capita. **29.** The star Pollux is about 1.99×10^{14} miles from Earth. **30.** $\dfrac{k^2}{9h^4}$ **31.** $\dfrac{c^8}{d^5}$ **32.** $\dfrac{3}{b^3}$ **33.** $\dfrac{z^4}{3}$

34. $\dfrac{a^{12}}{125b^6}$ **35.** $\dfrac{12y}{x^6}$ **36.** $\dfrac{9a^6}{b^{20}}$ **37.** $\dfrac{a^6}{b^8}$ **38.** $\dfrac{144a^{14}}{b^6}$ **39.** Each character is 1.66×10^{-1} or about 0.166 inch. **40.** The ratio of the atomic radius of chlorine to the atomic radius of sodium is 33 to 62. **41. (a)** The equatorial radius is 44,432.278 miles. **(b)** The volume is about 3.674×10^{14} cubic miles. **42.** $5x^4 + 7x^3 + 5x^2 + 6x + 4$ **43.** $3.57z^3 + 3.56z^2 + 5.79z + 2.74$ **44.** $4a^4 - a^3 - 2a^2 - 3a - 4$

45. $65z^4 - 16z^3 + 27z^2 - 8z + 24$ **46.** $\dfrac{1}{8}b^4 + \dfrac{7}{8}b^3 - \dfrac{9}{8}b^2 + \dfrac{3}{8}b - \dfrac{1}{4}$ **47. (a)** $C(x) = 10 + 3.5x$ **(b)** $R(x) = 10x$ **(c)** $P(x) = 6.5x - 10$

(d) The profit is \$55 for 10 items and \$152.50 for 25 items.

48. $C(x) = 175 + 29.5x$
$R(x) = 125x$
$P(x) = 95.5x - 175$

49. The difference is $(0.066x^2 - 1.787x + 42.8)$ pounds.   **50.** $-15a^4b^4$ **51.** $-23.46x^4z^7$ **52.** $18x^5 + 12x^4 - 42x^3$ **53.** $-21a^7 - 7a^5 + 14a^3$
54. $8a^3 - 12a^2b + 4a^2c$ **55.** $p^2 - 3p - 54$ **56.** $5x^2 + 53x - 22$ **57.** $2x^2 + xy - y^2$ **58.** $6x^3 + 13x^2 - 3x - 4$ **59.** $a^3 - 27$
60. $x^4 + x^3 + 6x^2 + 7x + 15$ **61.** $z^4 + 4z^3 - 2z^2 - 12z + 9$ **62.** $b^3 - 12b^2 + 48b - 64$ **63.** $4x^2 - 25$ **64.** $\dfrac{16}{25}x^2 - \dfrac{1}{4}$
65. $z^4 - 100$ **66.** $y^2 + 18y + 81$ **67.** $9x^2 - 30x + 25$ **68.** $x^6 + 6x^3 + 9$ **69. (a)** $4x^2 - 5x + 1$ **(b)** $-2x^2 - 4x$
70. $f(x + h) = x^2 + 2xh + h^2 - 4x - 4h + 3$ **71. (a)** length: $(x + 3)$ in.; width: $(x - 3)$ in.; height: x in.   **(b)** The volume is $(x^3 - 9x)$ in^3.
72. (a) The current area is $3x^2$ ft^2.   **(b)** The new area is $(6x^2 + 18x)$ ft^2.   **(c)** The difference is $(3x^2 + 18x)$ square feet.   **73.** Let x = the length,
$s(x)$ = the square of the width; $s(x) = 4x^2 + 36x + 81$ **74.** Let x = the number of increases, $R(x)$ = the revenue;

$R(x) = -10x^2 + 275.1x + 3746.26$ **75.** $R(x) = -2.8x^2 - 17x + 225$ **76.** $\dfrac{72xy}{z^2}$ **77.** $\dfrac{2}{a} + \dfrac{6}{b}$ **78.** $-3b^3 + 2b^2 + 5b - \dfrac{6}{5b}$

79. $3x + 8$ **80.** $4x - 5 - \dfrac{4}{2x + 3}$ **81.** $x^2 - 7x + 5$ **82.** $z^2 + 2z + 4$ **83.** $4a - 5$ **84.** $2x + 9$ **85.** $6 + \dfrac{12}{x^2 - 4x + 4}$

86. (a) $C(x) = 35.00 + 1.25x$ **(b)** $R(x) = 3.75x$ **(c)** $P(x) = 2.50x - 35.00$ **(d)** $A(x) = 2.50 - \dfrac{35.00}{x}$ **(e)** The average profit is \$1.10 per pumpkin.

87. (a) $C(x) = 0.75x + 25.00$ **(b)** $R(x) = 2.50x - 0.25x^2$ **(c)** $P(x) = -0.25x^2 + 1.75x - 25.00$ **(d)** $A(x) = -0.25x + 1.75 - \dfrac{25.00}{x}$

88. $2000t^3 + 2000t^2 + 2000t + 2000$; the total charge is about \$6373.

CHAPTER 7 MIXED REVIEW

1. $\dfrac{n^5}{m^7}$ **2.** $\dfrac{a^{10}}{9b^8}$ **3.** $\dfrac{9x^2}{y^{10}}$ **4.** $\dfrac{64t^3}{125s^4}$ **5.** $\dfrac{4b^3}{a^5}$ **6.** $\dfrac{2}{7x^3y^4}$ **7.** $\dfrac{k^4}{25h^6}$ **8.** s^{10} **9.** $(m + n)^6$ **10.** $27y^6$ **11.** c^3 **12.** 1 **13.** $-15a^3b^7$

14. $\dfrac{z^7}{2}$ **15.** b^{35} **16.** $729d^6$ **17.** $-27d^3$ **18.** $x^{16}y^{20}z^4$ **19.** $5b^2$ **20.** $(a + 2b)^7$ **21.** $-16p^3q^6$ **22.** $4096x^6$ **23.** $\dfrac{c^6}{64d^6}$ **24.** $\dfrac{-27a^6}{64b^3}$

25. $\dfrac{a^2}{2}$ **26.** $\dfrac{9a^6}{b^8}$ **27.** $10y^2 - 8y + 12$ **28.** $\dfrac{9}{8}a^3 + \dfrac{1}{8}a^2 - \dfrac{3}{16}a + \dfrac{15}{16}$ **29.** $4.9z^3 - 1.92z^2 + 10.17z - 6.47$ **30.** $-2x^3 - 11x^2 - 8x + 7$
31. $a^4 - 4a^3 + 2a + 4$ **32.** $117z^4 - 18z^3 + 43z^2 - 50z + 56$ **33.** $143x^7y^{12}$ **34.** $-12x^5 + 24x^4 - 36x^3 - 48x^2 + 60x$
35. $36a^6 + 18a^4 - 27a^2$ **36.** $m^2 - 121$ **37.** $z^2 - 16z + 64$ **38.** $4a^2 + 45a - 91$ **39.** $169 - x^2$ **40.** $b^6 + 8b^3 + 16$
41. $t^3 + 6t^2 + 12t + 8$ **42.** $7x^3 + 26x^2 - 29x + 6$ **43.** $p^2 + q^2 + r^2 + 2pq + 2qr + 2pr$ **44.** $b^3 - 64$ **45.** $y^2 - 4y - 45$
46. $x^4 + 2x^3 + 2x^2 + 11x + 4$ **47.** $\dfrac{3x^3y}{z}$ **48.** $-2b^3 + 3b^2 + 5b - \dfrac{24}{7}$ **49.** $\dfrac{4}{c} + \dfrac{2}{d}$ **50.** $8x + 1$ **51.** $x - 9 - \dfrac{5}{2x + 5}$
52. $9a^2 + 6a + 4$ **53.** $5x^2 + x + 8$ **54.** $-3 \cdot d \cdot d \cdot d \cdot d$ **55.** $-3 \cdot -3 \cdot -3 \cdot -3 \cdot d \cdot d \cdot d \cdot d$ **56.** $2x^3 - 4x^2$ **57.** $2 - \dfrac{35}{x^2 - 8x + 16}$

58. $a^2 + 2ah + h^2 - 3a - 3h + 4$ **59. (a)** $C(x) = 35.00 + 2.75x$ **(b)** $R(x) = 10x$ **(c)** $P(x) = 7.25x - 35.00$ **(d)** $A(x) = 7.25 - \dfrac{35.00}{x}$

(e) The average profit is \$3.75 per child.   **60.** $25s^4 + 25s^3 + 25s^2 + 25s + 25$; the total amount received is about \$113.11.   **61.** The distance is
9.44×10^{15} miles.   **62. (a)** length: $(2x + 3)$ in.; width: x in.; height: x in.   **(b)** The volume is $(2x^3 + 3x^2)$ in^3.   **(c)** The volume is 1216 in^3.

63. (a) The area is $\left(x^2 + \dfrac{5}{2}x\right)$ cm^2.   **(b)** The area is 174 cm^2.   **64. (a)** The current area is x^2 ft^2.   **(b)** The new area will be $(4x^2 + 10x)$ ft^2.   **(c)** The

difference is $(3x^2 + 10x)$ square feet.   **65.** The difference of the price functions is $1.55x^2 - 11.15x + 38.1$.   **66. (a)** Approximately 3.08 to 1
(b) The volume is approximately 3.20×10^{-23} cubic centimeter.   **67.** Approximately 3.32×10^{-12} mole is equivalent to 2×10^{12} molecules.
68. Let x = the number of decreases (multiple units), $R(x)$ = the revenue; $R(x) = 125x - 10x^2$ **69.** $R(x) = -2.5x^2 + 17x + 80$

CHAPTER 7 TEST

1. $(2x - 1)^9$ **2.** $\dfrac{3x^2}{z^3}$ **3.** $\dfrac{n^4}{m^9}$ **4.** $-\dfrac{y^3}{8x^6}$ **5.** a^7 **6.** $\dfrac{9q^2}{64p^6}$ **7.** $\dfrac{8ac^3}{b^5}$ **8.** $\dfrac{a^4b^7}{c}$ **9.** $4y^4 + 5y^3 + 9y^2 + 5$

10. $7x^5 - 2x^4 + 23x^3 + 21x^2 + 2x - 30$ **11.** $-11.4p^9q^2r^3$ **12.** $-8t^4 + 12t^3 + 32t^2 - 24t$ **13.** $81 - 25d^2$ **14.** $15x^2 - x - 28$

15. $8z^3 - 10z^2 + 23z - 15$ **16.** $x^2 + 6x + 9$ **17.** $3x^4 + 5x^3 - \dfrac{1}{x}$ **18.** $5x + 7$ **19.** $3x^2 - 20x + 25$ **20.** $3 - \dfrac{4}{x^2 + 2x + 1}$

21. $h^2 - h$ **22. (a)** The volume is $(2x^3 + 8x^2)$ in^3.   **(b)** The volume is 450 in^3.   **23. (a)** $C(x) = 5.75x + 235$ **(b)** $R(x) = 25x$

(c) $P(x) = 19.25x - 235$ **(d)** $A(x) = 19.25 - \dfrac{235}{x}$ **(e)** The average profit is \$14.03 per basket.   **24.** The population of China is approximately

5.8467×10^5 or 584,670 people.   **25.** The total income was 1.744 times that of the private donations.   **26. (a)** The radius of the oxygen atom is
6.6×10^{-11} meter.   **(b)** The radius of the oxygen atom is 6.6×10^{-9} centimeter.   **(c)** The volume of the oxygen atom is approximately
1.2×10^{-24} cubic centimeter.   **27.** The difference in the amount sold is $-11.5x^2 + 24.5x + 96$.   **28.** Let x = the number of pizzas ordered (discounts), $R(x)$ = the revenue; $R(x) = 12.50x - 0.25x^2$ **29.** $R(x) = -7.00x^2 + 82.50x + 1687.50$ **30.** Answers will vary.

CHAPTER 8

SECTION 8.1 EXERCISES

1. $10a^2bc^2$ **2.** $45x^2yz$ **3.** $36x^2$ **4.** $63u^3v^2$ **5.** 45 **6.** 8 **7.** $7xyz$ **8.** $10a^2bc$ **9.** $30ab^2c$ **10.** $30xy^2z$ **11.** $4(x + 3y)$
12. $-7(x - 3y)$ **13.** $4(2x^3 - x^2 + 3x - 6)$ **14.** $3(3d^5 - 4d^3 + 7d + 8)$ **15.** $a^2(3a^2 - 5a + 7)$ **16.** $-p^3(4p^2 + 9p + 11)$
17. $-3x^3(x^2 + 3x + 4)$ **18.** $5m(m^2 - 3m + 6)$ **19.** $x^2y^2(7x^2 - 3 + 9y^2)$ **20.** $-uv(3u^2 - 4uv + 8v^2)$ **21.** $4a^3(2a^2b^3c + ab^2 + 4c)$
22. $7xy^3(x^2y^2 - 3xy + 9)$ **23.** $22u^3v^3(3v - 4u)$ **24.** $-13c^2d^2(3d - 4c)$ **25.** does not factor **26.** does not factor **27.** $(x + 3)(5x - 4)$
28. $(y + 7)(3y - 5)$ **29.** $(2x + y)(x + 2y)$ **30.** $(a + 3b)(3a + b)$ **31.** $(3x + 5)(2x + 7)$ **32.** $(5x + 2)(3x + 2)$ **33.** $(x + 8)(x + 1)$
34. $(y + 4)(y + 1)$ **35.** $(2a + 3)(a - 1)$ **36.** $(2z + 7)(z - 1)$ **37.** $(2x + y)(x + 2y)$ **38.** $(p + 3q)(3p + q)$ **39.** $(x + y)(x - y)$
40. $(m + n)(m - n)$ **41.** $(2x - 11)(5y + 12)$ **42.** $(4x + 3)(7y - 9)$ **43.** $(4a + b)(3c + d)$ **44.** $(2m + n)(5p + 2q)$
45. $(2xy + 3)(xy - 4)$ **46.** $(7ab - 2)(ab + 3)$ **47.** $-1(x + 3)(x + y)$ **48.** $-1(a + b)(a + 7)$ **49.** $(x^2 + y^2)(x^2 + 2y^2)$
50. $(p + q)(p - q)(3p^2 + q^2)$ **51.** $(a + b)(c + d)$ **52.** $(x + y)(y + z)$ **53.** $4(2x + 1)(x + 3)$ **54.** $7(3y + 2)(y + 4)$
55. $u^2(u + v)(u - 2v)$ **56.** $a^2(a + b)(a + 2b)$ **57.** $6a^2(a + b^2)(a + b)$ **58.** $5c^2(c + d^2)(c^2 + d)$ **59.** $-2x(x + 3)(2x + 1)$
60. $-5y(y - 5)(2y + 3)$ **61.** $(2x + 3z)^2$ **62.** $(3u + 4v)^2$ **63.** $(6a - 5b)^2$ **64.** $(4x + 3y)^2$ **65.** $5m(m + n)^2$ **66.** $7p(p - q)^2$
67. $(2x^2 + 3)(x + 4)$ **68.** $(5c^3 + 7)(c - 3)$ **69.** $(5a^2 + 2b^2)(x + 3y)$ **70.** $(2a^2 + 3b^2)(c + 7d)$ **71.** $A = P(1 + rt)$

72. $s(t) = -t(16t - v_0)$ **73.** $S = 2\pi r(r + h)$ **74.** $A = \dfrac{1}{2}h(b + B)$ **75. (a)** She will receive $(9x + 36)$ dollars. **(b)** $9(x + 4)$. **(c)** The

binomial $(x + 4)$ is the average amount in dollars that she will receive for each of her nine goals. **(d)** She will receive $126. **76. (a)** She smoked
$(7c - 42)$ cigarettes the first week. **(b)** $7(c - 6)$ **(c)** The binomial $(c - 6)$ represents the average number of cigarettes she smoked for each of
seven days. **(d)** She smoked 98 cigarettes; yes; she smoked eight cigarettes on the seventh. **77. (a)** $n(n - 1)$ **(b)** Each equals 420 times. **(c)** The
factored expression was easier to evaluate; answers will vary. **78. (a)** $n(n - 2)(n - 1)$ **(b)** Each equals 990 times. **(c)** The factored expression
was easier to evaluate; answers will vary. **79.** $w(w + 5)$; the length is 5 more than the width. **80.** $b(b - 3)$; the height is 3 less than the base.
81. The rectangle's length is $(x + 7)$ units and width is $(x - 3)$ units. **82.** The length of the square's side is $(2x + 3)$ units. **83. (a)** The area of
the green strip is $(4x^2 + 500x)$ square feet. **(b)** $4x(x + 125)$; the area is equivalent to the area of a rectangle $4x$ feet by $(x + 125)$ feet. **(c)** The area
is 5400 ft^2. **84. (a)** The area of the frame is $(4x^2 + 108x)$ square inches. **(b)** $4x(x + 27)$; the area is equivalent to the area of a rectangle $4x$ inches
by $(x + 27)$ inches. **(c)** The area is 640 in^2. **85.** $R(x) = x(100 - 3x)$; the cost of the package was reduced $3 per package.
86. $R(x) = x(25 - x)$; the cost of the dinner was reduced $1 per person. **87.** $R(x) = (5 + 2x)(12 - x)$; the $12 charge is reduced $1 per decrease;
the number of children, 5, is increased 2 children per decrease. **88.** $R(x) = (100 - x)(50 + 3x)$; the $100 charge is reduced $1 per decrease; the
number of customers, 50, is increased 3 customers per decrease. **89.** $R(x) = 125(40 - 3x)(3 + x)$ **90.** $R(x) = 5(23 + 5x)(4 + x)$
91. $6x(2x + 1)(4x + 1)$ **92.** $6x^2(3x - 1)(5x - 1)$

8.1 CALCULATOR EXERCISES

Part 1

1. $21xyz^2$ **2.** $13c$ **3.** $12x^2$ **4.** $32abc$

Part 2

1. $30 = 2 \cdot 3 \cdot 5$ **2.** $108 = 2^2 \cdot 3^3$ **3.** $525 = 3 \cdot 5^2 \cdot 7$ **4.** $1287 = 3^2 \cdot 11 \cdot 13$ **5.** $1547 = 7 \cdot 13 \cdot 17$ **6.** $4500 = 2^2 \cdot 3^2 \cdot 5^3$

SECTION 8.2 EXERCISES

1. $(x + 2)^2$ **2.** $(p + 7)^2$ **3.** $(4z + 5)^2$ **4.** $(6x + 7)^2$ **5.** does not factor **6.** does not factor **7.** $(x - 5)^2$ **8.** $(y - 8)^2$
9. $(6z - 5)^2$ **10.** $(8m - 3)^2$ **11.** does not factor **12.** does not factor **13.** $(a + 4)^2(a - 4)^2$ **14.** $(b + 7)^2(b - 7)^2$
15. $(2x + 3)^2(2x - 3)^2$ **16.** $(5y + 2)^2(5y - 2)^2$ **17.** $3(x + 4)^2$ **18.** $16(x + 1)^2$ **19.** $2(a - 3)^2$ **20.** $5(x - 7)^2$ **21.** $p(p + q)^2$

22. $z^2(y + 2z)^2$ **23.** $2p(p + q)^2(p - q)^2$ **24.** $5u(u + 2v)^2(u - 2v)^2$ **25.** $m(m^2 + n^2)^2$ **26.** $p^3(p^2 + q^2)^2$ **27.** $(x + 10)(x - 10)$
28. $(y + 8)(y - 8)$ **29.** $(11 + c)(11 - c)$ **30.** $(14 + b)(14 - b)$ **31.** $(7a + 2)(7a - 2)$ **32.** $(5z + 3)(5z - 3)$ **33.** $(5 + 2y)(5 - 2y)$
34. $(8 + 3x)(8 - 3x)$ **35.** $(4u + 3v)(4u - 3v)$ **36.** $(6a + 5b)(6a - 5b)$ **37.** $7(z + 2)(z - 2)$ **38.** $8(x + 1)(x - 1)$ **39.** does not factor
40. does not factor **41.** $(x^2 + 25)(x + 5)(x - 5)$ **42.** $(a^2 + 36)(a + 6)(a - 6)$ **43.** $(16 + z^2)(4 + z)(4 - z)$ **44.** $(25 + b^2)(5 + b)(5 - b)$
45. $(x^4 + 1)(x^2 + 1)(x + 1)(x - 1)$ **46.** $(y^4 + 16)(y^2 + 4)(y + 2)(y - 2)$ **47.** $(x - 3)(x^2 + 3x + 9)$ **48.** $(z - 7)(z^2 + 7z + 49)$
49. $(a + 4)(a^2 - 4a + 16)$ **50.** $(m + 1)(m^2 - m + 1)$ **51.** $(3x + 4y)(9x^2 - 12xy + 16y^2)$ **52.** $(5p + 3q)(25p^2 - 15pq + 9q^2)$
53. $(2p - 5q)(4p^2 + 10pq + 25q^2)$ **54.** $(3u - 2v)(9u^2 + 6uv + 4v^2)$ **55.** $p(p + 4q)(p^2 - 4pq + 16q^2)$ **56.** $y(5x + y)(25x^2 - 5xy + y^2)$
57. $3u(3u - v)(9u^2 + 3uv + v^2)$ **58.** $2b(a - 3b)(a^2 + 3ab + 9b^2)$ **59.** $x^2 - 16 = (x + 4)(x - 4)$ **60.** $4x^2 - 9 = (2x + 3)(2x - 3)$
61. $\pi b^2 - \pi a^2 = \pi(b + a)(b - a)$ **62.** $4\pi R^2 - 4\pi r^2 = 4\pi(R + r)(R - r)$ **63.** $a^3 - b^3 = (a - b)(a^2 + ab + b^2)$
64. $x^3 - y^3 = (x - y)(x^2 + xy + y^2)$ **65. (a)** The garden area is $(x^2 - 225)$ ft^2. **(b)** The rectangular plot has dimensions of $(x + 15)$ ft by

$(x - 15)$ ft. **(c)** Yes, the plot that is 100 ft on each side has a larger garden area than the 85-by-100-foot plot. **66. (a)** The area is $\left(y^2 - \dfrac{1}{4}x^2\right)$ in^2.

(b) An equivalent area is that of a rectangle measuring $\left(y + \dfrac{1}{2}x\right)$ in. by $\left(y - \dfrac{1}{2}x\right)$ in. **(c)** The dimensions are 14 in. by 10 in.

67. $(35 + 2x)(35 + 2x)$; the dimensions of the stage are 35 feet by 35 feet. The area of the stage and mosh pit is 7225 ft^2. The area of the stage is
1225 ft^2. The area of the mosh pit is 6000 ft^2. **68.** $(65 - 2x)(65 - 2x)$; the dimensions of the yard are 65 feet by 65 feet. The central area of the yard
is 3025 ft^2. The area of the yard is 4225 ft^2. The area of the shrub trim is 1200 ft^2. **69.** $4x^2 - 100 = 4(x + 5)(x - 5)$
70. $9x^2 - 49 = (3x + 7)(3x - 7)$ **71.** $16x^2 - 64 = 16(x + 2)(x - 2)$ **72.** $0.25x^2 - 30.25 = 0.25(x + 11)(x - 11)$

73. $x^3 + 125 = (x + 5)(x^2 - 5x + 25)$ **74.** $\dfrac{1}{27}x^3 + 216 = \left(\dfrac{1}{3}x + 6\right)\left(\dfrac{1}{9}x^2 - 2x + 36\right)$ **75.** $27x^3 - 64 = (3x - 4)(9x^2 + 12x + 16)$

76. $8x^3 - 27,000 = 8(x - 15)(x^2 + 15x + 225)$

8.2 CALCULATOR EXERCISES

1. perfect square **2.** perfect cube **3.** perfect square **4.** perfect square and perfect cube **5.** $(x - 35)(x + 35)$
6. $(a - 19)(a^2 + 19a + 361)$ **7.** $(16y - 21)(16y + 21)$ **8.** $(7b - 12)(49b^2 + 84b + 144)$ **9.** $(z - 27)(z + 27)$ **10.** $(z - 9)(z + 9z + 81)$

SECTION 8.3 EXERCISES

1. $(x + 5)(x + 9)$ **2.** $(p + 6)(p + 8)$ **3.** $(y - 7)(y - 8)$ **4.** $(u - 2)(u + 13)$ **5.** $(p + 3)(p - 12)$ **6.** $(v + 1)(v - 13)$ **7.** does not factor **8.** does not factor **9.** $(x^2 + 9)(x^2 + 16)$ **10.** $(b^2 + 4)(b^2 + 25)$ **11.** $(x^2 + 1)(x^2 - 3)$ **12.** $(d^2 - 7)(d^2 + 25)$ **13.** $3(a + 5)(a + 11)$ **14.** $7(b - 4)(b - 6)$ **15.** $4(c - 2)(c + 13)$ **16.** $7(p + 4)(p - 5)$ **17.** $(x - 3y)(x - 8y)$ **18.** $(a - 8b)(a - 9b)$ **19.** $(x - y)(x + 12y)$ **20.** $(a + 6b)(a - 15b)$ **21.** $-3(a + 2b)(a + 3b)$ **22.** $-5(x - 3y)(x - 4y)$ **23.** $-2(x + 2y)(x - 9y)$ **24.** $-6(x + 3y)(x - 7y)$ **25.** $(3x + 1)(x + 3)$ **26.** does not factor **27.** $(x - 7)(2x - 1)$ **28.** $(x - 11)(3x - 1)$ **29.** $(x - 1)(3x + 2)$ **30.** $(x - 1)(5x + 3)$ **31.** $(m + 2)(5m - 1)$ **32.** $(p + 5)(7p - 1)$ **33.** does not factor **34.** does not factor **35.** $(a + 6)(4a + 1)$ **36.** $(c + 4)(10c + 1)$ **37.** $(d - 1)(9d - 4)$ **38.** $(b - 1)(8b - 9)$ **39.** $(x - 4)(6x + 1)$ **40.** $(x - 8)(4x + 1)$ **41.** $(y + 2)(8y - 9)$ **42.** $(z + 4)(6z - 5)$ **43.** $(2b + 3)(3b + 4)$ **44.** $(5a + 6)(3a + 2)$ **45.** $(5x - 4)(4x - 3)$ **46.** $(2z + 3)(7z - 4)$ **47.** $(3x - 4)(6x + 5)$ **48.** $(2x - 9)(4x + 7)$ **49.** $3(2p - 7)(3p + 1)$ **50.** $-3(7x + 8)(3x - 2)$ **51.** $(2x^2 + 9)(x^2 + 1)$ **52.** $(4x^2 - 3)(6x^2 - 1)$ **53.** $(m^2 + 4)(4m^2 - 3)$ **54.** $(z^2 + 9)(5z^2 - 6)$ **55.** $-1(2x - 7)(3x + 8)$ **56.** $-1(b + 3)(4b - 7)$ **57.** $(2x + 3y)(3x - 2y)$ **58.** $(2a + 3b)(7a + 2b)$ **59.** $(u - 8v)(4u - 7v)$ **60.** $(x - 4y)(3x - 8y)$ **61.** $(x^2 + y^2)(9x^2 + 4y^2)$ **62.** $(x^2 + y^2)(16x^2 + 25y^2)$ **63.** $(2xy + 3)(5xy - 7)$ **64.** $(3pq - 2)(7pq + 4)$ **65.** $x + 4$ **66.** $2x + 3$ **67. (a)** The increased width is $(w + 2)$ in and the increased length is $(w + 12)$ in. **(b)** The width was increased by 2 in. **(c)** The length was increased by 4 in. **68. (a)** The new width is $(x - 3)$ in and the new length is $(x - 1)$ in. **(b)** The width was increased by 2 in. **(c)** The length was decreased by 1 in. **69. (a)** The lengths of the legs are $(x + 8)$ in and $(2x + 5)$ in. **(b)** They were each increased by 8 in. **(c)** The expression is $(2x - 3)$ in. **70. (a)** The lengths of the legs are $(x - 4)$ in and $(3x - 12)$ in. **(b)** They were each decreased by 4 in. **(c)** The expression is $(3x - 8)$ in. **71.** $4(x + 18)(x + 139)$ or $(2x + 36)(2x + 78)$; the dimensions of the playing area are 36 feet by 78 feet. **72.** $2(4x + 53)(x + 50)$ or $(4x + 53)(2x + 100)$; the dimensions of the playing area are 53 yards by 100 yards. **73.** $(4x - 7)(3x + 5)$; the angles measure 13° and 20°. **74.** $(2x + 3)(3x - 5)$; the angles measure 13° and 10°. **75.** $(x + 16)(7x - 2)$; yes **76.** $(9x + 7)(x + 33)$; no **77.** $-6(x - 15)(x + 4)$ **78.** $-50(2x + 5)(x - 12)$ **79.** $(23 + 5x)(4 + x)$ **80.** $10(15 + x)(9 + x)$ **81.** $-1(4t + 1)(4t - 27)$ **82.** $-1(16t - 25)(t + 5)$

8.3 CALCULATOR EXERCISES

1. $(5x + 12)(8x - 15)$ **2.** $(4x - 9)(20x - 13)$ **3.** $(9x - 11)(12x - 5)$ **4.** $(12x + 13)(15x + 11)$

SECTION 8.4 EXERCISES

1. $(3x + 4)(x + 5)$ **2.** $(5x + 4)(x + 3)$ **3.** $(3x + 5)(2x + 7)$ **4.** $(7x + 2)(4x + 3)$ **5.** $(5q + 11)(2q + 1)$ **6.** $(4p + 13)(2p + 1)$ **7.** cannot be factored **8.** cannot be factored **9.** cannot be factored **10.** $(5y - 2)(8y - 3)$ **11.** $(3m - 2)(2m - 3)$ **12.** $(5k - 2)(2k - 5)$ **13.** $(7p - 1)(8p + 3)$ **14.** $(8x - 1)(9x + 4)$ **15.** $(5p - 2)(3p - 4)$ **16.** cannot be factored **17.** $(4x + 1)(8x - 5)$ **18.** $(6x + 1)(4x - 3)$ **19.** $(4k - 9)(7k + 11)$ **20.** $(8k - 9)(7k + 5)$ **21.** $(8m - 9)(3m + 13)$ **22.** $(5x + 12)(6x - 5)$ **23.** $4(5x - 1)(2x - 7)$ **24.** $2(9x - 2)(3x - 4)$ **25.** $3(2x + 5)(5x + 2)$ **26.** $5(3x + 2)(2x + 3)$ **27.** $2(8x - 3)(x + 3)$ **28.** $2(9x - 4)(x + 4)$ **29.** $-3(2x - 3)(3x - 8)$ **30.** $-4(2x - 5)(3x - 2)$ **31.** $4(4x^2 - 13x - 20)$ **32.** $6(4y^2 - y - 11)$ **33.** $x(2x + 5)(3x + 5)$ **34.** $y(10y^2 + 29y + 35)$ **35.** $(3x^2 + 2)(2x^2 + 1)$ **36.** $(5x^2 + 1)(2x^2 + 3)$ **37.** $(4x^2 + 9)(2x^2 + 7)$ **38.** $(6y^2 + 5)(2y^2 + 3)$ **39.** $(3x^2 - 5)(2x^2 - 3)$ **40.** $(3x^2 - 5)(4x^2 - 7)$ **41.** $(3x^2 - 2)(4x^2 - 3)$ **42.** $(3x^2 - 7)(2x^2 - 5)$ **43.** $(4m^2 + 5)(2m^2 - 3)$ **44.** $(6p^2 + 5)(2p^2 - 3)$ **45.** $(3x^2 - 2)(5x^2 + 8)$ **46.** $(3x - 2)(3x + 2)(2x^2 + 3)$ **47.** $3(4y^2 + 7)(5y^2 - 4)$ **48.** $2(7x^2 - 3)(4x^2 + 5)$ **49.** $-2(6x^2 - 5)(2x^2 - 1)$ **50.** $-3(5y^2 + 4)(3y^2 + 2)$ **51.** $(3x + 4y)(2x - 5y)$ **52.** $(3x - 4y)(7x + 2y)$ **53.** $(8p - 7q)(5p - 4q)$ **54.** $(6p - 5q)(9p - 2q)$ **55.** $\frac{1}{2}(3x + 7)(4x + 7)$; the enlarged triangle has a height of $(3x + 7)$ feet and a base of $(4x + 7)$ feet; the base and height were increased by 7 feet. **56.** $\frac{1}{2}(5x - 6)(x - 6)$; the reduced triangle has a height of $(x - 6)$ feet and a base of $(5x - 6)$ feet; the base and height were reduced by 6 feet. **57.** $(2x + 7)(x + 6)$; the length is $(2x + 7)$ meters and the width is $(x + 6)$ meters, which indicates that the free space added to each side of the width is 3 meters; since $x = 6$, the dimensions of the total area are 12 meters by 19 meters with an area of 228 square meters. **58.** $(2x + 7)(x + 7)$; the length is $(2x + 7)$ meters and the width is $(x + 7)$ meters, which indicates that the free space added to each side is 3.5 meters; since $x = 1.8$, the dimensions of the total area are 8.8 meters by 10.6 meters with an area of 93.28 square meters. **59.** $(7x + 90)(x + 15)$; no **60.** $(3x - 7)(5x - 17)$; no **61.** $(2x - 9)(9x + 7)$ **62.** $(5x + 7)(9x - 4)$ **63.** $(3x + 8)(6x - 17)$ **64.** $(7x + 61)(2x + 1)$ **65.** $(3x + 7)(7x - 57)$ **66.** $(5x - 54)(2x - 25)$ **67.** $-1(16t + 5)(t - 15)$ **68.** $-1(9.8t - 9)(t + 10)$

8.4 CALCULATOR EXERCISES

1. $2(4x - 1)(12x + 1)$ **2.** $(3x + 5)(8x - 11)$ **3.** $(2x + 3)(16x + 27)$ **4.** $(3x - 2)(24x - 17)$ **5.** $(p^2 + 25)(4p^2 + 9)$

SECTION 8.5 EXERCISES

1. $3y(y^2 + y + 1)$ **2.** $5x(2x^2 + 7x - 1)$ **3.** $5ab(2c^2 + 3c - 4)$ **4.** $2xy(3z^2 + 5z - 3)$ **5.** $-8a(5a + 3b - 6c)$ **6.** $-7x(4x + 5y - 3z)$ **7.** $3x^3(6x + 5)(6x - 5)$ **8.** $2u(4u + 7)(4u - 7)$ **9.** $-8xy(5x + 2y)(5x - 2y)$ **10.** $-2ab(3a + 8b)(3a - 8b)$ **11.** $x(x - 8)^2$ **12.** $z(z - 5)^2$ **13.** $3v(2u + 3v)^2$ **14.** $2x(5x + 2y)^2$ **15.** $(x + 4)(x - 4)(3x^2 + 7)$ **16.** $(x + 3)(x - 3)(2x^2 + 5)$ **17.** $(p + 3)(p - 3)(2p + 1)(2p - 1)$ **18.** $(z + 2)(z - 2)(3z + 2)(3z - 2)$ **19.** $-2(3y - 1)(7y + 1)$ **20.** $-3(4y - 1)(6y + 1)$ **21.** $4(uv + 2)(uv + 7)$ **22.** $5(ab + 3)(ab + 4)$ **23.** $4x(x - 2)(8x - 7)$ **24.** $3x(5x - 6)(x - 4)$ **25.** $2x^2(x + 3)(6x - 5)$ **26.** $5z^2(z + 2)(3z - 4)$ **27.** $(x^3 - 5y^3)(x^3 + 3y^3)$ **28.** $(p^3 + 2q^3)(p^3 - 5q^3)$ **29.** $x(x - 5)(x^2 + 8)$ **30.** $2y(y + 3)(y^2 + 4)$ **31.** $(1 + k^4)(1 + k^2)(1 + k)(1 - k)$ **32.** $(16s^4 + 1)(4s^2 + 1)(2s + 1)(2s - 1)$ **33.** $2x - 3$ **34.** $x - 3$ **35.** $2r + 1$ **36.** $3r - 2$ **37.** $x - 1$ **38.** $x - 2$ **39.** $x - 3$ **40.** $x - 6$ **41.** $2x + 5$ **42.** x **43.** $x(9 - 2x)(15 - 2x)$; the dimensions are x inches by $(9 - 2x)$ inches by $(15 - 2x)$ inches; if $x = 2$, the dimensions are 2 inches by 5 inches by 11 inches with a volume of 110 cubic inches. **44.** $x(x + 20)(x + 10)$; the dimensions are x inches by $(x + 20)$ inches by $(x + 10)$ inches; if $x = 5$, the dimensions are 5 inches by 25 inches by

15 inches with a volume of 1875 cubic inches. **45.** $\pi x(2x - 5)^2$; the radius is $(2x - 5)$ inches; if $x = 8$, the radius is 11 inches and the volume is 968π cubic inches or about 3041 cubic inches. **46.** $\pi x(x - 8)^2$; the radius is $(x - 8)$ inches and the diameter is $(2x - 16)$ inches; if $x = 15$, the radius is 7 inches, the diameter is 14 inches, the height is 15 inches and the volume is 735π cubic inches or about 2309 cubic inches. **47.** $(x - 6)(x^2 + 6x + 36)$; no, since $V = e^3$ for a cube; each side of the smaller cube was 6 inches. **48.** $(x + 24)(x^2 - 24x + 576)$; no; the larger cube is 24 inches on each side. **49.** $x(14.75 - 0.95x)$; the regular price is $14.75; for every additional pizza, a discount of $0.95 will be given; yes. **50.** $x(15.70 - 2.24x)$; CD's regularly cost $15.70; for every additional CD, a discount of $2.24 will be given; yes. **51.** $x(19.95 + 2.99x)$; a doll costs $19.95; for every doll purchased, a surcharge of $2.99 will be given. **52.** $x(4.95 + 2x)$; a turkey costs $4.95; for every turkey purchased, x, a charge of $2 will be given. **53.** $16(t_2 + t_1)(t_2 - t_1)$ **54.** $9.8(t_2 + t_1)(t_2 - t_1)$ **55.** $\frac{1}{R}(V + V_2)(V - V_2)$ **56.** $\frac{k}{2}(x_2 + x_1)(x_2 - x_1)$ **57.** Let $x =$ the number of years after 2000, $a(x) =$ the number of active Army personnel, $a(x) = -3x^2 + 300$; $a(x) = -3(x + 10)(x - 10)$ **58.** Let $x =$ the number of years after 1998, $t(x) =$ the estimated cost of yearly undergraduate tuition, $t(x) = 3x^2 + 364x + 10,033$; $t(x) = (3x + 127)(x + 79)$ **59.** Let $x =$ the number of weeks after June 15, $f(x) =$ the number of fish, $f(x) = 14x^2 + 25x - 150$; $f(x) = (2x - 5)(7x + 30)$; the results are equal in value and equal to the actual value. **60.** Let $x =$ the age of the child, $e(x) =$ the yearly expense, $e(x) = 5x^2 + 61x - 228$; $e(x) = (x - 3)(5x + 76)$; the results are equal to the actual value.

8.5 CALCULATOR EXERCISES

1. $(2x + 9)(4x - 3)(2x - 7)$ **2.** $(2x + 1)(5x - 3)(5x + 3)$ **3.** $(3x + 7)(5x - 4)(6x + 5)$ **4.** $(3x + 8)(3x - 8)(2x - 5)$

CHAPTER 8 SUMMARY

Vocabulary Review

1. factor **2.** greatest common factor (GCF) **3.** factoring by grouping **4.** *ac* method **5.** trial-and-error method

Reflections

1–9. Answers will vary.

CHAPTER 8 SECTION-BY-SECTION REVIEW

1. $4a^2(5a^4 - 7a^2 + 11)$ **2.** $22u^2v^2(u + v)$ **3.** $(x^2 + 1)(3x + 1)$ **4.** $7(a^2 + b^2)^2$ **5.** $(5c + 6d)(3a + 4b)$ **6. (a)** $\frac{1}{2}n(n + 1)$ **(b)** The sum is 78. **(c)** The factored expression is easier to evaluate; answers will vary. **7.** The width is $(x - 3)$ units and the length is $(2x + 5)$ units. **8.** $x + (x + 10) + (x + 20) + (x + 30) + (x + 40) + (x + 50) + (x + 60)$; $7(x + 30)$; the employee earns an average of $(x + 30)$ dollars for each of 7 months; the salary is $6930. **9.** The area is $(4x^2 + 78x)$ square feet; $2x(2x + 39)$; the area of the border is equivalent to the area of a rectangle $2x$ feet by $(2x + 39)$ feet; if $x = 3$, the area is 270 square feet. **10.** $R(x) = x(300 - 7x)$; the cost is reduced $7 per package (reduction). **11.** $R(x) = (50 - 3x)(100 + 5x)$; each increase of $5 will result in 3 fewer customers. **12.** $(p + 6)^2$ **13.** $(q - 8)^2$ **14.** $(3x + 5)^2$ **15.** $(7y - 8)^2$ **16.** does not factor **17.** $x^3(x^2 + 3y)^2$ **18.** $(x - 13)(x + 13)$ **19.** $(25 - a)(25 + a)$ **20.** $3(2x + 5)(2x - 5)$ **21.** $(p - q)(p + q)$ **22.** does not factor **23.** $(3x - 5y)(3x + 5y)$ **24.** $(4x^2 + 9)(2x + 3)(2x - 3)$ **25.** $(x^4 + 1)(x^2 + 1)(x + 1)(x - 1)$ **26.** $(c + 3)(c^2 - 3c + 9)$ **27.** $(c - 3)(c^2 + 3c + 9)$ **28.** $(2z - 5)(4z^2 + 10z + 25)$ **29.** $5(h + 2k)(h^2 - 2hk + 4k^2)$ **30. (a)** $x^2 - 4$ **(b)** $(x + 2)(x - 2)$ **(c)** No, because some of the rectangle is filled in with light blue material. **31.** $\pi(x + 100)^2$; the radius is 100 feet; the area of the pond and exercise space is about 45,239 square feet; the area of the pond is about 31,416 square feet; the area of the exercise space is about 13,823 square feet. **32.** $9x^2 - 81 = 9(x + 3)(x - 3)$ **33.** $0.216x^3 - 216.00 = 0.216(x - 10)(x^2 + 10x + 100)$ **34.** $(z - 9)(z + 11)$ **35.** $(p - 6q)(p + 11q)$ **36.** $6(a + 3)(a + 13)$ **37.** $(x^2 + 3)(x^2 + 5)$ **38.** $4q(q + 5)(q - 12)$ **39.** $(xy + 9)(xy - 13)$ **40.** $-7(x - 2)(x - 12)$ **41.** $(x - 5)(2x - 1)$ **42.** $(2x + 5)(3x + 1)$ **43.** $7(ab + 3)(4ab + 1)$ **44.** $-3x(3x + 8)(5x - 2)$ **45. (a)** The base is $(2x + 7)$ units and the height is $(2x + 3)$ units. **(b)** The base was increased by 7 units. **(c)** The height was increased by $(x + 3)$ units. **46. (a)** The new length is $(x + 15)$ units and the new width is $(x + 2)$ units. **(b)** It was increased by 15 units. **(c)** It was increased by 8 units. **47.** $2(2x + 15)(x + 14)$ or $(2x + 15)(2x + 28)$; the dimensions of the basketball court are 15 meters by 28 meters. **48.** $(6x + 7)(2x + 3)$; yes **49.** $R(x) = 10(x + 9)(x + 75)$ **50.** $d(t) = -16(t - 1)(t + 5)$ **51.** cannot be factored **52.** $(4x + 9)(2x + 1)$ **53.** $(5y - 3)(3y - 4)$ **54.** cannot be factored **55.** $(3y + 2)(4y - 7)$ **56.** $(4x^2 + 5)(2x^2 + 3)$ **57.** $(5x^2 - 3)(2x^2 + 3)$ **58.** cannot be factored **59.** cannot be factored **60.** $4(2x + 1)(3x + 8)$ **61.** $-5(4x^2 - 7)(2x^2 + 5)$ **62.** $(3x + 4y)(2x - 5y)$ **63.** $(6x + 5y)(2x + 5y)$ **64.** $(4x - 3y)(5x - 3y)$ **65.** $(19x + 9)(x + 3)$; the dimensions of the total area are 4 meters by 28 meters; the total area is 112 square meters; the dimensions of the lane are 1 meter by 19 meters with an area of 19 square meters. **66.** $(5x + 6)(3x + 4)$; no **67.** $p(x) = -1(x - 95)(2x + 7)$ **68.** $s(t) = -8(t - 25)(2t + 1)$ **69.** $-3x(2x - 5y)^2$ **70.** $7x^2(x^2 + x + 1)$ **71.** $3x(2x + 9)(2x - 9)$ **72.** $8x(2x + 1)^2$ **73.** $2x(4x - 9)(3x + 5)$ **74.** $(4x + 3)^2(4x - 3)^2$ **75.** $(3x + 2)(3x - 2)(2x + 1)(2x - 1)$ **76.** $2x(x + 7)(x - 2)(x + 2)$ **77. (a)** The land area not covered is $(4x^2 - 25)$ ft². **(b)** The dimensions would be $(2x + 5)$ ft by $(2x - 5)$ ft. **(c)** The dimensions would be 165 ft by 155 ft. **78.** $x(19.95 - 0.10x)$; for every instructor, x, there is a 10¢ discount. **79.** $16(2 + t)(2 - t)$ **80.** Let $x =$ the number of times F2 key is used, $a(x) =$ the area of the character, $a(x) = 12x^2 + 25x - 50$; $a(x) = (3x + 10)(4x - 5)$

CHAPTER 8 MIXED REVIEW

1. $(z + 15)(z - 6)$ **2.** $(a - 6)(a - 12)$ **3.** $(x + 9y)(x + 5y)$ **4.** $5(a + 7)^2$ **5.** $2(a^2 + 4ab + 6b^2)$ **6.** $(x^2 + 3)(x^2 + 7)$ **7.** $3q(q + 3)(q - 14)$ **8.** $-6(x + 5)(x - 12)$ **9.** $(x + 2)(x + 5)$ **10.** $(x + 17)(x - 17)$ **11.** $(x - 1)(x^2 + x + 1)$ **12.** $4(x + 4)(x - 4)$ **13.** does not factor **14.** $(6x + 7y)(6x - 7y)$ **15.** $(9x^2 + 1)(3x + 1)(3x - 1)$ **16.** $(p + 11)^2$ **17.** $(q - 15)^2$ **18.** $(3a + 4b)(9a^2 - 12ab + 16b^2)$ **19.** $3(3ab - 4)^2$ **20.** $-2x(5x - 6y)^2$ **21.** $2x(4x^3 - x^2 + 3x - 6)$ **22.** $5u^2v^2(7u + 5v)$ **23.** $(x^2 + 5)(2x + 1)$ **24.** $(m - 2n)(m - 8n)$ **25.** $4(a^2 + 2b^2)^2$ **26.** $(x - 1)(2x - 11)$ **27.** $(6c + 5d)(4a + 3b)$ **28.** $(x - 3)(7x + 2)$ **29.** $(2x - 3)(5x + 2)$ **30.** $6(2a + 1)(3a + 4)$ **31.** $-2(3x - 2)(5x + 8)$ **32.** $(3x^2 + 1)(4x^2 + 3)$ **33.** $6x(3x + 1)^2$ **34.** $(3x + 2)^2(3x - 2)^2$ **35.** $(2x + 5)(2x - 5)(x + 3)(x - 3)$ **36.** $3x(2x + 3)(2x - 5)$ **37.** $3x(x + 5)(x + 3)(x - 3)$ **38.** The width is $(2x + 1)$ units and the length is $(4x - 3)$ units. **39. (a)** The new length is $(3x + 1)$ in and the new width is $(2x - 4)$ in. **(b)** The length was increased by $(2x + 1)$ in. **(c)** The width was increased by $(x - 2)$ in. **40. (a)** The base is $(2x + 16)$ units and the height is $(x + 4)$ units. **(b)** The base was increased by 16 units. **(c)** The height was increased by 4 units. **41.** $x(50 + 25x)$; a judge sets a fine of $75 for the first penalty and then adds on $25 for x number of times cited in the future. **42. (a)** $x^2 - 9$ **(b)** $(x + 3)(x - 3)$ **(c)** Yes **43.** $\pi(610 + x)^2$; the radius is $(610 + x)$ mm;

the area is $372,100\pi$ mm^2 or about 1,168,987 mm^2.   **44.** $312x + 4x^2$; $4x(78 + x)$ or $2x(156 + 2x)$; if $x = 16$, the area is 6016 square inches.
45. $x(35 - 4x)$; the cost of the package is reduced \$4 per package purchased (or reduction).   **46.** $R(x) = (100 + 3x)(50 - x)$; each increase of \$3 in the cost will result in 1 fewer purchase.   **47.** $0.04x^2 - 225.00 = 0.04(x + 75)(x - 75)$ **48.** $0.027x^3 + 8.00 = (0.3x + 2.00)(0.09x^2 - 0.6x + 4.00)$
49. $5(200 - 14x + x^2)$ **50.** $s(t) = -1(2t + 9)(8t - 33)$ **51.** $p(x) = (3x + 4)(4x - 29)$ **52.** $(5 + 4t)(5 - 4t)$ **53.** $(10x + 3)(5x + 1)$; no
54. Let $x =$ the number of discounts, $R(x) =$ the revenue in dollars, $R(x) = -2x^2 + 5x + 150$; $R(x) = -1(2x + 15)(x - 10)$

CHAPTER 8 TEST

1. $9a(3a + 1)^2$ **2.** $(p + 5)(p^2 - 5p + 25)$ **3.** $-4a^2b^2(a + 4b)(2a + b)$ **4.** $(a^2 + b^2)(a - 5b)$ **5.** $(5x - 7y)(3x + 2y)$
6. $(8a + 7b)(8a - 7b)$ **7.** $(5x - 7)^2$ **8.** $3x(x - 1)(x - 8)$ **9.** $(x + 3y)(x - 7y)$ **10.** $(2x + 1)(7x + 9)$ **11.** $(x^2 + 7)(2x + 1)(2x - 1)$
12. does not factor   **13.** $x(2x - 1)(x + 3)$; the width is $(2x - 1)$ inches; the length is $(x + 3)$ inches.   **14. (a)** $\frac{1}{2}(x + 12)(x + 5)$; the base is
$(x + 12)$ inches and the height is $(x + 5)$ inches.   **(b)** The base and height were increased by 5 inches each.   **(c)** The base of the original triangle was $(x + 7)$ inches.   **15. (a)** $s^3 - 8$ **(b)** $(s - 2)(s^2 + 2s + 4)$; no since $V = e^3$.   **(c)** You will need 1720 cubic inches of gelatin to fill the larger crate and boxed egg.   **16.** $\pi(x + 9)^2$; the radius of the center tray is 9 inches; the total area is 121π square inches or about 380 square inches; the area of the center is 81π square inches or about 254 square inches; the area of the border is 40π square inches or about 126 square inches.
17. $R(x) = x(49 - 2x)$; the package cost is reduced \$2 per connection (or reduction).   **18.** $R(x) = (55 - 3x)(100 + x)$; for each \$3 reduction in the price of the package one additional package is purchased.   **19.** $9x^2 - 64 = (3x + 8)(3x - 8)$ **20.** $p(x) = (2x - 11)(3x - 31)$
21. $(9 + 4t)(9 - 4t)$ **22.** $(6x - 5)(2x - 1)$; yes   **23. (a)** factor by grouping **(b)** He did not factor completely. **(c)** $(3x + 7)(2x + 3)(2x - 3)$

CHAPTER 9

SECTION 9.1 EXERCISES

1. polynomial; cubic   **2.** not a polynomial   **3.** not a polynomial   **4.** polynomial; cubic   **5.** polynomial   **6.** polynomial; cubic
7. polynomial; quadratic   **8.** not a polynomial   **9.** not a polynomial   **10.** polynomial; cubic   **11.** polynomial; quadratic   **12.** polynomial; quadratic   **13.** $2x^2 + x = x + 8$, $x = -2$, $x = 2$ **14.** $2x(x + 1) = 2x^2 + 2x$; all real numbers   **15.** $x^2 + 4x + 8 = 4$; $x = -2$
16. $x^2 + 2 = x^2 - 1$; no solution   **17.** 2 and 4   **18.** -3 and 2   **19.** noninteger between 0 and 1.   **20.** nonintegers between -4 and -5 and between 3 and 4.   **21.** no solution   **22.** no solution   **23.** all real numbers   **24.** all real numbers   **25.** no real-number solution   **26.** no real-number solution   **27.** -6 and 2   **28.** -4 and 3   **29.** -3 and 3   **30.** -4 and 4   **31.** -1 and 3   **32.** -4 and -2 **33.** -2, 0, and 2
34. 2   **35.** -2 and 5   **36.** -3, -1, and 1   **37.** no solution   **38.** no real-number solution   **39.** no real-number solution   **40.** no solution
41. all real numbers   **42.** all real numbers   **43.** -1, 0, and 4   **44.** -3, 0, and 2   **45.** no solution   **46.** no solution   **47.** $\frac{1}{3}$ and -4
48. $-\frac{2}{3}$ and 1   **49.** $-\frac{5}{3}$ and $\frac{5}{3}$ **50.** $-\frac{4}{3}$ and $\frac{4}{3}$ **51.** -0.8, 0.5, and 1   **52.** -1, 0.5, and 2.5   **53.** -2.8 and 3.7   **54.** 0.8 and 4.2
55. -3.6, -1.5, and 1.4   **56.** -2.4, -0.2, and 2.5   **57.** It will hit the ground in approximately 1.58 seconds.   **58.** They will hit the ground in 1 second.   **59.** The dagger will hit the ground in approximately 1.43 seconds.   **60.** The branch will hit the ground in approximately 0.94 second.
61. It will hit the ground in 1.75 seconds.   **62.** The hammer will hit the ground in 1 second.   **63.** The price of gas will be \$4.32 in 2011.   **64.** The cost will be \$20,000 in 2021.   **65.** The foreign-born population was 14.6% of the population in 1906 and 1912.   **66.** The foreign-born population was 7% of the population in 1953 and 1983.   **67.** The number of cars will be 662,970 in 2000 and 2005.   **68.** The number of cars will be 1200 in 2006.

9.1 CALCULATOR EXERCISES

Students should verify solutions with the calculator.

SECTION 9.2 EXERCISES

1. x-intercepts: $(-4, 0)(2, 0)$; $(x + 4)(x - 2) = 0$; $x = -4$, $x = 2$ **2.** x-intercepts: $(3, 0)(-1, 0)$; $(x - 3)(x + 1) = 0$; $x = 3$, $x = -1$
3. x-intercepts: $\left(\frac{1}{2}, 0\right)\left(-\frac{5}{3}, 0\right)$; $(2x - 1)(3x + 5) = 0$; $x = \frac{1}{2}$, $x = -\frac{5}{3}$ **4.** x-intercepts: $\left(-\frac{3}{2}, 0\right)\left(\frac{1}{3}, 0\right)$; $(2x + 3)(3x - 1) = 0$; $x = -\frac{3}{2}$, $x = \frac{1}{3}$
5. -11 and -6 **6.** -13 and -9 **7.** -9, 0, and $\frac{5}{2}$ **8.** $-\frac{1}{6}$, 0, and 4   **9.** -6, $-\frac{3}{4}$, and $\frac{9}{2}$ **10.** $-\frac{7}{2}$, $\frac{8}{3}$, and 7   **11.** -34 and 1.3   **12.** -3 and 4
13. -6 and -4 **14.** -8 and -5 **15.** 3 and 11   **16.** 4 and 13   **17.** -6 and $-\frac{5}{4}$ **18.** -2 and $-\frac{8}{7}$ **19.** $-\frac{8}{5}$ and 1   **20.** $-\frac{5}{3}$ and 4
21. 0 and $\frac{7}{3}$ **22.** 0 and $\frac{7}{2}$ **23.** $-\frac{5}{3}$ and $\frac{1}{6}$ **24.** $-\frac{3}{2}$ and $\frac{7}{4}$ **25.** $-\frac{9}{4}$ **26.** $\frac{2}{7}$ **27.** $-\frac{5}{2}$ **28.** $-\frac{4}{3}$ **29.** -8 and 8   **30.** -12 and 12
31. $-\frac{5}{3}$ and $\frac{5}{3}$ **32.** $-\frac{9}{8}$ and $\frac{9}{8}$ **33.** -8 and 6   **34.** -4 and 8   **35.** -4 and 9   **36.** -6 and 7   **37.** -12 and 9   **38.** -20 and 15
39. 7, -3, and 3   **40.** -5, -4, and 4   **41.** $-\frac{5}{2}$, $-\frac{5}{3}$, and $\frac{5}{3}$ **42.** -3.5, -3, and 3.5   **43.** 1   **44.** 8   **45. (a)** The volume is $\left(\frac{3}{2}x^2 + 3x\right)$ ft^3.
(b) The dimensions are 6 ft by 3 ft by 4 ft.   **46. (a)** The volume is $(32x^2 + 4x)$ cm^3. **(b)** The dimensions are 5 cm by 4 cm by 41 cm.
47. (a) The surface area is $(26x^2 + 10x)$ in^2. **(b)** The dimensions are 15 in by 5 in by 22 in.   **48. (a)** The surface area is $(84x^2 + 24x)$ units^2.
(b) The dimensions are 3 in by 15 in by 23 in.   **49. (a)** The area is $\left(\frac{1}{2}x^2 + 2x\right)$ ft^2. **(b)** The dimensions are 6 ft base, 10 ft height.
50. (a) The area is $\left(\frac{5}{2}x^2 + x\right)$ m^2. **(b)** The dimensions are 10 m height, 52 m base.   **51.** The height of the triangle is 12 feet.   **52.** The length of the larger box is 10 inches.   **53.** $V^2 = 30(0.40)(243)$; the vehicle was traveling at 54 mph.   **54.** $V^2 = 30(0.27)(250)$; the vehicle was traveling at 45 mph.   **55.** There were 9 or 13 staff members on this day.   **56.** There were 12 birthday parties scheduled.   **57.** There were 20 deliveries made to his shops.   **58.** There were 9 television appearances made by the athlete.   **59.** 14 salespeople worked on that day.   **60.** 20 tables were served.

61. Let x = the number of years after 2000, y = the personal consumption expenditures for household operations (in billions of dollars), $y = 4x^2 + x + 390$; expenditures will reach 800 billion dollars in 2010. **62.** Let x = the number of years after 1990, y = the world commercial catch of fish, crustaceans, and mollusks in thousands of metric tons, $y = -50x^2 + 2300x + 12{,}070$; in 2013 there will be 38,520,000 metric tons of fish, crustaceans, and mollusks caught.

9.2 CALCULATOR EXERCISES

Students should verify solutions with the calculator.

SECTION 9.3 EXERCISES

1. $3\sqrt{7}$ **2.** $4\sqrt{5}$ **3.** $9\sqrt{3}$ **4.** $5\sqrt{3}$ **5.** $7\sqrt{3}$ **6.** $-8\sqrt{2}$ **7.** $-5\sqrt{5}$ **8.** $3\sqrt{3}$ **9.** $-3 + 2\sqrt{5}$ **10.** $-4 + 2\sqrt{7}$ **11.** $2 - 5\sqrt{2}$

12. $7 - 4\sqrt{2}$ **13.** $1 - \sqrt{3}$ **14.** $1 - \sqrt{2}$ **15.** $-2 + \sqrt{5}$ **16.** $-2 + \sqrt{6}$ **17.** $\dfrac{5}{3} + \sqrt{2}$ **18.** $\dfrac{3}{2} + \sqrt{10}$ **19.** $2 + \sqrt{6}$

20. $2 + \sqrt{11}$ **21.** $\dfrac{4\sqrt{5}}{5}$ **22.** $\dfrac{3\sqrt{7}}{7}$ **23.** $\dfrac{5\sqrt{6}}{12}$ **24.** $\dfrac{\sqrt{30}}{4}$ **25.** $\sqrt{21}$ **26.** $\sqrt{10}$ **27.** $12\sqrt{6}$ **28.** $6\sqrt{15}$ **29.** $\dfrac{\sqrt{10}}{5}$ **30.** $\dfrac{\sqrt{21}}{7}$

31. $5\sqrt{2}$ **32.** $7\sqrt{2}$ **33.** $24\sqrt{2}$ **34.** $30\sqrt{2}$ **35.** $\sqrt{5}$ **36.** $\sqrt{5}$ **37.** 5 **38.** 3 **39.** $\sqrt{10}$ **40.** $\sqrt{21}$ **41.** 5

42. 1 **43.** not a real number **44.** not a real number **45.** $2\sqrt{13}$ **46.** $2\sqrt{3}$ **47.** $8\pi\sqrt{41}$ **48.** $6\pi\sqrt{73}$ **49.** $24\pi\sqrt{10}$ **50.** $98\pi\sqrt{2}$
51. The distance is $90\sqrt{2}$ feet or approximately 127.28 feet. **52.** The wire is 100 feet. **53.** It is 11 inches high. **54.** The kite is 80 feet high.
55. The distance is 4000 feet. **56.** The tower is 120 meters tall. **57.** It would rise approximately 51.4 feet. **58.** It would rise about 24.5 inches.
59. The ladder rests at $\sqrt{589}$ feet or approximately 24.27 feet. **60.** The distance is $\sqrt{82.64}$ feet or about 9.10 feet. **61.** 5 units **62.** 8 units

63. $\sqrt{65}$ units **64.** $\sqrt{53}$ units **65.** $\sqrt{106}$ units **66.** $\sqrt{185}$ units **67.** $4\sqrt{2}$ units **68.** $3\sqrt{2}$ units **69.** $\dfrac{\sqrt{13}}{6}$ units **70.** $\dfrac{\sqrt{41}}{10}$ units

71. $\sqrt{10} + \sqrt{13} + \sqrt{5}$ units **72.** $\sqrt{10} + \sqrt{5} + \sqrt{5}$ units **73. (a)** According to the Pythagorean theorem, $c^2 = a^2 + b^2$ or
$\left(\sqrt{26}\right)^2 = \left(2\sqrt{2}\right)^2 + \left(3\sqrt{2}\right)^2$. **(b)** The area is 6 square units. **74. (a)** According to the Pythagorean theorem, $c^2 = a^2 + b^2$ or
$\left(5\sqrt{2}\right)^2 = \left(4\sqrt{2}\right)^2 + \left(3\sqrt{2}\right)^2$. **(b)** The area is 12 square units. **75.** $(0,0)$ and $(541, 236)$; the ships are $\sqrt{348{,}377}$ miles or approximately 590 miles apart.

76. $(0,0)$ and $(-3, -3)$; Chad is $3\sqrt{2}$ miles or about 4.24 miles from camp. **77.** $(2,3)$ and $(-3, -2)$; no **78.** $(3, -4)$ and $(-2, -5)$; yes

9.3 CALCULATOR EXERCISES

7 in., 8 in., 10 in., 11 in., 13 in., 14 in., 16 in., 17 in.

SECTION 9.4 EXERCISES

1. ± 12 **2.** ± 11 **3.** $\pm\sqrt{13}$ **4.** $\pm\sqrt{15}$ **5.** $\pm 7\sqrt{2}$ **6.** $\pm 10\sqrt{2}$ **7.** ± 4 **8.** ± 3 **9.** $\pm\dfrac{\sqrt{6}}{3}$ **10.** $\pm\dfrac{\sqrt{35}}{5}$

11. no real-number solution **12.** no real-number solution **13.** 5 **14.** $\dfrac{7}{2}$ **15.** 5 and 9 **16.** -9 and -3 **17.** $\dfrac{1}{4}$ and $\dfrac{5}{4}$ **18.** $\dfrac{4}{3}$ and 2

19. -5 and -1 **20.** 1 and 11 **21.** 1 and 7 **22.** -11 and -7 **23.** -8 and -2 **24.** -3 and 17 **25.** $-\dfrac{11}{3}$ and $\dfrac{13}{3}$ **26.** $-\dfrac{9}{5}$ and $\dfrac{7}{5}$

27. $7 \pm \sqrt{6}$ **28.** $12 \pm \sqrt{5}$ **29.** $\dfrac{-1 \pm \sqrt{10}}{2}$ **30.** $\dfrac{5 \pm \sqrt{2}}{4}$ **31.** $-3 \pm 2\sqrt{3}$ **32.** $15 \pm 2\sqrt{3}$ **33.** $\pm\dfrac{2\sqrt{5}}{5}$ **34.** $\pm\dfrac{3\sqrt{7}}{7}$ **35.** $\pm\dfrac{5\sqrt{2}}{2}$

36. $\pm\dfrac{4\sqrt{11}}{11}$ **37.** 81 **38.** 16 **39.** $\dfrac{81}{4}$ **40.** $\dfrac{25}{4}$ **41.** $\dfrac{9}{64}$ **42.** $\dfrac{9}{100}$ **43.** $\dfrac{1}{4}$ **44.** $\dfrac{1}{4}$ **45.** -11 and 5 **46.** -5 and 13 **47.** -4 and 7

48. -8 and 5 **49.** $-\dfrac{3}{7}$ and $-\dfrac{1}{7}$ **50.** $-\dfrac{4}{5}$ and $-\dfrac{2}{5}$ **51.** -10 and 9 **52.** -7 and 8 **53.** $3 \pm \sqrt{11}$ **54.** $-4 \pm \sqrt{21}$ **55.** $\dfrac{-9 \pm \sqrt{85}}{2}$

56. $\dfrac{5 \pm \sqrt{33}}{2}$ **57.** $\dfrac{-4 \pm \sqrt{178}}{9}$ **58.** $\dfrac{-3 \pm \sqrt{58}}{7}$ **59.** $\dfrac{1 \pm \sqrt{21}}{2}$ **60.** $\dfrac{-1 \pm \sqrt{41}}{2}$ **61.** no real-number solution

62. no real-number solution **63.** $\dfrac{-3 \pm \sqrt{11}}{2}$ **64.** $\dfrac{-3 \pm 2\sqrt{3}}{2}$ **65.** $\dfrac{-1 \pm \sqrt{85}}{6}$ **66.** -1 and $\dfrac{3}{5}$ **67.** 7 **68.** -5 **69.** $\dfrac{5}{2}$ **70.** $-\dfrac{2}{3}$

71. $-5 \pm \sqrt{29}$ **72.** $3 \pm \sqrt{6}$ **73.** In 1990, the top was about 189.41 feet above the ground. In 2001, the top was about 189.52 feet above the ground. **74.** The pole's height is about 19.94 feet. **75.** The distance is $25\sqrt{2}$, or approximately 35.36 feet. **76.** The perimeter is $40\sqrt{2}$, or approximately 56.57 cm. **77.** The ball was about 7.14 feet high. The ball missed the bar by 0.86 feet. **78.** The ball was about 8.57 feet high. The ball cleared the bar by 0.57 feet. **79.** The annual interest rate was 8.5%. **80.** The annual interest rate was 5.5%. **81.** The annual interest rate was 9.54%. **82.** The annual interest rate was 15.47%. **83.** The annual interest rate was 12.55%. **84.** The annual interest rate was 18.5%.
85. They break even when 10 tickets or 26 tickets are sold. **86.** They break even when 4 tickets or 14 tickets are sold. **87.** They break even when 13 people or 65 people are in the group. **88.** They break even when 20 licenses or 30 licenses are purchased. **89.** The number of cars is 5.
90. $f(x) = 0.5x^2 + 5x$; a total of 10 dolls can be purchased. **91.** The price should be set at $19. **92.** The price should be set at $42. **93.** The contract should be about $10,400,000. **94.** The contract should be for about $7,400,000. **95.** The width is 9 in. and the length is 13 in.
96. The height is 10 cm and the base is 18 cm. **97.** The length is 12.1 ft and the width is 7.1 ft. **98.** The lengths of the legs are 13.22 ft and 21.22 ft.
99. The width is about 7.76 units. **100.** The height of the smaller triangle is about 15.4 units. **101. (a)** $0 = -16t^2 + 32t + 16$

(b) It will take $1 + \sqrt{2}$ seconds. **(c)** It will take approximately 2.4 seconds. **102. (a)** $0 = -16t^2 + 88t + 8$ **(b)** It will take $\dfrac{11 + \sqrt{129}}{4}$ seconds.

(c) It will take approximately 5.6 seconds.   **103.** It will take 4.3 seconds for the balloon to reach a height of 100 feet.   **104.** It will reach a height of 10 feet in 5.9 seconds.   **105.** It will take $\dfrac{5\sqrt{70}}{2}$, or approximately 20.9 seconds.   **106.** It will take $\dfrac{25\sqrt{3}}{2}$, or approximately 21.65 seconds.

107. (a) $y = -0.5x^2 + 3.5x + 30$ **(b)** In 2006, there will be 33 million people below the poverty level.   **108. (a)** $y = 1.2x^2 - 7.35x + 15.5$ **(b)** In 2001 and 2005, the yield is about 8.75.   **109. (a)** $y = 17x^2 - 24x + 132$ **(b)** In 2004, the city failed to meet the air-quality standards on 300 days.   **110. (a)** $y = -35x^2 + 25x + 1360$ **(b)** In 2004, there were one million grandchildren living with grandparents with no parent present.

9.4 CALCULATOR EXERCISES

1. -5 and -3 **2.** no real-number solution   **3.** approximately -1.618 and 0.618 **4.** -4 and -1.5 **5.** no real-number solution   **6.** approximately -1.435 and 0.435

SECTION 9.5 EXERCISES

1. 3 and 9   **2.** 5 and 7   **3.** $-\dfrac{7}{2}$ and 3   **4.** $-\dfrac{8}{3}$ and 2   **5.** -5 and $-\dfrac{1}{2}$ **6.** -9 and $-\dfrac{4}{3}$ **7.** $\dfrac{1}{4}$ **8.** $-\dfrac{2}{5}$ **9.** no real-number solution

10. no real-number solution   **11.** no real-number solution   **12.** no real-number solution   **13.** $\dfrac{5 \pm \sqrt{17}}{2}$ **14.** $\dfrac{3 \pm \sqrt{5}}{2}$ **15.** $2 \pm \sqrt{3}$

16. $-3 \pm \sqrt{2}$ **17.** $\dfrac{5 \pm 5\sqrt{257}}{32}$ **18.** $\dfrac{-5 \pm 5\sqrt{129}}{32}$ **19.** $\pm\dfrac{\sqrt{21}}{3}$ **20.** $\pm\dfrac{\sqrt{30}}{2}$ **21.** 5 and 11   **22.** -12 and -6 **23.** 1.5 and 4.8

24. -3.2 and -0.5 **25.** $-2.8 \pm \sqrt{9.64}$ **26.** $0.9 \pm \sqrt{7.01}$ **27.** 4.9   **28.** -7.1 **29.** no real-number solution   **30.** no real-number solution

31. $\dfrac{8 \pm \sqrt{1534}}{9.8}$ **32.** $\dfrac{-12 \pm \sqrt{2104}}{9.8}$ **33.** two rational solutions   **34.** no real-number solution   **35.** one rational solution

36. two irrational solutions   **37.** no real-number solution   **38.** one rational solution   **39.** two rational solutions   **40.** two rational solutions   **41.** two irrational solutions   **42.** two rational solutions   **43.** two irrational solutions   **44.** no real-number solution   **45.** one rational solution   **46.** two irrational solutions   **47.** no real-number solution   **48.** one rational solution   **49. (a)** $R(x) = x(9 - 0.1x)$ **(b)** $C(x) = 7.50 + 6x$ **(c)** $P(x) = -0.1x^2 + 3x - 7.50$ **(d)** He breaks even when he sells 2.75 pounds at \$8.73 per pound or 27.2 pounds at \$6.28 per pound.   **50. (a)** $R(x) = x(3.25 - 0.05x)$ **(b)** $C(x) = 3.00 + 2x$ **(c)** $P(x) = -0.05x^2 + 1.25x - 3.00$ **(d)** She breaks even when she sells 3 ribbons at \$3.10 each or 23 ribbons at \$2.10 each.   **51. (a)** $R(x) = 50x$ **(b)** $C(x) = x(20 - 0.25x) + 600$ **(c)** $P(x) = 0.25x^2 + 30x - 600$ **(d)** The promoter breaks even when there are 18 guests and he pays the caterer \$15.50 per guest.   **52. (a)** $R(x) = 250x$ **(b)** $C(x) = x(75 - 5x) + 500$ **(c)** $P(x) = 5x^2 + 175x - 500$ **(d)** The firm breaks even when the job lasts about 3 days with a variable cost of \$60 per day.   **53. (a)** $R(x) = 225 + 13x - 0.4x^2$ **(b)** $C(x) = 237.50 + 3x$ **(c)** $P(x) = -12.50 + 10x - 0.4x^2$ **(d)** 2 and 23 tickets will result in a slight profit.   **54. (a)** $R(x) = 5437.50 + 432.50x - 7x^2$ **(b)** $C(x) = 7175 - 30x$ **(c)** $P(x) = -1737.50 + 462.50x - 7x^2$ **(d)** 4 and 62 fares will result in a slight profit.   **55. (a)** $R(x) = 1035 + 61.2x - x^2$ **(b)** $C(x) = 2000 - 8x$ **(c)** $P(x) = -965 + 69.20x - x^2$ **(d)** 20 and 49 tickets will result in a slight profit.   **56. (a)** $R(x) = 3182.5 + 360x - 22.5x^2$ **(b)** $C(x) = 2480 + 345x$ **(c)** $P(x) = 702.50 + 15x - 22.50x^2$ **(d)** 5 boxes will result in a slight profit.   **57.** The width is about 18 feet and the length is about 63 feet.   **58.** The height is about 12.1 decimeters and the base is about 79.7 decimeters.   **59.** The angle is about 80.9 degrees.   **60.** The width is about 3.10 inches.   **61.** $(x + 12)^2 = x^2 + (x + 6)^2$; The measurements are 18 ft height, 24 ft base, and 30 ft hypotenuse.   **62.** $\left(x + \dfrac{1}{2}\right)^2 = x^2 + \left(\dfrac{3}{4}x\right)^2$; The measurements are 2 in base, $1\dfrac{1}{2}$ in height, and $2\dfrac{1}{2}$ in hypotenuse.

63. She will land on the safety net in about 2.06 seconds.   **64.** It will be at a height of 400 feet in about 6.98 seconds.   **65.** In 2011, the per capita expenditure on spectator sports will reach \$25.   **66.** In 2002, the number of cable TV systems was 130,000.   **67.** In 2009, there will be 750,000 robberies in the United States.   **68.** In 2002, there were one million burglaries in the United States.

9.5 CALCULATOR EXERCISES

Equation	Value of Discriminant	Types of Roots	Number of Unlike Roots	Roots
1. $x^2 + 6 = 5x$	1	rational	2	2, 3
2. $9x^2 + 6x = -1$	0	rational	1	$-\dfrac{1}{3}$
3. $2x^2 + 1 = 7x$	41	irrational	2	0.149, 3.351
4. $x^2 + 6x = -10$	-4	not real	2	not real
5. $x^2 = 6 - x$	25	rational	2	$-3, 2$
6. $5x^2 - 6x = 0$	36	rational	2	0, 1.2
7. $x^2 + 0.36 = 1.2x$	0	rational	1	0.6
8. $1.7x^2 + x + 1.9 = 0$	-11.92	not real	2	not real
9. $1.5x^2 + 1.2x = 3.6$	23.04	rational	2	$-2, 1.2$
10. $\dfrac{1}{4}x^2 + x = \dfrac{1}{8}$	1.125	irrational	2	$-4.121, 0.121$
11. $x^2 - \dfrac{1}{6}x = \dfrac{1}{6}$	$0.69\overline{4}$	rational	2	$-0.\overline{3}, 0.5$
12. $\dfrac{1}{5}x^2 + \dfrac{2}{3}x = -\dfrac{7}{8}$	$-0.2\overline{5}$	not real	2	not real

SECTION 9.6 EXERCISES

1. $c = \pm\sqrt{\dfrac{E}{m}}$ or $\pm\dfrac{\sqrt{Em}}{m}$ **2.** $r = \pm\dfrac{1}{2}\sqrt{\dfrac{A}{\pi}}$ or $\pm\dfrac{\sqrt{A\pi}}{2\pi}$ **3.** $r = \pm\sqrt{\dfrac{V}{\pi h}}$ or $\pm\dfrac{\sqrt{V\pi h}}{\pi h}$ **4.** $v = \pm\sqrt{\dfrac{FR}{m}}$ or $\pm\dfrac{\sqrt{FRm}}{m}$ **5.** $v = \pm\sqrt{\dfrac{2E}{m}}$ or $\pm\dfrac{\sqrt{2Em}}{m}$

6. $r = \pm\sqrt{\dfrac{10A}{\pi S}}$ or $\pm\dfrac{6\sqrt{10A\pi S}}{\pi S}$ **7.** $n = \dfrac{1 \pm \sqrt{1 + 8C}}{2}$ **8.** $n = \dfrac{-1 \pm \sqrt{1 + 8S}}{2}$ **9.** $x = \pm\sqrt{y^2 + c^2}$ **10.** $x = \pm\sqrt{r^2 - y^2}$

11. $w = \pm\sqrt{\dfrac{F}{mr}}$ **12.** $I = \pm\sqrt{\dfrac{w}{Rt}}$ **13.** $c = \pm\sqrt{\dfrac{w_k}{m - m_0}}$ **14.** $f = \pm\sqrt{\dfrac{a}{-4\pi^2 x}}$ **15.** $t = \pm\sqrt{\dfrac{2s}{a}}$ **16.** $v = \pm\sqrt{\dfrac{3P}{Nm_1}}$

17. $v_0 = \pm\sqrt{v^2 - 2as}$ **18.** $w_0 = \pm\sqrt{w_1^2 - 2a\theta}$ **19.** $r = \pm\sqrt{\dfrac{c}{I}}$ **20.** $r = \pm\sqrt{\dfrac{kq_1}{E}}$ **21.** $r = \pm\sqrt{\dfrac{gmM}{F}}$ **22.** $B = \pm\sqrt{\dfrac{Em}{er}}$

23. $r_2 = \pm\sqrt{\dfrac{I - m_1 r_1^2}{m_2}}$ **24.** $h = \pm\sqrt{\dfrac{I - I_G}{m}}$ **25.** $x = \pm\sqrt{\dfrac{2F + ky^2}{k}}$ **26.** $y = \pm\sqrt{\dfrac{2F - kx^2}{-k}}$ **27.** $x = -7 \pm \dfrac{\sqrt{3 - y}}{2}$

28. $x = -5 \pm \sqrt{6y - y^2}$ **29.** $r = \dfrac{-\pi h \pm \sqrt{\pi^2 h^2 + 2\pi S}}{2\pi}$ **30.** $b = c + a$

31. $r = -1 \pm \dfrac{\sqrt{AP}}{P}$ **32.** $t = \dfrac{-g \pm \sqrt{g^2 + 64S}}{32}$ **33.** The hypotenuse measures approximately 5.30 m.   **34.** The hypotenuse measures approximately 9.26 feet.   **35.** The lengths are approximately 5.37 feet.   **36.** The lengths are approximately 10.54 cm.   **37.** The wire is approximately 28.28 feet.   **38.** The wire is approximately 21.21 feet.   **39.** The building is approximately 30.05 feet tall.   **40.** The tower is approximately 102.53 feet high.   **41.** Yes, 28.28 feet is less than 30 feet.   **42.** No, 35.36 feet is greater than 30 feet.   **43.** The lengths are approximately 10.7 in. and 21.5 in.   **44.** The lengths are approximately 1.3 cm and 2.5 cm.   **45.** The lengths are 11 in and approximately 19.1 in.   **46.** The lengths are 17 cm and approximately 29.4 cm.   **47.** The lengths are 42 cm and approximately 36.4 cm.   **48.** The lengths are 16.4 in and approximately 14.2 in.   **49.** The horizontal distance is about 6928 ft and the slanted distance is 8000 ft.   **50.** The horizontal distance is approximately 69.3 ft and the length of string is approximately 138.6 ft.   **51.** The height of the pole is approximately 13.9 ft and the length of the wire is 16 ft.   **52.** The amount of wire is approximately 15.0 m, and it should be anchored approximately 7.5 m from the base of the pole.

53. $11\sqrt{2}$ meters   **54.** $\dfrac{7\sqrt{2}}{2}$ meters   **55.** $5\sqrt{3}$ centimeters   **56.** $3\sqrt{3}$ feet   **57.** The height is $3\sqrt{3}$ yards. The area is $9\sqrt{3}$ square yards.

58. The height is $5\sqrt{3}$ feet. The area is $25\sqrt{3}$ square feet.   **59.** The height is 2 feet. The area is 4 square feet. The perimeter is $4 + 4\sqrt{2}$ feet.   **60.** The base is 14 meters. The area is 49 square meters. The perimeter is $14 + 14\sqrt{2}$ meters.

9.6 CALCULATOR EXERCISES

1. (a) yes   **(b)** no   **(c)** yes   **(d)** no   **2. (a)** yes   **(b)** no   **(c)** no   **(d)** no   **(e)** yes

SECTION 9.7 EXERCISES

1. (a) domain: $(-\infty, \infty)$; range: $[-4, \infty)$ **(b)** x-intercepts: $(-3, 0)$, $(1, 0)$; y-intercepts: $(0, -3)$ **(c)** concave: upward   **(d)** vertex: $(-1, -4)$; axis of symmetry: $x = -1$ **(e)** relative maximum: none; relative minimum: -4 when $x = -1$ absolute maximum: none; absolute minimum: -4 when $x = -1$; increasing: $(-1, \infty)$; decreasing: $(-\infty, -1)$ **(f)** x-values for which y-values equal 0: -3 and 1   **(g)** solutions: -3 and 1   **2. (a)** domain $(-\infty, \infty)$; range $[-9, \infty)$ **(b)** x-intercepts: $(-5, 0)$, $(1, 0)$; y-intercept: $(0, -5)$ **(c)** concave: upward   **(d)** vertex: $(-2, -9)$; axis of symmetry: $x = -2$ **(e)** relative maximum: none; relative minimum: -9 when $x = -2$; absolute maximum: none; absolute minimum: -9 when $x = -2$; increasing: $(-2, \infty)$; decreasing: $(-\infty, -2)$ **(f)** x-values for which y-values equal 0: -5 and 1   **(g)** solutions: -5 and 1   **3. (a)** domain: $(-\infty, \infty)$; range: $(-\infty, 9]$ **(b)** x-intercepts: $(-1, 0)$, $(5, 0)$; y-intercept: $(0, 5)$ **(c)** concave: downward   **(d)** vertex: $(2, 9)$; axis of symmetry: $x = 2$ **(e)** relative maximum: 9 when $x = 2$; relative minimum: none; absolute maximum: 9 when $x = 2$; absolute minimum: none; increasing: $(-\infty, 2)$; decreasing: $(2, \infty)$ **(f)** x-values for which y-values equal 0: -1 and 5   **(g)** solutions: -1 and 5   **4. (a)** domain: $(-\infty, \infty)$; range: $(-\infty, 4]$ **(b)** x-intercepts: $(-1, 0)$, $(3, 0)$; y-intercept: $(0, 3)$ **(c)** concave: downward   **(d)** vertex: $(1, 4)$; axis of symmetry: $x = 1$ **(e)** relative maximum: 4 when $x = 1$; relative minimum: none; absolute maximum: 4 when $x = 1$; absolute minimum: none; increasing: $(-\infty, 1)$; decreasing: $(1, \infty)$ **(f)** x-values for which y-values equal 0: -1 and 3   **(g)** solutions: -1 and 3   **5. (a)** domain: $(-\infty, \infty)$; range: $[2, \infty)$ **(b)** x-intercepts: none; y-intercept: $(0, 3)$ **(c)** concave: upward   **(d)** vertex: $(-1, 2)$; axis of symmetry: $x = -1$ **(e)** relative maximum: none; relative minimum: 2 when $x = -1$; absolute maximum: none; absolute minimum: 2 when $x = -1$; increasing: $(-1, \infty)$; decreasing $(-\infty, -1)$ **(f)** x-values for which y-values equal 0: none   **(g)** solutions: none   **6. (a)** domain: $(-\infty, \infty)$; range: $(-\infty, -2]$ **(b)** x-intercepts: none; y-intercept: $(0, -3)$ **(c)** concave: downward   **(d)** vertex: $(1, -2)$; axis of symmetry: $x = 1$ **(e)** relative maximum: -2 when $x = 1$; relative minimum: none; absolute maximum: -2 when $x = 1$; absolute minimum: none; increasing: $(-\infty, 1)$; decreasing: $(1, \infty)$ **(f)** x-values for which y-values equal 0: none   **(g)** solutions: none   **7. (a)** domain: $(-\infty, \infty)$; range: $(-\infty, 0]$ **(b)** x-intercept: $(-2, 0)$; y-intercepts: $(0, -4)$ **(c)** concave: downward   **(d)** vertex: $(-2, 0)$; axis of symmetry $x = -2$ **(e)** relative maximum: 0 when $x = -2$; relative minimum: none; absolute maximum: 0 when $x = -2$; absolute minimum: none; increasing: $(-\infty, -2)$; decreasing: $(-2, \infty)$ **(f)** x-value for which y-values equal 0: -2 **(g)** solution: -2 **8. (a)** domain: $(-\infty, \infty)$; range: $[0, \infty)$ **(b)** x-intercept: $(3, 0)$; y-intercept: $(0, 9)$ **(c)** concave: upward   **(d)** vertex: $(3, 0)$; axis of symmetry: $x = 3$ **(e)** relative maximum: none; relative minimum: 0 when $x = 3$; absolute maximum: none; absolute minimum: 0 when $x = 3$; increasing: $(3, \infty)$; decreasing: $(-\infty, 3)$ **(f)** x-values for which y-values equal 0: 3   **(g)** solution: 3   **9.** x-intercepts: $(-3, 0)$ and $(2, 0)$; y-intercept: $(0, -6)$ **10.** x-intercepts: $(5, 0)$ and $(-4, 0)$; y-intercept: $(0, -20)$ **11.** x-intercepts: $(3, 0)$ and $(-3, 0)$; y-intercept: $(0, -9)$ **12.** x-intercepts: $(4, 0)$ and $(-4, 0)$; y-intercept: $(0, -16)$ **13.** x-intercepts: $\left(-3 \pm \sqrt{13}, 0\right)$; y-intercept: $(0, 4)$ **14.** x-intercepts: $\left(2 \pm \sqrt{11}, 0\right)$; y-intercept: $(0, 7)$ **15.** x-intercepts: none; y-intercept: $(0, 5)$ **16.** x-intercepts: none; y-intercept: $(0, 7)$ **17.** vertex: $(-2, 1)$; axis of symmetry: $x = -2$ **18.** vertex: $(1, 3)$; axis of symmetry: $x = 1$ **19.** vertex: $(0, -9)$; axis of symmetry: $x = 0$ **20.** vertex: $(0, -16)$; axis of symmetry: $x = 0$ **21.** vertex: $(1, 2)$; axis of symmetry: $x = 1$ **22.** vertex: $(-2, 5)$; axis of symmetry: $x = -2$ **23.** vertex: $\left(-\dfrac{1}{3}, \dfrac{2}{3}\right)$; axis of symmetry: $x = -\dfrac{1}{3}$ **24.** vertex: $(-1, 3)$ axis of symmetry: $x = -1$

25.
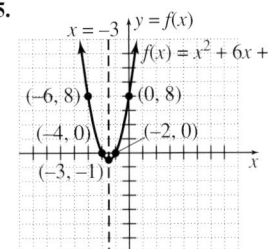

26.
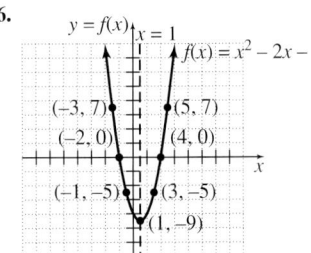

27.
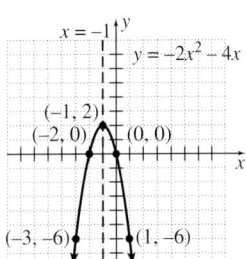

28.
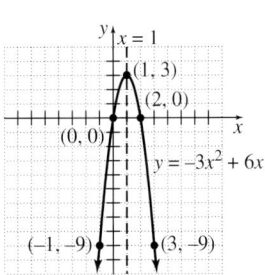

29.
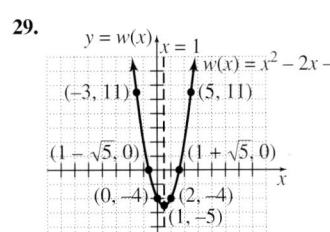

30.
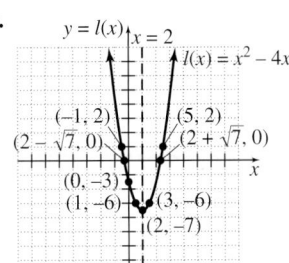

31.
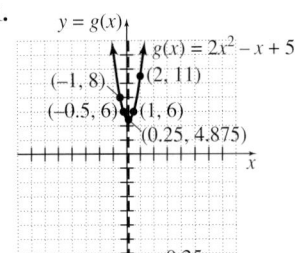

32.
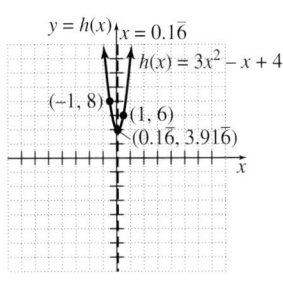

33. $f(x) = x^2 + x - 12$ **34.** $f(x) = x^2 - x - 6$ **35.** $f(x) = 12x^2 - 11x + 2$ **36.** $f(x) = 10x^2 - 11x + 3$ **37.** $f(x) = x^2 - 5.5x + 5.46$

38. $f(x) = x^2 - 3.6x + 2.75$ **39.** $f(x) = x^2 - 125.50x$ **40.** $f(x) = x^2 - 234.75x$ **41.** $f(x) = x^2 - 8x + 16$ **42.** $f(x) = x^2 + 4x + 4$

43. (a) 0 meter   **(b)** 40 meters   **(c)** 45 meters   **(d)** 3 seconds   **(e)** 10 meters at about 5.6 seconds   **44. (a)** 25 meters   **(b)** about 27 meters   **(c)** 28 meters   **(d)** about 0.7 second   **(e)** about 2.8 seconds

45. (a) 586 feet   **(b)** 875 feet, 6.25 seconds   **(c)** 12.5 seconds   **(d)** about 13.65 seconds   **(e)**

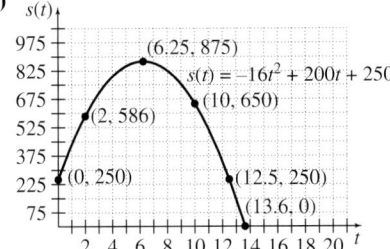

46. (a) 83.5 feet   **(b)** about 84.77 feet, about 0.78 second   **(c)** about 1.56 seconds   **(d)** about 3.08 seconds   **(e)**

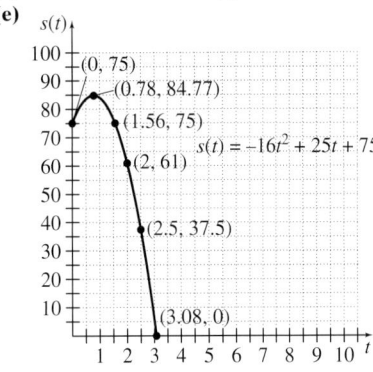

47. (a) about 110.75 meters   **(b)** about 113.27 meters, about 0.82 second   **(c)** about 1.63 seconds   **(d)** about 5.62 seconds   **(e)**

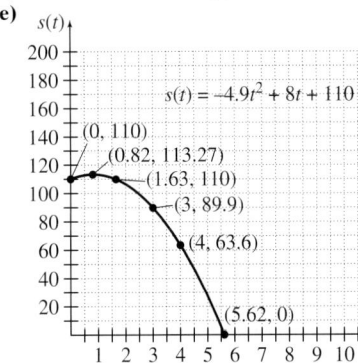

48. (a) 3173.6 meters   **(b)** about 15,483.67 meters, about 56.12 seconds   **(c)** about 22.67 seconds and about 89.58 seconds   **(d)** about 112.34 seconds   **(e)**

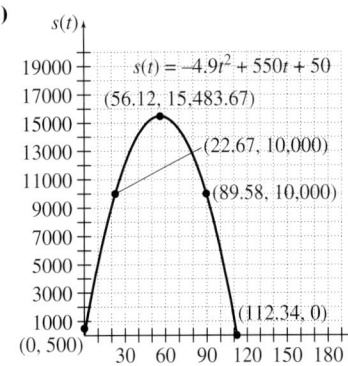

49. (a) (2, 300) and (18, 1100); Mrs. Tilley will break even when she produces and sells 2 and 18 units of pottery.   **(b)** 15, $1150   **(c)** (2, 0) and (18, 0); Mrs. Tilley will break even when she produces and sells 2 and 18 units of pottery.   **(d)** 10, $300   **50. (a)** (5, 4000) and (65, 22,000); Mr. Tilley will break even when he produces and sells 5 and 65 go-carts.   **(b)** 50, $25,000   **(c)** (5, 0) and (65, 0); Mr. Tilley will break even when he produces and sells 5 and 65 go-carts.   **(d)** 35, $9000

51. (a) $R(x) = 14x - 0.75x^2$ **(b)** $C(x) = 3x + 10$
(c) $P(x) = -0.75x^2 + 11x - 10$ **(d)** There will be $0 in revenue for 0 people and a loss of $4.75 in revenue for 19 people.   **(e)** 9, $65.25
(f) There will be a loss of $10 for 0 people and a loss of $3 for 14 people.
(g) 7, $30.25   **(h)** There will be a slight profit for 1 person ($0.25) and 13 people ($6.25).
(i)

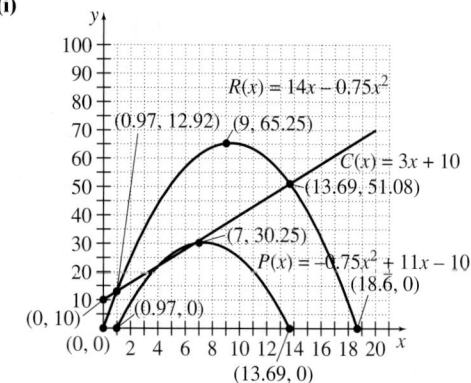

52. (a) $R(x) = 28.75x - 0.80x^2$ **(b)** $C(x) = 3.50x + 125$
(c) $P(x) = -0.80x^2 + 25.25x - 125$ **(d)** There will be $0 in revenue for 0 children and a loss of $1.80 for 36 children.   **(e)** 18, $258.30
(f) There will be a loss of $2.30 for 6 children and a loss of $9.30 for 26 children.   **(g)** 16, $74.20   **(h)** There will be a slight profit for 7 children ($12.55) and 25 children ($6.25).
(i)

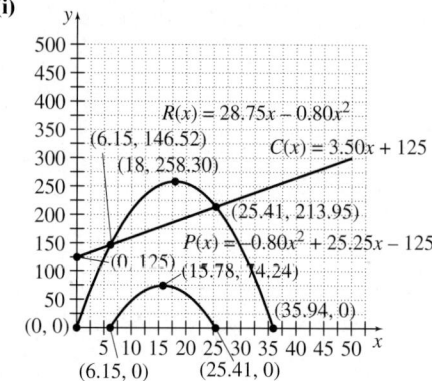

53. (a) $R(x) = 5.50x - 0.10x^2$ **(b)** $C(x) = 0.75x + 25$
(c) $P(x) = -0.10x^2 + 4.75x - 25$ **(d)** There will be $0 in revenue for 0 deliveries and 55 deliveries.   **(e)** The maximum revenue will be $75.60 for 27 and 28 deliveries.   **(f)** There will be a loss of $0.10 for 6 deliveries and a loss of $1.90 for 42 deliveries.   **(g)** 24, $31.40   **(h)** There will be a slight profit for 7 deliveries ($3.35) and 41 deliveries ($1.65).
(i)

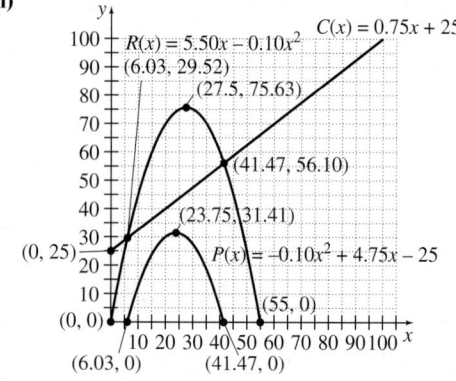

54. (a) $R(x) = 5.50x - 0.05x^2$ **(b)** $C(x) = 0.75x + 50$
(c) $P(x) = -0.05x^2 + 4.75x - 50$ **(d)** There will be $0 in revenue for 0 tickets and 110 tickets.   **(e)** The maximum revenue will be $151.25 for 55 tickets.   **(f)** There will be a loss of $0.20 for 12 tickets and 83 tickets.
(g) The maximum profit is $62.80 for 47 tickets and 48 tickets.
(h) There will be a slight profit of $3.30 for 13 tickets and 82 tickets.
(i)

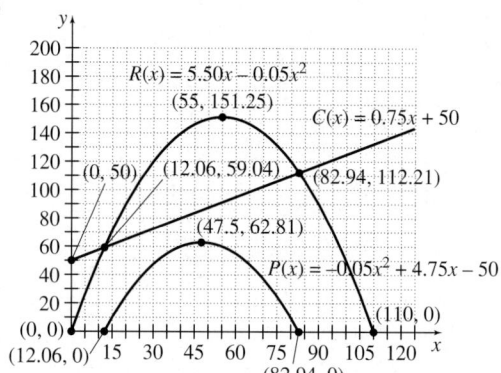

55. (a) The maximum yearly depreciation is $121,500 in 2004.   **(b)** In 2010, the yearly depreciation will be $67,000.   **(c)** In 2001 and 2007, the yearly depreciation will be $108,000.   **56. (a)** Darlene's maximum yearly payment is $18,000 6 years after obtaining the loan.   **(b)** Her fifth year payment will be $17,500.   **(c)** She will pay $10,000 two years and ten years after obtaining the loan.   **57. (a)** The maximum revenue of about $7,770,000,000 occurred 3.5 months after September 2004 or in the middle of December 2004.   **(b)** In June 2005, the total revenue was $7,470,000,000. In January 2006, the total revenue was $6,210,000,000.   **(c)** In September 2005, the total revenue was $7,000,000,000.   **58. (a)** The maximum revenue of about $555,610,000 occurred 4.7 months after August 2004 or late December.   **(b)** In June 2005, the total revenue was $358,600,000. In December 2005, the total revenue was a loss of $345,800,000.   **(c)** In May 2005, the total revenue was $425,000,000.   **59. (a)** The maximum gross profit of about $4,700,000,000 occurred 2.6 months after September 2004 or mid-November 2004.   **(b)** In January 2005, the gross profit was $4,480,000,000. In January 2006, the gross loss was $15,080,000,000.   **(c)** In late March 2005 (6.96 months after September 2004), the gross profit was $2,600,000,000.
60. (a) The maximum gross loss of about $251,860,000 occurred 5.1 months after August 2004 or early January 2005.   **(b)** In December 2004, the gross profit was $249,260,000. In December 2005, the gross profit was $5,540,000.   **(c)** In August 2005 (12.1 months after August 2004), the gross profit was $150,000,000.   **61. (a)** The maximum area (50,625 square feet) occurs at a width of 225 feet.   **(b)** The area is 0 square feet when the width is 0 feet and 450 feet (at this width, the length will be 0 feet).   **(c)** The area is 20,000 square feet.   **(d)** The area is 34,750 square feet when the width is about 351 feet or about 99 feet.   **62. (a)** The maximum area (81,225 square yards) occurs at a length of 285 yards.   **(b)** The area is 0 square yards when the length is 0 yards or 570 yards (at this length, the width will be 0 yards).   **(c)** The area is 26,000 square yards.   **(d)** The area is 54,000 square yards when the length is 120 yards and 450 yards.   **63. (a)** $A(x) = 100x - x^2$ **(b)** The maximum area of 2500 square feet occurs when the width is 50 feet.
(c) The minimum area of 0 square feet occurs when the width is 0 feet and 100 feet.   **(d)** The area is 1875 square feet.   **(e)** The area is 2000 square feet when the width is about 72.36 feet and 27.64 feet.   **64. (a)** $A(x) = 50x - x^2$ **(b)** The maximum area is 625 square feet when the length is 25 feet.   **(c)** The minimum area of 0 square feet occurs when the length is 0 feet and 50 feet.   **(d)** The area is 525 square feet.   **(e)** The area is 500 square feet when the length is about 13.82 feet and 36.18 feet.

9.7 CALCULATOR EXERCISES

1. $y = x^3 - 2x^2 + 3x - 4$ **2.** $y = x^4 - x^3 + x^2 - x + 1$ **3.** $y = -1.5x^3 + 10x^2 - 9.5x - 6$ **4.** $y = 0.5x^4 - 0.2x^3 - 7x + 6$

SECTION 9.8 EXERCISES

1. quadratic inequality **2.** not a quadratic inequality **3.** quadratic inequality **4.** not a quadratic inequality **5.** not a quadratic inequality **6.** quadratic inequality **7.** quadratic inequality **8.** quadratic inequality **9.** not a quadratic inequality **10.** not a quadratic inequality **11.** not a quadratic inequality **12.** quadratic inequality **13.** all integers less than or equal to -5 and greater than or equal to 3 **14.** all integers greater than or equal to -4 and less than or equal to 2 **15.** all integers greater than -4 and less than 1 **16.** all integers greater than -3 and less than 2 **17.** all integers less than 0 or greater than 8 **18.** all integers less than -3 or greater than 0 **19.** $(-\infty, -3) \cup (1, \infty)$ **20.** $(-\infty, 1] \cup [7, \infty)$ **21.** $(-2.5, 2)$ **22.** $[-1, 5]$ **23.** $(-\infty, -2) \cup (8, \infty)$ **24.** $(-\infty, -1) \cup (8, \infty)$ **25.** $[-3, 3]$ **26.** $(-\infty, -5) \cup (2, \infty)$ **27.** no solution **28.** no solution **29.** $(-\infty, \infty)$ **30.** -2 **31.** $(-\infty, \infty)$ **32.** $(-\infty, \infty)$

33. $(-\infty, -4] \cup [6, \infty)$ **34.** $[-5, 7]$ **35.** $(-3, 5)$ **36.** $(-3, 6)$ **37.** $\left[\dfrac{1}{2}, \dfrac{5}{2}\right]$ **38.** $(-\infty, -4] \cup [-1, \infty)$ **39.** $(-\infty, -2) \cup (7, \infty)$

40. $(-5, 6)$ **41.** $(-\infty, -4] \cup [3, \infty)$ **42.** $[-2, 6]$ **43.** $(-\infty, -3) \cup (1, \infty)$ **44.** $(-\infty, -2) \cup (4, \infty)$ **45.** $[-2, 3]$

46. $\left(-\infty, \dfrac{1}{2}\right] \cup [5, \infty)$ **47.** $\dfrac{3}{2}$ **48.** $(-\infty, \infty)$ **49.** $\left(-\infty, \dfrac{1}{2}\right) \cup \left(\dfrac{1}{2}, \infty\right)$ **50.** no solution **51.** $(-\infty, \infty)$ **52.** 4 **53.** no solution

54. $(-\infty, -4) \cup (-4, \infty)$ **55.** Cost will exceed \$12,500 for 25 or more faculty members. **56.** Cost will be above \$50 for less than 6 apprentice hours. **57.** Cost will be between \$11.25 and \$14.00 for one and four tools. **58.** Costs will be between \$75 and \$150 for three to six, inclusive, visits. **59.** Her revenue will be less than \$200 for less than 22 sessions and more than 28 sessions. **60.** Revenue will exceed \$15,000 for more than 26 paintings. **61.** Revenue will be between \$300 and \$500 for 17 to 21, inclusive, orders. **62.** Revenue will be between \$20,000 and \$30,000 for 14 to 19, inclusive, tables. **63.** His profit will be greater than \$1000 for 13 or more works. **64.** She needs to make 19 or more calls to earn \$25 or more. **65.** Profits are less than \$9000 for 15 to 52, inclusive, weeks. **66.** Profits are less than \$28 for less than 4 sites and more than 7 sites. **67.** The egg is higher than the stand between 0 and 1.875 seconds. **68.** The arrow is above the point of origin between 0 and 2.5 seconds. **69.** He is between 411 and 500 feet for time between 5 and 5.5 seconds. **70.** The weight is between 23 and 29 meters for time between 0.603 and 1.006 seconds. **71.** The soccer ball will be between 2.2 and 2.7 meters for time between 1 and 1.5 seconds. **72.** The rock will be between 12.8 and 13.2 meters for time between 2 and 2.25 seconds and 4 and 4.25 seconds. **73.** The boulder is between 100 and 175 meters above the surface between 3.68 and 7.35 seconds. **74.** The rock is between 2 and 2.5 meters above the surface between 0.09 and 0.28 seconds and 1.56 and 1.74 seconds. **75.** The price of gas will be between \$3 and \$5 per gallon between 2008 and 2012. **76.** The wage will be less than \$25 between 2000 and 2007. **77.** $c(x) = 8.3x^2 - 55.9x + 123.6$; the cassette sales were below 40 million in 2001 and 2003. **78.** $n(x) = -13.5x^2 + 24.5x + 769$; nuclear-based electricity generation was below 550 million kilowatt hours in 2000 to 2005, inclusive.

9.8 CALCULATOR EXERCISES

Answers will vary.

CHAPTER 9 SUMMARY

Vocabulary Review

1. cubic function **2.** quadratic function **3.** hypotenuse **4.** isosceles right triangle **5.** equilateral triangle **6.** root

Reflections

1–6. Answers will vary.

CHAPTER 9 SECTION-BY-SECTION REVIEW

1. -3 and 4 **2.** -9 and -3 **3.** 1 and 5 **4.** -1 and 5 **5.** -4 and 4 **6.** -4 and 1.5 **7.** -5 and 11 **8.** approximately -6.83 and -1.17 **9.** -3, 3, and 1.5 **10.** It will reach the ground in approximately 2.45 seconds. **11.** $s = -16t^2 + 550t + 15$; the rocket will be at a height of 3000 feet in 6.75 and 27.62 seconds. **12.** $s = -16t^2 - 8t + 40$; the firework will be at a height of 25 feet in 0.75 second. **13.** At age 41, 15% of people have a hearing problem. **14.** -2 and 3 **15.** $-\dfrac{7}{2}$ and $\dfrac{11}{3}$ **16.** -1 and 8 **17.** -5 and 12 **18.** no solution

19. $\dfrac{4}{3}$ and $\dfrac{3}{2}$ **20.** $\dfrac{5}{2}$ and -7 **21.** $\pm\dfrac{7}{3}$ **22.** x-intercepts: $(-2, 0)$ $(1, 0)$; $(x + 2)(x - 1) = 0$; $x = -2$, $x = 1$ **23.** $5w + w^2 = 300$; The dimensions are 15 feet by 20 feet. **24.** The width is 1 yard. **25.** The stand was opened 65 hours. **26.** Let x = the ranking, y = the area in thousands of square miles, $y = -x^2 - 28x + 366$; Madagascar has a ranking of 4. **27.** -7 **28.** $10\sqrt{2}$ **29.** $4\sqrt{2}$ **30.** $2\sqrt{2}$ **31.** $-6\sqrt{2}$

32. $-\dfrac{6}{5} - \sqrt{2}$ **33.** $1 + \dfrac{\sqrt{2}}{2}$ **34.** $\dfrac{1 - \sqrt{3}}{2}$ **35.** $2 - \sqrt{5}$ **36.** $\dfrac{6\sqrt{5}}{5}$ **37.** $\dfrac{\sqrt{5}}{2}$ **38.** $2\sqrt{15}$ **39.** $18\sqrt{2}$ **40.** 5 **41.** $\sqrt{21}$

42. $3 + \sqrt{57}$ **43.** $\sqrt{26}$ **44.** $2\sqrt{5}$ **45.** $\sqrt{10} + \sqrt{5} + \sqrt{13}$ **46.** The horizontal distance is $10\sqrt{10}$ ft, or approximately 31.6 ft.

47. $(0, 0)$ $(5, 5)$; $5\sqrt{2} \approx 7.07$ **48.** ± 5 **49.** ± 2 **50.** $\pm 2\sqrt{3}$ **51.** no real-number solution **52.** 1 and 7 **53.** -13 and -5 **54.** $2 \pm \sqrt{2}$

55. -8 and 12 **56.** $-\dfrac{3}{2}$ and 4 **57.** $\dfrac{-1 \pm \sqrt{17}}{4}$ **58.** They will break even selling 10 figurines. **59.** $x^2 + 4x - 45 = 0$; the dimensions are 5 in. by 18 in. **60.** The interest rate is 8%. **61.** They would free-fall about 24 seconds, with wind resistance and maneuvering ignored.

62. (a) $y = -1.45x^2 + 6.75x + 6.1$ (b) $x \approx 4$; in 2004, the percent of sales revenue will be 9.7. **63.** -7 and 9 **64.** $\dfrac{3 \pm \sqrt{21}}{2}$ **65.** $\dfrac{1}{5}$

66. $-\dfrac{3}{4}$ and $\dfrac{2}{5}$ **67.** -4.5 and 2.4 **68.** no real-number solution **69.** $5 \pm \sqrt{19}$ **70.** $\dfrac{2 \pm 2\sqrt{10}}{3}$ **71.** no real-number solution

72. one rational solution **73.** two rational solutions **74.** two irrational solutions **75.** (a) $R(x) = x(6.50 - 0.50x)$ (b) $C(x) = 2.50x + 3.95$ (c) $P(x) = -0.5x^2 + 4x - 3.95$ (d) The break-even points are sales of two cakes at \$5.50 each or six cakes at \$3.50 each. **76.** The rectangle is 12 meters by 44 meters. **77.** In 2012 the death rate due to heart disease will decrease to 150 per 100,000. **78.** $s = -16t^2 + 50$; $t = \dfrac{\pm\sqrt{50 - s}}{4}$ **79.** $d = \dfrac{2\sqrt{\pi A}}{\pi}$

80. $x = \pm \dfrac{\sqrt{b(a-c)}}{b}$ **81.** $t = \dfrac{-v_0 \pm \sqrt{(v_0)^2 + 64(s_0 - s)}}{-32}$ **82.** $H = \sqrt{D^2 - L^2 - W^2}$; the height is 8 inches.   **83.** The rope is $7\sqrt{2}$ ft, or approximately 9.9 feet.   **84.** The lengths of the sides are 10 in and $10\sqrt{3}$ in, or approximately 17.3 in.   **85.** The height is $4\sqrt{3}$ feet. The area is $16\sqrt{3}$ square feet.   **86. (a)** The domain is $(-\infty, \infty)$. The range is $[-1, \infty)$.   **(b)** x-intercepts: (2, 0) and (4, 0), y-intercept: (0, 8)   **(c)** upward   **(d)** vertex: $(3, -1)$, axis of symmetry: $x = 3$ **(e)** relative maximum: none, relative minimum: -1 at $x = 3$, absolute maximum: none, absolute minimum: -1 at $x = 3$, increasing: $(3, \infty)$, decreasing: $(-\infty, 3)$ **(f)** 2 and 4   **(g)** 2 and 4   **87.** x-intercepts: (3, 0) and $(-6, 0)$, y-intercept: $(0, -18)$

88. x-intercepts: $\left(\dfrac{5 + \sqrt{17}}{4}, 0\right)$ and $\left(\dfrac{5 - \sqrt{17}}{4}, 0\right)$, y-intercept: (0, 1)   **89.** vertex: $(-2, -16)$; axis of symmetry: $x = -2$ **90.** vertex: $(-1, 7)$; axis of symmetry: $x = -1$ **91.**

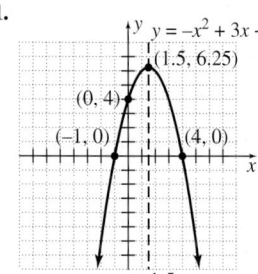

92.

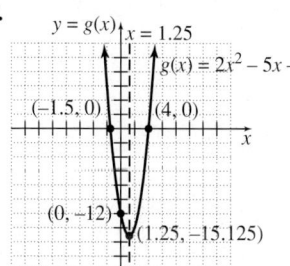

93.

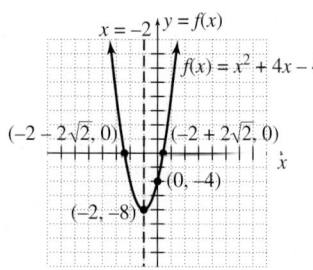

94. $f(x) = x^2 + 2x - 8$ **95.** $f(x) = 6x^2 - 7x + 2$ **96. (a)** 0 feet   **(b)** 12 feet   **(c)** 16 feet   **(d)** 1 second   **(e)** about 7 feet at 1.75 seconds   **97. (a)** (25, 5000) and (85, 10,500); the manufacturer breaks even at 25 and 85 units.   **(b)** The maximum revenue is $11,000 for 70 units.   **(c)** (25, 0) and (85, 0); there is no profit for 25 and 85 units.   **(d)** 55 units will maximize the profit. The maximum profit is $2000.

98. (a) The diver's maximum height is 202.5 meters.   **(b)** The maximum height occurs at about 0.71 seconds.   **(c)** The diver reached a height of 150 meters at about 3.99 seconds.   **(d)** She hit the surface of the water in about 7.14 seconds.   **(e)** She will be 4 meters below the surface in about 7.21 seconds.   **(f)**

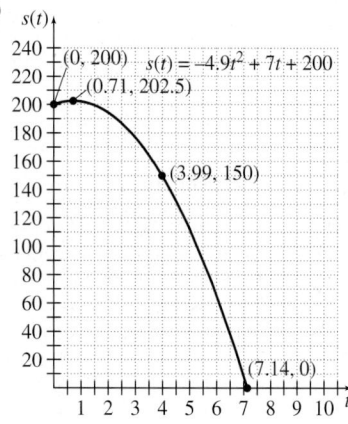

99. (a) $R(x) = 52.50x - 0.25x^2$ **(b)** $C(x) = 15x + 600$ **(c)** $P(x) = -0.25x^2 + 37.50x - 600$ **(d)** There will be $0 in revenue for 0 guests and 210 guests.   **(e)** The maximum revenue is $2756.25 for 105 guests.   **(f)** There will be a loss of $6 for 18 guests and 132 guests.   **(g)** The maximum profit is $806.25 for 75 guests.   **(h)** There will be a slight profit of $22.25 for 19 guests and 131 guests.   **(i)**

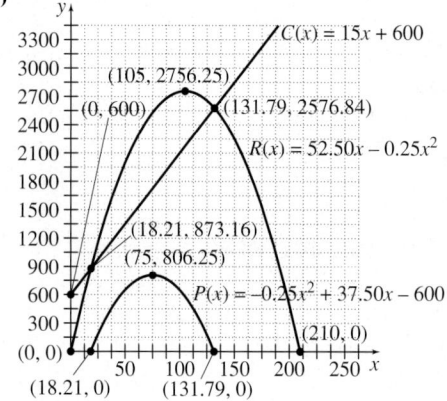

100. all integers greater than or equal to -6 and less than or equal to 4   **101.** all integers less than -2 or greater than 2   **102.** $(-\infty, -4] \cup [2, \infty)$

103. $[-3, 3]$ **104.** $(-1, 4)$ **105.** no solution   **106.** $(-\infty, 3) \cup (3, \infty)$ **107.** 4   **108.** (1.59, 4.41)   **109.** $\left(2 - \dfrac{2}{3}\sqrt{6}, 2 + \dfrac{2}{3}\sqrt{6}\right)$

110. $[-3, 2]$ **111.** $(-1, 3)$ **112.** $(-\infty, -3) \cup (-3, \infty)$ **113.** $(-\infty, \infty)$ **114.** no solution   **115.** $\left(3 - \sqrt{10}, 3 + \sqrt{10}\right)$ **116.** The booth can be rented up to four days.   **117.** The dart is above the ground from 0 second to approximately 2.358 seconds.   **118.** The profits are between $100 and $195 for less than 5 staff on duty and between 13 and 23 staff on duty.   **119.** Let $t =$ time in seconds, $s =$ position in feet, $s = -16t^2 + 300t + 50$; the object is less than 500 feet and above the ground level for time between 0 and 1.64, including 0, seconds and between 17.11 seconds and 18.915 seconds.

CHAPTER 9 MIXED REVIEW

1. $5\sqrt{2}$ **2.** $-4\sqrt{3}$ **3.** $-1 + \sqrt{2}$ **4.** $-2 + 2\sqrt{5}$ **5.** $\dfrac{5\sqrt{6}}{6}$ **6.** $3\sqrt{7}$ **7.** $30\sqrt{2}$ **8.** $\sqrt{13}$ **9.** 4   **10.** $2\sqrt{10}$ **11.** -1 and 3

12. -3 and 3   **13.** -5 and -1 **14.** $-2\dfrac{2}{3}$ and $1\dfrac{4}{5}$ **15.** -3 and 1   **16.** approximately -8.14 and -0.86 **17.** approximately -0.85 and 5.65

18. -4 and 10   **19.** -5 and 9   **20.** -1 and 5   **21.** $-\dfrac{3}{4}$ and $\dfrac{2}{3}$ **22.** -11 and 8   **23.** -7 and $\dfrac{2}{5}$ **24.** $\pm\dfrac{4}{7}$ **25.** ± 6 **26.** no real-number solution   **27.** 5 and 13   **28.** $7 \pm \sqrt{3}$ **29.** $-6 \pm \sqrt{3}$ **30.** $\dfrac{-7 \pm \sqrt{37}}{2}$ **31.** -3.6 and 1.2 **32.** all real numbers   **33.** -14 and -6

34. $-\dfrac{5}{2}$ and 1   **35.** $\dfrac{-4 \pm 3\sqrt{2}}{2}$ **36.** $-4 \pm 2\sqrt{3}$ **37.** $\dfrac{7 \pm \sqrt{57}}{2}$ **38.** $\dfrac{5}{6}$ **39.** no real-number solution   **40.** -11 and 5   **41.** -4 and $\dfrac{9}{4}$

42. $x = \dfrac{-1 \pm \sqrt{1 + 8a}}{2}$ **43.** $y = \pm\sqrt{r^2 - x^2 - z^2}$ **44.** $r = \pm\dfrac{\sqrt{A\pi}}{2\pi}$ **45.** all integers greater than or equal to -3 and less than or equal to 5

46. all integers greater than or equal to -7 and less than or equal to 2   **47.** $(-6, 1)$ **48.** $(-\infty, -3) \cup (5, \infty)$

49. $\left(-\infty, -1 - \sqrt{2}\right) \cup \left(-1 + \sqrt{2}, \infty\right)$ **50.** $\left(-\infty, 4 - 3\sqrt{2}\right) \cup \left(4 + 3\sqrt{2}, \infty\right)$ **51.** $\left[-\dfrac{5}{3}, 6\right]$ **52.** $(-\infty, -3] \cup [4, \infty)$

53. $(-\infty, -1] \cup [6, \infty)$ **54.** no solution   **55.** $(-3, 5)$
56. $(-4, 4)$ **57.** $(-\infty, -3.58) \cup (-0.42, \infty)$
58. $(-\infty, -5) \cup (-5, \infty)$ **59.** $(0.88, 5.12)$ **60.** 3
61. $f(x) = x^2 + 2x - 15$ **62. (a)** The domain is $(-\infty, \infty)$. The range is $[-2, \infty)$.   **(b)** x-intercepts: $(1, 0)$ and $(3, 0)$; y-intercept: $(0, 6)$
(c) upward   **(d)** vertex: $(2, -2)$; axis of symmetry: $x = 2$ **(e)** relative minimum of -2 at $x = 2$, relative maximum: none; absolute minimum of -2 at $x = 2$, absolute maximum: none; increasing: $(2, \infty)$, decreasing: $(-\infty, 2)$ **(f)** 1 and 3   **(g)** 1 and 3

63.
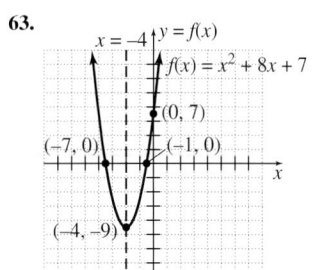

64. The number is about 16 items.   **65.** It will reach the ground in $2 + \sqrt{6}$ seconds or approximately 4.45 seconds.   **66.** It will take $\sqrt{437.5}$ seconds or approximately 20.92 seconds.   **67.** The other leg is 25.5 meters.   **68.** The dimensions are 8 cm by 18 cm.   **69.** The interest rate is 5%.
70. The interest rate is approximately 11.8%.   **71. (a)** $R(x) = x(10.50 - 0.50x)$ **(b)** $C(x) = 7.50x + 3.00$ **(c)** $P(x) = -0.5x^2 + 3x - 3$
(d) The break-even point occurs by selling two baskets at $9.50 or four baskets at $8.50.   **72.** The hypotenuse is 52 inches.   **73.** They each measure $7.105\sqrt{2}$ cm, or approximately 10 cm.   **74.** The rope is $11\sqrt{2}$ feet long, or approximately 15.6 feet.   **75.** The sides measure 16 in. and $16\sqrt{3}$ in., or approximately 27.7 in.   **76.** The booth can be rented up to seven days.   **77.** Let $t = $ time in seconds, $s = $ position in feet above ground, $s = -16t^2 + 55$; the ball will hit the ground in $\dfrac{\sqrt{55}}{4}$ seconds or about 1.85 seconds.   **78.** Let $t = $ time in seconds, $s = $ position in feet above ground, $s = -16t^2 + 50t + 100$; the projectile will be at a height of 90 feet at about 3.31 seconds.   **79.** Let $t = $ time in seconds, $s = $ position in feet above ground, $s = -4.9t^2 - 3t + 30$; the flower pot will be 4 meters above the ground in about 2.02 seconds.   **80.** $(-5, 10)$; Karla is $5\sqrt{5}$ yards or about 11.18 yards.   **81.** In 1999 and 2004, the number of passenger cars imported to the United States from Sweden was about 189,000.   **82.** In 2006, there will be 200,000 grandchildren living with grandparents with both parents present.

83. (a) The height of the ball is about 2.7 meters.   **(b)** The maximum height is about 2.81 meters in about 1.88 seconds.   **(c)** The ball will be at a height of 2.7 meters at 1.5 seconds and 2.25 seconds.   **(d)** The ball will hit the surface in 3.75 seconds.

(e)
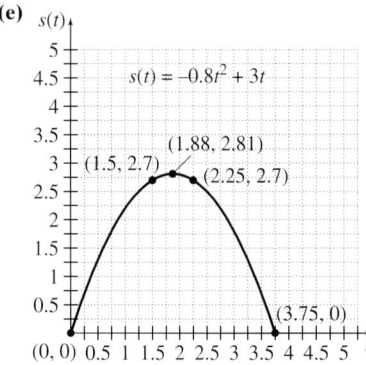

84. (a) $R(x) = 350x - 5x^2$ **(b)** $C(x) = 105x + 2500$
(c) $P(x) = -5x^2 + 245x - 2500$ **(d)** There will be $0 in revenue for 0 computers and 70 computers.   **(e)** The maximum revenue is $6125 for 35 computers.   **(f)** There will be a loss of $50 for 14 computers and 35 computers.   **(g)** The maximum profit is $500 for 24 and 25 computers.
(h) There will be a slight profit of $50 for 15 computers and 34 computers.
(i)
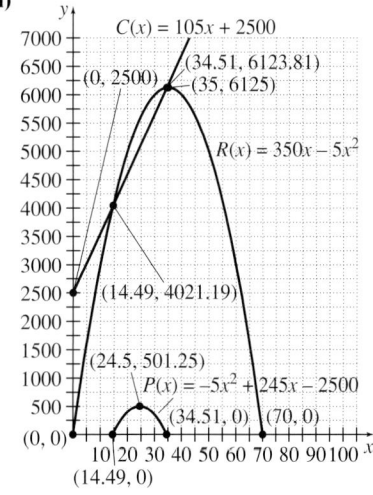

85. Her profit will be between $2000 and $5000 for 31 to 48, inclusive, houses.   **86.** In 2021 and after, the cost will exceed $20,000.
87. Let $x = $ the time in seconds, $s = $ the position of the object in meters, $s = -5x^2 - 2x + 148$; The object is between 90 and 100 meters for time between 2.9 and 3.2 seconds.

CHAPTER 9 TEST

1. $4\sqrt{2}$ **2.** $-1 + \sqrt{5}$ **3.** $\dfrac{3\sqrt{5}}{5}$ **4.** $42\sqrt{3}$ **5.** $\sqrt{15}$

21.

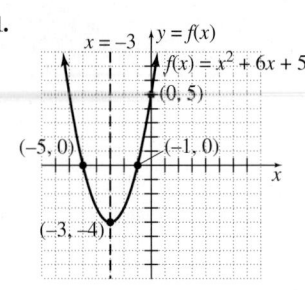

6. $5\sqrt{2}$ **7. (a)** -2 and 3 **(b)** -2 and 3 **(c)** -2 and 3 **8.** -2 and 8
9. $-5.5, -2$, and 3 **10.** no real-number soution **11.** no real-number solution **12.** 0.5 and 4 **13.** -0.82 and 1.82 **14.** $[-3, 4]$

15. $(-3, 5)$ **16.** $(-\infty, -4] \cup \left[\dfrac{5}{2}, \infty\right)$ **17.** 200; two irrational solutions; $8 \pm 5\sqrt{2}$ **18.** -39; no real-number solutions

19. $t = \pm\dfrac{\sqrt{a(s-c)}}{a}$ **20.** $f(x) = 2x^2 + 5x - 3$

22. (a) The domain is $(-\infty, \infty)$. The range is $(-\infty, 4]$. **(b)** x-intercepts: $(-4, 0)$ and $(0, 0)$, y-intercept: $(0, 0)$ **(c)** downward **(d)** vertex: $(-2, 4)$, axis of symmetry: $x = -2$ **(e)** relative maximum of 4 at $x = -2$, relative minimum: none; absolute maximum of 4 at $x = -2$, absolute minimum: none; increasing: $(-\infty, -2)$, decreasing: $(-2, \infty)$ **(f)** -4 and 0 **(g)** -4 and 0 **23.** The legs are 14 in and $14\sqrt{3}$ in, or approximately 24.2 in.
24. The interest rate must be approximately 6%. **25. (a)** $R(x) = x(12.50 - 0.50x)$ **(b)** $C(x) = 9.50x + 3.95$ **(c)** $P(x) = -0.50x^2 + 3x - 3.95$
(d) Break-even point occurs when two arrangements are sold at $11.50 each. **26.** The horizontal distance is $10\sqrt{15}$ feet or about 38.7 feet.
27. The revenue will be more than $135 for the number of customers between 5 and 20. **28.** $(4, 3)$ and $(-3, -2)$; the distance is $\sqrt{74}$ miles or about 8.6 miles; no **29.** Let $t =$ the time in seconds, $s =$ the position in meters, $s = -4.9t^2 + 8t + 2.75$; the ball will be 5 meters above the floor 0.36 second and 1.27 seconds. **30.** Let $t =$ time in seconds, $s =$ the position in feet, $s = -16t^2 + 234$; the ball will reach the surface in about 3.82 seconds.

31. (a) The height after one-half of a second is 28.5 feet. **(b)** The maximum height of 30.39 feet occurs in 0.2 second. **(c)** The diver hits the surface in 1.5 seconds. **(d)** He will be 3 feet below the surface in about 1.6 seconds.

(e)

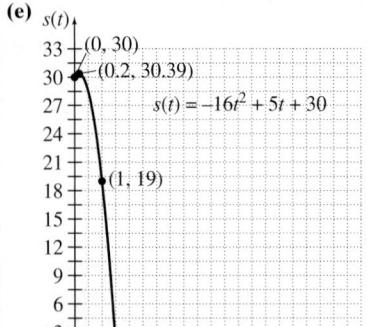

32. (a) $R(x) = 25x - 0.50x^2$ **(b)** $C(x) = 15x + 25$
(c) $P(x) = -0.50x^2 + 10x - 25$ **(d)** There will be $0 in revenue for 0 children and 50 children. **(e)** The maximum revenue is $312.50 for 25 children. **(f)** There will be a loss of $7 for 2 children and 18 children.
(g) The maximum profit is $25 for 10 children. **(h)** There will be a slight profit of $0.50 for 3 children and 17 children.

(i)

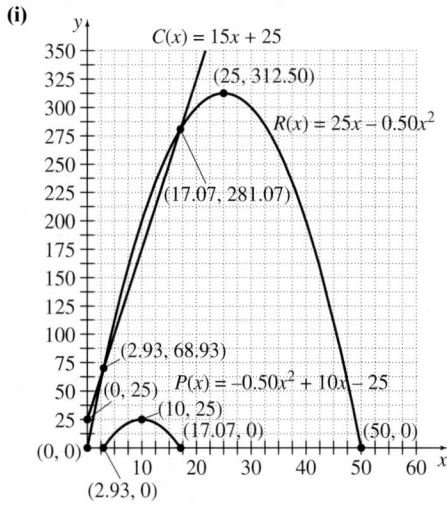

33. Answers will vary.

CHAPTER P–9 CUMULATIVE REVIEW

1. $3a^2 + 4ab - 5b^2$ **2.** $x^2 + xy$ **3.** $6x^2 - 16x - 6$ **4.** $25x^2 + 10x + 1$ **5.** $4x^2 - 9$ **6.** $6.3x^2y^5z^3$ **7.** $\dfrac{6x^2}{y}$ **8.** $\dfrac{1}{2x^2y}$ **9.** $\dfrac{25b^2}{64a^6}$

10. $-8p^5q^2r^2$ **11.** $x + 2 - \dfrac{3}{x}$ **12.** $x - 1$ **13.** -16 **14.** 0.0056 **15.** $-3{,}400{,}000$ **16.** $\dfrac{2A}{h} = b$ **17.** $t = \dfrac{\pm\sqrt{5} - s}{4}$

18. $(x + 5)(x - 3)$ **19.** $(5s - 4)(2s + 3)$ **20.** $(3x - 4)(3x + 4)$ **21.** $(2x + 3)^2$ **22.** $(a + 3)(a^2 - 3a + 9)$ **23.** $2(a + 2)(a - 2)(a^2 + 4)$

24. $x = \dfrac{25}{6}$ $y = \dfrac{11}{6}$ **25.** possible solution: $(1, 2)$

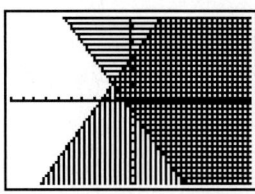

26. 4 and 2 **27.** $2.5 \pm \sqrt{18.25}$ **28.** −3 and 1 **29.** no solution **30.** no real-number solution **31.** 2.64 and −1.14 **32.** $\dfrac{5}{3}$ **33.** all real numbers **34.** no solution **35.** $-\dfrac{3}{2}$ and $\dfrac{5}{2}$ **36.** −3 and 3 **37.** $(-\infty, -9)$ **38.** $(-\infty, -1] \cup [6, \infty)$ **39.** $\left(2 - \sqrt{5}, 2 + \sqrt{5}\right)$

40. (a)

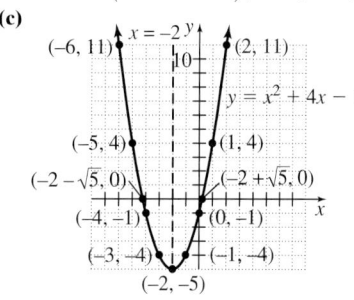

(b) Yes; it passes the vertical-line test. **(c)** Decreasing for all x
(d) Domain is all real numbers; range is all real numbers.
(e) x int: $\left(\dfrac{4}{3}, 0\right)$
  y int: $(0, 4)$

41. (a) x int: $\left(-2 \pm \sqrt{5}, 0\right)$ y int: $(0, -1)$ **(b)** $(-2, -5)$
(c)

(d) Domain is all real numbers; range is $y \geq -5$.

42. $y = 3x - 11$ **43.** $y = \dfrac{3}{2}x + \dfrac{7}{2}$ **44.** He should mix 2 pounds of peanuts with 5 pounds of cashews. **45.** It will take about 2.2 seconds to drop 77 feet. **46.** She should invest $15,000. **47. (a)** $y = -0.6x^2 + 0.9x + 9.5$ **(b)** The profit will drop to $3.5 million in the year 2003.
48. (a) $R(x) = x(3.50 - 0.25x)$ **(b)** $C(x) = 2x + 1.50$ **(c)** $P(x) = -0.25x^2 + 1.50x - 1.50$ **(d)** The break-even points are about 2 and 5. He must sell two sparklers at $3.00 each. **49.** The legs are both $4\sqrt{2}$ meters or about 5.7 meters long. **50.** Janet must score between 68 and 88 inclusive.

CHAPTER 10

SECTION 10.1 EXERCISES

1. rational expression **2.** not a rational expression **3.** rational expression **4.** rational expression **5.** not a rational expression
6. rational expression **7.** rational expression **8.** not a rational expression **9.** rational expression **10.** not a rational expression
11. rational expression **12.** rational expression **13.** rational expression **14.** rational expression **15.** not a rational expression
16. rational expression **17.** 0; $x \neq 0$ **18.** −5 and −3; $x \neq -5, x \neq -3$ **19.** 5 and 6; $x \neq 5, x \neq 6$ **20.** −3 and 0; $x \neq -3, x \neq 0$
21. −2 and 2; $x \neq -2, x \neq 2$ **22.** −1, 1, and 4; $x \neq -1, x \neq 1, x \neq 4$ **23.** 0 and 5; $x \neq 0, x \neq 5$ **24.** 0; $x \neq 0$ **25.** 2; $x \neq 2$
26. −2; $x \neq -2$ **27.** −5 and $-\dfrac{7}{2}$; $x \neq -5, x \neq -\dfrac{7}{2}$ **28.** $-\dfrac{3}{5}$; $x \neq -\dfrac{3}{5}$ **29.** $-\dfrac{3}{2}$ and $\dfrac{3}{4}$; $x \neq -\dfrac{3}{2}, x \neq \dfrac{3}{4}$
30. −5, −4, and 4; $x \neq -5, x \neq -4, x \neq 4$ **31.** $-\dfrac{9}{2}$; $x \neq -\dfrac{9}{2}$ **32.** $-\dfrac{9}{7}$ and $-\dfrac{1}{2}$; $x \neq -\dfrac{9}{7}, x \neq -\dfrac{1}{2}$ **33.** 11; $x \neq 11$ **34.** no restricted values; all real numbers **35.** $-\dfrac{5}{3}$ and $\dfrac{5}{3}$; $x \neq -\dfrac{5}{3}, x \neq \dfrac{5}{3}$ **36.** −3 and $\dfrac{5}{6}$; $x \neq -3, x \neq \dfrac{5}{6}$ **37.** −3, −2, and 3; $x \neq -3, x \neq -2, x \neq 3$
38. $-\dfrac{7}{4}$ and $\dfrac{7}{4}$; $x \neq -\dfrac{7}{4}, x \neq \dfrac{7}{4}$ **39.** no restricted values; all real numbers **40.** $\dfrac{4}{3}$; $x \neq \dfrac{4}{3}$ **41.** $-\dfrac{3}{2}$; $x \neq -\dfrac{3}{2}$ **42.** $-\dfrac{3}{2}$ and $\dfrac{6}{5}$; $x \neq -\dfrac{3}{2}, x \neq \dfrac{6}{5}$

43.

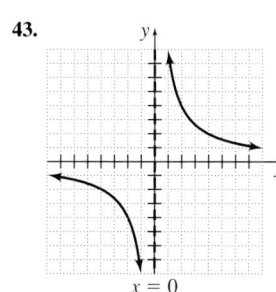

$x = 0$

44.

$x = 0$

45.

$x = 0$

46.

$x = 0$

47.

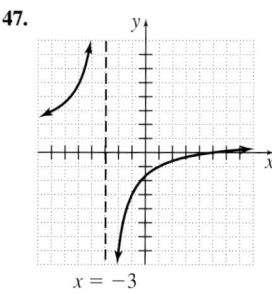

$x = -3$

48.

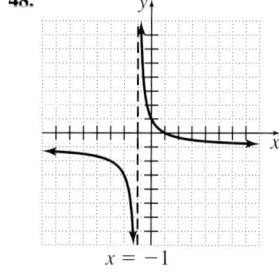

$x = -1$

49.

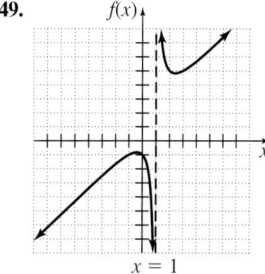

$x = 1$

50.

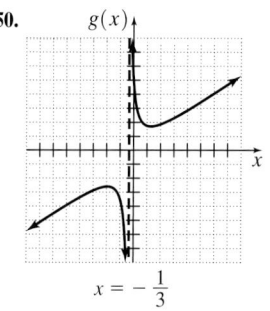

$x = -\dfrac{1}{3}$

51.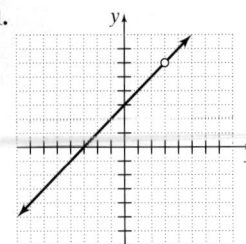

52.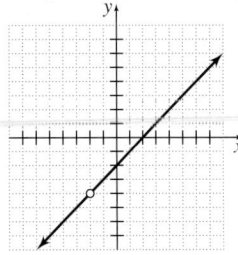

53.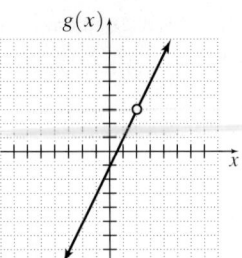

54.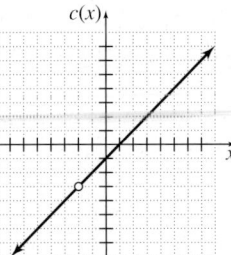

55.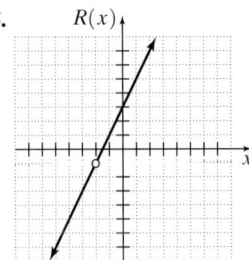

56.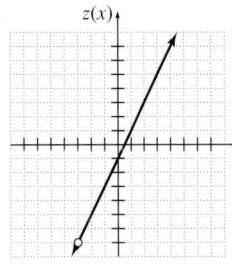

57.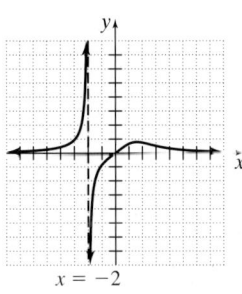

58.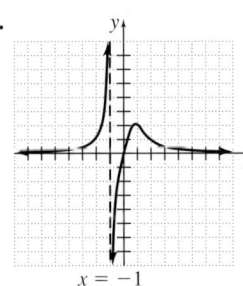

59.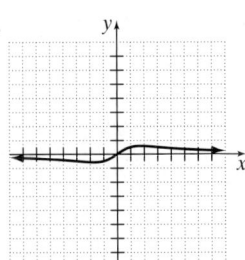

60.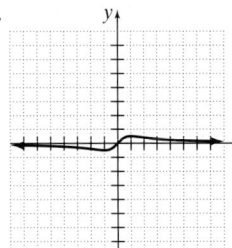

61.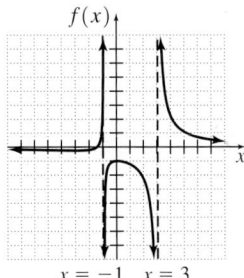

62.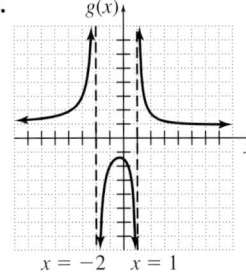

63. (a) The domain is
$(-\infty, -2) \cup (-2, 2) \cup (2, \infty)$.

(b)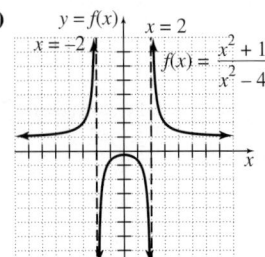

(c) The relative maximum of $-\dfrac{1}{4}$ at $x = 0$.

64. (a) The domain is
$(-\infty, -2) \cup (-2, 2) \cup (2, \infty)$.

(b)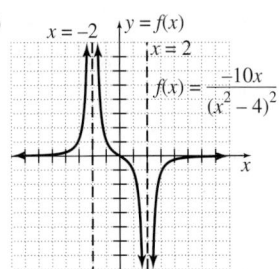

(c) There is no relative maximum or relative minimum.

65. (a) $C_{ave}(x) = \dfrac{6500 + 100x + 25x^2}{x}$

(b) The minimum average cost per year would be about \$906.25, when $x = 16$.

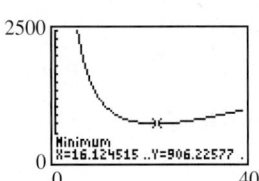

(c) The customer would want to buy a new system after 16 years.

66. (a) $C_{ave}(x) = \dfrac{10{,}000 + 900x + 300x^2}{x}$

(b) The minimum average cost per year would be about \$4364.10, when $x = 5.8$.

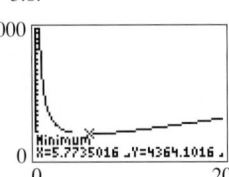

(c) After about five years and nine months, the customer would want to buy a new copier.

67. (a) $P_{ave}(x) = \dfrac{-0.02x^2 + 12x - 100}{x}$

(b)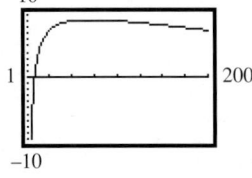

(c) The maximum average profit is approximately \$9.17 per player when 71 compact disc players are produced and sold.

68. (a) $P_{ave}(x) = \dfrac{-0.02x^2 + 20x - 320}{x}$

(b)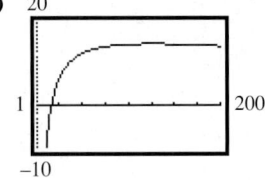

(c) The maximum average profit is approximately \$14.94 per lawn mower when 126 lawn mowers are produced and sold.

69. The domain is $(0, \infty)$. The maximum volume is 96.225 cubic inches when the square base is 5.77 inches on a side.   **70.** The domain is $(0, \infty)$.

The maximum volume is 144 cubic inches when the width of the base is 4 inches.   **71. (a)** $A(x) = \dfrac{D(x)}{N(x)} = \dfrac{1961x^2 - 6374x + 5564}{68x^2 - 257x + 288}$

(b) In 2004, the average number of days missed per worker was at a maximum of 33 days. In 2002, the average number of days per worker was at a minimum of 7 days.   **72. (a)** $A(x) = \dfrac{E(x)}{N(x)} = \dfrac{-0.79x^2 + 15.24x + 478.75}{-0.15x + 34.17}$ **(b)** In 2011, the average earnings per hour will be a maximum of \$16.94. In 2000, the average earnings per hour will be a minimum of \$14.01.   **73. (a)** $C(x) = 88.5x^2 - 215.5x + 5859$ **(b)** $T(x) = 102.5x^2 - 256.5x + 7038$

(c) $R(x) = \dfrac{C(x)}{T(x)} = \dfrac{88.5x^2 - 215.5x + 5859}{102.5x^2 - 256.5x + 7038}$ **(d)** In 2003, the percentage is 83.6%. In 2000, the minimum percent of 83.2% occurred. In 2025, the maximum percent of 86.7% will occur.   **74. (a)** $T(x) = -908.5x^2 - 633.5x + 88{,}153$ **(b)** $E(x) = -5480x^2 + 11{,}272 + 106{,}262$

(c) $R(x) = \dfrac{T(x)}{E(x)} = \dfrac{-908.5x^2 - 633.5x + 88{,}153}{-5480x^2 + 11{,}272 + 106{,}262}$ **(d)** In 2002, the minimum percent from transportation was 76.8%. In 2005, the percent will exceed 100%.

10.1 CALCULATOR EXERCISES

1. (window: $-5, 5, 1, -10, 10, 5, 1$)   **2.** (window: $-2, 2, 1, -10, 10, 5, 1$)   **3.** (window: $-2, 2, 1, -5, 5, 1, 1$)

SECTION 10.2 EXERCISES

1. $\dfrac{2xz}{3y^3}$ **2.** $\dfrac{3y^3}{5x^2z^2}$ **3.** $-\dfrac{2a}{3c}$ **4.** $-\dfrac{11b^3c}{8a^2}$ **5.** $\dfrac{3(x-3)}{2(3x-1)}$ **6.** $\dfrac{2(x+2)}{3(2x+1)}$ **7.** -1 **8.** -1 **9.** $\dfrac{y(x+2y)}{3-4x}$ **10.** $\dfrac{x(5-3x)}{y(2x+y)}$

11. $\dfrac{-2x+3y-z}{x-7y+z}$ **12.** $\dfrac{-x+4y-2z}{2x-y+z}$ **13.** $\dfrac{x-2}{x-4}$ **14.** $\dfrac{x-3}{x-7}$ **15.** $\dfrac{x-3}{x+7}$ **16.** $\dfrac{x+8}{x-5}$ **17.** $\dfrac{x+2}{x-4}$ **18.** $\dfrac{x+5}{x-9}$ **19.** $\dfrac{3x-2}{2x-3}$

20. $\dfrac{5x-4}{4x-5}$ **21.** $\dfrac{(x+1)(2x+1)}{2(x-2)(3x+1)}$ **22.** $\dfrac{2(x+1)(2x-1)}{3(x+2)(3x-1)}$ **23.** $\dfrac{2x-y}{3x+y}$ **24.** $\dfrac{5x-y}{4x+y}$ **25.** $-\dfrac{1}{x+2}$ **26.** $-\dfrac{1}{x+3}$ **27.** $\dfrac{2x+3}{x^2+11}$

28. $\dfrac{3x+4}{x^2+9}$ **29.** $\dfrac{28ac}{45b}$ **30.** $\dfrac{9a^2}{10b^2d^2}$ **31.** $-\dfrac{3x^2}{4}$ **32.** $-\dfrac{2y^2}{13x^2}$ **33.** $\dfrac{8.06x^3}{y^2}$ **34.** $\dfrac{21x^2y}{2z}$ **35.** $\dfrac{2a^2}{9b}$ **36.** $\dfrac{14a^3}{15b^2}$ **37.** $\dfrac{x^2(x+5)}{x+4}$

38. $\dfrac{x(x+15)}{x-11}$ **39.** $\dfrac{x-4}{x+4}$ **40.** $\dfrac{x+7}{x-7}$ **41.** $\dfrac{(x+7)(5x+2)}{x(2x+1)}$ **42.** $\dfrac{(3x+5)(x+4)}{x(2x+9)}$ **43.** $\dfrac{(x-3)(x-1)}{(x+1)(x+3)}$ **44.** $\dfrac{(x+5)(x+2)}{(x-2)(x-5)}$

45. $\dfrac{x(x-2y)}{(x+3y)(x-y)}$ **46.** $\dfrac{y(x+y)}{(x+2y)(x+5y)}$ **47.** $\dfrac{3a^2}{2}$ **48.** $\dfrac{7a}{8b}$ **49.** $-3xyz$ **50.** $-\dfrac{3}{x^2y^2z}$ **51.** $\dfrac{4c}{b}$ **52.** $3ab^2c^2$ **53.** $-\dfrac{7x}{yz^3}$

54. $-\dfrac{2x}{y^3z^2}$ **55.** $\dfrac{1}{5(3a-1)}$ **56.** $\dfrac{7}{6a+1}$ **57.** $(x-4)(5y+2)$ **58.** $(x-7)(4y-3)$ **59.** $\dfrac{(2x+1)(x-3)}{(x+2)(3x+1)}$ **60.** $\dfrac{(x-4)^2}{(x-1)(3x+2)}$

61. $\dfrac{1}{2x+1}$ **62.** $\dfrac{1}{3x-2}$ **63.** $\dfrac{3x+4}{2x+1}$ **64.** $\dfrac{5x-2}{2x-5}$ **65.** $\dfrac{x+7}{3x-5}$ **66.** $\dfrac{5(2x+1)}{7(4x+3)}$ **67.** $\dfrac{x(x-y)}{y(x+y)}$ **68.** $\dfrac{y(x+2y)}{x(x-2y)}$ **69.** $\dfrac{2(x+2y)}{x-4y}$

70. $\dfrac{4(x+7y)}{3(x-2y)}$ **71.** $\dfrac{170}{x}$ hours; $(x-10)\left(\dfrac{170}{x}\right)$ miles; the distance is 136 miles.   **72.** $\dfrac{155}{x}$ hours; $(x+8)\left(\dfrac{155}{x}\right)$ miles; the distance is $182\dfrac{5}{9}$ miles.

73. $w(x) = \dfrac{10x^3 - 11x - 6x}{2x - 3}$; $w(x) = 5x^2 + 2x$; the width is 259 yards.   **74.** $b(x) = \dfrac{18x^3 + 39x^2 + 15x}{3x + 5}$; $b(x) = 6x^2 + 3x$; the height is 315 feet.

75. $L = \dfrac{V}{WH}$; the length is $(5x - 1)$ inches; height: 4 inches; width: 14 inches; length: 19 inches   **76.** $h = \dfrac{V}{\pi r^2}$; the height is $(6x - 5)$ inches; the height is 4 inches.   **77.** $m(x) = 500(1 + x + x^2)$; the total amount that Sharon's grandson received was \$1820.   **78.** $s(x) = 50{,}000(1 + x + x^2)$; the total amount of Alexandra's sales was \$190,625.   **79. (a)** $C(x) = 300 + 5x$; $R(x) = 25x$ **(b)** $\dfrac{5x}{60 + x}$ **(c)** The ratio is 2.

80. (a) $C(x) = 175 + 25x$; $R(x) = 75x$ **(b)** $\dfrac{7 + x}{3x}$ **(c)** The ratio is $\dfrac{57}{150} = \dfrac{19}{50}$.   **81.** $\dfrac{1225}{r(5r + 2)}$ **82.** $\dfrac{16(r - 2)}{15r}$ **83.** $\dfrac{16(3g + 2)}{27g}$ **84.** $\dfrac{(w - 4)(t + 7)}{11t}$

10.2 CALCULATOR EXERCISES

Value of n	Original Function	Simplified Function
2	$y = \dfrac{(1 - x^2)}{(1 - x)}$	$y = 1 + x$
3	$y = \dfrac{(1 - x^3)}{(1 - x)}$	$y = 1 + x + x^2$
4	$y = \dfrac{(1 - x^4)}{(1 - x)}$	$y = 1 + x + x^2 + x^3$
5	$y = \dfrac{(1 - x^5)}{(1 - x)}$	$y = 1 + x + x^2 + x^3 + x^4$
6	$y = \dfrac{(1 - x^6)}{(1 - x)}$	$y = 1 + x + x^2 + x^3 + x^4 + x^5$

SECTION 10.3 EXERCISES

1. $\dfrac{13}{x}$ 2. $\dfrac{12}{x}$ 3. $\dfrac{1}{y}$ 4. $\dfrac{1}{a}$ 5. $\dfrac{2x}{x+6}$ 6. $\dfrac{3x}{x+12}$ 7. $\dfrac{2}{b-5}$ 8. $\dfrac{3}{z-7}$ 9. 3   10. 4   11. $-\dfrac{5}{d}$ 12. $-\dfrac{8}{b}$ 13. $\dfrac{1}{x}$ 14. $-\dfrac{1}{y}$

15. $\dfrac{x}{x+9}$ 16. $\dfrac{3(x-1)}{x+8}$ 17. 2   18. 2   19. $\dfrac{-x+11}{x+11}$ 20. $\dfrac{2x+9}{x+13}$ 21. $z-4$ 22. $c-7$ 23. $\dfrac{3}{c+3}$ 24. $\dfrac{5}{b+2}$

25. $\dfrac{2(x+2)}{2x+3}$ 26. $\dfrac{-2x+3}{3x-4}$ 27. $-\dfrac{3}{x}$ 28. $\dfrac{6}{x}$ 29. 2   30. 3   31. $a+3$ 32. $5+c$ 33. $\dfrac{5}{x+3}$ 34. $\dfrac{7}{x+1}$ 35. $\dfrac{9x+7}{6x^2}$

36. $\dfrac{3(6x+1)}{10x^3}$ 37. $\dfrac{7x-2}{2(x-6)}$ 38. $\dfrac{5x-4}{2(x+9)}$ 39. $\dfrac{2x+3}{2x-3}$ 40. $\dfrac{2x-3}{5x+2}$ 41. $\dfrac{3(11x+5)}{(3x-5)(3x+5)}$ 42. $\dfrac{6(4x-1)}{(2x-3)(2x+3)}$ 43. $\dfrac{2(4x-17)}{(x-5)^2}$

44. $\dfrac{5x-12}{(x-8)^2}$ 45. $\dfrac{2(b^2+8b+32)}{b(b+8)}$ 46. $\dfrac{5a^2-6a+9}{2a(a-3)}$ 47. $\dfrac{x^2+3x+10}{4(x+3)(x-3)}$ 48. $\dfrac{2x^2-2x-1}{3(x+2)(x-2)}$ 49. $\dfrac{2(11x+2)}{(x+5)(x-3)(x+4)}$

50. $\dfrac{-x^2+6x-2}{(x+7)(x+1)(x-2)}$ 51. $\dfrac{a^2+5ab-b^2}{a^2b^2}$ 52. $\dfrac{p^2+q^2}{p^2q^2}$ 53. $\dfrac{3x-4y}{x-2y}$ 54. $\dfrac{x-3y}{5x-y}$ 55. $\dfrac{11x-16y}{(x-3y)(x+3y)}$

56. $\dfrac{2(8x+11y)}{(2x-3y)(2x+3y)}$ 57. $\dfrac{2(5x-9z)}{(x+3z)^2(x-3z)}$ 58. $\dfrac{4(2x+y)}{(x+2y)^2(x-2y)}$ 59. $\dfrac{4(2x+1)}{x-2}$ 60. $\dfrac{3x+1}{x-7}$ 61. $\dfrac{3}{x-2}$ 62. $\dfrac{5}{a-6}$

63. $\dfrac{x}{x+5}$ 64. $\dfrac{8x+17}{3(2x+3)}$ 65. $\dfrac{-4(x-20)}{(2x-5)(2x+5)}$ 66. $\dfrac{15x+13}{(3x-1)(3x+1)}$ 67. $\dfrac{-x(2x+13)}{(x+6)^2}$ 68. $\dfrac{-x^2+11x-25}{(x-7)^2}$ 69. $\dfrac{16(x-4)}{x(8-x)}$

70. $\dfrac{-20(x-5)}{x(x-10)}$ 71. $\dfrac{x-1}{3(x+4)}$ 72. $\dfrac{-2x+27}{x(x+3)(x-3)}$ 73. $\dfrac{15b+34}{(b+3)(b-3)(2b+5)}$ 74. $\dfrac{19a-31}{(a-5)(a+5)(2a+1)}$ 75. $\dfrac{14a-15b-15a^2b}{10a^2b^2}$

76. $\dfrac{15y-4xy-56x}{48x^2y^2}$ 77. $\dfrac{3(p-q)}{p+3q}$ 78. $\dfrac{x+3z}{x+5z}$ 79. $\dfrac{5x-27y}{(x+3y)^2(x-3y)}$ 80. $\dfrac{5(x-11y)}{(x+5y)^2(x-5y)}$ 81. $\dfrac{x-4}{x-5}$ 82. $\dfrac{2z+3}{z+9}$

83. $\dfrac{2x+1}{x+10}$ 84. $\dfrac{10x+3}{3x+1}$ 85. $\dfrac{10x+31}{2x+7}$ 86. $\dfrac{4}{x+4}$ 87. $\dfrac{x-10}{x+7}$ 88. $\dfrac{-31x+16}{9x-2}$ 89. $\dfrac{x^2+8x+18}{x+3}$ 90. $\dfrac{x^2+4x+5}{x+1}$

91. $\dfrac{2x^2-7x-7}{x-4}$ 92. $\dfrac{-10x(2x-1)}{4x-1}$ 93. (a) The total width is $\dfrac{65}{L}$ feet.   (b) The total width is $\dfrac{5(17L-20)}{L(2L-5)}$ feet.   94. (a) The difference is $\dfrac{8}{L}$ inches.   (b) The difference is $\dfrac{4(4L-15)}{L(2L+5)}$ inches.   95. The perimeter is $\dfrac{96(2x-1)}{(x-1)(x+1)}$ feet.   96. The perimeter is $\dfrac{x^2+246x+117}{2x(x+3)}$ inches.

97. (a) $T(x)=\dfrac{26}{x}+\dfrac{110}{x+20}$

(b)

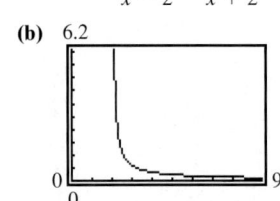

98. (a) $T(x)=\dfrac{1}{x-2}+\dfrac{1}{x+2}$

(b) 6.2

(c) The total time is approximately 6.7 hours.
(d) The average speeds for running and bicycling are approximately 6.6 mph and 26.6 mph, respectively.

(c) It will take approximately 2.2 hours.
(d) He should swim at approximately 2.8 mph.

99. The average speed is 29.2 mph.   100. The average speed is 111.1 mph.   101. $\dfrac{134r+50}{r(5r+2)}$ 102. $\dfrac{17g+15}{g(2g+3)}$ 103. $\dfrac{-14t+7w+wt-35}{t(t+7)}$

104. $\dfrac{-40(r+4)}{r(r-2)}$ 105. (a) $\dfrac{C(x)}{T(x)}=\dfrac{-2.5x^2+5.5x+34}{-2.5x^2+4.5x+40}$ (b) $\dfrac{P(x)}{T(x)}=\dfrac{-3x^2+7x+31}{-2.5x^2+4.5x+40}$ (c) $\dfrac{-5.5x^2+12.5x+65}{-2.5x^2+4.5x+40}$

106. (a) $\dfrac{C(x)}{P(x)}=\dfrac{-0.39x+23.48}{-0.105x^2+0.065x+71.22}$ (b) $\dfrac{N(x)}{P(x)}=\dfrac{-0.17x+8.48}{-0.105x^2+0.065x+71.22}$ (c) $\dfrac{-0.22x+15}{-0.105x^2+0.065x+71.22}$ 107. (a) Let $S_1(x)=$ the PE ratio for the first toy industry, $S_2(x)=$ the PE ratio for the second toy industry, $S_1(x)=\dfrac{9.31x+27.27}{0.35x+1.9}$, $S_2(x)=\dfrac{12.18x+14.81}{0.26x+0.96}$

(b) $\dfrac{-1.8424x^2-12.2977x-1.9598}{(0.35x+1.9)(0.26x+0.96)}$ 108. (a) Let $S_1(x)=$ the PE ratio for the first computer industry, $S_2(x)=$ the PE ratio for the second

computer industry, $S_1(x)=\dfrac{6.38x+23.82}{0.13x+1.29}$, $S_2(x)=\dfrac{30.59x+14.85}{0.21x+1.41}$ (b) $\dfrac{-2.6369x^2-27.3936x+14.4297}{(0.13x+1.29)(0.21x+1.41)}$

10.3 CALCULATOR EXERCISES

Students should use the method described to check the equivalent expressions.

SECTION 10.4 EXERCISES

1. rational   2. not rational   3. rational   4. not rational   5. not rational   6. rational   7. not rational   8. rational   9. rational

10. rational   11. rational   12. rational   13. $\dfrac{9}{11}$ 14. $\dfrac{63}{8}$ 15. 8   16. -24 17. 18   18. 14   19. -7 20. $\dfrac{3}{2}$ 21. 5   22. $\dfrac{19}{3}$

23. 9   **24.** −5   **25.** 7   **26.** 11   **27.** $\dfrac{3}{4}$ **28.** $\dfrac{4}{7}$ **29.** 1   **30.** −2 and 5   **31.** ±4   **32.** ±9   **33.** ±7   **34.** ±8   **35.** −2 and 5

36. −7 and 4   **37.** 4 and 8   **38.** 1 and 6   **39.** −4 and 9   **40.** −3 and 5   **41.** 7   **42.** 6   **43.** $\dfrac{1}{2}$ and 8   **44.** −5   **45.** −15   **46.** $\dfrac{56}{11}$

47. $\pm\dfrac{1}{3}$ **48.** $\pm\dfrac{1}{4}$ **49.** −6 and 10   **50.** −7 and 2   **51.** no solution   **52.** no solution   **53.** 11   **54.** −8   **55.** 5   **56.** −7 and 6

57. −9 and 1   **58.** −9   **59.** −4 and 8   **60.** −3 and 5   **61.** all real numbers not equal to 1   **62.** no solution   **63.** no solution

64. all real numbers not equal to 6   **65.** $-\dfrac{11}{2}$ and 6   **66.** −11 and 3   **67.** approximately −2.8117 and 2.3117   **68.** approximately −6.6714

and 5.1714   **69.** approximately −2.5811 and 0.5811   **70.** approximately −1.5774 and −0.4226   **71.** $w = -1$ and $w = \pm\sqrt{2}$

72. $v = 3$ and $v = \pm\sqrt{5}$ **73.** approximately −0.3024 and 1.2399   **74.** approximately −0.2758 and 3.4187   **75.** no solution   **76.** no solution

77. no solution   **78.** no solution   **79.** all real numbers except $b = 2$ and $b = 1$.   **80.** all real numbers except $x = -\dfrac{3}{2}$ and $x = 2$.

81. all integers not equal to −1 or 1.   **82.** all integers not equal to −3 or 3.   **83.** nonreal solutions   **84.** nonreal solutions   **85.** The interest on the first account is 6.5% and on the second account is 4.5%.   **86.** The first investment was for 2 years and the second for 3.5 years.   **87.** The focal

length needed is 60 millimeters.   **88.** The focal length needed is 30 millimeters.   **89. (a)** The length is $\dfrac{7 + 7\sqrt{5}}{2}$ feet or approximately 11.326 feet.

The width is 7 feet.   **(b)** The length is 13 centimeters. The width is $\dfrac{-13 + 13\sqrt{5}}{2}$ centimeters or approximately 8.03 centimeters.   **90. (a)** The height

is 7 feet. The base is $\dfrac{7 + 7\sqrt{5}}{2}$ feet or approximately 11.326 feet.   **(b)** The height is $\dfrac{-5 + 5\sqrt{5}}{2}$ inches or approximately 3.090 inches. The base is 5 feet.

91. (a) The dimensions are 7 feet by approximately 11.326 feet.   **(b)** The dimensions are approximately 4.854 meters by approximately 7.854 feet.
92. (a) The dimensions are approximately 7 feet by approximately 11.326 feet.   **(b)** The dimensions are approximately 4.854 meters by approximately
7.854 feet.   **93.** In 2009, the PE ratio will be 33.5.   **94.** In 2010, the PE ratio will be 30.   **95.** The resistance of the second vessel is 26.2 dynes.
96. The constant for the second spring is 2 pounds per square inch.   **97.** The radii are 12 meters and 2 meters.   **98.** The radii are 32 meters and

30 meters.   **99. (a)** $\dfrac{M(x)}{C(x)} = \dfrac{167x + 15{,}870}{549x + 11{,}876{,}120}$ **(b)** $\dfrac{R(x)}{C(x)} = \dfrac{-2920x + 426{,}477}{549x + 11{,}876{,}120}$ **(c)** The sum of the ratios will be equal to 0.031 in 2027.

100. (a) $\dfrac{B(x)}{C(x)} = \dfrac{35{,}344x + 2{,}081{,}187}{549x + 11{,}876{,}120}$ **(b)** $\dfrac{P(x)}{C(x)} = \dfrac{13{,}704x + 10{,}423{,}485}{549x + 11{,}876{,}120}$ **(c)** The ratio of property crimes to the number of crimes committed will be

0.671 more than the ratio of burglaries to the number of crimes committed in 2017.

10.4 CALCULATOR EXERCISES

1. $x = 7$ **2.** $c = 10$ and $c = \dfrac{1}{2}$ **3.** $x = 2$ **4.** $k = \dfrac{4}{5}$ **5.** $h = \dfrac{5}{3}$ **6.** $z = -4$ and $z = -1$

SECTION 10.5 EXERCISES

1. It will take them 1.75 hours working together.   **2.** It will take them 18 minutes working together.   **3.** It takes Jacques 10 hours and Simone 5 hours.   **4.** It will take Joe about 2.58 hours and Mary Lynne about 3.58 hours.   **5.** It will take 3.6 hours working together.   **6.** It will take 9.375 minutes working together.   **7.** It will take approximately 2.55 hours for both pipes together.   **8.** It will take 3 hours to drain when both are used.
9. It takes Line A 8 hours and Line B 12 hours.   **10.** It will take the first line about 8.3 hours and the second line about 9.8 hours.   **11.** There must

be an additional 15 points.   **12.** Another $\dfrac{1}{3}$ liter of pure vinegar should be added.   **13.** They should raise and spend $27.27.   **14.** He must raise

another $50.   **15.** His average rate is approximately 17.405 miles per hour.   **16.** Her average rate is approximately 38.734 miles per hour.
17. The average rate is approximately 2.536 miles per hour.   **18.** Her average rate is approximately 1.029 miles per hour.   **19.** XY measures 4
inches; PR measures 18 inches.   **20.** MN measures 2 mm; KL measures 28 mm.   **21.** PQ measures 10.075 cm; YZ measures 1.76 cm.   **22.** JK
measures 16.56 yards; MO measures 18.3 yards.   **23.** $MN = 12$; $AB = 16$ **24.** $AB = 5.625$; $AC = 6.25$ **25.** $CA = 10$; $BU = 5$; $CR = 8$;
$BG = 4$ **26.** $CA = 10$; $DO = 5$; $AT = 6$; $OG = 3$ **27.** The estimated height is 48 feet.   **28.** The flag pole is 15 feet high.

29. $r = \dfrac{v^2}{a}$ **30.** $m = \dfrac{kF}{a}$ **31.** $v = \sqrt{\dfrac{Fr}{m}}$ or $\dfrac{\sqrt{Frm}}{m}$ **32.** $t = \sqrt{\dfrac{2s}{a}}$ or $\dfrac{\sqrt{2sa}}{a}$ **33.** $w_0 = w_t - at$ **34.** $v_t = \dfrac{F_t + mv_0}{m}$

35. $w = v - em + en$; $n = \dfrac{em - v + w}{e}$ **36.** $v = em - en + w$; $m = \dfrac{v - w + en}{e}$ **37.** $G = \dfrac{4\pi^2 a^3}{MT}$ **38.** $D = \sqrt{\dfrac{kq_1 q_2}{F}}$ or $\dfrac{\sqrt{Fkq_1 q_2}}{F}$

39. The resistance of the resistors is 10 ohms and 15 ohms, respectively.   **40.** The resistance of the resistors is 5 ohms and 20 ohms, respectively.

10.5 CALCULATOR EXERCISES

1. $x = -4$ and $x = 3$ **2.** $x = \dfrac{3 \pm \sqrt{57}}{2}$ or $x \approx 5.27$ and $x \approx -2.27$ **3.** $x = -\dfrac{6}{5}$ and $x = 4$

CHAPTER 10 SUMMARY

Vocabulary Review

1. rational expression   **2.** restricted value   **3.** rational equation in one variable   **4.** extraneous solution   **5.** rate
6. corresponding angles; corresponding sides

Reflections

1–6. Answers will vary.

CHAPTER 10 SECTION-BY-SECTION REVIEW

1. rational expression **2.** nonrational expression **3.** rational expression **4.** rational expression **5.** $0; x \neq 0$

6. -8 and $3; x \neq -8, x \neq 3$ **7.** no restricted values; all real numbers **8.** $\pm\frac{3}{2}; x \neq -\frac{3}{2}, x \neq \frac{3}{2}$

9.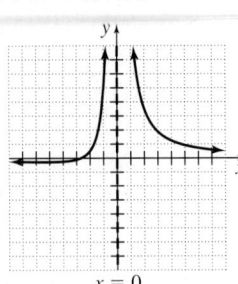

$x = 0$

10.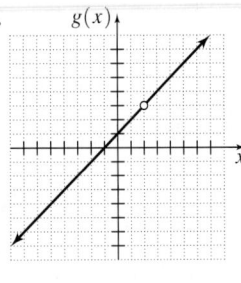

11.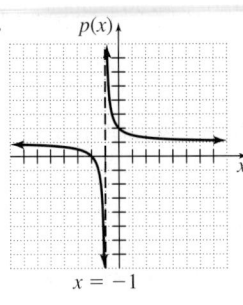

$x = -1$

12.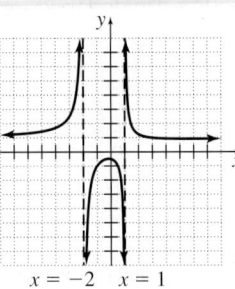

$x = -2 \quad x = 1$

13. (a) $C_{ave}(x) = \dfrac{1800 + 100x + 25x^2}{x}$

(b) 5000

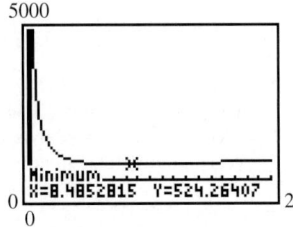

The minimum is 524.27 at $x = 8.5$.
This means that the minimum
average cost per year is $524.27.

(c) After $8\frac{1}{2}$ years, the cash register should be replaced.

14. (a) The domain is $(-\infty, -3) \cup (-3, 3) \cup (3, \infty)$.

(b)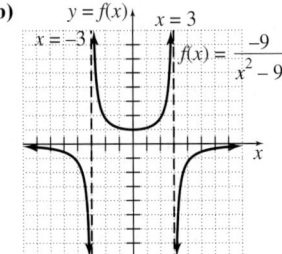

$f(x) = \dfrac{-9}{x^2 - 9}$

(c) The relative minimum of 1 at $x = 0$.

15. The domain is $(0, \infty)$. The maximum volume is approximately 769.8 cubic inches. **16. (a)** $R(x) = \dfrac{N(x)}{L(x)} = \dfrac{-63.5x^2 - 51.5x + 16,502}{594x^2 - 2438x + 124,326}$

(b) In 2005, the ratio of the number of union members to the number of people in the labor force is 0.12 or 12%. On this domain, the absolute maximum percentage in 2000 is 13% or the ratio is 0.13, and the minimum absolute percentage in 2010 is 6% or the ratio is 0.06.

17. (a) $C(x) = -42x + 2214.667$ **(b)** $T(x) = 4x^2 + 16x + 10,521$ **(c)** $R(x) = \dfrac{C(x)}{T(x)} = \dfrac{-42x + 2214.667}{4x^2 + 16x + 10,521}$ **(d)** On this domain, the maximum

percent is 21% in the year 2000; the minimum percent is 9% in the year 2025. The number of country format stations is decreasing. **18.** $-\dfrac{4x}{9y^2}$

19. $\dfrac{p - 3}{3p + 5}$ **20.** $-\dfrac{1}{2x}$ **21.** $\dfrac{2x - 5}{4x + 1}$ **22.** $\dfrac{b - 7}{b^2 + 2}$ **23.** $-\dfrac{3y}{14x^2}$ **24.** $\dfrac{(a + 5)(a + 1)}{a - 4}$ **25.** $\dfrac{4}{(m + 5)(2m + 7)}$ **26.** -1 **27.** $-\dfrac{x}{6y^2}$

28. $-\dfrac{1}{15}$ **29.** $-\dfrac{6yz^2}{5x}$ **30.** $\dfrac{6a^3b^3}{c^3d^2}$ **31.** $\dfrac{(x + 3)(x + 1)^2}{5(x - 2)}$ **32.** $\dfrac{3x}{2z^4}$ **33.** $14ac^2$ **34.** $\dfrac{x + 2}{x^2 + 4}$ **35.** $(x + 1)(2x + 3)$ **36.** $\dfrac{(a + 3)(a + 4)}{(a + 6)(a + 2)}$

37. 1 **38.** His average speed is $\dfrac{220}{t}$ mph; his new distance is $\dfrac{110(t + 2)}{t}$ miles. **39.** $H = \dfrac{V}{LW}$; the height is $(x + 3)$ inches.

40. (a) $C(x) = 500 + 40x; R(x) = 80x$ **(b)** The ratio is $\dfrac{25 + 2x}{4x}$. **41.** $w(x) = \dfrac{6x^3 - 13x^2 - 5x}{2x - 5}; w(x) = 3x^2 + x$; the width is 114 feet.

42. (a) $\dfrac{416}{t(t + 3)}$ **(b)** $\dfrac{8(t + 3)}{13t}$ **43.** $\dfrac{y(3 + 7y)}{5x}$ **44.** $\dfrac{b(5b^2 - 2)}{7a}$ **45.** 2 **46.** $\dfrac{10x^2 + 10x + 3}{(2x - 3)(2x + 3)}$ **47.** $\dfrac{12y + 7x}{15x^3y^2}$ **48.** $\dfrac{x(7x + 4)}{(x - 8)(x + 4)}$

49. $\dfrac{44}{(2x - 1)(x + 5)}$ **50.** $\dfrac{3}{x - y}$ **51.** $\dfrac{2(13x + 4)}{5(3x - 4)(3x + 4)}$ **52.** $\dfrac{29x - 3}{(2x + 1)(x - 3)(3x - 2)}$ **53.** $\dfrac{x + 55}{2(x - 9)(x + 9)}$

54. $\dfrac{10(2x - 1)}{(2x - 3)(x + 2)(3x - 2)}$ **55.** $\dfrac{5(x - 9)}{(x + 5)(x - 5)}$ **56.** $\dfrac{37x^2 - 32x - 44}{6x(x + 2)}$ **57.** The perimeter is $\dfrac{5x^2 - 4x - 5}{2x(x + 1)}$ units. **58.** The length is

$\dfrac{4x + 3}{x}$ units. **59. (a)** $t(x) = \dfrac{125}{10 + x} + \dfrac{80}{x}$ **(b)**

t(x) graph with axis markings 100, 80, 60, 40, 20 and x-axis 20 40 60 80 100

(c) The trip took 5.8 hours. **(d)** Gretchen's speed was 40 mph and Bob's speed was 50 mph.

60. $\dfrac{3(11m + 21)}{m(2m - 3)}$ **61. (a)** Let $S_1(x) =$ the PE ratio for the first stock, $S_2(x) =$ the PE ratio for the second stock,

$S_1(x) = \dfrac{21.57x + 33}{-0.07x + 1.08}$, $S_2(x) = \dfrac{9.11x + 20.88}{0.17x + 1.33}$ **(b)** $\dfrac{4.3046x^2 + 25.9209x + 21.3396}{(-0.07x + 1.08)(0.17x + 1.33)}$ **62. (a)** $\dfrac{D(x)}{T(x)} = \dfrac{2x^2 - 11x + 488}{4.5x^2 - 23.5x + 570}$

(b) $\dfrac{I(x)}{T(x)} = \dfrac{2.5x^2 - 12.5x + 82}{4.5x^2 - 23.5x + 570}$ **(c)** $\dfrac{-0.5x^2 + 1.5x + 406}{4.5x^2 - 23.5x + 570}$ **63.** not rational   **64.** not rational   **65.** rational   **66.** rational   **67.** -8 and 4

68. all real numbers not equal to -3 **69.** no solution   **70.** 7   **71.** -3 and $\dfrac{1}{2}$ **72.** 5   **73.** ± 10 **74.** -5 and 6   **75.** -4 **76.** -3 and 4

77. no solution   **78.** -3 and $\dfrac{9}{2}$ **79.** all real numbers except -4 **80.** $-\dfrac{3}{2}$ and 4   **81.** $\dfrac{5 \pm \sqrt{21}}{2}$ **82.** nonreal solutions

83. The first interest rate was 6%. The second interest rate was 7%.   **84.** In 2009, the ratio will be 30.   **85.** The base is $4 + 4\sqrt{5}$ centimeters or approximately 12.944 centimeters. The height is 8 centimeters.   **86.** The radii are approximately 23 meters and 117 meters.   **87.** It will take them $\dfrac{24}{7}$ hours, or approximately 3.4 hours.   **88.** It will take Ethel 55.4 minutes and Lucy 65.4 minutes.   **89.** It will take 6 minutes working together.

90. It will take the high-speed line $5\dfrac{1}{4}$ hours and the other line $10\dfrac{1}{2}$ hours, working alone.   **91.** She should add another $40.   **92.** Another two cups should be added.   **93.** The average rate is approximately 2.8.   **94.** $GE = 1; TH = 7$ **95.** $v = \sqrt{ar}$ **96. (a)** GI measures 12 in; KL measures 14 in.   **(b)** GH measures 7.52 feet; JL measures 3.52 feet.   **97.** The bluff is 48 feet high.   **98.** The tree's shadow was 96 feet long.

99. The resistances of the two resistors are 44 ohms and 93 ohms.   **100.** $f = \dfrac{f_1 f_2}{f_2 + f_1}$

CHAPTER 10 MIXED REVIEW

1.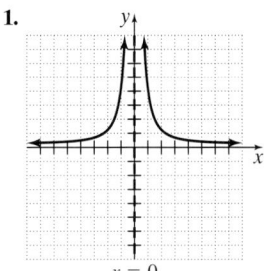
$x = 0$

2.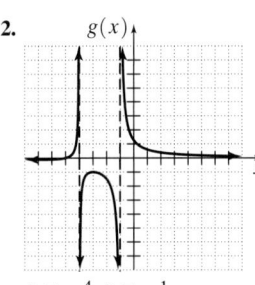
$x = -4$ $x = -1$

3.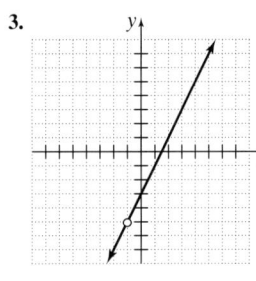

4.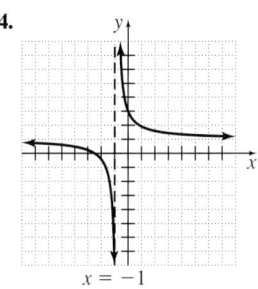
$x = -1$

5. no restricted values; all real numbers   **6.** $\pm\dfrac{5}{3}; x \neq -\dfrac{5}{3}, x \neq \dfrac{5}{3}$ **7.** $0; x \neq 0$ **8.** -2 and $\dfrac{4}{3}; x \neq -2, x \neq \dfrac{4}{3}$ **9.** $\dfrac{3x + 4}{2x + 3}$ **10.** $\dfrac{k + 5}{k^2 + 6}$

11. $-\dfrac{3x^3}{4y^4}$ **12.** $\dfrac{q - 3}{2(q + 2)}$ **13.** $\dfrac{-2x}{3(x + 2)}$ **14.** $\dfrac{x - 25}{(3x + 2)(x - 3)}$ **15.** $\dfrac{5}{a - b}$ **16.** $\dfrac{b(7 + 5b)}{3a}$ **17.** $\dfrac{p(3p - 2)}{4m}$ **18.** $\dfrac{5 + 2y^2}{4x^2 y^3}$

19. $\dfrac{x(5x + 7)}{(x + 3)(x - 5)}$ **20.** $\dfrac{8x + 5}{3(2x - 5)(2x + 5)}$ **21.** $\dfrac{31x + 9}{(2x - 1)(x + 3)(3x + 2)}$ **22.** 2   **23.** $\dfrac{2x - 1}{5x + 4}$ **24.** $\dfrac{x - 30}{(x + 6)(x - 6)}$ **25.** $\dfrac{x^2 - 9x - 6}{4x(x + 1)}$

26. $\dfrac{x - 27}{2(x + 5)(x - 5)}$ **27.** $\dfrac{7x - 2}{(4x - 5)(x - 3)(5x - 4)}$ **28.** $\dfrac{3(m + 6)}{2m + 5}$ **29.** -1 **30.** $-\dfrac{10b^2}{9a^3}$ **31.** $\dfrac{(2c + 3)(c + 7)}{c + 3}$ **32.** $-\dfrac{a}{3b^2}$ **33.** $-\dfrac{1}{4}$

34. $-\dfrac{4g^4 k}{3h^2}$ **35.** $\dfrac{6p^3 q^7}{5m^3 n^4}$ **36.** $\dfrac{75m^2 p^3}{2}$ **37.** $\dfrac{2x - 3}{4x^2 + 9}$ **38.** $\dfrac{(x + 2)^2}{2}$ **39.** $\dfrac{5b^2}{3c^7}$ **40.** $\dfrac{(z - 3)(z + 8)}{(z - 6)(z + 4)}$ **41.** 1   **42.** $(x + 5)(2x + 1)$

43. 4   **44.** approximately -0.51 and 4.71   **45.** 0   **46.** $\dfrac{1}{3}$ and 8   **47.** 5   **48.** $\dfrac{1}{7}$ and $\dfrac{1}{5}$ **49.** no solution   **50.** $-\dfrac{7}{4}$ **51.** 15   **52.** $\dfrac{7}{2}$

53. approximately -4.01 and 6.51   **54.** all real numbers except 3   **55.** -7 and 3   **56.** all real numbers except -3 **57.** all real numbers except 0

58. -1 and $\dfrac{4}{5}$ **59.** -9 and 9   **60.** no solution   **61.** -7 and 2   **62.** nonreal solutions   **63.** no solution   **64.** -2 **65.** It will take them $\dfrac{70}{17}$ hours, or approximately 4.1 hours.   **66.** Another 1 pint of glue is needed.   **67.** His average rate of speed is $\dfrac{120}{t}$ mph; the new distance is $\dfrac{80(t + 1)}{t}$ miles.

68. The tree is 24 feet high.   **69.** $H = \dfrac{V}{LW}$; the height is $(2x + 1)$ inches.   **70.** It would take the first line 6 hours and the second line 7.5 hours, working alone.   **71.** The perimeter is $\dfrac{(4x - 3)(x - 1)}{x(x - 3)}$ units.   **72.** She needs an additional $20.   **73.** Each resistor is approximately 45 ohms and 57 ohms.   **74.** $C = \dfrac{C_1 C_2}{C_2 + C_1}$ **75. (a)** $R(x) = \dfrac{C(x)}{P(x)} = \dfrac{-0.39x + 23.48}{-0.105x^2 + 0.065x + 71.22}$ **(b)** In 2003 and 2009, the percentage will be 31.6% or the

ratio will be 0.316. On the given domain, the minimum percentage is 31.16% or the ratio is 0.3116 in 2006.

76. (a) $C_{\text{ave}}(x) = \dfrac{18,000 + 162.5x + 37.5x^2}{x}$ **(b)** The minimum average cost is approximately $1805.67 per year.   **77.** The minimum surface area is

approximately 40.788 square inches when the radius is approximately 1.471 inches.   **78.** $b(x) = \dfrac{6x^3 + 7x^2 - 3x}{2x + 3}; b(x) = 3x^2 - x$; The base is

102 feet.   **79. (a)** $\dfrac{M(x)}{T(x)} = \dfrac{-563x^2 + 1844x + 55,311}{-1208x^2 + 4712x + 104,705}$ **(b)** $\dfrac{U(x)}{T(x)} = \dfrac{-76x^2 + 233x + 4736}{-1208x^2 + 4712x + 104,705}$ **(c)** $\dfrac{-487x^2 + 1611x + 50,575}{-1208x^2 + 4712x + 104,705}$

80. The dimensions are $2 + 2\sqrt{5}$ inches or approximately 6.472 inches and approximately 10.472 inches.   **81.** The two accelerations are approximately 1.768 and 6.536.   **82.** $AB = 3$; $BC = 4$; $XY = 3$ **83.** $m = \dfrac{kF}{a}$

CHAPTER 10 TEST

1. -3 and 0; $x \neq -3$, $x \neq 0$ **2.** -4 and 9; $x \neq -4$, $x \neq 9$ **3.**   **4.** $\dfrac{8}{3x - 7}$ **5.** $\dfrac{2z(z - 3)}{z^2 + 9}$ **6.** $\dfrac{7x - 15}{x(x + 4)(x - 3)}$

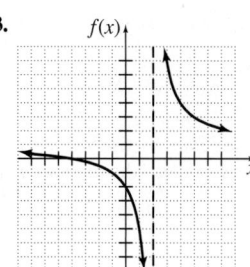

7. $\dfrac{1}{2}$ **8.** $\dfrac{x^2 + 15x + 5}{x(x + 5)^2}$ **9.** $\dfrac{9(x - 2y)}{2x(x + y)}$ **10.** -1 and 5

11. $11 \pm 4\sqrt{7}$ **12.** no real-number solutions   **13.** ± 15

14. -2 and $-\dfrac{1}{3}$ **15.** 3 **16.** 0 **17.** all real numbers

except -1 **18.** no solution   **19.** $s = \dfrac{x - m}{z}$

20. $c = \dfrac{2ab}{b + a}$ **21.** The dimensions are $4 + 4\sqrt{5}$ inches or approximately 12.944 inches and 8 inches.   **22.** $\dfrac{-12(t^2 - 2t - 2)}{t^2(t + 2)^2}$

23. (a) $C_{\text{ave}}(x) = \dfrac{75x^2 + 75x + 17{,}000}{x}$ **(b)** The minimum average cost is approximately \$2333.32 per year.

24. (a) $R(x) = \dfrac{N(x)}{P(x)} = \dfrac{-0.17x + 8.48}{-0.105x^2 + 0.065x + 71.22}$ **(b)** In 2015, the ratio will be 0.1225 or the percentage will be 12.25%. The minimum percent will

be approximately 10.95% or the ratio will be approximately 0.1095 in the year 2008.   **25.** The height is $21\dfrac{2}{3}$ feet.   **26.** Jill can rake the leaves in four hours.   **27.** Answers will vary.

CHAPTER 11

SECTION 11.1 EXERCISES

1. -6 **2.** -7 **3.** not a real number   **4.** not a real number   **5.** 6 **6.** 11 **7.** -6 **8.** -11 **9.** -6 **10.** -11 **11.** 10.488
12. 14.142 **13.** -10.488 **14.** -14.142 **15.** not a real number   **16.** not a real number   **17.** 4.791 **18.** 5.848 **19.** -4.791
20. -5.848 **21.** 1.821 **22.** 1.710 **23.** 2.321 **24.** 2.921 **25.** nonradical   **26.** radical   **27.** radical   **28.** nonradical   **29.** all real

numbers less than 3; $[3, \infty)$ **30.** all real numbers less than $-\dfrac{5}{3}$; $\left[-\dfrac{5}{3}, \infty\right)$ **31.** all real numbers less than 0; $[0, \infty)$ **32.** all real numbers less

than 0; $[0, \infty)$ **33.** no restricted values; $(-\infty, \infty)$ **34.** no restricted values; $(-\infty, \infty)$ **35.** all real numbers less than $\dfrac{1}{3}$; $\left[\dfrac{1}{3}, \infty\right)$

36. all real numbers less than 3; $[3, \infty)$ **37.** all real numbers between -2 and 0; $(-\infty, -2] \cup [0, \infty)$ **38.** all real numbers between 0 and 5;
$(-\infty, 0] \cup [5, \infty)$ **39.** all real numbers between 2 and 4; $(-\infty, 2] \cup [4, \infty)$ **40.** all real numbers between -2 and 5; $(-\infty, -2] \cup [5, \infty)$

41. 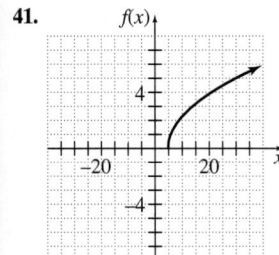   **42.** 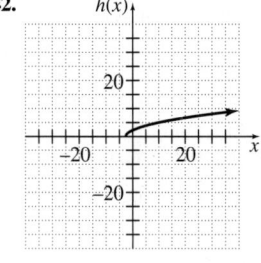   **43.** 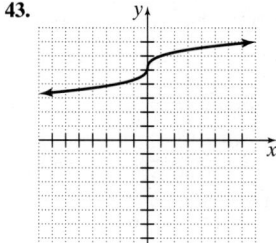   **44.**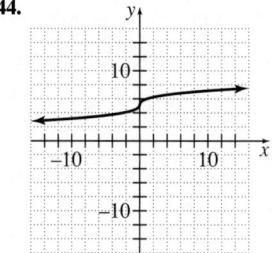

45. 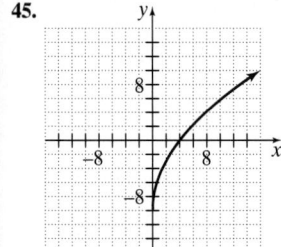   **46.** 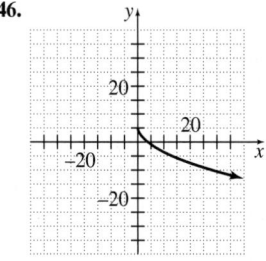   **47.** 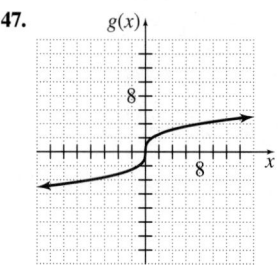   **48.**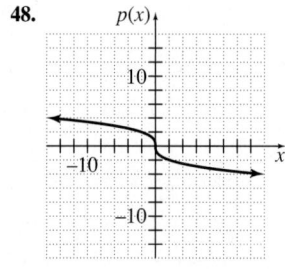

49.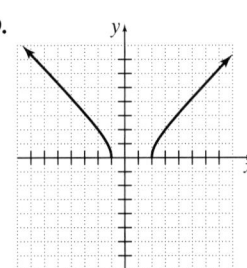

50.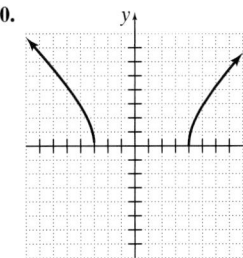

51. $\sqrt{65}$

52. $\sqrt{51}$

53. $45\sqrt{33}$

54. $100\sqrt{10}$

55. $f(x) = \sqrt{x(x-5)}$; $(-\infty, 0] \cup [5, \infty)$;

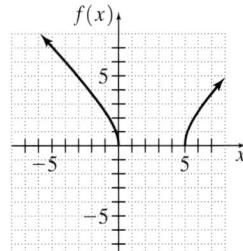

56. $f(x) = \sqrt{x(x+1)}$; $(-\infty, -1] \cup [0, \infty)$;

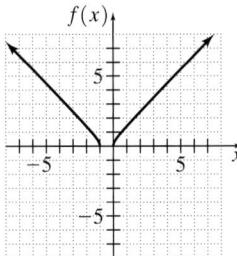

57. $f(x) = \sqrt{(x+3)(x-7)}$; $(-\infty, -3] \cup [7, \infty)$;

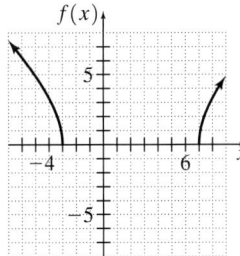

58. $f(x) = \sqrt{(x-5)(x-4)}$; $(-\infty, 4] \cup [5, \infty)$;

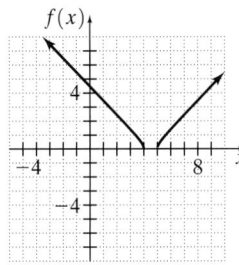

59. $s = \sqrt{A}$ **(a)** The length of the side is 17 ft.   **(b)** The length of the side is 9.5 inches.   **(c)** The length of the side is approximately 10.724 mm.   **60. (a)** The length of the side is 23 yards.   **(b)** The length of the side is 10.5 cm.   **(c)** The length of the side is approximately 6.708 feet.   **61.** $r = \sqrt{\dfrac{A}{\pi}}$ **(a)** The length of the radius is 14 inches.   **(b)** The length of the radius is $\dfrac{7}{\sqrt{\pi}} \approx 3.949$ yards.   **(c)** The length of the radius is $\sqrt{\dfrac{108}{\pi}} \approx 5.863$ meters.   **62. (a)** The length of the radius is 15 dm.   **(b)** The length of the radius is $\dfrac{19}{\sqrt{\pi}} \approx 10.720$ ft.   **(c)** The length of the radius is $\sqrt{\dfrac{200}{\pi}} \approx 7.979$ cm.

63. $r = \sqrt{\dfrac{8200}{\pi}}$ The radius and diameter are approximately 51.090 ft and 102.179 ft, respectively.   **64.** $s = \sqrt{377{,}000}$ The side is approximately 614 feet.

65.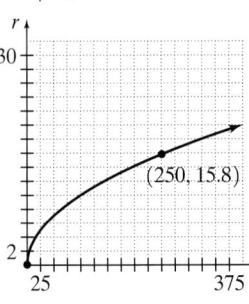

There should be about 16 rows in the table.

66.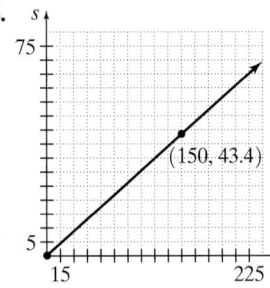

The variability is about 43.

67. (a) The cost of 10 units is $24.47. The cost of 15 units is $36.32.

(b)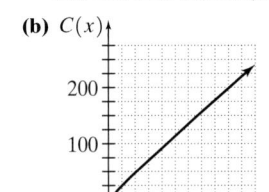

(c) increasing
(d) The cost of 54 units is $122.

68. (a) The cost of 10 units is $6.92. The cost of 15 units is $15.30.

(b)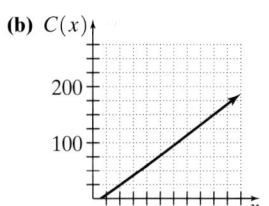

(c) increasing
(d) The cost of 72 units is $117.

69. (a) $R(x) = x\left(35 - \sqrt{x-2}\right)$
(b) The revenue of 10 units is $321.72. The revenue of 15 units is $470.92.
(c) $[2, \infty)$
(d) $R(x)$

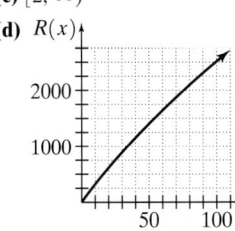

(e) increasing
(f) The revenue of 51 units is $1428.

70. (a) $R(x) = x\left(2.7 + \sqrt{3x+1}\right)$
(b) The revenue of 15 units is $142.23. The revenue of 20 units is $210.20.
(c) $[0, \infty)$
(d) $R(x)$

(e) increasing
(f) The revenue of 40 units is $548.

71. (a) $T(x)$

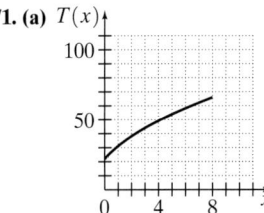

(b) increasing   **(c)** May

72. (a) $T(x)$

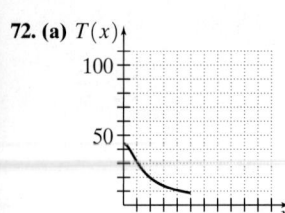

(b) decreasing   **(c)** November

73. (a) $P(x)$

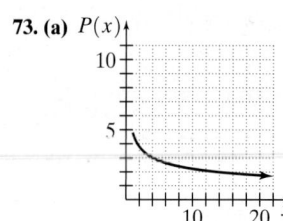

(b) decreasing   **(c)** 2007

74. (a) $A(t)$

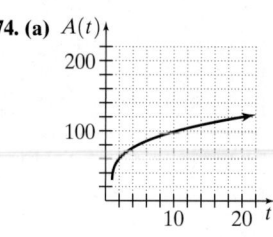

(b) increasing   **(c)** 2006

11.1 CALCULATOR EXERCISES

1. $f(x)$ simplifies to $f(x) = |x - 2|$.   **2.** $f(x)$ simplifies to $f(x) = |2x - 3|$.

SECTION 11.2 EXERCISES

1. $\sqrt{36} = 6$ **2.** $\sqrt{100} = 10$ **3.** $\sqrt[3]{216} = 6$ **4.** $\sqrt[3]{729} = 9$ **5.** $-\sqrt[4]{81} = -3$ **6.** $-\sqrt[4]{625} = -5$ **7.** $\sqrt[4]{-81}$, not a real number

8. $\sqrt[4]{-625}$, not a real number   **9.** $-\sqrt[3]{8} = -2$ **10.** $-\sqrt[3]{27} = -3$ **11.** $\sqrt[3]{-8} = -2$ **12.** $\sqrt[3]{-27} = -3$ **13.** $\dfrac{1}{\sqrt{36}} = \dfrac{1}{6}$ **14.** $\dfrac{1}{\sqrt{100}} = \dfrac{1}{10}$

15. $\dfrac{1}{\sqrt[3]{216}} = \dfrac{1}{6}$ **16.** $\dfrac{1}{\sqrt[3]{729}} = \dfrac{1}{9}$ **17.** $\dfrac{1}{\sqrt[4]{81}} = \dfrac{1}{3}$ **18.** $\dfrac{1}{\sqrt[4]{625}} = \dfrac{1}{5}$ **19.** $-\dfrac{1}{\sqrt[4]{81}} = -\dfrac{1}{3}$ **20.** $\dfrac{1}{\sqrt[4]{-625}}$, not a real number   **21.** $\dfrac{1}{\sqrt[3]{8}} = \dfrac{1}{2}$

22. $\dfrac{1}{\sqrt[3]{27}} = \dfrac{1}{3}$ **23.** $\dfrac{1}{\sqrt[3]{-8}} = -\dfrac{1}{2}$ **24.** $\dfrac{1}{\sqrt[3]{-27}} = -\dfrac{1}{3}$ **25.** $\sqrt{522} \approx 22.847$ **26.** $\sqrt[3]{478} \approx 7.819$ **27.** $\sqrt[4]{522} \approx 4.780$ **28.** $\sqrt[5]{478} \approx 3.435$

29. $\dfrac{1}{\sqrt[3]{522}} \approx 0.124$ **30.** $\dfrac{1}{\sqrt{478}} \approx 0.046$ **31.** $\dfrac{1}{\sqrt[5]{522}} \approx 0.286$ **32.** $\dfrac{1}{\sqrt[4]{478}} \approx 0.214$ **33.** $\left(\sqrt[3]{27}\right)^4 = 81$ **34.** $\left(\sqrt{25}\right)^3 = 125$

35. $\left(\sqrt[3]{-27}\right)^4 = 81$ **36.** $\left(\sqrt{-25}\right)^3$, not a real number   **37.** $\dfrac{1}{\left(\sqrt[3]{27}\right)^4} = \dfrac{1}{81}$ **38.** $\dfrac{1}{\left(\sqrt{25}\right)^3} = \dfrac{1}{125}$ **39.** $-\dfrac{1}{\left(\sqrt[3]{27}\right)^4} = -\dfrac{1}{81}$

40. $-\dfrac{1}{\left(\sqrt{25}\right)^3} = -\dfrac{1}{125}$ **41.** $\left(\sqrt{4}\right)^5 = 32$ **42.** $\left(\sqrt{9}\right)^3 = 27$ **43.** $\left(\sqrt[3]{8}\right)^7 = 128$ **44.** $\left(\sqrt[3]{125}\right)^5 = 3125$ **45.** $\dfrac{1}{\left(\sqrt{4}\right)^7} = \dfrac{1}{128}$

46. $\dfrac{1}{\left(\sqrt{16}\right)^5} = \dfrac{1}{1024}$ **47.** $-\left(\sqrt{16}\right)^3 = -64$ **48.** $-\left(\sqrt{64}\right)^3 = -512$ **49.** $\left(\sqrt{-9}\right)^3$, not a real number   **50.** $\left(\sqrt{-4}\right)^3$, not a real number

51. $-\dfrac{1}{\left(\sqrt{81}\right)^3} = -\dfrac{1}{729}$ **52.** $-\dfrac{1}{\left(\sqrt{36}\right)^3} = -\dfrac{1}{216}$ **53.** $\left(\sqrt[4]{28}\right)^5 \approx 64.409$ **54.** $\left(\sqrt[4]{36}\right)^5 \approx 88.182$ **55.** $\left(\sqrt[4]{-21}\right)^4 \approx 57.937$

56. $\left(\sqrt[3]{-15}\right)^2 \approx 6.082$ **57.** $\dfrac{1}{\left(\sqrt[5]{5}\right)^2} \approx 0.342$ **58.** $\dfrac{1}{\left(\sqrt[3]{7}\right)^2} \approx 0.273$ **59.** $-\dfrac{1}{\left(\sqrt[3]{42}\right)^2} \approx -0.083$ **60.** $-\dfrac{1}{\left(\sqrt[3]{36}\right)^2} \approx -0.092$ **61.** $\left(\sqrt[8]{-88}\right)^3$, not a

real number   **62.** $\left(\sqrt[6]{-66}\right)^5$, not a real number   **63.** The restricted values are all real numbers greater than $\dfrac{5}{4}$. The domain of the function is $\left(-\infty, \dfrac{5}{4}\right]$.
64. There are no restricted values. The domain is all real numbers, or $(-\infty, \infty)$.   **65.** There are no restricted values. The domain is all real numbers,
or $(-\infty, \infty)$.   **66.** The restricted values are all real numbers greater than $\dfrac{7}{2}$. The domain of the function is $\left(-\infty, \dfrac{7}{2}\right]$.

67.

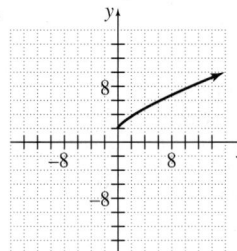

68.

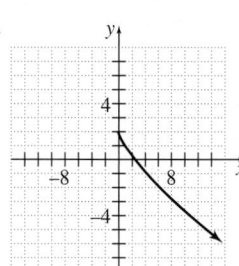

69.

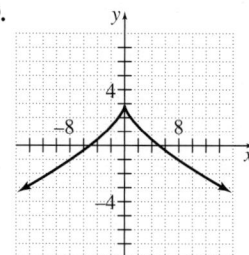

70.

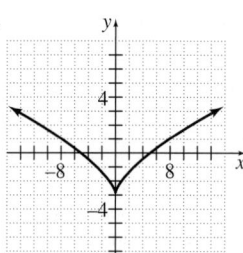

71.

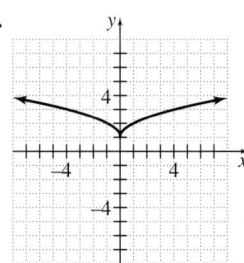

72.

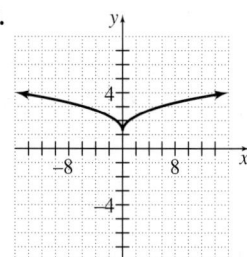

73.

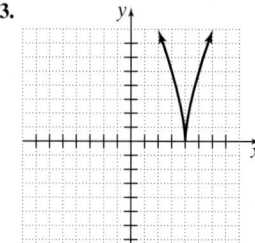

74.

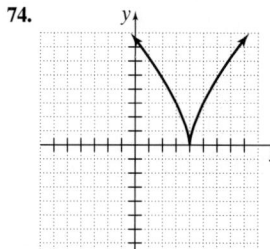

75. The average bacteria level was 58.179 bacteria per 100 ml.   **76.** The average bacteria level was 31.589 bacteria per 100 ml.   **77.** The average return was 1.08 or $1.08 per dollar.   **78.** The average return was 1.07 or $1.07 per dollar.   **79.** The average return was 1.11 or $1.11 per dollar. **80.** The average return was 1.05 or $1.05 per dollar.

81. (a)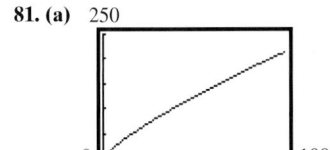

82. (a)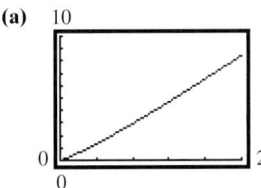

83. (a)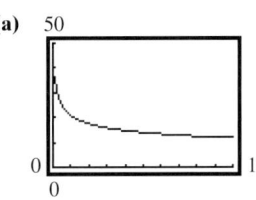

84. (a)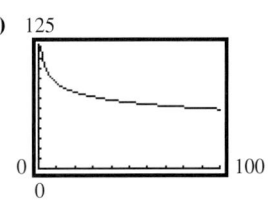

(b) increasing   **(c)** There are approximately 91 recovery plans for mammals.   **(d)** 363 types of fish are endangered or threatened.

(b) increasing   **(c)** In 2002, 0.46% of sales were in digital format.   **(d)** In 2008, 2.27% of sales will be in digital format.

(b) decreasing   **(c)** The wind chill will be 17.50°.   **(d)** The wind speed is 37 miles per hour.

(b) decreasing   **(c)** The earnings were 85.79 million dollars.   **(d)** The ranking is 7th.

11.2 CALCULATOR EXERCISES

1. 9   **2.** $(-27)^{2/3}, \left(\sqrt[3]{(-27)}\right)^2, ((-27)^{1/3})^2, \sqrt[3]{(-27)^2}$

SECTION 11.3 EXERCISES

1. $\dfrac{1}{3}$ **2.** $\dfrac{1}{3}$ **3.** 2   **4.** 2   **5.** 243   **6.** 512   **7.** 8   **8.** 8   **9.** 5   **10.** 4   **11.** 6   **12.** 5   **13.** $\dfrac{2}{3}$ **14.** $\dfrac{9}{25}$ **15.** $\dfrac{4}{3}$ **16.** $\dfrac{8}{27}$

17. $\dfrac{1}{8}$ **18.** $\dfrac{1}{16}$ **19.** $\dfrac{1}{x^{2/3}}$ **20.** $\dfrac{1}{x^{5/6}}$ **21.** $12y^{3/4}$ **22.** $2y^{4/7}$ **23.** $z^{17/12}$ **24.** $z^{13/8}$ **25.** $p^{1/6}$ **26.** $\dfrac{1}{x^{1/9}}$ **27.** $b^{2/3}$ **28.** $z^{3/8}$

29. $x^{3/2}y^{3/4}$ **30.** $p^{5/6}q^{5/2}$ **31.** $\dfrac{x^{5/3}}{y^{5/2}}$ **32.** $\dfrac{a^{7/3}}{b^{7/4}}$ **33.** $\dfrac{b^{1/3}}{a^{1/3}}$ **34.** $\dfrac{n^{3/4}}{m^{3/4}}$ **35.** $\dfrac{1}{c^{1/5}}$ **36.** $k^{2/7}$ **37.** $4a^{10/3}b^4$ **38.** $8c^{2/3}d^{3/2}$ **39.** $10a^{13/12}b^{4/5}$

40. $-6x^{4/5}y^{7/12}$ **41.** $\dfrac{m^{10/7}}{4}$ **42.** $64z^{7/3}$ **43.** $\dfrac{8a^{10/3}c^{13/6}}{9b^{13/4}}$ **44.** $\dfrac{z^3}{2y^{7/4}}$ **45.** $x^{11/12} - x^{21/20}$ **46.** $z^{11/12} - z$ **47.** $2x^{3/5} + 6x^{2/5}y^{2/5}$

48. $15a^{3/7} - 5a^{2/7}b^{4/7}$ **49.** $3a^{1/4}b^{1/3} - a^{3/4}b^{7/6}$ **50.** $x^{3/4}y^{9/8} - 4x^{1/4}y^{3/4}$ **51.** $x^{5/6} + x^{1/2}y^{1/3} - x^{1/3}y^{1/2} - y^{5/6}$

52. $c^{7/6} + c^{2/3}d^{1/2} - c^{1/2}d^{2/3} - d^{7/6}$ **53.** $x^{1/2} - y^{1/2}$ **54.** $p^{3/2} - q^{3/2}$ **55.** $x^{5/2} - x^2y^{1/2} + x^{1/2}y^2 - y^{5/2}$ **56.** $a^{5/3} - a^{2/3}b + ab^{2/3} - b^{5/3}$

57. $x^{2/3} - 4$ **58.** $16 - z^{1/2}$ **59.** $x^{1/2} + 4x^{1/4} + 4$ **60.** $x^{2/3} + 6x^{1/3} + 9$ **61.** $x^2 - 2xy^{1/2} + y$ **62.** $x - 2x^{1/2}y + y^2$

63. $a + 2a^{1/2}b^{1/2} + b$ **64.** $c - 2c^{1/2}d^{1/2} + d$ **65.** The side length should be doubled.   **66.** The side length should be tripled.

67. The time is increased by a factor of $\sqrt{3}$, or the time is about $1.732t$ seconds.   **68.** The time is increased by a factor of 2, or the time is $2t$ seconds. **69.** The answer is the same as that for Section Exercise 67. The change from feet to meters does not affect the change in time.   **70.** The answer is the same as that for Section Exercise 68. The change from feet to meters does not affect the change in time.   **71.** It is multiplied by a factor of about 0.577.   **72.** It is multiplied by a factor of about 1.414.   **73.** It is half as much; it is 10 times as great.   **74.** It is multiplied by a factor of about 0.707; it is three times as great.

11.3 CALCULATOR EXERCISES

1. x^2 **2.** $\dfrac{1}{x^2}$ **3.** $x^{7/4}$ **4.** $\dfrac{1}{x^{3/2}}$ **5.** $x^{9/4} - x^{17/12}$ **6.** $x^{2/3} - 1$

SECTION 11.4 EXERCISES

1. $2\sqrt{7}$ **2.** $5\sqrt{3}$ **3.** $-7\sqrt[3]{2}$ **4.** $-4\sqrt[3]{3}$ **5.** $2\sqrt[4]{7}$ **6.** $7\sqrt[4]{3}$ **7.** $-5\sqrt[5]{2}$ **8.** $-3\sqrt[5]{8}$ **9.** $2x^2yz\sqrt{5y}$ **10.** $2xy^4z^4\sqrt{3xy}$

11. $2mn^3\sqrt[3]{9m^2}$ **12.** $3p^2q^2\sqrt[3]{4pq^2}$ **13.** $3xy\sqrt[4]{2y}$ **14.** $2ab^2\sqrt[4]{5a^2}$ **15.** $3ab^2\sqrt[5]{2ac^2}$ **16.** $3yz^3\sqrt[5]{3x^2y^3}$ **17.** $(x+3)\sqrt{5}$

18. $(x+1)\sqrt{3x}$ **19.** $7\sqrt{2xy}$ **20.** $6\sqrt{2xy}$ **21.** $14xy\sqrt{2x}$ **22.** $-6p^2q\sqrt{21p}$ **23.** $(x+2y)\sqrt{21}$ **24.** $(p+2q)\sqrt{3p}$

25. $(x+2)\sqrt{x+1}$ **26.** $(x-7)\sqrt{x+1}$ **27.** $(x-1)\sqrt{(x+2)(x+4)}$ **28.** $(x+4)\sqrt{(x+2)(x-4)}$ **29.** $-2xy\sqrt[3]{3x^2}$

30. $-5x^2y^2\sqrt[3]{2y^2}$ **31.** $-\dfrac{6}{7}$ **32.** $-\dfrac{5}{9}$ **33.** $\dfrac{11}{12}$ **34.** $\dfrac{13}{14}$ **35.** $-\dfrac{2\sqrt{6}}{9}$ **36.** $-\dfrac{3\sqrt{15}}{25}$ **37.** $\dfrac{\sqrt[3]{4}}{5}$ **38.** $\dfrac{\sqrt[3]{5}}{8}$ **39.** $-\dfrac{\sqrt[3]{45}}{5}$ **40.** $-\dfrac{\sqrt[3]{70}}{7}$

41. $\dfrac{\sqrt[5]{2}}{2}$ **42.** $\dfrac{\sqrt[3]{9}}{9}$ **43.** $\dfrac{2x}{3y}$ **44.** $\dfrac{5\sqrt{x}}{7y}$ **45.** $\dfrac{\sqrt{3x}}{5y}$ **46.** $\dfrac{\sqrt{5p}}{7q}$ **47.** $\dfrac{2\sqrt{5xyz}}{5z}$ **48.** $\dfrac{6\sqrt{7abc}}{7c}$ **49.** $\dfrac{x\sqrt{3}}{3}$ **50.** $\dfrac{z^2\sqrt{5}}{5}$ **51.** $\dfrac{3x}{y^2}$

52. $\dfrac{-4x^2y}{z^3}$ **53.** $\dfrac{\sqrt[3]{15x}}{5x}$ **54.** $\dfrac{\sqrt[3]{42a}}{6a}$ **55.** $\dfrac{\sqrt[3]{75xy^2z^2}}{5yz}$ **56.** $\dfrac{\sqrt[3]{196ac^2}}{7c}$ **57.** $\dfrac{\sqrt{5x}}{x}$ **58.** $\dfrac{\sqrt{10y}}{y}$ **59.** $\dfrac{\sqrt{2y}}{2y}$ **60.** $\dfrac{\sqrt{3b}}{3b}$ **61.** $\dfrac{z\sqrt{2z}}{4}$

62. $\dfrac{p\sqrt{3p}}{9}$ **63.** $\dfrac{b\sqrt{ab}}{a}$ **64.** $\dfrac{\sqrt{cd}}{cd^2}$ **65.** $\dfrac{\sqrt{3x}}{6}$ **66.** $\dfrac{p\sqrt{2q}}{6q}$ **67.** $\dfrac{\sqrt[3]{3x}}{x}$ **68.** $\dfrac{\sqrt[3]{7a}}{a}$ **69.** $\dfrac{\sqrt[3]{2y^2}}{2y}$ **70.** $\dfrac{\sqrt[3]{2a^2}}{2a}$ **71.** $\dfrac{-2\sqrt[3]{9x^2z}}{3x}$

72. $\dfrac{-3\sqrt[3]{25b^2c}}{5b}$ **73.** The period is approximately 2.9 seconds.   **74.** The period is approximately 3.8 seconds.   **75.** The period is approximately

6.02 seconds. **76.** The period is approximately 5.31 seconds. **77.** It takes approximately 1.92 seconds. **78.** It takes approximately 1.4 seconds.
79. The time is about 2.48 seconds; the speed is about 14.52 feet per second. **80.** The time is about 2.11 seconds; the speed is about 15.17 feet per second.

81. $\dfrac{\sqrt{6xy}}{x^2y^4}$ **82.** $\dfrac{\sqrt{14xy}}{x^5y^4}$ **83.** $f = \dfrac{\sqrt{6}}{12\pi x^2}$ **84.** $f = \dfrac{\sqrt{15y}}{30\pi y^2}$

11.4 CALCULATOR EXERCISES

1. $19\sqrt[3]{2}$ **2.** $13\sqrt[4]{7}$ **3.** $-2\sqrt[9]{13}$ **4.** $29\sqrt{11}$

SECTION 11.5 EXERCISES

1. $\sqrt{7}$ **2.** $7\sqrt{6}$ **3.** $\dfrac{9}{10}\sqrt{10}$ **4.** $\dfrac{14}{13}\sqrt{13}$ **5.** $-2\sqrt[3]{3}$ **6.** $13\sqrt[3]{2}$ **7.** $23\sqrt{3}$ **8.** $12\sqrt{5}$ **9.** $14\sqrt{x}$ **10.** $-2\sqrt{bc}$ **11.** $11\sqrt{x}$

12. $20\sqrt{p}$ **13.** $-3x\sqrt{2x}$ **14.** $-y^2\sqrt{3y}$ **15.** $(3 + 4a)\sqrt{a}$ **16.** $(11b - 4)\sqrt{b}$ **17.** $14a\sqrt{b}$ **18.** $x\sqrt{y}$ **19.** $7\sqrt{pq} + 7\sqrt[3]{pq}$

20. $6\sqrt[3]{ab} - 8\sqrt{ab}$ **21.** $6xy\sqrt{xy}$ **22.** $-cd\sqrt{cd}$ **23.** $-xy\sqrt[3]{x^2yz}$ **24.** $7xy\sqrt[4]{xyz^2}$ **25.** $\sqrt{35} - 7$ **26.** $\sqrt{30} + 5$ **27.** $\sqrt{3x} - \sqrt{15}$

28. $2\sqrt{35} + 2\sqrt{5a}$ **29.** $6a - 15\sqrt{a}$ **30.** $24c + 32\sqrt{c}$ **31.** $8x - 12\sqrt[3]{x^2}$ **32.** $35\sqrt[3]{a^2} - 14a$ **33.** $6 + 2\sqrt{6} - 30\sqrt{2} - 20\sqrt{3}$

34. $3\sqrt{30} - 36\sqrt{2} + 2\sqrt{5} - 8\sqrt{3}$ **35.** $\sqrt{6} + \sqrt{3x} - \sqrt{2x} - x$ **36.** $\sqrt{10} + \sqrt{2z} - \sqrt{5z} - z$ **37.** 19 **38.** -1 **39.** $144 - p$

40. $169 - q$ **41.** $2x - 3y$ **42.** $6x - 3y$ **43.** $a + 8\sqrt{a} + 16$ **44.** $bc + 10\sqrt{bc} + 25$ **45.** $9b - 12\sqrt{b} + 4$ **46.** $81c - 54\sqrt{c} + 9$

47. $x - 2\sqrt{xy} + y$ **48.** $2x - 2\sqrt{6xy} + 3y$ **49.** $\sqrt{3x} - \sqrt{2}$ **50.** $\sqrt{2x} + \sqrt{6}$ **51.** $1 - \dfrac{12\sqrt{a}}{a}$ **52.** $\dfrac{9\sqrt{b}}{b} + 1$ **53.** $1 + \dfrac{\sqrt{xy}}{x} + \dfrac{\sqrt{xz}}{x}$

54. $\sqrt{a} - \dfrac{\sqrt{abc}}{b} + \sqrt{c}$ **55.** $6\left(\sqrt{6} - \sqrt{3}\right)$ **56.** $3\left(\sqrt{10} - \sqrt{2}\right)$ **57.** $5 + 2\sqrt{6}$ **58.** $5 - 2\sqrt{6}$ **59.** $\dfrac{3x\sqrt{x} + 6x}{x - 4}$ **60.** $\dfrac{12w + 4w\sqrt{w}}{9 - w}$

61. $\sqrt{3b} + 2$ **62.** $\sqrt{ab} - 1$ **63.** $\dfrac{x + 6\sqrt{x} + 9}{x - 9}$ **64.** $\dfrac{36 - 12\sqrt{p} + p}{36 - p}$ **65.** -1 **66.** -1 **67.** It will require $8\sqrt{10} \approx 25.3$ inches more

of material. **68.** It is $4\sqrt{6} \approx 9.8$ inches larger. **69.** The difference is $4\sqrt[3]{14} \approx 9.6$ inches. **70.** The difference is $20\sqrt[3]{2} \approx 25.2$ inches.

71. The building will become visible $5.85\sqrt{3}$ or approximately 10.13 nautical miles. **72.** The building will become visible $5.85\sqrt{5}$ or approximately 13.08 nautical miles. **73.** The length is $(3 + \sqrt{3})$ inches. **74.** The width is $(2 + \sqrt{2})$ feet. **75.** The width is $(1 + \sqrt{3})$ inches.

76. The length is $(2 + \sqrt{5})$ feet. **77.** The sum is $12\sqrt{5}$. **78.** The difference is $10\sqrt{5}$.

11.5 CALCULATOR EXERCISES

Students should check the results by one of the methods presented. **1.** $4\sqrt[3]{x} + 6\sqrt{x} + 7$ **2.** $\sqrt{x} - 2$ **3.** $6\sqrt[3]{2x^2} + 10\sqrt[3]{x}$ **4.** $8x + 5x\sqrt{2}$

5. $\sqrt{x} - 4$ **6.** $\dfrac{21\sqrt{x} + 147}{x - 49}$ **7.** $3x - 13\sqrt{x} - 41$

SECTION 11.6 EXERCISES

1. 64 **2.** 49 **3.** 7.84 **4.** 38.44 **5.** no solution **6.** no solution **7.** 12 **8.** 28 **9.** $\dfrac{9}{2}$ **10.** $\dfrac{3}{2}$ **11.** $\dfrac{3}{2}$ **12.** 3 **13.** 4 **14.** 22

15. 10 **16.** $\dfrac{8}{3}$ **17.** 20 **18.** 12 **19.** 1 **20.** 6 **21.** 5 **22.** $\dfrac{9}{2}$ **23.** -1 **24.** -2 **25.** 5 **26.** 7 **27.** 4 **28.** -2.42 and 2.75

29. all real numbers less than or equal to 7 **30.** all real numbers less than or equal to $\dfrac{3}{2}$ **31.** approximately 3.83 **32.** -4.70 **33.** 8 **34.** 12

35. 36 **36.** 64 **37.** 16 **38.** 1 **39.** no solution **40.** no solution **41.** no solution **42.** 6 **43.** -72 **44.** $-\dfrac{9}{2}$ **45.** 5000 **46.** 133

47. -16 **48.** -27 **49.** -8 **50.** 8 **51.** 256 **52.** 81 **53.** 13 **54.** -22 **55.** 21 **56.** 88 **57.** 124 **58.** 11 **59.** -8 and 1

60. -27 and 3 **61.** 9 **62.** 3 **63.** 10 **64.** 52 **65.** 3 **66.** 2 **67.** 0 **68.** 0 **69.** no solution **70.** no solution **71.** 2 **72.** $\dfrac{1}{2}$

73. 2 **74.** 1 **75.** ± 8 **76.** ± 125 **77.** -38 and 26 **78.** -72 and 56 **79.** 85 **80.** 25 **81.** $\pm\dfrac{1}{8}$ **82.** $\dfrac{1}{81}$ **83.** $\dfrac{406}{81}$ **84.** 155

85. $-\dfrac{122}{5}$ and $\dfrac{128}{5}$ **86.** $\dfrac{257}{6}$ **87.** no real-number solution **88.** no real-number solution **89.** 16 **90.** 243 **91.** The vertical distance is

5.3824 feet. His height of 6.583 feet added to this jump just about equals a 12-foot basket at 11.97 feet. **92.** The vertical distance is about 3.028 feet.

93. $t = 2\sqrt{\dfrac{d}{4.9}}$; the distance would be 1.65 meters. **94.** The vertical distance is about 0.550 meters. **95.** -8 and 16 **96.** -11 and 5 **97.** -10

and 6 **98.** 4 and -2 **99.** no solution **100.** no solution **101.** The original value was $969.03. **102.** The original value was $3606.10.
103. The final value is $694,166.95. **104.** The final value is $193,720.36. **105.** The energy was approximately 2.875×10^{17} ft-lb.
106. The energy was 1.5625×10^{16} ft-lb. **107.** The crushing load was 100 tons. **108.** The crushing load was 324 tons. **109. (a)** 35 meals were
made. **(b)** 36 meals were sold. **(c)** 135 meals made and sold will make a $2 profit. **110. (a)** 49 meals were made. **(b)** 29 meals were sold.
(c) 43 meals made and sold will make a $2 profit. **111. (a)** Randy made 22 lamps. **(b)** 50 lamps were sold. **(c)** The break-even point is 21 lamps
for a slight profit of $0.15. **112. (a)** 11 parts were made. **(b)** 40 parts were sold. **(c)** The break-even point is 9 parts for a profit of $7.05.

11.6 CALCULATOR EXERCISES

1. 40 **2.** 10 **3.** 20 **4.** -0.307 and 1.412 **5.** 2.462 **6.** -1.291 and 20.920

SECTION 11.7 EXERCISES

1. $10i$ **2.** $12i$ **3.** $\dfrac{4}{7}i$ **4.** $\dfrac{6}{11}i$ **5.** $4i\sqrt{2}$ **6.** $5i\sqrt{3}$ **7.** $10i\sqrt{2}$ **8.** $-21i\sqrt{2}$ **9.** $60i$ **10.** $26i$ **11.** $13i$ **12.** $26i$ **13.** $\dfrac{4}{5}$

14. $\dfrac{4}{5}$ **15.** $-20i$ **16.** $-15i$ **17.** $\sqrt{2}+2\sqrt{3}$ **18.** $\sqrt{15}-2\sqrt{2}$ **19.** 2 **20.** 8 **21.** $-5+4i$ **22.** $-2-9i$ **23.** $3-i$

24. $9+9i$ **25.** 1 **26.** $6i$ **27.** $\dfrac{7}{2}+\dfrac{13}{3}i$ **28.** $\dfrac{1}{2}-i$ **29.** $1.62+11.38i$ **30.** $17.3+9.07i$ **31.** $7\sqrt{3}+i\sqrt{2}$ **32.** $-2\sqrt{5}-7i\sqrt{3}$

33. $39+2i$ **34.** $69-6i$ **35.** 74 **36.** 130 **37.** 37 **38.** 29 **39.** $4.76-17.35i$ **40.** $5.04+2.58i$ **41.** $\dfrac{43}{75}-\dfrac{1}{5}i$ **42.** $\dfrac{121}{180}-\dfrac{3}{20}i$

43. $-\sqrt{6}+2i$ **44.** $-9\sqrt{5}-9i\sqrt{2}$ **45.** 8 **46.** 31 **47.** $1+3i$ **48.** $2+6i$ **49.** $-\dfrac{19}{10}+\dfrac{17}{10}i$ **50.** $9-i$ **51.** $-\dfrac{5}{2}-3i$

52. $-\dfrac{3}{2}+2i$ **53.** $-5-6i$ **54.** $1.5-2.1i$ **55.** $4-3.2i$ **56.** $2.5+3i$ **57.** $\sqrt{7}-i\sqrt{3}$ **58.** $-\sqrt{7}-i\sqrt{5}$ **59.** $\sqrt{3}+2i\sqrt{2}$

60. $3\sqrt{5}-2i\sqrt{2}$ **61.** $a=\pm i\sqrt{7}$ **62.** $b=\pm i\sqrt{11}$ **63.** $z=\pm 2i$ **64.** $m=\pm 4i$ **65.** $p=\pm 5i$ **66.** $q=\pm 4i$ **67.** $d=\pm i\sqrt{3}$

68. $c=\pm i\sqrt{2}$ **69.** $t=-1\pm 3i$ **70.** $s=3\pm 6i$ **71.** $x=5\pm i\sqrt{5}$ **72.** $x=-3\pm 2i\sqrt{2}$ **73.** $x=-\dfrac{5}{2}\pm i$ **74.** $y=\dfrac{1}{2}\pm\dfrac{5}{2}i$

75. $z=-2.5\pm 2.3i$ **76.** $y=1.4\pm 1.6i$ **77.** $b=\dfrac{1}{2}\pm\dfrac{1}{2}i$ **78.** $c=-\dfrac{2}{3}\pm\dfrac{3}{4}i$ **79.** $x=-1\pm i\sqrt{3}$ **80.** $x=3\pm i\sqrt{5}$

81. $b=5\pm i\sqrt{2}$ **82.** $x=-7\pm i\sqrt{2}$ **83.** $y=-\dfrac{1}{2}\pm i$ **84.** $x=-\dfrac{4}{3}\pm\dfrac{1}{3}i$ **85.** $p=\dfrac{2}{3}\pm\dfrac{2}{3}i$ **86.** $z=\dfrac{1}{4}\pm\dfrac{\sqrt{6}}{4}i$ **87.** $x=1.2\pm i\sqrt{2}$

88. $m=-2.1\pm i\sqrt{3}$ **89.** $y=\dfrac{1}{2}\pm\dfrac{3}{5}i$ **90.** $z=-0.6\pm 0.3i$ **91.** $x=\dfrac{1}{3}\pm\dfrac{1}{2}i$ **92.** $x=-\dfrac{1}{4}\pm\dfrac{1}{3}i$ **93.** $z=-\dfrac{1}{6}\pm\dfrac{1}{6}i$

94. $x=-\dfrac{1}{6}\pm\dfrac{1}{4}i$ **95.** $x=1\pm 3i$ **96.** $a=-\dfrac{3}{2}\pm\dfrac{3\sqrt{15}}{2}i$ **97.** $y=-\dfrac{5}{2}\pm\dfrac{\sqrt{159}}{2}i$ **98.** $b=1\pm 2i\sqrt{13}$ **99.** $z=-\dfrac{7}{8}\pm\dfrac{3i\sqrt{39}}{8}$

100. $c=-\dfrac{3}{4}\pm\dfrac{3i\sqrt{23}}{4}$ **101.** The magnitude of the total voltage is approximately 37.336 volts. **102.** The total voltage is $42+2i$ volts.

103. The magnitude of the current is 5 amperes. **104.** The magnitude of the current is approximately 8.2 amperes. **105.** $r=1.335\pm\dfrac{i\sqrt{3.8711}}{2}$

106. $r=1.335\pm\dfrac{i\sqrt{6.8711}}{2}$ **107.** $y=0,\pm 2i\sqrt{2}$ **108.** $y=0,\pm 4i\sqrt{2}$ **109.** $x=0,\pm i\sqrt{5}$ **110.** $x=0,\pm i\sqrt{17}$ **111.** $y=\pm\dfrac{i\sqrt{3}}{3}$

112. $y=\pm i$ **113.** $m=\pm 4i\sqrt{3}$ **114.** $m=\pm 4i\sqrt{5}$ **115.** $m=\dfrac{-7\pm i\sqrt{11}}{2}$ **116.** $m=\dfrac{-1\pm i\sqrt{3}}{2}$

117. $(3-2i)(3-2i)=9-12i-4=5-12i$ **118.** $(7-i)(7-i)=49-14i-1=48-14i$ **119. (a)** $\sqrt{5^2+3^2}$ **(b)** 34 **(c)** $5-3i$

(d) 34 **(e)** The values are equal. **120. (a)** $\sqrt{11^2+6^2}$ **(b)** 157 **(c)** $11-6i$ **(d)** 157 **(e)** The values are equal.

121. (a)

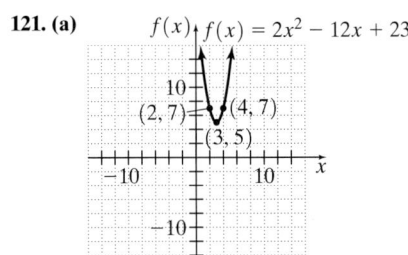

$f(x)=2x^2-12x+23$

(b) It is never equal to zero. **(c)** $x=3\pm\dfrac{i\sqrt{10}}{2}$

(d) The values in part **c**. **(e)** The graph represents real numbers, and the algebraic solutions are complex numbers.

122. (a)

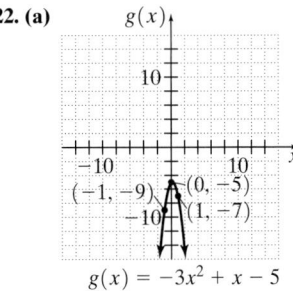

$g(x)=-3x^2+x-5$

(b) It is never equal to zero. **(c)** $x=\dfrac{-1\pm\sqrt{59}i}{-6}$

(d) The values in part **c**. **(e)** The graph represents real numbers, and the algebraic solutions are complex numbers.

11.7 CALCULATOR EXERCISES

1. $5i$ **2.** -3 **3.** $2+2i$ **4.** -2 **5.** $3+3i$ **6.** $10+10i$ **7.** $\dfrac{3}{2}-\dfrac{7}{2}i$ **8.** $\dfrac{2}{5}+\dfrac{16}{5}i$ **9.** $-\dfrac{9}{5}i$ **10.** 10 **11.** 10 **12.** 5.39 **13.** 22

14. 7 **15.** 1.73

CHAPTER 11 SUMMARY

Vocabulary Review

1. radical function **2.** conjugate **3.** radical equation in one variable **4.** imaginary unit i **5.** complex-number system

Reflections

1–11: Answers will vary.

CHAPTER 11 SECTION-BY-SECTION REVIEW

1. 15   **2.** 1.7   **3.** $\dfrac{7}{8}$ **4.** $\dfrac{3}{5}$ **5.** −6   **6.** not a real number   **7.** 12.247   **8.** −3.271   **9.** 2.627   **10.** all real numbers less than $\dfrac{7}{2}$; $\left[\dfrac{7}{2}, \infty\right)$

11. no restricted values; $(-\infty, \infty)$

12. $f(x) = 2\sqrt{x}$

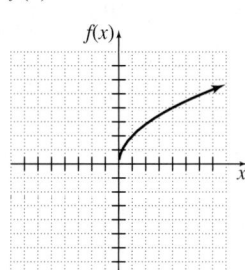

13. $y = \sqrt[3]{3x - 4}$

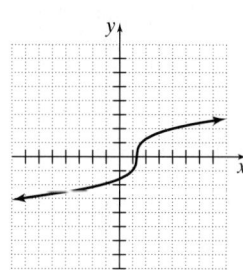

14. The variability is 6.78.   **15.** 11 inches

16. $\dfrac{5}{6}$ yard   **17.** The approximate radius is 2.5 cm and the diameter is 5 cm.

18. $f(x) = \sqrt{x(x + 5)}$; domain: $(-\infty, -5] \cup [0, \infty)$

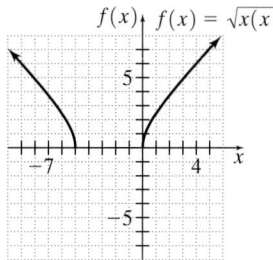

19. (a)

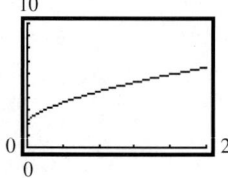

(b) increasing
(c) In 2008, barley will be \$4 per bushel.

20. (a) The price is \$11.40 if 25 units are sold. The price is \$11.10 if 35 units are sold.
(b) domain: $[0, \infty)$
(c)

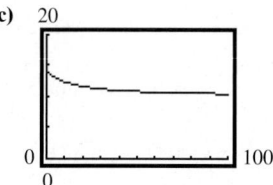

(d) decreasing
(e) The price is \$10.60 if 73 units are sold.

21. $\sqrt[3]{-64} = -4$ **22.** $-\sqrt[4]{16} = -2$ **23.** $\sqrt[4]{-16}$, not a real number   **24.** $-\dfrac{1}{\sqrt[3]{64}} = -\dfrac{1}{4}$ **25.** $-\left(\sqrt[3]{64}\right)^4 = -256$ **26.** $\left(\sqrt{-64}\right)^3$, not a real number   **27.** $\dfrac{1}{\left(\sqrt[4]{16}\right)^3} = \dfrac{1}{8}$ **28.** $\dfrac{1}{\left(\sqrt[4]{-16}\right)^3}$, not a real number   **29.** The restricted values are all real numbers less than $-\dfrac{9}{4}$. The domain is all real numbers greater than or equal to $-\dfrac{9}{4}$, or $\left[-\dfrac{9}{4}, \infty\right)$.   **30.** There are no restricted values. The domain is all real numbers, or $(-\infty, \infty)$.

31. $g(x) = x^{3/2} + 1$

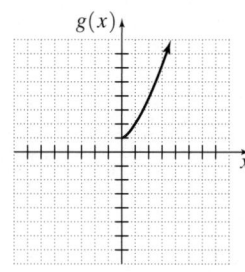

32. $y = (2x + 1)^{1/3}$

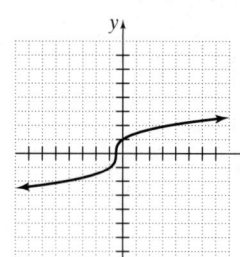

33.

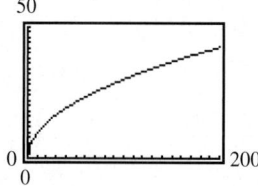

The approximate speed is 36.7 mph.

34. The average return was 1.11 or \$1.11 per dollar.

35. (a)

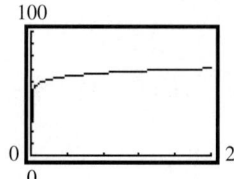

(b) increasing   **(c)** 65.2 million
(d) In 2023, the production will be 70 million.

36. 2   **37.** 128   **38.** $\left(\sqrt[3]{9}\right)^5 \approx 38.9$ **39.** $\dfrac{27}{8}$ **40.** $\dfrac{1}{27}$ **41.** 8   **42.** $\dfrac{1}{x^{1/6}}$ **43.** $y^{1/10}$ **44.** $z^{1/3}$

45. $\dfrac{b^{5/2}}{a^{5/4}}$ **46.** $16x^8 y^{12}$ **47.** $6a^{13/12}b$ **48.** $x - x^{2/3}$ **49.** The new side should be $\sqrt{5}$ times as large as the old side.   **50.** $30\sqrt{7}$ **51.** $-4\sqrt[3]{5}$ **52.** $3\sqrt[4]{2}$ **53.** $3x^2 y^3 z\sqrt{5y}$ **54.** $-4y^2\sqrt[3]{x^2 y}$

55. $(2x - 3)\sqrt{3}$ **56.** $4x^2$ **57.** $-2ab^2\sqrt[3]{5a}$ **58.** $(x - 2y)\sqrt{3x}$ **59.** $\dfrac{5}{8}$ **60.** $\dfrac{\sqrt{13}}{17}$

61. $\dfrac{3\sqrt{21}}{49}$ **62.** $\dfrac{\sqrt[3]{30}}{5}$ **63.** $\dfrac{\sqrt{30}}{6}$ **64.** $\dfrac{5a}{8b^2}$ **65.** $\dfrac{4\sqrt{5m}}{5}$ **66.** $\dfrac{z\sqrt[3]{6xy^2}}{2xy}$ **67.** $\dfrac{a\sqrt{2b}}{6b}$

68. The period is approximately 1.9 seconds.　　**69.** The time is about 0.79 second; the speed is about 4.43 feet per second.　　**70.** $7\sqrt{5}$

71. $11\sqrt{11}$　　**72.** $\dfrac{16}{15}\sqrt{15}$　　**73.** $7\sqrt[3]{2}$　　**74.** $2\sqrt{x}$　　**75.** $5ab\sqrt{ab}$　　**76.** $7\sqrt{2}-7$　　**77.** $6\sqrt{2a}+2a$　　**78.** $3-2\sqrt{5}$　　**79.** $5x-7y$

80. $x+16\sqrt{x}+64$　　**81.** $6x+3\sqrt[3]{x^2}$　　**82.** $\sqrt{3x}-\sqrt{6}$　　**83.** $1-\dfrac{5\sqrt{z}}{z}$　　**84.** $24\sqrt{5}-48$　　**85.** $\dfrac{x+4\sqrt{x}+4}{x-4}$　　**86.** -1　　**87.** $\sqrt{2x}+3$

88. It will require $24\sqrt{5}$ inches more material.　　**89.** The length is $(3+\sqrt{5})$ feet.　　**90.** The sum is $13\sqrt{5}$.　　**91.** 12　　**92.** 7　　**93.** 11　　**94.** 10

95. no solution　　**96.** -32　　**97.** 78　　**98.** -39 and 25　　**99.** $\dfrac{1}{4}$　　**100.** $\pm3\sqrt{3}$　　**101.** -6 and 2　　**102.** The skid mark would be approximately

152.4 feet long.　　**103.** It fell from a height of 579.6 feet.　　**104. (a)** 24 cakes were made.　　**(b)** 48 cakes were sold. (Actual revenue was $21.98.)

(c) The break-even point is 3 cakes for $0 profit.　　**105.** The final value is $2638.93.　　**106.** $8i$　　**107.** $\dfrac{5}{7}i$　　**108.** $2.5i$　　**109.** $5i\sqrt{2}$　　**110.** $\dfrac{9i\sqrt{2}}{2}$

111. $-20i\sqrt{2}$　　**112.** $12i$　　**113.** $4i$　　**114.** $66i$　　**115.** $4i$　　**116.** $\dfrac{13}{15}$　　**117.** $-30i$　　**118.** $-2\sqrt{3}+5i\sqrt{6}$　　**119.** $4\sqrt{2}$　　**120.** 4

121. $29-2i$　　**122.** $11-4i$　　**123.** $-26-7i$　　**124.** 130　　**125.** $4+5i$　　**126.** $3+2i$　　**127.** $7+3i$　　**128.** $8\sqrt{7}+6i\sqrt{13}$　　**129.** $6+3i\sqrt{2}$

130. $\dfrac{8}{15}-\dfrac{7}{90}i$　　**131.** $\sqrt{2}-4i\sqrt{3}$　　**132.** $z=\pm3i$　　**133.** $t=\pm5i$　　**134.** $a=\pm i\sqrt{11}$　　**135.** $r=5\pm6i$　　**136.** $x=-2\pm i\sqrt{3}$

137. $x=-\dfrac{1}{4}\pm\dfrac{3}{4}i$　　**138.** $m=-\dfrac{2}{5}\pm\dfrac{4}{5}i$　　**139.** $x=5\pm2i$　　**140.** $y=-\dfrac{1}{2}\pm\dfrac{3}{2}i$　　**141.** $z=-8\pm\sqrt{47}$　　**142.** $x=\dfrac{2}{3}\pm2i$

143. $x-0.5\pm1.1i$　　**144.** $x=\dfrac{3}{4}+\dfrac{1}{4}i$　　**145.** $x=\dfrac{9}{2}\pm\dfrac{i\sqrt{119}}{2}$　　**146.** $y=-\dfrac{1}{2}\pm\dfrac{i\sqrt{383}}{2}$　　**147.** $b=-\dfrac{11}{4}\pm\dfrac{i\sqrt{71}}{4}$　　**148.** The magnitude of

the total voltage is 59.0 volts.　　**149.** The magnitude of the impedance is $5\sqrt{2}$ ohms.　　**150.** $\pm\dfrac{4i\sqrt{6}}{3}$

CHAPTER 11 MIXED REVIEW

1. 14　　**2.** 2.1　　**3.** $-\dfrac{3}{4}$　　**4.** 4　　**5.** not a real number　　**6.** -3.072　　**7.** $\sqrt{121}=11$　　**8.** $\sqrt[3]{-125}=-5$　　**9.** $-\sqrt[4]{81}=-3$　　**10.** $\sqrt[4]{-81}$,

not a real number　　**11.** $\left(\sqrt[6]{729}\right)^5=243$　　**12.** $\left(\sqrt[6]{-729}\right)^5$, not a real number　　**13.** $\dfrac{1}{\left(\sqrt[3]{-8}\right)^2}=\dfrac{1}{4}$　　**14.** $\dfrac{1}{\left(\sqrt[4]{-81}\right)^3}$, not a real number　　**15.** 3

16. 2187　　**17.** $\left(\sqrt[3]{6}\right)^5\approx19.812$　　**18.** 6　　**19.** $\dfrac{64}{27}$　　**20.** $\dfrac{1}{\left(\sqrt{6}\right)^3}\approx0.068$　　**21.** $-\dfrac{6}{7}$　　**22.** $\dfrac{\sqrt{15}}{12}$　　**23.** $\dfrac{5}{13}$　　**24.** $-\dfrac{4}{5}$　　**25.** $5\sqrt{6}$　　**26.** $-4\sqrt[3]{7}$

27. $2\sqrt[4]{3}$　　**28.** $-3\sqrt[5]{2}$　　**29.** $5\sqrt{21}$　　**30.** $-\dfrac{4}{21}\sqrt{21}$　　**31.** $12\sqrt{13}$　　**32.** $11\sqrt{7}$　　**33.** $3\sqrt{2}-3$　　**34.** $60-2\sqrt{3}$　　**35.** 5　　**36.** $34\sqrt[3]{3}$

37. $\dfrac{1}{x^{1/12}}$　　**38.** $\dfrac{1}{z^{9/10}}$　　**39.** $\dfrac{q^{5/2}}{p^{5/4}}$　　**40.** $81x^{12}y^{16}$　　**41.** $6x^3yz^2\sqrt{2y}$　　**42.** $-4y^2\sqrt[3]{x^2y}$　　**43.** $6xy\sqrt{2y}$　　**44.** $-3a^2b^2\sqrt[3]{2b}$　　**45.** $(2x+7y)\sqrt{5}$

46. $\dfrac{6x}{7y^2}$　　**47.** $\dfrac{5\sqrt{3z}}{3}$　　**48.** $\dfrac{-3\sqrt[3]{a}}{b}$　　**49.** $\dfrac{\sqrt{2b}}{2b}$　　**50.** $\dfrac{\sqrt{xy}}{xy^2}$　　**51.** $2\sqrt{x}$　　**52.** $14cd\sqrt{cd}$　　**53.** $a+18\sqrt{a}+81$　　**54.** $3\sqrt{6a}+6a$

55. $3x-2y$　　**56.** $6x+10x\sqrt[3]{x}$　　**57.** $\sqrt{3x}-\sqrt{7}$　　**58.** $1-\dfrac{9\sqrt{m}}{m}$　　**59.** $6\left(\sqrt{7}-2\right)$　　**60.** $\dfrac{9+6\sqrt{x}+x}{9-x}$　　**61.** -1　　**62.** $5+\sqrt{7x}$

63. Restricted values are all real numbers less than 0.

64. Restricted values are all real numbers less than 0.

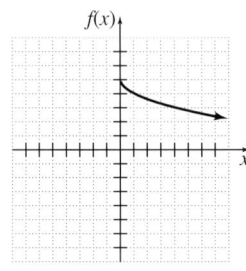

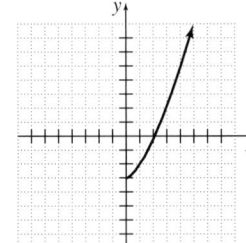

65. 2.681　　**66.** -0.429 and 1.061　　**67.** 81　　**68.** 45　　**69.** 8　　**70.** 7　　**71.** 4　　**72.** no solution　　**73.** -72　　**74.** 79

75. -248 and 238　　**76.** $\dfrac{1}{9}$　　**77.** $\pm3\sqrt{3}$　　**78.** $13i$　　**79.** $\dfrac{8}{9}i$　　**80.** $\dfrac{5i\sqrt{6}}{6}$　　**81.** $40i\sqrt{5}$　　**82.** $2.5i$　　**83.** $-6i\sqrt{3}$　　**84.** $30.85-4.23i$

85. $10i$　　**86.** $4i$　　**87.** $\dfrac{4}{3}-\dfrac{23}{18}i$　　**88.** $-6-4.35i$　　**89.** $59i$　　**90.** $-24i$　　**91.** $\sqrt{15}+2\sqrt{2}$　　**92.** 4　　**93.** $14-2i$　　**94.** $-72+54i$

95. $-3-2i$　　**96.** $7+6i$　　**97.** $\dfrac{5}{3}-6i$　　**98.** $\sqrt{2}+i\sqrt{5}$　　**99.** $\dfrac{17}{29}$　　**100.** $-\dfrac{37}{10}\pm\dfrac{i\sqrt{391}}{10}$　　**101.** $m=-7\pm5i$　　**102.** $y=3\pm i\sqrt{6}$

103. $x=8\pm i\sqrt{3}$　　**104.** $y=-\dfrac{5}{3}\pm\dfrac{i\sqrt{7}}{3}$　　**105.** $a=\pm9i$　　**106.** $b=\pm i\sqrt{13}$　　**107.** $y=\dfrac{3}{2}\pm\dfrac{\sqrt{281}}{2}$　　**108.** The side is 23 inches.

109. The variability is approximately 7.937.　　**110.** It fell from a height of 257.6 feet.　　**111.** The period is approximately 2.08 seconds.

112. $f(x) = \sqrt{(x+6)(x+2)}$; $(-\infty, -6] \cup [-2, \infty)$;

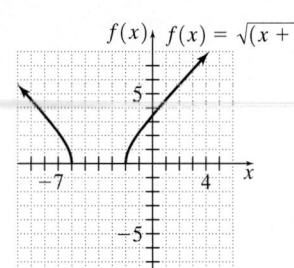

113. (a) $T(x)$

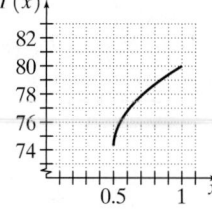

(b) increasing

(c) At 68% humidity, the temperature feels like 78 degrees.

114. (a) $R(x) = x\left(-\sqrt{x^2 - 5x - 14} + x\right)$

(b) The revenue of 100 units is $260.39; the revenue of 150 units is $385.30.

(c) domain: $[7, \infty)$

(d) $R(x)$

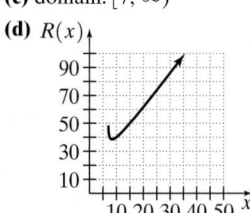

(e) decreasing: $(7, 8)$; increasing: $(8, \infty)$

(f) The revenue of 42 units is $115.80.

115. (a)

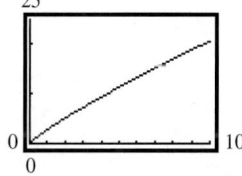

(b) increasing

(c) A library with 65 branches has a circulation of 14.24 million.

(d) A library with 20 branches has a circulation of 5 million.

116. The length is $(2 + \sqrt{3})$ feet.   **117. (a)** The cost of 12 meals was $10.77.   **(b)** The revenue of 40 meals was $20.07.   **(c)** The break-even point is 5 meals for $0 in profit.   **118.** The final value was $159,502.53.   **119.** -1 and 5   **120.** The magnitude of the current is approximately 5.8 amperes.   **121.** $y = \dfrac{\pm 3i\sqrt{2}}{2}$

CHAPTER 11 TEST

1. 14   **2.** 2.141   **3.** not a real number (or $5i$)   **4.** $-\dfrac{2}{5}$ **5.** 512   **6.** 9   **7.** $\dfrac{9}{4}$ **8.** $\sqrt{x}$ **9.** $2x - 5y$ **10.** $3x^2 y\sqrt{10y}$ **11.** $\dfrac{z\sqrt{6xz}}{2xy}$

12. $\dfrac{5\sqrt{y}}{7x}$ **13.** $7\sqrt{x}$ **14.** $10x + 15\sqrt[3]{x^2}$ **15.** $\dfrac{x + 3\sqrt{x} - 4}{x - 1}$ **16.** -5 **17.** 36   **18.** 5   **19.** 3

20. Restricted values are all real numbers less than -7.

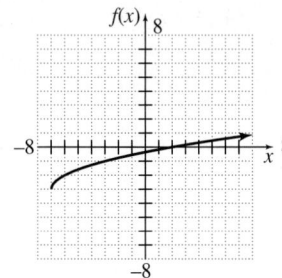

21. $16i$ **22.** $-28i$ **23.** $-\sqrt{14} - 4i\sqrt{7}$ **24.** $\dfrac{15}{17}$ **25.** 7   **26.** $-42 - 2i$ **27.** $3 + 7i$

28. $10.27 - 6.28i$ **29.** $-5\sqrt{3} + 3i\sqrt{5}$ **30.** $8 - 22i$ **31.** $x = \pm 14i$

32. $t = -2 \pm i\sqrt{15}$ **33.** $z = \pm 1.2i$ **34.** $x = 3 \pm 2i\sqrt{2}$ **35.** $x = \dfrac{1}{3} \pm \dfrac{i\sqrt{6}}{3}$

36. $y = \dfrac{3}{8} \pm \dfrac{i\sqrt{215}}{8}$ **37.** It will require $20\sqrt{5}$ inches more border.

38. $f(x) = \sqrt{x(x+1)}$; $(-\infty, -1] \cup [0, \infty)$;

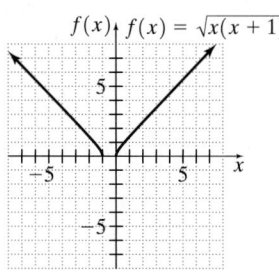

39. (a)

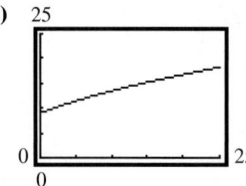

(b) increasing

(c) In 2009, one dollar will be equal to 13 pesos.

40. (a)

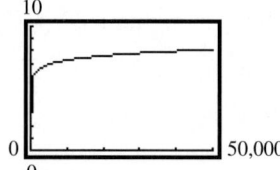

(b) increasing

(c) The magnitude was 7.4.

(d) The expected number of deaths from an earthquake of magnitude 8.0 is 41,559.

41. The time is about 1.86 seconds. The speed is about 3.23 feet per second.   **42.** The length is $(3 + \sqrt{2})$ feet.   **43. (a)** The cost of 24 cakes is $14.90.   **(b)** The revenue from 23 cakes is about $15.   **(c)** The break-even point is 9 cakes for a profit of $0.   **44.** The final value was $2199.11.   **45.** Answers will vary.   **46.** $y = \pm 4i$ **47.** The magnitude of the total voltage is approximately 97.4 volts.   **48.** Answers will vary.

CHAPTERS P–11 CUMULATIVE REVIEW EXERCISES

1. $\dfrac{y^2}{x}$ **2.** $9xy^{3/2}$ **3.** $\dfrac{27t^3}{64s^6}$ **4.** $5x^3 + 6x^2y + 2xy^2$ **5.** $-2.8a^2 - 6.31ab + 4.4b^2$ **6.** $-13.6m^3n^3p$ **7.** $6a^2 + 10ab - 4b^2$ **8.** $4x^2 - 9$

9. $4x^2 + 12x + 9$ **10.** $-5xy^2$ **11.** $1 + \dfrac{2}{m} - \dfrac{4n}{m^2}$ **12.** $\dfrac{x - 1}{x - 3}$ **13.** $\dfrac{x^2 + x + 6}{(x + 2)(x - 2)}$ **14.** $-\dfrac{3x^2 + 22x + 42}{(x + 2)(x - 3)(x + 4)}$ **15.** $\dfrac{2a - 1}{2a + 5}$

16. $\dfrac{x + 5}{2xy(2x + 1)}$ **17.** $-3\sqrt{2y}$ **18.** $5a\sqrt[3]{a^2b^2}$ **19.** -2 **20.** $\dfrac{c}{a}\sqrt{3c}$ **21.** $\dfrac{x + 3\sqrt{x} + 2}{x - 1}$ **22.** $x^{7/6} - x^{5/4}$ **23.** $(4a + 5b)(4a - 5b)$

24. $(x - 4)(x + 2)$ **25.** $3(x - 5)(x + 2)$ **26.** -11

27.

Domain: all real numbers
Range: all real numbers

28.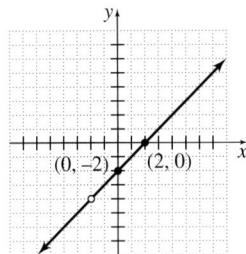

$x = -2$

Domain: all real numbers
Range: all real numbers ≥ 2

29.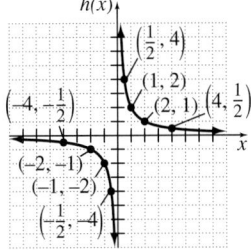

$x = \dfrac{1}{4}$

Domain: all real numbers
Range: all real numbers $\leq \dfrac{9}{8}$

30.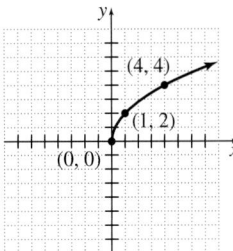

Domain: all real numbers $\neq -2$
Range: all real numbers $\neq -4$

31.

Domain: all real numbers $\neq 0$
Range: all real numbers $\neq 0$

32.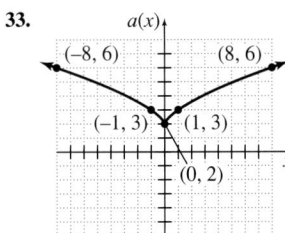

Domain: all real numbers ≥ 0
Range: all real numbers ≥ 0

33.

Domain: all real numbers
Range: all real numbers ≥ 2

34. 4 **35.** $\dfrac{3 \pm 3i\sqrt{3}}{2}$ **36.** -5 and 3 **37.** $\dfrac{-3 \pm \sqrt{41}}{4}$ **38.** -5 **39.** $\pm 2\sqrt{7}$ **40.** $\dfrac{19}{2}$ **41.** $\left(-\dfrac{3}{2}, 6\right)$ **42.** $(5, 3)$ **43.** $y = -x - 2$

44. $y = \dfrac{3}{2}x + 4$ **45.** $y = x^2 + 3x - 4$ **46.** The rectangle is 12 feet by 16 feet. **47.** The possible y-coordinates are 0 or 8. **48.** Yes, they can finish raking the leaves. **49.** The company must sell at least 1429 items in order to break even. **50.** The skydiver was free-falling for about 21.65 seconds.

CHAPTER 12

SECTION 12.1 EXERCISES

1. $h^{-1} = \{(5, -3), (4, -2), (3, -1), (2, 0), (1, 1), (0, 2)\}$ **2.** $d^{-1} = \{(25, 5), (16, 4), (9, 3), (4, 2), (1, 1), (0, 0)\}$

3. $A^{-1} = \{(6, 3), (7, 2), (8, 1), (8, 0), (7, -1), (6, -2)\}$ **4.** $J^{-1} = \{(1, -4), (2, 3), (1, -2), (2, 1), (1, 0), (2, -1)\}$ **5.** $y = \dfrac{1}{2}x + 4$ **6.** $y = \dfrac{1}{3}x - 2$

7. $y = -\dfrac{1}{3}x + \dfrac{2}{3}$ **8.** $y = -\dfrac{1}{2}x + \dfrac{5}{2}$ **9.** $y = \dfrac{4}{3}x - 12$ **10.** $y = -\dfrac{3}{2}x + 2$ **11.** $y = 8x + 20$ **12.** $y = -2.5x + 4.5$ **13.** $y = \pm\sqrt{x + 2}$

14. $y = \sqrt[3]{x} - 1$ **15.** function; yes **16.** function; no **17.** function; no **18.** function; yes **19.** not a function **20.** not a function

21. yes **22.** no **23.** no **24.** yes **25.** yes **26.** yes

27.

x	$f(x)$	x	$g(x)$	inverses
0	-3	-3	0	
1	4	4	1	

28.

x	$f(x)$	x	$g(x)$	inverses
2	0	0	2	
1	9	9	1	

29.

x	$f(x)$	x	$g(x)$	inverses
-1	3	3	-1	
1	21	21	1	

30.

x	$f(x)$	x	$g(x)$	not inverses
1	-6	18	1	
2	-9	12	2	

31.

x	$f(x)$	x	$g(x)$	not inverses
0	0	-2	0	
2	64	6	2	

32.

x	$f(x)$	x	$g(x)$	inverses
-1	-2	-2	-1	
2	1	1	2	

33. not an inverse   **34.** inverse   **35.** inverse   **36.** not an inverse   **37.** inverse   **38.** not an inverse

39. $g^{-1}(x) = \frac{1}{3}x + 2$

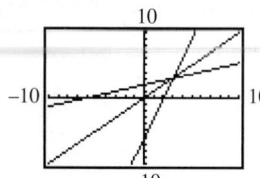

40. $f^{-1}(x) = -\frac{1}{4}x + \frac{1}{2}$

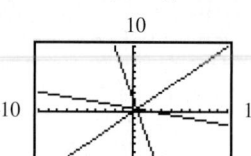

41. $y^{-1} = \frac{3}{2}x + 6$

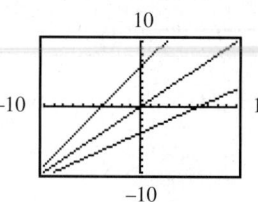

42. $y^{-1} = -\frac{5}{2}x + 10$

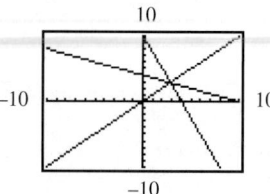

43. $h^{-1}(x) = \pm\sqrt{x+1}$

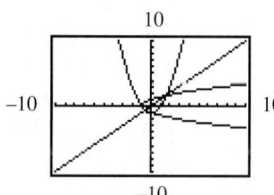

44. $r^{-1}(x) = \pm\sqrt{2-x}$

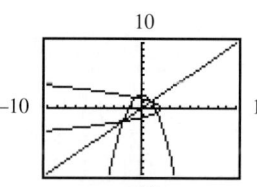

45. $y^{-1} = \sqrt[3]{3x+12}$

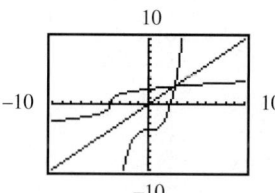

46. $y^{-1} = \sqrt[3]{4x-8}$

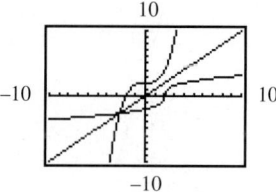

47. $f(x) = 1500 + 0.02x$
$f^{-1}(x) = 50x - 75{,}000$
The inverse function represents the amount of Julia's transactions in terms of her monthly income.

48. $f(x) = 125 + 0.15x$
$f^{-1}(x) = 6\frac{2}{3}x - 833\frac{1}{3}$
The inverse function represents the amount of Harvey's sales in terms of his weekly income.

49. $f(x) = 55x$
$f^{-1}(x) = \frac{x}{55}$
The inverse function represents the time in terms of the distance traveled.

50. $f(x) = 30x$
$f^{-1}(x) = \frac{x}{30}$
The inverse function represents the number of hours in terms of the number of pairs in jeans.

51. $f(x) = 2000 + 10x$
$f^{-1}(x) = \frac{1}{10}x - 200$
The inverse function represents the number of months in terms of the total amount to repay.

52. $f(x) = 1500 + 6x; f^{-1}(x) = \frac{1}{6}x - 250.$
The inverse function represents the number of months in terms of the amount earned.

53. $C(x) = 9.95 + 0.6x$
$C^{-1}(x) = \frac{x - 9.95}{0.6}$
The inverse function represents the number of songs burned.

54. $M(x) = 100 - 0.02x$
$M^{-1}(x) = \frac{x - 100}{-0.02}$
The inverse function represents the amount of purchases made for a given membership fee.

55. $V(x) = 15{,}000 - 1750x$
$V^{-1}(x) = \frac{x - 15{,}000}{-1750}$
The inverse function represents the year in which it has a given value.

56. $A(x) = 10{,}000 - 83x$
$A^{-1}(x) = \frac{x - 10{,}000}{-83}$
The inverse function represents the month in which she owes a given amount.

57. $y = \frac{1}{3}x - \frac{5}{3}; y = 3x + 5;$
they are inverses.

58. $y = -9x + 15; y = -\frac{1}{9}x + \frac{15}{9};$
they are inverses.

59. $y = \frac{3}{5}x + 4; y = \frac{3}{5}x - \frac{20}{3};$
they are inverses.

60. $y = 2.3x - 3.1; y \approx 0.44x + 1.35$
they are inverses.

12.1 CALCULATOR EXERCISES

1. $y^{-1} = \pm\sqrt{\frac{x+4}{0.3}}$

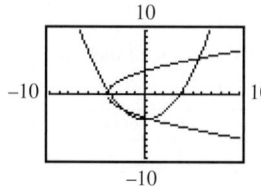

2. $f^{-1}(x) = \sqrt[3]{\frac{x-2}{0.1}}$

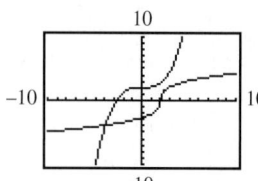

3. $g^{-1}(x) = \left(\frac{x+1.5}{5}\right)^2$

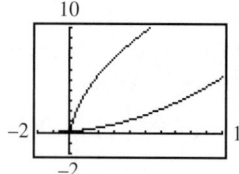

4. $y^{-1} = \frac{1}{x-2}$

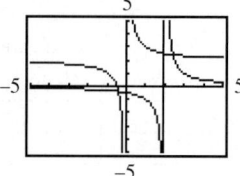

SECTION 12.2 EXERCISES

1. exponential   **2.** not exponential   **3.** exponential   **4.** exponential   **5.** not exponential   **6.** not exponential   **7.** exponential

8. exponential   **9.** not exponential   **10.** exponential   **11.** exponential   **12.** exponential   **13.** 4096   **14.** 65,536   **15.** $\frac{1}{256}$ **16.** $\frac{1}{16}$

17. 4   **18.** 8   **19.** ≈50.453   **20.** 1   **21.** ≈0.875   **22.** 0.512   **23.** ≈1.160   **24.** ≈0.689   **25.** ≈1.880   **26.** ≈0.369

27. $f(x) = 4^x$

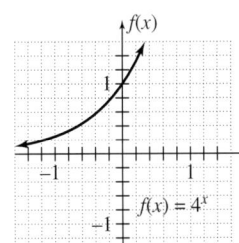

28. $C(x) = 3^x$

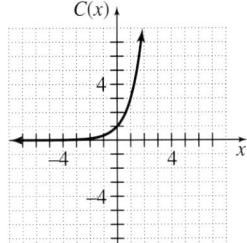

29. $g(x) = 4^{-x}$

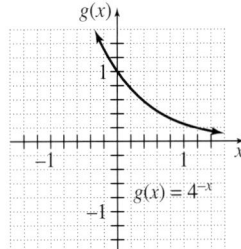

30. $D(x) = 3^{-2x}$

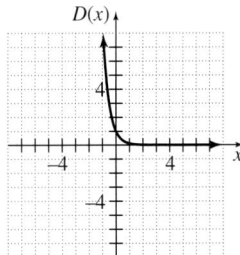

31. $h(x) = 4^{2x}$

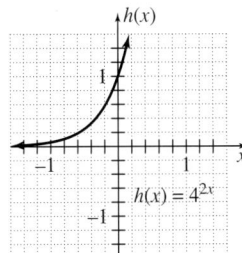

32. $F(x) = 3^{2x-1}$

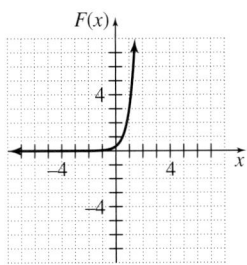

33. $j(x) = 4^{1/2x}$

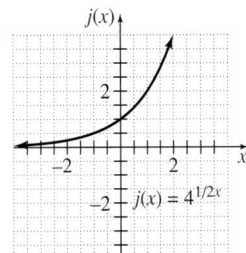

34. $K(x) = 3^{x/4}$

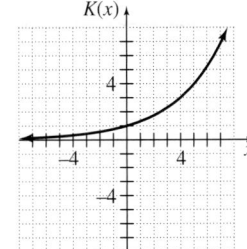

35. $k(x) = 4^{x-1}$

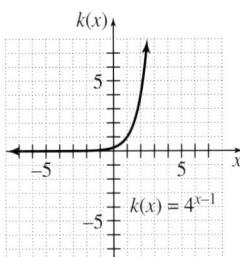

36. $L(x) = 3^x + 1$

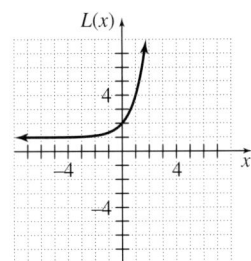

37. $m(x) = 4^x - 1$

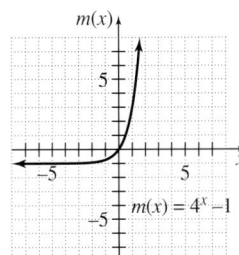

38. $M(x) = 3^{x+1} - 1$

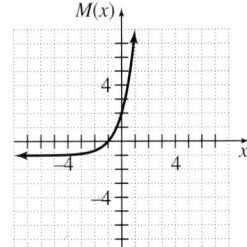

39. $y = e^{1/2x}$

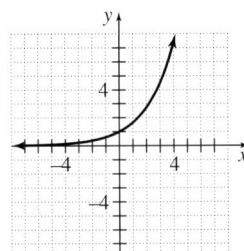

40. $y = e^{0.2x}$

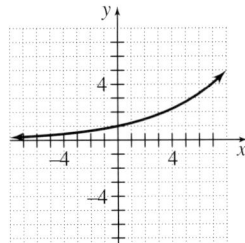

41. $y = \frac{1}{2}e^x$

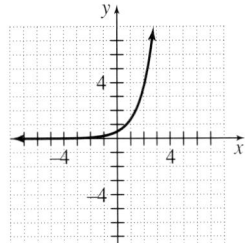

42. $y = 0.2e^x$

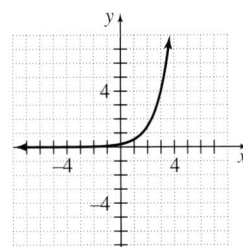

43. $y = e^{-1/2x}$

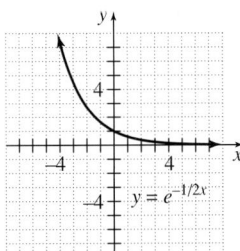

44. $y = e^{-0.2x}$

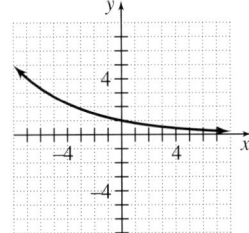

45. $y = e^x + \frac{1}{2}$

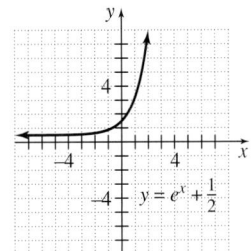

46. $y = e^{0.2x} + 0.2$

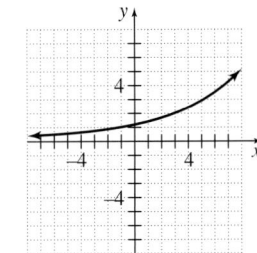

47. $y = \dfrac{1}{2}e^{1/2x}$

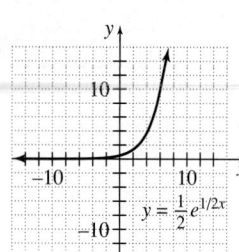

48. $y = 0.2e^{0.2x}$

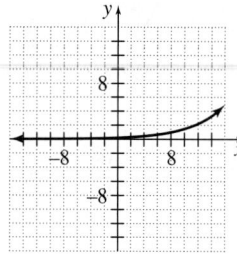

49.

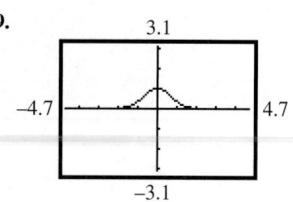

Domain: the set of all real numbers
Range: $(0, 1]$
Increasing $x < 0$
Decreasing $x > 0$
Maximum of 1 at $x = 0$

50.

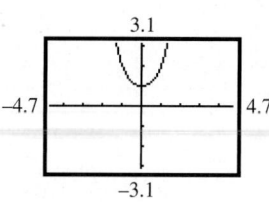

Domain: the set of all real numbers
Range: $[1, \infty)$
Increasing: $x > 0$
Decreasing: $x < 0$
Minimum of 1 at $x = 0$

51.

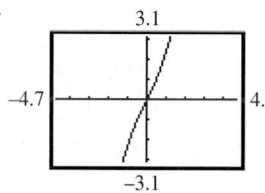

Domain: the set of all real numbers
Range: the set of all real numbers
Increasing on its domain
No max/min values

52.

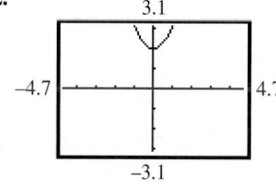

Domain: the set of all real numbers
Range: $[2, \infty)$
Increasing: $x > 0$
Decreasing: $x < 0$
Minimum of 2 at $x = 0$

53. $A = 6000(1.055)^t$

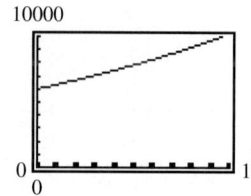

The investment was worth $8728.08.

54. $A = 3000(1.062)^t$

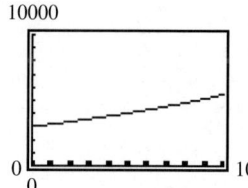

The investment was worth $3816.10.

55. $A = 8000e^{0.048t}$

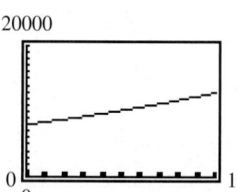

She will have earned $2169.99.

56. $A = 4500e^{0.075t}$

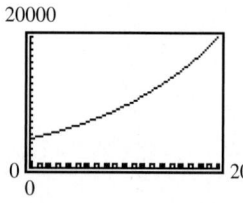

The investment will be worth $9526.50

57. The amounts that need to be deposited are $714.29, $587.64, and $282.67.   **58.** The amounts that need to be deposited are $917.43, $649.93, and $178.43.   **59.** The effective annual rates for an investment of this type are 7.123%, 7.186%, and 7.229%.   **60.** The effective annual rates for an investment of this type are 1.038%, 1.047%, and 1.052%.   **61.** In 2010, the emissions will be 7416 million metric tons of carbon equivalent. **62.** In 2010, there will be 54,115 new cases.

12.2 CALCULATOR EXERCISES

Part 1

1. (a)

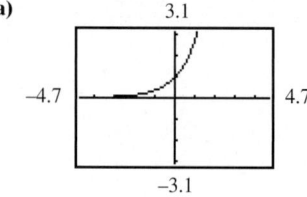

(b)

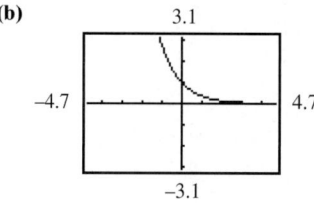

2. (a)

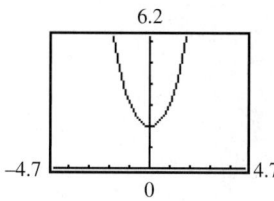

(b)

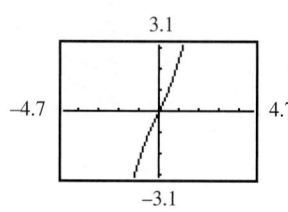

3. (a)

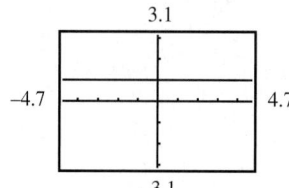

(b)

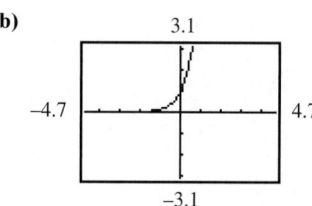

4. (a)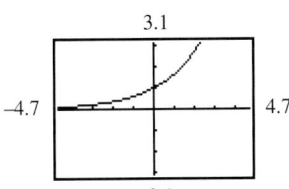

(b)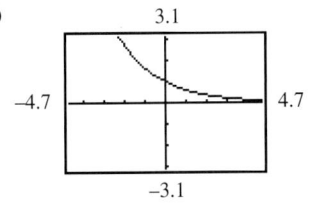

5. (a)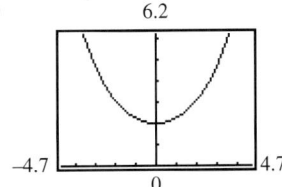

(b)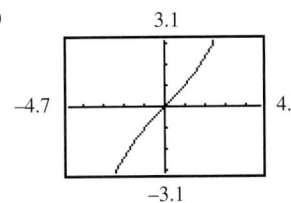

6. (a)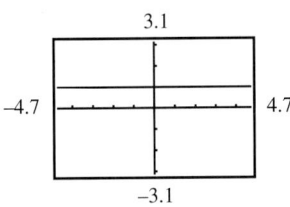

(b)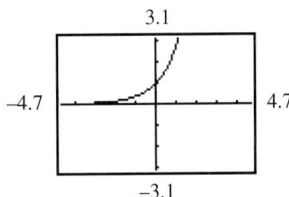

Part 2

1. $P(x) = 30.056(0.938)^x$, where x is the number of years after 2000; 18.012%; 2013   **2.** $P(x) = 10,715(0.908)^x$, where x is the number of years after 2001; 4081.790 thousand troy ounces; 2013   **3.** $S(x) = 8,456,491(0.951)^x$, where x is the number of years after 2001; 5,116,764; 2013

SECTION 12.3 EXERCISES

1. $f^{-1}(x) = \log_{11} x$ **2.** $h^{-1}(x) = \log_{15} x$ **3.** $g^{-1}(x) = \log_6 x$ **4.** $p^{-1}(x) = \log_{29} x$ **5.** $H^{-1}(x) = \log_k x$ **6.** $J^{-1}(x) = \log_b x$ **7.** 6   **8.** 7
9. 5   **10.** 6   **11.** 4   **12.** 3   **13.** -3 **14.** -2 **15.** -1 **16.** -3 **17.** -4 **18.** -3 **19.** 1   **20.** 4   **21.** -4 **22.** -6 **23.** 3
24. 7   **25.** -5 **26.** -8 **27.** -5 **28.** -7 **29.** ≈ 1.176 **30.** ≈ 1.362 **31.** ≈ -1.079 **32.** ≈ -1.279 **33.** ≈ 0.130 **34.** ≈ 1.097
35. ≈ 2.639 **36.** ≈ 3.296 **37.** ≈ 1.047 **38.** ≈ 2.451 **39.** ≈ -1.609 **40.** ≈ -2.708 **41.** ≈ 1.792 **42.** ≈ 2.070 **43.** ≈ 3.322
44. ≈ 3.322 **45.** ≈ 0.657 **46.** ≈ 2.447 **47.** ≈ -0.252 **48.** ≈ -0.465 **49.** ≈ 1.302 **50.** ≈ 1.984 **51.** ≈ 1.616 **52.** ≈ 0.679
53. ≈ -1.209 **54.** ≈ -0.442

55. $Y1 = \dfrac{\log x}{\log 5}$

56. $Y1 = \dfrac{\log x}{\log 7}$

57. $Y1 = \log(x + 2)$

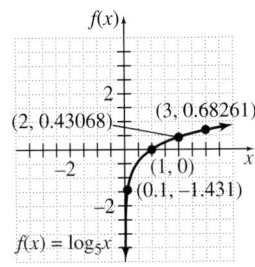

$f(x) = \log_5 x$

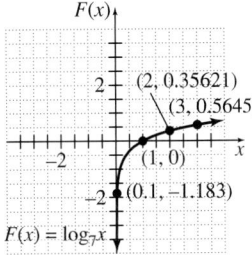

$F(x) = \log_7 x$

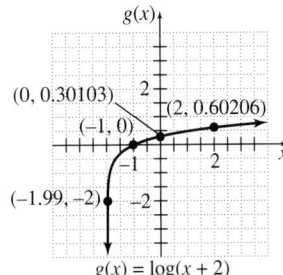

$g(x) = \log(x + 2)$

58. $Y1 = \log(x - 2)$

59. $Y1 = \ln(x + 2)$

60. $Y1 = \ln(x - 2)$

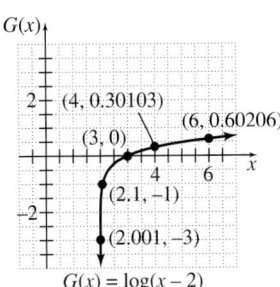

$G(x) = \log(x - 2)$

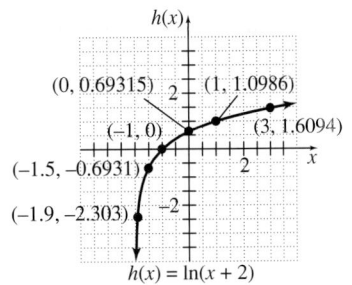

$h(x) = \ln(x + 2)$

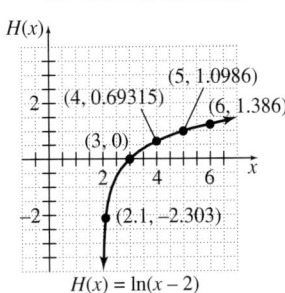

$H(x) = \ln(x - 2)$

61.

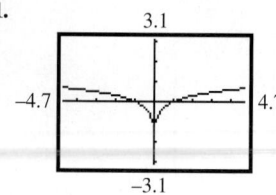

Domain: the set of all real numbers except 0
Range: $(-1, \infty)$
Increasing: $x > 0$
Decreasing: $x < 0$
No max/min values $(0, -1)$ is not a true minimum

62.

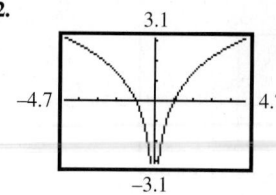

Domain: the set of all real numbers except 0
Range: the set of all real numbers
Increasing: $x > 0$
Decreasing: $x < 0$
No max/min values

63.

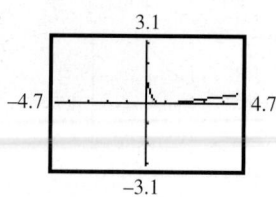

Domain: $(0, \infty)$
Range: $[0, \infty)$
Increasing: $x > 1$
Decreasing: $0 < x < 1$
Minimum value of 0 at $x = 1$

64.

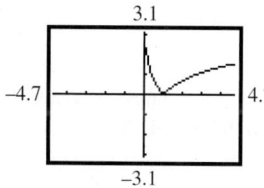

Domain: $(0, \infty)$
Range: $[0, \infty)$
Increasing: $x > 1$
Decreasing: $0 < x < 1$
Minimum value of 0 at $x = 1$

65. The hydrogen ion concentration is 0.0000006 mole per liter.   **66.** The hydrogen ion concentration is 0.001 mole per liter.   **67.** The pH is approximately 8.5.   **68.** The pH is approximately 6.4.   **69.** The larger earthquake's intensity was 63095.7 times as great as the smaller earthquake's intensity.   **70.** The larger earthquake's intensity was 39.8 times as great as the smaller earthquake's intensity.   **71.** In 2007, there will be 327 such stations. In 2020, there will be 315 such stations.   **72.** In 2007, cassette sales will be 1.11% of recorded music sales. In 2019, cassette sales will no longer be part of recorded music sales.

12.3 CALCULATOR EXERCISES

Part 1

1.

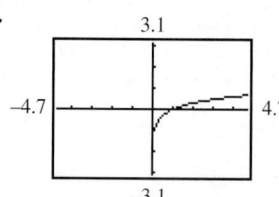

2.

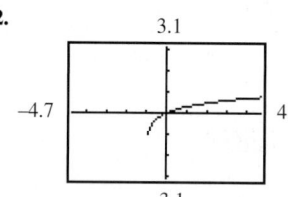

3.

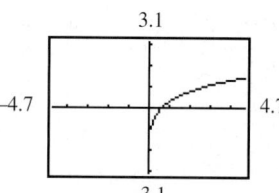

4.

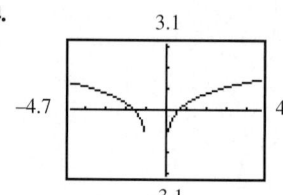

5.

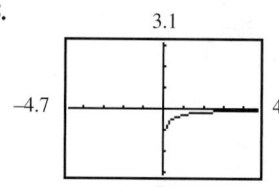

6.

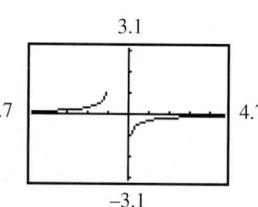

Part 2

1. $P(x) = 8.451 + 0.696 \ln x$, where x is the number of years after 2000; 9.898%; 2010   **2.** $P(x) = 25,499 + 4236 \ln x$, where x is the number of years after 2000; 35,253 thousand tons; 2013   **3.** $I(x) = 7467 + 600 \ln x$, where x is the number of years after 2000; about 8715 billion dollars; 2013

SECTION 12.4 EXERCISES

1. $\log 12 + \log a$ **2.** $\ln 25 + \ln c$ **3.** $3 \ln x$ **4.** $3 \log z$ **5.** $\log_5 x - 1$ **6.** $1 - \log_7 y$ **7.** $\log 2 + 2 \log x - \log y$

8. $2 \log x - \log 5 - 3 \log y$ **9.** $3 \log_3 x + 2 \log_3 y$ **10.** $2 \log_2 a + 4 \log_2 b$ **11.** $\frac{1}{3} \ln x + \frac{2}{3} \ln y$ **12.** $\frac{3}{4} \log x + \frac{1}{4} \log y$

13. $\frac{1}{2} \log 2 + \frac{1}{2} \log x - \frac{1}{3} \log y$ **14.** $\frac{1}{3} \ln 3 + \frac{2}{3} \ln x - \frac{1}{2} \ln 2 - \frac{1}{2} \ln y$ **15.** $1 + \log_3 a$ **16.** $1 + \log_5 z$ **17.** $\log_5 10 + \log_5 x + \log_5 y$

18. $\log_3 x + \log_3 y - \log_3 6$ **19.** $1 + 2 \log_a b$ **20.** $\log_6 3 + \log_6 a + 2 \log_6 b$ **21.** $\log x(x + 5)$ **22.** $\log(x^2 - 1)$ **23.** $\ln x^2 y^3$ **24.** $\ln \frac{b^3}{c^2}$

25. $\log_3 \frac{(x + 3)^2}{x - 1}$ **26.** $\log_5(a - 5)^5 a^2$ **27.** $\ln \frac{\sqrt{x}}{\sqrt[5]{x + 1}}$ **28.** $\log \frac{\sqrt[4]{z}}{\sqrt[3]{z + 5}}$ **29.** $\log \frac{y}{z}$ **30.** $\log pq^2$ **31.** The power gain is approximately

11.249 decibels.   **32.** The power gain is approximately 11.761 decibels.   **33.** The depth is approximately 15.033 units.   **34.** The depth is approximately 17.918 units.   **35.** It will take approximately 22 years.   **36.** It will take approximately 15.4 years.   **37.** It will take approximately

15.4 years.   **38.** It will take approximately $12\frac{1}{2}$ years.

12.4 CALCULATOR EXERCISES

1.
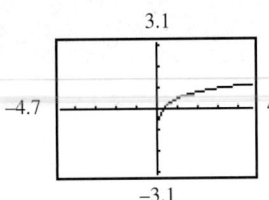

2.
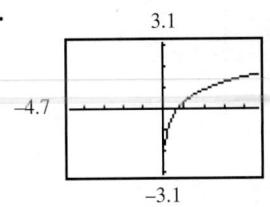

3.
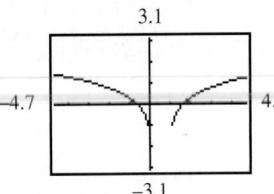

4.
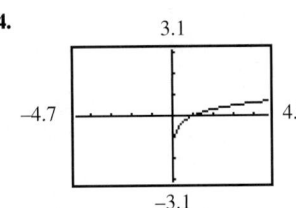

5. no   **6.** no   **7.** The logarithm of a sum is not equivalent to the sum of the logarithms.
8. The logarithm of a difference is not equivalent to the difference of the logarithms.

SECTION 12.5 EXERCISES

1. logarithmic   **2.** exponential   **3.** neither   **4.** logarithmic   **5.** exponential   **6.** neither   **7.** neither   **8.** neither   **9.** 2   **10.** 2

11. ≈0.693   **12.** ≈0.231   **13.** 0   **14.** ≈−0.631   **15.** ≈0.405   **16.** ≈−0.693   **17.** 1   **18.** $\frac{1}{2}$ **19.** 3   **20.** 4   **21.** $\frac{1}{2}$ and 3

22. 1 and 4   **23.** −2 and 5   **24.** −5 and $\frac{3}{2}$ **25.** no solution   **26.** no solution   **27.** all real numbers   **28.** all real numbers   **29.** 2

30. 11   **31.** $-\frac{1}{2}$ **32.** 5   **33.** −3 and $\frac{1}{2}$ **34.** −2 and $\frac{1}{3}$ **35.** ≈2.773   **36.** ≈0.602   **37.** ≈1.984   **38.** ≈1.228   **39.** 3125   **40.** 16

41. 1   **42.** 10   **43.** 1   **44.** ≈7.389   **45.** 9   **46.** 625   **47.** $\frac{1}{125}$ **48.** $\frac{1}{81}$ **49.** 7   **50.** 5   **51.** ≈1.649   **52.** ≈0.135   **53.** $\frac{1}{100}$

54. 100   **55.** 1   **56.** ≈2.718   **57.** 3   **58.** 5   **59.** 8   **60.** 11   **61.** all real numbers greater than 0   **62.** all real numbers greater than 0

63. no solution   **64.** 0   **65.** 4   **66.** $\frac{3}{4}$ **67.** $\frac{2}{3}$ **68.** 2   **69.** 2   **70.** 7   **71.** $A(t) = 210e^{0.0567t}$; in 2010, approximately $652.7 million will

be spent.   **72.** $A(t) = 52e^{0.0283t}$; in 2010, approximately 91.6 million households will have cable television in the United States.   **73.** It will double its value in the year 2036.   **74.** It will be 1.5 times its value in the year 2021.   **75.** The decay factor ≈−0.154; it will take approximately 0.131 billion years.   **76.** It will take approximately 0.684 billion years.   **77.** When the temperature is 25 degrees, 20 hours had passed.   **78.** When the temperature is 20 degrees, 26 hours had passed.   **79.** The employee needs to work 8 weeks to reach this level.   **80.** The student will score 43 on the first test, 68 on the tenth test, and 75 on the 16th test. The highest score is 79.

12.5 CALCULATOR EXERCISES

Answers will vary.

CHAPTER 12 SUMMARY

Vocabulary Review

1. one-to-one function   **2.** inverse   **3.** horizontal-line test   **4.** exponential function   **5.** natural logarithmic function

Reflections

1–7. Answers will vary.

CHAPTER 12 SECTION-BY-SECTION REVIEW

1. $h^{-1} = \{(4.5, 2), (3.5, 4), (2.5, 6), (1.5, 8), (0.5, 10)\}$ **2.** $y^{-1} = \frac{1}{3}x + 3$ **3.** $y^{-1} = \pm\sqrt{x - 1}$ **4.** $y^{-1} = \sqrt[3]{x + 1}$ **5.** not a function

6. function   **7.** no   **8.** yes   **9.** no

10. $f^{-1}(x) = \frac{4}{3}x + 4$ **11.** $y^{-1} = \sqrt[3]{x - 8}$ **12.**

x	$f(x)$	x	$g(x)$	inverses
−2	1	1	−2	
5	2	2	5	

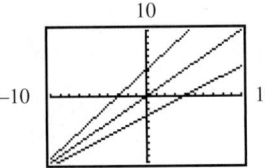

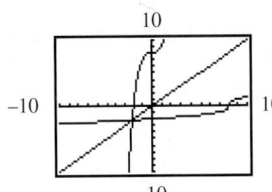

13. inverses; answers will vary   **14.** $f(x) = 570 + 0.03x$; $f^{-1}(x) = 33.\overline{3}x - 19{,}000$, which represents the value of all sales in terms of Motomo's weekly salary.   **15.** $f(x) = 15x$; $f^{-1}(x) = \frac{x}{15}$, which represents the number of hours in terms of the number of problems solved.   **16.** exponential

17. not exponential   **18.** 1.4641   **19.** ≈0.826   **20.** 1   **21.** 1.1   **22.** ≈1.059   **23.** ≈1.309

24.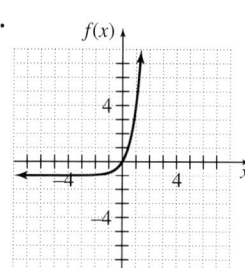

25.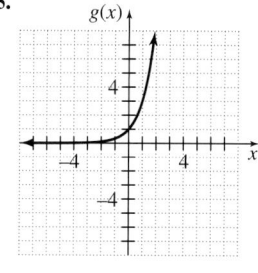

26.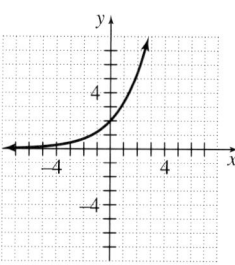

27.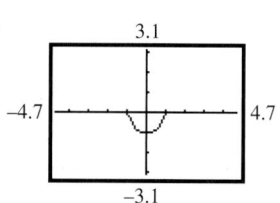

Domain: the set of all real numbers
Range: $[-1, 0)$
Increasing: $x > 0$
Decreasing: $x < 0$
Minimum of -1 at $x = 0$

28. $A = 1000(1.04)^t$

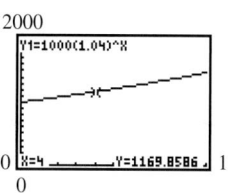

The investment was worth
$1169.86 after 4 years.

29. The estimated revenue predicted for the year 2010 will be about $168 million.

30.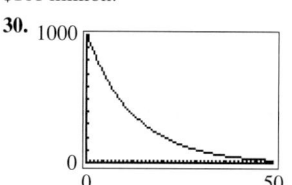

The amounts that need to be deposited are $925.93 (1 year), $680.58 (5 years), and $214.55 (20 years).

31. $h^{-1}(x) = \log_8 x$ **32.** $A^{-1}(x) = \dfrac{1}{k}\ln\dfrac{x}{A}$ **33.** 2   **34.** 4   **35.** -3 **36.** ≈ 0.176 **37.** 4   **38.** ≈ 2.303 **39.** -2 **40.** ≈ -0.222

41. ≈ 1.683

42. $Y1 = \dfrac{\log x}{\log 3}$

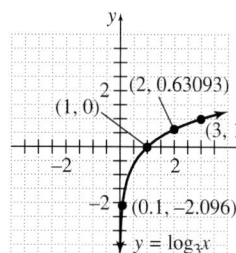

43. $Y1 = \ln(x - 2)$

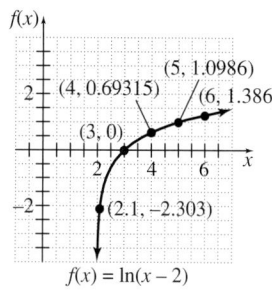

$f(x) = \ln(x - 2)$

44.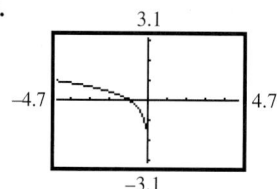

Domain: $(-\infty, 0)$
Range: the set of all real numbers
Increasing: does not increase
Decreasing: decreases on its domain
No max/min values

45. The pH is approximately 2.208.   **46.** The hydrogen ion concentration is 3.98×10^{-8} mole per liter.   **47.** $\log 2 + 4 \log x$

48. $1 + \log_7 x - \log_7 y$ **49.** $\ln 25 + 2\ln x + 3\ln y + \ln z$ **50.** $\dfrac{1}{3}\ln 2 + \dfrac{2}{3}\ln x + \dfrac{1}{3}\ln y - \dfrac{1}{2}\ln y - \dfrac{1}{2}\ln z$ **51.** $\log(x^2 - 9)$ **52.** $\ln\dfrac{x^5}{y^3}$

53. $\log\dfrac{\sqrt[3]{x}}{\sqrt{y}}$ **54.** $\log ad$ **55.** It will take approximately 18.3 years.   **56.** exponential   **57.** neither   **58.** logarithmic   **59.** neither

60. exponential   **61.** neither   **62.** 4   **63.** ≈ -0.322 **64.** 0   **65.** $\dfrac{3}{2}$ **66.** no solution   **67.** -3 and 1   **68.** all real numbers

69. ≈ 0.262 **70.** 2.569×10^{41} **71.** 19,683   **72.** ≈ 2.718 **73.** 1   **74.** $\dfrac{1}{1000}$ **75.** $\dfrac{1}{4}$ **76.** ≈ 1.396 **77.** -5 and $\dfrac{3}{2}$ **78.** 5

79. no solution   **80.** all real numbers greater than 0   **81.** $A(t) = 3.022e^{0.035t}$ The model projects that in 2015 the resident population for those 85 years and older will be about 7.249 million. This is higher than the given number.   **82.** The time since the skeleton's demise is 3351 years.   **83.** The body was deceased 5.8 hours.

CHAPTER 12 MIXED REVIEW

1. -3 **2.** 3   **3.** -6 **4.** ≈ 0.708 **5.** -3 **6.** ≈ 4.605 **7.** 1   **8.** ≈ -0.560 **9.** ≈ 3.262 **10.** $\log 3 + 2\log x + \log y$

11. $2 + \log_3 a - \log_3 b$ **12.** $\ln 100 + 3\ln p + 2\ln q + \ln r$ **13.** $\dfrac{1}{5}\log 6 + \dfrac{3}{5}\log x - \dfrac{1}{2}\log x - \dfrac{1}{2}\log y$ **14.** $\log(x - 3)$ **15.** $\log\dfrac{c^2}{d^5}$

16. $\ln\dfrac{\sqrt{x}}{y^3}$ **17.** $\log 6y^2$ **18.** $y^{-1} = 5 - x$ **19.** $y^{-1} = \pm\sqrt{1 - x}$ **20.** $y^{-1} = \sqrt[3]{4 - x}$ **21.** $y^{-1} = -\dfrac{5}{4}x + \dfrac{5}{2}$ **22.** $m^{-1}(x) = \log_5 x$

23. $G^{-1}(x) = \log_b\left(\dfrac{x}{a}\right)$ **24.** ≈ 1.088 **25.** $\dfrac{13}{4}$ **26.** 2   **27.** $1\dfrac{2}{3}$ **28.** ≈ 1.296 **29.** ≈ 5.074

30.

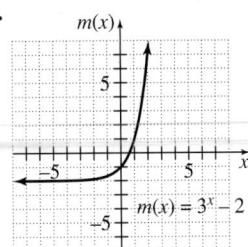

$m(x) = 3^x - 2$

31.

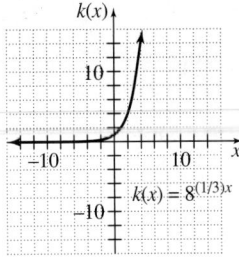

$k(x) = 8^{(1/3)x}$

32.

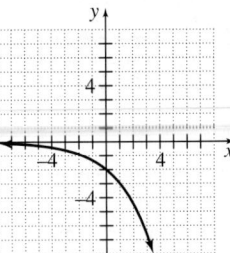

33.

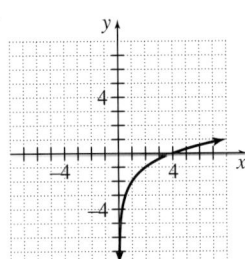

34.

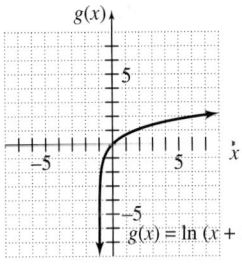

$g(x) = \ln(x + 1)$

35.

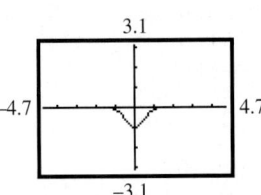

Domain: the set of all real numbers
Range: $(0, -1]$
Increasing: $x > 0$
Decreasing: $x < 0$
Minimum of -1 at $x = 0$

36.

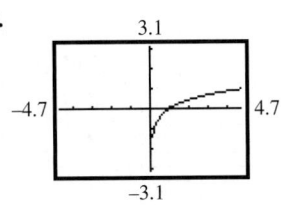

Domain: $(0, \infty)$
Range: the set of all real numbers
Increasing: increases on its domain
Decreasing: does not decrease
No max/min values

37. 6^{216} **38.** 27 **39.** 10 **40.** 1 **41.** $\dfrac{1}{20,000}$ **42.** 243 **43.** ≈ 3.162 **44.** -3 and $\dfrac{3}{2}$

45. -1 **46.** no solution **47.** all real numbers greater than 0 **48.** 6 **49.** 0 **50.** ≈ 0.514

51. $-\dfrac{5}{3}$ **52.** no solution **53.** -1 and 4 **54.** all real numbers **55.** ≈ 0.530

56. $f(x) = 1200 + 0.025x$; $f^{-1}(x) = 40x - 48,000$; the inverse function represents her total sales in terms of her monthly income. **57.** $f(x) = 95x$; $f^{-1}(x) = \dfrac{x}{95}$; The inverse function represents the number of hours in terms of the distance traveled.

58. $A = 8500(1.065)^t$

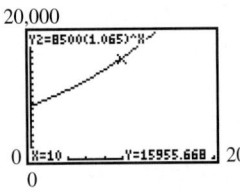

The investment was worth $15,955.67.

59.

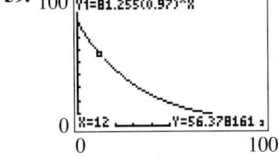

In 2012, there will be 56.378 million people enrolled in HMOs.

60. The pH is approximately 3.796. **61.** The hydrogen ion concentration is approximately 2.5×10^{-2} mole per liter.
62. It will take approximately 12.4 years. **63.** $A(t) = 696e^{0.0670t}$; in 2010, national health expenditures will be approximately 2658 billion dollars. **64.** It has been about 7573 years since the organism died. **65.** When the temperature is 30 degrees, 9 hours have passed.

CHAPTER 12 TEST

1. $f(x) = x^3$
$f^{-1}(x) = \sqrt[3]{x}$

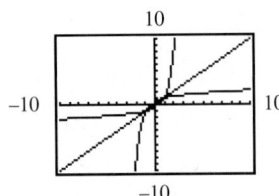

2.

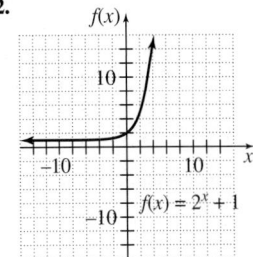

$f(x) = 2^x + 1$

3.

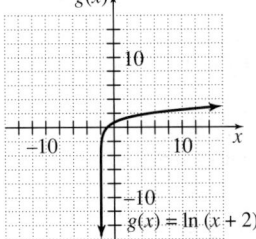

$g(x) = \ln(x + 2)$

4. $F^{-1}(x) = \dfrac{1}{2}x + 4$ **5. (a)** $\dfrac{1}{4}$ **(b)** 1 **(c)** 256 **(d)** ≈ 1.516 **(e)** ≈ 11.036 **6.** $\log 3 + 2\log x + 3\log y + \log z$ **7.** $2 + 2\log_3 a - \log_3 b$

8. $\log x^2(x - 4)$ **9.** $\ln \dfrac{\sqrt{x}}{y^2}$

10.

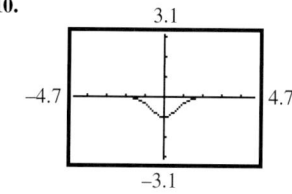

Domain: the set of all real numbers
Range: $[-1, 0)$
Increasing: $x > 0$
Decreasing: $x < 0$
Minimum of -1 at $x = 0$

11.

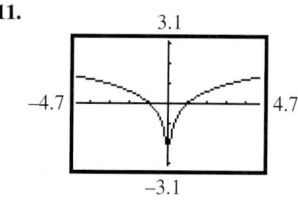

Domain: the set of all real numbers
except 0
Range: the set of all real numbers
Increasing: $x > 0$
Decreasing: $x < 0$
No max/min values

12. (a) 1 **(b)** 1 **(c)** 1 **13.** $\dfrac{5}{3}$ **14.** ≈ 4.711 **15.** all real numbers greater than 0 **16.** ≈ 0.732 **17. (a)** $f(x) = 400 + 0.03x$
(b) $f^{-1}(x) = 33.\overline{3}x - 13,333.\overline{3}$ **(c)** The inverse function represents the value of weekly sales in terms of his weekly income.
18. $f(x) = 2000(1.05)^x$; the investment was worth approximately $5306.60. **19.** It will take approximately 9.24 years.
20. $A(t) = 23,078e^{0.039t}$ The estimated personal income per capita will be about $50,344 in 2015. **21.** The body was deceased 6.9 hours.
22. Answers will vary.

CHAPTERS P–12 CUMULATIVE REVIEW EXERCISES

1. $\dfrac{y^2}{25}$ **2.** $\dfrac{4y^4}{x^6}$ **3.** $16x^2$ **4.** $-0.8a^2 - 5.2ab + 2.7b^2$ **5.** $-9x^2y^3z$ **6.** $9x^2 - 4y^2$ **7.** $4x^2 + 6x - 18$ **8.** $x^2 - 8x + 16$ **9.** $-5xy^3z$

10. $r + 2 - \dfrac{4s}{r}$ **11.** $\dfrac{x + 2}{x + 3}$ **12.** $\dfrac{x^2 + 2x + 5}{(x + 2)(x - 2)}$ **13.** $-\dfrac{(x + 2)(x + 1)}{(x + 4)(x - 2)}$ **14.** 1 **15.** $\dfrac{4(y - 5)}{xy^2(y - 3)}$ **16.** $6\sqrt{2x}$ **17.** $4ab\sqrt[3]{2b}$ **18.** -1

19. $\dfrac{2}{x}\sqrt{yz}$ **20.** $\dfrac{x + 7\sqrt{x} + 12}{x - 9}$ **21.** $x^{17/12} - x$ **22.** $(5m + 6n)(5m - 6n)$ **23.** $2(x - 4)(x + 2)$ **24.** does not factor

25.

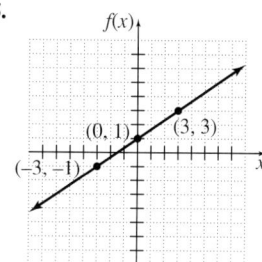

Domain: all real numbers
Range: all real numbers

26.

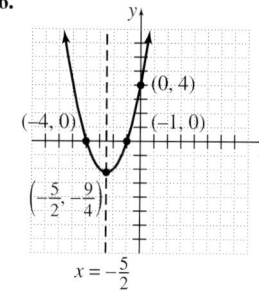

Domain: all real numbers
Range: all real numbers $\geq -\dfrac{9}{4}$

27.

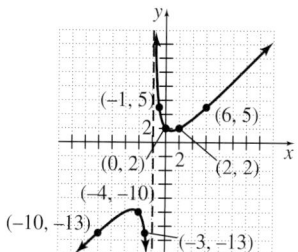

Domain: all real numbers $\neq -2$
Range: all real numbers ≤ -9.66 or ≥ 1.66

28.

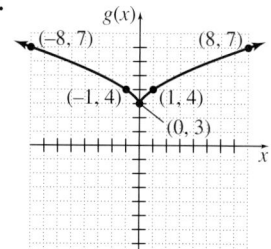

Domain: all real numbers ≥ 5
Range: all real numbers ≥ 0

29.

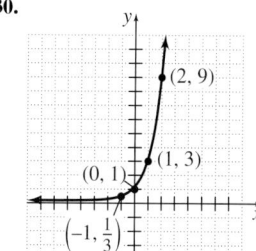

Domain: all real numbers
Range: all real numbers ≥ 3

30.

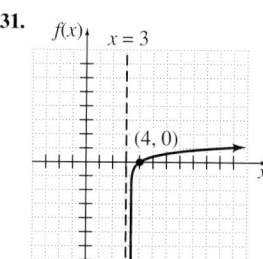

Domain: all real numbers
Range: all real numbers > 0

31.

Domain: all real numbers > 3
Range: all real numbers

32. -6 **33.** no solution **34.** 6 and -4 **35.** $\dfrac{5}{2} \pm \dfrac{\sqrt{11}}{2}i$ **36.** $-\dfrac{5}{3}$ **37.** 8 **38.** 2 **39.** $\sqrt{5}$ **40.** $(9, \infty)$

41. $\left(-\infty, -1 - \sqrt{3}\right] \cup \left[-1 + \sqrt{3}, \infty\right)$ **42.** $(4, 4)$ **43.** $y = -\dfrac{3}{5}x + \dfrac{4}{5}$ **44.** $y = 4x + 9$ **45.** $y = \dfrac{3}{2}x^2 + \dfrac{9}{2}x - 6$ **46.** $f^{-1}(x) = \dfrac{3}{2}x - 9$

47. The company must sell 53 books in order to break even. **48.** The dimensions are 9 feet by 12 feet. **49.** It will take the drains about 2.5 hours to drain the tank. **50.** It will take about 24.4 years for the money to triple.

Index

Slope of a Line (m)

$$m = \frac{y_2 - y_1}{x_2 - x_1}$$

(x_1, y_1) and (x_2, y_2) are coordinates of two points on a line

Linear Equation in Two Variables

Standard Form
$ax + by = c$
a, b, and c are real numbers and a and b are not both equal to zero

Slope–Intercept Form
$y = mx + b$
m is the slope of the graphed line, and b is the y-coordinate of the y-intercept of the graph

Point–Slope Form
$y - y_1 = m(x - x_1)$
m is the slope of the graphed line, and (x_1, y_1) are coordinates of a point on the line

Special Cases

$y = k$

$x = h$

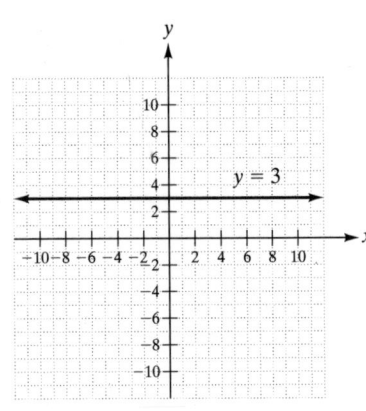

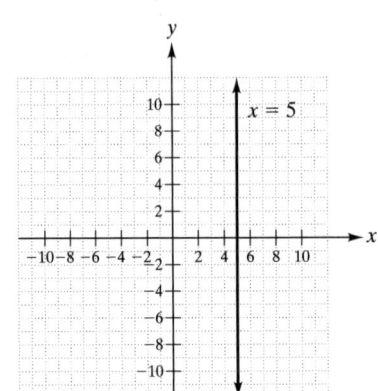

Standard Form for a Quadratic Function

$f(x) = ax^2 + bx + c$

a, b, and c are real numbers and $a \neq 0$

Calculator Windows

This text uses the following notation to identify the calculator window setting:

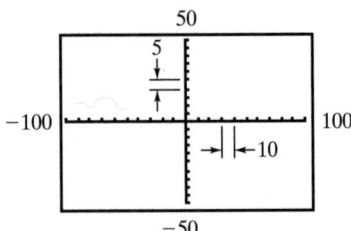

$(-100, 100, 10, -50, 50, 5, 1)$
(x minimum value, x maximum value, x scale, y minimum value, y maximum value, y scale, x resolution)

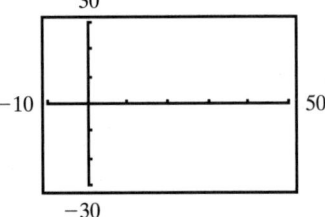

$(-10, 50, -30, 30)$
(x minimum value, x maximum value, y minimum value, y maximum value)

Sample Functions

Linear Function

$f(x) = ax, a > 0$

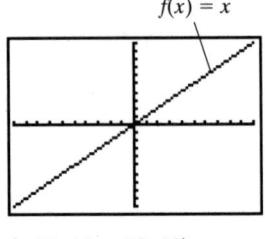

$(-10, 10, -10, 10)$

$f(x) = ax, a < 0$

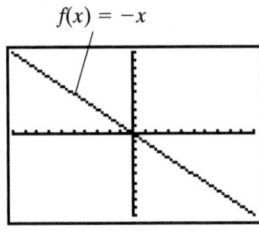

$(-10, 10, -10, 10)$